Stanley Gibbons
Stamp Catalogue

Commonwealth and British Empire Stamps 1840 – 1970

120th edition 2018

Stanley Gibbons Ltd · London and Ringwood

By Appointment to
Her Majesty The Queen
Philatelists
Stanley Gibbons Ltd
London

Published by Stanley Gibbons Ltd
Editorial and Publications:
7 Parkside, Christchurch Road, Ringwood,
Hants BH24 3SH

British Library Cataloguing in
Publication Data.
A catalogue record for this book is available
from the British Library.

ISBN-13: 978-1-911304-02-9
ISBN-10: 1-911304-02-X

Item No. R 2813-18

Printed and bound in Italy
by Lego SpA

Contents

Rhodesia (British South Africa Company) 1905 2s.6d. black,
one of a set of six issued to celebrate the opening of
the Victoria Falls Bridge.

Preface to the 2018 Edition

When Edward Stanley Gibbons issued his first 'Price list and Catalogue' in November 1865, it was simply a priced list of what he held in stock at the time (with a used Penny Black at 1d.), although to some extent it was already becoming a reference to what existed (the Canada Twelve Pence Black was included, but unpriced).

When the catalogue was split into two parts in 1895, to create the first British Empire catalogue – now in its 120th edition – it was already very much more than a price list of stamps for sale. It was an important reference work which collectors could use to see what existed and in most cases what Stanley Gibbons could sell it for, information which also allowed hundreds of other stamp dealers all over the world to set their prices.

I will return to the subject of prices below, but as a work of reference the Stanley Gibbons catalogue has continued to grow, with every one of its 120 editions containing new listings, information and guidance for the collector, each one rendering its predecessor as out-of-date as yesterday's newspaper.

But while the prices are set by Stanley Gibbons Commonwealth Stamp Department, based on current stock holdings and recent sales, the listings have been based on the work of an army of eminent philatelists, generously passing on the benefits of their research and experience to their fellow collectors by allowing us to publish the information in the pages of this catalogue.

To those we must add the even larger body of collectors, who through their diligence and observational skills have been able to add new watermark varieties (there are another 30 or so of these added this time), revise issue dates, add plate flaws and provide a plethora of other invaluable information.

We continue to welcome offers to assist with new listings and information, to add single items or suggest improvements and add new varieties. Initial contact by email is welcome (*hjefferies@ stanleygibbons.com*) with a scan or scans of the item(s) in question. Many items may require a personal inspection before listing can take place, although a certificate of genuineness from either the expert committee of the Royal Philatelic Society London or the British Philatelic Association are acceptable alternatives. It has to be remembered that overprints, cancellations, plate flaws and even watermark varieties have been extensively forged, so in some cases expert viewing is necessary before listing can take place.

As ever, the 2018 edition of Commonwealth and British Empire Stamps, 1840-1970 catalogue includes a vast amount of new information, provided by specialist and general collectors, dealers and auction houses, while prices have once again been carefully reviewed throughout the catalogue.

PRICES
The first and most important thing to report is that the market for Commonwealth stamps remains very healthy indeed and, while prices in certain other areas may be stagnant or falling, those in this catalogue remain firm or are moving up.

With inflation continuing to run at historically low levels and the effects of the currently weak UK currency not having had an impact on stamp pricing, we can be sure that those price increases which have been made are the result of increased demand from collectors and, while there have been significant increases for a number of stamps with a six-figure price ticket, increases for more modestly priced stamps are far more widespread, as collectors seek to fill gaps in their collections if and when they get the chance.

We are aware that it can be infuriating when a stamp which you own used is only priced in unused condition, and a particular effort has been made to add prices throughout the book where previously there have only been 'blanks'. It must be said, however, that we can only price what we know to exist and, once again many of those new prices are there thanks to collectors who have shown us or sent a scan of the item in question, so if you have something which is currently unpriced, you know what to do!

There are a few areas which see wholesale price increases for this edition, but in general it is more a case of widespread but selective adjustments and, while most of them are fairly modest, there are some which can only be described as spectacular, such as the 1942 4d. Koala stamp of Australia with inverted watermark (No. 188w), up from £4000 to £10,000 used.

India continues to see a significant number of price increases, with the **Convention and Feudatory States** also moving up. **Australian States** are also on the rise, especially for unused material.

Elsewhere, increases are less widespread, but the stamps of the first half of the 20th century, both mint and used, see a number of increases in the **West Indies**, **Africa**, the **Gulf**, the **Malayan States** and some of the **Pacific Islands**. In all areas, varieties of watermark clearly continue to be popular and there are increases to several of the 'back of the book' listings, such as postage dues, telegraphs, postal fiscals and official stamps. The process of pricing fiscally used high values continues, with the addition of prices for the **Ceylon** high value keyplates of King George V.

Great Britain prices remain firm and there are increases to be found throughout the section, from line-engraved right through to low-value Queen Elizabeth definitives.

REVISIONS TO THIS EDITION
In **Great Britain** the popular Mulready envelopes and letter sheets with advertisements printed on the inside are now included in this catalogue and there have been some additions to the **British Post Offices Abroad** section.

Probably one of the most long-awaited additions comes in **Aden**, where there is a new listing of Indian stamps used there. A number of collectors have contributed to this, but I would particularly like to thank Ray Brown of Dorset, whose collection provided the basis for the listing. As availability of material from the two main post offices at Aden and Aden Camp are comparable, we have combined these into a single listing and it is hoped that a future edition of the catalogue will also show listings of stamps used at the smaller offices, such as Kamaran, Khormaksar and Sheikh Othman; scans of covers or Indian stamps cancelled at these offices would greatly help in this endeavour.

Australia has received further attention, with Glen Stephens providing new illustrations and guidance on the early stamps of New South Wales, while there are extended notes on the two types of the 1903-10 9d. of Queensland and in Australia itself on the sheet positions of the Die II 3d, first watermark and the Die II 9d. on the third and subsequent watermarks. The 1962 Inland Mission 5d. with red omitted has been deleted and a note added that these are now considered to have been faked. In Papua there are illustrations for the 'POSTAGIE' and 'C' for 'O' varieties on the Lakatois, thanks to Mark 'Robbo' Robinson.

Recent research by Richard Watkins, now published in *Bermuda Post*, has shown that the original 1873 3d. of **Bermuda** was in the orange shade, with the yellow-buff coming from a subsequent printing. The revised listing reflects this important new information.

In **Cyprus** there is a new listing of the 17mm handstamped 'HALF-PENNY' surcharge of 1881 – currently only known used. This scarce new variety is clearly illustrated.

The stamps issued during the **British Occupation of the Faröe Islands** during World War II are now listed for the first time – all are overprints on the stamps of Denmark, which was under German occupation at the time.

New notes have been added to the listings of **British Occupation of Baghdad**, following Freddy Khalastchy's fine article on the subject in *Gibbons Stamp Monthly* in February 2017.

In **Malaysia** there are expanded notes in Straits Settlements concerning the 1880 10c. on 30c. (33/9) and in Johore on the 1884-6 overprints, while, thanks to Len Stanway, there is helpful guidance on the compound perforations of certain Federation period definitives.

Another important article in *GSM*, this time by Richard Garcia, has led to a new note on the use of British stamps in **Morocco**, while two new varieties have also been added to the overprinted stamps on Gibraltar.

New Zealand sees two new plate flaws on the 'Second Sidefaces' and one on the 3d. 'Christchurch Exhibition stamp of 1906, thanks to Paul Wreglesworth and Robin Gwynn, respectively, and there is a new note on telegraphic use of the 'long' fiscal stamps with postal cancellations provided by David Smitham. The background to the '"Tahae" joined' 1s. stamp of Niue (No. 15) is well worth reading, whether you are interested in Niue or not!.

In **Palestine** there is reference to the trials of the 1920 'Palestine' overprints and on the different papers used for the 1927-45 pictorials, with the types used for each value indicated.

The ever-popular 'Badge' set of **St. Helena** now includes the distinctive 'Storm over rock' variety, as well as the startling new discovery of the 1d. stamp with sideways watermark.

In **Sudan** the Official and Army Service perfins are now illustrated and the Military telegraph stamps, hitherto only listed when used in Bechuanaland are now also included with distinctive Sudan cancellations.

I should also mention that there have been changes and additions to the 'General Philatelic Information' section of this catalogue, which I would urge everyone to re-read every year. We all think we know all we need to know, but my in-box of queries and questions continues to suggest that we don't!

Finally, I would like to thank all those who have helped with this edition of 'Part 1' and to take a moment to remember some of those who have assisted us in the past, but who are, sadly, no longer with us. Those who come immediately to mind include Alan Drysdall, Charles Freeland, John Hillson, John Holman, Ted Proud and Iain Stevenson, while long-time member of the Commonwealth stamp department in the Strand, the late Brian Lucas, would regularly provide important corrections and improvements. Our world is a much poorer place without them.

Hugh Jefferies
Catalogue Editor
August 2017

The Stanley Gibbons Group Plc

Stanley Gibbons Limited,
Stanley Gibbons Auctions
399 Strand, London WC2R 0LX
Tel: +44 (0)207 836 8444
Fax: +44 (0)207 836 7342
E-mail: help@stanleygibbons.com
Website: www.stanleygibbons.com
for all departments, Auction and Specialist Stamp
Departments.

Open Monday–Friday 9.30 a.m. to 5 p.m.
Shop. Open Monday–Friday 9 a.m. to 5.30 p.m.
and Saturday 9.30 a.m. to 5.30 p.m.

Stanley Gibbons Publications, *Gibbons Stamp*
Monthly and *Philatelic Exporter*
7 Parkside, Christchurch Road, Ringwood,
Hampshire BH24 3SH.
Tel: +44 (0)1425 472363
Fax: +44 (0)1425 470247
E-mail: help@stanleygibbons.com
Publications Mail Order.
FREEPHONE 0800 611622

Monday–Friday 8.30 a.m. to 5 p.m.

Stanley Gibbons (Guernsey) Limited,
Roseneath, The Grange, St Peter Port,
Guernsey GY1 2QJ.
Tel: +44 (0)1481 708270
Fax: +44 (0)1481 708279
E-mail: investment@stanleygibbons.com

Stanley Gibbons (Jersey) Limited
2nd Floor, Minden House, Minden Place,
St Helier, Jersey, Channel Islands JE2 5WQ.
Tel: +44 (0)1534 766711
Fax: +44 (0)1534 766177
E-mail: investment@stanleygibbons.com

Stanley Gibbons Investments
Tel: +44 (0)845 026 7170 *or* +44 1534 766 711
E-mail: investment@stanleygibbons.com
Web: sginvest.co.uk

Stanley Gibbons (Asia) Limited
6/F, 100 Queen's Road Central
Central
Hong Kong
Tel: +852 3180 9370
E-mail: elee@stanleygibbons.com

Fraser's
(a division of Stanley Gibbons Group plc)
Bloomsbury House, 24 Maddox Street,
Mayfair, London W1S 1PP
Autographs, photographs, letters and documents
Tel: +44 (0)207 836 9325
Fax: +44 (0)207 495 9499
E-mail: sales@frasersautographs.com
Website: www.frasersautographs.com

Monday–Friday 9 a.m. to 5.30 p.m.
and Saturday 10 a.m. to 4 p.m.

Stanley Gibbons Publications Overseas Representation
Stanley Gibbons Publications are represented overseas by the following

Australia
Renniks Publications Pty Ltd
Unit 3 37-39 Green Street,
Banksmeadow, NSW 2019, Australia
Tel: +612 9695 7055
Website: www.renniks.com

Canada
Unitrade Associates
99 Floral Parkway, Toronto,
Ontario M6L 2C4, Canada
Tel: +1 416 242 5900
Website: www.unitradeassoc.com

Germany
Schaubek Verlag Leipzig
Am Glaeschen 23, D-04420
Markranstaedt, Germany
Tel: +49 34 205 67823
Website: www.schaubek.de

Italy
Ernesto Marini S.R.L.
V. Struppa, 300, Genova, 16165, Italy
Tel: +3901 0247-3530
Website: www.ernestomarini.it

Japan
Japan Philatelic
PO Box 2, Suginami-Minami,
Tokyo 168-8081, Japan
Tel: +81 3330 41641
Website: www.yushu.co.jp

Netherlands (also covers Belgium
Denmark, Finland & France)
Uitgeverij Davo BV
PO Box 411, Ak Deventer, 7400
Netherlands
Tel: +315 7050 2700
Website: www.davo.nl

New Zealand
House of Stamps
PO Box 12, Paraparaumu,
New Zealand
Tel: +61 6364 8270
Website: www.houseofstamps.co.nz

New Zealand
Philatelic Distributors
PO Box 863
15 Mount Edgecumbe Street
New Plymouth 4615, New Zealand
Tel: +6 46 758 65 68
Website: www.stampcollecta.com

Norway
SKANFIL A/S
SPANAV. 52 / BOKS 2030
N-5504 HAUGESUND, Norway
Tel: +47-52703940
E-mail: magne@skanfil.no

Singapore
C S Philatelic Agency
Peninsula Shopping Centre #04-29
3 Coleman Street, 179804, Singapore
Tel: +65 6337-1859
Website: www.cs.com.sg

South Africa
Peter Bale Philatelics
PO Box 3719, Honeydew,
2040, South Africa
Tel: +27 11 462 2463
Tel: +27 82 330 3925
E-mail: balep@iafrica.com

Sweden
Chr Winther Sorensen AB
Box 43, S-310 20 Knaered, Sweden
Tel: +46 43050743
Website: www.collectia.se

Stamps Added

Country	Stamps
Great Britain	O75a
Aden	Z1-Z279
Australia	286b
Queensland	115a
South Australia	161a
Western Australia	74a, 114a
Papua	O28a
Barbados	97a, 203x, 205b, 226sa
Basutoland	58b, D2ae
Bechuanaland	D10a
Stellaland	5a
Bermuda	37y, 84sa, 89d
Botswana	D13a
British Guiana	303g
British Honduras	105ax
British Occupation of Italian Colonies	M9aa
Burma	52a, 69b
Cyprus	8b
Dominica	47by
Falkland Islands Dependencies	Z45a
Fiji	337a
Ghana	461d
Grenada	35b, 46d, 47g, 154ab, 156ab, 408b, D5b, D7b
Hong Kong	102aw, 124b
British Post Offices in China	2x
India	O36a, O168w
Used in Iran	Z147a
Gwalior	14aw
Bundi	O19d
Sirmoor	3b
Travancore	44b
Iraq	107e
Issues for Baghdad	20ab, 20ac
Ireland	13y, 46a
Jamaica	87a, 101w
Kenya, Uganda and Tanganyika	44a
Malaysia	
Straits Settlements	56w, 202bx
Federation of Malaya	1w
Kedah	43d, 44d
Pahang	28a
Malta	73y, 242a, 242b, 252a
Mauritius	38a, 167aw, 168aw
Morocco Agencies	1c, 2c, 4c, 5c, 5d, 5fc, 5fd, 6fc, 7c, 7fc, 8c, 13d, 137b
New Zealand	27a, 217x, 226g, 230c, 235b, 239b, 245b, 372a, 468ab, 728w, 921w, 924w, O195ax, L31aw
Nigeria	52aba
Lagos	12w
Niger Coast Protectorate	67x
North Borneo	
Labuan	8a, 19a, 30xs, 31bxs, 32a, 39a, 85da, D9d
St. Helena	20y, 92d, 97f, 98d, 99d, 100d, 101d, 105d#
St. Vincent	161sa
South Africa	31c, 122a, O50a
Natal	21y
New Republic	32c, 53c, 76ab
Orange Free State	PF2a
Transvaal	RO28
South West Africa	40as
Swaziland	Z41
Transjordan	67a
Turks and Caicos Islands	102x

Catalogue Numbers Altered

The table below is a cross-reference of those catalogue numbers which have been altered in this edition.

	Old	New
Great Britain	216pa	deleted
Australia	343	deleted
Queensland	115a/c	115b/d
Bermuda	5	5a
	5b	5
Fiji	SB1a	deleted
Grenada	154a	154b
	154ab	154ba
	154ac	154bb
	156a	156b
	156ab	156ba
	156ac	156bb
India		
Used in Iran	Z147a	Z147b
Sirmoor	3b	3c
	3ba	3ca
Travancore	44b	44c
	44c	44d
Malaysia		
British Military Administration	1a	1b
	1b	1c
Malta	237a	237aa
	237b	237a

	Old	New
Mauritius	259a	deleted
Morocco Agencies	1c	1d
	2b	2g
	2c	2a
	2d	2b
	5c	5f
	5ca	5fa
	6c	6f
	7c	7f
North Borneo		
Labuan	31b	31c
	31ba	31ca
	31bw	31cw
	31bx	31cx
St. Helena	97fw	97gw
	97g	97h
	97ga	97ha
	97gc	97hc
	99dw	99ew
	99dx	99ex
	99e	99f
	99ea	99fa
	99ec	99fc
Samoa	120	119c

	Old	New
South Africa	31cw	31dw
	31d	31e
	31da	31ea
	31dw	31ew
	31e	31f
	122a	122b
Transvaal	129b	deleted
Trinidad and Tobago	214	213a

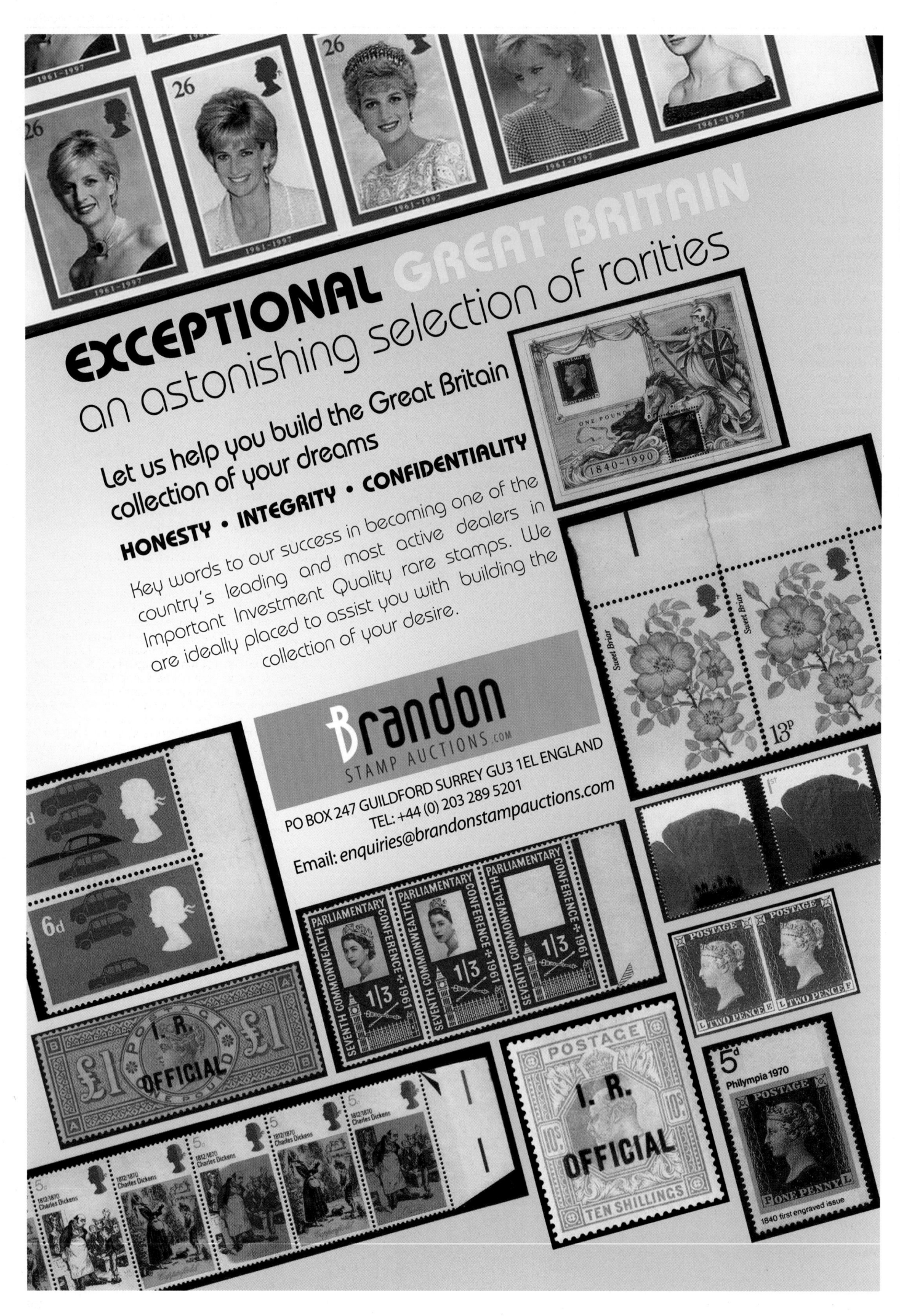

The Importance of Condition

The prices in the Stanley Gibbons Catalogue are for stamps in 'fine condition' – but what exactly does 'fine' mean, and what effect might a slight defect have upon the price? We visit Stanley Gibbons Specialist Stamp Department to find out

To quote in full the relevant paragraph in the introduction to the current Stanley Gibbons Commonwealth and British Empire Stamps Catalogue; 'The prices quoted in this catalogue are the estimated selling prices of Stanley Gibbons Ltd at the time of publication. They are, unless it is specifically stated otherwise, for examples in fine condition for the issue concerned. Superb examples are worth more, those of a lower quality, considerably less.' This single paragraph is probably the most significant piece of information in the entire catalogue – but one that is frequently ignored or forgotten. The big question, of course, is just how much more is 'more' and how much less is 'less'?

Not surprisingly, the ability to answer that question depends on experience. A knowledgeable philatelist will be able to assess fairly quickly what the price of a particular stamp should be in relation to that quoted in the catalogue. Many sellers, however, both professional and collector, find it simpler to price items for sale by a standard percentage of 'catalogue'; probably only marking down those that are actually damaged. This can mean that stamps in better than 'fine' condition are underpriced, while poorer ones are too expensive; something which buyers need to bear in mind.

Talking to the experts, it quickly becomes obvious that every single feature of a stamp needs to be considered separately before a judgement on its overall condition can be passed. So this article will look at each of those features individually, before drawing them all together and attempting to assess how much more than catalogue price a superb example might be worth and, conversely, how low a price should be put on one of lower quality.

Gum

This would seem to be a relatively easy one – after all, it says in the catalogue; 'The prices for unused stamps of Queen Victoria to King George V are for lightly hinged examples. Unused prices for King Edward VIII to Queen Elizabeth issues are for unmounted mint.' Well, at least the definition of unmounted is pretty clear, while lightly hinged means, in theory, a single hinge mark, although, apparently, two or three might be acceptable if the hinges have been lightly applied and carefully removed. The stamps printed by De La Rue for the majority of Colonial postal administrations during the first three decades of the twentieth century have stood up reasonably well to stamp hinges, so finding lightly mounted examples of such stamps should not be too difficult. However, Canadian stamps, for example, which were printed on softer paper and had thicker gum, are more difficult to find in fine mounted condition and should be valued accordingly.

Heavier hinging is acceptable for stamps issued before around 1890 but the majority of the gum should be clear and 'unblemished'. If the stamp has been mounted on a number of occasions or if there is a heavy hinge still attached, the price would drop to about half catalogue and from there on would decline fairly rapidly.

For a twentieth century stamp without gum a price of about one tenth of catalogue would be more or less the order of the day (unless it was normally issued that way, of course!). However,

many early issues are extremely rare with gum and in these cases anything up to full catalogue price would be appropriate. Prices for early Western **Australia** and Sarawak are, for example, without gum, gummed stamps being worth a premium. The first perforated issues of British Guiana are also rarely found with gum, so ungummed examples would be worth a higher proportion of catalogue price than usual – about one third, or more – while Turks Islands provisionals and early **New Zealand** Chalon heads without gum might rate half catalogue or above.

As for the premium that should be put on earlier stamps in unmounted condition, that will vary from issue to issue and from country to country. Clearly, the older the stamp the less likely it is that it will be easy to find by those seeking 'unmounted' perfection. The *Great Britain Concise* catalogue gives both mounted and unmounted prices for all stamps issued between 1887 and 1935 and the premium ranges from zero up to 100 per cent, or even more, depending on the relative scarcity of the stamp in unmounted condition.

Some stamps are more acceptable than others without gum

The discounts for mounted issues of the Third Reich period can be dramatic

As for post-1935 stamps in lightly mounted condition, the story is just as complicated. As it says in the catalogue; 'Some stamps from the King George VI period are often difficult to find in un-mounted mint condition. In such instances we would expect that collectors would need to pay a high proportion of the price quoted to obtain mounted mint examples. Generally speaking, lightly mounted mint stamps from this reign, issued before 1945, are in considerable demand.' This may hold good for Commonwealth stamps, but on the continent the demand for unmounted has severely affected the market for even lightly mounted specimens. The current *Part 7, Germany, Catalogue* provides some clear examples of this. This catalogue gives unmounted and mounted mint prices for all Third Reich issues, from 1933 to 1945, with unmounted prices only for later issues. The differences are quite dramatic, with the 1936 Local Government Congress set (SG 614/7) rated at £22.00 unmounted, but only £4.75 lightly hinged, and the 1942 Hamburg Derby stamp (SG 804) is priced at £26.00 and £7.25, respectively. Thus, for most mounted mint post-war

European stamps, one should probably be thinking in terms of deducting 75 or 85 per cent from the catalogue price.

Even for King George VI stamps the discount for mounted mint can vary

As suggested earlier, Commonwealth collectors are fortunate in that the price differential is not nearly so dramatic. On average, mounted mint prices for post-war King George VI sets are approximately 'half catalogue'. Again, there are exceptions. To take three examples; the first King George VI 3d. of Ascension, the black and ultramarine stamp (42), would only rate around 25 per cent of catalogue in mounted condition, on the other hand, the 1938 set of Perak (103/21) would be more like two thirds, while for some of the Indian Convention States high values the proportion would be even higher, providing the gum is white and not toned. For the first issues of the present reign the proportion drops to around a third, but after about 1965 there is really very little demand for mounted examples of anything other than the more expensive sets, even in fine lightly hinged condition.

Some gum toning can be acceptable on certain King George VI issues

Whether or not a hinge has been attached to it is not the only gum feature that can affect the value of a stamp. Discoloration or toning can also be significant. Stamps which have spent time in the tropics frequently suffer from gum browning and, in extreme cases, cracking and 'crazing', sometimes affecting the face of the stamp as well as the back. The value of such specimens should be marked down accordingly. For stamps of King George VI one would normally aim for no gum toning at all, but the first 10s. definitive of Grenada only exists toned, so that would be considered 'fine for the issue concerned'; later stamps in the series should have cream or white gum, depending on the original issue. Again, the vast majority of the first Hong Kong definitives have at least some gum toning, so here the discount for lightly toned examples would be smaller than usual.

The demand for unmounted mint, as well as very real concerns that the gum applied to nineteenth

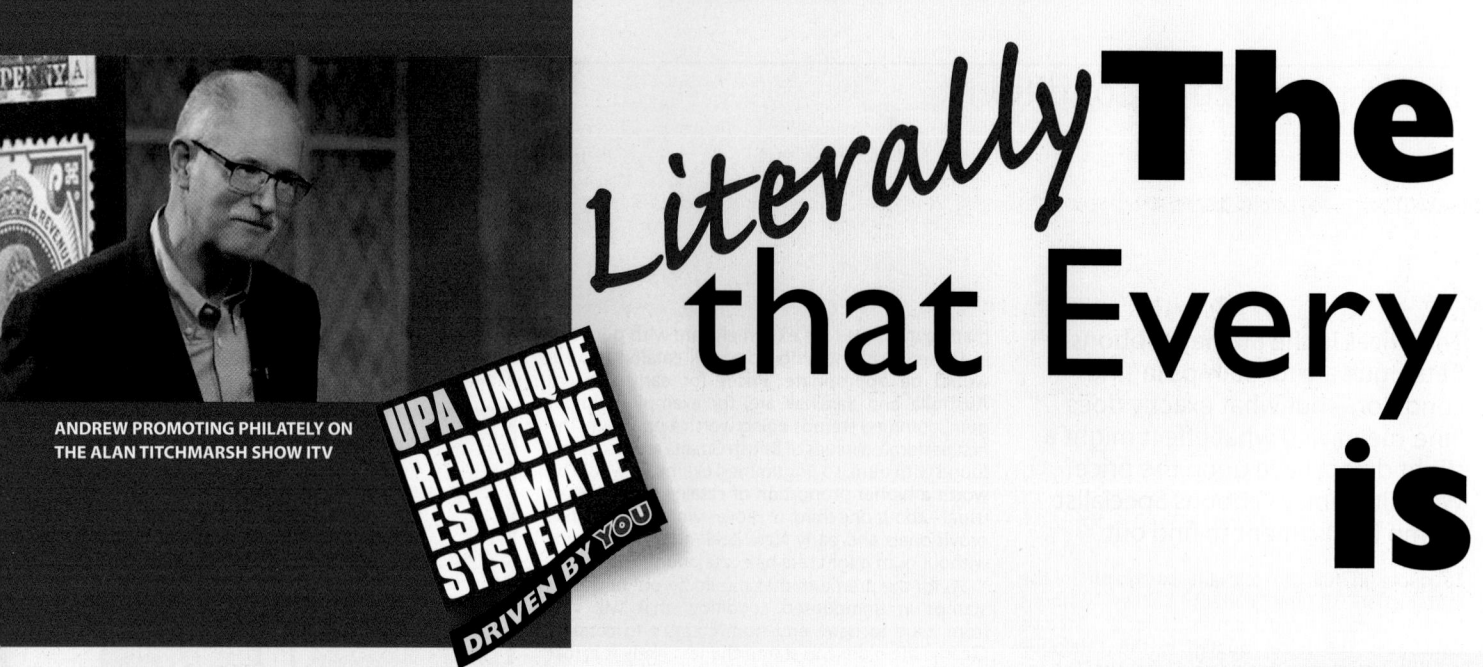

Literally **The** that Every is

ANDREW PROMOTING PHILATELY ON THE ALAN TITCHMARSH SHOW ITV

UPA UNIQUE REDUCING ESTIMATE SYSTEM DRIVEN BY YOU

Dear Colleague,
For the first time, in this open letter, I'm going to give you the thinking, the 'mindset' if you will, of how and why my stamp auction thrives where others do not...

1st £55 FREE WINNINGS

As many of you will attest. At certain 'peak' times in our auction 'cycle,' I personally answer the telephone to callers. It's a wonderfully enjoyable and rewarding thing for me to do, because, you kindly inform me of your likes and dislikes, about us, and other auctions that you may have dealt with before discovering U P A...

One of the most common 'threads' that I have learnt from You, and from other Dealers and Auctioneers, is simply 'how does U P A do it?' How is it that we have become the largest Stamp Auction in the UK and almost the largest globally? How can we afford to expend more upon advertising worldwide than most dealers sell in a year? Simply put: How can we afford to offer more and charge less – indeed – how can we afford to offer more and charge you no extra w-h-a-t-s-o-e-v-e-r ??

The fundamental reason why is because, unlike others, everything we do is Driven by You.. Over the course of the past 17 years I have discovered that combining this 'bottom-up' thinking with offering *simply MASSIVE Philatelic Choice* – permits us to offer you a Unique Collector-Driven Stamp Auction Experience. Think about it: whilst the rest of our philatelic industry works 'top-down' – issuing diktats, regulation, charges and fees, and few guarantees – ever increasingly we throw these off encouraged by more and more collectors joining us, who crucially continue to participate in auction after auction... rewarding us by their loyalty, enriching their collections... enabling us, in turn, to reward them.

...So that, when you inform us that You don't like 'X' (extra shipping and insurance charges), and You dislike 'Y' (paying credit card charges) and you positively abhor paying 'Z' – up to 25% buyer's premiums... (particularly when you may realise that you are possibly or probably paying a buyer's premium upon that dealer's own stamps that they are selling to You)... we take that valuable knowledge you've imparted and 'dial' it back into our auction system, not purely for your benefit BUT for our mutual benefit because over the 17 years that U P A has been auctioning I have discovered that if we have enough participating bidders in our auctions we can offer you a *radically superior service and a radically different deal than others*...

Shield Yourself & Save

I SUPPORT NO BP SUPPORT NO BUYER'S PREMIUM DRIVEN BY YOU

NO SURCHARGE MasterCard DRIVEN BY YOU

NEW POST-FREE UPA Loyalty Bonus DRIVEN BY YOU

Discover the Difference

UNIVERSAL PHILATELIC AUCTIONS SINCE 1958

Philately Understood

Stanley Gibbons Stamp Catalogues

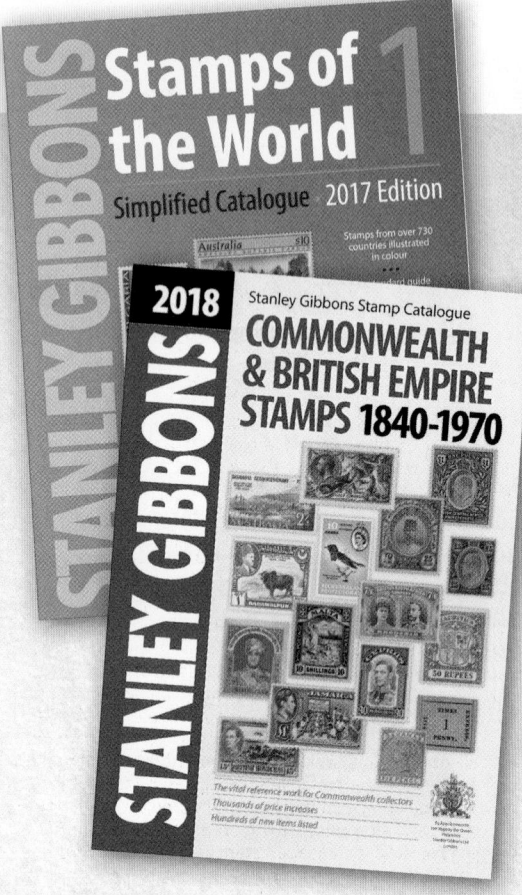

We have catalogues to suit every aspect of stamp collecting

Our catalogues cover stamps issued from across the globe - from the Penny Black to the latest issues. Whether you're a specialist in a certain reign or a thematic collector, we should have something to suit your needs. All catalogues include the famous SG numbering system, making it as easy as possible to find the stamp you're looking for.

Commonwealth & British Empire Stamps 1840–1970 (120th edition, 2018)

Commonwealth Country Catalogues

Australia & Dependencies
(10th Edition, 2016)
Bangladesh, Pakistan & Sri Lanka
(3rd edition, 2015)
Belize, Guyana, Trinidad & Tobago
(2nd edition, 2013)
Brunei, Malaysia & Singapore
(4th edition, 2013)
Canada (6th edition, 2016)
Cyprus, Gibraltar & Malta
(4th edition, 2014)
East Africa with Egypt & Sudan
(3rd edition, 2014)
Eastern Pacific (3rd edition, 2015)
Falkland Islands (7th edition, 2016)
Hong Kong (5th edition, 2015)
India (including Convention & Feudatory States) (4th edition, 2013)
Indian Ocean (3rd edition, 2016)
Ireland (6th edition, 2015)
Leeward Islands (3rd edition, 2017)
New Zealand (6th edition, 2016)
Northern Caribbean, Bahamas & Bermuda
(4th edition, 2016)
St. Helena & Dependencies
(6th edition, 2017)
Southern & Central Africa
(2nd edition, 2014)
West Africa (2nd edition, 2012)
Western Pacific (4th edition, 2017)
Windward Islands & Barbados
(3rd edition, 2015)

Stamps of the World 2018

Volume 1	Abu Dhabi – Charkhari
Volume 2	Chile – Georgia
Volume 3	German Commands – Jasdan
Volume 4	Jersey – New Republic
Volume 5	New South Wales – Singapore
Volume 6	Sirmoor – Zululand

Great Britain Catalogues

2017 Collect British Stamps
(68th edition, 2017)

Collect Channel Islands & Isle of Man
(30th edition, 2016)
Great Britain Concise Stamp Catalogue
(32nd edition, 2017)

Great Britain Specialised

Volume 1	Queen Victoria (16th edition, 2012)
Volume 2	King Edward VII to King George VI (14th edition, 2015)
Volume 3*	Queen Elizabeth II Pre-decimal issues (12th edition, 2011)
Volume 4*	Queen Elizabeth II Decimal Definitive Issues – Part 1 (10th edition, 2008)

Queen Elizabeth II Decimal Definitive Issues – Part 2* (10th edition, 2010)

Foreign Countries

Antarctica (2nd edition, 2012)
Arabia (1st edition, 2016)
Belgium & Luxembourg
(1st edition, 2015)
Central America (3rd edition, 2007)
China (11th edition, 2015)
Czech Republic and Slovakia
(1st edition, 2017)
Finland and Sweden
(1st edition, 2017)
France, Andorra and Monaco
(1st edition, 2015)
French Colonies (1st edition, 2016)
Germany (11th edition, 2014)
Japan & Korea (5th edition, 2008)
Netherlands & Colonies
(1st edition, 2017)
Poland (1st edition, 2015)
Russia (7th edition, 2014)
South-East Asia (5th edition, 2012)
United States of America
(8th edition, 2015)

*Currently out of stock.

STANLEY GIBBONS
LONDON 1856

399 Strand, WC2R 0LX, London
Phone: **+44 1425 472 363** | Email: **support@stanleygibbons.com**
www.stanleygibbons.com

century issues was, in itself, potentially damaging, has inevitably led to a certain amount of regumming. Stanley Gibbons' policy is not to sell stamps which have been regummed, especially since the new layer of gum may disguise damage or attempts at repair. It is important, therefore, that the edges of early mint stamps be checked very carefully to make sure that there are no suspicious signs of gum on the surface. (There is one set of stamps, China SG 457/9, which was gummed after printing and perforating, while stamps printed on top of the gum are clearly not a problem – but these are very much the exceptions.)

Margins

Another feature which has long been a part of the 'Stamp Improver's' repertoire has been the adding of margins to stamps which have been deficient in them. Once again, this 'service' has developed because of the premium placed by collectors on 'fine four-margin' examples of stamps like the Penny Black. For some years now the *Part 1* and *GB Concise* catalogues have provided guidance on this matter; illustrating 'good', 'fine', 'very fine' and 'superb' examples of the first postage stamp. As stated, the standard adopted in the catalogue is for stamps described as 'fine', which, in terms of margins, means that the area outside the printed design should be 'approximately one half of the distance between two adjoining unsevered stamps' – on all four sides, of course! Anything more than this will take the stamp into the 'very fine' or 'superb' categories, with the stamp's price rising accordingly. Ultimately, one arrives at a point where the stamp has 'stolen' the margins from all of its neighbours, in which case exaggerated expressions such as 'gargantuan' or 'jumbo' margins are frequently resorted to. Such examples are, indeed, rare and would expect to be valued accordingly; at least double catalogue price and probably more, if other aspects of its condition are 'up to scratch'.

Beware of stamps to which margins have been added

*Stamps with abnormally large
margins are worth a substantial premium*

One factor which needs to be borne in mind is that the distance between two adjoining unsevered stamps varied quite a lot in the early days. So what would be considered only 'fair', or even 'narrow', for the Indian lithographs or the first issue of Norway would be 'enormous' on the early issues of several British colonies whose stamp printing plates were laid down by Perkins Bacon. Ceylon, Queensland and Tasmania are typical examples of countries whose stamps, suffer from this problem – and where narrow margins do not necessarily prevent a stamp being described as 'fine'.

Mention of the **India**n lithographs raises the issue of octagonal stamps which have been cut to shape – often to fit into the spaces provided for them by the manufacturers of early stamp albums! Again, the catalogue provides helpful guidance with a note explaining that 'catalogue prices for Four Annas stamps are for cut-square specimens with clear margins and in good condition. Cut-to-shape copies are worth from 3% to 20% of these prices according to condition.'

For more conventionally-shaped imperforate issues, a stamp which has lost one of its margins might be priced as high as half catalogue if it is fine

in all other respects, but the price declines rapidly if more than one side is affected. Of course, there are exceptions; the Penny Black, because of its unique desirability, can merit a higher proportion of catalogue price, even with no margins at all, than just about any other stamp – certainly more than its much scarcer partner, the Two Pence Blue!

What might be described as 'narrow margins' for one stamp could be wide for another

Perforations

When we look at the influence which perforations have on value, the situation is no less complicated. Here there are two factors to consider, the condition of the perforations themselves and centring of the stamp image within them.

It makes sense to seek out stamps that are perfectly centred

Centring is easy to understand; in a perfect stamp the space between the edge of the design and the perforations should be equal on all sides. For most modern stamps, perforated on comb machines, good centring is normal and perfect centring would not merit a premium. Even 100 years ago the quality controls at De La Rue, where most British and colonial stamps were produced, were such that poorly centred stamps, particularly the keyplate types, are seldom encountered, so once again, it is hardly an issue. The attractive engraved pictorials, popular with post offices in the mid-twentieth century and popular with collectors to this day, were more variable – irrespective of which firm printed and perforated them. A stamp slightly off-centre could still merit the description 'fine', but if it is visibly off-centre in more than one direction or the design touches the perforations, then a discount from catalogue price could be expected – the clearer the displacement, the bigger the discount. If, of course, the perforations pass right through the middle of the stamp, it becomes an error – and that's a completely different story!

Early stamps are seldom found perfectly centred, especially those printed from plates laid down before perforating was introduced

The moral is that it certainly makes sense to try and seek out stamps that are perfectly centred, although in the case of the above issues it would be unlikely that you would be charged extra for them.

When discussing the problem of finding imperf stamps with good margins, it was noted that the designs were sometimes placed so close together on the plate that it required considerable care on the part of the post office clerk to separate stamps from the sheet without cutting into them. This became even more of a problem when stamps printed from those same plates were required to be perforated. It is not surprising that, in view of the materials they had to work with and the experimental nature of perforating machinery at the time, early stamps are seldom found perfectly centred. For this reason it would be unrealistic to suggest that a slightly off-centre perforated Penny Red was less than 'fine', although to command full catalogue price, the perforations should not touch the design.

Centring is also an important issue among more modern line-perforated stamps, notably those of the USA and Canada – right up to quite recent times. Here, poorly centred stamps were the norm and even a slightly off-centre example could merit the description 'fine'. Because of the inaccuracy of the perforating machines, the stamps can also vary in size quite a bit, and oversized, well-centred stamps, because of their relative scarcity, can be the subject of fierce competition when they come up at auction and can fetch prices vastly in excess of catalogue. In the case of cheaper stamps five or ten times catalogue price is not unknown.

Nibbled, Short or Pulled?

Perforations are easily damaged, especially if the gauge is coarse and the paper soft. On a De La Rue keyplate issue, with a standard perforation of 14, one would expect a 'fine' stamp to have all its perforation 'teeth' intact. One 'nibbled' or 'nibbed' perf tooth (slightly short) would call for a slight discount, but the more teeth affected or the shorter the tooth the greater the reduction in price. Incidentally, a 'short perf' would still show a vestigial 'tooth', a 'missing perf' shows no tooth at all and a 'pulled perf' signifies that there is a 'hole' in the stamp where the perforation tooth was pulled away). Even worse than a short perf on one of the sides is a short corner. Here again, the more of the corner missing the lower the price – but if the damage has resulted in part of the stamp design being torn away then the stamp would be unlikely to be worth more than a tenth of catalogue and possibly much less.

*Canadian coil stamps with full perfs
are far from common*

Whereas on a perf 14 stamp a damaged perforation tooth would be considered a defect which would force a reduction in the price, on a perf 8 stamp, such as some of the Canadian coil stamps of the 1920s and 30s, stamps with full perfs are far from common. Here, one or two shortish perfs would probably be acceptable, providing they were not too short. Such a stamp with all its perforations could command a premium over full catalogue price, especially if it was also well centred. As the gauge increases, however, the impact of short perfs increases, so that a King George V 'Seahorse' with one or two short perfs would probably carry a 20 per cent discount, any more than that and the price would drop to half catalogue.

Check the perfs on King George V Seahorses

Today, only a small premium is paid for plate number examples of most colonial stamps

Great Britain control numbers are widely available

Booklet stamps

Damaged perforations are not only caused by careless separation. Until very recently, most stamp booklets were made up from reels of stamps, bound into covers by stapling, stitching or gluing and then guillotined to produce the finished books. Inevitably, this cutting was seldom totally accurate, resulting in the majority of booklet panes being trimmed on at least one side. Prices for stamp booklets in the Stanley Gibbons catalogues are for examples with 'average' perforations – that is, slightly trimmed; the prices for booklet panes are for examples with full perforations. If a pane of six has good perforations at the top and side, but is trimmed along the foot, then its value should be based on the three stamps in the top row, the three stamps at the bottom being virtually discounted.

A single stamp which only occurs in booklet panes, such as most of the definitive watermark varieties of Queen Elizabeth **Great Britain**, should also have full perforations. Trimmed perfs bring the price down significantly and if they are missing completely than even a scarce variety would only merit a tenth of catalogue.

Wing margins

Another perforation issue is 'wing margins'. When De La Rue began producing the surface-printed stamps of Great Britain, their printing plates were made up of separate sections which printed as 'panes'. In the case of the 1861 3d., for example, the printed sheet of 240 stamps was made up of 12 panes of 20 stamps. Between each pane there was a 'gutter' and where the panes were side-by-side the gutter was perforated down the centre, giving the stamps at the side of the pane a wide (5mm) margin – the 'wing margin'. Wing margins were frowned upon by early collectors, who liked their stamps to fit exactly into the stamp-size rectangles printed for them by album manufacturers. As a result, stamps with wing margins generally commanded a lower price than stamps from the centre of the pane which had 'normal' perforations and many stamps had their wing margins cut off or had fake perforations added to provide collectors with stamps of the required shape.

Fashions change, and wing margins are now no longer despised, indeed, because of their slightly larger size, they frequently compare well with a 'normal' and they certainly show a postmark to better advantage. Thus, there is no longer a discount for a wing margined stamp, although we have not yet reached a situation where one has to pay a premium for their relative scarcity!

Sadly, however, those stamps which were 'doctored' in order to appeal to earlier fashions are now considered to be considerably devalued, except in the case of a good basic stamp such as the 2s. brown, or perhaps where the stamp has some other redeeming feature such as an attractive cancellation. For more run-of-the-mill stamps a price of one tenth of catalogue would usually be appropriate. With this in mind, of course, it pays to be aware of the corner letters of British surface-printed stamps which should have wing margins, in order to spot ones which have had fake perforations added. This information is given in both 'Part 1' and the GB Specialised Catalogue.

De La Rue printed stamps by the same technique for many British colonies; stamps which do not have corner letters to allow today's collectors to identify those with 'dodgy perfs'. The early stamps of Hong

One might expect to pay a premium for a modern plate block

Catalogue prices for booklet panes are for examples with full perforations

Kong are an obvious example and, bearing in mind the prices which these can fetch in fine condition, it behoves us all to be aware of stamps which may have had wing margins removed and to check them carefully before purchase.

Wing margins were frowned upon by early collectors but not any longer!

Marginal premium

For modern stamps, an intact sheet margin should not add to the value, although one might expect to pay a small premium for a plate block or imprint block over the price for a plain block of four. For most earlier twentieth century stamps, also, a plain margin will do little for a stamp's value, but if that piece of margin includes a control number, plate number or printer's imprint then the difference can be very significant indeed! Great Britain control numbers were widely collected at the time they were current and are widely available to this day. Reference to volume 2 of the *Great Britain Specialised Catalogue* demonstrates that, in spite of the fact that there was only one control single in a sheet of 240 stamps, apart from a few rare examples, they generally only merit a premium of between 50 and 100 per cent over the price of a normal mounted mint example. Plate number singles of colonial stamps occurred once or twice a sheet but, judging from the infrequency with which one encounters them, they were not sought after at the time of issue and are still undervalued today – again a small premium over the price of a fine mint basic stamp is all one should expect.

However, perhaps the Australian market indicates that this may not always be the case. In Australia huge premiums are now being paid for imprint strips and singles at auction. At a recent sale in Australia a 5s. Kangaroo, third watermark, mounted mint 'CA' monogram single, catalogue price for a single stamp £250, sold for A$21,000 – getting on for £9000 after tax and premium were added!

Even a partial marginal inscription can make a great difference to the price of a Penny Red

The first stamps of Great Britain bore an inscription in the sheet margins, advising the public as to the price of the stamps, where they should be placed on the letter and warning against the removal of 'the cement'. The early surface-printed stamps also bore inscriptions in the sheet margins. The latter are not currently considered to impact significantly on the value of the stamp to which they are attached, but a partial marginal inscription can make a great difference to the price of a Penny Black or Penny Red, and a complete corner, with plate number attached, will be very desirable indeed.

What's the damage?
We have looked at some aspects of damage in this article, notably in relation to perforations, so let us conclude by reviewing other aspects of damage.

All young collectors are advised from the outset to avoid torn stamps, and the advice obviously holds good throughout one's philatelic life. However, that is not to say that all torn stamps are worthless, because even a torn example of a desirable stamp is still collectable and can therefore command a price. In a GB context, a fine used £5 orange or 2s. brown with a 3mm tear, but otherwise superb, would probably rate about one third of catalogue price. A more common stamp, such as a 2s.6d. or 5s. value, would be worth much less and, naturally, the larger or more obvious the tear, the greater its impact on the price.

A 'bend' will generally not be evident on the face of a stamp, only on the back, and will result in a 10 or 15 per cent reduction in price; a gum crease is the natural result of gum ageing and its effect on value will depend upon the damage caused to the face of the stamp. A crease is clearly evident on the surface of the stamp and will result in a more common stamp being worth between one fifth and one tenth of catalogue, depending on the harshness of the crease and where it is – a crease across a corner will be less significant than one right across the middle, for example. A 'wrinkle' gives the appearance of a series of light creases, whose effect on value will depend on its extent and clarity. Once again, a crease or wrinkle on a valuable stamp will be less significant in percentage terms than one on a more common one – all other factors being equal.

The impact a thin will have will similarly depend upon its extent and the effect it may have on the surface of the stamp; a surface abrasion having a greater impact than a hinge thin. Some of the chalk-surfaced key types of the early twentieth century are particularly prone to 'rubbing' and, again, this will always reduce the price of a stamp, the size of the reduction depending upon the degree of the damage and the scarcity of the stamp itself.

Perfins
Stamps bearing perforated initials were at one time treated as little better than rubbish and many were destroyed. The fact that there is now a specialist society devoted to perfins should indicate that the situation has changed; but it is fair to say that the majority of collectors avoid them like the plague. Many official perfins are now listed in the catalogue and some of them carry a price higher than they would as normals. Some, indeed, are very desirable, notably the China 'Large Dragons' perforated 'NCH' by the *North China Herald*. Demand from specialist perfin collectors has pushed up the price for 'proving covers' that is, covers which show which organisation used a particular set of initials, while some commercial perfins are sought after and command a premium over the price of an unperfined stamp. Nevertheless, a set of perforated initials would still usually result in an

otherwise fine stamp being worth only about one tenth of catalogue.

Perfins can enhance the value of a stamp

Fading
One of the reasons why the firm of De La Rue held such an important position in stamp production in the British Empire at the turn of the last century was the security offered by their fugitive inks. The green ink they used, in particular, dissolved into a pale yellow-green upon immersion in water. A footnote in the catalogue under the 1883 definitives of Great Britain comments; 'The above prices are for stamps in the true dull green colour. Stamps which have been soaked, causing the colour to run, are virtually worthless.' This seems rather harsh, particularly in the case of the difficult 9d., but fairly reflects the current market position. The comment is just as relevant to many other stamps, both from Britain and the colonies. The same inks were used in the production of many colonial middle and high values, such as the Federated Malay States 'elephants'. Such stamps, when water affected, would be worth from one fifth to one tenth of catalogue, depending on the degree of discolouration.

Water damage is not only a problem for the typographed issues of De La Rue. Although it is generally recognised that recess-printing inks are more stable, there are examples of such stamps which are susceptible to 'washing' – some of the Rhodesian 'double heads', for example, can be de-valued in this way.

Colour change is not, of course, brought about only through immersion in water; sunlight can sometimes have a very significant effect and seriously faded stamps should be viewed in the same way as 'washed' ones – more common items being 'virtually worthless', rarer ones rating up to one fifth of catalogue, providing that the fading is not too serious.

Tone spots – the brownish spots encountered on many stamps which have been stored in damp conditions – especially in the tropics – will also reduce the value of a stamp or cover; the degree of reduction once again depending upon the extent of the toning and the value of the stamp in fine condition. A few toned perforation tips should, say the experts, be viewed in the same way as if they were 'short'. A small brown spot in the centre of a stamp, providing it cannot be seen on the front, would reduce an otherwise fine King George VI stamp to around half catalogue, or quarter catalogue if it were mounted as well. Earlier stamps would require similar discounting but toned examples of more modern issues should be considered almost valueless. Similarly, any stamp with extensive or more disfiguring brown marks should be avoided, especially as the fault can 'migrate' to other stamps.

Fugitive inks were used for many colonial middle and high values

Cancellation quality
When describing the postmarks of the nineteenth century, the word 'obliteration' is synonymous with

'cancellation' – because, of course, that was what they were designed to do – to 'obliterate' the stamp in such a way as to prevent any opportunity for reuse. The Maltese cross is an attractive cancellation, especially when applied in red or one of the 'fancy' colours, but many early Great Britain line-engraved adhesives are heavily cancelled by over-inked black crosses, which detract considerably from the beauty of the stamps. A 'fine' cancellation should be lightly applied, if possible leaving a substantial part of the design – ideally including the Queen's profile – clear of the cancellation. Also desirable are well centred examples displaying all, or nearly all of the cancellation on the stamp. This is particularly true where the cancellation is more significant than the stamp, such as a Wotton-under-Edge Maltese cross. Here, you would want to have as full a cancellation as possible, although it would still be preferable to have it lightly applied.

The Maltese cross is an attractive cancellation, especially when applied in red

Where the cancellation is more important than the stamp it should be clear, upright and lightly applied

This rule remains valid after the arrival of the '1844' numeral cancellation. The duplex postmark, incorporating a circular datestamp alongside the numeral obliterator, was not introduced in London until early 1853, so for nine years nearly every stamp continued to be 'obliterated' by a barred numeral. On the odd occasion where another form of cancellation was used, such as the circular 'Town' marks or 'Penny Post' handstamps, the postmark has become more desirable than the stamp anyway. For stamps used during those nine years, therefore, lightly applied postmarks which leave a significant part of the design clear continue to be desirable and stamps which fall short of this will not be categorised as 'fine'.

Other countries followed the practices established by the British Post Office, using 'anonymous' cancels which can only be identified by individual peculiarities, or numeral postmarks of one form or another.

Numeral postmarks which leave a significant part of the design clear are desirable

Line-engraved stamps cancelled only by the datestamp would be rated 'superb'

Again, stamps with lightly applied cancellations should be sought out for preference, although it is necessary to bear in mind the current postal practices in the country or at the individual post office concerned. In spite of the fact that pen cancellations are not generally popular among collectors, where this was a normal method of cancellation, as on the first issue of St Helena, for example, they would be acceptable, although in practice most such examples have since been cleaned in an attempt to make them appear unused. Indeed, early GB stamps with manuscript cancels, such as the hand-drawn 'Maltese cross' of Dunnet, often fetch high prices at auction if their provenance is sound.

Circular datestamps

With the arrival of the Duplex cancellation, the possibility that a stamp might receive the circular dated portion of the handstamp increases, although this was not supposed to happen. Here, we should perhaps return to the statement in the front of the Stanley Gibbons catalogue, that: 'The prices are ... for examples in fine condition for the issue concerned. Superb examples are worth more, those of a lower quality, considerably less'. Thus, a postally used stamp cancelled by a lightly applied numeral portion of the postmark would generally be considered 'fine', while one which showed only the dater portion would be rated as 'superb', especially where that datestamp is upright, well-centred and lightly but clearly applied. A stamp in this condition could rate two or three times the price of a fine example, all other factors being equal.

Squared circles are collectable in their own right

As Duplex postmarks were replaced by new forms of cancellation such as squared circle handstamps and various forms of machine cancellation, new criteria come into play, but essentially the aim is the same, to find stamps which have been attractively cancelled. Squared circles were designed to combine the date and place of posting (in the central circle) and the obliteration (in the form of the corner bars) in one small and convenient handstamp. Their adoption by many postal administrations around the world would seem to indicate what a good idea they were felt to be at the time. In the case of squared circles it is necessary to make your own judgement: heavily inked bars obscuring the main feature of a stamp's design would not be 'fine', but a light but legible postmark which allows the design to show through would be. Of course, once again, squared circles are very collectable in their own right, so a clear complete (or almost complete) cancellation would almost certainly outweigh the 'marking down' which might normally be applied because the stamp itself was almost obscured.

'Socked on the nose' cancellations have become more popular, especially if they show something significant like the misspelling 'MAURITUS'

Just as in the case of wing margins and perfins, discussed above, fashions are changing in relation to cancellations. In the past, the aim was to find stamps on which the cancellation fell across just one corner of the design, leaving the major part of it clear. Today, interest in exactly where and when the stamp was cancelled, not to mention the

possibility that such partial cancellations may have been forged, have made clear, centrally applied or 'socked-on-the-nose' cancellations much more desirable – although, again, they do need to be lightly applied.

Towards the end of the nineteenth century, rubber packet, newspaper and parcel cancellers began to appear. These, inevitably, obliterated more of the stamp's design than a steel datestamp and any stamp cancelled in this way would fall well short of 'fine'. The rectangular parcel cancellations which replaced the old parcel labels in the twentieth century are also shunned by all, other than postal historians seeking particular markings

Manuscript cancellations

We have briefly touched upon this issue already, but it is worth pursuing in greater depth. The reason why many collectors eschew stamps cancelled by pen marks is that they very often suggest fiscal, rather than postal, use. Fiscally used stamps are normally much cheaper than postally used examples, even with the significant increase in interest in revenue stamps which has taken place in the last decade. However, individual post offices in a number of countries have resorted to this form of cancellation from time to time and examples are sometimes even more desirable than the same stamp with a clear dated postmark. On the other hand, Australian postage due stamps are often found correctly cancelled in manuscript, rather than by a dated postmark. Although these are perfectly collectable, they are certainly nowhere near as desirable as similar examples with a 'proper' postmark and would probably rate no more than 20 per cent of catalogue, if that.

Individual post offices have resorted to manuscript cancellations from time to time: the Gold Coast stamp was used in Dodowah

Returning to fiscal cancellations, these take a number of forms and, since the stamps concerned are often of high face value, some are more desirable than others. The early 'Arms' high values of Rhodesia are relatively common fiscally used, cancelled by rubber handstamps in a variety of colours and often perfined as well. Such examples would rate barely 5 per cent of the catalogue price of postally used examples. The New Zealand 'long' Queen Victoria and 'Arms' high values were designed for both postal and fiscal use and the prices given for them in the catalogue are for examples with clear postal cancellations. However, some revenue cancels are similar in form to postal ones, so it is important that sufficient of the cancel falls on the stamp to guarantee postal use. Again, fiscally used examples would generally rate only 5 per cent or so of the price of postally used ones, while, among stamps which have seen revenue use, clear black 'Stamp Office' and other similar types are much more desirable than purple rubber handstamps, embossed cancels, manuscript markings and stamps which have been perforated through.

Early 'Arms' high values of Rhodesia are relatively common fiscally used

It is important that sufficient of the cancel falls on the stamp to guarantee postal use

Telegraphic postmarks

Generally speaking, just as stamp collectors prefer stamps which have not been fiscally used, they are also not keen on those which have identifiable telegraphic cancellations. Often, the same canceller was used for both purposes, in which case a stamp, once removed from a telegraph form would be indistinguishable from a postally used example and would therefore be equally acceptable. However, Indian high values that have been used telegraphically can often be identified by their cancellations which have three concentric arcs in the segments of the postmark immediately above and below the band across the centre of the cancellation which contains the date of sending. It is noted in the catalogue, for example, that India SG 147, the Edward VII 25r., can be supplied at one third of the price quoted in the catalogue (currently £1500), with a telegraphic cancellation. Other values should be similarly discounted.

1s. greens from plates 5 and 6 are not worth a premium

In light of this, it may seem strange that Great Britain Queen Victoria high values which were almost exclusively used for telegraphic or accounting purposes should be more highly priced than any which were used postally, simply because the quality of cancellation is vastly superior and, here, the prices quoted in the catalogue would be for telegraphically used examples, since this would be the only way of obtaining 'fine used'. Probably, the vast majority of fine used middle values, from 4d. to 2s. were also once attached to telegraph forms and many are relatively common in this form; notably the 1s. green from plates 5 and 6, which would not be worth a premium over catalogue in this condition, while others, notably the 2½d. rosy mauve or any 9d. value would merit the premiums, sometimes substantial premiums, quoted in the catalogue for 'well centred, lightly used'.

It has sometimes been remarked upon that some GB surface-printed issues are more highly priced in the main GB listing than they are in some of the 'used abroad' sections. An 1873-80 2½d. rosy mauve (SG 141), for example, is priced at £80 in the GB listing, but £28 used in Suez, £24 used in Constantinople, £21 used in Gibraltar and just £17 used in Malta. This is not because there is less interest in GB used abroad, but because the prices are for 'fine condition for the issue concerned'. GB stamps used in Malta are generally fairly heavily cancelled by the 'A25' obliterator and the price quoted would be for an example in this form, whereas the price in the GB listing would be for a considerably better stamp. The two conclusions which can be drawn from this are that, firstly, a British stamp with a light Malta c.d.s. should be priced according to the GB listing, where that price is higher, and, secondly, that one should expect to pay very considerably less than the price in the GB section of the catalogue for a stamp with an 'average' numeral cancellation, which would only rate between 10 and 20 percent of catalogue, depending on the scarcity of the stamp and the extent to which it is obliterated by the postmark.

A British stamp with light Malta c.d.s. should be priced according to the GB listing

Wartime Malay States stamps should have identifiable pre-occupation datestamps (left), not post-war cancellations, such as that on the 6c. (right)

It is worth mentioning at this point that, to be worth full catalogue price, a stamp also needs to be used 'in period'. There are notes in the catalogue (such as that below Perak No. 121 or Muscat No. O10) indicating that the price shown is for a stamp with clearly identifiable contemporary cancellation. Stamps used later, in the case of Malayan States after the Japanese occupation had ended, are worth much less than catalogue price, even though they were still valid for postage in the early post-war period.

Collectors should be wary of any stamp with a non-contemporary cancellation, however fine it may appear in all other respects, and expect to pay proportionately less for it. It must be remembered, of course, that some stamps were in normal use over prolonged periods, so it pays to be aware of the 'correct' postmark types for all stamps.

Be wary of stamps with non-contemporary cancellations, however attractive they may seem

Forged cancellations

The problem of forged cancellations has gained much greater prominence in the last few years. This is at least partly due to the increased demand for fine quality insofar as mint stamps are concerned. Heavily mounted or toned stamps are, as commented earlier, worth only a small fraction of catalogue price, so there is clearly an opportunity for the unscrupulous to turn them into 'fine used', in order to enhance their value. Fiscally used stamps may also have had their cancellations removed and any remains of them covered up by forged postmarks, while a great many stamps simply command a higher price used than they do mint, having been little used at the time they were current.

The upshot is that we all need to be aware of stamps which, at first sight, appear to be used, but bear cancellations which cannot be identified, A nice clean ring across the corner of a stamp, an apparently smeared c.d.s. on which neither the place of posting nor the date can be seen, or a general black smudge, reminiscent of many modern British Post Office operational postmarks, should all be avoided, unless they are known to be typical of the place and period concerned.

Fiscally used stamps may have their cancellations removed and covered up

'Madame Joseph' cancellations are becoming very collectable

Such stamps are really of 'spacefiller' status only and would usually not merit a price of more than one tenth of catalogue, if that.

More sophisticated forged cancellations also exist, of course and it is fair to say that the extent of this problem has only recently been recognised. Some of them are becoming collectable in their own right. However, these have now become of such interest that a stamp catalogued at less than about £10 is often of greater value with a clear Madame Joseph cancellation than it would be genuinely used. Higher value stamps would be discounted, though, but would still rate around one third of the price of a genuine example, taking the cheaper of the used or unused prices. Thus, a 1933 Falkland Islands Centenary £1 with the famous Port Stanley, '6 JA 33' forged postmark sells for about £750. Other forged cancellations are of less interest, especially more modern ones and those which have been drawn on by hand!

Another new development is 'postmarks' applied by ink-jet printer. In such cases close magnification will show the cancellation to be made up of a series of dots rather than the clearly inked lines of a genuine marking.

Look out for forged cancellations which have been drawn by hand or applied by ink-jet printer!

'Chops' and manuscript endorsements bring down the value of a used stamp

While on the subject of 'drawn in by hand', collectors in the past – including some very eminent ones – were in the habit of 'enhancing' slightly

unclear postal markings by drawing over them in Indian ink. Less expensive stamps are seriously devalued in this condition, especially if the postmark is a heavy or disfiguring one. Major rarities would be less devalued in percentage terms, however, and could still rate up to about one third the price of an 'unenhanced' stamp with the same cancellation.

Many businesses in Asian countries, especially forwarding agents, were in the habit of cancelling their stamps with 'chops', while individuals frequently wrote across them in manuscript in order to discourage theft. Catalogue prices are for stamps without such endorsements, with a neat handstamped 'chop' reducing the price by at least one third and a handwritten one by around two thirds.

Cancelled to order

Prices in the catalogue are, generally, for fine postally used, but for many modern issues they relate to cancelled to order examples. This does not refer to the selling of cancelled stamps for less than face value for the making up of stamp packets, as was the practice in many Eastern European countries between the 1950s and 1990s, and in North Borneo up to 1912 or Ghana in the 1950s. These latter examples are noted in the catalogue, with separate prices for the North Borneo stamps, while it is noted that catalogue prices for Ghana refer to cancelled to order, properly postally used stamps being worth a little more.

As the volume of worldwide stamp issues has escalated in the last 30 years and the cost of having postally used stamps removed from envelopes, soaked, dried and sorted has risen, it is no longer practicable for the stamp trade to supply fine postally used examples of most modern issues. They are therefore supplied cancelled by the postal administration concerned at the same price as mint examples, although as new issues they may be slightly more expensive, owing to the extra handling costs involved. Catalogue price is therefore for stamps 'cancelled to order' or 'cancelled by favour', although fine postally used examples would merit the same price. Unfortunately, as collectors in Britain and the USA are aware, 'fine' and 'postally used' are two expressions which are rarely used together when discussing modern issues, since our respective postal administrations have deliberately returned to the philosophy of their Victorian predecessors and 'obliterated', rather than 'cancelled', any stamp being used to prepay postage. In the circumstances, therefore, catalogue price for used twentieth or twenty-first century GB refers to stamps cancelled by a light circular or oval datestamp. Rubber packet or parcel handstamps, ink-jet cancellations slogan postmarks or wavy lines are worthy only of a small proportion of catalogue, the size of that proportion depending, once again, on the appearance of the stamp and its relative scarcity.

Modern GB prices are for c.d.s. used, wavy lines are worth only a small proportion of catalogue

That, indeed, encapsulates the relationship between condition and price. In this article we have reviewed the various aspects of 'condition' and how they can vary from country to country and from issue to issue. The catalogue price is for 'fine for the issue concerned', meaning fine in every respect, although a better than fine cancellation might outweigh a slight deficiency in centring, to allow a stamp to still be classified as 'fine'.

The end result is that, when buying, it is vitally important to carefully consider the condition of the item as well as its price and whether or not you want it and, when satisfied on all three counts, make your purchase – before anyone else gets in first!

This is an updated version of a series of articles published in Gibbons Stamp Monthly *in 2003 under the title of "Defining 'Fine'".*

General Philatelic Information and Guidelines to the Scope of Stanley Gibbons Commonwealth catalogues

These notes reflect current practice in compiling the Stanley Gibbons Commonwealth Catalogues.

The Stanley Gibbons Stamp Catalogue has a very long history and the vast quantity of information it contains has been carefully built up by successive generations through the work of countless individuals. Philately is never static and the Catalogue has evolved and developed over the years. These notes relate to the current criteria upon which a stamp may be listed or priced. These criteria have developed over time and may have differed somewhat in the early years of this catalogue. These notes are not intended to suggest that we plan to make wholesale changes to the listing of classic issues in order to bring them into line with today's listing policy, they are designed to inform catalogue users as to the policies currently in operation.

PRICES

The prices quoted in this Catalogue are the estimated selling prices of Stanley Gibbons Ltd at the time of publication. They are, unless it is specifically stated otherwise, for examples in fine condition for the issue concerned. Superb examples are worth more; those of a lower quality considerably less.

All prices are subject to change without prior notice and Stanley Gibbons Ltd may from time to time offer stamps below catalogue price. Individual low value stamps sold at 399 Strand are liable to an additional handling charge. Purchasers of new issues should note the prices charged for them contain an element for the service rendered and so may exceed the prices shown when the stamps are subsequently catalogued. Postage and handling charges are extra.

No guarantee is given to supply all stamps priced, since it is not possible to keep every catalogued item in stock. Commemorative issues may, at times, only be available in complete sets and not as individual values.

Quotation of prices. The prices in the left-hand column are for unused stamps and those in the right-hand column are for used.

A dagger (†) denotes that the item listed does not exist in that condition and a blank, or dash, that it exists, or may exist, but we are unable to quote a price.

We welcome information concerning items which are currently unpriced. Such assistance may lead to them being priced in future editions.

Prices are expressed in pounds and pence sterling. One pound comprises 100 pence (£1 = 100p).

The method of notation is as follows: pence in numerals (e.g. 10 denotes ten pence); pounds and pence, up to £100, in numerals (e.g. 4.25 denotes four pounds and twenty-five pence); prices above £100 are expressed in whole pounds with the '£' sign shown.

Unused stamps. Great Britain and Commonwealth: the prices for unused stamps of Queen Victoria to King George V are for lightly hinged examples. Unused prices for King Edward VIII, King George VI and Queen Elizabeth issues are for unmounted mint or 'mint never hinged' (MNH).

Some stamps from the King George VI period are often difficult to find in unmounted mint condition. In such instances we would expect that collectors would need to pay a high proportion of the price quoted to obtain mounted mint examples. Generally speaking lightly mounted mint stamps from this reign, issued before 1945, are in considerable demand.

Used stamps. The used prices are normally for stamps fine postally used, which for the vast majority of those issued since 1900 refers to cancellation with a clear circular or oval dated postmark. It may also include stamps cancelled to order, where this practice exists, or with commemorative or 'first day' postmarks.

A pen-cancellation on early issues can sometimes correctly denote postal use. Instances are individually noted in the Catalogue in explanation of the used price given.

Prices quoted for bisects on cover or large piece are for those dated during the period officially authorised.

Stamps not sold unused to the public (e.g. some official stamps) are priced used only.

The use of 'unified' designs, that is stamps inscribed for both postal and fiscal purposes, results in a number of stamps of very high face value. In some instances these may not have been primarily intended for postal purposes, but if they are so inscribed we include them. The used prices shown refer to stamps postally used, although fiscally used examples are sometimes priced in brackets. Collectors should be careful to avoid stamps with fiscal cancellations that have had their cancellations removed and fraudulent postmarks applied.

Cover prices. To assist collectors, cover prices are quoted for issues up to 1945 at the beginning of each country.

The system gives a general guide in the form of a factor by which the corresponding used price of the basic loose stamp should be multiplied when found in fine average condition on cover.

Care is needed in applying the factors and they relate to a cover which bears a single of the denomination listed; if more than one denomination is present the most highly priced attracts the multiplier and the remainder are priced at the simple figure for used singles in arriving at a total.

The cover should be of non-philatelic origin; bearing the correct postal rate for the period and distance involved and cancelled with the markings normal to the offices concerned. Purely philatelic items have a cover value only slightly greater than the catalogue value for the corresponding used stamps. This applies generally to those high-value stamps used philatelically rather than in the normal course of commerce. Low-value stamps, e.g. ¼d. and ½d., are desirable when used as a single rate on cover and merit an increase in 'multiplier' value.

First day covers in the period up to 1945 are not within the scope of the system and the multiplier should not be used. As a special category of philatelic usage, with wide variations in valuation according to scarcity, they require separate treatment.

Oversized covers, difficult to accommodate on an album page, should be reckoned as worth little more than the corresponding value of the used stamps. The condition of a cover also affects its value. Except for 'wreck covers', serious damage or soiling reduce the value where the postal markings and stamps are ordinary ones. Conversely, visual appeal adds to the value and this can include freshness of appearance, important addresses, old-fashioned but legible hand-writing, historic town-names, etc.

The multipliers are a base on which further value would be added to take account of the cover's postal historical importance in demonstrating such things as unusual, scarce or emergency cancels, interesting routes, significant postal markings, combination usage, the development of postal rates, and so on.

Minimum price. The minimum catalogue price quoted is 10p. For individual stamps prices between 10p. and 95p. are provided as a guide for catalogue users. The lowest price charged for individual stamps or sets purchased from Stanley Gibbons Ltd is £1

Set prices. Set prices are generally for one of each value, excluding shades and varieties, but including major colour changes. Where there are alternative shades, etc., the cheapest is usually included. The number of stamps in the set is always stated for clarity. The prices for sets containing se-tenant pieces are based on the prices quoted for such combinations, and not on those for the individual stamps.

Varieties. Where plate or cylinder varieties are priced in used condition the price quoted is for a fine used example with the cancellation well clear of the listed flaw.

Specimen stamps. The pricing of these items is explained under that heading.

Stamp booklets. Prices are for complete assembled booklets in fine condition with those issued before 1945 showing normal wear and tear. Incomplete booklets and those which have been 'exploded' will, in general, be worth less than the figure quoted.

Repricing. Collectors will be aware that the market factors of supply and demand directly influence the prices quoted in this Catalogue. Whatever the scarcity of a particular stamp, if there is no one in the market who wishes to buy it cannot be expected to achieve a high price. Conversely, the same item actively sought by numerous potential buyers may cause the price to rise.

All the prices in this Catalogue are examined during the preparation of each new edition by the expert staff of Stanley Gibbons and repriced as necessary. They take many factors into account, including supply and demand, and are in close touch with the international stamp market and the auction world.

Commonwealth cover prices and advice on postal history material originally provided by Edward B Proud.

GUARANTEE

All stamps are guaranteed originals in the following terms:

If not as described, and returned by the purchaser, we undertake to refund the price paid to us in the original transaction. If any stamp is certified as genuine by the Expert Committee of the Royal Philatelic Society, London, or by BPA Expertising Ltd, the purchaser shall not be entitled to make any claim against us for any error, omission or mistake in such certificate.

Consumers' statutory rights are not affected by the above guarantee.

The recognised Expert Committees in this country are those of the Royal Philatelic Society, 41 Devonshire Place, London W1G, 6JY, and BPA Expertising Ltd, PO Box 1141, Guildford, Surrey GU5 0WR. They do not undertake valuations under any circumstances and fees are payable for their services.

CONDITION GUIDE

To assist collectors in assessing the true value of items they are considering buying or in reviewing stamps already in their collections, we now offer a more detailed guide to the condition of stamps on which this catalogue's prices are based.

For a stamp to be described as 'Fine', it should be sound in all respects, without creases, bends, wrinkles, pin holes, thins or tears. If perforated, all perforation 'teeth' should be intact, it should not suffer from fading, rubbing or toning and it should be of clean, fresh appearance.

Margins on imperforate stamps: These should be even on all sides and should be at least as wide as half the distance between that stamp and the next. To have one or more margins of less than this width, would normally preclude a stamp from being described as 'Fine'. Some early stamps were positioned very close together on the printing plate and in such cases 'Fine' margins would necessarily be narrow. On the other hand, some plates were laid down to give a substantial gap between individual stamps and in such cases margins would be expected to be much wider.

An 'average' four-margin example would have a narrower margin on one or more sides and should be priced accordingly, while a stamp with wider, yet even, margins than 'Fine' would merit the description 'Very Fine' or 'Superb' and, if available, would command a price in excess of that quoted in the catalogue.

Gum: Since the prices for stamps of King Edward VIII, King George VI and Queen Elizabeth are for 'unmounted' or 'never hinged' mint, even stamps from these reigns which have been very lightly mounted should be available at a discount from catalogue price, the more obvious the hinge marks, the greater the discount.

Catalogue prices for stamps issued prior to King Edward VIII's reign are for mounted mint, so unmounted examples would be worth a premium. Hinge marks on 20th century stamps should not be too obtrusive, and should be at least in the lightly mounted category. For 19th century stamps more obvious hinging would be acceptable, but stamps should still carry a large part of their original gum—'Large part o.g.'—in order to be described as 'Fine'.

Centring: Ideally, the stamp's image should appear in the exact centre of the perforated area, giving equal margins on all sides. 'Fine' centring would be close to this ideal with any deviation having an effect on the value of the stamp. As in the case of the margins on imperforate stamps, it should be borne in mind that the space between some early stamps was very narrow, so it was very difficult to achieve accurate perforation, especially when the technology was in its infancy. Thus, poor centring would have a less damaging effect on the value of a 19th century stamp than on a 20th century example, but the premium put on a perfectly centred specimen would be greater.

Cancellations: Early cancellation devices were designed to 'obliterate' the stamp in order to prevent it being reused and this is still an important objective for today's postal administrations. Stamp collectors, on the other hand, prefer postmarks to be lightly applied, clear, and to leave as much as possible of the design visible. Dated, circular cancellations have long been 'the postmark of choice', but the definition of a 'Fine' cancellation will depend upon the types of cancellation in use at the time a stamp was current—it is clearly illogical to seek a circular datestamp on a Penny Black.

'Fine', by definition, will be superior to 'Average', so, in terms of cancellation quality, if one begins by identifying what 'Average' looks like, then one will be half way to identifying 'Fine'. The illustrations will give some guidance on mid-19th century and mid-20th century cancellations of Great Britain, but types of cancellation in general use in each country and in each period will determine the appearance of 'Fine'.

As for the factors discussed above, anything less than 'Fine' will result in a downgrading of the stamp concerned, while a very fine or superb cancellation will be worth a premium.

Combining the factors: To merit the description 'Fine', a stamp should be fine in every respect, but a small deficiency in one area might be made up for in another by a factor meriting an 'Extremely Fine' description.

Some early issues are so seldom found in what would normally be considered to be 'Fine' condition, the catalogue prices are for a slightly lower grade, with 'Fine' examples being worth a premium. In such cases a note to this effect is given in the catalogue, while elsewhere premiums are given for well-centred, lightly cancelled examples.

Stamps graded at less than fine remain collectable and, in the case of more highly priced stamps, will continue to hold a value. Nevertheless, buyers should always bear condition in mind.

Contents. The Catalogue is confined to adhesive postage stamps, including miniature sheets. For particular categories the rules are:

(a) Revenue (fiscal) stamps are listed only where they have been expressly authorised for postal duty.

(b) Stamps issued only precancelled are included, but normally issued stamps available additionally with precancel have no separate precancel listing unless the face value is changed.

(c) Stamps prepared for use but not issued, hitherto accorded full listing, are nowadays foot-noted with a price (where possible).

(d) Bisects (trisects, etc.) are only listed where such usage was officially authorised.

(e) Stamps issued only on first day covers or in presentation packs and not available separately are not listed but may be priced in a footnote.

(f) New printings are only included in this Catalogue where they show a major philatelic variety, such as a change in shade, watermark or paper. Stamps which exist with or without imprint dates are listed separately; changes in

MARGINS ON IMPERFORATE STAMPS

| Superb | Very fine | Fine | Average | Poor |

GUM

| Unmounted | Very lightly mounted | Lightly mounted | Mounted/large part original gum (o.g.). | Heavily mounted small part o.g |

CENTRING

| Superb | Very fine | Fine | Average | Poor |

CANCELLATIONS

| Superb | Very fine | Fine | Average | Poor |

| Superb | Very fine |

| Fine | Average | Poor |

imprint dates are mentioned in footnotes.

(g) Official and unofficial reprints are dealt with by footnote.

(h) Stamps from imperforate printings of modern issues which occur perforated are covered by footnotes, but are listed where widely available for postal use.

Exclusions. The following are excluded:

(a) non-postal revenue or fiscal stamps;

(b) postage stamps used fiscally (although prices are now given for some fiscally used high values);

(c) local carriage labels and private local issues;

(d) bogus or phantom stamps;

(e) railway or airline letter fee stamps, bus or road transport company labels or the stamps of private postal companies operating under licence from the national authority;

(f) cut-outs;

(g) all types of non-postal labels and souvenirs;

(h) documentary labels for the postal service, e.g. registration, recorded delivery, air-mail etiquettes, etc.;

(i) privately applied embellishments to official issues and privately commissioned items generally;

(j) stamps for training postal officers.

Full listing. 'Full listing' confers our recognition and implies allotting a catalogue number and (wherever possible) a price quotation.

In judging status for inclusion in the catalogue broad considerations are applied to stamps. They must be issued by a legitimate postal authority, recognised by the government concerned, and must be adhesives valid for proper postal use in the class of service for which they are inscribed. Stamps, with the exception of such categories as postage dues and officials, must be available to the general public, at face value, in reasonable quantities without any artificial restrictions being imposed on their distribution.

For errors and varieties the criterion is legitimate (albeit inadvertent) sale through a postal administration in the normal course of business. Details of provenance are always important; printers' waste and deliberately manufactured material are excluded.

Certificates. In assessing unlisted items due weight is given to Certificates from recognised Expert Committees and, where appropriate, we will usually ask to see them.

Date of issue. Where local issue dates differ from dates of release by agencies, 'date of issue' is the local date. Fortuitous stray usage before the officially intended date is disregarded in listing.

Catalogue numbers. Stamps of each country are catalogued chronologically by date of issue. Subsidiary classes are placed at the end of the country, as separate lists, with a distinguishing letter prefix to the catalogue number, e.g. D for postage due, O for official and E for express delivery stamps.

The catalogue number appears in the extreme left-column. The boldface Type numbers in the next column are merely cross-references to illustrations.

A catalogue number with a suffix will normally relate to the main number, so 137a will be a variant of No. 137, unless the suffix appears as part of the number in the left-hand column such as Great Britain No. 20a, in which case that should be treated as the main number. A number with multiple suffixes will relate to the first letter or letters of that suffix, so 137ab will be a variant of 137a and 137aba a variant of 137ab. The exception is an "aa" suffix, which will precede an "a" and always refers to the main number, so 137aa relates to 137, not 137a.

Once published in the Catalogue, numbers are changed as little as possible; really serious renumbering is reserved for the occasions when a complete country or an entire issue is being rewritten. The edition first affected includes cross-reference tables of old and new numbers.

Our catalogue numbers are universally recognised in specifying stamps and as a hallmark of status.

Illustrations. Stamps are illustrated at three-quarters linear size. Stamps not illustrated are the same size and format as the value shown, unless otherwise indicated. Stamps issued only as miniature sheets have the stamp alone illustrated but sheet size is also quoted. Overprints, surcharges, watermarks and postmarks are normally actual size. Illustrations of varieties are often enlarged to show the detail. Stamp booklet covers are illustrated half-size, unless otherwise indicated.

Designers. Designers' names are quoted where known, though space precludes naming every individual concerned in the production of a set. In particular, photographers supplying material are usually named only where they also make an active contribution in the design stage; posed photographs of reigning monarchs are, however, an exception to this rule.

CONTACTING THE CATALOGUE EDITOR

The editor is always interested in hearing from people who have new information which will improve or correct the Catalogue. As a general rule he must see and examine the actual stamps before they can be considered for listing; photographs or photocopies are insufficient evidence.

Submissions should be made in writing to the Catalogue Editor, Stanley Gibbons Publications at the Ringwood office. The cost of return postage for items submitted is appreciated, and this should include the registration fee if required.

Where information is solicited purely for the benefit of the enquirer, the editor cannot undertake to reply if the answer is already contained in these published notes or if return postage is omitted. Written communications are greatly preferred to enquiries by telephone or e-mail and the editor regrets that he or his staff cannot see personal callers without a prior appointment being made. Correspondence may be subject to delay during the production period of each new edition.

The editor welcomes close contact with study circles and is interested, too, in finding reliable local correspondents who will verify and supplement official information in countries where this is deficient.

> We regret we do not give opinions as to the genuineness of stamps, nor do we identify stamps or number them by our Catalogue.

TECHNICAL MATTERS

The meanings of the technical terms used in the catalogue will be found in our *Philatelic Terms Illustrated*.

References below to (more specialised) listings are to be taken to indicate, as appropriate, the Stanley Gibbons *Great Britain Specialised Catalogue* in five volumes or the *Great Britain Concise Catalogue*.

1. Printing

Printing errors. Errors in printing are of major interest to the Catalogue. Authenticated items meriting consideration would include: background, centre or frame inverted or omitted; centre or subject transposed; error of colour; error or omission of value; double prints and impressions; printed both sides; and so on. Apparent "double prints" including overprints, on stamps printed by offset litho arising from movement of the rubber "blanket" involved in this process are however, outside the scope of this catalogue, although they may be included in more specialised listings. Designs *tête-bêche*, whether intentionally or by accident, are listable. *Se-tenant* arrangements of stamps are recognised in the listings or footnotes. Gutter pairs (a pair of stamps separated by blank margin) are not included in this volume. Colours only partially omitted are not listed. Stamps with embossing omitted are reserved for our more specialised listings.

Printing varieties. Listing is accorded to major changes in the printing base which lead to completely new types. In recess-printing this could be a design re-engraved; in photogravure or photolithography a screen altered in whole or in part. It can also encompass flat-bed and rotary printing if the results are readily distinguishable.

To be considered at all, varieties must be constant.

Early stamps, produced by primitive methods, were prone to numerous imperfections; the lists reflect this, recognising re-entries, retouches, broken frames, misshapen letters, and so on. Printing technology has, however, radically improved over the years, during which time photogravure and lithography have become predominant. Varieties nowadays are more in the nature of flaws and these, being too specialised for this general catalogue, are almost always outside the scope.

In no catalogue, however, do we list such items as: dry prints, kiss prints, doctor-blade flaws, colour shifts or registration flaws (unless they lead to complete omission of a colour from an individual stamp), lithographic ring flaws, and so on. Neither do we recognise fortuitous happenings like paper creases or confetti flaws.

"Varieties of the varieties". We no longer provide individual listings for combinations of two or more varieties; thus a plate variety or overprinting error will not be listed for various watermark orientations.

Overprints (and surcharges). Overprints of different types qualify for separate listing. These include overprints in different colours; overprints from different printing processes such as litho and typo; overprints in totally different typefaces, etc. Major errors in machine-printed overprints are important and listable. They include: overprint inverted or omitted; overprint double (treble, etc.); overprint diagonal; overprint double, one inverted; pairs with one overprint omitted, e.g. from a radical shift to an adjoining stamp; error of colour; error of type fount; letters inverted or omitted, etc. If the overprint is handstamped, few of these would qualify and a distinction is drawn. We continue, however, to list pairs of stamps where one has a handstamped overprint and the other has not.

Albino prints or double prints, one of them being albino (i.e. showing an uninked impression of the printing plate) are listable unless they are particularly common in this form (see the note below Travancore No. 32fa, for example). We do not, however, normally list reversed albino overprints, caused by the accidental or deliberate folding of sheets prior to overprinting (British Levant Nos. 51/8).

Varieties occurring in overprints will often take the form of broken letters, slight differences in spacing, rising spaces, etc. Only the most important would be considered for listing or footnote mention.

Sheet positions. If space permits we quote sheet positions of listed varieties and authenticated data is solicited for this purpose.

De La Rue plates. The Catalogue classifies the general plates used by De La Rue for printing British Colonial stamps as follows:

VICTORIAN KEY TYPE

Die I

1. The ball of decoration on the second point of the crown appears as a dark mass of lines.
2. Dark vertical shading separates the front hair from the bun.
3. The vertical line of colour outlining the front of the throat stops at the sixth line of shading on the neck.
4. The white space in the coil of the hair above the curl is roughly the shape of a pin's head.

Die II

1. There are very few lines of colour in the ball and it appears almost white.
2. A white vertical strand of hair appears in place of the dark shading.
3. The line stops at the eighth line of shading.
4. The white space is oblong, with a line of colour partially dividing it at the left end.

Plates numbered 1 and 2 are both Die I. Plates 3 and 4 are Die II.

GEORGIAN KEY TYPE

Die I

A. The second (thick) line below the name of the country is cut slanting, conforming roughly to the shape of the crown on each side.
B. The labels of solid colour bearing the words "POSTAGE" and "& REVENUE" are square at the inner top corners.
C. There is a projecting "bud" on the outer spiral of the ornament in each of the lower corners.

Die II

A. The second line is cut vertically on each side of the crown.
B. The labels curve inwards at the top.
C. There is no "bud" in this position.

Unless otherwise stated in the lists, all stamps with watermark Multiple Crown CA (w **8**) are Die I while those with watermark Multiple Crown Script CA (w **9**) are Die II. The Georgian Die II was introduced in April 1921 and was used for Plates 10 to 22 and 26 to 28. Plates 23 to 25 were made from Die I by mistake.

2. Paper

All stamps listed are deemed to be on (ordinary) paper of the wove type and white in colour; only departures from this are normally mentioned.

Types. Where classification so requires we distinguish such other types of paper as, for example, vertically and horizontally laid; wove and laid bâtonné; card(board); carton; cartridge; glazed; granite; native; pelure; porous; quadrillé; ribbed; rice; and silk thread.

Wove paper   Laid paper

Granite paper   Quadrillé paper

Burelé band

The various makeshifts for normal paper are listed as appropriate. The varieties of double paper and joined paper are recognised. The security device of a printed burelé band on the back of a stamp, as in early Queensland, qualifies for listing.

Descriptive terms. The fact that a paper is handmade (and thus probably of uneven thickness) is mentioned where necessary. Such descriptive terms as "hard" and "soft"; "smooth" and "rough"; "thick", "medium" and "thin" are applied where there is philatelic merit in classifying papers.

Coloured, very white and toned papers. A coloured paper is one that is coloured right through (front and back of the stamp). In the Catalogue the colour of the paper is given in italics, thus: black/*rose* = black design on rose paper.

Papers have been made specially white in recent years by, for example, a very heavy coating of chalk. We do not classify shades of whiteness of paper as distinct varieties. There does exist, however, a type of paper from early days called toned. This is off-white, often brownish or buffish, but it cannot be assigned any definite colour. A toning effect brought on by climate, incorrect storage or gum staining is disregarded here, as this was not the state of the paper when issued.

"Ordinary" and "Chalk-surfaced" papers. The availability of many postage stamps for revenue purposes made necessary some safeguard against the illegitimate re-use of stamps with removable cancellations. This was at first secured by using fugitive inks and later by printing on paper surfaced by coatings containing either chalk or china clay, both of which made it difficult to remove any form of obliteration without damaging the stamp design.

This catalogue lists these chalk-surfaced paper varieties from their introduction in 1905. Where no indication is given, the paper is "ordinary".

The "traditional" method of indentifying chalk-surfaced papers has been that, when touched with a silver wire, a black mark is left on the paper, and the listings in this catalogue are based on that test. However, the test itself is now largely discredited, for, although the mark can be removed by a soft rubber, some damage to the stamp will result from its use.

The difference between chalk-surfaced and pre-war ordinary papers is fairly clear: chalk-surfaced papers being smoother to the touch and showing a characteristic sheen when light is reflected off their surface. Under good magnification tiny bubbles or pock marks can be seen on the surface of the stamp and at the tips of the perforations the surfacing appears "broken". Traces of paper fibres are evident on the surface of ordinary paper and the ink shows a degree of absorption into it.

Initial chalk-surfaced paper printings by De La Rue had a thinner coating than subsequently became the norm. The characteristics described above are less pronounced in these printings.

During and after the Second World War, substitute papers replaced the chalk-surfaced papers, these do not react to the silver test and are therefore classed as "ordinary", although differentiating them without recourse to it is more difficult, for, although the characteristics of the chalk-surfaced paper remained the same, some of the ordinary papers appear much smoother than earlier papers and many do not show the watermark clearly. Experience is the only solution to identifying these, and comparison with stamps whose paper type is without question will be of great help.

Another type of paper, known as "thin striated" was used only for the Bahamas 1s. and 5s. (Nos. 155a, 156a, 171 and 174) and for several stamps of the Malayan states. Hitherto these have been described as "chalk-surfaced" since they gave some reaction to the silver test, but they are much thinner than usual chalk-surfaced papers, with the watermark showing clearly. Stamps on this paper show a slightly 'ribbed'

effect when the stamp is held up to the light. Again, comparison with a known striated paper stamp, such as the 1941 Straits Settlements Die II 2c. orange (No. 294) will prove invaluable in separating these papers.

Glazed paper. In 1969 the Crown Agents introduced a new general-purpose paper for use in conjunction with all current printing processes. It generally has a marked glossy surface but the degree varies according to the process used, being more marked in recess-printing stamps. As it does not respond to the silver test this presents a further test where previous printings were on chalky paper. A change of paper to the glazed variety merits separate listing.

Green and yellow papers. Issues of the First World War and immediate postwar period occur on green and yellow papers and these are given separate Catalogue listing. The original coloured papers (coloured throughout) gave way to surface-coloured papers, the stamps having "white backs"; other stamps show one colour on the front and a different one at the back. Because of the numerous variations a grouping of colours is adopted as follows:

Yellow papers

(1) The original *yellow* paper (throughout), usually bright in colour. The gum is often sparse, of harsh consistency and dull-looking. Used 1912–1920.
(2) The *white-backs*. Used 1913–1914.
(3) A bright lemon paper. The colour must have a pronounced greenish tinge, different from the "yellow" in (1). As a rule, the gum on stamps using this lemon paper is plentiful, smooth and shiny, and the watermark shows distinctly. Care is needed with stamps printed in green on yellow paper (1) as it may appear that the paper is this lemon. Used 1914–1916.
(4) An experimental *orange-buff* paper. The colour must have a distinct brownish tinge. It is not to be confused with a muddy yellow (1) nor the misleading appearance (on the surface) of stamps printed in red on yellow paper where an engraved plate has been insufficiently wiped. Used 1918–1921.
(5) An experimental *buff* paper. This lacks the brownish tinge of (4) and the brightness of the yellow shades. The gum is shiny when compared with the matt type used on (4). Used 1919–1920.
(6) A *pale yellow* paper that has a creamy tone to the yellow. Used from 1920 onwards.

Green papers

(7) The original "green" paper, varying considerably through shades of blue-green and yellow-green, the front and back sometimes differing. Used 1912–1916.
(8) The *white backs*. Used 1913–1914.
(9) A paper blue-green on the surface with *pale olive* back. The back must be markedly paler than the front and this and the pronounced olive tinge to the back distinguish it from (7). Used 1916–1920.
(10) Paper with a vivid green surface, commonly called *emerald-green*; it has the olive back of (9). Used 1920.
(11) Paper with *emerald-green* both back and front. Used from 1920 onwards.

3. Perforation and Rouletting

Perforation gauge. The gauge of a perforation is the number of holes in a length of 2 cm. For correct classification the size of the holes (large or small) may need to be distinguished; in a few cases the actual number of holes on each edge of the stamp needs to be quoted.

Measurement. The Gibbons *Instanta* gauge is the standard for measuring perforations. The stamp is viewed against a dark background with the transparent gauge put on top of it. Though the gauge measures to decimal accuracy, perforations read from it are generally quoted in the Catalogue to the nearest half. For example:

Just over perf 12¾ to just under 13¼ = perf 13
Perf 13¼ exactly, rounded up   = perf 13½
Just over perf 13¼ to just under 13¾ = perf 13½
Perf 13¾ exactly, rounded up   = perf 14

However, where classification depends on it, actual quarter-perforations are quoted.

Notation. Where no perforation is quoted for an issue it is imperforate. Perforations are usually abbreviated (and spoken) as follows, though sometimes they may be spelled out for clarity. This notation for rectangular stamps (the majority) applies to diamond shapes if "top" is read as the edge to the top right.

P 14: perforated alike on all sides (read: "perf 14").

P 14×15: the first figure refers to top and bottom, the second to left and right sides (read: "perf 14 by 15"). This is a compound perforation. For an upright triangular stamp the first figure refers to the two sloping sides and second to the base. In inverted triangulars the base is first and the second figure to the sloping sides.

P 14–15: perforation measuring anything between 14 and 15: the holes are irregularly spaced, thus the gauge may vary along a single line or even along a single edge of the stamp (read: "perf 14 to 15").

P 14 *irregular*: perforated 14 from a worn perforator, giving badly aligned holes irregularly spaced (read: "irregular perf 14").

P *comp(ound)* 14×15: two gauges in use but not necessarily on opposite sides of the stamp. It could be one side in one gauge and three in the other; or two adjacent sides with the same gauge. (Read: "perf compound of 14 and 15".) For three gauges or more, abbreviated as "P 12, 14½, 15 *or compound*" for example.

P 14, 14½: perforated approximately 14¼ (read: "perf 14 or 14½"). It does *not* mean two stamps, one perf 14 and the other perf 14½. This obsolescent notation is gradually being replaced in the Catalogue.

Imperf: imperforate (not perforated)

Imperf×P 14: imperforate at top ad bottom and perf 14 at sides.

P 14×*imperf*: perf 14 at top and bottom and imperforate at sides.

Such headings as "P 13×14 (*vert*) and P 14×13 (*horiz*)" indicate which perforations apply to which stamp format—vertical or horizontal.

Some stamps are additionally perforated so that a label or tab is detachable; others have been perforated for use as two halves. Listings are normally for whole stamps, unless stated otherwise.

Imperf×perf

Other terms. Perforation almost always gives circular holes; where other shapes have been used they are specified, e.g. square holes; lozenge perf. Interrupted perfs are brought about by the omission of pins at regular intervals. Perforations merely simulated by being printed as part of the design are of course ignored. With few exceptions, privately applied perforations are not listed.

In the 19th century perforations are often described as clean cut (clean, sharply incised holes), intermediate or rough (rough holes, imperfectly cut, often the result of blunt pins).

Perforation errors and varieties. Authenticated errors, where a stamp normally perforated is accidentally issued imperforate, are listed provided no traces of perforation (blind holes or indentations) remain. They must be provided as pairs, both stamps wholly imperforate, and are only priced in that form.

Note that several postal administrations and their agencies are now deliberately releasing imperforate versions of issued stamps in restricted quantities and at premium prices. These are not listable, but, where possible, their existance will be noted

Stamps imperforate between stamp and sheet margin are not listed in this catalogue, but such errors on Great Britain stamps will be found in the *Great Britain Specialised Catalogue*.

Pairs described as "imperforate between" have the line of perforations between the two stamps omitted.

Imperf between (horiz pair): a horizontal pair of stamps with perfs all around the edges but none between the stamps.

Imperf between (vert pair): a vertical pair of stamps with perfs all around the edges but none between the stamps.

Imperf between   Imperf horizontally
(vertical pair)   (vertical pair)

Where several of the rows have escaped perforation the resulting varieties are listable. Thus:

Imperf vert (horiz pair): a horizontal pair of stamps perforated top and bottom; all three vertical directions are imperf—the two outer edges and between the stamps.

Imperf horiz (vert pair): a vertical pair perforated at left and right edges; all three horizontal directions are imperf—the top, bottom and between the stamps.

Straight edges. Large sheets cut up before issue to post offices can cause stamps with straight edges, i.e. imperf on one side or on two sides at right angles. They are not usually listable in this condition and are worth less than corresponding stamps properly perforated all round. This does not, however, apply to certain stamps, mainly from coils and booklets, where straight edges on various sides are the manufacturing norm affecting every stamp. The listings and notes make clear which sides are correctly imperf.

Malfunction. Varieties of double, misplaced or partial perforation caused by error or machine malfunction are not listable, neither are freaks, such as perforations placed diagonally from paper folds, nor missing holes caused by broken pins.

Types of perforating. Where necessary for classification, perforation types are distinguished. These include:

Line perforation from one line of pins punching single rows of holes at a time.

Comb perforation from pins disposed across the sheet in comb formation, punching out holes at three sides of the stamp a row at a time.

Harrow perforation applied to a whole pane or sheet at one stroke.

Rotary perforation from toothed wheels operating across a sheet, then crosswise.

Sewing machine perforation. The resultant condition, clean-cut or rough, is distinguished where required.

Pin-perforation is the commonly applied term for pin-roulette in which, instead of being punched out, round holes are pricked by sharp-pointed pins and no paper is removed.

Mixed perforation occurs when stamps with defective perforations are re-perforated in a different gauge.

Punctured stamps. Perforation holes can be punched into the face of the stamp. Patterns of small holes, often in the shape of initial letters, are privately applied devices against pilferage. These (perfins) are outside the scope except for Australia, Canada, Cape of Good Hope, Papua and Sudan where they were used as official stamps by the national administration. Identification devices, when officially inspired, are listed or noted; they can be shapes, or letters or words formed from holes, sometimes converting one class of stamp into another.

Rouletting. In rouletting the paper is cut, for ease of separation, but none is removed. The gauge is measured, when needed, as for perforations. Tradi-

tional French terms descriptive of the type of cut are often used and types include:

Arc roulette (percé en arc). Cuts are minute, spaced arcs, each roughly a semicircle.

Cross roulette (percé en croix). Cuts are tiny diagonal crosses.

Line roulette (percé en ligne or *en ligne droite)*. Short straight cuts parallel to the frame of the stamp. The commonest basic roulette. Where not further described, "roulette" means this type.

Rouletted in colour or coloured roulette (percé en lignes colorées or *en lignes de coleur)*. Cuts with coloured edges, arising from notched rule inked simultaneously with the printing plate.

Saw-tooth roulette (percé en scie). Cuts applied zigzag fashion to resemble the teeth of a saw.

Serpentine roulette (percé en serpentin). Cuts as sharply wavy lines.

Zigzag roulette (percé en zigzags). Short straight cuts at angles in alternate directions, producing sharp points on separation. US usage favours "serrate(d) roulette" for this type.

Pin-roulette (originally *percé en points* and now *perforés trous d'epingle)* is commonly called pin-perforation in English.

4. Gum

All stamps listed are assumed to have gum of some kind; if they were issued without gum this is stated. Original gum (o.g.) means that which was present on the stamp as issued to the public. Deleterious climates and the presence of certain chemicals can cause gum to crack and, with early stamps, even make the paper deteriorate. Unscrupulous fakers are adept in removing it and regumming the stamp to meet the unreasoning demand often made for "full o.g." in cases where such a thing is virtually impossible.

The gum normally used on stamps has been gum arabic until the late 1960s when synthetic adhesives were introduced. Harrison and Sons Ltd for instance used polyvinyl alcohol known to philatelists as PVA. This is almost invisible except for a slight yellowish tinge which was incorporated to make it possible to see that the stamps had been gummed. It has advantages in hot countries, as stamps do not curl and sheets are less likely to stick together. Gum arabic and PVA are not distinguished in the lists except that where a stamp exists in both forms this is indicated in the footnotes. Our more specialised catalogues provide separate listing of gums for Great Britain

5. Watermarks

Stamps are on unwatermarked paper except where the heading to the set says otherwise.

Detection. Watermarks are detected for Catalogue description by one of four methods: (1) holding stamps to the light; (2) laying stamps face down on a dark background; (3) adding a few drops of petroleum ether 40/60 to the stamp laid face down in a watermark tray; (4) by use of the Stanley Gibbons Detectamark, or other equipment, which work by revealing the thinning of the paper at the watermark. (Note that petroleum ether is highly inflammable in use and can damage photogravure stamps.)

Listable types. Stamps occurring on both watermarked and unwatermarked papers are different types and both receive full listing.

Single watermarks (devices occurring once on every stamp) can be modified in size and shape as between different issues; the types are noted but not usually separately listed. Fortuitous absence of watermark from a single stamp or its gross displacement would not be listable.

To overcome registration difficulties the device may be repeated at close intervals (*a multiple watermark*), single stamps thus showing parts of several devices. Similarly, a *large sheet watermark* (or *all-over watermark*) covering numerous stamps can be used. We give informative notes and illustrations for them. The designs may be such that numbers of stamps in the sheet automatically lack watermark: this is not a listable variety. Multiple and all-over watermarks sometimes undergo modifications, but if the various types are difficult to distinguish from single stamps notes are given but not separate listings.

Papermakers' watermarks are noted where known but not listed separately, since most stamps in the sheet will lack them. Sheet watermarks which are nothing more than officially adopted papermakers' watermarks are, however, given normal listing.

Marginal watermarks, falling outside the pane of stamps, are ignored except where misplacement has caused the adjoining row to be affected, in which case they may be footnoted.

They usually consist of straight or angled lines and double-lined capital letters, they are particularly prevalent on some Crown CC and Crown CA watermark stamps.

Watermark errors and varieties. Watermark errors are recognised as of major importance. They comprise stamps intended to be on unwatermarked paper but issued watermarked by mistake, or stamps printed on paper with the wrong watermark. Varieties showing letters omitted from the watermark are also included, but broken or deformed bits on the dandy roll are not listed unless they represent repairs.

Watermark positions. The diagram shows how watermark position is described in the Catalogue. Paper has a side intended for printing and watermarks are usually impressed so that they read normally when looked through from that printed side. However, since philatelists customarily detect watermarks by looking at the back of the stamp the watermark diagram also makes clear what is actually seen.

Illustrations in the Catalogue are of watermarks in normal positions (from the front of the stamps) and are actual size where possible.

Differences in watermark position are collectable varieties. This Catalogue now lists inverted, sideways inverted and reversed watermark varieties on Commonwealth stamps from the 1860s onwards except where the watermark position is completely haphazard or, due to the method of printing, appear in equal quantities, upright and inverted (e.g. Papua Nos. 47/83). In such cases it should be assumed that the price is the same, either way.

Where a watermark comes indiscriminately in various positions our policy is to cover this by a general note: we do not give separate listings because the watermark position in these circumstances has no particular philatelic importance.

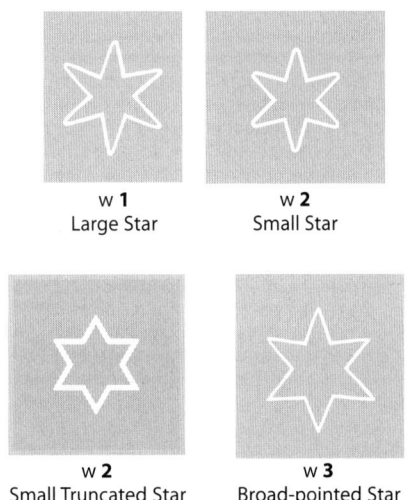

AS DESCRIBED (Read through front of stamp)		AS SEEN DURING WATERMARK DETECTION (Stamp face down and back examined
GvR	Normal	ЯvᎼ
ЯvᎼ	Inverted	ᎬʌЯ
ЯvᎼ	Reversed	GvR
ᎬʌЯ	Inverted and Reversed	GvR
GvR	Sideways	ᎬʌЯ
GvR	Sideways Inverted	ЯvᎼ

As shown in the diagram, a watermark described as 'sideways' will normally show the top of the watermark (as shown in its illustration), pointing to the left of the stamp, as seen from the front and to the right as seen from the back.

For clarification, or in cases where the 'normal' watermark is 'sideways inverted' a note is generally provided at the foot of the relevant listing, particularly where sideways and sideways inverted varieties exist.

Standard types of watermark. Some watermarks have been used generally for various British possessions rather than exclusively for a single colony. To avoid repetition the Catalogue classifies 11 general types, as under, with references in the headings throughout the listings being given either in words or in the form ("W w **9**") (meaning "watermark type w **9**"). In those cases where watermark illustrations appear in the listings themselves, the respective reference reads, for example, W **153**, thus indicating that the watermark will be found in the normal sequence of illustrations as (type) **153**.

The general types are as follows, with an example of each quoted.

W	Description	Example
w **1**	Large Star	St. Helena No. 1
w **2**	Small Star	Turks Is. No. 4
w **3**	Broad (pointed) Star	Grenada No. 24
w **4**	Crown (over) CC, small stamp	Antigua No. 13
w **5**	Crown (over) CC, large stamp	Antigua No. 31
w **6**	Crown (over) CA, small stamp	Antigua No. 21
w **7**	Crown CA (CA over Crown), large stamp	Sierra Leone No. 54
w **8**	Multiple Crown CA	Antigua No. 41
w **9**	Multiple Script CA	Seychelles No. 158
w **9**a	do. Error	Seychelles No. 158a
w **9**b	do. Error	Seychelles No. 158b
w **10**	V over Crown	N.S.W. No. 327
w **11**	Crown over A	N.S.W. No. 347

CC in these watermarks is an abbreviation for "Crown Colonies" and CA for "Crown Agents". Watermarks w **1**, w **2** and w **3** are on stamps printed by Perkins, Bacon; w **4** onwards on stamps from De La Rue and other printers.

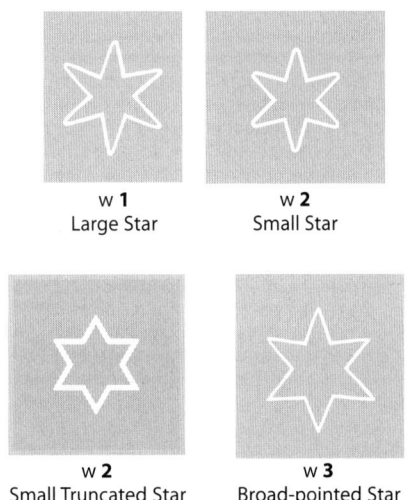

w **1**
Large Star

w **2**
Small Star

w **2**
Small Truncated Star

w **3**
Broad-pointed Star

Watermark w **1**, *Large Star*, measures 15 to 16 mm across the star from point to point and about 27 mm from centre to centre vertically between stars in the sheet. It was made for long stamps like Ceylon 1857 and St. Helena 1856.

Watermark w **2**, *Small Star* is of similar design but measures 12 to 13^1/$_2$mm from point to point and 24 mm from centre to centre vertically. It was for use with ordinary-size stamps such as Grenada 1863–71.

When the Large Star watermark was used with the smaller stamps it only occasionally comes in the centre of the paper. It is frequently so misplaced as to show portions of two stars above and below and this eccentricity will very often help in determining the watermark.

Watermark w **2**a, *Small Truncated Star*, only used for Queensland stamps of 1868-74.

Watermark w **3**, *Broad-pointed Star*, resembles w **1** but the points are broader.

w **4**
Crown (over) CC

w **5**
Crown (over) CC

Two *Crown (over) CC* watermarks were used:

w **4** was for stamps of ordinary size and w **5** for those of larger size.

w **6**
Crown (over) CA

w **7**
CA over Crown

Two watermarks of *Crown CA* type were used, w **6** being for stamps of ordinary size. The other, w **7**, is properly described as *CA over Crown*. It was specially made for paper on which it was intended to print long fiscal stamps: that some were used postally accounts for the appearance of w **7** in the Catalogue. The watermark occupies twice the space of the ordinary Crown CA watermark, w **6**. Stamps of normal size printed on paper with w **7** watermark show it *sideways*; it takes a horizontal pair of stamps to show the entire watermark.

w **8**
Multiple Crown CA

w **9**
Multiple Script CA

Multiple watermarks began in 1904 with w **8**, *Multiple Crown CA*, changed from 1921 to w **9**, *Multiple Script CA*. On stamps of ordinary size portions of two or three watermarks appear and on the large-sized stamps a greater number can be observed. The change to letters in script character with w **9** was accompanied by a Crown of distinctly different shape.

It seems likely that there were at least two dandy rolls for each Crown Agents watermark in use at any one time with a reserve roll being employed when the normal one was withdrawn for maintenance or repair.

Both the Mult Crown CA and the Mult Script CA types exist with one or other of the letters omitted from individual impressions. It is possible that most of these occur from the reserve rolls as they have only been found on certain issues. The MCA watermark experienced such problems during the early 1920s and the Script over a longer period from the early 1940s until 1951.

During the 1920s damage must also have occurred on one of the Crowns as a substituted Crown has been found on certain issues. This is smaller than the normal and consists of an oval base joined to two upright ovals with a circle positioned between their upper ends. The upper line of the Crown's base is omitted, as are the left and right-hand circles at the top and also the cross over the centre circle.

Substituted Crown

The *Multiple Script CA* watermark, w **9**, is known with two errors, recurring among the 1950–52 printings of several territories. In the first a crown has fallen away from the dandy-roll that impresses the watermark into the paper pulp. It gives w **9a**, *Crown missing*, but this omission has been found in both "Crown only" (*illustrated*) and "Crown CA" rows. The resulting faulty paper was used for Bahamas, Johore, Seychelles and the postage due stamps of nine colonies

w **9a**: Error, Crown missing

w **9b**: Error, St. Edward's Crown

When the omission was noticed a second mishap occurred, which was to insert a wrong crown in the space, giving w **9b**, St. Edward's Crown. This produced varieties in Bahamas, Perlis, St. Kitts-Nevis and Singapore and the incorrect crown likewise occurs in (Crown only) and (Crown CA) rows.

w **10**   w **11**
V over Crown   Crown over A

Resuming the general types, two watermarks found in issues of several Australian States are: w **10**, *V over Crown*, and w **11**, *Crown over A*.

w **12**   w **13**
Multiple St. Edward's   Multiple PTM
Crown Block CA

The *Multiple St. Edward's Crown Block CA* watermark, w **12**, was introduced in 1957 and besides the change in the Crown (from that used in Multiple Crown Script CA, w **9**) the letters reverted to block capitals. The new watermark began to appear sideways in 1966 and these stamps are generally listed as separate sets.

The watermark w **13**, *Multiple PTM*, was introduced for new Malaysian issues in November 1961.

6. Colours
Stamps in two or three colours have these named in order of appearance, from the centre moving outwards. Four colours or more are usually listed as multicoloured.

In compound colour names the second is the predominant one, thus:

orange-red = a red tending towards orange;
red-orange = an orange containing more red
             than usual.

Standard colours used. The 200 colours most used for stamp identification are given in the Stanley Gibbons Stamp Colour Key. The Catalogue has used the Stamp Colour Key as standard for describing new issues for some years. The names are also introduced as lists are rewritten, though exceptions are made for those early issues where traditional names have become universally established.

Determining colours. When comparing actual stamps with colour samples in the Stamp Colour Key, view in a good north daylight (or its best substitute; fluorescent "colour matching" light). Sunshine is not recommended. Choose a solid portion of the stamp design; if available, marginal markings such as solid bars of colour or colour check dots are helpful. Shading lines in the design can be misleading as they appear lighter than solid colour. Postmarked portions of a stamp appear darker than normal. If more than one colour is present, mask off the extraneous ones as the eye tends to mix them.

Errors of colour. Major colour errors in stamps or overprints which qualify for listing are: wrong colours; one colour inverted in relation to the rest; albinos (colourless impressions), where these have Expert Committee certificates; colours completely omitted, but only on unused stamps (if found on used stamps the information is footnoted) and with good credentials, missing colours being frequently faked.

Colours only partially omitted are not recognised, Colour shifts, however spectacular, are not listed.
Shades. Shades in philately refer to variations in the intensity of a colour or the presence of differing amounts of other colours. They are particularly significant when they can be linked to specific printings. In general, shades need to be quite marked to fall within the scope of this Catalogue; it does not favour nowadays listing the often numerous shades of a stamp, but chooses a single applicable colour name which will indicate particular groups of outstanding shades. Furthermore, the listings refer to colours as issued; they may deteriorate into something different through the passage of time.

Modern colour printing by lithography is prone to marked differences of shade, even within a single run, and variations can occur within the same sheet. Such shades are not listed.
Aniline colours. An aniline colour meant originally one derived from coal-tar; it now refers more widely to colour of a particular brightness suffused on the surface of a stamp and showing through clearly on the back.
Colours of overprints and surcharges. All overprints and surcharges are in black unless stated otherwise in the heading or after the description of the stamp.

7. Specimen Stamps
Originally, stamps overprinted SPECIMEN were circulated to postmasters or kept in official records, but after the establishment of the Universal Postal Union supplies were sent to Berne for distribution to the postal administrations of member countries.

During the period 1884 to 1928 most of the stamps of British Crown Colonies required for this purpose were overprinted SPECIMEN in various shapes and sizes by their printers from typeset formes. Some locally produced provisionals were handstamped locally, as were sets prepared for presentation. From 1928 stamps were punched with holes forming the word SPECIMEN, each firm of printers using a different machine or machines. From 1948 the stamps supplied for UPU distribution were no longer punctured.

Stamps of some other Commonwealth territories were overprinted or handstamped locally, while

stamps of Great Britain and those overprinted for use in overseas postal agencies (mostly of the higher denominations) bore SPECIMEN overprints and handstamps applied by the Inland Revenue or the Post Office.

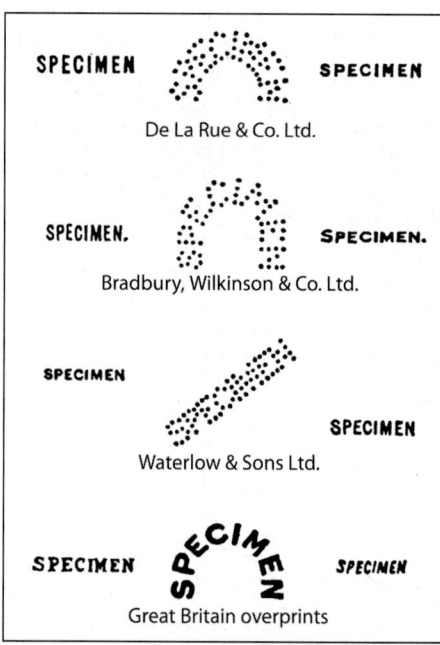

De La Rue & Co. Ltd.

Bradbury, Wilkinson & Co. Ltd.

Waterlow & Sons Ltd.

Great Britain overprints

Some of the commoner types of overprints or punctures are illustrated here. Collectors are warned that dangerous forgeries of the punctured type exist.

The *Stanley Gibbons Commonwealth Catalogues* record those Specimen overprints or perforations intended for distribution by the UPU to member countries and we are grateful to James Bendon, author and publisher of *UPU Specimen Stamps, 1878 – 1961*, a much expanded edition of which was published in 2015, for his assistance with these listings. The Specimen overprints of Australia and its dependent territories, which were sold to collectors by the Post Office, are also included.

Various Perkins Bacon issues exist obliterated with a "CANCELLED" within an oval of bars handstamp.

Perkins Bacon "CANCELLED"
Handstamp

This was applied to six examples of those issues available in 1861 which were then given to members of Sir Rowland Hill's family. 75 different stamps (including four from Chile) are recorded with this handstamp although others may possibly exist. The unauthorised gift of these "CANCELLED" stamps to the Hill family was a major factor in the loss of the Agent General for the Crown Colonies (the forerunner of the Crown Agents) contracts by Perkins Bacon in the following year. Where examples of these scarce items are known to be in private hands the catalogue provides a price.

For full details of these stamps see *CANCELLED by Perkins Bacon* by Peter Jaffé (published by Spink in 1998).

All other Specimens are outside the scope of this volume.

Specimens are not quoted in Great Britain as they are fully listed in the Stanley Gibbons *Great Britain Specialised Catalogue*.

In specifying type of specimen for individual high-value stamps, "H/S" means handstamped, "Optd" is overprinted and "Perf" is punctured. Some sets occur mixed, e.g. "Optd/Perf". If unspecified, the type is apparent from the date or it is the same as for the lower values quoted as a set.
Prices. Prices for stamps up to £1 are quoted in sets; higher values are priced singly. Where specimens

exist in more than one type the price quoted is for the cheapest. Specimen stamps have rarely survived even as pairs; these and strips of three, four or five are worth considerably more than singles.

8. Luminescence
Machines which sort mail electronically have been introduced in recent years. In consequence some countries have issued stamps on flourescent or phosphorescent papers, while others have marked their stamps with phosphor bands.

The various papers can only be distinguished by ultraviolet lamps emitting particular wavelengths. They are separately listed only when the stamps have some other means of distinguishing them, visible without the use of these lamps. Where this is not so, the papers are recorded in footnotes or headings.

For this catalogue we do not consider it appropriate that collectors be compelled to have the use of an ultraviolet lamp before being able to identify stamps by our listings. Some experience will also be found necessary in interpreting the results given by ultraviolet. Collectors using the lamps, nevertheless, should exercise great care in their use as exposure to their light is potentially dangerous to the eyes.

Phosphor bands are listable, since they are visible to the naked eye (by holding stamps at an angle to the light and looking along them, the bands appear dark). Stamps existing with or without phosphor bands or with differing numbers of bands are given separate listings. Varieties such as double bands, bands omitted, misplaced or printed on the back are not listed.

Detailed descriptions appear at appropriate places in the listings in explanation of luminescent papers; see, for example, Australia above No.363, Canada above Nos. 472 and 611, Cook Is. above 249, etc.

For Great Britain, where since 1959 phosphors have played a prominent and intricate part in stamp issues, the main notes above Nos. 599 and 723 should be studied, as well as the footnotes to individual listings where appropriate. In general the classification is as follows.

Stamps with phosphor bands are those where a separate cylinder applies the phosphor after the stamps are printed. Issues with "all-over" phosphor have the "band" covering the entire stamp. Parts of the stamp covered by phosphor bands, or the entire surface for "all-over" phosphor versions, appear matt. Stamps on phosphorised paper have the phosphor added to the paper coating before the stamps are printed. Issues on this paper have a completely shiny surface.

Further particularisation of phosphor – their methods of printing and the colours they exhibit under ultraviolet – is outside the scope of this catalogue. The more specialised listings should be consulted for this information.

9. Coil Stamps
Stamps issued only in coil form are given full listing. If stamps are issued in both sheets and coils the coil stamps are listed separately only where there is some feature (e.g. perforation or watermark sideways) by which singles can be distinguished. Coil stamps containing different stamps *se-tenant* are also listed.

Coil join pairs are too random and too easily faked to permit listing; similarly ignored are coil stamps which have accidentally suffered an extra row of perforations from the claw mechanism in a malfunctioning vending machine.

10. Stamp Booklets
Stamp booklets are now listed in this catalogue.

Single stamps from booklets are listed if they are distinguishable in some way (such as watermark or perforation) from similar sheet stamps.

Booklet panes are listed where they contain stamps of different denominations *se-tenant*, where stamp-size labels are included, or where such panes are otherwise identifiable. Booklet panes are placed in the listing under the lowest denomination present.

Particular perforations (straight edges) are covered by appropriate notes.

The majority of stamps booklets were made up from normal sheets and panes may be bound upright or inverted and booklets may be stapled or stitched at either the left or right-hand side. Unless specifically mentioned in the listings, such variations do not command a price premium.

11. Miniature Sheets and Sheetlets
We distinguish between "miniature sheets" and "sheetlets" and this affects the catalogue numbering. An item in sheet form that is postally valid, containing a single stamp, pair, block or set of stamps, with wide, inscribed and/or decorative margins, is a miniature sheet if it is sold at post offices as an indivisable entity. As such the Catalogue allots a single MS number and describes what stamps make it up. The sheetlet or small sheet differs in that the individual stamps are intended to be purchased separately for postal purposes. For sheetlets, all the component postage stamps are numbered individually and the composition explained in a footnote. Note that the definitions refer to post office sale—not how items may be subsequently offered by stamp dealers.

12. Forgeries and Fakes
Forgeries. Where space permits, notes are considered if they can give a concise description that will permit unequivocal detection of a forgery. Generalised warnings, lacking detail, are not nowadays inserted, since their value to the collector is problematic.

Forged cancellations have also been applied to genuine stamps. This catalogue includes notes regarding those manufactured by "Madame Joseph", together with the cancellation dates known to exist. It should be remembered that these dates also exist as genuine cancellations.

For full details of these see *Madame Joseph Forged Postmarks* by Derek Worboys (published by the Royal Philatelic Society London and the British Philatelic Trust in 1994) or *Madame Joseph Revisited* by Brian Cartwright (published by the Royal Philatelic Society London in 2005).

Fakes. Unwitting fakes are numerous, particularly "new shades" which are colour changelings brought about by exposure to sunlight, soaking in water contaminated with dyes from adherent paper, contact with oil and dirt from a pocketbook, and so on. Fraudulent operators, in addition, can offer to arrange: removal of hinge marks; repairs of thins on white or coloured papers; replacement of missing margins or perforations; reperforating in true or false gauges; removal of fiscal cancellations; rejoining of severed pairs, strips and blocks; and (a major hazard) regumming. Collectors can only be urged to purchase from reputable sources and to insist upon Expert Committee certification where there is any kind of doubt.

The Catalogue can consider footnotes about fakes where these are specific enough to assist in detection.

Abbreviations

Printers

A.B.N. Co.	American Bank Note Co, New York.
B.A.B.N.	British American Bank Note Co. Ottawa
B.W.	Bradbury Wilkinson & Co, Ltd.
C.B.N.	Canadian Bank Note Co, Ottawa.
Continental B.N. Co.	Continental Bank Note Co.
Courvoisier	Imprimerie Courvoisier S.A., La-Chaux-de-Fonds, Switzerland.
D.L.R.	De La Rue & Co, Ltd, London.
Enschedé	Joh. Enschedé en Zonen, Haarlem, Netherlands.
Harrison	Harrison & Sons, Ltd. London
P.B.	Perkins Bacon Ltd, London.
Waterlow	Waterlow & Sons, Ltd, London.

General Abbreviations

Alph	Alphabet
Anniv	Anniversary
Comp	Compound (perforation)
Des	Designer; designed
Diag	Diagonal; diagonally
Eng	Engraver; engraved
F.C. or f.c.	Fiscal Cancellation
H/S	Handstamped
Horiz	Horizontal; horizontally
Imp, Imperf	Imperforate
Inscr	Inscribed
L	Left
Litho	Lithographed
mm	Millimetres
MS	Miniature sheet
N.Y.	New York
Opt(d)	Overprint(ed)
P or P-c	Pen-cancelled
P, Pf or Perf	Perforated
Photo	Photogravure
Pl	Plate
Pr	Pair
Ptd	Printed
Ptg	Printing
R	Right
R.	Row
Recess	Recess-printed
Roto	Rotogravure
Roul	Rouletted
S	Specimen (overprint)
Surch	Surcharge(d)
T.C.	Telegraph Cancellation
T	Type
Typo	Typographed
Un	Unused
Us	Used
Vert	Vertical; vertically
W or wmk	Watermark
Wmk s	Watermark sideways

(†) = Does not exist

(–) (or blank price column) = Exists, or may exist, but no market price is known.

/ between colours means "on" and the colour following is that of the paper on which the stamp is printed.

Colours of Stamps
Bl (blue); blk (black); brn (brown); car, carm (carmine); choc (chocolate); clar (claret); emer (emerald); grn (green); ind (indigo); mag (magenta); mar (maroon); mult (multicoloured); mve (mauve); ol (olive); orge (orange); pk (pink); pur (purple); scar (scarlet); sep (sepia); turq (turquoise); ultram (ultramarine); verm (vermilion); vio (violet); yell (yellow).

Colour of Overprints and Surcharges
(B.) = blue, (Blk.) = black, (Br.) = brown,
(C.) = carmine, (G.) = green, (Mag.) = magenta, (Mve.) = mauve, (Ol.) = olive, (O.) = orange,
(P.) = purple, (Pk.) = pink, (R.) = red, (Sil.) = silver, (V.) = violet, (Vm.) or (Verm.) = vermilion,
(W.) = white, (Y.) = yellow.

Arabic Numerals
As in the case of European figures, the details of the Arabic numerals vary in different stamp designs, but they should be readily recognised with the aid of this illustration.

٠	١	٢	٣	٤	٥	٦	٧	٨	٩
0	1	2	3	4	5	6	7	8	9

International Philatelic Glossary

English	French	German	Spanish	Italian
Agate	Agate	Achat	Agata	Agata
Air stamp	Timbre de la poste aérienne	Flugpostmarke	Sello de correo aéreo	Francobollo per posta aerea
Apple Green	Vert-pomme	Apfelgrün	Verde manzana	Verde mela
Barred	Annulé par barres	Balkenentwertung	Anulado con barras	Sbarrato
Bisected	Timbre coupé	Halbiert	Partido en dos	Frazionato
Bistre	Bistre	Bister	Bistre	Bistro
Bistre-brown	Brun-bistre	Bisterbraun	Castaño bistre	Bruno-bistro
Black	Noir	Schwarz	Negro	Nero
Blackish Brown	Brun-noir	Schwärzlichbraun	Castaño negruzco	Bruno nerastro
Blackish Green	Vert foncé	Schwärzlichgrün	Verde negruzco	Verde nerastro
Blackish Olive	Olive foncé	Schwärzlicholiv	Oliva negruzco	Oliva nerastro
Block of four	Bloc de quatre	Viererblock	Bloque de cuatro	Bloco di quattro
Blue	Bleu	Blau	Azul	Azzurro
Blue-green	Vert-bleu	Blaugrün	Verde azul	Verde azzuro
Bluish Violet	Violet bleuâtre	Bläulichviolett	Violeta azulado	Vioitto azzurrastro
Booklet	Carnet	Heft	Cuadernillo	Libretto
Bright Blue	Bleu vif	Lebhaftblau	Azul vivo	Azzurro vivo
Bright Green	Vert vif	Lebhaftgrün	Verde vivo	Verde vivo
Bright Purple	Mauve vif	Lebhaftpurpur	Púrpura vivo	Porpora vivo
Bronze Green	Vert-bronze	Bronzegrün	Verde bronce	Verde bronzo
Brown	Brun	Braun	Castaño	Bruno
Brown-lake	Carmin-brun	Braunlack	Laca castaño	Lacca bruno
Brown-purple	Pourpre-brun	Braunpurpur	Púrpura castaño	Porpora bruno
Brown-red	Rouge-brun	Braunrot	Rojo castaño	Rosso bruno
Buff	Chamois	Sämisch	Anteado	Camoscio
Cancellation	Oblitération	Entwertung	Cancelación	Annullamento
Cancelled	Annulé	Gestempelt	Cancelado	Annullato
Carmine	Carmin	Karmin	Carmín	Carminio
Carmine-red	Rouge-carmin	Karminrot	Rojo carmín	Rosso carminio
Centred	Centré	Zentriert	Centrado	Centrato
Cerise	Rouge-cerise	Kirschrot	Color de ceresa	Color Ciliegia
Chalk-surfaced paper	Papier couché	Kreidepapier	Papel estucado	Carta gessata
Chalky Blue	Bleu terne	Kreideblau	Azul turbio	Azzurro smorto
Charity stamp	Timbre de bienfaisance	Wohltätigkeitsmarke	Sello de beneficenza	Francobollo di beneficenza
Chestnut	Marron	Kastanienbraun	Castaño rojo	Marrone
Chocolate	Chocolat	Schokolade	Chocolate	Cioccolato
Cinnamon	Cannelle	Zimtbraun	Canela	Cannella
Claret	Grenat	Weinrot	Rojo vinoso	Vinaccia
Cobalt	Cobalt	Kobalt	Cobalto	Cobalto
Colour	Couleur	Farbe	Color	Colore
Comb-perforation	Dentelure en peigne	Kammzähnung, Reihenzähnung	Dentado de peine	Dentellatura e pettine
Commemorative stamp	Timbre commémoratif	Gedenkmarke	Sello conmemorativo	Francobollo commemorativo
Crimson	Cramoisi	Karmesin	Carmesí	Cremisi
Deep Blue	Blue foncé	Dunkelblau	Azul oscuro	Azzurro scuro
Deep bluish Green	Vert-bleu foncé	Dunkelbläulichgrün	Verde azulado oscuro	Verde azzurro scuro
Design	Dessin	Markenbild	Diseño	Disegno
Die	Matrice	Urstempel. Type, Platte	Cuño	Conio, Matrice
Double	Double	Doppelt	Doble	Doppio
Drab	Olive terne	Trüboliv	Oliva turbio	Oliva smorto
Dull Green	Vert terne	Trübgrün	Verde turbio	Verde smorto
Dull purple	Mauve terne	Trübpurpur	Púrpura turbio	Porpora smorto
Embossing	Impression en relief	Prägedruck	Impresión en relieve	Impressione a relievo
Emerald	Vert-eméraude	Smaragdgrün	Esmeralda	Smeraldo
Engraved	Gravé	Graviert	Grabado	Inciso
Error	Erreur	Fehler, Fehldruck	Error	Errore
Essay	Essai	Probedruck	Ensayo	Saggio
Express letter stamp	Timbre pour lettres par exprès	Eilmarke	Sello de urgencia	Francobollo per espresso
Fiscal stamp	Timbre fiscal	Stempelmarke	Sello fiscal	Francobollo fiscale
Flesh	Chair	Fleischfarben	Carne	Carnicino
Forgery	Faux, Falsification	Fälschung	Falsificación	Falso, Falsificazione
Frame	Cadre	Rahmen	Marco	Cornice

English	French	German	Spanish	Italian
Granite paper	Papier avec fragments de fils de soie	Faserpapier	Papel con filamentos	Carto con fili di seta
Green	Vert	Grün	Verde	Verde
Greenish Blue	Bleu verdâtre	Grünlichblau	Azul verdoso	Azzurro verdastro
Greenish Yellow	Jaune-vert	Grünlichgelb	Amarillo verdoso	Giallo verdastro
Grey	Gris	Grau	Gris	Grigio
Grey-blue	Bleu-gris	Graublau	Azul gris	Azzurro grigio
Grey-green	Vert gris	Graugrün	Verde gris	Verde grigio
Gum	Gomme	Gummi	Goma	Gomma
Gutter	Interpanneau	Zwischensteg	Espacio blanco entre dos grupos	Ponte
Imperforate	Non-dentelé	Geschnitten	Sin dentar	Non dentellato
Indigo	Indigo	Indigo	Azul indigo	Indaco
Inscription	Inscription	Inschrift	Inscripción	Dicitura
Inverted	Renversé	Kopfstehend	Invertido	Capovolto
Issue	Émission	Ausgabe	Emisión	Emissione
Laid	Vergé	Gestreift	Listado	Vergato
Lake	Lie de vin	Lackfarbe	Laca	Lacca
Lake-brown	Brun-carmin	Lackbraun	Castaño laca	Bruno lacca
Lavender	Bleu-lavande	Lavendel	Color de alhucema	Lavanda
Lemon	Jaune-citron	Zitrongelb	Limón	Limone
Light Blue	Bleu clair	Hellblau	Azul claro	Azzurro chiaro
Lilac	Lilas	Lila	Lila	Lilla
Line perforation	Dentelure en lignes	Linienzähnung	Dentado en linea	Dentellatura lineare
Lithography	Lithographie	Steindruck	Litografía	Litografia
Local	Timbre de poste locale	Lokalpostmarke	Emisión local	Emissione locale
Lozenge roulette	Percé en losanges	Rautenförmiger Durchstich	Picadura en rombos	Perforazione a losanghe
Magenta	Magenta	Magentarot	Magenta	Magenta
Margin	Marge	Rand	Borde	Margine
Maroon	Marron pourpré	Dunkelrotpurpur	Púrpura rojo oscuro	Marrone rossastro
Mauve	Mauve	Malvenfarbe	Malva	Malva
Multicoloured	Polychrome	Mehrfarbig	Multicolores	Policromo
Myrtle Green	Vert myrte	Myrtengrün	Verde mirto	Verde mirto
New Blue	Bleu ciel vif	Neublau	Azul nuevo	Azzurro nuovo
Newspaper stamp	Timbre pour journaux	Zeitungsmarke	Sello para periódicos	Francobollo per giornali
Obliteration	Oblitération	Abstempelung	Matasello	Annullamento
Obsolete	Hors (de) cours	Ausser Kurs	Fuera de curso	Fuori corso
Ochre	Ocre	Ocker	Ocre	Ocra
Official stamp	Timbre de service	Dienstmarke	Sello de servicio	Francobollo di
Olive-brown	Brun-olive	Olivbraun	Castaño oliva	Bruno oliva
Olive-green	Vert-olive	Olivgrün	Verde oliva	Verde oliva
Olive-grey	Gris-olive	Olivgrau	Gris oliva	Grigio oliva
Olive-yellow	Jaune-olive	Olivgelb	Amarillo oliva	Giallo oliva
Orange	Orange	Orange	Naranja	Arancio
Orange-brown	Brun-orange	Orangebraun	Castaño naranja	Bruno arancio
Orange-red	Rouge-orange	Orangerot	Rojo naranja	Rosso arancio
Orange-yellow	Jaune-orange	Orangegelb	Amarillo naranja	Giallo arancio
Overprint	Surcharge	Aufdruck	Sobrecarga	Soprastampa
Pair	Paire	Paar	Pareja	Coppia
Pale	Pâle	Blass	Pálido	Pallido
Pane	Panneau	Gruppe	Grupo	Gruppo
Paper	Papier	Papier	Papel	Carta
Parcel post stamp	Timbre pour colis postaux	Paketmarke	Sello para paquete postal	Francobollo per pacchi postali
Pen-cancelled	Oblitéré à plume	Federzugentwertung	Cancelado a pluma	Annullato a penna
Percé en arc	Percé en arc	Bogenförmiger Durchstich	Picadura en forma de arco	Perforazione ad arco
Percé en scie	Percé en scie	Bogenförmiger Durchstich	Picado en sierra	Foratura a sega
Perforated	Dentelé	Gezähnt	Dentado	Dentellato
Perforation	Dentelure	Zähnung	Dentar	Dentellatura
Photogravure	Photogravure, Heliogravure	Rastertiefdruck	Fotograbado	Rotocalco
Pin perforation	Percé en points	In Punkten durchstochen	Horadado con alfileres	Perforato a punti
Plate	Planche	Platte	Plancha	Lastra, Tavola
Plum	Prune	Pflaumenfarbe	Color de ciruela	Prugna
Postage Due stamp	Timbre-taxe	Portomarke	Sello de tasa	Segnatasse
Postage stamp	Timbre-poste	Briefmarke, Freimarke, Postmarke	Sello de correos	Francobollo postale
Postal fiscal stamp	Timbre fiscal-postal	Stempelmarke als Postmarke verwendet	Sello fiscal-postal	Fiscale postale
Postmark	Oblitération postale	Poststempel	Matasello	Bollo
Printing	Impression, Tirage	Druck	Impresión	Stampa, Tiratura
Proof	Épreuve	Druckprobe	Prueba de impresión	Prova

English	French	German	Spanish	Italian
Provisionals	Timbres provisoires	Provisorische Marken. Provisorien	Provisionales	Provvisori
Prussian Blue	Bleu de Prusse	Preussischblau	Azul de Prusia	Azzurro di Prussia
Purple	Pourpre	Purpur	Púrpura	Porpora
Purple-brown	Brun-pourpre	Purpurbraun	Castaño púrpura	Bruno porpora
Recess-printing	Impression en taille douce	Tiefdruck	Grabado	Incisione
Red	Rouge	Rot	Rojo	Rosso
Red-brown	Brun-rouge	Rotbraun	Castaño rojizo	Bruno rosso
Reddish Lilac	Lilas rougeâtre	Rötlichlila	Lila rojizo	Lilla rossastro
Reddish Purple	Poupre-rouge	Rötlichpurpur	Púrpura rojizo	Porpora rossastro
Reddish Violet	Violet rougeâtre	Rötlichviolett	Violeta rojizo	Violetto rossastro
Red-orange	Orange rougeâtre	Rotorange	Naranja rojizo	Arancio rosso
Registration stamp	Timbre pour lettre chargée (recommandée)	Einschreibemarke	Sello de certificado lettere	Francobollo per raccomandate
Reprint	Réimpression	Neudruck	Reimpresión	Ristampa
Reversed	Retourné	Umgekehrt	Invertido	Rovesciato
Rose	Rose	Rosa	Rosa	Rosa
Rose-red	Rouge rosé	Rosarot	Rojo rosado	Rosso rosa
Rosine	Rose vif	Lebhaftrosa	Rosa vivo	Rosa vivo
Roulette	Percage	Durchstich	Picadura	Foratura
Rouletted	Percé	Durchstochen	Picado	Forato
Royal Blue	Bleu-roi	Königblau	Azul real	Azzurro reale
Sage green	Vert-sauge	Salbeigrün	Verde salvia	Verde salvia
Salmon	Saumon	Lachs	Salmón	Salmone
Scarlet	Écarlate	Scharlach	Escarlata	Scarlatto
Sepia	Sépia	Sepia	Sepia	Seppia
Serpentine roulette	Percé en serpentin	Schlangenliniger Durchstich	Picado a serpentina	Perforazione a serpentina
Shade	Nuance	Tönung	Tono	Gradazione de colore
Sheet	Feuille	Bogen	Hoja	Foglio
Slate	Ardoise	Schiefer	Pizarra	Ardesia
Slate-blue	Bleu-ardoise	Schieferblau	Azul pizarra	Azzurro ardesia
Slate-green	Vert-ardoise	Schiefergrün	Verde pizarra	Verde ardesia
Slate-lilac	Lilas-gris	Schierferlila	Lila pizarra	Lilla ardesia
Slate-purple	Mauve-gris	Schieferpurpur	Púrpura pizarra	Porpora ardesia
Slate-violet	Violet-gris	Schieferviolett	Violeta pizarra	Violetto ardesia
Special delivery stamp	Timbre pour exprès	Eilmarke	Sello de urgencia	Francobollo per espressi
Specimen	Spécimen	Muster	Muestra	Saggio
Steel Blue	Bleu acier	Stahlblau	Azul acero	Azzurro acciaio
Strip	Bande	Streifen	Tira	Striscia
Surcharge	Surcharge	Aufdruck	Sobrecarga	Soprastampa
Tête-bêche	Tête-bêche	Kehrdruck	Tête-bêche	Tête-bêche
Tinted paper	Papier teinté	Getöntes Papier	Papel coloreado	Carta tinta
Too-late stamp	Timbre pour lettres en retard	Verspätungsmarke	Sello para cartas retardadas	Francobollo per le lettere in ritardo
Turquoise-blue	Bleu-turquoise	Türkisblau	Azul turquesa	Azzurro turchese
Turquoise-green	Vert-turquoise	Türkisgrün	Verde turquesa	Verde turchese
Typography	Typographie	Buchdruck	Tipografia	Tipografia
Ultramarine	Outremer	Ultramarin	Ultramar	Oltremare
Unused	Neuf	Ungebraucht	Nuevo	Nuovo
Used	Oblitéré, Usé	Gebraucht	Usado	Usato
Venetian Red	Rouge-brun terne	Venezianischrot	Rojo veneciano	Rosso veneziano
Vermilion	Vermillon	Zinnober	Cinabrio	Vermiglione
Violet	Violet	Violett	Violeta	Violetto
Violet-blue	Bleu-violet	Violettblau	Azul violeta	Azzurro violetto
Watermark	Filigrane	Wasserzeichen	Filigrana	Filigrana
Watermark sideways	Filigrane couché liegend	Wasserzeichen	Filigrana acostado	Filigrana coricata
Wove paper	Papier ordinaire, Papier uni	Einfaches Papier	Papel avitelado	Carta unita
Yellow	Jaune	Gelb	Amarillo	Giallo
Yellow-brown	Brun-jaune	Gelbbraun	Castaño amarillo	Bruno giallo
Yellow-green	Vert-jaune	Gelbgrün	Verde amarillo	Verde giallo
Yellow-olive	Olive-jaunâtre	Gelboliv	Oliva amarillo	Oliva giallastro
Yellow-orange	Orange jaunâtre	Gelborange	Naranja amarillo	Arancio giallastro
Zig-zag roulette	Percé en zigzag	Sägezahnartiger Durchstich	Picado en zigzag	Perforazione a zigzag

Specialist Philatelic Societies

Requests for inclusion on this page should be sent to the Catalogue Editor.

Great Britain Philatelic Society
Membership Secretary – Victoria Lajer,
Stanley Gibbons Ltd., 399 Strand,
London WC2R 0LX

Great Britain Collectors Club
Secretary - Mr S. McGill
103309 Brookhollow Circle,
Highlands Ranch, CO 80129, USA

Channel Islands Specialists Society
Membership Secretary – Sheila Marshall
1 Grove Farm Drive, Leeds, West Yorkshire
LS16 6DD

GB Overprints Society
Membership Secretary – Mr A. Haymes,
20 Sheldon Drive, Wells, Somerset BA5 2HB.

Aden & Somaliland Study Group
UK Representative – Mr M. Lacey
108 Dalestorth Road, Sutton-in-Ashfield
Notts NG17 3AA

Ascension Study Circle
Secretary – Dr. R.C.F. Baker
Greys, Tower Road, Whitstable,
Kent CT5 3ER

Australian States Study Circle
Royal Sydney Philatelic Club
Membership Secretary – Mr P. Brigden
c/o R.S.P.C., GPO Box 1751,
Sydney, NSW 2001,
Australia

British Society of Australian Philately
Secretary – Dr P.G.E. Reid
12 Holly Spring Lane, Bracknell,
Berks RG12 2JL

Society of Australasian Specialists/Oceania
Secretary – Mr S. Leven
P.O. Box 24764, San Jose, CA 95154-4764 U.S.A.

Bechuanalands and Botswana Society
Membership Secretary – Mr O. Peetoom,
Roos, East Yorkshire
HU12 0LD

Bermuda Collectors Society
President – Mr J. Pare
405 Perimeter St, Mt. Horeb,
Wisconsin 52572, USA

British Caribbean Philatelic Study Group
Overseas Director – Mr D.N. Druett
Pennymead Auctions, 1 Brewerton Street,
Knaresborough, North Yorkshire HG5 8AZ

British West Indies Study Circle
Membership Secretary – Mr S. Jarvis
5 Redbridge Drive, Andover,
Hampshire SP10 2LF

Burma (Myanmar) Philatelic Study Circle
Secretary – Mr M. Whittaker,
1 Ecton Leys, Rugby, Warwickshire,
CV22 5SL, UK

Canadian Philatelic Society of Great Britain
Secretary – Mr J. Watson,
Lyngarth, 106 Huddersfield Road, Penistone
South Yorkshire S36 7BX

Cape and Natal Study Circle
Acting Secretary – Mr J. Dickson,
Lismore House, Great Lane, Shepton Beauchamp,
Somerset TA19 0LJ

Ceylon Study Circle
Secretary – Mr R.W.P. Frost
42 Lonsdale Road, Cannington, Bridgewater,
Somerset TA5 2JS

Cyprus Study Circle
Secretary – Mr R. Wheeler
47 Drayton Avenue, Ealing, London
W13 0LE

East Africa Study Circle
Secretary – Mr M.D. Vesey-Fitzgerald,
Gambles Cottage, 18 Clarence Road,
Lyndhurst, Hants SO43 7AL

Egypt Study Circle
Secretary – Mr M. Murphy,
109 Chadwick Road, Peckham, London SE15 4PY

Falklands Islands Study Group
Membership Secretary – Mr M. Burton,
16 Bonneycroft Lane,
Easingwold, N Yorkshire YO61 3AW

Gibraltar Study Circle
Membership Secretary – Mr E. D. Holmes,
29 Highgate Road, Woodley, Reading RG5 3ND

Hong Kong Study Circle
Membership Secretary -- Mr N Halewood
Midoricho 1-9-204, Ashiya-shi
Japan 659-0042

Indian Ocean Study Circle
Secretary – Mrs S. Hopson
Field Acre, Hoe Benham, Newbury,
Berkshire RG20 8PD

India Study Circle
Secretary – Mr D Haskell
1 Badburgham Court, Waltham Abbey
EN9 3EB

Irish Philatelic Circle
Acting Secretary – Mr B. Warren
PO Box 12624, Rathfarnham,
Dublin 16, Ireland

King George V Silver Jubilee Study Circle
President – Mr N. Donen
31-4525 Wilkinson Road, Victoria, BC,
V8Z 5C3, Canada

King George VI Collectors Society
Membership Secretary – Mr M. Axe
Barbizon Cottage, Marringdean Road,
Billingshurst RH14 9HQ

Kiribati & Tuvalu Philatelic Society
Honorary Secretary - Mr D. Baines
20 Jasmin Close, Sheppey Minster,
Isle of Sheppey, Kent MB12 3FL

Malaya Study Group
Membership Secretary - Mr D. Tett
4 Amenbury Court, Harpenden,
Herts AL5 2BU

Malta Study Circle
Membership Secretary – Mr C. Searle
4 Sunderland Place Wellesbourne,
Warwick CV35 9LE

New Zealand Society of Great Britain
Membership Secretary - Mrs E. Diamond
9 Ashley Drive, Walton on Thames,
Surrey KT12 1JL

Orange Free State Study Circle
Secrertary – Mr J.R. Stroud
28 Oxford Street, Burnham-on-Sea,
Somerset TA8 1LQ

Pacific Islands Study Circle
Honorary Secretary – Mr J.D. Ray
24 Woodvale Avenue, London SE25 4AE

Pakistan Study Circle
Membership Secretary – Mr M. Robinson
35 Ethelburt Avenue, Bassett Green,
Southampton SO16 3DG

Papuan Philatelic Society
Membership Secretary – Mr M. Robinson
P.O. Box 3275, Birkdale,
Queensland 4159, Australia

Pitcairn Islands Study Group (U.K.)
Honorary Secretary – Mr D. Sleep
6 Palace Gardens, 100 Court Road, Eltham,
London SE9 5NS

Rhodesian Study Circle
Membership Secretary - Mr A. Plumbe
25 Oakwood Drive, Bingley,
West Yorkshire BD16 4SJ

Royal Philatelic Society of New Zealand
Secretary – Mr G. Wilson
P.O. Box 1269, Wellington, New Zealand

St. Helena, Ascension and Tristan da Cunha Philatelic Society
Secretary – Mr. Klaus D. Hahn
P.O. Box 14, 71145 Bondorf,
Germany

Samoa Specialists, Fellowship of
Secretary – Mr S.G. Zirinsky
P.O. Box 230049, Ansonia Station
New York, NY10023, USA

Sarawak Specialists Society
(also Brunei, North Borneo and Labuan)
Secretary – Dr. R.G. Johnson
9 Chipstead Park Close, Sevenoaks, Kent TN13 2ST

South African Collectors' Society
General Secretary – Mr C. Oliver
Telephone 020 8940 9833

Philatelic Society of Sri Lanka
Secretary – Mr H. Goonawardena, J.P.
44A Hena Road, Mt. Lavinia 10370, Sri Lanka

Sudan Study Group
Secretary – Mr P. Grigg
19 Howmead, Berkeley, Glos GL13 9AR

Transvaal Study Circle
Honorary Treasurer – Mr J. Woolgar
c/o 9 Meadow Road, Gravesend,
Kent DA11 7LR

West Africa Study Circle
Membership Secretary – Mr J. Hossack
28 Saxon's Close, Leighton Buzzard
LU7 3LT

Western Australia Study Circle
Secretary – Mr B. Pope
P.O Box 423, Claremount
Western Australia 6910

Select Bibliography

The literature on British Commonwealth stamps is vast, but works are often difficult to obtain once they are out of print. The selection of books below has been made on the basis of authority together with availability to the general reader, either as new or secondhand. Very specialised studies, and those covering aspects of postal history to which there are no references in the catalogue, have been excluded.

The following abbreviations are used to denote publishers:

CRL   Christie's Robson Lowe;
HH   Harry Hayes;
PB   Proud Bailey Co. Ltd. and Postal
       History Publications Co.;
PC   Philip Cockrill;
RPSL   Royal Philatelic Society, London;
SG   Stanley Gibbons Ltd.

Where no publisher is quoted, the book is published by its author.

GENERAL

Encylopaedia of British Empire Postage Stamps. Vols 1-6. Edited Robson Lowe. (CRL, 1951–1991)

Specimen Stamps of the Crown Colonies 1857-1948. Marcus Samuel. (RPSL, 1976 and 1984 Supplement)

Cancelled by Perkins Bacon. P. Jaffé. (Spink & Son Ltd., 1998)

U.P.U. Specimen Stamps 1878-1961. J. Bendon. (2015)

King George V Key Plates of the Imperium Postage and Revenue Design. P. Fernbank. (Second edition, British West Indies Study Circle, 2013)

Silver Jubilee of King George V Stamps Handbook. A.J. Ainscough. (Ainweel Developments, 1985)

The Commemorative Stamps of the British Commonwealth. H.D.S. Haverbeck. (Faber, 1955)

The Printings of King George VI Colonial Stamps. W.J.W. Potter & Lt-Col R.C.M. Shelton. (1952 and later facsimile edition)

King George VI Large Key Type Stamps of Bermuda, Leeward Islands, Nyasaland. R.W. Dickgiesser and E.P. Yendall. (Triad Publications, 1985)

The King George VI Large Key Type Revenue and Postage High Value Stamps 1937–1952. E. Yendall (RPSL, 2008)

War Tax Stamps of the British Empire, First World War – The West Indies. J.G.M. Davis (RPSL, 2009)

Madame Joseph Forged Postmarks. D. Worboys. (RPSL, 1994)

Madame Joseph Revisited. B.M. Cartwright. (RPSL, 2005)

G.B. Used Abroad: Cancellations and Postal Markings. J. Parmenter. (The Postal History Society, 1993)

GREAT BRITAIN

For extensive bibliographies see G.B. Specialised Catalogues. Vols 1-5. (Stanley Gibbons)

Stamps and Postal History of the Channel Islands. W. Newport. (Heineman, 1972)

ADEN

The Postal History of British Aden 1839-1967. Major R.W. Pratt. (PB, 1985)

The Postal History of Aden and Somaliland Protectorate. E. B. Proud. (PB, 2004)

ANTIGUA

Antigua, the Stamps and Postal History. C Freeland and J.M. Jordan (B.W.I. Study Circle, 2016)

ASCENSION

Ascension. The Stamps and Postal History. J.H. Attwood. (CRL, 1981)

AUSTRALIA

The Postal History of New South Wales 1788-1901. Edited J.S. White. (Philatelic Association of New South Wales, 1988)

South Australia. The Long Stamps 1902-12. J.R.W. Purves. (Royal Philatelic Society of Victoria, 1978)

The Departmental Stamps of South Australia. A.R. Butler. (RPSL, 1978)

A Priced Listing of the Departmental Stamps of South Australia. A.D. Presgrave. (2nd edition, 1999)

Stamps and Postal History of Tasmania. W.E. Tinsley. (RPSL, 1986)

The Pictorial Stamps of Tasmania 1899-1912. K.E. Lancaster. (Royal Philatelic Society of Victoria, 1986)

The Stamps of Victoria. G. Kellow. (B. & K. Philatelic Publishing, 1990)

Western Australia. The Stamps and Postal History. Edited M. Hamilton and B. Pope. (W. Australian Study Group, 1979)

Postage Stamps and Postal History of Western Australia. Vols 1-3. M. Juhl. (1981-83)

The Chapman Collection of Australian Commonwealth Stamps. R. Chapman. (Royal Philatelic Society of Victoria, 1999)

Nauru 1915--1923. K. Buckingham. (The British Philatelic Association Expertising Educational Charity, 2004)

The Postal History of British New Guinea and Papua 1885-1942. R. Lee. (CRL, 1983)

Collector's Guide to the Stamps of British New Guinea and the Territory of Papua, 1884-1942. M. L. Parr and M. Robinson (PnR Publications, 2013)

The Stamps of the Territory of New Guinea, 1952–1932 Huts Issues. R. Heward, R. Garratt and D. Heward (2008)

Norfolk Island. A Postal and Philatelic History, 1788-1969. P. Collas & R. Breckon. (B. & K. Philatelic Publishing, 1997)

BAHAMAS

The Postage Stamps and Postal History of the Bahamas. H.G.D. Gisburn, (SG, 1950 and later facsimile edition)

Bahamas Stamps and Postal Stationery to 1970. Ed. P. Fernbank (B.W.I. Study Circle, 2017)

BARBADOS

The Stamps of Barbados. E.A. Bayley. (1989)

Advanced Barbados Philately. H.F. Deakin. (B.W.I. Study Circle, 1997)

Barbados, The Britannia Issues. M.F. Roett. (B.W.I. Study Circle, 2013)

BASUTOLAND

The Cancellations and Postal Markings of Basutoland/ Lesotho Post Offices. A. H. Scott. (Collectors Mail Auctions (Pty) Ltd., 1980)

BATUM

British Occupation of Batum. P.T. Ashford. (1989)

BECHUANALAND

The Postage Stamps, Postal Stationery and Postmarks of the Bechuanalands. H.R. Holmes. (RPSL, 1971)

BERMUDA

The Postal History and Stamps of Bermuda. M.H. Ludington. (Quarterman Publications Inc., 1978)

The King George V High-value Stamps of Bermuda, 1917-1938. M. Glazer. (Calaby Publishers, 1994)

The Postal History of Bermuda. E.B. Proud. (PB, 2003)

BRITISH GUIANA

The Postage Stamps and Postal History of British Guiana. W.A. Townsend & F.G. Howe. (RPSL, 1970)

British Guiana: The provisionals of 1882. R. Maisel (B.W.I. Study Circle, 2013)

BRITISH HONDURAS

The Postal History of British Honduras. E.B. Proud. (PB, 1999)

BRITISH INDIAN OCEAN

The Postal History of B.I.O.T., Maldive Islands and Seychelles. E. B. Proud (PB, 2006)

BRITISH OCCUPATION OF GERMAN COLONIES

G.R.I. R.M. Gibbs. (CRL, 1989)

BRITISH PACIFIC OCEAN

The Postal History of the British Solomon Islands and Tonga. E.B. Proud (PB, 2006)

The Postal History of the Gilbert and Ellice Islands and New Hebrides. E.B. Proud. (PB, 2006)

BRITISH POSTAL AGENCIES IN EASTERN ARABIA

The Postal Agencies in Eastern Arabia and the Gulf. N. Donaldson. (HH, 1975) and Supplement (Bridger & Kay Guernsey Ltd., 1994)

BRITISH SOLOMON ISLANDS

British Solomon Islands Protectorate. Its Postage Stamps and Postal History. H.G.D. Gisburn. (T. Sanders (Philatelist) Ltd., 1956)

BRITISH WEST AFRICA

The Postal History and Handstamps of British West Africa. C. McCaig. (CRL, 1978)

BRITISH WEST INDIES

The Postal History of the Cayman Islands and Turks & Caicos Islands. E.B. Proud (PB, 2006)

The Postal History of St. Lucia and St. Vincent. E.B. Proud and J. C. Aleong (PB, 2006)

BURMA

Burma Postal History. G. Davis and D Martin. (CRL, 1971 and 1987 Supplement).

The Postal History of Burma. E.B. Proud. (PB, 2002)

CAMEROONS

The Postal Arrangements of the Anglo-French Cameroons Expeditionary Force 1914-1916. R.J. Maddocks. (1996)

CANADA

The Postage Stamps and Postal History of Newfoundland. W.S. Boggs. (Quarterman Publications Inc., 1975)

Stamps of British North America. F. Jarrett. (Quarterman Publications Inc., 1975)

The Postage Stamps and Postal History of Canada. W.S. Boggs. (Quarterman Publications Inc., 1974)

The First Decimal Issue of Canada 1859-68. G. Whitworth. (RPSL, 1966)

The Five Cents Beaver Stamp of Canada. G. Whitworth. (RPSL, 1985)

The Small Queens of Canada. J. Hillson. (CRL, 1989)

Canada Small Queens Re-Appraised. J. Hillson. (Canadian Philatelic Society of Great Britain, 1999)

Canada's Postage Stamps of the Small Queen Era, 1870-1897. J. Hillson and J.E. Nixon (Vincent Graves Greene Philatelic Research Foundation, 2008)

The Edward VII Issue of Canada, G.C. Marler, (National Postal Museum, Canada, 1975)

The Admiral Issue of Canada. G.C. Marler. (American Philatelic Society, 1982)

CEYLON

The Postal History of Ceylon. E. B. Proud (PB, 2006)

CYPRUS

Cyprus 1353-1986. W. Castle. (CRL 3rd edition, 1987)

DOMINICA

Dominica Postal History, Stamps and Postal Stationery to 1935. E.V. Toeg. (B.W.I. Study Circle, 1994)

EGYPT

Egypt Stamps & Postal History. P.A.S. Smith. (James Bendon, 1999)

The Nile Post. J. H. Chalhoub. (2003)

FALKLAND ISLANDS

The Postage Stamps of the Falkland Islands and Dependencies. B.S.H. Grant. (SG, 1952 and later facsimile edition)

The Falkland Islands Philatelic Digest. Nos. 1 & 2. M. Barton and R Spafford. (HH, 1975 and 1979)

The De La Rue Definitives of the Falkland Islands 1901-1929. J.P. Bunt. (1986 and 1996 Supplement)

The Falkland Islands. The 1891 Provisionals. M. Barton. (BPA Expertising Educational Trust, 2002)

The War Stamp Overprints of the Falkland Islands 1918-1920. J.P. Bunt. (1981)

The Falkland Islands. Printings of the Pictorial Issue of 1938-49. C.E. Glass. (CRL, 1979)

The Postal History of the Falkland Islands and Dependencies. E.B. Proud (PB, 2006)

FIJI

Fiji's Times Express Stamps. D.E. Gillis (Pacific Islands Study Circle, 2011)

Fiji Philatelics. D.E.F. Alford. (Pacific Islands Study Circle, 1994)

Fiji Queen Victoria One Shilling and Five Shillings Postage Stamps 1881-1902. R.F. Duberal. (Pacific Islands Study Circle, 2003)

The Postal History of Fiji 1911-1952. J.G. Rodger. (Pacific Islands Study Circle, 1991)

GAMBIA

The Stamps and Postal History of the Gambia. Edited J.O. Andrew. (CRL, 1985)

The Postal History of the Gambia. E.B. Proud. (PB, 1994)

GIBRALTAR

Posted in Gibraltar. W. Hine-Haycock. (CRL, 1978 and 1983 Supplement)

Gibraltar. The Postal History and Postage Stamps. Vol 1 to 1885. G. Osborn. (Gibraltar Study Circle, 1995)

The Postal History of Gibraltar. R.J.M. Garcia & E.B. Proud. (PB, 1998)

Gibraltar, Collecting King George VI. E. Chambers. (The Gibraltar Study Circle, 2003)

GOLD COAST

The Postal History of the Gold Coast. E.B. Proud. (PB, 1995)

The Postal Services of the Gold Coast, 1901-1957. Edited M. Ensor. (West Africa Study Circle, 1998)

The Postal Services of the Gold Coast to 1901. Edited J. Sacher. (RPSL, 2003)

HONG KONG

The Philatelic History of Hong Kong. Vol 1. (Hong Kong Study Circle, 1984)

Hong Kong Postage Stamps of the Queen Victoria Period. R.N. Gurevitch. (1993)

Hong Kong. The 1898 10c. on 30c. Provisional Issue. A.M. Chu. (1998)

The Postal History History of Hong Kong. E.B. Proud (PB, 2004)

British Post Offices in the Far East. E.B. Proud. (PB, 1991)

Cancellations of the Treaty Ports of Hong Kong. H. Schoenfield. (1988)

The Crown Colony of Wei Hai Wei. M.Goldsmith and C.W. Goodwyn. (RPSL, 1985)

INDIA

C.E.F. The China Expeditionary force 1900-1923. D.S. Virk, J.C. Hume, G. Sattin. (Philatelic Congress of India, 1992)

India Used Abroad. V.S. Dastur. (Mysore Philatelics, 1982)

The Indian Postal Agencies in the Persian Gulf Area. A. Parsons. (Sahara Publications Ltd., 2001)

A Handbook on Gwalior Postal History and Stamps. V.K. Gupta. (1980)

The Stamps of Jammu & Kashmir. F. Staal. (The Collectors Club, 1983)

Sorath Stamps and Postal History. R.A. Malaviya. (Ravi Prakashan, 1999)

IRAQ

The Postal History of Iraq. P.C. Pearson and E.B. Proud. (PB, 1996)

Baghdad in British Occupation: The Story of the 1917 Provisional Stamps. F. Khalastchy (RPSL, 2017)

IRELAND

Irish Stamp Booklets 1931-1991. C.J. Dulin. (1998)

British Stamps Overprinted for use in Ireland during the Transitional Period. Barry Cousins (Irish Philatelic Circle, 2008)

JAMAICA

Encyclopaedia of Jamaican Philately. Vol 1. D.Sutcliffe & S. Jarvis. (1997); *Vol 6.* S. Jarvis. (2001) (B.W.I. Study Circle)

Jamaica, the Definitive and Commemorative Stamps and Postal Stationery of the Reign of King George VI. H.A.H. James. (The King George VI Collectors Society, 1999)

KENYA

British East Africa. The Stamps and Postal Stationery. J. Minns. (RPSL, 1982 and 1990 Supplement) (New edition, revised and updated, George T. Krieger, 2006)

The Postal History of Kenya. E.B. Proud. (PB, 1992)

LEEWARD ISLANDS

The Leeward Islands – Notes for Philatelists. M.N. Oliver. (B.W.I. Study Circle, second edition, 2011)

MALAYA

The Postal History of British Malaya. Vols 1-3. E.B. Proud. (PB, 2nd edition, 2000)

The Postage Stamps of Federated Malay States. W.A. Reeves. (Malaya Study Group, 1978)

Kedah and Perlis. D.R.M. Holley. (Malaya Study Group, 1995)

Kelantan. Its Stamps and Postal History. W.A. Reeves and B.E. Dexter. (Malaya Study Group, 1992)

The Postal History of the Occupation of Malaya and British Borneo 1941-1945. E.B. Proud and M.D. Rowell. (PB, 1992)

Pahang 1888 to 1903, The Chersonese Collection (BPA Expertising Educational Charity, 2009)

MALTA

Malta. The Postal History and Postage Stamps. Edited R.E. Martin. (CRL, 1980 and 1985 Supplement)

MAURITIUS

The Postal History and Stamps of Mauritius. P. Ibbotson. (RPSL, 1991); Revisions and additions Supplement (Indian Ocean Study Circle, 1995)

The Postal History of Mauritius. E.B. Proud. (PB, 2001)

MONTSERRAT

Montserrat to 1965. L.E. Britnor. (B.W.I. Study Circle. 3rd edition, 2010)

MOROCCO AGENCIES

British Post Offices and Agencies in Morocco 1857-1907 and Local Posts 1891-1914. R.K. Clough. (Gibraltar Study Circle, 1984)

The Stamps of the Morocco Agencies. Ed. D.A. Stotter (GB Overprints Society, 2011)

NEW ZEALAND

The Postage Stamps of New Zealand. Vols I-VII. (Royal Philatelic Society of New Zealand. 1939—98)

The Early Cook Islands Post Office. A.R. Burge (Hawthorn Pres, 1978)

The Postal History and Postage Stamps of the Tokelau/Union Islands. A.H. Burgess. (Pacific Islands Study Circle, 2nd edition, 1998)

A Postal History of the Samoan Islands (Parts I and II). Edited R. Burge. (Royal Philatelic Society of New Zealand, 1987-89)

The Stamps and Postal History of Nineteenth Century Samoa. R.P. Odenweller. (RPSL and The Royal Philatelic Society of New Zealand, 2004)

The 1893 New Zealand Advertisement Stamps. J.A. Robb (Christchurch (N.Z.) Philatelic Society, 2006)

New Zealand Stamps Overprinted "O.P.S.O". C. Capill (New Zealand Society of Great Britain and Royal Philatelic Society of New Zealand, 2010)

The Postage Stamps of New Zealand 1855-1873: The Chalon Head Issues and *Chalon Sorting Guide* R.P. Odenweller (RPSL, 2009 and 2014)

The 1898 Pictorial Issue of New Zealand its Design, Printing and Use. D. Diamond (New Zealand Society of Great Britian, 2014)

NIGERIA

The Postal Services of the British Nigeria Region. J. Ince and J. Sacher. (RPSL, 1992)

The Postal History of Nigeria. E.B. Proud (PB, 1995)

The Oil Rivers and Niger Coast Surcharged Provisionals and Bisected Stamps. J. Sacher (RPSL, 2009)

NORTH BORNEO

A Concise Guide to the Queen Issues of Labuan. R. Price. (Sarawak Specialists Society, 1991)

The Stamps and Postal History of North Borneo. Parts 1-3. L.H. Shipman and P.K. Cassells. (Sarawak Specialists Society, 1976-88)

The Postal History of British Borneo. E.B. Proud. (PB, 2003)

NORTHERN RHODESIA

Northern Rhodesia – The Mkushi Postage Dues and the renamed Old Mkushi Post Office Otto Peetoom (2005)

The King George VI Postage and Revenue Stamps of Northern Rhodesia Alan Drysdall, Ian Lane and Jean Cheston (Rhodesia Study Circle, 2006)

NYASALAND

The Postal History of Nyasaland. E.B. Proud. (PB, 1997)

PALESTINE

The Stamps & Postal Stationery of Palestine Mandate 1918-1948. D. Dorfman. (Edward G. Rosen, 2001)

The Postal History of Palestine and Transjordan. E.B. Proud. (PB, 2006)

PITCAIRN ISLANDS

Pitcairn Islands Philately. D.E. Hume. (3rd edition, 2006)

RHODESIA

Mashonaland. A Postal History 1890—96. Dr. A.R. Drysdall and D. Collis. (CRL, 1990)

Rhodesia. A Postal History. R.C. Smith. (1967 and 1970 Supplement)

The Rhodesia Philatelist. (Ormskirk Stamps)

ST. HELENA

St. Helena, Postal History and Stamps. E. Hibbert. (CRL, 1979)

The George V Badge Issues of St Helena and Ascension. R. Stanton and W. Thorpe (West Africa Study Circle, 2012)

The Postal History of Ascension, St. Helena & Tristan da Cunha. E.B. Proud. (PB, 2005)

ST. KITTS-NEVIS

A Study of the King George VI Stamps of St. Kitts-Nevis. P.L. Baldwin. (Murray Payne Ltd., 2nd edition, 1997)

The Philately of Nevis. F. Borromeo. (British West Indies Study Circle, 2001)

Nevis-The Stamps and Postal History (1661-1890). F. Borromeo and C. Freeland (British West Indies Study Circle, 2015)

ST VINCENT

St Vincent 1899-1965. C. Freeland, R. Bond and R. Boylan (B.W.I, Study Circle 2017).

SARAWAK

The Stamps and Postal History of Sarawak. W.A. Forrester-Wood. (Sarawak Specialists Society, 1959 and 1970 Supplement)

Sarawak: The Issues of 1871 and 1875. W. Batty-Smith and W.E.Watterson. (1990)

SEYCHELLES

Seychelles Postal History and Postage Stamps to 1976. S. Hopson & B.M. McCloy. (Indian Ocean Study Circle, 2002)

The Postal History of B.I.O.T., Maldive Islands and Seychelles. E.B Proud (PB 2006)

Select Bibliography

SIERRA LEONE

The Postal Service of Sierra Leone. P.O. Beale. (RPSL, 1988)

The Postal History of Sierra Leone. E.B. Proud. (PB, 1994)

Sierra Leone King George VI Definitive Stamps. F. Walton. (West Africa Study Circle, 2001)

SOUTH AFRICA

Postmarks of the Cape of Good Hope. R. Goldblatt. (Reijger Publishers (Pty) Ltd., 1984)

Stamps of the Orange Free State. Parts 1-3. G.D. Buckley & W.B. Marriott. (O.F.S. Study Circle, 1967--80)

The Postal History of the Orange Free State. R Allison. (BPA Expertising, 2016)

Transvaal Philately. Edited I.B. Mathews. (Reijer Publishers (Pty) Ltd., 1986)

Transvaal. The Provisional Issues of the First British Occupation. Dr. A.R. Drysdall. (James Bendon, 1994)

Die Pietersburg-seëls ran die Anglo-Boereoorlog. C. Breedt and J. Groenewald (Philatelic Federation of South Africa, 2007)

The Wherewithal of Wolmaransstad. H. Birkhead and J. Groenewald. (Philatelic Foundation of Southern Africa, 1999)

Die Vryburg-seëls van die Anglo-Boereoorlog. J Groenewald. (Philatelic Federation of South Africa, 2010)

SOUTH WEST AFRICA

The Overprinted Stamps of South West Africa to 1930. N. Becker. (Philatelic Holdings (Pty) Ltd., 1990)

SUDAN

Sudan. The Stamps and Postal Stationery of 1867 to 1970. E.C.W. Stagg. (HH, 1977)

The Camel Postman 1898-1998. R. Stock. (Sudan Study Group, 2001)

The Postal History of Sudan. E. B Proud (PB, 2006)

SWAZILAND

Swaziland Philately to 1968. Ed. P. van der Molen (RPSL, 2013)

TANGANYIKA

The Postal History of Tanganyika. 1915-1961. E.B. Proud. (PB, 1989)

TOGO

Togo-The Postal History of the Anglo-French Occupation 1914-22. J. Martin and F. Walton. (West Africa S.C., 1995)

Togo Overprints on Stamps of the Gold Coast 1915–1920. P. Duggan. (West Africa S.C. 2005)

TRANSJORDAN

The Stamps of Jordan 1920—1965. A.H. Najjar. (Sahara Publications Ltd., 1998)

TRINIDAD AND TOBAGO

The Postal History of Trinidad and Tobago. J.C. Aleong and E.B. Proud. (PB, 1997)

Trinidad, a Philatelic History to 1913. Sir J. Marriott, KCVO, RDP, M. Medlicott and R.A. Ramkissoon (British West Indies Study Circle and British Caribbean Philatelic Study Group, 2010)

Tobago, the Philatelic Story of a Small Island. P.C. Ford, C. Freeland and E. Barrow (British West Indies Study Circle, 2014)

TRISTAN DA CUNHA

The History and Postal History of Tristan da Cunha. G. Crabb. (1980)

TURKS AND CAICOS ISLANDS

Turks Islands and Caicos Islands to 1950. J.J. Challis. (Roses Caribbean Philatelic Society, 1983)

UGANDA

The Postal History of Uganda and Zanzibar. E.B. Proud. (PB, 1993)

ZANZIBAR

Zanzibar 1895 – 1904. T.W. Hall. (Reprint, East Africa Study Circle, 2002)

The Postage Dues of Zanzibar 1875 – 1964, The Stamps, the Covers and their Story. J. Griffith-Jones (B.P.A. Expertising, 2014)

Come and Visit us at 399 Strand

| 1856 | 1896 | 1936 | 1976 | 2017 |

- Get advice from our experienced and knowledgeable staff
- See first hand our superb range of top quality stamps, albums and accessories
- Get insider tips on how to enhance and expand your collection
- Ask for guidance on techniques for care and storage of your stamps and covers
- View our specialist material
- All Stanley Gibbons stamps come with a lifetime guarantee of authenticity from our stamp specialists.

Everything for the stamp collector.

399 Strand opening hours
- Mon-Fri 9am-5.30pm   • Sat 9:30am-5.30pm
- Sun Closed

For more information visit
stanleygibbons.com

Great Britain

STAMPS ON COVER. Prices are quoted, as a third price column, for those Victorian and Edwardian issues usually found used on cover. In general these prices refer to the cheapest version of each basic stamp with other shades, plates or varieties, together with unusual frankings and postmarks, being worth more.

UNITED KINGDOM OF GREAT BRITAIN AND IRELAND

QUEEN VICTORIA
20 June 1837—22 January 1901

PARLIAMENTARY ENVELOPES. When the Uniform Penny Postage was introduced on 10 January 1840 the free franking privileges of Members of Parliament were abolished. During the same month, special envelopes were introduced for mail posted from the Houses of Parliament and these remained in use until the introduction of stamps and the Mulready stationery in May 1840. Envelopes are priced in used condition only.

Inscribed "Houses of Parliament" in black (16 Jan 1840)			
PE2	1d. envelope	....from	£18000
PE3	2d. envelope	....from	£45000
PE4	4d. envelope	....from	

Inscribed "House of Lords" in vermilion (Jan 1840)			
PE5	1d. envelope	....from	£25000
PE8	2d. envelope		

Inscribed "House of Commons" in black (Jan 1840)			
PE9	1d. envelope	....from	£6000

MULREADY ENVELOPES AND LETTER SHEETS, so called from the name of the designer, William Mulready, were issued concurrently with the first British adhesive stamps

POSTAGE ONE PENNY

A large number of letter sheets and a much smaller quantity of envelopes were sold by businesses advertising to promote their services.

1d. Black

ME1	1d.	Letter sheet..	£325	£525
		a. With advertisements printed inside		
		....from	£750	£825
ME2	1d.	Envelope..	£350	£550
		a. With advertisements printed inside		
		....from	£2500	£4000

2d. Blue

ME3	2d.	Letter sheet..	£425	£2400
		a. With advertisements printed inside		
		....from	—	£3200
ME4	2d.	Envelope..	£450	£2500

LINE-ENGRAVED ISSUES
GENERAL NOTES

Brief notes on some aspects of the line-engraved stamps follow, but for further information and a full specialist treatment of these issues collectors are recommended to consult Volume 1 of the Stanley Gibbons *Great Britain Specialised Catalogue*.

Alphabet I	Alphabet II

Alphabet III	Alphabet IV

Typical Corner Letters of the four Alphabets

Alphabets. Four different styles were used for the corner letters on stamps prior to the issue with letters in all four corners, these being known to collectors as:

Alphabet I. Used for all plates made from 1840 to the end of 1851. Letters small.

Alphabet II. Plates from 1852 to mid-1855. Letters larger, heavier and broader.

Alphabet III. Plates from mid-1855 to end of period. Letters tall and more slender.

Alphabet IV. 1861. 1d. Die II, Plates 50 and 51 only. Letters were hand-engraved instead of being punched on the plate. They are therefore inconsistent in shape and size but generally larger and outstanding.

While the general descriptions and the illustrations of typical letters given above may be of some assistance, only long experience and published aids can enable every letter to be allocated to its particular Alphabet without hesitation, as certain letters in each are similar to those in one of the others.

Blued Paper. The blueing of the paper of the earlier issues is believed to be due to the presence of prussiate of potash in the printing ink, or in the paper, which, under certain conditions, tended to colour the paper when the sheets were damped for printing. An alternative term is bleuté paper.

Corner Letters. The corner letters on the early British stamps were intended as a safeguard against forgery, each stamp in the sheet having a different combination of letters. Taking the first 1d. stamp, printed in 20 horizontal rows of 12, as an example, the lettering is as follows:

Row 1.	A A,	A B,	A C,	etc. to	A L.
Row 2.	B A,	B B,	B C,	etc. to	B L.
		and so on to			
Row 20.	T A,	T B,	T C,	etc. to	T L.

On the stamps with four corner letters, those in the upper corners are in the reverse positions to those in the lower corners. Thus in a sheet of 240 (12 × 20) the sequence is:

Row 1.	A A	B A	C A		L A
	A A	A B	A C	etc. to	A L
Row 2.	A B	B B	C B		L B
	B A	B B	B C	etc. to	B L
		and so on to			
Row 20.	A T	B T	C T	etc. to	L T
	T A	T B	T C		T L

Placing letters in all four corners was not only an added precaution against forgery but was meant to deter unmarked parts of used stamps being pieced together and passed off as an unused whole.

Dies. The first die of the 1d. was used for making the original die of the 2d., both the No Lines and White Lines issues. In 1855 the 1d. Die I was amended by retouching the head and deepening the lines on a transferred impression of the original. This later version, known to collectors as Die II, was used for making the dies for the 1d. and 2d. with letters in all four corners and also for the 1½d.

The two dies are illustrated above No. 17 in the catalogue.

Double letter   Guide line in corner

Guide line through value

Double Corner Letters. These are due to the workman placing his letter-punch in the wrong position at the first attempt, when lettering the plate, and then correcting the mistake; or to a slight shifting of the punch when struck. If a wrong letter was struck in the first instance, traces of a wrong letter may appear in a corner in addition to the correct one. A typical example is illustrated.

Guide Lines and Dots. When laying down the impressions of the design on the early plates, fine vertical and horizontal guidelines were marked on the plates to assist the operative. These were usually removed from the gutter margins, but could not be removed from the stamp impressions without damage to the plate, so that in such cases they appear on the printed stamps, sometimes in the corners, sometimes through "POSTAGE" or the value. Typical examples are illustrated.

Guide dots or cuts were similarly made to indicate the spacing of the guide lines. These too sometimes appear on the stamps.

Ivory Head

"Ivory Head." The so-called "ivory head" variety is one in which the Queen's Head shows white on the back of the stamp. It arises from the comparative absence of ink in the head portion of the design, with consequent absence of blueing. (See "Blued Paper" note above.)

Line-engraving. In this context "line-engraved" is synonymous with recess-printing, in which the engraver cuts recesses in a plate and printing (the coloured areas) is from these recesses. "Line-engraved" is the traditional philatelic description for these stamps; other equivalent terms found are "engraving in *taille-douce*" (French) or in "*intaglio*" (Italian).

Plates. Until the introduction of the stamps with letters in all four corners, the number of the plate was not indicated in the design of the stamp, but was printed on the sheet margin. By long study of identifiable blocks and the minor variations in the position of the corner letters, philatelists are now able to allot many of these stamps to their respective plates. Specialist collectors often endeavour to obtain examples of a given stamp from its different plates and our catalogue accordingly reflects this depth of detail.

Maltese Cross   Type of Town postmark

Type of Penny Post cancellation

Example of 1844 type postmark

Postmarks. The so-called "Maltese Cross" design was the first employed for obliterating British postage stamps and was in use from 1840 to 1844. Being hand-cut, the obliterating stamps varied greatly in detail and some distinctive types can be allotted to particular towns or offices. Local types, such as those used at Manchester, Norwich, Leeds, etc., are keenly sought. A red ink was first employed, but was superseded by black, after some earlier experiments, in February 1841. Maltese Cross obliterations in other colours are rare.

Obliterations of this type, numbered 1 to 12 in the centre, were used at the London Chief Office in 1843 and 1844.

Some straight-line cancellations were in use in 1840 at the Penny Post receiving offices, normally applied on the envelope, the adhesives then being obliterated at the Head Office. They are nevertheless known, with or without Maltese Cross, on the early postage stamps.

In 1842 some offices in S.W. England used dated postmarks in place of the Maltese Cross, usually on the back of the letter since they were not originally intended as obliterators. These town postmarks have likewise been found on adhesives.

In 1844 the Maltese Cross design was superseded by numbered obliterators of varied type, one of which is illustrated. They are naturally comparatively scarce on the first 1d. and 2d. stamps. Like the Maltese Cross they are found in various colours, some of which are rare.

Re-entry

"Union Jack" re-entry

Re-entries. Re-entries on the plate show as a doubling of part of the design generally at top or bottom. Many re-entries are very slight while others are most marked. A typical one is illustrated.

The "*Union Jack*" *re-entry*, so called owing to the effect of the re-entry on the appearance of the corner stars (*see illustration*) occurs on stamp L K of Plate 75 of the 1d. red, Die I.

T A (T L)   M A (M L)
Varieties of Large Crown Watermark

I   II
Two states of Large Crown Watermark

Watermarks. Two watermark varieties, as illustrated, consisting of crowns of entirely different shape, are found in sheets of the Large Crown paper and fall on stamps lettered M A and T A (or M L and T L when the paper is printed on the wrong side). Both varieties are found on the 1d. rose-red of 1857, while the M A (M L) variety comes also on some plates of the 1d. of 1864 (Nos. 43, 44) up to about Plate 96. On the 2d. the T A (T L) variety is known on plates 8 and 9, and the M A (M L) on later prints of plate 9. These varieties may exist inverted, or inverted reversed, on stamps lettered A A and A L and H A and H L, and some are known.

In 1861 a minor alteration was made in the Large Crown watermark by the removal of the two vertical strokes, representing *fleurs-de-lis*, which projected upwards from the uppermost of the three horizontal curves at the base of the Crown. Hence two states are distinguishable, as illustrated.

CONDITION—IMPERFORATE LINE-ENGRAVED ISSUES

The prices quoted for the 1840 and 1841 imperforate Line-engraved issues are for "fine" examples. As condition is most important in assessing the value of a stamp, the following definitions will assist collectors in the evaluation of individual examples.

Four main factors are relevant when considering quality.
(a) **Impression**. This should be clean and the surface free of any rubbing or unnatural blurring which would detract from the appearance.
(b) **Margins**. This is perhaps the most difficult factor to evaluate. Stamps described as "fine", the standard adopted in this catalogue for pricing purposes, should have margins of the recognised width, defined as approximately one half of the distance between two adjoining unsevered stamps. Stamps described as "very fine" or "superb" should have margins which are proportionately larger than those of a "fine" stamp. Examples with close margins should not, generally, be classified as "fine".
(c) **Cancellation**. On a "fine" stamp this should be reasonably clear and not noticeably smudged. A stamp described as "superb" should have a neat cancellation, preferably centrally placed or to the right.
(d) **Appearance**. Stamps, at the prices quoted, should always be without any tears, creases, bends or thins and should not be toned on either the front or back. Stamps with such defects are worth only a proportion of the catalogue price.

Good

Fine

Very Fine

Superb

The above actual size illustrations of 1840 1d. blacks show the various grades of quality. When comparing these illustrations it should be assumed that they are all from the same plate and that they are free of any hidden defects.

PRINTERS. Nos. 1/53*a* were recess-printed by Perkins, Bacon & Petch, known from 1852 as Perkins, Bacon & Co.

1   **1a**   **2** Small Crown

(Eng Charles and Frederick Heath)

1840 (6 May). Letters in lower corners. Wmk Small Crown. W **2**. Imperf.

			Un	Used	Used on cover
1	**1**	1d. intense black	£17500	£525	
2		1d. black	£12500	£375	£750
		Wi. Wmk inverted	£50000	£2500	
3		1d. grey-black (worn plate)	£16500	£500	
4	**1a**	2d. deep full blue	£45000	£1150	
5		2d. blue	£38000	£900	£2750
		Wi. Wmk inverted	£90000	£6250	
6		2d. pale blue	£48000	£1000	

The 1d. stamp in black was printed from Plates 1 to 11. Plate 1 exists in two states (known to collectors as 1a and 1b), the latter being the result of extensive repairs.

Repairs were also made to Plates 2, 5, 6, 8, 9, 10 and 11, and certain impressions exist in two or more states.

The so-called "Royal reprint" of the 1d. black was made in 1864, from Plate 66, Die II, on paper with Large Crown watermark, inverted. A printing was also made in carmine, on paper with the same watermark, normal.

For 1d. black with "VR" in upper corners *see* No. VI under Official Stamps.

The 2d. stamps were printed from Plates 1 and 2.

Plates of 1d. black

Plate		Un	Used
1*a*		£18500	£375
1*b*		£12500	£375
2		£13000	£400
3		£20000	£500
4		£13000	£400
5		£12500	£375
6		£13500	£375
7		£13500	£400
8		£16500	£525
9		£21000	£625
10		£26500	£950
11		£23000	£4600

Varieties of 1d. black.

		Un	Used
a.	On *bleuté* paper (Plates 1 to 8) ....from		£775
b.	Double letter in corner ....from	£13000	£400
bb.	Re-entry ....from	£13500	£450

		Un	Used
bc.	"PB" re-entry (Plate 5, 3rd state)	—	£10500
c.	Guide line in corner	£13000	£400
cc.	Large letters in each corner (E J, I L, J C and P A) (Plate 1*b*) ....from	£13500	£550
d.	Guide line through value	£13000	£450
g.	Obliterated by Maltese Cross		
	In red	—	£425
	In black	—	£375
	In blue	—	£12000
	In magenta	—	£3000
	In yellow	—	—
h.	Obliterated by Maltese Cross with number in centre ....from		
	No. 1	—	£20000
	No. 2	—	£20000
	No. 3	—	£20000
	No. 4	—	£20000
	No. 5	—	£20000
	No. 6	—	£20000
	No. 7	—	£20000
	No. 8	—	£20000
	No. 9	—	£20000
	No. 10	—	£20000
	No. 11	—	£20000
	No. 12	—	£20000
i.	Obliterated "Penny Post" in black (without Maltese Cross) ....from	—	£5500
j.	Obliterated by town postmark (without Maltese Cross)		
	In black ....from	—	£17000
	In yellow ....from	—	£60000
	In red ....from	—	£18500
k.	Obliterated by 1844 type postmark in black ....from	—	£1800

Plates of 2d. blue

Plate		Un	Used
1	*Shades from*	£38000	£900
2	*Shades from*	£48000	£1000

Varieties of 2d. blue.

		Un	Used
a.	Double letter in corner	—	£975
aa.	Re-entry	—	£1100
b.	Guide line in corner	—	£925
c.	Guide line through value	—	£925
e.	Obliterated by Maltese Cross		
	In red	—	£1100
	In black	—	£900
	In blue	—	£15000
	In magenta	—	£12000
f.	Obliterated by Maltese Cross with number in centre ....from		
	No. 1	—	£18000
	No. 2	—	£18000
	No. 3	—	£18000
	No. 4	—	£18000
	No. 5	—	£18000
	No. 6	—	£18000
	No. 7	—	£18000
	No. 8	—	£18000
	No. 9	—	£18000
	No. 10	—	£18000
	No. 11	—	£18000
	No. 12	—	£18000
g.	Obliterated "Penny Post" in black (without Maltese Cross) ....from	—	£16000
h.	Obliterated by town postmark (without Maltese Cross) in black ....from	—	£10000
i.	Obliterated by 1844 type postmark		
	In black ....from	—	£2500
	In blue ....from	—	£18000

1841 (10 Feb). Printed from "black" plates. Wmk W **2**. Paper more or less blued. Imperf.

			Un	Used	Used on cover
7	**1**	1d. red-brown *(shades)*	£2700	£130	£240
		a. "PB" re-entry (Plate 5, 3rd state)	—	£2600	
		Wi. Wmk inverted (Plates 1b, 8 and 10) ....from	—	£3250	

The first printings of the 1d. in red-brown were made from Plates 1*b*, 2, 5 and 8 to 11 used for the 1d. black.

1d. red-brown from "black" plates.

Plate		Un	Used
1*b*		£23000	£375
2		£25000	£325
5		£12000	£200
8		£13000	£190
9		£6500	£190
10		£2800	£190
11		£11500	£130

1841 (late Feb). Plate 12 onwards. Wmk W **2**. Paper more or less blued. Imperf.

			Un	Used	Used on cover
8	**1**	1d. red-brown	£600	35·00	45·00
		Wi. Wmk inverted	£5000	£400	
8*a*		1d. red-brown on very blue paper	£700	35·00	
9		1d. pale red-brown (worn plates)	£675	45·00	
10		1d. deep red-brown	£900	50·00	
11		1d. lake-red	£5250	£800	
12		1d. orange-brown	£2000	£275	
		Error. No letter "A" in right lower corner (Stamp B(A), Plate 77)		
12*a*	**1**	1d. red-brown	—	£26000

The error "No letter A in right corner" was due to the omission to insert this letter on stamp B A of Plate 77. The error was discovered some months after the plate was registered and was then corrected.

There are innumerable variations in the colour and shade of the 1d. "red" and those given in the above list represent colour groups each covering a wide range.

Varieties of 1d. red-brown, etc.

			Un	Used
b.	Major re-entry ....*from*		—	90·00
c.	Double letter in corner ....*from*		—	40·00
d.	Double Star (Plate 75) "Union Jack" re-entry.	£34000	£3000
e.	Guide line in corner		—	35·00
f.	Guide line through value		—	40·00
g.	Thick outer frame to stamp		—	38·00
h.	Ivory head		£600	38·00
j.	Left corner letter "S" inverted (Plates 78, 105, 107) ....*from*		—	£160
k.	P converted to R (Plates 30/1, 33, 83, 86) ....*from*		—	80·00
l.	Obliterated by Maltese Cross			
	In red		—	£4800
	In black		—	65·00
	In blue		—	£675
m.	Obliterated by Maltese Cross with number in centre			
	No. 1		—	£180
	No. 2		—	£180
	No. 3		—	£225
	No. 4		—	£600
	No. 5		—	£180
	No. 6		—	£160
	No. 7		—	£160
	No. 8		—	£160
	No. 9		—	£180
	No. 10		—	£320
	No. 11		—	£350
	No. 12		—	£350
n.	Obliterated "Penny Post" in black (without Maltese Cross)		—	£1100
o.	Obliterated by town postmark (without Maltese Cross)			
	In black ....*from*		—	£825
	In blue ....*from*		—	£2700
	In green ....*from*		—	£5500
	In yellow ....*from*		—	—
	In red ....*from*		—	£15000
p.	Obliterated by 1844 type postmark			
	In blue ....*from*		—	£250
	In red ....*from*		—	£9750
	In green ....*from*		—	£3250
	In violet ....*from*		—	£4000
	In black ....*from*		—	35·00

Stamps with thick outer frame to the design are from plates on which the frame-lines have been strengthened or recut, particularly Plates 76 and 90.

For "Union Jack" re-entry *see* General Notes to Line-engraved Issues. In "P converted to R" the corner letter "R" is formed from the "P", the distinctive long tail having been hand-cut.

KEY TO LINE-ENGRAVED ISSUES

S.G. No.	Description	Date	Wmk	Perf	Die	Alphabet
	THE IMPERFORATE ISSUES					
1/3	1d. black	6.5.40	SC	Imp	I	I
4/6	2d. no lines	8.5.40	SC	Imp	I	I
	PAPER MORE OR LESS BLUED					
7	1d. red-brown	Feb 1841	SC	Imp	I	I
8/12	1d. red-brown	Feb 1841	SC	Imp	I	I
8/12	1d. red-brown	6.2.52	SC	Imp	I	II
13/15	2d. white lines	13.3.41	SC	Imp	I	I
	THE PERFORATED ISSUES					
ONE PENNY VALUE						
16*a*	1d. red-brown	1848	SC	Roul	I	I
16*b*	1d. red-brown	1850	SC	16	I	I
16*c*	1d. red-brown	1853	SC	16	I	II
17/18	1d. red-brown	Feb 1854	SC	16	I	II
22	1d. red-brown	Jan 1855	SC	14	I	II
24/5	1d. red-brown	28.2.55	SC	14	II	II
21	1d. red-brown	1.3.55	SC	16	II	II
26	1d. red-brown	15.5.55	LC	14	II	II
29/33	1d. red-brown	Aug 1855	LC	14	II	III
	NEW COLOURS ON WHITE PAPER					
37/41	1d. rose-red	Nov 1856	LC	14	II	III
36	1d. rose-red	26.12.57	LC	16	II	III
42	1d. rose-red	1861	LC	14	II	IV
	TWO PENCE VALUE					
19, 20	2d. blue	1.3.54	SC	16	I	I
23	2d. blue	22.2.55	SC	14	I	I
23*a*	2d. blue	5.7.55	SC	14	I	II
20*a*	2d. blue	18.8.55	SC	16	I	II
27	2d. blue	20.7.55	LC	16	I	II
34	2d. blue	20.7.55	LC	14	I	II
35	2d. blue	2.7.57	LC	14	I	III
36*a*	2d. blue	1.2.58	LC	16	I	III
	LETTERS IN ALL FOUR CORNERS					
48/9	½d. rose-red	1.10.70	W **9**	14	—	
43/4	1d. rose-red	1.4.64	LC	14	II	
53*a*	1½d. rosy mauve	1860	LC	14	II	
51/3	1½d. rose-red	1.10.70	LC	14	II	
45	2d. blue	July 1858	LC	14	I	
46/7	2d. thinner lines	7.7.69	LC	14	II	

Watermarks: SC   Small Crown, T **2**.
                 LC   Large Crown, T **4**.

Dies: See notes above No. 17 in the catalogue.
Alphabets: See General Notes to this section.

3 White lines added

1841 (13 Mar)–**51**. White lines added. Wmk W **2**. Paper more or less blued. Imperf.

			Un	Used	Used on cover
13	**3**	2d. pale blue	£9500	£110	
14		2d. blue	£6250	90·00	£350
		Wi. Wmk inverted	£24000	£875	
15		2d. deep full blue	£8500	£110	
15aa		2d. violet-blue (1851)	£28000	£1800	

The 2d. stamp with white lines was printed from Plates 3 and 4. No. 15aa came from Plate 4 and the price quoted is for examples on thicker, lavender tinted paper.

Plates of 2d. blue

Plate		Un	Used
3	Shades............from	£6250	£100
4	Shades............from	£6250	90·00

Varieties of 2d. blue

		Un	Used
a.	Guide line in corner	—	£110
b.	Guide line through value	£6750	£110
bb.	Double letter in corner		£120
be.	Re-entry	£8250	£200
c.	Ivory head	£6250	£100
e.	Obliterated by Maltese Cross		
	In red	—	—
	In black	—	£275
	In blue	—	£5000
f.	Obliterated by Maltese Cross with number in centre		
	No. 1	—	£700
	No. 2	—	£700
	No. 3	—	£700
	No. 4	—	£700
	No. 5	—	£850
	No. 6	—	£700
	No. 7	—	£1200
	No. 8	—	£1000
	No. 9	—	£1200
	No. 10	—	£1500
	No. 11	—	£850
	No. 12	—	£550
g.	Obliterated by town postmark (without Maltese Cross)		
	In black............from	—	£3500
	In blue............from	—	£4500
h.	Obliterated by 1844 type postmark		
	In black............from	—	90·00
	In blue............from	—	£1000
	In red............from	—	£28000
	In green............from	—	£9000
	In olive-yellow............from	—	£2000

1841 (Apr). Trial printing (unissued) on Dickinson silk-thread paper. No wmk. Imperf.

16	**1**	1d. red-brown (Plate 11)	£7750

Eight sheets were printed on this paper, six being gummed, two ungummed, but we have only seen examples without gum.

1848. Wmk Small Crown, W **2**. Rouletted approx 11½ by Henry Archer.

16a	**1**	1d. red-brown (Plates 70, 71)	£25000

1850. Wmk Small Crown, W **2**. P 16 by Henry Archer.

			Un	Used	Used on cover
16b	**1**	1d. red-brown (Alph 1) (from Plates 90–101)............from	£3500	£625	£2000

Stamps on cover dated prior to February 1854 are worth a premium of 50% over the price on cover quoted above.

1853. Government Trial Perforation. Wmk Small Crown. W **2**.

			Un	Used
16c	**1**	1d. red-brown (P 16) (Alph II) (on cover)		†

SEPARATION TRIALS. Although the various trials of machines for rouletting and perforating were unofficial, Archer had the consent of the authorities in making his experiments, and sheets so experimented upon were afterwards used by the Post Office.

As Archer ended his experiments in 1850 and plates with corner letters Alphabet II did not come into issue until 1852, perforated stamps with corner letters of Alphabet I may safely be assumed to be Archer productions, if genuine.

The Government trial perforation is believed to have been done on Archer's machines after they had been purchased in 1853. As Alphabet II was by that time in use, the trials can only be distinguished from the perforated stamps listed below by being dated prior to 24 February 1854, the date when the perforated stamps were officially issued.

Die I Alphabet I, stamps from plates 74 and 113 perforated 14 have been recorded for many years, but it is now generally recognised that the type of comb machine used, producing one extension hole in the side margins, cannot be contemporary with other trials of this period.

Die I

Die II

4 Large Crown

Die I: The features of the portrait are lightly shaded and consequently lack emphasis.

Die II: (Die I retouched): The lines of the features have been deepened and appear stronger.

The eye is deeply shaded and made more lifelike. The nostril and lips are more clearly defined. the latter appearing much thicker. A strong downward stroke of colour marks the corner of the mouth. There is a deep indentation of colour between lower lip and chin. The band running from the back of the ear to the chignon has a bolder horizontal line below it than in Die I.

One Penny. The numbering of the 1d. plates recommenced at 1 on the introduction of Die II. Plates 1 to 21 were Alphabet II from which a scarce plum shade exists. Corner letters of Alphabet III appear on Plate 22 and onwards.

As an experiment, the corner letters were engraved by hand on Plates 50 and 51 in 1856, instead of being punched (Alphabet IV), but punching was again resorted to from Plate 52 onwards. Plates 50 and 51 were not put into use until 1861.

Two Pence. Unlike the 1d. the old sequence of plate numbers continued. Plates 3 and 4 of the 2d. had corner letters of Alphabet I, Plate 5 Alphabet II and Plate 6 Alphabet III. In Plate 6 the white lines are thinner than before.

1854–57. Paper more or less blued.

*(a) Wmk Small Crown, W **2**. P 16*

			Un	Used*	Used on cover
17	**1**	1d. red-brown (Die I) (24.2.54)	£375	35·00	60·00
		a. Imperf three sides (horiz pair)	†	£7500	
		Wi. Wmk inverted		£200	
18		1d. yellow brown (Die I)	£450	50·00	
19	**3**	2d. deep blue (Plate 4) (12.3.54)	£4700	£100	£200
		a. Imperf three sides (horiz pair)	†	—	
		Wi. Wmk inverted	—	£325	
20		2d. pale blue (Plate 4)	£5500	£110	
20a		2d. blue (Plate 5) (18.8.55)	£10000	£350	£550
		aWi. Wmk inverted		£900	
21	**1**	1d. red-brown (Die II) (22.5.55)	£550	65·00	£110
		a. Imperf			
		Wi. Wmk inverted	£1750	£260	

*(b) Wmk Small Crown, W **2**. P 14*

22	**1**	1d. red-brown (Die I) (1.55)	£900	90·00	£160
		Wi. Wmk inverted	—	£300	
23	**3**	2d. blue (Plate 4) (22.2.55)	£13000	£225	£375
		Wi. Wmk inverted	£18500	£650	
23a		2d. blue (Plate 5) (4.7.55)	£14000	£350	£525
		aWi. Wmk inverted		£750	
		b. Imperf (Plate 5)			
24	**1**	1d. red-brown (Die II) (27.2.55)	£675	70·00	£110
		Wi. Wmk inverted	£2400	£350	
24a		1d. deep red-brown (very blue paper) (Die II)	£825	£110	
25		1d. orange-brown (Die II)	£1900	£170	

*(c) Wmk Large Crown, W **4**. P 16*

26	**1**	1d. red-brown (Die II) (15.5.55)	£2400	£130	£240
		a. Imperf (Plate 7)			
		Wi. Wmk inverted	—	£450	
27	**3**	2d. blue (Plate 5) (20.7.55)	£18500	£450	£575
		a. Imperf	—	£12000	
		Wi. Wmk inverted	—	£1000	

*(d) Wmk Large Crown, W **4**. P 14*

29	**1**	1d. red-brown (Die II) (6.55)	£240	22·00	40·00
		a. Imperf (shades) (Plates 22, 24, 25, 32, 43)	£4000	£3500	
		Wi. Wmk inverted	£1000	£150	
30		1d. brick-red (Die II)	£375	45·00	
31		1d. plum (Die II) (2.56)	£3800	£900	
32		1d. brown-rose (Die II)	£375	55·00	
33		1d. orange-brown (Die II) (3.57)	£725	60·00	
34	**3**	2d. blue (Plate 5) (20.7.55)	£2850	70·00	£200
		Wi. Wmk inverted	—	£325	
35		2d. blue (Plate 6) (2.7.57)	£3400	70·00	£200
		a. Imperf	—	£12000	
		b. Imperf horiz (vert pair)	†	—	
		Wi. Wmk inverted	—	£325	

***17/35a** For well-centred, lightly used +125%.*

1856–58. Wmk Large Crown, W **4**. Paper no longer blued.

(a) P 16

36	**1**	1d. rose-red (Die II) (26.12.57)	£2750	70·00	£160
		Wi. Wmk inverted	—	£475	
36a	**3**	2d. blue (Plate 6) (1.2.58)	£14500	£375	£550
		Wi. Wmk inverted	—	£1000	

(b) Die II. P 14

37	**1**	1d. red-brown (11.56)	£2400	£375	£1100
38		1d. pale red (9.4.57)	£100	35·00	
		a. Imperf	£4800	£3600	
39		1d. pale rose (3.57)	£110	35·00	
40		1d. rose-red (9.57)	50·00	12·00	23·00
		a. Imperf	£5000	£3800	
		b. Imperf vert (horiz pair)	†	—	
		Wi. Wmk inverted	£180	85·00	
41		1d. deep rose-red (7.57)	£160	20·00	

1861. Letters engraved on plate instead of punched (Alphabet IV).

42	**1**	1d. rose-red (Die II) (Plates 50 and 51)	£250	40·00	70·00
		a. Imperf	—	£5750	
		Wi. Wmk inverted	£750	£200	

***36/42a** For well-centred, lightly used +125%.*

In both values, varieties may be found as described in the preceding issues—ivory heads, inverted watermarks, re-entries, and double letters in corners.

The change of perforation from 16 to 14 was decided upon late in 1854 since the closer holes of the former gauge tended to cause the sheets of stamps to break up when handled, but for a time both gauges were in concurrent use. Owing to faulty alignment of the impressions on the plates and to shrinkage of the paper when damped, badly perforated stamps are plentiful in the line-engraved issues.

5　　　　　　6

Showing position of the plate number on the 1d. and 2d. values. (Plate 170 shown)

1864–79. Letters in all four corners. Wmk Large Crown, W **4**. Die II. P 14.

43	**5**	1d. rose-red (1.4.64)	27·00	2·75	8·00
44		1d. lake-red	27·00	2·75	
		a. Imperf from	£8500	£4500	
		Wi. Wmk inverted	£110	35·00	

***43/4a** For well-centred, lightly used +125%.*

Plate	Un	Used	Plate	Un	Used
71	55·00	4·00	150	28·00	2·75
72	60·00	5·00	151	80·00	11·00
73	60·00	4·00	152	80·00	7·50
74	60·00	2·75	153	£140	11·00
76	55·00	2·75	154	70·00	2·75
77	—	£600000	155	70·00	3·00
78	£130	2·75	156	65·00	2·75
79	48·00	2·75	157	70·00	2·75
80	65·00	2·75	158	48·00	2·75
81	65·00	3·00	159	48·00	2·75
82	£130	5·00	160	48·00	2·75
83	£155	9·00	161	80·00	9·00
84	80·00	3·00	162	70·00	9·00
85	60·00	4·00	163	70·00	4·00
86	70·00	5·00	164	70·00	4·00
87	48·00	2·75	165	65·00	6·50
88	£190	9·50	166	65·00	7·00
89	60·00	2·75	167	65·00	2·75
90	60·00	2·75	168	70·00	10·00
91	75·00	7·00	169	80·00	9·00
92	55·00	2·75	170	55·00	2·75
93	70·00	2·75	171	28·00	2·75
94	65·00	6·00	172	48·00	2·75
95	60·00	2·75	173	95·00	11·00
96	65·00	2·75	174	48·00	2·75
97	60·00	4·50	175	80·00	4·50
98	70·00	7·00	176	80·00	3·00
99	75·00	6·00	177	60·00	2·75
100	80·00	3·00	178	80·00	4·50
101	80·00	11·00	179	70·00	3·00
102	65·00	2·75	180	80·00	6·50
103	70·00	4·50	181	65·00	2·75
104	£100	6·00	182	£130	6·50
105	£130	9·00	183	75·00	4·00
106	75·00	2·75	184	48·00	3·00
107	80·00	9·00	185	70·00	4·00
108	£110	3·00	186	90·00	3·00
109	£120	4·50	187	70·00	2·75
110	80·00	11·00	188	95·00	12·00
111	70·00	3·00	189	95·00	8·50
112	90·00	3·00	190	70·00	7·00
113	70·00	15·00	191	48·00	9·00
114	£325	15·00	192	70·00	2·75
115	£130	3·00	193	48·00	2·75
116	£100	11·00	194	70·00	10·00
117	65·00	2·75	195	70·00	10·00
118	70·00	2·75	196	70·00	6·50
119	65·00	2·75	197	75·00	11·00
120	28·00	2·75	198	60·00	7·00
121	60·00	11·00	199	75·00	7·00
122	28·00	2·75	200	70·00	2·75
123	60·00	2·75	201	48·00	6·00
124	42·00	2·75	202	80·00	10·00
125	60·00	2·75	203	48·00	20·00
127	75·00	3·00	204	75·00	3·00
129	60·00	10·00	205	75·00	4·00
130	75·00	3·00	206	75·00	11·00
131	85·00	20·00	207	80·00	11·00
132	£190	27·00	208	75·00	18·00
133	£160	11·00	209	65·00	10·00
134	28·00	2·75	210	90·00	15·00
135	£130	30·00	211	95·00	25·00
136	£130	24·00	212	90·00	13·00
137	42·00	3·00	213	80·00	13·00
138	32·00	2·75	214	90·00	23·00
139	80·00	20·00	215	90·00	23·00
140	32·00	2·75	216	95·00	23·00
141	£160	11·00	217	95·00	9·00
142	95·00	30·00	218	90·00	10·00
143	80·00	17·00	219	£130	85·00
144	£130	25·00	220	60·00	9·00
145	48·00	3·00	221	95·00	20·00
146	60·00	7·00	222	£110	50·00
147	70·00	4·00	223	£130	75·00
148	60·00	4·00	224	£160	65·00
149	60·00	7·00	225	£3200	£800

The following plate numbers are also known imperf and used (No. 44a); 72, 79, 80, 81, 82, 83, 84, 85, 86, 87, 88, 90, 91, 92, 93, 96, 97, 98, 100, 101, 102, 103, 104, 105, 107, 108, 109, 112, 113, 114, 116, 117, 120, 121, 122, 136, 137, 142, 146, 148, 158, 162, 164, 166, 171, 174, 191 and 202.

The numbering of this series of 1d. red plates follows after that of the previous 1d. stamp, last printed from Plate 68.

Plates 69, 70, 75, 126 and 128 were prepared for this issue but rejected owing to defects, and stamps from these plates do not exist, so that specimens which appear to be from these plates (like many of those which optimistic collectors believe to be from Plate 77) bear other plate numbers. Owing to faulty engraving or printing it is not always easy to identify the plate number. Plate 77 was also rejected but some stamps printed from it were used. One specimen is in the Tapling Collection and six or seven others are known. Plates 226 to 228 were made but not used.

Specimens from most of the plates are known with inverted watermark. The variety of watermark described in the General Notes

to this section occurs on stamp M A (or M L) on plates up to about 96 (Prices from £110 used). Re-entries in this issue are few, the best being on stamps M K and T K of Plate 71 and on S L and T L, Plate 83.

1858-76 Wmk Large Crown, W **4**, Die II . P 14.

			Un	Used*	Used on cover
45	6	2d. blue (thick lines) (7.58)........	£350	15·00	50·00
		a. Imperf (Plate 9)		£13000	
		Wi. Wmk inverted	£1700	£240	
		Plate 7	£2000	65·00	
		Plate 8	£1850	42·00	
		Plate 9	£350	15·00	
		Plate 12	£3000	£140	
46		2d. blue (thin lines) (1.7.69)	£375	27·00	75·00
		Wi. Wmk inverted	£2250	£300	
47		2d. deep blue (thin lines)	£375	27·00	
		a. Imperf (Plate 13)..................		£12000	
		Plate 13...........................	£375	30·00	
		Plate 14...........................	£500	38·00	
		Plate 15...........................	£525	38·00	

45/7 For well-centred, lightly used +125%.

Plates 10 and 11 of the 2d. were prepared but rejected. Plates 13 to 15 were laid down from a new roller impression on which the white lines were thinner.

There are some marked re-entries and repairs, particularly on Plates 7, 8, 9 and 12. Stamps with inverted watermark may be found and also the T A (T L) and M A (M L) watermark varieties (see General Notes to this section).

Though the paper is normally white, some printings showed blueing and stamps showing the "ivory head" may therefore be found.

7	Showing the plate number (9)

9

1870 (1 Oct). Wmk W **9**, extending over three stamps. P 14.

48	7	½d. rose-red...............	£110	30·00	70·00
49		½d. rose	£110	30·00	
		a. Imperf (Plates 1, 4, 5, 6, 8, 14) .... *from*	£4500	£3200	
		Wi. Wmk inverted	£450	£150	
		Wi. Wmk reversed	£450	£150	
		Wi. Wmk inverted and reversed	£300	£100	
		Plate 1	£325	£100	
		Plate 3	£240	55·00	
		Plate 4	£150	30·00	
		Plate 5	£110	30·00	
		Plate 6	£120	30·00	
		Plate 8	£600	£120	
		Plate 9	£6000	£850	
		Plate 10	£130	30·00	
		Plate 11	£120	30·00	
		Plate 12	£120	30·00	
		Plate 13	£120	30·00	
		Plate 14	£120	30·00	
		Plate 15	£175	50·00	
		Plate 19	£300	65·00	
		Plate 20	£350	85·00	

49/9a For well-centred, lightly used +200%.

The ½d. was printed in sheets of 480 (24 × 20) so that the check letters run from to

	A A		X T
	A A	to	T X

Plates 2, 7, 16, 17 and 18 were not completed while Plates 21 and 22, though made, were not used.

Owing to the method of perforating, the outer side of stamps in either the A or X row (ie the left or right side of the sheet) is imperf.

Stamps may be found with watermark inverted or reversed, or without watermark, the latter due to misplacement of the paper when printing.

8	Position of plate Number

1870 (1 Oct). Wmk W **4**. P 14.

51	8	1½d. rose-red	£500	75·00	£275
52		1½d. lake-red	£600	75·00	
		a. Imperf (Plates 1 and 3)........ *from*	£10000	†	
		Wi. Wmk inverted	£3000	£500	
		Plate			
		(1)	£725	£110	
		3	£500	75·00	
		Error of lettering. OP–PC for CP–PC (Plate 1)			
53	8	1½d. rose-red	£30000	£2000	£7500
		Prepared for use in 1860 but not issued; blued paper			
53a	8	1½d. rosy mauve (Plate 1).......	£8500	—	
		b. Error of lettering, OP–PC for CP–PC...........................	—	†	

51/3 For well-centred, lightly used +125%.

Owing to a proposed change in the postal rates, 1½d. stamps were first printed in 1860, in rosy mauve, No. 53a, but the change was not approved and the greater part of the stock was destroyed, although three or four postally used examples have been recorded.

In 1870 a 1½d. stamp was required and was issued in rose-red.

Plate 1 did not have the plate number in the design of the stamps, but on stamps from Plate 3 the number will be found in the frame as shown above.

The error of lettering OP-PC on Plate 1 was apparently not noticed by the printers, and therefore not corrected.

Plate 2 was defective and was not used.

EMBOSSED ISSUES

Volume 1 of the Stanley Gibbons *Great Britain Specialised Catalogue* gives further detailed information on the embossed issues.

PRICES. The prices quoted are for cut-square stamps with average to fine embossing. Stamps with exceptionally clear embossing are worth more.

10	**11**

12 **13**

Position of die number

(Primary die engraved at the Royal Mint by William Wyon. Stamps printed at Somerset House.)

1847–54. Imperf. (For paper and wmk see footnote.)

			Un	Used	Used on Cover
54	10	1s. pale green (11.9.47)............	£24000	£1000	£1900
55		1s. green.........................	£24000	£1000	
56		1s. deep green	£28500	£1200	
		Die 1 (1847).....................	£24000	£1000	
		Die 2 (1854).....................	£26500	£1100	
57	11	10d. brown (6.11.48)...............	£11500	£1500	£3200
		Die 1 (1848).....................	£12000	£1500	
		Die 2 (1850).....................	£11500	£1500	
		Die 3 1853)......................	£11500	£1500	
		Die 4 (1854).....................	£13000	£1750	
58	12	6d. mauve (wmk reversed) (1.3.54)............................	£19500	£1000	
59		6d. dull lilac.....................	£19500	£1000	£1900
60		6d. purple (wmk upright)........	£19500	£1000	
		Wi. Wmk inverted	£19500	£1000	
		Wk. Wmk inverted and reversed	£19500	£1000	
61		6d. violet	£32000	£4000	

The 1s. and 10d. are on "Dickinson" paper with "silk" threads (actually a pale blue twisted cotton yarn). The 6d. is on paper watermarked V R in single-lined letters, W 13, which may be found in four ways—upright, inverted, upright reversed, and inverted reversed, upright reversed being the most common.

The die numbers are indicated on the base of the bust. Only Die 1 (1 WW) of the 6d. was used for the adhesive stamps. The 10d. is from Die 1 (W.W.1 on stamps), and Dies 2 to 4 (2 W.W., 3 W.W. and, 4 W.W.) but the number and letters on stamps from Die 1 are seldom clear and many specimens are known without any trace of them. Because of this the stamp we previously listed as "No die number" has been deleted. That they are from Die I is proved by the existence of blocks showing stamps with and without the die number. The 1s. is from Dies 1 and 2 (W.W.1, W.W.2).

The normal arrangement of the "silk" threads in the paper was in pairs running down each vertical row of the sheet, the space between the threads of each pair being approximately 5 mm and between pairs of threads 20 mm. Varieties due to misplacement of the paper in printing show a single thread on the first stamp from the sheet margin and two threads 20 mm apart on the other stamps of the row. Faulty manufacture is the cause of stamps with a single thread in the middle.

Through bad spacing of the impressions, which were handstruck, all values may be found with two impressions more or less overlapping. Owing to the small margin allowed for variation of spacing, specimens with good margins on all sides are not common. Double impressions are known of all values.

Later printings of the 6d. had the gum tinted green to enable the printer to distinguish the gummed side of the paper.

SURFACE-PRINTED ISSUES
GENERAL NOTES

Volume 1 of the Stanley Gibbons *Great Britain Specialised Catalogue* gives further detailed information on the surface-printed issues.

"Abnormals". The majority of the great rarities in the surface-printed group of issues are the so-called "abnormals", whose existence is due to the practice of printing six sheets from every plate as soon as made, one of which was kept for record purposes at Somerset House, while the others were perforated and usually issued. If such plates were not used for general production or if, before they came into full use, a change of watermark or colour took place, the six sheets originally

printed would differ from the main issue in plate, colour or watermark and, if issued, would be extremely rare.

The abnormal stamps of this class listed in this Catalogue and distinguished, where not priced, by an asterisk (*), are:

No.		
78	3d.	Plate 3 (with white dots)
152	4d.	vermilion, Plate 16
153	4d.	sage-green, Plate 17
109	6d.	mauve, Plate 10
124/a	6d.	chestnut and 6d. pale chestnut, Plate 12
145	6d.	pale buff, Plate 13
88	9d.	Plate 3 (hair lines) 989d. Plate 5 (*see* footnote to No. 98)
113	10d.	Plate 2 911s. Plate 3 ("Plate 2")
148/50	1s.	green, Plate 14
120	2s.	blue, Plate 3

Those which have been issued, but of which no specimens are known, are 2½d. wmk Anchor, Plates 4 and 5; 3d. wmk Emblems, Plate 5; 3d. wmk Spray, Plate 21; 6d. grey, wmk Spray, Plate 18; 8d. orange, Plate 2; 1s. wmk Emblems, Plate 5; 5s. wmk Maltese Cross, Plate 4.

The 10d. Plate 1, wmk Emblems (No. 99), is sometimes reckoned among the abnormals, but was an error, due to the use of the wrong paper.

Corner Letters. With the exception of the 4d., 6d. and 1s. of 1855–57, the ½d., 1½d., 2d. and 5d. of 1880, the 1d. lilac of 1881 and the £5 (which have letters in lower corners only, and in the reverse order to the normal), all the surface-printed stamps issued prior to 1887 had letters in all four corners, as in the later line-engraved stamps. The arrangement is the same, the letters running in sequence right across and down the sheets, whether these were divided into ones or not. The corner letters existing naturally depend on the number of stamps in the sheet and their arrangement.

Imprimaturs and Imperforate Stamps. The Post Office retained in their records (now in the National Postal Museum) one imperforate sheet from each plate, known as the Imprimatur (or officially approved) sheet. Some stamps were removed from time to time for presentation purposes and have come on to the market, but these imperforates are not listed as they were not issued. Full details can be found in Volume I of the *Great Britain Specialised Catalogue*.

However, other imperforate stamps are known to have been issued and these are listed where it has been possible to prove that they do not come from the Imprimatur sheets. It is therefore advisable to purchase these only when accompanied by an Expert Committee certificate of genuineness.

Plate Numbers. All stamps from No. 75 to No. 163 bear in their designs either the plate number or, in one or two earlier instances, some other indication by which one plate can be distinguished from another. With the aid of these and of the corner letters it is thus possible to "reconstruct" a sheet of stamps from any plate of any issue or denomination.

Surface-printing. In this context the traditional designation "surface-printing" is synonymous with typo(graphy)—a philatelic term—or letterpress—the printers' term—as meaning printing from (the surface of) raised type. It is also called relief-printing, as the image is in relief (in French, *en épargne*), unwanted parts of the design having been cut away. Duplicate impressions can be electrotyped or stereotyped from an original die, the resulting *clichés* being locked together to form the printing plate.

Wing Margins. As the vertical gutters (spaces) between the panes, into which sheets of stamps of most values were divided until the introduction of the Imperial Crown watermark, were perforated through the centre with a single row of holes, instead of each vertical row of stamps on the inner side of the panes having its own line of perforation as is now usual, a proportion of the stamps in each sheet have what is called a "wing margin" about 5 mm wide on one or other side.

The stamps with "wing margins" are the watermark Emblems and Spray of Rose series (3d., 6d., 9d., 10d., 1s. and 2s.) with letters D, E, H or I in S.E. corner, and the watermark Garter (4d. and 8d.) with letters F or G in S.E. corner. Knowledge of this lettering will enable collectors to guard against stamps with wing margin cut down and reperforated, but note that wing margin stamps of Nos. 62 to 73 are also to be found re-perforated.

'Used' Prices. In the case of high value surface-printed issues, used prices refer to stamps bearing telegraphic cancellations.

PRINTERS. The issues of Queen Victoria, Nos. 62/214, were typo by Thomas De La Rue & Co.

PERFORATIONS. All the surface-printed issues of Queen Victoria are Perf 14, with the exception of Nos. 126/9.

KEY TO SURFACE-PRINTED ISSUES 1855–83

S.G. Nos.	Description	Watermark	Date of Issue
	NO CORNER LETTERS		
62	4d. carmine	Small Garter	31.7.55
63/5	4d. carmine	Medium Garter	25.2.56
66/a	4d. carmine	Large Garter	Jan 1857
69/70	6d. lilac	Emblems	21.10.56
71/3	1s. green	Emblems	1.11.56
	SMALL WHITE CORNER LETTERS		
75/7	3d. carmine	Emblems	1.5.62
78	3d. carmine (dots)	Emblems	Aug 1862
79/82	4d. red	Large Garter	15.1.62
83/5	6d. lilac	Emblems	1.12.62
86/8	9d. bistre	Emblems	15.1.62
89/91	1s. green	Emblems	1.12.62
	LARGE WHITE CORNER LETTERS		
92	3d. rose	Emblems	1.3.65
102/3	3d. rose	Spray	July 1867
93/4	4d. vermilion	Large Garter	4.7.65
96/7	6d. lilac	Emblems	7.3.65
104/7	6d. lilac	Spray	21.6.67
108/9	6d. lilac	Spray	8.3.69
122/4	6d. chestnut	Spray	12.4.72

www.philasearch.com   www.numissearch.com   www.antiquessearch.com

125	6d. grey	Spray	24.4.73
98	9d. straw	Emblems	30.10.65
110/11	9d. straw	Spray	3.10.67
99	10d. brown	Emblems	11.11.67
112/14	10d. brown	Spray	1.7.67
101	1s. green	Emblems	19.1.65
115/17	1s. green	Spray	13.7.67
118/20*b*	2s. blue	Spray	1.7.67
121	2s. blue	Spray	27.2.80
126/7	5s. rose	Cross	1.7.67
128	10s. grey	Cross	26.9.78
129	£1 brown-lilac	Cross	26.9.78
130, 134	5s. rose	Anchor	25.11.82
131, 135	10s. grey-green	Anchor	Feb 1883
132, 136	£1 brown-lilac	Anchor	Dec 1882
133, 137	£5 orange	Anchor	21.3.82

LARGE COLOURED CORNER LETTERS

166	1d. Venetian red	Crown	1.1.80
138/9	2½d. rosy mauve	Anchor	1.7.75
141	2½d. rosy mauve	Orb	1.5.76
142	2½d. blue	Orb	5.2.80
157	2½d. blue	Crown	23.3.81
143/4	3d. rose	Spray	5.7.73
158	3d. rose	Crown	Jan 1881
159	3d. on 3d. lilac	Crown	1.1.83
152	4d. vermilion	Large Garter	1.3.76
153	4d. sage-green	Large Garter	12.3.77
154	4d. brown	Large Garter	15.8.80
160	4d. brown	Crown	9.12.80
145	6d. buff	Spray	15.3.73
146/7	6d. grey	Spray	20.3.74
161	6d. grey	Crown	1.1.81
162	6d. on 6d. lilac	Crown	1.1.83
156*a*	8d. purple-brown	Large Garter	July 1876
156	8d. orange	Large Garter	11.9.76
148/50	1s. green	Spray	1.9.73
151	1s. brown	Spray	14.10.80
163	1s. brown	Crown	24.5.81

Watermarks: Anchor	W **40, 47**
Cross	W **39**
Crown	W **49**
Emblems	W **20**
Large Garter	W **17**
Medium Garter	W **16**
Orb	W **48**
Small Garter	W **15**
Spray	W **33**

Please note that all watermark illustrations are *as seen from the front of the stamp.*

14 **15** Small Garter

16 Medium Garter **17** Large Garter

1855–57. No corner letters.

(a) Wmk Small Garter, W **15**. *Highly glazed, deeply blued paper (31 July 1855)*

				Un	Used*	Used on cover
62	**14**	4d. carmine (*shades*)		£8500	£450	£780
		a. Paper slightly blued		£9000	£450	
		b. White paper		£20000	£1100	
		Wi. Wmk inverted		£11000	£1200	

(b) Wmk Medium Garter, W **16**

(i) Thick, blued highly glazed paper (25 February 1856)

63	**14**	4d. carmine (*shades*)	£14000	£575	£1100
		a. White paper	£12000		
		Wi. Wmk inverted	—	—	£1250

(ii) Ordinary thin white paper (September 1856)

64	**14**	4d. pale carmine	£13000	£475	£1000
		a. Stamp printed double	†	—	

(iii) Ordinary white paper, specially prepared ink (1 November 1856)

65	**14**	4d. rose or deep rose	£13000	£500	£1000
		Wi. Wmk inverted	†	—	

(c) Wmk Large Garter, W **17**. *Ordinary white paper (January 1857)*

66	**14**	4d. rose-carmine	£2100	£150	£225
		a. Rose	£1750	£150	
		*a*Wi. Wmk inverted	£4800	£400	
		*a*Wk. Wmk inverted and reversed	—	—	
		b. Thick glazed paper	£6500	£350	
		*b*Wi. Wmk inverted	—	—	

*62/6b For well-centred, lightly used +125%.

---

18 **19** **20** Emblems wmk (normal)

20a Wmk error, three roses and shamrock **20b** Wmk error, three roses and thistle

(d) Wmk Emblems, W **20**

68	**18**	6d. lilac (21.10.56)	£1350	£110	£240
69		6d. deep lilac (21.10.56)	£1800	£175	
70		6d. pale lilac	£1350	£125	£240
		a. Azure paper	£9000	£950	
		b. Thick paper	£4000	£425	
		c. Error. Wmk W **20a**			
		Wi. Wmk inverted	£3000	£400	
		Wj. Wmk reversed	—	£450	
		Wk. Wmk inverted and reversed	—	—	
71	**19**	1s. deep green (1.11.56)	£5750	£550	
72		1s. green	£3250	£350	£425
73		1s. pale green	£3250	£350	
		a. Azure paper	—	£2000	
		b. Thick paper	—	£400	
		c. Imperf		†	—
		Wi. Wmk inverted	—	£700	
		Wj. Wmk reversed	—	£1400	
		Wk. Wmk inverted and reversed	—	—	

*69/73b For well-centred, lightly used +125%.

21 **22**

23 **24** **25** Plate 2

A. White dots added B. Hair lines

1862–64. A small uncoloured letter in each corner, the 4d. wmk Large Garter. W **17**, the others Emblems, W **20**.

75	**21**	3d. deep carmine-rose (Plate 2) (1.5.62)	£4800	£575	
76		3d. bright carmine-rose	£2700	£350	£600
		a. Error. Wmk W **20b** (stamp TF)		£9000	
		Wi. Wmk inverted	—	£1200	
77		3d. pale carmine-rose	£2700	£350	
		b. Thick paper	£4000	£475	
		Wj. Wmk reversed	—	—	
78		3d. rose (with white dots, Type A, Plate 3) (8.62)	£45000	£17000	
		a. Imperf (Plate 3)	£6750		
79	**22**	4d. bright red (Plate 3) (15.1.62)	£2200	£170	
80		4d. pale red	£2000	£140	£300
		Wi. Wmk inverted	—	£375	
81		4d. bright red (Hair lines, Type B, Plate 4) (16.10.63)	£2300	£185	
82		4d. pale red (Hair lines, Type B, Plate 4)	£2100	£150	£300
		a. Imperf (Plate 4)	£3700		
		Wi. Wmk inverted	£6700	£375	
83	**23**	6d. deep lilac (Plate 3) (1.12.62)	£2800	£160	
84		6d. lilac	£2250	£140	£225
		a. Azure paper	—	£1400	
		b. Thick paper	—	£375	
		c. Error. Shamrock missing from wmk (stamp TF)			
		d. Error. Wmk W **20b** (stamp TF)	—	£8000	
		e. Hyphen omitted (KA)*		£7750	
		Wi. Wmk inverted	£8250	£450	
		Wj. Wmk reversed	—	£550	

		Wk. Wmk inverted and reversed	£12000	—	
85		6d. lilac (Hair lines, Plate 4) (20.4.64)	£3000	£250	£350
		a. Imperf (wmk inverted)	£4250		
		Eb. Imperf and wmk upright	£4750	—	
		c. Thick paper	£4000	£280	
		d. Error. Wmk W **20b** (stamp TF)			
		Wi. Wmk inverted	£8250	£475	
		Wj. Wmk reversed	—	—	
		Wk. Wmk inverted and reversed	—	—	
86	**24**	9d. bistre (Plate 2) (15.1.62)	£5800	£575	£1200
		Wi. Wmk inverted	£10000	£700	
		Wj. Wmk reversed	—	£850	
		Wk. Wmk inverted and reversed	—	—	
87		9d. straw	£4000	£475	£1000
		a. On azure paper			
		b. Thick paper	£6000	£550	
		c. Error. Watermark W **20b** (stamp TF)	†		
		Wi. Wmk inverted	£6800	£650	
88		9d. bistre (Hair lines, Plate 3) (5.62)	£32000	£13500	
89	**25**	1s. deep green (Plate No. 1 = Plate 2) (1.12.62)	£4800	£500	
90		1s. green (Plate No. 1 = Plate 2)	£3200	£300	£450
		a. "K" in lower left corner in white circle (stamp KD)	£20000	£2750	
		*a*Wi. Wmk inverted	—	£4250	
		aa. "K" normal (stamp KD)	—	£2200	
		b. On azure paper			
		c. Error. Wmk **20b** (stamp TF)			
		d. Thick paper			£375
		da. Thick paper, "K" in circle as No. 90a	—	£3750	
		Wi. Wmk inverted	—	£450	
		Wj. Wmk reversed	—	—	
		Wk. Wmk inverted and reversed	—	£475	
91		1s. deep green (Plate No. 2 = Plate 3)	£35000		
		a. Imperf	£7250		
		*a*Wi. Wmk inverted	—	£7250	

*75/91 For well-centred, lightly used +125%.

The 3d. as Type 21, but with network background in the spandrels which is found overprinted SPECIMEN, was never issued.

The plates of this issue may be distinguished as follows:

3d.	Plate 2.	No white dots.
	Plate 3.	White dots as Illustration A.
4d.	Plate 3.	No hair lines. Roman I next to lower corner letters.
	Plate 4.	Hair lines in corners. (Illustration B.). Roman II.
6d.	Plate 3.	No hair lines.
	Plate 4.	Hair lines in corners.
9d.	Plate 2.	No hair lines.
	Plate 3.	Hair lines in corners. Beware of faked lines.
1s.	Plate 2.	Numbered 1 on stamps.
	Plate 3.	Numbered 2 on stamps and with hair lines.

*One used example on piece has been recorded, cancelled by a Glasgow Duplex postmark dated 06.1.1863.

The 9d. on azure paper (No. 87a) is very rare, only one confirmed example being known.

The variety "K" in circle, No. 90a, is believed to be due to a damaged letter having been cut out and replaced. It is probable that the punch was driven in too deeply, causing the flange to penetrate the surface, producing an indentation showing as an uncoloured circle.

The watermark variety "three roses and a shamrock" illustrated in W **20a** was evidently due to the substitution of an extra rose for the thistle in a faulty watermark bit. It is found on stamp TA of Plate 4 of the 3d., Plates 1 (No. 70c), 3, 5 and 6 of the 6d., Plate 4 of the 9d. and Plate 4 of the 1s.

Similar problems occurred on stamp TF of the 6d. and 9d. Here the shamrock item became detached by a used example of the 6d. (No. 84) is known showing it omitted. It was replaced by a third rose (W **20b**) and this variety exists on the 6d. (Nos. 84/5 and 97) and 9d. (Nos. 87 and 98).

26 **27**

28 (with hyphen) **28a** (without hyphen)

29 **30** **31**

1865–73. Large uncoloured corner letters. Wmk Large Garter (4d.); others Emblems.

92	26	3d. rose (Plate 4) (1.3.65)...	£2500	£250	£500
		a. Error. Wmk W **20a**	£6500	£1250	
		b. Thick paper	£3500	£325	
		Wi. Wmk inverted	—	£600	
		Wj. Wmk reversed	—	—	
		Wk. Wmk inverted and reversed			
93	27	4d. dull vermilion (4.7.65).	£650	90·00	
94		4d. vermilion	£575	75·00	£140
		a. Imperf (Plates 11, 12).	£8500		
		Wi. Wmk inverted	£575	75·00	
		Plate			
		7 (1865)	£650	£130	
		8 (1866)	£600	90·00	
		9 (1867)	£600	90·00	
		10 (1868)	£825	£150	
		11 (1869)	£625	90·00	
		12 (1870)	£575	75·00	
		13 (1872)	£650	75·00	
		14 (1873)	£775	£100	
96	28	6d. deep lilac (with hyphen) (7.3.65)	£1900	£190	
97		6d. lilac (with hyphen)	£1200	£140	£225
		a. Thick paper	£1600	£175	
		b. Stamp doubly printed (Pl 6)	—	£15000	
		c. Error. Wmk W **20a** (Pl 5, 6)	*from* —	£2400	
		d. Error. Wmk W **20b** (Plate 5)			
		e. Imperf (plate 5)			
		Wi. Wmk inverted	—	£250	
		Wj. Wmk reversed	—	—	
		Wk. Wmk inverted and reversed	†	—	
		Plate			
		5 (1865)	£1100	£140	
		6 (1867)	£3800	£275	
98	29	9d. straw (Plate 4) (30.10.65)	£4800	£600	£1400
		a. Thick paper	£5800	£850	
		b. Error. Wmk W **20a**		£2500	
		c. Error. Wmk W **20b** (stamp TF)	£13000		
		Wi. Wmk inverted		£1650	
99	30	10d. red-brown (Pl 1) (11.11.67)		† £55000	
101	31	1s. green (Plate 4) (19.1.65)	£2850	£275	£450
		a. Error. Wmk W **20a**		£1700	
		b. Thick paper	£3500	£380	
		c. Imperf between (vert pair)	—	£16000	
		Wi. Wmk inverted	—	£650	
		Wia. Imperf wmk inverted..	—	—	
		Wk. Wmk inverted and reversed	—	£650	

*92/101c **For well-centred, lightly used +100%.**

From mid-1866 to about the end of 1871 4d. stamps of this issue appeared generally with watermark inverted.

Unused examples of No. 98 from Plate 5 exist, but this was never put to press and all evidence points to such stamps originating from a portion of the Imprimatur sheet which was perforated by De La Rue in 1887 for insertion in albums to be presented to members of the Stamp Committee (*Price* £18000 un).

The 10d. stamps, No. 99, were printed in error on paper watermarked "Emblems" instead of on "Spray of Rose".

32	**33** Spray of Rose	**34**

1867–80. Wmk Spray of Rose, W **33**.

102	26	3d. deep rose (12.7.67)	£800	£100	
103		3d. rose	£525	60·00	£110
		a. Imperf (Plates 5, 6, 8)	*from* £11000		
		Wi. Wmk inverted	£2250	£300	
		Plate			
		4 (1867)	£1850	£300	
		5 (1868)	£525	70·00	
		6 (1870)	£550	70·00	
		7 (1871)	£650	70·00	
		8 (1872)	£625	60·00	
		9 (1872)	£625	70·00	
		10 (1873)	£875	£150	
104	28	6d. lilac (with hyphen) (Plate 6) (21.6.67)	£1850	£150	£225
		a. Imperf		£6000	
		Wi. Wmk inverted	—	£350	
105		6d. deep lilac (with hyphen) (Plate 6)	£1850	£150	
106		6d. purple (with hyphen) (Pl 6)	£1850	£190	
107		6d. bright violet (with hyphen) (Plate 6) (22.7.68)	£1750	£190	
108		6d. dull violet (without hyphen) (Plate 8) (8.3.69)	£1250	£190	
		Wi. Wmk inverted		£275	
109		6d. mauve (without hyphen)	£700	90·00	£140
		a. Imperf (Plate Nos. 8 and 9)	£12000	£5000	
		Wi. Wmk inverted	—	£250	
		Plate			

		8 (1869, mauve)	£800	£140	
		9 (1870, mauve)	£700	90·00	
		10 (1869, mauve)	*	£3750	
110	29	9d. straw (Plate No. 4) (3.10.67)	£2500	£325	£525
		Wi. Wmk inverted	—	£650	
111		9d. pale straw (Plate No. 4)	£2400	£300	
		a. Imperf (Plate 4)	£22000		
112	30	10d. red-brown (1.7.67)	£3600	£400	£850
		Wi. Wmk inverted	—	£1000	
113		10d. pale red-brown	£3600	£400	
114		10d. deep red-brown	£5000	£600	
		a. Imperf (Plate 1)	£17000		
		Plate			
		1 (1867)	£3600	£400	
		2 (1867)	£55000	£17000	
115	31	1s. deep green (13.7.67)	£1300	70·00	
117		1s. green	£800	45·00	90·00
		a. Imperf between (horiz pair) (Plate 7)	—	£6500	
		b. Imperf (Plate 4)	£10000	£6500	
		Wi. Wmk inverted	£2400	£180	
		Plate			
		4 (1867)	£975	65·00	
		5 (1871)	£800	45·00	
		6 (1871)	£1200	45·00	
		7 (1873)	£1400	90·00	
118	32	2s. dull blue (1.7.67)	£4200	£225	£825
		Wi. Wmk inverted	—	£900	
119		2s. deep blue	£5000	£240	
		a. Imperf (Plate 1)	£23000		
120		2s. pale blue	£5000	£275	
		aa. Imperf (Plate 1)	£22000		
120*a*		2s. cobalt	£25000	£3000	
120*b*		2s. milky blue	£24000	£2000	
		Plate			
		1 (1867)	£4200	£225	
		3 (1868)	*	£16500	
121		2s. brown (Plate No. 1) (27.2.80)	£30000	£4200	
		a. Imperf	£30000		
		b. No watermark	†	—	
		Wi. Wmk inverted	—	£6000	

*102/21 **For well-centred, lightly used +75%.**

Examples of the 1s. from Plates 5 and 6 without watermark are postal forgeries used at the Stock Exchange Post Office in the early 1870's.

1872–73. Uncoloured letters in corners. Wmk Spray, W **33**.

122	34	6d. deep chestnut (Plate II) (12.4.72)	£1300	£125	
122*a*		6d. chestnut (Plate II) (22.5.72)	£800	65·00	£150
		*a*Wi. Wmk inverted	—	£325	
122*b*		6d. pale chestnut (Plate II) (1872)	£700	65·00	
123		6d. pale buff (19.10.72)	£1100	£125	£250
		Wi. Wmk inverted	—	£375	
		Plate			
		11 (1872, pale buff)	£1100	£125	
		12 (1872, pale buff)	£3400	£350	
124		6d. chestnut (Plate 12) (1872)	*	£3800	
124*a*		6d. pale chestnut (Plate 12) (1872)	*	£3500	
125		6d. grey (Plate 12) (24.4.73)	£1900	£300	£375
		a. Imperf	£15000		
		Wi. Wmk inverted	£6250	—	

*122/5 **For well-centred, lightly used +50%.**

35	**36**

37

38

39 Maltese Cross	**40** Large Anchor

1867–83. Uncoloured letters in corners.

				Un	Used*
		(a) Wmk Maltese Cross, W **39**. *P 15½ × 15*			
126	35	5s. rose (1.7.67)		£11000	£675
127		5s. pale rose		£11000	£675
		a. Imperf (Plate 1)		£18000	
		Plate			
		1 (1867)		£11000	£675
		2 (1874)		£18000	£1500
128	36	10s. greenish grey (Plate 1) (26.9.78)		£60000	£3200
129	37	£1 brown-lilac (Plate 1) (26.9.78)		£90000	£4500
		(b) Wmk Anchor, W **40**. *P 14*			
		(i) Blued paper			
130	35	5s. rose (Plate 4) (25.11.82)		£42000	£4800
		Wi. Wmk inverted		—	£18000
131	36	10s. grey-green (Plate 1) (2.83)		£135000	£5200
132	37	£1 brown-lilac (Plate 1) (12.82)		£175000	£10000
133	38	£5 orange (Plate 1) (21.3.82)		£70000	£15000
		(ii) White paper			
134	35	5s. rose (Plate 4)		£35000	£4200
135	36	10s. greenish grey (Plate 1)		£160000	£4500
136	37	£1 brown-lilac (Plate 1)		£200000	£9000
137	38	£5 orange (Plate 1)		£14500	£4750

*126/37 **For well-centred, lightly used +75%.**

41	**42**	**43**

44	**45**	**46**

47 Small Anchor	**48** Orb

1873–80. Large coloured letters in the corners.

			Un	Used*	Used on cover
		(a) Wmk Anchor, W **47**			
138	41	2½d. rosy mauve (*blued paper*) (1.7.75)	£875	£190	
		a. Imperf			
		Wi. Wmk inverted	£3000	£350	
		Plate			
		1 (*blued paper*) (1875).	£875	£190	
		2 (*blued paper*) (1875).	£8000	£1650	
		3 (*blued paper*) (1875).	—	£5750	
139		2½d. rosy mauve (white paper)	£650	£120	£180
		Wi. Wmk inverted	£2750	£250	
		Plate			
		1 (*white paper*) (1875).	£650	£120	
		2 (*white paper*) (1875).	£650	£120	
		3 (*white paper*) (1875).	£1000	£175	
		Error of Lettering L H—F L for L H—H L (Plate 2)			
140	41	2½d. rosy mauve	£34000	£2750	
		(b) Wmk Orb, W **48**			
141	41	2½d. rosy mauve (1.5.76)	£525	85·00	£125
		Wi. Wmk inverted	£1900	£225	
		Plate			
		3 (1876)	£1350	£150	
		4 (1876)	£525	80·00	
		5 (1876)	£525	80·00	
		6 (1876)	£525	80·00	
		7 (1877)	£525	80·00	
		8 (1877)	£525	80·00	
		9 (1877)	£525	80·00	
		10 (1878)	£550	95·00	
		11 (1878)	£525	80·00	
		12 (1878)	£525	80·00	
		13 (1878)	£525	80·00	
		14 (1879)	£525	80·00	
		15 (1879)	£525	80·00	
		16 (1879)	£525	80·00	
		17 (1880)	£1700	£300	
142		2½d. blue (5.2.80)	£575	55·00	90·00
		Wi. Wmk inverted	£2100	£275	
		Plate			
		17 (1880)	£575	70·00	
		18 (1880)	£575	55·00	

		19 (1880)	£575	55·00	
		20 (1880)	£575	55·00	

(c) Wmk Spray, W 33

143	42	3d. rose (5.7.73)	£450	80·00	£120
		Wi. Wmk inverted	£1650	£350	
144		3d. pale rose	£450	80·00	
		Plate			
		11 (1873)	£450	80·00	
		12 (1873)	£525	80·00	
		14 (1874)	£525	80·00	
		15 (1874)	£450	80·00	
		16 (1875)	£450	80·00	
		17 (1875)	£525	80·00	
		18 (1875)	£525	80·00	
		19 (1876)	£450	80·00	
		20 (1879)	£850	£140	
145	43	6d. pale buff (Plate 13) (15.3.73)	*	£25000	
146		6d. deep grey (20.3.74)	£600	£120	£150
147		6d. grey	£500	90·00	
		Wi. Wmk inverted	£1800	£350	
		Plate			
		13 (1874)	£500	90·00	
		14 (1875)	£500	90·00	
		15 (1876)	£500	90·00	
		16 (1878)	£500	90·00	
		17 (1880)	£950	£180	
148	44	1s. deep green (1.9.73)	£1100	£225	
150		1s. green	£650	£160	£240
		Wi. Wmk inverted	£2400	£400	
		Plate			
		8 (1873)	£825	£175	
		9 (1874)	£825	£175	
		10 (1874)	£775	£200	
		11 (1875)	£775	£175	
		12 (1875)	£650	£160	
		13 (1876)	£650	£160	
		14 (—)	*	£40000	
151		1s. orange-brown (Plate 13) (14.10.80)	£4750	£700	£1800
		Wi. Wmk inverted	£11000	£1800	

(d) Wmk Large Garter, W 17

152	45	4d. vermilion (1.3.76)	£3200	£525	£1100
		Wi. Wmk inverted	—	£1000	
		Plate			
		15 (1876)	£3200	£525	
		16 (1877)	*	£35000	
153		4d. sage-green (12.3.77)	£1400	£300	£600
		Wi. Wmk inverted	£3000	£625	
		Plate			
		15 (1877)	£1600	£325	
		16 (1877)	£1400	£300	
		17 (1877)	*	£20000	
154		4d. grey-brown (Plate 17) (15.8.80)	£2800	£550	£1700
		a. Imperf	£22000		
		Wi. Wmk inverted	—	£1200	
156	46	8d. orange (Plate 1) (11.9.76)	£1850	£350	£625
		Wi. Wmk inverted		£900	

*138/56 **For well-centred, lightly used +100%.**

1876 (July). Prepared for use but not issued.

156a	46	8d. purple-brown (Plate 1)	£9750	

49 Imperial Crown	**(50)**

1880–83. Wmk Imperial Crown. W **49**.

157	41	2½d. blue (23.3.81)	£450	35·00	55·00
		Wi. Wmk inverted	—	£550	
		Plate			
		21 (1881)	£500	45·00	
		22 (1881)	£450	45·00	
		23 (1881)	£450	35·00	
158	42	3d. rose (3.81)	£500	£100	£175
		Wi. Wmk inverted	—	£580	
		Plate			
		20 (1881)	£900	£150	
		21 (1881)	£500	£100	
159	50	3d. on 3d. lilac (C.) (Plate 21) (1.1.83)	£650	£160	£450
		Wi. Wmk inverted	—	—	
160	45	4d. grey-brown (8.12.80)	£450	75·00	£190
		Wi. Wmk inverted	—	£650	
		Plate			
		17 (1880)	£475	80·00	
		18 (1882)	£450	75·00	
161	43	6d. grey (1.1.81)	£400	80·00	£120
		Wi. Wmk inverted	—	£650	
		Plate			
		17 (1881)	£425	80·00	
		18 (1882)	£400	80·00	
162	50	6d. on 6d. lilac (C.) (Plate 18) (1.1.83)	£675	£150	£425
		a. Slanting dots (various) *from*	£1800	£450	
		b. Opt double	—	£12500	
		Wi. Wmk inverted	£3500	£850	
163	44	1s. orange-brown (24.5.81)	£750	£170	£550
		Wi. Wmk inverted	£3250	£950	
		Plate			
		13 (1881)	£875	£170	
		14 (1881)	£750	£170	

*157/63 **For well-centred, lightly used +75%.**
The 1s. Plate 14 (line perf 14) exists in purple, but was not issued in this shade (*Price £8000 unused*). Examples were included in a few of the Souvenir Albums prepared for members of the "Stamp Committee of 1884".

52	**53**

54	**55**	**56**

1880–81. Wmk Imperial Crown, W **49**.

164	52	½d. deep green (14.10.80)	55·00	22·00	30·00
		a. Imperf	£5000		
		b. No watermark	£10000		
		Wi. Wmk inverted	£2400	£575	
165		½d. pale green	55·00	22·00	
166	53	1d. Venetian red (1.1.80)	35·00	15·00	30·00
		a. Imperf	£5800		
		b. Error. Wmk 48	†	£27000	
		Wi. Wmk inverted	—	£350	
167	54	1½d. Venetian red (14.10.80)	£250	60·00	£160
		Wi. Wmk inverted	†		
168	55	2d. pale rose (8.12.80)	£340	£120	£300
		Wi. Wmk inverted	£3000	£850	
168a		2d. deep rose	£360	£120	
169	56	5d. indigo (15.3.81)	£725	£175	£325
		a. Imperf	£6750	£4500	
		Wi. Wmk inverted	—	£4800	

*164/9 **For well-centred, lightly used +75%.**
Two used examples of the 1d. value have been reported on the Orb (fiscal) watermark.

Die I	**57**	Die II

1881. Wmk Imperial Crown. W **49**.

(a) 14 dots in each corner, Die I (12 July)

170	57	1d. lilac	£225	45·00	60·00
		Wi. Wmk inverted	—	£600	
171		1d. pale lilac	£225	45·00	

(b) 16 dots in each corner, Die II (13 December)

172	57	1d. lilac	2·75	2·20	4·00
		Wi. Wmk inverted	60·00	35·00	
172a		1d. bluish lilac	£475	£150	
173		1d. deep purple	2·75	2·20	
		a. Printed both sides	£900	†	
		b. Frame broken at bottom	£975	£350	
		c. Printed on gummed side	£900	†	
		d. Imperf three sides (pair)	£8250	†	
		e. Printed both sides but impression on back inverted	£1000	†	
		f. No watermark	£8000	†	
		g. Blued paper	—		
174		1d. mauve	2·75	1·70	
		a. Imperf (pair)	£7500		

*170/4 **For well-centred, lightly used +50%.**
1d. stamps with the words "PEARS SOAP" printed on the back in orange, blue or mauve *price from £550, unused.*
The variety "frame broken at bottom" (No. 173b) shows a white space just inside the bottom frame-line from between the "N" and "E" of "ONE" to below the first "N" of "PENNY", breaking the pearls and cutting into the lower part of the oval below "PEN".

KEY TO SURFACE-PRINTED ISSUES 1880–1900

S.G. Nos.	Description	Date of Issue
164/5	½d. green	14.10.80
187	½d. slate-blue	1.4.84
197/e	½d. vermilion	1.1.8
721	3½d. blue-green	17.4.1900
166	1d. Venetian red	1.1.80
170/	1⅟d. lilac, Die 1	12.7.81
172/4	1d. lilac, Die 11	12.12.81
167	1½d. Venetian red	14.10.80
188	1½d. lilac	1.4.84
198	2d. purple and green	1.1.87
168/a	2d. rose	8.12.80
189	2d. lilac	1.4.84
199/200	2d. green and red	1.1.87
190	2½d. lilac	1.4.84
201	2½d purple on blue paper	1.1.87
191	3d. lilac	1.4.84
202/4	3d. purple on yellow paper	1.1.87
192	4d. dull green	1.4.84
205/a	4d. green and brown	1.1.87
206	4½d. green and carmine	15.9.92
169	5d. indigo	15.3.81
193	5d. dull green	1.4.84

S.G. Nos.	Description	Date of Issue
207	5d. purple and blue, Die I	1.1.87
207a	5d. purple and blue, Die II	1888
194	6d. dull green	1.4.84
208/a	6d. purple on rose-red paper	1.1.87
195	9d. dull green	1.8.83
209	9d. purple and blue	1.1.87
210/b	10d. purple and carmine	24.2.90
196	1s. dull green	1.4.84
211	1s. green	1.1.87
214	1s. green and carmine	11.7.1900
175	2s.6d. lilac on blued paper	2.7.83
178/9	2s.6d. lilac	1884
176	5s. rose on blued paper	1.4.84
180/1	5s. rose	1884
177/a	10s. ultramarine on blued paper	1.4.84
182/3a	10s. ultramarine	1884
185	£1 brown-lilac, wmk Crowns	1.4.84
186	£1 brown-lilac, wmk Orbs	6.1.88
212	£1 green	28.1.91

Note that the £5 value used with the above series is listed as Nos. 133 and 137.

58	**59**

60

1883–84. Coloured letters in the corners. Wmk Anchor, W **40**.

(a) Blued paper

			Un	Used
175	58	2s.6d. lilac (2.7.83)	£6750	£1500
176	59	5s. rose (1.4.84)	£18000	£4000
177	60	10s. ultramarine (1.4.84)	£40000	£8250
177a		10s. cobalt (5.84)	£62000	£13500

(b) White paper

178	58	2s.6d. lilac	£600	£160
179		2s.6d. deep lilac	£825	£225
		a. On blued paper	£9000	£3600
		Wi. Wmk inverted	—	£11500
180	59	5s. rose	£1100	£250
		Wi. Wmk inverted	†	£12500
181		5s. crimson	£975	£250
182	60	10s. cobalt	£42000	£8250
183		10s. ultramarine	£2250	£525
183a		10s. pale ultramarine	£2500	£550

*175/83a **For well-centred, lightly used +50%.**
For No. 180 perf 12 see second note below No. 196.

61

Broken frames, Plate 2

1884 (1 Apr). Wmk Three Imperial Crowns, W **49**.

185	61	£1 brown-lilac	£32000	£2800
		a. Frame broken	£60000	£5000
		Wi. Wmk inverted	—	£38000

1888 (Jan). Wmk Three Orbs, W **48**.

186	61	£1 brown-lilac	£72000	£4250
		a. Frame broken	£140000	£9000

*185/6a **For well-centred, lightly used +50%.**
The December 1887 printing of the £1 brown-lilac was produced on paper watermarked Three Orbs in error. The decision was taken to issue date stamps for normal postal use and the earliest recorded postmark is 6 January 1888 at Leadenhall Street, London EC.
The broken-frame varieties, Nos. 185a and 186a, are on Plate 2 stamps JC and TA, as illustrated. See also No. 212a.

62	**63**	**64**

65 **66**

1883 (1 Aug.) (9d.) or **1884** (1 Apr) (others). Wmk Imperial Crown, W **49** (sideways on horiz designs).

			Un	Used*	Used on cover
187	52	½d. slate-blue	35·00	10·00	20·00
		a. Imperf	£3750		
		Wi. Wmk inverted	£3000	£350	
188	62	1½d. lilac	£125	45·00	£120
		a. Imperf	£3750		
		Wi. Wmk inverted	£3000	£280	
189	63	2d. lilac	£230	80·00	£150
		a. Imperf	£4800		
		Wi. Wmk sideways inverted	—		
190	64	2½d. lilac	95·00	20·00	30·00
		a. Imperf	£4800		
		Wi. Wmk sideways inverted	£600		—
191	65	3d. lilac	£280	£100	£180
		a. Imperf	£4800		
		Wi. Wmk inverted	†	£1200	
192	66	4d. dull green	£580	£210	£350
		a. Imperf	£4800		
193	62	5d. dull green	£580	£210	£350
		a. Imperf	£5500		
194	63	6d. dull green	£625	£240	£380
		a. Imperf	£5750		
		Wi. Wmk sideways inverted	£1400		—
195	64	9d. dull green (1.8.83)	£1250	£480	£4750
		Wi. Wmk sideways inverted	£2000	£775	
196	65	1s. dull green	£1600	£325	£625
		a. Imperf	£8750		
		Wi. Wmk inverted	—		

*187/96 **For well-centred, lightly used +100%**

The normal sideways watermark shows the top of the crown pointing to the right, *as seen from the back of the stamp*.

The above prices are for stamps in the true dull green colour. Stamps which have been soaked, causing the colour to run, are virtually worthless.

Stamps of the above set and No. 180 are also found perf 12; these are official perforations, but were never issued. A second variety of the 5d. is known with a line instead of a stop under the "d" in the value; this was never issued and is therefore only known unused (*Price* £28000).

71 **72** **73**

74 **75** **76**

77 **78** **79**

80 **81** **82**

Die I Die II

Die I: Square dots to right of "d".
Die II: Thin vertical lines to right of "d".

1887 (1 Jan)–**92**. "Jubilee" issue. New types. The bicoloured stamps have the value tablets, or the frames including the value tablets, in the second colour. Wmk Imperial Crown, W **49** (Three Crowns on £1).

197	71	½d. vermilion	1·75	1·20	7·00
		a. Printed on gummed side	£3500		
		b. Printed both sides			

---

			c. Doubly printed	£32000		
			d. Imperf	£5000		
			Wi. Wmk inverted	60·00	60·00	
197e			½d. orange-vermilion	1·75	1·20	
198	72	1½d. dull purple and pale green		18·00	8·00	25·00
			a. Purple part of design double		£9000	
			Wi. Wmk inverted	£1200	£500	
199	73	2d. green and scarlet		£425	£260	
200		2d. grey-green and carmine		35·00	15·00	28·00
			Wi. Wmk inverted	£1200	£525	
201	74	2½d. purple/*blue*		25·00	5·00	8·00
			a. Printed on gummed side	£15000		
			b. Imperf three sides	£9500		
			c. Imperf	£12000		
			Wi. Wmk inverted	£3500	£1400	
202	75	3d. purple/*yellow*		25·00	5·00	38·00
			a. Imperf (wmk inverted)	£11000		
			Wi. Wmk inverted	—	£725	
203		3d. deep purple/*yellow*		30·00	5·00	
204		3d. purple/*orange* (1890)		£800		
205	76	4d. green and purple-brown		40·00	18·00	42·00
			aa. Imperf	£11000		
			Wi. Wmk inverted	£1200	£650	
205a		4d. green and deep brown		40·00	18·00	
206	77	4½d. green and carmine (15.9.92)		11·00	45·00	£100
			Wi. Wmk inverted	—		
206a		4½d. green and deep bright carmine		£750	£650	
207	78	5d. dull purple and blue (Die I)		£800	£120	£275
207a		5d. dull purple and blue (Die II) (1888)		42·00	15·00	50·00
			Wi. Wmk inverted	£17000	£1250	
208	79	6d. purple/*rose-red*		40·00	15·00	95·00
			Wi. Wmk inverted	£7500	£2000	
208a		6d. deep purple/*rose-red*		40·00	15·00	
209	80	9d. dull purple and blue		75·00	48·00	£275
			Wi. Wmk inverted	£8000	£2800	
210	81	10d. dull purple and carmine (*shades*) 24.2.90)		60·00	45·00	£300
			aa. Imperf	£17000		
			Wi. Wmk inverted	£9500	£3000	
210a		10d. dull purple and deep dull carmine		£625	£250	
210b		10d. dull purple and scarlet		95·00	65·00	
211	82	1s. dull green		£275	80·00	£190
			Wi. Wmk inverted	£1700	£975	
212	61	£1 green (28.1.91)		£4000	£800	
			a. Frame broken	£8500	£2000	
			Wi. Wmk inverted	£110000	£13000	

*197/212a **For well-centred, lightly used +50%**.

The broken-frame varieties, No. 212a, are on Plate 2 stamps JC or TA, as illustrated above No. 185.

½d. stamps with "PEARS SOAP" printed on the back in orange, blue or mauve, *price from* £525 *each*.

No used price is quoted for No. 204 as it is not possible to authenticate the paper colour on stamps in used condition.

1900. Colours changed. Wmk Imperial Crown, W **49**.

213	71	½d. blue-green (17.4)	2·00	2·25	6·50
		a. Printed on gummed side		†	
		b. Imperf	£7250		
		Wi. Wmk inverted	75·00	75·00	
214	82	1s. green and carmine (11.7)	65·00	£140	£1000
		Wi. Wmk inverted	£1900	£1100	
197/214 *Set of 14*			£650	£375	

*213/14 **For well-centred, lightly used +50%**.

The ½d., No. 213, in bright blue, is a colour changeling caused by a constituent of the ink used for some months in 1900.

KING EDWARD VII
22 January 1901–6 May 1910

PRINTINGS. Distinguishing De La Rue printings from the provisional printings of the same values made by Harrison & Sons Ltd. or at Somerset House may prove difficult in some cases. For very full guidance Volume 2 of the Stanley Gibbons *Great Britain Specialised Catalogue* should prove helpful.

Note that stamps perforated 15×14 must be Harrison; the 2½d., 3d. and 4d. in this perforation are useful reference material, their shades and appearance in most cases matching the Harrison perf 14 printings. Except for the 6d. value, all stamps on chalk-surfaced paper were printed by De La Rue.

Of the stamps on ordinary paper, the De La Rue impressions are usually clearer and of a higher finish than those of the other printers. The shades are markedly different except in some printings of the 4d., 6d. and 7d. and in the 5s., 10s. and £1.

Used stamps in good, clean, unrubbed condition and with dated postmarks can form the basis of a useful reference collection, the dates often assisting in the assignment to the printers.

USED STAMPS. For well-centred, lightly used examples of King Edward VII stamps, add the following percentages to the used prices quoted below:

De La Rue printings (Nos. 215/66)—3d. values +35%, 4d. orange + 100%, 6d. +75%, 7d. and 1s. +25%, all other values + 50%.
Harrison printings (Nos. 267/86)—all values and perforations +75%.
Somerset House printings (Nos. 287/320)—1s. values +25%, all other values +50%.

---

83 **84** **85**

86 **87** **88**

89 **90** **91**

92 **93** **94**

95 **96**

97

(Des E. Fuchs)

1902 (1 Jan)–**10**. Printed by De La Rue & Co. Wmk Imperial Crown (½d. to 1s.): Anchor (2s.6d. to 10s.); Three Crowns (£1). Ordinary paper. P 14.

215	83	½d. dull blue-green (1.1.02)	2·00	1·50	2·50
		Wi. Wmk inverted	£2750	£2000	
216		½d. blue-green	2·00	1·50	
217		½d. pale yellowish green (26.11.04)	2·00	1·50	2·50
218		½d. yellowish green	2·00	1·50	
		a. Booklet pane. Five stamps plus St. Andrew's Cross label (6.06)	£700		
		b. Doubly printed (bottom row on one pane) (Control H9)	£27500		
		Wi. Wmk inverted	12·00	9·00	
219		1d. scarlet (1.1.02)	2·00	1·50	2·50
220		1d. bright scarlet	2·00	1·50	
		a. Imperf (pair)	£30000		
		Wi. Wmk inverted	4·00	3·00	
221	84	1½d. dull purple and green (21.3.02)	48·00	24·00	
222		1½d. slate-purple and green	50·00	24·00	50·00
		Wi. Wmk inverted	—	£900	
223		1½d. pale dull pur and green (*chalk-surfaced paper*) (7.05)	45·00	24·00	
224		1½d. slate-purple and bluish green (*chalk-surfaced paper*)	45·00	22·00	
225	85	2d. yellowish green and carmine-red (25.3.02)..	70·00	25·00	50·00
		Wi. Wmk inverted	—	—	
226		2d. grey-grn and carm-red (1904)	70·00	35·00	
227		2d. pale grey-green and carmine-red (*chalk-surfaced paper*) (4.06)	45·00	32·00	
		Wi. Wmk inverted	£20000		
228		2d. pale grey-green and scarlet (*chalk-surfaced paper*) (1909)	45·00	32·00	
229		2d. dull blue-green and carm (*chalk-surfaced paper*) (1907)	90·00	50·00	
230	86	2½d. ultramarine (1.1.02)	20·00	12·00	25·00
231		2½d. pale ultramarine	20·00	12·00	
		Wi. Wmk inverted	—	£4200	

			Un	Used	
232	87	3d. dull purple/*orange-yellow* (20.3.02)	50·00	18·00	35·00
		Wi. Wmk inverted	—	—	
		a. Chalk-surfaced paper (3.06)	£225	90·00	
232b		3d. deep purple/*orange-yellow*	45·00	18·00	
232c		3d. pale reddish pur/*orge-yell* (*chalk-surfaced paper*) (3.06)	£225	85·00	
233		3d. dull reddish pur/*yell* (*lemon back*) (*chalk-surfaced paper*)	£225	85·00	
233b		3d. pale purple/*lemon* (*chalk-surfaced paper*)	45·00	20·00	
234		3d. pur/*lemon* (*chalk-surfaced paper*)	45·00	20·00	
235	88	4d. green and grey-brown (27.3.02)	70·00	35·00	
		Wi. Wmk inverted	—	—	
236		4d. green and chocolate-brown	70·00	35·00	
		Wi. Wmk inverted	—	£9500	
		a. Chalk-surfaced paper (1.06)	40·00	20·00	45·00
238		4d. dp green and choc-brn (*chalk-surfaced paper*) (1.06)	40·00	20·00	
239		4d. brown-orange (1.11.09)	£180	£140	
240		4d. pale orange (12.09)	20·00	18·00	40·00
241		4d. orange-red (12.09)	20·00	18·00	
242	89	5d. dull purple and ultramarine (14.5.02)	65·00	22·00	50·00
		a. Chalk-surfaced paper (5.06)	55·00	22·00	
244		5d. slate-pur and ultram (*chalk-surfaced paper*) (5.06)	50·00	22·00	
		Wi. Wmk inverted	£5500	—	
245	83	6d. pale dull purple (1.1.02)	45·00	22·00	60·00
		a. Chalk-surfaced paper (1.06)	45·00	22·00	
246		6d. slate-purple	45·00	22·00	
248		6d. dull purple (*chalk-surfaced paper*) (1.06)	45·00	22·00	
		Wi. Wmk inverted	—	£3500	
249	90	7d. grey-black (4.5.10)	15·00	22·00	£200
249a		7d. deep grey-black	£115	£100	
250	91	9d. dull purple and ultramarine (7.4.02)	£140	75·00	£250
		a. Chalk-surfaced paper (6.05)	£140	75·00	
		aWi. Wmk inverted	—	£3500	
251		9d. slate-purple and ultramarine	£140	75·00	
		a. Chalk-surfaced paper (6.05)	£120	75·00	
254	92	10d. dull purple and carmine (3.7.02)	£150	75·00	£225
		a. No cross on crown	£425	£300	
		b. Chalk-surfaced paper (9.06)	£140	75·00	
255		10d. slate-purple and carm (*chalk-surfaced paper*) (9.06)	£140	75·00	
		a. No cross on crown	£450	£275	
256		10d. dull purple and scarlet (*chalk-surfaced paper*) (9.10)	£140	75·00	
		a. No cross on crown	£425	£250	
257	93	1s. dull green and carmine (24.3.02)	£100	40·00	£175
		a. Chalk-surfaced paper (9.05)	£100	40·00	
259		1s. dull green and scarlet (*chalk-surfaced paper*) (9.10)	£100	55·00	
260	94	2s.6d. lilac (5.4.02)	£280	£150	£1250
		Wi. Wmk inverted	£5000	£3500	
261		2s.6d. pale dull purple (*chalk-surfaced paper*) (7.10.05)	£350	£180	
		Wi. Wmk inverted	£7500	£4250	
262		2s.6d. dull purple (*chalk-surfaced paper*)	£350	£180	
263	95	5s. bright carmine (5.4.02)	£450	£220	£1850
		Wi. Wmk inverted	£65000	£5750	
264		5s. deep bright carmine	£450	£220	
265	96	10s. ultramarine (5.4.02)	£1000	£500	
		Wi. Wmk inverted	—	£40000	
266	97	£1 dull blue-green (16.6.02)	£2000	£825	
		Wi. Wmk inverted	£110000	£24000	

97a

1910 (May). Prepared for use by De La Rue but not issued. Wmk Imperial Crown, W **49**. P 14.

266a	**97a**	2d. Tyrian plum	£115000	

One example of this stamp is known used, but it was never issued to the public.

1911. Printed by Harrison & Sons. Ordinary paper. Wmk Imperial Crown.

(a) P 14

267	**83**	½d. dull yellow-green (3.5.11)	2·75	4·00	6·00
		Wi. Wmk inverted	60·00	60·00	

268		½d. dull green	3·00	4·00	
269		½d. deep dull green	11·00	10·00	
270		½d. pale bluish green	40·00	40·00	
		a. Booklet pane. Five stamps plus St. Andrew's Cross label	£800		
		b. Wmk sideways	†	£35000	
		c. Imperf (pair)	£40000	†	
271		½d. bright green (fine impression) (6.11)	£275	£170	
272		1d. rose-red (3.5.11)	8·00	15·00	18·00
		a. No wmk (brick red)	50·00	—	
		Wi. Wmk inverted	50·00	50·00	
273		1d. deep rose-red	8·00	15·00	
274		1d. rose-carmine	55·00	30·00	
275		1d. aniline pink (5.11)	£750	£375	
275a		1d. aniline rose	£180	£140	
276	86	2½d. bright blue (10.7.11)	65·00	38·00	55·00
		Wi. Wmk inverted	£1250	—	
277	87	3d. purple/*lemon* (12.9.11)	£150	£250	£550
277a		3d. grey/*lemon*	£4500		
278	88	4d. bright orange (12.7.11)	£120	55·00	£175

(b) P 15×14

279	83	½d. dull green (30.10.11)	40·00	45·00	£100
		Wi. Wmk inverted	†	£3500	
279a		½d. deep dull green	40·00	45·00	
280		1d. rose-red (4.10.11)	45·00	25·00	
281		1d. rose-carmine	15·00	15·00	30·00
		Wi. Wmk inverted	†	—	
282		1d. pale rose-carmine	22·00	15·00	
283	86	2½d. bright blue (14.10.11)	22·00	15·00	35·00
284		2½d. dull blue	22·00	15·00	
		Wi. Wmk inverted	—	£3000	
285	87	3d. purple/*lemon* (22.9.11)	45·00	15·00	40·00
285a		3d. grey/*lemon*	£3250		
286	88	4d. bright orange (11.11.11)	30·00	15·00	65·00
		279/86 *Set of 5*	£130	90·00	

No. 272a was probably a trial printing.

1911–13. Printed at Somerset House. Ordinary paper. Wmk as 1902–1910. P 14.

287	84	1½d. reddish purple and bright green (13.7.11)	45·00	38·00	
288		1½d. dull purple and green	30·00	30·00	60·00
289		1½d. slate-purple and green (9.12)	30·00	30·00	
290	85	2d. dp dull green and red (8.8.11)	28·00	22·00	55·00
291		2d. deep dull green and carmine	28·00	22·00	
292		2d. grey-green and bright carmine (carmine shows clearly on back) (11.3.12)	28·00	28·00	
293	89	5d. dull reddish purple and bright blue (7.8.11)	30·00	22·00	65·00
294		5d. deep dull reddish purple and bright blue	30·00	22·00	
295	83	6d. royal purple (31.10.11)	50·00	90·00	
296		6d. bright magenta (*chalk-surfaced paper*) (31.10.11)	£12500		
297		6d. dull purple	30·00	22·00	90·00
298		6d. reddish purple (11.11)	30·00	28·00	
		a. No cross on crown (*various shades*)	£1200		
299		6d. very dp reddish purple (11.11)	55·00	45·00	
300		6d. dark purple (3.12)	30·00	22·00	
301		6d. dull purple ("Dickinson" coated paper) (3.13)	£250	£190	
303		6d. deep plum (7.13)	30·00	75·00	
		a. No cross on crown	£1250		
305	90	7d. slate-grey (1.8.12)	15·00	22·00	£200
306	91	9d. reddish purple and light blue (24.7.11)	95·00	75·00	
306a		9d. deep dull reddish purple and deep bright blue (9.11)	95·00	75·00	
307		9d. dull reddish purple and blue (10.11)	60·00	60·00	£190
307a		9d. deep plum and blue (7.13)	60·00	60·00	
308		9d. slate-purple and cobalt-blue (3.12)	£140	£110	
309	92	10d. dull purple and scarlet (9.10.11)	95·00	75·00	
310		10d. dull reddish pur and aniline pink	£275	£225	
311		10d. dull reddish purple and carmine (5.12)	80·00	60·00	£225
		a. No cross on crown	£1800		
312	93	1s. dark green and scarlet (13.7.11)	£120	60·00	
313		1s. deep green and scarlet (9.10.11)	80·00	40·00	
		Wi. Wmk inverted	£150	†	
314		1s. green and carmine (15.4.12)	60·00	35·00	£200
315	94	2s.6d. dull greyish purple (15.9.11)	£950	£450	
316		2s.6d. dull reddish purple (15.9.11)	£300	£180	£1700
		Wi. Wmk inverted	†	—	
317		2s.6d. dark purple	£325	£190	
318	95	5s. carmine (29.2.12)	£425	£200	£1750
319	96	10s. blue (14.1.12)	£1100	£600	
320	97	£1 deep green (3.9.11)	£2000	£750	

*No. 301 was on an experimental coated paper which does not respond to the silver test.

KING GEORGE V
6 May 1910–20 January 1936

Further detailed information on the issues of King George V will be found in Volume 2 of the Stanley Gibbons *Great Britain Specialised Catalogue*.

PRINTERS. Types **98** to **102** were typographed by Harrison & Sons Ltd, with the exception of certain preliminary printings made at Somerset House and distinguishable by the controls "A.11", B.11" or "B.12" (the Harrison printings do not have a full stop after the letter). The booklet stamps, Nos. 334/7 and 344/5 were printed by Harrisons only.

WATERMARK VARIETIES. Many British stamps to 1967 exist without watermark owing to misplacement of the paper, and with either inverted, reversed, or inverted and reversed watermarks. A proportion of the low-value stamps issued in booklets have the watermark inverted in the normal course of printing.

Low values with *watermark sideways* are normally from stamp rolls used in machines with sideways delivery or, from June 1940, certain booklets.

STAMPS WITHOUT WATERMARK. Stamps found without watermark, due to misplacement of the sheet in relation to the dandy roll, are not listed here, but will be found in the *Great Britain Specialised Catalogue*.
The 1½d. and 5d. 1912–22, and 2d. and 2½d., 1924–26, listed here, are from *whole* sheets completely without watermark.

98   **99**

For type differences with T **101/2** *see* notes below the latter.

Die A   Die B

Dies of Halfpenny

Die A. The three upper scales on the body of the right hand dolphin form a triangle; the centre jewel of the cross inside the crown is suggested by a comma.
Die B. The three upper scales are incomplete; the centre jewel of the cross is suggested by a crescent.

Die A   Die B

Dies of One Penny

Die A. The second line of shading on the ribbon to the right of the crown extends right across the wreath; the line nearest to the crown on the right hand ribbon shows as a short line at the bottom of the ribbon.
Die B. The second line of shading is broken in the middle; the first line is little more than a dot.

(Des Bertram Mackennal and G. W. Eve. Head from photograph by W. & D. Downey. Die eng J. A. C. Harrison)

1911–12. Wmk Imperial Crown, W **49**. P 15×14.

			Un	Used
321	**98**	½d. pale green (Die A) (22.6.11)	5·00	4·00
322		½d. green (Die A) (22.6.11)	4·00	4·00
		a. Error. Perf 14 (8.11)	£20000	£1000
		Wi. Wmk inverted	—	£2000
323		½d. bluish green (Die A)	£300	£180
324		½d. yellow-green (Die A)	12·00	1·50
325		½d. bright green (Die B)	8·00	1·50
		a. Wmk sideways	—	£5500
		Wi. Wmk inverted	20·00	7·50
326		½d. bluish green (Die B)	£160	£100
327	**99**	1d. carmine-red (Die A) (22.6.11)	4·50	2·50
		c. Wmk sideways	†	£17000
		Wi. Wmk inverted	£1500	£1250
328		1d. pale carmine (Die A) (22.6.11)	14·00	3·00
		a. No cross on crown	£850	£500
329		1d. carmine (Die B)	10·00	3·00
		Wi. Wmk inverted	20·00	7·50
330		1d. pale carmine (Die B)	10·00	4·00
		a. No cross on crown	£800	£500
331		1d. rose-pink (Die B)	£125	45·00
332		1d. scarlet (Die B) (6.12)	45·00	18·00
		Wi. Wmk inverted	45·00	18·00
333		1d. aniline scarlet (Die B)	£240	£110

For note on the aniline scarlet No. 333 see below No. 343.

100 Simple Cypher

1912 (28 Sept). Booklet stamps. Wmk Royal Cypher ("Simple"), W **100**. P 15×14.

334	**98**	½d. pale green (Die B)	45·00	40·00
335		½d. green (Die B)	45·00	40·00
		Wi. Wmk inverted	45·00	40·00
		Wj. Wmk reversed	£1100	£800
		Wk. Wmk inverted and reversed	£1100	£800
336	**99**	1d. scarlet (Die B)	30·00	30·00
		Wi. Wmk inverted	30·00	30·00
		Wj. Wmk reversed	£1100	£800
		Wk. Wmk inverted and reversed	—	£850
337		1d. bright scarlet (Die B)	30·00	30·00

101

102

103 Multiple Cypher

Type differences

½d. In T **98** the ornament above "P" of "HALFPENNY" has two thin lines of colour and the beard is undefined. In T **101** the ornament has one thick line and the beard is well defined.1d. In T **99** the body of the lion is unshaded and in T **102** it is shaded.

1912 (1 Jan). Wmk Imperial Crown, W **49**. P 15 × 14.

338	**101**	½d. deep green	15·00	8·00
339		½d. green	8·00	4·00
340		½d. yellow-green	8·00	4·00
		a. No cross on crown	£100	55·00
		Wi. Wmk inverted	£1100	£650
341	**102**	1d. bright scarlet	5·00	2·00
		a. No cross on crown	£110	55·00
		b. Printed double, one albino	£180	
		Wi. Wmk inverted	£425	£400
342		1d. scarlet	5·00	2·00
343		1d. aniline scarlet*	£175	£100
		a. No cross on crown	£1400	

*Our prices for the aniline scarlet 1d. stamps, Nos. 333 and 343, are for specimens in which the colour is suffused on the surface of the stamp and shows through clearly on the back. Specimens without these characteristics but which show "aniline" reactions under the quartz lamp are relatively common.

1912 (Aug). Wmk Royal Cypher ("Simple"), W **100**. P 15×14.

344	**101**	½d. green	7·00	3·00
		a. No cross on crown	£200	£125
		Wi. Wmk inverted	£350	£225
		Wj. Wmk reversed	£350	£225
		Wk. Wmk inverted and reversed	8·00	4·50
345	**102**	1d. scarlet	8·00	4·50
		a. No cross on crown	£100	50·00
		Wi. Wmk inverted	18·00	25·00
		Wj. Wmk reversed	£125	£125
		Wk. Wmk inverted and reversed	12·00	20·00

1912 (Sept–Oct). Wmk Royal Cypher ("Multiple"), W **103**. P 15×14.

346	**101**	½d. green (10.12)	12·00	8·00
		a. No cross on crown	£175	£125
		b. Imperf	£175	
		c. Wmk sideways	†	£4000
		d. Printed on gummed side	—	†
		Wi. Wmk inverted	12·00	20·00
		Wj. Wmk reversed	15·00	20·00
		Wk. Wmk inverted and reversed	£100	£100
347		½d. yellow-green	15·00	8·00
348		½d. pale green	15·00	8·00
349	**102**	1d. bright scarlet	18·00	10·00
350		1d. scarlet	18·00	10·00
		a. No cross on crown	£150	60·00
		b. Imperf	£150	
		c. Wmk sideways	£190	£220
		d. Wmk sideways. No cross on crown	£750	
		Wi. Wmk inverted	22·00	28·00
		Wj. Wmk reversed	22·00	28·00
		Wk. Wmk inverted and reversed	£1000	£650

104

105

106

No. 357a

No. 357ab

No. 357ac

107

108

Die I

Die II

Dies of 2d.

Die I.— Inner frame-line at top and sides close to solid of background. *Four* complete lines of shading between top of head and oval frame-line. These four lines do *not* extend to the oval itself. White line round "TWOPENCE" thin.

Die II.— Inner frame-line farther from solid of background.*Three* lines between top of head and extending to the oval. White line round "TWOPENCE" thicker.

(Des Bertram Mackennal (heads) and G. W. Eve (frames). Coinage head (½, 1½, 2, 3 and 4d.); large medal head (1d., 2½d.); intermediate medal head (5d. to 1s.); small medal head used for fiscal stamps. Dies eng J. A. C. Harrison)

(Typo by Harrison & Sons Ltd., except the 6d. printed by the Stamping Department of the Board of Inland Revenue, Somerset House. The latter also made printings of the following which can only be distinguished by the controls: ½d. B.13; 1½d. A.12; 2d. C.13; 2½d. A.12; 3d. A.12, B.13, C.13; 4d. B.13; 5d. B.13; 7d. C.13; 8d. C.13; 9d. agate B.13; 10d. C.13; 1s. C.13)

1912–24. Wmk Royal Cypher, W **100**. Chalk-surfaced paper (6d.). P 15×14.

351	**105**	½d. green (16.1.13)	1·00	1·00
		a. Partial double print (half of bottom row from Control G15)	£25000	
		b. Gummed both sides	—	—
		Wi. Wmk inverted	3·00	1·50
		Wj. Wmk reversed	55·00	55·00
		Wk. Wmk inverted and reversed	4·00	3·50
352		½d. bright green	1·00	1·00
353		½d. deep green	5·00	2·00
354		½d. yellow-green	6·00	3·00
355		½d. very yellow (Cyprus) green (1914)	£9000	†
356		½d. blue-green	40·00	25·00
357	**104**	1d. bright scarlet (8.10.12)	1·00	1·00
		a. "Q" for "O" (R. 1/4) (Control E14)	£175	£175
		ab. "Q" for "O" (R. 4/11) (Control T22)	£350	£190
		ac. Reversed "Q" for "O" (R. 15/9) (Control T22)	£300	£240
		ad. Inverted "Q" for "O" (R. 20/3)	£375	£240
		b. *Tête-bêche* (pair)	£80000	†
		Wi. Wmk inverted	2·00	1·00
		Wj. Wmk reversed	95·00	95·00
		Wk. Wmk inverted and reversed	3·00	3·00
358		1d. vermilion	5·00	2·50
359		1d. pale rose-red	20·00	5·00
360		1d. carmine-red	11·00	5·00
361		1d. scarlet-vermilion	£125	50·00
		a. Printed on back†	£300	†
362	**105**	1½d. red-brown (15.10.12)	6·00	1·50
		a. "PENCF" (R. 15/12)	£300	£250
		b. Booklet pane. Four stamps plus two printed labels (2.24)	£600	
		Wi. Wmk inverted	5·00	2·00
		Wj. Wmk reversed	50·00	50·00
		Wk. Wmk inverted and reversed	8·00	8·00
363		1½d. chocolate-brown	11·00	2·00
		a. Without wmk	£240	£240
364		1½d. chestnut	3·00	1·00
		a. "PENCF" (R. 15/12)	£125	£110
365		1½d. yellow-brown	20·00	16·00
366	**106**	2d. orange-yellow (Die I) (20.8.12)	8·00	3·00
367		2d. reddish orange (Die I) (11.13)	6·00	3·00
368		2d. orange (Die I)	4·00	3·00
		Wi. Wmk inverted	12·00	12·00
		Wj. Wmk reversed	15·00	12·00
		Wk. Wmk inverted and reversed	10·00	10·00
369		2d. bright orange (Die I)	5·00	3·00
370		2d. orange (Die II) (9.21)	5·00	3·50
		Wi. Wmk inverted	40·00	40·00
		Wk. Wmk inverted and reversed	£140	£130
371	**104**	2½d. cobalt-blue (18.10.12)	12·00	4·00
371a		2½d. bright blue (1914)	12·00	4·00
372		2½d. blue	12·00	4·00
		Wi. Wmk inverted	85·00	75·00
		Wj. Wmk reversed	65·00	65·00
		Wk. Wmk inverted and reversed	28·00	28·00
373		2½d. indigo-blue* (1920)	£3500	£2500
373a		2½d. dull Prussian blue* (1921)	£1500	£850
374	**106**	3d. dull reddish violet (9.10.12)	12·00	1·00
375		3d. violet	8·00	3·00
		Wi. Wmk inverted	95·00	£110
		Wj. Wmk reversed	£450	£450
		Wk. Wmk inverted and reversed	30·00	30·00
376		3d. bluish violet (11.13)	9·00	3·00
377		3d. pale violet	10·00	3·00
378		4d. deep grey-green (15.1.13)	45·00	25·00
379		4d. grey-green	15·00	2·00
		Wi. Wmk inverted	30·00	30·00
		Wj. Wmk reversed	£300	£300
		Wk. Wmk inverted and reversed	80·00	80·00
380		4d. pale grey-green	25·00	5·00
381	**107**	5d. brown (30.6.13)	15·00	5·00
		Wi. Wmk inverted	£1200	£1100
		Wj. Wmk reversed	†	
		Wk. Wmk inverted and reversed	£400	£400
382		5d. yellow-brown	15·00	5·00

		a. Without wmk	£1200	
383		5d. bistre-brown	£185	75·00
384		6d. dull purple (1.8.13)	25·00	10·00
385		6d. reddish purple (8.13)	15·00	7·00
		a. Perf 14 (9.20)	90·00	£110
		Wi. Wmk inverted	50·00	50·00
		Wj. Wmk reversed	£4500	
		Wk. Wmk inverted and reversed	£100	£100
386		6d. deep reddish purple	50·00	5·00
387		7d. olive (1.8.13)	20·00	10·00
		Wi. Wmk inverted	50·00	55·00
		Wj. Wmk reversed	†	
		Wk. Wmk inverted and reversed	£5000	
388		7d. bronze-green (1915)	70·00	25·00
389		7d. sage-green (1917)	70·00	18·00
390		8d. black/yellow (1.8.13)	32·00	11·00
		Wi. Wmk inverted	£150	£150
		Wj. Wmk reversed	£240	£240
		Wk. Wmk inverted and reversed	£5500	
391		8d. black/yellow-buff (granite) (5.17)	40·00	15·00
392	**108**	9d. agate (30.6.13)	15·00	6·00
		a. Printed double, one albino		
		Wi. Wmk inverted	£175	£175
		Wk. Wmk inverted and reversed	£175	£175
393		9d. deep agate	25·00	6·00
393a		9d. olive-green (9.22)	£110	30·00
		Wi. Wmk inverted	£900	£750
		Wk. Wmk inverted and reversed	£1100	£950
393b		9d. pale olive-green	£120	40·00
394		10d. turquoise-blue (1.8.13)	22·00	20·00
		Wi. Wmk inverted	£3000	£2000
		Wk. Wmk inverted and reversed	£325	£275
394a		10d. deep turquoise-blue	90·00	30·00
395		1s. bistre (1.8.13)	20·00	4·00
		Wi. Wmk inverted	£250	£200
		Wk. Wmk inverted and reversed	70·00	70·00
396		1s. bistre-brown	35·00	12·00
351/95		*Set of* 15	£250	95·00

Imperf stamps of this issue exist but may be war-time colour trials.

† The impression of No. 361a is set sideways and is very pale.

Nos. 362a and 364a occur on Plates 12 and 29 and are known from Controls L18, M18, M19, O19 and Q21. The flaws were corrected by 1921.

*No. 373 comes from Control O20 and also exists on toned paper. No. 373a comes from Control R21 and also exists on toned paper, but both are unlike the rare Prussian blue shade of the 1935 2½d. Jubilee issue.

See also Nos. 418/29.

For the 2d., T **106** bisected, see note under Guernsey, War Occupation Issues.

1913 (1 Aug). Wmk Royal Cypher ("Multiple"). W **103**. P 15×14.

397	**105**	½d. bright green	£150	£180
		a. Wmk sideways	†	£18000
		Wi. Wmk inverted	£900	
398	**104**	1d. dull scarlet	£225	£225
		Wi. Wmk inverted	£1100	

Both these stamps were originally issued in rolls only. Subsequently sheets were found, so that horizontal pairs and blocks are known but are of considerable rarity.

109

A

110 Single Cypher

Major Re-entries on 2s.6d.

Nos. 400a and 406/7a

No. 415b.

Philately Understood

What everybody ought to know about collecting and buying and selling stamps

Advance Notification of upcoming NEW 'Stamp Tips of the Trade' + 'Case Studies'

Some *Plain Talk* about the simple business of stamps which often seems complicated

Why is my business publishing this information?

I can remember the day I found my Father's stamp collection in the bottom drawer of the bureau in the dining room more than 45 years ago. Aged 11, I was excited travelling the world through his stamps. In those days every school had a stamp club and mine was no exception. I took the collection to school and joined the stamp club. When Mr. Armitage (the Chemistry Teacher who ran the club) asked what stamps we collected I said "Wurttemberg" – much to everybody's surprise. In fact they were from Austria and the page was misclassified. They were those imperforate 1920's Austrian Newspaper stamps which fascinated me and as everybody now knows are hardly worth anything ... but probably they helped me get started in stamps.

Over following years I found little help in understanding stamps, so much had to be learned the hard-way, which is why my company UPA publishes what I dare to hope are useful articles about collecting and buying and selling stamps. It is my hope that these prove valuable to you and that we may serve you if you decide to contact us ...

There are several different types of stamp businesses

In fact no two stamp dealers are alike. What a truism that is. Once in Amsterdam I made the mistake of admitting to the owner of the stamp shop I was visiting that I was a dealer. In almost perfect English **"We Don't sell to Dealers"** and he turned his back. So did I - as I left his shop. But over the years I discovered that the only way to succeed in stamps was to create a business of stamp selling systems and join them all together. This is what allows us to handle stamps from literally every single country in the world. Recently in coming articles which I shall call *'Case Studies'* the strength of this business model has become apparent.

> ## "We Don't sell to Dealers" and he turned his back

How can UPA help you?

If You are Collecting You can Request ...

1. **Auction**: Take £55 OFF Your 1st purchase (UK clients + selected countries) Offer: Request your Next Free UPA auction catalogue worth £15 comprising 20,000+/- lots from £'s to £1,000's. Apart from £55 OFF you'll benefit from UPA's Unique combination of features to collector colleagues – NO Buyer's Premium – Reducing Estimate System till sold or given away – All lots Guaranteed - Modest shipping + Free Insurance. **Request now – contact us in any way today**

2. **Approvals**: Take £25 OFF Your 1st Approvals purchase (UK clients + selected countries): Individually identified and priced stamp selections of stamps from most countries in the world sent to you on approval. You select those you want and return the rest with payment. Established 56 years. **Request now – contact us in any way today**

3. **OFF-paper WORLD / Country Mixtures** – Unit priced – buy those you want, return those you don't – UK clients SEND £6.45 – over 100,000 bags supplied. **Request now – contact us in any way today**

4. **On-line?** E-Bay clients – hundreds of lots starting 1p auctions though to £20,000 collections on-line. Visit www.upastampauctions.co.uk for links to eBay account ID's: upa-global, universalphilatelic, upa-collectables, upa-online

5. **PRIVATE TREATY:** A new UPA selling system – valuable collections sold / matched to clients on a commission basis. Modest fees, No sale, No charge. British Empire collections required to £250,000, GB collections to £500,000, Collections / Postal History / Foreign from £2,000 upwards

If You are Selling Please Contact Andrew / Elaine at UPA:

Valuable Collections wanted: We can use and have clients who require GB collections to £500,000, British Empire / British Commonwealth to £250,000 and Foreign required. **Telephone, Fax or E-mail now.**

Why does UPA make Promotional Offers?

Unlike most other stamp companies we believe in giving before hoping to receive. We believe in proving to YOU that your trust in dealing with UPA is well founded. Proving to YOU in advance of asking you to purchase from us is much of our model. Most collector colleagues stay with UPA which is why we can make you such an extraordinary offer. 2,199 different collectors (and some dealers) bid in our latest auction, 90% of whom won lots. Without pernicious buyer's premium average regular collector bidders save £250 a year at UPA. *Client loyalty is the reason why we can offer* 1st time buyers aged over 18 (!) £55 OFF your 1st auction purchase whether you spend more than £55 or not. '

Advance Notification of NEW 'Stamp Tips of the Trade' and 'Case Studies' to follow

We're going to be publishing more articles in the coming months. If you would like to know more about how my company may serve you ... **Please contact us in any way today...** if you are really interested please do it **NOW, don't forget to Request My 'Tips of the Trade' FREE booklet too!**

Looking forward to hearing from you.
Thank you for reading

Andrew

Andrew McGavin, Managing Director UPA

Please See Our Other Articles on Pages 42, 98, 210, 272 and 264

Contact us in any way today

ANDREW PROMOTING PHILATELY ON THE ALAN TITCHMARSH SHOW ITV

UNIVERSAL PHILATELIC AUCTIONS   (Part 1)
4 The Old Coalyard, West End Northleach, Glos. GL54 3HE UK
Telephone: 01451 861111 • Fax: 01451 861297
Email: info@upastampauctions.co.uk
Web: www.upastampauctions.co.uk

(Des Bertram Mackennal. Dies eng J. A. C. Harrison. Recess)

High values, so-called "Sea Horses" design: T **109**. Background around portrait consists of horizontal lines, Type A. Wmk Single Cypher, W **110**. P 11×12.

1913 (30 June–Aug). Printed by Waterlow Bros & Layton.

399		2s.6d. deep sepia-brown	£400	£200
400		2s.6d. sepia-brown	£300	£150
	a.	Re-entry (R. 2/1)	£1800	£775
401		5s. rose-carmine	£625	£320
402		10s. indigo-blue (1.8)	£1200	£475
403		£1 green (1.8)	£3500	£1400
404		£1 dull blue-green (1.8)	£3500	£1600

*399/404 For well-centred, lightly used +35%.

1915 (Sept–Dec). Printed by De La Rue & Co.

405		2s.6d. deep yellow-brown	£375	£250
	Wi.	Wmk inverted	£1500	—
406		2s.6d. yellow-brown	£325	£225
	a.	Re-entry (R. 2/1)	£2000	£950
	Wi.	Wmk inverted	£1250	£875
	Wj.	Wmk reversed	£1250	£1000
	Wk.	Wmk inverted and reversed	£4000	—
407		2s.6d. grey-brown	£400	£300
	a.	Re-entry (R. 2/1)	£2000	£950
	Wi.	Wmk inverted	£1250	£1000
	Wj.	Wmk reversed	£1250	£1000
408		2s.6d. sepia (seal-brown)	£325	£250
	Wi.	Wmk inverted	£1250	£1000
	Wj.	Wmk reversed	£1250	£1000
409		5s. bright carmine	£650	£400
	Wi.	Wmk inverted	£4750	—
	Wj.	Wmk reversed	£4500	—
	Wk.	Wmk inverted and reversed	£18000	†
410		5s. pale carmine	£800	£500
411		10s. deep blue (12.15)	£3750	£1000
412		10s. blue	£3250	£875
	Wk.	Wmk inverted and reversed	—	†
413		10s. pale blue	£3500	£875

*405/13 For well-centred, lightly used + 45%.

Nos. 406/7 were produced from the original Waterlow plates as were all De La Rue 5s. and 10s. printings. Examples of Nos. 406/7, 410 and 411 occur showing degrees of plate wear.

1918 (Dec)–**19**. Printed by Bradbury Wilkinson & Co, Ltd.

413a		2s.6d. olive-brown	£190	£100
414		2s.6d. chocolate-brown	£160	75·00
415		2s.6d. reddish brown	£160	75·00
415a		2s.6d. pale brown	£175	75·00
	b.	Major re-entry (R. 1/2)	£950	£475
416		5s. rose-red (1.19)	£325	£135
417		10s. dull grey-blue (1.19)	£475	£175
399/417 *Set of 4*			£4000	£1500

*413a/17 For well-centred, lightly used +35%.

DISTINGUISHING PRINTINGS. Note that the £1 value was only printed by Waterlow.

Waterlow and De La Rue stamps measure exactly 22.1 mm vertically. In the De La Rue printings the gum is usually patchy and yellowish, and the colour of the stamp, particularly in the 5s., tends to show through the back. The holes of the perforation are smaller than those of the other two printers, but there is a thick perforation tooth at the top of each vertical side.

In the Bradbury Wilkinson printings the height of the stamp is 22.6-23.1 mm due to the use of curved plates. On most of the 22.6 mm high stamps a minute coloured guide dot appears in the margin just above the middle of the upper frame-line.

For (1934) re-engraved Waterlow printings *see* Nos. 450/2.

UNITED KINGDOM OF GREAT BRITAIN AND NORTHERN IRELAND

111	**111a**

Block Cypher

The watermark Type **111a**, as compared with Type **111**, differs as follows: Closer spacing of horizontal rows (12½ *mm* instead of 14½ *mm*). Letters shorter and rounder. Watermark thicker.

(Typo by Waterlow & Sons, Ltd (all values except 6d.) and later, 1934-35, by Harrison & Sons, Ltd (all values). Until 1934 the 6d. was printed at Somerset House where a printing of the 1½d. was also made in 1926 (identifiable only by control E.26). Printings by Harrisons in 1934-35 can be identified, when in mint condition, by the fact that the gum shows a streaky appearance vertically, the Waterlow gum being uniformly applied, but Harrisons also used up the balance of the Waterlow "smooth gum" paper)

1924 (Feb)–**26**. Wmk Block Cypher, W **111**. P 15×14.

418	105	½d. green	1·00	1·00
	a.	Wmk sideways (5.24)	9·00	3·25
	aWi.	Wmk sideways inverted	£450	—
	b.	Doubly printed	£12000	†
	Wi.	Wmk inverted	3·50	1·00
419	104	1d. scarlet	1·00	1·00
	a.	Wmk sideways	20·00	15·00
	b.	Experimental paper, W **111a** (10.24)	22·00	
	c.	Partial double print, one inverted	—	
	d.	Inverted "Q" for "O" (R. 20/3)	£500	—
	Wi.	Wmk inverted	4·00	1·50
420	105	1½d. red-brown	1·00	1·00
	a.	*Tête-bêche* (pair)	£500	£800
	b.	Wmk sideways (8.24)	10·00	3·50

	bWi.	Wmk sideways inverted	£900	—
	c.	Printed on the gummed side	£750	
	d.	Booklet pane. Four stamps plus two printed labels (3.24)	£225	
	f.	Ditto. Wmk sideways	£10000	
	g.	Experimental paper, W **111a** (10.24)	£120	£120
	h.	Double impression	—	†
	Wi.	Wmk inverted	2·00	1·00
421	106	2d. orange (Die II) (7.24)	2·50	2·50
	a.	No wmk	£1800	
	b.	Wmk sideways (7.26)	£100	£100
	c.	Partial double print	£35000	†
	Wi.	Wmk inverted	55·00	55·00
422	104	2½d. blue (10.10.24)	5·00	3·00
	a.	No wmk	£2800	
	b.	Wmk sideways	†	£16000
	Wi.	Wmk inverted	90·00	90·00
423	106	3d. violet (10.10.24)	10·00	2·50
	Wi.	Wmk inverted	90·00	70·00
424		4d. grey-green (23.10.24)	12·00	2·50
	a.	Printed on the gummed side	£4250	†
	Wi.	Wmk inverted	£150	£150
425	107	5d. brown (17.10.24)	20·00	3·00
	Wi.	Wmk inverted	£150	£150
426		6d. reddish purple (*chalk-surfaced paper*) (9.24)	12·00	2·50
	Wi.	Wmk inverted	60·00	60·00
	Wk.	Wmk inverted and reversed	£450	£400
426a		6d. purple (6.26)	4·00	1·50
	aWi.	Wmk inverted	90·00	90·00
427	108	9d. olive-green (11.11.24)	12·00	3·50
	Wi.	Wmk inverted	£120	£120
428		10d. turquoise-blue (28.11.24)	40·00	40·00
	Wi.	Wmk inverted	£2750	£2000
429		1s. bistre-brown (10.24)	22·00	3·00
	Wi.	Wmk inverted	£375	£375
418/29 *Set of 12*			£110	60·00

There are numerous shades in this issue.

The normal sideways watermark shows the top of the Crown pointing to the right, *as seen from the back of the stamp*.

The 6d. on both chalk-surfaced and ordinary papers was printed by both Somerset House and Harrisons. The Harrisons printings have streaky gum, differ slightly in shade, and that on chalk-surfaced paper is printed in a highly fugitive ink. The prices quoted are for the commonest (Harrison) printing in each case.

The dandy roll to produce watermark Type **111a** was provided by Somerset House in connection with experiments in paper composition undertaken during 1924–25. These resulted in a change from rag only paper to that made from a mixture including esparto and sulphite.

112

(Des H. Nelson. Eng J. A. C. Harrison, Recess Waterlow)

1924–25. British Empire Exhibition. W **111**. P 14.

(a) Dated "1924" (23.4.24)

430	112	1d. scarlet	10·00	11·00
431		1½d. brown	15·00	15·00

(b) Dated "1925" (9.5.25)

432	112	1d. scarlet	15·00	30·00
433		1½d. brown	40·00	70·00

113	**114**	**115**

116 St. George and the Dragon

117

(Des J. Farleigh (T **113** and **115**), E. Linzell (T **114**) and H. Nelson (T **116**). Eng C. G. Lewis (T **113**), T. E. Storey (T **115**), both at the Royal Mint; J. A. C. Harrison, of Waterlow (T **114** and **116**). Typo by Waterlow from plates made at the Royal Mint, except T **116**, recess by Bradbury, Wilkinson from die and plate of their own manufacture)

1929 (10 May). Ninth UPU Congress, London.

*(a) W **111** P 15×14*

434	113	½d. green	2·25	2·25
	a.	Wmk sideways	55·00	50·00
	Wi.	Wmk inverted	15·00	12·00
435	114	1d. scarlet	2·25	2·25
	a.	Wmk sideways	95·00	90·00
	Wi.	Wmk inverted	15·00	12·00
436		1½d. purple-brown	2·25	1·75
	a.	Wmk sideways	60·00	55·00
	b.	Booklet pane. Four stamps plus two printed labels	£375	
	Wi.	Wmk inverted	5·00	6·00
437	115	2½d. blue	10·00	10·00
	Wi.	Wmk inverted	£2750	£1100

*(b) W **117**. P 12*

438	116	£1 black	£750	£550
434/7 *Set of 4 (to 2½d.)*			15·00	14·50

PRINTERS. All subsequent issues were printed in photogravure by Harrison and Sons Ltd *except where otherwise stated.*

118	**119**	**120**

121	**122**

1934–36. W **111**. P 15×14.

439	118	½d. green (17.11.34)	50	50
	a.	Wmk sideways	10·00	5·00
	aWi.	Wmk sideways inverted	£450	£150
	b.	Imperf three sides	£5250	
	Wi.	Wmk inverted	11·00	1·50
440	119	1d. scarlet (24.9.34)	50	50
	a.	Imperf (pair)	£5000	
	b.	Printed on the gummed side	£750	
	c.	Wmk sideways (30.4.35)	20·00	12·00
	cWi.	Wmk sideways inverted	£125	
	d.	Double impression	†	£24000
	e.	Imperf between (pair)	£8500	
	f.	Imperf three sides (pair)	£7000	
	Wi.	Wmk inverted	9·00	3·00
441	118	1½d. red-brown (20.8.34)	50	50
	a.	Imperf (pair)	£1250	
	b.	Imperf three sides (lower stamp in vert pair)	£4800	
	c.	Imperf between (horiz pair)		
	d.	Wmk sideways	10·00	5·00
	dWi.	Wmk sideways inverted	—	†
	e.	Booklet pane. Four stamps plus two printed labels (1.35)	£200	
	Wi.	Wmk inverted	4·00	1·00
442	120	2d. orange (19.1.35)	75	75
	a.	Imperf (pair)	£5750	
	b.	Wmk sideways (30.4.35)	£125	90·00
443	119	2½d. ultramarine (18.3.35)	1·50	1·25
444	120	3d. violet (18.3.35)	1·50	1·25
	Wi.	Wmk inverted	—	£9000
445		4d. deep grey-green (2.12.35)	2·00	1·25
	Wi.	Wmk inverted	†	£9000
446	121	5d. yellow-brown (17.2.36)	6·50	2·75
447	122	9d. deep olive-green (2.12.35)	12·00	2·25
448		10d. turquoise-blue (24.2.36)	15·00	10·00
449		1s. bistre-brown (24.2.36)	15·00	1·25
	a.	Double impression	—	†
439/49 *Set of 11*			50·00	20·00

Owing to the need for wider space for the perforations the size of the designs of the ½d. and 2d. were once, and the 1d. and 1½d. twice, reduced from that of the first printings.

There are also numerous minor variations, due to the photographic element in the process.

The normal sideways watermark shows the top of the Crown pointing to the right, *as seen from the back of the stamp*.

The ½d. imperf three sides, No. 439b, is known in a block of four, from a sheet, to which the bottom pair is imperf at top and sides.

For No. 442 bisected, see Guernsey, War Occupation Issues.

B	**123**

(Eng J. A. C. Harrison. Recess Waterlow)

1934 (16 Oct). T **109** (re-engraved). Background around portrait consists of horizontal and diagonal lines. Type B. W **110**. P 11×12.

450	109	2s.6d. chocolate-brown	80·00	40·00
451		5s. bright rose-red	£175	85·00
452		10s. indigo	£350	80·00
450/2 *Set of 3*			£575	£190

There are numerous other minor differences in the design of this issue.

1935 (7 May). Silver Jubilee. W **111**. P 15×14.

453	**123**	½d. green		1·00	1·00
		Wi. Wmk inverted		8·00	3·00
454		1d. scarlet		1·50	2·00
		Wi. Wmk inverted		8·00	4·00
455		1½d. red-brown		1·00	1·00
		Wi. Wmk inverted		3·00	1·50
456		2½d. blue		5·00	6·50
456*a*		2½d. Prussian blue		£13750	£15000
453/6 *Set of 4*				7·50	9·50

The 1½d. and 2½d. values differ from T **123** in the emblem in the panel at right.

Four sheets of No. 456*a*, printed in the wrong shade, were issued in error by the Post Office Stores Department on 25 June 1935. It is known that three of the sheets were sold from the sub-office at 134 Fore Street, Upper Edmonton, London. between that date and 4 July.

KING EDWARD VIII
20 January–10 December 1936

Further detailed information on the stamps of King Edward VIII will be found in Volume 2 of the Stanley Gibbons *Great Britain Specialised Catalogue.*

124   **125**

(Des H. Brown, adapted Harrison using a photo by Hugh Cecil)

1936. W **125**. P 15×14.

457	**124**	½d. green (1.9.36)		30	30
		a. Double impression		10·00	5·00
		Wi. Wmk inverted		10·00	5·00
458		1d. scarlet (14.9.36)		60	50
		Wi. Wmk inverted		9·00	5·00
459		1½d. red-brown (1.9.36)		30	30
		a. Booklet pane. Four stamps plus two printed labels (10.36)		85·00	
		b. Imperf (pair)		£40000	
		Wi. Wmk inverted		1·00	1·00
460		2½d. bright blue (1.9.36)		30	85
457/60 *Set of 4*				1·25	1·75

KING GEORGE VI
11 December 1936–6 February 1952

Further detailed information on the stamps of King George VI will be found in Volume 2 of the Stanley Gibbons *Great Britain Specialised Catalogue.*

126 King George VI and Queen Elizabeth

Colon flaw (Cyl 7 No dot, R 10/1, later corrected

(Des E. Dulac)

1937 (13 May). Coronation. W **127**. P 15×14.

461	**126**	1½d. maroon		30	30
		a. Colon flaw		70·00	

127   **128**

129   **130**

King George VI and National Emblems

(Des T **128/9**, E. Dulac (head) and E. Gill (frames). T **130**, E. Dulac (whole stamp))

1937–47. W **127**. P 15×14.

462	**128**	½d. green (10.5.37)		30	25
		a. Wmk sideways (1.38)		75	60
		ab. Booklet pane of 4 (6.40)		£110	
		Wi. Wmk inverted		10·00	60
463		1d. scarlet (10.5.37)		30	25
		a. Wmk sideways (2.38)		20·00	9·00
		ab. Booklet pane of 4 (6.40)		£175	
		Wi. Wmk inverted		40·00	3·00
464		1½d. red-brown (30.7.37)		30	25
		a. Wmk sideways (2.38)		1·25	1·25
		b. Booklet pane. Four stamps plus two printed labels (8.37)		£140	

		e. Imperf three sides (pair)		£6500	
		Wi. Wmk inverted		15·00	1·25
465		2d. orange (31.1.38)		1·20	50
		a. Wmk sideways (2.38)		75·00	40·00
		b. Bisected (*on cover*)		†	50·00
		Wi. Wmk inverted		60·00	22·00
466		2½d. ultramarine (10.5.37)		40	25
		a. Wmk sideways (6.40)		75·00	35·00
		b. *Tête-bêche* (horiz pair)		£22000	
		Wi. Wmk inverted		55·00	22·00
467		3d. violet (31.1.38)		5·00	1·00
468	**129**	4d. grey-green (21.11.38)		60	75
		a. Imperf (pair)		£9000	
		b. Imperf three sides (horiz pair)		£9500	
469		5d. brown (21.11.38)		3·50	85
		a. Imperf (pair)		£8500	
		b. Imperf three sides (horiz pair)		£9000	
470		6d. purple (30.1.39)		1·50	60
471	**130**	7d. emerald-green (27.2.39)		5·00	60
		a. Imperf three sides (horiz pair)		£9000	
472		8d. bright carmine (27.2.39)		7·50	80
473		9d. deep olive-green (1.5.39)		6·50	80
474		10d. turquoise-blue (1.5.39)		7·00	80
		aa. Imperf (pair)			
474*a*		11d. plum (29.12.47)		3·00	2·75
475		1s. bistre-brown (1.5.39)		9·00	75
462/75 *Set of 15*				45·00	10·00

For later printings of the lower values in apparently lighter shades and different colours, see Nos. 485/90 and 503/8.

No. 465b was authorised for use in Guernsey. See notes on War Occupation Issues.

Nos. 468b and 469b are perforated at foot only and each occurs in the same sheet as Nos. 468a and 469a.

No. 471a is also perforated at foot only, but occurs on the top row of a sheet.

131 King George VI   **132** King George VI

133

Mark in shield (R. 1/7)   Gashed diadem (R. 2/7)

Gashed crown (R. 5/5)   Broken stem (R. 1/4)

Blot on scroll (R. 2/5)   Scratch on scroll (R. 4/6)

(Des E. Dulac (T **131**) and Hon. G. R. Bellew (T **132**). Eng J. A. C. Harrison. Recess Waterlow)

1939–48. W **133**. P 14.

476	**131**	2s.6d. brown (4.9.39)		95·00	8·00
		aa. Mark in shield		£190	85·00
		ab. Gashed diadem		£190	85·00
		ac. Gashed crown		£190	85·00
476*b*		2s.6d. yellow-green (9.3.42)		15·00	1·50
477		5s. red (21.8.39)		20·00	2·00
478	**132**	10s. dark blue (30.10.39)		£260	22·00
		aa. Broken stem		£275	80·00
		ab. Blot on scroll		£275	80·00
		ac. Scratch on scroll		£350	£100
478*b*		10s. ultramarine (30.11.42)		45·00	5·00
478*c*		£1 brown (1.10.48)		25·00	26·00
476/8c *Set of 6*				£425	60·00

134 Queen Victoria and King George VI.

(Des H. L. Palmer)

1940 (6 May). Centenary of First Adhesive Postage Stamps. W **127**. P 14½×14.

479	**134**	½d. green		30	75
480		1d. scarlet		1·00	75
481		1½d. red-brown		50	1·50
482		2d. orange		1·00	75
		a. Bisected (*on cover*)		†	40·00
483		2½d. ultramarine		2·25	50
484		3d. violet		3·00	3·50
479/84 *Set of 6*				8·75	5·25

No. 482a was authorised for use in Guernsey. See notes on War Occupation Issues.

1941–42. Head as Nos. 462/7, but with lighter background to provide a more economic use of the printing ink. W **127**. P 15×14.

485	**128**	½d. pale green (1.9.41)		30	30
		a. *Tête-bêche* (horiz pair)		£18000	
		b. Imperf (pair)		£8500	
		Wi. Wmk inverted		4·00	50
486		1d. pale scarlet (11.8.41)		30	30
		a. Wmk sideways (10.42)		5·00	4·50
		b. Imperf (pair)		£8000	
		c. Imperf three sides (horiz pair)		£8500	
487		1½d. pale red-brown (28.9.42)		60	80
488		2d. pale orange (6.10.41)		50	50
		a. Wmk sideways (6.42)		28·00	19·00
		b. *Tête-bêche* (horiz pair)		£18000	
		c. Imperf (pair)		£7500	
		d. Imperf pane*		£20000	
		Wi. Wmk inverted		4·00	1·00
489		2½d. light ultramarine (21.7.41)		30	30
		a. Wmk sideways (8.42)		15·00	12·00
		b. *Tête-bêche* (horiz pair)		£18000	
		c. Imperf (pair)		£4800	
		d. Imperf pane*		£15000	
		e. Imperf three sides (horiz pair)		£7500	
		Wi. Wmk inverted		1·50	1·00
490		3d. pale violet (3.11.41)		2·50	1·00
485/90 *Set of 6*				3·50	2·75

The *tête-bêche* varieties are from defectively made-up stamp booklets.

Nos. 486c and 489e are perforated at foot only and occur in the same sheets as Nos. 486b and 489c.

*BOOKLET ERRORS. Those listed as "imperf panes" show one row of perforations either at the top or at the bottom of the pane of six.

135   **136** Symbols of Peace and Reconstruction

Extra porthole aft (Cyl. 11 No dot, R. 16/1)   Extra porthole fore (Cyl. 8 Dot, R. 5/6)   Seven berries (Cyl. 4 No dot, R. 12/5)

(Des H. L. Palmer (T **135**) and R. Stone (T **136**))

1946 (11 June). Victory. W **127**. P 15×14.

491	**135**	2½d. ultramarine		20	20
		a. Extra porthole aft		95·00	
		b. Extra porthole fore		£120	
492	**136**	3d. violet		20	50
		a. Seven berries		50·00	

137   **138** King George VI and Queen Elizabeth

(Des G. Knipe and Joan Hassall from photographs by Dorothy Wilding)

1948 (26 Apr). Royal Silver Wedding. W **127**. P 15×14 (2½d.) or 14×15 (£1).

493	**137**	2½d. ultramarine		35	20
494	**138**	£1 blue		40·00	40·00

1948 (10 May). Stamps of 1d. and 2½d. showing seaweed-gathering were on sale at eight Head Post Offices in Great Britain, but were primarily for use in the Channel Islands and are listed there (see after Great Britain Postal Fiscals).

139 Globe and Laurel Wreath   **140** "Speed"

141 Olympic Symbol   **142** Winged Victory

Crown Flaw (Cyl. 1 No dot,
R. 20/2, later retouched)

(Des P. Metcalfe (T **139**), A. Games (T **140**), S. D. Scott (T **141**) and
E. Dulac (T **142**))

1948 (29 July). Olympic Games. W **127**. P 15×14.

495	**139**	2½d. ultramarine	50	10
496	**140**	3d. violet	50	50
		a. Crown flaw	75·00	
497	**141**	6d. bright purple	3·25	75
498	**142**	1s. brown	4·50	2·00
495/8 *Set of 4*			8·00	3·00

143 Two Hemispheres   **144** UPU Monument, Berne

145 Goddess Concordia, Globe   **146** Posthorn and Globe
and Points of Compass

Lake in Asia (Cyl. 3 Dot,   Lake in India (Cyl. 2 No Dot,
R. 14/1)   R. 18/2)

(Des Mary Adshead (T **143**), P. Metcalfe (T **144**), H. Fleury (T **145**)
and Hon. G. R. Bellew (T **146**))

1949 (10 Oct). 75th Anniv of Universal Postal Union. W **127**.
P 15×14.

499	**143**	2½d. ultramarine	25	10
		a. Lake in Asia	£145	
		b. Lake in India	£100	
500	**144**	3d. violet	25	50
501	**145**	6d. bright purple	50	75
502	**146**	1s. brown	1·00	1·25
499/502 *Set of 4*			1·50	2·50

1950–52. 4d. as Nos. 468 and others as Nos. 485/9, but colours
changed. W **127**. P 15×14.

503	**128**	½d. pale orange (3.5.51)	30	30
		a. Imperf (pair)	£6500	
		b. *Tête-bêche* (horiz pair)	£18000	
		c. Imperf pane	£18000	
		Wi. Wmk inverted	50	50
504		1d. light ultramarine (3.5.51)	30	30
		a. Wmk sideways (5.51)	1·10	1·25
		b. Imperf (pair)	£4800	
		c. Imperf three sides (horiz pair)	£6500	
		d. Booklet pane. Three stamps plus		
		three printed labels (3.52)	18·00	
		e. Ditto. Partial *tête-bêche* pane	£8500	
		Wi. Wmk inverted	4·50	2·50
505		1½d. pale green (3.5.51)	65	60
		a. Wmk sideways (9.51)	3·25	5·00
		Wi. Wmk inverted	6·00	1·00
506		2d. pale red-brown (3.5.51)	75	40
		a. Wmk sideways (5.51)	1·75	2·00
		b. *Tête-bêche* (horiz pair)	£18000	
		c. Imperf three sides (horiz pair)	£8000	
		Wi. Wmk inverted	6·00	6·50
507		2½d. pale scarlet (3.5.51)	60	40
		a. Wmk sideways (5.51)	1·75	1·75
		b. *Tête-bêche* (hoiz pair)		
		Wi. Wmk inverted	2·00	1·25
508	**129**	4d. light ultramarine (2.10.50)	2·00	1·75
		a. Double impression	†	£7000
503/8 *Set of 6*			4·00	3·25

No. 504c is perforated at foot only and occurs in the same sheet
as No. 504b.No. 506c is also perforated at foot only.

*BOOKLET ERRORS. Those listed as "imperf panes" show one row
of perforations either at the top or at the bottom of the pane of 6.

147 HMS *Victory*   **148** White Cliffs of Dover

149 St. George and the Dragon   **150** Royal Coat of Arms

(Des Mary Adshead (T **147/8**), P. Metcalfe (T **149/50**).
Recess Waterlow)

1951 (3 May). W **133**. P 11×12.

509	**147**	2s.6d. yellow-green	7·50	1·00
510	**148**	5s. red	35·00	1·00
511	**149**	10s. ultramarine	15·00	7·50
512	**150**	£1 brown	45·00	18·00
509/12 *Set of 4*			£100	25·00

151 "Commerce and Prosperity"   **152** Festival Symbol

(Des E. Dulac (T **151**), A. Games (T **152**))

1951 (3 May). Festival of Britain. W **127**. P 15×14.

513	**151**	2½d. scarlet	20	15
514	**152**	4d. ultramarine	30	35

QUEEN ELIZABETH II

6 February 1952

Further detailed information on the stamps of Queen Elizabeth II will
be found in volumes 3, 4 and 5 of the Stanley Gibbons *Great Britain
Specialised Catalogue.*

USED PRICES. For Nos. 515 onwards the used prices quoted are for
examples with circular dated postmarks.

153 Tudor Crown   **154**

155   **156**   **157**

158   **159**   **160**

Queen Elizabeth II and National Emblems

I   II

Types of 2½d. Type I:—In the frontal cross of the diadem, the top
line is only half the width of the cross.
Type II:—The top line extends to the full width of the cross and there
are signs of strengthening in other parts of the diadem.

(Des Enid Marx (T **154**), M. Farrar-Bell (T **155/6**), G. Knipe (T **157**),
Mary Adshead (T **158**), E. Dulac (T **159/60**). Portrait by Dorothy
Wilding)

1952–54. W **153**. P 15×14.

515	**154**	½d. orange-red (31.8.53)	25	15
		Wi. Wmk inverted	2·00	2·00
516		1d. ultramarine (31.8.53)	30	20
		a. Booklet pane. Three stamps plus		
		three printed labels	40·00	
		Wi. Wmk inverted	6·00	3·00
517		1½d. green (5.12.52)	25	20
		a. Wmk sideways (15.10.54)	1·20	1·20
		b. Imperf pane*		

		Wi. Wmk inverted	1·30	1·30
518		2d. red-brown (31.8.53)	30	20
		a. Wmk sideways (8.10.54)	2·00	2·00
		Wi. Wmk inverted	30·00	22·00
519	**155**	2½d. carmine-red (Type I) (5.12.52)	30	15
		a. Wmk sideways (15.11.54)	12·00	12·00
		b. Type II (Booklets) (5.53)	1·30	1·00
		bWi. Wmk inverted	1·00	1·00
520		3d. deep lilac (18.1.54)	1·50	90
521	**156**	4d. ultramarine (2.11.53)	3·25	1·30
522	**157**	5d. brown (6.7.53)	1·00	3·50
523		6d. reddish purple (18.1.54)	4·00	1·00
		a. Imperf three sides (pair)	£3750	
524		7d. bright green (18.1.54)	9·50	5·50
525	**158**	8d. magenta (6.7.53)	1·25	85
526		9d. bronze-green (8.2.54)	23·00	4·75
527		10d. Prussian blue (8.2.54)	18·00	4·75
528		11d. brown-purple (8.2.54)	35·00	15·00
529	**159**	1s. bistre-brown (6.7.53)	80	50
530	**160**	1s.3d. green (2.11.53)	4·50	3·25
531	**159**	1s.6d. grey-blue (2.11.53)	14·00	3·75
515/31 *Set of 17*			£100	40·00

*BOOKLET ERRORS—This pane of six stamps is completely imperf
(see No. 540a etc.).
See also Nos. 540/56, 561/6, 570/94 and 599/618a.

161   **162**

163   **164**

(Des E. Fuller (2½d.), M. Goaman (4d.), E. Dulac (1s.3d.), M. Farrar-
Bell (1s.6d.), Portrait (except 1s.3d.) by Dorothy Wilding)

1953 (3 June). Coronation. W **153**. P 15×14.

532	**161**	2½d. carmine-red	20	25
533	**162**	4d. ultramarine	1·10	1·90
534	**163**	1s.3d. deep yellow-green	5·00	3·00
535	**164**	1s.6d. deep grey-blue	10·00	4·75
532/5 *Set of 4*			16·00	9·00

165 St. Edward's Crown   **166** Carrickfergus Castle

167 Caernarvon Castle   **168** Edinburgh Castle

169 Windsor Castle

(Des L. Lamb. Portrait by Dorothy Wilding. Recess Waterlow
(until 31.12.57) and De La Rue (subsequently))

1955–58. W **165**. P 11×12.

536	**166**	2s.6d. black-brown (23.9.55)	15·00	2·00
		a. De La Rue printing (17.7.58)	30·00	2·50
		aWi. Wmk inverted	†	£3000
537	**167**	5s. rose-carmine (23.9.55)	40·00	4·00
		a. De La Rue printing (30.4.58)	65·00	10·00
538	**168**	10s. ultramarine (1.9.55)	90·00	14·00
		a. De La Rue printing. *Dull ultramarine* (25.4.58)	£225	22·00
539	**169**	£1 black (1.9.55)	£140	35·00
		a. De La Rue printing (28.4.58)	£350	65·00
536/9 *Set of 4*			£250	50·00
536a/9a *Set of 4*			£600	100·00

See also Nos. 595/8a and 759/62.

On 1 January 1958 the contract for printing the high values, T **166** to
169 was transferred to De La Rue & Co, Ltd.
The De La Rue sheets are printed in pairs and have a ⊣ or ⊢ shaped
guide-mark at the centre of one side-margin, opposite the middle row
of perforations, indicating left- and right-hand sheets respectively.
The Waterlow sheets have a small circle (sometimes crossed) instead
of a "⊢" and this is present in both side–margins opposite the 6th row
of stamps, though one is sometimes trimmed off. Short dashes are
also present in the perforation gutter between the marginal stamps
marking the middle of the four sides and a cross is at the centre of
the sheet. The four corners of the sheet have two lines forming a
right-angle as trimming marks, but some are usually trimmed off.
All these gutter marks and sheet-trimming marks are absent in the
De La Rue printings.

The work of the two printers is very similar, but the following notes will be helpful to those attempting to identify Waterlow and De La Rue stamps of the W **165** issue.

De La Rue used the Waterlow die and no alterations were made to it, so that no difference exists in the design or its size, but the making of new plates at first resulted in slight but measurable variations in the width of the gutters between stamps, particularly the horizontal, as follows:

	W.	D.L.R.
Horiz gutters, mm	3.8 to 4.0	3.4 to 3.8

Later D.L.R. plates were however less distinguishable in this respect. For a short time in 1959 the D.L.R. 2s.6d. appeared with one dot in the bottom margin below the first stamp.

It is possible to sort singles with reasonable certainty by general characteristics. The individual lines of the D.L.R. impression are cleaner and devoid of the whiskers of colour of Waterlow's, and the whole impression lighter and softer.

Owing to the closer setting of the horizontal rows the strokes of the perforating comb are closer; this results in the topmost tooth on each side of De La Rue stamps being narrower than the corresponding teeth in Waterlow's which were more than normally broad.

Shades also help. The 2s.6d. D.L.R. is a warmer, more chocolate shade than the blackish brown of W.; the 5s a lighter red with less carmine than W's; the 10s. more blue and less ultramarine; the £1 less intense blue.

The paper of D.L.R. printings is uniformly white, identical with that of W. printings from February 1957 onwards, but earlier W. printings are on paper which is creamy by comparison.

In this and later issues of T **166/9** the dates of issue given for changes of watermark or paper are those on which supplies were first sent by the Supplies Department to Postmasters.

1955–58. W **165.** P 15×14.

540	**154**	½d. orange-red (booklets 8.55, sheets 12.12.55)	20	15
		a. Part perf pane*	£5250	
		Wi. Wmk inverted	45	40
541		1d. ultramarine (19.9.55)	30	15
		a. Booklet pane. Three stamps plus three printed labels	18·00	
		b. *Tête-bêche* (horiz pair)	65	
		Wi. Wmk inverted	65	60
542		1½d. green (booklets 8.55, sheets 11.10.55)	25	30
		a. Wmk sideways (7.3.56)	35	70
		b. *Tête-bêche* (horiz pair)	—	
		Wi. Wmk inverted	75	70
543		2d. red-brown (6.9.55)	25	35
		aa. Imperf between (vert pair)	£4750	
		a. Wmk sideways (31.7.56)	55	70
		ab. Imperf between (horiz pair)	£4750	
		aWi. Wmk inverted	11·00	9·00
543b		2d. light red-brown (17.10.56)	30	20
		ba. *Tête-bêche* (horiz pair)	—	
		bb. Imperf pane*	£6000	
		bc. Part perf pane*	£6000	
		bWi. Wmk inverted	9·00	7·00
		d. Wmk sideways (5.3.57)	8·00	7·00
544	**155**	2½d. carmine-red (Type I) (28.9.55)	1·50	
		a. Wmk sideways (Type I) (23.3.56)	1·50	1·80
		b. Type II (booklets 9.55, sheets 1957)	45	45
		ba. *Tête-bêche* (horiz pair)	—	
		bb. Imperf pane*	—	
		bc. Part perf pane*	£5250	
		bWi. Wmk inverted	55	70
545		3d. deep lilac (17.7.56)	40	25
		aa. *Tête-bêche* (horiz pair)	£3000	
		a. Imperf three sides (pair)	£2750	
		b. Wmk sideways (22.11.57)	18·00	17·00
		Wi. Wmk inverted	1·25	1·25
546	**156**	4d. ultramarine (14.11.55)	1·25	45
547	**157**	5d. brown (21.9.55)	6·00	6·00
548		6d. reddish purple (20.12.55)	4·50	1·20
		aa. Imperf three sides (pair)	£5250	
		a. *Deep claret* (8.5.58)	4·50	1·40
		ab. Imperf three sides (pair)	£5250	
549		7d. bright green (23.4.56)	50·00	10·00
550	**158**	8d. magenta (21.12.55)	7·00	1·30
551		9d. bronze-green (15.12.55)	20·00	2·75
552		10d. Prussian blue (22.9.55)	20·00	2·75
553		11d. brown-purple (28.10.55)	1·00	1·10
554	**159**	1s. bistre-brown (3.11.55)	22·00	65
555	**160**	1s.3d. green (27.3.56)	30·00	1·60
556	**159**	1s.6d. grey-blue (27.3.56)	23·00	1·60
540/56		*Set of 18*	£160	27·00

The dates given for Nos. 540/556 are those on which they were first issued by the Supplies Dept to postmasters.

In December 1956 a completely imperforate sheet of No. 543b was noticed by clerks in a Kent post office, one of whom purchased it against PO regulations. In view of this irregularity we do not consider it properly issued.

Types of 2½d. In this issue, in 1957, Type II formerly only found in stamps from booklets began to replace Type I on sheet stamps.

*BOOKLET ERRORS. Those listed as "imperf panes" show one row of perforations either at top or bottom of the booklet pane; those as "part perf panes" have one row of three stamps imperf on three sides.

170 Scout Badge and "Rolling Hitch"

171 "Scouts coming to Britain"

172 Globe within a Compass

(Des Mary Adshead (2½d.), P. Keely (4d.), W. H. Brown (1s.3d.))

1957 (1 Aug). World Scout Jubilee Jamboree. W **165.** P 15×14.

557	**170**	2½d. carmine-red	50	50
558	**171**	4d. ultramarine	75	1·50
559	**172**	1s.3d. green	5·50	4·50
557/9		*Set of 3*	6·00	5·75

173

½d. to 1½d., 2½d. and 3d.

2d.

Graphite-line arrangements (Stamps viewed from back)

(Adapted F. Langfield)

1957 (12 Sept). 46th Inter-Parliamentary Union Conference. W **165.** P 15×14.

560	**173**	4d. ultramarine	2·00	1·50

GRAPHITE-LINED ISSUES. These were used in connection with automatic sorting machinery, first introduced experimentally at Southampton in December 1957.

The graphite lines were printed in black on the back, beneath the gum; two lines per stamp, except for the 2d.

In November 1959 phosphor bands were introduced (see notes after No. 598).

1957 (19 Nov). Graphite-lined issue. Two graphite lines on the back, except 2d. value, which has one line. W **165.** P 15×14.

561	**154**	½d. orange-red	60	60
562		1d. ultramarine	80	80
563		1½d. green	2·00	1·75
		a. Both lines at left	£1600	£600
564		2d. light red-brown	2·40	2·40
		a. Line at left	£700	£250
565	**155**	2½d. carmine-red (Type II)	8·50	7·00
566		3d. deep lilac	1·50	1·50
561/66		*Set of 6*	15·00	13·00

No. 564a results from a misplacement of the line and horizontal pairs exist showing one stamp without line. No. 563a results from a similar misplacement.

See also Nos. 587/94.

176 Welsh Dragon

177 Flag and Games Emblem

178 Welsh Dragon

(Des R. Stone (3d.), W. H. Brown (6d.), P. Keely (1s.3d.))

1958 (18 July). Sixth British Empire and Commonwealth Games, Cardiff. W **165.** P 15×14.

567	**176**	3d. deep lilac	20	20
568	**177**	6d. reddish purple	60	45
569	**178**	1s.3d. green	2·25	2·50
567/9		*Set of 3*	2·50	2·75

179 Multiple Crowns

1958–65. W **179.** P 15×14.

570	**154**	½d. orange-red (25.11.58)	10	10
		a. Wmk sideways (26.5.61)	75	75
		c. Part perf pane*	£4500	
		Wi. Wmk inverted	1·50	1·50
		k. Chalk-surfaced paper (15.7.63)	2·50	2·75
		kWi. Wmk inverted	2·75	3·00
		l. Booklet pane. No. 570a×4	7·50	
		m. Booklet pane. No. 570k×3 se-tenant with 574k	9·00	
		n. Booklet pane. No. 570a×2 se-tenant with 574l (1.7.64)	2·25	
571		1d. ultramarine (booklets 11.58, sheets 24.3.59)	10	10
		aa. Imperf (vert pair from coil)		
		a. Wmk sideways (26.5.61)	1·50	1·50
		b. Part perf pane*	£5000	
		c. Imperf pane	£6500	
		d. *Tête-bêche* (horiz pair)		
		Wi. Wmk inverted	50	50
		l. Booklet pane. No. 571a×4	10·00	
		m. Booklet pane. No. 571a×2 se-tenant with 575a×2 (1d. values at left) (16.8.65)	12·00	
		ma. Ditto. 1d. values at right	13·00	
572		1½d. green (booklets 12.58, sheets 30.8.60)	10	15
		a. Imperf three sides (horiz strip of 3)	£8500	
		b. Wmk sideways (26.5.61)	9·00	9·00
		c. *Tête-bêche* (horiz pair)		
		Wi. Wmk inverted	1·50	1·25
		l. Booklet pane. No. 572b×4	40·00	
573		2d. light red-brown (4.12.58)	10	10
		a. Wmk sideways (3.4.59)	1·00	1·00
		Wi. Wmk inverted	£140	70·00
574	**155**	2½d. carmine-red (Type II) (booklets 11.58, sheets 15.9.59)	10	20
		a. Imperf strip of 3	—	
		b. *Tête-bêche* (horiz pair)	—	
		c. Imperf pane	—	
		ca. Part perf pane	£3750	
		Wi. Wmk inverted (Type II) (11.58)	4·50	3·00
		e. Wmk sideways (Type I) (10.11.60)	40	60
		ea. Imperf strip of 3	—	
		f. Type I (wmk upright) (4.10.61)	70	70
		k. Chalk-surfaced paper (Type II) (15.7.63)	50	80
		kWi. Wmk inverted	75	1·30
		l. Wmk sideways (Type II) Ord paper (1.7.64)	75	1·30
575		3d. deep lilac (booklets 11.58, sheets 8.12.58)	20	30
		a. Wmk sideways (24.10.58)	50	55
		b. Imperf pane*	£4250	
		c. Part perf pane*	£4000	
		d. Phantom "R" (Cyl 41 no dot)	£375	
		e. Phantom "R" (Cyl 37 no dot)	55·00	
		Wi. Wmk inverted	50	55
		l. Booklet pane. No. 575a×4 (26.5.61)	3·25	
576	**156**	4d. ultramarine (29.10.58)	45	35
		a. *Deep ultramarine*†† (28.4.65)	15	15
		ab. Wmk sideways (31.5.65)	70	55
		ac. Imperf pane*	£5500	
		ad. Part perf pane*	£4500	
		al. Booklet pane. No. 576ab×4 (16.8.65)	3·25	
		aWi. Wmk inverted	60	75
577		4½d. chestnut (9.2.59)	10	25
578	**157**	5d. brown (10.11.58)	30	40
579		6d. deep claret (23.12.58)	30	25
		a. Imperf three sides (pair)	£4000	
		b. Imperf (pair)	£4500	
580		7d. bright green (26.11.58)	50	45
581	**158**	8d. magenta (24.2.60)	60	40
582		9d. bronze-green (24.3.59)	60	40
583		10d. Prussian blue (18.11.58)	1·00	75
584	**159**	1s. bistre-brown (30.10.58)	75	30
585	**160**	1s.3d. green (17.6.59)	75	30
586	**159**	1s.6d. grey-blue (16.12.58)	5·00	40
570/86		*Set of 17*	9·00	4·25

*BOOKLET ERRORS. See note after No. 556.

††This "shade" was brought about by making more deeply etched cylinders, resulting in apparent depth of colour in parts of the design. There is no difference in the colour of the ink.

Sideways watermark. The 2d., 2½d., 3d. and 4d. come from coils and the ½d., 1d., 1½d., 2½d., 3d. and 4d. come from booklets. In coil stamps the sideways watermark shows the top of the watermark to the left as seen from the front of the stamp. In the booklet stamps it comes equally to the left or right.

Nos. 570k and 574k only come from 2s. "Holiday Resort" Experimental undated booklets issued in 1963, in which one page contained 1×2½d. se-tenant with 3×½d. (See No. 570m).

No. 574l comes from coils, and the "Holiday Resort" Experimental booklets dated "1964" comprising four panes each containing two of these 2½d. stamps se-tenant vertically with two ½d. No. 570a (See No. 570n).

2½d. imperf No. 574a comes from a booklet with watermark upright. No. 574ea is from a coil with sideways watermark.

No. 574f comes from sheets bearing cylinder number 42 and is also known on vertical delivery coils.

Phantom "R" varieties

Nos. 575d and 615a (Cyl 41 no dot)

No. 575Eda

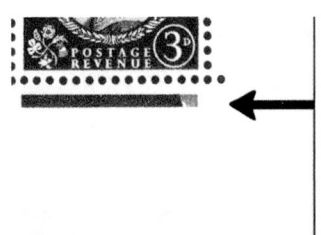

No. 575e (Cyl 37 no dot)

Nos. 575d and 615a occurred below the last stamp of the sheet from Cyl 41 (no dot), where an incomplete marginal rule revealed an "R". The cylinder was later twice retouched. The stamps listed show the original, unretouched "R". The rare variety, No. 575d, is best collected in a block of four or six with full margins in order to be sure that it is not No. 615a with phosphor lines removed.

No. 575e is a similar variety but from Cyl 37 (no dot). The marginal rule is much narrower and only a very small part of the" R" is revealed. The cylinder was later retouched. The listed variety is for the original, unretouched state.

No. 575 is known imperforate and tête-bêche. These came from booklet sheets which were not issued (price £25 per pair).

WHITER PAPER. On 18 May 1962 the Post Office announced that a whiter paper was being used for the current issue (including Nos. 595/8). This is beyond the scope of this catalogue, but the whiter papers are listed in Vol. 3 of the Stanley Gibbons *Great Britain Specialised Catalogue*.

1958 (24 Nov)–**61**. Graphite-lined issue. Two graphite lines on the back, except 2d. value, which has one line. W **179**. P 15×14.

587Wi	**154**	½d. orange-red (15.6.59)	9·00	9·00
		Wi. Wmk inverted	3·25	4·00
588		1d. ultramarine (18.12.58)	2·00	1·50
		a. Misplaced graphite lines (7.61)*	80	1·20
		Wi. Wmk inverted	1·50	2·00
589Wi		1½d. green (4.8.59)	90·00	80·00
		Wi. Wmk inverted	75·00	60·00
590		2d. light red-brown (24.11.58)	10·00	3·50
		a. Band at extreme left as seen from back	£975	
591	**155**	2½d. carmine-red (Type II) (9.6.59)	12·00	10·00
		Wi. Wmk inverted	65·00	50·00
592		3d. deep lilac (24.11.58)	90	65
		a. Misplaced graphite lines (5.61)*	£550	£425
		Wi. Wmk inverted	1·00	1·25
593	**156**	4d. ultramarine (29.4.59)	5·50	5·00
		a. Misplaced graphite lines (1961)*	£2400	
594		4½d. chestnut (3.6.59)	6·50	5·00
587/94 *Set of 8*			£110	70·00

Nos. 587/9 were only issued in booklets or coils (587/8).

*No. 588a (in coils), and Nos. 592a and 593a (both in sheets) result from the use of a residual stock of graphite-lined paper. As the use of graphite lines had ceased, the register of the lines in relation to the stamps was of no importance and numerous misplacements occurred—two lines close together, one line only, etc. No. 588a refers to two lines at left or at right; No. 592a refers to stamps with two lines only at left and both clear of the perforations and No. 593a to stamps with two lines at left (with left line down perforations) and traces of a third line down the opposite perforations.

(Recess D.L.R. (until 31.12.62), then B. W.)

1959–68. W **179**. P 11×12.

595	**166**	2s.6d. black-brown (22.7.59)	10·00	75
		Wi. Wmk inverted	—	3250
		a. BW printing (1.7.63)	35	40
		aWi. Wmk inverted	£3250	£280
		k. Chalk-surfaced paper (30.5.68)	50	1·50
596	**167**	5s. scarlet-vermilion (15.6.59)	45·00	2·00
		Wi. Wmk inverted	£9000	£600
		a. BW ptg. Red (shades) (3.9.63)	1·20	80
		ab. Printed on the gummed side	£1600	
		aWi. Wmk inverted	£400	£300
597	**168**	10s. blue (21.7.59)	55·00	5·00
		a. BW ptg. Bright ultramarine (16.10.63)	4·50	4·50
		aWi. Wmk inverted	—	£3250
598	**169**	£1 black (23.6.59)	£120	12·00
		Wi. Wmk inverted	—	£2500
		a. B. W. printing (14.11.63)	13·00	8·00
		aWi. Wmk inverted	£15000	£3750
		k. Chalk-surfaced paper	£5250	
595/8 *Set of 4*			£195	17·00
595a/8a *Set of 4*			15·00	11·00

The B.W. printings have a marginal Plate Number. They are generally more deeply engraved than the D.L.R., showing more of the Diadem detail and heavier lines on Her Majesty's face. The vertical perf is 11.9 to 12 as against D.L.R. 11.8.

See also Nos. 759/62.

PHOSPHOR BAND ISSUES. These are printed on the front and are wider than graphite lines. They are not easy to see but show as broad vertical bands at certain angles to the light.

Values representing the rate for printed papers (and when this was abolished in 1968 for second class mail) have one band and others two, three or four bands as stated, according to the size and format.

In the small size stamps the bands are on each side with the single band at left (except where otherwise stated). In the large-size commemorative stamps the single band may be at left, centre or right, varying in different designs. The bands are vertical on both horizontal and vertical designs except where otherwise stated.

The phosphor was originally applied typographically but later usually by photogravure and sometimes using flexography, a typographical process using rubber cylinders.

Three different types of phosphor have been used, distinguishable by the colour emitted under an ultra-violet lamp, the first being green, then blue and later violet. Different sized bands are also known. All these are fully listed in Vol. 3 of the Stanley Gibbons *Great Britain Specialised Catalogue*.

Varieties. Misplaced and missing phosphor bands are known but such varieties are beyond the scope of this Catalogue.

1959 (18 Nov). Phosphor-Graphite issue. Two phosphor bands on front and two graphite lines on back, except 2d. value, which has one band on front and one line on back. P 15×14.

(a) W **165**

599	**154**	½d. orange-red	4·50	4·50
600		1d. ultramarine	12·00	12·00
601		1½d. green	5·25	5·25

(b) W **179**

605	**154**	2d. light red-brown (1 band)	6·00	5·00
		a. Error. W **165**	£200	£175
606	**155**	2½d. carmine-red (Type II)	22·00	18·00
607		3d. deep lilac	12·00	9·00
608	**156**	4d. ultramarine	20·00	16·00
609		4½d. chestnut	30·00	20·00
599/609 *Set of 8*			£100	80·00

Examples of the 2½d., No. 606, exist showing watermark W **165** in error. It is believed that phosphor-graphite stamps of this value with this watermark were not used by the public for postal purposes.

1960 (22 June)–**67**. Phosphor issue. Two phosphor bands on front, except where otherwise stated. W **179**. P 15×14.

610	**154**	½d. orange-red	10	15
		a. Wmk sideways (14.7.61)	15·00	15·00
		l. Booklet pane. No. 610a×4	40·00	
		Wi. Wmk inverted	1·50	1·50
611		1d. ultramarine	10	10
		a. Wmk sideways (14.7.61)	1·10	1·10
		l. Booklet pane. No. 611a×4	10·00	
		m. Booklet pane. No. 611a×2 se-tenant with 615d×2 (1d. stamps at left) (16.8.65)	18·00	
		ma. Booklet pane. As. No. 611m, but 1d. stamps at right	18·00	
		n. Booklet pane. No. 611a×2 se-tenant with 615b×2†† (11.67)	10·00	
		Wi. Wmk inverted	65	65
612		1½d. green	15	15
		a. Wmk sideways (14.7.61)	18·00	18·00

		l. Booklet pane. No. 612a×4	45·00	
		Wi. Wmk inverted	25·00	22·00
613		2d. light red-brown (1 band)	22·00	22·00
613a	**154**	2d. lt red-brown (two bands) (4.10.61)	10	15
		aa. Imperf three sides*** (pair)	—	
		ab. Wmk sideways (6.4.67)	1·00	1·00
614	**155**	2½d. carmine-red (Type II) (2 bands)*	40	30
		Wi. Wmk inverted	£170	£140
614a		2½d. carmine-red (Type II) (1 band) (4.10.61)	60	75
		aWi. Wmk inverted	50·00	42·00
614b		2½d. carmine-red (Type I) (1 band) (4.10.61)	45·00	40·00
615		3d. deep lilac (2 bands)	60	55
		aa. Phantom "R" (Cyl 41 no dot)	55·00	
		a. Imperf three sides (horiz pair)	£2000	
		b. Wmk sideways (14.7.61)	1·80	1·80
		l. Booklet pane. No. 615b×4	25·00	
		Wi. Wmk inverted	50	90
615c		3d. deep lilac (1 side band) (29.4.65)	60	55
		cWi. Wmk inverted	8·00	7·00
		d. Wmk sideways (16.8.65)	5·50	5·00
		e. One centre band (8.12.66)	40	45
		ea. Wmk sideways (19.6.67)	1·00	1·00
		eWi. Wmk inverted	4·00	4·00
616	**156**	4d. ultramarine	3·50	3·50
		a. Deep ultramarine (28.4.65)	25	30
		aa. Part perf pane	£5500	
		ab. Wmk sideways (16.8.65)	1·10	1·10
		al. Booklet pane. No. 616ab×4	2·50	
		aWi. Wmk inverted	75	75
616b		4½d. chestnut (13.9.61)	55	30
616c	**157**	5d. brown (9.6.67)	55	35
617		6d. deep claret (27.6.60)	55	35
617a		7d. bright green (15.2.67)	70	50
617b	**158**	8d. magenta (28.6.67)	70	55
617c		9d. bronze-green (29.12.66)	70	65
617d		10d. Prussian blue (30.12.66)	1·00	1·00
617e	**159**	1s. bistre-brown (28.6.67)	1·00	35
618	**160**	1s.3d. green	1·90	2·50
618a	**159**	1s.6d. grey-blue (12.12.66)	2·00	2·00
610/18a *Set of 17*			10·50	8·00

The automatic facing equipment was brought into use on 6 July 1960 but the phosphor stamps may have been released a few days earlier.

The stamps with watermark sideways are from booklets except Nos. 613ab and 615ea which are from coils. No. 616ab comes from both booklets and coils.

No. 615aa. See footnote after No. 586.

*No. 614 with two bands on the creamy paper was originally from cylinder 50 dot and no dot. When the change in postal rates took place in 1965 it was reissued from cylinder 57 dot and no dot on the whiter paper. Some of these latter were also released in error in districts of S. E. London in September 1964. The shade of the reissue is slightly more carmine.

***This comes from the bottom row of a sheet which is imperf at bottom and both sides.

††Booklet pane No. 611n comes from 2s. booklets of January and March 1968. The two bands on the 3d. stamp were intentional because of the technical difficulties in producing one band and two band stamps se-tenant.

Unlike previous one-banded phosphor stamps. No. 615c has a broad band extending over two stamps so that alternate stamps have the band at left or right (same prices either way).

180 Postboy of 1660

181 Posthorn of 1660

(Des R. Stone (3d.), Faith Jaques (1s.3d.))

1960 (7 July). Tercentenary of Establishment of General Letter Office. W **179** (sideways on 1s.3d.). P 15×14 (3d.) or 14×15 (1s.3d.)

619	**180**	3d. deep lilac	50	50
620	**181**	1s.3d. green	3·75	4·25

182 Conference Emblem

(Des R. Stone (emblem, P. Rahikainen))

1960 (19 Sept). First Anniv of European Postal and Telecommunications Conference. Chalk-surfaced paper. W **179**. P 15×14.

621	**182**	6d. bronze-green and purple	2·00	50
622		1s.6d. brown and blue	9·50	5·00

183 Thrift Plant

184 "Growth of Savings"

185 Thrift Plant

(Des P. Gauld (2½d.), M. Goaman (others))

1961 (28 Aug). Centenary of Post Office Saving Bank. Chalk-surfaced paper. W **179** (sideways on 2½d.). P 14×15 (2½d.) or 15×14 (others).

A. "Timson" Machine

623A	**183**	2½d. black and red	25	25
		a. Black omitted	£27000	
624A	**184**	3d. orange-brown and violet	20	20
		a. Orange-brown omitted	£600	
625A	**185**	1s.6d. red and blue	2·75	3·00
623A/5A *Set of 3*			2·75	3·00

B. "Thrissell" Machine

623B	**183**	2½d. black and red	2·25	2·25
624B	**184**	3d. orange-brown and violet	40	40
		a. Orange-brown omitted	£1600	

2½d. TIMSON. Cyls 1E–1F. Deeply shaded portrait (brownish black). 2½d. THRISSELL. Cyls 1D–1B or 1D (dot)–1B (dot). Lighter portrait (grey-black).

3d. TIMSON. Cyls 3D–3E. Clear, well-defined portrait with deep shadows and bright highlights. 3d. THRISSELL. Cyls 3C–3B or 3C (dot)–3B (dot). Dull portrait, lacking in contrast.

Sheet marginal examples without single extension perf hole on the short side of the stamp are always "Timson", as are those with large punch-hole *not* coincident with printed three-sided box guide mark.

The 3d. "Timson" perforated completely through the right-hand side margin comes from a relatively small part of the printing perforated on a sheet-fed machine.

Normally the "Timsons" were perforated in the reel, with three large punch-holes in both long margins and the perforations completely through both short margins. Only one punch-hole coincides with the guide-mark.

The "Thrissells" have one large punch-hole in one long margin, coinciding with guide-mark and one short margin imperf (except sometimes for encroachments).

186 CEPT Emblem

187 Doves and Emblem

188 Doves and Emblem

(Des M. Goaman (doves T. Kurpershoek))

1961 (18 Sept). European Postal and Telecommunications (CEPT) Conference, Torquay. Chalk-surfaced paper. W **179**. P 15×14.

626	**186**	2d. orange, pink and brown	15	10
		a. Orange omitted	£18500	
627	**187**	4d. buff, mauve and ultramarine	15	15
628	**188**	10d. turquoise, pale green and Prussian blue	20	75
		a. Pale green omitted	£27500	
		b. Turquoise omitted	£8000	
626/8 *Set of 3*			40	60

189 Hammer Beam Roof, Westminster Hall

190 Palace of Westminster

(Des Faith Jaques)

1961 (25 Sept). Seventh Commonwealth Parliamentary Conference. Chalk-surfaced paper. W **179** (sideways on 1s.3d.). P 15×14 (6d.) or 14×15 (1s.3d.)

629	**189**	6d. purple and gold	25	25
		a. Gold omitted	£2750	
630	**190**	1s.3d. green and blue	2·50	2·75
		a. Blue (Queen's head) omitted	£45000	

191 "Units of Productivity"

192 "National Productivity"

193 "Unified Productivity"

(Des D. Gentleman)

1962 (14 Nov). National Productivity Year. Chalk-surfaced paper. W **179** (inverted on 2½d. and 3d.). P 15×14.

631	**191**	2½d. myrtle-green and carmine-red (*shades*)	20	20
		p. One phosphor band	60	50
632	**192**	3d. light blue and violet (*shades*)	50	25
		a. Light blue (Queen's head) omitted	£6500	
		p. Three phosphor bands	1·50	80
633	**193**	1s.3d. carmine, light blue and deep green	1·50	1·70
		a. Light blue (Queen's head) omitted	£17500	
		p. Three phosphor bands	35·00	22·00
631/3 *Set of 3*			2·00	1·90
631p/3p *Set of 3*			35·00	22·00

194 Campaign Emblem and Family   **195** Children of Three Races

(Des M. Goaman)

1963 (21 Mar). Freedom from Hunger. Chalk-surfaced paper. W **179** (inverted). P 15×14.

634	**194**	2½d. crimson and pink	25	10
		p. One phosphor band	3·00	1·20
635	**195**	1s.3d. bistre-brown and yellow	1·90	1·90
		p. Three phosphor bands	30·00	23·00

196 "Paris Conference"

(Des R. Stone)

1963 (7 May). Paris Postal Conference Centenary. Chalk-surfaced paper. W **179** (inverted). P 15×14.

636	**196**	6d. green and mauve	50	85
		a. Green omitted	£6500	
		p. Three phosphor bands	6·50	7·00

197 Posy of Flowers   **198** Woodland Life

(Des S. Scott (3d.), M. Goaman (4½d.))

1963 (16 May). National Nature Week. Chalk-surfaced paper. W **179**. P 15×14.

637	**197**	3d. yellow, green, brown and black	15	15
		p. Three phosphor bands	60	60
638	**198**	4½d. black, blue, yellow, magenta and brown-red	35	35
		p. Three phosphor bands	3·25	3·25

199 Rescue at Sea   **200** 19th-century Lifeboat

201 Lifeboatmen

(Des D. Gentleman)

1963 (31 May). Ninth International Lifeboat Conference, Edinburgh. Chalk-surfaced paper. W **179**. P 15×14.

639	**199**	2½d. blue, black and red	25	25
		p. One phosphor band	50	60
640	**200**	4d. red, yellow, brown, black and blue	50	50
		p. Three phosphor bands	50	60
641	**201**	1s.6d. sepia, yellow and grey-blue	3·00	3·25
		p. Three phosphor bands	48·00	28·00
639/41 *Set of 3*			3·25	3·50
639p/41p *Set of 3*			48·00	28·00

202 Red Cross   **203**

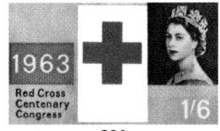

204

(Des H. Bartram)

1963 (15 Aug). Red Cross Centenary Congress. Chalk-surfaced paper. W **179**. P 15×14.

642	**202**	3d. red and deep lilac	25	25
		a. Red omitted	£18500	
		p. Three phosphor bands	1·10	1·00
		pa. Red omitted	£46000	
643	**203**	1s.3d. red, blue and grey	3·00	3·00
		p. Three phosphor bands	35·00	30·00
644	**204**	1s.6d. red, blue and bistre	3·00	3·00
		p. Three phosphor bands	35·00	27·00
642/4 *Set of 3*			5·00	5·75
642p/4p *Set of 3*			65·00	55·00

205 Commonwealth Cable

(Des P. Gauld)

1963 (3 Dec). Opening of COMPAC (Trans-Pacific Telephone Cable). Chalk-surfaced paper. W **179**. P 15×14.

645	**205**	1s.6d. blue and black	2·75	2·50
		a. Black omitted	£8750	
		p. Three phosphor bands	16·00	16·00

206 Puck and Bottom (*A Midsummer Night's Dream*)   **207** Feste (*Twelfth Night*)

208 Balcony Scene (*Romeo and Juliet*)   **209** "Eve of Agincourt" (*Henry V*)

210 Hamlet contemplating Yorick's Skull (*Hamlet*) and Queen Elizabeth II

(Des D. Gentleman. Photo Harrison & Sons (3d., 6d., 1s.3d., 1s.6d.). Des C. and R. Ironside. Recess B.W. (2s.6d.))

1964 (23 Apr). Shakespeare Festival. Chalk-surfaced paper. W **179**. P 11×12 (2s.6d.) or 15×14 (others).

646	**206**	3d. yellow-bistre, black and deep violet blue-black (*shades*)	15	15
		p. Three phosphor bands	25	30
647	**207**	6d. yellow, orange, black and yellow-olive (*shades*)	30	30
		p. Three phosphor bands	75	1·00
648	**208**	1s.3d. cerise, blue-green, black and sepia (*shades*)	75	1·00
		Wi. Wmk inverted	£950	
		p. Three phosphor bands	4·00	6·50
		pWi. Wmk inverted	£400	—
649	**209**	1s.6d. violet, turquoise, black and blue (*shades*)	1·00	1·10
		Wi. Wmk inverted	—	£1300
		p. Three phosphor bands	8·00	8·00
650	**210**	2s.6d. deep slate-purple (*shades*)	3·00	3·00
		Wi. Wmk inverted	£1000	
646/50 *Set of 5*			4·50	4·50
646p/9p *Set of 4*			12·00	14·00

211 Flats near Richmond Park ("Urban Development")   **212** Shipbuilding Yards, Belfast ("Industrial Activity")

213 Beddgelert Forest Park, Snowdonia ("Forestry")   **214** Nuclear Reactor, Dounreay ("Technological Development")

(Des D. Bailey)

1964 (1 July). 20th International Geographical Congress. London. Chalk-surfaced paper. W **179**. P 15×14.

651	**211**	2½d. black, olive-yell, olive-grey and turquoise-blue	10	10
		p. One phosphor band	40	50
652	**212**	4d. orange-brown, red-brown, rose, black and violet	30	30
		a. Violet (face value) omitted	£300	
		c. Violet and red-brown (dock walls) omitted	£550	
		d. Red-brown (dock walls) omitted	£850	—
		Wi. Wmk inverted		
		p. Three phosphor bands	1·20	1·20
653	**213**	8d. yellow-brown, emerald, green and black	75	85
		a. Green (lawn) omitted	£22500	
		Wi. Wmk inverted	£2200	
		p. Three phosphor bands	2·50	3·50
654	**214**	1s.6d. yellow-brown, pale pink, black and brown	3·50	3·50
		Wi. Wmk inverted	55·00	—
		p. Three phosphor bands	28·00	28·00
651/4 *Set of 4*			4·50	4·50
651p/4p *Set of 4*			30·00	25·00

A used example of the 4d. is known with the red-brown omitted.

215 Spring Gentian   **216** Dog Rose

217 Honeysuckle   **218** Fringed Water Lily

(Des M. and Sylvia Goaman)

1964 (5 Aug). Tenth International Botanical Congress, Edinburgh. Chalk-surfaced paper. W **179**. P 15×14.

655	**215**	3d. violet, blue and sage-green	25	25
		a. Blue omitted	£24000	
		b. Sage-green omitted	£28000	
		p. Three phosphor bands	40	40
656	**216**	6d. apple-green, rose, scarlet and green	50	50
		p. Three phosphor bands	2·50	2·75
657	**217**	9d. lemon, green, lake and rose-red	1·70	2·25
		a. Green (leaves) omitted	£26000	
		Wi. Wmk inverted	75·00	—
		p. Three phosphor bands	4·50	4·00
658	**218**	1s.3d. yellow, emerald, reddish violet and grey-green	2·50	2·50
		a. Yellow (flowers) omitted	£50000	
		Wi. Wmk inverted	£2500	—
		p. Three phosphor bands	25·00	20·00
655/8 *Set of 4*			4·50	4·50
655p/8p *Set of 4*			30·00	25·00

219 Forth Road Bridge   **220** Forth Road and Railway Bridges

(Des A. Restall)

1964 (4 Sept). Opening of Forth Road Bridge. Chalk-surfaced paper. W **179**. P 15×14.

659	**219**	3d. black, blue and reddish violet	10	10
		p. Three phosphor bands	1·00	1·50
660	**220**	6d. blackish lilac, light blue and carmine-red	40	40
		a. Light blue omitted	£7500	
		Wi. Wmk inverted	5·00	—
		p. Three phosphor bands	4·50	4·75
		Wi. Wmk inverted	£875	—

221 Sir Winston Churchill

(Des D. Gentleman and Rosalind Dease, from photograph by Karsh)

1965 (8 July). Churchill Commemoration. Chalk-surfaced paper. W **179**. P 15×14.

I. "REMBRANDT" Machine

661	**221**	4d. black and olive-brown	15	10
		Wi. Wmk inverted	3·00	—
		p. Three phosphor bands	25	25

II. "TIMSON" Machine

661a	**221**	4d. black and olive-brown	35	35

III. "L. & M. 4" Machine

662	–	1s.3d. black and grey	45	40
		Wi. Wmk inverted	£140	—
		p. Three phosphor bands	2·50	3·00

The 1s.3d. shows a closer view of Churchill's head.

4d. REMBRANDT. Cyls 1A–1B dot and no dot. Lack of shading detail on Churchill's portrait. Queen's portrait appears dull and coarse. This is a rotary machine which is sheet-fed.

4d. TIMSON. Cyls 5A–6B no dot. More detail on Churchill's portrait—furrow on forehead, his left eyebrow fully drawn and more shading on cheek. Queen's portrait lighter and sharper. This is a reel-fed, two-colour 12-in, wide rotary machine and the differences in impression are due to the greater pressure applied by this machine.

1s.3d. Cyls 1A–1B no dot. The "Linotype and Machinery No. 4" machine is an ordinary sheet-fed rotary press machine. Besides being used for printing the 1s.3d. stamps it was also employed for overprinting the phosphor bands on both values.

Two examples of the 4d. value exist with the Queen's head omitted, one due to something adhering to the cylinder and the other due to a paper fold. The stamp also exists with Churchill's head omitted, also due to a paper fold

222 Simon de Montfort's Seal

223 Parliament Buildings (after engraving by Hollar, 1647)

(Des S. Black (6d.), R. Guyatt (2s.6d.))

1965 (19 July). 700th Anniv of Simon de Montfort's Parliament. Chalk-surfaced paper. W **179**. P 15×14.

663	222	6d. olive-green	30	40
		p. Three phosphor bands	1·00	1·25
664	223	2s.6d. black, grey and pale drab	80	1·80
		Wi. Wmk inverted	65·00	

224 Bandsmen and Banner   **225** Three Salvationists

(Des M. Farrar-Bell (3d.), G. Trenaman (1s.6d.))

1965 (9 Aug). Salvation Army Centenary. Chalk-surfaced paper. W **179**. P 15×14.

665	224	3d. indigo, grey-blue, cerise, yellow and brown	25	25
		p. One phosphor band	25	40
666	225	1s.6d. red, blue, yellow and brown	1·00	1·50
		p. Three phosphor bands	2·50	2·75

226 Lister's Carbolic Spray   **227** Lister and Chemical Symbols

(Des P. Gauld (4d.), F. Ariss (1s.))

1965 (1 Sept). Centenary of Joseph Lister's Discovery of Antiseptic Surgery. Chalk-surfaced paper. W **179**. P 15×14.

667	226	4d. indigo, brown-red and grey-black	25	15
		a. Brown-red (tube) omitted	£650	
		b. Indigo omitted	£7000	
		p. Three phosphor bands	25	25
		pa. Brown-red (tube) omitted	£7500	
668	227	1s. black, purple and new blue	1·00	1·40
		Wi. Wmk inverted	£675	—
		p. Three phosphor bands	2·00	2·50
		pWi. Wmk inverted	£550	—

228 Trinidad Carnival Dancers   **229** Canadian Folk-dancers

(Des D. Gentleman and Rosalind Dease)

1965 (1 Sept). Commonwealth Arts Festival. Chalk-surfaced paper. W **179**. P 15×14.

669	228	6d. black and orange	20	20
		p. Three phosphor bands	30	50
670	229	1s.6d. black and light reddish violet	80	1·10
		p. Three phosphor bands	2·50	3·50

230 Flight of Supermarine Spitfires   **231** Pilot in Hawker Hurricane Mk I

232 Wing-tips of Supermarine Spitfire and Messerschmitt Bf 109   **233** Supermarine Spitfires attacking Heinkel HE-111H Bomber

 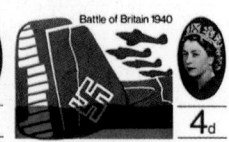

234 Supermarine Spitfire attacking Junkers Ju 87B "Stuka" Dive-bomber   **235** Hawker Hurricanes Mk 1 over Wreck of Dornier Do-17Z Bomber

236 Anti-aircraft Artillery in Action   **237** Air-battle over St. Paul's Cathedral

(Des D. Gentleman and Rosalind Dease (4d.×6 and 1s.3d.), A. Restall (9d.))

1965 (13 Sept). 25th Anniv of Battle of Britain. Chalk-surfaced paper. W **179**. P 15×14.

671	230	4d. yellow-olive and black	25	25
		a. Block of 6. Nos. 671/6	8·00	8·00
		p. Three phosphor bands	50	50
		pa. Block of 6. Nos. 671p/6p	10·00	12·00
672	231	4d. yellow-olive, olive-grey and black	25	25
		p. Three phosphor bands	50	50
673	232	4d. red, new blue, yellow-olive, olive-grey and black	25	25
		p. Three phosphor bands	50	50
674	233	4d. olive-grey, yellow-olive and black	25	25
		p. Three phosphor bands	50	50
675	234	4d. olive-grey, yellow-olive and black	25	25
		p. Three phosphor bands	50	50
676	235	4d. olive-grey, yellow-olive, new blue and black	25	25
		a. New blue omitted	†	£6500
		p. Three phosphor bands	50	50
677	236	9d. bluish violet, orange and slate-purple	1·70	1·70
		Wi. Wmk inverted	£100	—
		p. Three phosphor bands	1·70	2·50
678	237	1s.3d. light grey, deep grey, black, light blue and bright blue	1·70	1·70
		Wi. Wmk inverted	£190	—
		p. Three phosphor bands	1·70	2·50
		pWi. Wmk inverted	5·00	—
671/8	*Set of 8*		10·00	10·00
671p/8p	*Set of 8*		12·00	14·00

Nos. 671/6 were issued together *se-tenant* in blocks of six (3×2) within the sheet.

No. 676a is only known commercially used on cover from Truro.

238 Tower and Georgian Buildings   **239** Tower and "Nash" Terrace, Regent's Park

(Des C. Abbott)

1965 (8 Oct). Opening of Post Office Tower. Chalk-surfaced paper. W **179** (sideways on 3d.). P 14×14 (1s.3d.).

679	238	3d. olive-yellow, new blue and bronze-green	15	15
		a. Olive-yellow (Tower) omitted	£6750	£2400
		p. One phosphor band	15	15
680	239	1s.3d. bronze-green, yellow-green and blue	45	45
		Wi. Wmk inverted	£175	—
		p. Three phosphor bands	50	50
		pWi. Wmk inverted	£200	—

The one phosphor band on No. 679p was produced by printing broad phosphor bands across alternate vertical perforations. Individual stamps show the band at right or left (same prices either way).

240 U.N. Emblem   **241** I.C.Y. Emblem

(Des J. Matthews)

1965 (25 Oct). 20th Anniv of U.N.O. and International Co-operation Year. Chalk-surfaced paper. W **179**. P 15×14.

681	240	3d. black, yellow-orange and light blue	25	20
		p. One phosphor band	25	30

682	241	1s.6d. black, bright purple and light blue	1·00	80
		Wi. Wmk inverted	—	£2200
		p. Three phosphor bands	2·75	3·00

242 Telecommunications Network   **243** Radio Waves and Switchboard

(Des A. Restall)

1965 (15 Nov). I.T.U. Centenary. Chalk-surfaced paper. W **179**. P 15×14.

683	242	9d. red, ultramarine, deep slate violet, black and pink	50	40
		Wi. Wmk inverted	30·00	—
		p. Three phosphor bands	1·00	75
		pWi. Wmk inverted	£110	
684	243	1s.6d. red, greenish black, indigo, black and light pink	1·50	1·25
		a. Light pink omitted	£4500	£2500
		Wi. Wmk inverted	£300	
		p. Three phosphor bands	4·25	5·25

Originally scheduled for issue on 17 May 1965 supplies from the Philatelic Bureau were sent in error to reach a dealer on that date and another dealer received his supply on 27 May.

244 Robert Burns (after Skirving chalk drawing)   **245** Robert Burns (after Nasmyth portrait)

(Des G. Huntly)

1966 (25 Jan). Burns Commemoration. Chalk-surfaced paper. W **179**. P 15×14.

685	244	4d. black, deep violet-blue and new blue	20	15
		p. Three phosphor bands	50	50
686	245	1s.3d. black, slate-blue and yellow-orange	65	70
		p. Three phosphor bands	2·25	2·25

246 Westminster Abbey

247 Fan Vaulting, Henry VII Chapel

(Des Sheila Robinson. Photo Harrison (3d.). Des and eng Bradbury Wilkinson. Recess (2s.6d.))

1966 (28 Feb). 900th Anniv of Westminster Abbey. Chalk-surfaced paper (3d.). W **179**. P 15×14 (3d.) or 11×12 (2s.6d.).

687	246	3d. black, red-brown and new blue	20	20
		p. One phosphor band	20	25
688	247	2s.6d. black	1·00	1·20

248 View near Hassocks, Sussex

249 Antrim, Northern Ireland

250 Harlech Castle, Wales

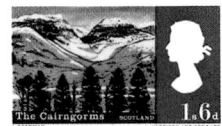

251 Cairngorm Mountains, Scotland

(Des L. Rosoman. Queen's portrait, adapted by D. Gentleman from coinage)

1966 (2 May). Landscapes. Chalk-surfaced paper. W **179**. P 15×14.

689	**248**	4d. black, yellow-green and new blue............................	10	15
		p. Three phosphor bands...............	10	15
690	**249**	6d. black, emerald and new blue....	15	20
		Wi. Wmk inverted........................	6·00	—
		p. Three phosphor bands...............	15	20
		pWi. Wmk inverted......................	£170	—
691	**250**	1s.3d. black, greenish yellow and greenish blue................	25	35
		p. Three phosphor bands...............	25	35
692	**251**	1s.6d. black, orange and Prussian blue.............................	40	35
		Wi. Wmk inverted........................	22·00	—
		p. Three phosphor bands...............	40	40
689/92	*Set of 4*...............................		80	95
689p/92p	*Set of 4*.............................		80	1·00

A block of four of No. 689 is known with the top right stamp showing the face value and the bottom right the Queen's head and the face value omitted due to a paper fold.

252 Players with Ball   **253** Goalmouth Mêlée

254 Goalkeeper saving Goal

(Des D. Gentleman (4d.), W. Kempster (6d.), D. Caplan (1s.3d.). Queen's portrait adapted by D. Gentleman from coinage)

1966 (1 June). World Cup Football Championship. Chalk-surfaced paper. W **179** (sideways on 4d.). P 14×15 (4d.) or 15×14 (others).

693	**252**	4d. red, reddish pur, bright blue, flesh and black................	10	25
		p. Two phosphor bands................	10	25
694	**253**	6d. black, sepia, red, apple-green and blue.......................	15	25
		a. Black omitted.........................	£225	
		b. Apple-green omitted...............	£7000	
		c. Red omitted...........................	£12500	
		Wi. Wmk inverted........................	5·00	—
		p. Three phosphor bands...............	15	25
		pa. Black omitted.......................	£3000	
695	**254**	1s.3d. black, blue, yellow, red and light yellow-olive........	50	1·00
		a. Blue omitted..........................	£380	
		Wi. Wmk inverted........................	£150	—
		p. Three phosphor bands...............	50	1·00
		pWi. Wmk inverted......................	2·00	—
693/5	*Set of 3*...............................		70	1·25
693p/5p	*Set of 3*..............................		70	1·25

255 Black-headed Gull

256 Blue Tit

257 European Robin

258 Blackbird

(Des J. Norris Wood)

1966 (8 Aug). British Birds. Chalk-surfaced paper. W **179**. P 15×14.

696	**255**	4d. grey, black, red, emerald-green, bright blue, greenish yellow and bistre......	20	20
		Wi. Wmk inverted........................	4·00	—
		a. Block of 4. Nos. 696/9.............	1·00	2·00
		ab. Block (value), etc. omitted* (block of 4).............	£20000	
		ac. Black only omitted*...............	£5000	
		aWi. Wmk inverted (block of 4).....	18·00	—
		p. Three phosphor bands...............	20	20
		pWi. Wmk inverted......................	20·00	—
		pa. Block of 4. Nos. 696p/9p........	1·00	2·00
		paWi. Wmk inverted (block of 4)...	85·00	—
697	**256**	4d. black, greenish yellow grey, emerald-green, bright blue and bistre..........	20	20
		Wi. Wmk inverted........................	4·00	—
		p. Three phosphor bands...............	20	20
		pWi. Wmk inverted......................	20·00	—
698	**257**	4d. red, greenish yellow, black, grey, bistre, reddish brown and emerald-green......	20	20
		a. Black only omitted.................	£15000	
		Wi. Wmk inverted........................	4·00	—
		p. Three phosphor bands...............	20	20
		pWi. Wmk inverted......................	20·00	—
699	**258**	4d. black, reddish brown, greenish yellow, grey and bistre**............	20	20
		Wi. Wmk inverted........................	4·00	—
		p. Three phosphor bands...............	20	20
		pWi. Wmk inverted......................	20·00	—
696/9	*Set of 4*...............................		1·00	2·00
696p/9p	*Set of 4*..............................		1·00	2·00

Nos. 696/9 were issued together *se-tenant* in blocks of four within the sheet.

*In No. 696ab the blue, bistre and reddish brown are also omitted but in No. 696ac only the black is omitted.

** On No. 699 the black was printed over the bistre.

Other colours omitted, and the stamps affected:

d.	Greenish yellow (Nos. 696/9)............	£1100
pd.	Greenish yellow (Nos. 696/9)............	£2000
e.	Red (Nos. 696 and 698)............	£1100
f.	Emerald-green (Nos. 696/8p)............	£200
pf.	Emerald-green (Nos. 696/8p)............	£200
g.	Bright blue (Nos. 696/9)............	£700
pg.	Bright blue (Nos. 696/7p)............	£6000
h.	Bistre (Nos. 696/9)............	£200
ph.	Bistre (Nos. 696p/9p)............	£2750
j.	Reddish brown (Nos. 698/9)............	£125
pj.	Reddish brown (Nos. 698p/9p)............	£175

The prices quoted are for each stamp.

259 Cup Winners

1966 (18 Aug). England's World Cup Football Victory. Chalk-surfaced paper. W **179** (sideways). P 14×15.

700	**259**	4d. red, reddish purple, bright blue, flesh and black............	30	30

These stamps were only put on sale at post offices in England, the Channel Islands and the Isle of Man, and at the Philatelic Bureau in London and also, on 22 August, in Edinburgh on the occasion of the opening of the Edinburgh Festival as well as at Army post offices at home and abroad.

260 Jodrell Bank Radio Telescope

261 British Motor-cars

262 "SRN 6" Hovercraft

263 Windscale Reactor

(Des D. and A. Gillespie (4d., 6d.), A. Restall (others))

1966 (19 Sept). British Technology. Chalk-surfaced paper. W **179**. P 15×14.

701	**260**	4d. black and lemon....................	15	10
		p. Three phosphor bands...............	10	10
702	**261**	6d. red, deep blue and orange........	25	20
		a. Red (Mini-cars) omitted...........	£22000	
		b. Deep blue (Jaguar and inscr) omitted.......	£18500	
		p. Three phosphor bands...............	15	25
703	**262**	1s.3d. black, orange-red, slate and light greenish blue........	50	40
		p. Three phosphor bands...............	35	40
704	**263**	1s.6d. black, yellow-green, bronze-green, lilac and deep blue.........	50	60
		p. Three phosphor bands...............	50	60
701/4	*Set of 4*...............................		1·25	1·10
701p/4p	*Set of 4*..............................		1·00	1·10

264

265

266

267

268

269

All the above show battle scenes and they were issued together *se-tenant* in horizontal strips of six within the sheet.

270 Norman Ship

271 Norman Horsemen attacking Harold's Troops

(All the above are scenes from the Bayeux Tapestry)

(Des D. Gentleman. Photo, Queen's head die-stamped (6d., 1s.3d.))

1966 (14 Oct). 900th Anniv of Battle of Hastings. Chalk-surfaced paper. W **179** (sideways on 1s.3d.). P 15×14.

705	**264**	4d. black, olive-green, bistre, deep blue, orange, magenta, green, blue and grey......	10	10
		Wi. Wmk inverted........................	7·00	—
		a. Strip of 6. Nos. 705/10............	1·90	2·25
		aWi. Wmk inverted (strip of 6)......	45·00	—

	p. Three phosphor bands..............		10	10
	pWi. Wmk inverted		3·00	—
	pa. Strip of 6. Nos. 705p/10p		1·90	2·25
	paWi. Wmk inverted (strip of 6) ...		20·00	—
706 **265**	4d. black, olive-green, bistre, deep blue, orange, mag, grn, blue and grey....................................		10	10
	Wi. Wmk inverted		7·00	—
	p. Three phosphor bands..............		10	10
	pWi. Wmk inverted		2·00	—
707 **266**	4d. black, olive-green, bistre, deep blue, orange, mag, grn, blue and grey....................................		10	10
	Wi. Wmk inverted		7·00	—
	p. Three phosphor bands..............		10	10
	pWi. Wmk inverted		2·00	—
708 **267**	4d. black, olive-green, bistre, deep blue, magenta, green, blue and grey....................................		10	10
	Wi. Wmk inverted		7·00	—
	p. Three phosphor bands..............		10	10
	pWi. Wmk inverted		2·00	—
709 **268**	4d. black, olive-green, bistre, deep blue, orange, mag, grn, blue and grey....................................		10	10
	Wi. Wmk inverted		7·00	—
	p. Three phosphor bands..............		10	10
	pWi. Wmk inverted		2·00	—
710 **269**	4d. black, olive-green, bistre, deep blue, orange, mag, grn, blue and grey....................................		10	10
	Wi. Wmk inverted		7·00	—
	p. Three phosphor bands..............		10	10
	pWi. Wmk inverted		2·00	—
711 **270**	6d. black, olive-grn, vio, bl, grn and gold..................................		10	10
	Wi. Wmk inverted		42·00	—
	p. Three phosphor bands..............		10	10
	pWi. Wmk inverted		55·00	—
712 **271**	1s.3d. black, lilac, bronze-green, rosine, bistre-brown and gold...		20	75
	Wi. Wmk sideways inverted (top of crown pointing to right)*...........		35·00	—
	a. Lilac omitted		£5250	
	p. Four phosphor bands................		20	75
	pa. Lilac omitted		£1500	
	pWi. Wmk sideways inverted (top of crown pointing to right)*........		35·00	—

705/12 *Set of 8*.. 2·00 2·75
705p/12p *Set of 8*... 2·00 2·75

*The normal sideways watermark shows the tops of the Crowns pointing to the left, *as seen from the back of the stamp*.

Other colours omitted on the 4d. values and the stamps affected:

b. Olive-green (Nos. 705/10)....................................	65·00
pb. Olive-green (Nos. 705p/10p)............................	65·00
c. Bistre (Nos. 705/10)..	65·00
pc. Bistre (Nos. 705p/10).......................................	65·00
d. Deep blue (Nos. 705/10).....................................	75·00
pd. Deep blue (Nos. 705p/10p)...............................	75·00
e. Orange (Nos. 705p/7 and 709/10).......................	65·00
pe. Orange (Nos. 705p/7 and 709p/10p)..................	65·00
f. Magenta (Nos. 705/10)..	65·00
pf. Magenta (Nos. 705 /10p)...................................	65·00
g. Green (Nos. 705/10)..	65·00
pg. Green (Nos. 705p/10p)......................................	65·00
h. Blue (Nos. 705/10)..	65·00
ph. Blue (Nos. 705/10p)..	65·00
j. Grey (Nos. 705/10)...	65·00
pj. Grey (Nos. 705p/10p)...	65·00
pk. Magenta and green (Nos. 705p/10p).................	75·00

The prices quoted are for each stamp.

Nos. 705 and 709, with grey and blue omitted, have been seen commercially used, posted from Middleton-in-Teesdale.

Three examples of No. 712 in a right-hand top corner block of ten (2×5) are known with the Queen's head omitted as a result of a double paper fold prior to die-stamping The perforation is normal. Of the other seven stamps, four have the Queen's head misplaced and three are normal.

MISSING GOLD HEADS. The 6d and 1s.3d. were also issued with the die-stamped gold head omitted but as these can also be removed by chemical means we are not prepared to list them unless a way is found of distinguishing the genuine stamps from the fakes which will satisfy the Expert Committees.
The same remarks apply to Nos. 713/14.

272 King of the Orient

273 Snowman

(Des Tasveer Shemza (3d.), J. Berry (1s.6d.) (winners of children's design competition). Photo, Queen's head die-stamped)

1966 (1 Dec). Christmas. Chalk-surfaced paper. W **179** (sideways on 3d.). P 14×15.

713 **272**	3d. black, blue, green, yell, red and gold....................................		10	25
	a. Queen's head double...............		£7000	†
	ab. Queen's head double, one albino...................................		£650	
	b. Green omitted		10	25
	p. One phosphor band.................		10	25
714 **273**	1s.6d. blue, red, pink, black and gold .		30	50
	a. Pink (hat) omitted		£4500	
	Wi. Wmk inverted		30·00	—
	p. Two phosphor bands................		30	50
	pWi. Wmk inverted		90·00	—

See note below Nos. 679/80 which also applies to No. 713p.

---

274 Sea Freight

275 Air Freight

(Des C. Abbott)

1967 (20 Feb). European Free Trade Association (EFTA). Chalk-surfaced paper. W **179**. P 15×14.

715 **274**	9d. deep blue, red, lilac, green, brown, new blue, yellow and black..		25	20
	a. Black (Queen's head, etc.), brown, new blue and yellow omitted...................................		£1300	
	b. Lilac omitted		£3500	
	c. Green omitted		£3500	
	d. Brown (rail trucks) omitted........		95·00	
	e. New blue omitted		—	
	f. Yellow omitted		£3500	
	p. Three phosphor bands..............		25	20
	pb. Lilac omitted		£225	
	pc. Green omitted		£135	
	pd. Brown omitted		95·00	
	pe. New blue omitted		£135	
	pf. Yellow omitted		£180	
	pWi. Wmk inverted		£2000	
716 **275**	1s.6d. violet, red, deep blue, brown, green, blue-grey, new bl, yell & black..		50	45
	a. Red omitted		—	
	b. Deep blue omitted		£135	
	c. Brown omitted		£135	
	d. Blue-grey omitted		£135	
	e. New blue omitted		£135	
	f. Yellow omitted		£135	
	g. Green omitted		£3750	
	Wi. Wmk inverted		30·00	—
	p. Three phosphor bands..............		25	40
	pb. Deep blue omitted		£250	
	pc. Brown omitted		95·00	
	pd. Blue-grey omitted		£135	
	pf. New blue omitted		£135	
	pWi. Wmk inverted		30·00	—

276 Hawthorn and Bramble

277 Larger Bindweed and Viper's Bugloss

278 Ox-eye Daisy, Coltsfoot and Buttercup

279 Bluebell, Red Campion and Wood Anemone

The above were issued together *se-tenant* in blocks of four within the sheet.

280 Dog Violet

281 Primroses

(Des Rev. W. Keble Martin (T **276/9**), Mary Grierson (others))

1967 (24 Apr). British Wild Flowers. Chalk-surfaced paper. W **179**. P 15×14.

717 **276**	4d. grey, lemon, myrtle-green, red, agate and slate-purple..............		20	20
	Wi. Wmk inverted		2·00	—
	a. Block of 4. Nos. 717/20.............		80	2·25
	aWi. Wmk inverted (block of 4)		9·00	
	b. Grey double*..........................			
	c. Red omitted		£5000	
	f. Slate-purple omitted		£5500	
	p. Three phosphor bands..............		10	15
	pWi. Wmk inverted		2·00	—
	pa. Block of 4. Nos. 717p/20p........		80	2·00
	paWi. Wmk inverted (block of 4)		9·00	
	pd. Agate omitted		£4500	
	pf. Slate-purple omitted		£550	
718 **277**	4d. grey, lemon, myrtle-green, red, agate and violet......................		20	20
	b. Grey double*..........................			
	Wi. Wmk inverted		2·00	—
	p. Three phosphor bands..............		10	15
	pd. Agate omitted		£4500	
	pe. Violet omitted			
	pWi. Wmk inverted		2·00	—
719 **278**	4d. grey, lemon, myrtle-green, red and agate..............................		20	20
	b. Grey double*..........................			
	Wi. Wmk inverted		2·00	—
	p. Three phosphor bands..............		10	15
	pd. Agate omitted		£4500	
	pWi. Wmk inverted		2·00	—
720 **279**	4d. grey, lemon, myrtle-green, reddish purple, agate and violet...................................		20	20
	b. Grey double*..........................			
	c. Reddish purple omitted		£2250	
	d. Value omitted†......................		£12000	
	Wi. Wmk inverted		2·00	—
	p. Three phosphor bands..............		10	15
	pd. Agate omitted		£4500	
	pe. Violet omitted			
	pWi. Wmk inverted		2·00	—
721 **280**	9d. lavender-grey, green, reddish violet and orange-yellow...........		20	25
	Wi. Wmk inverted		1·30	—
	p. Three phosphor bands..............		15	25
722 **281**	1s.9d. lavender-grey, green, greenish yellow and orange..............		25	35
	p. Three phosphor bands..............		20	30

717/22 *Set of 6*.. 1·00 2·25
717p/22p *Set of 6*... 1·00 2·00

*The double impression of the grey printing affects the Queen's head, value and inscription.

†No. 720d was caused by something obscuring the face value on R. 14/6 during the printing of one sheet.

PHOSPHOR BANDS. Issues from No. 723 are normally with phosphor bands only, except for the high values. However, most stamps have appeared with the phosphor bands omitted in error, but they are outside the scope of this catalogue. They are listed in Volumes 3, 4 and 5 of the Stanley Gibbons *Great Britain Specialised Catalogue* and in the *Great Britain Concise Catalogue*.
See also further notes after No. X1058.

PHOSPHORISED PAPER. Following the adoption of phosphor bands the Post Office started a series of experiments involving the addition of the phosphor to the paper coating before the stamps were printed. No. 743c was the first of these experiments to be issued for normal postal use. See also notes after No. X1058.

PVA GUM. Polyvinyl alcohol was introduced by Harrisons in place of gum arabic in 1968. As it is almost invisible a small amount of pale yellowish colouring was introduced to make it possible to check that the stamps had been gummed. Such gum varieties are outside the scope of this catalogue, but they are listed in the *Great Britain Concise Catalogue*. See further notes *re* gum after Nos. 744 and 762.

282   **282a**

I   II

Two types of the 2d.

I. Value spaced away from left side of stamp (cylinders 1 no dot and dot).

II. Value close to left side from new multipositive used for cylinders 5 no dot and dot onwards. The portrait appears in the centre, thus conforming to the other values

(Des after plaster cast by Arnold Machin)

1967 (5 June)–**70**. Chalk-surfaced paper. Two phosphor bands except where otherwise stated. No wmk. P 15×14.

723 **282**	½d. orange-brown (5.2.68)...........		30	75
724	1d. light olive (*shades*) (2 bands) (5.2.68).................................		20	10
	a. Imperf (coil strip).....................		£3500	
	b. Part perf pane*.......................			
	c. Imperf pane*...........................		£5750	
	d. Uncoated paper**...................		£150	
	l. Booklet pane. No. 724×2, *se-tenant* with 730×2 (6.3.68)		3·00	
	m. Booklet pane. No. 724×4, *se-tenant* with 734×2 (6.1.69)		3·50	
	n. Booklet pane. No. 724×6, 731×6 and 735×3 *se-tenant* (1.12.69)...............................		8·50	
	na. Uncoated paper**.................		£925	
725	1d. yellowish olive (1 centre band) (16.9.68).........................		45	55
	l. Booklet pane. No. 725×d, *se-tenant* with 732×2.............		4·00	

	m. Coil strip. No. 728×2, *se-tenant* with 729, 725 and 733 (27.8.69)	1·90	1·90
726	2d. lake-brown (Type I) (2 bands) (5.2.68)	20	15
727	2d. lake-brown (Type II) (2 bands) (1969)	30	40
728	2d. lake-brown (Type II) (1 centre band) (27.8.69)	1·00	1·50
729	3d. violet (*shades*) (1 centre band) (8.8.67)	30	10
	a. Imperf (pair)	£950	
730	3d. violet (2 bands) (6.4.68)	30	45
	a. Uncoated paper**		
731	4d. deep sepia (*shades*) (2 bands)	30	30
	b. Part perf pane*	£4000	
732	4d. deep olive-brown (*shades*) (1 centre band) (16.9.68)	30	45
	a. Part perf pane)	£4250	
	l. Booklet pane. Two stamps plus two printed labels	1·00	
733	4d. bright vermilion (1 centre band) (6.1.69)	20	10
	a. *Tête-bêche* (horiz pair)	£5000	
	b. Uncoated paper**	20·00	
	l. Booklet pane. Two stamps plus two printed labels (3.3.69)	1·00	
734	4d. bright vermilion (1 side band) (6.1.69)	1·90	2·50
	a. Uncoated paper*	£425	
735	5d. royal blue (*shades*) (1.7.68)	20	20
	a. Imperf pane*	£3500	
	b. Part perf pane	£2500	
	c. Imperf (pair)††	£275	
	d. Uncoated paper**	40·00	
736	6d. bright reddish purple (*shades*) (5.2.68)	50	40
737 282a	7d. bright emerald (1.7.68)	1·00	1·00
738	8d. bright emerald (1.7.68)	1·25	1·75
739	8d. light turquoise-blue (6.1.69) ..	1·00	1·50
740	9d. myrtle-green (8.8.67)	1·00	1·50
741 282	10d. drab (1.7.68)	1·00	1·25
	a. Uncoated paper**	60·00	
742	1s. light bluish violet (*shades*)	45	45
743	1s.6d. greenish blue and deep blue (*shades*) (8.8.67)	50	50
	a. Greenish blue omitted	£160	
	c. Phosphorised paper. Prussian blue and indigo (10.12.69)	1·40	1·40
	ca. Prussian blue omitted	£450	
744	1s.9d. dull orange and black (*shades*)	1·00	1·00
723/44 *Set of 16*		7·00	8·00

*BOOKLET ERRORS. See note after No. 556.

**Uncoated paper. This does not respond to the chalky test, and may be further distinguished from the normal chalk-surfaced paper by the fibres which clearly show on the surface, resulting in the printing impression being rougher, and by the screening dots which are not so evident. The 1d., 4d. and 5d. come from the £1 "Stamps for Cooks" Booklet (1970); and the 3d. and 10d. from sheets (1969). The 20p. and 50p. high values (Nos. 830/1) exist with similar errors.

†No. 724a occurs in a vertical strip of four, top stamp perforated on three sides, bottom stamp imperf three sides and the two middle stamps completely imperf.

††No. 735c comes from the original state of cylinder 15 which is identifiable by the screening dots which extend through the gutters of the stamps and into the margins of the sheet. This must not be confused with imperforate stamps from cylinder 10, a large quantity of which was stolen from the printers early in 1970.

The 1d. with centre band (725) only came in the September 1968 booklets (PVA gum) and the coil strip (725m) (gum arabic); the 2d. with centre band (728) was only issued in the coil strip (725m); the 3d. (No. 730) appeared in booklets on 6.4.68 from coils during December 1968 and from sheets in January 1969; and the 4d. with one side band (734) only in 10s. (band at left) and £1 (band at left or right) booklets.

Gum. The 1d. (725), 3d. (729), 4d. (731 and 733), 9d., 1s., 1s.6d. and 1s.9d. exist with gum arabic as well as the PVA gum; the 2d. (728) and coil strip (725m) exist only with gum arabic; and the remainder exist with PVA gum only.

The 4d. (731) in shades of washed-out grey are colour changelings which we understand are caused by the concentrated solvents used in modern dry cleaning methods.

For decimal issue, sec Nos. X841, etc.

283 *"Master Lambton"* (Sir Thomas Lawrence)

284 *"Mares and Foals in a Landscape"* (George Stubbs)

285 *"Children Coming Out of School"* (L. S. Lowry)

(Des S. Rose)

1967 (10 July). British Paintings. Chalk-surfaced paper. Two phosphor bands. No wmk. P 14×14 (others).

748	283	4d. rose-red, lemon, brown, black, new blue and gold	10	10
		a. Gold (value and Queen's head) omitted	£350	
		b. New blue omitted	£21000	

749	284	9d. Venetian red, ochre, grey-black, new blue, greenish yellow and black	15	15
		a. Black (Queen's head and value) omitted	£12000	
		b. Black (Queen's head only) omitted	£2500	
750	285	1s.6d. greenish yellow, grey, rose, new blue grey-black and gold..	35	35
		a. Gold (Queen's head) omitted	£350	
		b. New blue omitted	£350	
		c. Grey (clouds and shading) omitted	£175	
748/50 *Set of 3*			50	50

286 *Gypsy Moth IV*

(Des M. and Sylvia Goaman)

1967 (24 July). Sir Francis Chichester's World Voyage. Chalk-surfaced paper. Three phosphor bands. No wmk. P 15×14.

751	286	1s.9d. black, brown-red, light emerald and blue	45	45

287 *Radar Screen*

288 *Penicillium notatum*

289 *Vickers VC-10 Jet Engines*

290 *Television Equipment*

(Des C. Abbott (4d., 1s.), Negus-Sharland team (others))

1967 (19 Sept). British Discovery and Invention. Chalk-surfaced paper. Three phosphor bands (4d.) or two phosphor bands (others). W **179** (sideways on 1s.9d.). P 14×15 (1s.9d.) or 15×14 (others).

752	287	4d. greenish yellow, black and vermilion	10	10
753	288	1s. blue-green, light greenish blue, slate purple and bluish violet	35	35
		Wi. Wmk inverted	20·00	—
754	289	1s.6d. black, grey, royal blue, ochre and turquoise-blue	45	45
		Wi. Wmk inverted	£240	—
755	290	1s.9d. black grey-blue, pale olive-grey, violet and orange	50	50
		a. Pale olive-grey omitted	£4500	
		b. Orange (Queen's head) omitted	£30000	
752/5 *Set of 4*			1·20	1·20

WATERMARK. All issues from this date are on unwatermarked paper.

291 *"The Adoption of the Sheperds"* (School of Seville)

292 *"Madonna and Child"* (Murillo)

293 *"The Adoration of the Shepherds"* (Louis le Nain)

(Des S. Rose)

1967. Christmas. Chalk-surfaced paper. One phosphor band (3d.) or two phosphor bands (others). P 15×14 (1s.6d.) or 14×15 (others).

756	291	3d. ol-yell, rose, bl, blk and gold (27.11)	10	15

---

		a. Gold (value and Queen's head) omitted	£110	
		ab. Gold (Queen's head only) omitted		
		b. Printed on the gummed side	£625	
		c. Rose omitted	£3700	
757	292	4d. bright purple, greenish yellow, new blue, grey-black and gold (18.10)	10	15
		a. Gold (value and Queen's head) omitted	80·00	
		ab. Gold (Queen's head only) omitted	£4500	
		b. Gold ("4D" only) omitted	£3000	
		c. Greenish yellow (Child, robe and Madonna's face) omitted	£7500	
		d. Greenish yellow and gold omitted	£15000	
758	293	1s.6d. bright purple, bistre, lemon, black, orange-red, ultramarine and gold (27.11)	15	15
		a. Gold (value and Queen's head) omitted	£18000	
		ab. Gold (Queen's head only) omitted	£3000	
		b. Ultramarine omitted	£850	
		c. Lemon omitted	£20000	
756/8 *Set of 3*			30	30

Distinct shades exist of the 3d. and 4d. values but are not listable as they are intermediate shades. For the 4d. stamps from one machine show a darker background and give the appearance of the yellow colour being omitted, but this is not so and these should not be confused with the true missing yellow No. 757c.

No. 757b comes from stamps in the first vertical row of a sheet. The 3d. and 4d. values are known imperforate. They are of proof status.

(Recess Bradbury, Wilkinson)

1967–68. No wmk. White paper. P 11×12.

759	166	2s.6d. black-brown (1.7.68)	30	45
760	167	5s. red (10.4.68)	70	75
761	168	10s. bright ultramarine (10.4.68)	7·75	4·00
762	169	£1 black (4.12.67)	7·50	4·50
759/62 *Set of 4*			15·00	8·00

PVA GUM. All the following issues from this date have PVA gum *except where footnotes state otherwise.*

294 *Tarr Steps, Exmoor*

295 *Aberfeldy Bridge*

296 *Menai Bridge*

297 *M4 Viaduct*

(Des A. Restall (9d.), L. Roseman (1s.6d.), J. Matthews (others))

1968 (29 Apr). British Bridges. Chalk-surfaced paper. Two phosphor bands. P 15×14.

763	294	4d. black, bluish violet, turquoise-blue and gold	10	10
		a. Printed on gummed side	35·00	
764	295	9d. red-brown, myrtle-green, ultramarine, olive-brown, black and gold	15	15
		a. Gold (Queen's head) omitted	£280	
		b. Ultramarine omitted	†	£7000
765	296	1s.6d. olive-brown, red-orange, bright green, turquoise-green and gold	25	25
		a. Gold (Queen's head) omitted	£425	
		b. Red-orange (roof tops) omitted	£425	
766	297	1s.9d. olive-brown, greenish yellow, dull green, deep ultramarine and gold	30	30
		a. Gold (Queen's head) omitted	£425	
763/6 *Set of 4*			70	70

No. 764b is only known on first day covers posted from Canterbury, Kent. or the Philatelic Bureau, Edinburgh.

298 *"TUC" and Trades Unionists*

299 Mrs. Emmeline Pankhurst (statue)

300 Sopwith Camel and English Electric Lightning Fighters

301 Captain Cook's *Endeavour* and Signature

(Des D. Gentleman (4d.), C. Abbott (others))

1968 (29 May). British Anniversaries. Events described on stamps. Chalk-surfaced paper. Two phosphor bands. P 15×14.

767	**298**	4d. emerald, olive, blue and black..	10	10
768	**299**	9d. reddish violet, bluish grey and black	15	15
769	**300**	1s. olive-brown, blue, red, slate-blue and black	25	30
770	**301**	1s.9d. yellow-ochre and blackish brown	55	60
767/70 *Set of 4*			1·00	1·00

302 *"Queen Elizabeth I"* (unknown artist)

303 *"Pinkie"* (Lawrence)

304 *"Ruins of St. Mary Le Port"* (Piper)

305 *"The Hay Wain"* (Constable)

(Des S. Rose)

1968 (12 Aug). British Paintings. Queen's head embossed. Chalk-surfaced paper. Two phosphor bands. P 15×14 (1s.9d.) or 14×15 (others).

771	**302**	4d. black, vermilion, greenish yellow, grey and gold	10	10
		a. Gold (value and Queen's head) omitted	£350	
		b. Vermilion omitted*	£700	
772	**303**	1s. mauve, new blue, greenish yellow, black, magenta and gold	10	20
		Eb. Gold (value and Queen's head) omitted*	£750	
773	**304**	1s.6d. slate, orange, black, mauve, greenish yellow, ultramarine and gold	20	25
		a. Gold (value and Queen's head) omitted	£350	
774	**305**	1s.9d. greenish yellow, black, new blue, red and gold	25	40
		a. Gold (value and Queen's head) and embossing omitted	£1000	
		b. Red omitted	£13500	
771/4 *Set of 4*			60	85

*The effect of this is to leave the face and hands white and there is more yellow and olive in the costume.

The 4d., 1s. and 1s.9d. are known with the embossing only omitted. No. 774a is only known with the phosphor also omitted.

*No. 772Eb also has the embossing and phosphor omitted. The stamp with gold omitted but embossing and phosphor present (No. 772a) is £7500.

306 Boy and Girl with Rocking Horse

307 Girl with Doll's House

308 Boy with Train Set

(Des Rosalind Dease. Head printed in gold and then embossed)

1968 (25 Nov). Christmas. Chalk-surfaced paper. One centre phosphor band (4d.) or two phosphor bands (others). P 15×14 (4d.) or 14×15 (others).

775	**306**	4d. black, orange, vermilion, ultramarine, bistre and gold	10	15
		a. Gold omitted	£6000	
		b. Vermilion omitted*	£650	
		c. Ultramarine omitted	£550	
		d. Bistre omitted	†	—
		e. Orange omitted	†	—
776	**307**	9d. yellow-olive. black, brown, yellow, magenta, orange, turquoise green and gold	15	25
		a. Yellow omitted	£175	
		b. Turquoise-green (dress) omitted	£22000	
777	**308**	1s.6d. ultramarine. yellow-orange, bright purple. blue-green, black and gold	15	50
775/7 *Set of 3*			35	80

*The effect of the missing vermilion is shown on the rocking horse, saddle and faces which appear orange instead of red.

A single used example of the 4d. exists with the bistre omitted.

No. 775c is only known with the phosphor also omitted. All values exist with the embossing of Queen's head omitted.

309 *Queen Elizabeth 2*

310 Elizabethan Galleon

311 East Indiaman

312 *Cutty Sark*

313 *Great Britain*

314 *Mauretania I*

(Des D. Gentleman)

1969 (15 Jan). British Ships. Chalk-surfaced paper. Two vertical phosphor bands at right (1s.), one horizontal phosphor band (5d.) or two phosphor bands (9d.). P 15×14.

778	**309**	5d. black, grey, red and turquoise...	10	15
		a. Black Queen's head, value, (hull and inset) omitted	£3500	
		b. Grey (decks, etc.) omitted	£280	
		c. Red (inscription) omitted	£300	
779	**310**	9d. red, blue, ochre, brown, black and grey	10	25
		a. Strip of 3. Nos. 779/81	1·30	1·50
		ab. Red and blue omitted	£3800	
		ac. Blue omitted	£3800	
780	**311**	9d. ochre, brown, black and grey	10	25
781	**312**	9d. ochre, brown, black and grey....	10	25

782	**313**	1s. brown, black, grey, green and greenish yellow	40	35
		a. Pair. Nos. 782/3	1·30	1·50
		ab. Greenish yellow omitted	£4800	
783	**314**	1s. red, black, brown, carmine and grey	40	35
		a. Carmine (hull overlay) omitted.	£40000	
		b. Red (funnels) omitted	£30000	
		c. Carmine and red omitted	£30000	
778/83 *Set of 6*			2·40	2·75

The 9d. and 1s. values were arranged in horizontal strips of three and pairs respectively throughout the sheet.

No. 779ab is known only with the phosphor also omitted.

315 Concorde in Flight

316 Plan and Elevation Views

317 Concorde's Nose and Tail

(Des M. and Sylvia Goaman (4d.), D. Gentleman (9d., 1s.6d.))

1969 (3 Mar). First Flight of Concorde. Chalk-surfaced paper. Two phosphor bands. P 15×14.

784	**315**	4d. yellow-orange, violet, greenish blue, blue-green and pale green	25	25
		a. Violet (value, etc.) omitted	£850	
		b. Yellow-orange omitted	£850	
785	**316**	9d. ultramarine, emerald, red and grey-blue	55	75
		a. Face value and inscr omitted	£40000	
786	**317**	1s.6d. deep blue, silver-grey and light blue	75	1·00
		a. Silver-grey omitted	£850	
784/6 *Set of 3*			1·00	1·50

No. 785a is caused by a colour shift of the grey-blue. On the only known example the top of the Queen's head appears across the perforations at foot.

No. 786a affects the Queen's head which appears in the light blue colour.

318 Queen Elizabeth II. (See also Type **357**)

(Des after plaster cast by Arnold Machin. Recess Bradbury, Wilkinson)

1969 (5 Mar). P 12.

787	**318**	2s.6d. brown	35	30
788		5s. crimson-lake	1·80	60
789		10s. deep ultramarine	6·00	7·00
790		£1 bluish black	3·25	1·50
787/90 *Set of 4*			10·00	8·50

For decimal issue, see Nos. 829/31*b* and notes after No. 831*b*.

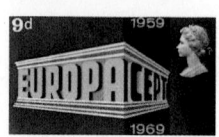

319 Page from *Daily Mail*, and Vickers FB-27 Vimy Aircraft

320 Europa and CEPT Emblems

321 ILO Emblem

322 Flags of NATO Countries

323 Vickers FB-27 Vimy Aircraft and Globe showing Flight

(Des P. Sharland (5d., 1s., 1s.6d.), M. and Sylvia Goaman (9d., 1s.9d.))

1969 (2 Apr). Anniversaries. Events described on stamps. Chalk-surfaced paper. Two phosphor bands. P 15×14.

791	319	5d. black, pale sage-green, chestnut and new blue...............		10	15
792	320	9d. pale turquoise, deep blue, light emerald-green and black.		15	25
		a. Uncoated paper*..........................		£1800	
793	321	1s. bright purple, deep blue and lilac..		15	25
794	322	1s.6d. red, royal blue, yellow-green, black, lemon and new blue.......		15	30
		e. Black omitted.................................		£125	
		f. Yellow-green (from flags) omitted......................................		90·00	
		g. Lemon (from flags) omitted.......		†	£4500
795	323	1s.9d. yellow-olive, greenish yellow and pale turquoise-green...........		40	40
		a. Uncoated paper*..........................		£275	
791/5		*Set of 5*...		60	1·00

*Uncoated paper. The second note after No. 744 also applies here.
No. 794g is only known used on first day cover from Liverpool.

324 Durham Cathedral

325 York Minster

326 St. Giles' Cathedral, Edinburgh

327 Canterbury Cathedral

328 St. Paul's Cathedral

329 Liverpool Metropolitan Cathedral

(Des P. Gauld)

1969 (28 May). British Architecture. Cathedrals. Chalk-surfaced paper. Two phosphor bands. P 15×14.

796	324	5d. grey-black, orange, pale bluish violet and black........................		10	10
		a. Block of 4. Nos. 796/9................		1·10	1·25
		ab. Block of 4. Uncoated paper**....		£1000	
		b. Pale bluish violet omitted........		£24000	
797	325	5d. grey-black, pale bluish violet, new blue and black................		10	10
		b. Pale bluish violet omitted..........		£24000	
798	326	5d. grey-black, purple, green and black..		10	10
		c. Green omitted*............................		£100	
799	327	5d. grey-black, green, new blue and black...............................		10	10
800	328	9d. grey-black,ochre, pale drab, violet and black..........................		25	30
		a. Black (value) omitted...................		£300	

801	329	1s.6d. grey-black, pale turquoise, pale reddish violet, pale yellow-olive and black.................		25	35
		a. Black (value) omitted...................		£5000	
		b. Black (value) double...................		£5000	
796/801		*Set of 6*...		1·40	1·70

The 5d. values were issued together *se-tenant* in blocks of four throughout the sheet.

*The missing green on the roof top is known on R. 2/5, R. 8/5 and R. 10/5, but all from different sheets, and it only occurred in part of the printing, being "probably caused by a batter on the impression cylinder". Examples are also known with the green partly omitted.
**Uncoated paper. The second note after No. 744 also applies here.

330 The King's Gate, Caernarvon Castle

331 The Eagle Tower, Caernarvon Castle

332 Queen Eleanor's Gate, Caernarvon Castle

333 Celtic Cross, Margam Abbey

334 HRH The Prince of Wales (after photo by G. Argent)

(Des D. Gentleman)

1969 (1 July). Investiture of HRH The Prince of Wales. Chalk-surfaced paper. Two phosphor bands. P 14×15.

802	330	5d. deep olive-grey, light olive-grey, deep grey, light grey, red, pale turquoise-green, black and silver...............................		10	15
		a. Strip of 3. Nos. 802/4................		50	1·00
		b. Black (value and inscr) omitted		£750	
		c. Red omitted*................................		£1700	
		d. Deep grey omitted*....................		£575	
		e. Pale turquoise-green omitted...		£1600	
		f. Light grey omitted......................		£14000	
803	331	5d. deep olive-grey, light olive-grey, deep grey, light grey, red, pale turquoise-green, black and silver...............................		10	15
		b. Black (value and inscr) omitted		£750	
		c. Red omitted*................................		£1700	
		d. Deep grey omitted**...................		£575	
		e. Pale turquoise-green omitted...		£1600	
		f. Light grey (marks on walls, window frames, etc) omitted....		£14000	£8000
804	332	5d. deep olive-grey, light olive-grey, deep grey, light grey, red, pale turquoise-green, black and silver...............................		10	15
		b. Black (value and inscr) omitted		£750	
		c. Red omitted*................................		£1700	
		d. Deep grey omitted**...................		£575	
		e. Pale turquoise-green omitted...		£16000	
		f. Light grey omitted......................		£14000	
805	333	9d. deep grey, light grey, black and gold..................................		15	30
806	334	1s. blackish yellow-olive and gold.		15	30
802/6		*Set of 5*...		75	1·40

The 5d. values were issued together, *se-tenant*, in strips of three throughout the sheet.

*The 5d. value is also known with the red misplaced downwards and where this occurs the red printing does not take very well on the silver background and in some cases is so faint that it could be mistaken for a missing red. However, the red can be seen under a magnifying glass and caution should therefore be exercised when purchasing copies of Nos. 802/4c.
**The deep grey affects the dark portions of the windows and doors. No. 803f is only known commercially used on cover.

335 Mahatma Gandhi

(Des B. Mullick)

1969 (13 Aug). Gandhi Centenary Year. Chalk-surfaced paper. Two phosphor bands. P 15×14.

807	335	1s.6d. black, green, red-orange and grey..............................		40	30
		a. Printed on the gummed side		£1700	

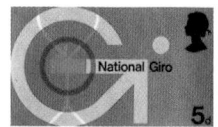

336 National Giro "G" Symbol

337 Telecommunications—International Subscriber Dialling

338 Telecommunications—Pulse Code Modulation

339 Postal Mechanisation—Automatic Sorting

(Des D. Gentleman. Litho De La Rue)

1969 (1 Oct). Post Office Technology Commemoration. Chalk-surfaced paper. Two phosphor bands. P 13½×14.

808	336	5d. new bl, greenish bl, lavender and black................................		10	10
809	337	9d. emerald, violet-blue and black.		20	25
810	338	1s. emerald, lavender and black		20	25
811	339	1s.6d. brt purple, lt blue, grey-blue and black...............................		50	50
808/11		*Set of 4*...		90	1·00

340 Herald Angel

341 The Three Shepherds

342 The Three Kings

(Des F. Wegner. Queen's head (and stars 4d., 5d. and scroll-work 1s.6d.) printed in gold and then embossed)

1969 (26 Nov). Christmas. Chalk-surfaced paper. Two phosphor bands (5d., 1s.6d.) or one centre band (4d.). P 15×14.

812	340	4d. vermilion, new blue, orange, bright purple, light green, bluish violet, blackish brown and gold..................................		10	10
		a. Gold (Queen's head etc.) omitted		£13000	
813	341	5d. magenta, light blue, royal blue, olive-brown, green, greenish yellow, red and gold.................		15	15
		a. Light blue (sheep, etc) omitted		£110	
		b. Red omitted*...............................		£2700	
		c. Gold (Queen's head) omitted		£1200	
		d. Green omitted..............................		£450	
		e. Olive-brown, red and gold omitted......................................		£17000	
814	342	1s.6d. greenish yell, bright purple, bluish violet, deep slate, orange, green, new blue and gold.....................................		20	20
		a. Gold (Queen's head etc.) omitted		£180	
		b. Deep slate (value) omitted.........		£550	
		c. Greenish yellow omitted............		£550	
		e. New blue omitted.........................		£140	
812/14		*Set of 3*...		40	40

*The effect of the missing red is shown on the hat, leggings and purse which appear as dull orange.
The 5d. and 1s.6d. values are known with the embossing omitted.
No. 813e was caused by a paper fold and also shows the phosphor omitted.
Used copies of the 5d. have been seen with the olive-brown or greenish yellow (tunic at left) omitted.

343 Fife Harling

344 Cotswold Limestone

345 Welsh Stucco

346 Ulster Thatch

(Des D. Gentleman (5d., 9d.), Sheila Robinson (1s., 1s.6d.))

1970 (11 Feb). British Rural Architecture. Chalk-surfaced paper. Two phosphor hands. P 15×14.

815	343	5d. grey, grey-blk, blk, lemon, greenish blue, orange-brown, ultramarine and green	10	10
		a. Lemon omitted	£175	
		b. Grey (Queen's head and cottage shading) omitted		
		c. Greenish blue (door) omitted	†	£4800
		d. Grey-black (inscription and face value) omitted	£20000	
		e. Grey-black (face value only) omitted	£17000	
		f. Green omitted (cobblestones)		
816	344	9d. orange-brown, olive-yellow, bright green, black, grey-black and grey	20	25
817	345	1s. deep blue, reddish lilac, drab and new blue	25	25
		a. New blue omitted	£150	
818	346	1s.6d. greenish yellow, black, turquoise-blue and lilac	30	40
		a. Turquoise-blue omitted	£21000	
815/18 *Set of 4*			75	90

Used examples of the 5d. exist, one of which is on piece, with the greenish blue colour omitted.

347 Signing the Declaration of Arbroath

348 Florence Nightingale attending Patients

349 Signing of International Co-operative Alliance

350 Pilgrims and *Mayflower*

351 Sir William Herschel, Francis Baily, Sir John Herschel and Telescope

(Des F. Wegner (5d., 9d., and 1s.6d.), Marjorie Saynor (1s., 1s.9d.). Queen's head printed in gold and then embossed)

1970 (1 Apr). Anniversaries. Events described on stamps. Chalk-surfaced paper. Two phosphor bands. P 15×14.

819	347	5d. black yellow-olive, blue, emerald, greenish yellow, rose-red, gold and orange-red	10	10
		a. Gold (Queen's head) omitted	£4250	
		b. Emerald omitted	£550	
820	348	9d. ochre, deep blue, carmine, black, blue-green, yellow-olive, gold and blue	15	15
		a. Ochre omitted	£550	
821	349	1s. green, greenish yellow, brown, black, cerise, gold and light blue	20	25
		a. Gold (Queen's head) omitted	90·00	
		c. Green omitted	£170	
		d. Brown omitted	£320	
822	350	1s.6d. greenish yellow, carmine, deep yellow-olive, emerald, black, blue gold and sage-green	20	30
		a. Gold (Queen's head) omitted	£320	
		b. Emerald omitted	£170	
823	351	1s.9d. black, slate, lemon, gold and bright purple	25	30
		a. Lemon (trousers and document) omitted	£10000	£6000
819/23 *Set of 5*			80	1·00

The 9d., 1s. and 1s.6d. are known with the embossing omitted. No. 821c also exists with embossing omitted.

No. 823a is known mint, or used on first day cover postmarked London WC.

352 "Mr. Pickwick and Sam" (*Pickwick Papers*) **353** "Mr. and Mrs. Micawber" (*David Copperfield*) **354** David Copperfield and Betsy Trotwood" (*David Copperfield*)

355 "Oliver asking for more" (*Oliver Twist*) **356** "*Grasmere*" (from engraving by J. Farrington, R.A.)

T **352/5** were issued together *se-tenant* in blocks of four throughout the sheet.

(Des Rosalind Dease. Queen's head printed in gold and then embossed)

1970 (3 June). Literary Anniversaries. Death Centenary of Charles Dickens (novelist) (5d.×4) and Birth Bicentenary of William Wordsworth (poet) (1s.6d.). Chalk-surfaced paper. Two phosphor bands. P 14×15.

824	352	5d. black, orange, silver, gold and magenta	10	25
		a. Block of 4. Nos. 824/7	75	1·50
		ab. Imperf (block of four)	£2500	
		ac. Silver (inscr) omitted	—	
825	353	5d. black, magenta, silver, gold and orange	10	25
826	354	5d. black, light greenish blue, silver, gold and yellow-bistre	10	25
		b. Yellow-bistre (value) omitted	£10000	
827	355	5d. black, yellow-bistre, silver, gold and light greenish blue	10	25
		b. Yellow-bistre (background) omitted	£25000	
		c. Light greenish blue (value) omitted*	£825	
		d. Light greenish blue and silver (inscr at foot) omitted	£35000	
828	356	1s.6d. light yellow-olive, black, silver, gold and bright blue	25	50
		a. Gold (Queen's head) omitted	£10000	
		b. Silver ("Grasmere") omitted	£250	
		c. Bright blue (face value) omitted	£22500	
		d. bright blue and silver omitted	£27500	
824/8 *Set of 5*			90	1·80

*No 827c (unlike No. 827b) comes from a sheet on which the colour was only partially omitted so that, although No. 827 was completely without the light greenish blue colour, it was still partially present on No. 826.

The 1s.6d. is known with embossing omitted.

Essays exist of Nos. 824/7 showing the Queen's head in silver and with different inscriptions.

357 (Value redrawn)

(Des after plaster cast by Arnold Machin. Recess B.W.)

1970 (17 June)–72. Decimal Currency. Chalk-surfaced paper or phosphorised paper (10p.). P 12.

829	357	10p. cerise	50	75
830		20p. olive-green	60	25
831		50p. deep ultramarine	1·50	40
831b		£1 bluish black (6.12.72)	3·50	80
829/31b *Set of 4*			5·50	2·00

The 20p. and 50p. exist on thinner, uncoated paper and are listed in the *Great Britain Concise Catalogue*.

A whiter paper was introduced in 1973. The £1 appeared on 27 Sept. 1973, the 20p. on 30 Nov. 1973 and the 50p. on 20 Feb. 1974.

The 50p. was issued on 1 Feb. 1973 on phosphorised paper. This cannot be distinguished from No. 831 with the naked eye.

The £1, T **318**, was also issued, on 17 June 1970, in sheets of 100 (10×10) instead of panes of 40 (8×5) but it is not easy to distinguish from No. 790 in singles. It can be readily differentiated when in large strips or marginal pieces showing sheet markings or plate numbers.

358 Runners **359** Swimmers

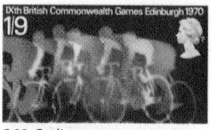

360 Cyclists

(Des A. Restall. Litho D.L.R.)

1970 (15 July). Ninth British Commonwealth Games. Chalk-surfaced paper. Two phosphor bands. P 13½×14.

832	358	5d. pk, emer, greenish yell and deep yellow-green	25	25
		a. Greenish yellow omitted	£20000	
833	359	1s.6d. light greenish blue, lilac, bistre brown and Prussian blue	50	50
834	360	1s.9d. yellow-orange, lilac, salmon and deep red-brown	50	50
832/4 *Set of 3*			1·10	1·10

361 1d. Black (1840) **362** 1s. Green (1847)

363 4d. Carmine (1855)

(Des D. Gentleman)

1970 (18 Sept). "Philympia 70" Stamp Exhibition. Chalk-surfaced paper. Two phosphor bands. P 14×14½.

835	361	5d. grey-black, brownish bistre, black and dull purple	25	10
		a. Grey-black (Queen's head) omitted	—	
836	362	9d. light drab, bluish green, stone, black and dull purple	25	30
837	363	1s.6d. carmine, light drab, black and dull purple	25	45
835/7 *Set of 3*			70	75

364 Shepherds and Apparition of the Angel **365** Mary, Joseph, and Christ in the Manger

366 The Wise Men bearing gifts

(Des Sally Stiff after De Lisle Psalter. Queen's head printed in gold and then embossed)

1970 (25 Nov). Christmas. Chalk-surfaced paper. One centre phosphor band (4d.) or two phosphor bands (others). P 14×15.

838	364	4d. brown-red, turquoise-green, pale chestnut, brn, grey-blk, gold and vermilion	15	10
839	365	5d. emerald, gold, blue, brown-red, ochre, grey-black and violet	15	15
		a. Gold (Queen's head) omitted	†	£3500
		b. Emerald omitted	£140	
		c. Imperf (pair)	£500	
		d. Ochre omitted	£8000	
840	366	1s.6d. gold, grey-black, pale turquoise-green, salmon, ultramarine, ochre and yellow-green	25	30
		a. Salmon omitted	£220	
		b. Ochre omitted	£140	
838/40 Set of 3			50	50

The 4d. and 5d. are known with embossing omitted, and the 1s.6d. is known with embossing and phosphor omitted.

REGIONAL ISSUES

For Regional issues of Guernsey and Jersey, *see* after Great Britain Postal Fiscals

Printers (£ s. d. stamps of all regions);—Photo Harrison & Sons. Portrait by Dorothy Wilding Ltd.

DATES OF ISSUE. Conflicting dates of issue have been announced for some of the regional issues, partly explained by the stamps being released on different dates by the Philatelic Bureau in Edinburgh or the Philatelic Counter in London and in the regions. We have adopted the practice of giving the earliest known dates, since once released the stamps could have been used anywhere in the U.K.

I. ISLE OF MAN

1 **2**

(Des J. Nicholson. Portrait by Dorothy Wilding Ltd. Photo Harrison)

1958 (18 Aug)–**68**. W **179**. P 15×14.

1	1	2½d. carmine-red (8.6.64)	90	1·75
2	2	3d. deep lilac	50	20
		a. Chalk-surfaced paper (17.5.63)	12·00	12·00
		p. One centre phosphor band (27.6.68)	20	50
3		4d. ultramarine (7.2.66)	1·50	2·00
		p. Two phosphor bands (5.7.67)	30	40
1/3p Set of 3			1·00	2·50

No. 2a was released in London sometime after 17 May 1963, this being the date of issue in Douglas.

1968–69. No wmk. Chalk-surfaced paper. PVA gum. One centre phosphor band (Nos. 5/6) or two phosphor bands (others). P 15×14.

4	2	4d. blue (24.6.68)	25	30
5		4d. olive-sepia (4.9.68)	25	30
6		4d. bright vermilion (26.2.69)	45	75
7		5d. royal blue (4.9.68)	45	75
4/7 Set of 4			1·25	2·00

II. NORTHERN IRELAND

N 1 **N 2** **N 3**

(Des W. Hollywood (3d., 4d., 5d.), L. Pilton (6d., 9d.), T. Collins (1s.3d., 1s.6d.))

1958–67. W **179**. P 15×14.

NI1	N 1	3d. deep lilac (18.8.58)	15	15
		p. One centre phosphor band (9.6.67)	25	25
NI2		4d. ultramarine (7.2.66)	15	15
		p. Two phosphor bands (10.67)	15	15
NI3	N 2	6d. deep claret (29.9.58)	50	50
NI4		9d. bronze-green (2 phosphor bands) (1.3.67)	30	70
NI5	N 3	1s.3d. green (29.9.58)	40	80
NI6		1s.6d. grey-blue (2 phosphor bands) (1.3.67)	40	80

1968–69. No wmk. Chalk-surfaced paper. One centre phosphor band (Nos. NI8/9) or two phosphor bands (others). P 15×14.

NI7	N 1	4d. deep bright blue (27.6.68)	25	25
NI8		4d. olive-sepia (4.9.68)	25	25
NI9		4d. bright vermilion (26.2.69)	30	30
NI10		5d. royal blue (4.9.68)	40	40
NI11	N 3	1s.6d. grey-blue (20.5.69)	2·50	2·75

No. N17 was only issued in Northern Ireland with gum arabic. After it had been withdrawn from Northern Ireland but whilst still on sale at the philatelic counters elsewhere, about 50 sheets with PVA gum were sold over the London Philatelic counter on 23 October 1968, and some were also on sale at the British Philatelic Exhibition Post Office in October, without any prior announcement. The other values exist with PVA gum only.

III. SCOTLAND

S 1 **S 2** **S 3**

(Des G. Huntly (3d., 4d., 5d.), J. Fleming (6d., 9d.), A. Imrie (1s.3d., 1s.6d.))

1958–67. W **179**. P 15×14.

S1	S 1	3d. deep lilac (18.8.58)	15	15
		p. Two phosphor bands (29.1.63)	13·00	4·00
		pa. One side phosphor band (30.4.65)	20	25
		pb. One centre phosphor band (9.11.67)	20	25
S2		4d. ultramarine (7.2.66)	20	20
		p. Two phosphor bands	20	20
S3	S 2	6d. deep claret (29.9.58)	25	25
		p. Two phosphor bands (29.1.63)	25	25
S4		9d. bronze-green (2 phosphor bands) (1.3.67)	35	40
S5	S 3	1s.3d. green (29.9.58)	40	40
		p. Two phosphor bands (29.1.63)	50	50
S6		1s.6d. grey-blue (2 phosphor bands) (1.3.67)	60	60

The one phosphor band on No. S1pa was produced by printing broad phosphor bands across alternate vertical perforations. Individual stamps show the band at right or left (same prices either way).

1967–70. No wmk. Chalk-surfaced paper. One centre phosphor band (S7, S9/10) or two phosphor bands (others). P 15×14.

S7	S 1	3d. deep lilac (16.5.68)	15	15
S8		4d. deep bright blue (28.11.67)	30	30
S9		4d. olive-sepia (4.9.68)	15	15
S10		4d. bright vermilion (26.2.69)	15	15
S11		5d. royal blue (4.9.68)	25	25
S12	S 2	9d. bronze-green (29.9.70)	6·00	6·00
S13	S 3	1s.6d. grey-blue (12.12.68)	1·75	1·50

Nos. S7/8 exist with both gum arabic and PVA gum; others with PVA gum only.

IV. WALES

From the inception of the Regional stamps, the Welsh versions were tendered to members of the public at all Post Offices within the former County of Monmouthshire but the national alternatives were available on request. By August 1961 the policy of "dual stocking" of definitive stamps was only maintained at Abergavenny, Chepstow, Newport and Pontypool. Offices with a Monmouthshire postal address but situated outside the County, namely Beachley, Brockweir, Redbrook. Sedbury, Tutshill, Welsh Newton and Woodcroft, were not supplied with the Welsh Regional stamps.

W 1 **W 2** **W 3**

(Des R. Stone)

1958–67. W **179**. P 15×14.

W1	W 1	3d. deep lilac (18.8.58)	15	15
		p. One centre phosphor band (16.5.67)	20	15
W2		4d. ultramarine (7.2.66)	20	25
		p. Two phosphor bands (10.67)	20	25
W3	W 2	6d. deep claret (29.9.58)	35	40
W4		9d. bronze-green (2 phosphor bands) (1.3.67)	40	50
W5	W 3	1s.3d. green (29.9.58)	40	55
W6		1s.6d. grey-blue (2 phosphor bands) (1.3.67)	45	55

1967–69. No wmk. Chalk-surfaced paper. One centre phosphor band (W 7, W 9/10) or two phosphor bands (others). P 15×14.

W7	W 1	3d. deep lilac (6.12.67)	15	20
W8		4d. ultramarine (21.6.68)	15	20
W9		4d. olive-sepia (4.9.68)	15	20
W10		4d. bright vermilion (26.2.69)	15	20
W11		5d. royal blue (4.9.68)	15	30
W12	W 3	1s.6d. grey-blue (1.8.69)	3·50	3·50

The 3d. exists with gum arabic only; the remainder with PVA gum only.

STAMP BOOKLETS

For a full listing of Great Britain stamp booklets see the *Great Britain Concise Catalogue* published each Spring.

POSTAGE DUE STAMPS

PERFORATIONS. All postage due stamps to No. D89 are perf 14×15.

WATERMARKS. The normal sideways watermark shows the tops of the crowns pointing to the right, *as seen from the back of the stamp.*

D 1 **D 2**

(Des G. Eve. Typo Somerset House (early trial printings of ½d., 1d., 2d. and 5d.; all printings of 1s.) or Harrison (later printings of all values except 1s.)).

1914 (20 Apr)–**22**. W **100** (Simple Cypher) sideways.

D1	D 1	½d. emerald	50	25
		Wi. Wmk sideways-inverted	1·00	1·00
		Wj. Wmk sideways-reversed	18·00	20·00
		Wk. Wmk sideways-inverted and reversed	—	20·00
D2		1d. carmine	50	25
		a. Pale carmine	75	50
		Wi. Wmk sideways-inverted	1·00	1·00
		Wj. Wmk sideways-reversed	—	20·00
		Wk. Wmk sideways-inverted and reversed	18·00	20·00
D3		1½d. chestnut (1922)	48·00	20·00
		Wi. Wmk sideways-inverted	70·00	20·00
D4		2d. agate	50	25
		Wi. Wmk sideways-inverted	2·00	2·00
		Wk. Wmk sideways-inverted and reversed	15·00	18·00
D5		3d. violet (1918)	5·00	75
		a. Bluish violet	6·00	2·75
		Wi. Wmk sideways-inverted	15·00	10·00
		Wk. Wmk sideways-inverted and reversed	—	—
D6		4d. dull grey-green (12.20)	£150	50·00
		Wi. Wmk sideways-inverted	40·00	5·00
D7		5d. brownish cinnamon	7·00	3·50
		Wi. Wmk sideways-inverted	16·00	16·00
D8		1s. bright blue (1915)	40·00	5·00
		a. Deep bright blue	40·00	5·00
		Wi. Wmk sideways-inverted	40·00	40·00
		Wk. Wmk sideways-inverted and reversed	—	—
D1/8 Set of 8			£130	32·00

The 1d. is known bisected from various offices between 1914 and 1924, the 2d. bisected for use as a 1d. between 1918 and 1923, the 3d. bisected for use as a 1½d. in 1922 at Warminster and trisected for use as a 1d. in 1921 at Malvern.

(Typo Waterlow)

1924. As 1914–22, but on thick chalk-surfaced paper.

D9	D 1	1d. carmine	6·00	6·00
		Wi. Wmk sideways-inverted		

(Typo Waterlow and (from 1934) Harrison)

1924–31. W **111** (Block Cypher) sideways.

D10	D 1	½d. emerald (6.25)	1·25	75
		Wi. Wmk sideways-inverted	3·00	1·50
D11		1d. carmine (4.25)	60	25
		Wi. Wmk sideways-inverted	—	30·00
D12		1½d. chestnut (10.24)	47·00	22·00
		Wi. Wmk sideways-inverted	—	75·00
D13		2d. agate (7.24)	1·00	25
		Wi. Wmk sideways-inverted	—	30·00
D14		3d. dull violet (10.24)	1·50	25
		a. Printed on gummed side	£125	†
		Wi. Wmk sideways-inverted	20·00	40·00
		b. Experimental paper W **111a**	95·00	95·00
D15		4d. dull grey-green (10.24)	15·00	4·25
		Wi. Wmk sideways-inverted	40·00	40·00
D16		5d. brownish cinnamon (1.31)	65·00	45·00
D17		1s. deep blue (9.24)	8·50	50
		Wi. Wmk sideways-inverted	55·00	—
D18	D 2	2s.6d. purple/yellow (5.24)	85·00	1·75
		Wi. Wmk sideways-inverted	—	40·00
D10/18 Set of 8			£200	70·00

The 1d. is known bisected from various offices between 1925 and 1932 and the 2d. exists bisected to make up the 2½d. rate at Perranwell Station, Cornwall, in 1932.

1936–37. W **125** (E 8 R) sideways.

D19	D 1	½d. emerald (6.37)	15·00	10·50
D20		1d. carmine (5.37)	2·00	1·75
D21		2d. agate (5.37)	15·00	12·00
D22		3d. dull violet (3.37)	2·00	2·00
D23		4d. dull grey-green (12.36)	65·00	34·00
D24		5d. brownish cinnamon (11.36)	90·00	30·00
		a. Yellow-brown (1937)	40·00	28·00
D25		1s. deep blue (12.36)	25·00	8·50
D26	D 2	2s.6d. purple/yellow (5.37)	£350	12·00
D19/26 Set of 8 (cheapest)			£450	90·00

The 1d. is known bisected at Solihull in 1937.

1937–38. W **127** (G VI R) sideways.

D27	D 1	½d. emerald (5.38)	13·00	3·75
D28		1d. carmine (5.38)	3·00	50
		Wi. Wmk sideways-inverted	£150	
D29		2d. agate (5.38)	2·75	30
		Wi. Wmk sideways-inverted	£150	
D30		3d. violet (12.37)	10·50	30
		Wi. Wmk sideways-inverted	£150	
D31		4d. dull grey-green (9.37)	£110	10·00
		Wi. Wmk sideways-inverted	£300	
D32		5d. yellow-brown (11.38)	16·50	75
		Wi. Wmk sideways-inverted	£150	
D33		1s. deep blue (10.37)	78·00	75
		Wi. Wmk sideways-inverted	£150	
D34	D 2	2s.6d. purple/yellow (9.38)	85·00	1·25
D27/34 Set of 8			£290	16·00

The 2d. is known bisected at various offices between 1951 and 1954.

DATES OF ISSUE. The dates for Nos. D35/9 are those on which stamps were first issued by the Supplies Department to postmasters.

1951–52. Colours changed and new value (1½d.). W **127** (G VI R) sideways.

D35	D **1**	½d. yellow-orange (18.9.51)........	3·50	3·50
		a. Bright orange..........	40·00	
D36		1d. violet-blue (6.6.51)...........	1·50	75
		Wi. Wmk-inverted..........	—	—
D37		1½d. green (11.2.52)........	2·00	2·00
		Wi. Wmk-inverted..........	£120	£120
D38		4d. blue (14.8.51)..........	50·00	22·00
		Wi. Wmk-inverted...........	†	£1000
D39		1s. ochre (6.12.51)........	28·00	5·25
		Wi. Wmk-inverted..........	£2800	
D35/9 *Set of 5*			75·00	30·00

The 1d. is known bisected at Capel, Dorking in 1952 and at Camberley in 1954.

1954–55. W **153** (Mult Tudor Crown and E 2 R) sideways.

D40	D **1**	½d. orange (8.6.55)........	7·00	5·25
		Wi. Wmk-inverted..........	£125	—
D41		2d. agate (28.7.55)........	26·00	23·00
		Wi. Wmk-inverted..........	—	—
D42		3d. violet (4.5.55)........	75·00	60·00
D43		4d. blue (14.7.55)........	26·00	32·00
		a. Imperf (pair)..........	£250	
D44		5d. yellow-brown (19.5.55)....	20·00	20·00
D45	D **2**	2s.6d. purple/*yellow* (11.54)........	£150	5·75
		Wi. Wmk sideways-inverted....	—	—
D40/5 *Set of 6*			£250	£130

1955–57. W **165** (Mult St. Edward's Crown and E 2 R) sideways.

D46	D **1**	½d. orange (16.7.56)........	2·75	3·25
		Wi. Wmk sideways-inverted....	85·00	—
D47		1d. violet-blue (7.6.56)........	5·00	1·50
D48		1½d. green (13.2.56)........	8·50	7·00
		Wi. Wmk sideways-inverted....	85·00	—
D49		2d. agate (22.5.56)........	45·00	3·50
D50		3d. violet (5.3.56)........	6·00	1·50
		Wi. Wmk sideways-inverted....	£100	—
D51		4d. blue (24.4.56)........	25·00	6·00
		Wi. Wmk sideways-inverted....	£175	—
D52		5d. brown-ochre (23.3.56)........	26·00	20·00
D53		1s. ochre (22.11.55)........	65·00	2·25
		Wi. Wmk sideways-inverted....	—	—
D54	D **2**	2s.6d. purple/*yellow* (28.6.57)........	£200	8·25
		Wi. Wmk sideways-inverted....	—	—
D55		5s. scarlet/*yellow* (25.1.55)........	£150	32·00
		Wi. Wmk sideways-inverted....	—	—
D46/55 *Set of 10*			£475	75·00

The 1d. is known bisected in September 1956 and June 1957, the 2d. in June and July 1956, the 3d. in May 1957 (London S.E.D.O.) and the 4d. in December 1958 (Poplar).

1959–63. W **179** (Mult St. Edward's Crown) sideways.

D56	D **1**	½d. orange (18.10.61)........	15	1·25
		Wi. Wmk sideways-inverted....	2·00	—
D57		1d. violet-blue (9.5.60)........	15	50
		Wi. Wmk sideways-inverted....	£125	—
D58		1½d. green (5.10.60)........	2·50	2·50
D59		2d. agate (14.9.59)........	1·10	50
		Wi. Wmk sideways-inverted....	£200	—
D60		3d. violet (24.3.59)........	30	30
		Wi. Wmk sideways-inverted....	85·00	—
D61		4d. blue (17.12.59)........	30	30
		Wi. Wmk sideways-inverted....	£300	—
D62		5d. yellow-brown (6.11.61)........	45	60
		Wi. Wmk sideways-inverted....	5·00	6·00
D63		6d. purple (29.3.62)........	50	30
		Wi. Wmk sideways-inverted....	£300	—
D64		1s. ochre (11 .4.60)........	90	30
		Wi. Wmk sideways-inverted....	60·00	—
D65	D **2**	2s.6d. purple/*yellow* (11.5.61)........	3·00	50
		Wi. Wmk sideways-inverted....	15·00	2·00
D66		5s. scarlet/*yellow* (8.5.61)........	8·25	1·00
		Wi. Wmk sideways-inverted....	25·00	3·00
D67		10s. blue/*yellow* (2.9.63)........	11·50	5·75
		Wi. Wmk sideways-inverted....	40·00	20·00
D68		£1 black/*yellow* (2.9.63)........	45·00	8·25
D56/68 *Set of 13*			65·00	20·00

Whiter paper. The note after No. 586 also applies to Postage Due stamps.

The 1d. is known bisected at various offices between November 1961 and July 1964. The 2d. is known bisected at Doncaster.

1968–69. Typo. No wmk. Chalk-surfaced paper.

D69	D **1**	2d. agate (11.4.68)........	75	1·00
D70		3d. violet (9.9.68)........	1·00	1·00
D71		4d. blue (6.5.68)........	1·00	1·00
D72		5d. orange-brown (3.1.69)........	8·00	11·00
D73		6d. purple (9.9.68)........	2·25	1·75
D74		1s. ochre (19.11.68)........	4·00	2·50
D69/74 *Set of 6*			15·00	16·00

The 2d. and 4d. exist with gum arabic and PVA gum; remainder with PVA gum only.

The 6d. is known bisected, in October 1968 (Kilburn, London NW).

1968–69. Photo. No wmk. Chalk-surfaced paper. PVA gum.

D75	D **1**	4d. blue (12.6.69)........	7·00	6·75
D76		8d. red (3.10.68)........	50	1·00

Nos. D75/6 are smaller, 21½×17½ mm.
The 4d. is known bisected in April 1970 (Northampton).

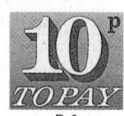

D **3**   D **4**

(Des J. Matthews. Photo Harrison)

1970 (17 June)–**75.** Decimal Currency. Chalk-surfaced paper.

D77	D **3**	½p. turquoise-blue (15.2.71)........	15	2·50
D78		1p. deep reddish purple (15.2.71)...	15	15
D79		2p. myrtle-green (15.2.71)........	20	15
D80		3p. ultramarine (15.2.71)........	20	15
D81		4p. yellow-brown (15.2.71)........	25	15
D82		5p. violet (15.2.71)........	25	15
D83		7p. red-brown (21.8.74)........	35	1·00
D84	D **4**	10p. carmine........	30	30
D85		11p. slate-green (18.6.75)........	50	1·00
D86		20p. olive-brown........	60	25
D87		50p. ultramarine........	2·00	1·25
D88		£1 black........	4·00	1·00
D89		£5 orange-yellow and black (2.4.73)........	36·00	1·50
D77/89 *Set of 13*			40·00	7·75

The 2p. was bisected at Exeter on 25 October 1977.

OFFICIAL STAMPS

In 1840 the 1d. black (Type **1**), with "V R" in the upper corners, was prepared for official use, but never issued for postal purposes. Obliterated specimens are those which were used for experimental trials of obliterating inks, or those that passed through the post by oversight.

V 1

1840. Prepared for use but not issued; "V" "R" in upper corners. Imperf.

			Un	Used	Used on cover
V1	V **1**	1d. black............	£32000	£35000	

The following Official stamps would be more correctly termed Departmental stamps as they were exclusively for the use of certain government departments. Until 1882 official mail used ordinary postage stamps purchased at post offices, the cash being refunded once a quarter. Later the government departments obtained Official stamps by requisition. Official stamps may have been on sale to the public for a short time at Somerset House but they were not sold from post offices. The system of only supplying the Government departments was open to abuse so that all Official stamps were withdrawn on 13 May 1904.

OVERPRINTS, PERFORATIONS, WATERMARKS. All Official stamps were overprinted by Thomas De La Rue & Co. and are perf 14. They are on Crown watermarked paper unless otherwise stated.

INLAND REVENUE

These stamps were used by revenue officials in the provinces, mail to and from Head Office passing without a stamp. The London Office used these stamps only for foreign mail.

I.R. (O **1**)   **I. R.** (O **2**)

OFFICIAL

Optd with Types O **1** (½d. to 1s.) or O **2** (others)

1882–1901. Stamps of Queen Victoria.

(a) Issues of 1880–81

O 1		½d. deep green (1.11.82)........	£135	60·00	£120
O 2		½d. pale green........	90·00	40·00	
O 3		1d. lilac (Die II) (1.10.82)........	8·00	6·00	30·00
		a. Optd in blue-black........	£300	£125	
		b. "OFFICIAL" omitted........	—	£12500	
		c. Imperf........	£4500		
		ca. Imperf, optd in blue-black....	£4500	—	
		Wi. Wmk inverted........	—	£2200	
O 4		6d. grey (Plate 18) (3.11.82)........	£575	£140	

No. O3 with the lines of the overprint transposed is an essay.

(b) Issues of 1884–1888

O 5		½d. slate-blue (8.5.85)........	85·00	35·00	£135
O 6		2½d. lilac (12.3.85)........	£525	£180	£1400
O 7		1s. dull green (12.3.85)........	£6000	£1900	
O 8		5s. rose (*blued paper*) (wmk Anchor) (12.3.85)........	£17500	£6500	
		a. Raised stop after "R"........	£18500	£7250	
O 9		5s. rose (wmk Anchor) (3.90)........	£12000	£2500	
		a. Raised stop after "R"........	£14000	£3200	
		b. Optd in blue-black........	£14000	£3200	
O 9c		10s. cobalt (*blued paper*) (wmk Anchor) (12.3.85)........	£38000	£9500	
		ca. Raised stop after "R"........			
		cb. White paper........	£22000	£7750	
O 9d		10s. ultramarine (*blued paper*) (wmk Anchor) (12.3.85)........	£25000	£7500	
		da. Raised stop after "R"........	£27000	£8500	
O 10		10s. ultramarine (wmk Anchor) (3.90)........	£11500	£3750	
		a. Raised stop after "R"........	£12500	£4500	
		b. Optd in blue-black........	£12500	£4500	
O 11		£1 brown-lilac (wmk Crowns) (12.3.85)........	£75000	£30000	
		a. Frame broken........	£100000		
O 12		£1 brown-lilac (wmk Orbs) (3.90)........	£100000	£40000	
		a. Frame broken........	£150000		
		b. Optd in blue-black........	£160000		

(c) issues of 1887–92

O13		½d. vermilion (15.5.88)........	15·00	7·00	£110
		a. Without "I.R."........	£7000		
		b. Imperf........	£7000		
		c. Opt double (imperf)........	£8000		
O14		2½d. purple/*blue* (2.92)........	£175	30·00	£450
O15		1s. dull green (9.89)........	£1000	£375	£3750
		a. Optd in blue-black........	£2250		
O16		£1 green (6.92)........	£12500	£2500	
		a. No stop after "R"........	—	£4000	

b. Frame broken........ £20000 £5250

Nos. O3, O13, O15 and O16 may be found showing worn impressions of the overprints with thicker letters.

(d) Issues of 1887 and 1900

O17		½d. blue-green (4.01)........	20·00	15·00	£350
O18		6d. purple/*rose-red* (1.7.01)........	£500	£150	
O19		1s. green and carmine (12.01)........	£4250	£1800	

O1/19 For well-centred, lightly used +35%.

1902–04. Stamps of King Edward VII. Ordinary paper.

O20		½d. blue-green (4.2.02)........	32·00	4·50	£150
O21		1d. scarlet (4.2.02)........	22·00	3·00	95·00
O22		2½d. ultramarine (19.2.02)........	£1000	£280	
O23		6d. pale dull purple (14.3.04)......	£475000	£300000	
O24		1s. dull green and carmine (29.4.02)........	£3750	£900	
O25		5s. bright carmine (29.4.02)........	£45000	£11000	
		a. Raised stop after "R"........	£50000	£13000	
O26		10s. ultramarine (29.4.02)........	£100000	£48000	
		a. Raised stop after "R"........	£125000	£48000	
O27		£1 dull blue-green (29.4.02)....	£62500	£25000	

OFFICE OF WORKS

These were issued to Head and Branch (local) offices in London and to Branch (local) offices at Birmingham, Bristol, Edinburgh, Glasgow, Leeds, Liverpool, Manchester and Southampton. The overprints on stamps of value 2d. and upwards were created later in 1902, the 2d. for registration fees and the rest for overseas mail.

O.W.

OFFICIAL

(O **3**)

Optd with Type O **3**

1896 (24 Mar)–**02.** Stamps of Queen Victoria.

O31		½d. vermilion........	£350	£150	£800
O32		½d. blue-green (2.02)........	£475	£225	
O33		1d. lilac (Die II)........	£500	£150	£1000
O34		5d. dull purple and blue (II) (29.4.02)........	£4000	£1400	
O35		10d. dull purple and carmine (28.5.02)........	£7250	£2250	

1902 (11 Feb)–**03.** Stamps of King Edward VII. Ordinary paper.

O36		½d. blue-green (2.02)........	£575	£180	£2000
O37		1d. scarlet........	£575	£180	£425
O38		2d. yellowish green and carmine-red (27.4.02)........	£2000	£450	£3250
O39		2½d. ultramarine (29.4.02)........	£3400	£675	£4250
O40		10d. dull purple & carmine (28.5.03)........	£47500	£7000	

O31/40 For well-centred, lightly used +25%.

ARMY

Letters to and from the War Office in London passed without postage. The overprinted stamps were distributed to District and Station Paymasters nationwide, including Cox and Co., the Army Agents, who were paymasters to the Household Division.

ARMY (O **4**)   **ARMY** (O **5**)   **ARMY** (O **6**)

OFFICIAL

1896 (1 Sept)–**01.** Stamps of Queen Victoria optd with Type O **4** (½d., 1d.) or O **5** (2½d., 6d.).

O41		½d. vermilion........	8·00	3·00	65·00
		a. "OFFICIAI" (R. 13/7)........	£300	£130	
		b. Lines of opt transposed......	£4500		
		Wi. Wmk inverted........	£800	£375	
O42		½d. blue-green (6.00)........	10·00	15·00	
		Wi. Wmk inverted........	£1000	£650	
O43		1d. lilac (Die II)........	8·00	7·00	£110
		a. "OFFICIAI" (R. 13/7)........	£240	£150	
O44		2½d. purple/*blue*........	50·00	35·00	£775
O45		6d. purple/*rose-red* (20.9.01)......	£110	60·00	£1700

Nos. O41a and O43a occur on sheets overprinted by Forme 1.

1902–03. Stamps of King Edward VII optd with Type O **4** (Nos. O48/50) or Type O **6** (No. O52). Ordinary paper.

O48		½d. blue-green (11.2.02)........	5·50	2·25	£100
O49		1d. scarlet (11.2.02)........	5·50	2·25	£100
		a. "ARMY" omitted........	†	—	
O50		6d. pale dull purple (23.8.02)......	£175	80·00	
O52		6d. pale dull purple (12.03)........	£3000	£1600	

GOVERNMENT PARCELS

These stamps were issued to all departments, including the Head Office, for use on parcels weighing over 3 lb. Below this weight government parcels were sent by letter post to avoid the 55% of the postage paid from accruing to the railway companies, as laid down by parcel-post regulations. Most government parcels stamps suffered heavy postmarks in use.

GOVT

PARCELS

(O **7**)

Optd as Type O **7**

1883 (1 Aug)–**86.** Stamps of Queen Victoria.

			Un	Used*
O61		1½d. lilac (1.5.86)........	£400	£100

	a. No dot under "T"	£775	£175
	b. Dot to left of "T"	£775	£175
O62	6d. dull green (1.5.86)	£3500	£1400
O63	9d. dull green	£2750	£1200
O64	1s. orange-brown (wmk Crown, Pl 13)	£1750	£300
	a. No dot under "T"	£2750	£500
	b. Dot to left of "T"	£2750	£500
O64c	1s. orange-brown (Pl 14)	£3500	£600
	ca. No dot under "T"	£4500	£850
	cb. Dot to left of "T"		

1887–90. Stamps of Queen Victoria.

O65	1½d. dull purple and pale green (29.10.87)	£160	28·00
	a. No dot under "T"	£260	75·00
	b. Dot to right of "T"	£260	75·00
	c. Dot to left of "T"	£260	75·00
O66	6d. purple/rose-red (19.12.87)	£275	75·00
	a. No dot under "T"	£375	£120
	b. Dot to right of "T"	£375	£120
	c. Dot to left of "T"	£375	£120
O67	9d. dull purple and blue (21.8.88)	£425	£120
	a. Optd in blue-black		
	Wi. Wmk inverted		
O68	1s. dull green (25.3.90)	£700	£275
	b. Dot to right of "T"	£1000	£500
	c. Dot to left of "T"	£1000	£500
	d. Optd in blue-black	£1000	£500

1891–1900. Stamps of Queen Victoria.

O69	1d. lilac (Die II) (18.6.97)	£100	30·00
	a. No dot under "T"	£160	75·00
	b. Dot to left of "T"	£160	75·00
	c. Opt inverted	£7500	£3500
	d. Ditto. Dot to left of "T"	£8500	£4500
	Wi. Wmk inverted	—	£500
O70	2d. grey-green and carmine (24.10.91)	£250	50·00
	a. No dot under "T"	£400	£125
	b. Dot to left of "T"	£400	£125
O71	4½d. green and carmine (29.9.92)	£400	£275
	b. Dot to right of "T"	—	£9000
	Wi. Wmk inverted		
O72	1s. green and carmine (11.00)	£650	£275
	a. Opt inverted †	†	£17500

*O61/72 **For well-centred, lightly used +100%.**
The "no dot under T" variety occurred on R. 12/3 and 20/2. The "dot to left of T" comes four times in the sheet on R. 2/7, 6/7, 7/9 and 12/9. The best example of the "dot to right of T" is on R. 20/1. All three varieties were corrected around 1897.

1902. Stamps of King Edward VII. Ordinary paper.

O74	1d. scarlet (30.10.02)	75·00	22·00
O75	2d. yellowish green and carmine-red (29.4.02)	£225	60·00
O76	6d. pale dull purple (19.2.02)	£275	60·00
	a. Opt double, one albino	£35000	
O77	9d. dull purple and ultramarine (28.8.02)	£650	£175
O78	1s. dull green and carmine (17.12.02)	£1350	£300

BOARD OF EDUCATION

BOARD

OF

EDUCATION

(O **8**)

Optd with Type O **8**

1902 (19 Feb). Stamps of Queen Victoria.

		Un	Used*	Used on cover
O81	5d. dull purple and blue (II)	£5750	£1500	
O82	1s. green and carmine	£12000	£6000	

1902 (19 Feb)–04. Stamps of King Edward VII. Ordinary paper.

O83	½d. blue-green	£180	40·00	£550
O84	1d. scarlet	£180	40·00	£550
O85	2½d. ultramarine	£4850	£450	
O86	5d. dull purple and ultram (6.2.04)	£35000	£10000	
O87	1s. dull green and carmine (23.12.02)	£200000		

ROYAL HOUSEHOLD

R.H.

OFFICIAL

(O **9**)

1902. Stamps of King Edward VII optd with Type O **9**. Ordinary paper.

O91	½d. blue-green (29.4.02)	£375	£200	£1100
O92	1d. scarlet (19.2.02)	£325	£175	£1000

ADMIRALTY

ADMIRALTY   **ADMIRALTY**

OFFICIAL   **OFFICIAL**

(O **10**)   (O **11**) (with different "M")

1903 (1 Apr). Stamps of King Edward VII optd with Type O **10**. Ordinary paper.

O101	½d. blue-green	30·00	15·00

O102	1d. scarlet	20·00	8·00	£300
O103	1½d. dull purple and green	£325	£150	
O104	2d. yellowish green and carmine-red	£350	£160	
O105	2½d. ultramarine	£475	£150	
O106	3d. purple/yellow	£425	£160	

1903–04. Stamps of King Edward VII optd with Type O **11**. Ordinary paper.

O107	½d. blue-green (9.03)	60·00	25·00	£500
O108	1d. scarlet (12.03)	60·00	25·00	£160
O109	1½d. dull purple and green (2.04)	£1200	£650	
O110	2d. yellowish green and carmine red (3.04)	£2700	£900	
O111	2½d. ultramarine (3.04)	£2900	£950	
O112	3d. dull purple/orange-yellow (12.03)	£2600	£400	

Stamps of various issues perforated with a Crown and initials ("H.M.O.W.", "O.W.", "B.T." or "S.O.") or with initials only ("H.M.S.O." or "D.S.I.R.") have also been used for official purposes, but these are outside the scope of the catalogue.

POSTAL FISCAL STAMPS

PRICES. Prices in the used column are for stamps with genuine postal cancellations dated from the time when they were authorised for use as postage stamps. Beware of stamps with fiscal cancellations removed and fraudulent postmarks applied.

VALIDITY. The 1d. Surface-printed stamps were authorised for postal use from 1 June 1881 and at the same time the 1d. postage issue, No. 166, was declared valid for fiscal purposes. The 3d. and 6d. values, together with the Embossed issues were declared valid for postal purposes by another Act effective from 1 January 1883

SURFACE-PRINTED ISSUES
(Typo Thomas De La Rue & Co)

F **1** Rectangular Buckle

F **2**

F **3** Octagonal Buckle

F **4**

F **5** Double-lined Anchor   F **6** Single-lined Anchor

1853–57. P 15½×15.

*(a) Wmk F **5** (inverted) (1853–55)*

			Un	Used	Used on cover
F1	F **1**	1d. light blue (10.10.53)	50·00	65·00	£225
		Wi. Wmk upright	£180	—	
		Wj. Emk reversed*	£180	—	
F2	F **2**	1d. ochre (10.53)	£130	£160	£600
		a. Tête-bêche (in block of four)	£22000		
		Wi. Wmk upright	—	—	
F3	F **3**	1d. pale turquoise-blue (12.53)	38·00	60·00	£350
F4		1d. light blue/blue (12.53)	90·00	95·00	£550
		Wi. Wmk upright	£160	£225	
F5	F **4**	1d. reddish lilac/blue glazed paper (25.3.55)	£130	£160	£450
		Wi. Wmk upright	£200	£300	

*Watermark reversed: with the stamp upright and *viewed from the front*, the cable finishes to the right of the base of the anchor shaft. Only one example is known of No. F2a outside the National Postal Museum and the Royal Collection.

*(b) Wmk F **6** (1856–57)*

F6	F **4**	1d. reddish lilac (shades)	12·00	9·50	£180
		Wi. Wmk inversed	£160	—	
		Wj. Wmk reversed	£180	—	
F7		1d. reddish lilac/bluish (shades) (1857)	12·00	9·50	£180
		Wj. Wmk reversed	£180	—	

INLAND **REVENUE**

(F **7**)

1860 (3 Apr). No. F7 optd with Type F **7**, in red

F8	F **4**	1d. dull reddish lilac/blue.	£900	£725	£1500
		Wj. Wmk reversed	—	—	

BLUE PAPER. In the following issues we no longer distinguish between bluish and white paper. There is a range of papers from white or greyish to bluish.

F **8**   F **9**

F **10**

1860–67. Bluish to white Paper. P 15½×15.

*(a) Wmk F **6** (1860)*

F9	F **8**	1d. reddish lilac (5.60)	14·00	18·00	£180
		Wi. Wmk inverted	£130	—	
F10	F **9**	3d. reddish lilac (6.60)	£550	£340	£550
F11	F **10**	6d. reddish lilac (10.60)	£220	£220	£450
		Wi. Wmk inverted	£275	£220	
		Wj. Wmk reversed	£275	£220	

*(b) W **40** (Anchor 16 mm high) (1864)*

F12	F **8**	1d. pale reddish lilac (Nov)	12·00	14·00	£180
		Wi. Wmk inverted	—	—	
F13	F **9**	3d. pale reddish lilac	£275	£210	£550
F14	F **10**	6d. pale reddish lilac	£240	£210	£550
		Wi. Wmk inverted	£360	—	

*(c) W **40** (Anchor 18 mm high) (1867)*

F15	F **8**	1d. reddish lilac	25·00	27·00	£275
F16	F **9**	3d. reddish lilac	£120	£120	£450
F17	F **10**	6d. reddish lilac	£110	95·00	£300

For stamps perf 14, see Nos. F24/7.

F **11**   F **12**

Four Dies of Type F 12

Nos. F19/21 show "O" of "ONE" circular. No. F22 (Die 4) shows a horizontal oval

Four Dies of Type F 12

Round "O" (Dies 1 to 3)

Oval "O" (Die 4)

Small corner ornaments (Dies 1 and 2)

Medium corner ornaments (Die 3)

Large corner ornaments (Die 4)

Four lines of shading In left-hand ribbon (Die 1)

Two lines of shading in left-hand ribbon (Die 2)

Three lines of shading In left-hand ribbon (Die 3)

Heavy shading in both ribbons (Die 4)

Band of crown shaded (Dies 1 and 2)

Band of crown unshaded (Die 3)

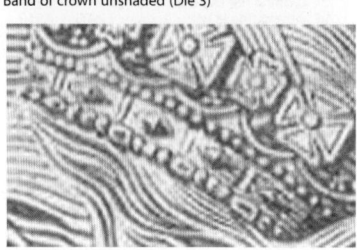
Band of crown unshaded at front only (Die 4)

Die 1: Round "O" in "ONE"
Small corner ornaments
Four lines of shading in left-hand ribbon
Band of crown shaded

Die 2: Round "O" in "ONE"
Small corner ornaments
Two lines of shading in left-hand ribbon
Band of crown shaded

Die 3: Round "O" in "ONE"
Medium corner ornaments
Three lines of shading in left-hand ribbon
Band of crown unshaded

Die 3: Oval "O" in "ONE"
Large corner ornaments
Heavy shading in both ribbons
Band of crown unshaded at front only

1867–81. White to bluish paper. P 14.

(a) W 47 (Small Anchor)

F18	F **11**	1d. purple (1.9.67)	22·00	24·00	£140
		Wi. Wmk inverted	£130	—	
F19	F **12**	1d. purple (Die 1) (6.68)	7·50	9·00	£140
		Wi. Wmk inverted	90·00	—	
F20		1d. purple (Die 2) (6.76)	27·00	22·00	£300
F21		1d. purple (Die 3) (3.77)	14·00	18·00	£220
F22		1d. purple (Die 4) (7.78)	8·50	10·00	£120

(b) W 48 (Orb)

F23	F **12**	1d. purple (Die 4) (1.81)	8·50	5·00	£110
		Wi. Wmk inverted	£130	—	

1881. White to bluish paper. P 14.

(a) W 40 (Anchor 18 mm high) (Jan)

F24	F **9**	3d. reddish lilac	£850	£525	£1000
F25	F **10**	6d. reddish lilac	£400	£225	£450

(b) W 40 (Anchor 20 mm high) (May)

F26	F **9**	3d. reddish lilac	£625	£425	£700
F27	F **10**	6d. reddish lilac	£360	£210	£450

ISSUES EMBOSSED IN COLOUR

(Made at Somerset House)

The embossed stamps were struck from dies not appropriated to any special purpose on paper which had the words "INLAND REVENUE" previously printed, and thus became available for payment of any duties for which no special stamps had been provided.

The die letters are included in the embossed designs and holes were drilled for the insertion of plugs showing figures indicating dates of striking.

F **13**

F **14**

(F **15**)

INLAND
REVENUE

(F **16**)

1860 (3 Apr)–**71**. Types F **13/14** and similar types embossed on bluish paper. No wmk. Imperf.

		Un	*Used*
F28	2d. pink (Die A) (1.1.71)	£775	
F29	3d. pink (Die C)	£210	
	a. Tête-bêche (vert pair)	£1700	
F30	3d. pink (Die D)	£775	

F31	6d. pink (Die T)		
F32	6d. pink (Die U)	£400	
	a. Tête-bêche (vert pair)		
F33	9d. pink (Die C) (1.1.71)	£1000	
F34	1s. pink (Die E) (28.6.61)	£775	
	a. Tête-bêche (vert pair)		
F35	1s. pink (Die F) (28.6.61)	£300	
	a. Tête-bêche (vert pair)	£1200	
F36	2s. pink (Die K) (6.8.61)	£775	
F37	2s.6d. pink (Die N) (28.6.61)		
F38	2s.6d. pink (Die O) (28.6.61)	£400	

1871 (Aug). As last but perf 12½.

F39	2d. pink (Die A)	£500	
	a. Tête-bêche (vert pair)		
F42	9d. pink (Die C)	£1200	
F43	1s. pink (Die E)	£775	
F44	1s. pink (Die F)	£700	
F45	2s.6d. pink (Die O)	£400	

1874 (Nov). Type F **15** embossed on white paper. Underprint Type F **16**, in green. W **47** (Small Anchor). P 12½.

F48	1s. pink (Die F)	£775	

It is possible that the 2d., 9d. and 2s.6d. may not exist with the thin underprint, Type F **16**, in this shade

1875 (Nov)–**80**. Types F **13/15** and similar but colour changed and underprint as **15**. On white or bluish paper.

F50	2d. vermilion (Die A) (1880)	£600	
F51	9d. vermilion (Die C) (1876)	£775	
F52	1s. vermilion (Die E)	£500	
F53	1s. vermilion (Die F)	£1200	
F54	2s.6d. vermilion (Die O) (1878)	£500	

1882 (Oct). As last but W **48** (Orbs).

F55	2d. vermilion (Die A)	†	
F56	9d. vermilion (Die C)	†	
F57	1s. vermilion (Die E)	†	
F58	2s.6d. vermilion (Die O)	£1000	£775

Although specimen overprints of Nos. F55/7 are known there is some doubt if these values were issued.

The sale of Inland Revenue stamps up to the 2s. value ceased from 30 December 1882 and stocks were called in and destroyed. The 2s.6d. value remained on sale until 2 July 1883 when it was replaced by the 2s.6d. "Postage & Revenue" stamp. Inland Revenue stamps still in the hands of the public continued to be accepted for revenue and postal purposes.

TELEGRAPH STAMPS. A priced listing of the Post Office telegraph stamps appears in Volume 1 of the Stanley Gibbons *Great Britain Specialised Catalogue* and in the *Great Britian Concise Catalogue*. The last listing for the private telegraph companies in the Part 1 Catalogue was in the 1940 edition. For military telegraph stamps, see under Bechuanaland, Egypt and British Field Offices in South Africa.

CHANNEL ISLANDS

GENERAL ISSUE

C **1** Gathering Vraic

C **2** Islanders gathering Vraic

Broken Wheel (R. 20/5)

(Des J. R. R. Stobie (1d.) or from drawing by E. Blampied (2½d.). Photo Harrison)

1948 (10 May). Third Anniv of Liberation. W **127** of Great Britain. P 15×14.

C1	C **1**	1d. scarlet	25	55
C2	C **2**	2½d. ultramarine	25	60
		a. Broken Wheel	75·00	

Supplies of these stamps were also available from eight head post offices on the mainland of Great Britain.

GUERNSEY

WAR OCCUPATION ISSUES

Stamps issued under the authority of the Guernsey States during the German Occupation

BISECTS. On 24 December 1940 authority was given, by Post Office notice, that prepayment of penny postage could be effected by using half a British 2d. stamp, diagonally bisected. Such stamps were first used on 27 December 1940.

The 2d. stamps generally available were those of the Postal Centenary issue, 1940 (S.G. 482) and the first colour of the King George VI issue (S.G. 465). These are listed under Nos. 482a and 465b. A number of the 2d. King George V, 1912–22, and of the King George V photogravure stamp (S.G. 442) which were in the hands of philatelists, were also bisected and used.

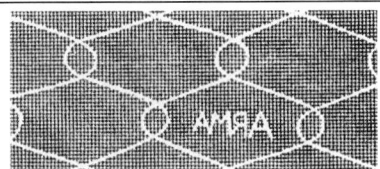

1a Loops (*half actual size*)

(Des E. W. Vaudin. Typo Guernsey Press Co Ltd)

1941–44. Rouletted.

(a) White paper. No wmk

1	**1**	½d. light green (7.4.41)....................	6·00	3·50
		a. Emerald-green (6.41).................	6·00	2·00
		b. Bluish green (11.41)...................	35·00	13·00
		c. Bright green (2.42)	22·00	10·00
		d. Dull green (9.42)	4·00	2·00
		e. Olive-green (2.43)......................	45·00	25·00
		f. Pale yellowish green (7.43 and later) (shades).................	4·00	3·00
		g. Imperf (pair)...............................	£250	
		h. Imperf between (horiz pair)......	£800	
		i. Imperf between (vert pair)........	£950	
2		1d. scarlet (18.2.41)......................	3·25	2·00
		a. Pale vermilion (7.43) (etc.)........	5·00	2·00
		b. Carmine (1943)...........................	3·50	2·00
		c. Imperf (pair)...............................	£200	90·00
		d. Imperf between (horiz pair).......	£800	
		da. Imperf vert (centre stamp of horiz strip of 3)........	£950	
		e. Imperf between (vert pair).........	£950	
		f. Printed double (scarlet shade)..	£150	
3		2½d. ultramarine (12.4.44)..............	18·00	15·00
		a. Pale ultramarine (7.44)..............	15·00	12·00
		b. Imperf (pair)...............................	£550	
		c. Imperf between (horiz pair).......	£1250	

*(b) Bluish French bank-note paper. W **1a** (sideways)*

4	**1**	½d. bright green (11.3.42).................	32·00	25·00
5		1d. scarlet (9.4.42)........................	18·00	25·00

The dates given for the shades of Nos. 1/3 are the months in which they were printed as indicated on the printer's imprints. Others are issue dates.

REGIONAL ISSUES

DATES OF ISSUE. Conflicting dates of issue have been announced for some of the regional issues, partly explained by the stamps being released on different dates by the Philatelic Bureau in Edinburgh or the Philatelic Counter in London and in the regions. We have adopted the practice of giving the earliest known dates, since once released the stamps could have been used anywhere in the U.K

2   **3**

(Des E. A. Piprell. Portrait by Dorothy Wilding Ltd. Photo Harrison & Sons)

1958 (18 Aug)–**67.** W **179** of Great Britain. P 15×14.

6	**2**	2½d. rose-red (8.6.64).....................	40	50
7	**3**	3d. deep lilac (............................	30	40
		p. One centre phosphor band (24.5.67)	20	30
8		4d. ultramarine (7.2.66)	40	50
		p. Two phosphor bands (24.10.67)	15	25
6/8p		*Set of 3*	70	1·25

1968–69. No wmk. Chalk-surfaced paper. PVA gum*. One centre phosphor band (Nos. 10/11) or two phosphor bands (others). P 15×14.

9	**3**	4d. pale ultramarine (16.4.68)...........	10	20
10		4d. olive-sepia (4.9.68)..................	10	15
11		4d. bright vermilion (26.2.69)........	20	25
12		5d. royal blue (4.9.68)...................	30	40
9/12		*Set of 4*	50	1·00

No. 9 was not issued in Guernsey until 22 April.
* PVA Gum. See note after No. 722 of Great Britain.

INDEPENDENT POSTAL ADMINISTRATION

4 Castle Cornet and Edward the Confessor

5 View of Sark Two Types of 1d. and 1s.6d.

6 Martello Tower and Henry II

7 Arms of Sark and King John

8 Arms of Alderney and Edward III

9 Guernsey Lily and Henry V

10 Arms of Guernsey and Elizabeth I

11 Arms of Alderney and Charles II

12 Arms of Sark and George III

13 Arms of Guernsey and Queen Victoria

14 Guernsey Lily and Elizabeth I

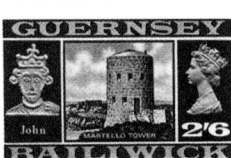

15 Martello Tower and King John

16 View of Sark

17 View of Alderney

18 View of Guernsey

(Des R. Granger Barrett. Photo Harrison (½d. to 2s.6d.), Delrieu (others))

1969 (1 Oct)–**70.** Perf 14 (½d. to 2s.6d.) or 12½ (others), all comb.

13	**4**	½d. deep magenta and black (a).....	10	10
		a. Thin paper...........................	60	60
14	**5**	1d. bright blue and black (I) (a).......	10	10
		a. Thin paper (b)........................	50	50
14b		1d. bright blue and black (thin paper) (II) (eg)........	30	30
		c. Booklet stamp with margins (thick paper) (C)........	40	40
15	**6**	1½d. yellow-brown and black (a)......	10	10
16	**7**	2d. gold, bright red, deep blue and black (a)........	10	10
		a. Thin paper (g)........................	40	40
17	**8**	3d. gold, pale greenish yellow, orange-red and black (a)..........	15	15
		a. Error. Wmk Block CA.............	£1400	
		ai. Wmk inverted........................	£1250	
		b. Thin paper (g)........................	50	50
18	**9**	4d. multicoloured (a)......................	20	10
		a. Booklet stamp with margins (C)	40	45
		ab. Yellow omitted......................	£775	
		ac. Emerald (stem) omitted............	£775	
19	**10**	5d. gold, bright vermilion, bluish violet and black (a)........	20	10
		a. Booklet stamp with margins (C)........	50	50
		b. gold (inscription etc.) omitted (booklets)........	£1400	
20	**11**	6d. gold, pale greenish yellow, light bronze-green and black (a).......	20	30
		a. Thin paper (g)........................	45	45
21	**12**	9d. gold, bright red, crimson and black (a)........	30	30
		a. Thin paper (g)	3·00	1·70
22	**13**	1s. gold, bright vermilion, bistre and black (a)........	30	30
		a. Thin paper (g)	1·00	75
23	**5**	1s.6d. turquoise-green and black (I) (a)........	25	30
		a. Thin paper (d)........................	1·70	3·25
23b		1s.6d. turquoise-green and black (thin paper) (II) (eg)........	2·00	1·70
24	**14**	1s.9d. multicoloured (a)......................	1·00	1·00
		a. Emerald (stem) omitted...........	£875	
		b. Thin paper (g)........................	1·50	1·90
25	**15**	2s.6d. brt reddish violet and black (a)........	3·00	2·50
		a. Thin paper (g)........................	4·50	4·00
26	**16**	5s. multicoloured (a).....................	2·50	2·75
27	**17**	10s. multicoloured (a)...................	12·00	14·00
		a. Perf 13½×13 (f).......................	26·00	32·00
28	**18**	£1 multicoloured (a).....................	2·20	2·20
		a. Perf 13½×13 (fh).....................	2·20	2·20
13/28a		*Set of 16*	20·00	23·00

The booklet panes consist of single perforated stamps with wide margins all round intended to fit automatic machines designed for the Great Britain 2s. booklets. They are therefore found with three margins when detached from booklets or four margins when complete.

There was no postal need for the ½d. and 1½d. values as the ½d. coin had been withdrawn prior to their issue in anticipation of decimalisation. These values were only on sale at the Philatelic Bureau and the Crown Agents as well as in the USA

Nos. 14b and 23b are known only on thin paper and Nos. 13, 14, 16, 17, 20, 21, 22, 23, 24 and 25 also exist on thin paper.

 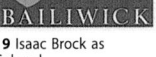

19 Isaac Brock as Colonel

23 HMS *L103* (landing craft) entering St. Peter's Harbour

(Litho Format)

1969 (1 Dec). Birth Bicentenary of Sir Isaac Brock. T **19** and similar multicoloured designs. P 13½×14 (2s.6d.) or 14×13½ (others).

29		4d. Type **19**	20	20
30		5d. Sir Isaac Brock as Major-General	20	20
31		1s.9d. Isaac Brock as Ensign	60	50
32		2s.6d. Arms and flags (*horiz*)	60	50
29/32		*Set of 4*	1·40	1·25

(Des and photo Courvoisier)

1970 (9 May). 25th Anniv of Liberation. T **23** and similar designs. Granite paper. P 11½.

33	4d. blue and pale blue	20	20
34	5d. brown-lake and pale grey	30	20
35	1s.6d. bistre-brown and buff	75	75
33/5	Set of 3	1·00	1·00

Designs: Horiz—5d. HMS *Bulldog* and HMS *Beagle* (destroyers) entering St. Peter's Port. Vert—1s.6d. Brigadier Snow reading Proclamation.

26 Guernsey "Toms"

32 St. Peter Church, Sark

(Des and photo Courvoisier)

1970 (12 Aug). Agriculture and Horticulture. T **26** and similar horiz designs. Multicoloured. Granite paper. P 11½.

36	4d. Type **26**	55	20
37	5d. Guernsey Cow	60	20
38	9d. Guernsey Bull	1·25	75
39	1s.6d. Freesias	1·50	2·00
36/9	Set of 4	3·50	2·75

(Des and photo Courvoisier)

1970 (11 Nov). Christmas. Guernsey Churches (1st series). T **32** and similar multicoloured designs. Granite paper. P 11½.

40	4d. St. Anne's Church, Alderney (*horiz*) ..	20	10
41	5d. St. Peter's Church (*horiz*)	20	10
42	9d. Type **32**	80	60
43	1s.6d. St. Tugual Chapel, Herm	1·00	1·00
40/3	Set of 4	2·00	1·60

Further stamps in this series appear after 1970.

STAMP BOOKLETS

For a full listing of Guernsey stamp booklets see *Collect Channel Islands and Isle of Man Stamps.*

POSTAGE DUE STAMPS

D 1 Castle Cornet

(Des R. Granger Barrett. Photo Delrieu)

1969 (1 Oct). Value in black; background colour given. No wmk. P 12½×12.

D1	**D 1**	1d. plum	1·50	1·20
D2		2d. bright green	1·50	1·20
D3		3d. vermilion	2·25	3·00
D4		4d. ultramarine	2·50	3·50
D5		5d. yellow-ochre	4·50	3·50
D6		6d. turquoise-blue	4·50	3·50
D7		1s. lake-brown	7·50	6·50
D1/7	Set of 7		22·00	20·00

JERSEY
WAR OCCUPATION ISSUES

Stamps issued under the authority of the Jersey States during the German Occupation

5

(Des Major N. V. L. Rybot. Typo Jersey Evening Post, St. Helier)

1941–43. White paper (thin to thick). No wmk. P 11.

1	**5**	½d. bright green (29.1.42)	8·00	6·00
		a. Imperf between (vert pair)	£900	
		b. Imperf between (horiz pair)	£800	
		c. Imperf (pair)	£300	
		d. On greyish paper (1.43)	12·00	12·00
2		1d. scarlet (1.4.41)	8·00	5·00
		a. Imperf between (vert pair)	£900	
		b. Imperf between (horiz pair)	£800	
		c. Imperf (pair)	£325	
		d. On chalk-surfaced paper	55·00	48·00
		e. On greyish paper (1.43)	14·00	14·00

6 Old Jersey Farm

7 Portelet Bay

---

8 Corbière Lighthouse

9 Elizabeth Castle

10 Mont Orgueil Castle

11 Gathering Vraic (seaweed)

(Des E. Blampied. Eng H. Cortot. Typo French Govt Works, Paris)

1943–44. No wmk. P 13½.

3	**6**	½d. green (1.6.43)	12·00	12·00
		a. Rough, grey paper (6.10.43)	15·00	14·00
4	**7**	1d. scarlet (1.6.43)	3·00	50
		a. On newsprint (28.2.44)	3·50	75
5	**8**	1½d. brown (8.6.43)	8·00	5·75
6	**5**	2d. orange-yellow (8.6.43)	7·50	2·00
7	**9**	2½d. blue (29.6.43)	3·00	1·00
		a. On newsprint (25.2.44)	1·00	1·75
		ba. Thin paper*	£225	
8	**11**	3d. violet (29.6.43)	3·00	2·00
3/8	Set of 6		30·00	21·00

*On No. 7ba the design shows clearly through the back of the stamp.

REGIONAL ISSUES

DATES OF ISSUE. The note at the beginning of the Guernsey Regional Issues also applies here

INVALIDATION. The regional issues for Jersey were invalidated for use in Jersey and Guernsey on 1 November 1969 but remained valid for use in the rest of the United Kingdom. Nos. 15/41 (except No. 29) and Nos. D1/6 were invalidated on 14 February 1972

12

13

(Des E. Blampied (T **12**), W Gardner (T **13**) Portrait by Dorothy Wilding Ltd. Photo Harrison & Sons)

1958 (18 Aug)–**67**. W **179** of Great Britain. P 15×14.

9	**12**	2½d. carmine-red (8.6.64)	75	1·00
		a. Imperf three sides (pair)	£3250	
10	**13**	3d. deep lilac	30	40
		p. One centre phosphor band (9.6.67)	15	25
11		4d. ultramarine (7.2.66)	25	30
		p. Two phosphor bands (5.9.67)	15	25
9/11p	Set of 3		80	1·25

1968–69. No wmk. Chalk-surfaced paper. PVA gum*. One centre phosphor band (4d. values) or two phosphor bands (5d.). P 15×14.

12	**13**	4d. olive-sepia (4.9.68)	15	25
13		4d. bright vermilion (26.2.69)	15	25
14		5d. royal blue (4.9.68)	15	50
12/14	Set of 3		40	90

*PVA Gum. See note after No. 722 of Great Britain.

INDEPENDENT POSTAL ADMINISTRATION

14 Elizabeth Castle

23 Queen Elizabeth II (after Cecil Beaton)

27 Queen Elizabeth II (after Cecil Beaton)

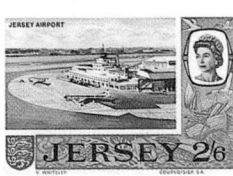

24 Jersey Airport

(Des V. Whiteley. Photo Harrison (½d. to 1s.9d.); Courvoisier (others))

1969 (1 Oct). T **14/27** and similar horiz designs as T **14** (½d. to 1s.6d.) or T **24** (5s., 10s., £1). Multicoloured. Granite paper (2s.6d. to £1). P 14 (½d. to 1s.9d.) or 12 (others).

15	½d.	Type **14**	10	60
16	1d.	La Hougue Bie (prehistoric tomb)	10	10
		a. Booklet stamp with blank margins..	75	
17	2d.	Portelet Bay	10	10
18	3d.	La Corbière Lighthouse	10	10
		b. Orange omitted	£425	
19	4d.	Mont Orgueil Castle by night	10	10
		a. Booklet stamp with blank margins ..	50	
		c. Gold omitted		
20	5d.	Arms and Royal Mace	10	10
21	6d.	Jersey Cow	10	10
22	9d.	Chart of English Channel	10	20
23	1s.	Mont Orgueil Castle by day	25	25
24	1s.6d.	As 9d.	80	80
25	1s.9d.	Type **23**	1·00	1·00
26	2s.6d.	Type **24**	1·60	1·60
27	5s.	Legislative Chamber	4·50	4·50
28	10s.	The Royal Court	9·00	9·00
		a. Error. Green border*	£5500	
29	£1	Type **27** (*shades*)	1·90	1·90
15/29	Set of 15		17·00	17·00

*During the final printing of the 10s. a sheet was printed in the colours of the 50p., No. 56, i.e. green border instead of slate.

The 3d. is known with the orange omitted.

There was no postal need for the ½d. value as the ½d. coin had been withdrawn prior to its issue in anticipation of decimalisation.

Nos. 16a and 19a come from 2s. booklets for the automatic machines formerly included for the Great Britain 2s. booklets (see also note after Guernsey No. 28).

Various papers were used by Harrisons. The ½d. and 1d. exist on much thicker paper from 2s. booklets and the 2d. to 1s.9d. exist on thinner paper having white instead of creamy gum.

28 First Day Cover

29 Lord Coutanche, former Bailiff of Jersey

(Des R. Sellar. Photo Harrison)

1969 (1 Oct). Inauguration of Post Office. P 14.

30	**28**	4d. multicoloured	10	15
31		5d. multicoloured	10	10
32		9d. multicoloured	30	50
33		1s.9d. multicoloured	60	80
30/3	Set of 4		1·00	1·40

(Des Rosalind Dease. Photo Courvoisier)

1970 (9 May). 25th Anniv of Liberation. T **29** and similar multicoloured designs. Granite paper. P 11½.

34	4d.	Type **29**	20	20
35	5d.	Sir Winston Churchill	20	20
36	1s.6d.	"Liberation" (Edmund Blampied) (*horiz*)	60	80
37	1s.9d.	SS *Vega* (*horiz*)	80	80
34/7	Set of 4		1·40	1·75

33 "A Tribute to Enid Blyton"

(Des Jennifer Toombs. Photo Courvoisier)

1970 (28 July). "Battle of Flowers" Parade. T **33** and similar horiz designs. Multicoloured. Granite paper. P 11½.

38	4d.	Type **29**	20	10
39	5d.	"Rags to Riches" (Cinderella and pumpkin)	20	20
40	1s.6d.	"Gourmet's Delight" (lobster and cornucopia)	1·75	1·75
41	1s.9d.	"We're the Greatest" (ostriches)	1·75	1·75
38/41	Set of 4		3·50	3·50

37 Martello Tower, Archirondel

(Des V. Whiteley. Photo Harrison (½ to 9p.), Courvoisier (others))

1970 (1 Oct)–**74**. Decimal Currency. Designs as Nos. 15/28, but with values inscr in decimal currency as in T **37**, and new horiz design as T **14** (6p). Chalk-surfaced paper (4½, 5, 8p.); granite paper (10, 20, 50p.). P 14 (½p. to 9p.) or 12 (others).

42	½p.	Type **14** (15.2.71)	10	10
		a. Booklet stamp with blank margins....	20	
43	1p.	La Corbière Lighthouse (*shades*) (15.2.71)	10	10
		a. Orange omitted	£500	
44	1½p.	Jersey Cow (15.2.71)	10	10

45	2p. Mont Orgueil Castle by night (15.2.71)		10	10
	a. Booklet stamp with blank margins....		60	
46	2½p. Arms and Royal Mace (15.2.71)		10	10
	a. Booklet stamp with blank margins....		60	
	ab. Gold (Mace) omitted		£775	
	ac. Gold (Mace) printed double		£575	
47	3p. La Hougue Bie (prehistoric tomb) (15.2.71)		10	10
	a. Booklet stamp with blank margins (1.12.72)		60	
48	3½p. Portelet Bay (15.2.71)		10	10
	a. Booklet stamp with blank margins (1.7.74)		25	
49	4p. Chart of English Channel (15.2.71)		10	10
49a	4½p. Arms and Royal Mace (1.11.74)		75	75
	ab. Uncoated paper		£400	
50	5p. Mont Orgueil Castle by day (15.2.71)		10	10
50a	5½p. Jersey Cow (1.11.74)		75	75
51	6p. Type **37** (15.2.71)		20	10
52	7½p. Chart of English Channel (15.2.71)		50	50
52a	8p. Mont Orgueil Castle by night (1.11.74)		75	75
53	9p. Type **23** (15.2.71)		70	70
54	10p. Jersey Airport		40	30
55	20p. Legislative Chamber		90	80
56	50p. The Royal Court		1·50	1·20
	42/56 *Set of 18*		4·50	4·50

Original printings of the ½p. to 4p.. 5p. and 6p. were with PVA gum; printings from 1974 (including original printings of the 4½p. and 5½p.) have dextrin added (see notes after 1971 Great Britain Decimal Machin issue). The 10p. to 50p. have gum arabic.

The border of No. 56 has been changed from turquoise-blue to dull green.

STAMP BOOKLETS

For a full listing of Jersey stamp booklets see Collect *Channel Islands and Isle of Man Stamps.*

POSTAGE DUE STAMPS

D **1**   D **2** Map

(Des F. Gudnier. Litho Bradbury, Wilkinson)

1969 (1 Oct). P 14×13½.

D1	D **1**	1d. bluish violet	65	1·10
D2		2d. sepia	90	1·10
D3		3d. magenta	1·00	1·10
D4	D **2**	1s. bright emerald	5·50	5·00
D5		2s.6d. olive-grey	13·00	14·00
D6		5s. vermilion	15·00	16·00
		D1/6 *Set of 6*	32·00	35·00

British Post Offices Abroad

The origins of the network of Post Offices, Postal Agencies and Packet Agents can be recognised from the 18th- century, but the system did not become established until the expansion of trade, following the end of the Napoleonic Wars in 1815.

Many offices were provided in newly acquired dependent territories, and were then, eventually, transferred from the control of the British Post Office to the evolving local administrations.

Those in foreign countries, nearly always based on existing British Consular appointments, were mostly connected to the network of British Packet lines which had been re-established in 1814. They tended to survive until the country in which they were situated established its own efficient postal service or joined the UPU The term "Post Office Agent" was employed by the British GPO and "Packet Agent" by the shipping lines to describe similar functions.

Listed in this section are the Crowned-circle handstamps and G.B. stamps used in the Post Offices and Agencies situated in foreign countries. Those for the territories within the scope of this catalogue will be found under the following headings:

Prices. Catalogue prices quoted in this section, and throughout the volume, covering stamps of Great Britain used abroad are for used examples with the cancellation or handstamp clearly legible. Poor impressions of the cancellations and handstamps are worth much less than the prices quoted.

They also take into account the fact that many identifiable cancellations of the post offices abroad render the stamps they obliterate in less than 'fine' condition. As a result, some stamps listed in this section are priced at less than the same items used in Great Britain, where the prices are for fine examples. Lightly cancelled stamps used in offices abroad would be worth a premium over the prices quoted.

CROWNED-CIRCLE HANDSTAMPS

Following the introduction, in 1840, of adhesive stamps in Great Britain there was considerable pressure from a number of the dependent territories for the British Post Office to provide something similar for their use.

Such suggestions were resisted, however, because of supposed operational problems, but the decision was taken, in connection with an expansion of the Packet Service, to issue a uniform series of handstamps and date stamps to the offices abroad, both in the dependent territories and in foreign countries.

Under the regulations circulated in December 1841, letters and packets forwarded through these offices to the United Kingdom or any of its territories were to be sent unpaid, the postage being collected on delivery. Where this was not possible, for example from a British colony to a foreign colony or between two foreign ports, then a *crowned-circle handstamp* was to be applied with the postage, paid in advance, noted alongside in manuscript.

Examples of these handstamps were supplied over 20 years from 1842, but many continued to fulfil other functions long after the introduction of adhesive stamps in the colony concerned.

Our listings cover the use of these handstamps for their initial purpose and the prices quoted are for examples used on cover during the pre-adhesive period.

In most instances the dates quoted are those on which the handstamp appears in the G.P.O. Record Books, but it seems to have been normal for the handstamps to be sent to the office concerned immediately following this registration. The only known examples of certain hanstamps are those in The Record Books; these include St. Michaels (Azores), Cobija (Bolivia), St Vincent (Cape Verde Islands), Cartagena (CC1) and Chagres (Colombia), Cap Haitien (Haiti), Greytown (Nicaragua), Corunna (Spain), and Charleston, Mobile, New Orleans and Savannah (United States of America).

Many of the handstamps were individually cut by hand, so that each has its own characteristics, but for the purposes of the listing they have been grouped into nine Types as shown in the adjacent column. No attempt has been made to identify them by anything but the most major differences, so that minor differences in size and in the type of the crown have been ignored.

DOUBLE CIRCLE

CC **1**

CC **1a**

Curved "PAID"

CC **1b**

CC **1c**

Curved "PAID"

CC **2**
Straight "PAID"

SINGLE CIRCLE

CC **3**
Straight "PAID"

CC **4**

CC **5**
Curved "PAID"

CC **6** Straight "PAID"

CC **7** Curved "PAID"

GREAT BRITAIN STAMPS USED ABROAD

Prices quoted are for single stamps not on cover unless otherwise stated. Stamps on cover are worth considerably more in most cases.

In many instances obliterators allocated to post offices abroad were, at a later date re-allocated to offices at home. Postmarks on issues later than those included in our lists can therefore safely be regarded as *not* having been "used abroad".

INDEX

BRITISH POST OFFICES ABROAD

TYPES OF OBLITERATOR FOR GREAT BRITAIN STAMPS USED ABROAD

HORIZONTAL OVAL

(1)   (2)   (3)   (4)

(5)

(6)

(7)

VERTICAL OVAL

(8)   (9)

(10)

(11)

(11A)

(12)

(13)

(14)

(14A)

(14B)

(15)

CIRCULAR DATE STAMPS

(16)

(16A)

(17)

(17A)

(17B)   (18)

(19)　　　　　　(20)

(21)

(22)

ARGENTINE REPUBLIC

BUENOS AYRES

The first regular monthly British mail packet service was introduced in 1824, replacing a private arrangement which had previously existed for some years.

Great Britain stamps were used from 1860 until the office closed at the end of June 1873. Until 1878 the British Consul continued to sell stamps which were used in combination with an Argentine value prepaying the internal rate. The British stamps on such covers were cancelled on arrival in England.

CROWNED-CIRCLE HANDSTAMPS

CC1　CC **7** BUENOS AYRES (Black or B.) (5.1.1851)
.... *Price on cover*　£850

Stamps of GREAT BRITAIN *cancelled* "B 32" *as Types* **2**, **12** *or* **13** *in black or blue.*

1860–73.

Z1	1d. rose-red (1857)	45·00
Z2	1d. rose-red (1864) .... *From*	38·00
	Plate Nos. 71, 72, 73, 74, 76, 78, 79, 80, 81,	
	82, 85, 87, 89, 90, 91, 92, 93, 94, 95, 96, 97,	
	99, 101, 103, 104, 107, 108, 110, 112, 113,	
	114, 117, 118, 119, 120, 121, 123, 125, 127,	
	129, 130, 131, 135, 136, 138, 139, 140, 142,	
	143, 145, 147, 149, 150, 151, 155, 159, 163,	
	164, 166, 169, 172.	
Z3	2d. blue (1858–69) .... *From*	45·00
	Plate Nos. 8, 9, 12, 13, 14.	
Z4	3d. carmine-rose (1862)	£270
Z5	3d. rose (1865) (Plate No. 4)	£110
Z6	3d. rose (1867–73) .... *From*	55·00
	Plate Nos. 4, 5, 6, 7, 8, 9, 10.	
Z7	4d. rose (1857)	£120
Z8	4d. red (1862) (Plate Nos. 3, 4)	£110
Z9	4d. vermilion (1865–73) .... *From*	50·00
	Plate Nos. 7, 8, 9, 10, 11, 12, 13.	
Z10	6d. lilac (1856)	£100
Z11	6d. lilac (1862) (Plate Nos. 3, 4)	
Z12	6d. lilac (1865–67) (Plate Nos. 5, 6) ... *From*	80·00
Z13	6d. lilac (1867) (Plate No. 6)	90·00
Z14	6d. violet (1867–70) (Plate Nos. 6, 8, 9) ... *From*	70·00
Z15	6d. buff (1872) (Plate No. 11)	85·00
Z16	6d. chestnut (1872) (Plate No. 11)	50·00
Z17	9d. bistre (1862)	£325
Z18	9d. straw (1862)	£300
Z19	9d. straw (1865)	£475
Z20	9d. straw (1867)	£300
Z21	10d. red-brown (1867)	£325
Z22	1s. green (1856)	£275
Z23	1s. green (1862)	£170
Z24	1s. green (1865) (Plate No. 4)	£160
Z25	1s. green (1867–73) (Plate Nos. 4, 5, 6, 7) ..... *From*	45·00
Z26	1s. green (1873–77) (Plate No. 8)	
Z27	2s. blue (1867)	£175
Z28	5s. rose (1867) (Plate No. 1)	£500

A "B 32" obliteration was later used by Mauritius on its own stamps.

AZORES

ST. MICHAELS (SAN MIGUEL)

A British Postal Agency existed at Ponta Delgada, the chief port of the island, to operate with the services of the Royal Mail Steam Packet Company.

CROWNED-CIRCLE HANDSTAMPS

CC1　CC **1b** ST. MICHAELS (27.5.1842)...........................
Although recorded in the G.P.O. Proof Books, no example of No. CC1 is known on cover.

BOLIVIA

COBIJA

It is believed that the British Postal Agency opened in 1862. The stamps of Great Britain were used between 1865 and 1878. They can be found used in combination with Bolivia adhesive stamps paying the local postage. The Agency closed in 1881, the town having been occupied by Chile in 1879.

CROWNED-CIRCLE HANDSTAMPS

CC1　CC **4** COBIJA (29.3.1862)......................................
Although recorded in the GPO Proof Books, no example of No. CC1 is known on cover.

Stamps of GREAT BRITAIN *cancelled* "C 39" *as Types* **4**, **8** *or* **12**.

1865–78.

Z1	1d. rose-red (Plate Nos. 93, 95, 156)	
Z2	2d. blue (1858–69) (Plate No. 14)	
Z3	3d. rose (1867–73) (Plate No. 6)	
Z4	3d. rose (1873–76) (Plate Nos. 16, 19)	
Z5	4d. sage-green (1877) (Plate No. 15)	£1000
Z6	6d. violet (1867–70) (Plate No. 9)	£1000
Z7	6d. buff (1872) (Plate No. 11)	
Z8	6d. grey (1874–76) (Plate Nos. 13, 14, 15, 16)	£800
Z9	1s. green (1867–73) (Plate Nos. 4, 5)	£850
Z10	1s. green (1873–77) (Plate Nos. 10, 11, 12, 13)	£850
Z11	2s. blue (1867)	£1300
Z12	5s. rose (1867–74) (Plate No. 2)	£2400

BRAZIL

The first packets ran to Brazil in 1808 when the Portuguese royal family went into exile at Rio de Janeiro. The Agencies at Bahia and Pernambuco did not open until 1851. All three agencies used the stamps of Great Britain from 1866 and these can be found used in combination with Brazil adhesive stamps paying the local postage. The agencies closed on 30 June 1874.

BAHIA

CROWNED-CIRCLE HANDSTAMPS

CC1　CC **7** BAHIA (Black or B.) (6.1.1851)
.... *Price on cover From*　£3750

Stamps of GREAT BRITAIN *cancelled* "C 81" *as Type* **12**.

1866–74.

Z1	1d. rose-red (1864–79) .... *From*	45·00
	Plate Nos. 90, 93, 96, 108, 113, 117, 135, 140,	
	147, 155.	
Z2	1½d. lake-red (1870–74) (Plate No. 3)	£110
Z3	2d. blue (1858–59) (Plate Nos. 9, 12, 13, 14)	65·00
Z4	3d. rose (1865) (Plate No. 4)	
Z5	3d. rose (1867–73) (Plate Nos. 4, 6, 8, 9, 10)	70·00
Z6	3d. rose (1873–79) (Plate No. 11)	
Z7	4d. vermilion (1865–73) .... *From*	50·00
	Plate Nos. 8, 9, 10, 11, 12, 13.	
Z8	6d. lilac (1865–67) (Plate No. 5)	
Z9	6d. lilac (1867) (Plate No. 6)	£100
Z10	6d. violet (1867–70) (Plate Nos. 6, 8, 9) ... *From*	£95
Z11	6d. buff (1872–73) (Plate Nos. 11, 12) .... *From*	£100
Z12	6d. chestnut (1872) (Plate No. 11)	£100
Z13	6d. grey (1873) (Plate No. 12)	£225
Z14	6d. grey (1874–76) (Plate No. 13)	
Z15	9d. straw (1865)	£425
Z16	9d. straw (1867)	£250
Z17	1s. green (1865) (Plate No. 4)	£170
Z18	1s. green (1867–73) (Plate Nos. 4, 5, 6, 7) ..... *From*	60·00
Z19	1s. green (1873–77) (Plate Nos. 8, 9)	90·00
Z20	2s. blue (1867)	£275
Z21	5s. rose (1867) (Plate No. 1)	£500

PERNAMBUCO

CROWNED-CIRCLE HANDSTAMPS

CC2　CC **7** PERNAMBUCO (Black or R.) (6.1.1851)
.... *Price on cover From*　£3750

Stamps of GREAT BRITAIN *cancelled* "C 82" *as Type* **12** *or with circular date stamp as Type* **16** *in black or blue.*

1866–74.

Z22	1d. rose-red (1864–79) .... *From*	45·00
	Plate Nos. 85, 108, 111, 130, 131, 132, 149,	
	157, 159, 160, 187.	
Z23	2d. blue (1858–69) .... *From*	55·00
	Plate Nos. 9, 12, 13, 14.	
Z23a	3d. rose (1865) (Plate No. 4)	£110
Z24	3d. rose (1867–73) (Plate Nos. 4, 5, 6, 7, 10)	65·00
Z25	3d. rose (1873–77) (Plate No. 11)	
Z26	4d. vermilion (1865–73) .... *From*	50·00
	Plate Nos. 9, 10, 11, 12, 13, 14.	
Z27	6d. lilac (1865–67) (Plate Nos. 5, 6)	
Z28	6d. lilac (1867) (Plate No. 6)	85·00
Z29	6d. violet (1867–70) (Plate Nos. 8, 9) ... *From*	75·00
Z30	6d. buff (1872–73) (Plate Nos. 11, 12) .... *From*	80·00
Z31	6d. chestnut (1872) (Plate No. 11)	60·00
Z32	6d. grey (1873) (Plate No. 12)	
Z33	9d. straw (1865)	£425
Z34	9d. straw (1867)	£225
Z35	10d. red-brown (1867)	£325
Z36	1s. green (1865) (Plate No. 4)	£170
Z37	1s. green (1867–73) (Plate Nos. 4, 5, 6, 7) ..... *From*	60·00
Z38	2s. blue (1867)	£250
Z39	5s. rose (1867–74) (Plate Nos. 1, 2) .... *From*	£500

RIO DE JANEIRO

CROWNED-CIRCLE HANDSTAMPS

CC3　CC **7** RIO DE JANEIRO (Black, B. or G.) (6.1.1851)
.... *Price on cover From*　£850

Stamps of GREAT BRITAIN *cancelled* "C 83" *as Type* **12**.

1866–74.

Z40	1d. rose-red (1857)	45·00
Z41	1d. rose-red (1864–79) .... *From*	38·00
	Plate Nos. 71, 76, 80, 82, 86, 94, 103, 113,	
	117, 119, 123, 130, 132, 134, 135, 146, 148,	
	159, 161, 166, 185, 200, 204.	
Z42	2d. blue (1858–69) .... *From*	40·00
	Plate Nos. 9, 12, 13, 14.	
Z43	3d. rose (1867–73) .... *From*	55·00
	Plate Nos. 4, 5, 6, 7, 8, 9.	
Z44	3d. rose (1873–77) (Plate No. 11)	
Z45	4d. vermilion (1865–73) .... *From*	50·00
	Plate Nos. 8, 9, 10, 11, 12, 13, 14.	

CAPE VERDE ISLANDS

Z46	6d. lilac (1865–67) (Plate No. 5)	£100
Z47	6d. lilac (1867) (Plate No. 6)	75·00
Z48	6d. violet (1867–70) (Plate Nos. 6, 8, 9) .... *From*	70·00
Z49	6d. buff (1872) (Plate No. 11)	75·00
Z50	6d. chestnut (1872) (Plate No. 11)	45·00
Z51	6d. grey (1873) (Plate No. 12)	
Z52	9d. straw (1865)	£400
Z53	9d. straw (1867)	£200
Z54	10d. red-brown (1867)	£275
Z55	1s. green (1865) (Plate No. 4)	£140
Z56	1s. green (1867–73) (Plate Nos. 4, 5, 6, 7) ..... *From*	45·00
Z57	1s. green (1873–77) (Plate Nos. 8, 9).	70·00
Z58	2s. blue (1867)	£160
Z59	5s. rose (1867–74) (Plate Nos. 1, 2) .... *From*	£450

The British Packet Agency at St. Vincent opened in 1851 as part of the revised service to South America. The agency was closed by 1860.

CROWNED-CIRCLE HANDSTAMPS

CC1　CC **6** ST. VINCENT C.DE.V. (6.1.1851) ....
Although recorded in the GPO Proof Books, no example of No. CC1 is known on cover.

CHILE

The British Postal Agency at Valparaiso opened on 7 May 1846, to be followed by further offices at Caldera (1858) and Coquimbo (1863). The stamps of Great Britain were introduced in 1865 and can be found used in combination with Chile adhesives paying the local postage. All three offices closed on 31 March 1881 when Chile joined the UPU

CALDERA

Stamps of GREAT BRITAIN *cancelled* "C 37" *as in Type* **4** *in black and blue.*

1865–81.

Z1	1d. rose-red (1864–79) .... *From*	65·00
	Plate Nos. 71, 72, 88, 90, 95, 160, 195.	
Z2	1½d. lake-red (1870–74) (Plate No. 3)	
Z3	2d. blue (1858–69) (Plate Nos. 9, 13)	75·00
Z4	3d. rose (1865) (Plate No. 4)	£110
Z5	3d. rose (1867–73) (Plate Nos. 5, 7)	80·00
Z6	3d. rose (1873–79) .... *From*	75·00
	Plate Nos. 11, 12, 16, 17, 18, 19.	
Z7	4d. red (1862) (Plate No. 4)	
Z8	4d. vermilion (1865–73) .... *From*	75·00
	Plate Nos. 8, 11, 12, 13, 14.	
Z9	4d. sage-green (1877) (Plate No. 16)	
Z10	6d. lilac (1862) (Plate No. 4)	£100
Z11	6d. lilac (1865–67) (Plate Nos. 5, 6) .... *From*	£130
Z12	6d. violet (1867–70) (Plate Nos. 6, 8, 9) .... *From*	90·00
Z13	6d. buff (1872) (Plate No. 11)	
Z14	6d. chestnut (1872) (Plate No. 11)	
Z15	6d. grey (1873) (Plate No. 12)	
Z16	6d. grey (1874–80) .... *From*	70·00
	Plate Nos. 13, 14, 15, 16, 17.	
Z17	8d. orange (1876)	£350
Z18	9d. straw (1867)	£300
Z19	10d. red-brown (1867)	£350
Z20	1s. green (1865) (Plate No. 4)	
Z21	1s. green 1867–73 (Plate Nos. 4, 5, 6) .... *From*	70·00
Z22	1s. green (1873–77) .... *From*	90·00
	Plate Nos. 8, 10, 11, 12, 13.	
Z23	2s. blue (1867)	£225
Z23a	2s. cobalt (1867)	
Z24	2s. brown (1880)	£2250
Z25	5s. rose (1867–74) (Plate No. 2)	£700

COQUIMBO

Stamps of GREAT BRITAIN *cancelled* "C 40" *as in Type* **4** *or with circular date stamp as Type* **16**.

1865–81.

Z26	½d. rose-red (1870–79) (Plate No. 14)	
Z27	1d. rose-red (1857)	
Z28	1d. rose-red (1864–79) (Plate Nos. 85, 204)	
Z29	2d. blue (1858–69) (Plate Nos. 9, 14)	
Z30	3d. rose (1865)	
Z31	3d. rose (1872) (Plate No. 8)	
Z32	3d. rose (1873–76) (Plate No. 18, 19) .... *From*	75·00
Z33	4d. red (1863) (Plate No. 4) (*Hair lines*)	
Z34	4d. vermilion (1865–73) (Plate Nos. 12, 14)	75·00
Z35	4d. sage-green (1877) (Plate Nos. 15, 16) ..... *From*	£225
Z36	6d. lilac (1862) (Plate Nos. 3, 4) .... *From*	95·00
Z37	6d. lilac (1865–67) (Plate No. 5)	
Z38	6d. lilac (1867) (Plate No. 6)	90·00
Z39	6d. violet (1867–70) (Plate Nos. 6, 8, 9) .... *From*	85·00
Z40	6d. buff (1872–73) (Plate Nos. 11, 12) .... *From*	90·00
Z41	6d. chestnut (1872) (Plate No. 11)	
Z42	6d. grey (1873) (Plate No. 12)	£225
Z43	6d. grey (1874–76) .... *From*	70·00
	Plate Nos. 13, 14, 15, 16.	
Z44	8d. orange (1876)	
Z45	9d. straw (1862)	£325
Z46	9d. straw (1867)	£250
Z47	10d. red-brown (1867)	£325
Z48	1s. green (1865) (Plate No. 4)	£170
Z49	1s. green (1867–73) (Plate Nos. 4, 5, 6)	70·00
Z50	1s. green (1873–77) .... *From*	90·00
	Plate Nos. 8, 10, 11, 12, 13.	
Z51	2s. blue (1867)	£200
Z51a	2s. cobalt (1867)	
Z52	2s. brown (1880)	£2250
Z53	5s. rose (1867–74) (Plate Nos. 1, 2) .... *From*	£700

VALPARAISO

CROWNED-CIRCLE HANDSTAMPS

CC1	CC **1** VALPARAISO (R.) (*without stop*) (13.1.1846)	
	.... *Price on cover*	£450
CC2	VALPARAISO. (R.) (*with stop*) (16.7.1846)	
	.... *Price on cover*	£500

Stamps of GREAT BRITAIN *cancelled* "C 30", *as in Types* **12**, **14** *and* **14A** *(without* "PAID" *before 1870) or with circular date stamp as Type* **16** *in black blue or red.*

1865–81.

Z54	½d. rose-red (1870–79)............................ *From*	65·00
	Plate Nos. 6,11, 12, 13, 14.	
Z55	1d. rose-red (1864–79)........................... *From*	35·00
	Plate Nos. 80, 84, 85, 89, 91, 101, 106, 113,	
	116, 122, 123, 138, 140, 141, 146, 148, 149,	
	152, 157, 158, 162, 166, 167, 175, 178, 181,	
	185, 186, 187, 189, 190, 195, 197, 198, 199,	
	200, 201, 207, 208, 209, 210, 211, 212, 213,	
	214, 215, 217.	
Z56	1½d. lake-red (1870–74) (Plate Nos, 1, 3)......*From*	65·00
Z57	2d. blue (1858–69) (Plate Nos. 9, 13, 14, 15).........	45·00
Z58	2½d. rosy mauve (1875), white paper..................	£200
	Plate No. 2.	
Z59	2½d. rosy mauve (1876) (Plate Nos. 4, 8)...........	£180
Z60	3d. carmine-rose (1862)	
Z61	3d. rose (1865) (Plate No. 4)	
Z62	3d. rose (1867–73)................................. *From*	50·00
	Plate Nos. 5, 6, 7, 8, 9, 10.	
Z63	3d. rose (1873–76).............................. *From*	38·00
	Plate Nos. 11, 12, 14, 16, 17, 18, 19.	
Z63a	4d. red (1862) (Plate Nos. 3, 4)	
Z64	4d. vermilion (1865–73)........................ *From*	50·00
	Plate Nos. 9, 10, 11, 12, 13, 14.	
Z65	4d. vermilion (1876) (Plate No. 15)................	£300
Z66	4d. sage-green (1877) (Plate Nos. 15, 16)......*From*	£200
Z67	4d. grey-brown (1880) wmk Large Garter.............	
	Plate No. 17.	
Z68	6d. lilac (1862) (Plate Nos. 3, 4)	£100
Z69	6d. lilac (1865) (Plate Nos. 5, 6)	
Z70	6d. lilac (1867) (Plate No. 6)	
Z71	6d. violet (1867–70) (Plate Nos. 6, 8, 9)...........	70·00
Z72	6d. buff (1872–73) (Plate Nos. 11, 12)......... *From*	80·00
Z73	6d. chestnut (1872) (Plate No. 11)	45·00
Z74	6d. grey (1873) (Plate No. 12).....................	£210
Z75	6d. grey (1874–80)............................. *From*	45·00
	Plate Nos. 13, 14, 15, 16, 17.	
Z76	6d. grey (1881) (Plate No. 17)	
Z77	8d. orange (1876).................................	£300
Z78	9d. straw (1862)	
Z79	9d. straw (1865)	
Z80	9d. straw (1867)..................................	£200
Z81	10d. red-brown (1867).............................	£275
Z82	1s. green (1865) (Plate No. 4)	
Z83	1s. green (1867–73).............................. *From*	38·00
	Plate Nos. 4, 5, 6, 7.	
Z84	1s. green (1873–77)............................. *From*	65·00
	Plate Nos. 8, 9, 10, 11, 12, 13.	
Z85	1s. orange-brown (1880) (Plate No. 13)............	£375
Z86	2s. blue (1867)...................................	£120
Z86a	2s. cobalt (1867).................................	£1500
Z87	2s. brown (1880).................................	£1900
Z88	5s. rose (1867–74) (Plate Nos. 1, 2).......... *From*	£400
Z89	10s. grey-green (1878) (wmk Cross)................	£4000
Z90	£1 brown-lilac (1878) (wmk Cross).................	£5000

1880.

Z91	1d. Venetian red.................................	£100
Z92	1½d. Venetian red................................	£150

COLOMBIA

The system of British Postal Agencies in the area was inaugurated by the opening of the Carthagena office in 1825. In 1842 agencies at Chagres, Panama and Santa Martha were added to the system. A further office opened at Colon in 1852, this port also being known as Aspinwall. During 1872 the system was further enlarged by an office at Savanilla, although this agency was later, 1878, transferred to Barranquilla.

Stamps of Great Britain were supplied to Carthagena, Panama and Santa Martha in 1865, Colon in 1870 and Savanilla in 1872. Combination covers with Colombia stamps paying the local postage are known from Santa Martha and Savanilla as are similar covers from Panama showing Costa Rica and El Salvador stamps.

All offices, except Chagres which had ceased to operate in 1855, closed for public business on 30 June 1881. Colon and Panama continued to exist as transit offices to deal with the mail across the isthmus. Both finally closed on 31 March 1921.

CARTHAGENA

CROWNED-CIRCLE HANDSTAMPS

CC1	CC **1b** CARTHAGENA (15.1.1841)......................	
CC2	CC **1** CARTHAGENA (Black or R.) (1.7.1846)........	
	...................................*Price on cover From*	£1000

Although recorded in the GPO Proof Books, no example of No. CC1 is known on cover.

Stamps of GREAT BRITAIN *cancelled* "C 56" *as in Type* **4**.

1865–81.

Z1	½d. rose-red (1870–79) (Plate No. 10)	
Z2	1d. rose-red (1864–79) .... *From*	55·00
	Plate Nos. 78, 87, 100, 111, 113, 117, 119,	
	125, 172, 189, 217.	
Z3	2d. blue (1858–69) (Plate Nos. 9, 14).........	55·00
Z4	3d. rose (1865) (Plate No. 4)	
Z5	3d. rose (1865–68) (Plate Nos. 4, 5).	
Z6	3d. rose (1873–79) (Plate Nos. 12, 17, 18) ...... *From*	60·00
Z7	4d. vermilion (1865–73)........................ *From*	55·00
	Plate Nos. 7, 8, 9, 10, 11, 12, 13, 14.	
Z8	4d. vermilion (1876) (Plate No. 15)...............	£300
Z9	4d. sage-green (1877) (Plate Nos. 15, 16)......*From*	£200
Z10	6d. lilac (1865–67) (Plate Nos. 5, 6)	
Z11	6d. violet (1867–70) (Plate Nos. 6, 8)........... *From*	75·00
Z12	6d. grey (1873) (Plate No. 12).....................	£210
Z13	6d. grey (1874–76)............................. *From*	60·00
	Plate Nos. 13, 14, 15, 16.	
Z14	8d. orange (1876).................................	£350
Z15	9d. straw (1865)	
Z16	1s. green (1865)	
Z17	1s. green (1867–73) (Plate Nos. 4, 5, 7)........ *From*	60·00

Z18	1s. green (1873–77).............................. *From*	70·00
	Plate Nos. 8, 9, 10, 11, 12, 13.	
Z19	1s. orange-brown (1880)	
Z20	2s. blue (1867)..................................	£300
Z21	5s. rose (1867) (Plate No. 1)....................	£550

Cancelled "C 65" *(incorrect handstamp, supplied in error) as Type* **12**.

1866–81.

Z22	½d. rose-red (1870–79) (Plate No. 10)	
Z23	1d. rose-red (1864–79)........................... *From*	75·00
	Plate Nos. 100, 106, 111, 123.	
Z23a	1½d. lake-red (1870) (Plate No. 3)	
Z24	2d. blue (1858–69) (Plate Nos. 9, 14)...........	75·00
Z25	2d. blue (1880)	
Z26	2½d. blue (1880) (Plate No. 19)	
Z27	3d. rose (1867–73) (Plate No. 9)	
Z28	3d. rose (1873–79) (Plate Nos. 14, 17, 19, 20)	
Z29	4d. vermilion (1865–73) .... *From*	60·00
	Plate Nos. 7, 8, 9, 10, 11, 12, 13 14.	
Z30	4d. vermilion (1876) (Plate No. 15)................	£300
Z31	4d. sage-green (1877) (Plate Nos. 15, 16).....*From*	£200
Z32	6d. violet (1867–70) (Plate Nos. 6, 8).............	90·00
Z33	6d. pale buff (1872) (Plate No. 11)	
Z34	6d. grey (1873) (Plate No. 12).....................	£210
Z35	6d. grey (1874–80).............................. *From*	60·00
	Plate Nos. 13, 14, 15, 16, 17.	
Z36	8d. orange (1876).................................	£400
Z37	9d. straw (1865)...................................	£450
Z38	1s. green (1865) (Plate No. 4)....................	£130
Z39	1s. green (1867) (Plate Nos. 4, 5, 6, 7)	65·00
Z40	1s. green (1873–77).............................. *From*	75·00
	Plate Nos. 8, 11, 12, 13.	
Z41	1s. orange-brown (1880)	
Z42	2s. blue (1867)..................................	£650
Z43	2s. brown (1880).................................	£2750
Z44	5s. rose (1867) (Plate Nos. 1, 2)............... *From*	£650

CHAGRES

CROWNED-CIRCLE HANDSTAMPS

CC3	CC **1** CHAGRES (16.9.1843)	

Although recorded in the GPO Proof Books, no example of No. CC3 is known on cover.

COLON

CROWNED-CIRCLE HANDSTAMPS

CC4	CC **5** COLON (R.) (21.6.1854)................ *Price on cover*	£4750

Stamps of GREAT BRITAIN *cancelled* "E 88" *as in Type* **12** *or circular date stamp as Type* **16**, **16A** *and* **17A**.

1870–81.

Z45	1d. rose-red (1864–79)........................... *From*	50·00
	Plate Nos. 107, 121, 122, 123, 125, 127, 130,	
	131, 133, 136, 138, 142, 150, 151, 152, 153,	
	155, 156, 157, 158, 160, 169, 170, 171, 174,	
	176, 178, 179, 184, 187, 188, 194, 195, 201,	
	209, 213, 214, 217.	
Z46	1d. Venetian red (1880)...........................	£120
Z47	1½d. lake-red (1870–74) (Plate No. 3).............	£100
Z48	2d. blue (1858–69) (Plate Nos. 14, 15)............	50·00
Z49	2d. pale rose (1880).............................	£150
Z50	3d. rose (1867–73) (Plate Nos. 6, 9)..............	
Z51	3d. rose (1873–76)............................... *From*	60·00
	Plate Nos. 11, 12, 16, 18, 19, 20.	
Z52	4d. vermilion (1865–73)......................... *From*	60·00
	Plate Nos. 10, 11, 12, 13 14.	
Z53	4d. vermilion (1876) (Plate No. 15)................	£300
Z54	4d. sage-green (1877) (Plate Nos. 15, 16)......*From*	£225
Z55	4d. grey-brown (1880) wmk Large Garter.............	£350
	Plate No. 17.	
Z56	4d. grey-brown (1880) wmk Crown..................	75·00
	Plate No. 17.	
Z57	6d. violet (1867–70) (Plate Nos. 6, 8, 9)...........	
Z58	6d. buff (1872) (Plate No. 11)	
Z59	6d. chestnut (1872) (Plate No. 11)...............	70·00
Z60	6d. grey (1873) (Plate No. 12)	
Z61	6d. grey (1874–80)............................. *From*	60·00
	Plate Nos. 13, 14, 15, 16, 17.	
Z62	8d. orange (1876).................................	£375
Z63	9d. straw (1867).................................	£275
Z63a	10d. red-brown (1867)	
Z64	1s. green (1867–73).............................. *From*	50·00
	Plate Nos. 4, 5, 6, 7.	
Z65	1s. green (1873–77).............................. *From*	65·00
	Plate Nos. 8, 9, 10, 11, 12, 13.	
Z66	1s. orange-brown (1880) (Plate 13)...............	£375
Z67	1s. orange-brown (1881) (Plate 13)...............	£140
Z68	2s. blue (1867)..................................	£225
Z69	2s. brown (1880).................................	£2250
Z70	5s. rose (1867) (Plate Nos. 1, 2)............... *From*	£700

PANAMA

CROWNED-CIRCLE HANDSTAMPS

CC5	CC **1** PANAMA (R.) (24.8.1846)............ *Price on cover*	£1900

Stamps of GREAT BRITAIN *cancelled* "C 35" *as in Type* **4**, **11A**, **14B** *or as* **21**.

1865–81.

Z71	½d. rose-red (1870–79) .... *From*	50·00
	Plate Nos. 10, 11, 12, 13, 14, 15, 19.	
Z72	1d. rose-red (1864–79)........................... *From*	35·00
	Plate Nos. 71, 72, 76, 81, 85, 87, 88, 89, 93,	
	95, 96, 101, 104, 114, 122, 124, 130, 138, 139,	
	142, 159, 168, 171, 172, 174, 177, 179, 180,	
	182, 184, 185, 187, 189, 191, 192, 193, 196,	
	197, 200, 203, 204, 205, 207, 208, 209, 210,	
	211, 213, 214, 215, 218, 224.	
Z73	1½d. lake-red (1870–74) (Plate No. 3)	65·00
Z74	2d. blue (1858–69)............................... *From*	40·00
	Plate Nos. 9, 12, 13, 14, 15.	
Z75	2½d. rosy mauve (1875) (Plate No. 1)..............	£250
Z76	2½d. rosy mauve (1876–80) (Plate Nos. 4, 12,16).....	£200
Z77	2½d. blue (1880) (Plate No. 19)	

Z78	2½d. blue (1881) (Plate Nos. 22, 23)	
Z79	3d. carmine-rose (1862)...........................	£300
Z80	3d. rose (1865) (Plate No. 4)	
Z81	3d. rose (1867–73)............................... *From*	50·00
	Plate Nos. 4, 5, 6, 7, 8, 9.	
Z82	3d. rose (1873–76)............................... *From*	38·00
	Plate Nos. 12, 14, 15, 16, 17, 18, 19, 20.	
Z83	3d. rose (1881) (Plate Nos. 20, 21)	
Z84	4d. red (1863) (Plate No. 4) (Hair lines)........	£110
Z85	4d. vermilion (1865–73)......................... *From*	50·00
	Plate Nos. 7, 8, 9, 10, 11, 12, 13, 14.	
Z86	4d. vermilion (1876) (Plate No. 15)................	£300
Z87	4d. sage-green (1877) (Plate Nos. 15, 16)......*From*	£200
Z88	4d. grey-brown (1880) *wmk* Crown .... *From*	55·00
	Plate Nos. 17 18.	
Z89	6d. lilac (1862) (Plate Nos. 3, 4) .... *From*	95·00
Z90	6d. lilac (1865–67) (Plate Nos. 5, 6) .... *From*	75·00
Z91	6d. lilac (1867) (Plate No. 6)	
Z92	6d. violet (1867–70) (Plate Nos. 6, 8, 9).........	70·00
Z93	6d. buff (1872–73) (Plate Nos. 11, 12)......... *From*	75·00
Z94	6d. chestnut (Plate No. 11)......................	50·00
Z95	6d. grey (1873) (Plate No. 12).....................	£210
Z96	6d. grey (1874–80)............................. *From*	50·00
	Plate Nos. 13, 14, 15, 16, 17.	
Z97	6d. grey (1881) (Plate No. 17).....................	70·00
Z98	8d. orange (1876).................................	£300
Z99	9d. straw (1862).................................	£350
Z100	9d. straw (1867).................................	£250
Z101	10d. red-brown (1867).............................	£275
Z102	1s. green (1865) (Plate No. 4)...................	£140
Z103	1s. green (1867–73).............................. *From*	45·00
	Plate Nos. 4, 5, 6, 7.	
Z104	1s. green (1873–77).............................. *From*	60·00
	Plate Nos. 8, 9, 10, 11, 12, 13.	
Z105	1s. orange-brown (1880) (Plate No. 13)............	£400
Z106	1s. orange-brown (1881) (Plate No. 13)............	£110
Z107	2s. blue (1867)..................................	£140
Z108	2s. brown (1880).................................	£1900
Z109	5s. rose (1867–74) (Plate Nos. 1, 2)........... *From*	£450

1880.

Z110	1d. Venetian red.................................	55·00
Z111	2d. rose..	£110
Z112	5d. indigo..	£190

Later stamps cancelled "C 35" are believed to originate from sailors' letters or other forms of maritime mail.

SANTA MARTHA

CROWNED-CIRCLE HANDSTAMPS

CC6	CC **1b** SANTA MARTHA (R.) (15.12.1841)	
	.... *Price on cover*	£1900

Stamps of GREAT BRITAIN *cancelled* "C 62" *as in Type* **4**.

1865–81.

Z113	½d. rose-red (1870–79) (Plate No. 6).............	90·00
Z114	1d. rose-red (1864–79) (Plate No. 106)...........	65·00
Z115	2d. blue (1858–69) (Plate Nos. 9, 13)............	90·00
Z116	4d. vermilion (1865–73)......................... *From*	60·00
	Plate Nos. 7, 8, 9, 11, 12, 13, 14.	
Z117	4d. sage-green (1877) (Plate No. 15)..............	£250
Z118	4d. grey-brown (1880) wmk Large Garter.............	£375
	Plate No. 17.	
Z119	4d. grey-brown (1880) wmk Crown..................	85·00
	Plate No. 17.	
Z120	6d. lilac (1865–67) (Plate No. 5).................	£100
Z121	6d. grey (1873) (Plate No. 12)	
Z122	6d. grey (1874–76) (Plate No. 14)	
Z123	8d. orange (1876).................................	£375
Z123a	9d. bistre (1862)	
Z124	1s. green (1865) (Plate No. 4)....................	£160
Z125	1s. green (1867–73) (Plate Nos. 5, 7) .... *From*	75·00
Z126	1s. green (1873–77) (Plate No. 8)	
Z127	2s. blue (1867)..................................	£325
Z128	5s. rose (1867) (Plate No. 2)....................	£600

SAVANILLA (BARRANQUILLA)

Stamps of GREAT BRITAIN *cancelled* "F 69" *as in Type* **12**.

1872–81.

Z129	½d. rose-red (1870–79) (Plate No. 6).............	90·00
Z130	1d. rose-red (1864–79) (Plate Nos. 122, 171).....	65·00
Z131	1½d. lake-red (1870–74) Plate No. 3).............	£110
Z131a	2d. blue (1858–69) (Plate No. 15)	
Z132	3d. rose (1867–73) (Plate No. 7)	
Z133	3d. rose (1873–76) (Plate No. 20)................	£110
Z134	3d. rose (1881) (Plate No. 20)....................	£110
Z135	4d. verm (1865–73).............................. *From*	65·00
	Plate Nos. 12, 13, 14.	
Z136	4d. vermilion (1876) (Plate No. 15)................	£325
Z137	4d. sage-green (1877) (Plate Nos. 15, 16)......*From*	£225
Z138	4d. grey-brown (1880) wmk Large Garter.............	£375
	Plate No. 17.	
Z139	4d. grey-brown (1880) wmk Crown..................	75·00
	Plate No. 17.	
Z140	6d. buff (1872) (Plate No. 11)	
Z141	6d. grey (1878) (Plate Nos. 16, 17)...............	80·00
Z142	8d. orange (1876).................................	£375
Z143	1s. green (1867–73) (Plate No. 5,7)...............	85·00
Z144	1s. green (1873–77) (Plate Nos. 8, 11, 12, 13)...	90·00
Z145	1s. orange-brown (1880)..........................	£400
Z146	2s. blue (1867)..................................	£300
Z147	5s. rose (1867–74) (Plate No. 2).................	£600

CUBA

The British Postal Agency at Havana opened in 1762, the island then being part of the Spanish Empire. A further office, at St. Jago de Cuba, was added in 1841.

Great Britain stamps were supplied to Havana in 1865 and to St. Jago de Cuba in 1866. They continued in use until the offices closed on 30 May 1877.

HAVANA

CROWNED-CIRCLE HANDSTAMPS

1890.
CC1	CC **1b** HAVANA (13.11.1841)	*Price on cover*	£1200
CC2	CC **1c** HAVANA (1848)	*Price on cover*	£1200
CC3	CC **2** HAVANA (14.7.1848)	*Price on cover*	£1000

*Stamps of GREAT BRITAIN cancelled "C 58" as in Type **4**, or as Type **14**, **14B**.*

1865–77.
Z1	½d. rose-red (1870) (Plate Nos. 6, 12)	75·00
Z2	1d. rose-red (1864–79)	60·00
	Plate Nos. 86, 90, 93, 115, 120, 123, 144, 146, 171, 174, 208.	
Z3	2d. blue (1858–69) (Plate Nos. 9, 14, 15)	75·00
Z4	3d. rose (1867–73) (Plate No. 4)	£140
Z5	3d. rose (1873–76) (Plate Nos. 18, 19)	
Z6	4d. vermilion (1865–73)	65·00
	Plate Nos. 7, 8, 10, 11, 12, 13, 14.	
Z7	4d. vermilion (1876) (Plate No. 15)	£300
Z8	6d. lilac (1865) (with hyphen) (Plate No. 5)	
Z9	6d. grey (1874–76) (Plate No. 15)	
Z10	8d. orange (1876)	£375
Z11	9d. straw (1867)	£300
Z12	10d. red-brown (1867)	£325
Z13	1s. green (1865) (Plate No. 4)	£160
Z14	1s. green (1867–73) (Plate Nos. 4, 5, 7)........*From*	65·00
Z15	1s. green (1873–77) (Plate Nos. 10, 12, 13)	
	....*From*	90·00
Z16	2s. blue (1867)	£275
Z17	5s. rose (1867–74) (Plate Nos. 1, 2)..............*From*	£650

ST. JAGO DE CUBA

CROWNED-CIRCLE HANDSTAMPS

CC4	CC **1b** ST JAGO-DE-CUBA (R.) (15.12.1841)		
	.... *Price on cover*		£6000

*Stamps of GREAT BRITAIN cancelled "C 88" as Type **12**.*

1866–77.
Z18	½d. rose-red (1870–79) (Plate Nos. 4, 6, 14)	
Z19	1d. rose-red (1864–79)................*From*	£225
	Plate Nos. 100, 105, 106, 109, 111, 120, 123, 138, 144, 146, 147, 148, 171, 208.	
Z20	1½d. lake-red (1870–74) (Plate No. 3)	
Z21	2d. blue (1858–69) (Plate Nos. 9, 12, 13, 14)	£325
Z22	3d. rose (1867) (Plate No. 5).	
Z23	4d. vermilion (1865–73)................*From*	£350
	Plate Nos. 9, 10, 11, 12, 13, 14.	
Z24	4d. vermilion (1876) (Plate No. 15)	£850
Z25	6d. violet (1867–70) (Plate Nos. 6, 8, 9)........*From*	£700
Z26	6d. buff (Plate No. 11)	
Z27	9d. straw (1865)	
Z27a	9d. straw (1867)	£900
Z28	10d. red-brown (1867)	£900
Z29	1s. green (1867–73) (Plate Nos. 4, 5, 6) ....*From*	£700
Z30	1s. green (1873–77) (Plate Nos. 9, 10, 12, 13)	
Z31	2s. blue (1867)	
Z32	5s. rose (1867) (Plate 1).	

DANISH WEST INDIES

ST. THOMAS

The British Postal Agency at St. Thomas opened in January 1809 and by 1825 was the office around which many of the packet routes were organised.

Great Britain stamps were introduced on 3 July 1865 and can be found used in combination with Danish West Indies adhesives paying the local postage.

Following a hurricane in October 1867 the main British packet office was moved to Colon in Colombia.

The British Post Office at St. Thomas closed to the public on 1 September 1877, but continued to operate as a transit office for a further two years.

CROWNED-CIRCLE HANDSTAMPS

CC1	CC **1** ST. THOMAS (R.) (20.2.49) ....*Price on cover*		£500
CC2	CC **6** ST. THOMAS (R.) (1.5.1855)........*Price on cover*		£1800

*Stamps of GREAT BRITAIN cancelled "C 51" as in Types **4**, **12** or **14**.*

1865–79.
Z1	½d. rose-red (1870–79)	38·00
	Plate Nos. 5, 6, 8, 10, 11, 12.	
Z2	1d. rose-red (1857)	
Z3	1d. rose-red (1864–79)................*From*	27·00
	Plate Nos. 71, 72, 79, 81, 84, 85, 86, 87, 88, 89, 90, 93, 94, 95, 96, 97, 98, 99, 100, 101, 102, 105, 106, 107, 108, 109, 110, 111, 112, 113, 114, 116, 117, 118, 119, 120, 121, 122, 123, 124, 125, 127, 129, 130, 131, 133, 134, 136, 137, 138, 139, 140, 141, 142, 144, 145, 146, 147, 148, 149, 150, 151, 152, 154, 155, 156, 157, 158, 159, 160, 161, 162, 163, 164, 165, 166, 167, 169, 170, 171, 172, 173, 174, 175, 176, 177, 178, 179, 180, 181, 182, 184, 185, 186, 187, 189, 190, 197.	
Z4	1½d. lake-red (1870–74) (Plate Nos. 1, 3)	65·00
Z5	2d. blue (1858–69)................*From*	32·00
	Plate Nos. 9, 12, 13, 14, 15.	
Z6	3d. rose (1865) (Plate No. 4)	90·00
Z7	3d. rose (1867–73)................*From*	45·00
	Plate Nos. 4, 5, 6, 7, 8, 9, 10.	
Z8	3d. rose (1873–76)................*From*	32·00
	Plate Nos. 11, 12, 14, 15, 16, 17, 18, 19.	
Z9	4d. red (1862) (Plate Nos. 3, 4)	75·00
Z10	4d. vermilion (1865–73)................*From*	50·00
	Plate Nos. 7, 8, 9, 10, 11, 12, 13, 14.	
Z11	4d. vermilion (1876) (Plate No. 15)	£300
Z12	4d. sage-green (1877) (Plate Nos. 15, 16)..*From*	£200
Z14	6d. lilac (1864) (Plate No. 4)	£150
Z15	6d. lilac (1865–67) (Plate Nos. 5, 6) ....*From*	75·00
Z16	6d. lilac (1867) (Plate No. 6)	75·00
Z17	6d. violet (1867–70) (Plate Nos. 6, 8, 9) ....*From*	70·00
Z18	6d. buff (1872–73) (Plate Nos. 11, 12)	75·00
Z19	6d. chestnut (1872) (Plate No. 11)	45·00

Z20	6d. grey (1873) (Plate No. 12)	£210
Z21	6d. grey (1874–76) .... *From*	45·00
	Plate Nos. 13, 14, 15, 16.	
Z22	8d. orange (1876)	£275
Z23	9d. straw (1862)	£275
Z24	9d. bistre (1862)	£300
Z25	9d. straw (1865)	£375
Z26	9d. straw (1867)	£200
Z27	10d. red-brown (1867)	£275
Z28	1s. green (1865) (Plate No. 4)	£140
Z29	1s. green (1867–73) (Plate Nos. 4, 5, 6, 7)....*From*	32·00
Z30	1s. green (1873–77)	60·00
	Plate Nos, 8, 9, 10, 11, 12, 13.	
Z31	2s. blue (1867)	£130
Z32	5s. rose (1867–74) (Plate Nos. 1, 2)	£450

DOMINICAN REPUBLIC

British Postal Agencies may have existed in the area before 1867, but it is only from that year that details can be found concerning offices at Porto Plata and St. Domingo. Both were closed in 1871, but re-opened in 1876.

Although postmarks were supplied in 1866 it seems likely that Great Britain stamps were not sent until the offices re-opened in 1876.

Covers exist showing Great Britain stamps used in combination with those of Dominican Republic with the latter paying the local postage. Both agencies finally closed in 1881.

PORTO PLATA

*Stamps of GREAT BRITAIN cancelled "C 86" or circular date stamp as in Types **8** or **17**.*

1876–81.
Z1	½d. rose-red (1870–79)................................ *From*	90·00
	Plate Nos. 10, 12, 14.	
Z2	1d. rose-red (1864–79)................................ *From*	70·00
	Plate Nos. 123, 130, 136, 146, 151, 178, 199, 200, 205, 217.	
Z3	1½d. lake-red (1870–74) (Plate No. 3)	£110
Z4	2d. blue (1858–69) (Plate Nos. 14, 15)	£120
Z5	2½d. rosy mauve (1876–79) .... *From*	£250
	Plate Nos. 13, 14.	
Z6	3d. rose (1873–76) (Plate No. 18)	£120
Z7	4d. vermilion (1873) (Plate No. 14)	£120
Z8	4d. vermilion (1876) (Plate No. 15)	£325
Z9	4d. sage-green (1877) (Plate No. 15)	£275
Z10	6d. violet (1867–70) (Plate No. 8)	
Z11	6d. grey (1874–76) (Plate No. 15)	£100
Z12	8d. orange (1876)	£425
Z13	1s. green (1867–73) (Plate Nos. 4, 7)	£100
Z14	1s. green (1873–77)	£100
	Plate Nos. 11, 12, 13.	
Z15	2s. blue (1867)	£300
Z15a	5s. rose (1867–83) (Plate No. 2)	

ST. DOMINGO

*Stamps of GREAT BRITAIN cancelled "C 87" or circular date stamp as in Types **12** or **16**.*

1876–81.
Z16	½d. rose-red (1870–79)................................ *From*	£120
	Plate Nos. 5, 6, 8, 10, 11, 13.	
Z17	1d. rose-red (1864–79)................................ *From*	£100
	Plate Nos. 146, 154, 171, 173, 174, 176, 178, 133, 136, 190, 197, 220.	
Z18	1½d. lake-red (1870–74) (Plate No. 3)	£150
Z19	2d. blue (1858–69) (Plate Nos. 13, 14)	£150
Z20	3d. rose (1873–76) (Plate No. 18)	
Z21	4d. vermilion (1865–73)................................ *From*	£150
	Plate Nos. 11, 12, 14.	
Z22	4d. vermilion (1876) (Plate No. 15)	£500
Z23	4d. sage-green (1877) (Plate No. 15)	£350
Z24	6d. grey (1874–76) (Plate No. 15)	
Z25	9d. straw (1867)	
Z26	1s. green (1867) (Plate No. 4)	
Z27	1s. green (1873–77) .... *From*	£140
	Plate Nos. 10, 11, 12, 13.	
Z28	2s. blue (1867)	

ECUADOR

GUAYAQUIL

The first British Postal Agent in Guayaquil was appointed in 1848.

Great Britain stamps were supplied in 1865 and continued to be used until the agency closed on 30 June 1880. They can be found used in combination with stamps of Ecuador with the latter paying the local postage.

*Stamps of GREAT BRITAIN cancelled "C 41" as Type **4**.*

1865–80.
Z1	½d. rose-red (1870–79) (Plate Nos. 5, 6)	60·00
Z2	1d. rose-red (1857)	
Z3	1d. rose-red (1864–79) .... *From*	45·00
	Plate Nos. 74, 78, 85, 92, 94, 105, 110, 115, 133, 140, 145, 166, 174, 180, 216.	
Z4	1½d. lake-red (1870–74) (Plate No. 3)	90·00
Z5	2d. blue (1858–69) (Plate Nos. 9, 13, 14) ..... *From*	50·00
Z6	3d. carmine-rose (1862)	£275
Z7	3d. rose (1865) (Plate No. 4)	£120
Z8	3d. rose (1867–73) (Plate Nos. 5, 6, 7, 9, 10)..*From*	50·00
Z9	3d. rose (1873–76) .... *From*	50·00
	Plate Nos. 11, 12, 15, 16, 17, 18, 19, 20.	
Z10	4d. red (1862) (Plate Nos. 3, 4)	£120
Z11	4d. vermilion (1865–73) .... *From*	55·00
	Plate Nos. 7, 8, 9, 10, 11, 12, 13, 14.	
Z12	4d. vermilion (1876) (Plate No. 15)	£300
Z13	4d. sage-green (1877) (Plate Nos. 15, 16).....*From*	£200
Z14	6d. lilac (1864) (Plate No. 4)	£150
Z15	6d. lilac (1865–67) (Plate Nos. 5, 6)	75·00
Z16	6d. lilac (1867) (Plate No. 6)	
Z17	6d. violet (1867–70) (Plate Nos. 6, 8, 9) .....*From*	70·00
Z18	6d. buff (1872–73) (Plate Nos. 11,12)	80·00
Z19	6d. chestnut (1872)	
Z20	6d. grey (1873) (Plate No. 12)	

Z21	6d. grey (1874–76) .... *From*	50·00
	Plate Nos. 13, 14, 15, 16.	
Z22	8d. orange (1876)	£350
Z23	9d. straw (1862)	£300
Z24	9d. straw (1867)	£225
Z25	10d. red-brown (1867)	£325
Z26	1s. green (1865) (Plate No. 4)	£160
Z27	1s. green (1867–73) (Plate Nos. 4, 5, 6, 7)....*From*	45·00
Z28	1s. green (1873–77) .... *From*	75·00
	Plate Nos. 8, 9, 10, 11, 12, 13.	
Z29	2s. blue (1867)	£175
Z30	2s. brown (1880)	£2500
Z31	5s. rose (1867–74) (Plate Nos. 1, 2). .... *From*	£525

FERNANDO PO

The British government leased naval facilities on this Spanish island from 1827 until 1834. A British Consul was appointed in 1849 and a postal agency was opened on 1 April 1858.

The use of Great Britain stamps was authorised in 1858, but a cancellation was not supplied until 1874. The office remained open until 1877.

CROWNED-CIRCLE HANDSTAMPS

CC1	CC **4** FERNANDO-PO (R.) (19.2.1859) *Price on cover*		£7000

*Stamps of GREAT BRITAIN cancelled "247" as Type **9**.*

1874–77.
Z1	4d. vermilion (1865–72) (Plate Nos. 13, 14)...........	£2250
Z2	4d. vermilion (1876) (Plate No. 15)	£2000
Z3	6d. grey (1874–76) (Plate Nos. 13, 14, 15, 16).......	£2000

GUADELOUPE

A British Packet Agency was established on Guadeloupe on 1 October 1848 and continued to function until 1874.

No. CC1 is often found used in conjunction with French Colonies (General Issues) adhesive stamps.

A similar packet agency existed on Martinique from 1 October 1848 until 1879, but no crowned-circle handstamp was issued for it.

CROWNED-CIRCLE HANDSTAMPS

CC1	CC **1** GUADALOUPE (R., B. or Black) (9.3.1849)		
	.... *Price on cover*		£2250

HAITI

The original British Postal Agencies in Haiti date from 1830 when it is known a Packet Agency was established at Jacmel. An office at Port-au-Prince followed in 1842, both these agencies remaining in operation until 30 June 1881.

During this period short-lived agencies also operated in the following Haitian towns: Aux Cayes (1848 to 1863), Cap Haitien (1842 to 1863), Gonaives (1849 to 1857) and St. Marc (1854 to 1861). A further agency may have operated at Le Mole around the year 1841.

Great Britain stamps were supplied to Jacmel in 1865 and to Port-au-Prince in 1869.

CAP HAITIEN

CROWNED-CIRCLE HANDSTAMPS

CC1	CC **1b** CAPE-HAITIEN (R.) (31.12.1841)...............
	Although recorded in the GPO Proof Books, no example of No. CC1 is known on cover.

JACMEL

CROWNED-CIRCLE HANDSTAMPS

CC2	CC **1b** JACMEL (R.) (29.6.1843)............... *Price on cover*		£950

*Stamps of GREAT BRITAIN cancelled "C 59" as Type **4** or with circular date stamp as Type **16A**.*

1865–81.
Z1	½d. rose-red (1870–79) .... *From*	60·00
	Plate Nos. 4, 5, 6, 10, 11, 12, 14, 15.	
Z2	1d. rose-red (1864–79) .... *From*	45·00
	Plate Nos. 74, 81, 84, 87, 95, 106, 107, 109, 122, 136, 137, 139, 146, 148, 150, 151, 152, 156, 157, 159, 160, 162, 164, 166, 167, 170, 171, 179, 181, 183, 184, 186, 187, 189, 192, 194, 198, 200, 204, 206, 215, 219.	
Z3	1½d. lake-red (1870–74) (Plate No. 3)	65·00
Z4	2d. blue (1858–69) (Plate Nos. 9, 13, 14, 15)	45·00
Z5	2½d. rosy mauve (1876) (Plate No. 4)	
Z6	3d. rose (1867–73) .... *From*	50·00
	Plate Nos. 5, 6, 7, 8, 9, 10.	
Z7	3d. rose (1873–76)	50·00
	Plate Nos. 11, 12, 14, 16, 17, 18, 19.	
Z8	4d. red (1863) (Plate No. 4) (Hair lines)	£120
Z9	4d. vermilion (1865–73) .... *From*	50·00
	Plate Nos. 7, 8, 9, 10, 11, 12, 13, 14.	
Z10	4d. vermilion (1876) (Plate No. 15)	£300
Z11	4d. sage-green (1877) (Plate Nos. 15, 16)....*From*	£200
Z12	4d. grey-brown (1880) *wmk* Large Garter................	£325
	Plate No. 17.	
Z13	4d. grey-brown (1880) *wmk* Crown................	55·00
	Plate No. 17.	
Z14	6d. lilac (1867) (Plate Nos. 5, 6)	80·00
Z15	6d. violet (1867–70) (Plate Nos. 8, 9)	75·00
Z16	6d. buff (1872–73) (Plate Nos. 11, 12)	80·00
Z17	6d. chestnut (1872) (Plate No. 11)	
Z18	6d. grey (1873) (Plate No. 12)	
Z19	6d. grey (1874–76) .... *From*	55·00
	Plate Nos. 13, 14, 15, 16, 17.	
Z20	8d. orange (1876)	£325
Z21	9d. straw (1862)	£275
Z22	9d. straw (1867)	£200
Z23	10d. red-brown (1867)	£325
Z24	1s. green (1865) (Plate No. 4)	£140
Z25	1s. green (1867–73) (Plate Nos. 4, 5, 6, 7) ....*From*	45·00

Z26	1s. green (1873–77).................................. *From*	65·00
	Plate Nos. 8, 9, 10, 11, 12, 13.	
Z27	1s. orange-brown (1880) (Plate No. 13)..................	£375
Z28	1s. blue (1867)...	£150
Z29	2s. brown (1880)...	£2500
Z30	5s. rose (1867–74) (Plate Nos. 1, 2)............... *From*	£500

1880.

Z31	½d. green (1880)...	80·00
Z32	1d. Venetian red..	80·00
Z33	1½d. Venetian red...	£110
Z34	2d. rose..	£150

PORT-AU-PRINCE

CROWNED-CIRCLE HANDSTAMPS

CC3	CC **1b** PORT-AU-PRINCE (R.) (29.6.1843)	
	.... *Price on cover*	£2500

Stamps of GREAT BRITAIN cancelled "E 53" as in Types **8**, **12** *or* **16**.

1869–81.

Z35	½d. rose-red (1870–79)............................ *From*	60·00
	Plate Nos. 5, 6, 10, 11, 12, 13, 14.	
Z36	1d. rose-red (1864–79)............................ *From*	45·00
	Plate Nos. 87, 134, 154,146, 159, 167, 171,	
	173, 174, 177, 181, 183, 187, 189, 193, 199,	
	200, 201, 202, 206, 209, 210, 218, 219.	
Z37	1½d. lake-red (1870–74) (Plate No. 3)	80·00
Z38	2d. blue (1858–69) (Plate Nos. 9, 14, 15)	50·00
Z40	2½d. rosy mauve (1876–79) (Plate Nos. 3, 9).....*From*	£175
Z41	3d. rose (1867–73) (Plate Nos. 6, 7)	
Z42	3d. rose (1873–79) (Plate Nos. 17, 18, 20)	50·00
Z43	4d. vermilion (1865–73) .... *From*	50·00
	Plate Nos. 11, 12, 13, 14.	
Z44	4d. vermilion (1876) (Plate No. 15).................	£300
Z45	4d. sage-green (1877) (Plate Nos. 15, 16)....*From*	£200
Z46	4d. grey-brown (1880) wmk	£325
	Large Garter Plate No. 17.	
Z47	4d. grey-brown (1880) wmk Crown	55·00
	Plate No. 17.	
Z48	6d. grey (1874–76) (Plate Nos. 15, 16)	
Z49	8d. orange (1876)	£350
Z50	1s. green (1867–73) (Plate Nos. 4, 5, 6, 7).....*From*	45·00
Z51	1s. green (1873–77)............................... *From*	65·00
	Plate Nos. 8, 9, 10, 11, 12, 13.	
Z52	1s. orange-brown (1880) (Plate No. 13)...........	£375
Z53	1s. orange-brown (1880) (Plate No. 13)...........	£120
Z54	2s. blue (1867).......................................	£175
Z55	2s. brown (1880).....................................	£2750
Z56	5s. rose (1867–74) (Plate Nos. 1, 2)............. *From*	£550
Z57	10s. greenish grey (1878)	£4500

1880.

Z58	½d. green	80·00
Z59	1d. Venetian red	80·00
Z60	1½d. Venetian red	£110
Z61	2d. rose	£150

MACAO

A British Consular Post Office opened in 1841. It had been preceded by the Macao Boat Office, possibly a private venture, which operated in the 1830s. The office closed when the consulate closed on 30 September 1845, but was back in operation by 1854.

The Agency continued to function, in conjunction with the Hong Kong Post Office, until 28 February 1884 when Portugal joined the UPU.

CROWNED-CIRCLE HANDSTAMPS

Z 2

CC1	– PAID AT MACAO (crowned-oval 20 mm	
	wide) (R.) (1844) .... *Price on cover*	£32500
CC2	Z **2** Crown and Macao (1881)......................	

No. CC2 with the Crown removed was used by the Portuguese post office in Macao as a cancellation until 1890.

A locally-cut mark, as Type CC **2**, inscribed "PAGO EM MACAO" is known on covers between 1870 and 1877. It was probably used by the Portuguese postmaster to send letters via the British Post Office (*Price £10000*).

MADEIRA

The British Packet Agency on this Portuguese island was opened in 1767 and was of increased importance from 1808 following the exile of the Portuguese royal family to Brazil. The South American packets ceased to call in 1858. It appears to have closed sometime around 1860.

CROWN-CIRCLE HANDSTAMPS

CC1	CC **1b** MADEIRA (R.) (28.2.1842)............ *Price on cover*	£17500

MEXICO

The British Postal Agency at Vera Cruz opened in 1825, following the introduction of the Mexican Packet service. No handstamps were supplied, however, until 1842, when a similar agency at Tampico was set up.

Great Britain stamps were used at Tampico from 1867 but, apparently, were never sent to the Vera Cruz office. Combination covers exist showing the local postage paid by Mexican adhesives.

The Agency at Vera Cruz closed in 1874 and that at Tampico in 1876.

TAMPICO

CROWNED-CIRCLE HANDSTAMPS

CC1	CC **1b** TAMPICO (R.) (13.11.1841).......... *Price on cover*	£1800

No. CC1 may be found on cover, used in conjunction with Mexico adhesive stamps.

Stamps of GREAT BRITAIN cancelled "C 63" as Type 4.

1867–76.

Z1	1d. rose-red (1864–79)............................ *From*	£150
	Plate Nos. 81, 89, 96, 103, 117, 139, 147.	
Z2	2d. blue (1858–69) (Plate Nos. 9, 14)...........	£200
Z3	4d. vermilion (1865–73) .... *From*	£150
	Plate Nos. 7, 8, 10, 11, 12, 13, 14.	
Z4	1s. green (1867–73) (Plate Nos. 4, 5, 7, 8).......	£225
Z5	2s. blue (1867)	£600

VERA CRUZ

CROWNED-CIRCLE HANDSTAMPS

CC2	CC **1b** VERA CRUZ (R.) (13.11.1841) .....*Price on cover*	£2250
CC3	VERA CRUZ (Black) (*circa* 1845).*Price on cover*	£1000

NICARAGUA

GREYTOWN

British involvement on the Mosquito Coast of Nicaragua dates from 1655 when contacts were first made with the indigenous Misquito Indians. A formal alliance was signed in 1740 and the area was considered as a British dependency until the Spanish authorities negotiated a withdrawal in 1786.

The Misquitos remained under British protection, however, and, following the revolutionary period in the Spanish dominions, this eventually led to the appropriation, by the Misquitos with British backing, of the town of San Juan del Norte, later renamed Greytown.

The port was included in the Royal West Indian Mail Steam Packet Company's mail network from January 1842, forming part of the Jamaica District. This arrangement only lasted until September of that year, however, although packets were once again calling at Greytown by November 1844. Following the discovery of gold in California the office increased in importance, owing to the overland traffic, although the first distinctive postmark is not recorded in use until February 1856.

A subsidiary agency, without its own postmark, operated at Bluefields from 1857 to 1863.

The British Protectorate over the Misquitos ended in 1860, but the British Post Office at Greytown continued to operate, being supplied with Great Britain stamps in 1865. These are occasionally found in combination with Nicaragua issues, which had only internal validity.

The British Post Office at Greytown closed on 1 May 1882 when the Republic of Nicaragua joined the UPU

CROWNED-CIRCLE HANDSTAMPS

CC1	C **4** GREYTOWN (R.) (14.4.1859)................................	

Although recorded in the GPO Proof Books, no example of No. CC1 is known on cover.

Stamps of GREAT BRITAIN cancelled "C 57" as in Types **4** (issued 1865), **14A** (issued 1875), or with circular postmark as Type **16** (issued 1864).

1865–82.

Z1	½d. rose-red (1870–79) (Plate Nos. 5, 10, 11)........	80·00
Z2	1d. rose-red (1864–79)............................ *From*	50·00
	Plate Nos. 180, 197, 210.	
Z3	1½d. lake-red (1870) (Plate No. 3).................	75·00
Z4	2d. blue (1858–69) (Plate Nos. 9, 14, 15).......	
Z5	3d. rose (1873–76) (Plate Nos. 17, 18, 19, 20)...	55·00
Z6	3d. rose (1881) (Plate No. 20)......................	
Z7	4d. vermilion (1865–73) .... *From*	55·00
	Plate Nos. 8, 10, 11, 12, 13, 14.	
Z8	4d. vermilion (1876) (Plate No. 15).................	£300
Z9	4d. sage-green (1877) (Plate Nos. 15, 16).....*From*	£200
Z10	4d. grey-brown (1880) wmk Large Garter.............	£325
	Plate No. 17.	
Z11	4d. grey-brown (1880) wmk Crown	90·00
	Plate No. 17.	
Z12	6d. grey (1874–76) (Plate Nos. 14, 15, 16, 17)...	95·00
Z13	8d. orange (1876)	£325
Z14	1s. green (1865) (Plate No. 4)	
Z15	1s. green (1867–73) (Plate Nos. 6, 7)	
Z16	1s. green (1873–77)............................... *From*	65·00
	Plate Nos. 8, 10, 12, 13.	
Z17	1s. orange-brown (1880) (Plate No. 13)...........	£375
Z18	1s. orange-brown (1881) (Plate No. 13)...........	£110
Z19	2s. blue (1867).......................................	£200
Z20	2s. brown (1880).....................................	£2750
Z21	5s. rose (1867–74) (Plate Nos. 1, 2)............. *From*	£550
Z22	5s. rose (1882) (Plate No. 4), *blue paper*........	£3000
Z23	10s. greenish grey (1878)	£4500

1880.

Z24	1d. Venetian red..................................	80·00
Z25	1½d. Venetian red.................................	80·00

PERU

British Agencies in Peru date from 1846 when offices were established at Arica and Callao. The network was later expanded to include agencies at Paita (1848), Pisco (1868) and Iquique and Islay (both 1869). This last office was transferred to Mollendo in 1877.

It is believed that a further agency existed at Pisagua, but no details exist.

Great Britain stamps were supplied from 1865 and are often found in combination with Peru adhesives which paid the local postal tax.

The Postal Agency at Pisco closed in 1870 and the remainder in 1879, the towns of Arica, Iquique and Pisagua passing to Chile by treaty in 1883.

ARICA

CROWNED-CIRCLE HANDSTAMPS

CC1	CC **1** ARICA (Black) (5.11.1850) ....*Price on cover*	£4750

Stamps of Great Britain cancelled "C 36" as Types **4**, **12**, **14B** *and* **16A** *in black, blue or red.*

1865–79.

Z1	½d. rose-red (1870–79)............................ *From*	75·00
	Plate Nos. 5, 6, 10, 11, 13.	
Z2	1d. rose-red (1864–79)............................ *From*	65·00
	Plate Nos. 102, 139, 140, 163, 167.	
Z3	1½d. lake-red (1870–74) (Plate No. 3)	
Z4	2d. blue (1858–69) (Plate Nos. 13, 14)	75·00
Z5	3d. rose (1867–73) (Plate Nos. 5, 9)...............	
Z6	3d. rose (1873–76) .... *From*	65·00
	Plate Nos. 11, 12, 17, 18, 19.	
Z7	4d. vermilion (1865–73) .... *From*	65·00
	Plate Nos. 10, 11, 12, 13, 14.	
Z8	4d. vermilion (1876) (Plate No. 15).	
Z9	4d. sage-green (1877) (Plate Nos. 15, 16).........	£225
Z10	6d. lilac (1862) (Plate Nos. 3, 4).	
Z11	6d. lilac (1865–67) (Plate No. 5).	
Z12	6d. violet (1867–70) (Plate Nos. 6, 8, 9)...... *From*	80·00
Z13	6d. buff (1872) (Plate No. 11)	£100
Z14	6d. chestnut (1872) (Plate No. 11)	£100
Z15	6d. grey (1873) (Plate No. 12)	£225
Z16	6d. grey (1874–76) .... *From*	55·00
	Plate Nos. 13, 14, 15, 16.	
Z17	8d. orange (1876)	
Z18	9d. straw (1862)	
Z19	9d. straw (1865)	
Z20	9d. straw (1867)	£250
Z21	10d. red-brown (1867)	
Z22	1s. green (1862)	
Z23	1s. green (1865)	
Z24	1s. green (1867–73) (Plate Nos. 4, 5, 6, 7).......	60·00
Z25	1s. green (1873–77)............................... *From*	70·00
	Plate Nos. 8, 9, 10, 11, 12, 13.	
Z26	2s. blue (1867)	£225
Z27	5s. rose (1867–74) (Plate Nos. 1, 2)............. *From*	£600

CALLAO

CROWNED-CIRCLE HANDSTAMPS

CC2	CC **1** CALLAO (R.) (13.1.1846) .... *Price on cover*	£800

A second version of No. CC 2, showing "PAID" more curved, was supplied in July 1847.

No. CC2 can be found used on covers from 1865 showing the local postage paid by a Peru adhesive.

Stamps of GREAT BRITAIN cancelled "C 38" as in Types **4**, **12** *and* **14B**, *with circular date stamp as* **16A** *or with boxed handstamp Type* **22**.

1865–79.

Z28	½d. rose-red (1870–79)............................ *From*	45·00
	Plate Nos. 5, 6, 10, 11, 12, 13, 14.	
Z29	1d. rose-red (1864–79)............................ *From*	35·00
	Plate Nos. 74, 88, 89, 93, 94, 97, 108, 120,	
	121, 123, 127, 128, 130, 134, 137, 139, 140,	
	141, 143, 144, 145, 146, 148, 149, 156, 157,	
	160, 163, 167, 171, 172, 173, 175, 176, 180,	
	181, 182, 183, 185, 187, 190, 193, 195, 198,	
	199, 200, 201, 204, 206, 209, 210, 212, 213,	
	215.	
Z30	1½d. lake-red (1870–74) (Plate No. 3)	
Z31	2d. blue (1858–69) .... *From*	35·00
	Plate Nos. 9, 12, 13, 14, 15.	
Z32	3d. carmine-rose (1862)	
Z33	3d. rose (1865) (Plate No. 4).	£100
Z34	3d. rose (1867–73) .... *From*	45·00
	Plate Nos. 5, 6, 7, 8, 9, 10.	
Z35	3d. rose (1873–76) .... *From*	45·00
	Plate Nos. 11, 12, 14, 15, 16, 17, 18, 19.	
Z36	4d. red (1862) (Plate Nos. 3, 4).	
Z37	4d. vermilion (1865–73) .... *From*	38·00
	Plate Nos. 8, 10, 11, 12, 13, 14.	
Z38	4d. vermilion (1876) (Plate No. 15)	£300
Z39	4d. sage-green (1877) (Plate Nos. 15, 16)	£200
Z40	6d. lilac (1862) (Plate Nos. 3, 4)	
Z40a	6d. lilac (1865) (Plate No. 5)	
Z41	6d. lilac (1867)	
Z42	6d. violet (1867–70) .... *From*	70·00
	Plate Nos. 6, 8, 9.	
Z43	6d. buff (1872–73) (Plate Nos. 11, 12) ...... *From*	70·00
Z44	6d. chestnut (1872) (Plate No. 11)	50·00
Z45	6d. grey (1873) (Plate No. 12)	£210
Z46	6d. grey (1874–80) .... *From*	50·00
	Plate Nos. 13, 14, 15, 16.	
Z47	8d. orange (1876)	£275
Z48	9d. straw (1862)	
Z49	9d. straw (1865)	£400
Z50	9d. straw (1867)	£200
Z51	10d. red-brown (1867)	£275
Z52	1s. green (1865)	
Z53	1s. green (1867–73) .... *From*	38·00
	Plate Nos. 4, 5, 6, 7.	
Z54	1s. green (1873–77)............................... *From*	55·00
	Plate Nos. 8, 9, 10, 11, 12, 13.	
Z55	2s. blue (1867)	£120
Z56	5s. rose (1867–74) (Plate Nos. 1, 2)............. *From*	£450

IQUIQUE

Stamps of GREAT BRITAIN cancelled "D 87" as Type **12** *in black or blue.*

1865–79.

Z57	½d. rose-red (1870–79) (Plate Nos. 5, 6, 13, 14).....	75·00
Z58	1d. rose-red (1864–79)............................ *From*	55·00
	Plate Nos. 76, 179, 185, 205.	
Z59	2d. blue (1858–69) (Plate Nos. 9, 12, 13, 14)	55·00
Z60	3d. rose (1867–73) (Plate Nos. 5, 6, 7, 8, 9) ...*From*	65·00
Z61	3d. rose (1873–76) (Plate Nos. 12, 18, 19)	75·00
Z62	4d. vermilion (1865–73) .... *From*	70·00
	Plate Nos. 12, 13, 14.	
Z63	4d. vermilion (1876) (Plate No. 15)	£300
Z64	4d. sage-green (1877) (Plate Nos. 15, 16)....*From*	£200
Z65	6d. mauve (1869) (Plate Nos. 8, 9)	
Z66	6d. buff (1872–73) (Plate Nos. 11, 12) ...... *From*	£110
Z67	6d. chestnut (1872) (Plate No. 11)	
Z68	6d. grey (1873) (Plate No. 12)	£225
Z69	6d. grey (1874–76) (Plate Nos. 13, 14, 15, 16)....	80·00
Z70	8d. orange (1876)	£350

Z71	9d. straw (1867)		£200
Z72	10d. red-brown (1867)		
Z73	1s. green (1867–73) (Plate Nos. 4, 6, 7)	From	60·00
Z74	1s. green (1873–77)	From	80·00
	Plate Nos. 8, 9, 10, 11, 12, 13.		
Z75	2s. blue (1867)		£250
Z75a	5s. rose (1857) (Plate No. 2)		

ISLAY (later MOLLENDO)

CROWNED-CIRCLE HANDSTAMPS

CC4	CC **1** ISLAY (Black) (23.10.1850) .... *Price on cover*		£5000

Stamps of GREAT BRITAIN cancelled "C 42" as Type **4** or with circular date stamp as Type **16**.

1865–79.

Z76	1d. rose-red (1864–79)	From	55·00
	Plate Nos. 78, 84, 87, 88, 96, 97, 103, 125, 134.		
Z77	1½d. lake-red (1870–74) (Plate No. 3)		
Z78	2d. blue (1858–69) (Plate Nos. 9, 13, 15)		55·00
Z79	3d. carmine-rose (1862)		
Z80	3d. rose (1865)		£110
Z81	3d. rose (1867–73) (Plate Nos. 4, 5, 6, 10)	From	70·00
Z82	4d. red (1862) (Plate Nos. 3, 4)		£130
Z83	4d. vermilion (1867–73)	From	70·00
	Plate Nos. 9, 10, 11, 12, 13.		
Z84	4d. vermilion (1876) (Plate No. 15)		
Z85	4d. sage-green (1877) (Plate Nos. 15, 16)	From	£200
Z86	6d. lilac (1862) (Plate Nos. 3, 4)	From	90·00
Z87	6d. lilac (1865) (Plate No. 5)		80·00
Z88	6d. violet (1867–70) (Plate Nos. 6, 8, 9)		80·00
Z88a	6d. chestnut (1872) (Plate No. 11)		
Z89	6d. buff (1873) (Plate No. 12)		
Z90	6d. grey (1873) (Plate No. 12)		
Z91	6d. grey (1874–76)		65·00
	Plate Nos. 13, 14, 15, 16.		
Z92	9d. straw (1865)		£375
Z93	9d. straw (1867)		£225
Z94	10d. red-brown (1867)		£300
Z95	1s. green (1865) (Plate No. 4)		
Z96	1s. green (1867–73) (Plate Nos. 4, 5, 6, 7)	From	60·00
Z97	1s. green (1873–77)	From	80·00
	Plate Nos. 8, 10, 12, 13.		
Z98	2s. blue (1867)		
Z99	5s. rose (1867) (Plate No. 1)		

PAITA

CROWNED-CIRCLE HANDSTAMPS

CC5	CC **1** PAITA (Black) (5.11.1850) ....*Price on cover*		£6500

Stamps of GREAT BRITAIN cancelled "C 43" as Type **4** or with circular date stamp as Type **16A** in black or blue.

1865–79.

Z99a	½d. rose-red (Plate No. 6)		
Z100	1d. rose-red (1864–79) (Plate Nos. 127, 147)		£100
Z101	2d. blue (1858–69) (Plate Nos. 9, 14)		£100
Z102	3d. rose (1867–73) (Plate Nos. 5, 6)		£100
Z103	3d. rose (1876) (Plate Nos. 17, 18, 19)		£100
Z104	4d. vermilion (1865–73)	From	£100
	Plate Nos. 9, 10, 11, 12, 13, 14.		
Z104a	4d. vermilion (1876) (Plate No. 15)		£400
Z105	4d. sage-green (1877) (Plate No. 15)		£150
Z106	6d. lilac (1862) (Plate No. 3)		£140
Z107	6d. lilac (1865–67) (Plate Nos. 5, 6)	From	£140
Z108	6d. violet (1867–70) (Plate Nos. 6, 8, 9)	From	£140
Z109	6d. buff (1872–73) (Plate Nos. 11, 12)	From	£100
Z110	6d. chestnut (Plate No. 11)		
Z111	6d. grey (1873) (Plate No. 12)		£375
Z112	6d. grey (1874–76) (Plate Nos. 13, 14, 15)		
Z113	9d. straw (1862)		
Z114	10d. red-brown (1867)		£450
Z115	1s. green (1865) (Plate No. 4)		
Z116	1s. green (1867–73) (Plate No. 4)		£120
Z117	1s. green (1873–77) (Plate Nos. 8, 9, 10, 13)		£140
Z118	2s. blue (1867)		£400
Z119	5s. rose (1867) (Plate No. 1)		£850

PISAGUA(?)

Stamps of GREAT BRITAIN cancelled "D 65" as Type **12**.

Z119a	1d. rose-red (1864–79)	
Z119b	2d. blue (1858–69)	
Z120	2s. blue (1867)	

There is no record of an office opening at Pisagua. The few known examples of "D 65" in red are on loose stamps. The 2s. blue listing, based on a single cover cancelled "D 65" in black, is without any datestamp confirming its origin.

We continue to list this office pending further research.

PISCO AND CHINCHA ISLANDS

Stamps of GREAT BRITAIN cancelled "D 74" as Type **12**.

1865–70.

Z121	2d. blue (1858–69) (Plate No. 9)	
Z122	4d. vermilion (1865–73) (Plate Nos. 10, 12)	£1200
Z123	6d. violet (1868) (Plate No. 6)	£1800
Z124	1s. green (1867) (Plate No. 4)	
Z125	2s. blue (1867)	£2400

PORTO RICO

A British Postal Agency operated at San Juan from 1844. On 24 October 1872 further offices were opened at Aguadilla, Arroyo, Mayaguez and Ponce, with Naguabo added three years later.

Great Britain stamps were used from 1865 to 1877, but few letters appear to have used the San Juan postal agency between 1866 and 1873 due to various natural disasters and the hostile attitude of the local authorities. All the British Agencies closed on 1 May 1877.

AGUADILLA

Stamps of GREAT BRITAIN cancelled "F 84" as Type **8**.

1873–77.

Z1	½d. rose-red (1870) (Plate No. 6)		£125
Z2	1d. rose-red (1864–79)		£110
	Plate Nos. 119, 122, 139, 149, 156, 160.		
Z3	2d. blue (1858–69) (Plate No. 14)		
Z4	3d. rose (1867–73) (Plate Nos. 7, 8, 9)		
Z5	3d. rose (1873–76) (Plate No. 12)		
Z6	4d. vermilion (1865–73)	From	80·00
	Plate Nos. 12, 13, 14.		
Z7	4d. vermilion (1876) (Plate No. 15)		£325
Z7a	6d. pale buff (1872–73) (Plate No. 11)		
Z8	6d. grey (1874–76) (Plate Nos. 13, 14)		
Z9	9d. straw (1867)		£400
Z10	10d. red-brown (1867)		£450
Z11	1s. green (1867–73) (Plate Nos. 4, 5, 6, 7)	From	£100
Z12	1s. green (1873–77)	From	£100
	Plate Nos. 8, 9, 10, 11, 12.		
Z13	2s. blue (1867)		£350

ARROYO

Stamps of GREAT BRITAIN cancelled "F 83" as Type **8** (black or red) or with circular date stamps as Types **17** and **17B**.

1873–77.

Z14	½d. rose-red 1870 (Plate No. 5)		£110
Z15	1d. rose-red (1864–79)		90·00
	Plate Nos. 149, 150, 151, 156, 164, 174, 175...		
Z16	1½d. lake-red (1870) (Plate Nos. 1, 3)		
Z17	2d. blue (1858–69) (Plate No. 14)		
Z18	3d. rose (1867–73) (Plate Nos. 5, 7, 10)	From	90·00
Z19	3d. rose 1873–76	From	90·00
	Plate Nos. 11, 12, 14, 16, 18.		
Z20	4d. verm (1865–73) (Plate Nos. 12, 13, 14)	From	75·00
Z21	4d. vermilion (1876) (Plate No. 15)		£350
Z22	6d. chestnut (1872) (Plate No. 11)		£100
Z23	6d. pale buff (1872) (Plate No. 11)		£100
Z23a	6d. grey (1873) (Plate No. 12)		
Z24	6d. grey (1874–76) (Plate Nos. 13, 14, 15)		80·00
Z25	9d. straw (1867)		£350
Z26	10d. red-brown (1867)		£400
Z27	1s. green (1865) (Plate No. 4)		
Z28	1s. green (1867–73) (Plate Nos. 4, 5, 6, 7)	From	80·00
Z29	1s. green (1873–77)	From	£100
	Plate Nos. 8, 9, 10, 11, 12, 13.		
Z30	2s. blue (1867)		£325
Z31	5s. rose (1867–74) (Plate No. 2)		

MAYAGUEZ

Stamps of GREAT BRITAIN cancelled "F 85" as Type **8** in black or blue.

1873–77.

Z32	½d. rose-red (1870)	From	55·00
	Plate Nos. 4, 5, 6, 8, 10, 11.		
Z33	1d. rose-red (1864–79)	From	40·00
	Plate Nos. 76, 120, 121, 122, 124, 134, 137, 140, 146, 148, 149, 150, 151, 154, 155, 156, 157, 160, 167, 170, 171, 174, 175, 176, 178, 180, 182, 185, 186, 189.		
Z34	1½d. lake-red (1870–74) (Plate Nos. 1, 3)		50·00
Z35	2d. blue (1858–69) (Plate Nos. 13, 14, 15)		50·00
Z36	3d. rose (1867–73) (Plate Nos. 7, 8, 9, 10)	From	65·00
Z37	3d. rose (1873–76)	From	60·00
	Plate Nos. 11, 12, 13, 14.		
Z38	4d. vermilion (1865–73)	From	50·00
	Plate Nos. 11, 12, 13, 14.		
Z39	4d. vermilion (1876) (Plate No. 15)		£300
Z40	4d. sage-green (1877) (Plate No. 15)		
Z41	6d. mauve (1870) (Plate No. 9)		£120
Z42	6d. buff (1872) (Plate No. 11)		80·00
Z43	6d. chestnut (1872) (Plate No. 11)		70·00
Z44	6d. grey (1873) (Plate No. 12)		£200
Z45	6d. grey (1874–80)	From	60·00
	Plate Nos. 13, 14, 15, 16.		
Z46	8d. orange (1876)		£325
Z47	9d. straw (1867)		£275
Z48	10d. red-brown (1867)		£350
Z49	1s. green (1867–73) (Plate Nos. 4, 5, 6, 7)	From	45·00
Z50	1s. green (1873–77)	From	60·00
	Plate Nos. 8, 9, 10, 11, 12.		
Z51	2s. blue (1867)		£200
Z52	5s. rose (1867–74) (Plate Nos. 1, 2)		£600

NAGUABO

Stamps of GREAT BRITAIN cancelled "582" as Type **9**.

1875–77.

Z53	½d. rose-red (1870–79) (Plate Nos. 12, 14)		
Z54	1d. rose-red (1864–79) (Plate Nos. 150, 159, 165)		£800
Z55	3d. rose (1873–76) (Plate Nos. 17, 18)		£1100
Z56	4d. vermilion (1872–73) (Plate Nos. 13, 14)	From	£1100
Z57	4d. vermilion (1876) (Plate No. 15)		£1500
Z58	6d. grey (1874–76) (Plate Nos. 14, 15)		
Z59	9d. straw (1867)		
Z60	10d. red-brown (1867)		£1700
Z61	1s. green (1873–77) (Plate Nos. 11, 12)		£1100
Z62	2s. dull blue (1867) (Plate No. 1)		£1900

PONCE

Stamps of GREAT BRITAIN cancelled "F 88" as Type **8**.

1873–77.

Z63	½d. rose-red (1870) (Plate Nos. 5, 10, 12)		55·00
Z64	1d. rose-red (1864–79)		45·00
	Plate Nos. 120, 121, 122, 123, 124, 146, 148, 154, 156, 157, 158, 160, 167, 171, 174, 175, 179, 186, 187.		
Z65	1½d. lake-red (1870–74) (Plate No. 3)		£110
Z66	2d. blue (1858–69) (Plate Nos. 13, 14)		60·00
Z67	3d. rose (1867–73) (Plate Nos. 7, 8, 9)		
Z68	3d. rose (1873–76)		70·00
	Plate Nos. 12, 16, 17, 18, 19.		
Z69	4d. vermilion (1865–73)	From	55·00
	Plate Nos. 8, 9, 12, 13, 14.		

Z70	4d. vermilion (1876) (Plate No. 15)		£300
Z71	4d. sage-green (1877) (Plate No. 15, 16)	From	£200
Z72	6d. buff (1872–73) (Plate Nos. 11, 12)	From	75·00
Z73	6d. chestnut (1872) (Plate No. 11)		65·00
Z74	6d. grey (1873) (Plate No. 12)		
Z75	6d. grey (1874–76) (Plate Nos. 13, 14, 15)	From	60·00
Z76	6d. straw (1867)		£275
Z77	10d. red-brown (1867)		£325
Z78	1s. green (1867–73) (Plate Nos. 4, 6, 7)		50·00
Z79	1s. green (1873–77)	From	60·00
	Plate Nos. 8, 9. 10, 11, 12, 13.		
Z80	2s. blue (1867).		
Z81	5s. rose (1867–74) (Plate Nos. 1, 2)	From	£650

SAN JUAN

CROWNED-CIRCLE HANDSTAMPS

CC1	CC **1** SAN JUAN PORTO RICO (R. or Black) (25.5.1844) ...... *Price on cover*		£650

No. CC1 may be found on cover, used in conjunction with Spanish colonial adhesive stamps paying the local postage.

Stamps of GREAT BRITAIN cancelled "C 61" as in Types **4**, **8**, **12**, **14A** or **16**.

1865–77.

Z82	½d. rose-red (1870) (Plate Nos. 5, 10, 15)	From	50·00
Z83	1d. rose-red (1857)		
Z84	1d. rose-red (1864–79)	From	40·00
	Plate Nos. 72, 73, 74, 81, 84, 90, 94, 100, 101, 102, 107, 117, 122, 124, 125, 127, 130, 137, 138, 139, 140, 145, 146, 149, 153, 156, 159, 160, 162, 163, 169, 171, 172, 173, 174, 175, 179, 180, 182, 186.		
Z85	1½d. lake-red (1870–74) (Plate Nos. 1, 3)	From	65·00
Z86	2d. blue (1858–69) (Plate Nos. 9, 13, 14)	From	40·00
Z87	3d. rose (1865) (Plate No. 4)		90·00
Z88	3d. rose (1867–73)		50·00
	Plate Nos. 5, 6, 7, 8, 9, 10.		
Z89	3d. rose (1873–76)	From	50·00
	Plate Nos. 11, 12, 14, 15, 16, 17, 18.		
Z90	4d. vermilion (1865–73)	From	50·00
	Plate Nos. 7, 8, 9, 10, 11, 12, 13, 14.		
Z91	4d. vermilion (1876) (Plate No. 15)		£300
Z92	6d. lilac (1865–67) (Plate Nos. 5, 6)		75·00
Z93	6d. lilac (1867) (Plate No. 6)		75·00
Z94	6d. violet (1867–70) (Plate Nos. 6, 8, 9)		70·00
Z95	6d. buff (1872–73) (Plate Nos. 11, 12)		75·00
Z96	6d. chestnut (1872) (Plate No. 11)		50·00
Z97	6d. grey (1873) (Plate No. 12)		
Z98	6d. grey (1874–76) (Plate Nos. 13, 14, 15)	From	50·00
Z99	9d. straw (1862)		£300
Z100	9d. straw (1865)		£375
Z101	9d. straw (1867)		£200
Z102	10d. red-brown (1867)		£275
Z103	1s. green (1865) (Plate No. 4)		£140
Z104	1s. green (1867–73) (Plate Nos. 4, 5, 6, 7)	From	45·00
Z105	1s. green (1873–77)	From	60·00
	Plate Nos. 8, 9, 10, 11, 12, 13.		
Z106	2s. blue (1867)		£140
Z107	5s. rose (1867) (Plate Nos. 1, 2)	From	£450

RUSSIA

ARMY FIELD OFFICES IN THE CRIMEA, THE BLACK SEA AND CONSTANTINOPLE

1854–56.

Crown between Stars

Z1	1d. red-brown (1841), imperf	£875
Z2	1d. red-brown (1854), Die I, wmk Small Crown, perf 16	
Z3	1d. red-brown (1855), Die II, wmk Small Crown, perf 16	£275
Z4	1d. red-brown, Die I, wmk Small Crown, perf 14 .	
Z5	1d. red-brown (1855), Die II, Small Crown, perf 14	
Z6	2d. blue (1841), imperf	£1800
Z7	2d. blue, Small Crown (1854), perf 16 (Plate No. 4)	
Z8	1s. green (1847), embossed	£2800

Star between Cyphers

Z9	1d. red-brown (1841), imperf	
Z10	1d. red-brown (1854), Die I, wmk Small Crown, perf 16	85·00
Z11	1d. red-brown (1855), Die II, wmk Small Crown, perf 16	85·00
Z12	1d. red-brown (1855), Die I, wmk Small Crown, perf 14	85·00
Z13	1d. red-brown (1855), Die II, wmk Small Crown, perf 14	85·00
Z14	1d. red-brown (1855), Die II, wmk Large Crown, perf 16	£110
Z15	1d. red-brown (1855), Die II, wmk Large Crown, perf 14	45·00
Z16	2d. blue (1841), imperf	£2000
Z17	2d. blue (1854), wmk Small Crown, perf 16 ...From	£150
	Plate Nos. 4, 5.	
Z18	2d. blue (1855), wmk Small Crown, perf 14	£250
	Plate No. 4.	
Z19	2d. blue (1855), wmk Large Crown, perf 16	£300
	Plate No. 5.	

Z20	2d. blue (1855), wmk Large Crown, perf 14.	£180
	Plate No. 5.	
Z22	6d. violet (1854), embossed	£2100
Z23	1s. green (1847), embossed	£2100

On 12 March 1854 Britain, France and Turkey signed an alliance against Russia. A British force arrived in Constantinople in April 1854 and the Anglo-French Black Sea Fleet based itself at Varna, Bulgaria, the following month. "Crown between Stars" obliterators were supplied for use at Army Field Post Offices at Constantinople and Varna from July 1854 and in the Crimea, following the arrival of Allied Forces, on 14 September 1854. The "Star between Cyphers" obliterator was in use from March 1855 in the Crimea and at the British barracks at Scutari, near Constantinople.

SPAIN

Little is known about the operation of British Packet Agencies in Spain, other than the dates recorded for the various postal markings in the GPO Proof Books. The Agency at Corunna is said to date from the late 17th century when the Spanish packets for South America were based there. No. CC1 was probably issued in connection with the inauguration of the P. & O. service to Spain in 1843. The Spanish port of call was changed to Vigo in 1846 and the office at Corunna was then closed. Teneriffe became a port-of-call for the South American packets in 1817 and this arrangement continued until 1858.

CORUNNA

CROWNED-CIRCLE HANDSTAMPS

CC1　　CC **1b** CORUNNA (28.2.1842)

Although recorded in the G.P.O. Proof Books no example of No. CC1 on cover is known.

TENERIFFE (CANARY ISLANDS)

CROWNED-CIRCLE HANDSTAMPS

CC2	CC **7** TENERIFFE (6.1.1851)	*Price on cover*	£3750
CC3	CC **4** TENERIFFE (23.10.1857)	*Price on cover*	£3750

No. CC2/3 can be found used on covers from Spain to South America with the rate from Spain to Teneriffe paid in Spanish adhesive stamps.

UNITED STATES OF AMERICA

The network of British Packet Agencies, to operate the trans-Atlantic Packet system, was re-established in 1814 after the War of 1812.

The New York Agency opened in that year to be followed by further offices at Boston, Charleston (South Carolina), New Orleans, Savannah (Georgia) (all in 1842), Mobile (Alabama) (1848) and San Francisco (1860). Of these agencies Charleston and Savannah closed the same year (1842) as did New Orleans, although the latter was re-activated from 1848 to 1850. Mobile closed 1850, Boston in 1865, New York in 1882 and San Francisco, for which no postal markings have been recorded, in 1883.

Although recorded in the GPO Proof Books no actual examples of the Crowned-circle handstamps for Charleston, Mobile, New Orleans and Savannah are known on cover.

The GPO Proof Books record, in error, a Crowned-circle handstamp for St. Michaels, Maryland. This handstamp was intended for the agency on San Miguel in the Azores.

CHARLESTON

CROWNED-CIRCLE HANDSTAMPS

CC1　　CC **1b** CHARLESTON (15.12.1841)

MOBILE

CROWNED-CIRCLE HANDSTAMPS

CC2　　CC **1b** MOBILE (15.12.1841)

NEW ORLEANS

CROWNED-CIRCLE HANDSTAMPS

CC3　　CC **1b** NEW ORLEANS (15.12.1841)
CC4　　CC **1** NEW ORLEANS (27.4.1848)

NEW YORK

CROWNED-CIRCLE HANDSTAMPS

CC5　　CC **1b** NEW YORK (R.) (15.12.1841) ..... *Price on cover* £35000

SAVANNAH

CROWNED-CIRCLE HANDSTAMPS

CC6　　CC **1b** SAVANNAH (15.12.1841)

Although recorded in the GPO Proof Books, no examples of Nos. CC1/4 or CC6 are known on cover.

URUGUAY

MONTEVIDEO

British packets commenced calling at Montevideo in 1824 on passage to and from Buenos Aires.

Great Britain stamps were in use from 1864. Combination covers exist with the local postage paid by Uruguay adhesive stamps. The agency was closed on 31 July 1873.

CROWNED-CIRCLE HANDSTAMPS

CC1　　CC **5** MONTEVIDEO (Black) (6.1.1851) *Price on cover* £1400

Stamps of GREAT BRITAIN *cancelled* "C 28" *as Type* **4**.

1864–73.

Z1	1d. rose-red (1864)	60·00
	Plate Nos. 73, 92, 93, 94, 119, 148, 154, 157, 171.	
Z2	2d. blue (1858–69) (Plate Nos. 9, 13)	70·00
Z3	3d. rose (1865) (Plate No. 4)	
Z4	3d. rose (1867–71) (Plate Nos. 4, 5, 7) .... *From*	80·00
Z6	4d. rose (1857)	
Z7	4d. red (1862) (Plate No. 4)	
Z8	4d. vermilion (1865–73) .... *From*	80·00
	Plate Nos. 7, 8, 9, 10, 11, 12.	
Z9	6d. lilac (1856)	

Z10	6d. lilac (1862) (Plate No. 4)	£175
Z11	6d. lilac (1865–67) (Plate Nos. 5, 6) .... *From*	£100
Z12	6d. lilac (1867) (Plate No. 6)	
Z13	6d. violet (1867–70) (Plate Nos. 8, 9)	90·00
Z14	6d. buff (1872)	
Z15	6d. chestnut (1872)	
Z16	9d. straw (1862)	
Z17	9d. straw (1865)	
Z18	9d. straw (1867)	£325
Z19	10d. red-brown (1867)	£375
Z20	1s. green (1862)	£190
Z21	1s. green (1865) (Plate No. 4)	£170
Z22	1s. green (1867–73) (Plate Nos. 4, 5) .... *From*	80·00
Z23	2s. blue (1867)	£275
Z24	5s. rose (1867) (Plate No. 1)	£675

VENEZUELA

British Postal Agencies were initially opened at La Guayra and Porto Cabello on 1 January 1842. Further offices were added at Maracaibo in 1842 and Ciudad Bolivar during January 1868. Porto Cabello closed in 1858 and Maracaibo was also short-lived. The remaining offices closed at the end of 1879 when Venezuela joined the UPU.

Great Britain stamps were used at La Guayra from 1865 and at Ciudad Bolivar from its establishment in 1868. They can be found used in combination with Venezuela adhesives paying the local postage.

CIUDAD BOLIVAR

Stamps of GREAT BRITAIN *cancelled* "D 22" *as Type* **12**, *or circular date stamps as Types* **16** *(black) or* **17** *(red).*

1868–79.

Z1	1d. rose-red (1864–79) (Plate No. 133)	£300
Z2	2d. blue (1858–69) (Plate No. 13)	
Z3	3d. rose (1867–73) (Plate No. 5)	
Z4	3d. rose (1873–79) (Plate No. 11)	£400
Z5	4d. vermilion (1865–73) .... *From*	£400
	Plate Nos. 9, 11, 12, 14.	
Z6	4d. sage-green (1877) (Plate Nos. 15, 16)....*From*	£450
Z7	4d. grey-brown (1880) wmk Crown (Plate No. 17)	£1100
Z8	9d. straw (1867)	£550
Z9	10d. red-brown (1867)	
Z10	1s. green (1867–73) (Plate Nos. 4, 5, 7) .... *From*	£400
Z11	1s. green (1873–77) (Plate Nos. 10, 12, 13) ...*From*	£575
Z12	2s. blue (1867)	£1200
Z13	5s. rose (1867–74) (Plate Nos. 1, 2) .... *From*	£2200

LA GUAYRA

CROWNED-CIRCLE HANDSTAMPS

CC1　　CC **1b** LA GUAYRA (Black) (15.12.1841)

.... *Price on cover* £3250

Stamps of GREAT BRITAIN *cancelled* "C 60" *as Type* **4**, *circular date stamp as Types* **16** *and* **17** *or with No.* CC1.

1865–80.

Z14	½d. rose-red (1870) Plate No. 6)	
Z15	1d. rose-red (1864–79) .... *From*	60·00
	Plate Nos. 81, 92, 96, 98, 111, 113, 115, 131, 138, 144, 145, 154, 177, 178, 180, 196.	
Z16	1½d. lake-red (1870–74) (Plate No. 3)	
Z17	2d. blue (1858–69) (Plate Nos. 13, 14)	60·00
Z18	3d. rose (1873–76) .... *From*	70·00
	Plate Nos. 14, 15, 17, 18, 19.	
Z19	4d. vermilion (1865–73) .... *From*	60·00
	Plate Nos. 7, 9, 11, 12, 13, 14.	
Z20	4d. vermilion (1876) (Plate No. 15)	£300
Z21	4d. sage-green (1877) (Plate Nos. 15, 16)....*From*	£225
Z22	6d. lilac (1865) (Plate No. 5)	
Z23	6d. violet (1867–70) (Plate Nos. 6, 8)	
Z24	6d. buff (1872–73) (Plate Nos. 11, 12)	£100
Z25	6d. grey (1873) (Plate No. 12)	£225
Z26	6d. grey (1874–76) (Plate Nos. 13, 14, 15, 16)	60·00
Z27	8d. orange (1876)	£300
Z28	9d. straw (1862)	
Z29	9d. straw (1867)	
Z30	10d. red-brown (1867)	
Z31	1s. green (1865) (Plate No. 4)	£160
Z32	1s. green (1867–73) (Plate Nos. 4, 7)	
Z33	1s. green (1873–77) .... *From*	75·00
	Plate Nos. 8, 9, 10, 11, 12, 13.	
Z34	2s. blue (1867)	£275
Z35	5s. rose (1867–74) (Plate Nos. 1, 2) .... *From*	£600

MARACAIBO

CROWNED-CIRCLE HANDSTAMPS

CC2　　CC **1b** MARACAIBO (31.12.1841)

No examples of No. CC2 on cover have been recorded.

PORTO CABELLO

CROWNED-CIRCLE HANDSTAMPS

CC3　　CC **1b** PORTO-CABELLO (R.) (15.12.1841)

.... *Price on cover* £3500

MAIL BOAT OBLITERATIONS

The following cancellations were supplied to GPO sorters operating on ships holding mail contracts from the British Post Office. They were for use on mail posted on board, but most examples occur on letters from soldiers and sailors serving overseas which were forwarded to the mailboats without postmarks.

P. & O. MEDITERRANEAN AND FAR EAST MAILBOATS

The first such cancellation, "A 17" as Type **2**, was issued to the Southampton–Alexandria packet in April 1858, but no examples have been recorded.

The GPO Proof Book also records "B 16", in Type **2**, as being issued for marine sorting in November 1859, but this postmark was subsequently used by the Plymouth and Bristol Sorting Carriage.

Sorting on board P. & O. packets ceased in June 1870 and many of the cancellation numbers were subsequently reallocated using

Types **9**, **11** or **12**.

Stamps of GREAT BRITAIN *cancelled* "A 80" *as Type* **2**.

1859 (Mar)–70.

Z1	1d. rose-red (1857), Die II, wmk Large Crown, perf 14.	40·00
Z2	6d. lilac (1856)	£160

Stamps of GREAT BRITAIN *cancelled* "A 81" *as Type* **2**.

1859 (Mar)–70.

Z3	1d. rose-red (1857), Die II, wmk Large Crown, perf 14.	40·00
Z4	1d. rose-red (1864–79) .... *From*	35·00
	Plate Nos. 84, 85, 86, 91, 97.	
Z5	2d. blue (1858–69) (Plate No. 9).	50·00
Z6	4d. red (1862) (Plate No. 4).	£120
Z7	4d. vermilion (1865–73) (Plate No. 8).	60·00
Z8	6d. lilac (1856).	£160
Z9	6d. lilac (1862) (Plate No. 3).	£120
Z10	6d. lilac (1865–67) (Plate Nos. 5, 6) .... *From*	£100
Z11	6d. lilac (1867) (Plate No. 6).	£100
Z12	6d. violet (1867–70) (Plate Nos. 6, 8)............	75·00
Z13	10d. red-brown (1867).	£500
Z14	1s. red-brown (1856).	£275

Stamps of GREAT BRITAIN *cancelled* "A 82" *as Type* **2**.

1859 (Mar)–70.

Z15	1d. rose-red (1857), Die II, wmk Large Crown, perf 14.	50·00
Z16	2d. blue (1858) (Plate No. 7).	55·00
Z17	4d. red (1862).	£225
Z18	6d. lilac 1856.	£200
Z19	6d. lilac (1865–67) (Plate Nos. 5, 6) .... *From*	£130
Z20	6d. lilac (1867) (Plate No. 6).	£110

Stamps of GREAT BRITAIN *cancelled* "A 83" *as Type* **2**.

1859 (Apr)–70.

Z21	1d. rose-red (1857), Die II, wmk Large Crown, perf 14.	40·00
Z22	1d. rose-red (1864–79) .... *From*	35·00
	Plate Nos. 73, 74, 84, 91, 92, 109.	
Z23	3d. carmine-rose (1862).	£275
Z24	4d. rose (1857).	£200
Z25	4d. red (1862).	£110
Z26	4d. vermilion (1865–73) (Plate Nos. 9, 10) ... *From*	60·00
Z27	6d. lilac (1856).	£160
Z28	6d. lilac (1862).	£125
Z29	6d. lilac (1865–67) (Plate Nos. 5, 6) .... *From*	£100
Z30	6d. violet (1867–70) (Plate Nos. 6, 8)............ *From*	75·00
Z31	10d. red-brown (1867).	£500
Z32	1s. green (1862).	£275

Stamps of GREAT BRITAIN *cancelled* "A 84" *as Type* **2**.

1859 (Apr)–70.

Z33	1d. rose-red (1857), Die II, wmk Large Crown, perf 14.	£110

Stamps of GREAT BRITAIN *cancelled* "A 85" *as Type* **2**.

1859 (Apr)–70.

Z34	1d. rose-red (1857), Die II, wmk Large Crown, perf 14.	40·00
Z35	1d. rose-red (1864–79) .... *From*	35·00
	Plate Nos. 79, 97, 103.	
Z36	3d. carmine-rose (1862).	£275
Z37	4d. red (1862).	£110
Z38	6d. lilac (1856).	£160
Z39	6d. lilac (1862) (Plate Nos. 3, 4) .... *From*	£120
Z40	6d. lilac (1865–67) (Plate No. 5).	£100
Z41	6d. lilac (1867) (Plate No. 6).	90·00
Z42	1s. green (1862).	£300

Stamps of GREAT BRITAIN *cancelled* "A 86" *as Type* **2**.

1859 (Apr)–70.

Z43	1d. rose-red (1857), Die II, wmk Large Crown, perf 14.	40·00
Z44	1d. rose-red (1864–79) .... *From*	35·00
	Plate Nos. 73, 84, 94, 97, 114, 118.	
Z45	3d. rose (1865).	£250
Z46	3d. rose (1867–73) (Plate Nos. 4, 5) .... *From*	75·00
Z47	4d. rose (1857).	£200
Z48	4d. red (1862) (Plate No. 4).	£110
Z49	4d. vermilion (1865–73) (Plate No. 10).	80·00
Z50	6d. lilac (1856).	£160
Z51	6d. lilac (1862) (Plate Nos. 3, 4) .... *From*	£120
Z52	6d. lilac (1865–67) (Plate Nos. 5, 6) .... *From*	£100
Z53	6d. lilac (1867) (Plate Nos. 6, 8) .... *From*	75·00
Z54	10d. red-brown (1867).	£450
Z55	1s. green (1862).	£275

Stamps of GREAT BRITAIN *cancelled* "A 87" *as Type* **2**.

1859 (Apr)–70.

Z56	1d. rose-red (1857), Die II, wmk Large Crown, perf 14.	55·00
Z57	4d. rose (1856).	£250
Z58	6d. lilac (1867) (Plate No. 6).	£120

Stamps of GREAT BRITAIN *cancelled* "A 88" *as Type* **2**.

1859 (Apr)–70.

Z59	1d. rose-red (1857), Die II, wmk Large Crown, perf 14.	40·00
Z60	1d. rose-red (1864–79) .... *From*	35·00
	Plate Nos. 74, 80, 85.	
Z61	4d. rose (1857).	£225
Z62	4d. red (1862).	£120
Z63	4d. vermilion (1865–73) (Plate No. 8).	60·00
Z64	6d. lilac (1856).	
Z65	6d. lilac (1862) (Plate No. 4).	£160
Z66	6d. lilac (1865–67) (Plate No. 5).	£120
Z67	6d. lilac (1867) (Plate No. 6).	£100
Z68	6d. violet (1867–70) (Plate No. 8).	75·00
Z69	10d. red-brown (1867).	£525
Z70	1s. green (1856).	£300

Stamps of GREAT BRITAIN cancelled "A 89" as Type **2**.

1859 (Apr)–**70**.

Z71	1d. rose-red (1857), Die II, wmk Large Crown, perf 14	£110
Z72	6d. lilac (1856)	£300

Stamps of GREAT BRITAIN cancelled "A 90" as Type **2**.

1859 (June)–**70**.

Z73	1d. rose-red (1857), Die II, wmk Large Crown, perf 14	65·00
Z74	4d. rose (1856)	£250
Z75	6d. lilac (1856)	£250
Z76	6d. lilac (1865–67) (Plate Nos. 5, 6) .... *From*	£160
Z77	9d. straw (1867)	

Stamps of GREAT BRITAIN cancelled "A 99" as Type **2**.

1859 (June)–**70**.

Z78	1d. rose-red (1857), Die II, wmk Large Crown, perf 14	40·00
Z79	1d. rose-red (1864–79) .... *From* Plate Nos. 93, 97, 99, 118.	35·00
Z80	4d. rose (1857)	£200
Z81	4d. red (1862)	£110
Z82	4d. vermilion (1865–73) (Plate No. 11)	60·00
Z83	6d. lilac (1856)	
Z84	6d. lilac (1862)	£160
Z85	6d. lilac (1865–67) (Plate Nos. 5, 6) .... *From*	£120
Z86	10d. red-brown (1867)	£500

Stamps of GREAT BRITAIN cancelled "B 03" as Type **2**.

1859 (Aug)–**70**.

Z87	1d. rose-red (1857), Die II, wmk Large Crown, perf 14	55·00
Z88	1d. rose-red (1864–79) (Plate Nos. 109, 116) .. *From*	40·00
Z89	3d. rose (1865) (Plate No. 4)	£100
Z90	6d. lilac (1856)	£170
Z91	6d. lilac (1867) (Plate No. 6)	£140
Z92	6d. violet (1867–70) (Plate Nos. 6, 8) .... *From*	£100
Z93	10d. red-brown (1867)	£550

Stamps of GREAT BRITAIN cancelled "B 12" as Type **2**.

1859 (Oct)–**70**.

Z94	1d. rose-red (1857), Die II, wmk Large Crown, perf 14	55·00
Z95	1d. rose-red (1864–79) (Plate No. 94)	40·00
Z96	3d. rose (1865) (Plate No. 4)	£100
Z97	4d. red (1862)	£120
Z98	4d. vermilion (1865–73) (Plate No. 8)	75·00
Z99	6d. lilac (1856)	
Z100	6d. lilac (1862)	£170
Z101	6d. lilac (1865–67) (Plate Nos. 5, 6) .... *From*	£140
Z102	6d. violet (1867–70) (Plate No. 8)	95·00

Stamps of GREAT BRITAIN cancelled "B 56" as Type **2**.

1861 (July)–**70**.

Z103	1d. rose-red (1864–70) (Plate Nos. 84, 97)	40·00
Z104	2d. blue (1858–69) (Plate No. 9)	60·00
Z105	4d. red (1862) (Plate No. 4)	£120
Z106	4d. vermilion (1865–73) (Plate Nos. 7, 8)	65·00
Z107	6d. lilac (1862) (Plate Nos. 3, 4) .... *From*	£140
Z108	6d. lilac (1865–67) (Plate Nos. 5, 6) .... *From*	£120
Z109	6d. violet (1867–71) (Plate Nos. 6, 8) .... *From*	£100

Stamps of GREAT BRITAIN cancelled "B 57" as Type **2**.

1861 (July)–**70**.

Z110	1d. rose-red (1857), Die II, wmk Large Crown, perf 14	50·00
Z111	1d. rose-red (1864–79) (Plate No. 81)	40·00
Z112	2d. blue (1858–69) (Plate No. 9)	60·00
Z113	4d. red (1862)	£120
Z114	4d. vermilion (1865–73) (Plate Nos. 7, 8)	65·00
Z115	6d. lilac (1865–67) (Plate Nos. 5, 6) .... *From*	£120

Stamps of GREAT BRITAIN cancelled "C 79" as Type **12**.

1866 (June)–**70**.

Z116	6d. violet (1867–70) (Plate Nos. 6, 8) .... *From*	95·00
Z117	10d. red-brown (1867)	£450

CUNARD LINE ATLANTIC MAILBOATS

These were all issued in June 1859. No examples arc known used after August 1868. "B 61" is recorded as being issued in March 1862, but no examples are known. Cancellation numbers were subsequently reallocated to offices in Great Britain or, in the case of "A 91", the British Virgin Islands.

Stamps of GREAT BRITAIN cancelled "A 91" as Type **2**.

1859 (June)–**68**.

Z130	1d. rose-red (1857), Die II, wmk Large Crown, perf 14	70·00
Z131	1d. rose-red (1864–79) (Plate No. 121)	60·00
Z132	2d. blue (1855), wmk Small Crown, perf 14	
Z133	2d. blue (1858–69) (Plate Nos. 8, 9)	95·00
Z134	4d. rose (1857)	£250
Z135	4d. red (1862)	£130
Z136	6d. lilac (1856)	£175
Z137	6d. lilac (1862)	£150
Z138	6d. lilac (1865–67)	£120
Z139	9d. straw (1862)	
Z140	1s. green (1856)	£325

Stamps of GREAT BRITAIN cancelled "A 92" as Type **2**.

1859 (June)–**68**.

Z141	1d. rose-red (1857), Die II, wmk Large Crown, perf 14	70·00
Z142	1d. rose-red (1864–79) (Plate Nos. 93, 97) ....*From*	60·00
Z143	6d. lilac (1856)	£175
Z144	6d. lilac (1862) (Plate No. 3)	£160
Z145	6d. lilac (1865–67) (Plate Nos. 5, 6) .... *From*	£120

Stamps of GREAT BRITAIN cancelled "A 93" as Type **2**.

1859 (June)–**68**.

Z146	1d. rose-red (1857), Die II, wmk Large Crown, perf 14	70·00
Z147	1d. rose-red (1864–79) (Plate No. 85)	60·00

Z148	6d. lilac (1856)	£175
Z149	6d. lilac (1865–67) (Plate No. 6)	£160
Z150	10d. red-brown (1867)	£525

Stamps of GREAT BRITAIN cancelled "A 94" as Type **2**.

1859 (June)–**68**.

Z151	1d. rose-red (1857), Die II, wmk Large Crown, perf 14	95·00
Z152	1d. rose-red (1864–79) (Plate Nos. 74, 97)	70·00
Z153	4d. vermilion (1865–73) (Plate No. 7)	£100
Z154	6d. lilac (1856)	£200
Z155	6d. lilac (1862)	£160
Z156	6d. lilac (1865–67) (Plate Nos. 5, 6) .... *From*	£140

Stamps of GREAT BRITAIN cancelled "A 95" as Type **2**.

1859 (June)–**68**.

Z157	1d. rose-red (1857), Die II, wmk Large Crown, perf 14	65·00
Z158	1d. rose-red (1864–79) .... *From* Plate Nos. 72, 89, 97.	55·00
Z159	3d. rose (1867–73) (Plate No. 5)	95·00
Z160	4d. red (1862)	£130
Z161	4d. vermilion (1865–73) (Plate No. 8)	70·00
Z162	6d. lilac (1862)	£190
Z163	6d. lilac (1865–67) (Plate No. 5)	£160
Z164	6d. lilac (1867) (Plate No. 6)	£130
Z165	1s. green (1856)	£275

Stamps of GREAT BRITAIN cancelled "A 96" as Type **2**.

1859 (June)–**68**.

Z166	1d. rose-red (1857), Die II, wmk Large Crown, perf 14	70·00
Z167	4d. vermilion (1865–73) (Plate No. 7)	£100
Z168	6d. lilac (1856)	£180
Z169	1s. green (1856)	£300

Stamps of GREAT BRITAIN cancelled "A 97" as Type **2**.

1859 (June)–**68**.

Z170	1d. rose-red (1857), Die II, wmk Large Crown, perf 14	70·00
Z171	1d. rose-red (1864–79) (Plate No. 71)	60·00
Z172	4d. Ted (1862) (Plate No. 3)	£140

Stamps of GREAT BRITAIN cancelled "A 98" as Type **2**.

1859 (June)–**68**.

Z173	1d. rose-red (1857), Die II, wmk Large Crown, perf 14	70·00
Z174	4d. red (1862)	£140
Z175	6d. lilac (1856)	£200
Z176	6d. lilac (1862) (Plate No. 4)	£160
Z177	6d. lilac (1865–67) (Plate Nos. 5, 6) .... *From*	£120

ALLAN LINE ATLANTIC MAILBOATS

British G.P.O. sorters worked on these Canadian ships between November 1859 and April 1860. Cancellations as Type **2** numbered "B 17", "B 18", "B 27", "B 28", "B 29" and "B 30" were issued to them, but have not been reported used on Great Britain stamps during this period. All were subsequently reallocated to British post offices.

SPANISH WEST INDIES MAILBOATS

"D 26" was supplied for use by British mail clerks employed on ships of the Herrara Line operating between St. Thomas (Danish West Indies), Cuba, Dominican Republic and Porto Rico.

Stamps of GREAT BRITAIN cancelled "D 26" as Type **12**.

1868–71.

Z190	1d. rose-red (1864–79) (Plate Nos. 98, 125)	
Z191	4d. vermilion (1865–73) (Plate Nos. 9, 10, 11)	£1500
Z192	6d. violet (1867–70) (Plate No. 8)	
Z193	1s. green (1867) (Plate No. 4)	£1500

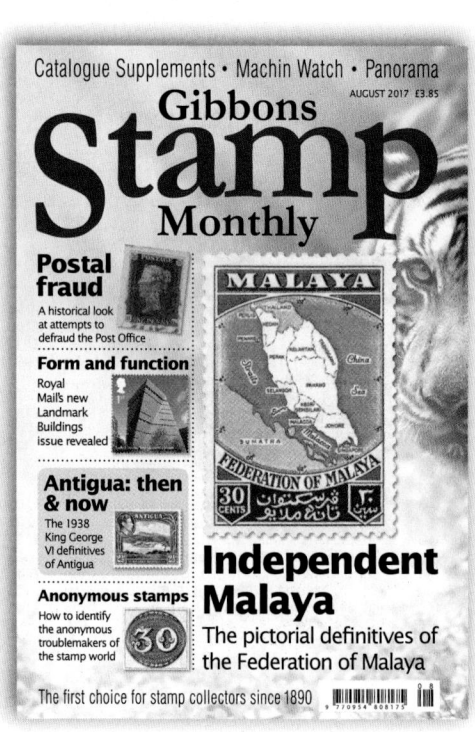

Abu Dhabi

1964. 100 Naye Paise = 1 Rupee 1966. 1000 Fils = 1 Dinar

Abu Dhabi is the largest of the former Trucial States on the Persian Gulf, which are now combined to form the United Arab Emirates. The others, which all issued stamps, are Ajman (with Manama), Dubai, Fujeira, Ras al Khaima, Sharjah and Umm al Qiwain. They were known as the Trucial States because in May 1853 they all signed the Perpetual Maritime Truce Agreement with the United Kingdom, under which they undertook to give up piracy and the slave trade.

Sheikh Shakhbut bin Sultan
1928–6 August 1966

BRITISH POSTAL ADMINISTRATION

The postal service was established on 30 March 1963 and the stamps of the British Postal Agencies in Eastern Arabia (see *British Postal Agencies in Eastern Arabia* in this catalogue) were used until 29 March 1964.

1 Sheikh Shakhbut bin Sultan

2 Mountain Gazelle

3 Ruler's Palace

4 Oil Rig and Camels

(Des M. C. Farrar-Bell. Photo Harrison (T **1/2**). Des C. T. Kavanagh (T **3**), Miss P. M. Goth (T **4**). Recess Bradbury Wilkinson)

1964 (30 Mar). P 14½ (T **1/2**) or 13×13½ (T **3/4**).

1	**1**	5n.p. green	6·00	6·00
2		15n.p. red-brown	4·75	3·75
3		20n.p. ultramarine	4·75	2·25
		a. Perf 13×13½	£600	
4		30n.p. red-orange	4·75	2·25
5	**2**	40n.p. reddish violet	8·50	1·50
6		50n.p. bistre	8·50	3·50
7		75n.p. black	11·00	8·00
8	**3**	1r. emerald	6·50	3·25
9		2r. black	11·00	6·00
10	**4**	5r. carmine-red	25·00	15·00
11		10r. deep ultramarine	29·00	17·00
1/11	*Set of 11*		£110	60·00

5

6

7

Saker Falcon on Gloved Hand

(Des V. Whiteley. Photo Harrison)

1965 (30 Mar). Falconry. P 14½.

12	**5**	20n.p. light brown and grey-blue	15·00	3·25
13	**6**	40n.p. light brown and blue	18·00	3·25
14	**7**	2r. sepia and turquoise-green	32·00	16·00
12/14	*Set of 3*		60·00	20·00

Sheikh Zaid bin Sultan al Nahyan
6 August 1966

فلس Fils

(8)

(Surch by Arabian Ptg & Publishing House, Bahrain)

1966 (1 Oct). New Currency. Nos. 1/11 surch as T **8**, with bars obliterating portrait of deposed Sheikh. P 13×13½ (20f.), others as before.

15	**1**	5f. on 5n.p. green	15·00	7·00
16		15f. on 15n.p. red-brown	22·00	13·00
17		20f. on 20n.p. ultramarine	22·00	9·00
		b. Perf 14½	£275	£300
		ba. Surch inverted	£800	£1400
18		30f. on 30n.p. red-orange	20·00	25·00
		a. Arabic "2" for "3" in surch (R. 7/8)	£9000	
		b. Surch double, one albino	£400	
19	**2**	40f. on 40n.p. reddish violet	18·00	1·50
20		50f. on 50n.p. bistre	60·00	60·00
21		75f. on 75n.p. black	60·00	60·00
		a. Surch double, one albino	£400	
22	**3**	100f. on 1r. emerald	18·00	5·00
23		200f. on 2r. black	18·00	15·00
24	**4**	500f. on 5r. carmine-red	30·00	38·00
25		1d. on 10r. deep ultramarine	55·00	70·00
		a. Short extra bar below portrait (R. 7/3)	£475	
15/25	*Set of 11*		£300	£275

The 40f., 50f. and 75f. are surcharged "Fils" only, as in Type **8**. The remainder have the new value expressed in figures also. On the 1d. the old value is obliterated by bars.

No. 18a was quickly corrected. Only five sheets with the error are believed to have been sold.

The Abu Dhabi Post Department took over the postal services on 1 January 1967. Later stamp isssues will be found in Stanley Gibbons *Arabia Catalogue*.

Aden

The first post office in Aden opened during January 1839, situated in what became known as the Crater district. No stamps were initially available, but, after the office was placed under the Bombay Postal Circle, stocks of the 1854 ½a. and 1a. stamps were placed on sale in Aden from 10 October 1854. Supplies of the 2a. and 4a. values did not arrive until December. Most Indian issues from the 1854 lithographs up to 1935 Silver Jubilee set can be found with Aden postmarks.

During January 1858 a further office, Aden Steamer Point, was opened in the harbour area and much of the business was transferred to it by 1869. The original Aden post office, in Crater, was renamed Aden Cantonment, later to be changed again to Aden Camp.

The first cancellation used with the Indian stamps was a plain diamond of dots. This type was also used elsewhere so that attribution to Aden is only possible when on cover. Aden was assigned "124" in the Indian postal number system, with the sub-office at Aden Steamer Point being "132". After a short period "124" was used at both offices, cancellations being identifiable by the spacing and shape of the numerals. It is possible that "132" was also used at an office in India.

1858 "124" Cancellation

1870 Aden Duplex

1872 Aden Steamer Point Duplex

Both post offices used "124" until 1871 when Aden Cantonment was assigned "125", only to have this swiftly amended to "124A" in the same year.

1871 Aden Cantonment "125" Cancellation

1871 Aden Cantonment "124A" Cancellation

Cancellations inscribed "Aden Steamer Point" disappear after 1874 and this office was then known simply as Aden. Following this change the office was given number "B-22" under the revised Indian PO scheme and this number appears as a major part of the cancellations from 1875 to 1886, either on its own or as part of a duplex. Aden Camp, the alternative name for the Cantonment office, became "B-22/1".

1875 Aden Duplex

Squared-circle types for Aden and Aden Cantonment were introduced in 1884 and 1888 to be in turn replaced by standard Indian double and single circle from 1895 onwards.

INDIA USED IN ADEN

Aden – Steamer Point/GPO or Aden Camp

1854-55 (Nos. 2/31)

Z1	½a. blue Die I	£100
Z2	½a. blue Die II	£250
Z3	½a. blue Die III	£200
Z4	1a. red Die I	£150
Z5	1a. red Die II	£150
Z6	1a. red Die III	£750
Z7	2a. green	£100
Z8	4a. blue and red (Head Die I)	£1400
Z9	4a. blue and red (Head Die II)	£1500
Z10	4a. blue and red (Head Die III)	£1100

ADEN

1855 Blue glazed paper (Nos. 35/6)

Z14	4a. black	50·00
Z15	8a. carmine	75·00

1856-64 No wmk (Nos. 37/49)

Z16	½a. blue	35·00
Z17	1a. brown	20·00
Z18	2a. dull pink	80·00
Z19	2a. yellow-buff	75·00
Z20	2a. yellow	85·00
Z21	2a. orange	85·00
Z22	4a. black	20·00
Z23	4a. green	£120
Z24	8a. carmine	75·00

1860 (Nos. 51/3)

Z25	8p. purple/*bluish*	
Z26	8p. purple/*white*	50·00

1865 Watermark T **13** (Nos. 51/65)

Z27	½a. blue	30·00
Z28	8p. purple	50·00
Z29	1a. brown	10·00
Z30	2a. orange	15·00
Z31	4a. green	85·00
Z32	8a. carmine (Die I)	£200

1866 Opt on 6a. fiscal (Nos. 66/8)

Z34	6a. purple (Type **15**)	£550
Z35	6a. purple (Type **16**)	£850

1866-78 (Nos. 69/76)

Z36	½a. blue Die II	6·00
Z37	4a. green Die I	18·00
Z38	4a. green Die II	15·00
Z39	6a.8p. slate	90·00
Z40	8a. rose Die II	20·00

1874-76 Additional values (Nos. 77/82)

Z41	9p. mauve	60·00
Z42	6a. pale brown	15·00
Z43	12a. Venetian red	90·00
Z44	1r. slate	£100

1882-90 (Nos. 84/101)

Z45	½a. blue-green	2·00
Z46	9p. rose	15·00
Z47	1a. brown-purple	2·00
Z48	1a.6p. sepia	8·00
Z49	2a. blue	3·00
Z50	3a. orange	18·00
Z51	3a. brown-orange	5·00
Z52	4a. olive-green	6·00
Z53	4a.6p. yellow-green	12·00
Z54	8a. magenta	10·00
Z55	12a. purple/*red*	25·00
Z56	1r. slate	18·00

1891 Surcharge (No. 102)

ZX58	2½a. on 4a.6p. yellow-green	10·00

1892-97 (Nos. 103/9)

Z59	2a.6p. yellow-green	4·00
Z60	1r. green and carmine	15·00
Z61	2r. carmine and yellow-brown	50·00
Z62	3r. brown and green	55·00
Z63	5r. ultramarine and violet	85·00

1898 Surcharge (No. 110)

Z64	¼ on ½a. blue-green	12·00

1899-1902 Changed colours (Nos. 111/18)

Z65	3p. aniline carmine	3·00
Z66	3p. grey	£250*
Z67	½a. yellow-green	4·00
Z68	1a. carmine	3·00
Z69	2a. pale violet	10·00
Z70	2a.6p. ultramarine	12·00

*The 3p. grey was never placed on sale in Aden, but was of course valid for postage there. Most purported examples with Aden cancels are forgeries.

1902 King Edward VII (Nos. 119/41)

Z71	3p. grey	3·00
Z72	½a. green	1·50
Z73	1a. carmine	1·50
Z74	2a. mauve	2·50
Z75	2a.6p. ultramarine	2·00
Z76	3a. orange-brown	3·00
Z77	4a. olive	4·00
Z78	6a. maize	7·00
Z79	8a. purple	6·00
Z80	12a. purple/*red*	15·00
Z81	1r. green and carmine	9·00
Z82	2r. carmine and yellow-brown	35·00
Z83	3r. brown and green	65·00
Z84	5r. ultramarine and violet	£110

1905 (No. 148)

Z88	¼ on ½a. green	9·00

1906 Inscr 'POSTAGE AND REVENUE' (Nos. 149/50)

Z89	½a. green	1·50
Z90	1a. carmine	1·50

1911-22 King George V Wmk Single Star (Nos. 151/91)

Z91	3p. grey	3·00
Z92	½a. green	1·25
Z93	1a. carmine	1·25
Z94	1½a. chocolate (Type A)	7·00
Z95	1½a. chocolate (Type B)	18·00
Z96	2a. purple	2·00
Z97	2a.6p. ultramarine (No. 170)	14·00
Z98	2a.6p. ultramarine (No. 171)	1·50
Z99	3a. orange	1·75
Z100	4a. olive-green	2·25
Z101	6a. brown-ochre	3·50
Z102	8a. deep mauve	4·00
Z103	12a. carmine-lake	6·00
Z104	1r. brown and green	7·00

Z105	2r. carmine and brown	12·00
Z106	5r. ultramarine and violet	25·00

1921-22 Surcharges (Nos. 192/6)

Z110	¼ on ½a. green	10·00
Z111	9p. on 1a. carmine	12·00

1922-26 Wmk Single Star (Nos. 197/200)

Z112	1a. chocolate	2·00
Z113	1½a. rose-carmine	5·00
Z114	2a.6p. orange	8·00
Z115	3a. ultramarine	4·00

1926-33 Wmk Multiple Star (Nos. 201/19)

Z116	3p. slate	1·50
Z117	½a. green	1·25
Z118	1a. chocolate	1·00
Z119	1½a. rose-carmine	4·00
Z120	2a. bright purple (No. 205)	40·00
Z121	2a. purple (No. 206)	1·25
Z122	2a.6p. orange	2·00
Z123	3a. ultramarine	2·50
Z124	4a. sage-green (No. 210)	2·50
Z125	4a. sage-green (No. 211)	2·00
Z126	8a. reddish purple	3·00
Z127	12a. claret	3·50
Z128	1r. chocolate and green	3·00
Z129	2r. carmine and orange	4·00
Z130	5r. ultramarine and purple	25·00
Z131	10r. green and scarlet	40·00
Z132	15r. blue and olive	

1931 Inauguration of New Delhi (Nos. 226/31)

Z140	¼a. olive-green and orange-brown	15·00
Z141	½a. violet and green	1·75
Z142	1a. mauve and chocolate	1·75
Z143	2a. green and blue	3·00
Z144	3a. chocolate and carmine	6·00
Z145	1r. violet and green	75·00

1932-36 (Nos. 232/9)

Z146	½a. green	2·00
Z147	9p. deep green	3·00
Z148	1a. chocolate	1·50
Z149	1a.3p. mauve	3·50
Z150	2a. vermilion (No. 236)	15·00
Z151	+2a. vermilion (No. 236*b*)	3·00
Z152	2a. vermilion (No. 236*c*)	5·00
Z153	3a. carmine	3·00
Z154	3a.6p. ultramarine	5·00

1935 Silver Jubilee (Nos. 240/6)

Z156	½a. black and yellow-green	3·00
Z157	9p. black and grey-green	3·50
Z158	1a. black and brown	2·50
Z159	1¼a. black and bright violet	3·00
Z160	2½a. black and orange	7·00
Z161	3½a. black and dull ultramarine	22·00
Z162	8a. black and purple	12·00

OFFICIAL STAMPS

1866 No Watermark (Nos. O1/5)

Z201	½a. blue	
Z202	1a. brown	
Z203	8a. carmine	£225

1866-72 Wmk T **13** (Nos. O6/14)

Z204	½a. blue	£180
Z205	8p. purple	
Z206	1a. brown	£180
Z207	2a. yellow	£375
Z208	4a. green (Type **11**)	£450
Z209	4a. green (Type **17**)	

1867-73 (Nos. O20/30a)

Z211	½a. blue (Die I)	30·00
Z212	½a. blue (Die II)	
Z213	1a. brown	30·00
Z214	2a. yellow	30·00
Z215	4a. green	25·00
Z216	8a. rose	35·00

1874-82 (Nos. O31/5)

Z217	½a. blue	15·00
Z218	1a. brown	15·00
Z219	2a. orange	30·00
Z220	4a. green	25·00
Z221	8a. rose	40·00

1883-99 (Nos. O37a/48)

Z224	3p. aniline carmine	15·00
Z225	½a. deep blue-green	10·00
Z226	1a. brown-purple	10·00
Z227	2a. blue	15·00
Z228	4a. olive-green	20·00
Z229	8a. magenta	28·00
Z230	1r. green and carmine	50·00

1900 (Nos. O49/52)

Z231	½a. yellow-green	15·00
Z232	1a. carmine	12·00
Z233	2a. mauve	20·00

1902-09 King Edward VII (Nos. O54/65)

Z234	3p. grey	15·00
Z235	½a. green	8·00
Z236	1a. carmine	7·00
Z237	2a. mauve	12·00
Z238	4a. olive	15·00
Z239	6a. olive-bistre	20·00
Z240	8a. claret	18·00
Z241	1r. green and carmine	35·00

1906 New Types (Nos. O66/7)

Z242	½a. green	8·00
Z243	1a. carmine	8·00

1909 (Nos. O68/9)

Z244	2r. carmine and yellow-brown	45·00
Z245	5r. ultramarine and violet	55·00

1912-13 King George V (wmk Single Star) (Nos. O73/92)

Z249	3p. grey	6·00
Z250	½a. light green	3·00
Z251	1a. carmine	3·00
Z252	2a. purple	5·00
Z253	4a. olive-green	10·00
Z254	6a. yellow-bistre	15·00
Z255	8a. deep mauve	15·00
Z256	1r. brown and green	18·00
Z257	2r. rose-carmine and brown	30·00

1922 (No. O98)

Z263	1a. chocolate	5·00

1926-31 (Wmk Multiple Star) (Nos. O109/17)

Z272	3p. slate	5·00
Z273	½a. green	4·00
Z274	1a. chocolate	4·00
Z275	2a. purple	5·00
Z276	4a. sage-green	7·00
Z277	8a. reddish purple	10·00
Z278	12a. claret	20·00
Z279	1r. chocolate and green	20·00

A number of other post offices were opened between 1891 and 1937:

Dthali (opened *1903, initially using "EXPERIMENTAL P.O. B-84" postmark; closed 1907*)
Kamaran (opened *c 1915, but no civilian postmarks known before 1925*)
Khormaksar (opened *1892; closed 1915; reopened 1925*)
Maalla (opened *1923; closed 1931*)
Nobat-Dakim (opened *1904, initially using "EXPERIMENTAL P.O. B-84" postmark; closed 1905*)
Perim (opened *1915; closed 1936*)
Sheikh Othman (opened *1891; closed 1915; reopened 1922; closed 1937*)

PRICES FOR STAMPS ON COVER TO 1945

Nos. 1/15	*from* × 6
Nos. 16/27	*from* × 3

(Currency. 12 pies = 1 anna; 16 annas = 1 rupee)

1 Dhow

(Recess D.L.R.)

1937 (1 Apr). Wmk Mult Script CA sideways. P 13×12.

1	**1**	½a. yellow-green	4·50	3·00
2		9p. deep green	4·75	3·75
3		1a. sepia	3·75	2·00
4		2a. scarlet	6·00	3·25
5		2½a. bright blue	8·00	2·50
6		3a. carmine	11·00	8·50
7		3½a. grey-blue	9·00	6·00
8		8a. pale purple	27·00	13·00
9		1r. brown	60·00	13·00
10		2r. yellow	£120	40·00
11		5r. deep purple	£300	£140
		a. Bright aniline purple	£425	£180
12		10r. olive-green	£750	£650
1/12 Set of 12			£1200	£800
1s/12s Perf "SPECIMEN" Set of 12			£800	

1937 (12 May). Coronation. As Nos. 95/7 of Antigua, but ptd by D.L.R. P 14.

13		1a. sepia	65	1·40
14		2½a. light blue	75	1·40
		w. Wmk inverted	£2000	£3250
15		3½a. grey-blue	1·00	3·25
13/15 Set of 3			2·25	5·50
13s/15s Perf "SPECIMEN" Set of 3			£160	

3 Aidrus Mosque, Crater   **4** Adenese Camel Corps

5 The Harbour   **6** Adenese Dhow

7 Mukalla   **8** "Capture of Aden, 1839" (Captain Rundle)

(Recess Waterlow)

1939 (19 Jan)–**48**. Wmk Mult Script CA. P 12½.

16	**3**	½a. yellowish green	2·25	60
		a. Bluish green (13.9.48)	5·50	4·00

2

17	4	¾a. red-brown	3·00	1·25
18	5	1a. pale blue	1·75	40
19	6	1½a. scarlet	3·00	60
20	3	2a. sepia	2·00	25
21	7	2½a. deep ultramarine	2·00	30
22	8	3a. sepia and carmine	2·00	25
23	7	8a. red-orange	2·50	40
23a	8	14a. sepia and light blue (15.1.45)	4·75	1·00
24	6	1r. emerald-green	5·50	2·75
25	5	2r. deep blue and magenta	13·00	3·25
26	4	5r. red-brown and olive-green	40·00	17·00
27	8	10r. sepia and violet	50·00	18·00
16/27 Set of 13			£120	40·00
16s/27s Perf "SPECIMEN" Set of 13			£375	

1½a. Accent over "D" (R. 7/1)

1946 (15 Oct). Victory. As Nos. 110/11 of Antigua.

28		1½a. carmine	40	1·75
		a. Accent over "D"	60·00	75·00
29		2½a. blue	1·00	1·00
		w. Wmk inverted	£2000	
28s/29s Perf "SPECIMEN" Set of 2			£140	

Examples of the "Accent over 'D'" are known officially corrected by scratching out the mark with a sharp point.

1949 (17 Jan). Royal Silver Wedding. As Nos. 112/13 of Antigua.

30		1½a. scarlet (P 14×15)	75	2·25
31		10r. mauve (P 11½×11)	40·00	55·00

1949 (10 Oct). 75th Anniv of UPU. As Nos. 114/17 of Antigua, surch with new values by Waterlow.

32		2½a. on 20c. ultramarine	60	1·50
33		3a. on 30c. carmine-red	2·00	1·50
34		8a. on 50c. orange	2·00	2·00
		a. "C" of "CA" omitted from watermark	£1600	
35		1r. on 1s. blue	1·60	5·50
32/35 Set of 4			5·50	9·50

(New Currency. 100 cents = 1 shilling)

5 CENTS
(12)

1951 (1 Oct). Nos. 18 and 20/7 surch with new values, in cents or shillings, as T **12**, or in one line between bars (30c.) by Waterlow.

36		5c. on 1a. pale blue	35	40
37		10c. on 2a. sepia	25	45
38		15c. on 2½a. deep ultramarine	55	1·25
		a. Surch double	£1600	
39		20c. on 3a. sepia and carmine	50	40
40		30c. on 8a. red-orange (R.)	1·00	65
41		50c. on 8a. red-orange	1·75	35
		a. Surch double, one albino	£3500	
42		70c. on 14a. sepia and light blue	2·50	1·50
43		1s. on 1r. emerald-green	3·25	30
44		2s. on 2r. deep blue and magenta	16·00	3·75
		a. Surch albino	£1500	
45		5s. on 5r. red-brown and olive-green	30·00	17·00
46		10s. on 10r. sepia and violet	42·00	17·00
36/46 Set of 11			85·00	38·00

1953 (2 June). Coronation. As No. 120 of Antigua.

47		15c. black and green	1·75	1·50

14 Minaret

15 Camel transport

16 Crater

17 Mosque

18 Dhow

19 Map

20 Salt works

21 Dhow building

21a Colony's badge

22 Aden Protectorate levy

23 Crater Pass

24 Tribesman

25 "Aden in 1572" (F. Hogenberg)

25c. Crack in wall (R. 1/5)

(Recess Waterlow, D.L.R. from 5 Dec 1961)

1953 (15 June)–**63**. T **14/25**. Wmk Mult Script CA. P 13½×13 (No. 72), 12×13½ (Nos. 57, 64, 66, 68) or 12 (others).

48	14	5c. yellowish green	20	10
49		5c. bluish green (1.6.55)	3·00	3·50
		a. Perf 12×13½ (12.4.56)	35	1·25
50	15	10c. orange	40	10
51		10c. vermilion (1.2.55)	1·50	30
52	16	15c. blue-green	1·50	60
53		15c. greenish grey (26.4.59)	10·00	6·50
		a. Deep greenish grey (16.1.62)	23·00	24·00
		b. Greenish slate (13.11.62)	30·00	20·00
54	17	25c. carmine-red	1·00	55
		a. Crack in wall	65·00	35·00
55		25c. deep rose-red (15.3.56)	7·00	2·00
		a. Rose-red (13.3.62)	23·00	8·50
56	18	35c. deep ultramarine	2·50	1·00
57		35c. deep blue (15.10.58)	7·00	5·50
		a. Violet-blue (17.2.59)	15·00	4·25
58	19	50c. dull blue	50	10
59		50c. deep blue (1.7.55)	4·25	2·25
		a. Perf 12×13½ (12.4.56)	1·25	20
		aw. Wmk inverted	†	£900
60	20	70c. brown-grey	70	10
61		70c. black (20.9.54)	1·75	1·25
		a. Perf 12×13½ (12.4.56)	2·00	20
62	21	1s. sepia and reddish violet	70	10
63		1s. black and violet (1.7.55)	1·75	10
64	21a	1s.25 blue and black (16.7.56)	15·00	60
		a. Dull blue and black (16.1.62)	23·00	1·25
65	22	2s. sepia and rose-carmine	1·50	50
66		2s. black and carmine-red (1.3.56)	16·00	50
		aw. Wmk inverted		
		b. Black and carmine-rose (22.1.63)	48·00	18·00
67	23	5s. sepia and dull blue	3·00	1·00
68		5s. black and deep dull blue (11.4.56)	17·00	1·25
		a. Black and blue (11.12.62)	45·00	18·00
69	24	10s. sepia and olive	3·25	8·00
70		10s. black and bronze-green (20.9.54)	17·00	1·75
71	25	20s. chocolate and reddish lilac	8·50	10·00
72		20s. black and deep lilac (7.1.57)	65·00	22·00
		a. Deep black and deep lilac (14.5.58)	85·00	27·00
48/72 Set of 25			£160	55·00

On No. 70 the tribesman's skirt is shaded with cross-hatching instead of with mainly diagonal lines as in No. 69.

1954 (27 Apr). Royal Visit. As No. 62 but inscr "ROYAL VISIT 1954" at top.

73		1s. sepia and reddish violet	1·00	1·00

تعديل
الدستور
١٩٥٩

REVISED CONSTITUTION 1959

(26)   (27)

1959 (26 Jan). Revised Constitution. No. 53 optd with T **26**, and No. 64 optd with T **27**, in red, by Waterlow.

74		15c. slate-green	60	2·50
75		1s.25 blue and black	1·00	1·50

1963 (4 June). Freedom from Hunger. As No. 146 of Antigua.

76		1s.25 bluish green (Protein foods)	1·25	2·25

1964 (5 Feb)–**65**. As Nos. 48, etc. but wmk w **12**. P 12 (10c., 15c., 25c., 1s.) or 12×13½ (others).

77	14	5c. green (16.2.65)	4·75	12·00
78	15	10c. bright orange	2·25	1·25
79	16	15c. greenish grey	1·00	6·50
		w. Wmk inverted	£130	
80	17	25c. carmine-red	3·25	50
81	18	35c. indigo-violet	8·00	6·00
82	19	50c. indigo-blue	1·50	1·50
		a. Pale indigo-blue (16.2.65)	2·50	2·50
		aw. Wmk inverted		
83	20	70c. black	3·00	5·00
		a. Brownish grey (16.2.65)	6·00	12·00
84	21	1s. black and violet (10.3.64)	12·00	3·50
85	21a	1s.25 ultramarine and black (10.3.64)	18·00	2·25
86	22	2s. black and carmine-rose (16.2.65)	7·50	38·00
77/86 Set of 10			55·00	65·00

The Stamps of Aden were withdrawn on 31 March 1965 and superseded by those of the South Arabian Federation.

ADEN PROTECTORATE STATES

KATHIRI STATE OF SEIYUN

The stamps of ADEN were used in Kathiri State of Seiyun from 22 May 1937 until 1942. A further office was opened at Tarim on 11 December 1940.

PRICES FOR STAMPS ON COVER TO 1945
Nos. 1/11   from × 10

1 Sultan of Seiyun

2 Seiyun

3 Tarim

4 Mosque, Seiyun

5 Fortress, Tarim

6 Mosque, Seiyun

7 South Gate, Tarim

8 Kathiri House

9 Mosque Entrance, Tarim

VICTORY ISSUE 8TH JUNE 1946
(10)

(Recess D.L.R.)

1942 (July–Oct). T **1/9** Wmk Mult Script CA. T **1**, P 14; others P 12×13 (vert) or 13×12 (horiz).

1	1	½a. blue-green	20	2·00
2		¾a. brown	60	4·50
3		1a. blue	70	2·25
4	2	1½a. carmine	70	2·75
5	3	2a. sepia	50	2·75
6	4	2½a. blue	1·25	2·75
7	5	3a. sepia and carmine	1·75	4·50
8	6	8a. red	3·25	1·50
9	7	1r. green	5·50	5·00
10	8	2r. blue and purple	16·00	27·00
11	9	5r. brown and green	38·00	35·00
1/11 Set of 11			60·00	80·00
1s/11s Perf "SPECIMEN" Set of 11			£325	

1946 (15 Oct). Victory. No. 4 optd with T **10**, and No. 6 optd similarly but in four lines, by De La Rue.

12	1½a. carmine		20	65
13	2½a. blue (R.)		20	35
	a. Opt inverted		£1300	
	b. Opt double		£1800	
12s/13s Perf "SPECIMEN" *Set of 2*			£120	

A flaw occurred on the plate to the right of the top of the fort on R. 10/6 (not known on No. 4), all examples of which were officially scratched out with a sharp point.

1949 (17 Jan). Royal Silver Wedding. As Nos. 112/13 of Antigua.

14	1½a. scarlet		30	4·50
15	5r. green		18·00	16·00

1949 (10 Oct). 75th Anniv of UPU. As Nos. 114/17 of Antigua, surch with new values by Waterlow.

16	2½a. on 20c. ultramarine		15	1·75
17	3a. on 30c. carmine-red		1·25	3·50
18	8a. on 50c. orange		25	6·50
19	1r. on 1s. blue		30	2·25
16/19 *Set of 4*			1·75	12·50

5 CTS (11)   **50 CENTS** (12)   **5/-** (13)

1951 (1 Oct). Currency changed. Nos. 3 and 5/11 surch as T **11** (5c.), **12** (10c. ("CTS"), 15c. ("CTS"), 20c. and 50c.) or **13** (1s. to 5s.), by Waterlow.

20	5c. on 1a. blue (R.)		15	2·50
21	10c. on 2a. sepia		30	2·00
22	15c. on 2½a. blue		15	2·75
23	20c. on 3a. sepia and carmine		20	3·00
24	50c. on 8a. red		1·00	2·00
25	1s. on 1r. green		3·00	4·50
26	2s. on 2r. blue and purple		14·00	42·00
27	5s. on 5r. brown and green		38·00	65·00
20/27 *Set of 8*			50·00	£110

1953 (2 June). Coronation. As No. 120 of Antigua.

28	15c. black and deep green (Queen Elizabeth II)		60	1·75

14 Sultan Hussein

15 Tarim

(Des Freya Stark and H. Ingram. Recess D.L.R.)

1954 (15 Jan). As Nos. 1/11 (but with portrait of Sultan Hussein as in T **14/15**). Wmk Mult Script CA. T **14**, P 12½; others P 12×13 (vert) or 13×12 (horiz).

29	**14**	5c. sepia		10	25
30		10c. deep blue		15	25
31	**2**	15c. deep bluish green		20	25
32	**15**	25c. carmine-red		20	25
33	**4**	35c. deep blue		20	25
34	**5**	50c. deep brown and carmine-red		20	20
35	**6**	1s. brown-orange		20	20
36	**7**	2s. deep yellow-green		5·00	3·25
37	**8**	5s. deep blue and violet		11·00	14·00
38	**9**	10s. yellow-brown and violet		12·00	14·00
29/38 *Set of 10*				26·00	29·00

16 Qarn Adh Dhabi

17 Seiyun

18 Gheil Omer

(Recess D.L.R.)

1964 (1 July). T **16/18**. W w **12**. P 12×13 (70c.) or 13×12 (others).

39	**16**	70c. black		4·00	2·50
40	**17**	1s.25 blue-green		4·00	11·00
41	**18**	1s.50 deep reddish violet		4·00	11·00
39/41 *Set of 3*				11·00	22·00

Stamps after this date can be found listed under South Arabia.

QU'AITI STATE IN HADHRAMAUT

The stamps of ADEN were used in Qu'aiti State in Hadhramaut from 22 April 1937 until 1942. The main post office was at Mukalla. Other offices existed at Du'an (*opened* 1940), Gheil Ba Wazir (*opened* 1942), Haura (*opened* 1940), Shibam (*opened* 1940) and Shihr (*opened* 1939).

PRICES FOR STAMPS ON COVER TO 1945

Nos. 1/11   *from* × 15

I. ISSUES INSCR "SHIHR AND MUKALLA".

1 Sultan of Shihr and Mukalla

2 Mukalla Harbour

3 Gateway of Shifir

4 Shibam

5 Outpost of Mukalla

6 'Einat

7 Du'an

8 Mosque in Hureidha

9 Meshhed

VICTORY ISSUE 8TH JUNE 1946 (10)

(Recess D.L.R.)

1942 (July)–**46**. **1/9**. Wmk Mult Script CA. P 14 (½ to 1a.), 12×13 (1½, 2, 3a. and 1r.) or 13×12 (others).

1	**1**	½a. blue-green		1·75	50
		a. Olive-green (12.46)		30·00	42·00
2		¾a. brown		2·50	30
3		1a. blue		1·00	1·00
4	**2**	1½a. carmine		2·00	50
5	**3**	2a. sepia		2·00	1·75
6	**4**	2½a. blue		50	30
7	**5**	3a. sepia and carmine		1·25	1·00
8		8a. red		1·25	40
9	**7**	1r. green		7·50	4·75
		a. "A" of "CA" missing from wmk		£1300	£1200
10	**8**	2r. blue and purple		20·00	17·00
11	**9**	5r. brown and green		40·00	23·00
1/11 *Set of 11*				70·00	45·00
1s/11s Perf "SPECIMEN" *Set of 11*			£325	

1946 (15 Oct). Victory. No. 4 optd. with T **10** and No. 6 optd similarly, but in three lines, by De La Rue.

12	1½a. carmine		15	1·25
13	2½a. blue (R.)		15	50
12s/13s Perf "SPECIMEN" *Set of 2*			£120	

1949 (17 Jan). Royal Silver Wedding. As Nos. 112/13 of Antigua.

14	1½a. scarlet		50	4·50
15	5r. green		17·00	17·00

1949 (10 Oct). 75th Anniv of UPU. As Nos. 114/17 of Antigua, surch with new values by Waterlow.

16	2½a. on 20c. ultramarine		15	70
17	3a. on 30c. carmine-red		1·40	3·75
18	8a. on 50c. orange		25	3·75
19	1r. on 1s. blue		30	50
	a. Surch omitted		£4000	
16/19 *Set of 4*			1·90	8·00

1951 (1 Oct). Currency changed. Surch with new values in cents or shillings as T **11** (5c.), **12** (10c. ("CTS"), 15c., 20c. and 50c.) or **13** (1s. to 5s.), by Waterlow.

20	5c. on 1a. blue (R.)		15	30
21	10c. on 2a. sepia		15	30
22	15c. on 2½a. blue		15	30
23	20c. on 3a. sepia and carmine		30	1·00
	a. Surch double, one albino		£600	
24	50c. on 8a. red		50	3·00
25	1s. on 1r. green		2·25	55
26	2s. on 2r. blue and purple		8·50	32·00
27	5s. on 5r. brown and green		23·00	45·00
20/27 *Set of 8*			32·00	75·00

1953 (2 June). Coronation. As No. 120 of Antigua.

28	15c. black and deep blue (Queen Elizabeth II)		1·00	65

II. ISSUES INSCR "HADHRAMAUT"

11 Metal Work

12 Mat-making

13 Weaving   **14** Pottery

15 Building

16 Date cultivation

17 Agriculture

18 Fisheries

19 Lime burning   **20** Dhow building

21 Agriculture

22 Metal Work

(Des Mme M. de Sturler Raemaekers. Recess D.L.R.)

1955 (1 Sept)–**63**. T **11/21**. Wmk Mult Script CA. P 11½×13-13½ (vert) or 14 (horiz).

29	5c. greenish blue		1·00	10
30	10c. grey-black		1·25	10
31	15c. deep green		1·00	10
	a. Bronze-green (9.3.63)		1·00	40
32	25c. carmine-red		50	10
33	35c. blue		1·00	10
34	50c. orange-red		1·50	10
	a. Red-orange (9.3.63)		1·00	30
35	90c. sepia		70	15
36	1s. black and deep lilac		1·00	10
37	1s.25 black and red-orange		75	55
38	2s. black and indigo		4·00	10
39	5s. black and bluish green		5·00	3·00
40	10s. black and lake		18·00	8·00
29/40 *Set of 12*			30·00	11·50

1963 (20 Oct). As Nos. 29/40 but with inset portrait of Sultan Awadh bin Saleh el-Qu'aiti as in T **22** and wmk w **12**.

41	5c. greenish blue	10	1·75
42	10c. grey-black	10	1·50
43	15c. bronze-green	10	1·75
44	25c. carmine-red	15	75
45	35c. blue	15	2·00
46	50c. red-orange	15	1·00
47	70c. deep brown (as 90c.)	20	75
48	1s. black and deep lilac	25	30
49	1s.25 black and red-orange	60	6·50
50	2s. black and indigo-blue	3·25	3·50
51	5s. black and bluish green	16·00	32·00
52	10s. black and lake	32·00	32·00
41/52 *Set of 12*		48·00	75·00

Stamps after this date can be found listed under South Arabia.

Aitutaki see Cook Islands

Anguilla

Following the grant of Associated Statehood to St. Christopher, Nevis and Anguilla, on 27 February 1967, the Island Council of Anguilla declared the island independent and the St. Kitts-Nevis authorities left the island on 30 May 1967. Mail communications, which had all been via St. Kitts, were severed for four weeks and when they were resumed, via St. Thomas in the US Virgin Islands, prepayment was denoted by a rectangular handstamp in violet with the postage rate incorporated within it. Nos. 1/16 were subsequently issued by the Island Council and were accepted for international mail. On 7 July 1969 the Anguilla post office was officially recognised by the Government of St. Christopher, Nevis and Anguilla and normal postal communications via St. Christopher were resumed. By the Anguilla Act of 21 July 1971, Anguilla was restored to direct British control.

A degree of internal self-government with an Executive Council was introduced on 10 February 1976 and the links with St. Kitts-Nevis were officially severed on 18 December 1980.

(Currency. 100 cents = 1 Eastern Carribean dollar)

Independent Anguilla
(**1**)

2 Mahogany Tree, The Quarter

1967 (4 Sept). Nos. 129/44 of St. Kitts-Nevis optd as T **1**, by Island Press Inc, St. Thomas, US Virgin Islands.

1	½c. New lighthouse, Sombrero	70·00	26·00
2	1c. Loading sugar cane, St. Kitts	80·00	11·00
3	2c. Pall Mall Square, Basseterre	75·00	3·00
4	3c. Gateway, Brimstone Hill Fort, St. Kitts	80·00	8·50
	w. Wmk inverted	—	50·00
5	4c. Nelson's Spring, Nevis	80·00	6·50
6	5c. Grammar School, St. Kitts	£400	50·00
7	6c. Crater, Mt. Misery, St. Kitts	£130	19·00
8	10c. Hibiscus	75·00	11·00
9	15c. Sea Island cotton, Nevis	£150	17·00
10	20c. Boat building, Anguilla	£400	26·00
11	25c. White-crowned Pigeon	£375	50·00
	w. Wmk inverted	£275	80·00
12	50c. St. George's Church Tower, Basseterre	£6000	£850
13	60c. Alexander Hamilton	£9000	£1900
14	$1 Map of St. Kitts-Nevis	£4250	£750
15	$2.50 Map of Anguilla	£3250	£475
16	$5 Arms of St. Christopher, Nevis and Anguilla	£3500	£500
1/16 *Set of 16*		£25000	£4250

Owing to the limited stocks available for overprinting, the sale of the above stamps was personally controlled by the Postmaster and no orders from the trade were accepted.

(Des John Lister Ltd. Litho A. & M.)

1967 (27 Nov)–**68**. T **2** and similar horiz designs. P 12½×13.

17	1c. dull green, bistre-brown and pale orange	10	1·00
18	2c. bluish green and black (21.3.68)	10	3·00
19	3c. black and light emerald (10.2.68)	10	10
20	4c. cobalt-blue and black (10.2.68)	10	10
21	5c. multicoloured	10	10
22	6c. light vermilion and black (21.3.68)	10	10
23	10c. multicoloured	15	10
24	15c. multicoloured (10.2.68)	3·25	20
25	20c. multicoloured	1·25	2·75
26	25c. multicoloured	60	20
27	40c. apple green, light greenish blue and black	1·00	25
28	60c. multicoloured (10.2.68)	5·00	6·00
29	$1 multicoloured (10.2.68)	1·75	3·25
30	$2.50 multicoloured (21.3.68)	2·00	7·50
31	$5 multicoloured (10.2.68)	3·00	4·25
17/31 *Set of 15*		16·00	25·00

Designs:—2c. Sombrero Lighthouse; 3c. St. Mary's Church; 4c. Valley Police Station; 5c. Old Plantation House, Mt. Fortune; 6c. Valley Post Office; 10c. Methodist Church, West End; 15c. Wall-Blake Airport; 20c. Beech A90 King Air aircraft over Sandy Ground; 25c. Island Harbour; 40c. Map of Anguilla; 60c. Hermit Crab and Starfish; $1 Hibiscus; $2.50, Local scene; $5, Spiny Lobster.

17 Yachts in Lagoon

18 Purple-throated Carib

(Des John Lister Ltd. Litho A. & M.)

1968 (11 May). Anguillan Ships. T **17** and similar horiz designs. Multicoloured. P 14.

32	10c. Type **17**	35	10
33	15c. Boat on beach	40	10
34	25c. *Warspite* (schooner)	55	15
35	40c. *Atlantic Star* (schooner)	65	20
32/35 *Set of 4*		1·75	50

(Des John Lister Ltd. Litho A. & M.)

1968 (8 July). Anguillan Birds. T **18** and similar multicoloured designs. P 14.

36	10c. Type **18**	65	20
37	15c. Bananaquit	80	25
38	25c. Black-necked Stilt (*horiz*)	85	25
39	40c. Royal Tern (*horiz*)	90	40
36/39 *Set of 4*		3·00	1·00

19 Guides' Badge and Anniversary Years

(Des John Lister Ltd. Litho A. & M.)

1968 (14 Oct). 35th Anniv of Anguillan Girl Guides. T **19** and similar multicoloured designs. P 13×13½ (10, 25c.) or 13½×13 (others).

40	10c. Type **19**	10	25
41	15c. Badge and silhouettes of Guides (*vert*)	15	25
42	25c. Guides' badge and Headquarters	20	35
43	40c. Association and Proficiency badges (*vert*)	25	50
40/43 *Set of 4*		65	1·25

20 The Three Kings

(Des John Lister Ltd. Litho A. & M.)

1968 (18 Nov). Christmas. T **20** and similar designs. P 13.

44	1c. black and cerise	10	10
45	10c. black and light greenish blue	10	10
46	15c. black and chestnut	15	10
47	40c. black and blue	15	10
48	50c. black and dull green	20	15
44/48 *Set of 5*		60	50

Designs: Vert—10c. The Wise Men; 15c. Holy Family and manger. Horiz—40c. The Shepherds; 50c. Holy Family and donkey.

21 Bagging Salt

INDEPENDENCE JANUARY, 1969 (**21a**)

(Des John Lister Ltd. Litho A. & M.)

1969 (4 Jan). Anguillan Salt Industry. T **21** and similar horiz designs. Multicoloured. P 13.

49	10c. Type **21**	25	35
50	15c. Packing salt	30	40
51	40c. Salt pond	35	45
52	50c. Loading salt	35	75
49/52 *Set of 4*		1·10	1·75

1969 (17 Jan*). Expiration of Interim Agreement on Status of Anguilla. Nos. 17/24 and 26/7 optd with T **21a**.

52a	1c. dull green, bistre-brown and pale orange	10	40
52b	2c. bluish green and black	10	40
52c	3c. black and light emerald	10	40
52d	4c. cobalt-blue and black	10	40
52e	5c. multicoloured	10	20
52f	6c. light vermilion and black	10	20
52g	10c. multicoloured	10	30
52h	15c. multicoloured	90	30
52i	25c. multicoloured	80	30
52j	40c. apple green, light greenish blue and black	1·50	40
52a/j *Set of 10*		3·25	3·00

*Earliest known postmark date. The remaining values of the 1967–68 series, Nos. 17/31, also come with this overprint. The complete set exists on large first day covers postmarked 9 January 1969. The values listed above have been reported used on commercial mail from Anguilla.

22 The Crucifixion (Studio of Massys)

(Des John Lister Ltd. Litho Format)

1969 (31 Mar). Easter Commemoration. T **22** and similar vert design. P 13½.

53	25c. multicoloured	25	15
54	40c. multicoloured	35	15

Design:—10c. *The Last Supper* (ascribed to Roberti).

23 Amaryllis

(Des John Lister Ltd. Litho Format)

1969 (10 June). Flowers of the Caribbean. T **23** and similar horiz designs. Multicoloured. P 14.

55	10c. Type **23**	15	20
56	15c. Bougainvillea	15	25
57	40c. Hibiscus	20	50
58	50c. Cattleya Orchid	1·00	1·60
55/58	Set of 4	1·40	2·25

24 Superb Gaza, Channelled Turban, Chestnut Turban and Carved Star Shell

(Des John Lister Ltd. Litho A. & M.)

1969 (22 Sept). Sea Shells. T **24** and similar horiz designs. Multicoloured. P 14.

59	10c. Type **24**	30	25
60	15c. American Thorny Oyster	30	25
61	40c. Scotch, Royal and Smooth Scotch Bonnets	45	30
62	50c. Atlantic Trumpet Triton	50	30
59/62	Set of 4	1·40	1·00

(25) (26) (27)

(28) (29)

1969 (1 Oct). Christmas. Nos. 17, 25/8 optd with T **25/29**.

63	1c. dull green, bistre-brown and light orange	10	10
64	20c. multicoloured	20	10
65	25c. multicoloured	20	10
66	40c. apple-green, light greenish blue and black	25	15
67	60c. multicoloured	40	20
63/67	Set of 5	1·00	55

30 Spotted Goatfish   **31** "Morning Glory"

(Des John Lister Ltd. Litho A. & M.)

1969 (1 Dec). Fish. T **30** and similar horiz designs. Multicoloured. P 14.

68	10c. Type **30**	45	15
69	15c. Blue-striped Grunt	60	15
70	40c. Nassau Grouper	75	20
71	50c. Banded Butterflyfish	80	20
68/71	Set of 4	2·40	65

(Des John Lister Ltd. Litho A. & M.)

1970 (23 Feb). Flowers. T **31** and similar vert designs. Multicoloured. P 14.

72	10c. Type **31**	25	10
73	15c. Blue Petrea	30	10
74	40c. Hibiscus	40	20
75	50c. "Flame Tree"	45	25
72/75	Set of 4	1·25	55

32 The Crucifixion (Masaccio)   **33** Scout Badge and Map

(Des John Lister Ltd. Litho Format)

1970 (26 Mar). Easter. T **32** and similar multicoloured designs. P 13½.

76	10c. The Ascent to Calvary (Tiepolo) (horiz)	15	10
77	20c. Type **32**	20	10
78	40c. Deposition (Rosso Fiorentino)	25	15
79	60c. The Ascent to Calvary (Murillo) (horiz)	25	15
76/79	Set of 4	75	45

(Des John Lister Ltd. Litho A. & M.)

1970 (10 Aug). 40th Anniv of Scouting in Anguilla. T **33** and similar horiz designs. Multicoloured. P 13.

80	10c. Type **33**	15	30
81	15c. Scout camp and cubs practising first-aid	20	30
82	40c. Monkey Bridge	25	40
83	50c. Scout HQ Building and Lord Baden-Powell	35	55
80/83	Set of 4	85	1·40

34 Boatbuilding

(Des John Lister Ltd. Litho Format)

1970 (23 Nov). Various horiz designs as T **34**. Multicoloured. P 14.

84	1c. Type **34**	30	40
85	2c. Road Construction	30	40
86	3c. Quay, Blowing Point	30	20
87	4c. Broadcaster, Radio Anguilla	30	50
88	5c. Cottage Hospital Extension	40	50
89	6c. Valley Secondary School	30	50
90	10c. Hotel Extension	30	30
91	15c. Sandy Ground	30	30
92	20c. Supermarket and Cinema	70	30
93	25c. Bananas and Mangoes	35	1·00
94	40c. Wall Blake Airport	4·00	3·25
95	60c. Sandy Ground Jetty	65	3·50
96	$1 Administration Buildings	1·25	1·40
97	$2.50 Livestock	1·50	4·00
98	$5 Sandy Hill Bay	3·25	3·75
84/98	Set of 15	13·00	18·00

35 The Adoration of the Shepherds (Reni)

(Des John Lister Ltd. Litho Questa)

1970 (11 Dec). Christmas. T **35** and similar vert designs. Multicoloured. P 13½.

99	1c. Type **35**	10	15
100	20c. The Virgin and Child (Gozzoli)	30	20
101	25c. Mystic Nativity (detail, Botticelli)	30	25
102	40c. The Santa Margherita Madonna (detail, Mazzola)	40	25
103	50c. The Adoration of the Magi (detail, Tiepolo)	40	25
99/103	Set of 5	1·25	1·00

Antigua

It is believed that the first postmaster for Antigua was appointed under Edward Dummer's scheme in 1706. After the failure of his service, control of the overseas mails passed to the British GPO Mail services before 1850 were somewhat haphazard, until St. John's was made a branch office of the British GPO in 1850. A second office, at English Harbour, opened in 1857.

The stamps of Great Britain were used between May 1858 and the end of April 1860, when the island postal service became the responsibility of the local colonial authorities. In the interim period, between the take-over and the appearance of Antiguan stamps, the crowned-circle handstamps were again utilised and No. CC1 can be found used as late as 1869.

For illustrations of the handstamp and postmark types see BRITISH POST OFFICES ABROAD notes, following GREAT BRITAIN.

CC **1**   CC **3**

ST. JOHN'S

CROWNED-CIRCLE HANDSTAMPS

CC1	CC **1** ANTIGUA (St. John's) (9.3.1850) (R).	*Price on cover*	£650

Stamps of GREAT BRITAIN cancelled "A 02" as Type **2**.

1858–60.

Z1	1d. rose-red (1857), P 14	£750
Z2	2d. blue (1855), P 14 (Plate No. 6)	£1800
Z3	2d. blue (1858) (Plate Nos. 7, 8, 9)	£1000
Z4	4d. rose (1857)	£600
Z5	6d. lilac (1856)	£180
Z6	1s. green (1856)	£3250

ENGLISH HARBOUR

CROWNED-CIRCLE HANDSTAMPS

CC2	CC **3** "ENGLISH HARBOR" (10.12.1857)	*Price on cover*	£9000

Stamps of GREAT BRITAIN cancelled "A 18" as Type **2**.

1858–60.

Z6a	1d. rose red (1857)	£3250
Z7	2d. blue (1858) (Plate No. 7)	£6000
Z8	4d. rose (1857)	£6000
Z9	6d. lilac	£2000
Z10	1s. green (1856)	£2000

PRICES FOR STAMPS ON COVER TO 1945	
No. 1	*from* × 10
Nos. 2/4	†
Nos. 5/10	*from* × 20
Nos. 13/14	*from* × 30
No. 15	*from* × 60
Nos. 16/18	*from* × 50
Nos. 19/23	*from* × 12
No. 24	*from* × 50
Nos. 25/30	*from* × 10
Nos. 31/51	*from* × 4
Nos. 52/4	*from* × 10
Nos. 55/61	*from* × 4
Nos. 62/80	*from* × 3
Nos. 81/90	*from* × 4
Nos. 91/4	*from* × 5
Nos. 95/7	*from* × 4
Nos. 98/109	*from* × 3

CROWN COLONY

1   **3**

(Eng C. Jeens after drawing by Edward Corbould. Recess P.B.)

1862 (Aug). No wmk.

(a) Rough perf 14 to 16

1	**1**	6d. blue-green	£800	£550

(b) P 11 to 12½

2	**1**	6d. blue-green	£7500	

(c) P 14 to 16×11 to 12½

3	**1**	6d. blue-green	£3250	

(d) P 14 to 16 compound with 11 to 12½

4	**1**	6d. blue-green	£3250	

Nos. 2/4 may be trial perforations. They are not known used.

1863 (Jan)-**67**. Wmk Small Star. W w **2** (sideways on 6d.). Rough perf 14 to 16.

5	**1**	1d. rosy mauve	£130	80·00
6	**1**	1d. dull rose (1864)	£120	55·00
		a. Imperf between (vert pair)	£32000	

7		1d. vermilion (1867)	£250	30·00
	a.	Imperf between (horiz pair)	£32000	
	b.	Wmk sideways	£250	42·00
8		6d. green (shades)	£700	26·00
	a.	Wmk upright		£190
9		6d. dark green	£750	26·00
10		6d. yellow-green	£4250	£100

Caution is needed in buying No. 10 as some of the shades of No. 8 verge on yellow-green.

The 1d. rosy mauve exists showing trial perforations of 11 to 12½ and 14 to 16 (Price, £8500 unused).

(Recess D.L.R. from P.B. plates)

1872. Wmk Crown CC. P 12½.

13	**1**	1d. lake	£200	17·00
	w.	Wmk inverted	£275	80·00
	x.	Wmk reversed	£180	17·00
	y.	Wmk inverted and reversed		
14		1d. scarlet	£200	24·00
	w.	Wmk inverted	£200	65·00
	x.	Wmk reversed	—	32·00
15		6d. blue-green	£550	11·00
	w.	Wmk inverted		£120
	x.	Wmk reversed	£500	14·00
	y.	Wmk inverted and reversed	—	£140

1876. Wmk Crown CC. P 14.

16	**1**	1d. lake	£225	11·00
	a.	Bisected (½d.) (1883) (on cover)	†	£8000
	x.	Wmk reversed		38·00
17		1d. lake-rose	£225	11·00
	w.	Wmk inverted	£400	£100
	y.	Wmk inverted and reversed	—	35·00
18		6d. blue-green	£425	21·00
	w.	Wmk inverted	†	£140
	x.	Wmk reversed	£350	22·00
	y.	Wmk inverted and reversed	£500	85·00

(Recess (T **1**); typo (T **3**) De La Rue & Co).

1879. Wmk Crown CC. P 14.

19	**3**	2½d. red-brown	£600	£170
	a.	Large "2" in "2½" with slanting foot	£11000	£2750
20		4d. blue	£250	13·00

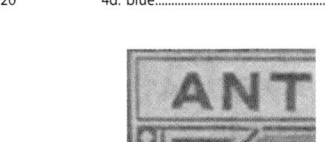

Top left triangle detached
(Pl 2 R. 3/3 of right pane)

1882. Wmk Crown CA. P 14.

21	**3**	½d. dull green	5·00	20·00
	a.	Top left triangle detached	£350	£550
22		2½d. red-brown	£190	55·00
	a.	Top left triangle detached		
	b.	Large "2" in "2½" with slanting foot	£3500	£1300
23		4d. blue	£275	13·00
	a.	Top left triangle detached	—	£750

1884. Wmk Crown CA. P 12.

24	**1**	1d. carmine-red	60·00	20·00
	w.	Wmk inverted		
	x.	Wmk inverted and reversed		

The 1d. scarlet is a colour changeling.

1884–87. Wmk Crown CA. P 14.

25	**1**	1d. carmine-red	2·25	3·75
	w.	Wmk inverted	—	£110
	x.	Wmk reversed	75·00	35·00
	y.	Wmk inverted and reversed		
26		1d. rose	60·00	12·00
27	**3**	2½d. ultramarine (1887)	7·00	14·00
	a.	Large "2" in "2½" with slanting foot	£160	£250
	b.	Top left triangle detached	£400	£475
28		4d. chestnut (1887)	2·25	3·00
	a.	Top left triangle detached	£350	£375
29	**1**	6d. deep green	60·00	£120
30	**3**	1s. mauve (1886)	£160	£140
	a.	Top left triangle detached	£2000	£2000
25/30		Set of 5	£200	£250
27s, 28s, 30s		Optd "SPECIMEN" Set of 3	£150	

Nos. 25 and 26 postmarked "A 12" in place of "A 02" were used in St. Christopher.

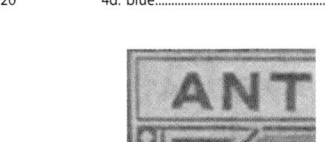

2½ 2½ 2½

A   B   C

The variety "Large '2' in '2½' with slanting foot" occurs on R. 7/1 of the duty plate on all printings. At this position the "NN" of "PENNY" also sustained damage in about 1886, leaving three vertical strokes shortened. A and B (above) represent two states of the flaw at R. 7/1. Head plate 2, first used for Antigua in 1886, was a double-pane plate of 120, but the same 60-set duty plate remained in use, the variety thus occurring on R. 7/1 of each pane. A very similar flaw (C above) appeared at R. 3/1 of the duty plate (on which the "NN" was undamaged) early in the life of No. 27 and thus occurs on both panes of that stamp.

From 31 October 1890 until July 1903 Leeward Islands general issues were used. Subsequently both general issues and the following separate issues were in concurrent use until July 1956, when the general Leeward Islands stamps were withdrawn.

---

4   **5**

(Typo D.L.R.)

1903 (July)–**07.** Wmk Crown CC. Ordinary paper. P 14.

31	**4**	½d. grey-black and grey-green	3·75	6·50
32		1d. grey-black and rose-red	14·00	1·25
	w.	Wmk inverted	†	£400
33		2d. dull purple and brown	7·50	25·00
34		2½d. grey-black and blue	18·00	23·00
	a.	Chalk-surfaced paper (1907)	50·00	70·00
35		3d. grey-green and orange-brown	11·00	20·00
36		6d. purple and drab	32·00	55·00
	w.	Wmk inverted	£190	£250
37		1s. blue and dull purple	55·00	65·00
	a.	Chalk-surfaced paper (1907)	75·00	£140
38		2s. grey-green and pale violet	90·00	£120
39		2s.6d. grey-black and purple	27·00	70·00
40	**5**	5s. grey-green and violet	£110	£160
	a.	Chalk-surfaced paper (1907)	£190	£250
31/40		Set of 10	£325	£500
31s/40s		Optd "SPECIMEN" Set of 10	£200	

1908–17. Wmk Mult Crown CA. Chalk-surfaced paper (2d., 3d. to 2s.). P 14.

41	**4**	½d. green	4·75	4·75
	w.	Wmk inverted	†	£400
42		½d. blue-green (1917)	8·00	7·50
43		1d. red (1909)	12·00	2·25
44		1d. scarlet (5.8.15)	9·00	3·25
	w.	Wmk inverted		£425
45		2d. dull purple and brown (1912)	4·75	32·00
46		2½d. ultramarine	23·00	18·00
	a.	Blue	38·00	25·00
47		3d. grey-green and orange-brown (1912)	6·50	19·00
48		6d. purple and drab (1911)	7·50	40·00
49		1s. blue and dull purple	27·00	70·00
50		2s. grey-green and violet (1912)	£110	£130
41/50		Set of 8	£170	£275
41s, 43s, 46s		Optd "SPECIMEN" Set of 3	90·00	

1913. As T **5**, but portrait of George V. Wmk Mult Crown CA. Chalk-surfaced paper. P 14.

51		5s. grey-green and violet	95·00	£150
	s.	Optd "SPECIMEN"	90·00	

WAR STAMP

(7)   **8**

1916 (Sept)–**17.** No. 41 optd with T **7** by D.L.R.

52	**4**	½d. green (Bk.)	4·75	3·75
53		½d. green (R.) (1.10.17)	1·50	3·50
	w.	Wmk inverted	†	—

1918 (July). Optd with T **7**. Wmk Mult Crown CA. P 14.

54	**4**	1½d. orange	1·75	1·75
52s/4s		Optd "SPECIMEN" Set of 3	£120	

(Typo D.L.R.)

1921 (July)–**29.** P 14.

(a) Wmk Mult Crown CA. Chalk-surfaced paper

55	**8**	3d. purple/pale yellow	4·75	15·00
56		4d. grey-black and red/pale yellow (1922)	2·25	5·50
57		1s. black/emerald	4·25	9·00
	y.	Wmk inverted and reversed		£400
58		2s. purple and blue/blue	13·00	38·00
59		2s.6d. black and red/blue	18·00	65·00
60		5s. green and red/pale yellow (1922)	8·50	50·00
61		£1 purple and black/red (1922)	£275	£375
55/61		Set of 7	£300	£500
55s/61s		Optd "SPECIMEN" Set of 7	£200	

(b) Wmk Mult Script CA. Chalk-surfaced paper (3d. to 4s.)

62	**8**	½d. dull green	3·00	50
63		1d. carmine-red	4·25	50
64		1d. bright violet (1923)	8·50	1·50
	a.	Mauve (1926?)	20·00	7·00
65		1d. bright scarlet (1929)	42·00	4·25
66		1½d. dull orange (1922)	6·00	5·00
67		1½d. carmine-red (1926)	9·00	1·75
68		1½d. pale red-brown (1929)	3·00	60
69		2d. grey	4·50	75
	a.	Wmk sideways	†	£3500
70		2½d. bright blue	9·50	17·00
71		2½d. orange-yellow (1923)	2·50	17·00
72		2½d. ultramarine (1927)	17·00	3·25
73		3d. purple/pale yellow (1925)	15·00	6·50
74		6d. dull and bright purple	8·00	4·25
75		1s. black/emerald (1929)	6·00	3·25
76		2s. purple and blue/blue (1927)	11·00	65·00
77		2s.6d. black and red/blue (1927)	50·00	48·00
78		3s. green and violet (1922)	50·00	£100
79		4s. grey-black and red (1922)	50·00	75·00
62/80		Set of 18	£200	£300
62s/80s		Optd or Perf (Nos. 65, 69, 76) "SPECIMEN" Set of 18	£450	

---

9 Old Dockyard, English Harbour   **10** Government House, St. John's

11 Nelson's *Victory*   **12** Sir Thomas Warner's *Concepcion*

(Des Mrs. J. Goodwin (5s.), Waterlow (others). Recess Waterlow)

1932 (27 Jan). Tercentenary. Wmk Mult Script CA. P 12½.

81	**9**	½d. green	4·50	7·50
82		1d. scarlet	6·00	9·00
83		1½d. brown	4·75	4·75
84	**10**	2d. grey	8·50	27·00
85		2½d. deep blue	8·50	8·50
86		3d. orange	8·50	12·00
87	**11**	6d. violet	15·00	12·00
88		1s. olive-green	20·00	32·00
89		2s.6d. claret	55·00	80·00
90	**12**	5s. black and chocolate	£120	£160
81/90		Set of 10	£225	£325
81s/90s		Perf "SPECIMEN" Set of 10	£250	

Examples of all values are known showing a forged St. John's postmark dated "MY 18 1932".

13 Windsor Castle

(Des H. Fleury. Recess D.L.R.)

1935 (6 May). Silver Jubilee. Wmk Mult Script CA. P 13½×14.

91	**13**	1d. deep blue and carmine	3·00	4·25
	f.	Diagonal line by turret	£100	£120
92		1½d. ultramarine and grey	2·75	1·75
93		2½d. brown and deep blue	7·00	1·75
	g.	Dot to left of chapel	£225	£250
94		1s. slate and purple	8·50	18·00
	a.	Frame printed double, one albino	£2000	
	h.	Dot by flagstaff	£375	£550
91/94		Set of 4	19·00	23·00
91s/4s		Perf "SPECIMEN" Set of 4	£110	

For illustrations of plate varieties see Ominbus section following Zanzibar.

14 King George VI and Queen Elizabeth

(Des D.L.R. Recess B.W.)

1937 (12 May). Coronation. Wmk Mult Script CA. P 11×11½.

95	**14**	1d. carmine	1·00	3·25
96		1½d. yellow-brown	1·00	3·00
97		2½d. blue	2·25	3·25
95/7		Set of 3	3·75	8·50
95s/97s		Perf "SPECIMEN" Set of 3	£100	

15 English Harbour   **16** Nelson's Dockyard

16a Fort James   **16b** St. John's Harbour

(Recess Waterlow)

1938 (15 Nov)–**51.** Wmk Mult Script CA. P 12½.

98	**15**	½d. green	40	1·25
99	**16**	1d. scarlet	3·50	2·50
	a.	Red (8.42)	5·50	3·00

100		1½d. chocolate-brown	10·00	2·50
		a. Dull reddish brown (12.43)	3·00	4·25
		b. Lake-brown (7.49)	32·00	14·00
101	15	2d. grey	1·50	1·50
		a. Slate-grey (6.51)	9·50	10·00
102	16	2½d. deep ultramarine	1·75	80
103	16a	3d. orange	1·50	1·00
104	16b	6d. violet	5·50	1·25
105		1s. black and brown	8·00	2·25
		a. Black and red-brown (7.49)	32·00	11·00
		ab. Frame ptd double, one albino ..	£6000	
		b. "A" of "CA" missing from wmk..	£1100	
106	16a	2s.6d. brown-purple	55·00	22·00
		a. Maroon (8.42)	38·00	22·00
107	16b	5s. olive-green	18·00	15·00
108	16	10s. magenta (1.4.48)	22·00	38·00
109	16a	£1 slate-green (1.4.48)	45·00	70·00
98s/109 Set of 12			£130	£140
98s/109s Perf "SPECIMEN" Set of 12			£300	

17 Houses of Parliament, London

(Des and recess D.L.R.)

1946 (1 Nov). Victory. Wmk Mult Script CA. P 13½×14.

110	17	1½d. brown	30	10
111		3d. red-orange	30	50
110s/11s Perf "SPECIMEN" Set of 2			90·00	

18 King George VI and Queen Elizabeth

19

(Des and photo Waterloo (T **18**). Design recess; name typo B.W. (T **19**))

1949 (3 Jan). Royal Silver Wedding. Wmk Mult Script CA.

| 112 | 18 | 2½d. ultramarine (P 14×15) | 1·00 | 2·75 |
| 113 | 19 | 5s. grey-olive (P 11½×11) | 15·00 | 15·00 |

20 Hermes, Globe and Forms of Transport

21 Hemispheres, Jet-powered Vickers Viking Airliner and Steamer

22 Hermes and Globe

23 UPU Monument

(Recess Waterloo (T **20, 23**). Designs recess, name typo B.W. (T **21/2**))

1949 (10 Oct). 75th Anniv of Universal Postal Union. Wmk Mult Script CA.

114	20	2½d. ultramarine (P 13½–14)	40	1·00
115	21	3d. orange (P 11×11½)	2·00	4·00
116	22	6d. purple (P 11×11½)	45	3·75
117	23	1s. red-brown (P 13½–14)	45	1·25
114/17 Set of 4			3·00	9·00

(New Currency. 100 cents = 1 West Indian, later Eastern Caribbean, dollar)

24 Arms of University

25 Princess Alice

(Recess Waterloo)

1951 (16 Feb). Inauguration of BWI University College. Wmk Mult Script CA. P 14×14½.

| 118 | 24 | 3c. black and brown | 1·00 | 2·25 |
| 119 | 25 | 12c. black and violet | 1·00 | 2·25 |

26 Queen Elizabeth II

27 Martello Tower

(Des and eng B.W. Recess D.L.R.)

1953. (2 June). Coronation. Wmk Mult Script CA. P 13½×13.

| 120 | 26 | 2c. black and deep yellow-green | 30 | 75 |

(Recess Waterloo until 1961, then D.L.R.)

1953 (2 Nov)–**62**. Designs previously used for King George VI issue, but with portrait of Queen Elizabeth II as in T **27**. Wmk Mult Script CA. P 13×13½ (horiz) or 13½×13 (vert).

120a	16a	½c. brown (3.7.56)	40	40
121	15	1c. slate-grey	30	2·50
		a. Slate (7.11.61)	3·75	5·50
122	16	2c. green	30	10
123		3c. black and orange-yellow	40	20
		a. Black and yellow-orange (5.12.61)	3·50	3·75
124	15	4c. scarlet	1·25	10
		a. Brown-red (11.12.62)	1·25	50
125	16	5c. black and slate-lilac	2·50	40
126	16a	6c. yellow-ochre	2·75	10
		a. Dull yellow-ochre (5.12.61)	13·00	3·50
127	27	8c. deep blue	2·50	10
128	16b	12c. violet	2·50	10
129		24c. black and chocolate	6·00	15
130	27	48c. purple and deep blue	14·00	4·00
131	16a	60c. maroon	13·00	2·25
132	16b	$1·20 olive-green	4·50	70
		a. Yellowish olive (10.8.55)	4·00	1·00
133	16	$2·40 bright reddish purple	20·00	12·00
134	16a	$4·80 slate-blue	28·00	35·00
120a/134 Set of 15			85·00	50·00

See also Nos. 149/58.

28 Federation Map

COMMEMORATION
ANTIGUA
CONSTITUTION
1960
(**29**)

(Recess B.W.)

1958 (22 Apr). Inauguration of British Caribbean Federation. W w **12**. P 11½×11.

135	28	3c. deep green	1·60	40
136		6c. blue	1·60	3·00
137		12c. scarlet	1·75	75
135/137 Set of 3			4·50	3·75

MINISTERIAL GOVERNMENT

1960 (1 Jan). New Constitution. Nos. 123 and 128 optd with T **29**.

| 138 | | 3c. black and orange-yellow (R) | 20 | 30 |
| 139 | | 12c. violet | 20 | 20 |

30 Nelson's Dockyard and Admiral Nelson

31 Stamp of 1862 and RMSP *Solent I* at English Harbour

(Recess B.W.)

1961 (14 Nov). Restoration of Nelson's Dockyard. W w **12**. P 11½×11.

| 140 | 30 | 20c. purple and brown | 2·00 | 1·60 |
| 141 | | 30c. green and blue | 2·00 | 3·50 |

(Des A. W. Morley. Recess B.W.)

1962 (1 Aug). Stamp Centenary. W w **12**. P 13½.

142	31	3c. purple and deep green	90	10
143		10c. blue and deep green	1·00	10
144		12c. deep sepia and deep green	1·10	10
145		50c. orange-brown and deep green	1·50	3·00
142/145 Set of 4			4·00	3·00

32 Protein Foods

33 Red Cross Emblem

(Des M. Goaman. Photo Harrison)

1963 (4 June). Freedom from Hunger. W w **12**. P 14×14½.

| 146 | 32 | 12c. bluish green | 20 | 15 |

(Des V. Whiteley. Litho B.W.)

1963 (2 Sept). Red Cross Centenary. W w **12**. P 13½.

| 147 | 33 | 3c. red and black | 30 | 1·00 |
| 148 | | 12c. red and blue | 45 | 1·25 |

(Recess D.L.R.)

1963 (16 Sept)–**65**. As 1953–61 but wmk w **12**.

149	16a	1c. brown (13.4.65)	2·75	1·50
150	15	1c. slate (13.4.65)	1·50	1·00
151	16	2c. green	70	30
152		3c. black and yellow-orange	45	20
153	15	4c. brown-red	30	3·75
154	16	5c. black and slate-lilac	20	20
		a. Black and reddish violet (15.1.65)	20	20
155	16a	6c. yellow-ochre	75	30
156	27	8c. deep blue	40	20
157	16b	12c. violet	3·00	20
158		24c. black and deep chocolate	8·50	1·00
		a. Black and chocolate-brown (28.4.65)	12·00	3·75
149/158 Set of 10			16·00	7·75

34 Shakespeare and Memorial Theatre, Stratford-upon-Avon

(**35**)

(Des R. Granger Barrett. Photo Harrison)

1964 (23 Apr). 400th Birth Anniv of William Shakespeare. W w **12**. P 14×14½.

| 164 | 34 | 12c. orange-brown | 30 | 10 |
| | | w. Wmk inverted | 80·00 | |

1965 (1 Apr). No. 157 surch with T **35**.

| 165 | | 15c. on 12c. violet | 20 | 10 |

36 ITU Emblem

(Des M. Goaman. Litho Enschedé)

1965. I.T.U. Centenary. W w **12**. P 11×11½.

| 166 | 36 | 2c. light blue and light red | 25 | 15 |
| 167 | | 50c. orange-yellow and ultramarine | 75 | 1·25 |

37 ICY Emblem

(Des V. Whiteley. Litho Harrison)

1965 (25 Oct). International Co-operation Year. W w **12**. P 14½.

| 168 | 37 | 4c. reddish purple and turquoise-green | 25 | 45 |
| 169 | | 15c. deep bluish green and lavender | 40 | 25 |

38 Sir Winston Churchill, and St. Paul's Cathedral in Wartime

(Des Jennifer Toombs. Photo Harrison)

1966 (24 Jan). Churchill Commemoration. Printed in black, cerise and gold and with background in colours stated. W w **12**. P 14.

170	38	½c. new blue	10	2·50
		a. Value omitted	£850	
171		4c. deep green	65	10
172		25c. brown	1·50	45
173		35c. bluish violet	1·50	55
170/3 Set of 4			3·25	3·25

No. 170a was caused by misplacement of the gold and also shows "ANTIGUA" moved to the right.

39 Queen Elizabeth II and Duke of Edinburgh

(Des H. Baxter. Litho B.W.)

1966 (4 Feb). Royal Visit. W w **12**. P 11×12.

| 174 | 39 | 6c. black and ultramarine | 1·50 | 1·10 |
| 175 | | 15c. black and magenta | 1·50 | 1·40 |

40 Footballer's Legs, Ball and
Jules Rimet Cup

(Des V. Whiteley. Litho Harrison)

1966 (1 July). World Cup Football Championship. W w **12** (sideways). P. 14.

176	**40**	6c. violet, yellow-green, lake and yellow-brown....................	20	75
177		35c. chocolate, blue-green, lake and yellow-brown......................	60	25

41 WHO Building

(Des M. Goaman. Litho Harrison)

1966 (20 Sept). Inauguration of WHO Headquarters, Geneva. W w **12** (sideways). P. 14.

178	**41**	2c. black, yellow-green and light blue............................	20	25
179		15c. black, light purple and yellow-brown....................	1·25	25

42 Nelson's Dockyard

43 Old Post Office, St John's

44 Health Centre

45 Teachers' Training College

46 Martello Tower, Barbuda

47 Ruins of Officers' Quarters, Shirley Heights

48 Government House, Barbuda

49 Princess Margaret School

50 Air Terminal Building

51 General Post Office

52 Clarence House

53 Government House, St John's

53a Administration Building

53b Courthouse, St John's

53c Magistrates' Court

53d St John's Cathedral

(Des, eng and recess B.W.)

1966 (1 Nov)–70. W w **12**. Ordinary paper. P 11½×11.

180	**42**	½c. green and turquoise-blue....	10	1·25
		a. Perf 13½ (24.6.69)...........	10	2·50
181	**43**	1c. purple and cerise	10	30
		a. Perf 13½ (24.6.69)...........	10	1·50
		ab. Glazed paper (30.9.69)	75	20
182	**44**	2c. slate-blue and yellow-orange................................	10	20
		a. Perf 13½ (24.6.69)...........	10	75
		ab. Glazed paper (30.9.69)	1·25	80
183	**45**	3c. rose-red and black.............	30	30
		a. Perf 13½ (24.6.69)...........	15	15
184	**46**	4c. slate-violet and brown.........	2·50	10
		a. Perf 13½ (24.6.69)...........	15	30
		ab. Glazed paper (6.4.70)	16·00	1·75
185	**47**	5c. ultramarine and yellow-olive................................	1·25	10
		a. Perf 13½ (24.6.69)...........	15	15
		ab. Glazed paper (30.9.69)	40	10
186	**48**	6c. salmon and purple	2·50	30
		a. Perf 13½ (24.6.69)...........	15	1·00
187	**49**	10c. emerald and rose-red..........	15	10
		a. Perf 13½ (24.6.69)...........	15	15
		ab. Glazed paper (30.9.69)	4·00	10
188	**50**	15c. brown and new blue...........	2·75	10
		a. Perf 13½ (glazed paper) (30.9.69).........................	70	10
189	**51**	25c. slate-blue and sepia.............	35	20
		a. Perf 13½ (glazed paper) (30.9.69).........................	45	10
190	**52**	35c. cerise and blackish brown...	1·50	55
		a. Perf 13½ (glazed paper) (30.9.69).........................	60	1·00
191	**53**	50c. dull green and black............	5·50	2·50
		a. Perf 13½ (glazed paper) (30.9.69).........................	70	2·25
192	**53a**	75c. greenish blue and ultramarine......................	7·50	5·00
193	**53b**	$1 cerise and yellow-olive......	15·00	2·50
		aa. Carmine and yellow-olive (14.5.68)........................	55·00	17·00
		a. Perf 13½ (glazed paper) (30.9.69).........................	1·25	5·00
194	**53c**	$2.50 black and cerise.............	14·00	10·00
		a. Perf 13½ (glazed paper) (30.9.69).........................	1·50	8·00
195	**53d**	$5 olive-green and slate-violet...............................	15·00	6·50
		a. Perf 13½ (glazed paper) (30.9.69).........................	14·00	24·00
180/195 Set of 16........................			55·00	25·00
180a/195a Set of 15.....................			18·00	40·00

54 "Education"

55 "Science"

56 "Culture"

(Des Jennifer Toombs. Litho Harrison)

1966 (1 Dec). 20th Anniv of UNESCO W w **12** (sideways). P. 14.

196	**54**	4c. slate-violet, red, yellow and orange.............................	20	10
197	**55**	25c. orange-yellow, violet and deep olive...........................	45	10
198	**56**	$1 black, bright purple and orange.............................	90	2·25
196/198 Set of 3.........................			1·40	2·25

ASSOCIATED STATEHOOD

57 State Flag and Maps

(Des W. D. Cribbs. Photo Harrison)

1967 (27 Feb). Statehood. T **57** and similar horiz designs. Multicoloured. W w **12** (sideways*). P. 14.

199		4c. Type **57**..........................	10	10
200		15c. State Flag..........................	10	20
		w. Wmk Crown to right of CA.................	1·25	
201		25c. Premier's Office and State Flag........	10	25
202		35c. As 15c..............................	15	25
199/202 Set of 4........................			40	70

*The normal sideways watermark shows Crown to left of CA, as seen from the back of the stamp.

60 Gilbert Memorial Church

4c. Line projecting from near corner of building stretching two thirds way up roof (R. 1/2)

(Des G. Drummond (from sketches by W. D. Cribbs). Photo Harrison)

1967 (18 May). Attainment of Autonomy by the Methodist Church. T **60** and similar horiz designs. W w **12**. P. 14½×13½.

203	4c. black and orange-red........................	10	10
	a. Roof flaw...................................	8·00	
204	25c. black and bright green....................	15	15
205	35c. black and bright blue.....................	15	15
203/205 Set of 3		35	35

Designs:—25c. Nathaniel Gilbert's House; 35c. Caribbean and Central American map.

63 Coat of Arms

64 Susan Constant (settlers' ship)

65 Van Risen's map of 1665

(Des V. Whiteley (from sketches by W. D. Cribbs). Photo Harrison)

1967 (21 July). 300th Anniv of Treaty of Breda and Grant of New Arms. W w **12** (sideways*). P 14½×14.

206	**63**	15c. multicoloured...................	20	10
		w. Wmk Crown to right of CA........	10·00	10·00
207		35c. multicoloured...................	20	10

*The normal sideways watermark shows Crown to left of CA, as seen from the back of the stamp.

(Des and recess B.W.)

1967 (14 Dec). 300th Anniv of Barbuda Settlement. T **64/5**. W w **12**. P 11½×11.

208	**64**	4c. deep ultramarine..............	45	10
209	**65**	6c. purple............................	45	1·50
210	**64**	25c. emerald..........................	50	20
211	**65**	35c. black.............................	55	25
208/11 Set of 4.........................			1·75	1·75

66 Tracking Station

70 Limbo-dancing

(Des G. Vasarhelyi. Photo Harrison)

1968 (29 Mar). NASA Apollo Project. Inauguration of Dow Hill Tracking Station. T **66** and similar vert designs in deep blue, orange yellow and black. W w **12** (sideways). P 14½×14.

212	**66**	4c. Type **66**..........................	10	10
213		15c. Antenna and spacecraft taking off........	20	10
214		25c. Spacecraft approaching Moon	20	10
215		50c. Re-entry of space capsule........	30	40
212/215 Set of 4.......................			70	60

(Des and photo Harrison)

1968 (1 July). Tourism. T **70** and similar horiz designs. Multicoloured. W w **12**. P 14½×14.

216	½c. Type **70**	10	50
217	15c. Water-skiing and bathers	30	10
218	25c. Yachts and beach	30	10
219	35c. Underwater swimming	30	10
220	50c. Type **70**	35	1·25
216/220 *Set of 5*		1·25	1·75

74 Old Harbour in 1768

(Des R. Granger Barrett. Recess B.W.)

1968 (31 Oct). Opening of St. John's Deep Water Harbour. T **74** and similar horiz designs. W w **12**. P 13.

221	2c. light blue and carmine	10	40
222	15c. light yellow-green and sepia	35	10
223	25c. olive-yellow and blue	40	10
224	35c. salmon and emerald	50	10
225	$1 black	90	2·00
221/225 *Set of 5*		2·00	2·25

Designs:—15c. Old Harbour in 1829; 25c. Freighter and chart of New Harbour; 35c. New Harbour, 1968; $1, Type **74**.

78 Parliament Buildings

(Des R. Granger Barrett. Photo Harrison)

1969 (3 Feb). Tercentenary of Parliament. T **78** and similar square designs. Multicoloured. W w **12** (sideways). P 12½.

226	4c. Type **78**	10	10
227	15c. Antigua Mace and bearer	20	10
228	25c. House of Representatives' Room	20	10
229	50c. Coat of Arms and Seal of Antigua	30	1·60
226/229 *Set of 4*		70	1·75

82 Freight Transport

(Des Jennifer Toombs. Litho D.L.R.)

1969 (14 Apr). First Anniv of CARIFTA (Caribbean Free Trade Area). T **82** and similar design. W w **12** (sideways on 4c, 15c). P 13.

230	4c. black and reddish purple	10	10
231	15c. black and turquoise-blue	20	30
232	25c. chocolate, black and yellow-ochre	25	30
233	35c. chocolate, black and yellow-brown	25	30
230/233 *Set of 4*		70	90

Designs: Horiz—4, 15c. Type **82**. Vert—25, 35c. Crate of cargo.

Nos. 234 to 248 are redundant.

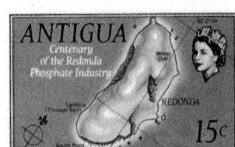

84 Island of Redonda (Chart)

(Des R. Granger Barrett. Photo Enschedé)

1969 (1 Aug). Centenary of Redonda Phosphate Industry. T **84** and similar horiz design. W w **12** (sideways). P 13×13½.

249	15c. Type **84**	20	10
250	25c. Redonda from the sea	20	10
251	50c. Type **84**	45	75
249/251 *Set of 3*		75	85

86 *The Adoration of the Magi* (Marcillat)

(**88**)

(Des adapted by V. Whiteley. Litho Enschedé)

1969 (15 Oct). Christmas. Stained-glass Windows. T **86** and similar vert design. Multicoloured. W w **12** (sideways*). P 13×14.

252	6c. Type **86**	10	10
253	10c. *The Nativity* (unknown German artist, 15th-century)	10	10
254	35c. Type **86**	25	10
255	50c. As 10c.	50	40
	w. Wmk Crown to right of CA	23·00	
252/255 *Set of 4*		85	60

*The normal sideways watermark shows Crown to left of CA, *as seen from the back of the stamp.*

1970 (2 Jan). No. 189 surch with T **88**.

256	20c. on 25c. slate-blue and sepia	20	10

89 Coat of Arms

90 Sikorsky S-38 Flying Boat

(Des and photo Harrison)

1970 (30 Jan)–**73**. Coil Stamps. W w **12**. P 14½×14.

A. Chalk-surfaced paper. Wmk upright (30.1.70)

257A	**89** 5c. blue	10	40
258A	10c. emerald	10	35
259A	25c. crimson	20	35
257A/259A *Set of 3*		35	1·00

B. Glazed paper. Wmk sideways (5.3.73)

257B	**89** 5c. blue	1·25	2·50
258B	10c. emerald	1·25	2·50
259B	25c. crimson	1·75	2·25
257B/9B *Set of 3*		3·75	6·50

These stamps were issued on Multiple Crown CA Diagonal paper in 1975.

(Des R. Granger Barrett. Litho J.W.)

1970 (16 Feb). 40th Anniv of Antiguan Air Services. T **90** and similar designs. Multicoloured. W w **12** (sideways). P 14½.

260	5c. Type **90**	50	10
261	20c. Dornier Do-X flying boat	80	10
262	35c. Hawker Siddeley H.S. 748	1·00	10
263	50c. Douglas C-124C Globemaster II	1·00	1·75
264	75c. Vickers Super VC-10	1·25	2·75
260/264 *Set of 5*		4·00	4·25

91 Dickens and Scene from *Nicholas Nickleby*

(Des Jennifer Toombs. Litho Walsall)

1970 (19 May). Death Centenary of Charles Dickens. T **91** and similar horiz designs. W w **12** (sideways). P 14.

265	5c. bistre, sepia and black	10	10
266	20c. light turquoise-blue, sepia and black.	20	10
267	35c. violet-blue, sepia and black	30	10
268	$1 rosine, sepia and black	75	80
265/268 *Set of 4*		1·25	1·00

Designs:—20c. Dickens and Scene from *Pickwick Papers*; 35c. Dickens and Scene from *Oliver Twist*; $1 Dickens and Scene from *David Copperfield*.

92 Carib Indian and War Canoe

93 *The Small Passion* (detail) (Dürer)

(Des J.W. Litho Questa)

1970 (19 Aug)–**75**. Horiz designs as T **92**. Multicoloured. Toned paper. W w **12** (sideways*). P 14.

269	½c. Type **92**	10	1·50
270	1c. Columbus and Nina	30	1·50
271	2c. Sir Thomas Warner's emblem and *Concepcion*	40	3·25
	a. Whiter paper (20.10.75)	1·50	3·25
272	3c. Viscount Hood and HMS *Barfleur*	40	1·75
	w. Wmk Crown to right of CA	4·00	4·00
273	4c. Sir George Rodney and HMS *Formidable*	40	3·00
274	5c. Nelson and HMS *Boreas*	50	40
275	6c. William IV and HMS *Pegasus*	1·75	4·75
276	10c. "Blackbeard" and pirate ketch	80	20
277	15c. Captain Collingwood and HMS *Pelican*	14·00	1·00
278	20c. Nelson and HMS *Victory*	1·25	40
279	25c. *Solent I* (paddle-steamer)	1·00	40
280	35c. George V (when Prince George) and HMS *Canada* (screw corvette)	3·50	80
281	50c. HMS *Renown* (battle cruiser)	3·00	6·00
282	75c. *Federal Maple* (freighter)	3·00	6·00
283	$1 *Sol Quest* (yacht) and class emblem	3·00	1·50
284	$2.50 HMS *London* (destroyer)	9·00	7·50
285	$5 *Pathfinder* (tug)	2·00	6·00
269/285 *Set of 17*		38·00	40·00

*The normal sideways watermark shows Crown to left of CA *as seen from the back of the stamp.*

Stamps in these designs were issued with upright watermark between 1972 and 1974 and the $5 value was issued with a change of watermark in 1975.

(Des G. Drummond. Recess and litho D.L.R.)

1970 (28 Oct). Christmas. T **93** and similar vert design. W w **12**. P 13½×14.

286	**93** 3c. black and turquoise-blue	10	10
287	– 10c. dull purple and pink	10	10
288	**93** 35c. black and rose-red	30	10
289	– 50c. black and lilac	45	50
286/289 *Set of 4*		85	70

Design:—10c., 50c. *Adoration of the Magi* (detail) (Dürer).

94 4th King's Own Regt, 1759

(Des P. W. Kingsland. Litho Questa)

1970 (14 Dec). Military Uniforms (1st series). T **94** and similar vert designs. Multicoloured. W w **12**. P 14×13½.

290	½c. Type **94**	10	10
291	10c. 4th West India Regiment, 1804	65	10
292	20c. 60th Regiment, The Royal American, 1809	1·00	10
293	35c. 93rd Regiment, Sutherland Highlanders, 1826–34	1·25	10
294	75c. 3rd West India Regiment, 1851	1·75	2·00
290/294 *Set of 5*		4·25	2·10
MS295 128×146 mm. Nos. 290/4		5·50	11·00

STAMP BOOKLET

1968 (2 Oct). Blue cover. Stitched.

SB1	$1.20 booklet containing 5c., 10c. and 15c. (Nos. 185, 187, 188) in blocks of 4		8·50

BARBUDA

DEPENDENCY OF ANTIGUA

PRICES FOR STAMPS ON COVER TO 1945
Nos. 1/11   *from* × 5

BARBUDA

(1)

1922 (13 July). Stamps of Leeward Islands optd with T **1**. All Die II. Chalk-surfaced paper.

(a) Wmk Mult Script CA

1	**11**	½d. deep green	1·50	13·00
2		1d. bright scarlet	1·50	13·00
		x. Wmk reversed	£850	£900
3	**10**	2d. slate-grey	1·50	7·00
		x. Wmk reversed	£100	
4	**11**	2½d. bright blue	1·50	7·50
		w. Wmk inverted	38·00	£120
5		6d. dull and bright purple	2·00	18·00
6	**10**	2s. purple and blue/*blue*	14·00	55·00
7		3s. bright green and violet	35·00	80·00
8		4s. black and red (R.)	45·00	80·00

(b) Wmk Mult Crown CA

9	**10**	3d. purple/*pale yellow*	1·75	16·00
10	**12**	1s. black/*emerald* (R.)	1·50	8·00
11		5s. green and red/*pale yellow*	65·00	£130
1/11 *Set of 11*			£150	£375
1s/11s Optd "SPECIMEN" *Set of 11*			£225	

Examples of all values are known showing a forged Barbuda postmark of "JU 1 23".

Stocks of the overprinted stamps were exhausted by October 1925 and issues of Antigua or Leeward Islands were then used in Barbuda until 1968.

The following issues for Barbuda were also valid for use in Antigua.

(New Currency. 100 cents = 1 Eastern Caribbean dollar)

2 Map of Barbuda

3 Greater Amberjack

(Des R. Granger Barrett. Litho Format)

1968 (19 Nov)–**70**. Designs as T **2/3**. P 14.

12	½c. brown, black and pink	65	3·75
13	1c. orange, black and flesh	1·75	35
14	2c. blackish brown, rose-red and rose	2·25	1·75

15	3c. blackish brown, orange-yellow and lemon	2·00	55
16	4c. black, bright green and apple-green	3·00	3·75
17	5c. blue-green, black and pale blue-green	2·25	20
18	6c. black, bright purple and pale lilac	1·50	3·25
19	10c. black, ultramarine and cobalt	2·00	1·75
20	15c. black, blue-green and turquoise-green	2·25	4·00
20a	20c. multicoloured (22.7.70)	2·00	2·00
21	25c. multicoloured (6.2.69)	1·50	25
22	35c. multicoloured (5.2.69)	3·00	25
23	50c. multicoloured (5.2.69)	1·00	2·25
24	75c. multicoloured (5.2.69)	1·00	80
25	$1 multicoloured (6.3.69)	50	1·50
26	$2.50 multicoloured (6.3.69)	55	2·00
27	$5 multicoloured (6.3.69)	65	2·25
12/27 *Set of 17*		24·00	27·00

Designs: ½ to 15c. Type **2**. Horiz as T **3**—20c. Great Barracuda; 35c. French Angelfish; 50c. Porkfish; 75c. Princess Parrotfish; $1, Long-spined Squirrelfish; $2.50, Bigeye; $5, Blue Chromis.

10 Sprinting and Aztec Sun-stone

14 *The Ascension* (Orcagna)

(Des R. Granger Barrett. Litho Format)

1968 (20 Dec). Olympic Games, Mexico. T **10** and similar horiz designs. Multicoloured. P 14.

28	25c. Type **10**	40	50
29	35c. High-jumping and Aztec statue	45	50
30	75c. Dinghy-racing and Aztec lion mask	50	1·75
28/30 *Set of 3*		1·25	2·50
MS31	85×76 mm. $1 Football and engraved plate	2·00	3·25

(Des R. Granger Barrett. Litho Format)

1969 (24 Mar). Easter Commemoration. P 14.

32	**14**	25c. black and light blue	15	45
33		35c. black and deep carmine	15	50
34		75c. black and bluish lilac	15	55
32/34 *Set of 3*			40	1·40

15 Scout Enrolment Ceremony | **18** *Sistine Madonna* (Raphael)

(Des R. Granger Barrett. Litho Format)

1969 (7 Aug). Third Caribbean Scout Jamboree. T **15** and similar horiz designs. Multicoloured. P 14.

35	25c. Type **15**	35	55
36	35c. Scouts around camp fire	45	65
37	75c. Sea Scouts rowing boat	55	1·40
35/37 *Set of 3*		1·25	2·40

(Des R. Granger Barrett. Litho Format)

1969 (20 Oct). Christmas. P 14.

38	**18**	½c. multicoloured	10	30
39		25c. multicoloured	10	15
40		35c. multicoloured	10	20
41		75c. multicoloured	20	35
38/41 *Set of 4*			30	90

19 William I (1066–87) | **(20)**

20c

(Des R. Granger Barrett. Litho Format (Nos. 42/9) or Questa (others))

1970–71. English Monarchs. T **19** and similar vert designs. Multicoloured. P 14½×14.

42	35c. Type **19** (16.2.70)	30	15
43	35c. William II (2.3.70)	10	15
44	35c. Henry I (16.3.70)	10	15
45	35c. Stephen (1.4.70)	10	15
46	35c. Henry II (15.4.70)	10	15
47	35c. Richard I (1.5.70)	10	15
48	35c. John (15.5.70)	10	15
49	35c. Henry III (1.6.70)	10	15
50	35c. Edward I (15.6.70)	10	15
51	35c. Edward II (1.7.70)	10	15
52	35c. Edward III (15.7.70)	10	15
53	35c. Richard II (1.8.70)	10	15
54	35c. Henry IV (15.8.70)	10	15
55	35c. Henry V (1.9.70)	10	15
56	35c. Henry VI (15.9.70)	10	15
57	36c. Edward IV (1.10.70)	10	15
58	35c. Edward V (15.10.70)	10	15
59	35c. Richard III (2.11.70)	10	15
60	35c. Henry VII (16.11.70)	35	15
61	35c. Henry VIII (1.12.70)	35	15
62	35c. Edward VI (15.12.70)	35	15
63	35c. Lady Jane Grey (2.1.71)	35	15
64	35c. Mary I (15.1.71)	35	15
65	35c. Elizabeth I (1.2.71)	35	15
66	35c. James I (15.2.71)	35	15
67	35c. Charles I (1.3.71)	35	15
68	35c. Charles II (15.3.71)	35	15
69	35c. James II (1.4.71)	35	15
70	35c. William III (15.4.71)	35	15
71	35c. Mary II (1.5.71)	35	15
72	35c. Anne (15.5.71)	35	15
73	35c. George I (1.6.71)	35	15
74	35c. George II (15.6.71)	35	15
75	35c. George III (1.7.71)	35	15
76	35c. George IV (15.7.71)	35	15
77	35c. William IV (2.8.71)	35	60
78	35c. Victoria (16.8.71)	35	60
42/78 *Set of 37*		7·50	6·00

Further values in this series were issued in 1984.

1970 (26 Feb). No. 12 surch with T **20**.

79	**2**	20c. on ½c. brown, black and pink	20	20
		a. Surch inverted	60·00	
		b. Surch double	55·00	

21 *The Way to Calvary* (Ugolino) | **22** Oliver is introduced to Fagin (*Oliver Twist*)

(Des R. Granger Barrett. Litho Questa)

1970 (16 Mar). Easter Paintings. T **21** and similar vert designs. Multicoloured. P 14.

80	25c. Type **21**	15	35
	a. Horiz strip of 3. Nos. 80/2	40	1·00
81	35c. *The Deposition from the Cross* (Ugolino)	15	35
82	75c. *Crucifix* (The Master of St. Francis)	15	40
80/82 *Set of 3*		40	1·00

Nos. 80/2 were printed together, *se-tenant*, in horizontal strips of three throughout the sheet.

(Des R. Granger Barrett. Litho Questa)

1970 (10 July). Death Centenary of Charles Dickens. T **22** and similar horiz design. Multicoloured. P 14.

83	20c. Type **22**	45	40
84	75c. Dickens and Scene from *The Old Curiosity Shop*	80	1·25

23 *Madonna of the Meadow* (Bellini) | **24** Nurse with Patient in Wheelchair

(Des R. Granger Barrett. Litho Questa)

1970 (15 Oct). Christmas. T **23** and similar horiz designs. Multicoloured. P 14.

85	20c. Type **23**	10	25
86	50c. *Madonna, Child and Angels* (from Wilton diptych)	15	35
87	75c. *The Nativity* (della Francesca)	15	50
85/7 *Set of 3*		30	1·00

(Des R. Granger Barrett. Litho Questa)

1970 (21 Dec). Centenary of British Red Cross. T **24** and similar multicoloured designs. P 14.

88	20c. Type **24**	15	40
89	35c. Nurse giving patient magazines (*horiz*)	20	45
90	75c. Nurse and mother weighing baby (*horiz*)	25	85
88/90 *Set of 3*		55	1·50

Ascension

DEPENDENCY OF ST. HELENA

Ascension, first occupied in 1815, was retained as a Royal Navy establishment from 1816 until 20 October 1922 when it became a dependency of St. Helena by Letters Patent.

Under Post Office regulations of 1850 (ratings) and 1854 (officers) mail from men of the Royal Navy serving abroad had the postage prepaid in Great Britain stamps, supplies of which were issued to each ship. Great Britain stamps used on Ascension before 1860 may have been provided by the naval officer in charge of the postal service.

The British GPO assumed responsibility for such matters in 1860, but failed to send any stamps to the island until January 1867.

Until about 1880 naval mail, which made up most early correspondence, did not have the stamps cancelled until arrival in England. The prices quoted for Nos. Z1/3 and Z6 are for examples on cover showing the Great Britain stamps cancelled on arrival and an Ascension postmark struck elsewhere on the front of the envelope.

The use of British stamps ceased in December 1922.

The following postmarks were used on Great Britain stamps from Ascension:

Z 1 | Z 2

Z 3 | Z 4

Z 5

Postmark Type	Approx Period of Use	Diameter	Index Letter
Z **1**	1862	20 mm	A
Z **2**	1864–1872	20 mm	A
	1872–1878	21½ mm	A
	1879–1889	19½ mm	A
	1891–1894	21½ mm	C
	1894–1902	22 mm	A
	1903–1907	20½ mm	A
	1908–1920	21 mm	A or none
	1909–1920	23 mm	C sideways (1909), none (1910–11), B (1911–20)
Z **3**	1920–1922	24 mm	none
Z **4**	1897–1903 Reg'd	23 mm	none
Z **5**	1900–1902 Reg'd	28 mm	C
	1903–1904 Reg'd	29 mm	A

Postmark Type Z **1** appears in the G.P.O. proof book for 1858, but the first recorded use is 3 November 1862.

Forged postmarks exist. Those found most frequently are genuine postmarks of the post-1922 period with earlier date slugs fraudulently inserted, namely a 20 mm postmark as Type Z **2** (because of the shape of the "O" in "ASCENSION" this is often known as the "Square O" postmark) and a 24 mm postmark as Type Z **3** but with the index letter A.

Stamps of GREAT BRITAIN cancelled with Types Z **2/5**. *Prices quoted for Nos. Z1/6 are for complete covers.*

Line-engraved issues.

Z1	1d. red-brown (1855)	£9000
Z2	1d. rose-red (1864–79) *From*	£3250
	Plate Nos. 71, 74, 76, 78, 83, 85, 96, 100, 102, 103, 104, 122, 134, 138, 154, 155, 157, 160, 168, 178	

Surface-printed issues (1856–1883)

Z2a	6d. lilac (1856)	
Z3	6d. lilac (1865) (Plate No. 5)	£9000
Z4	1s. green (1865) (Plate No. 4)	
Z5	1s. green (1867) (Plate No. 7)	
Z6	6d. grey (1874) (Plate Nos. 15, 16)	£7500
Z6a	6d. on 6d. lilac (1883)	
Z7	1d. lilac (1881) (16 dots)	90·00

1887–92.

Z8	½d. vermilion	£130
Z9	1½d. purple and green	£850
Z10	2d. green and carmine	£350
Z11	2½d. purple/*blue*	£170
Z12	3d. purple/*yellow*	£700
Z13	4d. green and brown	£450
Z14	4½d. green and carmine	£1300
Z15	5d. dull purple and blue	£500

Z16	6d. purple/*rose-red*		£400
Z17	9d. purple and blue		£1100
Z17a	10d. dull purple and carmine		£1300
Z18	1s. green		£1300

1900.

Z19	½d. blue-green		£160
Z20	1s. green and carmine		£1400

1902–11. King Edward VII issues.

Z21	½d. green		£100
Z22	1d. red		32·00
Z23	1½d. purple and green		£400
Z24	2d. green and carmine		£200
Z25	2½d. blue		£225
Z26	3d. purple/*yellow*		£400
Z27	4d. green and brown		£1000
Z28	4d. orange (1909)		£400
Z29	5d. purple and ultramarine		£400
Z30	6d. purple		£350
Z31	7d. grey-black (1910)		£475
Z32	9d. purple and ultramarine (1910)		£600
Z32a	10d. dull purple and scarlet		£800
Z33	1s. green and carmine		£200
Z33a	2s.6d. dull reddish purple (1911)		£1800
Z34	5s. carmine		£2500
Z35	10s. ultramarine		£3750
Z35a	£1 green		£8500

1911–12. T **98/9** of Great Britain.

Z36	½d. green (Die A)		£225
Z37	½d. yellow-green (Die B)		£100
Z38	1d. scarlet (Die B)		£100

1912. T **101/2** of Great Britain.

Z38a	½d. green		£100
Z38b	1d. scarlet		95·00

1912–22.

Z39	½d. green (1913)		85·00
Z40	1d. scarlet		38·00
Z41	1½d. red-brown		£100
Z42	2d. orange (Die I)		95·00
Z42a	2d. orange (Die II) (1921)		£900
Z43	2½d. blue		£130
Z44	3d. violet		£180
Z45	4d. grey-green (1913)		£225
Z46	5d. brown (1913)		£325
Z47	6d. purple (1913)		£180
Z47a	7d. green (1913)		£750
Z47b	8d. black/*yellow* (1913)		£800
Z48	9d. agate (1913)		£700
Z49	9d. olive-green (1922)		£1900
Z50	10d. turquoise-blue (1913)		£750
Z51	1s. bistre (1913)		£225
Z52	2s.6d. brown (1918)		£2250
Z53	5s. rose-red (1919)		£3750

Supplies of some values do not appear to have been sent to the island and known examples originate from maritime or, in the case of high values, philatelic mail.

PRICES FOR STAMPS ON COVER

Nos. 1/34	from × 5
Nos. 35/7	from × 10
Nos. 38/47	from × 6

ASCENSION
(1)

2d. Line through "P" of "POSTAGE" (R. 3/6)   **2d.** Blot on scroll (R. 3/10)

1922 (2 Nov). Stamps of St. Helena, showing Government House or the Wharf, optd with T **1** by D.L.R.

(a) Wmk Mult Script CA

1		½d. yellow and green	7·50	29·00
	x.	Wmk reversed		£1500
2		1d. green	8·00	28·00
3		1½d. rose-scarlet	17·00	48·00
4		2d. black and grey	17·00	13·00
	a.	Line through "P" of "POSTAGE"	£500	£650
	b.	Blot on scroll	£500	£650
5		3d. bright blue	13·00	29·00
6		8d. black and dull purple	27·00	55·00
7		2s. black and blue/*blue*	£110	£130
8		3s. black and violet	£140	£160

(b) Wmk Mult Crown CA

9		1s. black/*green* (R.)	28·00	48·00
1/9 *Set of 9*			£325	£475
1s/9s Optd "SPECIMEN" *Set of 9*			£800	

Nos. 1, 4 and 6/8 are on special printings which were not issued without overprint.

Examples of all values are known showing a forged Ascension postmark dated "MY 24 23".

PLATE FLAWS ON THE 1924–33 ISSUE. Many constant plate varieties exist on both the vignette and duty plates of this issue. The major varieties are illustrated and listed below.

This issue utilised the same vignette plate as the St. Helena 1922–37 set so that these flaws occur there also.

2 Badge of St. Helena

Broken mainmast. Occurs on R. 2/1 of all values.

Torn flag. Occurs on R. 4/6 of all values except the 5d. Retouched on sheets of ½d., 1d. and 2d. printed after 1927.

Cleft rock. Occurs on R. 5/1 of all values.

Broken scroll. (R. 1/4)   **1½d.** line through "C" (R. 1/6)

8d. "Shamrock" flaw (R. 4/1)

(Typo D.L.R.)

1924 (20 Aug)–**33**. Wmk Mult Script CA. Chalk-surfaced paper. P 14.

10	**2**	½d. grey-black and black	6·50	19·00
	a.	Broken mainmast	£130	£300
	b.	Torn flag	£200	£375
	c.	Cleft rock	£110	£275
11		1d. grey-black and deep blue-green	6·00	17·00
	a.	Broken mainmast	£140	£275
	b.	Torn flag	£150	£300
	c.	Cleft rock	£130	£275
11d		1d. grey-black and bright blue-green (1933)	£110	£500
	da.	Broken mainmast	£1000	
	dc.	Cleft rock	£1000	
12		1½d. rose-red	10·00	48·00
	a.	Broken mainmast	£150	£375
	b.	Torn flag	£160	£375
	c.	Cleft rock	£150	£375
	d.	Broken scroll	£180	£375
	e.	line through "C"	£180	£375
13		2d. grey-black and grey	24·00	12·00
	a.	Broken mainmast	£275	£275
	b.	Torn flag	£350	£275
	c.	Cleft rock	£250	£275
14		3d. blue	8·00	18·00
	a.	Broken mainmast	£160	£300
	b.	Torn flag	£160	£300
	c.	Cleft rock	£150	£275
15		4d. grey-black and black/*yellow*	50·00	95·00
	a.	Broken mainmast	£500	£850
	b.	Torn flag	£500	£850
	c.	Cleft rock	£475	£800
15d		5d. purple and olive-green (8.27)	23·00	26·00
	da.	Broken mainmast	£375	£450
	dc.	Cleft rock	£350	£450

16		6d. grey-black and bright purple	60·00	£120
	a.	Broken mainmast	£650	£1000
	b.	Torn flag	£650	£1000
	c.	Cleft rock	£650	£1000
17		8d. grey-black and bright violet	20·00	45·00
	a.	Broken mainmast	£325	£600
	b.	Torn flag	£325	£600
	c.	Cleft rock	£300	£550
	d.	"Shamrock" flaw	£375	£600
18		1s. grey-black and brown	21·00	55·00
	a.	Broken mainmast	£400	£650
	b.	Torn flag	£400	£650
	c.	Cleft rock	£375	£600
19		2s. grey-black and blue/*blue*	75·00	£110
	a.	Broken mainmast	£750	£950
	b.	Torn flag	£750	£950
	c.	Cleft rock	£700	£900
20		3s. grey-black and black/*blue*	£100	£100
	a.	Broken mainmast	£900	£1000
	b.	Torn flag	£900	£1000
	c.	Cleft rock	£850	£950
10/20 *Set of 12*			£350	£600
10s/20s Optd "SPECIMEN" *Set of 12*			£1000	

3 Georgetown   **4** Ascension Island

5 The Pier   **6** Long Beach

7 Three Sisters   **8** Sooty Tern and Wideawake Fair

9 Green Mountain

"Teardrops" flaw (R. 4/5)

(Des and recess D.L.R.)

1934 (2 July). T **3/9** and similar designs. Wmk Mult Script CA. P 14.

21	**3**	½d. black and violet	90	80
22	**4**	1d. black and emerald	1·75	1·50
	a.	Teardrops flaw	£150	£170
23	**5**	1½d. black and scarlet	1·75	2·25
24	**4**	2d. black and orange	1·75	2·50
	a.	Teardrops flaw	£275	£350
25	**6**	3d. black and ultramarine	2·50	1·50
26	**7**	5d. black and blue	2·25	3·25
27		8d. black and sepia	4·25	6·50
	a.	Teardrops flaw	£500	£650
28	**8**	1s. black and carmine	18·00	12·00
29	**4**	2s.6d. black and bright purple	45·00	48·00
	a.	Teardrops flaw	£1700	£1800
30	**9**	5s. black and brown	55·00	60·00
21/30 *Set of 10.*			£120	£120
21s/30s Perf "SPECIMEN" *Set of 10.*			£500	

1935 (6 May). Silver Jubilee. As Nos. 91/4 of Antigua, but ptd by Waterlow. P 11×12.

31		1½d. deep blue and scarlet	3·50	15·00
	l.	Kite and horizontal log	£475	£650
32		2d. ultramarine and grey	11·00	38·00
	l.	Kite and horizontal log	£750	
33		5d. green and indigo	23·00	32·00
	k.	Kite and vertical log	£400	£550
	l.	Kite and horizontal log	£800	£950
34		1s. slate and purple	23·00	42·00
	l.	Kite and horizontal log	£950	£1200
31/4 *Set of 4.*			55·00	£110
31s/4s Perf "SPECIMEN" *Set of 4.*			£425	

For illustrations of plate varieties see Omnibus section following Zanzibar.

1937 (19 May). Coronation. As Nos. 95/7 of Antigua, but printed by D.L.R. P 14.

35	1d. green	50	1·40
36	2d. orange	1·00	60
37	3d. bright blue	1·00	50
35/37 Set of 3		2·25	2·25
35s/7s Perf "SPECIMEN" Set of 3		£450	

10 Georgetown

11 Green Mountain

12 Three Sisters

13 The Pier

14 Long Beach

½d. Long centre bar to "E" in "GEORGETOWN" (R. 2/3)

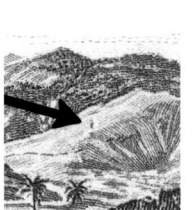
"Mountaineer" flaw (R. 4/4) (1d., 2d., and 4d. ptgs from 1945)

"Davit" flaw (R. 5/1) (all ptgs of 1½d. and 2s.6d.)

"Cut mast and railings" (R. 3/1) (1½d. and 2s.6d. ptgs from 1946)

"Boulder" flaw (R. 5/4) (6d. and 10s. part of 1938 ptg and all subsequent)

(Recess D.L.R.)

1938 (12 May)–**53**. T **10/14**. Wmk Mult Script CA. P 13½.

38	10	½d. black and violet	8·00	4·00
		a. Long centre bar to E	£325	£275
		b. Perf 13. *Black and bluish violet*		
		(17.5.44)	1·40	4·00
		ba. Long centre bar to E	90·00	£160
39	11	1d. black and green	45·00	13·00
39a		1d. black and yellow-orange		
		(8.7.40)	14·00	9·00
		b. Perf 13 (5.42)	45	60
		ba. Mountaineer flaw	£350	£350
		c. Perf 14 (17.2.49)	70	16·00
		ca. Mountaineer flaw	£225	£650

39d	12	1d. black and green, P 13		
		(1.6.49)	60	1·50
40	13	1½d. black and vermilion	9·00	1·40
		a. Davit flaw	£400	£225
		b. Perf 13 (17.5.44)	1·00	80
		ba. Davit flaw	£200	£170
		bb. Cut mast and railings	£275	£275
		c. Perf 14 (17.2.49)	3·75	13·00
		ca. Davit flaw	£350	£550
		cb. Cut mast and railings	£350	£550
40d		1½d. black and rose-carmine, P 14		
		(1.6.49)	2·25	1·00
		da. Davit flaw	£130	£190
		db. Cut mast and railings	£130	£190
		e. Black and carmine	12·00	5·00
		ea. Davit flaw	£450	£425
		eb. Cut mast and railings	£450	£425
		f. Perf 13 (25.2.53)	45	6·50
		fa. Davit flaw	£140	
		fb. Cut mast and railings	£140	£375
41	11	2d. black and red-orange	9·50	1·00
		a. Perf 13 (17.5.44)	80	40
		aa. Mountaineer flaw	£450	£450
		b. Perf 14 (17.2.49)	3·50	35·00
		ba. Mountaineer flaw	£350	£900
41c		2d. black and scarlet, P 14		
		(1.6.49)	1·50	1·75
		ca. Mountaineer flaw	£275	£400
42	14	3d. black and ultramarine	£100	26·00
42a		3d. black and grey (8.7.40)	20·00	4·00
		b. Perf 13 (17.5.44)	70	4·00
42c	11	4d. black and ultramarine		
		(8.7.40)	17·00	3·50
		d. Perf 13 (17.5.44)	5·00	2·50
		da. Mountaineer flaw	£1000	£700
43	12	6d. black and blue	13·00	2·25
		a. Boulder flaw	£225	£160
		b. Perf 13 (17.5.44)	12·00	7·00
		ba. Boulder flaw	£225	£200
44	10	1s. black and sepia	22·00	4·00
		a. Perf 13 (17.5.44)	4·75	2·00
45	13	2s.6d. black and deep carmine	45·00	12·00
		a. Frame printed double, one albino	£5000	£5000
		b. Davit flaw	£1600	£850
		c. Perf 13 (17.5.44)	27·00	38·00
		ca. Davit flaw	£1400	£1800
		cb. Cut mast and railings	£2500	£2750
46	14	5s. black and yellow-brown	95·00	12·00
		a. Perf 13 (17.5.44)	40·00	45·00
47	12	10s. black and bright purple	£110	48·00
		a. Boulder flaw	£900	£500
		b. Perf 13 (17.5.44)	48·00	60·00
		ba. Boulder flaw	£600	£600
38b/47b Set of 16			£250	£110
38s/47s Perf "SPECIMEN" Set of 13			£1000	

1946 (21 Oct). Victory. As Nos. 110/11 of Antigua.

48	2d. red-orange	40	1·00
49	4d. blue	40	1·00
48s/9s Perf "SPECIMEN" Set of 2		£450	

1948 (20 Oct). Royal Silver Wedding. As Nos. 112/13 of Antigua.

50	3d. black	50	30
51	10s. bright purple	50·00	50·00

1949 (10 Oct). 75th Anniv of Universal Postal Union. As Nos. 114/17 of Antigua.

52	3d. carmine	1·00	2·00
53	4d. deep blue	4·00	1·50
54	6d. olive	2·00	3·50
55	1s. blue-black	2·00	1·50
	a. "A" of "CA" missing from Wmk	—	£1500
52/55 Set of 4		8·00	7·75

1953 (2 June). Coronation. As No. 120 of Antigua.

56	3d. black and grey-black	1·00	2·75

15 Water Catchment

16 Map of Ascension

17 View of Georgetown

18 Map showing cable network

19 Mountain road

20 White-tailed Tropic Bird ("Boatswain Bird")

21 Yellow-finned Tuna

22 Rollers on the seashore

23 Young turtles

24 Land Crab

25 Sooty Tern ("Wideawake")

26 Perfect Crater

27 View of Ascension from North-west

(Recess B.W.)

1956 (19 Nov). T **19/27**. Wmk Mult Script CA. P 13.

57	15	½d. black and brown	10	50
58	16	1d. black and magenta	4·50	2·75
59	17	1½d. black and orange	1·50	1·25
60	18	2d. black and carmine-red	6·00	3·50
61	19	2½d. black and orange-brown	2·25	3·50
62	20	3d. black and blue	6·00	1·25
63	21	4d. black and deep turquoise-green	1·25	2·00
64	22	6d. black and indigo	1·75	2·75
65	23	7d. black and deep olive	4·25	2·00
66	24	1s. black and vermilion	1·50	1·75
67	25	2s.6d. black and deep dull purple	30·00	9·00
68	26	5s. black and blue-green	42·00	19·00
69	27	10s. black and purple	55·00	40·00
57/69 Set of 13			£140	80·00

28 Brown Booby

(Des after photos by N. P. Ashmole. Photo Harrison)

1963 (23 May). T **28** and similar horiz designs. W w **12**. P 14×14½.

70	1d. black, lemon and new blue	1·50	30
71	1½d. black, cobalt and ochre	2·00	1·00
	a. Cobalt omitted	£130	
72	2d. black, grey and bright blue	1·25	30
73	3d. black, magenta and turquoise-blue	1·75	30
74	4½d. black, bistre-brown and new blue	1·75	30
	w. Wmk inverted	£500	
75	6d. bistre, black and yellow-green	1·25	30
76	7d. black, brown and reddish violet	1·25	30
77	10d. black, greenish yellow and blue-green	1·25	50
78	1s. multicoloured	1·25	30
79	1s.6d. multicoloured	4·50	1·75
80	2s.6d. multicoloured	8·50	12·00
81	5s. multicoloured	10·00	13·00
82	10s. multicoloured	13·00	15·00
83	£1 multicoloured	21·00	17·00
70/83 Set of 14		60·00	55·00

Designs:—1½d. White-capped Noddy; 2d. White Tern; 3d. Red Billed Tropic Bird; 4½d. Common Noddy; 6d. Sooty Tern; 7d. Ascension Frigate Bird; 10d. Blue-faced Booby; 1s. White-tailed Tropic Bird; 1s.6d. Red-billed Tropic Bird; 2s.6d. Madeiran Storm Petrel; 5s. Red-footed Booby (brown phase); 10s. Ascension Frigate Birds; £1 Red-footed Booby (white phase).

1963 (4 June). Freedom from Hunger. As Nos. 146 of Antigua.

84	1s.6d. carmine	75	40

1963 (2 Sept). Red Cross Centenary. As Nos. 147/8 of Antigua.

85	3d. red and black	1·00	1·25
86	1s.6d. red and blue	1·50	2·25

1965 (17 May). ITU Centenary. As Nos. 166/7 of Antigua.

87	3d. magenta and bluish violet	50	65
88	6d. turquoise-blue and light chestnut	75	65

1965 (25 Oct). International Co-operation Year. As Nos. 168/9 of Antigua.

89	1d. reddish purple and turquoise-green	40	60
90	6d. deep bluish green and lavender	60	90

1966 (24 Jan). Churchill Commemoration. As Nos. 170/3 of Antigua.

91	1d. new blue	40	75
92	3d. deep green	1·50	1·00
93	6d. brown	1·75	1·25
94	1s.6d. bluish violet	2·00	1·50
91/94 Set of 4		5·00	4·00

1966 (1 July). World Cup Football Championship. As Nos. 176/7 of Antigua.

95	3d. violet, yellow-green, lake and yellow-brown	75	1·00
96	6d. chocolate, blue-green, lake and yellow-brown	75	1·25

1966 (20 Sept). Inauguration of WHO Headquarters, Geneva. As Nos. 178/9 of Antigua.

97	3d. black, yellow-green and light blue	1·75	1·00
98	1s.6d. black, light purple and yellow-brown	4·75	2·00

ASCENSION

36 Satellite Station   **37** BBC Emblem

(Des V. Whiteley. Photo Harrison)

1966 (7 Nov). Opening of *Apollo* Communications Satellite Earth Station. W w **12**. (sideways). P 14×14½.

99	**36**	4d. black and reddish violet............	10	10
100		8d. black and deep bluish green.....	15	15
101		1s.3d. black and olive-brown...........	15	20
102		2s.6d. black and turquoise-blue.........	15	20
99/102 *Set of 4*			50	60

(Des BBC staff. Photo, Queen's head and emblem die-stamped, Harrison)

1966 (1 Dec). Opening of BBC Relay Station. W w **12**. P 14½.

103	**37**	1d. gold and ultramarine..............	10	10
104		3d. gold and myrtle-green..............	15	15
		w. Wmk inverted......................	50	1·00
105		6d. gold and reddish violet............	15	15
106		1s.6d. gold and red	15	15
103/106 *Set of 4*			50	50

1967 (1 Jan). 20th Anniv of UNESCO As Nos. 196/8 of Antigua.

107		3d. slate-violet, red, yellow and orange.	1·75	1·50
108		6d. orange-yellow, violet and deep olive...........	2·25	2·00
109		1s.6d. black, bright purple and orange......	3·25	2·50
107/109 *Set of 3*			6·50	5·50

44 Human Rights Emblem and Chain Links

(Des and litho Harrison)

1968 (8 July). Human Rights Year. W w **12** (sideways*). P 14½×14.

110	**44**	6d. light orange, red and black........	30	15
111		1s.6d. light grey-blue, red and black......	40	25
112		2s.6d. light green, red and black..........	40	30
		w. Wmk Crown to right of CA	£800	
110/112 *Set of 3*			1·00	65

*The normal sideways watermark shows Crown to left of CA, as seen from the back of the stamp.

45 Black Durgon ("Ascension Black-Fish")   **46** HMS *Rattlesnake*

(Des M. Farrar Bell. Litho D.L.R.)

1968 (23 Oct). Fish (1st series). T **45** and similar horiz designs. W w **12** (sideways*). P 13.

113		4d. black, slate and turquoise-blue	30	35
114		8d. multicoloured...........................	35	60
		w. Wmk Crown to right of CA	£475	
115		1s.9d. multicoloured......................	40	65
116		2s.3d. multicoloured......................	40	65
113/116 *Set of 4*			1·25	2·00

Designs:—8d. Scribbled Filefish ("Leather-jacket"); 1s.9d. Yellow-finned Tuna; 2s.3d. Short-finned Mako.
*The normal sideways watermark shows Crown to left of CA, as seen from the back of the stamp.
See also Nos. 117/20 and 126/9.

(Des M. Farrar Bell. Litho D.L.R.)

1969 (3 Mar). Fish (2nd series). Horiz designs as T **45**. Multicoloured. W w **12** (sideways). P 13½×13.

117		4d. Sailfish...............................	55	80
118		6d. White Seabream ("Old Wife")........	70	1·00
119		1s.6d. Yellowtail........................	90	2·00
120		2s.11d. Rock Hind ("Jack")..............	1·10	2·25
117/120 *Set of 4*			3·00	5·50

(Des L. Curtis. Photo Harrison)

1969 (1 Oct). Royal Naval Crests (1st series). T **46** and similar vert designs. W w **12** (sideways*). P 14×14½.

121		4d. multicoloured........................	50	30
122		9d. multicoloured........................	60	35
123		1s.9d. deep blue, pale blue and gold........	80	45
124		2s.3d. multicoloured.....................	90	55
121/124 *Set of 4*			2·50	1·50
MS125 165×105 mm. Nos. 121/4. P 14½.			6·50	13·00
		w. Wmk Crown to right of CA	£1300	

Designs:—9d. HMS *Weston*; 1s.9d. HMS *Undaunted*; 2s.3d. HMS *Eagle*.
*The normal sideways watermark shows Crown to left of CA, as seen from the back of the stamp.
See also Nos. 130/4.

(Des M. Farrar Bell. Litho D.L.R.)

1970 (6 Apr). Fish (3rd series). Horiz designs as T **45**. Multicoloured. W w **12** (sideways*). P 14.

126		4d. Wahoo...............................	3·50	2·75
		w. Wmk Crown to right of CA	£500	
127		9d. Ascension Jack ("Coalfish").........	4·00	2·75
		w. Wmk Crown to right of CA	1·75	1·25
128		1s.9d. Pompano Dolphin................	4·50	3·50
129		2s.3d. Squirrelfish ("Soldier")...........	4·50	3·50
		w. Wmk Crown to right of CA	1·75	1·50
126/129w *Set of 4*			10·50	8·00

*The normal sideways watermark shows Crown to left of CA, as seen from the back of the stamp.

(Des L. Curtis. Photo D.L.R.)

1970 (7 Sept). Royal Naval Crests (2nd series). Designs as T **46**. Multicoloured. W w **12**. P 12½.

130		4d. HMS *Penelope*......................	1·00	1·00
131		9d. HMS *Carlisle*........................	1·25	1·25
132		1s.6d. HMS *Amphion*....................	1·50	1·50
133		2s.6d. HMS *Magpie*.....................	1·50	1·50
130/133 *Set of 4*			4·75	4·75
MS134 153×96 mm. Nos. 130/3.			7·50	14·00

STAMP BOOKLET

1963 (23 May). Buff cover. Stitched.

SB1	10s.6d. booklet containing 1d., 1½d., 2d., 3d., 6d. and 1s.6d. (Nos. 70/3, 75, 79), each in block of 4................	70·00	

Australia

The Australian colonies of New South Wales, Queensland, South Australia, Tasmania, Victoria and Western Australia produced their own issues before federation in 1901. Stamps inscribed for the individual states continued in use after federation until the end of December 1912.

WATERMARK VARIETIES. Some stamp printers in the Australian colonies paid little attention to the position of the watermark in the sheets they produced so that some entire printings had the watermark inverted, some 50% upright and 50% inverted while on others the inverted watermarks were restricted to odd sheets. Reversed, inverted and reversed, and on stamps with sideways watermarks, sideways inverted and sideways inverted and reversed watermarks, are frequently encountered, especially on the stamps of New South Wales and the later issues of Tasmania, Victoria and Western Australia. In such circumstances it is impossible to provide adequate prices for such items, so, generally, only those watermark varieties occurring on stamps printed in Great Britain are included in the following listings.

DOUBLE PRINTS. Numerous examples of "double prints," also "printed double, one albino" varieties are found on the locally printed line-engraved stamps of the Australian colonies. These are particularly prevalent in the stamps of South Australia and Tasmania. We no longer list such varieties.

NEW SOUTH WALES

PRICES FOR STAMPS ON COVER	
Nos. 1/83	from × 2
Nos. 84/7	from × 3
No. 88	—
Nos. 89/96	from × 2
Nos. 97/8	—
Nos. 99/101	from × 2
Nos. 102/13	from × 3
No. 114	from × 10
Nos. 115/17	from × 2
Nos. 118/27	from × 3
Nos. 131/53	from × 2
Nos. 154/70	from × 3
Nos. 171/81	—
Nos. 186/202	from × 2
Nos. 203/6	from × 10
Nos. 207/21	from × 5
Nos. 222/37	from × 6
Nos. 238/42	—
Nos. 243/4	from × 6
Nos. 253/64	from × 10
Nos. 265/8	from × 15
Nos. 269/70	from × 2
Nos. 271/3	from × 10
Nos. 280/1	from × 2
Nos. 288/97	from × 10
Nos. 298/312	from × 12
Nos. 313/31	from × 10
No. 332	—
Nos. 333/49	from × 12
No. 350	—
Nos. 351/63	from × 12
No. O1	—
Nos. O2/12	from × 4
Nos. O13/18	—
Nos. O19/34	from × 20
Nos. O35/8	—
Nos. O39/47	from × 40
Nos. O48/53	—
Nos. O54/8	from × 20
No. O59	—
Nos. D1/7	from × 50
Nos. D8/10	—
Nos. D11/15	from × 50

EMBOSSED LETTER SHEETS AND ENVELOPES. From 1 November 1838 the Sydney G.P.O. supplied letter sheets pre-stamped with an albino embossing, as illustrated, at 1½d. each or 1s.3d. per dozen. From January 1841 the price was reduced to 1s. per dozen. The public were also able to present their own stationery for embossing. The circular design measures approximately 29 mm in diameter, and examples are known on laid or wove paper of varying colours. Embossing continued until 1 May 1852 after which the Post Office refused to carry mail which was not franked with postage stamps. The die was used for reprints in 1870 and 1898 before it was destroyed later the same year.

A 1

PRINTERS. The early issues of New South Wales were printed on a press supervised by the Inspector of Stamps, Charles Kay. On 1 January 1857 this responsibility passed to the Government printer who produced all subsequent issues, *unless otherwise stated*.

SPECIMEN OVERPRINTS. Those listed are from UPU distributions between 1892 and 1903. Further "Specimen" overprints exist, but these were used for other purposes. From 1891 examples of some of these Specimens, together with cancelled stamps, were sold to collectors by the N.S.W. Post Office.

NEW SOUTH WALES USED IN NEW CALEDONIA. From October 1859 mail for Europe from New Caledonia was routed via Sydney and franked with New South Wales stamps in combination with local issues. Such N.S.W. stamps were cancelled on arrival in Sydney.

1   2

(Eng Robert Clayton, Sydney)

1850 (1 Jan). T **1**. Plate I. No clouds.

(a) Soft yellowish paper

1	1d. crimson-lake	£13000	£550
2	1d. carmine	£13000	£500
3	1d. reddish rose	£12000	£475
4	1d. brownish red	£13000	£500

(b) Hard bluish paper

5	1d. pale red	£12000	£475
6	1d. dull lake	£13000	£500

1850 (Aug). T **2**. Plate I re-engraved by Henry C. Jervis, commonly termed Plate II. With clouds.

(a) Hard toned white to yellowish paper

7	1d. vermilion	£10000	£375
8	1d. dull carmine	£10000	£375
	a. No trees on hill (R. 2/2)	£13000	£750
	b. Hill unshaded (R. 2/3)	£13000	£750
	c. Without clouds (R. 3/5)	£13000	£750

(b) Hard greyish or bluish paper

9	1d. crimson-lake	£10000	£375
10	1d. gooseberry-red	£12000	£550
11	1d. dull carmine	£10000	£375
12	1d. brownish red	£10000	£350
	a. No trees on hill (R. 2/2)	£13000	£750
	b. Hill unshaded (R. 2/3)	£13000	£750
	c. Without clouds (R. 3/5)	£13000	£750

(c) Laid paper

13	1d. carmine	£15000	£700
14	1d. vermilion	£16000	£650
	a. No trees on hill (R. 2/2)	—	£1200
	b. Hill unshaded (R. 2/3)	—	£1200
	c. Without clouds (R. 3/5)	—	£1200

Each image was individually engraved on the plate.

The varieties quoted with the letters "a", "b", "c" of course exist in each shade; the prices quoted are for the commonest shade, and the same applies to the following portions of this list.

Nos. 1/14 were printed in sheets of 25 (5×5).

Note that in genuine examples of Nos 1/14 the star is directly below the "T" of "POSTAGE". Otherwise convincing forgeries exist where the star is between the "T" and the "A".

LAID PAPER. Nos. 13/14, 34/5, 38 and 43d/e can be found showing parts of the papermaker's watermark (T. H. SAUNDERS 1847 in double-lined capitals and the figure of Britannia seated in an oval beneath a crown).

3   4   A (Pl I)

Illustrations A, B, C and D are sketches of the lower part of the inner circular frame, showing the characteristic variations of each plate.

(Eng John Carmichael)

1850 (1 Jan). Plate I. Vertical-lined background. T **3**.

(a) Early impressions, full details of clouds, etc

15	2d. greyish blue	£18000	£550
16	2d. deep blue	—	£650
	a. Double lines on bale (R. 2/7)	—	£1100

(b) Intermediate impressions

16b	2d. greyish blue	£9500	£325
16c	2d. deep blue	£10000	£400

*(c) Later impressions, clouds, etc., mostly gone, T **4***

17	2d. greyish blue	£7500	£190
18	2d. dull blue	£7500	£180

(d) Stamps in the lower row partially retouched (end Jan)

19	2d. greyish blue	£8500	£300
20	2d. dull blue	£9000	£350

5   Pick and shovel omitted (R. 1/10)

B (Pl II)   C (Pl III)

(Plate entirely re-engraved by Henry C. Jervis)

1850 (Apr–July). T **5**. Plate II. Horizontal-lined background. Bale on left side supporting the seated figure, dated. Dot in centre of the star In each corner.

(a) Early impressions

21	2d. indigo	£13000	£350
22	2d. lilac-blue	—	£1300
23	2d. grey-blue	£13000	£300
24	2d. bright blue	£13000	£300
	a. Fan as in Pl III, but with shading outside (R. 1/1)	—	£550
	b. Fan as in Pl III, but without shading, and inner circle intersects the fan (R. 1/1)	—	£600
	c. Fan as B, but inner circle intersects fan (R. 1/3)	—	£600
	d. No whip and inner circle intersects fan (R. 1/4)	—	£600
	e. No whip (R. 1/8, 2/8)	—	£475
	f. Pick and shovel omitted (R. 1/10)	£16000	£600
	g. "CREVIT" omitted (R. 2/1)	—	£950

(b) Worn impressions

25	2d. dull blue	£7500	£170
26	2d. Prussian blue	£7500	£200
	a. Fan as in Pl III, but with shading outside (R. 1/1)	—	£425
	b. Fan as in Pl III, but without shading, and inner circle intersects the fan (R. 1/2)	—	£425
	c. Fan as B, but inner circle intersects fan (R. 1/3)	—	£425
	d. No whip and inner circle intersects fan (R. 1/4)	—	£425
	e. No whip (R. 1/8, 2/8)	£10000	£350
	f. Pick and shovel omitted (R. 1/10)	—	£425
	g. "CREVIT" omitted (R. 2/1)	£13000	£425

(c) Bottom row retouched with dots and dashes in lower spandrels (from July)

27	2d. Prussian blue	£8500	£325
28	2d. dull blue	£8500	£225
	e. No whip (R. 2/8)	—	£375
	g. "CREVIT" omitted (R. 2/1)	—	£550

(Plate re-engraved a second time by Henry C. Jervis)

1850 (Sept). Plate III. Bale not dated and single-lined, except on No. 30c which is doubled-lined. No dots in stars.

29	2d. ultramarine	£8500	£225
30	2d. deep blue	£8500	£225
	a. No whip (R. 2/3, 2/7)	—	£375
	b. Fan with 6 segments (R. 2/8)	—	£500
	c. Double lines on bale (R. 1/7, 1/10, 1/12)	—	£350

(Plate re-engraved a third time by Henry C. Jervis)

1851 (Jan). Plate IV. Double-lined bale, and circle in centre of each star.

(a) Hard bluish grey wove paper

31	2d. ultramarine	£8000	£200
32	2d. Prussian blue	£8000	£170
33	2d. bright blue	£8000	£190
	a. Hill not shaded (R. 1/12)	—	£325
	b. Fan with 6 segments (R. 2/8)	—	£325
	c. No clouds (R. 2/10)	—	£325
	d. Retouch (R. 2/1)	—	£400
	e. No waves (R. 1/9, 2/5)	—	£275

(b) Stout yellowish vertically laid paper

34	2d. ultramarine	£9000	£250
35	2d. Prussian blue	£10000	£275
	a. Hill not shaded (R. 1/12)	—	£425
	b. Fan with 6 segments (R. 2/8)	—	£425
	c. No clouds (R. 2/10)	—	£425
	d. Retouch (R. 2/1)	—	£500
	e. No waves (R. 1/9, 2/5)	—	£375
	f. "PENOE" (R. 1/10, 2/12)	—	£450

The retouch, Nos. 33d and 35d., occurs outside the left margin line on R. 2/1.

6   D (Pl V)   7

(Plate re-engraved a fourth time by Henry C. Jervis)

1851 (Apr). T **6**. Plate V. Pearl in fan.

(a) Hard greyish wove paper

36	2d. ultramarine	£8500	£180
37	2d. dull blue	£8500	£180
	a. Pick and shovel omitted (R. 2/5)	—	£375
	b. Fan with 6 segments (R. 2/8)	—	£375

(b) Stout yellowish vertically laid paper

38	2d. dull ultramarine	£12000	£425
	a. Pick and shovel omitted (R. 2/5)	—	£650
	b. Fan with 6 segments (R. 2/8)	—	£650

Nos. 15/38 were printed in sheets of 24 (12×2), although the existence of an inter-panneau *tête-bêche* pair from Plate II indicates that the printer applied two impressions of the plate to each sheet of paper. The two panes were normally separated before issue. The original Plate I was re-cut four times to form Plates II to V. An interesting variety occurs on R. 1/9-11 and 2/7 in all five plates. It consists of ten loops of the engine-turning on each side of the design instead of the normal nine loops.

(Eng Henry C. Jervis)

1850 (1 Jan)–51. T **7**.

(a) Soft yellowish wove paper

39	3d. yellow-green	£9500	£325
40	3d. myrtle green	£20000	£1400
41	3d. emerald-green	£11000	£350
	a. No whip (R. 4/3–4)	—	£500
	b. "SIGIIIUM" for "SIGILLUM" (R. 5/3)	—	£700

(b) Bluish to grey wove paper (July 1850)

42		3d. yellow-green	£9500	£275
43		3d. emerald-green	£10000	£275
	b.	No whip (R. 4/3–4)	—	£400
	c.	"SIGIIIUM" for "SIGILLUM" (R. 5/3)	—	£600

(c) Yellowish to bluish laid paper (Jan 1851)

43*d*		3d. bright green	£15000	£600
43*e*		3d. yellowish green	£13000	£500
	f.	No whip (R. 4/3–4)	—	£850
	g.	"SIGIIIUM" for "SIGILLUM" (R. 5/3)	—	£1200

Nos. 39/43*e* were printed in sheets of 25 (5×5).

8　　　**9**

(Des A. W. Manning from sketch by W. T. Levinge; eng on steel by John Carmichael, Sydney)

1851 (18 Dec)–**52**. Imperf.

(a) Thick yellowish paper

44	**8**	1d. carmine	£4250	£300
	a.	No leaves right of "SOUTH" (R. 1/7, 3/1)	—	£500
	b.	Two leaves right of "SOUTH" (R. 2/5)	—	£750
	c.	"WALE" (R. 1/9)	—	£750

(b) Bluish medium wove paper (1852)

45	**8**	1d. carmine	£2000	£160
46		1d. scarlet	£2000	£160
47		1d. vermilion	£2000	£140
48		1d. brick-red	£2000	£140
	a.	No leaves right of "SOUTH" (R. 1/7, 3/1)	£3750	£350
	b.	Two leaves right of "SOUTH" (R. 2/5)	—	£450
	c.	"WALE" (R. 1/9)	—	£450

(c) Thick vertically laid bluish paper (1852?)

49	**8**	1d. orange-brown	£6500	£450
50		1d. claret	£6500	£475
	a.	No leaves right of "SOUTH" (R. 1/7, 3/1)	—	£850
	b.	Two leaves right of "SOUTH" (R. 2/5)	—	£1100
	c.	"WALE" (R. 1/9)	—	£1200

Nos. 44/50 were printed in sheets of 50 (10×5).

(Eng John Carmichael (Nos. 51/9), Henry C. Jervis (Nos. 60/4))

1851 (24 July)–**55**. Imperf.

(a) Plate I

(i) Thick yellowish wove paper

51	**8**	2d. ultramarine	£1800	£120

(ii) Fine impressions, blue to greyish medium paper

52	**8**	2d. ultramarine	£1400	35·00
53		2d. chalky blue	£1300	35·00
54		2d. dark blue	£1300	35·00
55		2d. greyish blue	£1300	35·00

(iii) Worn plate, blue to greyish medium paper

56	**8**	2d. ultramarine	£900	35·00
57		2d. Prussian blue	£900	35·00

(iv) Worn plate, blue wove medium paper

58	**8**	2d. ultramarine	£800	35·00
59		2d. Prussian blue	£800	35·00

(b) Plate II. Stars in corners (Oct 1853)

(i) Bluish medium to thick wove paper

60	**9**	2d. deep ultramarine	£2000	£130
61		2d. indigo	£2100	£100
		a. "WAEES" (R. 3/3)	—	£475

(ii) Worn plate, hard blue wove paper

62	**9**	2d. deep Prussian blue	£2000	£120
		a. "WAEES" (R. 3/3)	—	£475

*(c) Plate III, being Plate I (T **8**) re-engraved by H. C. Jervis. Background of crossed lines (Sept 1855)*

(i) Medium bluish wove paper

63		2d. Prussian blue	£1100	75·00
	a.	"WALES" partly covered with wavy lines (R. 1/3)	—	£275

(ii) Stout white wove paper

64		2d. Prussian blue	£1100	75·00
	a.	"WALES" partly covered with wavy lines (R. 1/3)	£2750	£275

Nos. 51/64 were printed in sheets of 50 (10×5).

(Eng John Carmichael)

1852 (3 Dec). Imperf.

(a) Medium greyish blue wove paper

65	**8**	3d. deep green	£4000	£225
66		3d. green	£3500	£160
67		3d. dull yellow-green	£3250	£110
	a.	"WAEES" with centre bar of first "E" missing (R. 4/7)	—	£450

(b) Thick blue wove paper

69	**8**	3d. emerald-green	£4000	£250
71		3d. blue-green	£4000	£275
	a.	"WAEES" with centre bar of first "E" missing (R. 4/7)	—	£750

Nos. 65/71 were printed in sheets of 50 (10×5).

1852 (Apr)–**53**. Imperf.

(a) Plate I

(i) Medium white wove paper

72	**8**	6d. Vandyke-brown	—	£950
		a. "WALLS" (R. 2/3)	—	£1800

(ii) Medium bluish grey wove paper

73	**8**	6d. Vandyke-brown	£4000	£250
74		6d. yellow-brown	£4250	£275
75		6d. chocolate-brown	£4000	£250
76		6d. grey-brown	£4000	£250
		a. "WALLS" (R. 2/3)	—	£750

(b) Plate I re-engraved by H. C. Jervis. Coarse background (June 1853)

77		–	6d. brown	£4250	£300
78		–	6d. grey-brown	£4000	£300

Reprints from the original plates of the 6d. and 8d. were produced in a variety of colours, including those in which the stamps had been issued. Unused examples of Nos. 72/81 should only be purchased from a reliable source.

Nos. 72/6 and 77/8 were printed in sheets of 25 (5×5).

(Eng Henry C. Jervis)

1853 (May). Imperf. Medium bluish paper.

79		8d. dull yellow	£14000	£600
80		8d. yellow-orange	£14000	£600
81		8d. orange	£15000	£650
	a.	No bow at back of head (R. 1/9)	—	£1800
	b.	No leaves right of "SOUTH" (R. 3/1)	—	£1800
	c.	No lines in spandrel (R. 2/2, 3/2, 4/2)	—	£1000

Nos. 79/81 were issued in sheets of 50 (10×5).

10

NOTE. All watermarked stamps from No. 82 to No. 172 have double-lined figures, as T **10**.

1854 (Jan–Mar). Yellowish wove paper. Wmk double-line "**1**", "**2**", or "**3**" as T **10**, to match face value. Imperf.

82	**8**	1d. red-orange (2.54)	£475	35·00
83		1d. orange-vermilion	£475	35·00
	a.	No leaves right of "SOUTH" (R. 1/7, 3/1)	£850	£100
	b.	Two leaves right of "SOUTH" (R. 2/5)	£1200	£150
	c.	"WALE" (R. 1/9)	£1200	£150
84	–	2d. ultramarine (Pl III) (1.54)	£375	15·00
85	–	2d. Prussian blue (Pl III)	£375	15·00
86	–	2d. chalky blue (Pl III)	£375	12·00
	a.	"WALES" partly covered by wavy lines (R. 1/3)	£900	65·00
87	**8**	3d. yellow-green (3.54)	£650	50·00
	a.	"WAEES" with centre bar of first "E" missing (R. 4/7)	£1500	£180
	b.	Error. Wmk "**2**"	£6500	£1600

Nos. 82/7 were printed in sheets of 50 (10×5).

11　　　**12**

13　　　**14**

(6d. and 1s. des E. H. Corbould after sketches by W. T. Levinge. Printed by New South Wales Govt Ptg Dept from Perkins Bacon plates)

1854 (1 Feb)–**59**. Wmk double-line "**5**", "**6**", "**8**" or "**12**" to match face value. Imperf.

88	**11**	5d. dull green (1.12.55)	£1300	£650
89	**12**	6d. deep slate	£1900	35·00
	a.	Wmk sideways	†	£1200
90		6d. greenish grey	£1700	35·00
91		6d. slate-green	£1700	35·00
92		6d. bluish grey	£1700	55·00
93		6d. fawn	£1800	95·00
	a.	Wmk "**8**" (15.8.59)	£4000	£110
94		6d. grey	£1700	55·00
95		6d. olive-grey	£1700	35·00
96		6d. greyish brown	£1700	35·00
	a.	Wmk "**8**" (15.8.59)	£4000	£110
	ab.	Wmk sideways	—	£500
97	**13**	8d. golden yellow (1.12.55)	£18000	£1400
98		8d. dull yellow-orange	£17000	£1300
99	**14**	1s. rosy vermilion (2.54)	£4500	75·00
	a.	Wmk "**8**" (20.6.57)	£9000	£180
100		1s. pale red	£4000	70·00
101		1s. brownish red	£4500	80·00

Nos. 93a, 96a and 99a come from printings made when supplies of the correct numeral watermarks were unavailable.

Plate proofs of the 6d. and of the 1s. in deep blue on unwatermarked paper exist handstamped "CANCELLED" in oval of bars (see note on Perkins Bacon "CANCELLED" in Catalogue introduction) (*Price £12000 each*).

A single used example of No. 91 exists printed on both sides. It is in the Royal Philatelic Collection.

For further examples of Types **11/14** on different watermarks see Nos. 141/53, 160/70, 215, 218, 231/3, 236 and 329.

15　　　**16**

(Eng John Carmichael)

1856 (1 Jan)–**59**. For Registered Letters. No wmk. Imperf.

(a) Soft medium yellowish paper

102	**15**	(6d.) vermilion and Prussian blue	£1800	£170
		a. Frame printed on back	£12000	£5000
103		(6d.) salmon and indigo	£1700	£190
104		(6d.) orange and Prussian blue	£1700	£225
105		(6d.) orange and indigo	£1700	£200

(b) Hard medium bluish wove paper, with manufacturer's wmk in sans-serif, double-lined capitals across sheet and only showing portions of letters on a few stamps in a sheet

106	**15**	(6d.) orange and Prussian blue (4.59)	£2250	£250

For further examples of Type **15** on different watermarks see Nos. 119/27.

2d. Major retouch (Plate I, R. 2/12)

2d. Major retouch (Plate I, R. 9/8)

(Printed by New South Wales Govt Ptg Dept from plates engraved by Perkins Bacon & Co)

1856 (7 Jan)–**60**. Wmk double-line "**1**", "**2**" or "**3**" to match face value. Imperf.

(a) Recess

107	**16**	1d. orange-vermilion (6.4.56)	£350	24·00
		a. Error. Wmk "**2**"	†	£8500
108		1d. carmine-vermilion	£350	24·00
109		1d. orange-red	£375	24·00
		a. Printed on both sides	£3750	£2500
110		2d. deep turquoise-blue (Pl I)	£325	14·00
111		2d. ultramarine (Pl I)	£300	14·00
112		2d. blue (Pl I)	£300	14·00
		a. Major retouch (1858)	£2250	£450
		b. Error. Wmk "**1**"	†	£8500
		c. Wmk "**5**" (3.57)	£850	70·00
113		2d. pale blue	£300	14·00
114		2d. blue (Pl II) (1.60)	£850	65·00
115		3d. yellow-green (10.10.56)	£1600	£100
116		3d. bluish green	£1700	£110
117		3d. dull green	£1700	£110
		a. Error, Wmk "**2**"	—	£3750

(b) Lithographic transfer of Plate I

118	**16**	2d. pale blue (3.8.59)	—	£800
		a. Retouched	—	£2500

For further examples of Type **16** on different watermarks see Nos. 131/40, 154/8, 171/2, 211/12, 226/8 and 327/8.

Two plates were used for the 2d. The 2d. Plate I was retouched, on a total of ten positions, Nos. 112a and 133a refer to the third retouch of R. 2/12 and R. 9/8. Earlier retouches from these exist. Stamps from Plate II are wider apart and are more regularly spaced. There is also a white patch between "A" of "WALES" and the back of the Queen's head on later printings from Plate II, but this is not obvious on the early printings.

On the 3d. the value is in block letters on a white background. No. 112c comes from a printing made when supplies of the "2" paper were unavailable. There are only two known of No. 112b one of which is in the Royal Collection. Two used examples are known with "8" watermark, both of which are in museum collections.

The 1d. exists privately rouletted 10, a used pair of which is known postmarked 15 May 1861.

No. 114 was mainly used at post offices in Queensland.

The lithographic retouches (No. 118a) occur on the three stamps at the left of the bottom row of the sheet and consist of strong horizontal lines below "TWO PENCE".

STAMPS WITH STRAIGHT EDGES. Stamps between Nos. 119 and 244 and also Nos. 327/9 can be found with one or two sides imperforate. These come from the outside rows which were not perforated between the stamps and the sheet margins. Being from the edge of the sheet such stamps are often found without watermark or showing portions of the double-lined "NEW SOUTH WALES" marginal watermark.

1860 (Feb)–**63**. For Registered Letters.

(a) P 12

(i) Hard medium bluish wove paper with manufacturer's wmk in sans-serif, double-lined capitals across sheet, showing portions of letters on a few stamps

119	**15**	(6d.) orange and Prussian blue	£950	75·00
120		(6d.) orange and indigo	£950	80·00

(ii) Coarse, yellowish wove paper with manufacturer's wmk in Roman capitals (Feb 1860)

121	**15**	(6d.) rose-red and Prussian blue	£650	50·00
122		(6d.) rose-red and indigo	£750	95·00
123		(6d.) salmon and indigo		

(b) P 13

(i) Coarse, yellowish wove paper with manufacturer's wmk in Roman capitals (1862)

124	**15**	(6d.) rose-red and Prussian blue	£750	65·00

(ii) Yellowish wove paper. Wmk double-line "6" (May 1863)

125	**15**	(6d.) rose-red and Prussian blue	£300	24·00
126		(6d.) rose-red and indigo	£400	32·00
127		(6d.) rose-red and pale blue	£300	22·00

2d. Major retouch around neck and above "TWO PENCE" (Plate II, R. 5/9)

1860 (14 Feb)–**72**. Wmk double-lined figure of value.

(a) P 12

131	**16**	1d. orange-red	£325	24·00
132		1d. scarlet	£250	24·00
133		2d. pale blue (Pl I)	£650	£140
		a. Retouched	—	£1400
134		2d. greenish blue (Pl II)	£225	13·00
136		2d. Prussian blue (Pl II)	£225	13·00
		a. Error. Wmk "1"	—	£3500
		b. Retouched (shades)	—	£425
137		2d. Prussian blue (Pl I) (3.61)	£250	14·00
138		2d. dull blue (Pl I)	£225	13·00
139		3d. yellow-green (1860)	£1700	60·00
140		3d. blue-green	£850	48·00
141	**11**	5d. dull green (1863)	£425	£110
142		5d. yellowish green (1863)	£425	£110
143	**12**	6d. grey-brown	£750	65·00
144		6d. olive-brown	£750	75·00
145		6d. greenish grey	£850	60·00
146		6d. fawn	£800	85·00
147		6d. mauve	£750	38·00
148		6d. violet	£650	19·00
149	**13**	8d. lemon-yellow		£2000
150		8d. orange	£6500	£1200
151		8d. red-orange	£6500	£1200
152	**14**	1s. brownish red	£1500	70·00
153		1s. rose-carmine	£1500	70·00

(b) P 13

154	**16**	1d. scarlet (1862)	£150	24·00
155		1d. dull red	£150	24·00
156		3d. blue-green (12.62)	95·00	13·00
157		3d. yellow-green	£110	9·50
		a. Wmk "6" (7.72)	£225	15·00
158		3d. dull green	£110	9·00
		a. Wmk "6" (7.72)	£250	18·00
160	**11**	5d. bluish green (12.63)	£130	35·00
161		5d. bright yellow-green (8.65)	£250	75·00
162		5d. sea-green (1866)	£150	38·00
162a		5d. dark bluish green (11.70)	95·00	25·00
163	**12**	6d. reddish purple (Pl I) (7.62)	£225	6·50
164		6d. mauve	£225	6·50
165		6d. purple (Pl II) (1864)	£160	4·75
		a. Wmk "5" (7.66)	£750	28·00
		ab. Wmk "5" sideways	†	£1200
		b. Wmk "12" (12.66 and 1868)	£700	23·00
166		6d. violet	£170	6·50
		a. Wmk "5" (7.66)	—	38·00
167		6d. aniline mauve	£1300	£140
167a	**13**	8d. red-orange (1862)	£475	55·00
167b		8d. yellow-orange	£500	45·00
		ba. Wmk sideways	†	£1200
167c		8d. bright yellow	£475	45·00
168	**14**	1s. rose-carmine (1862)	£325	8·00
169		1s. carmine	£300	8·50
170		1s. crimson-lake	£300	8·50

(c) Perf compound 12×13

171	**16**	1d. scarlet (1862)	—	£1700
172		2d. dull blue (1.62)	£2250	£180

No. 133 was made by perforating a small remaining stock of No. 113. Nos. 137/8 were printed from the original plate after its return from London, where it had been repaired.

No. 136b refers to the second retouch on R. 5/9. Other retouches to plate II exist.

Nos. 157a, 158a and 165a/b come from printings made when supplies of paper with the correct face value were unavailable.

The Royal Philatelic Collection contains examples of Nos. 131 and 168 in imperf between pairs.

For later printings in these types, with different watermarks and perforations, see Nos. 195, 211/2, 215, 218, 226/8, 231/3, 236, 269/70 and 327/9.

24   **25**

(Des E. H. Corbould, R.I.)

1861–88. W **25**. Various perfs.

174	**24**	5s. dull violet, P 12 (1861)	£2000	£325
		a. Perf 13 (1861)	£325	35·00
175		5s. royal purple, P 13 (1872)	£800	70·00
176		5s. deep rose-lilac, P 13 (1875)	£225	35·00
177		5s. deep purple, P 13 (1880)	£275	50·00
		a. Perf 10 (1882)	£300	75·00
178		5s. rose-lilac, P 10 (1883)	£275	55·00
179		5s. purple, P 12 (1885)	—	70·00
		a. Perf 10×12 (1885)	—	£180
180		5s. reddish purple, P 10 (1886)	£275	60·00
		a. Perf 12×10 (1887)	£425	65·00
		b. Mixed perfs 10 and 12	—	†
181		5s. rose-lilac, P 11 (1888)	£325	£140

This value was replaced by Nos. 261, etc. in 1888 but reissued in 1897, see Nos. 297c/e.

26   **27**   **28**

(Printed by De La Rue & Co, Ltd, London and perf at Somerset House, London)

1862–65. Surfaced paper. P 14.

(i) W 27

186	**26**	1d. dull red (Pl I) (1.4.64)	£225	90·00

(ii) No wmk

187	**26**	1d. dull red (Pl I) (1.65)	£225	80·00
188	**28**	2d. pale blue (25.3.62)	£225	95·00

(Printed from the De La Rue plates in the Colony)

1862 (12 Apr). Wmk double-lined "2" (No. 189) or "5" (No. 190). P 13.

189	**28**	2d. blue	£110	35·00
		a. Perf 12	£200	50·00
		b. Perf 12×13	£600	£200
190		2d. dull blue (9.62)	£110	38·00

29

1863–69. W **29**. P 13.

191	**26**	1d. pale red (3.69)	£250	35·00
192	**28**	2d. pale blue (4.63)	55·00	3·00
		a. Perf 12		
193		2d. cobalt-blue	55·00	3·00
194		2d. Prussian blue	60·00	3·75

1864–65. W **27**. P 13.

195	**16**	1d. pale red (6.64)	£120	55·00
196	**26**	1d. dark red-brown (Pl I)	£300	45·00
197		1d. brownish red (Pl II)	80·00	9·50
		a. Imperf between (horiz pair)	†	£2500
198		1d. brick-red (Pl II)	80·00	9·50
		a. Highly surfaced paper (1865)	£300	£180
199	**28**	2d. pale blue	£225	6·00

Plates I and II were made from the same die; they can only be distinguished by the colour or by the marginal inscription.

1865–66. Thin to very thin wove paper. No wmk. P 13.

200	**26**	1d. brick-red	£200	45·00
201		1d. brownish red	£200	45·00
202	**28**	2d. pale blue (11.65)	£130	6·00

32   **34**

33   **35**

1867 (Sept)–**93**. W **33** and **35**.

203	**32**	4d. red-brown, P 13	£120	8·50
204		4d. pale red-brown, P 13	£120	8·50
205	**34**	10d. lilac, P 13	55·00	8·50
		a. Imperf between (horiz pair)	£3000	
		s. Optd "Specimen"	30·00	
206		10d. lilac, P 11 (1893)	18·00	9·00
		a. Perf 10	19·00	11·00
		b. Perf 10×11 or 11×10	27·00	11·00
		c. Perf 12×11	£160	16·00

See also Nos. 269/70.

---

36   **37**   **38**

NINEPENCE
(39)

From 1871 to 1903 the 9d. is formed from the 10d. by a black surch. (T **39**), 15 mm long on Nos. 219 to 220g, and 13½ mm long on subsequent issues.

1871–1902. W **36**.

207	**26**	1d. dull red, P 13 (8.71)	40·00	3·25
		a. Imperf vert (horiz pair)	†	£2750
		b. Imperf between (horiz pair)	†	£2750
208		1d. salmon, P 13 (1878)	40·00	3·50
		a. Perf 10 (6.80)	£250	40·00
		b. Perf 10×13 (6.80)	65·00	8·50
		ba. Perf 13×10	32·00	2·50
		c. Scarlet. Perf 10 (4.82)	—	£180
209	**28**	2d. Prussian-blue, P 13 (11.71)	50·00	1·75
		a. Perf 11×12, comb (11.84)	£250	40·00
		c. Imperf between (horiz pair)	†	£3250
210		2d. pale blue, P 13 (1876)	45·00	1·75
		a. Perf 10 (6.80)	£250	23·00
		b. Perf 10×13 (6.80)	£100	16·00
		ba. Perf 13×10	32·00	1·25
		c. Surfaced paper. Perf 13	—	£200
211	**16**	3d. yellow-green, P 13 (3.74)	75·00	5·00
		a. Perf 10 (6.80)	90·00	12·00
		b. Perf 11 (1902)	£160	£100
		c. Perf 12 (5.85)	—	£150
		d. Perf 10×12 or 12×10 (5.85)	£150	40·00
		e. Perf 11×12 (1902)	£130	40·00
212		3d. bright green, P 10 (6.80)	£120	20·00
		a. Perf 13×10 (6.80)	£110	24·00
		b. Perf 13		
213	**32**	4d. pale red-brown, P 13 (8.77)	£120	22·00
214		4d. red-brown, P 13	£120	17·00
		a. Perf 10 (6.80)	£225	60·00
		b. Perf 10×13 (6.80)	£150	24·00
		ba. Perf 13×10	£130	7·00
215	**11**	5d. bluish green, P 10 (8.84)	40·00	45·00
		a. Perf 12 (5.85)	£250	£100
		b. Perf 10×13 or 13×10 (6.80)		
		c. Perf 12×10 (5.85)	£120	65·00
		ca. Perf 12×10	60·00	45·00
216	**37**	6d. bright mauve, P 13 (1.1.72)	£100	2·25
		a. Imperf between (horiz pair)	†	£3000
217		6d. pale lilac, P 13 (1878)	£100	2·25
		a. Perf 10 (6.80)	£200	12·00
		b. Perf 10×13 (6.80)	£140	16·00
		ba. Perf 13×10	£120	2·50
		c. Imperf between (horiz pair). (Perf 13×10)	†	£3000
218	**13**	8d. yellow, P 13 (3.77)	£225	17·00
		a. Wmk sideways	†	
		b. Perf 10 (6.80)	£350	26·00
		c. Perf 13×10 (6.80)	£250	24·00
219	**34**	9d. on 10d. pale red-brown, P 13 (8.71)	75·00	5·50
220		9d. on 10d. red-brown, P 13 (1878)	75·00	13·00
		a. Perf 10 (6.80)	16·00	11·00
		b. Perf 12 (5.85)	23·00	20·00
		c. Perf 11 (12.85)	60·00	11·00
		d. Perf 10×12 (5.85)	£275	£180
		e. Perf 10×11 or 11×10 (12.85)	70·00	20·00
		g. Perf 12×11, comb (1.84)	18·00	6·00
		ga. Perf 11×12		
		gs. Optd "Specimen"	27·00	
221	**38**	1s. black, P 13 (1.4.76)	£170	13·00
		aa. Imperf horiz (vert pair)	†	£3000
		a. Perf 10 (6.80)	£225	25·00
		b. Perf 10×13 (6.80)	£250	48·00
		ba. Perf 13×10	£180	15·00
		c. Perf 11		
		e. Imperf (pair)	†	£2750

Stamps from this series without watermark are from the edge of the sheet.

A used horizontal pair of the 2d. Prussian-blue imperf vertically, is in the Royal Philatelic Collection.

Nos. 211b and 211e were printed in 1902 on wmk **36** paper, left over when it was superseded by wmk **40**.

Collectors should note that for issues prior to 1888 (other than those specifically described as "Perf 11×12, comb" our classification of perforations follows the long-standing convention whereby "Perf 12" denotes a perforation of 11½, 12 and "Perf 13" denotes one of 12½, 13.

BISECTS. Between 1887 and 1913 various 1d. and 2d. stamps can be found vertically or diagonally bisected. This was unauthorised.

40

1882 (Apr)–**97**. W **40**.

222	**26**	1d. salmon, P 10	42·00	3·00
		a. Perf 13		
		b. Perf 13×13	†	£200
		ba. Perf 13×10	65·00	2·75
223		1d. orange to scarlet, P 13	£850	£450
		a. Perf 10	24·00	2·25
		ab. Imperf between (horiz pair)	†	£3750

		b. Perf 10×13	£120	9·50
		c. Perf 10×12 or 12×10 (4.85)	£275	65·00
		d. Perf 11×10 (12.85)	£475	£120
		e. Perf 12×11 (12.85)	—	£120
		f. Perf 11×12, comb (1.84)	10·00	1·25
		h. Perf 11 (12.85)	—	£140
224	28	2d. pale blue, P 13	£450	90·00
		a. Perf 10	50·00	1·25
		b. Perf 10×13	£150	7·50
		ba. Perf 13×10	70·00	3·25
225		2d. Prussian blue, P 10	60·00	1·00
		b. Perf 12 (4.85)	—	£225
		c. Perf 11 (12.85)	—	£100
		d. Perf 12×11 (12.85)	£400	£100
		e. Perf 10×12 (4.85)	£225	65·00
		ca. Perf 12×10	£400	£100
		f. Perf 10×11 or 11×10 (12.85)	£450	£150
		g. Perf 11×12, comb (1.84)	13·00	1·00
		ga. Printed double	†	£700
		gb. Imperf three sides (left stamp of horizontal pair)	£2000	
226	16	3d. yellow-green, P 10 (1886)	32·00	2·25
		bs. Optd "Specimen"	27·00	
		c. Perf 10×11	£180	42·00
		ca. Perf 12×10	£140	18·00
		d. Perf 11	10·00	1·00
		da. Imperf vert (horiz pair)	£700	
		e. Perf 11×12 or 12×11	6·00	1·00
		f. Perf 12	15·00	2·50
		g. Imperf (pair)	£500	
227		3d. bluish green, P 10	35·00	2·25
		a. Wmk sideways	60·00	11·00
		b. Perf 11	26·00	2·50
		ba. Imperf between (horiz pair)		
		c. Perf 10×11	35·00	3·25
		ca. Perf 11×10	£100	35·00
		d. Perf 11×12 or 12×11	11·00	2·75
		e. Perf 10×12 or 12×10	50·00	4·25
228		3d. emerald-green, P 10 (1893)	65·00	10·00
		a. Wmk sideways	—	22·00
		b. Perf 10×11	65·00	6·50
		ba. Perf 11×10	£120	42·00
		c. Perf 10×12	60·00	6·50
		ca. Perf 12×10	80·00	9·00
		d. Perf 12×11	—	15·00
229	32	4d. red-brown, P 10	£120	5·50
		a. Perf 10×12 (4.85)	—	£160
		b. Perf 11×12, comb (1.84)	£120	3·00
230		4d. dark brown, P 10	£120	4·75
		a. Perf 12 (4.85)	£325	£200
		b. Perf 10×12 (4.85)	£225	60·00
		ba. Perf 12×10	£325	£150
		c. Perf 11×12, comb (1.84)	85·00	2·75
231	11	5d. dull green, P 10 (1890)	50·00	3·25
		as. Optd. "Specimen"	27·00	
		b. Perf 11×10	70·00	
		c. Perf 12×10 (4.85)	£100	8·00
232		5d. bright green, P 10	75·00	15·00
		b. Perf 10×11 (12.85)	80·00	10·00
		ba. Perf 11×10	80·00	13·00
		c. Perf 10×12 (4.85)	£160	45·00
		ca. Perf 12×10	£110	75·00
233		5d. blue-green, P 10	25·00	1·75
		a. Perf 12 (4.85)	26·00	1·75
		ab. Wmk sideways	80·00	
		aba. Mixed perfs 12 and 13		
		b. Perf 11 (12.85)	11·00	1·25
		c. Perf 11×12, comb (1.84)	50·00	3·25
		d. Perf 11×12 or 12×11 (12.85)	11·00	1·25
		da. Wmk sideways (P 11×12)	80·00	25·00
		e. Imperf (pair)	£475	
234	37	6d. pale lilac, P 10	95·00	1·50
		a. Perf 10×13 or 13×10	—	£300
		b. Perf 10×12 or 12×10 (4.85)	£100	1·75
235		6d. mauve, P 10	95·00	1·50
		a. Perf 12 (4.85)	£130	10·00
		b. Perf 11 (12.85)	£130	8·00
		c. Perf 10×12 (4.85)	£100	8·50
		ca. Perf 12×10	£100	2·50
		cb. Imperf between (horiz pair)	†	£2750
		d. Perf 11×12 (12.85)	£130	14·00
		da. Perf 12×11	£100	2·00
		e. Perf 11×10 or 10×11(12.85)	£110	2·75
236	13	8d. yellow, P 10 (1883)	£225	20·00
		a. Perf 12 (4.85)	£325	30·00
		b. Perf 11 (12.85)	£225	25·00
		c. Perf 10×12 (4.85)	£275	60·00
		ca. Perf 12×10	£250	55·00
236d	34	9d. on 10d. red-brown, P 11×12 (28.2.97)	19·00	22·00
		das. Optd "Specimen"	27·00	
		db. Perf 12	13·00	22·00
		dc. Perf 11	12·00	22·00
		dca. Surch double	£325	£425
236e		10d. violet, P 11×12 (1897)	35·00	26·00
		eas. Optd "Specimen"	30·00	
		eb. Perf 12×11½	12·00	22·00
		ec. Perf 12	23·00	28·00
		ed. Perf 11	27·00	30·00
237	38	1s. black, P 10	£150	7·50
		a. Perf 11 (12.85)	£275	19·00
		b. Perf 10×12	—	£250
		c. Perf 10×13		
		ca. Perf 13×10	£275	28·00
		d. Perf 11×12, comb (1.84)	£150	7·50

41

42

1885–86. W 41 (sideways).

(i) Optd "POSTAGE", in black

238	42	5s. lilac and green, P 13 (15.10.85)		
		a. Perf 10		
		b. Perf 12×10	£800	£140
239		10s. lilac and claret, P 13 (17.5.86)		
		a. Perf 12	£1600	£225
		ab. Opt double	—	†
240		£1 lilac and claret, P 13 (17.5.86)	—	£8000
		a. Perf 12	£10000	£5000

(ii) Overprinted in blue

241	42	10s. mauve and claret, P 10	£1800	£225
		as. Optd "Specimen"	75·00	
		b. Perf 12	£300	70·00
		c. Perf 12×11		
242		£1 rose-lilac and claret, P 12×10	£9000	£5000

1886–87. W 41.

243	26	1d. scarlet, P 10 (12.86)	60·00	16·00
		a. Perf 11×12, comb	19·00	9·00
244	28	2d. deep blue, P 10 (12.87)	£100	22·00
		a. Perf 11×12, comb	40·00	7·00
		b. Imperf (pair)	†	£3000

45 View of Sydney   **46** Emu   **47** Captain Cook

48 Queen Victoria and Arms of Colony   **49** Superb Lyrebird   **50** Eastern Grey Kangaroo

51 Map of Australia   **52** Capt. Arthur Phillip, first Governor and Lord Carrington, Governor in 1888

(Des M. Tannenberg (1d., 6d.), Miss Catherine Devine (2d., 8d.), H. A. Barraclough (4d.), Govt Ptg Office (1s.), C. Turner (5s.), Mrs Mary Stoddard (20s.). Eng W. Bell).

1888 (1 May)–89. Centenary of New South Wales.

(a) W **40**. P 11×12

253	45	1d. lilac (9.7.88)	15·00	1·00
		a. Perf 12×11½	24·00	1·25
		b. Perf 12	16·00	50
		c. Imperf (pair)	£2250	
		d. Mauve	14·00	50
		da. Imperf between (pair)		
		db. Perf 12×11½	17·00	70
		dc. Perf 12	17·00	70
254	46	2d. Prussian blue (1.9.88)	22·00	50
		a. Imperf (pair)	£375	£550
		b. Imperf three sides (right stamp of horiz pair)	£1700	
		c. Perf 12×11½	22·00	40
		d. Perf 12	22·00	40
		e. Chalky blue	17·00	40
		ea. Perf 12×11½		
		eb. Perf 12	22·00	60
255	47	4d. purple-brown (8.10.88)	28·00	5·50
		a. Perf 12×11½	50·00	8·50
		b. Perf 12	50·00	5·00
		c. Perf 11	£300	95·00
		d. Red-brown	17·00	5·00
		da. Perf 12×11½	20·00	4·50
		db. Perf 12	20·00	4·50
		e. Orange-brown, P 12×11½	40·00	5·00
		f. Yellow-brown, P 12×11½	23·00	5·00
256	48	6d. carmine (26.11.88)	35·00	4·50
		a. Perf 12×11½	50·00	5·00
		b. Perf 12	35·00	11·00
257	49	8d. lilac-rose (17.1.89)	25·00	9·00
		a. Perf 12×11½	60·00	16·00
		b. Perf 12	25·00	9·50
		c. Magenta	85·00	16·00
		ca. Perf 12×11½	40·00	9·50
		cb. Perf 12	45·00	9·50
258	50	1s. maroon (21.2.89)	50·00	2·50
		a. Perf 12×11½	50·00	3·00
		b. Perf 12	55·00	2·50
		c. Violet-brown	50·00	3·00
		ca. Imperf (pair)	£1400	
		cb. Perf 12×11½	80·00	4·75
		cc. Perf 12	80·00	2·75

253s/8s Optd "Specimen" *Set of 6* ... £190

(b) W **41**. P 11×12

259	45	1d. lilac (1888)	70·00	
		a. Mauve	48·00	7·00
260	46	2d. Prussian blue (1888)	£110	7·00

(c) W **25** (sideways on 20s.) P 10

261	51	5s. deep purple (13.3.89)	£425	55·00
		a. Deep violet	£425	60·00
262	52	20s. cobalt-blue (27.4.88)	£750	£160

Nos. 255c and 261/2 are line perforated, the remainder are comb. A lithographed postal forgery exists of the 2d. on unwatermarked paper and perforated 11 (*Price £450, used*). These were in use in Sydney between March and May 1895, a similar forgery of the 2s. 6d. is also known.

53   **54**

1890. W 53 (5s.) or **54** (20s.). P 10.

263	51	5s. lilac	£275	32·00
		a. Perf 11	£375	50·00
		ab. Imperf between (horiz pair)		
		b. Perf 12	£450	55·00
		c. Perf 10×11 or 11×10	£375	32·00
		d. Mauve	£375	32·00
		da. Perf 11	£375	50·00
264	52	20s. cobalt-blue	£475	£160
		a. Perf 11	£475	90·00
		b. Perf 10×11		
		c. Ultramarine, P 11	£425	90·00
		ca. Perf 12	£450	£150
		cb. Perf 11×12 or 12×11	£375	90·00

263s/4s Optd "SPECIMEN" (5s.) or "Specimen" *Set of 2* ... £200

55 Allegorical figure of Australia

SEVEN-PENCE

Halfpenny (56)   **HALFPENNY** (57)

(Des Miss Catherine Devine)

1890 (22 Dec). W 40.

265	55	2½d. ultramarine, P 11×12 comb	17·00	60
		as. Optd "Specimen"	27·00	
		b. Perf 12×11½, comb	50·00	50·00
		c. Perf 12, comb	22·00	1·00

WATERMARK VARIETIES: The attention of collectors is drawn to the note on inverted and reversed watermarks on the stamps of the Australian States at the top of the Australia listings.

1891 (5 Jan). Surch as T 56 and 57. W 40.

266	26	½d. on 1d. grey, P 11×12 comb	4·50	6·00
		b. Surch double	£750	
267	37	7½d. on 6d. brown, P 10	5·50	9·50
		a. Perf 11	5·00	3·50
		b. Perf 12	13·00	4·25
		c. Perf 11×12 or 12×11	6·50	3·50
		d. Perf 10×12	7·00	4·50
268	38	12½d. on 1s. red, P 10	18·00	32·00
		a. "HALFPENNY" omitted		
		b. Perf 11	14·00	26·00
		c. Perf 11×12, comb	14·00	18·00
		d. Perf 12×11½, comb	15·00	25·00
		e. Perf 12, comb	30·00	19·00

266/8s Optd "SPECIMEN" *Set of 3* ... 80·00

1891 (1 July). Wmk "10" as W 35. P 10.

269	16	3d. green	16·00	80·00
270		3d. dark green	6·50	19·00

58   Type I. Narrow "H" in "HALF"

1892 (21 Mar)–99. Type I. W 40.

271	58	½d. grey, P 10	65·00	2·50
		a. Perf 11	95·00	8·50
		b. Perf 10×12 or 12×10	90·00	12·00
		c. Perf 11×12	5·50	40
		cs. Optd "SPECIMEN"	22·00	
		d. Perf 12	5·50	1·00
		e. Imperf (pair)		
272		½d. slate, P 11×12 (1897)	4·75	40
		a. Perf 12×11½	4·75	55
		b. Perf 12	4·75	40
		c. Imperf three sides (left stamp of horiz pair). Perf 12×11½	£1800	
273		½d. bluish green, P 11×12 (1.99)	8·00	40
		a. Perf 12×11½	2·00	80
		b. Perf 12	8·00	1·50

The perforations 11×12, 12×11½, 12, are from comb machines. The die for Type **58** was constructed from an electro taken from the die of the De La Rue 1d., Type **26**, with "ONE" replaced by "HALF" and two "½" plugs added to the bottom corners. These alterations proved to be less hard-wearing than the remainder of the die and defects were visible by the 1905 plate of No. 333. It seems likely that repairs were undertaken before printing from the next plate in late 1907 which produced stamps as Type II.

59

1894–1904. Optd "POSTAGE" in blue. W **59** (sideways).

274	**42**	10s. mauve and claret, P 10	£600	£160
275		10s. violet and claret, P 12	£325	50·00
		a. Perf 11	£500	90·00
		b. Perf 12×11	£350	60·00
276		10s. violet and aniline crimson, P 12×11	£325	55·00
		a. Chalk-surfaced paper (1903)	£375	60·00
		b. Perf 12	£425	85·00
277		10s. violet and rosine (*chalk-surfaced paper*), P 12 (1904)	£375	85·00
		a. Perf 11	£425	90·00
		b. Perf 12×11	£375	55·00
278		10s. violet and claret (*chalk-surfaced paper*), P 12×11 (1904)	£475	95·00
279		£1 violet and claret, P 12×11		

60

61

(Des C. Turner. Litho Govt Printing Office, Sydney)

1897 (22–28 June). Diamond Jubilee and Hospital Charity. T **60/1**. W **40**. P 12×11 (1d.) or 11 (2½d.).

280	**60**	1d. (1s.) green and brown (22.6)	50·00	50·00
281	**61**	2½d. (2s.6d.) gold, carmine and blue (28.6)	£250	£225
280s/1s Optd "Specimen" *Set of 2*			£300	

These stamps, sold at 1s. and 2s.6d. respectively, paid postage of 1d. and 2½d. only, the difference being given to a Consumptives' Home.

62 **63** **64**

Dies of the 1d.

Die I Die II

1d. Die I. The first pearl on the crown on the left side is merged into the arch, the shading under the fleur-de-lis is indistinct, the "S" of "WALES" is open.

Die II. The first pearl is circular, the vertical shading under the fleur-de-lis clear, the "S" of "WALES" not so open.

Dies of the 2½d.

Die I Die II

2½d. Die I. There are 12 radiating lines in the star on the Queen's breast.

Die II. There are 16 radiating lines in the star and the eye is nearly full of colour.

(Des D. Souter (2d., 2½d.). Eng W. Amor)

1897 (22 June)–**99**. W **40** (sideways on 2½d.). P 12×11 (2½d.) or 11×12 (others).

288	**62**	1d. carmine (Die I)	5·00	1·00
		a. Perf 12×11½	5·00	1·00
		s. Optd "Specimen"	22·00	
289		1d. scarlet (Die I)	10·00	1·25
		a. Perf 12×11½	10·00	1·50
		b. Perf 12	10·00	1·75

		ba. Imperf horiz (vert pair)	£850	
290		1d. rose-carmine (Die II) (10.97)	5·00	50
		a. Perf 12×11½	4·00	50
		b. Perf 12	7·00	50
		c. Imperf (pair)	£750	†
		d. Imperf between (pair)	£1200	
291		1d. salmon-red (Die II) (P 12×11½)	7·50	1·25
		a. Perf 12	9·50	1·75
292	**63**	2d. deep dull blue	17·00	1·50
		a. Perf 12×11½	8·50	1·50
		b. Perf 12	17·00	1·50
		s. Optd "Specimen"	22·00	
293		2d. cobalt-blue	18·00	1·00
		a. Perf 12×11½	7·00	1·00
		b. Perf 12	15·00	1·00
294		2d. ultramarine (1.12.97)	15·00	50
		a. Perf 12×11½	4·25	50
		b. Perf 12	4·25	50
		s. Optd "Specimen"	23·00	
295	**64**	2½d. purple (Die I)	28·00	2·50
		a. Perf 11½×12	29·00	2·50
		b. Perf 11	29·00	3·75
		s. Optd "Specimen"	22·00	
296		2½d. deep violet (Die II) (11.97)	38·00	2·25
		a. Perf 11½×12	29·00	2·25
		b. Perf 12	30·00	2·25
297		2½d. Prussian blue (17.1.99)	26·00	3·25
		a. Perf 11½×12	7·00	3·50
		b. Perf 12	7·00	4·50

The perforations 11×12, 12×11½ and 12 are from comb machines, the perforation 11 is from a single-line machine.

Nos. 288/96 were originally issued in celebration of Queen Victoria's Diamond Jubilee.

1897–99. Reissue of T **24**. W **25**. P 11.

297c		5s. reddish purple (*shades*)	48·00	13·00
		ca. Imperf between (horiz pair)	£9500	
		d. Perf 12	70·00	42·00
		e. Perf 11×12 or 11×11	50·00	19·00

1898–99. W **40**. P 11×12.

297f	**48**	6d. emerald-green	32·00	30·00
		fa. Perf 12×11½	35·00	19·00
		fb. Perf 12	27·00	19·00
		fs. Optd "Specimen"	24·00	
297g		6d. orange-yellow (1899)	35·00	11·00
		ga. Perf 12×11½	17·00	10·00
		gb. Perf 12	35·00	10·00
		gc. Yellow, P 12×11½	17·00	5·50

1899 (Oct). Chalk-surfaced paper. W **40** (sideways on 2½d.). P 12×11½ or 11½×12 (2½d.), comb.

298	**58**	½d. blue-green (Type I)	3·75	1·00
		a. Imperf (pair)	£250	£350
299	**62**	1d. carmine (Die II)	6·00	1·00
		a. Imperf horiz (vert pair)	£1000	
300		1d. scarlet (Die II)	6·00	1·00
		a. Imperf three sides (block of four)	£1200	
		b. Perf 11	†	£1200
		c. Mixed perfs 12×11½ and 11		
301		1d. salmon-red (Die II)	22·00	1·75
		a. Imperf (pair)	£275	£350
		b. Mixed perfs 12×11½ and 11		
302	**63**	2d. cobalt-blue	5·50	1·00
		a. Imperf (pair)	£300	
		b. Imperf horiz (vert pair)	£1800	
303	**64**	2½d. Prussian blue (Die II)	9·00	1·00
		a. Imperf (pair)	£350	
303b	**47**	4d. red-brown	32·00	16·00
		c. Imperf (pair)	£600	
304		4d. orange-brown	16·00	7·50
305	**48**	6d. deep orange	48·00	4·75
		a. Imperf (pair)	£600	
306		6d. orange-yellow	15·00	9·00
307		6d. emerald-green	85·00	25·00
		a. Imperf (pair)	£600	
308	**49**	8d. magenta	42·00	5·50
309	**34**	9d. on 10d. dull brown	11·00	21·00
		a. Surcharge double	£275	£600
		b. Albino surcharge	£275	
310		10d. violet	25·00	27·00
311	**50**	1s. maroon	25·00	3·50
312		1s. purple-brown	25·00	4·25
		a. Imperf (pair)	£700	

65 The spacing between the Crown and "NSW" is 1 mm in T **65** as against 2 mm in T **40**

66 Superb Lyrebird

67

1902–03. Chalk-surfaced paper. W **65** (sideways on 2½d.). P 12×11½ or 11½×12 (2½d.), comb.

313	**58**	½d. blue-green (Type I)	4·75	40
		a. Perf 12×11	4·75	40
		b. Mixed perfs 12×11½ and 11	£650	
314	**62**	1d. carmine (Die II)	2·75	20
		a. Perf 11	†	£1100
315	**63**	2d. cobalt-blue	7·00	1·50
		a. Imperf (pair)	£400	
		b. Perf 11	—	—
		c. Mixed perfs 12×11½ and 11		
316	**64**	2½d. dark blue (Die II)	14·00	1·00
317	**47**	4d. orange-brown	55·00	13·00
318	**48**	6d. yellow-orange	20·00	8·50
319		6d. orange	29·00	3·25
320		6d. orange-buff	50·00	3·75
321	**49**	8d. magenta	22·00	8·50
322	**34**	9d. on 10d. brownish orange	10·00	5·00
323		10d. violet	25·00	25·00
324	**50**	1s. maroon	70·00	2·75

325		1s. purple-brown	70·00	2·75
326	**66**	2s.6d. green (1903)	45·00	23·00
		s. Optd "SPECIMEN"	75·00	

1903–08. W **65**.

327	**16**	3d. yellow-green, P 11	14·00	1·75
		a. Perf 12	14·00	1·75
		ba. Imperf between (horiz pair)		
		c. Perf 11×12 or 12×11	10·00	1·00
328		3d. dull green, P 12	50·00	5·00
		a. Perf 11×12 or 12×11	24·00	3·75
		b. Perf 11	24·00	3·75
329	**11**	5d. dark blue-green, P 11×12 or 12×11	10·00	1·50
		a. Wmk sideways	35·00	7·00
		b. Perf 11	28·00	1·50
		ba. Wmk sideways	—	65·00
		c. Perf 12	50·00	6·50
		ca. Wmk sideways	£120	65·00
		d. Imperf (pair)	£450	

Stamps from this series without watermark are from the edge of the sheet.

(Typo Victoria Govt Printer, Melbourne)

1903 (18 July). Wmk double-lined V over Crown. W w **10**.

330	**67**	9d. brown and ultramarine, P 12¼×12½, comb	17·00	3·25
		s. Optd "SPECIMEN."	48·00	
331		9d. brown and deep blue, P 12¼×12½, *comb*	17·00	3·25
332		9d. brown and blue, P 11	£4500	£1600

Type II. Broad "H" in "HALF" **68**

1905 (1 Oct)–**10.** Chalk-surfaced paper. W **68** (sideways on 2½d.). P 12×11½ or 11½×12 (2½d.) comb, unless otherwise stated.

333	**58**	½d. blue-green (Type I)	4·50	1·00
		a. Perf 11½×11	17·00	2·50
		b. Type II (1908)	2·75	1·25
		ba. Type I (substituted cliché) in pair with Die II	90·00	75·00
		bb. Perf 11½×11	3·25	1·25
		bc. Mixed perfs 12×11½ and 11		
334	**62**	1d. rose-carmine (Die II)	2·75	10
		a. Double impression	£550	£650
		b. Perf 11½×11	10·00	75
335	**63**	2d. deep ultramarine	2·25	40
		b. Perf 11½×11	2·75	40
		c. Perf 11		
336		2d. milky blue (1910)	4·75	20
		a. Perf 11	60·00	80·00
		b. Perf 11½×11	4·75	30
337	**64**	2½d. Prussian blue (Die II)	4·00	2·50
338	**47**	4d. orange-brown	10·00	4·00
339		4d. red-brown	13·00	5·00
340	**48**	6d. dull yellow	19·00	4·50
		a. Perf 11½×11	23·00	6·50
341		6d. orange-yellow	19·00	2·50
		a. Perf 11½×11	28·00	7·50
342		6d. deep orange	16·00	2·50
		a. Perf 11	£350	
343		6d. orange-buff	23·00	2·75
		a. Perf 11½×11	32·00	6·00
344	**49**	8d. magenta	26·00	8·00
345		8d. lilac-rose	55·00	8·00
346	**34**	10d. violet	18·00	9·00
		a. Perf 11½×11	13·00	5·50
		b. Perf 11	13·00	6·50
347	**50**	1s. maroon	27·00	1·75
348		1s. purple-brown (1908)	42·00	2·75
349	**66**	2s.6d. blue-green	85·00	45·00
		a. Perf 11½×11	75·00	19·00
		b. Perf 11	45·00	24·00

No. 333ba occurred when a block of four units from the Type II plate (R. 3/5-4/6) were replaced by new clichés, one of which (right pane, R. 4/6) was Type I.

69

1905 (Dec). W **69**. Chalk-surfaced paper. P 11.

350	**52**	20s. cobalt-blue	£375	80·00
		a. Perf 12	£400	85·00
		b. Perf 11×12 or 12×11	£375	70·00

(Typo Victoria Govt Printer, Melbourne)

1905 (Dec). Wmk double-lined "A" and Crown, W w **11**. P 12×12½ comb.

351	**67**	9d. brown and ultramarine	26·00	1·75
		a. Perf 11	£120	70·00
		b. Mixed perfs 12×12½ and 11	£1600	
352		9d. yellow-brown and ultramarine	17·00	1·75
		a. Perf 11	£120	70·00

1907 (July–Dec). W w **11** (sideways on 2½d.). P 12×11½ or 11½×12 (2½d.), comb, unless otherwise stated.

353	**58**	½d. blue-green (Type I)	4·75	6·50
354	**62**	1d. dull rose (Die II)	26·00	4·50

No.	Type	Description	Mint	Used
355	63	2d. cobalt-blue	7·50	4·50
		a. Wmk sideways	—	£325
356	64	2½d. Prussian blue (Die II)	70·00	£130
357	47	4d. orange-brown	30·00	30·00
358	48	6d. orange-buff	50·00	48·00
359	49	6d. dull yellow	50·00	48·00
360	49	8d. magenta	32·00	50·00
361	34	10d. violet, P 11 (12.07)	35·00	60·00
362	50	1s. purple-brown	75·00	12·00
		a. Perf 11	†	£1700
363	66	2s.6d. blue-green	£110	£110

Stamps from this series without watermark are from the edge of the sheet.

STAMP BOOKLETS

There are very few surviving examples of Nos. SB1/4. Listings are provided for those believed to have been issued with prices quoted for those known to still exist.

B **1** *(Illustration reduced. Actual size 150×175 mm)*

1904 (May)–**09**. Black on red cover as Type B **1** and picture of one of six different State G.P.O's on back. Stapled.
SB1 £1 booklet containing 240×1d. in four blocks of 30 and two blocks of 60
 a. Red on pink cover (1909)
 b. Blue on pink cover

1904 (May). Black on grey cover as No. SB1. Stapled.
SB2 £1 booklet containing 120×2d. in four blocks of 30

B **2** *(Illustration reduced. Actual size 85×57 mm)*

1910 (May). Black on cream. cover 80-85×55-57 mm, as Type B **2**.
SB3 2s. booklet containing 11×½d. (No. 333), either in block of 6 plus block of 5 or block of 11, and 18×1d. (No. 334), either in three blocks of 6 or block of 6 plus block of 12 ... £7000
Unsold stock of No. SB3 was uprated with one additional ½d. in May 1911.

1911 (Aug). Red on pink cover as No. SB3. Stapled.
SB4 2s. booklet containing 12×½d. (No. 333), either in two blocks of 6 or block of 12, and 18 1d. (No. 334) either in three blocks of 6 or one block of 6 plus block of 12 ... £6000

OFFICIAL STAMPS

O S O S O S
(O **1**) (O **2**) (O **3**)

The space between the letters is normally 7 mm as illustrated, except on the 5d. and 8d. (11–11½ mm), 5s. (12 mm) and 20s. (14 mm). Later printings of the 3d., W **40**, are 5½ mm, and these are listed. A wide (8.5 mm) variety exists at R. 4/4 on all values other than the 3d., 5d., 8d., 5s., 10s. and 20s.
Varieties of Type O **1** exist with "O" sideways.

*Nos. O1/35 overprinted with Type O **1***

1879. Wmk double-lined "6". P 13.

No.	Type	Description	Mint	Used
O1	16	3d. dull green	—	£600

1879 (Oct)–**85**. W **36**. P 13.

No.	Type	Description	Mint	Used
O2	26	1d. salmon	50·00	2·75
		a. Perf 10 (5.81)	£180	38·00
		b. Perf 13×10 (1881)	60·00	4·50
O3	28	2d. blue	50·00	2·50
		a. Perf 10 (7.81)	£225	35·00
		b. Perf 10×13 (1881)	75·00	25·00
		ba. Perf 13×10	60·00	3·50
		d. Perf 11×12 (11.84?)	—	£225
O4	16	3d. dull green (R.) (12.79)	£950	£350
O5		3d. dull green (3.80)	£325	75·00
		a. Perf 10 (1881)	£180	65·00
		b. Yellow-green. Perf 10 (10.81)	£170	30·00
		ba. Perf 13×10 (1881)	£160	30·00
		bb. Perf 12 (4.85)	£225	55·00
		be. Perf 10×12 or 12×10 (4.85)	£225	55·00
O6	32	4d. red-brown	£300	9·00
		a. Perf 10 (1881)	—	£225
		b. Perf 10×13 (1881)	£325	90·00
		ba. Perf 13×10 (1881)	£250	13·00
O7	11	5d. green, P 10 (8.84)	25·00	32·00
O8	37	6d. pale lilac	£300	7·00
		a. Perf 10 (1881)	£425	42·00
		b. Perf 13×10 (1881)	£250	42·00
O9	13	8d. yellow (R.) (12.79)	—	£550
		a. Perf 10 (1880)	—	50·00
O10		8d. yellow (1880)	£500	90·00
O11	34	9d. on 10d. brown, P 10 (30.5.80)	£1000	£900
		s. Optd "Specimen"	65·00	
O12	38	1s. black (R.)	£475	23·00
		a. Perf 10 (1881)	—	38·00
		b. Perf 10×13 (1881)	—	50·00
		ba. Perf 13×10	—	12·00

Other stamps are known with red overprint but their status is in doubt.

1880–88. W **25**.
(a) P 13

No.	Type	Description	Mint	Used
O13	24	5s. deep purple (15.2.80)	£850	£100
		a. Royal purple	—	£300
		b. Deep rose-lilac	£850	£100

(b) P 10

O14	24	5s. deep purple (9.82)	£850	£170
		a. Opt double	£4250	£1700
		b. Rose-lilac (1883)	£600	£120
		ba. Opt double, one albino		

(c) P 10×12

O15	24	5s. purple (10.86)		

(d) P 12×10

O16	24	5s. reddish purple (1886)	£750	£120

(e) P 12

O17	24	5s. purple	†	£650

(f) P 11

O18	24	5s. rose-lilac (1888)	£475	95·00

1880 (31 May). W **35**. P 13.

O18a	34	10d. lilac	£425	£120
		ab. Perf 10 and 11, compound	£425	£200
		ac. Perf 10	£425	
		aca. Opt double, one albino	£475	
		as. Optd "Specimen"	70·00	

1882–85. W **40**. P 10.

No.	Type	Description	Mint	Used
O19	26	1d. salmon	75·00	4·75
		a. Perf 13×10	—	£130
O20		1d. orange *to* scarlet	27·00	2·00
		a. Perf 10×13	—	£130
		b. Perf 11×12, comb (1.84)	13·00	1·40
		c. Perf 10×12 or 12×10 (4.85)	—	£110
		d. Perf 12×11 (12.85)		
O21	28	2d. blue	40·00	1·00
		a. Perf 10×13 or 13×10	£200	75·00
		c. Perf 11×12, comb (1.84)	9·00	1·00
		ca. Opt double	£950	£400
		e. Perf 12×11 (12.85)		
O22	16	3d. yellow-green (7 mm)	14·00	5·00
		aa. Opt double, one albino	£160	
		a. Wmk sideways	£225	£110
		b. Perf 12 (4.85)	£120	80·00
		ba. Opt double, one albino	£250	
		c. Perf 10×12 (4.85)	—	7·50
		ca. Opt double	†	£650
		d. Perf 12×11		
O23		3d. bluish green (7 mm)	30·00	8·50
		a. Perf 12 (4.85)	£120	80·00
		b. Perf 12×10 (4.85)		
		c. Perf 10×11 (12.85)		
O24		3d. yellow-green (5½ mm)	15·00	5·50
		a. Wmk sideways	40·00	38·00
		as. Optd "Specimen"	38·00	
		b. Perf 10×12 or 12×10 (4.85)	28·00	5·50
		c. Perf 10×11 or 11×10 (12.85)	—	7·00
O25		3d. bluish green (5½ mm)	12·00	11·00
		a. Wmk sideways		
		b. Perf 10×12 or 12×10 (4.85)	17·00	12·00
		c. Perf 10×11 or 11×10 (12.85)	5·00	4·25
O26	32	4d. red-brown	70·00	5·50
		a. Perf 11×12, comb (1.84)	18·00	4·00
		b. Perf 10×12 (4.85)	—	70·00
O27		4d. dark brown	40·00	4·00
		a. Perf 11×12, comb (1.84)	19·00	4·00
		b. Perf 12 (4.85)	£250	£150
		c. Perf 10×12 (4.85)	£250	90·00
O28	11	5d. dull green	24·00	26·00
		a. Perf 12×10 (4.85)		
O29		5d. blue-green	25·00	35·00
		a. Perf 12 (4.85)	£100	£120
		as. Optd "Specimen"	38·00	
		b. Perf 10×11	15·00	20·00
		c. Perf 11	†	£150
O30	37	6d. pale lilac	22·00	5·50
		a. Perf 11 (12.85)	55·00	8·00
O31		6d. mauve	22·00	7·00
		a. Perf 12 (4.85)	—	45·00
		b. Perf 10×12 or 12×10 (4.85)	22·00	6·50
		c. Perf 11×10 (12.85)	22·00	7·00
		e. Perf 11×12		
		ea. Perf 12×11 (12.85)	85·00	19·00
O32	13	8d. yellow	26·00	11·00
		aa. Opt double	—	†
		a. Perf 12 (4.85)	£150	45·00
		b. Perf 10×12 or 12×10 (4.85)	26·00	11·00
		ba. Opt double	†	
		d. Perf 11 (12.85)	26·00	28·00
		da. Opt double	£850	
		db. Opt treble	†	£1200
O33	38	1s. black (R.)	55·00	15·00
		a. Perf 11	—	60·00
		b. Perf 11×12, comb (1.84)	29·00	8·00
		ba. Opt double	—	£500

1886–87. W **41**. P 10.

No.	Type	Description	Mint	Used
O34	26	1d. scarlet	£100	8·00
O35	28	2d. deep blue	†	£600
		a. Perf 11×12, comb	†	£600

1887–90. Nos. 241/2 optd in black.
*(a) With Type O **1***

O36	42	10s. mauve and claret, P 12 (1890)	—	£3750

*(b) With Type O **2** (30 April 1889)*

O37	42	10s. mauve and claret P 12	£6000	£1400
		as. Optd "Specimen"	£110	
		b. Perf 10	£7500	£3000

*(c) With Type O **3** (7 Jan 1887)*

O38	42	£1 mauve and claret, P 12×10	£40000	£19000

Only nine examples of No. O38 are recorded, three of which are mint. One of the used stamps, in the Royal Collection, shows overprint Type O **3** double.

1888 (17 July)–**90**. Optd as Type O **1**.
*(a) W **40**. P 11×12*

No.	Type	Description	Mint	Used
O39	45	1d. lilac	6·00	75
		b. Mauve	3·50	75
		ba. Perf 12	3·75	75
O40	46	2d. Prussian blue (15.10.88)	4·50	40
		aa. Opt double, one albino	—	†
		ab. Opt double	—	†
		a. Perf 12	9·00	2·50
O41	47	4d. purple-brown (10.10.89)	11·00	4·25
		a. Perf 12	18·00	6·00
		b. Perf 11		
		c. Red-brown	13·00	3·75
		ca. Perf 12	†	£650
		cb. Perf 12	20·00	6·00
O42	48	6d. carmine (16.1.89)	9·00	10·00
		a. Perf 12	20·00	10·00
		ab. Opt double	—	†
O43	49	8d. lilac-rose (1890)	25·00	12·00
		a. Perf 12	55·00	17·00
O44	50	1s. maroon (9.1.90)	42·00	4·00
		a. Perf 12	42·00	4·50
		b. Purple-brown	40·00	4·75
		ba. Opt double		
		bb. Perf 12	42·00	6·50
O39s/44s Optd "Specimen" Set of 6			£250	

*(b) W **41**. P 11×12 (1889)*

O45	45	1d. mauve		
O46	46	2d. blue		

*(c) W **25**. P 10*

O47	51	5s. deep purple (R.) (9.1.90)	£2000	£800
O48	52	20s. cobalt-blue (10.3.90)	£19000	£1100

1890 (15 Feb)–**91**. Optd as Type O **1**. W **53** (5s.) or **54** (20s.). P 10.

O49	51	5s. lilac	£650	£170
		a. Mauve	£400	£100
		b. Dull lilac, P 12	£800	£170
O50	52	20s. cobalt-blue (3.91)	£20000	£1100
O49s/50s Optd "SPECIMEN" Set of 2			£250	

The used prices quoted for Nos. O48 and O50 are for cancelled-to-order examples.

1891 (Jan). Optd as Type O **1**. W **40**.
(a) On No. 265. P 11×12

O54	55	2½d. ultramarine	13·00	10·00

(b) On Nos. 266/8

O55	26	½d. on 1d. grey, P 11×12	70·00	80·00
		a. Opt double	£1500	†
O56	37	7½d. on 6d. brown, P 10	50·00	70·00
O57	38	12½d. on 1s. red, P 11×12	70·00	£110
O54s/7s Optd "Specimen" Set of 4			£150	

1892 (May). No. 271 optd as Type O **1**. P 10.

O58	58	½d. grey	14·00	19·00
		a. Perf 11×12	5·50	16·00
		as. Optd "SPECIMEN"	32·00	
		b. Perf 12	11·00	11·00
		c. Perf 12×11½	32·00	17·00

Official stamps were withdrawn from the government departments on 31 December 1894.

POSTAGE DUE STAMPS

D **1**

(Dies eng by A. Collingridge. Typo Govt Printing Office, Sydney)

1891 (1 Jan)–**97**. W **40**. P 10.

No.	Type	Description	Mint	Used
D1	D **1**	½d. green (21.1.92)	12·00	7·00
D2		1d. green	32·00	4·00
		a. Imperf vert (horiz pair)	†	£6000
		b. Perf 12 (1896)	22·00	3·50
		c. Perf 12	80·00	40·00
		d. Perf 12×10 (1892)	80·00	40·00
		e. Perf 10×11 (1894)	35·00	8·00
		f. Perf 11×12 or 12×11	24·00	3·50
D3		2d. green	24·00	4·00
		a. Perf 11	24·00	3·50
		b. Perf 12 (1897)	80·00	40·00
		c. Perf 12×10 (1894)	80·00	40·00
		d. Perf 10×11 (1894)	32·00	11·00
		e. Perf 11×12 or 12×11	24·00	4·00
		f. Wmk sideways	70·00	20·00
D4		3d. green	65·00	13·00
		a. Perf 10×11 (1893)	65·00	13·00
D5		4d. green	60·00	3·75
		a. Perf 11		
		b. Perf 10×11 (1893)	50·00	3·75
		c. Perf 12×10	†	£1000
D6		6d. green	60·00	15·00
D7		8d. green	£120	27·00

D8		5s. green	£275	50·00
		a. Perf 11	£700	£180
		b. Perf 11×12	—	£325
D9		10s. green	£750	70·00
		a. Perf 12×10	£550	
D10		20s. green	£850	£100
		a. Perf 12	£1400	
		a. Perf 12×10	£650	
D1s/10s Optd "SPECIMEN" *Set of 10* (incl D3fs)			£225	

Used prices for 10s. and 20s. are for cancelled-to-order stamps. Postally used examples are very rare.

1900. Chalk-surfaced paper. W **40**. P 11.

D12	D **1**	1d. emerald-green	26·00	4·75
		a. Perf 12	50·00	13·00
		b. Perf 11×12 or 12×11	28·00	4·25
D13		2d. emerald-green	32·00	6·50
		a. Perf 12	—	£100
		b. Perf 11×12 or 12×11	25·00	6·50
D14		3d. emerald-green, P 11×12 or 12×11	85·00	26·00
D15		4d. emerald-green (7.00)	55·00	13·00

TELEGRAPH STAMPS

T **1**

(Des of vignette H. T. Glover. Vignette litho, frame typo Govt Printer)

1871 (1 Feb). W **41** (sideways). Bluish paper. P 13.

T1	1d. black and brownish red	£180	
T2	2d. black and blue	£275	
T3	6d. black and Indian red	£275	
T4	1s. black and bright blue	£400	
T5	2s. black and brown	£750	
T6	4s. black and mauve	£950	
T7	6s. black and carmine	£1400	
T8	8s. black and lilac	£1700	
	a. Perf 10	£1500	

New South Wales became part of the Commonwealth of Australia on 1 January 1901

QUEENSLAND

The area which later became Queensland was previously part of New South Wales known as the Moreton Bay District. The first post office, at Brisbane, was opened in 1834 and the use of New South Wales stamps from the District became compulsory from 1 May 1854.

Queensland was proclaimed a separate colony on 10 December 1859, but continued to use New South Wales issues until 1 November 1860.

Post Offices opened in the Moreton Bay District before 10 December 1859, and using New South Wales stamps, were

Office	Opened	Numeral Cancellation
Brisbane	1834	95
Burnett's Inn/Goode's Inn/Nanango	1850	108
Callandoon	1850	74
Condamine	1856	151
Dalby	1854	133
Drayton	1846	85
Gayndah	1850	86
Gladstone	1854	131
Goode's Inn	1858	108
Ipswich	1846	87
Maryborough	1849	96
Rockhampton	1858	201
Surat	1852	110
Taroom	1856	152
Toowoomba	1858	214
Warwick	1848	81

PRICES FOR STAMPS ON COVER	
Nos. 1/3	*from* × 2
Nos. 4/56	*from* × 3
Nos. 57/8	—
Nos. 59/73	*from* × 4
Nos. 74/82	*from* × 2
Nos. 83/109	*from* × 3
Nos. 110/13	*from* × 2
Nos. 116/17	*from* × 3
Nos. 118/27	—
Nos. 128/50	*from* × 4
Nos. 151/65	—
Nos. 166/78	*from* × 10
Nos. 179/83	*from* × 4
Nos. 184/206	*from* × 15
No. 207	—
Nos. 208/28	*from* × 15
No. 229	*from* × 100
No. 230	—
Nos. 231/54	*from* × 15
Nos. 256/62c	*from* × 10
Nos. 264a/b	*from* × 2
Nos. 265/6	*from* × 20
Nos. 270/4	—
Nos. 281/5	*from* × 10
Nos. 286/308	*from* × 12
Nos. 309/13	—
Nos. F1/37	—

PERKINS BACON "CANCELLED". For notes on these handstamps, showing "CANCELLED" between horizontal bars forming an oval, see Catalogue Introduction.

1	**2** Large Star	**3** Small Star

(Dies eng W. Humphrys. Recess P.B.)

1860. W **2**.

		(a) Imperf		
1	1	1d. carmine-rose	£6500	£800
2		2d. blue	£16000	£1800
3		6d. green	£10000	£800
		(b) Clean-cut perf 14–16		
4	1	1d. carmine-rose	£2750	£300
5		2d. blue	£1400	£110
		a. Imperf between (horiz pair)	†	—
6		6d. green (15.11)	£1400	70·00

 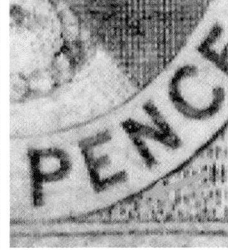

3d. re-entry   **3d.** retouch (R.2/8)

The 3d. re-entry which occurs on one stamp in the second row, shows doubling of the left-hand arabesque and the retouch has redrawn spandrel dots under "EN" of "PENCE", a single dot in the centre of the circle under "E" and the bottom outer frame line closer to the spandrel's frame line.

1860–61. W **3**.

		(a) Clean-cut perf 14–16		
7	1	2d. blue	£1000	£110
		a. Imperf between (horiz pair)	†	£11000
8		3d. brown (15.4.61)	£800	75·00
		a. Re-entry	—	£275
		b. Retouch	—	£275
9		6d. green	£1400	75·00
10		1s. violet (15.11.60) (H/S "CANCELLED" in oval £10000)	£1500	£110
11		"REGISTERED" (6d.) olive-yellow (1.61) (H/S "CANCELLED" in oval £10000)	£1000	£100
		a. Imperf between (pair)	£13000	
		(b) Clean-cut perf 14 at Somerset House (7.61)		
12	1	1d. carmine-rose (H/S "CANCELLED" in oval £9500)	£400	60·00
13		2d. blue (H/S "CANCELLED" in oval £9500)	£900	65·00
		(c) Rough perf 14–16 (9.61)		
14	1	1d. carmine-rose	£100	50·00
15		2d. blue	£300	28·00
		a. Imperf between (horiz pair)	£10000	
16		3d. brown (H/S "CANCELLED" in oval £11000)	85·00	32·00
		a. Imperf vert (horiz pair)	£10000	
		b. Re-entry	£400	£140
		c. Retouch (R. 2/8)	—	£140
17		6d. deep green (H/S "CANCELLED" in oval £10000)	£550	30·00
18		6d. yellow-green	£650	30·00
19		1s. violet	£1100	90·00
20		"REGISTERED" (6d.) orange-yellow	£110	40·00

The perforation of No. 8 is that known as "intermediate between clean-cut and rough", No. 20 can also be found with a similar perforation.

Line through design

(Printed and perforated by Thomas Ham, Brisbane)

1862–67. Thick toned paper. No wmk.

		(a) P 13 rough perforations (1862–63)		
21	1	1d. Indian red (16.12.62)	£500	75·00
22		1d. orange-vermilion (2.63)	£110	17·00
		a. Imperf (pair)	—	£2750
23		2d. pale blue (16.12.62)	£140	27·00
24		2d. blue	85·00	9·00
		a. Imperf (pair)	—	£2500
		b. Imperf between (horiz pair)	†	£15000
		c. Imperf between (vert pair)	£5000	
25		3d. brown	£120	45·00
		a. Re-entry	—	£140
		b. Retouch (R. 2/8)	—	£140
26		6d. apple green (17.4.63)	£180	15·00
		a. Line through design at right	—	£130
		b. Line through design at left	—	£130
27		6d. yellow-green	£170	12·00
		a. Imperf between (horiz pair)	†	£16000
		b. Line through design at right	—	£110
		c. Line through design at left	—	£110

28		6d. pale bluish green	£275	45·00
		a. Imperf (pair)	—	£2750
		b. Line through design at right	—	£225
		c. Line through design at left	—	£225
29		1s. grey (14.7.63)	£375	24·00
		a. Imperf between (horiz pair)	†	£17000
		b. Imperf between (vert pair)	†	
		s. Handstamped "SPECIMEN"	50·00	

The top or bottom row of perforations was sometimes omitted from the sheet, resulting in stamps perforated on three sides only.

Prior to the plates being printed from in Brisbane, damage occurred to the 6d. plate in the form of a scratch across two adjoining stamps. The position of the pair in the plate is not yet recorded. One joined pair is known.

This flaw was not corrected until around 1869 when, after plate cleaning, only faint traces remain. These are hard to see.

The Royal Philatelic Collection contains an example of No. 22 imperf between (horizontal pair), used.

1862–67. P 12½×13 rough (1863–67)

30	**1**	1d. orange-vermilion	£120	32·00
31		2d. blue	£110	20·00
32		3d. brown	£130	26·00
		a. Re-entry	—	£130
		b. Retouch (R. 2/8)	—	£130
33		6d. apple green	£225	50·00
		a. Line through design at right	—	£300
		b. Line through design at left	—	£300
34		6d. yellow-green	£225	50·00
		a. Line through design at right	—	£300
		b. Line through design at left	—	£300
35		6d. pale bluish green		
		a. Line through design at right		
		b. Line through design at left		
36		1s. grey	£600	45·00
		a. Imperf between (horiz pair)		

This paper was used again for a very limited printing in 1867 which can be properly regarded as the First Government Printing. The perforations were now clean-cut. The designs and the background to the head are very well defined, the plates having been cleaned when transferred to the Government Printing Office.

		(c) P 13 Clean-cut (1867)		
37		1d. orange-vermilion	£120	28·00
38		2d. blue	90·00	11·00
40		6d. apple green	£225	19·00
41		6d. yellow-green	£225	23·00
42		6d. deep green		

Previously listed and then removed, the significance of this issue has been reassessed and it is now re-listed under this paper.

Copies of the 3d. and 1s. have been identified with these characteristics but there are no records of them being printed at this time.

1864–65. W **3**.

		(a) P 13		
44	**1**	1d. orange-vermilion (1.65)	£120	60·00
		a. Imperf between (horiz pair)	£5500	
45		2d. pale blue (1.65)	£120	17·00
46		2d. deep blue	£120	17·00
		a. Imperf between (vert pair)	£8500	
		b. Imperf between (horiz pair)	†	£13000
		c. Bisected (1d.) (on cover)	†	£4000
47		6d. yellow-green (1.65)	£225	22·00
		a. Line through design at right	—	£160
		b. Line through design at left	—	£160
48		6d. deep green	£275	22·00
		a. Line through design at right	—	£160
		b. Line through design at left	—	£160
49		"REGISTERED" (6d.) orge-yell (21.6.64)	£170	35·00
		b. Imperf		
		(b) P 12½×13		
50	**1**	1d. orange-vermilion	£160	80·00
50a		2d. deep blue	£275	80·00

The "REGISTERED" stamp was reprinted in 1895. See note below No. 82.

1866 (24 Jan). Wmk "QUEENSLAND/POSTAGE — POSTAGE/STAMPS — STAMPS" in three lines in script capitals with double wavy lines above and below the wmk and single wavy lines with projecting sprays between each line of words. There are ornaments ("fleurons") between "POSTAGE" "POSTAGE" and between "STAMPS" "STAMPS". Single stamps only show a portion of one or two letters of this wmk.

		(a) P 13		
51	**1**	1d. orange-vermilion	£200	45·00
52		2d. blue	£100	17·00
		(b) P 12½×13		
52a		1d. orange-vermilion	£275	75·00
52b		2d. blue	£275	75·00

First transfer

Double transfer

1866–67. Lithographed on thick paper. No wmk. P 13.

		(a) First Transfer (Sept 1866) "FOUR" in taller thin letters		
53		4d. reddish lilac (shades)	£450	30·00
		a. Re-entry	—	£130
		b. Double transfer	£5500	£2500

54		4d. grey-lilac (*shades*)	£450	30·00
	a.	Re-entry	—	£130
	b.	Double transfer	—	£2500

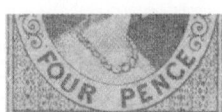

Second transfer

(b) Second Transfer (Feb 1867) "FOUR" in shorter letters

55		4d. lilac (*shades*)	£450	22·00
	a.	Retouch (R. 2/8)	—	£120
	b.	"FOUR" missing	—	£550
56		4d. grey-lilac (*shades*)	£450	22·00
	a.	Retouch (R. 2/8)	—	£120
	b.	"FOUR" missing	—	£600
	s.	Handstamped "SPECIMEN"	55·00	
57		5s. bright rose	£1300	£180
58		5s. pale rose	£1200	£140
	a.	Imperf between (vert pair)	†	£8500
	s.	Handstamped "SPECIMEN"	70·00	

The 4d. was lithographed from two separate transfers from the 3d. plate and the 5s. was taken from the 1s. plate.

The alterations in values were made by hand on the stones and there are minor varieties in the shape and position of the letters.

4

2d. Pl II. Dot by "U"   **2d.** Pl II. Dots near arabesque

1868–74. Wmk small truncated Star, W **4** on each stamp, and the word "QUEENSLAND" in single-lined Roman capitals four times in each sheet. P 13.

59	1	1d. orange-vermilion (18.1.71)	95·00	7·50
60		2d. pale blue (3.4.68) (Pl I)	80·00	5·00
61		2d. blue (18.1.71) (Pl I)	75·00	3·50
62		2d. bright blue (Pl I)	85·00	2·75
63		2d. greenish blue (Pl I)	£150	2·75
64		2d. dark blue (Pl I)	85·00	2·75
65		3d. olive-green (27.2.71)	£200	7·00
	a.	Re-entry	—	65·00
	b.	Retouch (R. 2/8)	—	65·00
66		3d. greenish grey	£225	6·50
	a.	Re-entry	—	60·00
	b.	Retouch (R. 2/8)	—	60·00
67		3d. brown	£120	5·50
	a.	Re-entry	—	55·00
	b.	Retouch (R. 2/8)	—	55·00
68		6d. yellow-green (10.11.71)	£250	7·50
69		6d. green	£225	10·00
70		6d. deep green	£300	17·00
71		1s. greenish grey (13.11.72)	£800	50·00
72		1s. brownish grey	£800	50·00
73		1s. mauve (19.2.74)	£400	23·00
59s/73s H/S "SPECIMEN" *Set of 5*			£250	

(b) P 12 (about Feb 1874)

74	1	1d. orange-vermilion	£500	29·00
75		2d. blue (Pl II)	£950	75·00
76		3d. greenish grey	—	£225
	a.	Re-entry		
	b.	Retouch (R. 2/8)		
77		3d. brown	£750	£225
	a.	Re-entry		
	b.	Retouch (R. 2/8)		
78		6d. green	£1800	50·00
79		1s. mauve	£850	55·00

(c) P 13×12

80	1	1d. orange-vermilion	—	£200
81		2d. blue (Pl II)	£1600	45·00
82		3d. greenish grey	—	£350

A second plate of the 2d. denomination was sent by Perkins Bacon to the Colony in 1872 and it was first printed from in August of that year. The new plate is helpful in separating many of the 2d. printings up to 1879.

Plate II of the 2d. may be identified by a smudged dot to the left of "U" in "QUEEN" and tiny dots near the lower curl of the right arabesque.

Reprints were made in 1895 of all five values on Wmk W **4**, and perforated 13; the colours are:—1d. orange and brownish orange, 2d. deep dull blue (Pl II), 3d. brown, 6d green, 1s. red-violet and dull violet. The "Registered" was also reprinted with these on the same paper, but perforated 12. One sheet of the 2d. reprint is known to have had the perforations missing between the fourth and fifth vertical rows.

5   6

 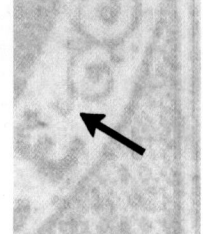

4d. First transfer   **4d.** Second transfer

The first transfer of the 4d. was taken from the 3d. plate, identified by the lack of the curl at the foot of the arabesque, the second was from Plate II of the 2d. On the first transfer the "P" of "POSTAGE" is to the right of the centre of the Queen's necklace, on the second transfer it is to the left of it.

(4d., litho. Other values recess)

1868–78. Wmk Crown and Q. W **5**.

(a) P 13 (1868–75)

83	1	1d. orange-vermilion (10.11.68)	£110	6·00
	a.	Imperf (pair)	£800	
84		1d. pale rose-red (4.11.74)	90·00	16·00
85		1d. deep rose-red	£160	16·00
86		2d. pale blue (20.11.68) (Pl I)	85·00	2·00
87		2d. deep blue (4.11.74) (Pl II)	80·00	4·50
88		3d. brown (11.6.75)	£130	14·00
	a.	Re-entry	—	85·00
	b.	Retouch (R. 2/8)	—	85·00
89		4d. yellow (*shades*) (1st transfer) (1.1.75)	£2250	£110
	s.	Handstamped "SPECIMEN"	£100	
90		6d. deep green (9.4.69)	£200	9·00
91		6d. yellow-green	£190	6·50
92		6d. pale apple-green (1.1.75)	£225	9·00
	a.	Imperf (pair)	£700	
93		1s. mauve	£400	65·00

(b) P 12 (1876–78)

94	1	1d. deep orange-vermilion	75·00	6·00
95		1d. pale orange-vermilion	85·00	6·00
96		1d. rose-red	85·00	11·00
97		1d. flesh	£120	13·00
98		2d. pale blue (Pl II)	£130	15·00
99		2d. bright blue (Pl II)	70·00	1·75
100		2d. deep blue (Pl II)	70·00	2·00
101		3d. brown	£120	9·50
	a.	Re-entry	—	70·00
	b.	Retouch (R. 2/8)	—	70·00
102		4d. yellow (*shades*) (1st transfer)	£1600	48·00
103		4d. buff-yellow (*shades*) (2nd transfer)	£1600	48·00
104		6d. deep green	£250	10·00
105		6d. green	£225	4·25
106		6d. yellow-green	£250	4·50
107		6d. apple-green	£275	7·00
108		1s. mauve	£100	9·00
109		1s. purple	£250	5·00
	a.	Imperf between (vert pair)	†	—

(c) P 13×12 or 12×13

110	1	1d. orange-vermilion	—	£150
110a		1d. rose-red	—	£180
111		2d. deep blue (Pl II)	£1400	£250
112		4d. yellow	—	£375
113		6d. deep green	—	£300

(d) P 12½×13 (1868)

114	1	1d. orange-vermilion	—	£350
115		2d. deep blue (Pl I)	—	£350
115a		3d. brown	—	£350
115b		6d. yellow-green	†	£1200

(e) P 12½ (1868)

| 115c | 1 | 2d. deep blue (Pl II) | † | £1000 |
| 115d | 1 | 2d. deep blue (Pl II) | † | £750 |

Reprints of the above were made in 1895 on thicker paper, Wmk W **6**, perf 12. The colours are:—1d. vermilion-red, 2d. deep dull blue and pale ultramarine, 3d. brown, 6d. dull yellow-green and 1s. lilac-grey.

The Royal Philatelic Collection contains an example of No. 95 imperf between (vert pair), used.

1879. No wmk. P 12.

| 116 | 1 | 6d. pale emerald-green | £400 | 27·00 |
| 117 | | 1s. mauve (*fiscal cancel* £5) | £225 | £100 |

No. 117 has a very indistinct lilac *burelé* band at back.
Nos. 116/17 can be found showing portions of a papermaker's watermark, either T. H. Saunders & Co or A. Pirie & Sons.

1880. Lithographed from transfers from the 1s. die. Wmk Crown and Q. W **6**. P 12.

118	1	2s. pale blue	£160	60·00
119		2s. blue (*fiscal cancel* £4)	£160	60·00
	a.	Imperf vert (horiz pair)	£8500	
120		2s. deep blue (*fiscal cancel* £4)	£190	60·00
121		2s.6d. dull scarlet	£325	80·00
122		2s.6d. bright scarlet (*fiscal cancel* £4)	£325	80·00
123		5s. pale yellow-ochre	£500	£120
124		5s. yellow-ochre (*fiscal cancel* £5)	£500	£120
125		10s. reddish brown	£900	£200
126		10s. bistre-brown	£900	£200
127		20s. rose (*fiscal cancel* £7)	£2000	£250

Of the 2s. and 20s. stamps there are five types of each, and of the other values ten types of each.
Beware of fiscally used copies that have been cleaned and provided with forged postmarks.

7

Die I   Die II

Dies I and II often occur in the same sheet.
Die I. The white horizontal inner line of the triangle in the upper right-hand corner merges into the outer white line of the oval above the "L".
Die II. The same line is short and does not touch the inner oval.

1879–81. Typo. P 12.

*(a) Wmk Crown and Q. W **5***

128	7	1d. reddish brown (Die I) (15.5.79)	£150	48·00
	a.	Die II	£225	48·00
	ab.	Imperf between (horiz pair)	†	£2250
	ac.	"QUEENSLAND"	£1700	£275
129		1d. orange-brown (Die I)	£200	48·00
130		2d. blue (Die I) (10.4.79)	£140	13·00
	a.	"PENGE" (R. 12/6)	£950	£130
	b.	"QUEENSbAND" (R. 5/6)	—	£130
	c.	"QU" joined	—	£130
131		4d. orange-yellow (6.6.79)	£1300	£100

(b) No wmk, with lilac burelé band on back

132	7	1d. reddish brown (Die I) (21.10.79)	£750	£120
	a.	Die II	£850	£140
	ab.	"QUEENSLAND"	—	£1900
133		2d. blue (Die I) (21.10.79)	£750	60·00
	a.	"PENGE" (R. 12/6)	£3750	£700
	b.	"QUEENSbAND" (R. 5/6)		

*(c) Wmk Crown and Q. W **6***

134	7	1d. reddish brown (Die I) (31.10.79)	85·00	9·50
	b.	Die II	£120	9·50
	ba.	"QUEENSLAND"	£500	60·00
135		1d. dull orange (Die I)	65·00	11·00
	a.	Die II	70·00	12·00
	ab.	"QUEENSLAND"	£250	45·00
	ac.	Imperf between (horiz pair)	†	
136		1d. scarlet (Die I) (7.3.81)	60·00	10·00
	aa.	Imperf vert (horiz pair)	†	£2250
	a.	Die II	65·00	10·00
	ab.	"QUEENSLAND"	£275	38·00
137		2d. blue (Die I) (10.4.79)	85·00	4·00
	a.	"PENGE"	£350	50·00
	b.	"QUEENSbAND"	£350	50·00
	c.	Die II	95·00	6·50
138		2d. grey-blue (Die I)	85·00	3·25
	a.	"PENGE"	£350	50·00
	b.	"QUEENSbAND"	£350	50·00
	c.	Die II	85·00	6·50
139		2d. bright blue (Die I)	90·00	3·00
	a.	"PENGE"	£350	50·00
	b.	"QUEENSbAND"	£350	50·00
	c.	Imperf between (horiz pair)	£2250	£2250
	d.	Die II	90·00	6·50
140		2d. deep blue (Die I)	90·00	3·25
	a.	"PENGE"	£350	50·00
	b.	"QUEENSbAND"	£350	50·00
	c.	Die II	80·00	8·50
141		4d. orange-yellow	£400	20·00
	a.	Imperf vert (horiz pair)	£12000	
142		6d. deep green	£170	7·50
143		6d. yellow-green	£180	7·00
	a.	Imperf between (horiz pair)		
144		1s. deep violet (3.80)	£180	10·00
145		1s. pale lilac	£170	16·00

The variety "QO" is No. 48 in the first arrangement, and No. 44 in a later arrangement on the sheets.

All these values have been seen imperf and unused, but we have no evidence that any of them were used in this condition.

The above were printed in sheets of 120, from plates made up of 30 groups of four electrotypes. There are four different types in each group, and two such groups of four are known of the 1d. and 2d., thus giving eight varieties of these two values. There was some resetting of the first plate of the 1d.; and there are several plates of the 2d.; the value in the first plate of the latter value is in thinner letters, and in the last plate three types in each group of four have the "TW" of "TWO" joined, the letters of "PENCE" are larger and therefore much closer together, and in one type the "O" of "TWO" is oval, that letter being circular in the other types.

Half-penny

(8)   9   10

1880 (21 Feb). Surch with T **8**.

151	7	½d. on 1d. (No. 134) (Die I)	£325	£180
	a.	Die II	£800	£475
	ab.	"QUEENSLAND"	£1900	£1300

Examples with "Half-penny" reading downwards are forged surcharges.

£1 Re-entry (R. 1/2)   £1 Retouch (R. 6/4)

(Eng H. Bourne. Recess Govt Printing Office, Brisbane, from plates made by B.W.)

1882 (13 Apr)–**95**. P 12.

*(a) W **5** (twice sideways). Thin paper*

152	**9**	2s. bright blue (14.4.82)	£275	65·00
153		2s.6d. vermilion (12.7.82)	£130	26·00
154		5s. rose	£130	27·00
155		10s. brown (12.7.82)	£250	50·00
156		£1 deep green (30.5.83)	£550	£140
		a. Re-entry (R. 1/2)	—	£325
		b. Retouch (R. 6/4)	—	£325
152s/6s		(ex 2s. 6d.) H/S "SPECIMEN" *Set of 4*	£275	

*(b) W **10**. Thick paper (10.11.86)*

157	**9**	2s. bright blue	£300	65·00
158		2s.6d. vermilion	55·00	27·00
159		5s. rose	55·00	42·00
160	**9**	10s. brown	£130	50·00
161		£1 deep green	£325	85·00
		a. Re-entry (R. 1/2)	£850	£200
		b. Retouch (R. 6/4)	£850	£200

*(c) W **6** (twice sideways). Thin paper (1895)*

162	**9**	2s. vermilion	85·00	45·00
163		5s. rose	90·00	26·00
164		10s. brown	£475	£110
165		£1 deep green	£375	£100
		a. Re-entry (R. 1/2)	£900	£250
		b. Retouch (R. 6/4)	£900	£250

The re-entry on the £1 shows as a double bottom frame line and the retouch occurs alongside the bottom right numeral.
See also Nos. 270/1, 272/4 and 309/12.

11   12

In T **12** the shading lines do not extend entirely across, as in T **11**, thus leaving a white line down the front of the throat and point of the bust.

4d. "PENGE" for   4d. "EN" joined in
"PENCE" (R. 9/1)   "PENCE" (R. 4/6)

1882 (1 Aug)–**91**. W **6**.

(a) P 12

166	**11**	1d. pale vermilion-red (23.11.82)	11·00	1·00
		a. Double impression		
167		1d. deep vermilion-red	11·00	1·00
168		2d. blue	23·00	1·00
		a. Imperf between (horiz pair)	†	£3000
169		4d. pale yellow (18.4.83)	48·00	3·25
		a. "PENGE" for "PENCE"	£275	50·00
		b. "EN" joined in "PENCE"	£225	35·00
		c. Imperf (11.91)	†	£475
170		6d. green (6.11.82)	32·00	2·00
171		1s. violet (6.2.83)	55·00	12·00
172		1s. lilac	27·00	7·50
173		1s. deep mauve	24·00	7·50
174		1s. pale mauve	13·00	7·50
		a. Imperf	†	—

(b) P 9½×12 (1884)

176	**11**	1d. pale red	£160	65·00
177		2d. blue	£550	85·00
178		1s. mauve	£275	80·00

The above were printed from plates made up of groups of four electrotypes as previously. In the 1d. the words of value are followed by a full stop. There are four types of the 4d., 6d. and 1s., eight types of the 1d., and 12 types of the 2d.

No. 169c is from a sheet used at Roma post office and comes cancelled with the "46" numeral postmark.

1887 (5 May)–**89**. W **6**.

(a) P 12

179	**12**	1d. vermilion-red	17·00	1·00
180		2d. blue	17·00	1·00
		a. Oval white flaw on Queen's head behind diadem (R. 12/5)	70·00	9·00
181		2s. deep brown (12.3.89)	80·00	80·00
182		2s. pale brown	70·00	70·00

(b) P 9½×12

183	**12**	2d. blue	£425	80·00

These are from new plates; four types of each value grouped as before. The 1d. is without stop. In all values No. 2 in each group of four has the "L" and "A" of "QUEENSLAND" joined at the foot, and No. 3 of the 2d. has "P" of word "PENCE" with a long downstroke.

The 2d. is known bisected and used as a 1d. value.

13   14

1890. W **6** (sideways on ½d.). P 12½, 13 (comb machine).

184	**13**	½d. pale green	20·00	2·00
185		½d. deep green	15·00	2·00
186		½d. deep blue-green	7·50	2·00
187	**12**	1d. vermilion-red	8·00	50
		a. Imperf (pair)	£300	£325
		b. Oval broken by tip of bust (R. 10/3)	45·00	5·00
		c. Double impression	†	£650
188		2d. blue (old plate)	9·00	50
189		2d. pale blue (old plate)	9·00	50
190		2d. pale blue (retouched plate)	11·00	1·00
		a. "FWO" for "TWO" (R. 8/7)	—	25·00
191	**14**	2½d. carmine	17·00	2·50
192	**12**	3d. brown	9·00	4·00
193	**11**	4d. yellow	18·00	4·00
		a. "PENGE" for "PENCE"	£100	28·00
		b. "EN" joined in "PENCE"	80·00	24·00
194		4d. orange	27·00	4·00
		a. "PENGE" for "PENCE"	£140	28·00
		b. "EN" joined in "PENCE"	£110	24·00
195		4d. lemon	29·00	8·00
		a. "PENGE" for "PENCE"	£150	30·00
		b. "EN" joined in "PENCE"	£120	30·00
196		6d. green	11·00	2·00
197	**12**	2s. red-brown	45·00	55·00
198		2s. pale brown	55·00	60·00

This issue is perforated by a new vertical comb machine, gauging about 12¾×12¾. The 3d. is from a plate similar to those of the last issue, No. 2 in each group of four types having "L" and "A" joined at the foot. The ½d. and 2½d. are likewise in groups of four types, but the differences are very minute. In the retouched plate of the 2d. the letters "L" and "A" no longer touch in No. 2 of each group and the "P" in No. 3 is normal.

1895. W **10**.

A. Thick paper

(a) P 12½, 13

202	**12**	1d. vermilion-red (16.1.95)	4·75	60
		a. Oval broken by tip of bust (R. 10/3)	42·00	6·50
203		1d. red-orange	4·75	60
		a. Oval broken by tip of bust (R. 10/3)	42·00	6·50
204		2d. blue (retouched plate) (16.1.95)	6·50	60
		a. "FWO" for "TWO" (R. 8/7)	80·00	22·00

(b) P 12

205	**11**	1s. mauve (8.95)	42·00	27·00

B. Unwmkd paper; with blue burelé band at back. P 12½, 13

206	**12**	1d. vermilion-red (19.2.95)	2·50	2·50
		a. Oval broken by tip of bust (R. 10/3)	22·00	22·00
		b. "PE" of "PENNY" omitted (R. 1/2)	£300	£325
206c		1d. red-orange	2·50	2·50

C. Thin paper. Crown and Q faintly impressed. P 12½, 13

207	**12**	2d. blue (retouched plate) (6.95)	13·00	£160
		a. "FWO" for "TWO" (R. 8/7)	£140	

15   16

17   18

1895–96.

*A. W **6** (sideways on ½d.)*

(a) P 12½, 13

208	**15**	½d. green (11.5.95)	3·25	2·00
		a. Double impression	£2000	£2000
209		½d. deep green	3·25	2·00
		a. Printed both sides	£275	
210	**16**	1d. orange-red (28.2.95)	3·75	50
211		1d. pale red	8·50	75
212		2d. blue (19.6.95)	35·00	50
213	**17**	2½d. carmine (8.95)	24·00	5·50
214		2½d. rose	24·00	5·00
215	**18**	5d. purple-brown (10.95)	27·00	5·00

(b) P 12

217	**16**	1d. red (8.95)	90·00	50·00
218		2d. blue (8.95)	80·00	30·00

*B. Thick paper. W **10** (sideways) (part only on each stamp)*

(a) P 12½, 13

219	**15**	½d. green (6.8.95)	2·75	6·50
220		½d. deep green	2·75	6·50

(b) P 12

221	**15**	½d. green	45·00	
222		½d. deep green	45·00	

C. No wmk; with blue burelé band at back

(a) P 12½, 13

223	**15**	½d. green (1.8.95)	10·00	8·00
		a. Without burelé band	75·00	
224		½d. deep green	10·00	

(b) P 12

225	**15**	½d. green	22·00	
		a. Without burelé band	£140	

Nos. 223a and 225a are from the margins of the sheet.

D. Thin paper, with Crown and Q faintly impressed. P 12½, 13.

227	**15**	½d. green	2·00	6·50
228	**16**	1d. orange-red	3·25	2·25

19

1896–1902. W **6**. P 12½, 13.

229	**19**	1d. vermilion	20·00	70
230		6d. green (1902)	†	£16000

Only used examples of No. 230 are known, mostly with readable postmarks from 1902. It is suggested that electrotypes of this unissued design were inadvertently entered in a plate of No. 249.

20   21   22

23   24   25

"Cracked plate"

Die I   Die II

Two Dies of 4d.:

Die I. Serif of horizontal bar on lower right 4d. is clear of vertical frame line.
Die II. Serif joins vertical frame line.

1897–1908. Figures in all corners. W **6** (sideways on ½d.). P 12½, 13 (comb).

231	**20**	½d. deep green	5·00	8·00
		a. Perf 12	—	£150
232	**21**	1d. orange-vermilion	2·50	40
233		1d. vermilion	2·50	40
		a. Perf 12 (1899)	8·00	3·50
234		2d. blue	8·00	40
		a. Cracked plate	£190	35·00
		b. Perf 12 (1905)	£1000	7·00
		ba. Cracked plate	£2750	£250
235		2d. deep blue	7·00	40
		a. Cracked plate	£170	35·00
236	**22**	2½d. rose (10.98)	17·00	28·00
237		2½d. purple/blue (20.1.99)	9·50	3·25
238		2½d. brown-purple/blue	9·50	3·25
239		2½d. slate/blue (5.08)	9·00	9·00
240	**21**	3d. brown (10.98)	10·00	3·00
241		3d. deep brown	8·00	3·00
242		3d. reddish brown (1906)	13·00	4·50
243		3d. grey-brown (1907)	25·00	5·00
244		4d. yellow (Die I) (10.98)	13·00	3·25
		a. Die II	32·00	11·00
245		4d. yellow-buff (Die I)	11·00	3·25
		a. Die II	26·00	11·00
246	**23**	5d. purple-brown	8·50	3·00
247		5d. dull brown (1906)	9·50	10·00
248		5d. black-brown (1907)	16·00	6·50
249	**21**	6d. green (1.4.98)	8·50	2·75
250		6d. yellow-green	7·00	3·50
251	**24**	1s. pale mauve (1.7.99)	14·00	3·75
252		1s. dull mauve	14·00	3·75
253		1s. bright mauve	19·00	5·00
254	**25**	2s. turquoise-green	35·00	50·00

Stamps of this issue also exist with the irregular line perforation 12½, 13.

The 1d. perf 12×9½ exists used and unused but their status has not yet been established (price £120 unused).

The cracked plate variety on the 2d. developed during 1901 and shows as a white break on the Queen's head and neck. The electro was later replaced.

1897–98. W **6**.

(a) Zigzag roulette in black
(ab) Zigzag roulette in green
(b) The same but plain
(c) Roulette (a) and also (b)
(d) Roulette (b) and perf 12½, 13
(e) Roulette (a) and perf 12½, 13
(f) Compound of (a), (b), and perf 12½, 13

256	**21**	1d. vermilion	17·00	13·00
		a. Zigzag roulette in green (ab)	£250	
257		1d. vermilion (b)	18·00	7·50

258		1d. vermilion (c)	19·00	26·00
259		1d. vermilion (d)	9·50	6·50
260		1d. vermilion (e)	75·00	95·00
261		1d. vermilion (f)	95·00	£100

26

(Des M. Kellar)

1899 (Sept.)–**1906**. W **6**. P 12½, 13 (comb).

262	**26**	½d. deep green	3·25	2·50
		a. Grey-green	2·50	2·50
		b. Green (P 12) (1905)	£110	60·00
		c. Pale green (1906)	11·00	4·50

Stamps of T **26** without wmk, are proofs.

Stamps of this issue also exist with the irregular line perforation 12½, 12.

27   **27a**

(Des F. Elliott)

1900 (19 June). Anglo-Boer War Patriotic Fund. W **6**. P 12.

263	**27**	1d. (6d.) claret	£140	£120
264	**27a**	2d. (1s.) violet	£350	£275

These stamps, sold at 6d. and 1s. respectively, paid postage of 1d. and 2d. only, the difference being contributed to The Anglo–Boer War Patriotic Fund.

28   A   B

TWO TYPES OF "QUEENSLAND". Three different pairs of plates were produced for Type **28**, each plate being of 120 impressions (12×10). In Type A the letters of "QUEENSLAND" are 1mm tall and in Type B they are 1.5mm.

Plate 1:	All Type A
Plate 2:	Initially, all Type A, but in 1905 Type B clichés were substituted at R. 1/6, 2/6 and 3/6
Plate 3:	All Type B
Plate 4:	All Type B
Plate 5:	All Type A
Plate 6:	All Type A

(Typo Victoria Govt Printer, Melbourne)

1903 (4 July)–**05**. W w **10**. P 12½.

265	**28**	9d. brown and ultramarine (A)	55·00	8·00
266		9d. brown and ultramarine (B)		
		(1905)	38·00	8·00

The first two printings, No. 265, were all from plates 1 and 2, prior to the substitutions on plate 2. The third printing in May 1905 involved both plates 1 and 2 (after substitutions), together with 3 and 4 (both Type B). For the final printing on W w **10** paper, plates 3 and 4 were again used.

1903 (Oct). As Nos. 162 and 165. W **6** (twice sideways). P 12½, 13 (irregular line).

270	**9**	2s.6d. vermilion	£200	55·00
271		£1 deep green	£2000	£700
		a. Re-entry (R. 1/2)	£4000	£1400
		b. Retouch (R. 6/4)	£4000	£1400

(Litho Govt Ptg Office, Brisbane, from transfers of the recess plates)

1905 (Nov)–**06**. W **6** (twice sideways).

(a) P 12½, 13 (irregular line)

272	**9**	£1 deep green	£1000	£170
		a. Re-entry (R. 1/2)	£2000	£375
		b. Retouch (R. 6/4)	£2000	£375

(b) P 12

273	**9**	5s. rose (7.06)	£160	£100
274		£1 deep green (7.06)	£550	£130
		a. Re-entry (R. 1/2)	£1000	£300
		b. Retouch (R. 6/4)	£1000	£300

30   **32**

Redrawn types of T 21

T **30**. The head is redrawn, the top of the crown is higher and touches the frame, as do also the back of the chignon and the point of the bust. The forehead is filled in with lines of shading, and the figures in the corners appear to have been redrawn also.

T **32**. The forehead is plain (white instead of shaded), and though the top of the crown is made higher, it does not touch the frame; but the point of the bust and the chignon still touch. The figure in the right lower corner does not touch the line below, and has not the battered appearance of that in the first redrawn type. The stamps are very clearly printed, the lines of shading being distinct.

1906 (Sept). W **6**. P 12½, 13 (comb).

281	**30**	2d. dull blue (shades)	10·00	5·50

(Typo Victoria Govt Printer, Melbourne)

1906 (Sept)–**10**. Wmk Crown and double-lined A, W w **11**.

(a) P 12×12½

282	**28**	9d. brown and ultramarine (A)		
		(1909)	75·00	7·50
283		9d. brown and ultramarine (B)	23·00	4·50
283a		9d. pale brown and blue (A) (1909)	70·00	7·50
284		9d. pale brown and blue (B)	14·00	4·50

(b) P 11 (1910)

285	**28**	9d. brown and blue (B)	£5000	£800

(c) Compound perf 12×12½ and 11

285a		9d. brown and ultramarine (B)	†	£1600

For the first three printings on W w **11** paper, plates 3 and 4 (Type B) were used. For the fourth printing in January 1909 plates 5 and 6 (Type A) were introduced and used in conjunction with 3 and 4. The final two printings in September 1911 and January 1912 were probably all from plates 3 and 4.

33

1907–11. W **33**.

(a) P 12½, 13 (comb)

286	**26**	½d. deep green	2·00	4·50
287		½d. deep blue-green	2·00	4·50
288	**21**	1d. vermilion	3·00	30
		a. Imperf (pair)	£400	
289	**30**	2d. dull blue	35·00	3·75
289a		2d. bright blue (3.08)	28·00	20·00
290	**32**	2d. bright blue (4.08)	4·50	30
291	**21**	3d. pale brown (8.08)	23·00	2·75
292		3d. bistre-brown	12·00	3·75
293		4d. yellow (Die I)	12·00	4·50
		a. Die II	42·00	14·00
294		4d. grey-black (Die I) (4.09)	25·00	6·50
		a. Die II	50·00	15·00
295	**23**	5d. dull brown	38·00	21·00
295a		5d. sepia (12.09)	21·00	25·00
296	**21**	6d. yellow-green	22·00	4·25
297		6d. bright green	19·00	8·00
298	**24**	1s. violet (1908)	22·00	3·75
299		1s. bright mauve	20·00	3·75
300	**25**	2s. turquoise-green (8.08)	38·00	48·00

Stamps of this issue also exist with the irregular line perforation 12½, 13. This was used when the comb perforation was under repair.

(b) P 13×11 to 12½ (May 1911)

301	**26**	½d. deep green	7·00	13·00
302	**21**	1d. vermilion	7·50	7·00
303	**32**	2d. blue	10·00	9·00
304	**21**	3d. bistre-brown	18·00	27·00
305		4d. grey-black	70·00	90·00
		a. Die II	£140	£160
306	**23**	5d. dull brown	26·00	70·00
307	**21**	6d. yellow-green	38·00	55·00
308	**23**	1s. violet	60·00	85·00

The perforation (b) is from a machine introduced to help cope with the demands caused by the introduction of penny postage. The three rows at top (or bottom) of the sheet show varieties gauging 13×11½, 13×11, and 13×12, respectively, these are obtainable in strips of three showing the three variations.

(Litho Govt Ptg Office, Brisbane)

1907 (Oct)–**11**. W **33** (twice sideways). P 12½, 13 (irregular line).

309	**9**	2s.6d. vermilion	42·00	50·00
		a. Dull orange (1910)	75·00	90·00
		b. Reddish orange (1911)	£180	£225
310		5s. rose (12.07)	80·00	65·00
		a. Deep rose (1910)	£100	90·00
		b. Carmine-red (1911)	£250	£275
311		10s. blackish brown	£150	75·00
		a. Sepia (1911)	£425	£300
312		£1 bluish green	£400	£130
		a. Re-entry (R. 1/2)	£800	£300
		b. Retouch (R. 6/4)	£800	£300
		c. Deep bluish green (1910)	£550	£350
		ca. Re-entry (R. 1/2)	£1200	£700
		cb. Retouch (R. 6/4)	£1200	£700
		d. Deep yellowish green (1911)	£1800	£1400
		da. Re-entry (R. 1/2)	£4250	£2750
		db. Retouch (R. 6/4)	£4250	£2750

The 1911 printings are on thinner, whiter paper.

The lithographic stones used for Nos. 272/4 and 309/12 took the full sheet of 30 so the varieties on the £1 recess-printed version also appear on the stamps printed by lithography.

1911. W **33**. Perf irregular compound, 10½ to 12½.

313	**21**	1d. vermilion	£1500	£700

This was from another converted machine, formerly used for perforating Railway stamps. The perforation was very unsatisfactory.

STAMP BOOKLETS

There are very few surviving examples of Nos. SB1/4. Listings are provided for those believed to have been issued with prices quoted for those known to still exist.

1904 (1 Jan)–**09**. Black on a red cover as Type B **1** of New South Wales. Stapled.

SB1	£1 booklet containing 240×1d. in four blocks of 30 and two blocks of 60
	a. Red on pink cover (1909)
	b. Blue on pink cover £15000

1904 (1 Jan). Black on grey cover as No. SB1. Stapled.

SB2	£1 booklet containing 120×2d. in four blocks of 30

1910 (May). Black on cream cover as Type B **2** of New South Wales. Stapled.

SB3	2s. booklet containing 11×½d. (No. 301), either in block of 6 plus block of 5 or block of 11 and 18×1d. (No 302), either in three blocks of 6 or block of 6 plus block of 12

Unsold stock of No. SB3 was uprated with one additional ½d. in May 1911.

1911 (Aug). Red on pink cover as No. SB3. Stapled.

SB4	2s. booklet containing 12×½d. (No. 301), either in two blocks of 6 or block of 12, and 18×1d. (No. 302), either in three blocks of 6 or block of 6 plus block of 12	£6000
	a. Red on white cover	£5500

POSTAL FISCALS

Authorised for use from 1 January 1880 until 1 July 1892

CANCELLATIONS. Beware of stamps which have had pen-cancellations cleaned off and then had faked postmarks applied. Used prices quoted are for postally used examples between the above dates.

F 1   **F 2**

1866–68. Litho, Govt Ptg Office.

A. No wmk. P 13

F1	**F 1**	1d. blue	£130	30·00
F2		6d. deep violet	£225	£130
F3		1s. blue-green	£200	90·00
F4		2s. brown	£375	£225
F5		2s.6d. dull red	£450	£180
F6		5s. yellow	£1200	£450
F6a		6s. light brown	£1800	
F7		10s. green	£1400	£600
F8		20s. rose	£2250	£1000

B. Wmk F 2. P 13

F9	**F 1**	1d. blue	70·00	70·00
F10		6d. deep violet	£225	£160
F11		6d. blue	£650	£400
F12		1s. blue-green	£200	95·00
F13		2s. brown	£375	£180
F13a		5s. yellow	£1200	£400
F14		10s. green	£1400	£600
F15		20s. rose	£2250	£1100

F 3   **F 3a**

1871–72. Litho, Govt Ptg Office. P 12 or 13.

A. Wmk Large Crown and Q, Wmk F 3a

F16	**F 3**	1d. mauve	60·00	24·00
F17		6d. red-brown	£110	50·00
		a. Imperf vert (horiz pair)		
F18		1s. green	£140	50·00
F19		2s. blue	£200	75·00
F20		2s.6d. brick-red	£375	£160
F21		5s. orange-brown	£475	£225
F22		10s. brown	£1000	£450
F23		20s. rose	£2000	£650

B. No wmk. Blue burelé band at back

F24	**F 3**	1d. mauve	70·00	24·00
F25		6d. red-brown	£110	48·00
F26		6d. mauve	£450	£150
F27		1s. green	£160	48·00
F28		2s. blue	£275	£160
F29		2s.6d. vermilion	£475	£180
F30		5s. yellow-brown	£650	£225
F31		10s. brown	£1100	£450
F32		20s. rose	£2000	£650

No. F19 is known imperforate horizontally (vert pair), with fiscal cancellation.

F 4	F 5

1878–79. Typo.

A. No wmk. Lilac burelé band at back. P 12

F33	F **4**	1d. violet	£200	£100

*B. Wmk Crown and Q, W **5**. P 12*

F34	F **4**	1d. violet	£120	70·00
		d. Imperf between (horiz pair).......		

Stamps as Type F **5** may not have been issued until after 1 July 1892 when the proper use of duty stamps for postal service was terminated but there are several examples which appear to have genuinely passed through the post during the 1890's. Unless they are dated during 1892 their postal use was certainly unauthorised although they may have been accepted.

Queensland became part of the Commonwealth of Australia on 1 January 1901.

SOUTH AUSTRALIA

PRICES FOR STAMPS ON COVER	
Nos. 1/3	*from* × 3
No. 4	†
Nos. 5/12	*from* × 2
Nos. 13/18	*from* × 3
Nos. 19/43	*from* × 4
Nos. 44/9b	—
Nos. 50/110	*from* × 3
No. 111	—
Nos. 112/34	*from* × 6
Nos. 135/45	*from* × 3
Nos. 146/66	*from* × 5
Nos. 167/70a	*from* × 10
Nos. 171/2a	—
Nos. 173/94a	*from* × 12
Nos. 195/208	—
Nos. 229/31	*from* × 12
No. 232	—
Nos. 233/42	*from* × 12
Nos. 268/75	*from* × 30
Nos. 276/9	—
Nos. 280/8	*from* × 30
Nos. 289/92	—
Nos. 293/304	*from* × 15
No. 305	—
Nos. O1/13	—
Nos. O14/36	*from* × 20
Nos. O37/42	*from* × 5
Nos. O43/4	*from* × 50
Nos. O45/7	—
Nos. O48/52	*from* × 30
No. O53	—
Nos. O54/85	*from* × 50
Nos. O86/7	—

SPECIMEN OVERPRINTS. Those listed are from U.P.U. distributions between 1889 and 1895. Further "Specimen" overprints exist, but these were used for other purposes.

PERKINS BACON "CANCELLED". For notes on these handstamps, showing "CANCELLED" between horizontal bars forming an oval, see Catalogue Introduction.

1	2 Large Star

(Eng Wm Humphrys. Recess P.B.)

1855 (1 Jan–Oct). Printed in London. W **2**. Imperf.

1	**1**	1d. dark green (10.55) (H/S "CANCELLED" in oval £12000)	£10000	£500
2		2d. rose-carmine (*shades*) (H/S "CANCELLED" in oval £11000)	£800	85·00
3		6d. deep blue (10.55) (H/S "CANCELLED" in oval £10000)	£4500	£170

Prepared and sent to the Colony, but not issued

4	**1**	1s. violet (H/S "CANCELLED" in oval £20000)	£27000	

A printing of 500,000 of these 1s. stamps was delivered, but, as the colour was liable to be confused with that of the 6d. stamp, this stock was destroyed on 5 June 1857. It is believed that surviving examples of No. 4 come from Perkins Bacon remainders which came on to the market in the late 1890s.

Proofs of the 1d. and 6d. without wmk exist, and these are found with forged star watermarks added, and are sometimes offered as originals.

For reprints of the above and later issues, see note after No. 194.

1856–58. Printed by Printer of Stamps, Adelaide, from Perkins Bacon plates. W **2**. Imperf.

5	**1**	1d. deep yellow-green (15.6.58)	£9500	£550
6		1d. yellow-green (11.10.58)	£8500	£650
7		2d. orange-red (4.58)	£2250	80·00
8		2d. blood-red (14.11.56)	£3000	60·00
		a. Printed on both sides	†	£1300
9		2d. red (*shades*) (23.4.56)	£750	40·00
		a. Printed on both sides	†	£850
10		6d. slate-blue (7.57)	£4750	£200
11		1s. red-orange (8.7.57)	—	£750
12		1s. orange (11.6.58)	£12000	£475

1858–59. Rouletted. (This first rouletted issue has the same colours as the local imperf issue). W **2**.

13	**1**	1d. yellow-green (8.1.59)	£1000	65·00
14		1d. light yellow-green (18.3.59)	£1000	70·00
		a. Imperf between (pair)		
15		2d. red (17.2.59)	£350	22·00
		a. Printed on both sides	†	£850
17		6d. slate-blue (12.12.58)	£900	65·00
18		1s. orange (18.3.59)	£2000	50·00
		a. Printed on both sides	†	£1900

3	4	(5)

The "TEN PENCE" surcharge (T **5**) was produced from a setting of six (3×2). There are noticable differences between the six types.

1860–69. Second rouletted issue, printed (with the exception of No. 24) in colours only found rouletted or perforated. Surch with T **5** (Nos. 35/7). W **2**.

19	**1**	1d. bright yellow-green (22.4.61)	£140	50·00
20		1d. dull blue-green (17.12.63)	£150	50·00
21		1d. sage-green (8.1.59)	£160	50·00
		a. Imperf between (horiz pair)		
22		1d. pale sage-green (27.5.65)	£140	
23		1d. deep green (1864)	£550	85·00
24		1d. deep yellow-green (1869)	£300	
24a		2d. pale red	£250	4·00
		b. Printed on both sides	†	£550
25		2d. pale vermilion (3.2.63)	£150	4·75
26		2d. bright vermilion (19.8.64)	£150	3·75
		a. Imperf between (horiz pair)	£3750	£750
27	**3**	4d. dull violet (24.1.67)	£170	48·00
28	**1**	6d. violet-blue (19.3.60)	£475	8·00
29		6d. greenish blue (11.2.63)	£300	4·50
30		6d. dull ultramarine (25.4.64)	£250	4·50
		a. Imperf between (horiz pair)	†	£2250
31		6d. violet-ultramarine (11.4.68)	£450	7·00
32		6d. dull blue (26.8.65)	£375	7·50
		a. Imperf between (pair)	†	£3000
33		6d. Prussian blue (7.9.69)	£1100	50·00
33a		6d. indigo	—	70·00
34	**4**	9d. grey-lilac (24.12.60)	£150	9·00
		a. Imperf between (horiz pair)	†	£4000
35		10d. on 9d. orange-red (B.) (20.7.66)	£550	50·00
36		10d. on 9d. yellow (B.) (29.7.67)	£750	30·00
37		10d. on 9d. yellow (Blk.) (14.8.69) ...	£4000	80·00
		a. Surch inverted at the top	†	£7000
		c. Roul×perf 10	†	—
38	**1**	1s. yellow (25.10.61)	£1400	32·00
		a. Imperf horiz (vert pair)	†	£5500
39		1s. grey-brown (10.4.63)	£425	32·00
40		1s. dark grey-brown (26.5.63)	£400	32·00
41		1s. chestnut (25.8.63)	£350	11·00
42		1s. lake-brown (27.3.65)	£325	12·00
		a. Imperf between (horiz pair)	†	£2250
43	**3**	2s. rose-carmine (24.1.67)	£500	32·00
		a. Imperf between (vert pair)	†	£2500

1868–71. Remainders of old stock subsequently perforated by the 11½–12½ machine.

(a) Imperf stamps. P 11½–12½

44	**1**	2d. pale vermilion (2.68)	—	£1300
45		2d. vermilion (18.3.68)	—	£1400

(b) Rouletted stamps. P 11½–12½

46	**1**	1d. bright green (9.11.69)	—	£750
47		2d. pale vermilion (15.8.68)	£2500	£650
48		6d. Prussian blue (8.11.69)	—	£400
		aa. Horiz pair perf all round, roul between		
48a		6d. indigo	—	£500
49	**4**	9d. grey-lilac (29.3.71)	£2750	£250
		a. Perf×roulette		£275
49b	**1**	1s. lake-brown (23.5.70)		

1867–70. W **2**. P 11½–12½×roulette.

50	**1**	1d. pale bright green (2.11.67)	£400	29·00
51		1d. bright green (1868)	£375	24·00
52		1d. grey-green (26.1.70)	£425	29·00
		a. Imperf between (horiz pair)		
53		1d. blue-green (29.1.71)	£550	65·00
54	**3**	4d. dull violet (7.68)	£3000	£160
55		4d. dull purple (1869)	—	£130
56	**1**	6d. bright pale blue (29.5.67)	£1000	19·00
57		6d. Prussian blue (30.7.67)	£950	19·00
		a. Printed on both sides		
58		6d. indigo (1.8.69)	£1100	26·00
59	**4**	10d. on 9d. yellow (B.) (2.2.69)	£1500	35·00
		a. Printed on both sides	—	£1200
60	**1**	1s. chestnut (4.68)	£500	20·00
61		1s. lake-brown (3.3.69)	£500	20·00

NOTE. The stamps perf 11½, 12½, or compound of the two, are here combined in one list, as both perforations are on the one machine, and all the varieties may be found in each sheet of stamps. This method of classifying the perforations by the machines is by far the most simple and convenient.

(6)	7 (=Victoria W **19**)

3-PENCE

1868–79. Surch with T **6** (Nos. 66/8). W **2**. P 11½–12½.

62	**1**	1d. pale bright green (8.2.68)	£375	70·00
63		1d. grey-green (18.2.68)	£325	70·00
64		1d. dark green (20.3.68)	£190	22·00
		a. Printed on both sides	†	£1100
65		1d. deep yellow-green (28.6.72)	£180	22·00
		a. Imperf between (horiz pair)	†	£3250
66	**3**	3d. on 4d. Prussian blue (Blk.) (7.2.71)	—	£850
67		3d. on 4d. sky-blue (Blk.) (12.8.70) ..	£600	18·00
		a. Imperf.		
		b. Rouletted	—	£1400
68		3d. on 4d. deep ultramarine (Blk.) (9.72)	£170	9·00
		a. Surch double	†	£3750
		b. Additional surch on back	—	£3000
		c. Surch omitted	£40000	£20000
70		4d. dull purple (1.2.68)	£120	15·00
71		4d. dull violet (1868)	£110	8·00
72	**1**	6d. bright pale blue (23.2.68)	£650	11·00
73		6d. Prussian blue (29.9.69)	£350	7·00
		a. Perf 11½×imperf (horiz pair) ...	†	£2250
74		6d. indigo (1869)	£350	17·00
75	**4**	9d. claret (7.72)	£200	8·00
76		9d. bright mauve (1.11.72)	£200	8·00
		a. Printed on both sides	†	£900
77		9d. red-purple (15.1.74)	£120	8·00
78		10d. on 9d. yellow (B.) (15.8.68)	£2250	50·00
		a. Wmk Crown and S A (W **10**) (1868)	—	£1700
79		10d. on 9d. yellow (Blk.) (13.9.69) ...	£475	65·00
80	**1**	1s. lake-brown (9.68)	£225	18·00
81		1s. chestnut (8.10.72)	£200	20·00
82		1s. dark red-brown	£170	12·00
83		1s. red-brown (6.1.69)	£180	12·00
84	**3**	2s. pale rose-pink (10.10.69)	£2000	£180
85		2s. deep rose-pink (8.69)	—	£120
86		2s. crimson-carmine (16.10.69)	£180	21·00
87		2s. carmine (1869)	£170	13·00
		a. Printed on both sides	†	£750

No. 68c comes from two sheets on which, it is believed, some stamps showed the surcharge omitted and others the surcharge double. One of the used examples of No. 68c is known postmarked in 1875 and many of the others in 1879.

No. 78a was a trial printing made to test the perforating machine on the new D.L.R. paper.

A used example of No. 70 in imperf between horiz pair is in the Royal Philatelic Collection.

1870–71. W **2**. P 10.

88	**1**	1d. grey-green (6.70)	£350	25·00
89		1d. pale bright green (9.8.70)	£350	22·00
90		1d. bright green (1871)	£300	22·00
91	**3**	3d. on 4d dull ultramarine (R.) (6.870)	£1500	£120
92		3d. on 4d pale ultramarine (Blk.) (14.2.71)	£550	35·00
93		3d. on 4d ultramarine (Blk.) (14.8.71)	£350	40·00
93a		3d. on 4d. Prussian blue (Blk.) (16.12.71)	—	£1000
94		4d. dull lilac (1870)	£200	11·00
95		4d. dull purple (1871)	£190	11·00
96	**1**	6d. bright blue (19.6.70)	£375	17·00
97		6d. indigo (11.10.71)	£550	16·00
98		1s. chestnut (4.1.71)	£350	42·00

NOTE. Stamps perf 10 all round were produced by a new rotary machine, introduced early in 1870. This machine was not large enough to perforate entire sheets, and perforation therefore had to be completed with the perf 11½–12½ line machine, giving rise to the compound perforations listed as Nos. 99/110.

1870–73. W **2**. P 10×11½–12½, 11½–12½×10, or compound.

99	**1**	1d. pale bright green (11.10.70)	£350	24·00
		a. Printed on both sides		
100		1d. grey-green	£325	18·00
101		1d. deep green (19.6.71)	£200	11·00
102	**3**	3d. on 4d. pale ultramarine (Blk.) (9.11.70)	£550	80·00
103		4d. dull lilac (11.5.72)	—	20·00
104		4d. slate-lilac (5.3.73)	£200	20·00
105	**1**	6d. Prussian blue (2.3.70)	£300	8·00
106		6d. bright Prussian blue (26.10.70) .	£325	10·00
107	**4**	10d. on 9d. yellow (Blk.) (1.70)	£325	60·00
108	**1**	1s. chestnut (17.6.71)	£400	80·00
109	**3**	2s. rose-pink (24.4.71)	—	£225
110		2s. carmine (3.4.72)	£350	65·00

1871 (17 July). W **7**. P 10.

111	**3**	4d. dull lilac	£5500	£325
		a. Printed on both sides	†	£4250

8 Broad Star	(9)

8 PENCE

1876–1900. Surch with T **9** (Nos. 118/21). W **8**.

(a) P 11½–12½

112	**3**	3d. on 4d. ultramarine (1.6.79)	£170	32·00
		a. Surch double................................	†	£1800

113		4d. violet-slate (15.3.79)	£160	15·00
114		4d. plum (16.4.80)	90·00	7·50
115		4d. deep mauve (8.6.82)	90·00	6·00
116	**1**	6d. indigo (2.12.76)	£200	5·00
		a. Imperf between (horiz pair)	†	—
117		6d. Prussian blue (7.78)	£160	4·50
118	**4**	8d. on 9d. brown-orange (7.76)	£225	9·50
119		8d. on 9d. burnt umber (1880)	£225	11·00
		a. Surch double	†	—
120		8d. on 9d. brown (9.3.80)	£225	11·00
		a. Imperf between (vert pair)	£3000	
121		8d. on 9d. grey-brown (10.5.81)	£190	7·00
		a. Surch double	—	£2500
122		9d. purple (9.3.80)	£100	11·00
		a. Printed on both sides	—	£650
123		9d. rose-lilac (21.8.80)	27·00	4·50
		a. Printed on both sides	†	£600
124		9d. rose-lilac (*large holes*) (26.5.00)	16·00	4·50
125	**1**	1s. red-brown (3.11.77)	90·00	2·75
		a. Imperf between (horiz pair)	†	£900
126		1s. reddish lake-brown (1880)	90·00	3·75
127		1s. lake-brown (9.1.83)	95·00	3·00
128		1s. Vandyke brown (1891)	£100	8·50
129		1s. dull brown (1891)	90·00	3·25
130		1s. chocolate (*large holes*) (6.5.97)	27·00	3·50
		a. Imperf vert (horiz pair)	£450	
131		1s. sepia (*large holes*) (22.5.00)	27·00	6·00
		a. Imperf between (vert pair)	£600	
132	**3**	2s. carmine (15.2.77)	48·00	7·50
		a. Imperf between (horiz pair)	†	£2750
133		2s. rose-carmine (1885)	60·00	8·00
134		2s. rose-carmine (*large holes*) (6.12.98)	40·00	8·00

The perforation with larger, clean-cut holes resulted from the fitting of new pins to the machine.

No. 123a is known with the impression on the back either sideways or inverted. The Royal Philatelic Collection contains an unused marginal pair of the former.

		(b) P 10		
135	**1**	6d. Prussian blue (11.11.79)	£200	24·00
136		6d. bright blue (1879)	£225	19·00
136a		1s. reddish lake-brown	£500	

		(c) P 10×11½–12½, 11½–12½×10, or compound		
137	**3**	4d. violet-slate (21.5.79)	£180	24·00
138		4d. dull purple (4.10.79)	85·00	2·75
139	**1**	6d. Prussian blue (29.12.77)	£140	2·75
140		6d. bright blue	£170	6·00
141		6d. bright ultramarine	£120	2·75
142		1s. reddish lake-brown (9.2.85)	£140	11·00
143		1s. dull brown (29.6.86)	£180	14·00
144	**3**	2s. carmine (27.12.77)	95·00	6·50
145		2s. rose-carmine (1887)	90·00	6·00
		a. Imperf between (horiz pair)	†	£1900

10	11	12

1901–02. Wmk Crown SA (wide). W **10**. P 11½–12½ (*large holes*).

146	**4**	9d. claret (1.2.02)	20·00	25·00
147	**1**	1s. dark brown (12.6.01)	22·00	16·00
148		1s. dark reddish brown (1902)	25·00	18·00
		a. Imperf horiz (vert pair)	£2750	£2750
149		1s. red-brown (aniline) (18.7.02)	25·00	35·00
150	**3**	2s. crimson (29.8.01)	45·00	16·00
151		2s. carmine	27·00	12·00

(Plates and electrotypes by D.L.R. Printed in Adelaide)

1868–76. W **10**.

		(a) Rouletted		
152	**12**	2d. deep brick-red (8.68)	£150	7·00
153		2d. pale orange-red (5.10.68)	£140	2·75
		a. Printed on both sides	†	£700
		b. Imperf between (horiz pair)	†	£1300
		c. Imperf horiz (vert pair)	†	£1700

		(b) P 11½–12½		
154	**11**	1d. blue-green (10.1.75)	£170	45·00
155	**12**	2d. pale orange-red (5.5.69)	£1400	£250

		(c) P 11½–12½×roulette		
156	**12**	2d. pale orange-red (20.8.69)	—	£170

		(d) P 10×roulette		
157	**12**	2d. pale orange-red (7.5.70)	£500	42·00

		(e) P 10		
158	**11**	1d. blue-green (4.75)	£100	8·00
159	**12**	2d. brick-red (4.70)	60·00	4·00
160		2d. orange-red (1.7.70)	23·00	1·00
		a. Printed on both sides	†	£425

		(f) P 10×11½–12½, 11½–12½×10, or compound		
161	**11**	1d. blue-green (27.8.75)	£190	45·00
		a. Imperf between (horiz pair)	†	£1500
162	**12**	2d. brick-red (19.1.71)	£750	38·00
163		2d. orange-red (3.2.71)	£200	38·00
		a. Imperf (8.76)	£1200	£1100

1869. Wmk Large Star W **2**.

		(a) Rouletted		
164	**12**	2d. orange-red (13.3.69)	£170	25·00

		(b) P 11½–12½×roulette		
165	**12**	2d. orange-red (18.69)	£2000	£120

		(c) P 11½–12½		
165a	**12**	2d. orange-red (7.69)	—	£1200

1871 (15 July). Wmk V and Crown, W **7**. P 10.

166	**12**	2d. brick-red	£180	50·00

13	(14)

1876–1904. Wmk Crown SA (close). W **13**.

		(a) P 10 (1876–85)		
167	**11**	1d. blue-green (9.2.76)	40·00	1·50
		a. Yellowish green (11.78)	50·00	1·75
		b. Deep green (11.79)	28·00	30
		bb. Printed double	†	—
168	**12**	2d. orange-red (8.76)	50·00	50
		a. Dull brick-red (21.5.77)	55·00	1·00
		b. Blood-red (31.10.79)	£300	4·50
		c. Pale red (4.85)	18·00	40

		(b) P 10×11½–12½, 11½–12½×10 or compound (1877–80)		
169	**11**	1d. deep green (11.2.80)	80·00	14·00
		a. Blue-green (2.3.80)	38·00	7·50
170	**12**	2d. orange-red (4.9.77)	£180	14·00
		a. Dull brick-red (6.80)	£180	14·00

		(c) P 11½–12½ (1877–84)		
171	**11**	1d. blue-green (2.84)	—	£160
172	**12**	2d. orange-red (14.9.77)	—	£160
		a. Blood-red (1.4.80)	—	£160

		(d) P 15 (1893)		
173	**11**	1d. green (8.5.93)	48·00	1·00
174	**12**	2d. pale orange (9.2.93)	28·00	1·00
		a. Orange-red	27·00	1·00
		b. Imperf between (vert pair)	£950	

		(e) P 13 (1895–1903)		
175	**11**	1d. pale green (11.1.95)	12·00	1·00
		a. Green	12·00	20
		b. Imperf between (vert pair)	£1800	
176		1d. rosine (8.8.99)	12·00	65
		a. Scarlet (23.12.03)	8·00	1·25
		b. Deep red	9·50	1·50
177	**12**	2d. pale orange (19.1.95)	16·00	20
		a. Orange-red (9.5.95)	22·00	20
178		2d. bright violet (10.10.99)	6·50	20

		(f) P 12×11½ (comb) (1904)		
179	**11**	1d. rosine (2.2.04)	14·00	1·75
		a. Scarlet (25.7.04)	8·50	1·00
180	**12**	2d. bright violet (11.10.04)	14·00	1·00

Examples of the 1d. pale green with thicker lettering come from a worn plate.

1882 (1 Jan). No. 167 surch with T **14**.

181	**11**	½d. on 1d. blue-green	14·00	13·00

15	16	17	18

1883–99. W **13** (sideways on ½d.).

		(a) P 10 (1883–95)		
182	**15**	½d. chocolate (1.3.83)	18·00	2·25
		a. Imperf between (horiz pair)	†	£1500
		b. Red-brown (4.4.89)	10·00	2·25
		c. Brown (1895)	5·50	4·50
183	**16**	3d. sage-green (12.86)	38·00	2·75
		a. Olive-green (6.6.90)	25·00	5·50
		b. Deep green (12.4.93)	23·00	5·50
		s. Optd "SPECIMEN"	40·00	
184	**17**	4d. pale violet (3.90)	55·00	3·00
		a. Aniline violet (3.1.93)	50·00	8·00
		s. Optd "SPECIMEN"	40·00	
185	**18**	6d. pale blue (4.87)	70·00	3·75
		a. Blue (5.5.87)	55·00	1·25
		s. Optd "SPECIMEN"	40·00	

		(b) P 10×11½–12½, 11½–12½×10 or compound (1891)		
186	**15**	½d. red-brown (25.9.91)	35·00	12·00
		a. Imperf between (horiz pair)	£375	

		(c) P 11½–12½ (1890)		
187	**15**	½d. red-brown (12.10.90)	45·00	9·50

		(d) P 15 (1893–94)		
188	**15**	½d. pale brown (1.93)	12·00	1·50
		aa. Imperf between (horiz pair)	†	
		a. Deep brown	12·00	1·50
		b. Imperf between (horiz pair)	£400	
		c. Perf 12½ between (pair)	£325	85·00
189	**17**	4d. purple (1.1.94)	48·00	4·00
		a. Slate-violet	48·00	4·25
190	**18**	6d. blue (20.11.93)	70·00	4·00

		(e) P 13 (1895–99)		
191	**15**	½d. pale brown (9.95)	5·00	45
		a. Imperf between (horiz pair)	†	
		b. Deep brown (9.95)	6·00	30
192	**16**	3d. pale olive-green (26.7.97)	15·00	3·25
		a. Deep olive-green (27.11.99)	6·00	3·25
193	**17**	4d. violet (21.1.96)	6·00	1·00
194	**18**	6d. pale blue (3.96)	12·00	1·50
		a. Blue	11·00	1·50

REPRINTS. In 1884, and in later years, reprints on paper wmkd Crown SA, W **10**, were made of Nos. 1, 2, 3, 4, 12, 13, 14, 15, 19, 24, 27, 28, 32, 33, 34, 35, 36, 37, 38, 40, 43, 44, 49a, 53, 65, 67, 67 with surcharge in red, 70, 71, 72, 73, 78, 79, 81, 83, 86, 90, 118, 119, 120, 121, 122, 155, 158, 159, 164, 181, 182. They are overprinted "REPRINT".

In 1889 examples of the reprints for Nos. 1/3, 12, 15, 19, 27, 32/8, 44, 67, 67 surcharged in red, 70/1, 73, 83, 86, 118, 121/2, 158/9, 164 and 181/2, together with No. 141 overprinted "SPECIMEN", were supplied to the UPU for distribution.

19	(20)	(21)

(Plates and electrotypes by D.L.R. Printed in Adelaide)

1886 (20 Dec)**–96.** T **19** (inscr "POSTAGE & REVENUE"). W **13**. Parts of two or more wmks, on each stamp, sometimes sideways. P 10.

195		2s.6d. mauve	£130	17·00
		a. Perf 11½–12½. *Dull violet*	95·00	9·00
		bb. *Bright aniline violet*	£100	9·00
196		5s. rose-pink	£150	19·00
		a. Perf 11½–12½	£120	19·00
		ab. *Rose-carmine*	£120	22·00
197		10s. green	£300	75·00
		a. Perf 11½–12½	£250	70·00
198		15s. brownish yellow	£750	£375
		a. Perf 11½–12½	£800	£250
199		£1 blue	£600	£180
		a. Perf 11½–12½	£500	£170
200		£2 Venetian red	£4250	£550
		a. Perf 11½–12½	£4000	£500
201		50s. dull pink	£5000	£750
		a. Perf 11½–12½	£4750	£650
202		£3 sage green	£6000	£700
		a. Perf 11½–12½	£5500	£600
203		£4 lemon	£11000	
		a. Perf 11½–12½	£9000	£1400
204		£5 grey	£9000	
		a. Perf 11½–12½	£9000	
205		£5 brown (P 11½–12½) (1896)	£5500	£1000
206		£10 bronze	£9500	£1800
		a. Perf 11½–12½	£9000	£1400
207		£15 silver	£32000	
		a. Perf 11½–12½	£30000	£2500
208		£20 claret	£40000	
		a. Perf 11½–12½	£38000	£2750
		195s/208s Optd "SPECIMEN" *Set of 14**	£1300	

Variations exist in the length of the words and shape of the letters of the value inscription.

The 2s.6d. dull violet, 5s. rose-pink, 10s., £1 and £5 brown exist perf 11½–12½ with either large or small holes; the 2s.6d. aniline, 5s. rose-carmine, 15s., £2 and 50s. with large holes only and the remainder only with small holes.

Stamps perforated 11½–12½ small holes, are, generally speaking, rather rarer than those with the 1895 (large holes) gauge.

Stamps perf 10 were issued on 20 Dec 1886. Stamps perf 11½–12½ (small holes) are known with earliest dates covering the period from June 1890 to Feb 1896. Earliest dates of stamps with large holes range from July 1896 to May 1902.

*The listing of the "SPECIMEN" set distributed by the UPU comprises stamps with W **13**, perf 10, with an overprint 12¼ mm long, except No. 205 which is perf 11½–12½, with an overprint 15¼ mm long. These should not be confused with the same values with other "SPECIMEN" overprints, usually on stamps perf 11½–12½, and often with W **10**, which were prepared for presentation purposes and for inclusion in sets for sale to collectors.

1891 (1 Jan)**–93.** T **17/18** surch with T **20/1**. W **13**.

		(a) P 10		
229	**17**	2½d. on 4d. pale green (Br.)	8·00	2·50
		a. Fraction bar omitted	£110	80·00
		b. Deep green	8·00	1·75
		ba. Fraction bar omitted	£110	75·00
		bb. "2" and "½" closer together	26·00	18·00
		bc. Imperf between (horiz pair)		
		bd. Imperf between (vert pair)	†	£3250
		s. Optd "SPECIMEN"	32·00	
230	**18**	5d. on 6d. pale brown (C.)	19·00	7·50
		a. *Deep brown*	19·00	7·00
		b. No stop after "5D"	£170	
		s. Optd "SPECIMEN"	32·00	

		(b) P 10×11½–12½ or 11½–12½×10		
231	**17**	2½d. on 4d. pale green (Br.)	65·00	6·50
		a. *Deep green*	65·00	6·50

		(c) P 11½–12½		
232	**17**	2½d. on 4d. deep green	80·00	85·00

		(d) P 15		
233	**17**	2½d. on 4d. green (14.10.93)	55·00	2·75
		a. Fraction bar omitted		
		b. "2" and "½d." closer	£130	22·00

On Nos. 229bb and 233b the base of the "1" of "½" and the back of the large "2" are 0.5 mm apart. On normal stamps the spacing is 1 mm.

22 Red Kangaroo	23	24 GPO, Adelaide

(Des M. Tannenberg, plates by D.L.R.)

1894 (1 Mar)**–1906.** W **13**.

		(a) P 15		
234	**22**	2½d. violet-blue	48·00	7·50
235	**23**	5d. brown-purple	42·00	3·75
		234s/5s Optd "SPECIMEN" *Set of 2*	70·00	

		(b) P 13		
236	**22**	2½d. violet-blue (11.2.95)	32·00	1·00
237		2½d. indigo (25.3.98)	10·00	2·00
238	**23**	5d. Brown-purple (1.96)	10·00	1·75
		a. Purple	10·00	1·75

(c) P 12×11½ (comb)

239	**22**	2½d. indigo (4.7.06)	16·00	5·50
240	**23**	5d. dull purple (1.05)	21·00	2·50

(Typo D.L.R.)

1899 (27 Dec)–**1905**. W **13**.

(a) P 13

241	**24**	½d. yellow-green	7·50	1·50

(b) P 12×11½ (comb)

242	**24**	½d. yellow-green (7.05)	8·00	2·50

25

The measurements given indicate the length of the value inscription in the bottom label. The dates are those of the earliest known postmarks.

1902–04. As T **19**, but top tablet as T **25** (thin "POSTAGE"). W **13**.

(a) P 11½–12½

268		3d. olive-green (18½ mm) (1.8.02)	18·00	3·00
		a. Wmk sideways	†	£1700
269		4d. red-orange (17 mm) (29.11.02)	35·00	4·75
270		6d. blue-green (16–16½ mm)		
		(29.11.02)	13·00	3·25
271		8d. ultramarine (mm) (25.4.02)	8·50	18·00
272		8d. ultramarine (16½ mm) (22.3.04)	12·00	18·00
		a. "EIGNT" (R.2/9)	£2500	£3000
273		9d. rosy lake (19.9.02)	16·00	12·00
		a. Imperf between (vert pair)		£2500
274		10d. dull yellow (29.11.02)	18·00	19·00
275		1s. brown (18.8.02)	26·00	8·00
		a. Imperf between (horiz pair)		£2500
		b. Imperf between (vert pair)		£2500
		c. "POSTAGE" and value in red-brown .	£1300	£1100
276		2s.6d. pale violet (19.9.02)	80·00	50·00
		a. Bright violet (2.2.03)	42·00	15·00
277		5s. rose (17.10.02)	£120	75·00
278		10s. green (1.11.02)	£200	90·00
279		£1 blue (1.11.02)	£500	£250

(b) P 12

280		3d. olive-green (20 mm) (15.4.04)	32·00	3·50
		a. "POSTAGE" omitted; value below "AUSTRALIA"	£4500	
281		4d. orange-red (17½–18 mm)		
		(18.2.03)	25·00	3·00
282		6d. blue-green (15 mm) (14.11.03)	26·00	17·00
283		9d. rosy lake (2.12.03)	£130	32·00

No. 280a comes from the bottom row of the sheet. Other stamps show the value below "AUSTRALIA" with "POSTAGE" over the bottom frame (*Price* £950, *unused*).

A used example of No. 273 in imperf between horiz pair is in the Royal Philatelic Collection.

PRINTER. Stamp printing in Adelaide ceased in 1909 when the Printer of Stamps, J. B. Cooke, was appointed head of the Commonwealth Stamp Printing Branch in Melbourne. From 9 March 1909 further printings of current South Australia stamps were made in Melbourne.

26

V   X

In Type X the letters in the bottom line are slightly larger than in Type V, especially the "A", "S" and "P".

 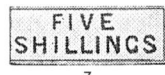

Y   Z

In Type Z the letters "S" and "G" are more open than in Type Y.
Nos. 196/a and 277 are similar to Type Y with all letters thick and regular and the last "S" has the top curve rounded instead of being slightly flattened.

1904–11. As T **19**, but top tablet as T **26** (thick "POSTAGE"). W **13**. P 12.

284		6d. blue-green (27.4.04)	42·00	3·00
		a. Imperf between (vert pair)	£4750	
285		8d. bright ultramarine (4.7.05)	18·00	8·50
		a. Value closer (15¼ mm)	70·00	28·00
		b. Dull ultramarine (2.4.08)	26·00	6·50
		ba. Ditto. Value closer (15¼ mm)	£110	20·00
286		9d. rosy lake (17–17¼ mm) (18.7.04)	24·00	6·50
		a. Value closer (16½–16¾ mm)	65·00	8·50
		b. Brown-lake. Perf 12½ small holes		
		(11.3.11)	17·00	26·00
287		10d. dull yellow (8.07)	18·00	25·00
		a. Imperf between (horiz pair)	£2750	£3000
		b. Imperf between (vert pair)	£4000	
288		1s. brown (12.4.04)	32·00	4·00
		a. Imperf between (vert pair)	£2500	
		b. Imperf between (horiz pair)	£2750	
289		2s.6d. bright violet (V.) (14.7.05)	75·00	42·00
		a. Dull violet (8.06)	75·00	27·00
290		5s. rose-scarlet (Y) (13.7.04)	75·00	48·00
		a. Scarlet (Z) (8.06)	75·00	48·00
		b. Pale rose. Perf 12½ (small holes) (Z)		
		(6.10)	£120	70·00
291		10s. green (26.8.08)	£200	£150
292		£1 blue (29.12.04)	£325	£170
		a. Perf 12½ (*small holes*) (6.10)	£250	£160

The "value closer" variety on the 8d. occurs six times in the sheet of 60. The value normally measures 16½ mm but in the variety it is 15¼ mm.

The 9d., 5s. and £1, perf 12½ (small holes), are late printings made in 1910–11 to use up the Crown SA paper.

No. 286b has the value as Type C of the 9d. on Crown over A paper.

27

1905–12. W **27**. P 12×11½ (new comb machine).

293	**24**	½d. pale green (4.07)	17·00	1·25
		a. Yellow-green	8·50	1·25
		b. Thin ready gummed paper		
		(1912)	6·00	8·00
		ba. Perf 11½×11½ and 12½	£850	
294	**11**	1d. rosine (2.12.05)	7·50	20
		a. Scarlet (4.11)	4·00	1·25
295	**12**	2d. bright violet (2.2.06)	27·00	30
		aa. Imperf three sides (horiz pair)	£3000	
		a. Mauve (4.08)	7·50	30
296	**22**	2½d. indigo-blue (14.9.10)	9·00	15·00
297	**23**	5d. brown-purple (11.3.08)	30·00	6·50

No. 295aa is perforated at foot.

Three types of the 9d., perf 12½, distinguishable by the distance between "NINE" and "PENCE".
A. Distance 1¾ mm. B. Distance 2¼ mm. C. Distance 2½ mm.

1906–12. T **19** ("POSTAGE" thick as T **26**). W **27**. P 12 or 12½ (small holes).

298		3d. sage-green (19 mm) (26.6.06)	16·00	5·50
		a. Imperf between (horiz pair)	†	£5500
		b. Perf 12½. Sage-green (17 mm)		
		(9.12.09)	17·00	11·00
		c. Perf 12½. Deep olive (20 mm) (7.10)....	75·00	11·00
		d. Perf 12½. Yellow-olive (19 mm)		
		(16.12.11)	80·00	60·00
		da. Perf 12½. Bright olive-green		
		(19–19¾ mm) Thin ready gummed		
		paper (8.9.11)	12·00	25·00
		e. Perf 11 (17 mm) (1910)	£1000	£700
299		4d. orange-red (10.9.06)	12·00	3·00
		a. Orange	12·00	3·00
		b. Perf 12½. Orange	25·00	8·50
		c. Thin ready gummed paper		
		(19.8.12)	25·00	32·00
300		6d. blue-green (1.9.06)	17·00	2·50
		a. Perf 12½ (21.4.10)	8·00	9·50
		ab. Perf 12½. Imperf between (vert pair)..	£2250	£2500
		b. Thin ready gummed paper (3.12)	10·00	19·00
301		8d. bright ultramarine (P 12½) (8.09)	10·00	22·00
		a. Value closer (8.09)	45·00	85·00
302		9d. brown-lake (3.2.06)	23·00	5·50
		aa. Imperf between (horiz strip of		
		three)	£4750	
		a. Imperf between (vert pair)	£2000	
		b. Deep lake (9.5.08)	50·00	9·00
		c. Perf 12½. Lake (A) (5.9.09)	11·00	10·00
		d. Perf 12½. Lake (B) (7.09)	45·00	11·00
		e. Perf 12½. Brown-lake	45·00	11·00
		ea. Perf 12½. Deep lake. Thin paper (C)..	35·00	11·00
		f. Perf 11 (1909)	†	£1500
303		1s. brown (30.5.06)	12·00	5·00
		aa. Imperf between (vert pair)	£3250	
		a. Imperf between (horiz pair)	£3500	
		b. Perf 12½ (10.3.10)	10·00	7·50
		c. Thin ready gummed paper (4.8.11)	14·00	16·00
304		2s.6d. bright violet (X) (10.6.09)	75·00	32·00
		a. Perf 12½. Pale violet (X) (6.10)	75·00	35·00
		ab. Perf 12½. Deep purple (X) Thin		
		ready gummed paper (15.11.12).......	£120	£120
305		5s. bright rose (P 12½) (Z) Thin ready		
		gummed paper (24.4.11)	£140	£140

The "value closer" variety of the 8d. occurred 11 times in the sheet of 60 in the later printing only. On No. 301 the value measures 16½ mm while on No. 301a it is 15¼ mm.

The 1s. brown, perf compound of 11½ and 12½, formerly listed is now omitted, as it must have been perforated by the 12 machine, which in places varied from 11½ to 13. The 4d. has also been reported with a similar perforation.

STAMP BOOKLETS

There are very few surviving examples of Nos. SB1/4. Listings are provided for those believed to have been issued with prices quoted for those known still to exist.

1904 (1 Jan)–**09**. Black on red cover as Type B **1** of New South Wales. Stapled.

SB1	£1 booklet containing 240×1d. in four blocks of 30 and two blocks of 60	
	a. Red on pink cover (1909)	
	b. Blue on pink cover	£15000

1904 (1 Jan). Black on grey cover as No. SB1. Stapled.

SB2	£1 booklet containing 120×2d. in four blocks of 30	

1910 (May). Black on cream cover as Type B **2** of New South Wales. Stapled.

SB3	2s. booklet containing 11×½d. (No. 241), either in block of 6 plus block of 5 or block of 11, and 18×1d. (No. 176a), either in three blocks of 6 or block of 6 plus block of 12	

Unsold stock of No. SB3 was uprated with one additional ½d. in May 1911.

1911 (Aug). Red on pink cover as No. SB3. Stapled.

SB4	2s. booklet containing 12×½d. (No. 241), either in two blocks of 6 or block of 12, and 18×1d. (No. 176a), either in three blocks of 6 or block of 6 plus block of 12	£7000

OFFICIAL STAMPS

A. Departmentals

Following suspected abuses involving stamps supplied for official use it was decided by the South Australian authorities that such supplies were to be overprinted with a letter, or letters, indicating the department of the administration to which the stamps had been invoiced.

The system was introduced on 1 April 1868 using overprints struck in red. Later in the same year the colour of the overprints was amended blue, and, during the latter months of 1869, to black.

In 1874 the Postmaster-General recommended that this some-what cumbersome system be replaced by a general series of "O.S." overprints with the result that the separate accounting for the Departmentals ceased on 30 June of that year. Existing stocks continued to be used, however, and it is believed that much of the residue was passed to the Government Printer to pay postage on copies of the *Government Gazette*.

We are now able to provide a check list of these most interesting issues based on the definitive work. *The Departmental Stamps of South Australia* by A. R. Butler, FRPSL, RDP, published by the Royal Philatelic Society, London in 1978.

No attempt has been made to assign the various overprints to the catalogue numbers of the basic stamps, but each is clearly identified by both watermark and perforation. the colours are similar to those of the contemporary postage stamps, but there can be shade variations. Errors of overprint are recorded in footnotes, but not errors occurring on the basic stamps used.

Most departmental overprints are considered to be scarce to rare in used condition, with unused examples, used multiples and covers being regarded as considerable rarities.

Forgeries of a few items do exist, but most can be readily identified by comparison with genuine examples. A number of forged overprints on stamps not used for the genuine issues also occur.

A. (Architect)

Optd in red with stop. W **2**. 2d. (Roul), 4d. (P 11½–12½), 6d. (Roul), 1s. (Roul)

Optd in red without stop W **2**. Roul. 1d., 2d., 6d., 1s.

Optd in black. (*a*) W **2**. 4d. (P 10×11½–12½), 6d. (P 11½–12½), 2s. (Roul)

(*b*) W **10**. 2d. D.L.R. (Roul), 2d. D.L.R. (P 10)

A.G. (Attorney-General)

Optd in red. W **2**. Roul. 1d., 2d., 6d., 1s.

Optd in blue. (*a*) W **2**. Roul. 6d.

(*b*) W **10**. Roul. 2d. D.L.R.

Optd in black. (*a*) W **2**. 1d (P 11½–12½×Roul), 4d. (P 11½–12½), 4d. (P 10), 6d. (P 11½–12½×Roul), 6d. (P 11½–12½×Roul), 1s. (P 11½–12½×Roul), 1s. (P 11½–12½) 1s. (P 10)

(*b*) W **10**. 2d. D.L.R. (Roul), 2d. D.L.R. (P 10)

A.O. (Audit Office)

Optd in red. W **2**. 2d. (Roul), 4d. (P 11½–12½), 6d. (Roul)

Optd in blue. (*a*) W **2**. P 11½–12½. 1d., 6d.

(*b*) W **10**. Roul. 2d. D.L.R.

Optd in black. (*a*) W **2**. 1d. (P 11½–12½×Roul), 1d. (P 10), 2d. D.L.R. (Roul), 4d. (P 11½–12½) 4d. (P 10), 4d. (P 10×11½–12½), 6d. (Roul), 6d. (P 11½–12½), 1s. (P 11½–12½), 1s. (P 11½–12½×Roul)

(*b*) W **7**. P 10. 4d.

(*c*) W **10**. 2d. D.L.R. (Roul), 2d. D.L.R. (P 10)

B.D. (Barracks Department)

Optd in red. W **2**. Roul. 2d., 6d., 1s.

B.G. (Botanic Garden)

Optd in black. (*a*) W **2**. 1d. (P 11½–12½×Roul), 1d. (P 11½–12½), 1d. (P 10×11½–12½), 2d. D.L.R. (Roul), 6d. (Roul), 6d. (P 11½–12½×Roul), 6d. (P 11½–12½×Roul), 1s. (P 11½–12½), 1s. (P 10), 1s. (P 10×11½–12½)

(*b*) W **7**. P 10, 2d. D.L.R.

(*c*) W **10**. 2d. D.L.R. (Roul), 2d. D.L.R. (P 10)

The 6d. (W **2**. Roul) is known without stop after "B".

B.M. (Bench of Magistrates)

Optd in red. W **2**. Roul. 2d.

Optd in black. W **10**. Roul. 2d. D.L.R.

C. (Customs)

Optd in red. W **2**. 1d. (Roul), 2d. (Roul), 4d. (Roul), 6d. (Roul), 1s. (Roul)

Optd in blue (*a*) W **2**. Roul. 1d., 4d., 6d., 1s., 2s.

(*b*) W **10**. Roul. 2d. D.L.R.

Optd in black. (*a*) W **2**. 1d. (Roul), 1d. (P 10), 1d. (P 10×11½–12½), 4d. (P 11½–12½), 4d. (P 10), 4d. (P 10×11½–12½), 6d. (Roul), 6d. (P 11½–12½), 6d. (P 10), 1s. (P 11½–12½×Roul), 1s. (P 11½–12½), 2s. (Roul)

(*b*) W **7**. P 10. 2d. D.L.R.

(*c*) W **10**. 2d. D.L.R. (Roul), 2d. D.L.R. (P 10×Roul), 2d. D.L.R. (P 10), 2d. D.L.R. (P 10×11½–12½)

The 2d. (W **10**. Roul) with black overprint is known showing the error "G" for "C".

C.D. (Convict Department)

Optd in red. W **2**. 2d., 4d. (P 11½–12½), 6d. (Roul), 1s. (Roul)

Optd in black. (*a*) W **2**. 1d. (P 11½–12½×Roul), 2d. D.L.R. (Roul), 4d. (P 11½–12½), 6d. (Roul), 6d. (P 11½–12½×Roul), 1s. (P 11½–12½)

(*b*) W **10**. 2d. D.L.R. (Roul), 2d. D.L.R. (P 10), 2d. D.L.R. (P 11½–12½×Roul)

C.L. (Crown Lands)

Optd in red. W **2**. 2d., 4d. (P 11½–12½), 6d. (Roul), 1s. (Roul)

Optd in blue. (*a*) W **2**. Roul. 4d., 6d.

(*b*) W **10**. Roul. 2d. D.L.R.

Optd in black. (*a*) W **2**. 2d. D.L.R. (Roul), 4d. (P 10), 4d. (P 11½–12½), 6d. (Roul), 6d. (P 11½–12½×Roul), 1s. (Roul), 2s. (Roul), 2s. (P 11½–12½)

(*b*) W **7**. P 10. 2d. D.L.R., 4d.

(*c*) W **10**. 2d. D.L.R. (Roul), 2d. D.L.R. (P 10), 2d. D.L.R. (P 10×11½–12½)

The 2s. (W **2**. P 11½–12½) with black overprint is known showing the stop omitted after "L".

C.O. (Commissariat Office)

Optd in red. W **2**, 4d. (P 11½–12½) 6d. (Roul), 1s. (Roul)

Optd in black. (*a*) W **2**. 4d. (P 10), 4d. (P 10×11½–12½), 6d. (P 11½–12½), 1s. (P 11½–12½), 2s. (Roul), 2s. (P 11½–12½)

(*b*) W **10**. 2d. D.L.R. (Roul), 2d. D.L.R. (P 10)

The 6d. (W **2**) with red overprint is known showing the error "O" for "C", and the 2s. (W **2**. P 11½–12½) with black overprint with the stop omitted after "O".

C.P. (Commissioner of Police)

Optd in red. W **2**. 2d. (Roul). 4d. (P 11½–12½) 6d. (Roul)

C.S. (Chief Secretary)

Optd in red. W **2**. 2d. (Roul), 4d. (P 11½–12½), 6d. (Roul), 1s. (Roul)

Optd in blue. (*a*) W **2**. Roul. 4d., 6d.

(*b*) W **10**. Roul. 2d. D.L.R.

Optd in black. (*a*) W **2**. 2d. D.L.R. (Roul), 4d. (Roul), 4d. (P 11½–12½×Roul), 4d. (P 11½–12½), 4d. (P 10), 4d. (P 10×11½–12½), 6d. (P 11½–12½), 6d. (P 11½–12½×Roul), 6d. (P 11½–12½), 6d. (P 10), 6d. (P 10×11½–12½), 1s. (P 11½–12½), 1s. (P 10), 1s. (P 10×11½–12½), 2s. (P 10×11½–12½)

(*b*) W **7**. P 10. 2d.

(*c*) W **10**. 2d. D.L.R. (Roul), 2d. D.L.R. (P 10)

The 6d. and 1s. (W **2**. Roul) with red overprint are known showing the error "G" for "C".

C.Sgn. (Colonial Surgeon)

Optd in red. W **2**. 2d. (Roul), 4d. (P 11½–12½) 6d. (Roul)

Optd in black. (*a*) W **2**. 2d. D.L.R. (Roul), 4d. (P 10), 4d. (P 10×11½–12½), 6d. (Roul), 6d. (P 11½–12½×Roul) 6d. (P 11½–12½)

(*b*) W **10**. 2d. D.L.R. (Roul), 2d. D.L.R. (P 10×Roul), 2d. D.L.R. (P 10)

Two types of overprint exist on the 2d. D.L.R., the second type having block capitals instead of the serifed type used for the other values.

D.B. (Destitute Board)

Optd in red. W **2**. 1d. (Roul), 2d. (Roul), 4d. (P 11½–12½), 6d. (Roul), 1s. (Roul)

Optd in blue. (*a*) W **2**. 2d. D.L.R. (Roul), 4d. (P 11½–12½), 6d. (Roul)

(*b*) W **10**. Roul. 2d. D.L.R.

Optd in black. (*a*) W **2**. 1d. (Roul), 4d. (P 11½–12½), 4d. (P 10), 6d. (P 10×11½–12½) 1s (P 10)

(*b*) W **10**. 2d. D.L.R. (Roul), 2d. D.L.R. (P 10), 2d. D.L.R. (P 10×11½–12½)

The 2d. D.L.R. (W **10**. P 10) with black overprint is known showing the stop omitted after "D".

D.R. (Deeds Registration)

Optd in red. W **2**. Roul, 2d., 6d.

E. (Engineer)

Optd in red. W **2**. 2d. (Roul), 4d. (P 11½–12½), 6d. (Roul), 1s. (Roul)

Optd in blue. (*a*) W **2**. Roul. 1s.

(*b*) W **10**. Roul. 2d. D.L.R.

Optd in black. (*a*) W **2**. 4d. (P 11½–12½), 4d. (P 10), 4d. (P 10×11½–12½), 6d. (P 11½–12½), 1s. (P 11½–12½×Roul), 1s. (P 10×11½–12½)

(*b*) W **7**. P 10. 4d.

(*c*) W **10**. P 10. 2d. D.L.R.

E.B. (Education Board)

Optd in red. W **2**. 4d. (P 11½–12½), 6d. (Roul)

Optd in blue. (*a*) W **2**. Roul. 4d., 6d.

(*b*) W **10**. Roul. 2d. D.L.R.

Optd in black. (*a*) W **2**. 2d. D.L.R. (Roul), 4d (Roul), 4d. (P 11½–12½), 4d. (P 10), 6d. (P 11½×12½×Roul), 6d. (P 11½×12½)

(*b*) W **7**. P 10. 2d. D.L.R.

(*c*) W **10**. 2d. D.L.R. (Roul), 2d. D.L.R. (P 10), 2d. D.L.R. (P 10×11½–12½)

G.F. (Gold Fields)

Optd in black. (*a*) W **2**. Roul. 6d.

(*b*) W **10**. 2d. D.L.R. (P 10×Roul), 2d. D.L.R. (P 10)

G.P. (Government Printer)

Optd in red. W **2**. Roul. 1d., 2d., 6d., 1s.

Optd in blue. (*a*) W **2**. Roul. 1d., 6d., 1s., 2s.

(*b*) W **10**. Roul. 2d. D.L.R.

Optd in black. (*a*) W **2**. 1d. (Roul), 1d. (P 11½–12½×Roul), 1d. (P 11½–12½) 1d. (P 10) 1d. (P 10×11½–12½), 6d. (P 11½–12½×Roul), 1s. (P 10×11½–12½), 2s. (Roul), 2s. (P 11½–12½) 2s. (P 10×11½–12½)

(*b*) W **10**. 2d. D.L.R. (Roul), 2d. D.L.R. (P 10)

The 1d. and 1s. (W **2**. Roul) with red overprint are known showing "C.P." instead of "G.P.".

G.S. (Government Storekeeper)

Optd in black. W **2**. Roul. 2d.

G.T. (Goolwa Tramway)

Optd in red. W **2**. 1d. (Roul), 2d. (Roul), 4d. (P 11½–12½), 6d. (Roul), 1s. (Roul)

Optd in black. (*a*) W **2**. 2d. D.L.R. (Roul), 4d. (P 11½–12½)

(*b*) W **10**. Roul. 2d. D.L.R.

The 2d. and 6d. (both W **2**. Roul) with red overprint are known showing the stop omitted after "T". The 6d, and 1s. (W **2**. Roul) with red overprint are known showing "C.T.", instead of "G.T.".

H. (Hospitals)

Optd in black. (*a*) W **2**. P 10×11½–12½. 4d.

(*b*) W **7**. P 10. 2d. D.L.R.

(*c*) W **10**. 2d. D.L.R. (P 10), 2d. D.L.R. (P 10×11½–12½)

H.A. (House of Assembly)

Optd in red. W **2**. 1d. (Roul), 2d. (Roul), 4d. (P 11½–12½), 6d. (Roul), 1s. (Roul)

Optd in black. (*a*) W **2**. 1d. (P 11½–12½), 1d. (P 10) 1d. (P 10×11½–12½), 4d. (P 11½–12½), 4d. (P 10) 6d. (Roul), 6d. (P 11½–12½) 1s. (P 11½–12½×Roul), 1s. (P 11½–12½)

(*b*) W **10**. 2d. D.L.R. (Roul), 2d. D.L.R. (P 10)

I.A. (Immigration Agent)

Optd in red. W **2**. 1d. (Roul), 2d. (Roul), 4d. (P 11½–12½), 6d. (Roul)

I.E. (Intestate Estates)

Optd in black. W **10**. P 10. 2d. D.L.R.

I.S. (Inspector of Sheep)

Optd in red. W **2**. Roul. 2d., 6d.

Optd in blue. W **2**. P 11½–12½. 6d.

Optd in black. (*a*) W **2**. 2d. D.L.R. (Roul), 6d. (P 11½–12½×Roul)

(*b*) W **10**. 2d. D.L.R. (Roul). 2d. D.L.R. (P 10)

L.A. (Lunatic Asylum)

Optd in red. W **2**. 1d. (Roul), 2d. (Roul), 4d. (P 11½–12½), 6d. (Roul), 1s. (Roul)

Optd in black. (*a*) W **2**. 4d. (P 11½–12½), 4d. (P 10), 4d. (P 10×11½–12½), 6d. (P 11½–12½), 1s. (P 11½–12½), 2s. (Roul)

(*b*) W **10**. 2d. D.L.R. (Roul), 2d. D.L.R. (P 10)

L.C. (Legislative Council)

Optd in red. W **2**. Roul. 2d., 6d.

Optd in black. (*a*) W **2**. Roul. 6d.

(*b*) W **10**. 2d. D.L.R. (Roul), 2d. D.L.R. (P 10×Roul)

The 2d. and 6d. (both W **2**. Roul) with red overprint are known showing the stop omitted after "C".

L.L. (Legislative Librarian)

Optd in red. W **2**. 2d. (Roul), 4d. (P 11½–12½), 6d. (Roul)

Optd in black. (*a*) W **2**. P 11½–12½. 6d.

(*b*) W **10**. P 10. 2d. D.L.R.

The 2d. and 6d. (both W **2**. Roul) with red overprint are known showing the stop omitted from between the two letters.

L.T. (Land Titles)

Optd in red. W **2**. 2d. (Roul), 4d. (P 11½–12½), 6d. (Roul), 1s. (Roul)

Optd in blue. W **10**. Roul. 2d. D.L.R.

Optd in black. (*a*) W **2**. 4d. (P 11½–12½), 4d. (P 10), 4d. (P 10×11½–12½), 6d. (P 11½–12½×Roul), 6d. (P 11½–12½), 6d. (P 10), 6d. (P 10×11½–12½)

(*b*) W **7**. P 10. 2d. D.L.R.

(*c*) W **10**. 2d. D.L.R. (Roul), 2d. D.L.R. (P 10)

The 2d. and 6d. (both W **2**. Roul) with red overprint are known showing the stop omitted after "T".

M. (Military)

Optd in red. W **2**. Roul. 2d., 6d., 1s.

Optd in black. W **2**. 6d. (P 11½–12½×Roul), 1s. (P 11½–12½×Roul), 2s. (Roul)

M.B. (Marine Board)

Optd in red. W **2**. 1d. (Roul), 2d. (Roul), 4d. (Roul), 4d. (P 11½–12½), 6d. (Roul), 1s. (Roul)

Optd in black. (*a*) W **2**. 1d. (Roul), 1d. (P 11½–12½×Roul), 2d. (Roul), 4d. (P 11½–12½×Roul), 4d. (P 10), 4d. (P 10×11½–12½), 6d. (Roul), 6d. (P 11½–12½), 6d. (P 10), 6d. (P 10×11½–12½), 1s. (P 11½–12½×Roul), 1s. (P 11½–12½), 1s. (P 10×11½–12½)

(*b*) W **7**. P 10. 4d.

(*c*) W **10**. Roul. 2d. D.L.R.

M.R. (Manager of Railways)

Optd in red. W **2**. Roul. 2d., 6d.

Optd in black. (*a*) W **2**. 1d. (P 11½–12½), 1d. (P 10), 2d. D.L.R. (Roul), 4d. (Roul), 4d. (P 11½–12½×Roul), 6d. (P 11½–12½×Roul), 6d. (P 11½–12½×Roul), 2s. (P 11½–12½ 1, 2s. (P 10×11½–12½)

(*b*) W **10**. 2d. D.L.R. (Roul), 2d. D.L.R. (P 10), 2d. D.L.R. (P 10×11½–12½)

M.R.G. (Main Roads Gambierton)

Optd in red without stops. W **2**. Roul. 2d., 6d.

Optd in blue without stops. W **10**. Roul. 2d. D.L.R.

Optd in black without stops. W **10**. 2d. D.L.R. (Roul), 2d. D.L.R. (Roul 10)

Optd in black with stops. W **10**. 2d. D.L.R. (Roul), 2d. D.L.R. (Roul 10)

The 2d. D.L.R. (W **10**. P 10) with black overprint is known showing the stops omitted after "M" and "R".

N.T. (Northern Territory)

Optd in black (*a*) W **2**. P 11½–12½. 1d., 3d. on 4d., 6d., 1s.

(*b*) W **10**. 2d. D.L.R. (Roul), 2d. D.L.R. (P 10)

O.A. (Official Assignee)

Optd in red. W **2**. 2d. (Roul), 4d. (P 11½–12½)

Optd in blue. W **10**. Roul. 2d. D.L.R.

Optd in black. W **2**. P 10. 4d.

(*b*) W **7**. P 10. 2d. D.L.R.

(*c*) W **10**. 2d. D.L.R. (Roul), 2d. D.L.R. (P 10×roul), 2d. D.L.R. (P 10)

P. (Police)

Optd in blue. (*a*) W **2**. Roul. 6d.

(*b*) W **10**. Roul. 2d. D.L.R.

Optd in black. (*a*) W **2**. 6d. (P 11½–12½×Roul), 6d. (P 11½–12½), 6d. (P 10)

(*b*) W **7**. P 10. 2d. D.L.R.

(*c*) W **10**. 2d. D.L.R. (Roul), 2d. D.L.R. (P 11½–12½×Roul), 2d. D.L.R. (P 10×Roul), 2d. D.L.R. (P 10), 2d. D.L.R. (P 10×11½–12½)

P.A. (Protector of Aborigines)

Optd in red. W **2**. Roul. 2d., 6d.

Optd in black. (*a*) W **2**. P. D.L.R., 6d.

(*b*) W **10**. 2d. D.L.R. (Roul), 2d. D.L.R. (P 10)

P.O. (Post Office)

Optd in red. W **2**. Roul. 1d., 2d., 6d., 1s.

Optd in blue. W **2**. Roul. 2d.

(*b*) W **10**. Roul. 2d. D.L.R.

Optd in black. (*a*) W **2**. 1d. (P 10×11½–12½), 2d. (Roul), 2d. D.L.R. (P 11½–12½×Roul), 2d. (P 11½–12½), 6d. (Roul), 6d. (P 11½–12½), 1s. (P 11½–12½×Roul), 1s. (P 11½12½) 1s. (P 11½–12½), 1s. (P 10) 1s. (P 10×11½–12½)

(*b*) W **10**. 2d. D.L.R. (Roul), 2d. (P 11½–12½×Roul), 2d. D.L.R. (P 10×Roul), 2d. D.L.R. (P 10)

The 4d. (W **2**. P 11½–12½) with black overprint is known showing the stop omitted after "O".

P.S. (Private Secretary)

Optd in red. W **2**. 1d. (Roul), 2d. (Roul), 4d. (P 11½–12½), 6d. (Roul), 1s. (Roul)

Optd in black. (*a*) W **2**. 1d. (P 11½–12½×Roul), 1d. (P 11½–12½), 1d. (P 10), 2d. (Roul), 3d. (in black) on 4d. (P 11½–12½), 3d. (in red) on 4d. (P 10), 3d. (in black) on 4d. (P 10), 4d. (P 11½–12½), 4d. (P 10), 4d. (P 10×11½–12½) 6d. (Roul), 6d. (P 11½–12½), 6d. (P 11½–12½), 9d. (Roul), 9d. (P 11½–12½) 10d. on 9d. (P 10), 10d. on 9d. (P 10×11½–12½), 1s. (P 11½–12½×Roul)

(*b*) W **7**. P 10. 2d. D.L.R.

(*c*) W **10**. 2d. D.L.R. (Roul), 2d. D.L.R. (P 10)

P.W. (Public Works)

Optd in red without stop after "W". W **2**. Roul. 2d., 6d., 1s.

Optd in black. (*a*) W **2**. 2d. D.L.R. (Roul), 4d. (P 10), 6d. (Roul), 6d. (P 11½–12½), 1s. (P 11½–12½×Roul)

(*b*) W **10**. 2d. D.L.R. (Roul), 2d. D.L.R. (P 10)

R.B. (Road Board)

Optd in red. W **2**. 1d. (Roul), 2d. (Roul), 4d. (P 11½–12½), 6d. (Roul), 1s. (Roul)

Optd in blue without stops. W **10**. Roul. 2d D.L.R

Optd in black. (*a*) W **2**. 1d. (P 11½–12½×Roul), 1d. (P 10), 4d. (P 10), 6d. (P 10), 2s. (Roul)

(*b*) W **7**. P 10. 2d. D.L.R.

(*c*) W **10**. 2d. D.L.R. (Roul), 2d. D.L.R. (P 10×Roul), 2d. D.L.R. (P 10)

The 6d. (W **2**. Roul) with red overprint is known showing the stop omitted after "B".

R.G. (Registrar-General)

Optd in red. W **2**. Roul. 2d., 6d., 1s.

Optd in blue. (*a*) W **2**. P 11½–12½×Roul. 6d.

(*b*) W **10**. 2d. D.L.R. (P 11½–12½×Roul)

Optd in black. (*a*) W **2**. 2d. D.L.R. (Roul), 6d. (P 10), 6d. (P 10×11½–12½), 1s. (P 11½–12½×Roul), 1s. (P 10)

(*b*) W **7**. P 10. 2d. D.L.R.

(*c*) W **10**. 2d. D.L.R. (Roul), 2d. D.L.R. (P 10×Roul), 2d. D.L.R. (P 10), 2d. D.L.R. (P 10×11½–12½)

The 2d. (W **2**. Roul) with red overprint is known showing "C" for "G".

S. (Sheriff)

Optd in red. W **2**. Roul. 2d., 6d.

Optd in blue. W **10**. Roul. 2d. D.L.R.

Optd in black. (*a*) W **2**. 6d. (Roul), 6d. (P 11½–12½×Roul), 6d. (P 11½–12½), 6d. (P 10)

(*b*) W **10**. 2d. D.L.R. (Roul), 2d. D.L.R. (P 10×Roul), 2d. D.L.R. (P 10)

S.C. (Supreme Court)

Optd in red. W **2**. Roul. 2d. 6d.

Optd in black. W **10**. P 10. 2d. D.L.R.

S.G. (Surveyor-General)

Optd in red. W **2**. 2d. (Roul), 4d. (P 11½–12½) 6d. (Roul)

Optd in blue. (*a*) W **2**. Roul. 4d.

(*b*) W **10**. Roul. 2d. D.L.R.

Optd in black. (*a*) W **2**. 2d. D.L.R. (Roul), 4d. (P 11½–12½), 4d. (P 10) 4d. (P 10×11½–12½), 6d. (P 11½–12½×Roul), 6d. (P 11½–12½), 6d. (P 10), 6d. (P 10×11½–12½)

(*b*) W **7**. P 10. 2d. D.L.R.

(*c*) W **10**. 2d. D.L.R. (Roul), 2d. D.L.R. (P 11½–12½), 2d. D.L.R. (P 10×Roul), 2d. D.L R (P 10)

The 2d. (W **7** and W **10**. P 10) with black overprint are known showing "C" for "G".

S.M. (Stipendiary Magistrate)

Optd in red. W **2**. 1d., 2d., 4d., 6d., 1s.

Optd in blue. (*a*) W **2**. Roul. 2d., 4d., 6d.

(*b*) W **10**. Roul. 2d. D.L.R.

Optd in black. (*a*) W **2**. 1d. (P 11½–12½), 1d. (P 10), 2d. D.L.R. (Roul), 4d. (Roul), 4d. (P 11½–12½×Roul), 4d. (P 11½–12½), 4d. (P 10), 4d. (P 10×11½–12½), 6d. (P 11½–12½×Roul), 6d. (P 11½–12½), 6d. (P 10), 6d. (P 10×11½–12½), 1s. (P 11½–12½×Roul)

(*b*) W **7**. P 10. 2d. D.L.R.

(*c*) W **10**. 2d. D.L.R. (Roul), 2d. D.L.R. (P 11½–12½), 2d. D.L.R. (P 10×Roul), 2d. D.L.R. (P 10), 2d D.L.R. (P 10×11½–12½)

The 2d. and 4d. (both W **2**. Roul) with red overprint are known showing the stop omitted after "M".

S.T. (Superintendent of Telegraphs)

Optd in red. W **2**. Roul. 2d., 6d.

Optd in blue. W **10**. Roul. 2d. D.L.R.

Optd in black. (*a*) W **2**. Roul. 2d. D.L.R., 6d.
(*b*) W **7**. P 10. 2d. D.L.R.
(*c*) W **10**. 2d. D.L.R. (Roul), 2d. D.L.R. (P 10×Roul), 2d. D.L.R. (P 10)
The 2d. and 6d. (both W **2**. Roul) with red overprint are known showing the stop omitted after "T".

T. (Treasury)

Optd in red. W **2**. 1d. (Roul), 2d. (Roul), 4d. (P 11½–12½×Roul), 6d. (Roul), 1s. (Roul)
Optd in blue. (*a*) W **2**. Roul. 1d., 4d., 6d.
(*b*) W **10**. Roul. 2d. D.L.R.
Optd in black. (*a*) W **2**. 1d. (P 10), 2d. D.L.R. (Roul), 4d. (Roul), 4d. (P 11½–12½), 4d. (P 10), 6d. (Roul), 6d. (P 11½–12½), 1s. (P 11½–12½×Roul), 1s. (P 10×11½–12½), 2s. (Roul), 2s. (P 11½–12½), 2s. (P 10×11½–12½)
(*b*) W **7**. P 10. 2d. D.L.R.
(*c*) W **10**. 2d. D.L.R. (Roul), 2d. D.L.R. (P 10)

T.R. (Titles Registration)

Optd in black. (*a*) W **2**. 4d. (P 11½–12½), 4d. (P 10×11½–12½), 6d. (P 11½–12½), 1s. (P 11½–12½)
(*b*) W **10**. P 10. 2d. D.L.R.

V. (Volunteers)

Optd in black. (*a*) W **2**. 4d. (P 10×11½–12½), 6d. (P 11½–12½), 1s. (P 11½–12½)
(*b*) W **7**. P 10. 2d. D.L.R.
(*c*) W **10**. 2d. D.L.R. (Roul), 2d. D.L.R. (P 10×Roul), 2d. D.L.R. (P 10)
The 2d. (W **10**. P 10×Roul) overprinted in black is only known showing the stop omitted after "V".

VA. (Valuator of Runs)

Optd in black without stop after "V". (*a*) W **2**. Roul. 4d.
(*b*) W **10**. P 10. 2d. D.L.R.

VN. (Vaccination)

Optd in black without stop after "V". W **2**. 4d. (P 10), 4d. (P 10×11½–12½)

W. (Waterworks)

Optd in red. W **2**. Roul. 2d.
Optd in black. W **10**. 2d. D.L.R. (Roul), 2d. D.L.R. (P 10)
The 2d. (W **2**. Roul) with red overprint is known showing the stop omitted after "W".

B. General

O.S. (O **1**)   **O.S.** (O **2**)

1874–77. Optd with Type O **1**. W **2**.

		(a) P 10		
O1	3	4d. dull purple (18.2.74)	£2750	£550
		(b) P 11½–12½×10		
O2	1	1d. green (2.1.74)	—	£475
O3	3	4d. dull violet (12.2.75)	£120	6·50
O4	1	6d. Prussian blue (20.10.75)	£180	11·00
O4a	3	2s. rose-pink (3.12.76)	—	£150
O5		2s. carmine (3.12.76)	—	£150
		(c) P 11½–12½		
O6	1	1d. deep yellow-green (30.1.74)	£3500	£400
		a. Printed on both sides	—	£1300
O7	3	3d. on 4d. ultramarine (26.6.77)	£8500	£3250
		a. No stop after "S"	—	£4250
O8		4d. dull violet (13.7.74)	85·00	9·00
		a. No stop after "S"	—	75·00
O9	1	6d. bright blue (31.8.75)	£275	22·00
		a. "O.S." double	—	£350
O10		6d. Prussian blue (27.3.74)	£250	9·50
		a. No stop after "S"	—	£100
O11	4	9d. red-purple (22.3.76)	£4250	£1700
		a. No stop after "S"	£4750	£2500
O12	1	1s. red-brown (5.8.74)	£110	6·50
		a. "O.S." inverted	—	£325
		b. No stop after "S"	£375	80·00
O13	3	2s. crimson-carmine (13.7.75)	£350	32·00
		a. No stop after "S"	—	£150
		b. No stops	—	£180
		c. Stops at top of letters		

1876–85. Optd with Type O **1**. W **8**.

		(a) P 10		
O14	1	6d. bright blue (1879)	£180	20·00
		(b) P 10×11½–12½, 11½–12½×10, or compound		
O15	3	4d. violet-slate (24.1.78)	£120	8·50
O16		4d. plum (29.11.81)	70·00	2·75
O17		4d. deep mauve	70·00	2·50
		a. No stop after "S"	£225	50·00
		b. No stop after "O"		
		c. "O.S." double		
		d. "O.S." inverted	—	£275
		e. Imperf between (horiz pair)		
O18	1	6d. bright blue (1877)	£150	5·50
		a. "O.S." inverted		
		b. No stop after "O"		
		c. Mixed perfs 10 and 11½–12½	—	†
O19		6d. bright ultramarine (27.3.85)	£150	5·50
		a. "O.S." inverted		
		b. "O.S." double		
		c. "O.S." double, one inverted	—	£550
		d. No stop after "S"	£600	75·00
		e. No stop after "O" and "S"		
O20		1s. red-brown (27.3.83)	95·00	7·00
		a. "O.S." inverted		
		b. No stop after "O"		
		c. No stop after "S"	—	80·00
O21	3	2s. carmine (16.3.81)	£300	9·00
		a. "O.S." inverted	—	£475
		b. No stop after "S"	—	£110

		(c) P 11½–12½		
O22	3	3d. on 4d. ultramarine	£8000	
O23		4d. violet-slate (14.3.76)	£200	27·00
O24		4d. deep mauve (19.8.79)	90·00	13·00
		a. "O.S." inverted	†	£800
		b. "O.S." double, one inverted	—	80·00
O25	1	6d. Prussian blue (6.77)	£140	7·50
		b. "O.S." double	—	£170
O26	4	8d. on 9d. brown (9.11.76)	£6000	£3000
		a. "O.S." double	£7000	
		b. "O" only	—	£3250
O26c		9d. purple	£8500	
O27	1	1s. red-brown (12.2.78)	55·00	8·50
		a. "O.S." inverted	£700	£250
		b. No stop after "S"	£350	85·00
O28		1s. lake-brown (8.11.83)	70·00	4·25
O29	3	2s. rose-carmine (12.8.85)	£250	8·50
		a. "O.S." double	—	£275
		b. "O.S." inverted	—	£325
		c. No stop after "S"	—	90·00

1891–1902. Optd with Type O **2**.

		(a) W 8. P 11½–12½		
O30	1	1s. lake-brown (18.4.91)	85·00	11·00
O31		1s. Vandyke brown	95·00	8·50
O32		1s. dull brown (2.7.96)	75·00	5·50
		a. No stop after "S"	—	90·00
O33		1s. sepia (*large holes*) (4.1.02)	70·00	5·50
		b. No stop after "S"	—	£450
O34	3	2s. carmine (26.6.00)	£150	15·00
		a. No stop after "S"		
		(b) W 8. P 10×11½–12½		
O35	3	2s. rose-carmine (9.11.95)	£150	10·00
		a. "O.S." inverted	£450	
		b. "O.S." double		
		(c) W 10. P 11½–12½		
O36	1	1s. dull brown (1902)	£100	48·00

1874–76. Optd with Type O **1**. W **10**.

		(a) P 10		
O37	11	1d. blue-green (30.9.75)	£225	40·00
		a. "O.S." inverted		
		b. No stop after "S"		
O38	12	2d. orange-red (18.2.74)	60·00	7·00
		a. "O.S." inverted	—	50·00
		(b) P 10×11½–12½, 11½–12½×10, or compound		
O39	11	1d. blue-green (16.9.75)		
		a. "O.S." inverted		
		b. No stop after "S"		
O40	12	2d. orange-red (27.9.76)	—	30·00
		(c) P 11½–12½		
O41	11	1d. blue-green (13.8.75)	—	60·00
		a. "O.S." inverted		
		b. No stop after "S"		
O42	12	2d. orange-red (20.5.74)	—	£150

1876–80. Optd with Type O **1**. W **13**.

		(a) P 10		
O43	11	1d. blue-green (2.10.76)	32·00	1·75
		a. "O.S." inverted	—	£110
		b. "O.S." double	£250	£110
		c. "O.S." double, one inverted		
		d. No stops	—	60·00
		e. No stop after "O"		
		f. No stop after "S"	—	21·00
		g. *Deep green*	50·00	1·00
		ga. "O.S." double	—	£150
O44	12	2d. orange-red (21.9.77)	16·00	1·00
		a. "O.S." inverted	—	65·00
		b. "O.S." double	£225	£120
		c. "O.S." double, one inverted	—	£350
		d. "O.S." double, both inverted	—	£110
		e. No stops		
		f. No stop after "O"	—	28·00
		g. No stop after "S"		
		h. *Dull brick-red*	75·00	1·00
		(b) P 10×11½–12½, 11½–12½×10 or compound		
O45	11	1d. deep green (14.8.80)	—	60·00
O46	12	2d. orange-red (6.4.78)	£100	29·00
		a. "O.S." inverted	—	£300
		b. No stop after "S"	—	£130
		(c) P 11½–12½		
O47	12	2d. orange-red (15.7.80)	—	90·00

1882 (20 Feb). No. 181 optd with Type O **1**.

O48	11	½d. on 1d. blue-green	£120	25·00
		a. "O.S." inverted		

1888 (15 Nov)–**91.** Nos. 184 and 185*a* optd with Type O **1**. P 10.

O49	17	4d. pale violet (24.1.91)	£130	11·00
O50	18	6d. blue	55·00	1·50
		a. "O.S." double		
		b. No stop after "S"		

1891. Nos. 229*b* and 231*a*/2 optd with Type O **1**.

		(a) P 10		
O51	17	2½d. on 4d. deep green (Br.) (1.8)	£130	14·00
		a. "2" and "½" closer together	—	50·00
		b. "O.S." inverted		
		c. "O.S." double		
		d. "OS" omitted (in vert pair with normal)		
		e. No stop after "S"		
		(b) P 10×11½–12½ or 11½–12½×10.		
O52	17	2½d. on 4d. deep green (Br.) (1.10)	£140	29·00
		(c) P 11½–12½		
O53	17	2½d. on 4d. deep green (Br.) (1.6)	£250	85·00

1891–96. Optd with Type O **2**. W **13**.

		(a) P 10		
O54	11	1d. deep green (22.4.91)	70·00	2·00
		a. "OS." double	£200	85·00
		b. "O.S." double, one inverted		

		c. No stop after "S"	£110	13·00
		d. Blackish blue opt	£250	4·50
O55	12	2d. orange-red (22.4.91)	60·00	3·50
		a. "O.S." double		
		b. "O.S." double, both inverted		
		c. "O.S." inverted	—	26·00
		(b) P 15		
O56	11	1d. green (8.9.94)	30·00	1·25
		a. "O.S." inverted		
		b. No stop after "S"		
		c. "O.S." double		
O57	12	2d. orange-red (16.6.94)	28·00	60
		a. "O.S." double	—	90·00
		b. "O.S." inverted	—	60·00
		(c) P 13		
O58	11	1d. green (20.5.95)	40·00	1·25
		a. No stop after "S"	£150	10·00
O59	12	2d. orange-red (11.2.96)	48·00	50
		a. "O.S." double	£350	
		b. No stop after "S"	£140	10·00

1891–99. Optd with Type O **2**. W **13** (sideways on ½d.).

		(a) P 10		
O60	15	½d. brown (2.5.94)	55·00	12·00
		a. "O.S." inverted	£250	
		b. No stop after "S"	£140	50·00
O61	17	4d. pale violet (13.2.91)	70·00	5·00
		a. "O.S." inverted		
		b. "S." omitted	—	£160
		c. No stop after "S"		
		d. *Aniline violet* (31.8.93)	70·00	12·00
		da. "O.S." inverted		
		dc. No stop after "S"		
O62	18	6d. blue (4.4.93)	45·00	2·50
		b. Blackish blue opt		
		(b) P 10×11½–12½		
O63	15	½d. brown (26.3.95)	50·00	8·00
		(c) P 11½–12½		
O64	15	½d. red-brown (13.6.91)	80·00	15·00
		(d) P 15		
O65	15	½d. pale brown (8.6.95)	75·00	21·00
O66	17	4d. slate-violet (4.4.95)	95·00	6·00
		a. "O.S." double	£500	£140
O67	18	6d. blue (20.9.93)	65·00	4·25
		(e) P 13		
O68	15	½d. deep brown (17.5.98)	65·00	6·00
		a. Opt triple, twice sideways	£375	
		b. "O.S." inverted		
O69	17	4d. violet (12.96)	£120	3·00
		a. "O.S." double	£475	£110
		b. No stop after "S"	£350	55·00
O70	18	6d. blue (13.9.99)	70·00	3·00
		a. No stop after "S"	£250	80·00

1891–95. Nos. 229*b*, 230*a* and 231*a* optd with Type O **2**.

		(a) P 10		
O71	17	2½d. on 4d. deep green (Br.) (18.8.94)	50·00	28·00
		a. Fraction bar omitted		
		b. "2" and "½" closer together	£120	55·00
		c. "O.S." inverted	£550	
		d. No stop after "S"	—	85·00
O72	18	5d. on 6d. deep brown (C.) (2.12.91)	55·00	18·00
		a. No stop after "5D"	£250	
		b. No stop after "S"	£190	70·00
		(b) P 10×11½–12½		
O73	17	2½d. on 4d. deep green (Br.) (17.9.95)	—	85·00

1897–1901. Nos. 235/6 and 238*a* optd with Type O **2**.

		(a) P 15		
O74	23	5d. brown-purple (29.3.01)	£120	22·00
		(b) P 13		
O75	22	2½d. violet-blue (12.5.97)	£110	7·50
			—	65·00
O76	23	5d. purple (29.9.01)	£120	27·00
		a. No stop after "S"		

O. S. (O **3**)

1899–1901. Optd with Type O **3**. W **13**. P 13.

O80	24	½d. yellow-green (12.2.00)	22·00	8·50
		a. "O.S." inverted	£150	
		b. No stop after "S"	85·00	
O81	11	1d. rosine (22.9.99)	28·00	1·60
		a. "O.S." inverted	£150	90·00
		b. "O.S." double	†	£475
		c. No stop after "S"	£100	18·00
O82	12	2d. bright violet (1.6.00)	32·00	80
		a. "O.S." inverted	£150	65·00
		b. "O.S." double		
		c. No stop after "S"	90·00	18·00
O83	22	2½d. indigo (2.10.01)	80·00	19·00
		a. "O.S." inverted	£475	£170
		b. No stop after "S"	£300	
O84	17	4d. violet (18.11.00)	80·00	5·50
		a. "O.S." inverted	£500	
		b. No stop after "S"	£250	
O85	18	6d. blue (8.10.00)	45·00	5·50
		a. No stop after "S"	£140	

1891 (May). Optd as Type O **3** but wider. W **13**. P 10.

O86	19	2s.6d. pale violet	£7500	£5500
O87	19	5s. pale rose	£8000	£6000

Only one sheet (60) of each of these stamps was printed.

The use of stamps overprinted "O S" was made invalid by the Posts and Telegraph Act of 1 November 1902.

South Australia became part of the Commonwealth of Australia on 1 January 1901.

TASMANIA

PRICES FOR STAMPS ON COVER	
Nos. 1/4	*from* × 6
Nos. 5/12	*from* × 5
Nos. 14/24	*from* × 3
Nos. 25/56	*from* × 5
Nos. 57/77	*from* × 6
Nos. 78/9	
Nos. 80/90	*from* × 3
No. 91	
Nos. 92/109	*from* × 3
No. 110	—
Nos. 111/23	*from* × 3
Nos. 124/6	
Nos. 127/34	*from* × 5
Nos. 135/55	*from* × 4
Nos. 156/8	*from* × 20
Nos. 159/66	*from* × 10
Nos. 167/9	*from* × 15
Nos. 170/4	*from* × 6
Nos. 216/22	*from* × 15
Nos. 223/5	
Nos. 226/7	*from* × 15
Nos. 229/36	*from* × 20
Nos. 237/57	*from* × 10
No. 258	—
Nos. 259/62	*from* × 10
Nos. F1/25	—
Nos. F26/9	*from* × 15
Nos. F30/9	—

SPECIMEN OVERPRINTS. Those listed are from UPU distributions between 1892 and 1904. Further "Specimen" overprints exist, but these were used for other purposes.

1	**2**	**3**

(Eng C.W. Coard. Recess H. and C. Best at the *Courier* newspaper, Hobart)

1853 (1 Nov). 24 varieties in four rows of six each. No wmk. Imperf.

(a) Medium soft yellowish paper with all lines clear and distinct

1	**1**	1d. pale blue	£12000	£1500
2		1d. blue	£12000	£1500

(b) Thin hard white paper with lines of the engraving blurred and worn

3	**1**	1d. pale blue	£11000	£1300
4		1d. blue	£11000	£1300

1853 (1 Nov). No wmk. Imperf. In each plate there are 24 varieties in four rows of six each.

(a) Plate I. Finely engraved. All lines in network and background thin, clear, and well defined

(i) First state of the plate, brilliant colours

5	**2**	4d. bright red-orange	£9000	£1000
6		4d. bright brownish orange	—	£1300

(ii) Second state of plate, with blurred lines and worn condition of the central background

7	**2**	4d. red-orange	£6500	£475
8		4d. orange	£6000	£450
9		4d. pale orange	—	£450

(b) Plate II. Coarse engraving, lines in network and background thicker and blurred

10	**2**	4d. orange	£6000	£425
11		4d. dull orange	£6000	£375
12		4d. yellowish orange	£6000	£375

In the 4d. Plate I, the outer frame-line is thin all round. In Plate II it is, by comparison with other parts, thicker in the lower left angle.

The 4d. is known on vertically laid paper from proof sheets. Examples from Plate I have the lines close together and those from Plate II wide apart (*Price* £10,000 *unused*).

In 1879 reprints were made of the 1d. in blue and the 4d., Plate I, in brownish yellow, on thin, tough, white wove paper, and perforated 11½. In 1887, a reprint from the other plate of the 4d. was made in reddish brown and black on thick white paper, imperforate, and in 1889 of the 1d. in blue and black, and of the 4d. (both plates) in yellow and in black on white card, imperforate. As these three plates were defaced after the stamps had been superseded, all these reprints show two, or three thick strokes across the Queen's head.

All three plates were destroyed in July 1950.

PERKINS BACON "CANCELLED". For notes on these handstamps, showing "CANCELLED" between horizontal bars forming an oval, see Catalogue Introduction.

(Eng W. Humphrys, after water-colour sketch by E. Corbould. Recess P.B.)

1855 (17 Aug–16 Sept). Wmk Large Star. W w **1**. Imperf.

14	**3**	1d. carmine (16.9) (H/S "CANCELLED" in oval £12000)	£10000	£900
15		2d. deep green (16.9)	£5500	£550
16		2d. green (16.9) (H/S "CANCELLED" in oval £13000)	£5500	£450
17		4d. deep blue	£5500	£130
18		4d. blue (H/S "CANCELLED" in oval £12000)	£5500	£130

Proofs of the 1d. and 4d. on thick paper, *without watermark*, are sometimes offered as the issued stamps. The 6d. dull lilac on this watermark was prepared, but not issued. Examples exist from a creased proof sheet (*Price* £750 *unused*).

(Recess H. and C. Best, Hobart, from P.B. plates)

1856 (Apr)–**57**. No wmk. Imperf.

(a) Thin white paper

19	**3**	1d. pale brick-red (4.56)	£13000	£650
20		2d. dull emerald-green (1.57)	£16000	£950
21		4d. deep blue (5.57)	£3000	£130

22		4d. blue (5.57)	£3000	£130
23		4d. pale blue (5.57)	—	£170

(b) Pelure paper

24	**3**	1d. deep red-brown (11.56)	£9000	£750

4	**7**	**8**

(Recess H. Best (August 1857–May 1859), J. Davies (August 1859–March 1862), J. Birchall (March 1863), M. Hood (October 1863–April 1864), Govt Printer (from July 1864), all from P.B. plates)

1857 (Aug)–**67**. Wmk double-lined numerals "1", "2" or "4" as W **4** on appropriate value. Imperf.

25	**3**	1d. deep red-brown	£1000	50·00
26		1d. pale red-brown	£650	40·00
27		1d. brick-red (1863)	£450	40·00
28		1d. dull vermilion (1865)	£375	35·00
29		1d. carmine (1867)	£375	30·00
30		2d. dull emerald-green	—	£130
31		2d. green	—	60·00
32		2d. yellow-green	£950	£110
33		2d. deep green (1858)	£900	70·00
34		2d. slate-green (1860)	£425	85·00
35		4d. deep blue	—	85·00
36		4d. pale blue	£475	26·00
37		4d. blue	£475	28·00
38		4d. bright blue	£475	28·00
		a. Printed on both sides	†	
39		4d. cobalt-blue	—	90·00

Printings before July 1864 were all carried out at the *Courier* printing works which changed hands several times during this period.

CANCELLATIONS. Beware of early Tasmanian stamps with pen-cancellations cleaned off and faked postmarks applied.

(Recess P.B.)

1858. Wmk double-lined numerals "6" or "12" as W **4**. Imperf.

40	**7**	6d. dull lilac (H/S "CANCELLED" in oval £13000)	£1200	90·00
41	**8**	1s. vermilion (*shades*) (H/S "CANCELLED" in oval £12000)	£800	80·00

(Recess J. Davies (March 1860), J. Birchall (April 1863), Govt Printer (from February 1865), all from P.B. plates)

1860 (Mar)–**67**. Wmk double-lined "6" as W **4**. Imperf.

44	**7**	6d. dull slate-grey	£900	85·00
45		6d. grey	—	90·00
46		6d. grey-violet (4.63)	£800	85·00
47		6d. dull cobalt (2.65)	£1300	£140
48		6d. slate-violet (2.65)	£900	75·00
49		6d. reddish mauve (4.67)	£1200	£180

In 1871 reprints were made of the 6d. (in mauve) and the 1s. on white wove paper, and perforated 11½. They are found with or without "REPRINT". In 1889 they were again reprinted on white card, imperforate. These later impressions are also found overprinted "REPRINT" and perforated 11½.

PERFORATED ISSUES. From 1 October 1857 the Tasmania Post Office only supplied purchasers requiring five or more complete sheets of stamps. The public obtained their requirements, at face value, from licensed stamp vendors, who obtained their stocks at a discount from the Post Office.

From 1863 onwards a number of the stamp vendors applied their own roulettes or perforations. The Hobart firm of J. Walch & Sons achieved this so successfully that they were given an official contract in July 1869 to perforate sheets for the Post Office. The Government did not obtain a perforating machine until late in 1871.

1863–71. Double-lined numeral watermarks. Various unofficial roulettes and perforations.

(a) By J. Walch & Sons, Hobart

(i) Roulette about 8, often imperf×roul (1863–68)

50	**3**	1d. brick-red	—	£475
51		1d. carmine	£900	£300
52		2d. yellow-green	—	£1200
53		2d. slate green	—	
54		4d. pale blue	—	£450
55	**7**	6d. dull lilac	—	£500
56	**8**	1s. vermilion	—	£1300

(ii) P 10 (1864–69)

57	**3**	1d. brick-red	£190	60·00
58		1d. dull vermilion	£190	50·00
59		1d. carmine	£150	50·00
60		2d. yellow-green	£800	£150
61		2d. slate-green	£800	£200
62		4d. pale blue	£400	20·00
63		4d. blue	£400	20·00
64	**7**	6d. grey-violet	£600	25·00
65		6d. dull cobalt	£800	£100
66		6d. slate-violet	—	50·00
67		6d. reddish mauve	£850	£100
68	**8**	1s. vermilion	£650	55·00
		a. Imperf vert (horiz pair)		

(iii) P 12 (1865–71—from July 1869 under contract to the Post Office)

69	**3**	1d. dull vermilion	£160	
70		1d. carmine	£120	23·00
		a. Error. Wmkd "2" (*pen cancel* £300)	—	£2750
71		2d. yellow-green	£600	95·00
72		4d. deep blue	£350	21·00
73		4d. blue	£350	23·00
74		4d. cobalt-blue	—	60·00
75	**7**	6d. slate-violet	£450	29·00
		a. Imperf between (vert pair)		
76		6d. reddish mauve	£180	42·00
		a. Imperf between (vert or horiz pair) (*pen cancel* £200)		
77	**8**	1s. vermilion	£450	70·00
		b. Imperf between (horiz pair) (*pen cancel* £275)	—	£3250

(iv) Perf compound 10×12 (1865–69)

78	**3**	1d. carmine	£3000	
79		4d. blue	—	£2500

(b) P 12½ by R. Harris, Launceston (1864–68)

80	**3**	1d. brick-red	£170	50·00
81		1d. dull vermilion	£160	50·00
82		1d. carmine	£100	25·00
83		2d. yellow-green	£750	£170
84		2d. slate-green	£650	£180
85		4d. blue	£450	55·00
86		4d. bright blue	£450	55·00
87	**7**	6d. dull cobalt	£800	£100
88		6d. slate-violet	£600	60·00
89		6d. reddish mauve	£850	£130
90	**8**	1s. vermilion	£700	£130
		a. Imperf between (horiz pair) (*pen cancel* £300)		

(c) Imperf×oblique roulette 11½ at Oatlands (1866)

91	**3**	4d. blue	—	£800
91*a*	**7**	6d. dull cobalt	†	

(d) Oblique roulette 10–10½, possibly at Deloraine (1867)

92	**3**	1d. brick-red	—	£750
93		1d. carmine	£2500	£650
94		2d. yellow-green	—	£1100
95		4d. bright blue	—	£850
96	**7**	6d. grey-violet	—	£1500

(e) Oblique roulette 14–15, probably at Cleveland (1867–69)

97	**3**	1d. brick-red	—	£1000
98		1d. dull vermilion	—	£1000
99		1d. carmine	—	£1000
100		2d. yellow-green	—	£1400
101		4d. pale blue	—	£1000
102	**7**	6d. grey-violet	—	£1800
103	**8**	1s. vermilion	—	£2250

(f) Pin-perf 5½ to 9½ at Longford (1867)

104	**3**	1d. carmine	£1000	£300
105		2d. yellow-green		
106		4d. bright blue	—	£550
107	**7**	6d. grey-violet	—	£550
108		6d. reddish mauve	—	£1200
109	**8**	1s. vermilion		

(g) Pin-perf 12 at Oatlands (1867)

110	**3**	4d. blue		

(h) Pin-perf 13½ to 14½ (1867)

111	**3**	1d. brick-red	—	£700
112		1d. dull vermilion	—	£700
113		1d. carmine		
114		2d. yellow-green	—	£1200
115		4d. pale blue	—	£600
116	**7**	6d. grey-violet	—	£1200
117	**8**	1s. vermilion		

(j) Serrated perf 19 at Hobart (1868–69)

118	**3**	1d. carmine (*pen-cancel* £20)	£750	£225
119		2d. yellow-green	—	£750
120		4d. deep blue	£1700	£225
121		4d. cobalt-blue	—	£225
122	**7**	6d. slate-violet	—	£1000
123	**8**	1s. vermilion		

(k) Roul 4½, possibly at Macquarie River (1868)

124	**3**	4d. blue		
125	**7**	6d. reddish mauve		
126	**8**	1s. vermilion		

An example of the 1d. carmine is known perforated 10 on three sides and serrated 19 on the fourth.

These local separations (Nos. 91/126) were sometimes applied only between the horizontal rows or vertical columns of sheets, so that pairs can be found 'imperforate vertically' or 'imperforate horizontally'.

For stamps perforated 11½ or 12 by the Post Office see Nos. 134*a*/43.

11	**12**

13	**14**

(Typo Govt Printer, Hobart, from plates made by D.L.R.)

1870 (1 Nov)–**71**. Wmk single-lined numerals W **12** (2d.), **13** (1d., 4d.) or **14** (10d.).

(a) P 12 by J. Walch & Sons

127	**11**	1d. rose-red (wmk "10")	£120	21·00
		b. *Deep rose-red*	£130	16·00
128		1d. rose-red (wmk "4") (3.71)	£140	65·00
		a. Imperf (pair)	†	
129		2d. yellow-green	£180	12·00
		b. *Blue-green*	£190	12·00
		ba. Double print		
130		4d. blue	£1200	£475
131		10d. black	24·00	50·00
		a. Imperf (pair)	£700	

(b) P 11½ by the Post Office (1871)

132	**11**	1d. rose-red (wmk "10")	£1100	
133		2d. yellow-green	£300	18·00
		a. Blue-green	£180	9·50
		ab. Double print	£5000	£1800
134		10d. black	50·00	50·00
		aa. Imperf vert (horiz pair)		

The above were printed on paper obtained from New South Wales. See also Nos. 144/55, 156/8, 159/66, 170/4, 226/7, 242 and 255/6.

(Recess P.B.)

1871. Wmk double-lined numeral "**12**". P 11½ by the Post Office.
134*a* 8 1s. vermilion...

(Recess Govt Printer, Hobart)

1871–91. Double-lined numeral watermarks as W **4**. Perforated by the Post Office.

(a) P 11½

135	7	6d. dull lilac....................................	£250	22·00
136		6d. lilac...	£225	22·00
		a. Imperf between (vert pair)........	—	£1700
		b. Imperf between (horiz pair)......		£1300
137		6d. deep slate-lilac (3.75).............	£225	22·00
		a. Imperf (pair).............................		£1300
138		6d. bright violet (5.78)..................	£250	35·00
		b. Imperf between (horiz pair)......	£3500	
139		6d. dull reddish lilac (10.79).........	£200	40·00
140	8	1s. brown-red (1.73)......................	£325	65·00
		a. Imperf between (horiz pair)......		
141		1s. orange-red (3.75)....................	£325	65·00
141*a*		1s. orange (5.78)...........................		

(b) P 12

142	7	6d. reddish purple (1884).............	£170	20·00
		a. Imperf between (horiz pair)......	£2250	
143		6d. dull claret (7.91).....................	50·00	14·00

The perforation machine used on Nos. 142/3 was previously owned by J. Walch and Sons and passed to the ownership of the Government in 1884. It may have been used to perforate leftover sheets of previous printings.

15 **16**

"Wedge" flaw (Right pane R. 10/6)

Line through "THREE PE" (Left pane R. 10/1)

(Typo Govt Printer, Hobart, from plates made by D.L.R.)

1871 (25 Mar)–**78**. W **15**.

(a) P 11½

144	11	1d. rose (5.71)...............................	16·00	2·50
		a. Imperf (pair) (*pen cancel* £150)...	—	£1300
		b. Bright rose...............................	15·00	2·50
		c. Carmine...................................	22·00	3·25
		d. Pink..	22·00	3·50
		e. Vermilion (4.75)........................	£275	75·00
		f. Wedge flaw.............................	£325	48·00
145		2d. deep green (11.72)..................	75·00	2·50
		a. Blue-green...............................	50·00	2·50
		b. Yellow-green (12.75).................	£250	4·50
146		3d. pale red-brown.......................	70·00	4·25
		a. Imperf (pair).............................	£600	£1000
		b. Imperf horiz (vert pair).............	£3500	
		c. Deep red-brown.......................	75·00	4·50
		d. Purple-brown (1.78)..................	75·00	4·25
		da. Line through "THREE PE"..........	£500	75·00
		e. Brownish purple.......................	65·00	4·25
147		4d. pale yellow (8.8.76).................	£160	48·00
		a. Ochre (7.78).............................	95·00	9·00
		b. Buff..	80·00	12·00
148		9d. blue (2.10.71).........................	29·00	8·00
		a. Imperf (pair).............................	£550	
		b. Double print............................	†	£3250
149		5s. purple (*pen cancel* £3.75).......	£350	80·00
		b. Mauve.....................................	£325	80·00

(b) P 12

150	11	1d. rose...	£140	30·00
		a. Carmine...................................	£150	32·00
		b. Wedge flaw.............................	—	£150
151		2d. green.......................................	£650	£140
152		3d. red-brown...............................	£130	22·00
		a. Deep red-brown.......................	£130	22·00
153		4d. buff...	£350	24·00
154		9d. pale blue.................................	55·00	
		a. Imperf between (horiz pair)......	£3750	
155		5s. purple......................................	£550	
		a. Mauve.....................................	£450	

(Typo D.L.R.)

1878 (28 Oct). W **16**. P 14.

156	11	1d. carmine...................................	12·00	1·00
		a. Rose-carmine...........................	6·50	1·00
		b. Scarlet.....................................	20·00	1·25
157		2d. pale green...............................	12·00	1·00
		a. Green.......................................	11·00	1·00
158		8d. dull purple-brown....................	14·00	10·00

(Typo Govt Printer, Hobart (some printings of 1d. in 1891 by *Mercury Press*) from plates made by Victoria Govt Printer, Melbourne (½d.) or D.L.R. (others))

1880 (Apr)–**91**. W **16**.

(a) P 11½

159	11	½d. orange (8.3.89)........................	3·00	3·25
		a. Deep orange.............................	3·00	3·25
160		1d. dull red (14.2.89)....................	15·00	3·50
		a. Vermilion-red............................	11·00	2·50
		b. Wedge flaw.............................	£130	35·00
161		3d. red-brown...............................	23·00	5·00
		a. Imperf (pair).............................	£450	
		b. Line through "THREE PE"...........	£250	75·00
162		4d. deep yellow (1.83)...................	85·00	18·00
		a. Chrome-yellow.........................	85·00	20·00
		b. Olive-yellow.............................	£150	27·00
		c. Buff..	40·00	9·50

(b) P 12

163	11	½d. orange.....................................	6·00	6·50
		a. Deep orange.............................	6·00	6·50
		ab. Wmk sideways.........................		
164		1d. pink (1891)..............................	40·00	16·00
		a. Imperf (pair).............................	£400	£425
		b. Rosine.....................................	38·00	12·00
		c. Dull rosine...............................	38·00	13·00
		ca. Imperf (pair)............................	£375	
		d. Wedge flaw.............................	£225	75·00
165		3d. red-brown...............................	8·00	8·50
		a. Imperf between (horiz pair)......	£2250	
		b. Line through "THREE PE"...........	95·00	80·00
166		4d. deep yellow.............................	£150	32·00
		a. Chrome-yellow.........................	£170	25·00
		ab. Printed both sides....................	£1500	

SPECIMEN AND PRESENTATION REPRINTS OF TYPE 11. In 1871 the 1d., 2d., 3d., 4d. blue, 9d., 10d. and 5s. were reprinted on soft white wove paper to be followed, in 1879, by the 4d. yellow and 8d. on rough white wove. Both these reprintings were perforated 11½. In 1886 it was decided to overprint remaining stocks with the word "REPRINT".

In 1889 Tasmania commenced sending sample stamps to the UPU in Berne and a further printing of the 4d. blue was made, imperforate, on white card. This, together with the 5s. in mauve on white card, both perforated 11½ and overprinted "REPRINT", were included in presentation sets supplied to members of the states' legislatures in 1901.

Halfpenny	$2\frac{1}{2}^{d.}$	$2\frac{1}{2}^{d.}$
(**17**)	(**18**) (2¼ *mm* between "d", and "2")	(**19**) (3½ *mm* between "d" and "2")

1889 (1 Jan). No. 156*b* surch locally with T **17**.

167	11	½d. on 1d. scarlet..........................	10·00	25·00
		a. "al" in "Half" printed sideways (R. 1/2).......	£2000	£1800

No. 167a occurred in a second printing and was later corrected.
A reprint on white card, perforated 11½ or imperforate, overprinted "REPRINT" was produced in 1901.

1891 (1 Jan–June). Surch locally by lithography. W **16**.

*(a) With T **18**. P 11½*

168	11	2½d. on 9d. pale blue....................	21·00	4·25
		a. Surch double, one inverted........	£700	£800
		b. Deep blue...............................	13·00	8·00

*(b) With T **19**. P 12*

169	11	2½d. on 9d. pale blue (5.91).........	5·00	3·50

A reprint, using a third setting, perforated 11½ and overprinted "REPRINT" was produced in 1901.

(Typo Govt Printer, Hobart)

1891 (Apr–Aug). W **15**.

(a) P 11½

170	11	½d. orange.....................................	75·00	55·00
		a. Brown-orange...........................	55·00	48·00
171		1d. rosine......................................	23·00	10·00
		a. Wedge flaw.............................	£225	90·00

(b) P 12

172	11	½d. orange.....................................	65·00	48·00
		a. Imperf (pair).............................	£300	
173		1d. dull rosine...............................	45·00	42·00
		a. Rosine.....................................	55·00	42·00
		b. Wedge flaw.............................	£350	£250
174		4d. bistre (8.91)............................	24·00	35·00

(Typo D.L.R.)

1892 (12 Feb)–**99**. W **16**. P 14.

216	20	½d. orange and mauve (11.92)........	2·75	1·25
217	21	2½d. purple....................................	2·75	1·75
218	20	5d. pale blue and brown................	7·00	3·75
219		6d. violet and black (11.92)...........	15·00	4·75
220	21a	10d. purple-lake and deep green (30.1.99)........	11·00	14·00
221	20	1s. rose and green (11.92).............	12·00	3·00
222		2s.6d. brown and blue (11.92)........	32·00	35·00
223		5s. lilac and red (3.2.97)..............	90·00	27·00
224		10s. mauve and brown (11.92)........	£190	£120
225		£1 green and yellow (2.97)............	£500	£500

216/25 Set of 10 .... £750 £650
216s/25s Optd "SPECIMEN" Set of 10 ...... £650
See also Nos. 243 and 257/8.

(Typo Govt Printer, Hobart)

1896. W **16**. P 12.

226	11	4d. pale bistre................................	15·00	7·00
227		9d. pale blue.................................	9·50	3·00
		a. Blue..	9·50	3·75

22 Lake Marion **23** Mount Wellington

24 Hobart **25** Tasman's Arch

26 Spring River, Port Davey **27** Russell Falls

28 Mount Gould, Lake St. Clair **29** Dilston Falls

30

(Eng L. Phillips. Recess D.L.R.)

1899 (Dec)–**1900**. W **30** (sideways on vert designs). P 14.

229	22	½d. deep green (31.3.00)...............	8·50	6·50
230	23	1d. bright lake (13.12.99)*...........	5·50	1·75
231	24	2d. deep violet (15.12.99)*..........	23·00	1·75
232	25	2½d. indigo (1900)........................	22·00	3·75
233	26	3d. sepia (1900)...........................	20·00	6·00
234	27	4d. deep orange-buff (1900).........	24·00	9·00
235	28	5d. bright blue (31.3.00)...............	38·00	11·00
236	29	6d. lake (31.3.00).........................	32·00	38·00

229/36 Set of 8 .... £150 £70·00
229s/36s Optd "Specimen" Set of 8 .... £550
*Earliest known postmark dates.
See also Nos. 237/9, 240/1, 245/8, 249/54, 259, 260 and 261/2.

DIFFERENCES BETWEEN LITHOGRAPHED AND TYPOGRAPHED PRINTINGS OF TYPES 22/9

LITHOGRAPHED	TYPOGRAPHED
General appearance fine.	*Comparatively crude and coarse appearance.*
½d. All "V over Crown" wmk.	All "Crown over A" wmk.
1d. The shading on the path on the right bank of the river consists of very fine dots. In printings from worn stones the dots hardly show.	The shading on the path is coarser, consisting of large dots and small patches of colour.
The shading on the white mountain is fine (or almost absent in many stamps).	The shading on the mountain is coarse, and clearly defined.
2d. Three rows of windows in large building on shore, at extreme left, against inner frame.	Two rows of windows.
3d. Clouds very white.	Clouds dark.
Stars in corner ornaments have long points.	Stars have short points.
Shading of corner ornaments is defined by a coloured outer line.	Shading of ornaments terminates against white background.
4d. Lithographed only.	
6d. No coloured dots at base of waterfall.	Coloured dots at base of waterfall.
Outer frame of value tablets is formed by outer line of design.	Thick line of colour between value tablets and outer line.
	Small break in inner frame below second "A" of "TASMANIA".

20 21 21a

(Litho, using transfers from D.L.R. plates, Victoria Government Printing Office, Melbourne)

1902 (Jan)–05. Wmk V over Crown, W w **10** (sideways on ½d., 2d.). P 12½.

237	**22**	½d. green (2.03)	5·00	1·50
		a. Wmk upright	28·00	27·00
		b. Perf 11 (1904)	6·50	15·00
		c. Perf comp of 12½ and 11	£200	£140
		d. Perf comp of 12½ and 12	£600	
		s. Optd "SPECIMEN"	£120	
238	**23**	1d. carmine-red	20·00	1·75
239	**24**	2d. deep reddish violet	13·00	70
		a. Perf 11	13·00	9·00
		b. Perf comp of 12½ and 11	£180	90·00
		c. Wmk upright (2.04)	90·00	17·00
		d. Deep rose-lilac (4.05)	20·00	2·00
		da. Perf 11	11·00	2·50
		db. Perf comp of 12½ and 11	£225	£100
		s. Optd "SPECIMEN"	£130	

As the V and Crown paper was originally prepared for stamps of smaller size, portions of two or more watermarks appear on each stamp.

We only list the main groups of shades in this and the following issues. There are variations of shade in all values, particularly in the 2d. where there is a wide range, also in the 1d. in some issues.

(Typo, using electrotyped plates, Victoria Govt Ptg Office, Melbourne)

1902 (Oct)–04. Wmk V over Crown, W w **10**. P 12½.

240	**23**	1d. pale red (wmk sideways)	18·00	4·50
		a. Perf 11	50·00	13·00
		b. Perf comp of 12½ and 11	£500	£100
		c. Wmk upright (1.03)	27·00	13·00
		ca. Perf 11	65·00	16·00
		d. Rose-red (wmk upright) (4.03)	15·00	4·25
		da. Perf 11	27·00	4·25
		db. Perf comp of 12½ and 11	£475	£100
		ds. Optd "SPECIMEN"	£120	
241		1d. scarlet (wmk upright) (9.03)	20·00	3·75
		a. Perf 11	25·00	
		b. Perf comp of 12½ and 11	—	55·00
		c. Rose-scarlet (1904)	20·00	3·75
		ca. Perf 11	9·00	4·25
		cb. Perf comp of 12½ and 11	£180	55·00

The 1d. scarlet of September 1903 was from new electrotyped plates which show less intense shading.

(Typo Victoria Govt Ptg Office, Melbourne)

1903 (Apr–Dec). Wmk V over Crown, W w **10**. P 12½.

242	**11**	9d. blue (4.03)	22·00	3·75
		a. Perf 11	8·50	18·00
		b. Perf comp of 12½ and 11	£950	£950
		c. Wmk sideways	£350	£160
		d. Pale blue	22·00	10·00
		e. Bright blue	23·00	12·00
		f. Ultramarine	£425	
		g. Indigo	£225	
243	**20**	1s. rose and green (12.03)	50·00	8·50
		a. Perf 11	90·00	80·00
		242s/3s Optd "SPECIMEN" Set of 2	£225	

ONE PENNY

(31)   (32)

1904 (29 Dec). No. 218 surch with T **31**.

244	**20**	1½d. on 5d. pale blue and brown	1·50	1·75
		s. Optd "SPECIMEN"	70·00	

Stamps with inverted surcharge or without surcharge *se-tenant* with stamps with normal surcharge were obtained irregularly and were not issued for postal use.

> **PRINTER.** The Victoria Govt Ptg Office became the Commonwealth Stamp Printing Branch in March 1909.

(Litho, using transfers from D.L.R. plates, Victoria Govt Office, Melbourne)

1905 (Sep)–12. Wmk Crown over A, W w **11** (sideways on horiz stamps). P 12½.

245	**24**	2d. deep purple	18·00	1·25
		a. Perf 11	50·00	2·75
		b. Perf comp of 12½ and 11	30·00	9·00
		c. Perf comp of 12½ and 12	£190	£120
		d. Perf comp of 11 and 12	£350	£200
		e. Slate-lilac (1906)	25·00	1·50
		ea. Perf 11	60·00	3·00
		eb. Perf comp of 12½ and 11		
		ed. Perf comp of 11 and 12	£325	£200
		ee. Perf comp of 12½ and 12		
		f. Reddish lilac (1907)	42·00	3·75
		fa. Perf 11	50·00	7·00
		fb. Perf comp of 12½ and 11	£160	
246	**26**	3d. brown (1906)	13·00	4·75
		a. Perf 11 (9.05)	32·00	40·00
		b. Perf comp of 12½ and 11	£275	£275
247	**27**	4d. pale yellow-brown (3.07)	21·00	4·75
		a. Perf 11	65·00	21·00
		b. Orange-buff (5.09)	65·00	5·50
		ba. Perf 11	65·00	30·00
		bb. Perf comp of 12½ and 11	£475	£475
		c. Brown-ochre (wmk sideways). Perf 11 (6.11)	30·00	55·00
		ca. Perf comp of 12½ and 11	—	£700
		d. Orange-yellow (3.12)	16·00	38·00
		da. Perf 11	48·00	65·00
		db. Perf comp of 12½ and 11	£475	£475
248	**29**	6d. lake (7.08)	80·00	9·00
		a. Perf 11	95·00	9·00
		b. Perf comp of 12½ and 11	£500	£500

Stamps with perf compound of 12½ and 12 or 11 and 12 are found on sheets which were sent from Melbourne incompletely perforated along the outside edge of the pane or sheet. The missing perforations were applied in Hobart using a line machine measuring 12 (11.8 is the exact gauge). This perforation can only occur on one side of a stamp.

(Typo, using electrotyped plates, Victoria Govt Ptg Office, Melbourne).

1905 (Aug)–11. Wmk Crown over A, W w **11** (sideways on horiz designs). P 12½.

249	**22**	½d. yellow-green (10.12.08)	2·75	75
		a. Perf 11	2·75	75
		b. Perf comp of 12½ and 11	£130	32·00
		c. Perf comp of 11 and 12	£300	
		d. Wmk upright (1909)	25·00	8·50
		da. Perf 11	£110	
250	**23**	1d. rose-red	7·50	30
		a. Perf 11	7·00	30
		b. Perf comp of 12½ and 11	5·50	7·00
		c. Perf comp of 12½ and 12	£170	60·00
		d. Perf comp of 11 and 12	£200	60·00
		e. Wmk sideways (1907)	25·00	3·00
		ea. Perf 11	26·00	4·00
		eb. Perf comp of 12½ and 11	95·00	23·00
		f. Imperf (pair)	£700	£750
250g		1d. carmine-red (3.10)	15·00	3·50
		ga. Perf 11	15·00	3·50
		gb. Perf comp of 12½ and 11	21·00	9·50
		gc. Perf comp of 12½ and 12	£170	55·00
		gd. Perf comp of 11 and 12	£200	60·00
		gf. Wmk sideways	15·00	3·25
		gg. Perf 11	16·00	3·25
		gh. Perf comp of 12½ and 11	19·00	9·00
		h. Carmine-vermilion (1911)	19·00	13·00
		ha. Perf 11	22·00	12·00
		hb. Perf comp of 12½ and 11	65·00	15·00
		hc. Perf comp of 12½ and 12		
		hd. Perf comp of 11 and 12		
251	**24**	2d. plum (8.07)	38·00	1·00
		a. Wmk upright	48·00	5·50
		b. Perf 11	6·50	30
		ba. Wmk upright (12.07)	48·00	5·50
		c. Perf comp of 12½ and 11	42·00	18·00
		d. Perf comp of 12½ and 12	£425	£140
		e. Perf comp of 11 and 12	£250	£110
		f. Bright reddish violet (1910)	13·00	4·25
		fa. Perf 11	12·00	2·25
		fb. Perf comp of 12½ and 11	55·00	22·00
		fc. Perf comp of 12½ and 12	£425	£130
253	**26**	3d. brown (3.09)	23·00	11·00
		a. Wmk upright		
		b. Perf 11	30·00	14·00
		c. Perf comp of 12½ and 11	£425	£450
254	**29**	6d. carmine-lake (12.10)	24·00	45·00
		a. Wmk upright	24·00	55·00
		b. Perf 11	£450	
		c. Dull carmine-red (3.11)	25·00	55·00
		ca. Wmk upright	60·00	65·00
		cb. Perf 11	27·00	65·00
		cc. Perf comp of 12½ and 11	£475	£500

The note after No. 248 re perfs compound with perf 12 also applies here.

Nos. 250/f were printed from the same plates as Nos. 241/cb. Nos. 250g/hd are from a further pair of new plates and the images are sharper.

(Typo Victoria Govt Printing Office, Melbourne).

1906–09. Wmk Crown over A, W w **11**. P 12½.

255	**11**	8d. purple-brown (1907)	27·00	24·00
		a. Perf 11	19·00	8·00
256		9d. blue (1907)	7·50	6·00
		a. Perf 11	7·50	9·50
		b. Perf comp of 12½ and 11 (1909)	£110	
		c. Perf comp of 12½ and 12 (1909)	£400	
		d. Perf comp of 11 and 12	£500	
257	**20**	1s. rose and green (1907)	13·00	9·00
		a. Perf 11 (1907)	29·00	48·00
		b. Perf comp of 12½ and 11	23·00	50·00
		c. Perf comp of 12½ and 12	£250	
258		10s. mauve and brown (1906)	£275	£275
		a. Perf 11	£475	£475
		b. Perf comp of 12½ and 12	£400	

The note after No. 248 re perfs compound with perf 12, also applies here.

(Typo, using stereotyped plates, Commonwealth Stamp Ptg Branch, Melbourne)

1911 (Jan). Wmk Crown over A, W w **11** (sideways). P 12½.

259	**24**	2d. bright violet	21·00	7·00
		a. Wmk upright	48·00	13·00
		b. Perf 11	9·50	5·50
		ba. Wmk upright	40·00	11·00
		c. Perf comp of 12½ and 11	£130	38·00

Stamps from this stereotyped plate differ from No. 251 in the width of the design (33 to 33¾ *mm*, against just over 32 *mm*), in the taller, bolder letters of "TASMANIA", in the slope of the mountain in the left background, which is clearly outlined in white, and in the outer vertical frame-line at left, which appears "wavy". Compare Nos. 260, etc, which are always from this plate.

1912 (Oct). No. 259 surch with T **32**. P 12½.

260	**24**	1d. on 2d. bright violet (R.)	1·00	1·00
		a. Perf 11	1·50	3·50
		b. Perf comp of 12½ and 11	£275	£300

(Typo, using electrotyped plates, Commonwealth Stamp Ptg Branch, Melbourne).

1912 (Dec). Thin ready gummed paper, white gum (as Victoria, 1912)*. W w **11** (sideways on 3d.). P 12½.

261	**23**	1d. carmine-vermilion	26·00	18·00
		a. Perf 11	21·00	18·00
		b. Perf comp of 12½ and 11	†	£600
262	**26**	3d. brown	70·00	£100

*See note below Victoria No. 455.

STAMP BOOKLETS

There are very few surviving examples of Nos. SB1/4. Listings are provided for those believed to have been issued with prices quoted for those known to still exist.

1904 (1 Jan)–09. Black on red cover as Type B **1** of New South Wales. Stapled.

SB1	£1 booklet containing 240×1d. in 12 blocks of 20 (5×4)	
	a. Red on pink cover (1909)	
	b. Blue on pink cover	

1904 (1 Jan). Black on grey cover No. SB1. Stapled.

SB2	£1 booklet containing 120×2d. in four blocks of 30	

1910 (1 May). Black on white cover as Type B **2** of New South Wales. Stapled.

SB3	2s. booklet containing 11×½d. (No. 249), either in block of 6 plus block of 5 or block of 11, and 18×1d. (No. 250), either in three blocks of 6 or blocks of 6 plus block of 12	£7500

Unsold stock No. SB3 was uprated with one additional ½d. in May 1911.

1911 (Aug). Red on pink cover as No. SB3. Stapled.

SB4	2s. booklet containing 12×½d. (No. 249), either in two blocks of 6 or block of 12, and 18×1d. (No. 250), either in three blocks of 6 or block of 6 plus block of 12	£6500

POSTAL FISCAL STAMPS

VALIDITY. Nos. F1/29 were authorised for postal purposes on 1 November 1882.

CLEANED STAMPS. Beware of postal fiscal stamps with pen-cancellations removed.

F **1**   F **2**

F **3**   F **4**

(Recess Alfred Bock, Hobart)

1863–80. Wmk double-lined "1". W **4**.

(a) Imperf

F1	F **1**	3d. green (1.65)	£700	£250
F2	F **2**	2s.6d. carmine (11.63)	£700	£250
F3		2s.6d. lake (5.80)		
F4	F **3**	5s. brown (1.64)	£1400	£800
F5		5s. sage-green (1880)	£900	£400
F6	F **4**	10s. orange (1.64)	£1700	£800
F7		10s. salmon (5.80)	£1400	£800

(b) P 10

F8	F **1**	3d. green	£450	£150
F9	F **2**	2s.6d. carmine	£400	
F10	F **3**	5s. brown	£600	
F11	F **4**	10s. orange	£550	

(c) P 12

F12	F **1**	3d. green	£400	£180
F13	F **2**	2s.6d. carmine	£350	£170
F14	F **3**	5s. brown	£600	
F15		5s. sage-green	£425	£170
F16	F **4**	10s. orange	£500	£250
F17		10s. salmon	£475	£200

(d) P 12½

F18	F **1**	3d. green	£650	
F19	F **2**	2s.6d. carmine	£600	
F20	F **3**	5s. brown	£900	
F21	F **4**	10s. orange-brown	£700	

(e) P 11½

F22	F **1**	3d. green	£800	
F23	F **2**	2s.6d. lake	£350	£190
F24	F **3**	5s. sage-green	£450	£180
F25	F **4**	10s. salmon	£600	£350

See also No. F30.

In 1879, the 3d., 2s.6d., 5s. (brown), and 10s. (orange) were reprinted on thin, tough, white paper, and are found with or without "REPRINT". In 1889 another reprint was made on white card, imperforate and perforated 12. These are also found with or without "REPRINT".

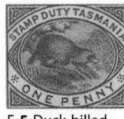

F **5** Duck-billed Platypus

(F **6**)

REVENUE

(Typo D.L.R.)

1880 (19 Apr). W **16** (sideways). P 14.

F26	F **5**	1d. slate	45·00	9·50
F27		3d. chestnut	26·00	4·75
F28		6d. mauve	95·00	2·50
F29		1s. rose-pink	£150	30·00
		a. Perf comp of 14 and 11		

All values are known imperf, but not used.

Reprints are known of the 1d. in deep blue and the 6d. in lilac. The former is on yellowish white, the latter on white card. Both values also exist on wove paper, perf 12, with the word "REPRINT".

1888. W **16**. P 12.

F30	F **2**	2s.6d. lake	£140	85·00
		a. Imperf between (horiz pair)	£2250	

1900 (15 Nov). Optd with Type F **6**.

*(a) On Types F **2** and F **4***

F32	F **2**	2s.6d. lake (No. F30)	£500	£500
		a. "REVFNUE"	£800	
		b. Opt inverted	£1600	
		c. Imperf (pair)	£1300	

F33	F **4**	10s. salmon (No. F17)	£800	£750
		a. "REVFNUE"		

(b) On Nos. F27 and F29

F34	F **5**	3d. chestnut	42·00	35·00
		a. Double opt, one vertical	£225	£250
F35		1s. rose-pink		

(c) On stamps as Nos. F26/9, but typo locally. W **16**. *P* 12

F36	F **5**	1d. blue	25·00	30·00
		b. Imperf vert (horiz pair)	£550	
		c. "REVENUE" inverted	£200	
		d. "REVENUE" double	£325	£325
		e. Pale blue	25·00	
F37		6d. mauve	£120	
		a. Double print	£800	
F38		1s. pink	£350	£325

(d) On No. 225

F39	**20**	£1 green and yellow	£275	£225
		a. Opt double, one vertical	£475	£450

It was not intended that stamps overprinted with Type F **6** should be used for postal purposes, but an ambiguity in regulations permitted such usage until all postal fiscal stamps were invalidated for postal purposes on 30 November 1900.

F38 is known with "REVENUE" inverted, fiscally used.

Printings of some of the above with different watermarks, together with a 2d. as Nos. F36/8, did not appear until after the stamps had become invalid for postal purposes.

Tasmania became part of the Commonwealth of Australia on 1 January 1901.

VICTORIA

During the expansion of the Australian settlements in the fourth decade of the 19-century the growing population of the Port Phillip District in the south of New South Wales led to a movement for its creation as a separate colony. This aspiration received the approval of the British Government in 1849, but the colony of Victoria, as it was to be called, was not to be created until 1 July 1851.

In the meantime the New South Wales Legislative Council voted for the introduction of postal reforms, including the use of postage stamps, from 1 January 1850, and this act was also to apply to the Port Phillip District where stamps inscribed "VICTORIA" would predate the creation of that colony by eighteen months.

Until the end of 1859 the stamps of Victoria, with the exception of Nos. 40 and 73, were produced by local contractors working under the supervision of the colonial administration.

HAM PRINTINGS. The first contractor was Thomas Ham of Melbourne. He was responsible for the initial printings of the "Half-Length" 1d., 2d. and 3d., together with the replacement "Queen-on-Throne" 2d. The first printings were produced from small sheets of 30 (5×6) laid down directly from the engraved die which showed a single example of each value. Subsequent printings, of which No. 4a was the first, were in sheets of 120 (two panes of 60) laid down using intermediate stones of various sizes. Impressions from the first printings were fine and clear, but the quality deteriorated when intermediate stones were used.

1 Queen Victoria ("Half Length")

(Lithographed by Thomas Ham, Melbourne)

1850 (3 Jan)–53. Imperf.

1d. Thin line at top

2d. Fine border and background

3d. White area to left of orb

(a) Original state of dies: 1d. (tops of letters of "VICTORIA" reach to top of stamp); 2d. (fine border and background); 3d. (thicker white outline around left of orb, central band of orb does not protrude at left). No frame-lines on dies

1	**1**	1d. orange-vermilion	£32000	£10000
		a. Orange-brown	†	£2250
		b. Dull chocolate-brown	£20000	£2500
2		2d. lilac-mauve (shades) (Stone A)	£15000	£1000
3		2d. brown-lilac (shades) (Stone B)	£13000	£500
		a. Grey-lilac	—	£550
4		3d. bright blue (shades)	£8000	£600
		a. Blue (shades)	£7000	£450
		ab. Retouched (between Queen's head and right border) (No. 11 in transfer group) (8 varieties)	—	£600
		ac. Retouched (under "V") (No. 10 in transfer group)	£14000	£1000

With the exception of No. 4a the above were printed from small stones of 30 (5×6) laid down directly from the engraved die which showed a single example of each value. There were two stones of the 2d. and one for each of the other values. No. 4a is the second printing of the 3d. for which the sheet size was increased to 120, the printing stone being constructed from an intermediate stone of 15 (5×3).

1d. Thick line at top

2d. Coarse background

3d. White area small and band protruding to left of orb

(b) Second state of dies: 1d. (more colour over top of letters of "VICTORIA"); 2d. (fine border as (a) but with coarse background); 3d. (thinner white outline around left of orb, central band of orb protrudes at left)

5	**1**	1d. red-brown (shades) (2.50)	£9500	£450
		a. Pale dull red-brown	£8000	£450
6		2d. grey-lilac (shades) (1.50)	£7000	£200
		a. Dull grey	£13000	£225
7		3d. blue (shades) (6.51)	£4750	£190
		a. Retouched (22 varieties) from	£6000	£350

Printed in sheets of 120 (10×12) with the printing stones constructed from intermediate stones of 30 (5×6) for the 1d. and 2d. or 10 (5×2) for the 3d. It is believed that the use of the smaller intermediate stone for the latter resulted in the many retouches.

Frame-lines added

(c) Third state of dies: As in (b) but with frame-lines added, very close up, on all four sides

8	**1**	1d. dull orange-vermilion (11.50)	£5500	£650
		a. Dull red (shades)	£4750	£200
9		1d. deep red-brown (5.51)	£12000	£1200
		a. Brownish red (shades)	£4500	£180
		b. Dull rose (shades)	£4500	£180
10		2d. grey (shades) (8.50)	£8000	£200
		a. Olive-grey (shades)	£8500	£200
11		3d. blue (shades) (12.52)	£2750	90·00
		a. Deep blue (shades)	£3250	90·00
		b. Pale greenish blue (shades)	£4000	£170

Printed in sheets of 120 (12×10) produced from intermediate stones of 30 (6×5) for No. 8 and 12 (6×2) for the others.

White veil

(d) As (c) but altered to give, for the 1d. and 3d., the so-called "white veils", and for the 2d., the effect of vertical drapes to the veil

12	**1**	1d. reddish brown (6.51)	£7000	£170
		a. Bright pinky red (shades)	£2250	£170
13		2d. drab (1.51)	£8000	£190
		a. Grey-drab (shades)	£8000	£180
		b. Lilac-drab (shades)	£8000	£180
		c. Red-lilac	—	£1300
		d. Void lower left corner	†	£22000
14		3d. blue (shades) (1.53)	£1200	80·00
		a. Deep blue (shades)	£1300	80·00
		b. Greenish blue (shades)	£1600	85·00
		c. Retouched (9 varieties)	£2750	£180

Printed in sheets of 120 (12×10) produced from intermediate stones of 12 (6×2) on which the details of the veil were amended as described above.

The "void corner" error occurred on the printing stone. It is believed that only four examples still exist.

2d. Coarse border and background

(e) Fourth state of 2d. die only: Coarse border and background. Veil details as in original die

15	**1**	2d. red-lilac (shades) (5.50)	£7500	£325
		a. Lilac	£7500	£350
		b. Grey	£9500	£425
		c. Dull brownish lilac	£7500	£180
		d. Retouched lower label—value omitted from	†	£15000
		e. Other retouches (17 varieties) from	£9500	£350

Printed in sheets of 120 (12×10) produced from an intermediate stone of 30 (6×5).

(f) 2d. as (e), but with veils altered to give effect of vertical drapes

16	**1**	2d. lilac-grey (1.51)	£5500	£170
		a. Deep grey	£6500	£170
		b. Brown-lilac (shades)	£5000	£110
17		2d. cinnamon (shades) (2.51)	£3500	£170
		a. Drab (shades)	£3750	95·00
		b. Pale dull brown (shades)	£3500	£120
		c. Greenish grey	£3500	£110
		d. Olive-drab (shades)	£3750	£190
		e. Buff	£12000	£250

Printed in sheets of 120 (12×10) produced from two successive intermediate stones of 30 (6×5) on which the details of the veil were amended as described above.

This was the final printing of the 2d. "Half Length" as the die for this value had been damaged. A replacement 2d. design was ordered from Thomas Ham.

For the later printings of the 1d. and 3d. in this design see Nos. 23/4, 26/31, 48/9 and 78/9.

2 Queen-on-Throne   **3**

(Recess-printed by Thomas Ham)

1852 (27 Dec). Imperf.

18	**2**	2d. reddish brown	£650	28·00
		a. Chestnut	—	£140
		b. Purple-brown	£8000	28·00

Printed in sheets of 50 (10×5) from a hand-engraved plate of the same size. Each stamp in the sheet had individual corner letters made-up of various combinations, none of which contained the letter "J".

Reprints were made in 1891 using the original plate, on paper wmk V over Crown, both imperf and perf 12½.

For later printings of this design see Nos. 19/22 and 36/9.

CAMPBELL & CO PRINTINGS. In May 1853 the Victoria postal authorities placed an order for 1d. and 6d. stamps in the "Queen-on-Throne" design with Perkins Bacon in London. These would not arrive for some time, however, and supplies of Ham's printings were rapidly becoming exhausted. Local tenders were, therefore, solicited for further supplies of the 1d. and 3d. "Half Lengths" and the 2d. "Queen-on-Throne". That received from J. S. Campbell & Co was accepted. The stamps were produced by lithography, using transfers from either the "Half Length" engraved die or the 2d. "Queen-on-Throne" engraved plate of 50. Stamps from the Campbell & Co printings can be distinguished from later printings in lithography by the good quality paper used.

(Lithographed by J. S. Campbell & Co, Melbourne, using transfers taken from Ham's engraved plate)

1854 (Jan–July). Good quality white or toned paper. Imperf.

(a) Clear impressions with details around back of throne generally complete

19	**2**	2d. brownish purple	£600	40·00
		a. Grey-brown	£750	40·00
		b. Purple-black	—	40·00
		c. Dull lilac-brown (toned paper only)	£800	50·00

(b) Poor impressions with details around back of throne not fully defined

20	**2**	2d. violet-black (2.54)	£750	48·00
		a. Grey-black	£800	48·00
		b. Grey-lilac	£750	48·00
		c. Dull brown (on toned)	£750	48·00
		ca. Substituted transfer (in pair)	—	£3000

(c) Weak impressions with background generally white without details. Toned paper only

21	**2**	2d. grey-purple (7.54)	£500	35·00
		a. Purple-black	£500	35·00

(d) Printings using an intermediate stone. Impression flat and blurred. Background details usually complete. Toned paper only

22	**2**	2d. grey-drab (shades) (5.54)	£700	40·00
		a. Black	—	£140

Nos. 19/21 were produced using transfers taken directly from the original Ham engraved plate. It is believed that the different strengths of the impressions were caused by the amount of pressure exerted when the transfers were taken. The stamps were printed in sheets of 100 (2 panes 10×5). On one stone a block of four at bottom left, lettered "FL GM" over "QV RW", was damaged and the stone was repaired by using a block of four substituted transfers. These were lettered "VZ WA" over "FL GM". No. 20ca covers any one of these substituted transfers in pair with normal. As horizontal pairs these are lettered "WA HN" or "GM SX" and as vertical pairs "VZ" over "VZ" or "WA" over "WA".

For No. 22 an intermediate stone was used to produce a printing stone of 300 (6 panes 10×5). The insertion of a further stage into the process caused the blurred appearance of stamps from this printing. No. 22a is believed to come from proof sheets issued to post offices for normal use. Examples are usually cancelled with Barred Oval 108 and Barred Numerals 1 and 2.

(Lithographed by J.S. Campbell & Co, Melbourne)

1854 (Feb–June). Good quality wove paper. Imperf.

23	**1**	1d. orange-red (shades)	£3000	£140
		a. Rose	£6500	£750
24		3d. blue (shades) (6.54)	£1100	50·00
		a. Retouched under "C" of "VICTORIA"		£150

The 1d. was produced in sheets of 192 (two panes of 96 (12×8)) and the 3d. in sheets of 320 (two panes of 160 (18×9). Both printing stones were constructed from transfers taken from intermediate stones of 24 (6×4). The spacing between stamps is far wider than on the Ham printings. The 3d. panes of 160 were constructed using six complete transfers of 24 and three of six with the final impression in the bottom two rows removed.

The 1d. Campbell printings have the frame lines almost completely absent due to lack of pressure when taking transfers.

The 3d. retouch, No. 24a, occurs on R. 3/5 of the intermediate stone.

(Lithographed by Campbell & Fergusson)

1854 (6 July). Poorer quality paper. Imperf.

25	**3**	1s. blue (shades)	£1000	40·00
		a. Greenish blue	£1200	40·00
		b. Indigo-blue	—	£190

No. 25 was produced in sheets of 100 (8×12 with an additional stamp appearing at the end of rows 6 to 9). The printing stones used each contained four such sheets. They were constructed from an intermediate stone of 40 (8×5) taken from a single engraved die. Each pane of 100 showed two complete transfers of 40, one of 20, and one of a vertical strip of four.

For this stamp rouletted or perforated see Nos. 54 and 81.

(Lithographed by Campbell & Fergusson)

1854 (July)–**57**. Poorer quality paper. Imperf.

26	**1**	1d. brown (shades)	£3000	£130
		a. Brick-red (shades)	£3250	£110
		b. Dull red (shades)	£3500	£110
27		1d. Orange-brown (shades) (8.55)	£3250	£140
		a. Dull rose-red (shades)	£3750	80·00
		b. Bright rose-pink	£6000	£160
		c. Retouched (6 varieties)	£6000	£450
28		1d. pink (shades) (2.55)	£1400	48·00
		a. Rose (shades)	£1400	48·00
		b. Lilac-rose (shades)	£1500	48·00
		c. Dull brown-red (shades)	£1700	£140
		d. Retouched (8 varieties)	£2500	£325
29		3d. bright blue (shades) (7.57)	£2250	50·00
		a. Greenish blue (shades)	£1900	55·00
		b. Retouch under "C" of "VICTORIA"	£3000	£130
30		3d. Prussian blue (shades) (11.56)	£3000	95·00
		a. Milky blue	£3750	£150
		b. Retouch under "C" of "VICTORIA"	—	£275
31		3d. steel-blue (shades) (heavier impression) (5.55)		65·00
		a. Greenish blue (shades)	£1900	48·00
		b. Blue (shades)	£1900	48·00
		c. Deep blue (shades)	£1600	48·00
		d. Indigo (shades)	—	55·00

The 1d. was produced in sheets of 400 (2 panes 20×10) constructed from transfers originating from the J. S. Campbell & Co intermediate stone. Each pane contained six complete transfers of 24, three of 12, two of eight and one of four.

The 3d. was produced in sheets of 320 (2 panes of 160) (No. 29), 200 (No. 30) or 400 (2 panes of 200) (No. 31.) The stone for No. 29 was constructed from transfers taken from the J. S. Campbell intermediate stone with the retouch on R. 3/5 still present. The panes of 160 contained six transfers of 24 and three of six with the last impression in both rows 8 and 9 removed. Quality of impression is generally poor. The stone for No. 30, once again taken from the Campbell intermediate stone, was laid down in the same combination of transfers as the 1d. value. Impressions from it were, however, so poor that transfers from a new intermediate stone were used for No. 31. Impressions from this stone, on which the panes of 200 were in a similar layout to the 1d. were much further apart than those on the stones used to produce Nos. 29/30.

The Campbell & Fergusson printings of the "Half Lengths" are listed in the order in which they were printed.

       4   **5**   **6**

(Typographed from woodblocks by Samuel Calvert)

1854 (1 Sept)–**55**. Imperf.

32	**4**	6d. reddish brown (13.9.54)	£1100	75·00
		a. Dull orange	£600	19·00
		b. Orange-yellow	£600	19·00
33	**5**	6d. ("TOO LATE") lilac and green (1.1.55)	£3000	£250
34	**6**	1s. ("REGISTERED") rose-pink and blue (1.12.54)	£3750	£200
35	**4**	2s. dull bluish green/*pale yellow*	£4000	£200

No. 33 was provided to pay the additional fee on letters posted after the normal closure of the mails. This service was only available in the larger towns; examples are usually postmarked Castlemaine, Geelong or Melbourne. The service was withdrawn on 30 June 1857 and remaining stocks of the "TOO LATE" stamps were used for normal postal purposes.

No. 34 was issued to pay the registration fee and was so used until 5 January 1858 after which remaining stocks were used for normal postage.

These four values were produced from individually-engraved boxwood woodblocks. The 6d. was in sheets of 100 printed by two impressions from two plates of 25. The 2s. was in sheets of 50 from a single plate of 25. The bicoloured "TOO LATE" and "REGISTERED" stamps are unusual in that Calvert used a common woodblock "key" plate of 25 for both values combined with "duty" plates made up from metal stereos. Both values were originally in sheets of 50, but the "REGISTERED" later appeared in sheets of 100 for which a second "key" plate of 25 was utilised.

For these stamps rouletted or perforated see Nos. 53, 55/8, 60/1 and 82.

(Lithographed by Campbell & Fergusson)

1855 (Mar)–**56**. Poorer quality paper. Imperf.

(a) Printings from stones which were not over-used; background around top of throne generally full and detail good

36	**2**	2d. dull lilac (shades) (7.55)	£500	32·00
		a. Purple (shades)	£500	32·00
		b. "TVO" for "TWO"	£9000	£1300

(b) Early printings from stones which were over-used. Similar characteristics to those above, though detail is not quite as full

37	**2**	2d. brown	—	80·00
		a. Brown-purple	£550	27·00
		b. Warm purple		27·00
		c. Rose-lilac		27·00
		d. Substituted transfer (pair)	—	£750

(c) Later printings from the same stones used for No. 37 when in a worn condition. Impressions heavy, coarse and overcoloured; details blurred; generally white background around top of throne

38	**2**	2d. dull lilac-mauve (1856)	£550	50·00
		a. Dull mauve	£550	50·00
		b. Grey-violet		50·00
		c. Red-lilac		50·00
		d. Substituted transfer (pair)	—	£750

(d) Printings from a stone giving blotchy and unpleasing results, with poor definition. Mainly shows in extra colour patches found on most stamps

39	**2**	2d. dull purple (7.55)		70·00
		a. Dull grey-lilac	£550	70·00
		b. On thick card paper	—	£650

The Campbell & Fergusson 2d. "Queen-on-Throne" printings were in sheets of 200 (4 panes 10×5) constructed from transfers taken from the original Ham engraved plate.

Four separate stones were used. On Stone A a creased transfer running through R. 4/8, 4/9 and 5/8 caused the "TVO" variety on the stamp from the bottom row of one pane. On Stone C the impression in the first vertical row of one pane were found to be so faulty that they were replaced by substituted transfers taken from elsewhere on the sheet causing abnormal horizontal pairs lettered "UY BF", "TX MQ", "DI WA", "SW GM" and "CH RW". The vertical pairs from the substituted transfers are lettered "UY" over "TX" and "DI" over "SW".

  7 Queen-on-Throne   **8** "Emblems"

(Recess Perkins Bacon & Co, London)

1856 (23 Oct). Wmk Large Star. Imperf.

40	**7**	1d. yellow-green (H/S "CANCELLED" in oval £12000)	£300	45·00

Supplies of this stamp, and the accompanying 6d. which was only issued rouletted (see No. 73), arrived in the colony at the end of 1854, but the 1d. was not placed on sale until almost two years later.

No. 40 was reprinted from the original plate in 1891. Examples, in either dull yellow-green or bright blue-green, are imperforate and on V over Crown watermarked paper.

(Typographed from electrotypes by Calvert) Imperf.

1857 (26 Jan–6 Sept).

(a) Wmk Large Star, W w 1

41	**8**	1d. yellow-green (18.2)	£250	28·00
		a. Deep green	£350	40·00
		b. Printed on both sides	†	£2750
42		4d. vermilion	£550	11·00
		a. Brown-vermilion	£500	9·50
		b. Printed on both sides	†	£2750
43		4d. dull red (6.7)	£400	8·50
44		4d. dull rose (6.9)	£500	8·50

(b) No wmk. Good quality medium wove paper

45		2d. pale lilac (25.5)	£650	11·00
		a. Grey-lilac	£650	11·00

Nos. 41/5 were produced in sheets of 120, arranged as four panes of 30 (6×5) (1d. and 4d.) or 12 panes of 10 (2×5) (2d.), using electrotypes taken from a single engraved die of each value.

The setting of the 4d. was rearranged before the printing of Nos. 43/4.

Only two examples of No. 41b and No. 42b have been recorded.

For this printing rouletted or perforated see Nos. 46/7, 50/2, 59, 74 and 77.

1857 (12 Aug–Sept). Rouletted 7–9 by counter clerks at GPO, Melbourne.

46	**8**	1d. yellow-green (No. 41)	£650	£110
47		2d. pale lilac (No. 45)	—	50·00
		a. Grey-lilac	—	50·00
48	**1**	3d. blue (shades) (No. 24)	£3250	£250
		a. Retouch under "C" of "VICTORIA"	†	£475
49		3d. bright blue (shades) (No. 29)		£250
		a. Greenish blue (shades)	£3250	£225
		b. Retouch under "C" of "VICTORIA"	†	£600
50	**8**	4d. vermilion (No. 42)	—	£100
51		4d. dull red (No. 43)	—	42·00
52		4d. dull rose (No. 44) (Sept)	—	28·00
53	**4**	6d. reddish brown (No. 32)	—	£100
		a. Dull orange		60·00
		b. Orange-yellow		70·00
54	**3**	1s. blue (shades) (No. 25)	—	£110
		a. Greenish blue	—	£110
55	**6**	1s. ("REGISTERED") rose-pink and blue (No. 34)	£10000	£400
56	**4**	2s. dull bluish green/*pale yellow* (No. 35)	£8500	£650

With the exception of the 1s., Nos. 54/a, these stamps are normally found rouletted on one or two sides only.

1857 (Oct). Rouletted by Calvert.

(a) Rouletted 7–9 on all four sides and with finer points than No. 53b

57	**4**	6d. orange-yellow (No. 32b)	—	£100

(b) Serpentine roulette 10–10½

58	**4**	6d. orange-yellow (No. 32b)	£3250	£180

(c) Serrated 18–19

59	**8**	2d. grey-lilac (No. 45a)	£1500	£600
60	**4**	6d. orange-yellow (No. 32b)	£4500	£160

(d) Compound of serrated 18–19 and serpentine 10–10½

61	**4**	6d. orange-yellow (No. 32b)	—	£600

No. 59 was not covered by the contract given to Calvert, but it is believed to be a test run for the rouletting machine. No. 61 always shows serrated 18–19 on three sides and the serpentine roulette at the top or bottom of the stamp.

(Typo from electrotypes by Calvert)

1858 (14 Jan–Apr). Good quality white wove paper. No wmk.

(a) Rouletted 7–9 on all four sides

62	**8**	1d. pale emerald	£550	30·00
		a. Emerald-green	£550	30·00
63		4d. rose-pink (18.1)	£425	7·00
		a. Bright rose	£425	7·00
		b. Reddish pink	—	11·00
		c. Imperf horiz (vert pair)	†	£650

(b) Imperf (Apr)

64	**8**	1d. pale emerald	£425	22·00
		a. Emerald-green	—	25·00
65		4d. rose-pink	£500	23·00
		a. Bright rose		23·00
		b. Reddish pink	—	30·00

Nos. 62/5 were produced in sheets of 120, arranged as four panes of 30 (6×5).

The Royal Collection contains a used horizontal pair of the 4d. showing the vertical roulettes omitted.

The majority of Nos. 64/5 were issued in April after Calvert's contracts had been terminated, although there is some evidence that imperforate sheets of the 4d., at least, were issued earlier.

For the 1d. of this issue perforated see No. 75.

(Typo from electrotypes by Robinson)
1858 (May–Dec).

(a) Imperf
(i) Coarse quality wove paper
| 66 | 8 | 4d. dull rose (*oily ink*) | — | 80·00 |

(ii) Smooth vertically-laid paper
67	8	4d. dull rose (*oily ink*)	—	55·00
		a. Dull rose-red	—	55·00
68		4d. dull rose-red (*normal ink*) (20.5)	£650	32·00

(b) Rouletted 5½–6½
(i) Smooth-laid paper
69	8	2d. brown-lilac (*shades*) (*horiz laid*) (6.58)	£300	11·00
		a. Vert laid paper (21.9)	£450	14·00
70		2d. violet (*horiz laid*) (27.11)	£375	6·50
		a. Dull violet	£425	18·00
71		4d. pale dull rose (*vert laid*) (1.6)	£325	4·00
		a. Horiz laid paper	†	£900
		b. Dull rose-red	£275	4·00
		c. Rose-red	£275	4·00
		ca. Serrated 19	†	£550

(ii) Good quality wove paper
| 72 | 8 | 1d. yellow-green (24.12) | £475 | 42·00 |

Nos. 66/72 were produced in sheets of 120, arranged as four panes of 30 (6×5).

For stamps of this issue perforated see Nos. 76 and 80.

(Recess Perkins Bacon & Co, London)
1858 (1 Nov). Wmk Large Star, W w **1**. Rouletted 5½–6½.
| 73 | 7 | 6d. bright blue | £500 | 18·00 |
| | | a. Light blue | £550 | 28·00 |

No. 73 was received from London at the same time as the 1d., No. 40, but was kept in store until November 1858 when the stock was rouletted by Robinson. When issued the gum was in a poor state.

Imperforate examples exist from Perkins Bacon remainders. Examples are known handstamped "CANCELLED" in oval of bars. *Price* £11000.

Imperforate reprints, in shades of indigo, were made from the original plate in 1891 on V over Crown watermarked paper.

1859 (Jan–May). P 12 by Robinson.
74	8	1d. yellow-green (No. 41)	—	£500
75		1d. emerald-green (No. 64*a*)	—	£500
		a. Imperf between (horiz pair)		
76		1d. yellow-green (as No. 72) (11.1)	£425	19·00
		a. Imperf horiz (vert pair)	—	£450
		b. Thin, glazed ("Bordeaux") paper...	†	£160
77		2d. pale lilac (No. 45)	—	£450
		a. Grey-lilac	—	£550
78	1	3d. blue (*shades*) (No. 24) (2.2)	£2500	£140
		a. Retouch under "C" of "VICTORIA"...	—	£400
79		3d. greenish blue (*shades*) (No. 29*a*)	†	£425
		a. Retouch under "C" of "VICTORIA"...	†	£1200
80	8	4d. dull rose-red (No. 68)	—	£325
81	3	1s. blue (*shades*) (No. 25) (4.2)	£400	16·00
		a. Greenish blue	£425	13·00
		b. Indigo-blue	—	45·00
		c. Retouched (shading omitted at left)		
82	4	2s. dull bluish green/*pale yellow* (No. 35) (5.59)	£650	55·00

The 1s. was reprinted in 1891 using transfers taken from the original die. These reprints were on V over Crown watermarked paper and perforated 12½.

For perforated 6d. black and 2s. blue both as Type **4** see Nos. 102 and 129/30.

(Typo from electrotypes by Robinson)
1859 (17 May–23 Dec). P 12.

(a) Good quality wove paper
| 83 | 8 | 4d. dull rose | £350 | 6·50 |
| | | a. Roul 5½–6½ | † | £850 |

(b) Poorer quality wove paper
84	8	1d. dull green (7.59)	£300	29·00
		a. Green (11.11)	£300	29·00
85		4d. rose-carmine (16.7)	£350	7·00
		a. Rose-pink (thick paper) (30.11)	—	15·00

A used vertical pair as No. 85 is known rouletted between, apparently to correct an imperforate between error.†

(c) Horizontally laid paper with the lines wide apart
86	8	1d. dull green (18.7)	£425	
		a. Laid lines close together	—	50·00
		b. Green (*shades*) (10.59)	£325	29·00
87		4d. rose-pink (*shades*) (23.12)	£300	7·50
		a. Laid lines close together	—	10·00

STAMP PRINTING BRANCH. On 1 January 1860 F. W. Robinson was appointed Printer of Postage Stamps and his equipment purchased by the Post Office to establish the Stamp Printing Branch. All later Victoria issues were printed by the Branch which became part of the Victoria Government Printing Office in December 1885. In 1909 the Commonwealth Stamp Printing Office under J. B. Cooke was established in Melbourne and produced stamps for both the states and Commonwealth until 1918.

9

10   11

(Des and eng F. Grosse. Typo from electrotypes)
1860 (31 Jan)–**66**. P 12.

(a) No wmk
88	9	3d. deep blue (*horiz laid paper*)	£650	75·00
		a. Light blue		
89		4d. rose-pink (*thin glazed Bordeaux paper*) (21.4.60)	—	38·00
		a. Rose	£600	38·00
		ab. Thicker coarser paper (7.60)	£600	38·00

(b) On paper made by T. H. Saunders of London wmkd with the appropriate value in words as W 10
90	9	3d. pale blue (1.61)	£325	7·00
		a. Bright blue (10.61)	£325	8·50
		b. Blue (4.63)	£325	6·00
		c. Deep blue (4.64)	£325	6·00
		d. "TRREE" for "THREE" in wmk	—	£700
91		3d. maroon (13.2.66)	£400	30·00
		a. Perf 13	£400	32·00
92		4d. rose-pink (1.8.60)	—	9·50
		a. Rose-red	£180	4·75
		b. Rose-carmine	—	9·50
		c. Dull rose	£180	4·75
		d. Printed on "FIVE SHILLINGS" diagonal wmk paper (11.9.62)	£3500	23·00
93		6d. orange (25.10.60)	£8000	£450
94		6d. black (20.8.61)	£425	8·50
		a. Grey-black	£425	8·50

(c) On paper made by De La Rue wmkd with the appropriate value as a single-lined numeral as W 11
95	9	4d. dull rose-pink (9.10.62)	£200	6·00
		a. Dull rose	£200	6·50
		b. Rose-red	—	6·00
		c. Roul 8 (28.7.63)	£2250	£250
		d. Imperf (14.7.63)	—	75·00
		e. Perf 12½×12		
		f. Perf 12½		

All three values were produced in sheets of 120, initially as four panes of 30 (6×5). Printings of the 3d. from 1864 were in a changed format of six panes of 20 (4×5).

The "TRREE" watermark error comes from early printings of No. 90 on R. 10/7.

Two examples of the 4d. on Saunders paper are known bisected in 1863, but such use was unauthorised.

Nos. 95c/d were issued during July and August 1863 when the normal perforating machine had broken down. They are best collected used on piece and cancelled within the period (July-September 1863).

Nos. 95e/f were perforated or part-perforated with a machine gauging 12¼-12½, borrowed from the Government Printer in 1863, while the perf 12 machine was being repaired.

Reprints, from new plates, were made of the 3d. and 4d. in 1891 on "V over Crown" paper and perforated 12½.

1860 (Apr)–**63**. P 12.

(a) No wmk
| 96 | 8 | 1d. bright green (*horiz laid paper*) | | |
| 97 | | 1d. bright green (*thin, glazed Bordeaux paper*) (25.5.60) | — | 75·00 |

(b) On paper made by T. H. Saunders of London wmkd with the appropriate value in words as W 10
98	8	1d. pale yellowish green (8.7.60)	£140	8·50
		a. Yellow-green	£160	8·50
		b. Error. Wmkd "FOUR PENCE"	†	£8500
99		2d. brown-lilac (7.7.61)	—	60·00
100		2d. bluish slate (8.61)	£225	6·00
		a. Greyish lilac (9.61)	£250	6·50
		b. Slate-grey (1.62)	—	6·00
		c. Printed on "THREE PENCE" wmkd paper. Pale slate (27.12.62)	£250	29·00
		ca. Bluish grey (2.63)	£275	29·00

(c) On paper made by De La Rue wmkd single-lined "2", W 11
101	8	2d. dull reddish lilac (24.4.63)	£350	16·00
		a. Grey-lilac (10.63)	£350	32·00
		ab. Error. Wmkd "6"	†	£6500
		b. Grey-violet (11.63)	£275	30·00
		c. Slate (12.63)	£350	42·00

Only two examples of No. 98b have been recorded, one of which is in the Royal Collection.

1861 (22 June). On paper made by T. H. Saunders of London wmkd "SIX PENCE" as W **10**. P 12.
| 102 | 4 | 6d. black | £450 | 75·00 |

No. 102 was produced as an emergency measure after the decision had been taken to change the colour of the current 6d. from orange (No. 93) to black (No. 94). During the changeover the old Calvert "woodblock" plates were pressed into service to provide two months' supply.

12   13

(Des, eng and electrotyped De Gruchy & Leigh, Melbourne. Typo)
1861 (1 Oct)–**64**. P 12.

(a) On paper made by T. H. Saunders of London. Wmk "ONE PENNY" as W 10
| 103 | 12 | 1d. pale green | £180 | 24·00 |
| | | a. Olive-green | — | 25·00 |

(b) On paper made by De La Rue. Wmk single-lined "1" as W 11
104	12	1d. olive-green (1.2.63)	£140	27·00
		a. Pale green (9.63)	£140	19·00
		b. Apple-green (4.64)	£140	18·00

(c) On paper supplied to Tasmania by Perkins Bacon. Wmk double-lined "1", W 4 of Tasmania
105	12	1d. yellow-green (10.12.63)	£250	25·00
		a. Dull green	—	25·00
		b. Imperf between (pair)	†	

All printings were in sheets of 120 containing four panes of 30 (6×5).

Reprints from new plates were made in 1891 on paper watermarked "V over Crown" and perforated 12½.

(Frame die eng F. Grosse. Typo from electrotypes.)
1862 (26 Apr)–**64**. Centre vignette cut from T **9** with a new frame as T **13**.

(a) On paper made by T. H. Saunders of London. Wmk "SIX PENCE" as W 10. P 12
106	13	6d. grey	£225	20·00
		a. Grey-black	£225	22·00
		b. Jet-black	£250	24·00

(b) On paper made by De La Rue. Wmk single-lined "6" as W 11
107	13	6d. grey (P 12) (18.6.63)	£180	7·00
		a. Jet-black	—	9·00
		b. Grey-black	£180	7·50
		c. Perf 13. Jet-black	£190	9·00
		ca. Grey-black	£190	9·00

Printings before August 1863 were in sheets of 120 containing four panes of 30 (6×5). For subsequent printings of No. 107 the format was changed to six panes of 20 (4×5).

Reprints from new plates were made in 1891 on paper watermarked "V over Crown" and perforated 12½.

SINGLE-LINED NUMERAL WATERMARK PAPERS. The first consignment of this paper, showing watermarks as W **11**, arrived in Victoria during October 1862. Five further consignments followed, all but the last supplied by De La Rue.

The complexity of the scheme for different watermarks for each value, together with the time required to obtain further supplies from Great Britain, resulted in the emergency use of paper obtained from Tasmania and of the wrong numeral watermark on certain printings.

The final order for this paper was placed, in error with the firm of T. H. Saunders of London. Although the actual watermarks are the same (the dandy rolls were the property of the Victoria Government and supplied to each firm in turn) there are considerable differences between the two types of paper. That manufactured by Saunders is of a more even quality and is smoother, thicker, less brittle and less white than the De La Rue type.

De La Rue supplied white paper watermarked "1", "2", "4", "6" and "8", blue paper watermarked "1" and green paper watermarked "2". The Saunders consignment of October 1865 contained white paper watermarked "1", "4" and "6", blue paper watermarked "1", green paper watermarked "2" and pink paper watermarked "10".

It is helpful for comparison purposes to note that all white paper watermarked "2" or "8" can only be De La Rue and all pink paper watermarked "10" can only be Saunders.

14   15   16

17   18

(Des and eng F. Grosse. Typo from electrotypes)
1863–73. "Laureated" series.

(a) On paper made by De La Rue wmkd with the appropriate value in single-lined numerals as W 11
108	14	1d. pale green (P 12) (9.9.64)	£120	15·00
		a. Perf 12½×12 (9.64)	£110	8·00
		b. Perf 13 (10.10.64)	£100	6·00
		c. Bluish green (P 13)	£110	6·00
		d. Green (P 12) (7.65)	£100	6·50
		da. Perf 13	£140	6·50
		ea. Perf 13	—	6·50
		eb. Perf 12×13	—	12·00
		f. Bright yellow-green (P 13)	—	23·00
109		2d. violet (P 12) (1.4.64)	£150	13·00
		a. Dull violet (P 12) (10.64)	£160	13·00
		ab. Perf 12½×12	£750	
		ac. Perf 12½		
		ad. Perf 13	£150	9·00
		b. Dull lilac (P 13) (4.65)	£130	9·00
		ba. Perf 12 (7.66)	—	18·00
		bb. Perf 12×13 (7.66)	—	19·00
		c. Reddish mauve (P 13) (11.65)	£140	19·00
		d. Rose-lilac (P 13) (1.66)	£130	11·00
		da. Perf 12×13 or 13×12	£120	11·00
		e. Grey (P 12) (7.66)	£180	14·00
		ea. Perf 13	£120	5·50
110		4d. deep rose (P 12) (11.9.63)	£250	5·50
		a. Printed double	†	£1500
		b. Rose-pink (P 12) (9.63)	£190	3·00
		c. Pink (P 12) (7.5.64)	£190	3·00
		ca. Error. Wmkd single-lined "8"	†	£8000
		cb. Perf 12½×12 (9.64)		
		d. Dull rose (P 13) (10.64)	£170	3·00
		e. Dull rose-red (P 13)	£170	3·00
		ea. Perf 12 (8.65)	£250	75·00
111	16	6d. blue (P 13) (13.2.66)	£130	11·00
		a. Perf 13	£130	4·75
		b. Perf 12×13	£120	11·00
112	14	8d. orange (P 13) (22.2.65)	£800	£110
113	17	1s. blue/*blue* (P 13) (10.4.65)	£275	6·00
		a. Perf 12×13 (4.66)	£275	6·00
		ab. Imperf between (vert pair)	†	£7000
		b. Bright blue/blue (P 13) (6.67)	£225	6·50
		c. Indigo-blue/blue (P 13) (3.68)	—	4·00
		d. Dull blue/blue (P 12) (6.74)	—	3·75

(b) Emergency printings on Perkins Bacon paper borrowed from Tasmania. Wmk double-lined "4" as W 4 of Tasmania
114	14	4d. deep rose (P 12) (7.1.64)	£250	11·00
		a. Pale rose (P 12)	—	11·00
		b. Dull reddish rose (P 13) (11.8.65)	£250	11·00
		ba. Perf 12	—	11·00
		bb. Perf 12×13	—	22·00
		c. Red (P 13) (4.12.65)	£250	11·00

(c) Emergency printings on De La Rue paper as W 11, but showing incorrect single-lined numeral. P 13

115	14	1d. bright yellow-green (wmkd "8") (27.12.66)	£300	28·00
116		1d. bright yellow-green (wmkd "6") (6.67)	—	70·00
117		2d. grey (wmkd "8") (18.1.67)	£275	6·50
118	15	3d. lilac (wmkd "8") (29.9.66)	£250	50·00
119	16	10d. grey (wmkd "8") (21.10.65)	£1000	£150
		a. Grey-black	£1000	£160

(d) On paper made by T. H. Saunders wmkd with the appropriate value in single-lined numerals as W 11

120	14	1d. deep yellow-green (P 12×13) (1.66)	£200	29·00
		a. Perf 13 (3.66)	£120	14·00
		b. Perf 12 (7.66)	—	29·00
121		4d. rose-red (P 13) (12.12.65)	£150	4·50
		aa. Wmk sideways	†	
		a. Perf 12×13 or 13×12 (2.66)	£225	9·50
		b. Perf 12 (4.66)	—	9·50
122	16	6d. blue (P 13) (28.5.66)	£130	3·50
		a. Perf 12	£130	7·00
		b. Perf 12×13	£130	4·50
123		10d. dull purple/*pink* (P 13) (22.3.66)	£300	7·00
		a. Perf 12×13	£350	8·00
		b. Blackish brown/*pink* (P 13) (12.69)	£300	7·00
		c. Purple-brown/*pink* (P 13) (11.70)	—	
124	17	1s. bright blue/*blue* (P 13) (5.12.70)	£160	4·75
		a. Pale dull blue/*blue* (P 12) (1.73)	£250	9·00
		ab. Perf 13	—	19·00
		b. Indigo-blue/*blue* (P 12) (9.73)	—	14·00
		ba. Perf 13	£160	7·00

(e) Emergency printings on Saunders paper as W 11, but showing incorrect single-lined numeral. P 13

125	14	1d. bright yellow-green (wmkd "4") (6.3.67)	£200	50·00
126		1d. bright yellow-green (wmkd "6") (6.67)	£300	65·00
127		2d. grey (wmkd "4") (21.2.67)	£225	9·00
128		2d. grey (wmkd "6") (13.5.67)	£350	9·50

The 1d., 2d., 4d. and 8d. were originally produced in sheets of 120 containing eight panes of 15 (3×5). The 3d. and 6d. were in sheets of 120 (12×10) from February 1866, 2d. (from July 1866) and 4d. (from April 1866) subsequently changed to this format. The 10d. was in sheets of 120 containing twenty panes of 6 (2×3). The 1s. was originally in sheets of 60 containing three panes of 20 (4×5), but this changed to 120 (12×10) in April 1866.

Nos. 108a, 109ab/ac and 110cb were perforated or part-perforated with a machine gauging 12½, borrowed from the Government Printer in September 1864, while the perf 12 machine was being repaired.

Only single examples are thought to exist of Nos. 110a, 110ca and 113ab and two of No. 108ca.

For later emergency printings on these papers see Nos. 153/66.

(Typo from composite woodblock and electrotype plate)

1864–80. Wmk single-lined "2" as W 11.

(a) On De La Rue paper.

129	4	2s. light blue/*green* (P 13) (22.11.64)	£450	12·00
		a. Dark blue/*green* (P 12) (9.65)	£475	20·00
		ab. Perf 13 (6.66)	£450	9·50
		b. Blue/*green* (P 13) (6.68)	£400	7·00
		c. Greenish blue/*green* (P 13) (7.73)	£400	9·50
		ca. Perf 12	£425	11·00
		d. Deep greenish blue/*green* (P 12½) (7.80)	£400	9·50

(b) On Saunders paper.

130	4	2s. dark blue/*green* (P 13) (23.11.67)	£450	8·50
		a. Blue/*green* (P 13) (10.71)	£450	8·50
		ab. Perf 12 (8.74)	£475	9·00
		c. Deep greenish blue/*green* (P 12½) (5.80)	£425	7·00

Nos. 129/30 were produced in sheets of 30 containing two panes of 15 (3×5). The plate contained eighteen of the original woodblock impressions and twelve electrotypes taken from them.

19	20

V OVER CROWN WATERMARKS. The changeover from the numeral watermarks to a general type to be used for all values was first suggested at the end of 1865, but the first supplies did not reach Melbourne until April 1867. Five different versions were used before the V over Crown watermark was superseded by the Commonwealth type in 1905. The five versions are listed as follows:

Type **19** De La Rue paper supplied 1867 to 1882. Shows four points at the top of the crown with the left and right ornaments diamond-shaped

Type **33** De La Rue paper supplied 1882 to 1895. No points at the top of the crown with the left and right ornaments oval-shaped

Type **82** Waterlow paper supplied 1896 to 1899. Wide base to crown

Type **85** Waterlow paper used for postal issues 1899 to 1905. Wide top to crown

Type **104** James Spicer and Sons paper used for postal issues August and September 1912. Narrow crown

(Typo from electrotypes)

1867–81. Wmk. V over Crown. W 19.

(a) P 13

131	14	1d. bright yellow-green (10.8.67)	£110	4·00
		a. Bright olive-green (1.69)	£170	24·00
		b. Yellow-green (4.69)	£120	4·00
		c. Dull green (3.70)	£120	3·75
		d. Pale green (10.70)	£110	3·75
		e. Grass-green (1871)	£110	4·00
		f. Bluish green (shades) (7.72)	£110	4·50
		fa. Wmk sideways	†	—
		g. Green (shades) (9.72)	£110	3·50
		ga. Wmk sideways	†	—
132		2d. slate-grey (shades) (26.8.67)	£130	3·75
		a. Grey-lilac (29.1.68)	£130	5·50

		b. Lilac (26.8.68)	£100	3·50
		ba. Wmk sideways	†	—
		c. Dull mauve (shades) (10.68)	£100	3·75
		d. Lilac-grey (1.69)	—	4·00
		e. Lilac-rose (2.69)	£110	3·50
		f. Mauve (4.69)	£130	3·75
		g. Red-lilac (5.69)	£110	3·25
		h. Dull lilac (5.69)	£110	2·75
		i. Silver-grey (9.69)	£200	10·00
133	15	3d. lilac (28.8.67)	£450	55·00
		a. Grey-lilac (6.68)	£475	60·00
134		3d. yellow-orange (12.6.69)	85·00	16·00
		aa. Wmk sideways	†	—
		a. Dull orange (6.70)	70·00	9·50
		ab. Wmk sideways	†	—
		b. Orange (3.73)	—	9·50
		c. Bright orange (3.73)	85·00	9·50
		d. Orange-brown (glazed paper) (10.78)	60·00	27·00
135	14	4d. dull rose (28.11.67)	£130	8·00
		a. Wmk sideways	†	70·00
		b. Aniline red (shades) (21.4.69)	—	11·00
		c. Rose-pink (11.69)	—	7·50
		d. Rose (shades) (8.71)	£130	3·75
		e. Dull rose (glazed paper) (5.3.79)	£130	6·50
		f. Dull rose-red (glazed paper) (11.79)	—	10·00
		g. Bright lilac-rose (aniline) (glazed paper) (2.80)	£140	6·00
		h. Rosine (aniline) (glazed paper) (9.80)	£350	9·50
136	16	6d. deep blue (15.1.68)	—	7·50
		a. Blue (21.12.68)	90·00	5·50
		ab. Wmk sideways	†	—
		b. Indigo-blue (10.69)	90·00	6·50
		c. Prussian blue (9.72)	90·00	6·50
		d. Indigo (4.73)	90·00	6·50
		e. Dull blue (worn plate) (3.74)	—	7·00
		f. Dull ultramarine (2.12.75)	£100	7·00
		g. Light Prussian blue (12.75)	£140	7·00
		h. Dull violet-blue (7.77)	—	17·00
		i. Blue (glazed paper) (6.78)	£110	7·00
		j. Dull milky-blue (glazed paper) (9.79)	£110	7·50
		k. Prussian blue (glazed paper) (4.80)	—	7·50
		l. Light blue (glazed paper) (4.81)	£110	8·00
		m. Deep blue (glazed paper) (10.81)	£110	7·50
137	14	8d. lilac-brown/*pink* (24.1.77)	£225	5·50
		a. Purple-brown/*pink* (2.78)	£225	5·50
		b. Chocolate/*pink* (8.78)	£250	10·00
		ba. Compound perf 13×12	†	£325
		c. Red-brown/*pink* (12.78)	£100	5·00
		d. Wmk sideways	†	£400
138	17	1s. light blue/*blue* (11.5.75)	£250	22·00
139	18	5s. blue/*yellow* (26.12.67)	£3750	£425
		a. Wmk reversed	—	£500
140		5s. indigo-blue and carmine (I) (8.10.68)	£700	55·00
		a. Blue and carmine (4.69)	£650	24·00
		b. Pale bright blue and carmine (glazed paper) (24.7.77)	£800	55·00
		c. Grey-blue and carmine (glazed paper) (4.78)	£650	28·00
		d. Wmk sideways. Deep lavender-blue and carmine (4.6.80)	£650	50·00
141		5s. bright blue and red (II) (glazed paper) (12.5.81)	£600	28·00
		a. Indigo-blue and red (glazed paper)	—	55·00

(b) P 12

142	14	1d. pale green (10.71)	£130	9·50
		a. Grass-green (1871)	£110	9·50
		b. Bluish green (shades) (7.72)	—	14·00
		c. Green (shades) (9.72)	£110	7·50
143	15	3d. dull orange (5.72)	75·00	7·50
		a. Orange (3.73)	—	3·00
		b. Bright orange (3.73)	—	3·00
		c. Dull orange-yellow (glazed paper) (12.80)	—	9·50
144	14	4d. rose (shades) (8.71)	£130	3·00
		a. Compound perf 12×13	—	£400
		b. Dull rose (glazed paper) (3.79)	—	3·25
		c. Dull rose-red (glazed paper) (11.79)	—	6·50
		d. Bright lilac-rose (aniline) (glazed paper) (2.80)	£250	18·00
		e. Rosine (aniline) (glazed paper) (9.80)	£150	15·00
145	16	6d. deep blue (2.2.72)	—	7·50
		a. Prussian blue (9.72)	95·00	9·00
		b. Indigo (4.73)	£100	9·50
		c. Dull blue (worn plate)	—	—
		d. Blue (glazed paper) (6.78)	—	9·00
		e. Dull milky-blue (glazed paper)	—	9·00
		f. Light blue (glazed paper) (4.81)	—	9·50
146	14	8d. red-brown/*pink* (glazed paper) (11.80)	£225	23·00
147	17	1s. light blue/*blue* (5.75)	—	13·00
148	18	5s. bright blue and red (II) (glazed paper) (5.81)	£600	15·00
		a. Indigo-blue and red	£700	19·00

(c) P 12½

149	15	3d. dull orange-yellow (glazed paper) (12.80)	£110	16·00
150	14	4d. rosine (aniline) (glazed paper) (9.80)	—	—
151	16	6d. Prussian blue (glazed paper) (4.80)	—	—
		a. Light blue (glazed paper) (4.81)	—	—
		b. Deep blue (glazed paper) (10.81)	£100	9·50
152	14	8d. lilac-brown/*pink* (8.77)	£225	23·00
		a. Red-brown/*pink* (glazed paper) (11.80)	†	£500

The same electrotypes as the previous issues were used for this series with the exception of the 5s. which was a new value. The 1d., 2d., 3d., 4d., 6d. and 1s. plates were arranged to print sheets of 120 (12×10) and the 8d. conformed to this when reintroduced in 1877. New plates for the 1d. (1868), 2d. (1869) and 6d. (1875) were constructed by Robinson's successor, J. P. Atkinson, using the improved facilities then available.

Atkinson was also responsible for the printing of the 5s. value. The original printings in blue on yellow paper were produced in sheets of 25, or possibly 50, using a vertical strip of five electrotypes. Due to its size the 5s. did not exactly fit the watermarked paper and, to avoid a preprinted sheet number, a proportion of the printing was made on the back of the paper creating the reversed watermark variety, No. 139a. These varieties occur in the first printing only as Atkinson created a plate of 25 for the second printing in March 1868.

Two Types of the 5s.: Printings of the 5s. bicoloured to April 1880 were made from electrotypes taken from the monocoloured plate. These showed a blue line beneath the crown (Type I). In early 1881 this plate was found to be too worn for further use and a new die was made from which a plate of 100 was constructed. Stamps from this plate are without the blue line beneath the crown (Type II).

PERFORATIONS 1859-1883. Collectors should note that our descriptions of perforations follow a longstanding convention.

"Perf 12" (1859 to mid–1866 and mid–1871 to 1883)–line perf machines perforating between 11½ and 12.

"Perf 13" (1864 to 1881)–line perf machines generally gauging between 12½ and 12¾, two of which were converted to comb perforation in 1871. It should be noted that, following a repair in 1879, one of these machines produced an irregular gauge varying between 12¼ and 13½.

"Perf 12½" (1863 and 1864)–a line perforating machine borrowed from the Government Printer while the perf 12 machine was being repaired. Stamps perforated (or part–perforated) on this machine were Nos. 95e/f, 108a, 109ab/ac and 110cb. All are rare.

"Perf 12½" (late 1879 onwards)–line or comb machines gauging exactly 12½.

"Mixed perforations"–this description covers stamps where both gauges are present on the same side or sides of the stamp, as a result of reperforation.

(Typo from electrotypes)

1867–70. Emergency printings on various papers due to shortages of V over Crown paper. P 13.

(a) Perkins Bacon paper borrowed from Tasmania. Wmk double-lined numerals as W 4 of Tasmania

153	14	1d. pale yellowish green (wmkd "1") (24.9.67)	£140	13·00
		a. Deep yellow-green (10.67)	£140	13·00
154		1d. pale yellow-green (wmkd "4") (27.5.68)	£2750	£130
155		2d. grey-lilac (wmkd "4") (3.2.68)	£275	5·00
		a. Slate (4.68)	£275	3·50
		b. Mauve (7.68)	—	4·50
		c. Imperf (pair)	†	£5500
156		2d. mauve (wmkd "1") (30.6.68)	£275	5·50
157	15	3d. grey-lilac (wmkd "1") (8.68)	£375	80·00
158	14	4d. dull rose-red (wmkd "4") (5.68)	£275	5·00
159	16	6d. blue (wmkd "4") (20.6.68)	£350	42·00
		a. Indigo-blue	—	45·00
160		6d. blue (wmkd "1") (28.7.68)	£190	13·00
161		6d. dull blue (wmkd "2") (1870)	†	£3750

(b) Saunders paper. Wmkd in words as W 10

162	14	1d. pale yellow-green (wmkd "SIX PENCE") (23.3.68)	£950	75·00
		a. Wmk sideways	†	—
164	16	6d. blue (wmkd "SIX PENCE") (20.5.68)	£750	60·00
		a. Indigo-blue	—	60·00
165		6d. dull blue (wmkd "THREE PENCE") (6.12.69)	£475	32·00
		a. Deep blue	—	38·00
166		6d. dull blue (wmkd "FOUR PENCE") (21.5.70)	£750	50·00
		a. Deep blue	—	55·00

(c) V over Crown, W 19, coloured paper

167	14	2d. mauve/*lilac* (7.68)	£190	6·50
		a. Lilac/*lilac*	£190	6·50

(d) Saunders single-lined numeral "4" as W 11

168	16	6d. dull blue (21.5.70)	†	£2250

The supply of paper was so short during 1868 that many odds and ends were utilised. Nos. 161 (five known) and 168 (ten known) are the rarest of these emergency printings.

The 2d. slate-grey is known watermarked "SIX PENCE". The single example is in the Royal Philatelic Collection.

(Printed in Melbourne from a double electrotyped plate of 240 supplied by D.L.R.)

1870 (28 Jan)**–73.** Wmk V over Crown. W 19.

169	20	2d. brown-lilac (P 13)	£120	3·00
		a. Dull lilac-mauve (9.70)	£110	1·25
		b. Mauve (worn plate) (3.73)	£110	1·25
170		2d. dull lilac-mauve (P 12) (28.7.71)	£110	2·50
		a. Mauve (worn plate) (3.73)	£110	2·25

9   9

NINEPENCE

(21)

1871 (22 Apr). No. 123c surch with T 21 in blue.

171	16	9d. on 10d. purple-brown/*pink*	£800	12·00
		a. Blackish brown/*pink*	£850	14·00
		b. Surch double	†	£2750
		c. Wmk sideways	†	—

22	23	24

	25		**26**		**27**

(Des and eng W. Bell. Typo from electrotyped plates)
1873 (25 Mar)–**74**. Saunders paper. Wmk single-lined "10" as W **11**.

172	25	9d. pale brown/*pink* (P 13)	£200	42·00
		a. Red-brown/*pink* (7.74)	£190	40·00
173		9d. pale brown/*pink* (P 12)	£225	42·00

HALF
(28)

1873 (25 June). No. 131*g* surch with T **28** in red.

174	14	½d. on 1d. green (P 13)	85·00	20·00
		a. Grass-green	90·00	20·00
		b. Short "1" at right (R. 1/3)	—	£100
		c. Mixed perf 13 and 12	†	
175		½d. on 1d. green (P 12)	£110	20·00
		a. Grass-green	£110	20·00
		b. Short "1" at right (R. 1/3)	—	£100

Die I   Die II

Two Dies of 2d.:
Die I. Single-lined outer oval
Die II. Double-lined outer oval

(Des and eng W. Bell. Typo from electrotyped plates)
1873–87. Wmk V over Crown, W **19** (sideways on ½d.).

(a) P 13

176	22	½d. rose-red (10.2.74)	35·00	3·00
		a. Lilac-rose (1874)	35·00	3·25
		b. Rosine (shades) (glazed paper)	32·00	3·00
		c. Pale red (glazed paper) (1882)	35·00	3·00
		d. Mixed perf 13 and 12	†	£400
		e. Perf 12×13		
177	23	1d. dull bluish green (14.12.75)	70·00	2·50
		a. Green (shades) (1877)	70·00	2·50
		b. Yellow-green (glazed paper)	80·00	2·25
		c. Mixed perf 13 and 12		
178	24	2d. deep lilac-mauve (I) (1.10.73)	95·00	1·00
		a. Dull violet-mauve	95·00	1·00
		b. Dull mauve	95·00	1·00
		c. Pale mauve (worn plate) (glazed paper) (1.79)	95·00	1·25
		d. Mixed perf 13 and 12	£600	£375
179		2d. lilac-mauve (II) (glazed paper) (17.12.78)	90·00	1·25
		a. Grey-mauve (1.80)	—	2·75
		b. Pale mauve (6.80)	£120	2·75
		c. Vert pair, lower stamp imperf horiz	†	£3250
180	26	1s. indigo-blue/*blue* (16.8.76)	£150	4·75
		a. Wmk sideways	†	£750
		b. Deep blue/*blue* (7.77)	£160	4·00
		c. Pale blue/*blue* (3.80)	£160	4·00
		ca. Wmk sideways	†	£750
		d. Bright blue/*blue* (9.80)	£180	7·50
		e. Bright blue/*blue* (glazed paper) (21.11.83)	£180	5·50
		f. Pale blue/*blue* (glazed paper)		
		g. Mixed perf 13 and 12	†	—

(b) P 12

181	22	½d. rose-red (1874)	35·00	6·50
		a. Lilac-rose (1874)	35·00	6·50
		b. Rosine (shades) (glazed paper)	35·00	6·50
		c. Pale red (glazed paper) (1882)	35·00	6·50
182	23	1d. dull bluish green (1875)	80·00	9·50
		a. Green (shades) (1877)	75·00	12·00
		b. Yellow-green (glazed paper)	—	11·00
183	24	2d. deep lilac-mauve (I) (1873)	—	14·00
		a. Dull violet-mauve	—	14·00
		b. Dull mauve	£120	6·00
		c. Pale mauve (worn plate) (glazed paper) (1879)	£130	7·00
184		2d. lilac-mauve (II) (glazed paper) (1878)	£130	6·00
		a. Grey-mauve (glazed paper) (1880)	—	7·00
		b. Pale mauve (glazed paper) (1880)	—	8·50
185	25	9d. lilac-brown/*pink* (1.12.75)	£275	18·00
186	26	1s. deep blue/*blue* (1880)	—	7·50
		a. Bright blue/*blue* (1880)	—	7·50

(c) P 12½

187	22	½d. rosine (shades) (glazed paper) (1880)		
		a. Pale red (glazed paper) (1882)		
188	23	1d. yellow-green (glazed paper) (1880)		
189	24	2d. grey-mauve (II) (glazed paper) (1880)		
		a. Pale mauve (1880)		
190	27	2s. deep blue/*green* (glazed paper) (8.7.81)	£275	24·00
		a. Light blue/*green* (glazed paper) (4.83)		
		ab. Wmk sideways	£275	24·00
		b. Ultramarine/*green* (glazed paper) (6.84)	—	28·00
		ba. Wmk sideways	—	60·00

8ᵈ **8ᵈ**

EIGHTPENCE
(29)

1876 (1 July). No. 185 surch with T **29** in blue.

191	25	8d. on 9d. lilac-brown/*pink*	£550	35·00
		a. "F.IGHTPENCE"	—	£500

No. 191a was caused by a broken "E" and it occurred once in each sheet of 120.

1877–79. Saunders paper. Wmk "10" as W **11**.

192	14	8d. lilac-brown/*pink* (P 13)	—	£500
		a. Purple-brown/*pink* (2.78)	£250	19·00
		b. Chocolate/*pink* (8.78)	†	£600
		c. Red-brown/*pink* (8.79)	£200	8·00
193		8d. red-brown/*pink* (P 12) (8.79)	£375	27·00
194		8d. red-brown/*pink* (P 12½) (8.79)	—	60·00

Nos. 192/4 occur amongst the V over Crown printings, the two types of pink paper having become mixed.

1878 (21 Feb–5 Apr). Emergency printings on coloured papers. Wmk V over Crown, W **19** (sideways on ½d.). P 13.

195	22	½d. rose-red/*pink* (1.3.78)	90·00	48·00
196	23	1d. yellow-green/*yellow* (5.3.78)	£150	38·00
197		1d. yellow-green/*drab* (5.4.78)	£275	70·00
198	24	2d. dull violet-mauve/*lilac* (21.2.78)	—	£1000
199		2d. dull violet-mauve/*green* (23.2.78)	£350	48·00
		a. Mixed perfs 12 and 13		
200		2d. dull violet-mauve/*brown* (21.3.78)	£325	48·00

There was a shortage of white V over Crown, W **19**, watermarked paper in the early months of 1878 and various coloured papers were used for printings of the ½d., 1d. and 2d. values until fresh stocks of white paper were received.

No. 198 is often misidentified. It can be confused with discoloured examples of Nos. 178/b, and has often been faked.

	30		**31**		**32**

(Des and eng C. Naish. Typo from electrotyped plates)
1880 (3 Nov)–**84**. Wmk V over Crown. W **19**.

201	30	1d. green (P 12½) (2.84)	£180	26·00
202	31	2d. sepia (P 12½)	75·00	3·00
		a. Sepia-brown (2.81)	75·00	3·00
		b. Brown (aniline) (5.81)	75·00	3·00
		c. Dull black-brown (10.81)	—	3·00
		d. Dull grey-brown (3.82)	70·00	3·00
203		2d. sepia (P 13)		
		a. Mixed perf 13 and 12	†	£650
204		2d. sepia (P 12)	—	£150
		a. Sepia-brown (2.81)	—	£150
		b. Brown (aniline) (5.81)	—	£150
205		2d. mauve (worn plate) (P 12½) (2.84)	£375	16·00
206	32	4d. rose-carmine (P 12½) (10.81)	£110	8·50
		aa. Wmk sideways	†	
		a. Rosine (7.82)	£110	8·00

Nos. 201 and 205 are subsequent printings of stamps first produced on watermark W **33**.

33

1882–84. Wmk V over Crown W **33** (sideways on ½d.). P 12½.

207	22	½d. rosine (3.83)	60·00	20·00
		a. Perf 12	—	42·00
208	23	1d. yellow-green (9.82)	80·00	7·00
		a. Perf 12		
209	30	1d. yellow-green (29.10.83)	80·00	5·00
		a. Green (1.84)	75·00	5·00
		b. Pale green (5.84)	75·00	3·25
210	31	2d. dull grey-brown (15.8.82)	60·00	2·25
		a. Chocolate (3.83)	60·00	2·25
		ab. Perf 12	†	£425
211		2d. mauve (20.12.83)	75·00	5·00
		a. Worn plate (2.84)	75·00	5·00
		b. Perf 12	†	£750
		c. Mixed perf 12 and 12½	†	£750
212	15	3d. yellow-orange (13.4.83)	£110	28·00
		a. Dull brownish orange	£110	38·00
213	32	4d. red-brown (3.83)	£110	17·00
214	16	6d. dull violet-blue (10.11.82)	95·00	6·50
		a. Indigo-blue (11.83)	95·00	6·50
		b. Light ultramarine (8.84)	95·00	8·50

Reprints were made in 1891 of the "Laureated" 1d., 2d., 3d. (in yellow), 4d., 6d., 8d. (in orange-yellow), 10d. (in greenish slate) and 5s. (in blue and red), of the Bell ½d., 1d., 2d. (Die II), 9d. and 1s. and of the Naish 2d. (in brown), 4d. (in pale red) and 2s. With the exception of the Bell 9d., which was watermarked W **19**, all were watermarked W **33** and perforated 12½. Some were from new plates.

THE POST OFFICE ACT OF 1883. Following official concern as to the number of different series of adhesive stamps, both fiscal and postal, used in Victoria it was decided that the system should be unified to the extent that the postage stamps, Stamp Statute fiscals and Stamp Duty fiscals should be replaced by a single series valid for all three purposes. As the Stamp Duty series contained the largest number of values it was adopted as the basis of the new range.

The regulations for the changeover were detailed in the Post Office Act of 1883 which came into force on 1 January 1884. From that date

all existing Stamp Statute (first produced in 1871) and Stamp Duty (first produced in 1879) issues became valid for postal purposes, and the previous postage stamps could be used for fiscal fees.

Until matters could be organised printings of some of the existing postage values continued and these will be found included in the listings above.

Printing of the Stamp Statute series was discontinued in early 1884. The existing Stamp Duty range was initially supplemented by postage stamps overprinted "STAMP DUTY" for those values where the available fiscal design was considered to be too large to be easily used on mail. These overprints were replaced by smaller designs inscribed "STAMP DUTY".

Stamp Statute and Stamp Duty values which became valid for postal purposes on 1 January 1884 have previously been listed in this catalogue as Postal Fiscals. Under the circumstances this distinction appears somewhat arbitrary and all such stamps are now shown in the main listing. Used prices quoted are for examples with postal cancellations. In some instances prices are also provided for fiscally used and these are marked "F.C.".

> Nos. 215/92 were extensively used for fiscal purposes. Collectors are warned against the many examples of these stamps which have been cleaned and provided with fake gum or forged cancels. In practice, many of these stamps are not known to exist in genuine unused or postally used condition and only fiscally cancelled examples are available. This applies especially to stamps of high face value such as Nos. 249/52.

	34		**35**		**36**

37

(Des and dies eng J. Turner (3d., 2s.6d.), W. Bell (others). Typo from electrotypes)

1884 (1 Jan*). Stamp Statute series. Vert designs as T **34/6**, and others showing Queen Victoria within various frames, and T **37**. P 13.

*(a) Wmk single-lined numerals according to face value, as W **11**, (sideways). Paper manufactured by T. H. Saunders unless otherwise stated*

215		1s. blue/*blue*	£225	48·00
		a. Perf 12	£250	50·00
216		2s. blue/*green* (D.L.R. paper)	£300	£100
		a. Perf 12	£300	£100
217		2s. deep blue/*green*	£275	
		a. Perf 12	—	£100
		b. Wmk upright		
218		10s. brown-olive/*pink*		
219		10s. red-brown/*pink*	£2500	£400
		a. Wmk upright Perf 12		

*(b) Wmk V over Crown W **19** (sideways). P 13*

220		1d. pale green	£120	65·00
		a. Green (wmk upright) (P 12½)	£170	£100
221		3d. mauve	£1800	£500
222		4d. rose	£1300	£450
		a. Wmk upright	£1400	
223		6d. blue	£200	48·00
		a. Ultramarine	£170	38·00
		ab. Perf 12	£190	40·00
224		1s. blue/*blue*	£180	48·00
		a. Ultramarine/*blue*	£200	50·00
		b. Ultramarine/*blue* (P 12½)	—	80·00
		ba. Perf 12		65·00
		c. Deep blue/*blue* (P 12½)	£200	48·00
		ca. Perf 12	£200	48·00
225		2s. blue/*green*	£350	£100
		a. Perf 12	£350	
		b. Deep blue/*blue-green* (glazed paper)	£350	£110
		ba. Perf 12	£350	£120
226		2s.6d. orange	—	£300
		a. Perf 12		
		b. Yellow (glazed paper)	£1400	
		ba. Perf 12	£1400	£325
		c. Orange-yellow (glazed paper) (P 12½)		£325
		ca. Perf 12		
227		5s. blue/*yellow*	£700	£120
		a. Perf 12	£700	
		b. Wmk upright		
		ba. Perf 12		
		c. Ultramarine/*lemon* (glazed paper) (P 12½)	£750	£140
		ca. Wmk upright		
228		10s. brown/*pink*	£2500	£400
		a. Purple-brown/*pink*	£2500	£400
		ab. Perf 12	£2500	
229		£1 slate-violet/*yellow*	£2750	£425
		a. Perf 12		
		b. Mauve/*yellow*		
		ba. Perf 12	£2750	£400
		bb. Perf 12½	£2750	£400
230		£5 black and yellow-green	£19000	
		a. Perf 12		
		b. Wmk upright. Perf 12½ (F.C. £425)	£19000	

(c) Wmk V over Crown (sideways) W **33**

231		1d. yellowish green (P 12½)	£130	£110
232		2s.6d. pale orange-yellow (P 12)	£1700	£325
233		£5 black and yellow-green (wmk upright) (P 12) (F.C. £350)	—	

½d

HALF
(38)

1884 (1 Jan*). No. 220 surch with T **38** in red.

234		½d. on 1d. pale green	£120	£110

*The dates quoted are those on which the stamps became valid for postal purposes. The ½d., 1d., 4d., 6d., 1s., 5s. and £1 were issued for fiscal purposes on 26 April 1871. The 10s. was added to the series in June 1871, the £5 in September 1871, the 2s.6d. in July 1876 and the 3d. in October 1879.

All values of the Stamp Statute series were reprinted in 1891 on paper watermarked W **19** (5s., 10s., £1) or W **33** (others). The £5 was pulled from the original plate, but the others were produced from new electrotypes taken from the original dies.

39   **40**   **41**

42   **43**   **44**

45   **46**   **47**

48   **49**   **50**

51   **52**   **53**

54   **55**

56   **57**

58   **59**

60

61

(Des H. Samson and F. Oxenbould

(T **39**), C. Jackson and L. Lang (all others except T **40**). Dies eng C. Jackson, J. Turner, J. Whipple, A. Williams and other employees of Sands & MacDougall. T **40** die eng C. Naish)

1884 (1 Jan*)–**96**. Existing Stamp Duty series.

(a) Litho. Wmk V over Crown. W **19** *(sideways). P 13*

235	**39**	1d. blue-green	£150	55·00
		a. Perf 12	£150	55·00
		b. Perf 12½		
236	**43**	1s.6d. rosine	£350	60·00
		a. Perf 12	—	70·00
		b. Perf 12½	£350	
237	**45**	3s. purple/*blue*	£900	95·00
		a. Perf 12	£900	95·00
		b. Perf 12½		
238	**46**	4s. orange-red	£170	22·00
		a. Perf 12	£170	22·00
		b. Perf 12½		
239	**48**	6s. apple-green	£500	70·00
		a. Perf 12½	£500	
240	**49**	10s. brown/*rose* (*glazed paper*)	£1700	£120
		a. Perf 12		
		b. Perf 12½		
		c. Wmk upright		
		cb. Perf 12½		
241	**50**	15s. mauve	£7500	£550
242	**51**	£1 red-orange	£1100	£110
		a. Perf 12½	£1100	£110
243	**52**	£1.5s. dull rose (wmk upright)	£5500	£550
244	**53**	£1.10s. deep grey-olive	£7000	£375
		a. Wmk upright	—	£400
245	–	35s. grey-violet (wmk upright) (F.C. £375)		£15000
246	**54**	£2 deep blue	—	£225
247	**55**	45s. dull brown-lilac	£10000	£500
248	**56**	£5 rose-red (wmk upright) (F.C. £150)		£15000
249	**57**	£6 blue/*pink* (wmk upright) (*glazed paper*) (F.C. £200)		£1600
250	**58**	£7 violet/*blue* (wmk upright) (F.C. £200)		
251	**59**	£8 brownish red/*yellow* (wmk upright) (*glazed paper*) (F.C. £200)		
252	**60**	£9 yellow-green/*green* (wmk upright) (*glazed paper*) (F.C. £200)		

(b) Typo from electrotypes
(i) Wmk V over Crown. W **19** *(sideways). P 13*

253	**39**	1d. yellowish green	£130	55·00
		a. Perf 12	£130	55·00
		b. Perf 12½	£130	

254	**40**	1d. pale bistre	70·00	13·00
		a. Perf 12	70·00	14·00
		b. Perf 12½		
255	**41**	6d. dull blue	£180	38·00
		a. Perf 12	£180	48·00
		b. Perf 12½		
256	**42**	1s. deep blue/*blue*	£225	7·50
		a. Perf 12	£225	12·00
		b. Perf 12½		
		c. *Bright blue/blue* (*glazed paper*) (P 12½)	£225	8·50
		ca. Perf 12	—	12·00
		d. *Ultramarine/blue* (*glazed paper*) (P 12½) (11.84)	£300	15·00
257		1s. chalky blue/*lemon* (*glazed paper*) (P 12½) (3.3.85)	£275	30·00
258	**44**	2s. deep blue/*green* (*glazed paper*)	£400	32·00
		a. Perf 12	—	42·00
		b. Perf 12½	£400	42·00
		c. *Indigo/green*	£375	42·00
		ca. Perf 12	£450	45·00
		cb. Perf 12½		
259	**45**	3s. maroon/*blue* (*glazed paper*) (P 12½) (8.8.84)	£700	70·00
260	**47**	5s. claret/*yellow* (*glazed paper*)	£110	18·00
		a. Perf 12	£130	19·00
		b. Perf 12½		
		c. *Pale claret/yellow* (P 12½)	£110	19·00
		ca. Perf 12	£140	20·00
		d. *Reddish purple/lemon* (P 12½) (6.87)	£100	14·00
		e. *Brown-red/yellow* (P 12½) (5.93)	£160	50·00
261	**49**	10s. chocolate/*rose* (*glazed paper*)	—	£120
		a. Perf 12		
		b. Perf 12½		
		c. Wmk upright		
262	**51**	£1 yellow-orange/*yellow* (P 12)	£1300	85·00
		a. *Orange/yellow* (P 12½) (8.84)	£1200	60·00
		b. *Reddish orange/yellow* (P 12½) (9.88)	£900	60·00
263	**54**	£2 deep blue (P 12)	—	£180
264	**61**	£10 dull mauve (P 12)		
		a. *Deep red-lilac* (P 12)	£16000	£400

(ii) Wmk V over Crown W **33** *(sideways). P 12½.*

265	**40**	1d. ochre	85·00	22·00
		a. Perf 12	85·00	22·00
266	**41**	6d. ultramarine	£180	40·00
		a. Perf 12	£180	40·00
267	**43**	1s.6d. pink (1.85)	£275	38·00
		a. *Bright rose-carmine* (4.86)	£300	24·00
268	**45**	3s. drab (20.10.85)	£130	16·00
		a. *Olive-drab* (1.93)	£120	16·00
269	**46**	4s. red-orange (5.86)	£130	16·00
		a. *Yellow-orange* (12.94)		
		ab. Wmk upright	£190	15·00
270	**47**	5s. rosine (8.5.96)	£150	20·00
271	**48**	6s. pea-green (12.11.91)	£300	65·00
		a. *Apple-green* (wmk upright)	£400	42·00
272	**49**	10s. dull bluish green (10.85)	£900	70·00
		a. *Grey-green* (5.86)	£800	38·00
273	**50**	15s. purple-brown (12.85)	£1600	£100
		a. *Brown* (wmk upright) (5.95)	£1500	£120
274	**52**	£1.5s. pink (wmk upright) (6.8.90)	£5500	£180
275	**53**	£1.10s. pale olive (6.88)	£5000	£160
276	**54**	£2 bright blue	£2000	£130
		a. *Blue* (7.88)	£1700	£130
277	**55**	45s. lilac (15.8.90)	£10000	£200
278	**56**	£5 rose-pink (P 12)	—	£1400
		a. *Pink* (P 12½)	—	£1500
279	**61**	£10 mauve (3.84)	£16000	£250
		a. *Lilac* (6.85)		£250

*This is the date on which the stamps became valid for postal use. The 1d., 6d., 1s., 1s.6d., 2s., 3s., 4s., 5s., 10s., 15s., £1, £1.10s., £2, £5 and £10 were issued for fiscal purposes on 18 December 1879 with the £1.5s., 35s., 45s., £6 and £9 added to the range later the same month and the 6s., £7 and £8 in January 1880.

Used prices for the £1.5s., £1.10s., £2 (No. 276a), 45s. and £10 watermarked W **33** are for examples from the cancelled-to-order sets sold to collectors by the Victoria postal authorities between September 1900 and 30 June 1902.

Similar Stamp Duty designs were prepared for 7s., 8s., 9s., 11s., 12s., 13s., 14s., 16s., 17s., 18s., and 19s., but were never issued.

The two different 1d. designs were reprinted in 1891 on W **33** paper.

For these designs with later watermarks see Nos. 345/50 and 369/71.

62

(Des C. Jackson and L. Lang. Dies eng C. Jackson)

1884 (1 Jan*)–**00**. High value Stamp Duty series.

(a) Recess-printed direct from the die
(i) Wmk V over Crown W **19** *(sideways). P 12½*

280	**62**	£25 yellow-green (F.C. £140)	
		a. Wmk upright	
		b. Perf 13	
		c. *Deep green* (F.C. £140)	
		ca. Wmk upright	
281		£50 bright mauve (F.C. £200)	
		a. Wmk upright	
		b. Perf 13	
282		£100 crimson-lake (F.C. £300)	
		a. Wmk upright	
		b. Perf 13	

(ii) Wmk V over Crown W **33** *(sideways). P 12½*

283	**62**	£25 yellow-green		
		a. Perf 12		
		b. *Deep green* (1.85) (F.C. £140)	£60000	£1300
		c. *Bright blue-green* (10.90) (F.C. £140)		
		ca. Wmk upright		

284		£50 dull lilac-mauve (wmk upright) (F.C. £180)		
		a. *Black-violet* (10.90) (F.C. £160)	£70000	£1300
		ab. Wmk upright		
285		£100 crimson (F.C. £300)		
		a. Wmk upright		
		b. Perf 12 (F.C. £300)		
		c. *Aniline crimson* (wmk upright) (2.85) (F.C. £300)	£80000	£1700
		d. *Scarlet-red* (5.95)	—	£1700
		da. Wmk upright		£1600

*(b) Litho. Wmk V over Crown W **19** (sideways). P 12½*

286	62	£25 dull yellowish green (1.86) (F.C. £100)		
		a. Wmk upright (11.87)		
		b. *Dull blue-green* (9.88) (F.C. £100)		
287		£50 dull purple (1.86) (F.C. £120)		
		a. Wmk upright		
		b. *Bright violet* (11.89) (F.C. £120)		
		ba. Wmk upright		
288		£100 rosine (1.86) (F.C. £200)		

*(c) Typo from electrotyped plates. Wmk V over Crown. W **33**. P 12½*

289	62	£25 dull blue-green (12.97)	—	£500
290		£50 bright mauve (10.97)	—	£600
291		£100 pink-red (10.1900)	—	£1000

*This is the date on which the stamps became valid for postal use. All three values were issued for fiscal purposes on 18 December 1879. Used prices for Nos. 283b, 284a, 285c/d and 289/91 are for examples from the cancelled-to-order sets described beneath No. 279a. "F.C." indicates that the price quoted is for a stamp with a fiscal cancellation. For the £25 and £50 with watermark W **82** see Nos. 351/2.

63

(Des and die eng C. Naish. Typo from electrotyped plates)

1884 (23 Apr)–**92**. New design inscr "STAMP DUTY". Wmk V over Crown, W **33** (sideways). P 12½.

292	63	2s.6d. brown-orange	£190	32·00
		a. *Yellow* (8.85)	£140	15·00
		b. *Lemon-yellow* (2.92)	£140	23·00

For this design on later watermarks see Nos. 344 and 370.

64 **65** **66**

67 **68**

(Des and dies eng C. Naish. Typo from electrotyped plates)

1885 (1 Jan)–**95**. New designs inscr "STAMP DUTY". P 12½.

*(a) W **19***

293	68	8d. rose/*pink*	50·00	11·00
		a. *Rose-red/pink* (2.88)	50·00	11·00
294	66	1s. deep dull blue/*lemon* (11.85)	£170	18·00
		a. *Dull blue/yellow* (6.86)	£170	19·00
295	68	2s. olive/*bluish green* (12.85)	£140	6·50

*(b) W **33***

296	64	½d. pale rosine	32·00	2·75
		a. *Deep rosine* (7.85)	38·00	3·50
		b. *Salmon* (9.85)	38·00	3·50
297	65	1d. yellowish green (1.85)	30·00	3·75
		a. *Dull pea-green* (2.85)	30·00	3·75
298	66	2d. lilac	50·00	2·75
		a. *Mauve* (1886)	50·00	2·75
		b. *Rosy-mauve* (1886)	60·00	2·75
299	65	3d. yellowish brown	60·00	4·00
		a. *Pale ochre* (9.86)	12·00	2·25
		b. *Bistre-yellow* (9.92)	12·00	2·25
300	67	4d. magenta	£110	7·00
		a. *Bright mauve-rose* (12.86)	£110	8·00
		b. Error. *Lilac* (12.86)	£10000	£1500
301	65	6d. chalky blue (1.85)	£170	11·00
		a. *Bright blue* (3.85)	£130	9·50
		b. *Cobalt* (7.85)	£130	4·75
302	68	8d. bright scarlet/*pink* (3.95)	32·00	16·00
303		2s. olive-green/*pale green* (1.90)	55·00	7·00
304		2s. apple-green (12.8.95)	32·00	90·00
		a. *Blue-green* (29.10.95)	22·00	45·00

The plates for the 1d., 6d., 1s. and 2s. were derived from the dies of the 2d. (1s.), 3d. (1d. and 6d.) and 8d. (2s.). In each instance lead moulds of six impressions were taken from the original die and the face values altered by hand creating six slightly different versions.

Two states of the 2d. exist with the second showing a break in the top frame line near the right-hand corner. This damaged die was used for seven impressions on Plate 1 and all 120 on Plate 2.

No. 300b occurred during the December 1886 printing of the 4d. when about fifty sheets were printed in the colour of the 2d. by mistake. The sheets were issued to Melbourne post offices and used examples are known postmarked between 21 December 1886 and 4 March 1887. Nine unused are also believed to exist.

Reprints of the ½d., 1d., 2d., 4d., 6d. and 1s. values were made in 1891 from the existing plates. The 1s. was watermarked W **19** and the remainder W **33**.

For some of these values used with later watermarks see Nos. 336, 343, 361 and 369.

STAMP DUTY

(69)

1885 (Feb–Nov). Optd with T **69**. P 12½.

*(a) W **19***

305	15	3d. dull orange-yellow (*glazed paper*) (B.) (11.85)	—	£850
306	26	1s. pale blue/*blue* (*glazed paper*) (P 13)	£130	50·00
		a. *Deep blue/blue*		55·00
		b. Blue opt (F.C. £350)	£5000	£2000
307	27	2s. ultramarine/*green* (*glazed paper*) (3.85)	£180	19·00
		a. Wmk sideways	£200	26·00

*(b) W **33***

308	15	3d. yellow-orange (B.) (11.85)	70·00	55·00
		a. *Dull brownish orange* (B.)	75·00	55·00
309	32	4d. rose-red (B.) (11.85)	60·00	80·00

Unauthorised reprints of the 4d. and 1s., both with blue overprints and watermarked W **33**, were made during 1895–96. The 4d. reprint, which is in pale red, also exists without the overprint.

70 **71** **72**

73 **74** **75**

76 **77** **78**

79 **80**

(Des S. Reading (1d.) (No. 313), M. Tannenberg (2½d., 5d.), C. Naish (1s.6d.), P. Astley (others). Dies eng C. Naish (2d., 4d. (both existing dies with lines added behind Queen's head) and 1s.6d.), S. Reading (originally as an employee of Fergusson & Mitchell) (others). Typo from electrotyped plates)

1886 (26 July)–**96**. W **33** (sideways on ½d., 1s., £5, £7 to £9). P 12½.

310	70	½d. lilac-grey (28.8.86)	42·00	12·00
		a. *Grey-black*	—	45·00
311		½d. pink (15.2.87)	40·00	2·25
		a. *Rosine* (aniline) (1889)	18·00	1·25
		b. *Rose-red* (1891)	14·00	1·00
		c. *Vermilion* (1896)	18·00	3·50
312	71	1d. green	21·00	3·75
		a. *Yellow-green* (1887)	21·00	3·75
313	72	1d. dull chestnut (1.1.90)	30·00	2·75
		a. *Deep red-brown* (1890)	30·00	2·75
		b. *Orange-brown* (1890)	30·00	75
		c. *Brown-red* (1890)	30·00	75
		d. *Yellow-brown* (1891)	30·00	50
		e. *Bright yellow-orange*	£120	32·00
		f. *Brownish orange* (1894)	14·00	40
314	73	2d. pale lilac (17.12.86)	38·00	70
		a. *Pale mauve* (1887)	42·00	30
		b. *Deep lilac* (1888, 1892)	18·00	30
		c. *Purple* (1894)	13·00	40
		d. *Violet* (1895)	13·00	40
		e. Imperf	—	£1000
315	74	2½d. red-brown/*lemon* (1.1.91)	38·00	4·00
		a. *Brown-red/yellow* (1892)	28·00	1·00
		b. *Red/yellow* (1893)	23·00	70
316	75	4d. red-orange (1.4.87)	55·00	1·50
		a. *Red* (1893)	26·00	1·50
317	76	5d. purple-brown (1.1.91)	35·00	3·50
		a. *Pale reddish brown* (1893)	14·00	3·25
318	77	6d. bright ultramarine (27.8.86)	60·00	5·00
		a. *Pale ultramarine* (1887)	45·00	60
		b. *Dull blue* (1891)	40·00	75
319	25	9d. apple-green (1.91)	30·00	15·00
320		9d. carmine-rose (15.10.95)	70·00	28·00
		a. *Rosine* (aniline) (1896)	70·00	26·00

321	78	1s. dull purple-brown (14.3.87)	£120	5·00
		a. *Lake* (1890)	95·00	6·00
		b. *Carmine-lake* (1892)	55·00	3·75
		c. *Brownish red* (1896)	55·00	7·50
322	79	1s.6d. pale blue (9.88)	£180	80·00
323		1s.6d. orange (19.9.89)	38·00	25·00
		a. *Red-orange* (1893)	38·00	13·00
324	80	£5 pale blue and maroon (7.2.88)†	£11000	£180
325		£6 yellow and pale blue (1.10.87)†	£12000	£200
326		£7 rosine and black (17.10.89)†	£13000	£250
327		£8 mauve and brown-orange (2.8.90)†	£14000	£275
328		£9 apple-green and rosine (21.8.88)†	£15000	£300

†The used prices provided for these stamps are for cancelled-to-order examples.

Unauthorised reprints of the ½d. lilac-grey and 1s.6d. pale blue were made in 1894–95 on W **33** paper and perforated 12½. These differ in shade from the originals and have rougher perforations. It should be noted that the original printing of No. 322 does not occur with inverted watermark, but the reprint does.

A single example of No. 314e is known postmarked "737" (Foster). A second, postmarked "249" (Mortlake), was reported in 1892. It is known that an imperforate sheet was sold at Mortlake P.O. in 1890. Other examples are believed to be clandestine.

Later printings of the £5 to £9 values, as No. 324/8 but on W **85** paper perforated 12½ or 11, were not valid for postal use (*Unused prices, £325 for £5 value, from £500 for £6 to £9 values*).

A £10 value as Type **80** was prepared, but not issued.

1891 (17 June). W **19**. P 12½.

329	72	1d. orange-brown/*pink*	17·00	4·50

No. 329 was an emergency printing during a shortage of white W **33** paper.

81 **82**

(Die eng A. Williams (1½d.). Typo from electrotyped plates).

1896 (11 June)–**99**. W **82** (sideways on ½d., 1½d., 1s., 2s.6d. to 15s.). P 12½.

330	70	½d. light scarlet (1.7.96)	11·00	6·00
		a. *Carmine-rose* (1897)	11·00	3·25
		b. *Deep carmine-red* (*coarse impression*) (1899)	—	7·00
		c. Wmk upright	£110	65·00
331		½d. emerald (1.8.99)	35·00	9·50
		a. Wmk upright	†	£100
332	72	1d. brown-red (13.6.96)	15·00	1·00
		a. *Brownish orange* (1897)	11·00	10
		b. Wmk sideways	†	—
333	81	1½d. apple-green (7.10.97)	3·00	8·00
334	73	2d. violet	28·00	50
		a. Wmk sideways	†	90·00
335	74	2½d. blue (1.8.99)	27·00	30·00
336	65	3d. ochre (11.96)	23·00	2·75
		a. *Buff* (1898)	13·00	2·75
		b. Wmk sideways	†	—
337	75	4d. red (6.97)	50·00	12·00
338	76	5d. red-brown (7.97)	38·00	2·25
339	77	6d. dull blue (9.96)	35·00	1·25
340	25	9d. rosine (8.96)	70·00	7·00
		a. *Rose-carmine* (1898)	—	7·00
		b. *Dull rose* (1898)	42·00	7·00
		c. Wmk sideways		
341	78	1s. brownish red (3.97)	35·00	4·75
		a. Wmk upright		
342	79	1s.6d. brown-orange (8.98)	90·00	65·00
343	68	2s. blue-green (4.97)	90·00	16·00
344	63	2s.6d. yellow (9.96)	£170	22·00
		a. Wmk upright (1898)	£190	22·00
345	45	3s. olive-drab (12.96)	£110	35·00
		a. Wmk upright (1898)	£110	35·00
346	46	4s. orange (9.97)	£150	50·00
347	47	5s. rosine (2.97)	£160	24·00
		a. *Rose-carmine* (1897)	£160	24·00
		b. Wmk upright. *Rosine* (1899)	£160	27·00
348	48	6s. pale yellow-green (4.99)†	£200	40·00
349	49	10s. grey-green (4.97)	£900	50·00
		a. *Blue-green* (1898)	£900	26·00
350	50	15s. brown (4.97)†	£900	85·00
351	62	£25 dull bluish green (1897)†	—	£350
352		£50 dull purple (1897)†	—	£500

†The used prices provided for these stamps are for cancelled-to-order examples.

83 **84**

(Des M. Tannenberg. Dies eng A. Mitchelhill. Typo from electrotyped plates)

1897 (22 Oct). Diamond Jubilee and Hospital Charity Fund. W **82** (sideways). P 12½.

353	83	1d. (1s.) blue	20·00	23·00
354	84	2½d. (2s.6d.) red-brown	£130	80·00
353s/4s Optd "Specimen" Set of 2			£200	

These stamps were sold at 1s. and 2s.6d., but only had postal validity for 1d. and 2½d. with the difference going to the Fund.

1899 (1 Aug). W **33** (sideways). P 12½.

355	81	1½d. brown-red/*yellow*	4·75	7·00

85

1899 (1 Aug)–**1901**. W **85** (sideways on ½d., 1s. and 2s.6d. to 10s.). P 12½.

356	**70**	½d. emerald	5·00	3·75
		a. Deep blue-green	6·50	2·25
		b. Wmk upright	—	13·00
357	**72**	1d. rose-red	16·00	1·00
		a. Rosine (1900)	7·00	10
		b. Wmk sideways	—	—
358		1d. olive (6.6.01)	13·00	4·00
359	**73**	2d. violet	42·00	1·50
		a. Wmk sideways	†	
360	**74**	2½d. blue (10.99)	48·00	3·00
361	**65**	3d. bistre-yellow (9.99)	7·50	9·00
		a. Wmk sideways	†	
362		3d. slate-green (20.6.01)	40·00	22·00
363	**75**	4d. rose-red (12.99)	28·00	11·00
364	**76**	5d. red-brown (10.99)	48·00	11·00
365	**77**	6d. dull ultramarine (1.00)	40·00	10·00
366	**25**	9d. rose-red (9.99)	23·00	3·75
		a. Wmk sideways	†	
367	**78**	1s. brown-red (5.00)	40·00	11·00
368	**79**	1s.6d. orange (2.00)	38·00	65·00
369	**68**	2s. blue-green (6.00)	50·00	50·00
370	**63**	2s.6d. yellow (1.00)	£600	38·00
371	**45**	3s. pale olive (4.00)†	£225	48·00
372	**47**	5s. rose-red (4.00)	£180	48·00
373	**49**	10s. green (3.00)†	£800	48·00

†The used prices provided for these stamps are for cancelled-to-order examples.

From 1 July 1901 stamps inscribed "STAMP DUTY" could only be used for fiscal purposes.

86 Victoria Cross   **87** Australian Troops in South Africa

(Des Sands and MacDougall (1d.), J. Sutherland (2d.). Dies eng S. Reading. Typo from electrotyped plates)

1900 (22 May). Anglo-Boer War Patriotic Fund. W **85** (sideways). P 12½.

374	**86**	1d. (1s.) olive-brown	£150	90·00
375	**87**	2d. (2s.) emerald-green	£275	£225

These stamps were sold at 1s. and 2s., but only had postal validity for 1d. and 2d. with the difference going to the Fund.

FEDERATION. The six Australian colonies were federated as the Commonwealth of Australia on 1 January 1901. Under the terms of the Post and Telegraph Act their postal services were amalgamated on 1 March 1901, but other clauses to safeguard the financial position of the individual States provided them with a large degree of independence until 13 October 1910 when issues of each state could be used throughout Australia. Postage stamps for the Commonwealth of Australia did not appear until January 1913.

It was agreed in 1901 that stamp printing should be centralised at Melbourne under J. B. Cooke of South Australia who was appointed Commonwealth Stamp Printer. By 1909 the Commonwealth Stamp Printing Branch in Melbourne was producing stamps for Papua, South Australia, Tasmania and Western Australia in addition to those of Victoria.

On federation it was decided to separate postal and fiscal stamp issues so Victoria needed urgent replacements for the current Stamp Duty series which reverted to fiscal use only on 30 June 1901.

1901 (29 Jan). Re-use of previous designs without "POSTAGE" inscr. W **82** (2s.) or W **85** (others) (sideways on ½d.). P 12½×12½.

376	**22**	½d. bluish green	2·75	3·75
		a. "VICTRIA" (R. 7/19)	42·00	60·00
377	**31**	2d. reddish violet	16·00	5·00
378	**15**	3d. dull orange	15·00	5·50
379	**32**	4d. bistre-yellow	25·00	30·00
380	**16**	6d. emerald	13·00	17·00
381	**26**	1s. yellow	80·00	48·00
382	**27**	2s. blue/pink	42·00	75·00
383	**18**	5s. pale red and deep blue	55·00	80·00

88 **89** **90**

91 **92** **93**

94 **95** **96**

97 **98** **99**

100 **101** **102**

I   II   III

Three die states of ½d.:

I. Outer vertical line of colour to left of "V" continuous except for a break opposite the top of "V". Triangles either end of "VICTORIA" are more or less solid colour.

II. Die re-engraved. Three breaks in outer line of colour left of "V". White lines added to left triangle.

III. Die re-engraved. As II, but equivalent triangle at right also contains white lines.

I

II

III

I and II   III

Three die states of 1d.:

I. Thick lines fill top of oval above Queen's head.

II. Die re-engraved. Lines thinner, showing white space between.

III. Die re-engraved. As II, but with bottom left value tablet recut to show full point separated from both "1" and the circular frame.

Two die states of 2d.:

I. Frame line complete at top right corner. Bottom right corner comes to a point.

II. Break in right frame line just below the top corner. Bottom right corner is blunted.

Two types of 1s.:

A. "POSTAGE" 6 mm long (produced by a hand punch applied twice to each impression on the previous 1s. electrotyped plate). Slight variations in position occur).

B. "POSTAGE" 7 mm long (produced from new electrotyped plates incorporating the "POSTAGE" inscriptions).

(Eng S. Reading after photo by W. Stuart (£1, £2))

1901 (29 Jan)–**10**. Previous issues with "POSTAGE" added and new designs (£1, £2). W **85** (sideways on ½d., 1½d., £1, £2).

(a) P 12×12½ (½d. to 2s.) or 12½ (½d., 5s. to £2)

384	**88**	½d. blue-green (I) (26.6.01)	7·50	1·00
		a. Wmk upright (1903)	3·25	3·25
		b. Die state II (6.04)	14·00	2·25
		ba. Wmk upright	14·00	1·75
		c. Die state III (6.05)	24·00	3·25
385	**89**	1d. rose (I)	21·00	1·75
		a. Dull red (12.02)	21·00	1·75
		ab. Wmk sideways	£200	75·00
		b. Die state II (4.01)	6·50	15
		ba. Dull red (12.02)	7·50	15
		bb. Wmk sideways	£200	75·00
		c. Die state III. Pale rose-red	6·00	3·00
		ca. Wmk sideways	60·00	60·00
386	**90**	1½d. maroon (9.7.01)	12·00	10·00
		a. Wmk upright. Brown-red/yellow (9.01)	4·75	55
		b. Dull red-brown/yellow (1906)	3·25	1·00
		ba. On yellow-buff back (1908)	3·75	1·50
387	**91**	2d. lilac (I) (26.6.01)	25·00	1·00
		a. Die state II	50·00	4·50
		b. Reddish violet (1902)	28·00	1·00
		ba. Die state II	55·00	3·25
		c. Bright purple (II) (1905)	9·50	1·50
		d. Rosy mauve (II) (1905)		
		e. Wmk sideways	42·00	
388	**92**	2½d. dull blue	16·00	40
		a. Deep blue (1902)	14·00	40
		b. Wmk sideways	†	£950
389	**93**	3d. dull orange-brown (5.7.01)	17·00	2·75
		a. Chestnut (1901)	19·00	1·00
		b. Yellowish brown (1903)	20·00	1·00
		ba. Wmk sideways	21·00	38·00
390	**94**	4d. bistre-yellow (26.6.01)	9·50	1·00
		a. Brownish bistre (1905)	13·00	2·25
391	**95**	5d. reddish brown	22·00	1·00
		a. Purple-brown (1903)	14·00	1·75
392	**96**	6d. emerald (5.7.01)	12·00	1·00
		a. Dull green (1904)	15·00	2·50
393	**97**	9d. dull rose-red (5.7.01)	30·00	4·25
		a. Wmk sideways (1901)	50·00	35·00
		b. Pale red (1901)	19·00	2·50
		c. Dull brownish red (1905)	40·00	7·50
394	**98**	1s. yellow-orange (A) (5.7.01)	35·00	3·50
		a. Yellow (1902)	24·00	3·50
		b. Type B (4.03)	23·00	3·50
		ba. Orange (1904)	21·00	3·00
		bb. Wmk sideways (1905)	75·00	35·00
395	**99**	2s. blue/rose (5.7.01)	30·00	2·00
		a. Wmk sideways	£1200	£1000
398	**100**	5s. rose-red and pale blue (5.7.01)	60·00	26·00
		a. Scarlet and deep blue	70·00	26·00
		b. Rosine and blue (12.04)	70·00	26·00
399	**101**	£1 carmine-rose (18.11.01)	£350	£130
400	**102**	£2 deep blue (2.6.02)	£750	£300

(b) P 11

401	**88**	½d. blue-green (I) (9.02)	22·00	9·00
		a. Wmk upright (1903)	3·25	5·00
		b. Die state II (6.04)	19·00	5·50
		ba. Wmk upright	19·00	7·50
		c. Die state III (6.05)	22·00	6·50
402	**89**	1d. dull red (I) (12.02)	90·00	50·00
		a. Die state II	28·00	11·00
		ab. Pale red (aniline) (3.03)	26·00	4·50
		ac. Pale rose (aniline) (1904)	48·00	9·00
		b. Die state III. Pale rose-red (7.05)	90·00	50·00
403	**90**	1½d. dull red-brown/yellow (1910)	£160	£100
404	**91**	2d. bright purple (II) (1905)	£750	£300
		a. Rosy mauve (II) (1905)	†	£250
405	**93**	3d. yellowish brown (1903)	6·00	17·00
		a. Wmk sideways	27·00	65·00
406	**96**	6d. emerald (2.03)	12·00	26·00
		a. Dull green (1905)	£1000	£550
407	**101**	£1 rose (5.05)	£375	£170
408	**102**	£2 deep blue (1905)	£2000	£1400

(c) Compound or mixed perfs of 12×12½ or 12½ and 11

409	**88**	½d. blue-green (I) (1901)	60·00	20·00
		a. Wmk upright (1903)	60·00	23·00
		b. Die state II (1904)	60·00	45·00
		ba. Wmk upright	65·00	50·00
410	**89**	1d. dull red (I) (1902)	—	£450
		a. Die state II	£900	£225
411	**90**	1½d. maroon/yellow (1903)	£1300	£800
412	**91**	2d. reddish violet (I) (1903)	†	£1200
413	**93**	3d. dull orange-brown (1902)	—	£1400
414	**96**	6d. emerald (1903)	†	£1400
415	**100**	5s. rosine and blue (12.04)	£3500	

Examples of the 1d. Die state II perforated 12×12½ exist with two black lines printed across the face of the stamp. These were prepared in connection with stamp-vending machine trials.

WATERMARK VARIETIES: The attention of collectors is drawn to the note on inverted and reversed watermarks on the stamps of the Australian States at the top of the Australia listings.

1905–13. Wmk Crown over A, W w **11** (sideways on ½d., £1, £2).

(a) P 12×12½ (½d. to 1s.) or 12½ (½d., 1d., 2½d., 6d., 5s. to £2)

416	**88**	½d. blue-green (shades) (III) (21.10.05)	4·25	1·75
		a. Wmk upright	15·00	8·00
		b. Thin, ready gummed paper (6.12)	5·00	13·00
		ba. Wmk upright	5·00	14·00
417	**89**	1d. rose-red (III) (16.7.05)	5·00	25
		a. Pale rose (1907)	2·00	10
		b. Rose-carmine (1911)	11·00	3·50
		c. Wmk sideways	14·00	10·00
		d. Thin, ready gummed paper (10.12)	4·50	5·50
418	**91**	2d. dull mauve (II) (13.9.05)	6·00	1·00
		a. Lilac (1906)	11·00	2·00
		b. Reddish violet (1907)	10·00	25
		c. Bright mauve (1910)	6·00	1·00
		ca. Thin, ready gummed paper (8.12)	42·00	8·00
419	**92**	2½d. deep dull blue (10.08)	5·00	1·75
		a. Dull blue (11.09)	3·00	40

88 **89** **90** **91** **92** **93**

420	93	3d. orange-brown (11.11.05)	22·00	1·25
		a. Yellow-orange (1908)	18·00	3·75
		b. Dull orange-buff (1909)	8·00	1·25
		c. Ochre (1912)	8·00	14·00
421	94	4d. yellow-bistre (15.1.06)	9·00	65
		a. Olive-bistre (1908)	8·50	65
		b. Yellow-olive (1912)	7·00	3·75
422	95	5d. chocolate (14.8.06)	8·50	9·00
		a. Dull reddish brown (1908)	7·50	7·50
		b. Wmk sideways	†	£850
		c. Thin, ready gummed paper (19.10.12)	13·00	25·00
423	96	6d. dull green (25.10.05)	26·00	80
		a. Dull yellow-green (1907)	16·00	80
		b. Emerald (1909)	16·00	1·10
		c. Yellowish green (1911)	19·00	5·50
		d. Emerald. Thin, ready gummed paper (11.12)	38·00	48·00
424	97	9d. brown-red (11.12.05)	40·00	10·00
		a. Orange-brown (1906)	35·00	10·00
		b. Red-brown (1908)	50·00	11·00
		c. Pale dull rose (1909)	20·00	11·00
		d. Rose-carmine (1910)	13·00	3·00
		e. Wmk sideways	£325	95·00
425	98	1s. orange (B) (13.2.06)	12·00	2·00
		a. Yellow-orange (1906)	11·00	2·00
		b. Yellow (1908)	17·00	2·00
		ba. Thin, ready gummed paper (11.12)	30·00	25·00
		c. Pale orange. Thin, ready gummed paper (1913)	30·00	50·00
430	100	5s. rose-red and ultramarine (12.07)	80·00	28·00
		a. Rose-red and blue (1911)	90·00	50·00
		ab. Wmk sideways	£120	55·00
431	101	£1 salmon (12.2.07)	£350	£140
		a. Dull rose (1910)	£350	£140
		ab. Wmk upright	£375	£160
432	102	£2 dull blue (18.7.06)	£750	£425

(b) P 11

433	88	½d. blue-green (*shades*) (III) (1905)	1·60	30
		a. Wmk upright. Thin, ready gummed paper (1912)	23·00	32·00
434	89	1d. rose-red (III) (1905)	8·50	3·00
		a. Pale rose (1907)	4·00	2·75
		b. Rose-carmine (1911)	7·00	8·00
		ba. Wmk sideways	35·00	30·00
		c. Thin, ready gummed paper (10.12)	16·00	5·50
435	91	2d. lilac (II) (1906)	†	£375
		a. Reddish violet (1907)	85·00	26·00
		b. Bright mauve (1910)	35·00	26·00
436	92	2½d. blue (1908)	60·00	35·00
		a. Indigo (1909)	20·00	26·00
437	93	3d. orange-brown (1905)	10·00	1·90
		a. Yellow-orange (1908)	†	£200
		b. Dull orange-buff (1909)	15·00	26·00
		c. Ochre (1912)	9·00	18·00
		d. Wmk sideways	†	£300
438	94	4d. yellow-bistre (1906)	15·00	28·00
		a. Olive-bistre (1909)		
		b. Yellow-olive (1912)	8·50	28·00
439	95	5d. chocolate (1906)	†	£1400
		a. Dull reddish brown (1908)	†	£1400
440	96	6d. emerald (1909)	10·00	26·00
		a. Yellowish green (1911)	21·00	38·00
441	97	9d. rose-carmine (1910)	†	£1200
442	98	1s. yellow-orange (B) (1906)	†	£375
		a. Orange (1910)	£1400	
443	100	5s. rose-red and ultramarine (12.07)	85·00	11·00
444	101	£1 salmon (12.2.07)	£475	£170
445	102	£2 dull blue (1.07)	£1300	£600

(c) Compound or mixed perfs of 12×12½ or 12½ and 11

446	88	½d. blue-green (*shades*) (III) (1905)	28·00	18·00
		a. Wmk upright. Thin, ready gummed paper (1912)	£200	£160
447	89	1d. rose-red (III) (1905)	95·00	80·00
		a. Pale rose (1907)	—	80·00
		b. Rose-carmine (1911)	—	80·00
448	91	2d. reddish violet (II) (1907)	£650	£375
449	93	3d. orange-brown (1905)	†	£1200
		a. Ochre (1912)	£650	
450	94	4d. bistre (1908)	†	£1500
451	96	6d. emerald (1909)	—	£1500
		a. Yellowish green (1911)	†	£850
452	97	9d. orange-brown (1906)	†	£1600
		a. Red-brown (1908)	†	£1600
453	98	1s. yellow-orange (1906)	£1900	
453a		£1 dull rose	†	£12000

(d) Rotary comb perf 11½×12¼

454		1d. scarlet-red	4·50	1·75
		a. Thin, ready gummed paper Rose-carmine	2·75	4·75
		ab. Rose-red	2·75	4·75
		ac. Wmk sideways	35·00	28·00
455	91	2d. lilac (II) (1906)	45·00	2·50

The original Crown over A watermark paper used by Victoria was of medium thickness and had toned gum applied after printing. Stocks of this paper lasted until 1912 when further supplies were ordered from a new papermakers, probably W. Joynson and Son. This paper was much thinner and was supplied with white gum already applied. The first delivery arrived in June 1912 and a second in September of the same year.

The rotary comb perforating machine gauging 11½×12¼ was transferred from South Australia in 1909 when J. B. Cooke moved to Melbourne.

Examples of the 1d. perforated 12½ or 11 exist with two black lines across the face of the stamp. These were prepared in connection with stamp-vending machine trials.

ONE PENNY
(103)   104

1912 (29 June). No. 455 surch with T **103** in red.

456	91	1d. on 2d. lilac (II)	1·00	60

1912 (1 Aug–Sept). W **104**.

(a) P 12½ (½d.) or 12×12½

457	88	½d. bluish green (III)	3·00	9·50
458	89	1d. rose-carmine (III)	6·00	6·50
		a. Wmk sideways	50·00	50·00
459	91	2d. reddish violet (II) (Sept)	3·00	9·00
		a. Lilac	6·50	14·00
460	97	9d. rose-carmine	32·00	48·00

(b) P 11

461	88	½d. bluish green (III)	20·00	45·00
462	89	1d. rose-carmine (III)	50·00	30·00
		a. Wmk sideways	£120	£120
463	97	9d. rose-carmine	50·00	75·00

(c) Compound perfs of 12×12½ or 12½ and 11

464	97	9d. rose-carmine	†	£1700

Nos. 457/64 were emergency printings caused by the non-arrival of stocks of the thin, ready gummed Crown over A watermarked paper. Paper watermarked W **104** had been introduced in 1911 and was normally used for Victoria fiscal stamps. This watermark can be easily distinguished from the previous W **85** by its narrow crown.

STAMP BOOKLETS

There are very few surviving examples of Nos. SB1/4. Listings are provided for those believed to have been issued with prices quoted for those known to still exist.

1904 (Mar)–**09**. Black on red cover as Type B **1** of New South Wales. Stapled.
SB1   £1 booklet containing 240×1d. in four blocks of 30 and two blocks of 60
   a. Red on pink cover (1909) £22000
   b. Blue on pink cover £20000

1904 (Mar). Black on grey cover as No. SB1. Stapled.
SB2   £1 booklet containing 120×2d. in four blocks of 30

1910 (May). Black on white cover as Type B **2** of New South Wales. Stapled.
SB3   2s. booklet containing 11×½d. (No. 426), either in block of 6 plus block of 5 or block of 11, and 18×1d. (No. 427), either in three blocks of 6 or block of 6 plus block of 12 .... £5500
   a. Black on pale green cover £6000
Unsold stock of No. SB3 was uprated with one additional ½d. in May 1911.

1911 (1 Aug). Red on pink cover as No. SB3. Stapled.
SB4   2s. Booklet containing 12×½d. (No. 426), either in two blocks of 6 or block of 12, and 18×1d. (No. 427), either in three blocks of 6 or block of 6 plus block of 12 .... £6000

POSTAGE DUE STAMPS

D 1

(Dies eng A. Williams (values) and J. McWilliams (frame). Typo)

1890 (1 Nov)–**94**. Wmk V over Crown, W **33**. P 12×12½.

D1	D 1	½d. dull blue and brown-lake (24.12.90)	8·50	8·50
		a. Dull blue and deep claret	6·50	6·50
D2		1d. dull blue and brown-lake	7·00	2·25
		a. Dull blue and brownish red (1.93)	16·00	2·50
D3		2d. dull blue and brown-lake	14·00	2·25
		a. Dull blue and brownish red (3.93)	27·00	2·50
D4		4d. dull blue and brown-lake	32·00	5·50
		a. Dull blue and pale claret (5.94)	35·00	10·00
D5		5d. dull blue and brown-lake	29·00	4·50
D6		6d. dull blue and brown-lake	24·00	9·50
D7		10d. dull blue and brown-lake	75·00	55·00
D8		1s. dull blue and brown-lake	50·00	11·00
D9		2s. dull blue and brown-lake	£140	70·00
D10		5s. dull blue and brown-lake	£190	£110
D1/10	*Set of 10*		£500	£250
D1as/10s	H/S *"Specimen."* Set of 10		£475	

A used example of the 6d. showing compound perforation of 12×12½ and 11 exists in the Royal Collection.

1895 (17 Jan)–**96**. Colours changed. Wmk V over Crown. W **33**. P 12×12½.

D11	D 1	½d. rosine and bluish green	10·00	2·25
		a. Pale scarlet and yellow-green (3.96)	5·50	3·75
D12		1d. rosine and bluish green	14·00	2·00
		a. Pale scarlet and yellow-green (3.96)	6·00	2·75
D13		2d. rosine and bluish green	27·00	3·00
		a. Pale scarlet and yellow-green (3.96)	25·00	1·50
D14		4d. rosine and bluish green	12·00	1·50
		a. Pale scarlet and yellow-green (3.96)	10·00	2·75
D15		5d. rosine and bluish green	35·00	35·00
		a. Pale scarlet and yellow-green (3.96)	19·00	24·00
D16		6d. rosine and bluish green	24·00	24·00
D17		10d. rosine and bluish green	48·00	10·00
D18		1s. rosine and bluish green	24·00	3·50
D19		2s. pale red and yellowish green (28.3.95)	90·00	26·00
D20		5s. pale red and yellowish green (28.3.95)	£140	40·00
D11/20	*Set of 10*		£350	£120

1897 (1 July)–**99**. Wmk V over Crown. W **82**. P 12×12½.

D21	D 1	1d. pale scarlet and yellow-green	21·00	2·00
		a. Dull red and bluish green (8.99)	19·00	2·50
D22		2d. pale scarlet and yellow-green	35·00	2·00
		a. Dull red and bluish green (6.99)	35·00	2·00

D23		4d. pale scarlet and yellow-green	55·00	2·50
		a. Dull red and bluish green (8.99)	55·00	2·50
D24		5d. pale scarlet and yellow-green	55·00	7·50
D25		6d. pale scarlet and yellow-green	15·00	7·50
D21/5	*Set of 5*		£160	19·00

1900 (1 June)–**04**. Wmk V over Crown. W **85**. P 12×12½.

D26	D 1	½d. rose-red and deep green	25·00	6·00
		a. Pale red and deep green (8.01)	7·00	5·00
		b. Scarlet and deep green (1.03)	—	30·00
		c. Aniline rosine and green (6.04)	18·00	10·00
D27		1d. rose-red and pale green	24·00	1·75
		a. Pale red and deep green (9.01)	26·00	1·50
		b. Scarlet and deep green (2.02)	26·00	1·00
		c. Aniline rosine and green (9.03)	26·00	1·25
D28		2d. rose-red and pale green	16·00	2·25
		a. Pale red and deep green (7.00)	26·00	3·25
		b. Scarlet and deep green (2.02)	26·00	1·25
		c. Aniline rosine and green (9.03)	26·00	2·00
D29		4d. rose-red and pale green (5.01)	50·00	14·00
		a. Pale red and deep green (9.01)	50·00	2·75
		b. Scarlet and deep green (6.03)	50·00	4·75
		c. Aniline rosine and green (6.04)	50·00	4·75
D30		5d. scarlet and deep green (1.03)	24·00	12·00
D31		1s. scarlet and deep green (3.02)	26·00	15·00
D32		2s. scarlet and deep green (1.03)	£180	95·00
D33		5s. scarlet and deep green (1.03)	£200	95·00
D26/33	*Set of 8*		£475	£200

1905 (Dec)–**09**. Wmk Crown over A, W w **11**. P 12×12½.

D34	D 1	½d. aniline rosine and pale green (1.06)	27·00	21·00
		a. Scarlet and pale yellow-green (7.07)	5·50	12·00
		b. Dull scarlet and pea-green (3.09)	6·50	13·00
		ba. Compound perf 12×12½ and 11.	£1600	£1600
D35		1d. aniline rosine and pale green (5.06)	70·00	9·00
		a. Scarlet and pale yellow-green (5.06)	6·50	2·75
		b. Dull scarlet and pea-green (1.07)	10·00	2·75
D36		2d. aniline scarlet and deep yellow-green (5.06)	45·00	6·00
		a. Dull scarlet and pea-green (11.07)	14·00	3·00
D37		4d. dull scarlet and pea-green (1908)	22·00	26·00
D34a/7	*Set of 4*		42·00	40·00

Prepared for use but not issued

D38		5d. dull scarlet and pea-green	£2750	£1600

The 5d. value on this paper was prepared in 1907-08 but not put into use. A few examples were subsequently included in presentation sets, either mint or cancelled-to-order.

WESTERN AUSTRALIA

PRICES FOR STAMPS ON COVER

Nos. 1/6	*from × 6*
Nos. 15/32	*from × 4*
Nos. 33/46	*from × 5*
Nos. 49/51	*from × 6*
Nos. 52/62	*from × 10*
Nos. 63/a	*from × 8*
No. 67	—
Nos. 68/92a	*from × 10*
Nos. 94/102	*from × 40*
Nos. 103/5	*from × 8*
Nos. 107/10a	*from × 12*
Nos. 111a/b	—
Nos. 112/16	*from × 25*
Nos. 117/25	*from × 10*
Nos. 126/8	—
Nos. 129/34	*from × 8*
Nos. 135/6	—
Nos. 138/48	*from × 12*
Nos. 151/63	*from × 5*
Nos. 168/9	*from × 20*
Nos. 170/1	*from × 4*
Nos. 172/3	*from × 40*
Nos. F11/22	*from × 10*
Nos. T1/2	—

SPECIMEN OVERPRINTS. Those listed are from U.P.U. distributions between 1889 and 1892. Further "Specimen" overprints exist, but those were used for other purposes.

1   2

 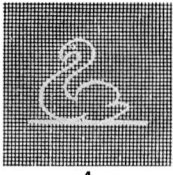

3   4

GUM. The 1854 and 1857–59 issues are hardly ever seen with gum, so the unused prices quoted are for examples without gum.

(Eng W. Humphrys. Recess P.B.)

1854 (1 Aug). W **4** (sideways).

(a) Imperf

1	1	1d. black	£1400	£275

(b) Rouletted 7½ to 14 and compound

2	1	1d. black	£4000	£700

ANDREW PROMOTING PHILATELY ON THE ALAN TITCHMARSH SHOW ITV

Selling Your Stamps?

Summary Tip #18:
When it comes to Selling – all collections are Not created Equal

by Andrew McGavin

Dear Colleague,

I will return to the surprisingly large subject of 'certificates' in another article – but this article is prompted by developments we have observed over the past few years when purchasing private stamp collections.

Traditionally there are 5 different ways to sell your stamps:

1. The Stamp Dealer or Stamp Auction buying on their own account.

2. Dealers 'runners'.

3. Private Treaty – the idea of Private Treaty is that collectors 'place' their collection with a dealer or auction that charges a small commission (or the buyer a commission) to purchase the collection outright. Historically 'Private Treaty' has acquired notoriety as an excuse for the company handling the transaction to 'buy-in' the collection for themselves. Fortunately things are more transparent now.

4. Selling through auction on your own account – the auction house charges you a commission and handling costs.

5. Finally – the internet now permits you to sell your stamps on-line upon your own account via internet giants such as 'eBay'.

In selling your stamps there are two principles to understand. Collectors want to buy stamps that are missing in their collections: this is why Dealers exist. Dealers buy collections to 'breakdown' into usually smaller units that collectors need for their collections: generally speaking breaking down

for sale into small/smaller units adds 'value' and profit for the dealer.

Some collectors are 'hoarders' and will buy general lots – other collectors will buy intermediate sized collections in order to 'extract' the stamps they want ... and then 'turn' the balance back for resale to dealer or auction. The idea that collectors will buy large complete intact collections at retail prices is quaint and outmoded. In almost 40 years of dealing I have seen few intact collections purchased by collectors and continued by new collectors. Collectors enjoy creating their own collections. Few collectors have the budget to purchase a substantial intact collection and develop it still further.

Know your 'strengths' – (know the strength of your collection).

Choosing who is best to approach to sell your stamps or handle them depends upon your knowing the 'strength' and merits of your collection. For example ... on a basic level – if your collection consists of all different modern British sets that you have bought from the Post Office at 'face value' ... the last thing you want to do is send this collection to auction. All you will be doing is paying an auction's commissions – up to 35% for them to sell your stamps, most probably, to a dealer below 'face value' – who will use a fair percentage of them upon commercial correspondence.

A few phone calls to dealers will elicit the percentage of 'face value'

that the trade is paying for stamps that there are too many of – because the Post Office has recently printed and sold them.

Just don't forget to ask if there is anything 'better' in the period that you are selling – that may command a higher price.

In our next article we'll focus on the merits of the 5 different ways to sell your stamps ... and which may be best for you.

Happy collecting from us all,

PS. If you find this 'tip' interesting please forward it to a philatelic friend.

Andrew McGavin
Managing Director: Universal Philatelic Auctions, Omniphil & Avon Approvals, Avon Mixtures, Universal Philatelic (Ebay)

To read the rest of this series 'SELLING YOUR STAMPS?' see the relevant pages listed below:

Summary Tip 18 – page 42 (Australia)
Summary Tip 19 – page 98 (Bechuanaland)
Summary Tip 20 – page 210 (Egypt)
Summary Tip 21 – page 272 (India)

To read the final instalment, Summary Tip 22 – 'Selling via Online Auction' simply e-mail and request to: *info@upastampauctions.co.uk*

Also, at the back of this catalogue to see how UPA can pay you upto 36% more for your collection

In addition to the supplies received from London a further printing, using the original plate and watermarked paper from Perkins, Bacon, was made in the colony before the date of issue.
The 1d. is also known pin-perforated.

(Litho H. Samson (later A. Hillman), Government Lithographer)
1854 (1 Aug)–**55**. W **4** (sideways).

(a) Imperf

3	**2**	4d. pale blue	£375	£200
		a. Blue	£450	£250
		b. Deep dull blue	£2750	£850
		c. Slate-blue (1855)	£4000	£1300
		d. "T" of "POSTAGE" shaved off to a point at foot (R. 7/5, 7/10, 7/15, 7/20)	£2250	£1000
		e. Top of letters of "AUSTRALIA" cut off so that they are barely 1 mm high	†	£30000
		f. "PEICE" instead of "PENCE"	†	£38000
		g. "CE" of "Pence" close together	†	£30000
		h. Frame inverted (R. 8/1, 8/6, 8/11, 8/16)	†	£140000
		i. Tilted border (R. 7/4, 7/9, 7/14, 7/19)	£3000	£1500
		j. "WEST" in squeezed-down letters and "F" of "FOUR" with pointed foot (R. 2/17)	£3750	£1600
		k. "ESTERN" in squeezed-down letters and "U" of "FOUR" squeezed up (R. 3/17)	£5250	£2500
		l. Small "S" in "POSTAGE" (R. 4/17)	£3750	£1600
		m. "EN" of "PENCE" shorter (R. 6/4)	£3000	£1300
		n. "N" of "PENCE" tilted to right with thin first downstroke (R. 6/16)	£3000	£1300
		o. Swan and water above "ENCE" damaged (R. 6/20)	£4000	£1600
		p. "F" of "FOUR" slanting to left (R. 7/17)	£3500	£1500
		q. "WESTERN" in squeezed-down letters only 1½ mm high (R. 8/17)	£4000	£1700
		r. "P" of "PENCE" with small head (R. 9/15)	£3500	£1400
		s. "RALIA" in squeezed-down letters only 1½ mm high (R. 9/16)	£3750	£1500
		t. "PE" of "PENCE" close together (R. 10/15)	£3500	£1400
		u. "N" of "PENCE" narrow (R. 10/16)	£3500	£1400
		v. Part of right cross-stroke and downstroke of "T" of "POSTAGE" cut off (R. 11/15)	£3000	£1300
		w. "A" in "POSTAGE" with thin right limb (R. 11/16)	£3500	£1400
		x. Coloured line above "AGE" of "POSTAGE" (R. 8/6)	£3500	£1500
		y. No outer line above "GE" of "POSTAGE" and coloured line under "FOU" of "FOUR" (R. 8/11)	£3500	£1700
4	**3**	1s. salmon	£25000	£4500
		a. Deep red-brown	£2000	£1100
		b. Grey-brown (1.55)	£650	£375
		c. Pale brown (10.55)	£475	£325

(b) Rouletted 7½ to 14 and compound

5	**2**	4d. pale blue	£3750	£700
		a. Blue	—	£700
		b. Slate-blue (1855)	—	£2500
6	**3**	1s. grey-brown (1.55)	£7500	£1200
		a. Pale brown (10.55)	£7000	£1100

Both values are also known pin-perforated.

The 4d. value was prepared by Horace Samson from the Perkins Bacon 1d. plate. A block of 60 (5×12, cols 16-20) was taken as a "plate to stone" transfer and each frame was then erased. A new lithographic frame, drawn on stone, was transferred 60 times to make up the intermediate stone.

There are a number of transfer varieties, one of the most prominent being the "T" of "POSTAGE" shaved at foot (No. 3d).

Four transfers were taken from the intermediate stone to make printing stone No. I with 240 impressions. Samson printed the initial supply of 100 sheets in deep dull blue (No. 3b) in July 1854.

Printing stone No. 1 had three scarce creased transfers whose positions in the sheet have yet to be established (Nos. 3e/g).

Further supplies were printed in January 1855 by Alfred Hillman, Samson's successor. A severe interruption to printing, almost certainly a broken stone, occurred when the fourth sheet was being pulled. On examining the intermediate stone preparatory to making a new printing stone it was found that the frame of R. 8/1 had been damaged and needed replacing.

This was done, but in so doing, Hillman accidentally produced the transfer error "Inverted Frame" (No. 3h). Printing Stone No. 2 was made as before and bore a range of transfer varieties (Nos. 3j/w) along with four "Inverted Frames". This printing was in blue (No. 3a). Some time after completion of the required 97 sheets, the "Inverted Frame" was corrected on each of the four positions to make printing stone No. 2A. All four corrections are identifiable and on two of them, traces of the inverted frame remain visible (Nos. 3x/y).

Printing stone No. 2A was used for the third printing undertaken in October 1855, producing 175 sheets of slate-blue (No. 3c.) stamps and for the fourth and final printing, totalling 1500 sheets in pale blue (No. 3), undertaken in December 1855.

The 1s. value was produced in much the same way, based on a transfer of cols. 10-14 from the Perkins Bacon 1d. plate.

5

(Litho A. Hillman, Government Lithographer)
1857 (7 Aug)–**59**. W **4** (sideways).

(a) Imperf

15	**5**	2d. brown-black/red (26.2.58)	£8000	£550
		a. Printed both sides	£10000	£800
16		2d. brown-black/Indian red (26.2.58)	£8000	£850

17		a. Printed both sides	£10000	£900
		6d. golden bronze	£21000	£2250
18		6d. black-bronze	£9000	£650
19		6d. grey-black (1859)	£9000	£550

(b) Rouletted 7½ to 14 and compound

20	**5**	2d. brown-black/red	£14000	£1900
		a. Printed both sides	—	£2250
21		2d. brown-black/Indian red	—	£1900
22		6d. black-bronze	£14000	£1300
23		6d. grey-black	—	£1300

The 2d. and 6d. are known pin-perforated.
Prices quoted for Nos. 15/23 are for "cut-square" examples. Collectors are warned against "cut-round" copies with corners added.

(Recess in the colony from P.B. plates)
1860 (11 Aug)–**64**. W **4** (sideways on 2d. and 6d.).

(a) Imperf

24	**1**	2d. pale orange	£130	80·00
25		2d. orange-vermilion	£140	80·00
25b		2d. deep vermilion	£1900	£800
		a. Wmk upright		
26		4d. blue (Wmk upright) (21.6.64)	£325	£2250
		a. Wmk sideways	£750	
27		4d. deep blue (Wmk upright)	£325	£2250
28		6d. sage-green (27.7.61)	£3000	£400
28a		6d. deep sage-green	—	£550

(b) Rouletted 7½ to 14

29	**1**	2d. pale orange	£800	£250
30		2d. orange-vermilion	£850	£250
31		4d. deep blue (Wmk upright)	£5500	
32		6d. sage-green	£5500	£700

WATERMARK VARIETIES: On several stamps, Nos. 1 to 46, watermark W **4** exists with the Swan's head to the left or right and reversed in either direction. We do not list these varieties.

PERKINS BACON "CANCELLED". For notes on these handstamps, showing "CANCELLED" between horizontal bars forming an oval, see Catalogue Introduction.

(Recess P.B.)
1861. W **4** (sideways).

(a) Intermediate perf 14–16

33	**1**	1d. rose	£750	£140
34		2d. blue	£250	40·00
35		4d. vermilion	£1800	£2000
36		6d. purple-brown	£1100	£110
37		1s. yellow-green	£2000	£250

(b) P 14 at Somerset House

38	**1**	1d. rose	£375	65·00
39		2d. blue	£160	45·00
40		4d. vermilion	£475	£180

(c) Perf clean-cut 14–16

41	**1**	2d. blue	£110	24·00
		a. Imperf between (pair)	†	—
42		6d. purple-brown	£550	50·00
43		1s. yellow-green	£800	80·00
		a. Wmk upright	£1200	£150

(d) P 14–16 very rough (July)

44	**1**	1d. rose-carmine (H/S "CANCELLED" in oval £18000)	£350	50·00
45		6d. purple/blued (H/S "CANCELLED" in oval £12000)	£4000	£500
46		1s. deep green (H/S "CANCELLED" in oval £11000)	£4500	£375

Perkins Bacon experienced considerable problems with their perforating machine during the production of these stamps.

The initial printing showed intermediate perforation 14–16. Further supplies were then sent, in late December 1860, to Somerset House to be perforated on their comb 14 machine. The Inland Revenue Board were only able to process the three lower values, although the 6d. purple-brown and 1s. yellow-green are known from this perforation overprinted "SPECIMEN".

The Perkins Bacon machine was repaired the following month and the 6d., 1s. and a further supply of the 2d. were perforated on it to give a clean-cut 14-16 gauge.

A final printing was produced in July 1861, but by this time the machine had deteriorated so that it produced a very rough 14–16.

(Recess D.L.R. from P.B. plates)
1863 (16 Dec)–**64**. No wmk. P 13.

49	**1**	1d. carmine-rose	75·00	4·50
50		1d. lake	75·00	4·50
51		6d. deep lilac (15.4.64)	£325	50·00
51a		6d. dull violet (15.4.64)	£375	55·00

Both values exist on thin and on thick papers, the former being the scarcer.

Both grades of paper show a marginal sheet watermark, "T H SAUNDERS 1860" in double-lined large and small capitals, but parts of this watermark rarely occur on the stamps.

(Recess D.L.R. from P.B. plates)
1864 (27 Dec)–**79**. Wmk Crown CC (sideways* on 1d.). P 12½.

52	**1**	1d. bistre	85·00	9·00
		w. Wmk Crown to right of CC	85·00	9·00
		x. Wmk sideways reversed	85·00	9·00
		y. Wmk Crown to right of CC and reversed	90·00	11·00
53		1d. yellow-ochre (16.10.74)	£110	14·00
		w. Wmk Crown to right of CC	£110	14·00
54		2d. chrome-yellow (18.1.65)	95·00	6·50
		x. Wmk reversed	£110	7·50
55		2d. yellow	£100	9·00
		a. Wmk sideways (5.79)	£250	24·00
		aw. Wmk Crown to right of CC	£250	24·00
		b. Error. Mauve (1879)	£21000	£15000
		w. Wmk inverted	£275	42·00
		x. Wmk reversed	£100	6·50
		y. Wmk inverted and reversed	£275	42·00
56		4d. carmine (18.1.65)	£140	7·00
		a. Doubly printed	£30000	
		w. Wmk inverted	£450	42·00
		x. Wmk reversed	£150	8·50
		y. Wmk inverted and reversed	—	60·00
57		6d. violet (18.1.65)	£170	6·00
		a. Doubly printed	†	£22000
		b. Wmk sideways		£800
		bw. Wmk Crown to right of CC		£325

---

		w. Wmk inverted	—	60·00
		x. Wmk reversed	£170	6·00
58		6d. indigo-violet	£450	35·00
		x. Wmk reversed	£450	35·00
59		6d. lilac (1872)	£275	6·00
		y. Wmk inverted and reversed	£400	
60		6d. mauve (12.5.75)	£250	6·00
		x. Wmk reversed	£250	6·00
		y. Wmk inverted and reversed	£400	
61		1s. bright green (18.1.65)	£250	20·00
		s. Handstamped "SPECIMEN."	£225	
		w. Wmk inverted		
		y. Wmk inverted and reversed	£300	
62		6d. sage-green (10.68)	£450	35·00

*The normal sideways watermark shows Crown to left of CC, *as seen from the back of the stamp.*
Beware of fakes of No. 55b made by altering the value tablet of No. 60.

7 (8)

ONE PENNY

(Typo D.L.R.)
1871 (29 Oct)–**73**. Wmk Crown CC (sideways). P 14.

63	**7**	3d. pale brown	60·00	6·00
		a. Cinnamon (1873)	60·00	4·75
		s. Handstamped "SPECIMEN."	£150	

1874 (10 Dec). No. 55 surch with T **8** by Govt Printer.

67	**1**	1d. on 2d. yellow (G.)	£700	55·00
		b. Surch triple	†	£6500
		x. Wmk reversed	£700	60·00
		y. Wmk inverted and reversed	—	£200

Forged surcharges of T **8** are known on stamps wmk Crown CC perf 14, and on Crown CA, perf 12 and 14.

(Recess D.L.R. from P.B. plates)
1876–81. Wmk Crown CC (sideways*). P. 14.

68	**1**	1d. ochre	90·00	3·75
		w. Wmk Crown to right of CC	90·00	3·75
69		1d. bistre (1878)	£160	5·50
		w. Wmk Crown to right of CC	—	6·50
		x. Wmk sideways reversed	£250	20·00
		y. Wmk Crown to right of CC and reversed	£250	20·00
70		1d. yellow-ochre (1879)	£100	2·75
71		2d. chrome-yellow	£110	1·75
		a. Wmk upright (1877)	£130	3·00
		aw. Wmk inverted	£325	50·00
		ax. Wmk inverted and reversed	£275	25·00
		ay. Wmk inverted and reversed		
		bw. Wmk Crown to right of CC	£110	2·00
		by. Wmk Crown to right of CC and reversed	£225	22·00
74		4d. carmine (1881)	£650	£120
		a. Wmk upright	†	—
		y. Wmk Crown to right of CC and reversed	£650	£150
75		6d. lilac (1877)	£200	4·00
		a. Wmk upright (1879)	£750	15·00
		bw. Wmk Crown to right of CC	£200	4·00
75c		6d. reddish lilac (1879)	£250	6·00

*The normal sideways watermark shows Crown to left of CC, *as seen from the back of the stamp.*

(Recess D.L.R. from P.B. plates)
1882 (Mar)–**85**. Wmk Crown CA (sideways*).

(a) P 14

76	**1**	1d. yellow-ochre	30·00	2·00
		w. Wmk Crown to right of CA	30·00	2·00
		x. Wmk sideways reversed		
		y. Wmk Crown to right of CA and reversed	—	20·00
77		2d. chrome-yellow	42·00	2·00
		a. Wmk upright	†	—
		w. Wmk Crown to right of CA	48·00	2·50
		x. Wmk sideways reversed	—	20·00
		y. Wmk Crown to right of CA and reversed	—	20·00
78		4d. carmine (8.82)	£190	15·00
		a. Wmk upright (1885)	—	£110
		aw. Wmk inverted	—	£200
		ax. Wmk reversed	—	£200
		w. Wmk Crown to right of CA	£190	15·00
		x. Wmk sideways reversed	—	42·00
79		6d. reddish lilac (1882)	£130	3·00
80		6d. lilac (1884)	£130	4·00
		s. Handstamped "SPECIMEN."	£150	
		w. Wmk Crown to right of CA	£140	5·00
		x. Wmk sideways reversed	—	35·00
		y. Wmk Crown to right of CA and reversed	£225	35·00

(b) P 12×14

81	**1**	1d. yellow-ochre (2.83)	£2750	£170

(c) P 12

82	**1**	1d. yellow-ochre (2.83)	95·00	5·50
		w. Wmk Crown to right of CA	£110	7·00
83		2d. chrome-yellow (6.83)	£160	5·00
		w. Wmk Crown to right of CA	£160	6·00
		y. Wmk Crown to right of CA and reversed	—	20·00
84		4d. carmine (5.83)	£300	60·00
		w. Wmk Crown to right of CA	£300	60·00
85		6d. lilac (6.83)	£550	55·00
		w. Wmk Crown to right of CA	£550	55·00
		y. Wmk Crown to right of CA and reversed	—	85·00

*The normal sideways watermark shows Crown to left of CA, *as seen from the back of the stamp.*

(Typo D.L.R.)
1882 (July)–**95**. Wmk Crown CA (sideways). P 14.

86	**7**	3d. pale brown	17·00	4·00
87		3d. brown (12.95)	10·00	4·00

The 3d. stamps in other colours, watermark Crown CA and perforated 12, are colour trials dating from 1883.

½ 1d. 1d.
(9)   **(10)**   **(11)**

1884 (19 Feb). Surch with T **9**, in red, by Govt Printer.
89	1	½d. on 1d. yellow-ochre (No. 76)......	30·00	45·00
		a. Thin bar....................................	£110	£160
		w. Wmk Crown to right of CA........	30·00	45·00
90		½d. on 1d. yellow-ochre (No. 82)......	17·00	30·00
		w. Wmk Crown to right of CA........	17·00	30·00

Inverted or double surcharges are forgeries made in London about 1886.

The "Thin bar" varieties occur on R. 12/3, R. 12/8, R. 12/13 and R. 12/18, and show the bar only 0.2 mm thick.

1885 (May). Nos. 63/a surch, in green, by Govt Printer.

*(a) Thick "1" with slanting top, T **10** (Horizontal Rows 1/5)*
91		1d. on 3d. pale brown..................	90·00	32·00
		a. Cinnamon...............................	85·00	32·00
		b. Vert pair. Nos. 91/2.................	£375	

*(b) Thin "1" with straight top, T **11** (Horizontal Row 6)*
92		1d. on 3d. pale brown..................	£200	75·00
		a. Cinnamon...............................	£180	75·00

12   **13**

14   **15**

(Typo D.L.R.)

1885 (May)–**93**. Wmk Crown CA (sideways). P 14.
94	12	½d. yellow-green..........................	7·00	1·00
		a. Green....................................	4·50	1·00
		w. Wmk Crown to right of CA......	—	£100
95	13	1d. carmine (2.90)........................	45·00	1·00
		w. Wmk Crown to right of CA......	—	65·00
96	14	2d. bluish grey (6.90)..................	32·00	4·00
		a. Grey.....................................	30·00	4·00
		w. Wmk Crown to right of CA......	—	£100
97	15	2½d. deep blue (1.5.92)................	26·00	2·25
		a. Blue.....................................	26·00	2·25
		w. Wmk Crown to right of CA......	—	£100
98		4d. chestnut (7.90)......................	15·00	2·50
99		5d. bistre (1.5.92)........................	19·00	4·25
100		6d. bright violet (1.93)................	21·00	2·00
		w. Wmk Crown to right of CA......	—	£140
101		1s. pale olive-green (4.90)............	42·00	5·50
102		1s. olive-green............................	38·00	5·00

94s/101s (ex 1d., 6d.) Handstamped "SPECIMEN." (Nos. 96, 98, 101) or optd "SPECIMEN" *Set of 6* £550

The normal sideways watermark shows Crown to left of CA, *as seen from the back of the stamp.*

(Recess D.L.R. from P.B. plates)

1888 (Mar–Apr). Wmk Crown CA (sideways). P 14.
103	1	1d. carmine-pink..........................	32·00	3·50
104		2d. grey....................................	85·00	1·25
		w. Wmk Crown to right of CA......	£120	
		y. Wmk Crown to right of CA and reversed...........................	£180	
105		4d. red-brown (4.88)....................	80·00	32·00
		x. Wmk sideways reversed..........	£120	

103s/5s H/S "SPECIMEN." *Set of 3*............ £275

The watermark shows Crown to right of CA on No. 103 and to the left of CA on 104/5, *as seen from the back of the stamp.*

ONE PENNY   **Half-penny**
(16)   **(17)**

1893 (Feb). Surch with T **16**, in green, by Govt Printer.
107	7	1d. on 3d. cinnamon (No. 63)........	15·00	9·50
108		1d. on 3d. cinnamon (No. 63a)......	15·00	9·50
		a. Double surcharge....................	£2000	
109		1d. on 3d. pale brown (No. 86)......	85·00	15·00

1895 (21 Nov). Surch with T **17** by Govt Printer.

(a) In green
110	7	½d. on 3d. pale brown (No. 63)........	10·00	42·00
110a		½d. on 3d. cinnamon (No. 63a)........	10·00	42·00
		b. Surcharge double....................	£1600	

(b) In red and in green
111a	7	½d. on 3d. cinnamon (No. 63a)......	£110	£300
111b		½d. on 3d. red-brown (No. 87)........	85·00	£180

Green was the adopted surcharge colour but a trial had earlier been made in red on stamps watermarked Crown CC. As they proved unsatisfactory they were given another surcharge in green. The trial stamps were inadvertently issued and, to prevent speculation, a further printing of the duplicated surcharge was made, but on both papers, Crown CC (No. 111a) and Crown CA (No. 111b).

18   **19**

---

20   **21**

(Typo D.L.R.)

1898 (Dec)–**1907**. Wmk W Crown A, W **18**. P 14.
112	13	1d. carmine................................	9·00	30
		w. Wmk inverted........................	—	£140
113	14	2d. bright yellow (1.99)................	32·00	3·00
		w. Wmk inverted........................	—	£140
114	19	2½d. blue (1.01)............................	16·00	1·25
		w. Wmk inverted........................	—	£350
115	20	6d. bright violet (10.06)................	45·00	4·50
		w. Wmk inverted........................	—	£275
116	21	1s. olive-green (4.07)..................	50·00	7·00
		w. Wmk inverted........................	—	£170

22   **23**   **24**

25   **26**   **27**

28   **29**   **30**

31   **32**   **33**

(Des M. Tannenberg (2s.6d., 5s.) Typo Victoria Govt Printer, Melbourne, Commonwealth Stamp Ptg Branch from March 1909)

1902 (Oct)–**11**. Wmk V and Crown, W **33** (sideways on horiz designs).

(a) P 12½ or 12½×12 (horiz), 12×12½ (vert)
117	22	1d. carmine-rose (1.03)................	28·00	1·00
		a. Wmk upright (10.02)................	25·00	3·00
118	23	2d. yellow (4.1.03)......................	28·00	4·75
		a. Wmk upright (1903)................	60·00	8·00
119	24	4d. chestnut (4.03)......................	45·00	4·25
		a. Wmk upright........................	£600	£600
120	15	5d. bistre (4.9.05)........................	£150	90·00
121	25	8d. apple-green (3.03)..................	21·00	4·50
122	26	9d. yellow-orange (5.03)................	55·00	35·00
		a. Wmk upright (11.03)................	£120	30·00
123	27	10d. red (3.03)............................	32·00	11·00
124	28	2s. bright red/*yellow*................	85·00	45·00
		a. Wmk sideways........................	£250	26·00
		b. Orange/*yellow* (7.06)............	55·00	12·00
		c. Brown-red/*yellow* (5.11)........	45·00	27·00
125	29	2s.6d. deep blue/*rose*................	55·00	21·00
126	30	5s. emerald-green........................	80·00	50·00
127	31	10s. deep mauve..........................	£170	£100
		a. Bright purple (1910)................	£900	£425
128	32	£1 orange-brown (1.11.02)............	£425	£190
		a. Orange (10.7.09)....................	£750	£350

(b) P 11
129	22	1d. carmine-rose........................	£400	50·00
		a. Wmk upright (1905)................	†	£500
130	23	2d. yellow................................	£425	60·00
		a. Wmk upright........................	†	£500
131	24	4d. chestnut..............................	£1400	£425
132	15	5d. bistre..................................	50·00	75·00
133	26	9d. yellow-orange........................	£180	£180
134	28	2s. bright red/*yellow*................	£300	£180
		a. Orange/*yellow*....................	£425	£225

(c) Perf compound of 12½ or 12½×12 and 11
135	22	1d. carmine-rose........................	£1300	£650
		a. Wmk upright........................	†	£650
136	23	2d. yellow................................	£1900	£1100
137	24	4d. chestnut..............................		

Type **22** is similar to Type **13** but larger.

> **WATERMARK VARIETIES:** The attention of collectors is drawn to the note on inverted and reversed watermarks on the stamps of the Australian States at the top of the Australia listings.

---

34   **35**

1905–12. Wmk Crown and A, W **34** (sideways).

(a) P 12½ or 12½×12 (horiz), 12×12½ (vert)
138	12	½d. green (6.10)..........................	4·50	8·50
139	22	1d. rose-pink (10.05)....................	22·00	3·75
		a. Wmk upright (1.06)..................	11·00	1·25
		b. Carmine (1909)......................	13·00	1·25
		c. Carmine-red (1912)................	13·00	11·00
140	23	2d. yellow (15.11.05)....................	8·50	2·00
		a. Wmk upright (4.10)................	†	£350
141	7	3d. brown (2.06)........................	65·00	5·00
142	24	4d. bistre-brown (12.06)................	60·00	18·00
		a. Pale chestnut (1908)................	45·00	17·00
		b. Bright brown-red (14.10.10)......	24·00	6·00
143	15	5d. pale olive-bistre (8.05)............	35·00	28·00
		a. Olive-green (1.09)....................	35·00	28·00
		b. Pale greenish yellow (2.12)......	60·00	£110
144	25	8d. apple-green (20.4.12)..............	23·00	80·00
		a. Wmk upright..........................	†	
145	26	9d. orange (11.5.06)....................	35·00	6·00
		a. Red-orange (6.10)...................	60·00	6·00
		b. Wmk upright (7.12)................	70·00	32·00
146	27	10d. rose-orange (16.2.10)............	24·00	29·00
148	30	5s. emerald-green (wmk upright) (9.07)........................	£180	£130

(b) P 11
150	12	½d. green..................................	£3000	
151	22	1d. rose-pink (1908)....................	50·00	32·00
		a. Carmine-red........................	60·00	30·00
		b. Wmk upright (2.06)................	90·00	30·00
152	23	2d. yellow................................	50·00	45·00
153	7	3d. brown................................	24·00	16·00
154	24	4d. yellow-brown........................	£1200	£275
		a. Pale chestnut........................	£1500	£400
155	15	5d. pale olive-bistre....................	60·00	11·00
		a. Olive-green............................	25·00	19·00
157	26	9d. orange................................	£200	£200
		a. Red-orange............................	—	£200
		b. Wmk upright (1912)................	£900	

(c) Perf compound of 12½ or 12½×12 and 11
161	22	1d. rose-pink (wmk upright)............	£1200	£500
		a. Wmk sideways........................	£1500	£800
162	23	2d. yellow................................	£1200	£550
163	7	3d. brown................................	£1500	£1500
163a		5d. olive-green............................	†	£1800
164	26	9d. red-orange............................		

The prices provided for Nos. 154/a are for examples perforated "OS".

1912 (25 Mar–9 Apr). Wmk Crown and A W **35** (sideways). P 11½×12.
168	20	6d. bright violet (9.4.12)................	18·00	28·00
169	21	1s. sage-green............................	32·00	45·00
		a. Perf 12½ (single line)..............	—	£2500

1912 (7 Aug). Thin, ready gummed paper with white gum (as Victoria*). W **34** (sideways).
170	7	3d. brown (P 12½)........................	75·00	75·00
		a. Wmk upright..........................	£200	£190
171		3d. brown (P 11)........................		
		a. Wmk upright..........................		

*See note below Victoria No. 455.

ONE PENNY
(36)

1912 (6 Nov). Nos. 140 and 162 surch with T **36** in Melbourne.

(a) P 12½ ×12
172	23	1d. on 2d. yellow........................	3·00	3·25
		a. Wmk upright..........................	8·50	16·00

(b) Perf compound of 12½×12 and 11
173	23	1d. on 2d. yellow........................	£750	£450
		a. Wmk upright..........................	£750	

STAMP BOOKLETS

There are very few surviving examples of Nos. SB1/4. Listings are provided for those believed to have been issued with prices quoted for those known to still exist.

1904 (1 Jan)–**09**. Black on red cover as Type B **1** of New South Wales. Stapled.
SB1	£1 booklet containing 240×1d. in four blocks of 30 and two blocks of 60..................	
	a. Red on pink cover (1909)................	£20000
	b. blue on pink cover.	

1904 (1 Jan). Black on grey cover as No. SB1. Stapled.
SB2	£1 Booklet containing 120×2d. in four blocks of 30..................................	

1910 (May). Black on cream cover as Type B **2** of New South Wales. Stapled.
SB3	2s. booklet containing 11×½d. (No. 138), either in block of 6 plus block of 5 or block of 11, and 18×1d. (No. 139) either in three blocks of 6 or block of 6 plus block of 12..................	£7500

Unsold stock of No. SB3 was uprated with one additional ½d. in May 1911.

1911 (1 Aug). Red on pink cover as No. SB3. Stapled.
SB4	2s. Booklet containing 12×½d. (No. 138), either in two blocks of 6 or block of 12, and 18×1d. (No. 139), either in three blocks of 6 or block of 6 plus block of 12..................	£7500

POSTAL FISCAL STAMPS

By the Post and Telegraph Act of 5 September 1893 the current issue of fiscal stamps up to and including the 1s. value, Nos. F11/15, was authorised for postal use.

These stamps had been initially supplied, for fiscal purposes, in February 1882 and had been preceded by a series of "I R" surcharges and overprints on postage stamps which were in use for a period of about six months. Examples of these 1881–82 provisionals can be found used postally under the terms of the 1893 Act but, as they had not been current for fiscal purposes for over eleven years, we no longer list them.

F **3**

(Typo D.L.R.)

1893 (5 Sept). Definitive fiscal stamps of Feb 1882. Wmk CA over Crown. P 14.

F11	F **3**	1d. dull purple		32·00	7·00
F12		2d. dull purple		£325	80·00
F13		3d. dull purple		£120	10·00
F14		6d. dull purple		£170	17·00
F15		1s. dull purple		£275	30·00

The 1s. value is as Type F **3** but with rectangular outer frame and circular frame surrounding swan.

Higher values in this series were not validated by the Act for postal use.

Two varieties of watermark exist on these stamps. Initial supplies showed an indistinct watermark with the base of the "A" 4 mm wide. From 1896 the paper used showed a clearer watermark on which the base of the "A" was 5 mm wide.

1897. Wmk W Crown A, W **18**. P 14.

F19	F **3**	1d. dull purple		38·00	7·00
F20		3d. dull purple		£120	10·00
F21		6d. dull purple		£160	12·00
F22		1s. dull purple		£275	40·00

The above were invalidated for postal purposes from 1 January 1901.

TELEGRAPH STAMPS

T **1**

1879 (9 Apr). Wmk Crown CC. P 14.

T1	T **1**	1d. bistre		£100	22·00
		a. Perf 12½		£100	22·00
T2		6d. lilac		£550	£225

The 1d. Telegraph Stamps were authorised for postal purposes from 25 October 1886.

OFFICIAL STAMPS

From 1 August 1862 stamps of various issues were punched with a circular hole, the earlier size being about 3 mm. in diameter and the latter 4 mm. These were used on official correspondence by the Commissariat and Convict Department, branches of the Imperial administration separate from the colonial government. This system of punching ceased in March 1886. Subsequently many stamps between Nos. 94 and 148 may be found punctured, "PWD", "WA" or "OS".

Western Australia became part of the Commonwealth of Australia on 1 January 1901.

COMMONWEALTH OF AUSTRALIA

On 1 March 1901 control of the postal service passed to the federal administration although it was not until 13 October 1910 that the issues of the various states became valid for use throughout Australia. Postal rates were standardised on 1 May 1911.

The first national postage due stamps appeared in July 1902, but it was not until January 1913 that postage stamps inscribed "AUSTRALIA" were issued.

PRICES FOR STAMPS ON COVER TO 1945	
Nos. 1/3	*from × 10*
No. 4	*from × 4*
Nos. 5/12	*from × 10*
Nos. 13/16	—
Nos. 17/19	*from × 10*
Nos. 20/3	*from × 10*
No. 24	*from × 8*
No. 25	*from × 2*
Nos. 26/7	*from × 8*
Nos. 28/30	—
Nos. 35/7	*from × 5*
Nos. 38/9	*from × 8*
Nos. 40/1	*from × 20*
Nos. 42/5	—
No. 47	*from × 5*
Nos. 48/51	*from × 8*
Nos. 52/3	*from × 5*
Nos. 56/7	*from × 10*
Nos. 58/61	*from × 8*
No. 62	*from × 5*

PRICES FOR STAMPS ON COVER TO 1945	
No. 63	*from × 2*
No. 64	*from × 15*
No. 65	*from × 5*
No. 66	—
No. 73	*from × 20*
Nos. 74/5	*from × 5*
Nos. 76/7	*from × 4*
Nos. 78/81	*from × 8*
Nos. 82/4	*from × 6*
Nos. 85/104	*from × 4*
No. 105	*from × 15*
Nos. 106/10	*from × 6*
Nos. 111/14	—
No. 115	*from × 3*
Nos. 116/18	*from × 5*
Nos. 119/20	*from × 8*
Nos. 121/9	*from × 5*
Nos. 130/1	*from × 25*
No. 132	*from × 3*
Nos. 133/5	*from × 10*
Nos. 136/8	*from × 4*
Nos. 139/a	*from × 3*
No. 140	*from × 8*
Nos. 141/2	*from × 4*
No. 143	*from × 6*
No. 146	*from × 20*
Nos. 147/8	*from × 3*
No. 149	*from × 6*
No. 150/2	*from × 3*
Nos. 153/a	*from × 12*
No. 154	*from × 15*
No. 155	*from × 4*
No. 156	*from × 15*
Nos. 157/8	*from × 3*
Nos. 159/60	*from × 6*
No. 161	*from × 10*
Nos. 162/3	*from × 4*
Nos. 164/211	*from × 2*
Nos. D1/118	*from × 8*
Nos. O1/3	*from × 10*
Nos. O4/6	*from × 4*
Nos. O7/8	*from × 10*
Nos. O9/15	—
Nos. O16/18	*from × 10*
No. O19	*from × 3*
No. O20	*from × 15*
No. O21	*from × 3*
Nos. O22/3	*from × 10*
No. O24/30	—
Nos. O31/4	*from × 10*
Nos. O35/7	—
Nos. O38/42	*from × 15*
Nos. O43/7	*from × 10*
No. O48	*from × 30*
Nos. O49/53	—
No. O54	*from × 6*
No. O60	*from × 4*
No. O61	*from × 30*
No. O62	—
No. O63	*from × 5*
Nos. O64/5	*from × 15*
Nos. O66/7	*from × 8*
No. O68	*from × 20*
No. O69	*from × 10*
Nos. O70/4	*from × 15*
No. O75	—
Nos. O76/7	*from × 15*
No. O78	—
Nos. O79/84	*from × 8*
No. O85	*from × 6*
Nos. O86/7	*from × 3*
No. O88	—
No. O89	*from × 15*
Nos. O90/6	*from × 6*
No. O97	*from × 20*
Nos. O98/110	*from × 6*
No. O111	*from × 10*
Nos. O112/17	*from × 20*
Nos. O118/b	—
Nos. O119/2	*from × 20*
No. O126	*from × 100*
No. O127	*from × 5*
No. O128	*from × 200*
Nos. O129/31	*from × 50*
Nos. O132/3	*from × 10*
Nos. O134/6	*from × 40*

PRINTERS. Except where otherwise stated, all Commonwealth stamps to No. 581 were printed under Government authority at Melbourne. Until 1918 there were two establishments (both of the Treasury Dept)—the Note Printing Branch and the Stamp Printing Branch. The former printed T **3** and **4**.

In 1918 the Stamp Printing Branch was closed and all stamps were printed by the Note Printing Branch. In 1926 control was transferred from the Treasury to the Commonwealth Bank of Australia, and on 14 January 1960 the branch was attached to the newly established Reserve Bank of Australia.

Until 1942 stamps bore in the sheet margin the initials or names of successive managers and from 1942 to March 1952 the imprint "Printed by the Authority of the Government of the Commonwealth of Australia". After November 1952 (or Nos. D129/31 for Postage Dues) imprints were discontinued.

SPECIMEN OVERPRINTS. These come from Specimen sets, first made available to the public on 15 December 1913. In these sets the lower values were cancelled-to-order, but stamps with a face value of over 5s. or later 50c. were overprinted "SPECIMEN" in different types. These overprints are listed as they could be purchased from the Australian Post Office.

It is, however, believed that examples of No. 112 overprinted "SPECIMEN" were distributed by the UPU in 1929. Supplies of the 1902 and 1902–04 postage due stamps overprinted "SPECIMEN" were supplied to the UPU by some of the states.

1

2

Die I   Die II

Dies of Type 1 (mono-coloured values only):—

Die I.   Break in inner frame line at lower left level with top of words of value.

Die II.   Die repaired showing no break.

Die I was only used for the ½d., 1d., 2d. and 3d. Several plates were produced for each except the 3d. When the second plate of the 3d. was being prepared the damage became aggravated after making 105 out of the 120 units when the die was returned for repair. This gave rise to the *se-tenant* pairs showing the two states of the die.

Die II was used until 1945 and deteriorated progressively with damage to the frame lines and rounding of the corners.

Specialists recognise seven states of this die, but we only list the two most major of the later versions.

Die IIA. This state is as Die II, but, in addition, shows a break in the inner left-hand frame line, 9 mm from the top of the design (occurs on 1d., 2d. and 6d.).

Die IIB. As Die IIA, but now also showing break in outer frame line above "ST", and (not illustrated) an incomplete corner to the inner frame line at top right (occurs on 3d., 6d., 9d., 1s. and £1 (No. 75)).

No. 9a shows a badly distorted second "E" in "PENCE", which is unmistakable. It occurs on the upper plate right pane R. 10/6 and was replaced by a substitute cliché in Die IIA (No. 9b) in the November 1913 printing.

(Des B. Young. Eng S. Reading. Typo J. B. Cooke)

1913 (2 Jan)–**14**. W **2**. P 12.

1	**1**	½d. green (Die I) (14.1.13)	10·00	6·50
		bw. Wmk inverted	85·00	32·00
		c. Wmk sideways	†	£35000
		cw. Wmk sideways inverted	†	£27000
2		1d. red (Die I)	19·00	1·75
		a. Wmk sideways	£1600	275
		aw. Wmk sideways inverted	£1800	£300
		b. Carmine	18·00	1·75
		cw. Wmk inverted	85·00	22·00
		d. Die II Red (16.1.13)	16·00	1·00
		da. Wmk sideways	£1600	£325
		daw. Wmk sideways inverted	£1800	£350
		db. Carmine	17·00	1·75
		dw. Wmk inverted	90·00	30·00
		e. Die IIA. *Red* (4.14)	29·00	1·25
		eb. Carmine	29·00	1·75
		ew. Wmk inverted	£170	32·00
3		2d. grey (Die I) (15.1.13)	55·00	6·50
		w. Wmk inverted	£130	35·00
4		2½d. indigo (Die II) (27.1.13)	50·00	22·00
5		3d. olive (Die I) (28.1.13)	80·00	11·00
		a. Imperf three sides (horiz pair)	£75000	
		aa. Imperf three sides (lower stamp of vert pair)	£42000	
		b. in pair with Die II	£1300	£700
		c. Yellow-olive	85·00	11·00
		ca. In pair with Die II	£1300	£700
		dw. Wmk inverted	£200	80·00

	e. Die II *Olive*	£475	95·00
	ea. Yellow-olive	£450	90·00
	ew. Wmk inverted	£950	£375
6	4d. orange (Die II) (19.2.13)	95·00	26·00
	a. Orange-yellow	£475	85·00
8	5d. chestnut (Die II) (18.1.13)	85·00	48·00
9	6d. ultramarine (Die II) (18.1.13)	75·00	20·00
	a. Retouched "E"	£2500	£950
	b. Die IIA (substituted cliché) (11.13)	£6000	£2000
	w. Wmk inverted	£1100	£400
10	9d. violet (Die II) (1.2.13)	80·00	27·00
11	1s. emerald (Die II) (25.1.13)	85·00	27·00
	a. Blue-green	£140	27·00
	w. Wmk inverted	£1500	80·00
12	2s. brown (Die II) (28.1.13)	£275	85·00
13	5s. grey and yellow (Die II) (20.3.13)	£450	£200
14	10s. grey and pink (Die II) (20.3.13)	£900	£700
15	£1 brown and ultramarine (Die II) (20.3.13)	£3000	£2500
16	£2 black and rose (Die II) (8.4.13)	£6500	£4000
1/16 *Set of 15*		£10000	£7000
14s/16s Handstamped "*Specimen*" *Set of 3*			£1300

The watermark on Nos. 1c, 2a and 2da shows the Crown pointing to the left and on Nos. 1cw, 2aw and 2daw pointing to the right, *as seen from the back of the stamp*. One example of 1c and two examples of 1cw are known, all used.

The 3d. was printed from two plates, of which the upper plate contained 105 stamps as Die I and 15 as Die II (at left pane R. 7/1-2, 8/1-5, 9/1-3, 10/1-5). The lower plate contained Die I stamps only.

No. 5a is from the top row of a sheet, with perforations at foot only. No. 5aa is from the bottom two rows of a different sheet.

See also Nos. 24/30 (W **5**), 35/45*b* (W **6**), 73/5 (W **6**, new colours), 107/14 (W **7**), 132/8 (W **15**), 212 (2s. re-engraved).

3

4 Laughing Kookaburra

(Des R. A. Harrison. Eng and recess T. S. Harrison)

1913 (9 Dec)–**14**. No wmk. P 11.

17	**3**	1d. red	4·25	6·50
		a. Imperf between (horiz pair)	£5000	
		b. Imperf between (vert pair)	£2500	
		c. Pale rose-red	10·00	16·00
		ca. Imperf between (vert pair)	£3000	
		cb. Imperf between (horiz pair)	£5000	
19	**4**	6d. claret (26.8.14)	75·00	55·00

All printings from Plate 1 of the 1d. were in the shade of No. 17*c*. This plate shows many retouches.

5

5a

Thin "1" in fraction at right (Plate 5 right pane R. 8/1)

Cracked electro (Plate 5 left pane R. 8/4)

1d. Die II

Dot before "1" (Plate 3 right pane R. 4/3)

"Secret mark" (Plate 4 left pane R. 1/1)

Flaw under neck (Plate 4 left pane R. 7/1)

"RA" joined (Plate 4 left pane R. 10/6)

4d. Line through "FOUR PENCE" (Pl. 2 right pane R. 2/6)

1d. Die II. The flaw distinguishing the so-called Die II, a white upward spur to the right of the base of the "1" in the left value tablet, is now known to be due to a defective roller-die. It occurred on all stamps in the second and third vertical rows of upper left plate, right pane. Each of the twenty defective impressions differs slightly; a typical example is illustrated above.

(Dies eng P.B. Typo J. B. Cooke until May 1918, then T. S. Harrison)

1914 (17 July)–**20**. W **5**. P 14¼×14 (comb).

20	**5a**	½d. bright green (22.2.15)	3·75	1·00
		a. Perf 14¼ (line) (12.15)	£12000	£600
		b. Green (1916)	3·75	1·00
		c. Yellow-green (1916)	32·00	13·00
		d. Thin "1" in fraction at right	£22000	£7500
		e. Cracked electro	£8500	£4000
		w. Wmk inverted	23·00	9·50
21		1d. carmine-red (*shades*) (Die I) (P 14¼ (line))	48·00	7·50
		a. Die II	£17000	£3000
		bw. Wmk inverted	†	£13000
		c. Perf 14¼×14 (comb)	13·00	1·00
		ca. Rusted cliché (Pl 2 rt pane R. 6/4 and 5) (9.16)	£18000	£450
		cb. Substituted cliché (Pl 2 right pane R. 6/5) (2.18)	£2000	60·00
		cc. Pale carmine (*shades*) (1917)	14·00	1·00
		cd. Rose-red (1917)	17·00	2·50
		ce. Carmine-pink (1918)	£170	11·00
		cf. Carmine (*aniline*) (1920)	20·00	3·25
		cg. Dot before "1"	£100	12·00
		ch. "Secret mark"	£100	12·00
		ci. Flaw under neck	£100	12·00
		cj. "RA" joined	£100	12·00
		cw. Wmk inverted	26·00	3·00
		cz. Wmk sideways	†	£50000
		d. Die II *Carmine-red* (*shades*)	£425	6·50
		db. Substituted cliché (Pl 2 right pane R. 6/4) (2.18)	£2000	60·00
		dc. Pale carmine (*shades*)	£450	7·50
		dw. Wmk inverted	£1200	£110
22		4d. orange (6.1.15)	42·00	2·50
		a. Yellow-orange (1915)	42·00	3·25
		b. Lemon-yellow (3.16)	85·00	14·00
		c. Pale orange-yellow (1.17)	£110	12·00
		d. Dull orange (1920)	55·00	3·25
		e. Line through "FOUR PENCE" (all shades) .... From	£350	£110
		w. Wmk inverted	45·00	12·00
23		5d. brown (P 14¼ (line)) (22.2.15)	50·00	7·50
		aw. Wmk inverted	£1400	£950
		b. Perf 14¼×14 (comb)	28·00	2·00
		ba. Yellow-brown (1920)	30·00	2·75
		bw. Wmk inverted	£750	£550

The variety No. 20d was caused by the engraving of a new fraction in a defective electro in 1918.

No. 21ca was caused by rusting on two positions of the steel Plate 2 and shows as white patches on the back of the King's neck and on, and beside, the top of the right frame (right pane R. 6/4) and on the left frame, wattles, head and ears of kangaroo (right pane R. 6/5). These were noticed in December 1916 when the damaged impressions were removed and replaced by a pair of copper electros (Die II for R. 6/4 and Die I for R. 6/5), the former also showing rounded corners and some frame damage, the former also showing a white spot under tail of emu. In time the tops of the crown quickly wore away.

One example of No. 21cz has been recorded. It shows wmk crown to right (*as seen from the back of the stamp*).

Most of Nos. 20/3 were perforated 14 by a comb machine (exact gauge 14.25×14), but printings of the ½d. in December 1915, of the 1d. in July and August 1914 and of the 5d. until June 1917 were perforated by a line machine measuring 14.2.

See also Nos. 47/k (W **5**, rough paper), 48/52 (W **6a**), 53/*a* (1d. Die III), 56/66*b* and 76/81 (W **5**, new colours), 82 (W **6a**), 83/4 (no wmk), 85/104 (W **7**), 124/31 (W **15**).

(Typo J. B. Cooke)

1915 (15 Jan–July). W **5**. P 12.

24	**1**	2d. grey (Die I)	£100	12·00
		w. Wmk inverted	†	£18000
25		2½d. indigo (Die II) (7.15)	90·00	32·00
26		6d. ultramarine (Die II) (4.15)	£200	22·00
		a. Bright blue	£425	70·00
		b. Die IIA. *Ultramarine* (substituted cliché) (Upper plate right pane R. 10/6)	£8000	£2750
		ba. Bright blue	£9500	£3750
		w. Wmk inverted	†	£40000

27		9d. violet (Die II) (9.7)	£200	48·00
		w. Wmk inverted	£4250	£1800
28		1s. blue-green (Die II) (4.15)	£180	35·00
29		2s. brown (Die II) (3.15)	£700	£120
30		5s. grey and yellow (Die II) (12.2)	£1000	£350
		a. Yellow portion doubly printed	£15000	£4000
		w. Wmk inverted	£1300	£500
24/30 *Set of 7*			£2250	£550

6

6a

2d. No. 35a (Upper plate left pane R. 10/1)

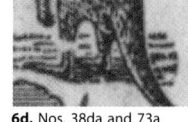

6d. Nos. 38da and 73a (Upper plate left pane R. 1/6)

(Typo J. B. Cooke (to May 1918), T. S. Harrison (to February 1926), A. J. Mullett (to June 1927) and thereafter J. Ash).

1915 (8 Oct)–**27**. W **6** (narrow Crown). P 12.

35	**1**	2d. grey (Die I) (11.15)	50·00	9·00
		a. Die IIA substituted cliché (upper plate left pane R. 10/1)*	£10000	£1800
		bw. Wmk inverted	75·00	32·00
		c. Silver-grey (*shiny paper*)	50·00	21·00
		d. Die IIA. *Silver-grey* (*shiny paper*) (3.18)	70·00	24·00
		daw. Wmk inverted	†	£10000
		dba. Grey (1920)	75·00	30·00
36		2½d. deep blue (Die II) (7.17)	27·00	10·00
		aw. Wmk inverted	£140	85·00
		b. Deep indigo (1919)	50·00	9·00
		ba. "1" of fraction omitted (Lower plate left pane R. 6/3)	£55000	£35000
37		3d. yellow-olive (Die I)	40·00	4·75
		a. In pair with Die II	£550	£400
		b. Olive-green (1917)	42·00	4·50
		ba. In pair with Die II	£600	£400
		cw. Wmk inverted	£100	48·00
		d. Die II *Yellow-olive*	£225	55·00
		da. Olive-green	£250	55·00
		dw. Wmk inverted	£600	£350
		e. Die IIB. *Light olive* (12.22)	60·00	13·00
38		6d. ultramarine (Die II) (15.12.15)	80·00	7·50
		a. Die IIA (substituted cliché) (Upper plate rt pane R. 10/6)	£7000	£1700
		b. Dull blue (6.18)	90·00	11·00
		ba. Die IIA (substituted cliché)	£7000	£1800
		cw. Wmk inverted	£450	£100
		d. Die IIB. *Bright ultramarine* (23.7.21)	90·00	22·00
		da. Leg of kangaroo broken	£2250	£700
		dw. Wmk inverted	£650	£250
39		9d. violet (Die II) (29.7.16)	65·00	11·00
		aw. Wmk inverted	£500	£110
		b. Die IIB. (16.4.19)	75·00	18·00
		bw. Wmk inverted	£300	£100
		c. Die II (substituted cliché) in pair with Die IIB	£700	£550
40		1s. blue-green (Die II) (6.16)	60·00	8·00
		aw. Wmk inverted	£275	£120
		b. Die IIB (11.20)	75·00	8·00
		ba. Wmk sideways (13.12.27)	60·00	£400
		bw. Wmk inverted	£275	£120
41		2s. brown (Die II) (6.16)	£275	14·00
		a. Imperf three sides (horiz pair)	£110000	
		b. Red-brown (*aniline*)	£3250	£500
		bw. Wmk inverted	£3750	£425
42		5s. grey and yellow (Die II) (4.18)	£275	£110
		a. Grey and orange (1920)	£425	£160
		b. Grey and deep yellow	£325	£130
		ba. Wmk sideways	†	£80000
		c. Grey and pale yellow	£275	£100
		w. Wmk inverted	£1300	£1100
43		10s. grey and pink (Die II) (5.2.17)	£550	£350
		a. Grey and bright aniline pink (10.18)	£500	£325
		ab. Wmk sideways	£42000	£18000
		aw. Wmk inverted	£2750	£1600
		b. Grey and pale aniline pink (1922)	£600	£350
44		£1 chocolate and dull blue (Die II) (7.16)	£3000	£1600
		a. Chestnut and bright blue (6.17)	£3250	£1800
		ab. Wmk sideways	†	£48000
		aw. Wmk inverted	£4500	£3500
		b. Bistre-brown and bright blue (7.19)	£3250	£1800
		ba. Frame printed double, one albino	£8000	
45		£2 black and rose (Die II) (12.19)	£5000	£3250
		a. Grey and crimson (1921)	£4750	£3250
		b. Purple-black and pale rose (6.24)	£4500	£2750
35/45*b Set of 11*			£8000	£4250
43s/5s Optd "SPECIMEN" *Set of 3*				£850

*The Die IIA of No. 35a is a substituted cliché introduced to repair a crack which occurred on R. 10/1 of the upper plate left pane. Its Die IIA characteristics are more pronounced than on the sheet stamps from this die, with the break at left extending to the outer, in addition to the inner, frame line.

One plate of the 3d. contained mixed Die I and Die II stamps as described.

No. 39c comes from eight substituted clichés taken from plate 2 (Die II) and inserted in plate 3 (Die IIB) at position left pane R. 3/6 and in plate 4 (Die IIB) at positions left pane R. 1/3-4, 2/3-4 and 8/6 and right pane R. 2/1 and R. 9/1. This substitution took place in August 1927 towards the end of the printings on W **6**. The variety can also be found on stamps with W **7** and W **15**, see Nos. 108a and 133a.

All values were printed by both Cooke and Harrison, and the 9d., 1s. and 5s. were also printed by Mullett and Ash.

The watermark on No. 40ba shows the Crown printing to the right, that on Nos. 42ba and 43ab shows the Crown pointing to the left *as seen from the back of the stamp.*

1916 (Nov)–**18.** Rough, unsurfaced paper, locally gummed. W **5**. P 14.

47	**5a**	1d. scarlet (Die I)	29·00	3·00
		a. Deep red (1917)	29·00	2·50
		b. Rose-red (1918)	35·00	2·75
		ba. Substituted cliché (Pl 2 rt pane R. 6/5)	£2000	75·00
		c. Rosine (1918)	£400	28·00
		ca. Substituted cliché (Pl 2 rt pane R. 6/5)	£3750	£425
		d. Dot before "1"	£140	20·00
		e. Secret mark	£140	20·00
		f. Flaw under neck	£140	20·00
		g. "RA" joined	£140	20·00
		hw. Wmk inverted	60·00	12·00
		i. Die II Rose-red (1918)	£500	23·00
		ia. Substituted cliché (Pl 2 rt pane R. 6/4)	£2000	75·00
		iw. Wmk inverted	£1200	£150
		j. Die II Rosine (1918)	£1500	£180
		ja. Substituted cliché (Pl 2 rt pane R. 6/4)	£3750	£425
		k. No wmk	£6500	£4750

All examples of the 5d. on this paper were perforated "OS" and will be found listed under No. O60.

No. 47k is the result of misplacement of the sheet during printing. To qualify, there should be no trace of the Crown over A or a line watermark.

(Typo J. B. Cooke to May 1918 thereafter T. S. Harrison)

1918 (4 Jan)–**20.** W **6a** (Mult). P 14.

48	**5a**	½d. green (shades)	8·50	2·00
		a. Thin 1 in fraction at right	£100	£140
		b. Wmk sideways	†	£30000
		bw. Wmk sideways inverted	†	£30000
		c. Cracked electro	£350	£375
		w. Wmk inverted	29·00	16·00
49		1d. carmine-pink (Die I) (23.1.18)	£250	£140
		aw. Wmk inverted	†	£27000
		b. Deep red (1918)	£5500	£3000
		bw. Wmk inverted	†	£40000
		c. Dot before "1"	£1200	£475
		d. Secret mark	£1200	£475
		e. Flaw under neck	£1200	£475
		f. "RA" joined	£1200	£475
50		1d. carmine (10.12.19)	30·00	16·00
		aw. Wmk inverted	£1400	£3000
		b. Deep red (aniline) (1920)	£800	£300
		c. Dot before "1"	£275	95·00
		d. Secret mark	£275	95·00
		e. Flaw under neck	£275	95·00
		f. "RA" joined	£275	95·00
51		1½d. black-brown (30.1.19)	6·00	4·00
		a. Very thin paper (2.19)	22·00	17·00
		w. Wmk inverted	45·00	35·00
52		1½d. red-brown (4.19)	13·00	2·25
		a. Chocolate (1920)	13·00	2·25
		w. Wmk inverted	£120	70·00

No. 48 was printed by Cooke and Harrison, Nos. 49/b by Cooke only and Nos. 50/2a by Harrison only. Nos. 49/b have rather yellowish gum, that of No. 50 being pure white.

The watermark on No. 48b shows the Crown pointing to the left and on No. 48bw pointing to the right, *as seen from the back of the stamp.* Two examples of No. 48b and two of No. 48bw are known.

1d. Die III

1d. Die III. In 1917 a printing (in sheets of 120) was made on paper originally prepared for printing War Savings Stamps, with watermark T **5**. A special plate was made for this printing, differing in detail from those previously used. The shading round the head is even; the solid background of the words "ONE PENNY" is bounded at each end by a white vertical line; and there is a horizontal white line cutting the vertical shading lines at left on the King's neck.

(Typo J. B. Cooke)

1918 (15 July). Printed from a new Die III plate on white unsurfaced paper, locally gummed. W **5**. P 14.

53	**5a**	1d. rose-red	75·00	38·00
		a. Rose-carmine	75·00	38·00
		w. Wmk inverted	£160	95·00

(Typo T. S. Harrison or A. J. Mullett (1s.4d. from March 1926))

1918 (9 Nov)–**23.** W **5**. P 14.

56	**5a**	½d. orange (8.11.23)	5·50	2·00

		w. Wmk inverted	8·50	11·00
57		1d. violet (shades) (12.2.22)	8·50	1·50
		a. Imperf three sides (horiz pair)	£50000	
		b. Red-violet	10·00	2·25
		c. Dot before "1"	70·00	17·00
		d. Secret mark	70·00	17·00
		e. Flaw under neck	70·00	17·00
		f. "RA" joined	70·00	17·00
58		1½d. black-brown	8·50	1·50
		w. Wmk inverted	60·00	22·00
59		1½d. deep red-brown (4.19)	16·00	1·00
		a. Chocolate (1920)	11·00	60
		w. Wmk inverted	65·00	35·00
60		1½d. bright red-brown (20.1.22)	38·00	4·00
61		1½d. green (7.3.23)	6·00	1·00
		a. Coarse unsurfaced paper (1923)	£450	£180
		w. Wmk inverted	†	£18000
62		2d. brown-orange (9.20)	14·00	1·00
		a. Dull orange (1921)	16·00	1·00
		w. Wmk inverted	†	£5500
63		2d. bright rose-scarlet (19.1.22)	19·00	1·50
		a. Dull rose-scarlet	19·00	1·50
		w. Wmk inverted		£19000
64		4d. violet (21.6.21)	18·00	15·00
		a. Line through "FOUR PENCE" (Pl 2 rt pane R. 2/6)	£32000	£8500
		b. "FOUR PENCE" in thinner letters (Pl 2 rt pane R. 2/6)	£475	£300
65		4d. ultramarine (shades) (23.3.22)	50·00	7·50
		a. "FOUR PENCE" in thinner letters (Pl 2 rt pane R. 2/6)	£475	£170
		b. Pale milky blue	90·00	14·00
		w. Wmk inverted	90·00	£275
66		1s.4d. pale blue (2.12.20)	90·00	35·00
		a. Dull greenish blue	95·00	28·00
		b. Deep turquoise (1922)	£3500	£2750
56/66		Set of 11	£225	55·00

In addition to a number of mint pairs of No. 57a from two sheets purchased at Gumeracha, South Australia, with the bottom row imperforate on three sides, a single used example of No. 57 imperforate on three sides is known.

No. 61a was printed on a batch of coarse unsurfaced paper during 1923. Examples may be indentified by a clear vertical mesh in the paper, with mint stamps having a yellowish gum.

The 4d. ultramarine was originally printed from the Cooke plates but the plates were worn in mid-1923 and Harrison prepared a new pair of plates. Stamps from these plates can only be distinguished by the minor flaws which are peculiar to them.

The variety of Nos. 64 and 65 with "FOUR PENCE" thinner, was caused by the correction of the line through "FOUR PENCE" flaw early in the printing of No. 64.

(Typo T. S. Harrison (to February 1926), A. J. Mullett (to June 1927), thereafter J. Ash)

1923 (6 Dec)–**24.** W **6**. P 12.

73	**1**	6d. chestnut (Die IIB)	28·00	1·75
		a. Leg of kangaroo broken (Upper plate lt pane R. 1/6)	75·00	£120
		w. Wmk inverted	†	£22000
74		2s. maroon (Die II) (1.5.24)	80·00	32·00
		w. Wmk inverted	£2250	£1600
75		£1 grey (Die IIB) (1.5.24)	£650	£325
		s. Optd "SPECIMEN"	£110	

The 6d. and 2s. were printed by all three printers, but the £1 only by Harrison.

No. 73a was corrected during the Ash printing.

(Typo T. S. Harrison (to February 1926), thereafter A. J. Mullett)

1924 (1 May–18 Aug). P 14.

*(a) W **5***

76	**5a**	1d. sage-green	6·00	1·50
		a. Dot before "1"	50·00	13·00
		b. Secret mark	50·00	13·00
		c. Flaw under neck	50·00	13·00
		d. "RA" joined	50·00	13·00
		w. Wmk inverted	24·00	10·00
77		1½d. scarlet (shades)	3·00	40
		a. Very thin paper	£110	50·00
		b. "HALEPENCE" (Pl 22 left pane R. 4/4)	30·00	38·00
		c. "RAL" of AUSTRALIA thin (Pl 22 Left pane R. 5/4)	32·00	38·00
		d. Curved "1" and thin fraction at left (Pl 24 rt pane R. 7/5)	32·00	38·00
		w. Wmk inverted	50·00	24·00
78		2d. red-brown	17·00	7·00
		a. Bright red-brown	22·00	8·00
		w. Wmk inverted	†	£24000
79		3d. dull ultramarine	26·00	2·00
		a. Imperf three sides (horiz pair)	£12000	
80		4d. olive-yellow	35·00	5·50
		a. Olive-green	32·00	6·00
		w. Wmk inverted	†	£17000
81		4½d. violet	24·00	3·50

*(b) W **6a***

82	**5a**	1d. sage-green (20.5)	15·00	11·00
		a. Dot before "1"	85·00	75·00
		b. Secret mark	85·00	75·00
		c. Flaw under neck	85·00	75·00
		d. "RA" joined	85·00	75·00
		w. Wmk inverted	†	£18000

(c) No wmk

83	**5a**	1d. sage-green (18.8)	7·50	11·00
		a. Dot before "1"	55·00	75·00
		b. Secret mark	55·00	75·00
		c. Flaw under neck	55·00	75·00
		d. "RA" joined	55·00	75·00
84		1½d. scarlet (14 Aug)	25·00	9·50
76/84		Set of 9	£140	45·00

Nos. 78/a and 82/4 were printed by Harrison only but the remainder were printed by both Harrison and Mullett.

In the semi-transparent paper of Nos. 51a and 77a the watermark is almost indistinguishable.

Nos. 77b, 77c and 77d are typical examples of retouching of which there are many others in these issues. In No. 77c the letters "RAL" differ markedly from the normal. There is a white stroke cutting the oval frame-line above the "L", and the right-hand outer line of the Crown does not cut the white frame-line above the "A".

It is believed that No. 79a occurs on the bottom row of at least four sheets purchased from post offices in Victoria during 1926.

7

I

II

New Dies

1d. For differences see note above No. 20.

1½d. From new steel plates made from a new die. Nos. 87a and 96a are the Ash printings, the ink of which is shiny.

2d. Die I. Height of frame 25.6 mm. Left-hand frame-line thick and uneven behind Kangaroo. Pearls in Crown vary in size.
Die II. Height of frame 25.6 mm. Left-hand frame-line thin and even. Pearls in Crown are all the same size.
Die III. Height 25.1 mm; lettering and figures of value bolder than Die I.

3d. Die II has bolder letters and figures than Die I, as illustrated above.

5d. Die II has a bolder figure "5" with flat top compared with Die I of the earlier issues.

(Typo A. J. Mullett or J. Ash (from June 1927))

1926–**30.** W **7**.

(a) P 14

85	**5a**	½d. orange (10.3.27)	6·50	7·50
		w. Wmk inverted	£120	£100
86		1d. sage-green (23.10.26)	5·50	1·00
		a. Dot before "1"	65·00	20·00
		b. Secret mark	65·00	20·00
		c. Flaw under neck	90·00	30·00
		d. "RA" joined	90·00	30·00
		w. Wmk inverted	26·00	12·00
87		1½d. scarlet (5.11.26)	13·00	2·50
		a. Golden scarlet (1927)	23·00	2·50
		w. Wmk inverted	30·00	10·00
89		2d. red-brown (Die I) (17.8.27)	40·00	48·00
90		3d. dull ultramarine (12.26)	30·00	5·00
		w. Wmk inverted	†	£12000
91		4d. yellow-olive (17.1.28)	55·00	40·00
92		4½d. violet (26.10.27)	23·00	3·75
93		1s.4d. pale greenish blue (6.9.27)	£130	80·00
		w. Wmk inverted	†	£23000
85/93		Set of 8	£275	£170

(b) P 13½×12½

94	**5a**	½d. orange (21.11.28)	2·50	1·00
95		1d. sage-green (Die I) (23.12.26)	5·00	70
		aa. Dot before "1"	£110	42·00
		ab. Secret mark	£140	60·00
		ac. Flaw under neck	£140	60·00
		ad. "RA" joined	£140	60·00
		aw. Wmk inverted	32·00	25·00
		b. Die II (6.28)	50·00	80·00
		bw. Wmk inverted	£1900	£1800
96		1½d. scarlet (14.1.27)	3·00	1·00
		a. Golden scarlet (1927)	5·00	1·00
		w. Wmk inverted	16·00	2·50
97		1½d. red-brown (16.9.30)	6·50	7·00
98		2d. red-brown (16.9.30)	18·00	9·50
99		2d. golden scarlet (Die II) (2.8.30)	24·00	2·75
		a. Die III (9.9.30)	8·00	1·00
		ab. No wmk	£1300	£2750
		ac. Tête-bêche (pair)	£200000	
		aw. Wmk inverted (from booklets)	9·50	1·60
100		3d. dull ultramarine (Die I) (28.2.28)	38·00	6·50
		aw. Wmk inverted	£190	£3000
		b. Die II Deep ultramarine (28.9.29)	20·00	1·40
		bw. Wmk inverted	†	£13000
102		4d. yellow-olive (19.4.29)	32·00	3·25
		w. Wmk inverted	†	£12000
103		4½d. violet Die I* (11.28)	70·00	32·00
103a		5d. orange-brown Die II (27.8.30)	45·00	7·00
104		1s.4d. turquoise (30.9.28)	£120	26·00
		w. Wmk inverted	†	£21000
94/104		Set of 11	£300	80·00

Owing to defective manufacture, part of the sheet of the 2d. (Die III), discovered in July 1931, escaped unwatermarked; while the watermark in other parts of the same sheet was faint or normal. Only one example of No. 99ac is known.
*For the 4½d. Die II see No. 120a.

8 Parliament House, Canberra

(Des R. A. Harrison. Die eng J. A. C. Harrison (Waterlow, London). Plates and printing by A. J. Mullett)

1927 (9 May). Opening of Parliament House, Canberra. No wmk. P 11.

105	**8**	1½d. brownish lake	50	50
		a. Imperf between (vert pair)	£5500	
		b. Imperf between (horiz pair)	£12000	£12000

(Eng H. W. Bell. Recess J. Ash)

1928 (29 Oct–2 Nov). Fourth National Stamp Exhibition, Melbourne. As T **4**. No wmk. P 11.

106		3d. blue (2.11)...................	4·50 6·50
MS106a	65×70 mm. No. 106×4............		£120 £200
	ab. Imperf (pane of four)............		£200000

No. MS106a comes from special sheets of 60 stamps divided into 15 blocks of 4 (5×3) and separated by wide gutters perforated down the middle, printed and sold at the Exhibition.

(Typo J. Ash)

1929 (Feb)–30. W **7**. P 12.

107	**1**	6d. chestnut (Die IIB) (25.9.29).........	38·00	4·50
108		9d. violet (Die IIB)...............	42·00	28·00
		a. Die II (substituted cliché) in pair with Die IIB........	£450	£475
109		1s. blue-green (Die IIB) (12.6.29).....	50·00	10·00
		w. Wmk inverted............	†	£22000
110		2s. maroon (Die II) (3.29)..........	85·00	17·00
111		5s. grey and yellow (Die II) (30.11.29).....	£250	£110
112		10s. grey and pink (Die II)............	£475	£500
114		£2 black and rose (Die II) (11.30).....	£4500	£750
107/14	Set of 7................		£5000	£1300
112s/14s Optd "SPECIMEN" Set of 2..........				£450

For No. 108a see note below No. 45b.

9 DH66 Biplane and Pastoral Scene

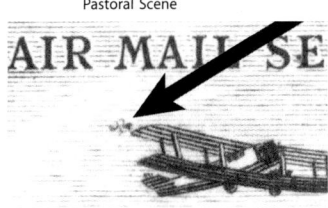

"Long wing" flaw (R. 2/1 of booklet pane)

(Des R. A. Harrison and H. Herbert. Eng A. Taylor. Recess J. Ash)

1929 (20 May). Air. No wmk. P 11.

115	**9**	3d. green (shades)...............	9·00	4·25
		a. Booklet stamp............	30·00	20·00
		b. "Long wing" flaw............	£275	£160

No. 115 was originally issued in preparation for the inauguration of the Perth to Adelaide air service on 2 June 1929.

Variations of up to ¾ mm in the design size of No. 115 are due to paper shrinkage on the printings produced by the "wet" process. The last printing, in 1935, was printed by the "dry" method.

Booklet stamps may be identified by a dot in the centre of the horizontal margin between each stamp. The dot may appear above or below the design and is sometimes removed by perforation.

10 Black Swan   11 Capt. Charles Sturt (J. H. Crossland)

Re-entry ("T" of "AUSTRALIA" clearly double) (Pl 2 R. 7/4)

(Des G. Pitt Morrison. Eng F. D. Manley. Recess J. Ash)

1929 (28 Sept). Centenary of Western Australia. No wmk. P 11.

116	**10**	1½d. dull scarlet.............	2·00	2·00
		a. Re-entry..........	60·00	80·00

(Des R. A. Harrison. Eng F. D. Manley. Recess J. Ash)

1930 (2 June). Centenary of Exploration of River Murray by Capt. Sturt. No wmk. P 11.

117	**11**	1½d. scarlet............	1·25	1·00
118		3d. blue............	9·00	9·00

No. 117 with manuscript surcharge of "2d. paid P M L H I" was issued by the Postmaster of Lord Howe Island during a shortage of 2d. stamps between 23 August and 17 October 1930 (*Price £750 un. or used*). A few copies of the 1½d. value No. 96a were also endorsed (*Price £1700 un. or used*). These provisionals are not recognized by the Australian postal authorities.

TWO

PENCE

(12)   13 Fokker F. VIIa/3m *Southern Cross* above Hemispheres

4½d. Original die

4½d. Redrawn die

1930 (28 July–2 Aug). T **5a** surch as T **12**. W **7**. P 13½×12½.

119	2d. on 1½d. golden scarlet............	2·75	1·00
120	5d. on 4½d. violet (2.8)............	15·00	16·00
	a. Without surcharge............	£6500	45·00

No. 120 is from a redrawn die in which the words "FOURPENCE HALFPENNY" are noticeably thicker than in the original die and the figure "4" has square instead of tapering serifs. The redrawn die also shows thin white lines to the left and right of the tablet carrying "FOURPENCE HALFPENNY".

Stamps from the redrawn die without the surcharge were not intended to be issued. Some stamps, *cancelled to order*, were included in sets supplied by the post office. A few mint copies, which escaped the cancellation were found and some may have been used postally.

6d. Re-entry ("FO" and "LD" double) (Pl 1 R. 5/5)

(Des and eng F. D. Manley. Recess John Ash)

1931 (19 Mar). Kingsford Smith's Flights. No wmk. P 11.

(a) Postage

121	**13**	2d. rose-red............	2·25	1·00
122		3d. blue............	8·50	6·50

(b) Air. Inscr "AIR MAIL SERVICE" at sides

123	**13**	6d. violet............	6·50	17·00
		a. Re-entry............	50·00	£110
121/3 Set of 3............			15·00	22·00

15   17 Superb Lyrebird

(Typo John Ash).

1931–36. W 15.

(a) P 13½×12½

124	**5a**	½d. orange (2.33)............	11·00	5·00
125		1d. green (Die I) (10.31)............	4·00	20
		w. Wmk inverted............	45·00	10·00
		x. Wmk reversed............	£2000	£1300
126		1½d. red-brown (10.36)............	9·00	14·00
127		2d. golden scarlet (Die III) (18.12.31)............	2·50	10
		w. Wmk inverted (*from booklets*)...	5·00	50
128		3d. ultramarine (Die II) (30.9.32).....	23·00	1·25
		w. Wmk inverted............	£16000	£16000
129		4d. yellow-olive (2.33)............	23·00	1·25
		w. Wmk inverted............	†	£10000
130		5d. orange-brown (Die II) (25.2.32).....	23·00	20
		w. Wmk inverted............	†	£8000
131		1s.4d. turquoise (18.8.32)............	50·00	2·75
		w. Wmk inverted............	†	£14000
124/31 Set of 8............			£130	22·00

(b) P 12

132	**1**	6d. chestnut (Die IIB) (20.4.32).....	40·00	40·00
133		9d. violet (Die IIB) (20.4.32).....	45·00	2·25
		a. Die II (substituted cliché) in pair with Die IIB............	£350	£275
134		2s. maroon (Die II) (6.8.35)............	12·00	1·00
135		5s. grey and yellow (Die II) (12.32).....	£170	20·00
136		10s. grey and pink (Die II) (31.7.32).....	£425	£150
137		£1 grey (Die IIB) (11.35)............	£650	£275
138		£2 black and rose (Die II) (6.34).....	£4250	£600
132/38 Set of 7............			£5000	£900
136s/8s Optd "SPECIMEN" Set of 3............				90·00

Stamps as No. 127, but without watermark and perforated 11, are forgeries made in 1932 to defraud the P.O. (*Price £400, unused*).

For re-engraved type of No. 134, see No. 212.

For No. 133a see note below No. 45b.

(Des and eng F. D. Manley. Recess John Ash)

1931 (4 Nov). Air Stamp. As T **13** but inscr "AIR MAIL SERVICE" in bottom tablet. No wmk. P 11.

139	6d. sepia............	22·00	17·00

1931 (17 Nov). Air. No. 139 optd with Type O **4**.

139a	6d. sepia............	32·00	60·00

This stamp was not restricted to official use but was on general sale to the public.

(Des and eng F. D. Manley. Recess John Ash)

1932 (15 Feb). No wmk. P 11.

140	**17**	1s. green............	45·00	2·75
		a. Yellow-green............	55·00	5·00

18 Sydney Harbour Bridge   19 Laughing Kookaburra

(Des R. A. Harrison. Eng F. D. Manley. Printed John Ash)

1932 (14 Mar). Opening of Sydney Harbour Bridge.

(a) Recess. No wmk. P 11

141	**18**	2d. scarlet............	7·00	4·25
142		3d. blue............	10·00	11·00
143		5s. blue-green............	£425	£200

(b) Typo. W 15. P 10½

144	**18**	2d. scarlet............	7·00	2·00
141/44 Set of 4............			£425	£200

Stamps as No. 144 without wmk and perf 11 are forgeries made in 1932 to defraud the P.O. (*Price £1000, unused*).

The used price for No. 143 is for a cancelled to order example. Postally used examples are worth more.

(Des and eng F. D. Manley. Recess John Ash)

1932 (1 June). W **15**. P 13½×12½.

146	**19**	6d. red-brown............	18·00	55
		w. Wmk inverted............	†	£7000

20 Melbourne and R. Yarra   21 Merino Ram

(Des and eng F. D. Manley. Recess John Ash)

1934 (2 July–Aug). Centenary of Victoria. W **15**. P 10½.

147	**20**	2d. orange-vermilion............	4·50	1·75
		a. Perf 11½ (8.34)............	14·00	1·75
148		3d. blue............	4·50	5·50
		a. Perf 11½ (8.34)............	7·00	8·00
149		1s. black............	55·00	22·00
		a. Perf 11½ (8.34)............	65·00	24·00
147/49 Set of 3............			55·00	26·00
147a/49a Set of 3............			75·00	30·00

Stamps were originally issued perforated 10½, and were subsequently changed to 11½ in August 1934 due to difficulties in separating stamps in the first perforation.

(Des and eng F. D. Manley. Recess John Ash)

1934 (1–26 Nov). Death Centenary of Capt. John Macarthur (founder of Australian sheep farming). W **15**. P 11½.

150	**21**	2d. carmine-red (A)............	8·00	1·75
150a		2d. carmine-red (B) (26.11)............	26·00	3·25
151		3d. blue............	17·00	18·00
152		9d. bright purple............	38·00	50·00
150/52 Set of 3 (excluding No. 150a)............			55·00	60·00

Type A of the 2d. shows shading on the hill in the background varying from light to dark (as illustrated). Type B has the shading almost uniformly dark.

22 Hermes   23 Cenotaph, Whitehall

(Des F. D. Manley. Eng E. Broad and F. D. Manley. Recess John Ash until April 1940; W. C. G. McCracken thereafter)

1934 (1 Dec)–48.

(a) No wmk. P 11

153	**22**	1s.6d. dull purple............	50·00	2·00

(b) W 15. Chalk-surfaced paper. P 13½×14

153a	**22**	1s.6d. dull purple (22.10.37)............	11·00	45
		b. Thin rough ordinary paper (12.2.48)............	2·50	1·40

(Des B Cottier; adapted and eng F. D. Manley. Recess John Ash)

1935 (18 Mar). 20th Anniv of Gallipoli Landing. W **15**. P 13½×12½ or 11 (1s.).

154	**23**	2d. scarlet............	3·25	30
155		1s. black (chalk-surfaced)............	50·00	45·00

The 1s. perforated 13½×12½ is a plate proof (*Price £1600, unused*).

24 King George V on *Anzac*   3d. Apostrophe after second "E" of "GEORGE" (Sheet C, lower pane R. 4/2)

25 Amphitrite and Telephone Cable

½d. Line to Kangaroo's ear (Right pane R. 6/8)

2d. Medal flaw
(Right pane R. 2/5)

6d. "Top hat" flaw (Lower plate, right pane R. 3/3)

1s. Roller flaw over "o" of "one"
(Upper plate, right pane R. 1-6/6)

(Des and eng F. D. Manley. Recess John Ash)

1935 (2 May). Silver Jubilee. Chalk-surfaced paper. W **15** (sideways). P 11½.

156	**24**	2d. scarlet	3·25	30
		a. Printed double, one albino	£300	£150
157		3d. blue	10·00	11·00
		a. Apostrophe flaw	£110	£110
158		2s. bright violet	35·00	48·00
156/58 *Set of 3*			42·00	55·00

(Des and eng F. D. Manley. Recess John Ash)

1936 (1 Apr). Opening of Submarine Telephone Link to Tasmania. W **15**. P 11½.

159	**25**	2d. scarlet	2·75	50
160		3d. blue	4·50	2·75

26 Site of Adelaide, 1836;
Old Gum Tree, Glenelg;
King William St, Adelaide

(Des and eng F. D. Manley. Recess John Ash)

1936 (3 Aug). Centenary of South Australia. W **15**. P 11½.

161	**26**	2d. carmine	4·00	40
162		3d. blue	11·00	3·50
163		1s. green	20·00	13·00
161/63 *Set of 3*			32·00	15·00

27 Wallaroo **28** Queen Elizabeth **28a** Queen Elizabeth

29 **30** King George VI **30a**

31 King George VI **32** Koala **33** Merino Ram

34 Laughing Kookaburra **35** Platypus **36** Superb Lyrebird

38 Queen Elizabeth **39** King George VI

40 King George VI and Queen Elizabeth

Dies of 3d.:

Die I Die Ia Die II

Die I. The letters "TA" of "POSTAGE" at right are joined by a white flaw; the outline of the chin consists of separate strokes.

No. 168a is a preliminary printing made with unsuitable ink and may be detected by the absence of finer details; the King's face appears whitish and the wattles are blank. The greater part of this printing was distributed to the Press with advance notices of the issue.

Die Ia. As Die I, but "T" and "A" have been clearly separated by individual retouches made on the plates.

Die II A completely new die. "T" and "A" are separate and a continuous line has been added to the chin. The outline of the cheek extends to about 1 mm above the lobe of the King's right ear.

Die III. Differs from Dies I and II in the King's left eyebrow which is shaded downwards from left to right instead of from right to left. This die also shows more of the epaulette at the right of the stamp, similar to the 1s.4d. value.

(Des R. A. Harrison (T **28/30**), F. D. Manley (T **27**, **31/6**), H. Barr (T **38/9**), H. Barr and F. D. Manley (T **40**). Eng F. D. Manley and T. C. Duffell (T **34**), T. C. Duffell (revised lettering for T **28a**, **30a**), F. D. Manley and E. Broad (T **38/40**), F. D. Manley (others). All recess with John Ash, W. C. G. McCracken or "By Authority ..." imprints)

1937–49. Chalk-surfaced paper (3d. (No. 168/c), 5s., 10s., £1). W **15** (sideways on 5d., 9d., 5s. and 10s.).

(a) P 13½×14 *(vert designs) or* 14×13½ *(horiz)*

164	**27**	½d. orange (3.10.38)	2·50	50
165	**28**	1d. emerald-green (10.5.37)	1·25	50
166	**29**	1½d. maroon (20.4.38)	9·00	5·50
167	**30**	2d. scarlet (10.5.37)	1·25	50
168	**31**	3d. blue (Die I) (2.8.37)	65·00	24·00
		a. "White wattles" (from 1st ptg)	£170	85·00
		b. Die Ia	£150	8·50
		c. Die II (3.38)	65·00	7·00
		ca. Bright blue (ordinary thin paper) (20.12.38)	60·00	4·00
170	**32**	4d. green (1.2.38)	7·00	2·25
171	**33**	5d. purple (1.12.38)	2·25	60
172	**34**	6d. purple-brown (2.8.37)	20·00	1·50
173	**35**	9d. chocolate (1.9.38)	9·00	2·50
174	**36**	1s. grey-green (2.8.37)	50·00	2·75
175	**31**	1s. 4d. pale magenta (3.10.38)	3·50	2·50
		a. Deep magenta (1943)	5·50	2·50

(b) P 13½

176	**38**	5s. claret (1.4.38)	28·00	2·00
		a. Thin rough ordinary paper (shades) (4.2.48)	5·50	4·00
177	**39**	10s. dull purple (1.4.38)	50·00	17·00
		a. Thin rough ordinary paper (11.48)	50·00	35·00
		s. Optd "SPECIMEN"	35·00	
178	**40**	£1 bluish slate (1.11.38)	70·00	35·00
		a. Thin rough ordinary paper (4.4.49)	70·00	75·00
		s. Optd "SPECIMEN"	£800	
164/78 *Set of 14*			£250	65·00

(c) P 15×14 *(vert designs) or* 14×15 *(horiz)* (1d. and 2d. redrawn with background evenly shaded and lettering strengthened)

179	**27**	½d. orange (28.1.42)	55	70
		a. Line to kangaroo's ear	42·00	32·00
		b. Coil pair (1942)	23·00	40·00
		ba. Coil block of four (1943)	£950	
180	**28a**	1d. emerald-green (1.8.38)	10·00	60
181		1d. maroon (10.12.41)	3·50	1·00
		a. Coil pair (1942)	14·00	28·00
182	**29**	1½d. maroon (21.11.41)	8·00	17·00
183		1½d. emerald-green (10.12.41)	2·50	2·50
184	**30a**	2d. scarlet (11.7.38)	9·00	20
		a. Coil pair (10.41)	£350	£450
		b. Medal flaw	£325	£120
		w. Wmk inverted (from booklets)	15·00	75
185		2d. bright purple (10.12.41)	75	2·00
		a. Coil pair (1942)	50·00	75·00
		b. Medal flaw	80·00	90·00
		w. Wmk inverted (from coils)	£170	£130
186	**31**	3d. bright blue (Die III) (11.40)	45·00	4·00
187		3d. purple-brown (Die III) (10.12.41)	1·25	10
188	**32**	4d. green (10.42)	1·00	10
		w. Wmk inverted	—	£10000
189	**33**	5d. purple (17.12.45)	65	2·25
190	**34**	6d. red-brown (6.42)	3·50	10
		a. Purple-brown (1944)	1·75	10
		ab. "Top hat" flaw	£1400	£1700
191	**35**	9d. chocolate (12.9.43)	1·00	10
192	**36**	1s. grey-green (29.3.41)	2·75	10
		a. Roller flaw	70·00	30·00
		w. Wmk inverted	£6000	£6000
179/92 *Set of 14*			75·00	27·00

The watermark on No. 191 shows Crown to the left of C of A, on Nos. 171, 173 and 189 it is to the right, *as seen from the back of the stamp*. For unwmkd issue, see Nos. 228/30d.

Thin paper. Nos. 176a, 177a, 178a. In these varieties the watermark is more clearly visible on the back and the design is much less sharp. On early printings of No. 176a the paper appears tinted.

SPECIAL COIL PERFORATION. This special perforation of large and small holes on the narrow sides of the stamps was introduced after 1939 for stamps issued in coils and was intended to facilitate separation. Where they exist they are listed as "Coil pairs".

The following with "special coil" perforation were placed on sale in *sheets*: Nos. 179, 205, 222a (1952), 228, 230, 237, 262 (1953), 309, 311, and 314. These are listed as "Coil blocks of four".

Coils with "normal" perforations also exist for Nos. 180 and 184.

41 *Governor Phillip at Sydney Cove* (J. Alcott) **2d.** "Man with tail" flaw (Left pane R. 7/1. Later retouched)

(Des and eng E. Broad and F. D. Manley. Recess J. Ash)

1937 (1 Oct). 150th Anniv of Foundation of New South Wales. W **15**. P 13½×14.

193	**41**	2d. scarlet	3·75	30
		a. "Man with tail" flaw	£700	£140
194		3d. bright blue	9·50	2·25
195		9d. purple	28·00	14·00
193/95 *Set of 3*			38·00	15·00

42 AIF and Nurse

(Des and eng F. D. Manley from drawing by Virgil Reilly. Recess W. C. G. McCracken)

1940 (15 July). Australian Imperial Forces. W **15** (sideways). P 14×13½.

196	**42**	1d. green	2·50	2·75
197		2d. scarlet	2·00	1·50
198		3d. blue	18·00	11·00
199		6d. brown-purple	35·00	30·00
196/99 *Set of 4*			50·00	40·00

(43) **(44)** **(45)**

(Opts designed by F. D. Manley)

1941 (10 Dec). Nos. 184, 186 and 171 surch with T **43/5**.

200	**30a**	2½d. on 2d. scarlet (V.)	1·00	70
		a. Pair, one without surcharge	£20000	
		b. Medal flaw	£450	£250
201	**31**	3½d. on 3d. bright blue (Y. on Black)	2·50	2·25
202	**33**	5½d. on 5d. purple (V.)	4·25	6·50
200/2 *Set of 3*			7·00	8·50

Nos. 200/2 were prepared in connection with the imposition of a ½d. "war tax" increase on most postage rates.

One sheet of the 2½d. on 2d. was discovered showing the surcharge omitted on R. 1/4 and R. 1/5.

46 Queen Elizabeth **46a** Queen Elizabeth **47** King George VI

48 King George VI **49** King George VI **50** Emu

(Des F. D. Maley. Eng F. D. Manley and T. C. Duffell (T **46/a**) or F. D. Manley (others))

1942–50. Recess. W **15**. P 15×14.

203	**46**	1d. brown-purple (2.1.43)	3·25	10
		a. Coil pair (1944)	22·00	42·00
204	**46a**	1½d. green (1.12.42)	3·00	10
		w. Wmk inverted	†	£10000
205	**47**	2d. bright purple (4.12.44)	1·75	2·00
		b. Coil pair (1.49)	90·00	£120
		ba. Coil block of four (5.50)	£2750	
206	**48**	2½d. scarlet (7.1.42)	60	10
		a. Imperf (pair)*	£6500	
		w. Wmk inverted (from booklets)	7·50	2·25
207	**49**	3½d. bright blue (3.42)	3·75	60
		a. Deep blue	2·50	60
208	**50**	5½d. slate-blue (12.2.42)	1·25	20
203/8 *Set of 6*			11·00	2·50

*No. 206a comes in horizontal pair with the right-hand stamp completely imperforate and the left-hand stamp imperforate at right only.

Coils with normal perforations exist for 1d.

For stamps as Nos. 204/5 but without watermark see Nos. 229/30.

The following items are understood to have been the subject of unauthorised leakages from the Commonwealth Note and Stamp Printing Branch and are therefore not listed by us.

It is certain that none of this material was distributed to post offices for issue to the public.

Imperforate all round. 1d. Princess Elizabeth; 1½d. Queen; 2½d. King; 4d. Koala; 6d. Kookaburra; 9d. Platypus; 1s. Lyrebird (small) (also imperf three sides); 1s.6d. Air Mail (Type **22**); 2½d. Mitchell; 2½d. Newcastle (also imperf three sides or imperf vertically).

Also 2½d. Peace, unwatermarked; 2½d. King, *tête-bêche;* 3½d. Newcastle, in dull ultramarine; 2½d. King on "toned" paper.

52 Duke and Duchess of Gloucester

(Des F. D. Manley. Eng F. D. Manley and T. C. Duffell. Recess)
1945 (19 Feb). Arrival of Duke and Duchess of Gloucester in Australia. W **15**. P 14½.
209	**52**	2½d. lake		20	10
210		3½d. ultramarine		40	1·25
211		5½d. indigo		50	1·25
209/11	*Set of 3*			1·00	2·25

A   B

1945 (24 Dec). Kangaroo type, as No. 134, but re-engraved as B. W **15**. P 12.
212	**1**	2s. maroon		4·50	7·50
		w. Wmk inverted		†	£24000

No. 134 has two background lines between the value circle and "TWO SHILLINGS"; No. 212 has only one line in this position. There are also differences in the shape of the letters.

53 Star and Wreath   **54** Flag and dove

55 Angel and Queensland   **56** Sir Thomas Mitchell

(Des F. D. Manley (2½d.), F. D. Manley and G. Lissenden (3½d.), G. Lissenden (5½d.). Eng F. D. Manley. Recess)
1946 (18 Feb). Victory Commemoration. W **15** (sideways on 5½d.). P 14½.
213	**53**	2½d. scarlet		20	10
214	**54**	3½d. blue		75	1·75
215	**55**	5½d. green		75	1·00
213/15	*Set of 3*			1·50	2·50

These designs were re-issued in 1995 with face values in decimal currency.

(Des F. D. Manley. Eng F. D. Manley and T. C. Duffell. Recess)
1946 (14 Oct). Centenary of Mitchell's Exploration of Central Queensland. W **15**. P 14½.
216	**56**	2½d. scarlet		25	10
217		3½d. blue		75	2·00
218		1s. grey-olive		75	75
216/18	*Set of 3*			1·60	2·50

57 Lt. John Shortland RN   **58** Steel Foundry   **59** Coal Carrier/Cranes

(Des and eng G. Lissenden (5½d.), F. D. Manley (others). Recess)
1947 (8 Sept). 150th Anniv of City of Newcastle, New South Wales. W **15** (sideways on 3½d.). P 14½ or 15×14 (2½d.).
219	**57**	2½d. lake		20	10
220	**58**	3½d. blue		60	60
221	**59**	5½d. green		60	75
219/21	*Set of 3*			1·25	2·00

60 Queen Elizabeth II when Princess

(Des R. A. Harrison. Eng. F. D. Manley. Recess)
1947 (20 Nov)–**52**. Marriage of Princess Elizabeth. P 14×15.

*(a) W **15** (sideways)*
222	**60**	1d. purple		15	1·00

(b) No wmk
222a	**60**	1d. purple (8.48)		10	10
		b. Coil pair (1.50)		2·25	5·50
		c. Coil block of four (9.52)		5·50	

No. 222 was originally prepared to mark the 21st birthday of Princess Elizabeth, but production delays resulted in it being issued on her wedding day instead.

61 Hereford Bull   **61a** Hermes and Globe

62 Aboriginal Art   **62a** Commonwealth Coat of Arms

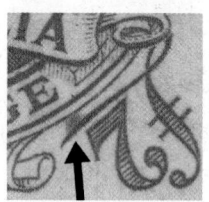

Roller flaw below "E" of "POSTAGE" (R. 4/1 and 5/1). Later retouched.

(Des G. Sellheim (T **62**), F. D. Manley (others). Eng G. Lissenden (T **62**), F. D. Manley (1s.3d., 1s.6d., 5s.), F. D. Manley and R. J. Becker (10s., £1, £2). Recess)
1948 (16 Feb)–**56**. W **15**.

(a) Wmk sideways. P 14½
223	**61**	1s.3d. brown-purple		2·50	2·00
223a	**61a**	1s.6d. blackish brown (1.9.49)		1·00	10
224	**62**	2s. chocolate		1·50	10

(b) Wmk upright. P 14½×13½
224a	**62a**	5s. claret (11.4.49)		4·00	20
		ab. Thin paper (1951)		£100	70·00
224b		10s. purple (3.10.49)		20·00	85
		bws. Wmk inverted, optd "SPECIMEN"		£3750	
224c		£1 blue (28.11.49)		42·00	4·25
224d		£2 green (16.1.50)		85·00	16·00
		da. Roller flaw		£150	£100
223/24d	*Set of 7*			£140	21·00
224bs/ds	Optd "SPECIMEN" *Set of 3*			£160	

(c) No wmk. P 14½
224e	**61a**	1s.6d. blackish brown (2.12.56)		12·00	1·50
224f	**62**	2s. chocolate (27.6.56)		8·50	1·50

The frames of Nos. 224b and 224c/d differ slightly from Type **62a**. No. 224ab is an emergency printing on white Harrison paper instead of the toned paper used for No. 224a.

63 William J. Farrer   **64** F. von Mueller   **65** Boy Scout

(Des and eng F. D. Manley. Recess)
1948 (12 July). William J. Farrer (wheat research) Commemoration. W **15**. P 15×14.
225	**63**	2½d. scarlet		40	10

(Des and eng F. D. Manley. Recess)
1948 (13 Sept). Sir Ferdinand von Mueller (botanist) Commemoration. W **15**. P 15×14.
226	**64**	2½d. lake		30	10

(Des and eng F. D. Manley. Recess)
1948 (15 Nov). Pan-Pacific Scout Jamboree, Wonga Park. W **15** (sideways). P 14×15.
227	**65**	2½d. lake		30	10

See also No. 254.

½d. Sky retouch (normally unshaded near hill) (Rt pane R. 6/8) (No. 228a retouched in 1951)

1s. "Green mist" retouch. A large area to the left of the bird's feathers is recut (Upper plate left pane R. 9/3)

1948–56. No wmk. P 15×14 or 14×15 (9d.).
228	**27**	½d. orange (15.9.49)		20	10
		a. Line to kangaroo's ear		38·00	40·00
		b. Sky retouch		60·00	65·00
		c. Coil pair (1950)		1·00	3·25
		ca. Line to kangaroo's ear		95·00	
		cb. Sky retouch (in pair)		£350	
		d. Coil block of four (1953)		2·75	
229	**46a**	1½d. green (17.8.49)		2·00	2·75
230	**47**	2d. bright purple (20.12.48)		1·75	3·25
		aa. Coil pair		3·50	14·00
230a	**32**	4d. green (18.8.56)		2·00	2·25
230b	**34**	6d. purple-brown (18.8.56)		8·50	1·00
230c	**35**	9d. chocolate (13.12.56)		22·00	4·50
230d	**36**	1s. grey-green (13.12.56)		5·00	1·25
		da. "Green mist" retouch		£4250	£3000
		db. Roller flaw		40·00	25·00
228/30d	*Set of 7*			35·00	13·50

66 Henry Lawson (Sir Lionel Lindsay)   **67** Mounted Postman and Convair CV 240 Aircraft

(Des F. D. Manley. Eng. E. R. M. Jones. Recess)
1949 (17 June). Henry Lawson (poet) Commemoration. P 15×14.
231	**66**	2½d. maroon		40	10

(Des Sir Daryl Lindsay and F. D. Manley. Eng F. D. Manley. Recess)
1949 (10 Oct). 75th Anniv of Founding of UPU P 15×14.
232	**67**	3½d. ultramarine		60	1·00

68 John, Lord Forrest of Bunbury   **69** Queen Elizabeth   **70** King George VI

(Des and eng F. D. Manley. Recess)
1949 (28 Nov). John, Lord Forrest of Bunbury (explorer and politician) Commemoration. W **15**. P 15×14.
233	**68**	2½d. lake		60	10

(Des and eng F. D. Manley. Recess)
1950 (12 Apr)–**52**.

*(a) W **15**. P 15×14*
234	**70**	2½d. scarlet		10	10
235		3d. scarlet (28.2.51)		15	25
		aa. Coil pair		17·00	50·00

(b) No wmk
236	**69**	1½d. green (19.6.50)		1·25	40
237		2d. yellow-green (28.3.51)		15	10
		a. Coil pair		6·50	10·00
		b. Coil block of four (11.52)		13·00	
237c	**70**	2½d. purple-brown (23.5.51)		15	65
237d		3d. grey-green (14.11.51)		15	10
		da. Coil pair (12.51)		24·00	55·00
234/37d	*Set of 6*			1·75	1·25

On 14 October 1951 No. 235 was placed on sale in sheets of 144 originally intended for use in stamp booklets. These sheets contain three panes of 48 (16×3) with horizontal gutter margin between.

71 Aborigine   **72** Reproduction of First Stamps of New South Wales   **73** Reproduction of First Stamps of Victoria

(Des and eng F. D. Manley. Recess)
1950 (14 Aug). W **15**. P 15×14.
238	**71**	8½d. brown		1·00	1·00

For T **71** in a larger size, see Nos. 253/b.

(Des and eng G. Lissenden (T **72**), E. R. M. Jones (T **73**). Recess)
1950 (27 Sept). Centenary of First Adhesive Postage Stamps in Australia. P 15×14.
239	**72**	2½d. maroon		50	10
		a. Horiz pair. Nos. 239/40		1·00	1·25
240	**73**	2½d. maroon		50	10

Nos. 239/40 were printed alternately in vertical columns throughout the sheet.

74 Sir Edmund Barton **75** Sir Henry Parkes

76 Opening First Federal Parliament (T. Roberts) **77** Federal Parliament House, Canberra

(Des and eng F. D. Manley. Recess)

1951 (1 May). 50th Anniv of Commonwealth of Australia. P 15×14.

241	**74**	3d. lake	1·50	10
		a. Horiz pair. Nos. 241/2	3·00	3·00
242	**75**	3d. lake	1·50	10
243	**76**	5½d. blue	65	2·25
244	**77**	1s.6d. purple-brown	1·25	50
241/44	Set of 4		4·50	2·75

Nos. 241/2 were printed alternately in vertical columns throughout the sheet.

78 E. H. Hargraves **79** C. J. Latrobe

(Des and eng F. D. Manley. Recess)

1951 (2 July). Centenaries of Discovery of Gold in Australia and of Responsible Government in Victoria. P 15×14.

245	**78**	3d. maroon	1·10	10
		a. Horiz pair. Nos. 245/6	2·25	3·75
246	**79**	3d. maroon	1·10	10

Nos. 245/6 were printed alternately in vertical columns throughout the sheet.

80 **81** King George VI **82**

(Des E. R. M. Jones (7½d.), F. D. Manley (others) Eng. F. D. Manley. Recess)

1951–52. W **15** (sideways on 1s.0½d.). P 14½ (1s.0½d.) or 15×14 (others).

247	**80**	3½d. brown-purple (28.11.51)	10	10
		a. Imperf between (horiz pair)	£18000	
248		4½d. scarlet (20.2.52)	15	1·25
249		6½d. brown (20.2.52)	20	1·75
250		6½d. emerald-green (9.4.52)	30	55
251	**81**	7½d. blue (31.10.51)	15	1·50
		a. Imperf three sides (vert pair)	£24000	
252	**82**	1s.0½d. indigo (19.3.52)	1·50	60
247/52	Set of 6		2·10	5·00

No. 251a occurs on the left-hand vertical row of one sheet.

(Des F. D. Manley. Eng E. R. M. Jones. Recess)

1952 (19 Mar)–**65.** P 14½.

(a) W **15** *(sideways*)*

253		2s.6d. deep brown	2·25	1·00
		aw. Wmk Crown to left of C of A	£5000	£1500

(b) No wmk

253b		2s.6d. deep brown (30.1.57)	3·50	75
		ba. Sepia (10.65)	13·00	14·00

Design:—2s.6d. As T **71** but larger (21×25½ mm).

*The normal sideways watermark on No. 253 shows Crown to right of C of A, *as seen from the back of the stamp.*

No. 253ba was an emergency printing and can easily be distinguished from No. 253b as it is on white Harrison paper, No. 253b being on toned paper.

(Des and eng F. D. Manley. Recess)

1952 (19 Nov). Pan-Pacific Scout Jamboree, Greystanes. As T **65**, but inscr "1952–53". W **15** (sideways). P 14×15.

254		3½d. brown-lake	20	10

83 Butter **84** Wheat **85** Beef

(Des P.O. artists; adapted G. Lissenden. Typo)

1953 (11 Feb). Food Production. P 14½.

255	**83**	3d. emerald	30	10
		a. Strip of 3. Nos. 255/7	1·60	2·75
256	**84**	3d. emerald	30	10
257	**85**	3d. emerald	30	10

258	**83**	3½d. scarlet	30	10
		a. Strip of 3. Nos. 258/60	1·60	2·75
259	**84**	3½d. scarlet	30	10
260	**85**	3½d. scarlet	30	10
255/60	Set of 6		3·00	55

The three designs in each denomination appear in rotation, both horizontally and vertically, throughout the sheet.

86 Queen Elizabeth II **87** Queen Elizabeth II

(Des F. D. Manley from photograph by Dorothy Wilding Ltd. Eng D. Cameron. Recess)

1953–56. P 15×14.

(a) No wmk

261	**86**	1d. purple (19.8.53)	15	15
261a		2½d. blue (23.6.54)	20	15
262		3d. deep green (17.6.53)	20	10
		aa. Coil pair	5·00	8·00
		ab. Coil block of four (9.53)	15·00	
262a		3½d. brown-red (2.7.56)	1·00	30
262b		6½d. orange (9.56)	1·75	2·50

(b) W **15**

263	**86**	3½d. brown-red (21.4.53)	20	10
263a		6½d. orange (23.6.54)	3·00	50
261/63a	Set of 7		6·00	3·25

(Des and eng F. D. Manley. Recess)

1953 (25 May). Coronation. P 15×14.

264	**87**	3½d. scarlet	40	10
265		7½d. violet	75	1·40
266		2s. dull bluish green	2·50	2·25
264/6	Set of 3		3·25	3·25

88 Young Farmers and Calf

(Des P.O. artist; adapted P. E. Morriss. Eng E. R. M. Jones. Recess)

1953 (3 Sept). 25th Anniv of Australian Young Farmers' Clubs. P 14½.

267	**88**	3½d. red-brown and deep green	10	10

89 Lt.-Gov. D. Collins **90** Lt.-Gov. W. Paterson

91 Sullivan Cove, Hobart, 1804

(Des E. R. M. Jones, eng D. Cameron (T **89**/90); des and eng G. Lissenden (T **91**). Recess)

1953 (23 Sept). 150th Anniv of Settlement in Tasmania. P 15×14.

268	**89**	3½d. brown-purple	50	10
		a. Horiz pair. Nos. 268/9	1·00	1·75
269	**90**	3½d. brown-purple	50	10
270	**91**	2s. green	1·25	3·25
268/70	Set of 3		2·00	3·25

Nos. 268/9 were printed alternately in vertical columns throughout the sheet.

92 Stamp of 1853

(Des R. L. Beck; eng G. Lissenden. Recess)

1953 (11 Nov). Tasmanian Postage Stamp Centenary. P 14½.

271	**92**	3d. rose-red	20	40

93 Queen Elizabeth II and Duke of Edinburgh

 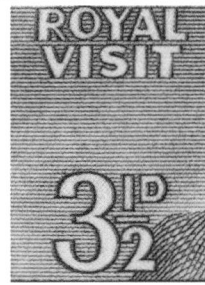

94 Queen Elizabeth II

Re-entry. Vertical lines doubled in "ROYAL VISIT" and "3½D." (Lower plate left pane R. 8/2)

(Des and eng F. D. Manley; border and lettering on 7½d. des by R. M. Warner. Recess)

1954 (2 Feb). Royal Visit. P 14.

272	**93**	3½d. scarlet	20	10
		a. Re-entry	45·00	21·00
273	**94**	7½d. purple	30	1·25
274	**93**	2s. dull bluish green	60	65
272/74	Set of 3		1·00	1·75

95 "Telegraphic Communications" **96** Red Cross and Globe

(Des R. M. Warner. Eng P. E. Morriss. Recess)

1954 (7 Apr). Australian Telegraph System Centenary. P 14.

275	**95**	3½d. brown-red	20	10

(Des B. Stewart. Eng P. E. Morriss. Design recess: cross typo)

1954 (9 June). 40th Anniv of Australian Red Cross Society. P 14½.

276	**96**	3½d. ultramarine and scarlet	20	10

97 Mute Swan **98** Locomotives of 1854 and 1954

(Des R. L. Beck. Eng G. Lissenden. Recess)

1954 (2 Aug). Western Australian Postage Stamp Centenary. P 14½.

277	**97**	3½d. black	20	10

(Des R. M. Warner. Eng G. Lissenden. Recess)

1954 (13 Sept). Australian Railways Centenary. P 14.

278	**98**	3½d. purple-brown	30	10

99 Territory Badge **100** Olympic Games Symbol **101** Rotary Symbol, Globe and Flags

(Des F. D. Manley. Eng G. Lissenden. Recess)

1954 (17 Nov). Australian Antarctic Research. P 14½×13½.

279	**99**	3½d. grey-black	20	10

(Des R. L. Beck. Eng P. E. Morriss. Recess)

1954 (1 Dec)–**55.** Olympic Games Propaganda. P 14.

280	**100**	2s. deep bright blue	1·00	1·00
280a		2s. deep bluish green (30.11.55)	2·00	2·50

(Des and eng D. Cameron. Recess)

1955 (23 Feb). 50th Anniv of Rotary International. P 14×14½.

281	**101**	3½d. carmine	10	10

101a Queen Elizabeth II **101b** Queen Elizabeth II **102** Queen Elizabeth II

(Des F. D. Manley from bas-relief by W. L. Bowles. Eng D. Cameron (7½d.), G. Lissenden (others). Recess)

1955 (9 Mar)–**57.** P 15×14 (T **101a/b**) or 14½ (T **102**).

(a) W **15** *(sideways)*

282	**102**	1s.0½d. deep blue	1·00	1·25

(b) No wmk

282a	**101a**	4d. lake (13.3.57)	55	10
		ab. Booklet pane of 6	7·50	
282b	**101b**	7½d. violet (13.11.57)	1·25	1·50
		ba. Double print	£5500	
282c	**101a**	10d. deep grey-blue (6.3.57)	60	1·00
282d	**102**	1s.7d. red-brown (13.3.57)	1·25	45
282/d	*Set of 5*		4·25	3·75

No. 282ab from booklet SB33 has the outer edges of the pane imperforate, producing single stamps with one or two adjacent sides imperforate.

The doubling on No. 282ba affects the lower part of the design only.

103 American Memorial, Canberra

104 Cobb and Co. Coach (from etching by Sir Lionel Lindsay)

(Des R. L. Beck (head by F. D. Manley). Eng F. D. Manley. Recess)

1955 (4 May). Australian–American Friendship. P 14×14½.

283	**103**	3½d. violet-blue	10	10

(Design adapted and eng by F. D. Manley. Recess)

1955 (6 July). Mail-coach Pioneers Commemoration. P 14½×14.

284	**104**	3½d. blackish brown	25	10
285		2s. reddish brown	1·00	1·75

105 YMCA Emblem and Map of the World

106 Florence Nightingale and Young Nurse

Broken triangle flaw (R. 8/5)

(Des E. Thake. Eng P. E. Morriss. Design recess; emblem typo)

1955 (10 Aug). World Centenary of YMCA P 14½×14.

286	**105**	3½d. deep bluish green and red	20	10
		a. Red (emblem) omitted	£28000	
		b. Broken triangle	15·00	

Only one unused example of No. 286a has been reported. A further defective example exists used on cover.

(Des and eng F. D. Manley. Recess)

1955 (21 Sept). Nursing Profession Commemoration. P 14×14½.

287	**106**	3½d. reddish violet	10	10

107 Queen Victoria

108 Badges of New South Wales, Victoria and Tasmania

(Des and eng D. Cameron. Recess)

1955 (17 Oct). Centenary of First South Australian Postage Stamps. P 14½.

288	**107**	3½d. green	10	10

Imperf pairs of No. 288 are known. They come from die proof blocks of four.

(Des and eng F. D. Manley. Recess)

1956 (26 Sept). Centenary of Responsible Government in New South Wales, Victoria and Tasmania. P 14½×14.

289	**108**	3½d. brown-lake	10	10

109 Arms of Melbourne

110 Olympic Torch and Symbol

111 Collins Street, Melbourne

112 Melbourne across R. Yarra

(Des P. E. Morriss; eng F. D. Manley (4d.). Des and eng F. D. Manley (7½d.) Recess. Des and photo Harrison from photographs by M. Murphy and sketches by L. Coles (1s.). Des and photo Courvoisier from photographs by M. Murphy (2s.))

1956 (31 Oct). Olympic Games, Melbourne. P 14½ (4d.), 14×14½ (7½d., 1s.) or 11½ (2s.).

290	**109**	4d. carmine-red	30	10
291	**110**	7½d. deep bright blue	55	1·40
292	**111**	1s. multicoloured	70	30
293	**112**	2s. multicoloured	1·40	2·50
290/93	*Set of 4*		2·75	3·75

115 South Australia Coat of Arms

116 Map of Australia and Caduceus

(Des and eng P. E. Morriss. Recess)

1957 (17 Apr). Centenary of Responsible Government in South Australia. P 14½.

296	**115**	4d. red-brown	10	10

(Des J. E. Lyle; adapted B. Stewart. Eng D. Cameron. Recess)

1957 (21 Aug). Flying Doctor Service. P 14½×14.

297	**116**	7d. ultramarine	15	10

117 "The Spirit of Christmas"

Re-entry. "ISTMAS" and "TRALI" double. (Upper plate left pane R. 10/1)

(Des and eng D. Cameron from a painting by Sir Joshua Reynolds. Recess)

1957 (6 Nov). Christmas. P 14½×14.

298	**117**	3½d. scarlet	10	20
		a. Re-entry	9·50	14·00
299		4d. purple	10	10

118 Lockheed L.1049 Super Constellation Airliner

Re-entry on final "A" of "AUSTRALIA" (Upper plate right pane R. 7/6)

(Des and eng P. E. Morriss. Recess)

1958 (6 Jan). Inauguration of Australian "Round the World" Air Service. P 14½×14.

301	**118**	2s. deep blue	1·00	1·00
		a. Re-entry	55·00	55·00

119 Hall of Memory, Sailor and Airman

120 Sir Charles Kingsford Smith and Fokker F.VIIa/3m *Southern Cross*

(Des and eng G. Lissenden. Recess)

1958 (10 Feb). T **119** and similar horiz design. P 14½×14.

302		5½d. brown-red	60	30
		a. Horiz pair. Nos. 302/303	1·50	5·50
303		5½d. brown-red	60	30

No. 303 shows a soldier and service-woman respectively in place of the sailor and airman. Nos. 302/3 are printed alternately in vertical columns throughout the sheet.

(Des J. E. Lyle. Eng F. D. Manley. Recess)

1958 (27 Aug). 30th Anniv of First Air Crossing of the Tasman Sea. P 14×14½.

304	**120**	8d. deep ultramarine	60	1·00

121 Silver Mine, Broken Hill

122 The Nativity

(Des R. H. Evans; adapted and eng F. D. Manley. Recess)

1958 (10 Sept). 75th Anniv of Founding of Broken Hill. P 14½×14.

305	**121**	4d. chocolate	30	10

(Des D. Cameron. Eng P. E. Morriss. Recess)

1958 (5 Nov). Christmas. P 14½×15.

306	**122**	3½d. deep scarlet	20	30
307		4d. deep violet	20	10

123

124

126

127

128 Queen Elizabeth II

129

Type I Short break in outer line to bottom right of "4"

Type II Line unbroken

Type A Four short lines inside "5"

Type B Five short lines inside "5"

1d. Re-entry. Line running through base of "RALIA" (Lower right plate, right pane R. 1/8).

3½d. Re-entry to "E" and left frame (Upper left plate, left pane R. 1/10)

(Des G. Lissenden from photographs by Baron Studios. Eng F. D. Manley (2d.), D. Cameron (3d.). P. E. Morriss (others). Recess)

1959–63. P 14×15 (horiz) or 15×14 (vert).

308	**123**	1d. deep slate-purple (2.2.59)	10	10
		a. Deep slate-lilac (1961)	2·00	30
		b. Re-entry	24·00	20·00
309	**124**	2d. brown (21.3.62)	60	20
		a. Coil pair (1962)	4·50	7·00
		b. Coil block of four (1963)	14·00	
311	**126**	3d. blue-green (20.5.59)	15	10
		a. Coil pair (8.59)	4·00	6·50
		b. Coil block of four	14·00	
312	**127**	3½d. deep green (18.3.59)	15	15
		a. Re-entry	24·00	24·00
313	**128**	4d. carmine-lake (Type I) (2.2.59)	3·00	10
		a. Carmine-red	3·00	10
		ab. Booklet pane of 6 (18.3.59)	20·00	
		b. Type II	3·00	10
		ba. Carmine-red	3·00	10

314	**129**	5d. deep blue (Type A or B)		
		(1.10.59)	1·50	10
		a. Vert *se-tenant* pair (A and B)	3·50	6·50
		b. Coil pair (18.7.60)	10·00	15·00
		c. Coil block of four (7.61)	50·00	
		d. Booklet pane of 6 (23.3.60)	11·00	
		da. Imperf between (horiz pair)	£11000	
308/14		*Set of 6*	4·75	65

No. 313. Produced in printer's sheets, of 640 split into sheets of 160 for issue. Type I occurs on the two upper sheets from the printers' sheet and on ten positions from the left pane of the lower right sheet. Type II occurs on all stamps from the lower sheets except for ten positions from the left pane of lower right sheet.

No. 314. Both types occur in alternate horizontal rows in the sheet (Type A in Row 1, Type B in Row 2, and so on), and their value is identical. Booklet pane No. 314d from SB35/6a contains two Type A and four Type B.

Nos. 309a/b, 311a/b and 314b/c have horizontal coil perforations as described after No. 191.

Nos. 313ab from booklets SB34 and 314d from booklets SB35/6a have the outer edges of the panes imperforate, producing stamps with one or two adjacent sides imperforate.

A single example (imperforate at base) of No.314da is known, apparently from a miscut booklet pane.

Printings of the 2d. (from March 1965) and of the 3d. (from April 1965), both including coils, were on Helecon paper.

131 Numbat

132 Tiger Cat

133 Eastern Grey Kangaroos

134 Common Rabbit-Bandicoot

135 Platypus

136 Thylacine

137 Christmas Bells

138 Flannel Flower

139 Wattle

140 Banksia

141 Waratah

142 Aboriginal Stockman

2s. "T" retouch (Right plate R. 6/8)

(Des Eileen Mayo (6d., 8d., 9d., 11d., 1s., 1s.2d.), B. Stewart (5s.), Margaret Stones (others). Eng P. Morriss (11d.) F. D. Manley (1s.), B. Stewart (others). Recess)

1959–64. T **131/42.** W **15** (5s.), no wmk (others). P 14×15 (1s.2d.), 15×14 (6d. to 1s.), 14½×14 (5s.) or 14½ (others).

316	**131**	6d. brown (30.9.60)	1·75	10
317	**132**	8d. red-brown (11.5.60)	1·00	10
		a. Pale red-brown (9.61)	1·50	20
318	**133**	9d. deep sepia (21.10.59)	2·25	55
319	**134**	11d. deep blue (3.5.61)	1·00	15
320	**135**	1s. deep green (9.9.59)	2·75	40
321	**136**	1s.2d. deep purple (21.3.62)	1·00	15
322	**137**	1s.6d. crimson/*yellow* (3.2.60)	2·25	1·25
323	**138**	2s. grey-blue (8.4.59)	70	20
		a. "T" retouch	55·00	45·00
324	**139**	2s.3d. green/*maize* (9.9.59)	1·00	10
324a		2s.3d. yellow-green (28.10.64)	2·50	75
325	**140**	2s.5d. brown/*yellow* (16.3.60)	4·50	1·00
326	**141**	3s. scarlet (15.7.59)	1·75	20
327	**142**	5s. red-brown (26.7.61)	14·00	3·00
		a. White paper. *Brown-red* (17.6.64)	90·00	7·50
316/327		*Set of 13*	32·00	6·50

No. 327 is on toned paper. No. 327a was a late printing on the white paper referred to in the note below No. 360.

An experimental printing of the 11d. was made on Helecon paper in December 1963. See note below No. 362.

All printings of the 8d., 11d., 1s.2d. and 2s.3d. (No. 324a) were on Helecon paper from April 1965.

---

143 Postmaster Isaac Nichols boarding the brig *Experiment*

144 Parliament House, Brisbane, and Arms of Queensland

(Des R. Shackel; adapted and eng F. D. Manley. Recess)

1959 (22 Apr). 150th Anniv of the Australian Post Office. P 14½×14.

331	**143**	4d. slate	15	10

(Des and eng G. Lissenden. Recess and typo)

1959 (5 June). Centenary of Self-Government in Queensland. P 14×14½.

332	**144**	4d. lilac and green	10	10

145 The Approach of the Magi

146 Girl Guide and Lord Baden-Powell

(Des and eng F. D. Manley. Recess)

1959 (4 Nov). Christmas. P 15×14.

333	**145**	5d. deep reddish violet	10	10

(Des and eng B. Stewart. Recess)

1960 (18 Aug). 50th Anniv of Girl Guide Movement. P 14½×14.

334	**146**	5d. deep ultramarine	30	15

147 *The Overlanders* (Sir Daryl Lindsay)

148 Archer and Melbourne Cup

Two types:

I. Mane rough

II. Mane smooth

Major re-entry below rider's right arm (Lower left plate R. 4/4). This occurs only on Type I.

Type II occurs on Pane A, Row 2 Nos. 8 and 9, Row 4 Nos. 1 to 12, Row 5 Nos. 10 to 12, and on Pane C, Row 4 Nos. 5 to 12, Row 5 Nos. 1 to 9, and Rows 6 to 10 inclusive; the stamps in Row 4 Nos. 5 to 12 and Row 5 Nos. 1 to 9 are considered to be of an intermediate type with the mane as in Type II but the ear and rein being as in Type I. All the rest are Type I.

(Adapted and eng P. E. Morriss. Recess)

1960 (21 Sept). Centenary of Northern Territory Exploration. P 15×14½.

335	**147**	5d. magenta (I)	50	15
		a. Major re-entry	60·00	42·00
		b. Type II	3·50	2·00

(Des F. D. Manley. Eng G. Lissenden. Recess)

1960 (12 Oct). 100th Melbourne Cup Race Commemoration. P 14½.

336	**148**	5d. sepia	20	10

149 Queen Victoria

150 Open Bible and Candle

(Des F. D. Manley. Eng B. Stewart. Recess)

1960 (2 Nov). Centenary of First Queensland Postage Stamp. P 14½×15.

337	**149**	5d. deep myrtle-green	25	10

Re-entry. "19" of "1960" partially double (Lower left plate R. 5/2). On upper left plate R. 10/10 there is a similar partial doubling of "19" but to right of "1" and inside "9". Same price for either variety.

(Des K. McKay. Adapted and eng B. Stewart. Recess)

1960 (9 Nov). Christmas. P 15×14½.

338	**150**	5d. carmine-red	10	10
		a. Re-entry	24·00	20·00

151 Colombo Plan Bureau Emblem

152 Melba (after bust by Sir Bertram Mackennal)

(Des and eng G. Lissenden. Recess)

1961 (30 June). Colombo Plan. P 14×14½.

339	**151**	1s. red-brown	30	10

No. 339 was issued on Helecon paper in April 1965. See note after No. 362.

(Des and eng B. Stewart. Recess)

1961 (20 Sept). Birth Centenary of Dame Nellie Melba (singer). P 14½×15.

340	**152**	5d. blue	30	15

153 Open Prayer Book and Text

(Des G. Lissenden. Eng P. E. Morriss. Recess)

1961 (8 Nov). Christmas. P 14½×14.

341	**153**	5d. brown	10	10

154 J. M. Stuart

155 Flynn's Grave and Nursing Sister

(Des W. Jardine. Eng P. E. Morriss. Recess)

1962 (25 July). Centenary of Stuart's Crossing of Australia from South to North. P 14½×15.

342	**154**	5d. brown-red	40	10

(Des F. D. Manley. Photo)

1962 (5 Sept). 50th Anniv of Australian Inland Mission. P 13½.

343	**155**	5d. multicoloured	40	15

Used examples apparently showing the red colour omitted are now considered to be faked.

156 "Woman"

157 Madonna and Child

(Des D. Dundas. Eng G. Lissenden. Recess)

1962 (26 Sept). "Associated Country Women of the World" Conference, Melbourne. P 14×14½.

344	**156**	5d. deep green	10	10

(Des and eng G. Lissenden. Recess)

1962 (17 Oct). Christmas. P 14½.

345	**157**	5d. violet	15	10

158 Perth and Kangaroo Paw (plant)   **159** Arms of Perth and Running Track

(Des R. M. Warner (5d.), G. Hamori (2s.3d.) Photo Harrison)

1962 (1 Nov). Seventh British Empire and Commonwealth Games, Perth. P 14 (5d.) or 14½×14 (2s.3d.).

346	**158**	5d. multicoloured	50	10
		a. Red omitted	£7000	
347	**159**	2s.3d. black, red, blue and green	2·00	2·75

160 Queen Elizabeth II   **161** Queen Elizabeth II and Duke of Edinburgh

(Des and eng after portraits by Anthony Buckley, P. E. Morriss (5d.), B. Stewart (2s.3d.). Recess)

1963 (18 Feb). Royal Visit. P 14½.

348	**160**	5d. deep green	35	10
349	**161**	2s.3d. brown-lake	1·50	3·25

162 Arms of Canberra and W. B. Griffin (architect)   **163** Centenary Emblem

(Des and eng B. Stewart. Recess)

1963 (8 Mar). 50th Anniv of Canberra. P 14½×14.

350	**162**	5d. deep green	15	10

(Des G. Hamori. Photo)

1963 (8 May). Red Cross Centenary. P 13½×13.

351	**163**	5d. red, grey-brown and blue	60	10

164 Blaxland, Lawson and Wentworth on Mt. York

(Des T. Alban. Eng P. E. Morriss. Recess)

1963 (28 May). 150th Anniv of First Crossing of Blue Mountains. P 14½×14.

352	**164**	5d. ultramarine	15	10

165 "Export"   **166** Queen Elizabeth II

(Des and eng B. Stewart. Recess)

1963 (28 Aug). Export Campaign. P 14½×14.

353	**165**	5d. red	10	10

(Des and eng P. E. Morriss from photograph by Anthony Buckley. Recess)

1963 (9 Oct)–65. P 15×14.

354	**166**	5d. deep green	1·00	10
		a. Booklet pane of 6	22·00	
		b. Imperf between (horiz pair) (31.7.64)	1·50	2·50
354c		5d. red (30.6.65)	55	10
		ca. Coil pair	19·00	38·00
		cb. Booklet pane of 6	22·00	

The 5d. deep green exists from both sheets and booklets on Helecon paper produced in error.

The 5d. red was issued with or without Helecon added to the ink. All coil and booklet printings included Helecon in the ink, except for a small printing produced in error. Examples of the sheet and booklet printings with Helecon ink have been found on Helecon *paper*.

Nos. 354a and 354cb have the outer edges of the panes imperforate producing single stamps with one or two adjacent sides imperforate. They come from booklets SB37/8a.

No. 354b comes from sheets of uncut booklet panes containing 288 stamps (16×18) with wide margins intersecting the sheet horizontally below each third row, alternate rows of stamps imperforate between vertically, and the outer left, right and bottom margins imperforate. This means that in each sheet there are 126 pairs of stamps imperf between vertically, plus a number with wide imperforate margins attached, as shown in the illustration.

A 5d. in a similar design, printed in blue and brown with vertical edges imperforate, was prepared, but not issued.

167 Tasman and *Heemskerk*   **168** Dampier and *Roebuck*

169 Captain Cook (after painting by Nathaniel Dance)   **170** Flinders and *Investigator*

171 Bass and *Tom Thumb* (whaleboat)   **172** Admiral King and *Mermaid* (survey cutter)

£2 Roller flaw, right-hand frame line at top (R. 1/3).

(Des W. Jardine. Eng B. Stewart (4s.), P. E. Morriss (5s., 7s., 6d., £1), M. Jones (10s). Recess)

1963–65. T **167/72**. No wmk (4s.) or W **15** (others), (sideways on 5s., £1). P 14 or 14½ (5s., £1, £2).

355	**167**	4s. ultramarine (9.10.63)	3·00	55
356	**168**	5s. red-brown (25.11.64)	5·00	1·25
357	**169**	7s.6d. olive (26.8.64)	19·00	21·00
358	**170**	10s. brown-purple (26.2.64)	25·00	5·00
		a. White paper. *Deep brown-purple* (14.1.65)	25·00	8·00
359	**171**	£1 deep reddish violet (26.2.64)	38·00	16·00
		a. White paper. *Deep bluish violet* (16.11.64)	48·00	30·00
360	**172**	£2 sepia (26.8.64)	55·00	75·00
		a. Roller flaw	£200	
355/60 Set of 6			£120	£110
357s/60s Optd "SPECIMEN" Set of 4			£475	

Nos. 358 and 359 were printed on a toned paper but all the other values are on white paper, the unwatermarked paper of the 4s. being rather thicker.

173 "Peace on Earth ..."   **174** "Commonwealth Cable"

(Des R. M. Warner. Eng B. Stewart. Recess)

1963 (25 Oct). Christmas. P 14½.

361	**173**	5d. greenish blue	10	10

(Des P. E. Morriss. Photo)

1963 (3 Dec). Opening of COMPAC (Trans-Pacific Telephone Cable). Chalk-surfaced paper. P 13½.

362	**174**	2s.3d. red, blue, black and pale blue	1·50	3·00

HELECON (PHOSPHOR) STAMPS. "Helecon", a chemical substance of the zinc sulphide group, has been incorporated in stamps in two different ways, either in the ink with which the stamps are printed, or included in the surface coating of the stamp paper.

Owing to the difficulty of identification without the use of a U.V. lamp we do not list the Helecon stamps separately but when in stock can supply them after testing under the lamp.

The first stamp to be issued on Helecon was the 11d. Bandicoot (No. 319) from an experimental printing of four million released to the public in December 1963. The next printing, on ordinary paper, was released in September 1964. The experimental printing was coarse, showing a lot of white dots and the colour is slate-blue, differing from both the ordinary and the later Helecon printings.

Further Helecon printings followed from March 1965. Almost all issues from No. 378 onwards were on Helecon paper or paper coated with Derby Luminescence.

175 Yellow-tailed Thornbill   **176** Black-backed Magpie

177 Galah   **178** Golden Whistler

179 Blue Wren   **180** Scarlet Robin

181 Straw-necked Ibis

(Des Betty Temple-Watts. Photo)

1964 (11 Mar)–**65**. Birds. T **175/81** and similar designs. Chalk-surfaced paper. P 13½.

363	**175**	6d. brown, yellow, black and bluish green (19.8.64)	1·50	50
		a. Brown, yellow, black and emerald-green	3·00	2·50
364	**176**	9d. black, grey and pale green	1·00	2·75
365	**177**	1s.6d. pink, grey, dull purple and black	75	1·40
366	**178**	2s. yellow, black and pink (21.4.65)	1·40	50
367	**179**	2s.5d. deep royal blue, light violet-blue, yellow-orange, grey and black	1·75	3·50
		a. Ordinary paper. *Deep blue, light blue, orange-brown, blue-grey and black* (7.65)	6·00	8·00
368	**180**	2s.6d. black, red, grey and green (21.4.65)	2·50	4·50
		a. Red omitted (white breast)	£18000	£18000
369	**181**	3s. black, red, buff and yellow-green (21.4.65)	2·50	2·25
363/69 Set of 7			10·00	18·00

No. 367a was from a printing, made in 1962, on unsurfaced Wiggins Teape paper, the rest of the set being on chalk-surfaced Harrison paper. Apart from the differences in shade, the inscriptions, particularly "BLUE WREN", stand out very much more clearly on No. 367a. Although two colours are apparent in both stamps, the grey and black were printed from one cylinder.

The 6d. (No. 363) and 2s.5d. were only issued on ordinary paper. The 9d. and 1s.6d. exist on ordinary or Helecon paper. The 6d. (No. 363a), 1s., 2s.6d. and 3s. were issued on Helecon paper only.

182 Bleriot XI Aircraft (type flown by M. Guillaux, 1914)

5d. Re-entry to second "A" of "AUSTRALIA" (Upper right plate, R. 4/4 subsequently retouched)

(Des K. McKay. Adapted and eng P. E. Morriss. Recess)

1964 (1 July). 50th Anniv of First Australian Airmail Flight. P 14½×14.

370	**182**	5d. olive-green	30	10
		a. Re-entry	£275	£180
371		2s.3d. scarlet	1·75	2·75

183 Child looking at Nativity Scene

184 Simpson and his Donkey

(Des P. E. Morriss and J. Mason. Photo)

1964 (21 Oct). Christmas. Chalk-surfaced paper. P 13½.

372	**183**	5d. red, blue, buff and black	10	10
		a. Red omitted	£5000	£3250
		b. Black omitted	£3000	

The red ink is soluble and can be removed by bleaching and it is therefore advisable to obtain a certificate from a recognised expert committee before purchasing No. 372a. The used price quoted is for an example on cover.

(Des C. Andrew (after statue, Shrine of Remembrance, Melbourne). Eng E. R. M. Jones. Recess)

1965 (14 Apr). 50th Anniv of Gallipoli Landing. P 14×14½.

373	**184**	5d. drab	50	10
374		8d. blue	75	2·50
375		2s.3d. reddish purple	1·50	2·50
373/75	Set of 3		2·50	4·50

185 "Telecommunications"

186 Sir Winston Churchill

(Des J. McMahon and G. Hamori. Photo)

1965 (10 May). ITU Centenary. Chalk-surfaced paper. P 13½.

376	**185**	5d. black, brown, orange-brown and blue	60	10
		a. Black (value and pylon) omitted	£5000	

(Des P. E. Morriss from photo by Karsh. Photo)

1965 (24 May). Churchill Commemoration. Chalk-surfaced paper. P 13½.

377	**186**	5d. black, pale grey, grey and light blue	30	10
		a. Pale grey (facial shading) omitted	£6000	
		b. Grey ("AUSTRALIA") omitted	†	£7000

No. 377a occurred on stamps from the bottom row of one sheet. No. 377 exists on ordinary or Helecon paper in approximately equal quantities.

187 General Monash

188 Hargrave and "Multiplane" Seaplane (1902)

(Des O. Foulkes and W. Walters. Photo)

1965 (23 June). Birth Centenary of General Sir John Monash (engineer and soldier). P 13½.

378	**187**	5d. multicoloured	15	10

(Des G. Hamori. Photo)

1965 (4 Aug). 50th Death Anniv of Lawrence Hargrave (aviation pioneer). P 13½.

379	**188**	5d. purple-brown, black, yellow-ochre and purple	25	10
		a. Purple (value) omitted	£500	£500

189 ICY Emblem

190 Nativity Scene

(Des H. Fallu from UN theme. Photo)

1965 (1 Sept). International Co-operation Year. P 13½.

380	**189**	2s.3d. emerald and light blue	1·00	1·50

(Des J. Mason. Photo)

1965 (20 Oct). Christmas. P 13½.

381	**190**	5d. multicoloured	15	10
		a. Gold omitted	£5500	
		b. Blue omitted	£1000	
		c. Brown omitted	£5000	

No. 381a comes from the bottom row of a sheet in which the gold is completely omitted, the background appearing as black with "CHRISTMAS 1965" and "AUSTRALIA" omitted. The row above had the gold missing from the lower two-fifths of the stamp.

(New Currency. 100 cents = 1 dollar)

191 Queen Elizabeth II

192 Blue-faced Honeyeater

193 White-tailed Dascyllus ("Humbug Fish")

Nos. 401 (top), 401a (centre) and 401b (bottom). No. 401b shows the final form of the variety with a plate crack visible in sky and across sail (Lower sheet left pane. R. 10/1)

(Des Betty Temple-Watts (6c. (No. 387), 13c., 24c.), Eileen Mayo (7c. (No. 388) to 10c.). Recess (T **191**, 40c. to \$4). Photo (others))

1966 (14 Feb)–**73**. Decimal currency. T **191**/3 and similar designs, some reused from previous issues. P 15×14 (T **191**), 14 (40c., 75c., \$1), 14½ (50c., \$2, \$4) or 13½ (others).

382	**191**	1c. deep red-brown	25	10
383		2c. olive-green	70	10
384		3c. slate-green	70	10
385		4c. red	20	10
		a. Booklet pane. Five stamps plus one printed label	16·00	
386	**175**	5c. brown, yellow, black and emerald-green	25	10
		a. Brown (plumage) omitted	£4500	
		b. Brown, yellow, black and blue-green (1.67)	25	20
386c	**191**	5c. deep blue (29.9.67)	70	10
		ca. Booklet pane. Five stamps plus one printed label	8·00	
		cb. Imperf in horiz strip of 3*	£3000	
387	**192**	6c. olive-yellow, black, blue and pale grey	1·00	1·25
		aa. Blue (eye markings) omitted	£3250	
387a	**191**	6c. orange (28.9.70)	1·00	10
388	**193**	7c. black, grey, salmon and brown	60	10
388a	**191**	7c. purple (1.10.71)	1·00	10
389	–	8c. red, yellow, blue-green and blackish green	60	1·00
390	–	9c. brown-red, purple-brown, black and light yellow-olive	60	20
391	–	10c. orange, blackish brown, pale turquoise blue and olive-brown	60	10
		a. Orange omitted	£5500	
392	–	13c. red black, grey and light turquoise-green	1·00	25
		a. Red omitted	£4500	
		b. Grey (plumage and legs) omitted	£4250	
393	**177**	15c. rose-carmine, black, grey and light bluish green	1·00	2·25
		a. Rose-carmine omitted	£7500	
		b. Grey omitted	£4000	
394	**178**	20c. yellow, black and pink	1·00	15
		a. Yellow (plumage) omitted	£5000	
395	–	24c. ultramarine, yellow, black and light brown	65	1·25
396	**180**	25c. black, red, grey and green	1·00	30
		a. Red omitted	£18000	

397	**181**	30c. black, red, buff and light yellow-green	2·75	1·75
		a. Red omitted	£4250	
398	**167**	40c. ultramarine	2·50	10
399	**168**	50c. red-brown	2·50	10
400	**169**	75c. olive	1·00	1·00
401	**170**	\$1 brown-purple (shades)	1·50	20
		a. Recut lines in sky	90·00	
		b. Recut lines and plate crack	£130	
		c. Perf 15×14† (5.73)	85·00	22·00
402	**171**	\$2 deep reddish violet	5·00	1·00
403	**172**	\$4 sepia	6·00	6·50
382/403	Set of 25		30·00	15·00
400s/3s	Optd "SPECIMEN" Set of 4		75·00	

Designs: Vert (as T **193**)—8c. Copper-banded Butterflyfish ("Coral Fish"); 9c. Hermit Crab; 10c. Orange Clownfish ("Anemone Fish"). (As T **192**)—13c. Red-necked Avocet; 15c. Galah; 20c. Golden Whistler; 30c. Straw-necked Ibis. Horiz (as T **192**)—24c. Azure Kingfisher; 25c. Scarlet Robin. As T **167**—75c. Captain Cook; \$1 Flinders and *Investigator*. As T **168**—\$2 Bass and whaleboat; \$4 Admiral King and *Mermaid* (survey cutter).

*This shows two stamps imperforate all round and one imperforate at left only.

†The exact gauge of No. 401c is 14.8×14.1. No. 401 is 14.25×13.95.

Nos. 385a (from booklets SB39/a) and 386ca (from booklets SB42/3a) have the outer edges of the pane imperforate producing single stamps with one or two adjacent sides imperforate.

No. 385 was normally printed in Helecon ink. Early in 1967 experimental printings on different kinds of paper coated with Helecon or Derby Luminescents phosphor were put on sale. These cannot be distinguished by the naked eye.

199 Queen Elizabeth II

200 "Saving Life"

1966 (14 Feb)–**67**. Coil stamps. Photo. P 15×imperf.

404	**199**	3c. black, light brown and green	45	1·25
405		4c. black, light brown and light vermilion	35	1·25
405a		5c. black, light brown and new blue (29.9.67)	40	10
404/5a	Set of 3		1·10	2·25

(Des L. Mason. Photo)

1966 (6 July). 75th Anniv of Royal Life Saving Society. P 13½.

406	**200**	4c. black, bright blue and blue	15	10

201 Adoration of the Shepherds

(Des L. Stirling, after medieval engraving. Photo)

1966 (19 Oct). Christmas. P 13½.

407	**201**	4c. black and yellow-olive	10	10
		a. Value omitted	£3750	

No. 407a was caused by a partial omission of the yellow-olive so that there was no colour surrounding the white face value.

202 Eendracht

203 Open Bible

(Des F. Eidlitz. Photo)

1966 (24 Oct). 350th Anniv of Dirk Hartog's Landing in Australia. P 13½.

408	**202**	4c. multicoloured	10	10
		a. Red (sphere) omitted	£5000	
		b. Gold omitted	£2750	

(Des L. Stirling. Photo)

1967 (7 Mar). 150th Anniv of British and Foreign Bible Society in Australia. P 13½.

409	**203**	4c. multicoloured	10	10

204 Ancient Keys and Modern Lock

Broken frame between "R" and "S" of "YEARS" (Left-hand pane, R. 8/1)

(Des G. Andrews. Photo)

1967 (5 Apr). 150th Anniv of Australian Banking. P 13½.

410	**204**	4c. black, light blue and emerald	10	10
		a. Broken frame	3·50	

205 Lions Badge and 50 Stars

206 YWCA Emblem

(Des M. Ripper. Photo)

1967 (7 June). 50th Anniv of Lions International. P 13½.
411 **205** 4c. black, gold and blue 10 10

(Des H. Williamson. Photo)

1967 (21 Aug). World YWCA Council Meeting, Monash University, Melbourne. P 13½.
412 **206** 4c. deep blue, ultramarine, light purple and light blue 10 10

207 Anatomical Figures

(208) 5c

(Des R. Ingpen. Photo)

1967 (20 Sept). Fifth World Gynaecology and Obstetrics Congress, Sydney. P 13½.
413 **207** 4c. black, blue and light reddish violet 10 10

1967 (29 Sept). No. 385 surch with T **208**.
414 **191** 5c. on 4c. red............................... 25 10
a. Booklet pane. Five stamps plus one printed label......................... 1·00

No. 414 was only issued in 50c. or $1 booklets, Nos. SB40/1ab, with the outer edges of the pane imperforate so all stamps have one or two adjacent sides imperforate. It only exists printed in Helecon ink.

209 Christmas Bells and Gothic Arches

210 Religious Symbols

(Des M. Ripper (5c.), Erica McGilchrist (25c.). Photo)

1967. (18 Oct-27 Nov) Christmas. P 13½.
415 **209** 5c. multicoloured (18.10.67) 20 10
a. Imperf three sides (vert pair)..... £13000
416 **210** 25c. multicoloured (27.11.67) .... 1·00 1·90

No. 415a show the stamps perforated at left only.

211 Satellite in Orbit

212 World Weather Map

(Des J. Mason. Photo)

1968 (20 Mar). World Weather Watch. P 13½.
417 **211** 5c. orange-brown, pale blue, black and ochre............................ 30 10
418 **212** 20c. orange-brown, blue and black . 1·10 3·00
a. White (radio waves) omitted £1500
b. Orange-brown (triangle) omitted £4250

213 Radar Antenna

214 Kangaroo Paw (Western Australia)

(Des R. Ingpen. Photo)

1968 (20 Mar). World Telecommunications via *Intelsat II*. P 13½.
419 **213** 25c. greenish blue, black and light blue-green .... 1·00 2·00

Type I.

Type II.

The 30c. was reprinted in 1971 from new cylinders so that Type II shows greater areas of white in the pink tones of the petals.

(Des Nell Wilson (6c., 30c.); R. and P. Warner (13c., 25c.); Dorothy Thornhill (15c.), 20c.). Photo)

1968 (10 July)–71. State Floral Emblems. T **214** and similar vert designs. Multicoloured. P 13½.
420 6c. Type **214**............................... 45 1·25
421 13c. Pink Heath (Victoria) 50 70
422 15c. Tasmanian Blue Gum (Tasmania)...... 50 40
423 20c. Sturt's Desert Pea (South Australia) . 1·00 75
424 25c. Cooktown Orchid (Queensland)....... 1·10 75
425 30c. Waratah (New South Wales) (Type I) 50 10
a. Green (leaves) omitted............ £3750
b. Type II (29.6.71) .... 4·75 2·00
420/25 Set of 6............................... 3·50 3·50

220 Soil Sample Analysis

(Des R. Ingpen. Photo)

1968 (6 Aug). International Soil Science Congress and World Medical Association Assembly. T **220** and similar horiz design. P 13½.
426 **220** 5c. orange-brown, stone, greenish blue and black...................... 10 10
a. Nos. 426/7 *se-tenant* with gutter margin between .... 6·00 14·00
427 – 5c. greenish blue, dull olive-yellow, rose and black................. 10 10

Design:—No. 427, Rubber-gloved hands, syringe and head of Hippocrates.

The above were printed in sheets of 100 containing a pane of 50 of each design.

The major shades formerly listed have been deleted as there is a range of intermediate shades.

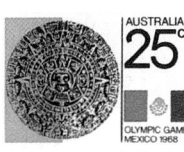

222 Athlete carrying Torch, and Sunstone Symbol

223 Sunstone Symbol and Mexican Flag

(Des H. Williamson. Photo)

1968 (2 Oct). Olympic Games, Mexico City. P 13½.
428 **222** 5c. multicoloured 30 10
429 **223** 25c. multicoloured .... 40 1·50
a. Green (left-hand panel) omitted £3500

224 Houses and Dollar Signs

225 Church Window and View of Bethlehem

(Des Erica McGilchrist. Photo)

1968 (16 Oct). Building and Savings Societies Congress. P 13½.
430 **224** 5c. multicoloured 10 60

(Des G. Hamori. Photo)

1968 (23 Oct). Christmas. P 13½.
431 **225** 5c. multicoloured 10 10
a. Green window (gold omitted) .. £850
b. Red (inscr) omitted £2500

226 Edgeworth David (geologist)

(Des Note Ptg Branch (Nos. 432, 434) A. Cook (others). Recess, background litho)

1968 (6 Nov). Famous Australians (1st series). T **226** and similar vert portraits. P 15×14.
432 5c. myrtle-green/*pale green* 25 20
a. Booklet pane. Five stamps plus one printed label........................ 1·10
433 5c. black/*pale blue* 25 20
a. Booklet pane. Five stamps plus one printed label........................ 1·10
434 5c. blackish brown/*pale buff* 25 20
a. Booklet pane. Five stamps plus one printed label........................ 1·10
435 5c. deep violet/*pale lilac*...................... 25 20
a. Booklet pane. Five stamps plus one printed label........................ 1·10
432/35 Set of 4............................... 90 70

Designs:—No. 432, Type **226**; No. 433, A. B. Paterson (poet); No. 434, Albert Namatjira (artist); No. 435, Caroline Chisholm (social worker).
Nos. 432/5 were only issued in $1 booklets, Nos. SB44/a, with the outer edges of the pane imperforate so all stamps have one or two adjacent sides imperforate.
See also Nos. 446/9, 479/82.

230 Macquarie Lighthouse

231 Pioneers and Modern Building, Darwin

(Des and eng Note Ptg Branch. Recess; background litho)

1968 (27 Nov). 150th Anniv of Macquarie Lighthouse. P 14½×13½.
436 **230** 5c. black and pale yellow.................. 50 1·00

Used examples are known with the pale yellow background colour omitted.

(Des Marietta Lyon. Photo)

1969 (5 Feb). Centenary of Northern Territory Settlement. P 13½.
437 **231** 5c. blackish brown, yellow-olive and yellow-ochre.................. 10 10

232 Melbourne Harbour

233 Concentric Circles (symbolising Management, Labour and Government)

(Des J. Mason. Photo)

1969 (26 Feb). Sixth Biennial Conference of International Association of Ports and Harbours, Melbourne. P 13½.
438 **232** 5c. multicoloured 20 10

(Des G. Hamori. Photo)

1969 (4 June). 50th Anniv of International Labour Organisation. P 13½.
439 **233** 5c. multicoloured 15 10
a. Gold (middle circle) omitted...... £3500

234 Sugar Cane

(Des R. Ingpen. Photo)

1969 (17 Sept). Primary Industries. T **234** and similar vert designs. Multicoloured. P 13½.
440 7c. Type **234**............................... 50 1·50
441 15c. Timber .... 75 2·00
a. Black ("Australia" and value) omitted ... £1700
442 20c. Wheat............................... 30 50
443 25c. Wool............................... 50 1·50
440/43 Set of 4............................... 1·90 5·00

238 The Nativity (stained-glass window)

240 Edmund Barton

(Des G. Hamori (5c.), J. Coburn (25c.). Photo)

1969 (15 Oct). Christmas. T **238** and similar multicoloured designs. P 13½.
444 5c. Type **238**............................... 20 10
a. Magenta (robe) omitted............ £1800
b. Yellow omitted £1800
445 25c. "Tree of Life", Christ in Crib and Christmas Star (abstract) .... 1·00 2·00

(Des from drawings by J. Santry. Recess, background litho)

1969 (22 Oct). Famous Australians (2nd series). Prime Ministers. T **240** and similar vert designs each black on pale green. P 15×14.

446	5c. Type **240**	30	20
	a. Booklet pane. Five stamps plus one printed label	1·40	
447	5c. Alfred Deakin	30	20
	a. Booklet pane. Five stamps plus one printed label	1·40	
448	5c. J. C. Watson	30	20
	a. Booklet pane. Five stamps plus one printed label	1·40	
449	5c. G. H. Reid	30	20
	a. Booklet pane. Five stamps plus one printed label	1·40	
446/49	Set of 4	1·10	70

Nos. 446/9 were only issued in $1 booklets, Nos. SB45/a, with the outer edges of the pane imperforate so all stamps have one or two adjacent sides imperforate.

244 Capt. Ross Smith's Vickers Vimy, 1919
247 Symbolic Track and Diesel Locomotive

(Des E. Thake. Photo)

1969 (12 Nov). 50th Anniv of First England–Australia Flight. T **244** and similar horiz designs. P 13½.

450	5c. olive-green, pale blue, black and red	15	15
	a. Strip of 3. Nos. 450/2	1·50	2·00
451	5c. black, red and olive-green	15	15
452	5c. olive-green, black, pale blue and red	15	15
450/52	Set of 3	1·50	40

Designs:—No. 450, Type **244**; No. 451, Lt. H. Fysh and Lt. P. McGinness on 1919 survey with Ford Model T runabout; No. 452, Capt. Wrigley and Sgt. Murphy in Royal Aircraft Factory B.E.2E taking off to meet the Smiths.

The three designs appear *se-tenant*, both horizontally and vertically, throughout the sheet.

(Des B. Sadgrove. Photo)

1970 (11 Feb). Sydney–Perth Standard Gauge Railway Link. P 13½.

453	**247**	5c. multicoloured	15	10

248 Australian Pavilion, Osaka
251 Australian Flag

(Des J. Copeland (5c.), A. Leydin (20c.). Photo)

1970 (16 Mar). World Fair, Osaka. T **248** and similar horiz design. P 13½.

454	5c. multicoloured	15	10
455	20c. orange-red and black	35	65

Design:—20c. "Southern Cross" and "from the Country of the South with warm feelings" (message).

(Des P.O. Artists (5c.), J. Mason (30c.). Photo)

1970 (31 Mar). Royal Visit. T **251** and similar horiz design. P 13½.

456	5c. black and deep ochre	35	15
457	30c. multicoloured	1·10	2·75

Design:—5c. Queen Elizabeth II and Prince Philip.

252 Lucerne Plant, Bull and Sun
253 Captain Cook and HMS *Endeavour*

5c. (No. 459). Red mark on sail at left (Top pane. R. 5/1)

(Des R. Ingpen. Photo)

1970 (13 Apr). 11th International Grasslands Congress, Queensland. P 13½.

458	**252**	5c. multicoloured	10	80

(Des R. Ingpen and "Team" (T. Kenealy, A. Leydin, J. R. Smith). Photo)

1970 (20 Apr). Bicentenary of Captain Cook's Discovery of Australia's East Coast. T **253** and similar multicoloured designs. P 13½.

459	5c. Type **253**	30	10

---

	a. Strip of 5. Nos. 459/63	1·40	1·50
	aa. Black omitted	£16000	
	b. Red mark on sail	3·00	
460	5c. Sextant and HMS *Endeavour*	30	10
461	5c. Landing in Botany Bay	30	10
462	5c. Charting and exploring	30	10
463	5c. Claiming possession	30	10
464	30c. Captain Cook, HMS *Endeavour*, sextant, aborigines and kangaroo (63 × 30 mm)	1·00	2·50
459/64	Set of 6	2·25	2·75
MS465	157×129 mm. Nos. 459/64. Imperf	5·00	5·00

The 5c. stamps were issued horizontally *se-tenant* within the sheet, to form a composite design in the order listed.

Several used single 5c. stamps are also known with the black omitted.

50,000 miniature sheets were made available by the Post Office to the organisers of the Australian National Philatelic Exhibition which overprinted them in the white margin at each side of the 30c. stamp with "Souvenir Sheet AUSTRALIAN NATIONAL PHILATELIC EXHIBITION" at left and "ANPEX 1970 SYDNEY 27 APRIL–1 MAY" at right in light red-brown and they were also serially numbered. These were put on sale at the exhibition on the basis of one sheet to each visitor paying 30c. for admission. Although still valid for postage, since the stamps themselves had not been defaced, these sheets were not sold at post offices.

Subsequently further supplies were purchased and similarly overprinted and numbered by a private firm without the authority of the Post Office and ANPEX took successful legal action to stop their further sale to the public. This firm also had the unoverprinted sheets rouletted in colour between the stamps whilst further supplies of the normal sheets were overprinted with reproductions of old coins and others with an inscription commemorating the opening of Melbourne Airport on 1st July 1970, but all these are private productions. Further private productions have been reported.

259 Sturt's Desert Rose

AUSTRALIA   AUSTRALIA
I.   II.

Two types of 2c.

I. "AUSTRALIA" thin: "2c" thin; flower name lightly printed.
II. Redrawn. "AUSTRALIA" thicker; "2c" much more heavily printed; flower name thicker and bolder.

(Des Note Ptg Branch. Photo)

1970–75. Coil Stamps. Vert designs as T **259**. Multicoloured. White fluorescent paper (10c.). Perf 15×imperf.

465a	2c. Type **259** (I) (1.10.71)	40	30
	ab. White fluorescent paper	40	
	b. Type II (white fluorescent paper)	1·50	1·25
	ba. Yellow omitted	£2000	
	bb. Grey omitted	£2250	
466	4c. Type **259** (27.4.70)	85	2·25
467	5c. Golden Wattle (27.4.70)	20	10
	aa. Yellow omitted	£2250	
	a. White fluorescent paper	20	
468	6c. Type **259** (28.9.70)	1·25	1·00
	a. Green (leaves) omitted	£3000	
468b	7c. Sturt's Desert Pea (1.10.71)	40	70
	ba. Black (berries, "7c." and inscr) omitted	£2000	
	bb. Buff (shadows on flowers) omitted	£225	
	bc. Buff and green (leaves) omitted	80·00	
	bd. White fluorescent paper (10.73)	40	
468d	6c. As 7c. (15.1.75)	60	2·00
465a/8d	Set of 6	3·25	5·50

Nos. 465a/8d have horizontal coil perforations described after No. 191.

One used example of No. 468 is known with the magenta omitted. Examples of No. 468bb also show the green colour displaced downwards.

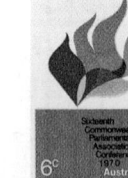

264 Snowy Mountains Scheme
265 Rising Flames

7c. Broken pylon leg (Left pane. R. 7/4).

(Des L. Mason (7c.), R. Ingpen (8c., 9c.), B. Sadgrove (10c.). Photo)

1970 (31 Aug). National Development (1st series). T **264** and similar horiz designs. Multicoloured. P 13½.

469	7c. Type **264**	20	1·75
	a. Broken pylon leg	8·00	
470	8c. Ord River Scheme	10	20
	a. Red omitted	£4250	
471	9c. Bauxite to aluminium	15	20
472	10c. Oil and Natural Gas	30	10
469/72	Set of 4	65	2·00

(Des G. Hamori, Photo)

1970 (2 Oct). 16th Commonwealth Parliamentary Association Conference, Canberra. P 13½.

473	**265**	6c. multicoloured	10	10

266 Milk Analysis and Dairy Herd
267 The Nativity

(Des R. Honisett. Photo)

1970 (7 Oct). 18th International Dairy Congress, Sydney. P 13½.

474	**266**	6c. multicoloured	10	10

(Des W. Beasley. Photo)

1970 (14 Oct). Christmas. P 13½.

475	**267**	6c. multicoloured	10	10
		a. Yellow omitted	£2250	

268 UN "Plant" and Dove of Peace
269 Boeing 707 and Avro 504

(Des Monad Design and Visual Graphics. Photo)

1970 (19 Oct). 25th Anniv of United Nations. P 13½.

476	**268**	6c. multicoloured	15	10

(Des G. Hamori. Photo)

1970 (2 Nov). 50th Anniv of QANTAS Airline. T **269** and similar horiz design. Multicoloured. P 13½.

477	6c. Type **269**	30	10
478	30c. Avro 504 and Boeing 707	70	2·25

270 The Duigan Brothers (Pioneer Aviators)

(Des A. Cook (No. 480), T. Adams (No. 482), Note Ptg Branch (others). Recess (background litho))

1970 (16 Nov). Famous Australians (3rd series). T **270** and similar vert designs. P 15×14.

479	6c. blue	35	20
	a. Booklet pane. Five stamps plus one printed label	1·60	
480	6c. black/*cinnamon*	35	20
	a. Booklet pane. Five stamps plus one printed label	1·60	
481	6c. purple/*pale pink*	35	20
	a. Booklet pane. Five stamps plus one printed label	1·60	
482	6c. brown-lake/*flesh*	35	20
	a. Booklet pane. Five stamps plus one printed label	1·60	
479/82	Set of 4	1·25	75

Designs:—No. 479 Type **270**; No. 480 Lachlan Macquarie (Governor of N.S.W.); No. 481 Adam Lindsay Gordon (poet); No. 482 E.J. Eyre (explorer).

Nos. 479/82 were only issued in 60c. or $1.20 booklets, Nos. SB46/8a, with the outer edges of the pane imperforate so all stamps have one or two adjacent sides imperforate.

STAMP BOOKLETS

Illustrations of booklet covers are reduced to ½ size, *unless otherwise stated.*

All booklets from 1913 to 1949 were stapled.

1913 (17 Jan). Red on pink cover, 75×60 mm as New South Wales Type B **2** (SB1) or blue on pink cover as New South Wales Type B **1** and picture of State G.P.O. on back, 150×175 mm (SB2).

SB1	2s. booklet containing 12×½d. and 18×1d. (Nos. 1/2) in blocks of 6	£2250
SB2	£1 booklet containing 240×1d. (No. 2) in blocks of 30	£18000

B 1 (Illustration reduced. Actual size 80×60 mm)

1914 (6 Oct)–**18**. Red on pink cover, 75×60 mm as Type B **1** (Nos. SB2a/3), black on red cover, 80×60 mm (No. SB4) or blue on pink cover as New South Wales Type B **1** and picture of State GPO on back, 150×175 mm (No. SB5).

SB2a	2s. booklet containing 12×½d. and 18×1d. (Nos. 1, 21c) in blocks of 6	£4000
SB3	2s. booklet containing 12×½d. and 18×1d. (Nos. 20, 21c) in blocks of 6 (1915)	£3500
SB4	2s. booklet containing 24×1d. (No. 21c) in blocks of 6 (10.5.17)	£3500
	a. Black on green cover	£4000
	b. Red on green cover	£3750
SB5	£1 booklet containing 240×1d. (No. 21c) in blocks of 30	£17000
	a. Back cover without G.P.O. picture (1918)	£19000

Records show that a £1 booklet containing one hundred and twenty 2d. stamps was issued in very limited quantities during 1914. No examples are known to have survived.

B **1a** (Illustration reduced. Actual size 80×60 mm)

COMMONWEALTH OF AUSTRALIA.

— 160 —

THREE-HALFPENNY STAMPS.

VALUE, ONE POUND.

ISSUED
BY THE
POSTMASTER-GENERAL.

B **1b** (Illustration reduced. Actual size 165×120 mm)

1919 (Jan–Apr). Black on pink, 80×60 mm, as Type B **1a** (Nos. SB6/7), black on green, 80×60 mm (Nos. SB8/9b) or black on green, 165×120 mm as Type B **1b** (Nos. 9c/d) covers.

SB6	2s.3d. booklet containing eighteen 1½d. (No. 58) in blocks of 6	£3000
	a. Black on green cover	£3000
SB7	2s.3d. booklet containing 18×1½d. (No. 51) in blocks of 6	£3000
	a. Black on green cover	£3000
SB8	2s.3d. booklet containing 18×1½d. (No. 59) in blocks of 6 (4.19)	£3000
	a. Black on pink cover	£3000
SB9	2s.3d. booklet containing 18×1½d. (No. 52) in blocks of 6 (4.19)	£3000
	a. Black on pink cover	£3000
	b. Black on blue cover	£3000
SB9c	£1 booklet containing 160×1½d. (No. 51) in blocks of 20	£19000
SB9d	£1 booklet containing 160×1½d. (No. 52) in blocks of 20 (Apr)	£17000

COMMONWEALTH OF AUSTRALIA

120
TWOPENNY STAMPS
VALUE ONE POUND

ISSUED
BY THE
POSTMASTER-GENERAL

SPECIAL NOTE.—The rate on letters to America is 3d. per half ounce or fraction of half ounce

B **1c** (Illustration reduced. Actual size 157×90 mm)

1920 (Dec)–**22**. Black on blue, 80×60 mm (Nos. SB10, SB12), black on white, 157×90 mm, as Type B **1c** (No. SB11) or black on brown (No. SB14) covers.

SB10	2s. booklet containing 12×2d. (No. 62) in blocks of 6	£3500
	a. Black on pink cover	£3500
	b. Black on orange cover (3.22)	£4000
SB11	2s. booklet containing 12×2d. (No. 63) in blocks of 6 (3.22)	£4250
	a. Black on orange cover (7.22)	£3750
	b. Black on pink cover	£3500
	c. Brown on buff cover	£3750
	d. Brown on pink cover	£3750
SB12	£1 booklet containing 120×2d. (No. 62) in blocks of 15 (1.21)	£18000
	a. Black on pink cover	£18000
SB13	£1 booklet containing 90×2d. and 15×4d. (Nos. 63, 65) in blocks of 15 (3.22)	£18000
SB14	£1 booklet containing 120×2d. (No. 63) in blocks of 15 (8.22)	£17000

COMMONWEALTH OF AUSTRALIA

≈ 160 ≈
*THREE HALFPENNY
STAMPS*

VALUE, ONE POUND

ISSUED BY THE
POSTMASTER-GENERAL

SPECIAL NOTE. THE RATE ON LETTERS TO AMERICA IS 3D. FOR THE FIRST OUNCE AND 1½D FOR EACH ADDITIONAL OUNCE

B **1d** (Illustration reduced. Actual size 155×90 mm)

1923 (Oct)–**24**. Black on rose, 80×60 mm (No. SB15), or green on pale green, 80×60 mm (No. SB16) or green on pale green, 155×90 mm, as Type B **1d** (Nos. 17/18) covers.

SB15	2s.3d. booklet containing 18×1½d. (No. 61) in blocks of 6	£3000
	a. Black on pale green cover	£3000
	b. Green on pale green cover	£2500
SB16	2s.3d. booklet containing 18×1½d. (No. 77) in blocks of 6 (5.24)	£2250
SB17	£1 booklet containing 160×1½d. (No. 61) in blocks of 20 (3.24)	£15000
SB18	£1 booklet containing 160×1½d. (No. 77) in blocks of 20 (5.24)	£15000

1927 (Jan–June). Green on pale green covers, 82×57 mm (Nos. SB19/20) or 150×100 mm (No. SB21).

SB19	2s.3d. booklet containing 18×1½d. (No. 87) in blocks of 6	£1400
SB20	2s.3d. booklet containing eighteen 1½d. (No. 96) in blocks of 6	£1400
SB21	£1 booklet containing 160× 1½d. (No. 96) in blocks of 20 (6.27)	£13000

B **1e** (Illustration reduced. Actual size 115×75 mm)

1927 (9 May). Opening of Parliament House, Canberra. Green on pale green cover 115×75 mm, as Type B **1e** with picture of HMS *Renown* on back (2s.).

SB22	2s. booklet containing 16×1½d. (No. 105) in blocks of 8	90·00

Examples of a 10s. booklet containing 80×1½d. (No. 105) are known without a front cover and with the back cover blank. There is no record that this was an official issue.

1928 (Nov). Green on pale green cover, 83×58 mm.

SB23	2s.3d. booklet containing 18×1½d. (No. 96a or 96w) in blocks of 6	£450

B **1f** (Illustration reduced. Actual size 85×60 mm)

B **1g** (Illustration reduced. Actual size 85×60 mm)

1930 (July)–**35**. Air. Black on blue cover, 85×60 mm, as Type B **1f** (No. SB24) or B **1g** (No. SB24a).

SB24	3s. booklet containing 24×3d. (No. 115a) in blocks of 4 plus two panes of air mail labels	£850
	a. Black on pale green cover (5.35)	£1700

1930 (9 Sep)–**33**. Green on pale green covers inscr "USE THE AIR MAIL" on the back (2s), 83×58 mm (Nos. 25/ab), 160×115 mm (Nos. 26/a).

SB25	2s. booklet containing 12×2d. (No. 99a or 99aw) in blocks of 6	£425
SB25a	2s. booklet containing 12×2d. (No. 127 or 127w) in blocks of 6 (1.32)	£425
	ab. Cover with parcel rates on back (1933)	£550
SB26	£1 booklet containing 120×2d. (No. 99) in blocks of 20	£11000
SB26a	£1 booklet containing 120×2d. (No. 99a) in blocks of 20	£11000

1934 (June). Black on cream cover inscr "Address your mail fully..." on front, 81×55 mm.

SB26b	2s. booklet containing 12×2d. (No. 127 or 127w) in blocks of 6	£650

1935–38. Black on green cover with Commonwealth Savings Bank advertisement on front inscr "WHEREVER THERE IS A MONEY ORDER POST OFFICE" 78×55 mm.

SB26c	2s. booklet containing 12×2d. (No. 127 or 127w) in blocks of 6	£475
	ca. Front cover inscr "IN MOST MONEY ORDER OFFICES" (1936)	£450
	cb. Ditto with waxed interleaves (1938)	£550

1938 (Dec). Black on green cover as No. SB26c but 70×46 mm. Postal rates on interleaves.

SB27	2s. booklet containing 12×2d. (No. 184 or 184w) in blocks of 6	£500
	a. With waxed interleaves. Postal rates on back cover	£850
	b. Black on buff cover	£700

1942 (Aug). Black on buff cover, size 73×47½ mm. Postal rates on interleaves.

SB28	2s.6d. booklet containing 12×2½d. (No. 206 or 206w) in blocks of 6, upright within the booklet	£110
	a. With waxed interleaves. Postal rates on back cover	£250

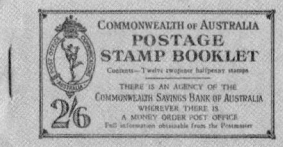

B **1h**

1949 (Sept). Black on buff cover, size 79½×42½ mm as Type B **1h**.

SB29	2s.6d. booklet containing 12×2½d. (No. 206) in blocks of 6, sideways within the booklet	80·00

B **1i**

1952 (24 June). Vermilion and deep blue on green cover as Type B **1i**.

SB30	3s.6d. booklet containing 12×3½d. (No. 247) in blocks of 6	17·00
	a. With waxed interleaves	90·00

B **1j**

1953 (8 July)–**56**. Vermilion and deep blue on green cover, 80×41 mm, as Type B **1j**.

SB31	3s.6d. booklet containing 12×3½d. (No. 263) in blocks of 6	11·00
	a. With waxed interleaves	30·00
SB32	3s.6d. booklet containing 12×3½d. (No. 262a) in blocks of 6 (7.56)	23·00
	a. With waxed interleaves	85·00

B **2**

1957 (13 Mar)–**59**. Vermilion and deep blue on green cover, 80×41 mm, as Type B **2**.

SB33	4s. booklet containing two panes of 6×4d. (No. 282ab)	16·00
	a. With waxed interleaves	55·00
SB34	4s. booklet containing two panes of 6×4d. (No. 313ab) (18.3.59)	38·00
	a. With waxed interleaves	90·00

B 3

1960 (23 Mar). Vermilion and deep blue on green cover, 80×41 mm, as Type B **3**.
SB35   5s. booklet containing two panes of
     6×5d. (No. 314d) .... 22·00
    a. With waxed interleaves....................... 50·00

B 4

1962 (1 July)–**65**. Rose and emerald on green cover, 80×41 mm, as Type B **4**.
SB36   5s. booklet containing two panes of
     6×5d. (No. 314d) .... 50·00
    a. With waxed interleaves (1963) £130
SB37   5s. booklet containing two panes of 6×5d.
     (No. 354a) (17.6.64) .... 50·00
    a. With waxed interleaves....................... £120
SB38   5s. booklet containing two panes of 6×5d.
     (No. 354cb) (13.7.65) .... 60·00
    a. With waxed interleaves....................... £150

B 5

1966 (14 Feb). Greenish blue and black on yellow-olive cover, 80×41 mm, as Type B **5**.
SB39   60c. booklet containing three panes of 5×4c.
     and 1 label (No. 385a) .... 45·00
    a. With waxed interleaves....................... £130

1967 (29 Sept). Greenish blue and black on yellow-olive covers, 80×41 mm, as Type B **5**.

(a) Surcharged covers
SB40   50c. booklet containing two panes of 5×5c. on
     4c. and 1 label (No. 414a) .... 12·00
SB41 $1 booklet containing four panes of 5×5c. on
     4c. and 1 label (No. 414a) .... 4·50
    a. Normal cover as Type B **5** .... 5·00
    ab. With waxed interleaves..................... 65·00

(b) Normal covers
SB42   50c. booklet containing two panes of 5×5c. and
     1 label (No. 386ca) .... 17·00
SB43 $1 booklet containing four panes of 5×5c. and
     1 label (No. 386ca) .... 23·00
    a. With waxed interleaves....................... 75·00

Booklets SB40/1ab were intended as provisional issues until supplies of the new 5c. became available in booklet form, but in the event these were put on sale on the same date.

B 6

1968 (6 Nov). Famous Australians (1st series). Black, red, white and blue cover, 80×41 mm, as Type B **6**.
SB44 $1 booklet containing four panes of 5×5c. and
     1 label (Nos. 432a, 433a, 434a, 435a) .... 4·00
    a. With waxed interleaves....................... 55·00

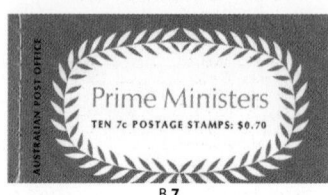

B 7

1969 (22 Oct). Famous Australians (2nd series). Olive-green, gold and black cover, 80×41 mm, as Type B **7**.
SB45 $1 booklet containing four panes of 5×5c. and
     1 label (Nos. 446a, 447a, 448a, 449a) .... 5·00
    a. With waxed interleaves....................... 65·00

Famous Australians

B 8

(Des B. Young. Eng S. Reading. Typo J. B. Cooke)
1970 (16 Nov). Famous Australians (3rd series). Multicoloured on white covers, 41×80 mm, as Type B **8**.
SB46   60c. booklet containing two panes of 5×6c. and
     1 label (Nos. 479a, 480a) .... 14·00
SB47   60c. booklet containing two panes of 5×6c. and
     1 label (Nos. 481a, 482a) .... 14·00
SB48 $1.20 booklet containing four panes of 5×6c. and
     1 label (Nos. 479a, 480a, 481a, 482a) ...... 7·00
    a. With waxed interleaves....................... 65·00

Military Post Booklets

Issued for the use of Australian Forces in Vietnam

MB 1

1967 (30 May–Sept). Yellow-green and black on white cover as Type MB **1**. Pane attached by selvedge.
MB1   50c. booklet containing 5c. (No. 386) in block
     of 10 .... 80·00
    a. Containing No. 386b (9.67) .... 80·00

1968 (1 Mar). Yellow-green and black on white cover as Type MB **1**. Pane attached by selvedge.
MB2   50c. booklet containing 5c. (No. 386c) in block
     of 10 .... 50·00

POSTAGE DUE STAMPS

POSTAGE DUE PRINTERS. Nos. D1/62 were typographed at the New South Wales Government Printing Office, Sydney. They were not used in Victoria.

     D 1   **D 2**   **D 3**

Type D **1** adapted from plates of New South Wales Type D **1**. No letters at foot.
1902 (1 July). Chalk-surfaced paper. Wmk Type D **2** (inverted on 1d., 3d. and 4d.).

(a) P 11½, 12

D1	D **1**	½d. emerald-green or dull green	3·50	7·00
D2		1d. emerald-green..........................	25·00	13·00
		w. Wmk upright.............................	45·00	26·00
D3		2d. emerald-green..........................	65·00	15·00
		w. Wmk inverted............................	£130	
D4		3d. emerald-green..........................	50·00	30·00
		w. Wmk upright.............................	55·00	38·00
D5		4d. emerald-green..........................	50·00	14·00
		w. Wmk upright.............................	65·00	25·00
D6		6d. emerald-green..........................	60·00	12·00
		w. Wmk inverted............................	55·00	12·00
D7		8d. emerald-green	£100	85·00
D8		5s. emerald-green or dull green	£200	75·00
D1/8 *Set of 8*			£475	£200
D1s/7s Opt "SPECIMEN" *Set of 7*			£350	

(b) P 11½, 12, compound with 11

D9	D **1**	1d. emerald-green..........................	£350	£160
		w. Wmk upright.............................	£375	£150
D10		2d. emerald-green..........................	£500	£180
		w. Wmk inverted............................	£600	£225

(c) P 11

D12	D **1**	1d. emerald-green (*wmk upright*)	£2500	£900

Stamps may be found showing portions of the marginal watermark "NEW SOUTH WALES POSTAGE".

1902 (July)–**04**. Type D **3** (with space at foot filled in). Chalk-surfaced paper. Wmk Type D **2** (inverted on 3d., 4d., 6d., 8d. and 5s.).

(a) P 11½, 12

D13	D **3**	1d. emerald-green (10.02).............	£275	£130
D14		2d. emerald-green (3.03)	—	£170
D15		3d. emerald-green (3.03)..............	£350	£100
D17		5d. emerald-green..........................	70·00	19·00
D18		10d. emerald-green or dull green......	95·00	23·00
D19		1s. emerald-green..........................	80·00	19·00
D20		2s. emerald-green..........................	£130	18·00

(b) P 11½, 12, compound with 11

D22	D **3**	½d. emerald-green or dull green (3.04)	21·00	17·00
D23		1d. emerald-green or dull green (10.02)..............................	20·00	4·50
		w. Wmk inverted............................	20·00	4·50
D24		2d. emerald-green or dull green (3.03)..............................	50·00	3·00
		w. Wmk inverted............................	50·00	3·00
D25		3d. emerald-green or dull green (3.03)..............................	90·00	17·00
		w. Wmk upright.............................	£120	32·00
D26		4d. emerald-green or dull green (5.03)..............................	75·00	22·00
		w. Wmk upright.............................	75·00	24·00
D27		5d. emerald-green..........................	65·00	23·00
D28		6d. emerald-green (3.04)...............	75·00	11·00
D29		8d. emerald-green (3.04)...............	£140	60·00
D30		10d. emerald-green (3.04).............	£120	19·00
D31		1s. emerald-green..........................	£110	28·00
D32		2s. emerald-green..........................	£190	27·00
D33		5s. emerald-green or dull green (5.03)..............................	£450	24·00

(c) P 11

D34	D **3**	½d. emerald-green or dull green (wmk inverted) (3.04)	£550	£300
D35		1d. emerald-green or dull green (10.02)..............................	£160	32·00
		w. Wmk inverted............................	£200	42·00
D36		2d. emerald-green (3.03)...............	£225	30·00
		w. Wmk inverted............................	£225	30·00
D37		3d. emerald-green or dull green (3.03)..............................	£150	60·00
		w. Wmk upright.............................	£160	60·00
D38		4d. emerald-green or dull green (5.03)..............................	£250	70·00
		w. Wmk upright.............................	£250	70·00
D39		5d. emerald-green..........................	£375	55·00
D40		6d. emerald-green (3.04)...............	£110	16·00
D41		1s. emerald-green..........................	£475	38·00
D42		5s. emerald-green (5.03)...............	£1600	£275
D43		10s. dull green (10.03).................	£2000	£1800
D44		20s. dull green (10.03).................	£4250	£2250
D13/44 *Set of 14*			£6500	£4000
D13s/44s Opt "SPECIMEN" *Set of 14*			£1100	

The 10s. and 20s. values were only issued in New South Wales.
The used prices quoted for Nos. D43/4 are for cancelled to order examples.

     D 4   **D 6**

1906 (Jan)–**08**. Chalk-surfaced paper. Wmk Type D **4**.

(a) P 11½, 12, compound with 11

D45	D **3**	½d. green (1.07)	16·00	18·00
		w. Wmk inverted............................	16·00	18·00
D46		1d. green....................................	28·00	5·00
		w. Wmk inverted............................	28·00	6·00
D47		2d. green....................................	75·00	9·00
		w. Wmk inverted............................	75·00	9·00
D48		3d. green (7.08)............................	£700	£325
D49		4d. green (4.07)............................	70·00	23·00
		w. Wmk inverted............................	70·00	23·00
D50		6d. green (3.08)............................	£300	25·00
		w. Wmk inverted............................	£300	25·00
D45/50 *Set of 6*			£1000	£350

(b) P 11

D51	D **3**	1d. dull green...............................	£3000	£1100
		aw. Wmk inverted..........................	£3000	£1100
D51b		2d. dull green...............................	†	£4750
D52		4d. dull green (4.07)......................	£5500	£3250

No. D51b is only known pen-cancelled.
Shades exist.

1907 (July–Sept). Chalk-surfaced paper. Wmk Type w **11** (Crown over double lined A) (inverted on ½d.). P 11½×11.

D53	D **3**	½d. green...................................	35·00	75·00
		w. Wmk upright.............................	55·00	£100
D54		1d. dull green (8.07)......................	£140	75·00
		w. Wmk inverted............................	£140	75·00
D55		2d. dull green (9.07)......................	£275	£160
		w. Wmk inverted............................	£300	£180
D56		4d. dull green (9.07)......................	£275	£150
		w. Wmk inverted............................	£275	£160
		y. Wmk inverted and reversed.........	£700	
D57		6d. dull green (9.07)......................	£325	£225
		w. Wmk inverted............................	—	£375
D53/7 *Set of 5*			£900	£600

1908 (Sept)–**09**. Stroke after figure of value. Chalk-surfaced paper. Wmk Type D **4** (inverted on 10s.).

(a) P 11½×11

D58	D **6**	1s. dull green (1909).....................	£130	17·00
D59		5s. dull green...............................	£250	48·00

(b) P 11

D60	D **6**	2s. dull green (1909).....................	£1000	£17000
D61		10s. dull green (1909)...................	£2500	£26000
D62		20s. dull green (1909)...................	£7000	£50000

Nos. D61/2 were only issued in New South Wales. The used prices quoted for Nos. D60/2 are for examples with verified postal cancellations from the period of issue.

D 7

Die I   Die II

1d.

Die I   Die II

2d.

(Typo J. B. Cooke, Melbourne)

1909 (1 July)–**10**. Wmk Crown over A, Type w **11**.

(a) P 12×12½ (comb)*

D63	D **7**	½d. rosine and yellow-green (8.09)	16·00	32·00
D64		1d. rosine and yellow-green (I)	14·00	4·00
		b. Die II (7.10)	35·00	2·00
D65		2d. rosine and yellow-green (I)	38·00	6·00
		a. Die II (8.10)	48·00	2·00
		aw. Wmk inverted	†	£5500
D66		3d. rosine and yellow-green (9.09)	40·00	19·00
D67		4d. rosine and yellow-green (8.09)	42·00	5·00
D68		6d. rosine and yellow-green (8.09)	27·00	2·75
D69		1s. rosine and yellow-green (8.09)	30·00	3·25
D70		2s. rosine and yellow-green (8.09)	70·00	10·00
D71		5s. rosine and yellow-green (10.09)	90·00	12·00
D72		10s. rosine and yellow-green (11.09)	£250	£150
D73		£1 rosine and yellow-green (11.09)	£500	£300
D63/73 *Set of 11*			£950	£475

(b) P 11 (line)

D74	D **7**	1d. rose and yellow-green (II)	£3750	£1400
D74a		2d. rose and yellow-green (II)	£24000	£15000
D75		6d. rose and yellow-green	£35000	£24000

*Nos. D64/b and D65a are also known perf 12½ (line).
Only one unused example, without gum, and another pen-cancelled are known of No. D74a.
The 1d. of this printing (No. D74) is distinguishable from No. D78 by the colours, the green being very yellow and the rose having less of a carmine tone. The paper is thicker and slightly toned, that of No D78 being pure white; the gum is thick and yellowish, No. D78 having thin white gum.
All later issues of the 1d. and 2d. are Die II.

(Typo J.B. Cooke (later ptgs by T. S. Harrison))

1913 (July)–**23**. Thin paper. White gum. W w **11**.

(a) P 12½ (line)

D76	D **7**	½d. scarlet and pale yellow-green (7.13)	32·00	27·00
		w. Wmk inverted	£110	£110

(b) P 11

D77	D **7**	½d. rosine and bright apple-green (10.14)	20·00	20·00
		a. Wmk sideways	6·50	13·00
D78		1d. rosine and bright apple-green (8.14)	22·00	3·75
		a. Wmk sideways	28·00	2·50
		w. Wmk inverted	£100	75·00

(c) P 14

D79	D **7**	½d. rosine and bright apple-green (11.14)	£225	£275
		a. Carmine and apple-green (Harrison) (1919)	9·00	17·00
D80		1d. rosine and bright apple-green (9.14)	£170	16·00
		a. Scarlet and pale yellow-green (2.18)	20·00	15·00
		aw. Wmk inverted	†	£1400
		b. Carmine and apple-green (Harrison) (1919)	18·00	3·75
D81		2d. scarlet and pale yellow-green (11.17)	17·00	11·00
		a. Carmine and apple-green (Harrison) (11.18)	29·00	6·00
D82		3d. rosine and apple-green (5.16)	85·00	32·00
		a. Wmk sideways	£7500	£4500
D83		4d. carmine and apple-green (Harrison) (4.21)	£110	55·00
		b. Carmine and pale yellow-green	£110	50·00
		ba. Wmk sideways	£1000	£475
D85		1s. scarlet and pale yellow-green (6.23)	25·00	15·00
D86		10s. scarlet and pale yellow-green (5.21)	£1400	
D87		£1 scarlet and pale yellow-green (5.21)	£950	£2750
D79a/87 *Set of 8*			£2250	

(d) Perf 14 compound with 11

D88	D **7**	1d. carmine and apple-green	£12000	

(Typo T. S. Harrison (to Feb 1926), A. J. Mullett (to June 1927) and J. Ash (thereafter))

1922 (Feb)–**30**. W **6**.

(a) P 14

D91	D **7**	½d. carmine and yellow-green (17.5.23)	3·50	8·00
D92		1d. carmine and yellow-green	4·00	1·00
		w. Wmk inverted	£6000	
D93		1½d. carmine and yellow-green (3.25)	1·50	9·00
		w. Wmk inverted	†	£6000
D94		2d. carmine and yellow-green	3·50	2·25
D95		3d. carmine and yellow-green	9·50	5·00
D96		4d. carmine and yellow-green	35·00	23·00
D97		6d. carmine and yellow-green (8.22)	26·00	16·00

(b) P 11

D98	D **7**	4d. carmine and yellow-green (22.9.30)	17·00	8·00
D91/98 *Set of 8*			90·00	65·00

All values perforated 14 were printed by Harrison and all but the 1d. by Mullett and Ash. The 4d. perforated 11 was produced by J. Ash. There is a wide variation of shades in this issue.

(Typo J. Ash)

1931 (Oct)–**36**. W **15**.

(a) P 14

D100	D **7**	1d. carmine and yellow-green (10.31)	7·00	11·00
		a. Imperf between (horiz pair)	†	£20000
D102		2d. carmine and yellow-green (19.10.31)	7·00	11·00

(b) P 11

D105	D **7**	½d. carmine and yellow-green (4.34)	12·00	19·00
D106		1d. carmine and yellow-green (21.11.32)	7·50	3·25
D107		2d. carmine and yellow-green (1933)	16·00	2·00
D108		3d. carmine and yellow-green (5.36)	75·00	70·00
D109		4d. carmine and yellow-green (23.5.34)	18·00	4·75
D110		6d. carmine and yellow-green (4.36)	£375	£325
D111		1s. carmine and yellow-green (8.34)	55·00	35·00
D105/11 *Set of 7*			£475	£400

D 8   **D 9**

A.   B.   C.

Type A. Solid rectangle inside "D" (ptgs of ½d., 1d., 2d., 4d. and 6d. from 1909 to 1945).
Type B. Shaded area inside "D" (ptgs of 3d. from 1909 to 1945).
Type C. Solid segment of circle inside "D" (ptgs of all values below 1s. from 1946).

D.   E.

Type D. Six lines of shading above numeral and four below (ptgs of 1s. from 1909 to 1945).
Type E. Larger "1" with only three background lines above; hyphen more upright (ptgs of 1s. from 1946 to 1953)

(Frame recess. Value typo J. Ash (to 1940, then W. C. G. McCracken))

1938 (July–Sept). W **15**. P 14½×14.

D112	D **8**	½d. carmine and green (A) (9.38)	3·00	6·00
D113		1d. carmine and green (A)	17·00	2·00
D114		2d. carmine and green (A)	25·00	3·25
D115		3d. carmine and green (B) (8.38)	65·00	26·00
D116		4d. carmine and green (A) (8.38)	9·00	1·00
D117		6d. carmine and green (A) (8.38)	75·00	48·00
D118		1s. carmine and green (D) (8.38)	40·00	12·00
D112/18 *Set of 7*			£200	85·00
Shades exist.				

1946–57. Redrawn as Type C and E (1s). W **15**. P 14½×14.

D119	D **9**	½d. carmine and green (9.56)	1·50	4·25
D120		1d. carmine and green (17.6.46)	1·25	80
		w. Wmk inverted	£6500	
D121		2d. carmine and green (9.46)	6·00	1·25
		w. Wmk inverted	†	£7000
D122		3d. carmine and green (6.8.46)	6·50	1·25
D123		4d. carmine and green (30.7.52)	8·50	2·50
D124		5d. carmine and green (16.12.48)	21·00	12·00
D125		6d. carmine and green (19.8.47)	13·00	24·00
D126		7d. carmine and green (26.8.53)	2·75	1·50
D127		8d. carmine and green (24.4.57)	4·50	15·00
D128		1s. carmine and green (9.47)	17·00	1·75
D119/28 *Set of 10*			70·00	38·00
There are many shades in this issue.				

D 10

1953 (26 Aug)–**59**. W **15**. P 14½×14.

D129		1s. carmine and yellow-green (17.2.54)	8·50	1·25
		a. Carmine and deep green	12·00	5·50
D130		2s. carmine and yellow-green	14·00	5·00
		a. Carmine and deep green	£400	£130
D131		5s. carmine and green	14·00	1·50
		a. Carmine and deep green (6.59)	12·00	1·00
D129/31 *Set of 3*			32·00	7·00
D129a/31a *Set of 3*			£400	£130

A new die was introduced for No. D131a. This differs from the original in having a distinct gap between the two arms of the "5". On No. D131 these two features are joined.

Two Dies of ½d.:
Die I. Six dots in base of "2"
Die II. Seven dots in base of "2"

I.   II.

Two Dies of 1d. to 10d.:
Die I. Numeral, "D" and stop, generally unoutlined.
Die II. Clear white line separates numeral, etc. from background.

1958–60. No wmk. P 14½×14.

D132		½d. carmine and dp green (I) (27.2.58)	4·75	4·75
		a. Die II (6.59)	2·50	1·25
D133		1d. carmine and dp green (I) (25.2.58)	2·50	3·00
		a. Die II (6.59)	2·50	75
D134		3d. carmine and dp green (II) (25.5.60)	2·00	3·00
D135		4d. carmine and dp green (I) (27.2.58)	9·50	7·00
		a. Die II (6.59)	2·75	4·00
D136		5d. carmine and dp green (I) (27.2.58)	11·00	21·00
		a. Die II (6.59)	60·00	70·00
D137		6d. carmine and dp green (II) (25.5.60)	2·50	2·00
D138		8d. carmine and dp green (II) (25.2.58)	6·00	28·00
D139		10d. carmine and dp green (II) (9.12.59)	3·50	1·75
D140		1s. carmine and deep green (6.5.58)	5·50	1·50
		a. Deep carmine and dp green (6.59)	6·50	1·00
D141		2s. dp carmine and dp green (8.3.60)	12·00	2·00
D132a/41 *Set of 10*			45·00	60·00

Nos. D140a and D141. Value tablets are re-engraved and have thicker and sharper printed lines than before.
The use of Postage Due stamps ceased on 13 January 1963.

OFFICIAL STAMPS

From 1902 the departments of the Commonwealth government were issued with stamps of the various Australian States perforated "OS" to denote official use. These were replaced in 1913 by Commonwealth of Australia issues with similar perforated initials as listed below.

During the same period the administrations of the Australian States used their own stamps and those of the Commonwealth perforated with other initials for the same purpose. These States issues are outside the scope of this catalogue.

Most shades listed under the postage issues also exist perforated "OS". Only those which are worth more than the basic colours are included below.

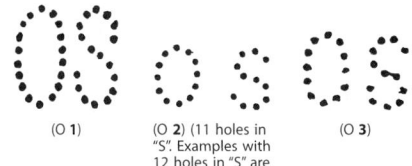

(O **1**)   (O **2**) (11 holes in   (O **3**)
            "S". Examples with
            12 holes in "S" are
            N.S.W. state issues)

1913 (Jan–Apr). Nos. 1/16 punctured as Type O **1**. W **2**. P 12.

O1	**1**	½d. green (Die I)	27·00	19·00
		w. Wmk inverted	†	£150
O2		1d. red (Die I)	17·00	4·75
		cw. Wmk inverted	£150	25·00
		d. Die II	42·00	15·00
		da. Wmk sideways	†	£1100
		dw. Wmk inverted	£150	25·00
O3		2d. grey (Die I)	55·00	22·00
O4		2½d. indigo (Die I)	£325	£140
O5		3d. olive (Die I)	£200	50·00
		ca. In pair with Die II	£1800	
		dw. Wmk inverted	£375	£150
		e. Die II	£700	£250
		ew. Wmk inverted	£1700	£450
O6		4d. orange (Die II)	£275	22·00
		a. Orange-yellow	£650	£180
O7		5d. chestnut (Die II)	£250	50·00
O8		6d. ultramarine (Die II)	£200	20·00
		a. Wmk inverted	£1800	£750
O9		9d. violet (Die II)	£300	65·00
		w. Wmk inverted	†	£10000

O10		1s. emerald (Die II)	350	28·00
		w. Wmk inverted	£2500	£1000
O11		2s. brown (Die II)	£600	£160
		a. Double print	†	£5000
O12		5s. grey and yellow	£1500	£700
O13		10s. grey and pink	£5500	£3250
O14		£1 brown and ultramarine	£10000	£7500
O15		£2 black and rose	£48000	£40000

1914. Nos. 1/16 punctured as Type O **2**. W **2**. P 12.

O16	**1**	½d. green (Die I)	26·00	10·00
			†	£180
O17		1d. red (Die I)	50·00	27·00
		d. Die II	42·00	3·75
		e. Die IIA	50·00	3·75
O18		2d. grey (Die I)	90·00	4·50
		w. Wmk inverted	£190	55·00
O19		2½d. indigo (Die II)	£375	£160
O20		3d. olive (Die II)	£180	16·00
		dw. Wmk inverted	£425	£100
		e. Die II	£750	£275
		ew. Wmk inverted	£1400	£500
O21		4d. orange (Die II)	£425	95·00
		a. Orange-yellow	£900	£300
O22		5d. chestnut (Die II)	£325	60·00
O23		6d. ultramarine (Die II)	£225	14·00
		w. Wmk inverted	†	£1000
O24		9d. violet (Die II)	£300	50·00
O25		1s. emerald (Die II)	£300	22·00
O26		2s. brown (Die II)	£950	£140
O27		5s. grey and yellow		
O28		10s. grey and pink	£11000	£8000
O29		£1 brown and ultramarine	£16000	£11000
O30		£2 black and rose	£42000	

1915. Nos. 24 and 26/30 punctured as Type O **2**. W **5**. P 12.

O31	**1**	2d. grey (Die II)	£200	12·00
O33		6d. ultramarine (Die II)	£425	21·00
		b. Die IIA	£7000	£3500
O34		9d. violet (Die II)	£900	£110
O35		1s. blue-green (Die II)	£900	£130
O36		2s. brown (Die II)	£1800	£160
O37		5s. grey and yellow	£1900	£225
		a. Yellow portion doubly printed	†	£4750
		w. Wmk inverted	£2000	£325

1914–21. Nos. 20/3 punctured as Type O **2**. W **5**. P 14¼×14 (comb).

O38	**5a**	½d. bright green	23·00	2·75
		a. Perf 14¼ (line)	†	£3500
		w. Wmk inverted	30·00	9·50
O39		1d. carmine-red (I) (No. 21c)	15·00	1·00
		gw. Wmk inverted	30·00	6·00
		h. Die II	£550	65·00
O41		4d. orange	85·00	3·50
		a. Yellow-orange	95·00	7·50
		b. Pale orange-yellow	£190	18·00
		c. Lemon-yellow	£650	95·00
		w. Wmk inverted	£130	28·00
O42		5d. brown (P 14¼ (line))	85·00	4·50
		aw. Wmk inverted	£1300	£700
		b. Printed on the gummed side (wmk inverted)	£9000	
		c. Perf 14¼×14 (comb)	85·00	4·00
		cw. Wmk inverted	£1200	£700

1915–28. Nos. 35/45 punctured as Type O **2**. W **6**. P 12.

O43	**1**	2d. grey (Die I)	60·00	13·00
		bw. Wmk inverted	£170	80·00
		d. Die IIA	85·00	26·00
		da. Printed double	†	£3750
O44		2½d. deep blue (Die II)	95·00	32·00
		w. Wmk inverted	—	£140
O45		3d. yellow-olive (Die I)	65·00	5·50
		cw. Wmk inverted	£140	75·00
		d. Die II	£350	£120
		dw. Wmk inverted	£650	£325
		e. Die IIB	80·00	29·00
		ew. Wmk inverted	£225	£110
O46		6d. ultramarine (Die II)	80·00	10·00
		d. Die IIA	£5500	£1700
		d. Die IIB	£150	45·00
		dw. Wmk inverted	£300	£150
O47		9d. violet (Die II)	95·00	32·00
		b. Die IIB	£110	38·00
		bw. Wmk inverted	†	£140
O48		1s. blue-green (Die II)	65·00	3·50
		aw. Wmk inverted	£1200	£800
		b. Die IIB	55·00	6·00
O49		2s. brown (Die II)	£475	17·00
		b. Red-brown (aniline)	£2250	£750
		w. Wmk inverted	£4000	£850
O50		5s. grey and yellow	£700	70·00
		w. Wmk inverted	£2000	£1300
O51		10s. grey and pink	£1200	75·00
O52		£1 chocolate and dull blue	£8500	£5500
		ab. Wmk sideways. Chestnut and bright blue	£160000	
		aw. Wmk inverted	£9500	£6500
O53		£2 black and rose	£5000	£2500

1916–20. Nos. 47/f and 5d. as No. 23 punctured as Type O **2**. Rough paper. W **5**. P 14.

O54	**5a**	1d. scarlet (Die I)	48·00	7·00
		a. Deep red	48·00	7·00
		b. Rose-red	48·00	7·00
		c. Rosine	£130	22·00
		dw. Wmk inverted	£100	21·00
		e. Die II. Rose-red	£475	38·00
		f. Die II. Rosine	£750	£120
		gw. Die II. Wmk inverted	£1000	£150
O60		5d. bright chestnut (P 14¼ (line)) (9.20)	£5000	£180

All examples of the 5d. on this paper were perforated "OS".

1918–20. Nos. 48/52 punctured as Type O **2**. W **6a**. P 14.

O61	**5a**	½d. green	30·00	2·00
		w. Wmk inverted	50·00	20·00

O62		1d. carmine-pink (I)	†	£2000
O63		1d. carmine (I)	£200	75·00
O64		1½d. black-brown	20·00	13·00
		a. Very thin paper	£150	65·00
		w. Wmk inverted	£110	55·00
O65		1½d. red-brown	42·00	2·50
		w. Wmk inverted	£130	60·00
O61/5		Set of 4	£250	80·00

1918–23. Nos. 56/9 and 61/6 punctured as Type O **2**. W **5**. P 14.

O66	**5a**	½d. orange	17·00	10·00
O67		1d. violet	50·00	15·00
		w. Wmk inverted	†	£25000
O68		1½d. black-brown	50·00	7·00
		w. Wmk inverted	£110	35·00
O69		1½d. deep red-brown	50·00	2·50
		aw. Wmk inverted	£130	60·00
O69b		1½d. bright red-brown	—	£120
O70		1½d. green	42·00	3·75
O71		2d. brown-orange	16·00	3·50
		w. Wmk inverted	£325	85·00
O72		2d. bright rose-scarlet	42·00	4·00
		w. Wmk inverted	£1300	£200
O73		4d. violet	90·00	13·00
O74		4d. ultramarine	80·00	11·00
O75		1s.4d. pale blue	£110	14·00
		b. Deep turquoise	£4250	£3500
O66/75		Set of 10	£450	75·00

1923–24. Nos. 73/5 punctured as Type O **2**. W **6**. P 12.

O76	**1**	6d. chestnut (Die IIB)	45·00	2·50
O77		2s. maroon (Die II)	£180	12·00
O78		£1 grey (Die IIB)	£1800	£1000
O76/8		Set of 3	£1900	£1000

1924. Nos. 76/84 punctured as Type O **2**. P 14.

(a) W **5**

O79	**5a**	1d. sage-green	24·00	5·50
O80		1½d. scarlet	15·00	1·00
		w. Wmk inverted	£130	30·00
		wa. Printed on the gummed side	£375	
O81		2d. red-brown	24·00	18·00
		a. Bright red-brown	80·00	38·00
O82		3d. dull ultramarine	55·00	6·00
O83		4d. olive-yellow	60·00	6·00
O84		4½d. violet	£275	17·00
		w. Wmk inverted	†	£15000

(b) W **6a**

O85	**5a**	1d. sage-green	42·00	32·00

(c) No wmk

O86	**5a**	1d. sage-green	85·00	85·00
O87		1½d. scarlet	90·00	85·00
O79/87		Set of 9	£550	£225

1926–30. Nos. 85/104 punctured as Type O **2**. W **7**.

(a) P 14

O88	**5a**	½d. orange	£400	£160
O89		1d. sage-green	12·00	3·25
O90		1½d. scarlet	42·00	4·75
		a. Golden scarlet	50·00	8·50
		w. Wmk inverted	60·00	12·00
O92		2d. red-brown (Die I)	£250	45·00
O93		3d. dull ultramarine	£100	13·00
		w. Wmk inverted	£120	90·00
O94		4d. yellow-olive	£275	50·00
O95		4½d. violet	£275	40·00
O96		1s.4d. pale greenish blue	£750	£250
O88/96		Set of 8	£1800	£475

(b) P 13½×12½

O97	**5a**	½d. orange	12·00	1·25
O98		1d. sage-green (Die I)	7·00	1·75
		b. Die II	£160	£160
O100		1½d. scarlet	19·00	2·50
		a. Golden scarlet	19·00	5·00
		w. Wmk inverted	21·00	5·00
O102		1½d. red-brown	38·00	5·00
O103		2d. red-brown (Die II)	55·00	16·00
O104		2d. golden scarlet (Die II)	24·00	4·50
		a. Die III	29·00	6·50
		aw. Wmk inverted	38·00	12·00
O106		3d. dull ultramarine (Die I)	50·00	6·50
		b. Die II. Deep ultramarine	23·00	1·50
		bw. Wmk inverted	£16000	£13000
O108		4d. yellow-olive	40·00	3·75
O109		4½d. violet	£250	£170
O110		5d. orange-brown (Die II)	90·00	7·00
O111		1s.4d. turquoise	£500	38·00
O97/111		Set of 11	£850	£225

1927 (9 May). Opening of Parliament House, Canberra. No. 105 punctured as Type O **3**.

O112	**8**	1½d. brownish lake	24·00	9·50

1928 (29 Oct). National Stamp Exhibition, Melbourne. No. 106 punctured as Type O **2**.

O113		3d. blue	13·00	9·00

1929–30. Nos. 107/14 punctured as Type O **2**. W **7**. P 12.

O114	**1**	6d. chestnut (Die IIB)	45·00	7·00
O115		9d. violet (Die IIB)	95·00	7·00
O116		1s. blue-green (Die IIB)	25·00	10·00
O117		2s. maroon (Die II)	£200	8·50
O118		5s. grey and yellow	£750	45·00
O118a		10s. grey and pink	£13000	£13000
O118b		£2 black and rose	£30000	£28000

1929 (20 May). Air. No. 115 punctured as Type O **3**.

O119	**9**	3d. green	32·00	12·00

1929 (28 Sept). Centenary of Western Australia. No. 116 punctured as Type O **3**.

O120	**10**	1½d. dull scarlet	26·00	22·00

1930 (2 June). Centenary of Exploration of River Murray by Capt. Sturt. Nos. 117/18 punctured as Type O **2**.

O121	**11**	1½d. scarlet	23·00	8·50
O122		3d. blue	30·00	8·50

O S

(O **4**)

1931 (4 May). Nos. 121/2 optd with Type O **4**.

O123	**13**	2d. rose-red	85·00	27·00
O124		3d. blue	£275	27·00

For No. 139 overprinted with Type O **4**, see No. 139a.

1932 (Feb)–**33**. Optd as Type O **4**.

(a) W **7**

(i) P 13½×12½

O125	**5a**	2d. golden scarlet (Die III)	26·00	1·50
		a. Opt inverted	†	£70000
		w. Wmk inverted	£4500	£3000
O126		4d. yellow-olive (3.32)	25·00	3·00

(ii) P 12

O127	**1**	6d. chestnut (3.32)	55·00	55·00

(b) W **15**

(i) P 13½×12½

O128	**5a**	½d. orange (11.7.32)	11·00	1·50
		a. Opt inverted	£28000	£20000
O129		1d. green (3.32)	4·25	45
		w. Wmk inverted	£1300	£800
		x. Wmk reversed	£2250	£900
O130		2d. golden scarlet (Die III)	24·00	55
		a. Opt inverted	†	£45000
O131		3d. ultramarine (Die II) (2.33)	7·50	4·75
O132		5d. orange-brown (7.32)	50·00	27·00

(ii) P 12

O133	**1**	6d. chestnut (9.32)	42·00	20·00
		a. Opt inverted	†	£70000

(c) Recess. No wmk. P 11

O134	**18**	2d. scarlet (3.32)	11·00	2·00
O135		3d. blue (3.32)	18·00	5·00
O136	**17**	1s. green (4.32)	50·00	30·00

No. O128a and probably the other inverted overprints were caused by the insertion of a stamp upside down into sheets repaired before surcharging.

Issue of overprinted official stamps ceased in February 1933 and remaining supplies were withdrawn from sale on 1 October 1935, Thereafter mail from the federal administration was carried free.

BRITISH COMMONWEALTH OCCUPATION FORCE (JAPAN)

Nos. J1/7 were used by the Australian forces occupying Japan after the Second World War. Initially their military post offices supplied unoverprinted Australian stamps, but it was decided to introduce the overprinted issue to prevent currency speculation.

B.C.O.F. JAPAN 1946

(1)

B.C.O.F. JAPAN 1946

(2)

O.F.   O.F.

1946   AN   AN

Wrong fount "6" (left pane R. 9/4)

Normal

Narrow "N" (right pane R. 1/8)

1946 (12 Oct)–**47**. Stamps of Australia optd as T **1** (1d., 3d.,) or T **2** (others) at Hiroshima Printing Co, Japan.

J1	**27**	½d. orange (No. 179)	9·00	14·00
		a. Wrong fount "6"	£190	£200
		b. Narrow "N"	£200	£225
		c. Stop after "JAPAN" (right pane R.5/5)	£300	£325
J2	**46**	1d. brown-purple (No. 203)	8·00	8·50
		a. Blue-black overprint	60·00	£110
J3	**31**	3d. purple-brown (No. 187)	3·00	5·50
		a. Opt double	£1200	£1300
J4	**34**	6d. purple-brown (No. 190a) (8.5.47)	29·00	23·00
		a. Wrong fount "6"	£300	£325
		b. Stop after "JAPAN" (right pane R. 5/5)	£425	£425
		c. Narrow "N"	£300	£325
J5	**36**	1s. grey-green (No. 192) (8.5.47)	20·00	25·00
		a. Wrong fount "6"	£350	£425
		b. Stop after "JAPAN" (right pane R. 5/5)	£550	£600
		c. Narrow "N"	£350	£425
		d. Roller flaw	£225	£250
J6	**1**	2s. maroon (No. 212) (8.5.47)	45·00	65·00
J7	**38**	5s. claret (No. 176) (8.5.47)	£140	£180
		a. Thin rough paper (No. 176a)	£110	£180
J1/7a		Set of 7	£190	£275

The ½d., 1d. and 3d. values were first issued on 12 October 1946, and withdrawn two days later, but were re-issued together with the other values on 8 May 1947.

The following values with T **2** in the colours given were from proof sheets which, however, were used for postage: ½d. (red) 1d. (red or black) and 3d. (gold, red or black). (Prices for black opts £100, each, and for red or gold from £325 each, all un).

The use of B.C.O.F. stamps ceased on 12 February 1949.

AUSTRALIAN ANTARCTIC TERRITORY

For use at the Antarctic bases of Casey (opened early 1969: used Wilkes postmark until early 1970), Davis (closed from 1965 until early 1969), Heard Island (seasonal occupation only), Macquarie Island, Mawson and Wilkes (closed January 1969). Stamps of Australia were used from the bases before 27 March 1957 and remained valid for use there after the introduction of Australian Antarctic Territory issues.

The following are also valid for use in Australia, where they are put on sale for a limited period when first issued.

DATES OF ISSUE. The dates given refer to release dates in Australia. Local release dates are usually later and where known they are given in footnotes.

1 1954 Expedition at Vestfold Hills and Map

(Des. T. Lawrence: adapted by artist of the Printing Branch. Recess)
1957 (27 Mar). P 14½.
1   1   2s. ultramarine .... 1·00   65

Issued Macquarie Island 11.12.57, Davis 6.2.58, Mawson 18.2.58, Wilkes 1.2.59.

2 Members of Shackleton Expedition at South Magnetic Pole, 1909   **3** Weazel and Team

4 Dog team and iceberg   **5** Map of Antarctica and Emperor Penguins

1959 (16 Dec). T **2/4**. T **3**. Recess; new values surch typo (5d., 8d.). P 14½ (5d.), 14½×14 (8d.) or 14×14½ (others).
2   **2**   5d. on 4d. black and sepia 60   15
3   **3**   8d. on 7d. black and indigo .... 1·75   2·25
4   **3**   1s. deep green .... 2·25   2·00
5   **5**   2s.3d. green .... 7·00   3·00
2/5 *Set of 4* .... 10·50   6·75

Issued Macquarie Island 26.12.59, Davis 30.1.60, Mawson 10.2.60, Wilkes 13.2.60.

6   **6**

7 Sir Douglas Mawson (Expedition leader)

Normal   Weak entry

Weak entry at left (R. 1/5 and 2/5)

1961 (5 July). Recess. P 14½.
6   **6**   5d. deep blue .... 1·60   20
            a. Weak entry .... 32·00

Issued Macquarie Island 6.12.61, Wilkes 10.1.62, Davis 20.1.62, Mawson 30.1.62.

1961 (18 Oct). 50th Anniv of 1911–14 Australasian Antarctic Expedition. Recess. P 14½.
7   **7**   5d. myrtle-green 55   20

Issued Macquarie Island 6.12.61, Wilkes 10.1.62, Davis 20.1.62, Mawson 30.1.62.

(New Currency. 100 cents = 1 Australian dollar)

8 Aurora and Camera Dome   **9** Bell 47G Trooper Helicopter

(Des J. Mason. Photo)
1966 (28 Sept)–**68**. Vert designs as T **8** (1c. to 15c.) or horiz as T **9** (20c. to $1). Multicoloured. Helecon paper (5c.). P 13½.
8   1c. Type **8** (*shades*) 70   30
9   2c. Emperor Penguins (*shades*) .... 3·00   80
10   4c. Ship and iceberg .... 1·00   90
11   5c. Banding Elephant-seals (25.9.68) ...... 2·25   1·75
12   7c. Measuring snow strata 80   80
13   10c. Wind gauges .... 1·25   1·10
14   15c. Weather balloon .... 5·00   2·00
15   20c. Type **9** .... 9·50   5·00
16   25c. Radio operator .... 1·75   2·25
17   50c. Ice compression tests .... 2·50   4·00
18    $1 Parahelion ("mock sun") .... 19·00   12·00
8/18 *Set of 11* .... 42·00   25·00

Nos. 13/15 and 17 have parts of the designs printed in bright orange fluorescent ink.

Nos. 8/10 and 12/18 placed on sale locally at Macquarie Island on 11.12.66, Wilkes 9.2.67 and Mawson 16.2.67.

No. 11 issued Macquarie Island 4.12.68, Mawson 13.1.69, Wilkes/Casey 9.2.69 and Davis 20.2.69.

CHRISTMAS ISLAND

Formerly a part of the Straits Settlements and then of the Colony of Singapore, Christmas Island was occupied by the Japanese from 31 March, 1942, until September, 1945. It reverted to Singapore after liberation, but subsequently became an Australian territory on 15 October 1958.

Stamps of the STRAITS SETTLEMENTS were used on Christmas Island from 1901 until 1942. Following liberation issues of MALAYA (BRITISH MILITARY ADMINISTRATION) and then SINGAPORE were used from 1946 to 1958.

(Currency. 100 cents = 1 Malayan dollar)

1 Queen Elizabeth II

(Des G. Lissenden. Recess with name and value typo in black. Note Printing Branch, Commonwealth Bank, Melbourne)
1958 (15 Oct). No wmk. P 14½.
1   **1**   2c. yellow-orange 55   80
2   4c. brown 60   30
3   5c. deep mauve 60   50
4   6c. grey-blue .... 1·00   30
5   8c. black-brown .... 1·75   50
6   10c. violet .... 1·00   30
7   12c. carmine .... 1·75   1·75
8   20c. blue .... 1·00   1·75
9   50c. yellow-green .... 2·00   1·75
10        $1 deep bluish green .... 2·00   1·75
1/10 *Set of 10* .... 11·00   8·75

PRINTERS. Nos. 11/32 were printed by the Note Printing Branch, Reserve Bank of Australia, Melbourne. Nos. 33/82 were printed in photogravure by Harrison and Sons, Ltd, London.

2 Map   **3** Moonflower

 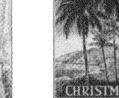

4 Robber crab   **5** Island scene

6 Phosphate train   **7** Raising phosphate

8 Flying Fish Cove   **9** Loading cantilever

10 Christmas Island Frigate Bird   **11** White-tailed Tropic Bird

(Des G. Lissenden (2, 8c.), P. Morriss (4, 5, 10, 20c.), B. Stewart (others). Recess)
1963 (28 Aug). T **2/11**. P 14½ × 14 ($1) or 14½ (others).
11   **2**   2c. orange .... 1·25   35
12   **3**   4c. red-brown 50   15
13   **4**   5c. purple 50   20
14   **5**   6c. indigo 30   35
15   **6**   8c. black .... 2·50   35
16   **7**   10c. violet 40   15
17   **8**   12c. brown-red 40   25
18   **9**   20c. blue .... 1·00   20
19   **10**   50c. green .... 1·00   20
20   **11** $1 yellow .... 1·75   35
11/20 *Set of 10* .... 8·50   2·25

I Thick lettering

II Thinner lettering

1965. 50th Anniversary of Gallipoli Landing. As T **184** of Australia but slightly larger (22×34½ *mm*) and colour changed. Photo. P 13½.
21   10c. sepia, black and emerald (I) (14.4).... 30   1·75
        a. *Black-brown, black and light emerald* (II) (24.4) .... 2·50   2·75

(New Currency. 100 cents = 1 Australian dollar)

12 Golden-striped Grouper   **13** Angel (mosaic)

(Des G. Hamori. Photo)
1968 (6 May)–**70**. Fish. T **12** and similar horiz designs. Multicoloured. P 13½.
22   1c. Type **12** 45   45
23   2c. Moorish Idol 60   20
24   3c. Long-nosed Butterflyfish 60   30
25   4c. Pink-tailed Triggerfish 60   20
        a. Deep blue (face value) omitted.... £3000
26   5c. Regal Angelfish 60   20
27   9c. White-cheeked Surgeonfish 60   40
28   10c. Lionfish 60   20
28a   15c. Saddle Butterflyfish (14.12.70) ...... 3·00   2·50
29   20c. Ornate Butterflyfish .... 1·50   55
29a   30c. Giant Ghost Pipefish (14.12.70) ...... 3·00   2·50
30   50c. Clown Surgeonfish .... 2·75   2·75
31    $1 Meyer's Butterflyfish .... 2·75   2·75
22/31 *Set of 12* .... 15·00   11·50

(Des G. Hamori. Photo)
1969 (10 Nov). Christmas. P 13½.
32   **13**   5c. red, deep blue and gold 20   30

14 *The Ansidei Madonna* (Raphael)

(Des Harrison)
1970 (26 Oct). Christmas. Paintings. T **14** and similar vert design. Multicoloured. P 14×14½.
33   3c. Type **14** 20   15
34   5c. *The Virgin and Child, St. John the Baptist and an Angel* (Morando) 20   15

COCOS (KEELING) ISLANDS

The Cocos (Keeling) Islands, which had been settled by the Clunies Ross family in the 1820s, were annexed by Great Britain in 1857. In 1878 the group was attached to Ceylon, but was transferred to the Straits Settlements on 7 February 1886. During the Second World War the islands were under British military control exercised from Ceylon. At the end of hostilities administration from Singapore was continued until the islands were transferred to Australia on 23 November 1955.

The stamps of the STRAITS SETTLEMENTS were used by a postal agency operating on Cocos (Keeling) Islands from 1 April 1933 until 1 March 1937. The postal agency reopened on 2 September 1952 and used the stamps of SINGAPORE until the islands were transferred to Australia in 1955. From 1955 until 1963 stamps of AUSTRALIA were in use.
Nos. 1/31 were also valid for use in Australia.

PRINTERS. All the following stamps to No. 31 were printed by the Note Printing Branch, Reserve Bank of Australia, Melbourne.

1 Copra Industry

2 Super Constellation

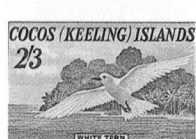

3 Map of islands

4 Palms

5 Dukong (sail boat)

6 White Tern

(Des K. McKay and E. Jones (5d.), E. Jones (others). Eng E. Jones. Recess)

1963 (11 June). T **1**/**6**. P 14½×14 (5d., 2s.3d.) or 14½ (others).

1	3d. chocolate	1·50	1·50
2	5d. ultramarine	2·25	80
3	8d. scarlet	1·00	1·75
4	1s. green	1·00	75
5	2s. deep purple	8·00	2·00
6	2s.3d. deep green	9·00	1·75
1/6 Set of 6		20·00	7·50

I Thick lettering

II Thinner lettering

1965 (14 Apr). 50th Anniv of Gallipoli Landing. As T **184** of Australia, but slightly larger (22×34½ *mm*) and colour changed. Photo. P 13½.

7	5d. sepia, black and light emerald (I)	60	45
	a. Black-brown, black and light emerald (II)	3·00	2·25

No. 7a comes from a second printing, using a new black cylinder, which was available from the end of April.

With the introduction of decimal currency on 14 February 1966, Australian stamps were used in Cocos Islands, until the appearance of the new definitives on 9 July 1969.

(New Currency. 100 cents = 1 Australian dollar)

7 Reef Clam
(*Tridacna derasa*)

8 Great Frigate Bird

(Des L. Annois (1c. to 6c.), P. Jones (10c. to $1). Photo)

1969 (9 July). Decimal Currency. T **8** or designs as T **7**. Multicoloured. P 13½.

8	1c. Lajonkaines Turbo shell (*Turbo lajonkairii*) (vert)	30	60
9	2c. Elongate or Small Giant Clam (*Tridacna maxima*) (vert)	60	80
10	3c. Type **7**	40	20
11	4c. Floral Blenny (fish)	30	50
	a. Salmon-pink omitted	£2750	
12	5c. *Porites cocosensis* (coral)	35	30
13	6c. Atrisignis Flyingfish	60	75
14	10c. Buff-banded Rail	60	70
15	15c. Java Sparrow	60	30
16	20c. Red-tailed Tropic Bird	60	30
17	30c. Sooty Tern	60	30
18	50c. Eastern Reef Heron (vert)	60	30
19	$1 Type **8**	1·25	75
8/19 Set of 12		6·00	5·25

NEW GUINEA

Stamps of Germany and later of GERMAN NEW GUINEA were used in New Guinea from 1888 until 1914.
During the interim period between the "G.R.I." surcharges and the "N.W. PACIFIC ISLANDS" overprints, stamps of AUSTRALIA perforated "OS" were utilised.

PRICES FOR STAMPS ON COVER

Nos. 1/30	from × 3
Nos. 31/2	—
Nos. 33/49	from × 3
Nos. 50/9	from × 2
Nos. 60/2	—
Nos. 63/4	from × 2
Nos. 64c/q	—
Nos. 65/81	from × 5
Nos. 83/5	—
Nos. 86/97	from × 5
No. 99	—
Nos. 100/16	from × 4
Nos. 117/18	—
Nos. 119/24	from × 4
Nos. 125/203	from × 2
Nos. 204/5	—
Nos. 206/11	from × 8
Nos. 212/25	from × 2
Nos. O1/54	from × 8

AUSTRALIAN OCCUPATION
Stamps of German New Guinea surcharged

G.R.I. G.R.I.
2d.   1s.   1
(1)   (2)   (3)

SETTINGS. The "G.R.I" issues of New Guinea were surcharged on a small hand press which could only accommodate one horizontal row of stamps at a time. In addition to complete sheets the surcharges were also applied to multiples and individual stamps which were first lightly affixed to plain paper backing sheets. Such backing sheets could contain a mixture of denominations, some of which required different surcharges.
Specialists recognise twelve settings of the low value surcharges (1d. to 8d.):

Setting 1	(Nos. 1/4, 7/11) shows the bottom of the "R" 6 mm from the top of the "d"
Setting 2	(Nos. 16/19, 22/6) shows the bottom of the "R" 5 mm from the top of the "d"
Setting 3	was used for the Official stamps (Nos. O1/2)
Setting 4, Setting 5	which included the 2½d. value for the first time, and showed individual stamps with either 6 mm or 5 mm spacing.

These five settings were for rows of ten stamps, but the remaining seven, used on odd stamps handed in for surcharging, were applied as strips of five stamps. One has, so far, not been reconstructed, but of the remainder three show the 6 mm spacing, two the 5 mm and one both.
On the shilling values the surcharges were applied as horizontal rows of four and the various settings divide into two groups, one with 3½ mm to 4½ mm between the bottom of the "R" and the top of numeral, and the second with 5½ mm between the "R" and numeral. The first group includes the very rare initial setting on which the space is 4 to 4½ mm.

G.R.I, G.R.I. G.R.I.
2d.   1d.   1s.
"1" for "I"   Short "1"   Large "S"
(Setting 1) (Setting 1) (Setting 1)

1914 (17 Oct)–**15**. Stamps of 1901 surch.

(a) As T 1. "G.R.I." and value 6 mm apart

1	1d. on 3pf. brown	£750	£850
	a. "I" for "1"	£2000	£2250
	b. Short "1"	£2000	£2250
	c. "1" with straight top serif (Setting 6)	£2000	
	d. "I" for "1" (Setting 12)	£3500	
2	1d. on 5pf. green	85·00	£110
	a. "I" for "1"	£350	£425
	b. Short "1"	£350	£425
	c. "1" with straight top serif (Settings 6 and 9)	£475	£550
3	2d. on 10pf. carmine	90·00	£120
	a. "1" for "I"	£400	£500
4	2d. on 20pf. ultramarine	90·00	£110
	a. "1" for "I"	£375	£425

	e. Surch double, one "G.R.I." albino	£5500	
	f. Surch inverted	£16000	
5	2½d. on 10pf. carmine (27.2.15)	95·00	£200
	a. Fraction bar omitted (Setting 9)	£3500	£3500
6	2½d. on 20pf. ultramarine (27.2.15)	£110	£225
	a. Fraction bar omitted (Setting 9)	†	£9500
7	3d. on 25pf. black and red/*yellow*	£375	£450
	a. "1" for "I"	£1100	£1300
8	3d. on 30pf. black and orange/*buff*	£475	£500
	a. "1" for "I"	£1300	£1500
	e. Surch double	£15000	£15000
9	4d. on 40pf. black and carmine	£475	£500
	a. "1" for "I"	£1500	
	e. Surch double	£4000	£4750
	f. Surch inverted	£16000	
10	5d. on 50pf. black and purple/*buff*	£850	£1000
	a. "1" for "I"	£2250	£3000
	e. Surch double	£16000	
	f. Surch inverted		
11	8d. on 80pf. black and carmine/*rose*	£1000	£1500
	a. "1" for "I"	£3250	£4250
	d. No stop after "d"	£4250	
	e. Error. Surch "G.R.I. 4d."	£15000	

(b) As T 2. "G.R.I." and value 3½ to 4 mm apart

12	1s. on 1m. carmine	£3500	£4250
	a. Large "s"	£13000	£13000
13	2s. on 2m. blue	£3250	£4000
	a. Large "s"	£12000	£14000
	c. Error. Surch "G.R.I. 5s."	£45000	
	d. Error. Surch "G.R.I. 2d." corrected by handstamped "S"	£50000	
14	3s. on 3m. violet-black	£5500	£7000
	a. Large "s"	£16000	
	b. No stop after "I" (Setting 3)	£13000	£13000
15	5s. on 5m. carmine and black	£14000	£16000
	a. Large "s"	£29000	
	b. No stop after "I" (Setting 3)	£18000	£20000
	c. Error. Surch "G.R.I. 1s."	£85000	

G.R.I.   G.R.I.
3d.   5d.
Thick "3"   Thin "5"
(Setting 2) (Setting 2)

1914 (16 Dec)–**15**. Stamps of 1901 surch.

(a) As T 1. "G.R.I." and value 5 mm apart

16	1d. on 3pf. brown	£100	£110
	a. "I" for "1" (Setting 11)	£750	
	b. Short "1"	£325	
	c. "1" with straight top serif (Settings 2 and 6)	£150	£180
	e. Surch double	£1500	£1800
	f. Surch double, one inverted	£8000	
	g. Surch inverted	£6000	
	h. Error. Surch "G.R.I. 4d."	£17000	
17	1d. on 5pf. green	35·00	50·00
	b. Short "1" (Setting 2)	£130	£190
	c. "1" with straight top serif (Setting 2)	50·00	80·00
	e. "d" inverted	†	£3750
	f. "1d" inverted	†	£11000
	g. "G.R.I." without stops or spaces	£11000	
	ga. "G.R.I." without stops, but with normal spaces	—	£11000
	h. "G.I.R." instead of "G.R.I."	£13000	£14000
	i. Surch double	£5000	£6000
18	2d. on 10pf. carmine	50·00	60·00
	e. No stop after "d" (Setting 2)	£180	£250
	f. Stop before, instead of after, "G" (Settings 4 and 5)	£11000	
	g. Surch double	£16000	£16000
	h. Surch double, one inverted	—	£13000
	i. In vert pair with No. 20	£20000	
	j. In horiz pair with No. 20	£28000	
	k. Error. Surch ".GR.I. 1d."	£12000	£12000
	l. Error. Surch "G.I.R. 3d."	£13000	
19	2d. on 20pf. ultramarine	50·00	70·00
	e. No stop after "d" (Setting 2)	£130	£190
	f. No stop after "I" (Setting 11)	£1500	
	g. "R" inverted (Settings 4 and 5)	—	£9000
	h. Surch double	£3500	£5000
	i. Surch double, one inverted	£4750	£7000
	j. Surch inverted	£10000	
	k. Albino surch (in horiz pair with normal)	£23000	
	l. In vert pair with No. 21	£18000	£21000
	m. Error. Surch "G.R.I. 1d."	£13000	£15000
20	2½d. on 10pf. carmine (27.2.15)	£225	£350
21	2½d. on 20pf. ultramarine (27.2.15)	£2000	£2500
	a. Error. Surch "G.R.I. 3d." (in vert pair with normal)	£40000	
22	3d. on 25pf. black and red/*yellow*	£190	£250
	e. Thick "3"	£600	£750
	f. Surch double	£11000	£13000
	g. Surch inverted	£11000	£13000
	h. Surch omitted (in horiz pair with normal)	£13000	
	i. Error. Surch "G.R.I. 1d."	£20000	
23	3d. on 30pf. black and orange/*buff*	£170	£225
	e. No stop after "d"	£800	
	f. Thick "3"	£550	
	g. Surch double	£4000	£4500
	h. Surch double, one inverted	£4500	£5500
	i. Surch double, both inverted	£13000	£14000
	j. Surch inverted	£10000	
	k. Albino surch	£12000	
	l. Surch omitted (in vert pair with normal)	£13000	
	m. Error. Surch "G.R.I. 1d."	£12000	£15000
24	4d. on 40pf. black and carmine	£180	£275
	e. Surch double	£3500	
	f. Surch double, one inverted	£5000	
	g. Surch double, both inverted	£13000	
	h. Surch inverted	£9500	
	i. Error. Surch "G.R.I. 1d."	£9000	
	ia. Error. Surch "G.R.I. 1d." inverted	£19000	
	j. Error. Surch "G.R.I. 3d." double	£27000	
	k. No stop after "I" (Setting 11)	£3250	

25 5d. on 50pf. black and purple/*buff* £325 £400
 e. Thin "5" £1400 £3250
 f. Surch double £4500 £5500
 g. Surch double, one inverted £10000 £10000
 h. Surch double, both inverted £13000 £14000
 i. Surch inverted £10000
 j. Error. Surch "G.I.R. 3d." £22000
26 8d. on 80pf. black and carmine/*rose* £425 £600
 e. Surch double £7000 £8000
 f. Surch double, one inverted £7000 £8000
 g. Surch triple £9500 £10000
 h. Surch inverted £14000
 i. Error. Surch "G.I.R. 3d." £18000

*(b) As T **2**. "G.R.I." and value 5½ mm apart*
27 1s. on 1m. carmine £5000 £8000
 a. No stop after "I" (Setting 7) £12000
28 2s. on 2m. blue £5000 £8000
 a. No stop after "I" (Setting 7) £12000
29 3s. on 3m. violet-black £10000 £15000
 a. "G.R.I." double £45000
30 5s. on 5m. carmine and black £40000 £45000

1915 (1 Jan). Nos. 18 and 19 further surch with T **3**.
31 1d. on 2d. on 10pf. £28000 £28000
32 1d. on 2d. on 20pf. £28000 £17000

German New Guinea Registration Labels surcharged

4

4a

G.R.I.
3d.
Sans serif "G"
and different "3"

1915 (Jan). Registration Labels surch "G.R.I. 3d." in settings of five or ten and used for postage. Each black and red on buff. Inscr "(Deutsch Neuguinea)" spelt in various ways as indicated. P 14 (No. 43) or 11½ (others).

*I. With name of town in sans-serif letters as T **4***
33 **Rabaul** "(Deutsch Neuguinea)" £275 £325
 a. "G.R.I. 3d." double £5000 £6500
 b. No bracket before "Deutsch" £900 £1300
 ba. No bracket and surch double £16000
 d. "(Deutsch-Neuguinea)" £425 £550
 da. "G.R.I. 3d." double £16000 £16000
 db. No stop after "I" £900
 dc. "G.R.I. 3d" inverted £16000
 dd. No bracket before "Deutsch" £1500 £2000
 de. No bracket after "Neuguinea" £1500 £2000
34 **Deulon** "(Deutsch Neuguinea)" £26000 £28000
35 **Friedrich-Wilhelmshafen**
 "(Deutsch Neuguinea)" £250 £800
 a. No stop after "d" £450
 b. Sans-serif "G" £7500
 c. Sans-serif "G" £16000
 d. Sans-serif "G" and different "3" £14000
 e. Surch inverted .... † £16000
 f. "(Deutsch-Neuguinea)" £275 £800
 fa. No stop after "I" £475
36 **Herbertshohe** "(Deutsch
 Neuguinea)" £300 £850
 a. No stop after "d" £500
 b. No stop after "I" £900 £1800
 c. "G" omitted £8500
 d. Surch omitted (in horiz pair with normal) £18000
 e. "(Deutsch Neu-Guinea)" £500 £1000
 f. "(Deutsch-Neuguinea)" ....
37 **Kawieng** "(Deutsch-Neuguinea)" £1000
 a. No bracket after "Neuguinea" £3750
 b. "Deutsch Neu-Guinea" £325 £650
 ba. No stop after "d" £550
 bb. "G.R.I." double £8000
 bc. "3d" double £8000
 bd. No stop after "I" £8500
38 **Kieta** "(Deutsch-Neuguinea)" £450 £800
 a. No bracket before "Deutsch" £1600 £2750
 b. No stop after "d" £850
 c. Surch omitted (right hand stamp of horiz pair) £16000
 e. No stop after "I" £1300
 f. "G" omitted £8000
39 **Manus** "(Deutsch Neuguinea)" £325 £900
 a. "G.R.I. 3d." double £9000
 b. No bracket before "Deutsch" £1500 £2500
40 **Stephansort** "(Deutsch Neu-Guinea)" .... — £4500
 a. No stop after "d" .... † £8500

*II. With name of town in letters with serifs as T **4a***
41 **Friedrich Wilhelmshafen**
 "(Deutsch-Neuguinea)" £275 £750
 b. No stop after "I" £450 £1100
 c. No stop after "d" £850 £1600
 d. No bracket before "Deutsch" £1600 £2250
 e. No bracket after "Neuguinea" £1600 £2250
42 **Kawieng** "(Deutsch Neuguinea)" £250 £650
 a. No stop after "d" £475
 b. No stop after "I" ....
43 **Manus** "(Deutsch Neuguinea)" £4250 £5000
 a. No stop after "d" £8500 £8000
Examples of Nos. 33db, 36b, 38e, 41c and 43a also show the stop after "R" either very faint or missing completely.

Stamps of Marshall Islands surcharged

SETTINGS. The initial supply of Marshall Islands stamps, obtained from Nauru, was surcharged with Setting 2 (5 mm between "R" and "d") on the penny values and with the 3½ to 4 setting on the shilling stamps.
 Small quantities subsequently handed in were surcharged, often on the same backing sheet as German New Guinea values, with Settings 6, 7 or 12 (all 6 mm between "R" and "d") for the penny values and with a 5½ mm setting for the shilling stamps.

1914 (16 Dec). Stamps of 1901 surch.
*(a) As T **1**. "G.R.I." and value 5 mm apart*
50 1d. on 3pf. brown £110 £170
 c. "1" with straight top serif (Setting 2) £180 £300
 d. ".G.R.I." and "1" with straight top serif (Settings 4 and 5) .... † £14000
 e. Surch inverted £9000
51 1d. on 5pf. green .... 80·00 85·00
 c. "1" with straight top serif (Settings 2 and 11) £140 £160
 d. "I" for "1" (Setting 11) £1200
 e. "1" and "d" spaced £300 £325
 f. Surch double £3750
 g. Surch inverted £5000
52 2d. on 10pf. carmine .... 27·00 50·00
 e. No stop after "G" (Setting 2) £850
 f. Surch double £3750
 g. Surch double, one inverted £5500
 h. Surch inverted £7000
 i. Surch sideways £10000
53 2d. on 20pf. ultramarine .... 27·00 50·00
 e. No stop after "d" (Setting 2) .... 70·00 £110
 g. Surch double £4000 £5000
 h. Surch double, one inverted £10000 £10000
 i. Surch inverted £11000 £11000
54 3d. on 25pf. black and red/*yellow* £450 £550
 e. No stop after "d" (Settings 2 and 11) £850 £1100
 f. Thick "3" £1000 £1400
 g. Surch double £4250 £4750
 h. Surch double, one inverted £4750
 i. Surch inverted £13000
55 3d. on 30pf. black and orange/*buff* £475 £600
 e. No stop after "d" (Setting 2) £900 £1200
 f. Thick "3" £1100
 g. Surch inverted £9000
 h. Surch double £7000
56 4d. on 40pf. black and carmine £170 £250
 e. No stop after "d" (Setting 2) £425 £650
 f. "d" omitted (Setting 2) .... † £7000
 g. Surch double £7000 £8000
 h. Surch triple £14000
 i. Surch inverted £10000
 j. Error. Surch "G.R.I. 1d." £17000
 k. Error. Surch "G.R.I. 3d." £17000
57 5d. on 50pf. black and purple/*buff* £300 £375
 e. Thin "5" £3750
 f. "d" omitted (Setting 2) £2000
 g. Surch double £10000
 h. Surch inverted £16000
58 8d. on 80pf. black and carmine/*rose* £475 £700
 e. Surch double £10000
 f. Surch double, both inverted £13000 £14000
 g. Surch triple £16000
 h. Surch inverted £11000

*(b) As T **2**. "G.R.I." and value 3½–4 mm apart*
59 1s. on 1m. carmine £4000 £5000
 b. No stop after "I" £6000 £9000
 e. Surch double £45000
 f. Error. Additional surch "1d." £45000
60 2s. on 2m. blue £1900 £4000
 b. No stop after "I" £3500 £6000
 e. Surch double £45000
 f. Surch double, one inverted £42000 £42000
61 3s. on 3m. violet-black £6500 £9500
 b. No stop after "I" £8500
 e. Surch double £40000 £45000
62 5s. on 5m. carmine and black £14000 £13500
 e. Surch double .... † £65000

1915 (Jan). Nos. 52 and 53 further surch with T **3**.
63 1d. on 2d. on 10pf. carmine £200 £275
 a. "1" double £16000
 b. "1" inverted £19000 £19000
 c. Small "1" £650
64 1d. on 2d. on 20pf. ultramarine £4000 £2500
 a. On No. 53e £9000 £4000
 b. "1" inverted £19000
The surcharged "1" on No. 63c is just over 4 mm tall. Type 3 is 6 mm tall.

1915. Stamps of 1901 surch.
*(a) As T **1**. "G.R.I." and value 6 mm apart*
64c 1d. on 3pf. brown £3500
 cc. "1" with straight top serif (Setting 6) £4250
 cd. "I" for "1" (Setting 12) £4250
 ce. Surch inverted £16000
64d 1d. on 5pf. green £3500
 dc. "1" with straight top serif (Setting 6) £4250
 dd. "I" for "1" (Setting 12) £4250
 de. Surch inverted £16000
 df. Surch double £16000
64e 2d. on 10pf carmine £4500
 ea. Surch sideways £16000
64f 2d. on 20pf. ultramarine £4000
 fe. Surch inverted £16000
64g 2½d. on 10pf. carmine £27000
64h 2½d. on 20pf. ultramarine £40000
64i 3d. on 25pf. black and red/*yellow* £6500
64j 3d. on 30pf. black and orange/*buff* £6500
 je. Error. Surch "G.R.I. 1d." £18000
64k 4d. on 40pf. black and carmine £6500
 ke. Surch double £18000
 kf. Surch inverted £18000
64l 5d. on 50pf. black and purple/*buff* £6000
 le. Surch double £18000
64m 8d. on 80pf. black and carmine/*rose* £7500
 me. Surch inverted £18000

*(b) As T **2**. "G.R.I." and value 5½ mm apart*
64n 1s. on 1m. carmine £17000
 na. Large "s" (Setting 7) £21000
 nb. No stop after "I" (Setting 7) £21000
64o 2s. on 2m. blue £14000
 a. Large "s" (Setting 5) £19000
 b. Surch double, one inverted £55000
64p 3s. on 3m. violet-black £27000
 pa. Large "s" (Setting 5) £38000
 pb. No stop after "I" (Setting 7) £38000
 pe. Surch inverted £65000
64q 5s. on 5m. carmine and black £38000
 qa. Large "s" (Setting 5) £50000

Stamps of Australia overprinted

N. W. PACIFIC ISLANDS.	N. W. PACIFIC ISLANDS.	N. W. PACIFIC ISLANDS.
(a)	(b)	(c)

(6)

1915–16. Stamps of Australia optd in black as T **6** (a), (b) or (c).
*(i) T **5a**. W **5** of Australia. P 14¼×14 (4 Jan–15 Mar 1915)*
65 ½d. green .... 3·00 9·00
 a. Bright green .... 3·00 10·00
 aw. Wmk inverted £2250 £2500
67 1d. pale rose (Die I) (4.1) .... 7·00 6·50
 a. Dull red .... 7·00 6·50
 b. Carmine-red .... 7·00 6·50
 ba. Substituted cliché (Pl 2 rt pane R. 6/5) £1900 £1500
 bb. Dot before "1" £120 £130
 bc. "Secret mark" £120 £130
 bd. Flaw under neck £120 £130
 be. "RA" joined £120 £130
 c. Die II. Carmine-red £110 £140
 ca. Substituted cliché (Pl 2 rt pane R. 6/4) £1900 £1500
70 4d. yellow-orange .... 4·00 15·00
 a. Pale orange-yellow .... 32·00 55·00
 b. Chrome-yellow £250 £275
 c. Line through "FOUR PENCE" (Pl 2 rt pane R. 2/6) (all shades) .... from £425 £700
72 5d. brown (P 14¼ (line)) .... 3·00 17·00
*(ii) T **1**. W **2** of Australia. P 12 (4 Jan 1915–March 1916)*
73 2d. grey (Die I) .... 20·00 65·00
74 2½d. indigo (Die II) (4.1.15) .... 2·75 16·00
76 3d. yellow-olive (Die I) .... 21·00 55·00
 a. Die II £350 £550
 ab. In pair with Die I £800 £1200
 c. Greenish olive £200 £275
 ca. In pair with Die I £1300
 cb. In pair with Die I £2250
78 6d. ultramarine (Die II) £110 £120
 a. Retouched "E" £7500 £8500
 w. Wmk inverted £300 £400
79 9d. violet (Die II) .... 55·00 65·00
81 1s. green (Die II) .... 60·00 70·00
83 5s. grey and yellow (Die II) (3.16) £2750 £3750
84 10s. grey and pink (Die II) (12.15) £150 £180
85 £1 brown and ultramarine (Die II) (12.15) £550 £700
*(iii) T **1**. W **5** of Australia. P 12 (Oct 1915–July 1916)*
86 2d. grey (Die I) .... 18·00 48·00
87 2½d. indigo (Die II) (7.16) £28000 £28000
88 6d. ultramarine (Die II) .... 10·00 12·00
89 9d. violet (Die II) (12.15) .... 16·00 21·00
90 1s. emerald (Die II) (12.15) .... 11·00 24·00
91 2s. brown (Die II) (12.15) £110 £130
92 5s. grey and yellow (Die II) (12.15) .... 75·00 £110
*(iv) T **1**. W **6** of Australia. P 12 (Dec 1915–1916)*
94 2d. grey (Die I) .... 6·50 32·00
96 3d. yellow-olive (Die I) .... 5·50 11·00
 a. Die II £110 £170
 ab. In pair with Die I £325
97 2s. brown (Die II) (8.16) .... 35·00 50·00
 w. Wmk inverted .... 30·00 90·00
99 £1 chocolate and dull blue (Die II) (8.16) £350 £450

Dates for Nos. 67 and 74 are issue dates at Rabaul. The stamps were in use from 2 January 1915 on Nauru. All other dates are those of despatch. Nos. 65/6, 68/73, 76/81 were despatched on 15 March 1915. For Die IIA of 2d. see note below Australia No. 45.

SETTINGS. Type 6 exists in three slightly different versions, illustrated above as (a), (b), and (c). These differ in the letters "S" of "ISLANDS" as follows:
(a) Both "SS" normal.
(b) First "S" with small head and large tail and second "S" normal.
(c) Both "SS" with small head and large tail.
Type 11, which also shows the examples of "S" as the normal version, can be identified from Type 6 (a) by the relative position of the second and third lines of the overprint. On Type 6 (a) the "P" of "PACIFIC" is exactly over the first "S" of "ISLANDS". On Type 11 the "P" appears over the space between "I" and "S".
It has been established, by the study of minor variations, that there are actually six settings of the "N.W. PACIFIC ISLANDS" overprint, including that represented by T 11, but the following are the different arrangements of Type 6 (a), (b), and (c) which occur.
A. Horizontal rows 1 and 2 all Type (a). Row 3 all Type (b). Rows 4 and 5 all Type (c).
B. (½d. green only.) As A, except that the types in the bottom row run (c) (c) (c) (c) (b) (c).
C. As A, but bottom row now shows types (a) (c) (c) (c) (b) (c).
Horizontal strips and pairs showing varieties (a) and (c), or (b) and (c) *se-tenant* are scarce.
The earliest printing of the 1d. and 2½d. values was made on sheets with margin attached on two sides, the later printings being on sheets from which the margins had been removed. In this printing the vertical distances between the overprints are less than in later printings, so that in the lower horizontal rows of the sheet the overprint is near the top of the stamp.
The settings used on King George stamps and on the Kangaroo type are similar, but the latter stamps being smaller the overprints are closer together in the vertical rows.

PURPLE OVERPRINTS. We no longer differentiate between purple and black overprints in the above series. In our opinion the two colours are nowadays insufficiently distinct to warrant separation.

PRICES. The prices quoted for Nos. 65 to 101 apply to stamps with opts Types 6 (a) or 6 (c). Stamps with opt Type 6 (b) are worth a 25 per cent premium. Vertical strips of three, showing (a), (b) and (c), are worth from four times the prices quoted for singles as Types 6 (a) or 6 (c).

N. W.
One Penny   **PACIFIC**
      ISLANDS.
(10)   (11)

1918 (23 May). Nos. 72 and 81 surch locally with T **10**.

100	1d. on 5d. brown	90·00	80·00
101	1d. on 1s. green	£100	80·00

Types **6** (*a*), (*b*), (*c*) occur on these stamps also.

1918–22. Stamps of Australia optd with T **11** ("P" of "PACIFIC" over space between "I" and "S" of "ISLANDS").

(i) T **5a**. W **5** of Australia. P 14¼×14

102	½d. green	1·75	3·50
	w. Wmk inverted	£3500	
103	1d. carmine-red (Die I)	3·75	1·60
	a. Substituted cliché (Pl 2 rt pane R. 6/5)	£1000	£650
	ab. Dot before "1"	90·00	80·00
	ac. "Secret mark"	90·00	80·00
	ad. Flaw under neck	90·00	80·00
	ae. "RA" joined	90·00	80·00
	b. Die II	£110	80·00
	ba. Substituted cliché (Pl 2 rt pane R. 6/4)	£1000	£650
104	4d. yellow-orange (1919)	4·50	16·00
	a. Line through "FOUR PENCE" (Pl 2 rt pane R. 2/6)	£850	£1300
105	5d. brown (1919)	4·00	12·00

(ii) T **1**. W **6** of Australia. P 12

106	2d. grey (Die I) (1919)	7·50	25·00
	a. Die II	12·00	50·00
107	2½d. indigo (Die II) (1919)	5·50	16·00
	a. "1" of "½" omitted	£14000	£17000
	b. Blue (1920)	15·00	48·00
109	3d. greenish olive (Die I) (1919)	23·00	26·00
	a. Die II	75·00	85·00
	ab. In pair with Die I	£425	£650
110	6d. ultramarine (Die II) (1919)	4·75	14·00
	a. Greyish ultramarine (1922)	42·00	65·00
	b. Die IIB. Greyish ultramarine	—	£750
112	9d. violet (Die IIB) (1919)	9·00	50·00
113	1s. emerald (Die II) (1919)	6·50	30·00
	a. Pale blue-green (Die IIB)	14·00	32·00
115	2s. brown (Die II) (1919)	21·00	38·00
116	5s. grey and yellow (Die II) (1919)	65·00	70·00
117	10s. grey and bright pink (Die II) (1919)	£170	£250
118	£1 bistre-brown and grey-blue (Die II) (1922)	£4500	£6000

(iii) T **5a**. W **6a**. of Australia (Mult Crown A). P 14

119	½d. green (1919)	5·50	7·50
	w. Wmk inverted	£130	£275

(iv) T **5a**. W **5** of Australia. Colour changes and new value

120	1d. violet (*shades*) (1922)	2·50	6·50
	a. Dot before "1"	75·00	£130
	b. "Secret mark"	75·00	£130
	c. Flaw under neck	75·00	£130
	d. "RA" joined	75·00	£130
121	2d. orange (1921)	9·00	2·50
122	2d. rose-scarlet (1922)	9·50	4·50
123	4d. violet (1922)	20·00	40·00
	a. "FOUR PENCE" in thinner letters (Pl 2 rt pane R. 2/6)	£800	£1400
124	4d. ultramarine (1922)	11·00	60·00
	a. "FOUR PENCE" in thinner letters (Pl 2 rt pane R. 2/6)	£900	£1800
	120/24 *Set of* 5	45·00	£100

Type **11** differs from Type **6** (*a*) in the position of the "P" of "PACIFIC", which is further to the left in Type **11**.

For 1d. rosine Dies I and II on rough unsurfaced paper see Nos. O16/b.

MANDATED TERRITORY OF NEW GUINEA

A civil administration for the Mandated Territory of New Guinea was established on 9 May 1921.

PRINTERS. See note at the beginning of Australia.

12 Native Village   (13)

(Des R. Harrison. Eng T. Harrison. Recess Note Printing Branch, Treasury, Melbourne, from 1926 Note Ptg Branch, Commonwealth Bank of Australia, Melbourne)

1925 (23 Jan)–**27**. P 11.

125	**12**	½d. orange	2·50	7·00
126		1d. green	2·50	5·50
126a		1½d. orange-vermilion (1926)	3·25	2·75
127		2d. claret	7·00	4·50
128		3d. blue	8·00	4·00
129		4d. olive-green	13·00	25·00
130		6d. brown-ochre	20·00	50·00
		a. Bistre (1.25)	6·00	50·00
		b. Yellow-brown (7.27)	14·00	48·00
131		9d. dull purple (*to violet*)	13·00	45·00
132		1s. dull blue-green (6.4.25)	15·00	27·00
133		2s. brown-lake (6.4.25)	30·00	48·00
134		5s. bistre (6.4.25)	50·00	65·00
135		10s. dull rose (6.4.25)	£120	£180
136		£1 dull olive-green (6.4.25)	£190	£300
		125/36 *Set of* 13	£400	£650

1931 (8 June). Air. Optd with T **13**. P 11.

137	**12**	½d. orange	1·50	9·00
138		1d. green	1·60	5·00
139		1½d. orange-vermilion	1·25	8·00
140		2d. claret	1·25	7·00
141		3d. blue	1·75	13·00
142		4d. olive-green	1·25	9·00
143		6d. light brown	1·75	14·00
144		9d. violet	3·00	17·00

145	1s. dull blue-green	3·00	17·00
146	2s. brown-lake	7·00	48·00
147	5s. olive-bistre	20·00	65·00
148	10s. bright pink	85·00	£110
149	£1 olive-grey	£160	£250
	137/49 *Set of* 13	£250	£500

AIR MAIL

14 Raggiana Bird of Paradise (Dates either side of value)   (15)

(Recess John Ash, Melbourne)

1931 (2 Aug). Tenth Anniv of Australian Administration. T **14** (with dates). P 11.

150	**14**	1d. green	4·25	7·00
151		1½d. vermilion	5·00	10·00
152		2d. claret	5·00	2·25
153		3d. blue	5·00	4·75
154		4d. olive-green	7·00	30·00
155		5d. deep blue-green	8·50	23·00
156		6d. bistre-brown	5·00	19·00
157		9d. violet	8·50	19·00
158		1s. pale blue-green	6·00	15·00
159		2s. brown-lake	10·00	48·00
160		5s. olive-brown	42·00	55·00
161		10s. bright pink	£120	£140
162		£1 olive-grey	£250	£275
		150/62 *Set of* 13	£425	£550

1931 (2 Aug). Air. Optd with T **15**.

163	**14**	½d. orange	3·25	3·25
164		1d. green	4·00	7·00
165		1½d. vermilion	3·75	10·00
166		2d. claret	3·75	3·00
167		3d. blue	6·00	6·50
168		4d. olive-green	6·00	6·00
169		5d. deep blue-green	6·00	11·00
170		6d. bistre-brown	7·00	26·00
171		9d. violet	8·00	15·00
172		1s. pale blue-green	7·50	15·00
173		2s. dull lake	16·00	50·00
174		5s. olive-brown	42·00	70·00
175		10s. bright pink	80·00	£120
176		£1 olive-grey	£150	£250
		163/76 *Set of* 14	£300	£500

1932 (30 June)–**34**. T **14** (redrawn without dates). P 11.

177	1d. green	7·50	20
178	1½d. claret	7·50	20·00
179	2d. vermilion	5·50	20
179a	2½d. green (14.9.34)	6·50	27·00
180	3d. blue	8·00	1·25
180a	3½d. aniline carmine (14.9.34)	13·00	22·00
181	4d. olive-green	6·50	6·50
182	5d. deep blue-green	7·00	70
183	6d. bistre-brown	7·50	5·00
184	9d. violet	9·50	26·00
185	1s. blue-green	6·50	10·00
186	2s. dull lake	5·00	17·00
187	5s. olive	32·00	48·00
188	10s. pink	55·00	70·00
189	£1 olive-grey	£120	£100
	177/89 *Set of* 15	£250	£300

The ½d. orange redrawn without dates exists without overprint, but it is believed that this was not issued (*Price* £110 un).

1932 (30 June)–**34**. Air. T **14** (redrawn without dates), optd with T **15**. P 11.

190	½d. orange	60	70
191	1d. green	1·25	3·50
192	1½d. claret	1·75	11·00
193	2d. vermilion	1·75	30
193a	2½d. green (14.9.34)	8·50	2·50
194	3d. blue	3·25	3·00
194a	3½d. aniline carmine (14.9.34)	4·75	3·25
195	4d. olive-green	4·50	10·00
196	5d. deep blue-green	7·00	7·50
197	6d. bistre-brown	4·50	15·00
198	9d. violet	6·00	9·00
199	1s. pale blue-green	6·00	12·00
200	2s. dull lake	14·00	50·00
201	5s. olive-brown	50·00	60·00
202	10s. pink	95·00	85·00
203	£1 olive-grey	85·00	55·00
	190/203 *Set of* 16	£250	£275

16 Bulolo Goldfields

(Recess John Ash, Melbourne)

1935 (1 May). Air. P 11.

204	**16**	£2 bright violet	£350	£140
205		£5 emerald-green	£750	£450

HIS MAJESTY'S JUBILEE. 1910 — 1935
(17)   **18**

1935 (27 June). Silver Jubilee. As Nos. 177 and 179, but shiny paper. Optd with T **17**.

206	1d. green	1·00	65
207	2d. vermilion	4·50	65

POSTAGE   **5d.**

Re-entry (design completely duplicated) (Pl 2a R. 5/2)

(Recess John Ash, Melbourne)

1937 (18 May). Coronation. P 11.

208	**18**	2d. scarlet	50	1·50
209		3d. blue	50	1·75
210		5d. green	50	1·75
		a. Re-entry	75·00	£130
211		1s. purple	50	2·25
		208/11 *Set of* 4	1·75	6·50

(Recess John Ash, Melbourne)

1939 (1 Mar). Air. Inscr "AIRMAIL POSTAGE" at foot. P 11.

212	**16**	½d. orange	4·00	9·00
213		1d. green	3·25	4·50
214		1½d. claret	4·00	18·00
215		2d. vermilion	9·00	3·50
216		3d. blue	18·00	18·00
217		4d. yellow-olive	15·00	8·50
218		5d. deep green	14·00	4·00
219		6d. bistre-brown	45·00	30·00
220		9d. violet	45·00	45·00
221		1s. pale blue-green	45·00	32·00
222		2s. dull lake	90·00	75·00
223		5s. olive-brown	£190	£160
224		10s. pink	£600	£425
225		£1 olive-grey	£140	£150
		212/25 *Set of* 14	£1100	£850

OFFICIAL STAMPS

O. S.
G.R.I.
1d.   **O S**   O   S
(O **1**)   (O **2**)   (O **3**)

1915 (27 Feb). Stamps of 1901 surch as Type O **1**. "G.R.I." and value 3½ mm apart.

O1	1d. on 3pf. brown	35·00	75·00
	a. "1" and "d" spaced	85·00	£170
	b. Surch double	£5500	
O2	1d. on 5pf. green	£100	£140
	a. "1" and "d" spaced	£200	£300

1919–23. Stamps of Australia optd with T **11** and punctured "O S" (8×15½ *mm* with eleven holes in the perforated "S").

(i) T **5a**. of Australia. W **5**. P 14¼×14

O3	1d. carmine-red (Die I)	£250	55·00
	ab. Dot before "1"	—	£275
	ac. "Secret mark"	—	£275
	ad. Flaw under neck	£850	£275
O4	4d. yellow-orange (19.5.19)	£375	£130
	a. Line through "FOUR PENCE" (Pl 2 rt pane R. 2/6)	—	£4250
O5	5d. brown (1921)	£450	£100

(ii) T **1**. of Australia. W **6**. P 12

O6	2d. grey (Die I)	£400	80·00
O7	2½d. indigo (Die II)	£600	£425
O8	3d. greenish olive (Die I) (1921)	£650	£140
O9	6d. ultramarine (Die II) (1921)	£700	£200
	a. Greyish ultramarine	£600	£200
	b. Die IIB. Greyish ultramarine	—	£250
O10	9d. violet (Die IIB) (1921)	£275	£150
O11	1s. emerald (Die II) (1921)	£375	£160
	a. Pale blue-green	£425	£170
O12	2s. brown (Die II) (1922)	£700	£350
O13	5s. grey and yellow (Die II) (1922)	—	£1500
O14	10s. grey and bright pink (Die II) (1921)..		

(iii) T **5a** of Australia. W **5**. Rough unsurfaced paper, locally gummed. P 14

O16	1d. rosine (Die I) (1920)	£1100	£190
	b. Die II	£4750	£950

(iv) T **5a** of Australia. W **5**. Colour changes and new value. P 14

O17	1d. violet (*shades*) (1923)	£350	50·00
O18	2d. orange (1921)	£150	48·00
O19	2d. rose-scarlet (1923)	£350	35·00
O20	4d. violet (23.7.21)	£250	£120
	a. "FOUR PENCE" in thinner letters (Pl 2 rt pane R. 2/6)	—	£4250
O21	4d. ultramarine (1.23)	£350	£150

Dates quoted for Nos. O3/21 are those of despatch from Australia. The earliest postmark date recorded is 2 April 1919 on No. O3. Their continued use on mail from government departments after the establishment of the civil administration is confirmed by a notice in the official *New Guinea Gazette* of 1 August 1921.

Australian postal archives indicate that nine sheets of the £1 Type **1** perforated "O S" were sent to New Guinea in September 1921. There is a pane of 30 of this stamp in the Royal Collection, but as no other examples are known it may not have been issued for postal purposes.

1925 (6 Apr)–**31**. Optd with Type O **2**. P 11.

O22	**12**	1d. green	5·00	4·50
O23		1½d. orange-vermilion (1931)	5·50	17·00
O24		2d. claret	3·00	3·75
O25		3d. blue	6·00	10·00
O26		4d. olive-green	4·50	8·50
O27		6d. bistre	27·00	35·00
		a. Yellow-brown (4.31)	7·50	35·00
O28		9d. violet	4·25	35·00
O29		1s. dull blue-green	5·50	35·00
O30		2s. brown-lake	42·00	65·00
		O22/30 *Set of* 9	75·00	£190

1931 (2 Aug). Optd with Type O **3**. P 11.

O31	**14**	1d. green	12·00	13·00
O32		1½d. vermilion	12·00	12·00
O33		2d. claret	12·00	7·00
O34		3d. blue	7·00	6·00
O35		4d. olive-green	7·50	8·50
O36		5d. deep blue-green	10·00	12·00
O37		6d. bistre-brown	14·00	17·00
O38		9d. violet	16·00	28·00
O39		1s. pale blue-green	16·00	28·00
O40		2s. brown-lake	40·00	70·00
O41		5s. olive-brown	£110	£180
O31/41	*Set of 11*		£225	£350

1932 (30 June)–**34**. T **14** (redrawn without dates), optd with Type O **3**. P 11.

O42		1d. green	19·00	20·00
O43		1½d. claret	19·00	20·00
O44		2d. vermilion	19·00	3·25
O45		2½d. green (14.9.34)	10·00	12·00
O46		3d. blue	11·00	42·00
		a. Double opt, one albino	£1000	
O47		3½d. aniline carmine (14.9.34)	9·00	9·00
O48		4d. olive-green	20·00	32·00
O49		5d. deep blue-green	9·00	30·00
O50		6d. bistre-brown	25·00	55·00
O51		9d. violet	15·00	48·00
O52		1s. pale blue-green	15·00	30·00
O53		2s. dull lake	30·00	75·00
O54		5s. olive-brown	£120	£180
O42/54	*Set of 13*		£275	£475

Civil Administration in New Guinea was suspended in 1942, following the Japanese invasion.

Various New Guinea stamps exist overprinted with an anchor and three Japanese characters in a style similar to the Japanese Naval Control Area overprints found on the stamps of Netherlands Indies. These overprints on New Guinea are bogus. Two different versions are known, one produced in Japan during 1947 and the other in Australia during the late 1980s.

On resumption, after the Japanese defeat in 1945, Australian stamps were used until the appearance of the issue for the combined territories of Papua & New Guinea.

NORFOLK ISLAND

Norfolk Island, first settled in 1788 from New South Wales, was transferred to Tasmania on 29 September 1844. It became a separate settlement on 1 November 1856 under the control of the Governor of New South Wales. The island was declared an Australian Territory on 1 July 1914. Unlike the other External Territories it retains an independent postal administration.

> A Post Office was opened on Norfolk Island in 1832. The stamps of TASMANIA were used on Norfolk Island from July 1854 until May 1855, such use being identified by the "72" numeral cancellation. Stamps of NEW SOUTH WALES were first used on the island in 1877, but were not regularly available until 1898. The first "NORFOLK ISLAND" cancellation was supplied in 1892, but not used until 1898. Stamps of AUSTRALIA were in use from 1913 to 1947.

1 Ball Bay

(Des and eng F. Manley. Recess Note Printing Branch, Reserve Bank of Australia)

1947 (10 June)–**59**. Toned paper. P 14.

1	**1**	½d. orange	85	60
		a. White paper (11.56)	3·25	17·00
2		1d. bright violet	50	60
		a. White paper (8.57)	5·00	35·00
3		1½d. emerald-green	50	70
		a. White paper (11.56)	9·00	28·00
4		2d. reddish violet	55	40
		a. White paper (11.56)	£130	£190
5		2½d. scarlet	80	30
6		3d. chestnut	70	70
6a		3d. emerald-green (*white paper*) (6.7.59)	15·00	12·00
7		4d. claret	1·75	40
8		5½d. indigo	70	30
9		6d. purple-brown	70	30
10		9d. magenta	1·25	40
11		1s. grey-olive	70	40
12		2s. yellow-bistre	1·25	1·75
12a		2s. deep blue (*white paper*) (6.7.59)	16·00	12·00
1/12a	*Set of 14*		35·00	28·00

Stamps as Type **1**, in different colours, perforated 11 were prepared in 1940 but never issued. Examples of the 1d. emerald, 2d. scarlet, 3d. ultramarine, 6d. chocolate and 1s. slate-green exist from sheets stolen prior to the destruction of these stocks.

2 Warder's Tower

3 Airfield

4 Old Stores (Crankmill)

5 Barracks entrance

6 Salt House

7 Bloody Bridge

(Des B. Stewart, eng. G. Lissenden (3½d.), D. Cameron (7½d.). Des and eng D. Cameron (6½d.), P. Morriss (8½d., 10d.) or G. Lissenden (5s.))

1953 (10 June). T **2**/**7**. P 14½×15 (vert) or 15×14½ (horiz).

13	**2**	3½d. brown-lake	1·00	90
14	**3**	6½d. deep green	2·25	4·25
15	**4**	7½d. deep blue	1·50	3·00
16	**5**	8½d. chocolate	1·75	4·75
17	**6**	10d. reddish violet	1·00	75
18	**7**	5s. sepia	35·00	8·50
13/18	*Set of 6*		38·00	20·00

8 Norfolk Island Seal and Pitcairners Landing

Two types of 2s.:

Type I	Type II

Alternate stamps on each horizontal row are with or without a dot in bottom right corner.

(Des and eng F. Manley)

1956 (8 June). Centenary of Landing of Pitcairn Islanders on Norfolk Island. P 15×14½.

19	**8**	3d. deep bluish green	1·00	40
20		2s. violet (I)	1·75	1·00
		a. Type II	1·75	1·00
		b. Deep violet (I)	2·75	1·75
		ba. Type II	2·75	1·75

(9)	(10)	(11)

1958 (1 July). Nos. 15/16 surch with T **9**/**10**.

21	7d. on 7½d. deep blue	1·25	1·00
22	8d. on 8½d. chocolate	1·25	1·00

1959 (7 Dec). 150th Anniv of Australian Post Office. No. 331 of Australia surch with T **11**.

23	5d. on 4d. slate (R.)	35	30

12 *Hibiscus insularis*

13 *Lagunaria patersonii*

14 White Tern

15 Lantana

16 Red Hibiscus

17 Queen Elizabeth II and Cereus

18 Fringed Hibiscus

19 Solander's Petrel

20 Passion Flower

21 Rose Apple

22 Red-tailed Tropic Bird

(Des G. Lissenden, eng P. Morriss (5s.). Des and eng G. Lissenden (10s.), P. Morriss (others). Recess and typo (2s.8d.), recess (others))

1960–62. T **6**/**7** and **12**/**22**. P 14½ or 14½×14 (10s.).

24	**12**	1d. bluish green (23.5.60)	15	10
25	**13**	2d. rose and myrtle-green (23.5.60)	20	10
26	**14**	3d. green (1.5.61)	70	15
27	**15**	5d. bright purple (20.6.60)	55	20
28	**16**	8d. red (20.6.60)	80	50
29	**17**	9d. ultramarine (23.5.60)	80	45
30	**6**	10d. brown and reddish violet (as No. 17) (27.2.61)	2·00	1·00
31	**18**	1s.1d. carmine-red (16.10.61)	80	35
32	**19**	2s. sepia (1.5.61)	4·00	1·00
33	**20**	2s.5d. deep violet (5.2.62)	1·00	40
34	**21**	2s.8d. cinnamon and deep green (9.4.62)	2·25	55
35	**7**	5s. sepia and deep green (as No. 18) (27.2.61)	3·00	75
36	**22**	10s. emerald-green (14.8.61)	26·00	38·00
		s. Optd "SPECIMEN"	42·00	
24/36	*Set of 13*		38·00	38·00

Nos. 30 and 35 are redrawn.

The SPECIMEN overprint on No. 36 is from sets sold by the Australian Post Office.

For Nos. 25 and 28 with face values in decimal currency see Nos. 600/1.

(23)	(24)	(25)

1960. As Nos. 13/15 but colours changed, surch with T **23**/**5**.

37	1s.1d. on 3½d. deep ultramarine (26.9.60)	2·00	1·50
38	2s.5d. on 6½d. bluish green (26.9.60)	3·00	2·25
39	2s.8d. on 7½d. sepia (29.8.60)	7·00	8·50
37/39	*Set of 3*	11·00	11·00

26 Queen Elizabeth II and Map

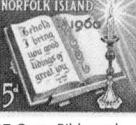

27 Open Bible and Candle

(Des and eng P. Morriss)

1960 (24 Oct). Introduction of Local Government. P 14.

40	**26**	2s.8d. reddish purple	4·00	7·00

(Des K. McKay. Adapted and eng B. Stewart. Recess)

1960 (21 Nov). Christmas. P 15×14½.

41	**27**	5d. bright purple	40	1·00

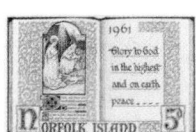

28 Open Prayer Book and Text

29 Stripey (*Atypichthys latus*)

(Des G. Lissenden. Eng P. Morriss. Recess)

1961 (20 Nov). Christmas. P 14½×14.

42	**28**	5d. slate-blue	30	70

> **PRINTERS**. All the following issues to No. 233 were printed in photogravure by Harrison and Sons, Ltd, London, *except where otherwise stated.*

1962–63. Fish. Horiz designs as T **29**. P 14½×14.

43		6d. sepia, yellow and deep bluish green (16.7.62)	60	25
44		11d. red-orange, brown and blue (25.2.63)	75	80
45		1s. blue, pink and yellow-olive (17.9.62)	60	25
46		1s.3d. blue, red-brown and green (15.7.63)	1·00	2·50
47		1s.6d. sepia, violet and light blue (6.5.63)	1·25	80
48		2s.3d. deep blue, red and greenish yellow (23.9.63)	1·50	1·25
43/48	*Set of 6*		5·00	5·00

Designs:—11d. Gold-mouthed Emperor (*Lethrinus chrysostomus*); 1s. Surge Wrasse ("Po'ov"); 1s.3d. Seachub ("Dreamfish"); 1s.6d. Giant Grouper (*Promicrops lanceolatus*); 2s.3d. White Trevally (*Carangidae*).

30 Madonna and Child

31 "Peace on Earth..."

(Des and eng G. Lissenden. Recess Note Ptg Branch, Reserve Bank of Australia)

1962 (19 Nov). Christmas. P 14½.
49   **30**   5d. ultramarine 45   80

(Des R. Warner. Eng B. Stewart. Recess Note Ptg Branch, Reserve Bank of Australia)

1963 (11 Nov). Christmas. P 14½.
50   **31**   5d. red 40   70

32 Overlooking Kingston

33 Norfolk Pine

1964 (24 Feb–28 Sept). Views. Horiz designs as T **32**. Multicoloured. P 14½×14.
51   5d. Type **32** 60   1·25
52   8d. Kingston .... 1·00   1·50
53   9d. The Arches (Bumboras) (11.5) .... 1·00   30
54   10d. Slaughter Bay (28.9) .... 1·00   30
51/54 *Set of 4* .... 3·25   3·00

(Photo Note Ptg Branch, Reserve Bank of Australia, Melbourne)
1964 (1 July). 50th Anniv of Norfolk Island as Australian Territory. P 13½.
55   **33**   5d. black, red and orange 40   15
56   8d. black, red and grey-green 40   1·10

34 Child looking at Nativity Scene

35 Nativity Scene

(Des P. Morriss and J. Mason. Photo Note Ptg Branch, Reserve Bank of Australia)

1964 (9 Nov). Christmas. P 13½.
57   **34**   5d. green, blue, buff and violet 30   40

1965 (14 Apr). 50th Anniv of Gallipoli Landing. As T **22** of Nauru. P 13½.
58   5d. sepia, black and emerald 15   10

(Des J. Mason. Photo Note Ptg Branch, Reserve Bank of Australia)
1965 (25 Oct). Christmas. Helecon paper. P 13½.
59   **35**   5d. multicoloured 15   10

(New Currency. 100 cents = 1 Australian dollar)

38 *Hibiscus insularis*

39 Headstone Bridge

1966 (14 Feb). Decimal currency. Various stamps surch in black on silver tablets, which vary slightly in size, obliterating old value as in T **38**. Surch typo.
60   **38**   1c. on 1d. bluish green (*value tablet* 4×5 *mm*) 20   10
      a. Value tablet larger, 5½×5½ mm.... 40   30
61   **13**   2c. on 2d. rose and myrtle-green (No. 25) 20   10
      a. Surch omitted (in pair with normal) £3000
62   **14**   3c. on 3d. green .... 1·50   1·00
      a. Silver tablet omitted £700
63   **15**   4c. on 5d. bright purple (No. 27) 25   10
64   **16**   5c. on 8d. red 30   10
65   **6**   10c. on 10d. brown and reddish violet (No. 30) .... 1·00   15
66   **18**   15c. on 1s.1d. carmine-red (No. 31).. 50   30
67   **19**   20c. on 2s. sepia (No. 32) .... 2·75   3·75
68   **20**   25c. on 2s.5d. deep violet (No. 33).... 1·00   40
69   **21**   30c. on 2s.8d. cinnamon and deep green .... 1·00   50
70   **7**   50c. on 5s. sepia and deep green (No. 35) .... 1·75   75
71   **22** $1 on 10s. emerald-green (*value tablet* 7×6½ *mm*) .... 2·50   2·50
      a. Value tablet smaller, 6½×4 mm .... 2·00   3·25
60/71a *Set of 12* (*cheapest*) .... 9·00   9·00
    No. 61a shows the black figure of value omitted, but the silver tablet is present.

1966 (27 June). Horiz designs as T **39**. Multicoloured. P 14½×14.
72   7c. Type **39** 40   15
73   9c. Cemetery Road 40   15

41 St. Barnabas' Chapel (interior)

42 St. Barnabas' Chapel (exterior)

1966 (23 Aug). Centenary of Melanesian Mission. P 14×14½.
74   **41**   4c. multicoloured 10   10
75   **42**   25c. multicoloured 20   20

43 Star over Philip Island

44 HMS *Resolution*, 1774

(Des B. G. W. McCoy)
1966 (24 Oct). Christmas. P 14½.
76   **43**   4c. multicoloured 10   10

(Des V. Whiteley)
1967 (17 Apr)–**68**. T **44** and similar horiz designs showing ships. Multicoloured. P 14×14½.
77   1c. Type **44** 10   10
78   2c. *La Boussole and L'Astrolabe*, 1788 15   10
79   3c. HMS *Supply*, 1788 15   10
80   4c. HMS *Sirius*, 1790 75   10
81   5c. *Norfolk* (sloop), 1798 (14.8.67).... 20   10
82   7c. HMS *Mermaid* (survey cutter), 1825 (14.8.67) 20   10
83   9c. *Lady Franklin*, 1853 (14.8.67) 20   10
84   10c. *Morayshire*, 1856 (14.8.67) 20   50
85   15c. *Southern Cross*, 1866 (18.3.68) 50   30
86   20c. *Pitcairn*, 1891 (18.3.68) 60   40
87   25c. *Black Billy* (Norfolk Island whaleboat), 1895 (18.3.68) .... 1·50   75
88   30c. *Iris* (cable ship), 1907 (18.6.68).... 1·50   2·00
89   50c. *Resolution*, 1926 (18.6.68) ..... 2·50   2·75
90     $1 *Morinda*, 1931 (18.6.68) .... 3·00   2·75
77/90 *Set of 14* .... 10·50   9·00

45 Lions Badge and 50 Stars

46 Prayer of John Adams and Candle

(Des M. Ripper. Photo Note Ptg Branch, Reserve Bank of Australia)
1967 (7 June). 50th Anniv of Lions International. P 13½.
91   **45**   4c. black, bluish green and olive-yellow 10   10

(Des B. G. W. McCoy)
1967 (16 Oct). Christmas. P 14.
92   **46**   5c. black, light yellow-olive and red 10   10

47 Queen Elizabeth II

(Photo Note Ptg Branch, Reserve Bank of Australia)
1968 (5 Aug)–**71**. Coil stamps. P 15×imperf.
93   **47**   3c. black, light brown and vermilion 10   10
94   4c. black, light brown and blue-green 10   10
95   5c. black, light brown and deep violet 10   10
95a   6c. black, light brown and lake-brown (25.8.71) 30   60
93/95a *Set of 4* 55   80

59 Avro Type 691 Lancastrian and Douglas DC-4 Aircraft

60 Bethlehem Star and Flowers

(Des Harrison)
1968 (25 Sept). 21st Anniv of QANTAS Air Service, Sydney-Norfolk Island. P 14.
96   **59**   5c. bluish black, carmine-red and light blue 15   10
97   7c. blackish brown, carmine-red and turquoise 15   10

(Des Betty Laing)
1968 (24 Oct). Christmas. P 14×14½.
98   **60**   5c. multicoloured 10   10

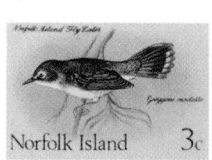

61 Captain Cook, Quadrant and Chart of Pacific Ocean Island

62 Van Diemen's Land, Norfolk and Sailing Cutter

(Des V. Whiteley from sketch by J. Cowap)
1969 (3 June). Captain Cook Bicentenary (1st issue). Observation of the transit of Venus across the Sun, from Tahiti. P 14.
99   **61**   10c. multicoloured 10   10
    See also Nos. 118/19. Further sets were issued in subsequent years.

(Des Mrs. A. Bathie and Mrs. M. J. McCoy)
1969 (29 Sept). 125th Anniv of the Annexation of Norfolk Island to Van Diemen's Land. P 14×14½.
100   **62**   5c. multicoloured 10   10
101   30c. multicoloured 50   1·00
      a. Inscr "VAN DIFMEN'S LAND" (R. 8/5) .... 16·00

63 The Nativity (carved mother-of-pearl plaque)

64 New Zealand Grey Flyeater

(Des J. Cowap)
1969 (27 Oct). Christmas. P 14½×14.
102   **63**   5c. multicoloured 10   10

(Des G. Mathews)
1970–71. Birds. T **64** and similar multicoloured designs. Chalk-surfaced paper. P 14.
103   1c. Scarlet Robins (22.7.70) 30   10
104   2c. Golden Whistler (24.2.71) 30   40
105   3c. Type **64** (25.2.70) 30   10
106   4c. Long-tailed Koels (25.2.70) 60   10
107   5c. Red-fronted Parakeet (24.2.71) .... 1·50   75
108   7c. Long-tailed Triller (22.7.70) 45   10
109   9c. Island Thrush (25.2.70) 70   10
110   10c. Boobook Owl (22.7.70) .... 1·50   2·75
111   15c. Norfolk Island Pigeon (24.2.71)........ 1·00   65
112   20c. White-chested White Eye .... 5·00   3·25
113   25c. Norfolk Island Parrots (22.7.70).... 1·00   40
      a. Error. Glazed, ordinary paper £450
114   30c. Collared Grey Fantail (16.6.71) .... 5·00   1·75
115   45c. Norfolk Island Starlings (25.2.70) 70   60
116   50c. Crimson Rosella (24.2.71) .... 1·00   2·25
117     $1 Sacred Kingfisher (16.6.71) .... 6·50   9·50
103/17 *Set of 15* .... 23·00   20·00
    Nos. 105, 106, 109, 112, 114, 115 and 117 are horizontal, and the remainder vertical designs.
    It is believed that only one sheet of No. 113a was issued.

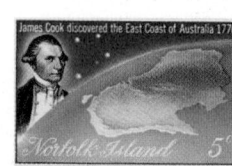

65 Capt. Cook and Map of Australia

66 First Christmas Service, 1788

(Des R. Bates)
1970 (29 Apr). Captain Cook Bicentenary (2nd issue). Discovery of Australia's East Coast. T **65** and similar horiz design. Multicoloured. P 14.
118   5c. Type **65** 15   10
119   10c. HMS *Endeavour* and aborigine.... 40   10

(Des R. Bates)
1970 (15 Oct). Christmas. P 14.
120   **66**   5c. multicoloured 10   10

PAPUA (BRITISH NEW GUINEA)

Stamps of QUEENSLAND were used in British New Guinea (Papua) from at least 1885 onwards. Post Offices were opened at Daru (1894), Kulumadau (Woodlarks) (1899), Nivani (1899), Port Moresby (1885), Samarai (1888), Sudest (1899) and Tamata (1899). Stamps were usually cancelled "N.G." (at Port Moresby from 1885) or "BNG" (without stops at Samarai or with stops at the other offices) from 1888. Queensland stamps were replaced in Papua by the issue of 1901.

PRICES FOR STAMPS ON COVER

Nos. 1/7	from × 15
No. 8	—
Nos. 9/15	from × 20
No. 16	—
Nos. 17/27	from × 6
No. 28	—
Nos. 34/45a	from × 5
Nos. 47/71	from × 8
Nos. 72/4	—
Nos. 75/92a	from × 8
Nos. 93/103	from × 6
Nos. 104/5	—
Nos. 106/11	from × 10
Nos. 112/14	from × 6
No. 115	—
Nos. 116/28	from × 5
Nos. 130/53	from × 4
Nos. 154/7	from × 12
Nos. 158/67	from × 4
No. 168	from × 3
Nos. O1/54	from × 10
Nos. O55/66a	from × 7
No. F1	from × 8

BRITISH NEW GUINEA

1 Lakatoi (trading canoe) with Hanuabada Village in Background

2 (Horizontal)

Normal   Thin "d" at left (R. 4/2)

Deformed "d" at left (R. 4/3)

(Recess D.L.R.)

1901 (1 July)–05. Wmk Mult Rosettes, W **2**. P 14.

A. Wmk horizontal. Thick paper. Line perf

1	**1**	½d. black and yellow-green	24·00	26·00
		a. Thin paper	£350	£275
2		1d. black and carmine	20·00	19·00
3		2d. black and violet	27·00	9·50
4		2½d. black and ultramarine	40·00	10·00
		a. Thin paper	£400	£225
		ab. *Black and dull blue*	£900	£475
		b. Thin "d" at left	£375	£130
5		4d. black and sepia	65·00	35·00
		a. Deformed "d" at left	£750	£475
6		6d. black and myrtle-green	65·00	35·00
7		1s. black and orange	75·00	70·00
8		2s.6d. black and brown (1.1.05)	£650	£550
1/8 *Set of 8*			£850	£650

B. Wmk vertical. Medium to thick paper. Line or comb perf

9	**1**	½d. black and yellow-green	23·00	3·75
		a. Thin paper (*comb perf*) (1905)	28·00	40·00
10		1d. black and carmine	13·00	2·00
11		2d. black and violet	13·00	4·25
		a. Thin paper (*comb perf*) (1905)	65·00	16·00
12		2½d. black and ultramarine (*shades*)	38·00	12·00
		a. Thin "d" at left	£350	£140
13		4d. black and sepia	45·00	55·00
		a. Deformed "d" at left	£650	£750
		b. Thin paper (*comb perf*) (1905)	£350	£1300
		ba. Deformed "d" at left	£3250	
14		6d. black and myrtle-green	65·00	90·00
		a. Thin paper (*comb perf*) (1905)	£1200	
15		1s. black and orange	65·00	£100
		a. Thin paper (*comb perf*) (1905)	£950	£4250

16		2s.6d. black and brown (1905)	£6000	£4000
		a. Thin paper (*comb perf*)	£600	£1400
9/16a *Set of 8* (*cheapest*)			£750	£1500

The paper used for Nos. 1/8 is white, of consistent thickness and rather opaque. The thin paper used for the horizontal watermark printings is of variable thickness, readily distinguishable from the thick paper by its greater transparency and by the gum which is thin and smooth.

Nos. 9/16 were initially printed on the same thick paper as the stamps with horizontal watermark and were line perforated. Values from ½d. to 2½d. were subsequently printed on medium paper on which the watermark was more visible. These were comb perforated. The thin paper with vertical watermark, produced in 1905, is much more transparent and has smooth gum. Printings were made on this paper for all values except the 2½d., but only the ½d. and 2d. were issued in Papua although used examples of the 4d., 1s. and 2s.6d. are also known. The entire printing of the 1d. on thin paper with vertical watermark was used for subsequent overprints.

The sheets of the ½d., 2d. and 2½d. show a variety known as "white leaves" on R. 4/5, while the 2d. and 2½d. (both R. 6/2) and the ½d. and 1s. (both R. 6/3) show what is known as the "unshaded leaves" variety.

TERRITORY OF PAPUA

Papua.   **Papua.**

(3)   (4)

1906 (8 Nov). I. Optd with T **3** (large opt), at Port Moresby.

A. Wmk horizontal. Thick paper. Line perf

16b		2½d. black and ultramarine	†	—
17	**1**	4d. black and sepia	£250	£170
		a. Deformed "d" at left	£2250	£1700
18		6d. black and myrtle-green	60·00	48·00
19		1s. black and orange	28·00	48·00
20		2s.6d. black and brown	£170	£190

B. Wmk vertical. Thin paper (½d., 1d., 2d.) or medium to thick paper (others). Comb perf (½d. to 2½d.) or line perf (others)

21	**1**	½d. black and yellow-green	12·00	20·00
22		1d. black and carmine	20·00	19·00
23		2d. black and violet	20·00	5·50
24		2½d. black and ultramarine	12·00	15·00
		a. Thin "d" at left	£130	£160
25		4d. black and sepia	£225	£160
		a. Deformed "d" at left	£2000	£1600
26		6d. black and myrtle-green	48·00	60·00
27		1s. black and orange	£1800	£1400
28		2s.6d. black and brown	£17000	£12000
19/26 *Set of 8*			£450	£450

1907 (May–June). Optd with T **4** (small opt), at Brisbane.

A. Wmk horizontal. Thick paper. Line perf

34	**1**	½d. black and yellow-green	—	
		a. Thin paper	75·00	90·00
35		2½d. black and ultramarine	£2000	
		a. Thin paper	80·00	85·00
		ac. *Black and dull blue*	£325	£350
		b. Thin "d" at left	£750	£800
36		1s. black and orange	£325	£400
37		2s.6d. black and brown	50·00	75·00
		a. Opt reading downwards	£7500	
		c. Opt double (*horiz*)	†	£6000
		d. Opt triple (*horiz*)	†	£4500

B. Wmk vertical. Thin paper (½d., 1d., 2d., 4d., 6d.) or medium to thick paper (2½d., 1s., 2s.6d.). Line or comb perf (2½d.) or comb perf (others)

38	**1**	½d. black and yellow-green	23·00	29·00
		a. Opt double	£3500	
39		1d. black and carmine	11·00	5·00
		a. Opt reading upwards	£8000	£3500
40		2d. black and violet	7·50	2·25
		a. Opt double	£4250	
41		2½d. black and ultramarine	21·00	20·00
		a. Thin "d" at left	£200	£225
42		4d. black and sepia	50·00	70·00
		a. Deformed "d" at left	£700	£800
43		6d. black and myrtle-green	50·00	45·00
		a. Opt double	£7000	£13000
44		1s. black and orange	80·00	90·00
		b. Thin paper (*comb perf*)	48·00	42·00
		ba. Opt double, one diagonal	£21000	£14000
45		2s.6d. black and brown	£18000	£10000
		a. Thin paper (*comb perf*)	55·00	90·00
38/45a *Set of 8*			£225	£250

In the setting of this overprint Nos. 10, 16, and 21 have the "p" of "Papua" with a defective foot or inverted "d" for "p", and in No. 17 the "pua" of "Papua" is a shade lower than the first "a".

No. 37a comes from a single sheet on which the overprints were sideways. Examples exist showing one, two or four complete or partial overprints.

> **PRINTERS.** All the following issues were printed at Melbourne by the Stamp Ptg Branch (to 1928) or Note Ptg Branch.

> **WATERMARK VARIETIES.** The lithographed issues Nos. 47/83 were printed using a "print-and-turn" technique. Thus, after one half of the sheet had been printed it was turned 180 degrees and the second half printed. As a result, upright and inverted (or sideways and sideways-inverted) watermarks were produced in equal quantities. Nos. 51/3, 55, 57, 62 and 69 are known with watermark reversed and others may well exist.

5 Large "PAPUA"   B   C

Three types of the 2s.6d.:—
A. Thin top to "2" and small ball. Thin "6" and small ball. Thick uneven stroke.
B. Thin top to "2" and large, round ball. Thin "6" and large ball. Very thick uneven stroke. Every stamp in Type B varies slightly.
C. Thick uniform figures with large oval balls Thin even stroke.
Type A is not illustrated as the stamp is distinguishable by perf and watermark.

The litho stones were prepared from the engraved plates of the 1901 issue, value for value except the 2s.6d. for which the original plate was mislaid. No. 48 containing Type A was prepared from the original ½d. plate with the value inserted on the stone and later a fresh stone was prepared from the 1d. plate and this contained Type B. Finally, the original plate of the 2s.6d. was found and a third stone was prepared from this, and issued in 1911. These stamps show Type C.

6 Small "PAPUA"

2s.6d. "POSTAGIE" at top left (R. 1/5)   **2d.** "C" for "O" in "POSTAGE" (R. 4/3)

(Litho Stamp Ptg Branch, Melbourne, from transfers taken from original engraved plates)

1907–10. A. Large "PAPUA". Wmk Crown over A, W w **11**.

(a) Wmk upright. P 11

47	**5**	½d. black and yellow-green (11.07)	4·50	3·50

(b) Wmk sideways. P 11

48	**5**	2s.6d. black and chocolate (A) (12.09)	75·00	90·00
		a. "POSTAGIE" at left (R.1/5)	£1600	£2000

B. Small "PAPUA" I. Wmk upright

(a) P 11 (1907–8)

49	**6**	1d. black and rose (6.08)	6·50	5·00
50		2d. black and purple (10.08)	27·00	4·50
51		2½d. black and bright ultramarine (7.08)	30·00	35·00
		a. *Black and pale ultramarine*	17·00	7·00
		b. Thin "d" at left	£160	95·00
52		4d. black and sepia (20.11.07)	7·00	17·00
		a. Deformed "d" at left	£140	£250
53		6d. black and myrtle-green (4.08)	16·00	16·00
54		1s. black and orange (10.08)	55·00	21·00

(b) P 12½ (1907–9)

55	**6**	2d. black and purple (10.08)	42·00	9·50
56		2½d. black and bright ultramarine (7.08)	£180	£190
		a. *Black and pale ultramarine*	65·00	85·00
		b. Thin "d" at left	£600	£700
57		4d. black and sepia (20.11.07)	9·00	8·00
		a. Deformed "d" at left	£170	£160
58		1s. black and orange (10.08)	75·00	£100

II. Wmk sideways

(a) P 11 (1909–10)

59	**6**	½d. black and yellow-green (12.09)	2·50	3·00
		a. *Black and deep green* (1910)	28·00	42·00
60		1d. black and carmine (1.10)	9·50	8·00
61		2d. black and purple (1.10)	27·00	8·00
62		2½d. black and dull blue (1.10)	4·50	26·00
		a. Thin "d" at left	90·00	£200
63		4d. black and sepia (1.10)	4·75	9·00
		a. Deformed "d" at left	£140	£170
64		6d. black and myrtle-green (11.09)	10·00	22·00
65		1s. black and orange (10.08)	55·00	75·00

(b) P 12½ (1909–10)

66	**6**	½d. black and yellow-green (12.09)	4·00	4·00
		a. *Black and deep green* (1910)	32·00	45·00
67		1d. black and carmine (1.10)	7·50	12·00
68		2d. black and purple (1.10)	10·00	14·00
69		2½d. black and dull blue (1.10)	10·00	45·00
		a. Thin "d" at left	£130	£275
70		6d. black and myrtle-green (11.09)	£5500	£14000
71		1s. black and orange (3.10)	19·00	65·00

(c) Perf compound of 11 and 12½

72	**6**	½d. black and yellow-green (12.09)	£5500	£5500
73		2d. black and purple (1.10)	£1700	

(d) Mixed perfs 11 and 12½

74	**6**	4d. black and sepia (1.10)	£16000	

Compound perforations on the 4d. are fakes.

The only known examples of No. 74 come from the top row of a sheet perforated 11 and with an additional line perf 12½ in the top margin.

Note that Nos. 59a and 66a are a strong shade of deep green, without any hint of yellow. They should not be confused with darker shades of the yellow-green, Nos. 59 and 66.

(Litho Stamp Ptg Branch, Melbourne, by J. B. Cooke, from new stones made from fresh transfers)

1910 (Sept)–11. Large "PAPUA". W w **11** (upright). P 12½.

75	**5**	½d. black and green (12.10)	4·75	15·00
76		1d. black and carmine	14·00	16·00
77		2d. black and dull purple (*shades*) (12.10)	6·50	5·00
		a. "C" for "O" in "POSTAGE" (R. 4/3)	£140	£130
78		2½d. black and blue-violet (10.10)	13·00	18·00
		a. Thin "d" at left	£130	£180
79		4d. black and sepia (10.10)	12·00	11·00
		a. Deformed "d" at left	£190	£190
80		6d. black and myrtle-green	8·50	13·00
81		1s. black and deep orange (12.10)	13·00	20·00
82		2s.6d. black and brown (B)	60·00	60·00
83		2s.6d. black and brown (C) (1911)	75·00	75·00
75/82 *Set of 8*			£110	£140

A variety showing a white line or "rift" in clouds occurs on R. 5/3 in Nos. 49/74 and the "white leaves" variety mentioned below No. 16 occurs on the 2d. and 2½d. values in both issues. Both are worth about three times the normal price.

ONE PENNY

8 **(9)**

(Eng S. Reading. Typo J. B. Cooke)

1911–15. Printed in one colour. W **8** (sideways*).

(a) P 12½ (1911–12)

84	**6**	½d. yellow-green (1911–12)	2·25	3·75
		a. Green	70	2·25
		w. Wmk Crown to right of A	24·00	
85		1d. rose-pink	2·00	75
		w. Wmk Crown to right of A	65·00	65·00
86		2d. bright mauve	4·00	75
		w. Wmk Crown to right of A	£170	£120
87		2½d. bright ultramarine	6·50	8·50
		a. Dull ultramarine	8·50	8·50
		aw. Wmk Crown to right of A	£180	
88		4d. pale olive-green	2·25	11·00
		w. Wmk Crown to right of A	£225	£180
89		6d. orange-brown	3·75	5·00
		w. Wmk Crown to right of A	£250	
90		1s. yellow	9·50	15·00
		w. Wmk Crown to right of A	£275	
91		2s.6d. rose-carmine	42·00	50·00
		w. Wmk Crown to right of A	£500	£750
84/91 *Set of 8*			60·00	85·00

(b) P 14

92	**6**	1d. rose-pink (6.15)	40·00	7·00
		a. Pale scarlet	22·00	2·00
		w. Wmk Crown to right of A	—	£225

*The normal sideways watermark shows Crown to left of A, *as seen from the back of the stamp.*

(Typo J. B. Cooke (1916–18), T. S. Harrison (1918–26), A. J. Mullett (No. 95*b* only) (1926–27), or John Ash (1927–31))

1916 (Aug)–**31**. Printed in two colours. W **8** (sideways*). P 14.

93	**6**	½d. myrtle and apple green (Harrison) (1919)	80	1·00
		a. Myrtle and pale olive-green (Ash) (1927)	1·75	3·25
		w. Wmk Crown to right of A	27·00	32·00
94		1d. black and carmine-red	1·75	1·25
		aw. Wmk Crown to right of A		
		b. Grey-black and red (1918)	1·75	1·25
		bw. Wmk Crown to right of A	5·50	50
		c. Intense black and red (Harrison) (wmk Crown to right of A) (1926)	2·50	2·50
95		1½d. pale grey-blue (*shades*) and brown (1925)	1·50	80
		aw. Wmk Crown to right of A	22·00	8·00
		b. Cobalt and light brown (Mullett) (wmk Crown to right of A) (1927)	10·00	3·25
		c. Bright blue and bright brown (1929)	3·00	2·00
		d. "POSTAGE" at right (R.1/1) (all printings)	From 40·00	40·00
96		2d. brown-purple and brown-lake (1919)	1·75	75
		a. Deep brown-purple and lake (1931)	25·00	1·75
		aw. Wmk Crown to right of A	42·00	5·00
		b. Brown-purple and claret (1931)	2·00	75
97		2½d. myrtle and ultramarine (1919)	4·75	12·00
98		3d. black and bright blue-green (12.16)	4·50	1·75
		a. Error. Black and deep greenish Prussian blue†	£1300	£1300
		b. Sepia-black and bright blue-green (Harrison)	22·00	20·00
		c. Black and blue-green (1927)	4·50	8·00
99		4d. brown and orange (1919)	2·50	5·00
		a. Light brown and orange (1927)	21·00	18·00
		aw. Wmk Crown to right of A	17·00	30·00
100		5d. bluish slate and pale brown (1931)	4·25	16·00
101		6d. dull and pale purple (*wmk Crown to right of A*) (1919)	4·50	9·50
		aw. Wmk Crown to left of A	32·00	
		b. Dull purple and red-purple (wmk Crown to left of A) (1927)	16·00	24·00
		c. "POSTACE" at left (R. 6/2) (all printings)	From 95·00	£140
102		1s. sepia and olive (1919)	5·50	7·00
		a. Brown and yellow-olive (1927)	8·50	14·00
103		2s.6d. maroon and pale pink (1919)	23·00	40·00
		a. Maroon and bright pink (shades) (1927)	20·00	55·00
104		5s. black and deep green (12.16)	55·00	48·00
105		10s. green and pale ultramarine (1925)	£180	£190
93/105 *Set of 13*			£250	£300

*The normal sideways watermark shows Crown to left of A, *as seen from the back of the stamp.*

†Beware of similar shades produced by removal of yellow pigment. No 98a is a colour trial, prepared by Cooke, of which, it is believed, five sheets were sold in error.

The printers of various shades can be determined by their dates of issue. The Ash printings are on whiter paper.

For 9d. and 1s.3d. values, see Nos. 127/8.

1917 (Oct). Nos. 84, 86/9 and 91 surch with T **9** by Govt Ptg Office, Melbourne.

106	**6**	1d. on ½d. yellow-green	1·50	1·60
		a. Green	1·00	1·25
		w. Wmk Crown to right of A	8·00	11·00
107		1d. on 2d. bright mauve	12·00	15·00
		w. Wmk Crown to right of A	£300	
108		1d. on 2½d. ultramarine	1·25	3·75
109		1d. on 4d. pale olive-green	1·75	4·50
		w. Wmk Crown to right of A	£180	£150

110		1d. on 6d. orange-brown	8·50	23·00
111		1d. on 2s.6d. rose-carmine	3·50	6·00
		a. Wmk upright (inverted)	£2250	
106/11 *Set of 6*			25·00	48·00

AIR MAIL

(10) **(11)**

1929 (Oct)–**30**. Air. Optd with T **10** by Govt Printer, Port Moresby.

(a) Cooke printing. Yellowish paper

112	**6**	3d. black and bright blue-green	3·00	19·00
		a. Opt omitted in vert pair with normal	£8000	

(b) Harrison printing. Yellowish paper

113	**6**	3d. sepia-black and bright blue-green	50·00	75·00
		a. Opt double	£4500	
		b. Opt double, one albino	£2500	

(c) Ash printing. White paper

114	**6**	3d. black and blue-green	2·00	10·00
		aa. Opt double (one albino)	£2500	
		a. Opt omitted (in horiz pair with normal)	£8000	
		b. Ditto, but vert pair	£7500	
		c. Opt vertical, on back	£6500	
		d. Opts tête-bêche (vert pair)	£12000	

1930 (15 Sept). Air. Optd with T **11**, in carmine by Govt Printer, Port Moresby.

(a) Harrison printings. Yellowish paper

115	**6**	3d. sepia-black and bright blue-green	£3750	£5500
116		6d. dull and pale purple (Wmk Crown to right of A)	3·00	12·00
		a. "POSTAGE" at left (R. 6/2)	80·00	£150
117		1s. sepia and olive	7·00	20·00
		a. Opt inverted	£15000	

(b) Ash printings. White paper

118		3d. black and blue-green	2·25	6·00
119		6d. dull purple and red-purple	5·50	19·00
		a. "POSTAGE" at left (R. 6/2)	£100	£180
120		1s. brown and yellow-olive	5·00	13·00
118/20 *Set of 3*			11·50	35·00

The rare Harrison printing with this overprint, No. 115, should not be confused with examples of the Ash printing, No. 118, which have been climatically toned.

5d.

TWO PENCE FIVE PENCE

(12) **(13)**

1931 (1 Jan). Surch with T **12** by Govt Printer, Port Moresby.

(a) Mullett printing

121	**6**	2d. on 1½d. cobalt and light brown	12·00	24·00
		a. "POSTAGE" at right (R. 1/1)	£150	£225

(b) Ash printing

122	**6**	2d. on 1½d. bright blue and bright brown	1·00	2·00
		a. "POSTAGE" at right (R. 1/1)	28·00	42·00

1931. Surch as T **13** by Govt Printer, Port Moresby.

(a) Cooke printing

123	**6**	1s.3d. on 5s. black and deep green	7·00	14·00

(b) Harrison printing. Yellowish paper

124	**6**	9d. on 2s.6d. maroon and pale pink (Dec)	6·00	27·00

(c) Ash printings. White paper

125	**6**	5d. on 1s. brown and yellow-olive (26.7)	1·25	2·00
126		9d. on 2s.6d. maroon and bright pink	5·50	9·00

(Typo J. Ash)

1932. W **15** of Australia (Mult "C of A"). P 11.

127	**5**	9d. lilac and violet	9·00	38·00
128		1s.3d. lilac and pale greenish blue	11·00	38·00
127s/8s Optd "SPECIMEN" *Set of 2*			£700	

15 Motuan girl

16 A Chieftain's son

17 Tree houses

18 Raggiana Bird of Paradise

---

19 Papuan dandy

20 Native mother and child

21 Masked dancer

22 Papuan motherhood

23 Papuan shooting fish

24 *Dubu*—or ceremonial platform

25 "Lakatoi"

26 Papuan art

27 Pottery making

28 Native policeman

29 Lighting a fire

30 Delta house

(Des F. E. Williams (2s., £1 and frames of other values), E. Whitehouse (2d., 4d., 6d., 1s., and 10s.); remaining centres from photos by Messrs F. E. Williams and Gibson. Recess J. Ash (all values) and W. C. G. McCracken (½d., 1d., 2d., 4d.))

1932 (14 Nov)–**40**. T **15/30**. No wmk. P 11.

130	**15**	½d. black and orange	4·25	3·75
		a. Black and buff (McCracken) (1940)	19·00	40·00
131	**16**	1d. black and green	3·50	60
132	**17**	1½d. black and lake	4·25	8·00
133	**18**	2d. red	12·00	30
134	**19**	3d. black and blue	4·25	6·50
135	**20**	4d. olive-green	12·00	9·50
136	**21**	5d. black and slate-green	6·50	3·00
137	**22**	6d. bistre-brown	7·50	5·50
138	**23**	9d. black and violet	11·00	21·00
139	**24**	1s. dull blue-green	9·00	8·50
140	**25**	1s.3d. black and dull purple	19·00	28·00
141	**26**	2s. black and slate-green	15·00	24·00
142	**27**	2s.6d. black and rose-mauve	25·00	35·00
143	**28**	5s. black and olive-brown	70·00	55·00
144	**29**	10s. violet	£150	£120
145	**30**	£1 black and olive-grey	£275	£180
130/145 *Set of 16*			£550	£450

31 Hoisting the Union Jack

32 Scene on HMS *Nelson*

(Recess J. Ash)

1934 (6 Nov). 50th Anniv of Declaration of British Protectorate. P 11.

146	**31**	1d. green	2·50	3·50
147	**32**	2d. scarlet	2·25	3·00

148	31	3d. blue	2·50	3·00
149	32	5d. purple	11·00	22·00
146/49		Set of 4	16·00	28·00

HIS MAJESTY'S JUBILEE.

(33)

(34)

MAJESTY'S
Normal

MAJESTY'S
"Accent" flaw (R.5/4)

1935 (9 July). Silver Jubilee. Nos. 131, 133/4 and 136 optd with T **33** or **34** (2d.).

150	16	1d. black and green	1·50	3·25
		a. "Accent" flaw	48·00	85·00
151	18	2d. scarlet	8·00	6·50
152	19	3d. black and blue	4·75	3·50
		a. "Accent" flaw	90·00	£110
153	21	5d. black and slate-green	4·75	3·50
		a. "Accent" flaw	95·00	£120
150/53		Set of 4	17·00	15·00

35

36 Port Moresby

(Recess J. Ash)

1937 (14 May). Coronation. P 11.

154	35	1d. green	45	20
155		2d. scarlet	45	1·25
156		3d. blue	45	1·25
157		5d. purple	45	1·75
154/57		Set of 4	1·60	4·00

Some covers franked with these stamps and posted on 2 June 1937 were postmarked 2 April 1937 in error.

(Recess J. Ash)

1938 (6 Sept). Air. 50th Anniv of Declaration of British Possession. P 11.

158	36	2d. rose-red	3·00	3·50
159		3d. bright blue	3·00	2·50
160		5d. green	3·00	3·75
161		8d. brown-lake	6·00	24·00
162		1s. mauve	25·00	27·00
158/62		Set of 5	35·00	55·00

37 Natives poling Rafts

(Recess J. Ash)

1939 (6 Sept). Air. P 11.

163	37	2d. rose-red	4·00	8·50
164		3d. bright blue	4·00	14·00
165		5d. green	3·50	2·50
166		8d. brown-lake	8·00	6·00
167		1s. mauve	14·00	10·00

(Recess W. C. G. McCracken)

1941 (2 Jan). Air. P 11½.

168	37	1s.6d. olive-green	30·00	42·00
163/168		Set of 6	55·00	75·00

OFFICIAL STAMPS

1908 (Oct). Punctured "OS".

O1	1	2s.6d. black and brown (No. 37)	£1200	38·00
O2		2s.6d. black and brown (No. 45)	£6500	£3750
		a. Thin paper (No. 45a)	£1700	£1700

1908 (Dec)–**10**. Nos. 49/71 punctured "OS".

I. Wmk upright

(a) P 11

O4	6	1d. black and rose	55·00	15·00
O5		2d. black and purple	65·00	5·00
O6		2½d. black and bright ultramarine	£100	40·00
		a. Black and pale ultramarine	60·00	£110
		b. Thin "d" at left	£550	£120
O7		4d. black and sepia	60·00	5·00
		a. Deformed "d" at left	£550	£140
O8		6d. black and myrtle-green	£140	55·00
O9		1s. black and orange	£140	21·00
O4/9		Set of 6	£475	95·00

(b) P 12½

O10	6	2d. black and purple	£110	29·00
O11		2½d. black and bright ultramarine	£350	£140
		a. Black and pale ultramarine	£180	95·00
		b. Thin "d" at left	£1300	£750
O12		4d. black and sepia	£120	9·50
		a. Deformed "d" at left	£900	£120
O13		1s. black and orange	£325	£100
O10/13		Set of 4	£650	£200

II. Wmk sideways

(a) P 11

O14	6	½d. black and yellow-green	55·00	4·75
		a. Black and deep green	90·00	38·00

O15		1d. black and carmine	£110	28·00
O16		2d. black and purple	32·00	2·50
O17		2½d. black and dull blue	75·00	6·00
		a. Thin "d" at left	£650	£110
O18		4d. black and sepia	55·00	11·00
		a. Deformed "d" at left	£500	£225
O19		6d. black and myrtle-green	95·00	6·00
O20		1s. black and orange	£325	90·00
O14/20		Set of 7	£650	£130

(b) P 12½

O21	6	½d. black and yellow-green	48·00	2·25
		a. Black and deep green	80·00	32·00
O22		1d. black and carmine	95·00	4·25
O23		2d. black and purple	60·00	3·25
O24		2½d. black and dull blue	£100	15·00
		a. Thin "d" at left	£850	£180
O25		6d. black and myrtle-green	—	£1400
O26		1s. black and orange	£140	38·00

No. O7 is known with watermark reversed.

1910. Nos. 47/8 punctured "OS".

O27	5	½d. black and yellow-green (wmk upright)	55·00	16·00
O28		2s.6d. black and chocolate (wmk sideways)	£325	£160
		a. "POSTAGIE" at left	—	£4250

1910–11. Nos. 75/83 punctured "OS".

O29	5	½d. black and green	55·00	26·00
O30		1d. black and carmine	£120	21·00
O31		2d. black and dull purple	55·00	26·00
		a. "C" for "O" in "POSTAGE"	£500	£275
O32		2½d. black and blue-violet	75·00	8·00
		a. Thin "d" at left	£600	£150
O33		4d. black and sepia	75·00	7·00
		a. Deformed "d" at left	£750	£150
O34		6d. black and myrtle-green	85·00	7·00
O35		1s. black and deep orange	£130	10·00
O36		2s.6d. black and brown (B)	£160	35·00
O37		2s.6d. black and brown (C)	£180	80·00
O29/36		Set of 8	£700	£120

1911–12. Nos. 84/91 punctured "OS".

O38	6	½d. yellow-green	30·00	2·25
		w. Wmk Crown to right of A	—	80·00
O39		1d. rose-pink	35·00	1·50
O40		2d. bright mauve	35·00	1·50
		w. Wmk Crown to right of A	—	£110
O41		2½d. bright ultramarine	45·00	25·00
O42		4d. pale olive-green	60·00	32·00
O43		6d. orange-brown	60·00	7·00
O44		1s. yellow	£100	18·00
O45		2s.6d. rose-carmine	£160	£110
O38/45		Set of 8	£450	£160

1930. Nos. 93/6a and 98c/103 punctured "OS".

O46	6	½d. myrtle and apple green	25·00	38·00
O47		1d. intense black and red	42·00	12·00
O48		1½d. bright blue and bright brown	28·00	40·00
		a. "POSTAGE" at right	£250	£300
O49		2d. deep brown-purple and lake	48·00	55·00
O50		3d. black and blue-green	£120	£140
O51		4d. light brown and orange	65·00	65·00
O52		6d. dull purple and pale purple	38·00	55·00
		a. "POSTACE" at left	£400	£600
O53		1s. brown and yellow-olive	90·00	95·00
O54		2s.6d. maroon and pale pink	£200	£250
O46/54		Set of 9	£600	£650

O S
(O **1**)

(Typo T. S. Harrison (1d. and 2s.6d.) and J. Ash)

1931 (29 July)–**32**. Optd with Type O **1**. W **7** or W **15** of Australia (9d., 1s.3d.). P 14 or 11 (9d., 1s.3d.).

O55	6	½d. myrtle and apple-green	3·00	4·75
O56		1d. Intense black and red	9·50	19·00
O57		1½d. bright blue and bright brown	2·00	12·00
		a. "POSTACE" at right	75·00	£200
O58		2d. brown-purple and claret	9·50	22·00
O59		3d. black and blue-green	2·75	22·00
O60		4d. light brown and orange (No. 99aw)	3·50	21·00
		w. Wmk Crown to left of A	4·00	25·00
O61		5d. bluish slate and pale brown	6·00	38·00
O62		6d. dull purple and red-purple	4·50	8·50
		a. "POSTACE" at left	£170	£325
O63		9d. lilac and violet (1932)	30·00	48·00
O64		1s. brown and yellow-olive	9·00	30·00
O65		1s.3d. lilac and pale greenish blue (1932)	30·00	48·00
O66		2s.6d. maroon and pale pink (Harrison)	48·00	95·00
		a. Maroon and bright pink (Ash)	55·00	95·00
O55/66		Set of 12	£130	£325

Civil Administration in Papua was suspended in 1942. On resumption, after the Japanese defeat in 1945, Australian stamps were used until the appearance of the issue of the combined territories of Papua & New Guinea.

POSTAL FISCAL STAMP

Stamp Duty.

F **1**

1912 (May) No. 85 Optd with T F **1** by Govt Printer, Port Moresby.

F1		1d. rose-pink	50·00	65·00
		a. Pair, one without opt	£4000	
		b. Opt double	£1600	£1600
		c. "Samp" for "Stamp" (R. 1/1)	£1300	

The use of No. F1 was authorised at Samarai in May 1912 and in early 1913 during shortages of 1d. stamps. Other values, including the 1d. with a curved sans-serif overprint are known used at other offices and at other times, but such use was not authorised.

PAPUA NEW GUINEA
AUSTRALIAN TRUST TERRITORY

Stamps of Australia were used in the combined territory following the defeat of the Japanese in 1945. They remained valid for postal purposes from Papua and New Guinea until 1 March 1953.

The name of the combined territory was changed from "Papua and New Guinea" to "Papua New Guinea" at the beginning of 1972.

SPECIMEN OVERPRINTS. These come from specimen sets in which the lower values were cancelled-to-order, but stamps above the value of 10s. were overprinted "SPECIMEN". These overprints are listed as they could be purchased from the Post Office.

1 Matschie's Tree Kangaroo

2 Buka Head-dresses

3 Native Youth

4 Greater Bird of Paradise

5 Native policeman

6 Papuan Headdress

7 Kiriwana Chief house

8 Kiriwana Yam house

9 Copra making

10 Lakatoi

11 Rubber tapping

12 Sepik dancing masks

13 Native shepherd and flock

14 Map of Papua and New Guinea

15 Papuan shooting Fish

(Recess Note Printing Branch, Commonwealth Bank, Melbourne)

1952 (30 Oct)–**58**. T **1/15**. P 14.

1	1	½d. emerald	30	10
2	2	1d. deep brown	20	10
3	3	2d. blue	35	10

4	**4**	2½d. orange	3·00	50
5	**5**	3d. deep green	50	10
6	**6**	3½d. carmine-red	50	10
6a		3½d. black (2.6.58)	5·00	1·25
7	**7**	6½d. dull purple	1·25	10
		a. Maroon (1956)	9·00	25
8	**8**	7½d. blue	2·50	1·00
9	**9**	9d. brown	2·50	40
10	**10**	1s. yellow-green	1·50	10
11	**11**	1s.6d. deep green	2·75	60
12	**12**	2s. indigo	2·50	40
13	**13**	2s.6d. brown-purple	2·50	40
14	**14**	10s. blue-black	32·00	13·00
15	**15**	£1 deep brown	45·00	15·00
1/15		Set of 16	90·00	29·00
14s/15s		Optd "SPECIMEN" Set of 2	90·00	

(16) **(17)**

1957 (29 Jan). Nos. 4 and 10 surch with T **16** or T **17**.
16		4d. on 2½d. orange	1·25	10
17		7d. on 1s. yellow-green	40	10

18 Cacao Plant | **19** Klinki Plymill

20 Cattle | **21** Coffee Beans

(Recess Note Ptg Branch, Commonwealth Bank, Melbourne)
1958 (2 June)–**60**. New values. P 14.
18	**18**	4d. vermilion	60	10
19		5d. green (10.11.60)	60	10
20	**19**	7d. bronze-green	2·00	40
21		8d. deep ultramarine (10.11.60)	60	1·00
22	**20**	1s.7d. red-brown	6·50	3·25
23		2s.5d. vermilion (10.11.60)	1·50	1·00
24	**21**	5s. crimson and olive-green	2·50	1·00
18/24		Set of 7	13·00	5·50

 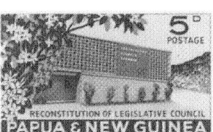

(22) | **23** Council Chamber, Port Moresby

1959 (1 Dec). No. 1 surch with T **22**.
25	**1**	5d. on ½d. emerald	75	10

(Photo Harrison)
1961 (10 Apr). Reconstitution of Legislative Council. P 15×14.
26	**23**	5d. deep green and yellow	75	25
27		2s.3d. deep green and light salmon	2·00	2·50

24 Female, Goroka, New Guinea | **25** Tribal elder, Tari, Papua

26 Female Dancer | **27** Male Dancer

28 Traffic Policeman

(Des Pamela M. Prescott, Recess Note Ptg Branch, Reserve Bank of Australia, Melbourne)
1961 (26 July)–**62**. T **24/8**. P 14½×14 (1d., 3d., 3s.) or 14×14½ (others).
28	**24**	1d. lake	70	10
29	**25**	3d. indigo	30	10
30	**26**	1s. bronze-green	1·00	15
31	**27**	2s. maroon	45	15
32	**28**	3s. deep bluish green (5.9.62)	1·00	2·00
28/32		Set of 5	3·00	2·25

 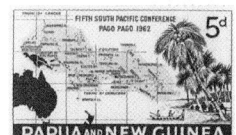

29 Campaign Emblem | **30** Map of South Pacific

(Recess Note Ptg Branch, Reserve Bank of Australia, Melbourne)
1962 (7 Apr). Malaria Eradication. P 14.
33	**29**	5d. carmine-red and light blue	30	15
34		1s. red and sepia	50	25
35		2s. black and yellow-green	60	1·25
33/35		Set of 3	1·25	1·50

(Des Pamela M. Prescott. Recess Note Ptg Branch, Reserve Bank of Australia, Melbourne)
1962 (9 July). Fifth South Pacific Conference, Pago Pago. P 14½×14.
36	**30**	5d. scarlet and light green	50	15
37		1s.6d. deep violet and light yellow	85	1·40
38		2s.6d. deep green and light blue	85	1·40
36/38		Set of 3	2·00	2·75

31 Throwing the Javelin | **33** Runners

(Des G. Hamori. Photo Courvoisier)
1962 (24 Oct). Seventh British Empire and Commonwealth Games, Perth. T **31**, **33** and similar design. P 11½.
39	**31**	5d. brown and light blue	20	10
		a. Pair. Nos. 39/40	40	50
40		5d. brown and orange	20	10
41	**33**	2s.3d. brown and light green	70	75
39/41		Set of 3	1·00	85

Design: (As T **31**)—5d. High jump.
Nos. 39/40 are arranged together se-tenant in sheets of 100.

34 Raggiana Bird of Paradise | **35** Common Phalanger

36 Rabaul | **37** Queen Elizabeth II

(Des S. T. Cham (10s.), A. Buckley (photo) (£1). Photo Harrison (£1), Courvoisier (others))
1963 (13 Feb–3 July). P 14½ (£1) or 11½ (others).
42	**34**	5d. yellow, chestnut and sepia (27.3)	70	10
43	**35**	6d. red, yellow-brown and grey (27.3)	50	1·00
44	**36**	10s. multicoloured (13.2)	8·50	4·50
45	**37**	£1 sepia, gold and blue-green (3.7)	1·25	1·75
		a. Gold ptd double		
42/45		Set of 4	10·00	6·50
44s/5s		Optd "SPECIMEN" Set of 2	90·00	

38 Centenary Emblem | **39** Waterfront, Port Moresby

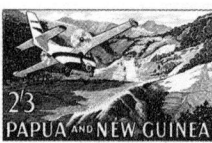

39a Piaggio P-166B Portofino aircraft landing at Tapini

(Des G. Hamori. Photo Note Ptg Branch, Reserve Bank of Australia, Melbourne)
1963 (1 May). Red Cross Centenary. P 13½×13.
46	**38**	5d. red, grey-brown and bluish green	75	10

(Des J. McMahon (8d.), Pamela M. Prescott (2s.3d.). Recess Note Ptg Branch, Reserve Bank of Australia, Melbourne)
1963 (8 May). T **39** and similar horiz design. P 14×13½.
47	**39**	8d. green	30	15
48	**39a**	2s.3d. ultramarine	30	30

40 Games Emblem | **41** Watam Head

(Des Pamela M. Prescott. Recess Note Ptg Branch, Reserve Bank of Australia, Melbourne)
1963 (14 Aug). First South Pacific Games, Suva. P 13½×14½.
49	**40**	5d. bistre	10	10
50		1s. deep green	30	60

(Des Pamela M. Prescott. Photo Courvoisier)
1964 (5 Feb). Native Artefacts. T **41** and similar vert designs. Multicoloured. P 11½.
51		11d. Type **41**	25	10
52		2s.5d. Watam Head (different)	30	1·75
53		2s.6d. Bosmun Head	30	10
54		5s. Medina Head	35	20
51/54		Set of 4	1·10	1·75

45 Casting Vote | **46** "Health Centres"

(Photo Courvoisier)
1964 (4 Mar). Common Roll Elections. P 11½.
55	**45**	5d. brown and drab	10	10
56		2s.3d. brown and pale blue	20	25

(Recess Note Ptg Branch, Reserve Bank of Australia, Melbourne)
1964 (5 Aug). Health Services. T **46** and similar vert designs. P 14.
57		5d. violet	10	10
58		8d. bronze-green	10	10
59		1s. blue	15	10
60		1s.2d. brown-red	20	35
57/60		Set of 4	50	60

Designs:—8d. "School health"; 1s. "Infant, child and maternal health"; 1s.2d. "Medical training".

50 Striped Gardener Bowerbird | **51** Emperor of Germany Bird of Paradise

(Photo Courvoisier)
1964 (28 Oct)–**65**. Vert designs as T **50** (1d. to 8d.) or **51** (others). Multicoloured; background colours given. P 11½ (1d. to 8d.) or 12×11½ (1s. to 10s.).
61	**50**	1d. pale olive-yellow (20.1.65)	40	10
62		3d. light grey (20.1.65)	40	30
63		5d. pale red (20.1.65)	40	10
64		6d. pale green	50	10
65		8d. lilac	1·00	20
66	**51**	1s. salmon	1·25	10

67	2s. light blue (20.1.65)		50	30
68	2s.3d. light green (20.1.65)		50	85
69	3s. pale yellow (20.1.65)		50	1·25
70	5s. cobalt (20.1.65)		5·00	1·00
71	10s. pale drab		1·25	6·50
	s. Optd "SPECIMEN"		85·00	
61/71 *Set of 11*			10·00	9·50

Designs:—3d. Adelbert Bowerbird; 5d. Blue Bird of Paradise; 6d. Lawes's Parotia; 8d. Black-billed Sicklebill; 2s. Brown Sicklebill; 2s.3d. Lesser Bird of Paradise; 3s. Magnificent Bird of Paradise; 5s. Twelve-wired Bird of Paradise; 10s. Magnificent Riflebird.

61 Canoe Prow

(Des Pamela M. Prescott. Photo Courvoisier)

1965 (24 Mar). Sepik Canoe Prows in Port Moresby Museum. T **61** and similar horiz designs showing carved prows. P 11½.

72	4d. multicoloured		30	10
73	1s.2d. multicoloured		1·00	1·75
74	1s.6d. multicoloured		30	10
75	4s. multicoloured		40	80
72/75 *Set of 4*			1·75	2·50

1965 (14 Apr). 50th Anniv of Gallipoli Landing. As T **22** of Nauru. P 13½.

76	2s.3d. sepia, black and emerald	20	10

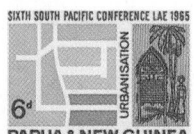

65 Urban Plan and Native House

(Des G. Hamori. Photo Courvoisier)

1965 (7 July). Sixth South Pacific Conference, Lae. T **65** and similar horiz design. P 11½.

77	6d. multicoloured		10	10
78	1s. multicoloured		10	10

No. 78 is similar to T **65** but with the plan on the right and the house on the left. Also "URBANISATION" reads downwards.

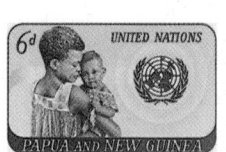

66 Mother and Child **67** Globe and UN Emblem

(Photo Courvoisier)

1965 (13 Oct). 20th Anniv of UNO T **66/7** and similar vert design. P 11½.

79	**66**	6d. sepia, blue and pale turquoise-blue		10	10
80	**67**	1s. orange-brown, blue and reddish violet		10	10
81		2s. blue, blue-green and light yellow-olive		10	10
79/81 *Set of 3*				25	25

Design:—2s. UN Emblem and globes.

(New Currency. 100 cents = 1 Australian dollar)

69 *Papilio ulysses* **71** *Ornithoptera priamus*

$1 Plate I

Black line through left blue patch on wing consists of two dots only. There are two blue lines extending from upper right edge of right wing towards two small patches of blue.

$1 Plate II

The black line through left blue patch on wing is continuous. Blue lines at upper right edge of wing are omitted. There is an extra short faint blue line extending from edge of lower right wing which is absent in Plate I.

$2 Plate I

In the lower left of the butterfly there are two short black lines from the edge to the yellow part.

In the lower part of the upper right wing there is a series of indeterminate short lines and dots.

$2 Plate II

The two black lines at lower left are lacking.

There are clear fine lines of shading in place of the thicker lines.

There are numerous other minor differences between the two plates of each value and also slight variations in the shades.

(Photo Courvoisier)

1966 (14 Feb)–**67**. Decimal Currency. Butterflies. Vert designs as T **69** (1 to 5c.), or horiz as T **71** (others). Multicoloured. P 11½.

82	1c. Type **69**		40	75
83	3c. *Cyrestis acilia*		40	1·00
84	4c. *Graphium weiskei*		40	1·00
85	5c. *Terinos alurgis*		40	10
86	10c. Type **71**		40	30
86a	12c. *Euploea callithoe* (12.10)		4·50	2·25
87	15c. *Papilio euchenor*		1·00	80
88	20c. *Parthenos sylvia*		40	10
89	25c. *Delias aruna*		50	1·00
90	50c. *Apaturina erminea*		8·00	1·00
91	$1 *Doleschallia dascylus* (Plate I)		2·50	2·00
	a. Plate II (8.67)		4·50	2·50
92	$2 *Ornithoptera paradisea* (Plate I)		3·50	10·00
	a. Plate II (8.67)		8·50	10·00
82/92 *Set of 12*			20·00	18·00

80 "Molala Harai" **84** Throwing the Discus

(Des Rev. H. A. Brown. Photo Courvoisier)

1966 (8 June). Folklore. Elema Art (1st series). T **80** and similar vert designs. P 11½.

93	2c. black and carmine		10	10
94	7c. black, light yellow and light blue		10	65
95	30c. black, carmine and apple-green		15	15
96	60c. black, carmine and yellow		40	65
93/96 *Set of 4*			65	1·40

Designs:—7c. "Marai"; 30c. "Meavea Kivovia"; 60c. "Toivita Tapaivita". Nos. 93/6 were supplementary values to the decimal currency definitive issue.

See also Nos. 152/5. A further set was issued in 1977.

(Photo Courvoisier)

1966 (31 Aug). South Pacific Games, Nouméa. T **84** and similar vert designs. Multicoloured. P 11½.

97	5c. Type **84**		10	10
98	10c. Football		15	10
99	20c. Tennis		20	40
97/99 *Set of 3*			40	55

87 *Mucuna novoguineensis* **91** "Fine Arts"

(Des Mrs. D. Pearce. Photo Courvoisier)

1966 (7 Dec). Flowers. T **87** and similar vert designs. Multicoloured. P 11½.

100	5c. Type **87**		15	10
101	10c. *Tecomanthe dendrophila*		15	10
102	20c. *Rhododendron macgregoriae*		20	10
103	60c. *Rhododendron konori*		50	1·40
100/3 *Set of 4*			90	1·50

(Des G. Hamori. Photo Courvoisier)

1967 (8 Feb). Higher Education. T **91** and similar horiz designs. Multicoloured. P 12½×12.

104	1c. Type **91**		10	10
105	3c. "Surveying"		10	15
106	4c. "Civil Engineering"		10	15
107	5c. "Science"		10	10
108	20c. "Law"		15	10
104/8 *Set of 5*			45	45

96 *Sagra speciosa* **100** Laloki River

(Des Pamela M. Prescott. Photo Courvoisier)

1967 (12 Apr). Fauna Conservation (Beetles). T **96** and similar vert designs. Multicoloured. P 11½.

109	5c. Type **96**		15	10
110	10c. *Eupholus schoenherri*		15	10
111	20c. *Sphingnotus albertisi*		25	10
112	25c. *Cyphogastra albertisi*		25	10
109/12 *Set of 4*			70	35

(Des G. Wade. Photo Courvoisier)

1967 (28 June). Laloki River Hydro-Electric Scheme, and "New Industries". T **100** and similar vert designs. Multicoloured. P 12½.

113	5c. Type **100**		10	10
114	10c. Pyrethrum		10	10
115	20c. Tea Plant		15	10
116	25c. Type **100**		15	10
113/16 *Set of 4*			45	35

103 Air Attack at Milne Bay **107** Papuan Lory

(Des R. Hodgkinson (2c.), F. Hodgkinson (5c.), G. Wade (20c., 50c.). Photo Courvoisier)

1967 (30 Aug). 25th Anniv of the Pacific War. T **103** and similar multicoloured designs. P 11½.

117	2c. Type **103**		10	50
118	5c. Kokoda Trail (*vert*)		10	10
119	20c. The Coast Watchers		25	10
120	50c. Battle of the Coral Sea		80	70
117/20 *Set of 4*			1·10	1·25

(Des T. Walcot. Photo Courvoisier)

1967 (29 Nov). Christmas. Territory Parrots. T **107** and similar vert designs. Multicoloured. P 12½.

121	5c. Type **107**		20	10
122	7c. Pesquet's Parrot		25	90
123	20c. Dusky Lory		30	10
124	25c. Edward's Fig Parrot		35	10
121/24 *Set of 4*			1·00	1·10

111 Chimbu Headdresses **112**

(Des P. Jones. Photo Courvoisier)

1968 (21 Feb). "National Heritage". T **111**/12 and similar multicoloured designs. P 12×12½ (5, 60c.) or 12½×12 (10, 20c.).

125	5c. Type **111**		10	10
126	10c. Southern Highlands Headdress (*horiz*)		15	10
127	20c. Western Highlands Headdress (*horiz*)		15	10
128	60c. Type **112**		40	45
125/28 *Set of 4*			70	65

115 *Hyla thesaurensis*   **119** Human Rights Emblem and Papuan Headdress (abstract)

(Des and photo Courvoisier)

1968 (24 Apr). Fauna Conservation (Frogs). T **115** and similar horiz designs. Multicoloured. P 11½.

129	5c. Type **115**		15	10
130	10c. *Hyla iris*		15	20
131	15c. *Ceratobatrachus guentheri*		15	30
132	20c. *Nyctimystes narinosa*		20	60
129/32 *Set of 4*			60	1·10

(Des G. Hamori. Litho Enschedé)

1968 (26 June). Human Rights Year. T **119** and similar horiz design. Multicoloured. P 13½×12½.

133	5c. Type **119**		10	10
134	10c. Human Rights in the World (abstract)		10	10

121 Leadership (abstract)   **123** Common Egg Cowrie (*Ovula ovum*)

(Des G. Hamori. Litho Enschedé)

1968 (26 June). Universal Suffrage. T **121** and similar horiz design. Multicoloured. P 13½×12½.

135	20c. Type **121**		15	20
136	25c. Leadership of the community (abstract)		15	30

(Des P. Jones. Photo Courvoisier)

1968–69. Sea Shells. Multicoloured designs as T **123**. P 12×12½ ($2), 12½×12 (1c. to 20c.) or 11½ (others).

137	1c. Type **123** (29.1.69)		10	10
138	3c. Laciniate Conch (*Strombus sinuatus*) (30.10.68)		30	1·25
139	4c. Lithograph Cone (*Conus litoglyphus*) (29.1.69)		20	1·25
140	5c. Marbled Cone (*Conus marmoreus marmoreus*) (28.8.68)		25	10
141	7c. Episcopal Mitre (*Mitra mitra*) (29.1.69)		35	10
142	10c. *Cymbiola rutila ruckeri* (30.10.68)		45	10
143	12c. Checkerboard Bonnet (*Phalium areola*) (29.1.69)		1·25	1·50
144	15c. Scorpion Conch (*Lambis scorpius*) (30.10.68)		45	75
145	20c. Fluted Giant Clam or Scale Tridacna (*Tridacna sqamosa*) (28.8.68)		50	10
146	25c. Camp Pitar Venus (*Lioconcha castrensis*) (28.8.68)		50	1·40
147	30c. Ramose Murex (*Murex ramosus*) (28.8.68)		50	75
148	40c. Chambered or Pearly Nautilus (*Nautilus pompilius*) (30.10.68)		50	1·00
149	60c. Trumpet Triton (*Charonia tritonis*) (28.8.68)		50	35
150	$1 Manus Green Papuina (*Papuina pulcherrima*) (30.10.68)		1·00	45
151	$2 Glory of the Sea Cone (*Conus gloriamaris*) (*vert*) (29.1.69)		7·00	1·00
137/51 *Set of 15*			12·00	9·00

The 1, 5, 7, 15, 40, 60c. and $1 exist with PVA gum as well as gum arabic.

138 Tito Myth   **139** Iko Myth

140 Luvuapo Myth   **141** Miro Myth

(Des from native motifs by Revd. H. A. Brown. Litho Enschedé)

1969 (9 Apr). Folklore. Elema Art (2nd series). P 12½×13½×Roul 9 between *se-tenant* pairs.

152	**138**	5c. black, yellow and red	10	60
		a. Pair. Nos. 152/3	20	1·10
153	**139**	5c. black, yellow and red	10	60
154	**140**	10c. black, grey and red	15	60
		a. Pair. Nos. 154/5	30	1·10
155	**141**	10c. black, grey and red	15	60
152/55 *Set of 4*			45	2·00

Nos. 152/3 and 154/5 were issued in vertical *se-tenant* pairs, separated by a line of roulette.

142 "Fireball" class Dinghy   **145** *Dendrobium ostrinoglossum*

(Des J. Fallas. Recess Note Ptg Branch, Reserve Bank of Australia)

1969 (25 June). Third South Pacific Games, Port Moresby. T **142** and similar designs. P 14×14½ (5c.) or 14½×14 (others).

156	5c. black		10	10
157	10c. deep bluish violet		10	20
158	20c. myrtle-green		15	30
156/58 *Set of 3*			30	50

Designs: Horiz—10c. Swimming pool, Boroko; 20c. Games arena, Konedobu.

(Des P. Jones. Photo Courvoisier)

1969 (27 Aug). Flora conservation (Orchids). T **145** and similar vert designs. Multicoloured. P 11½.

159	5c. Type **145**		25	10
160	10c. *Dendrobium lawesii*		25	70
161	20c. *Dendrobium pseudofrigidum*		30	90
162	30c. *Dendrobium conanthum*		30	70
159/62 *Set of 4*			1·00	2·25

149 Bird of Paradise   **150** Native Potter

(Des G. Hamori. Photo Note Ptg Branch, Reserve Bank of Australia)

1969 (24 Sept)–**71**. Coil stamps. P 15×imperf.

162*a*	**149**	2c. blue, black and red (1.4.71)	10	65
163		5c. bright green, brown and red-orange	10	10

(Des G. Hamori. Photo Courvoisier)

1969 (24 Sept). 50th Anniv of International Labour Organization. P 11½.

164	**150**	5c. multicoloured	10	10

151 Tareko   **155** Prehistoric Ambun Stone

(Des G. Hamori. Photo Courvoisier)

1969 (29 Oct). Musical Instruments. T **151** and similar horiz designs. P 12½×12.

165	5c. multicoloured		10	10
166	10c. black, olive-green and pale yellow		10	10
167	25c. black, yellow and brown		15	15
168	30c. multicoloured		25	15
165/68 *Set of 4*			55	45

Designs:—10c. Garamut; 25c. Iviliko; 30c. Kundu.

(Des R. Bates. Photo Courvoisier)

1970 (11 Feb). "National Heritage". T **155** and similar horiz designs. Multicoloured. P 12½×12.

169	5c. Type **155**		10	10
170	10c. Masawa canoe of Kula circuit		10	10
171	25c. Torres' Map, 1606		40	15
172	30c. HMS *Basilisk* (paddle-sloop), 1873		65	25
169/72 *Set of 4*			1·10	55

159 King of Saxony Bird Paradise

(Des T. Walcot. Photo Courvoisier)

1970 (13 May). Fauna Conservation (Birds of Paradise). T **159** and similar vert designs. Multicoloured. P 12.

173	5c. Type **159**		40	15
174	10c. King Bird of Paradise		40	45
175	15c. Raggiana Bird of Paradise		55	80
176	25c. Sickle-crested Bird of Paradise		65	50
173/76 *Set of 4*			1·75	1·75

163 Douglas Dc-6B and Mt Wilhelm   **164** Lockheed L.188 Electra and Mt. Yule

165 Boeing 727-100 and Mt. Giluwe   **166** Fokker F.27 Friendship and Manam Island

(Des D. Gentleman. Photo Harrison)

1970 (8 July). Australian and New Guinea Air Services. T **163**/6 and similar horiz designs. Multicoloured. P 14½×14.

177	5c. Type **163**		25	30
	a. Block of 4. Nos. 177/80		1·00	2·00
178	5c. Type **164**		25	30
179	5c. Type **165**		25	30
180	5c. Type **166**		25	30
181	25c. Douglas DC-3 and Matupi Volcano		35	40
182	30c. Boeing 707 and Hombrom's Bluff		35	60
177/82 *Set of 6*			1·50	2·50

Nos. 177/80 were issued together, *se-tenant*, in blocks of four throughout the sheet.

169 N. Miklouho-Maclay (scientist) and Effigy

(Des D. Gentleman. Photo Courvoisier)

1970 (19 Aug). 42nd ANZAAS (Australian—New Zealand Association for the Advancement of Science) congress, Port Moresby. T **169** and similar horiz designs. P 11½.

183	5c. multicoloured		10	10
184	10c. multicoloured		15	10
185	15c. multicoloured		60	25
186	20c. multicoloured		25	25
183/86 *Set of 4*			1·00	60

Designs:—10c. B. Malinowski (anthropologist) and native hut; 15c. T. Salvadori (ornithologist) and Double-wattled Cassowary; 20c. FRR Schlechter (botanist) and flower.

170 Wogeo Island Food Bowl

(Des P. Jones. Photo Courvoisier)

1970 (28 Oct). Native Artefacts. T **170** and similar multicoloured designs. P 12½×12 (30c.) or 12×12½ (others).

187	5c. Type **170**		10	10
188	10c. Lime Pot		20	10
189	15c. Aibom Sago Storage Pot		20	10
190	30c. Manus Island Bowl (*horiz*)		25	30
187/90 *Set of 4*			65	55

STAMP BOOKLETS

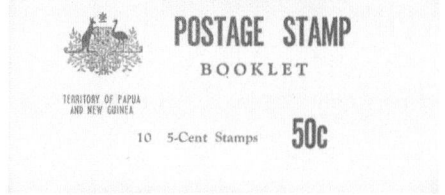

B **1**

1970 (28 Jan). Green on olive-yellow cover as Type B **1**, but "POSTAGE STAMP" in seriffed type. Stamps attached by selvedge.

SB1	50c. booklet containing 5c. (No. 140) in block of 10		£375

1970 (25 May). Green on cream cover as Type B **1** with "POSTAGE STAMP" without serifs. Stamps attached by selvedge.
SB2 50c. booklet containing 5c. (No. 140) in block of 10.. 15·00
No. SB2 shows "GP-P&NG/B112" imprint on reverse.
An example of No. SB2 has been reported containing No. 187 in block of 10.

POSTAGE DUE STAMPS

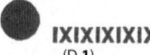

POSTAL CHARGES 6d.

POSTAL CHARGES 3s.

IXIXIXIXIX

(D **1**)   (D **2**)

1960 (1 Mar). Postage stamps surcharged.

(a) No. 8 with Type D **1**
D1 6d. on 7½d. blue (R.) £850 £450
   a. Surch double £4250 £2500

(b) Nos. 1, 4, 6a, 7/8 as Type D **2**
D2 1d. on 6½d. maroon .... 2·50 4·00
D3 3d. on ½d. emerald (B.) .... 5·00 1·25
   a. Surch double £1100
D4 6d. on 7½d. blue (R.) .... 40·00 5·50
   a. Surch double £1200
D5 1s. 3d. on 3½d. black (O.) .... 2·50 1·25
D6 3s. on 2½d. orange .... 10·00 2·25
D2/6 *Set of 5* .... 55·00 13·00

Genuine used examples of No. D1a should be postmarked at Goroko or Kawieng.
Examples of Nos. D1, D1a, D3a and D4a should only be purchased if accompanied by an expert committee's certificate.

D **3**

(Typo Note Ptg Branch, Reserve Bank of Australia, Melbourne)
1960 (2 June). W **15** of Australia. P. 14.
D7 D **3** 1d. orange 50 60
D8 3d. yellow-brown 50 50
D9 6d. blue 55 20
D10 9d. deep red .... 55 1·50
D11 1s. light emerald 55 25
D12 1s.3d. violet 75 75
D13 1s.6d. pale blue .... 2·50 4·00
D14 3s. yellow 75 25
D7/14 *Set of 8* .... 6·00 7·25

The use of Postal Charge stamps was discontinued on 12 February 1966, but they remained on sale at the Philatelic Bureau until 31 August 1966.

Bahamas

The British Post Office at Nassau was established during the early days of the West Indies packet system, and was certainly operating by 1733. The first known local postmark dates from 1802.
The crowned-circle handstamp No. CC1 was issued in 1846 and was generally replaced, for the public mails, by various stamps of Great Britain in 1858.
Local mail deliveries were rudimentary until 1859 when Nos. 1/2 were issued by the colonial authorities for interisland mails. Examples used for this purpose are usually cancelled in manuscript or with a "27" postmark. The "local" 1d. stamp became valid for overseas mails in May, 1860, when the colonial authorities took over this service from the British G.P.O.
For illustrations of the handstamp and postmark types see BRITISH POST OFFICES ABROAD notes, following GREAT BRITAIN.

NASSAU

CROWNED-CIRCLE HANDSTAMPS

CC1 CC **2** BAHAMAS (Nassau) (18.5.1846) (R.
.... *Price on cover* £2250
No. CC1 was later struck in black and used as an Official Paid mark in 1865 and between 1897 and 1937. Handstamps as Types CC **1** and CC **3** (only three known) struck in black were used for the same purpose from 1933 until 1953; but it is believed that these were never employed during the pre-stamp period. *Price on cover from* £50.

Stamps of GREAT BRITAIN cancelled "A 05" as Type **2**.
1858–60.
Z1 1d. rose-red (1857), perf 14 .... £2500
Z2 2d. blue (1858) (Plate Nos. 7, 8) £1600
Z3 4d. rose (1857) £475
Z3a 6d. purple (1854), embossed £5500
Z4 6d. lilac (1856) £375
Z5 1s. green (1856) £2750

PRICES FOR STAMPS ON COVER TO 1945	
No. 1	from × 10
No. 2	—
Nos. 3/6	from × 8
No. 7	—
Nos. 8/11	from × 10
Nos. 12/15	from × 4
Nos. 16/19a	from × 6
Nos. 20/5	from × 15
Nos. 26/8	from × 4
No. 29	—
Nos. 30/2	from × 15
No. 33	from × 30
Nos. 35/7	from × 6
Nos. 38/9	from × 10
No. 39b	from × 30
No. 40	from × 50
No. 41	from × 6
No. 42	from × 15
No. 43	from × 5
Nos. 44/a	from × 10
No. 45	from × 40
Nos. 47/57	from × 4
Nos. 58/89	from × 2
Nos. 90/130	from × 3
Nos. 131/2	from × 10
Nos. 141/5	from × 4
Nos. 146/8	from × 6
Nos. 149/57	from × 3
Nos. 158/60	from × 4
No. 161	from × 8
Nos. 162/75	from × 5
Nos. S1/3	from × 20

CROWN COLONY

1   2   3

(Eng and recess P.B.)
1859 (10 June)–**60**. No wmk. Imperf.
(a) Thick, opaque paper
1 **1** 1d. reddish lake (*shades*)................. £5000 £2250
(b) Thin paper
2 **1** 1d. dull lake (4.60) .... 65·00 £1500
No. 1, the printing on thick opaque paper, is very rare in unused condition. Unused remainders, on medium to thick, but slightly transparent, paper are worth about £250.
Collectors are warned against false postmarks upon the remainder stamps of 1d., imperf, on thin paper.

1860 (Oct). No wmk. Clean-cut perf 14 to 16.
3 1d. lake (H/S "CANCELLED" in oval
    (£8500) £5500 £750
For notes on "CANCELLED" examples see Catalogue Introduction. Examples with this handstamp on No. 3 are imperforate horizontally.

1861 (June)–**62**. No wmk.
(a) Rough perf 14 to 16
4 1d. lake £650 £325
5 **2** 4d. dull rose (12.61) £1400 £400
   a. Imperf between (pair) £38000
6 6d. grey-lilac (12.61) £4250 £600
   a. Pale dull lilac £3250 £500
(b) P 11 to 12½ (1862)
7 **1** 1d. lake £2250
No. 7 was a perforation trial on a new machine at Perkins Bacon. It was not sent out to the Colony and is also known part perforated.

(Recess D.L.R.)
1862. No wmk.*
(a) P 11½, 12
8 **1** 1d. carmine-lake £1000 £190
9 1d. lake £1600 £275
10 **2** 4d. dull rose £3750 £425
11 6d. lavender-grey £11000 £500
(b) P 11½, 12, compound with 11
12 **1** 1d. carmine-lake £2250 £850
13 1d. lake £2500 £950
14 **2** 4d. dull rose £21000 £2000
15 6d. lavender-grey £21000 £1900
(c) P 13
16 **1** 1d. lake £900 £170
17 1d. brown-lake £750 £140
18 **2** 4d. dull rose £2750 £375
19 6d. lavender-grey £3250 £475
   a. Lilac £2750 £450
*Stamps exist with part of papermaker's sheet wmk ("T. H. SAUNDERS" and date).

1863–77. Wmk Crown CC.
(a) P 12½
20 **1** 1d. brown-lake .... £100 70·00
   w. Wmk inverted £190 £120
   x. Wmk reversed .... — £180
   y. Wmk inverted and reversed .. — £180
21 1d. carmine-lake .... £120 70·00
   w. Wmk inverted £190 £100
   x. Wmk reversed .... £130 70·00
22 1d. carmine-lake (aniline) .... £150 75·00
   w. Wmk inverted £250
   x. Wmk reversed
23 1d. rose-red .... 70·00 45·00
   w. Wmk inverted £140
   x. Wmk reversed .... 70·00 45·00
24 1d. red .... 70·00 45·00
   w. Wmk inverted
   x. Wmk reversed .... — 45·00
25 1d. vermilion .... 75·00 45·00
   w. Wmk inverted .... £130 80·00
   x. Wmk reversed .... 75·00 45·00
   y. Wmk inverted and reversed .. £190 £100
26 **2** 4d. bright rose .... £300 60·00
   w. Wmk inverted .... — £250
   x. Wmk reversed .... — 85·00
27 4d. dull rose .... £400 60·00
   w. Wmk inverted .... — £250
   x. Wmk reversed .... £375 60·00
   y. Wmk inverted and reversed .. £1000 £250
28 4d. brownish rose (*wmk reversed*) .. £475 80·00
   w. Wmk inverted .... — £275
29 6d. rose-lilac .... — £2250
   w. Wmk inverted £6500
30 6d. lilac (*shades*) .... £425 75·00
   w. Wmk inverted .... — £250
   x. Wmk reversed
31 6d. deep violet £160 £120
   w. Wmk inverted £650 £250
   x. Wmk reversed .... £180 65·00
   y. Wmk inverted and reversed .. — £250
32 6d. violet (aniline) .... £250 90·00
   x. Wmk reversed .... £250 95·00
(b) P 14
33 **1** 1d. scarlet-vermilion (1877) ...... 70·00 15·00
   x. Wmk reversed .... 85·00 23·00
34 1d. scarlet (or scarlet-vermilion) (aniline) £1000
   x. Wmk reversed
35 **2** 4d. bright rose (1876) .... £400 40·00
   w. Wmk inverted £950 £225
36 4d. dull rose .... £1500 40·00
   w. Wmk inverted
37 4d. rose-lake .... £450 40·00
No. 29 is believed to be the shade of the first printing only and should not be confused with other lilac shades of the 6d.
No. 34 is not known postally used, although manuscript fiscal cancellations on this shade do exist.

(Typo D.L.R.)
1863–80. Wmk Crown CC.
(a) P 12½
38 **3** 1s. blue-green (1865) £2750 £300
(b) P 14
39 **3** 1s. deep green (1865) .... £400 50·00
   aw. Wmk inverted
   b. Green .... £120 30·00
   ba. Thick paper (1880) .... 9·00 11·00
   bw. Wmk inverted (thick paper) .. — £150

1882 (Mar). Wmk Crown CA.
(a) P 12
40 **1** 1d. scarlet-vermilion .... 60·00 14·00
   x. Wmk reversed .... — 65·00
41 **2** 4d. rose .... £550 45·00
(b) P 14
42 **1** 1d. scarlet-vermilion .... £475 60·00
   x. Wmk reversed £600
43 **2** 4d. rose .... £850 60·00
   x. Wmk reversed .... £950 70·00

1882 (Mar)–**98**. Wmk Crown CA. P. 14.
44 **3** 1s. green .... 50·00 14·00
44a 1s. blue-green (1898) .... 38·00 48·00

FOURPENCE
(**4**)   **5**

1883. No. 31 surch with T **4**.
45 **2** 4d. on 6d. deep violet................ £550 £400
   a. Surch inverted £18000 £10000
   x. Wmk reversed £600 £450
Type **4** was applied by handstamp and occurs in various positions. Caution is needed in buying Nos. 45/x.

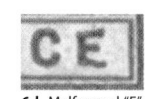

2½d. Sloping "2" (R. 10/6)   **6d.** Malformed "E"

(Typo D.L.R.)

1884–90. Wmk Crown CA. P 14.

47	**5**	1d. pale rose	90·00	14·00
48		1d. carmine-rose	8·00	2·00
49		1d. bright carmine (aniline)	6·00	5·50
50		2½d. dull blue (1888)	85·00	18·00
51		2½d. blue	50·00	8·00
		a. Sloping "2"	£450	£120
52		2½d. ultramarine	15·00	1·75
		a. Sloping "2"	£160	70·00
		s. Optd "SPECIMEN"	65·00	
		w. Wmk inverted	£250	£120
53		4d. deep yellow	9·50	4·50
54		6d. mauve (1890)	6·50	38·00
		a. Malformed "E" (R. 6/6)	£200	£400
		s. Optd "SPECIMEN"	65·00	
56		5s. sage-green	90·00	£100
57		£1 Venetian red	£275	£225
47/57 Set of 6			£350	£325

Examples of Nos. 54/7 are known showing a forged Bahamas postmark dated "AU 29 94".

6 Queen's Staircase, Nassau   **7**   **8**

(Recess D.L.R.)

1901 (23 Sept)–03. Wmk Crown CC. P 14.

58	**6**	1d. black and red	15·00	2·00
		w. Wmk inverted	£170	£170
		y. Wmk inverted and reversed	£300	£325
59		5d. black and orange (1.03)	9·50	50·00
		x. Wmk reversed	£300	
		y. Wmk inverted and reversed	£225	£350
60		2s. black and blue (1.03)	29·00	60·00
		x. Wmk reversed	£425	
61		3s. black and green (1.03)	50·00	65·00
		w. Wmk inverted	£140	£140
		y. Wmk inverted and reversed	£170	£160
58/61 Set of 4			90·00	£160
58s/61s Optd "SPECIMEN" Set of 4			£150	

For stamps in this design, but with Mult Crown CA or Mult Script CA watermarks see Nos. 75/80 and 111/14.

(Typo D.L.R.)

1902 (18 Dec)–10. Wmk Crown CA. P 14.

62	**7**	1d. carmine	1·50	1·50
63		2½d. ultramarine	12·00	1·25
		a. Sloping "2"	£250	£120
64		4d. orange	15·00	60·00
65		4d. deep yellow (3.10)	29·00	75·00
66		6d. brown	8·00	35·00
		a. Malformed "E" (R. 6/6)	£170	£300
67		1s. grey-black and carmine	22·00	55·00
68		1s. brownish grey and carmine (6.07)	22·00	55·00
69		5s. dull purple and blue	80·00	95·00
70		£1 green and black	£300	£350
62/70 Set of 7			£375	£550
62s/70s Optd "SPECIMEN" Set of 7			£300	

Examples of most values are known showing a forged Nassau postmark dated "2 MAR 10".

1906 (Apr)–11. Wmk Mult Crown CA. P 14.

71	**7**	½d. pale green (5.06)	5·00	3·50
		s. Optd "SPECIMEN"	55·00	
72		1d. carmine-rose	27·00	1·25
73		2½d. ultramarine (4.07)	27·00	26·00
		a. Sloping "2"	£350	£400
		w. Wmk inverted	£170	£170
74		6d. bistre-brown (8.11)	17·00	48·00
		a. Malformed "E" (R. 6/6)	£275	£475
71/4 Set of 4			65·00	70·00

1911 (Feb)–19. Wmk Mult Crown CA. P 14.

75	**6**	1d. black and red	25·00	2·75
		a. Grey-black and scarlet (1916)	5·50	2·75
		b. Grey-black and deep carmine-red (1919)	11·00	7·00
76		3d. purple/yellow (thin paper) (18.5.17)	7·00	45·00
		a. Reddish purple/buff (thick paper) (1.19)	7·50	13·00
		s. Optd "SPECIMEN"	50·00	
		x. Wmk reversed	†	£500
77		3d. black and brown (23.3.19)	3·25	2·75
		s. Optd "SPECIMEN"	50·00	
		w. Wmk inverted	†	£500
		x. Wmk reversed	†	£500
78		5d. black and mauve (18.5.17)	3·75	5·50
		s. Optd "SPECIMEN"	50·00	
79		2s. black and blue (11.16)	35·00	55·00
		w. Wmk inverted	£500	
		x. Wmk reversed	†	£500
80		3s. black and green (8.17)	70·00	55·00
		w. Wmk inverted	£350	£350
		y. Wmk inverted and reversed	£170	£160
75a/80 Set of 6			£110	£110

(Typo D.L.R.)

1912–19. Wmk Mult Crown CA. Chalk-surfaced paper (1s. to £1). P 14.

81	**8**	½d. green	80	70
		a. Yellow-green	2·75	17·00
82		1d. carmine (aniline)	3·50	30
		a. Deep rose	8·00	2·25

---

		b. Rose	11·00	3·00
		w. Wmk inverted	£350	£140
		y. Wmk inverted and reversed		†
83		2d. grey (1919)	2·25	3·00
84		2½d. ultramarine	4·75	35·00
		a. Deep dull blue	18·00	42·00
		b. Sloping "2"	£275	£425
85		4d. orange-yellow	5·50	27·00
		a. Yellow	2·50	22·00
86		6d. bistre-brown	1·75	9·00
		a. Malformed "E" (R. 6/6)	£130	£225
87		1s. grey-black and carmine	1·75	9·00
		a. Jet-black and carmine	15·00	22·00
88		5s. dull purple and blue	42·00	70·00
		a. Pale dull purple and deep blue	55·00	80·00
89		£1 dull green and black	£200	£350
		a. Green and black	£275	£375
81/9 Set of 9			£225	£425
81s/9s Optd "SPECIMEN" Set of 9			£325	

1.1.17.   WAR TAX
(9)   (10)

Long stroke to "7" (R. 4/6)

1917 (18 May). No. 75b optd with T **9** in red by D.L.R.

90	**6**	1d. grey-black and deep carmine-red	40	2·50
		a. Long stroke to "7"	40·00	75·00
		s. Optd "SPECIMEN"	65·00	

It was originally intended to issue No. 90 on 1 January 1917, but the stamps were not received in the Bahamas until May. Half the proceeds from their sale were donated to the British Red Cross Society.

1918 (21 Feb–10 July). Nos. 75/6, 81/2 and 87 optd at Nassau with T **10**.

91	**8**	½d. green	14·00	50·00
92		1d. carmine (aniline)	1·00	1·00
		w. Wmk inverted	£300	
		x. Wmk reversed	£400	
93	**6**	1d. black and red (10.7)	4·75	11·00
		a. Opt double, one inverted	£850	
		b. Opt double	£1700	£1800
		c. Opt inverted	£1500	£1600
		x. Wmk reversed	£350	
94		3d. purple/yellow (thin paper)	3·25	3·00
		a. Opt double	£1600	£1700
		b. Opt inverted	£1100	£1200
		c. "W" of "WAR" inserted by hand	£5000	
95	**8**	1s. grey-black and carmine	£110	£160
91/5 Set of 5			£120	£200

No. 93 was only on sale for ten days.

No. 94c occurred on R. 1/1 of one sheet, the original "W" having been omitted as a result of a paper fold.

Examples of Nos. 91/2 with overprint inverted, and of Nos. 91/2 and 95 with overprint double, are now considered to be forgeries.

WAR CHARITY

WAR TAX	**WAR TAX**	**3.6.18.**
(11)	(12)	(13)

1918 (20 July). Optd by D.L.R. in London with T **11** or **12** (3d.).

96	**8**	½d. green	1·75	1·75
		w. Wmk inverted	£300	
		x. Wmk reversed	£200	
97		1d. carmine	4·50	65
		a. Wmk sideways	£200	
		w. Wmk inverted	£170	
		y. Wmk inverted and reversed	£325	
98	**6**	3d. purple/yellow	1·00	1·50
		w. Wmk inverted	£170	
		x. Wmk reversed	£200	
99	**8**	1s. grey-black and carmine (R.)	14·00	7·50
96/9 Set of 4			19·00	10·00
96s/9s Optd "SPECIMEN" Set of 4			£170	

1919 (21 Mar). No. 77 optd with T **12** by D.L.R.

100	**6**	3d. black and brown	2·25	7·00
		a. "C" and "A" missing from wmk	£1800	
		s. Optd "SPECIMEN"	50·00	
		w. Wmk inverted	70·00	

No. 100a shows the "C" omitted from one impression and the "A" missing from the next one to the right (as seen from the front of the stamp). The "C" is badly distorted in the second watermark.

1919 (1 Jan). No. 75b optd with T **13** by D.L.R.

101	**6**	1d. grey-black and deep carmine-red (R.)	30	2·50
		a. Opt double	£2000	
		s. Optd "SPECIMEN"	55·00	
		w. Wmk inverted	80·00	
		x. Wmk reversed	85·00	95·00
		y. Wmk inverted and reversed	£160	

The date is that originally fixed for the issue of the stamp. The year 1918 was also the bicentenary of the appointment of the first Royal Governor.

WAR   WAR

TAX   TAX
(14)   (15)

1919 (14 July).

		(a) Optd with T **14** by D.L.R.		
102	**8**	½d. green (R.)	30	1·50
103		1d. carmine	1·50	2·25
104	–	1s. grey-black and carmine (R.)	27·00	60·00
		(b) No. 77 optd with T **15**		
105	**6**	3d. black and brown	2·00	9·50
		w. Wmk inverted	70·00	
		ws. Ditto. Optd "SPECIMEN"	£100	
		x. Wmk reversed	75·00	
		y. Wmk inverted and reversed	£130	
102/5 Set of 4			27·00	65·00
102s/5s Optd "SPECIMEN" Set of 4			£170	

16   **17** Great Seal of the Bahamas.

(Recess D.L.R.)

1920 (1 Mar). Peace Celebration. Wmk Mult Crown CA (sideways*). P 14.

106	**16**	½d. green	1·00	6·00
		a. "A" of "CA" missing from wmk	£850	
		x. Wmk sideways reversed	£350	£350
107		1d. carmine	2·75	1·00
		a. "A" of "CA" missing from wmk	†	£650
		x. Wmk sideways reversed	£375	
		y. Wmk Crown to right of CA and reversed	£375	
108		2d. slate-grey	2·75	8·50
		a. "C" of "CA" missing from wmk	£850	
109		3d. deep brown	2·75	9·00
		a. "A" of "CA" missing from wmk	£950	
		b. "C" of "CA" missing from wmk	£950	
		w. Wmk Crown to right of CA	£300	
110		1s. deep myrtle-green	15·00	38·00
		a. Substituted crown in wmk	£1800	
		b. "C" of "CA" missing from wmk	£1800	
		x. Wmk sideways reversed	£650	
106/10 Set of 5			22·00	55·00
106s/10s Optd "SPECIMEN" Set of 5			£170	

*The normal sideways watermark shows Crown to left of CA, as seen from the back of the stamp.

For illustration of the substituted watermark crown see Catalogue Introduction.

1921 (29 Mar)–29. Wmk Script CA. P 14.

111	**6**	1d. grey grey-red (R.)	3·75	4·50
		x. Wmk reversed	£350	
112		5d. black and purple (8.29)	3·75	45·00
113		2s. black and blue (11.22)	22·00	22·00
114		3s. black and green (9.24)	55·00	70·00
111/14 Set of 4			75·00	£130
111s/14s Optd or Perf (5d.) "SPECIMEN" Set of 4			£225	

Examples of all values are known showing a forged Nassau postmark dated "2 MAR 10".

½d. Elongated "E" (left pane R. 9/6)

1921 (8 Sept)–37. Wmk Mult Script CA. Chalk-surfaced paper (3d., 1s., 5s., £1). P 14.

115	**8**	½d. green (1924)	50	40
		a. Elongated "E"	95·00	£100
116		1d. carmine	1·00	15
117		1½d. brown-red (1934)	13·00	1·00
118		2d. grey (1927)	1·50	2·00
119		2½d. ultramarine (1922)	1·00	1·40
		y. Wmk inverted and reversed	†	£800
120		3d. purple/pale yellow (1931)	6·50	11·00
		a. Purple/orange-yellow (1937)	15·00	27·00
121		4d. orange-yellow (1924)	1·50	2·25
122		6d. bistre-brown (1922)	70	1·25
		a. Malformed "E" (R.6/6)	£100	£140
123		1s. black and carmine (1926)	9·50	5·50
124		5s. dull purple and blue (1924)	42·00	65·00
125		£1 green and black (1926)	£180	£375
115/25 Set of 11			£225	£425
115s/25s Optd or Perf (1½d., 3d.) "SPECIMEN" Set of 11			£550	

(Recess B.W.)

1930 (2 Jan). Tercentenary of Colony. Wmk Mult Script CA. P 12.

126	**17**	1d. black and scarlet	4·00	2·75
127		3d. black and deep brown	5·50	15·00
128		5d. black and deep purple	5·50	17·00
129		2s. black and deep blue	18·00	50·00
130		3s. black and green	48·00	85·00
126/30 Set of 5			70·00	£150
126s/30s Perf "SPECIMEN" Set of 5			£180	

18

(Recess B.W.)

1931 (14 July)–46. Wmk Mult Script CA. P 12.

131	**18**	2s. slate-purple and deep ultramarine	27·00	35·00
		a. Slate-purple and indigo (9.42)	£110	50·00

		b. Brownish black and indigo (13.4.43)	15·00	9·50
		c. Brownish black and steel-blue (6.44)	19·00	3·75
132		3s. slate-purple and myrtle-green...	38·00	32·00
		a. Brownish black and green (13.4.43)	13·00	4·50
		ab. "A" missing from wmk....	£1800	
		b. Brownish black and myrtle-green (1.10.46)	8·00	9·00
131s/2s Perf "SPECIMEN" *Set of 2*			95·00	

Most of the stamps from the September 1942 printing (No. 131*a* and further stocks of the 3s. similar to No. 132) were used for the 1942 "LANDFALL" overprints.

1935 (6 May). Silver Jubilee. As Nos. 91/4 of Antigua.

141		1½d. deep blue and carmine	1·00	3·50
		h. Dot by flagstaff	£130	£200
		i. Dash by turret	£325	
142		2½d. brown and deep blue	5·00	9·50
		f. Diagonal line by turret	£180	£250
		g. Dot to left of chapel	£375	£450
143		6d. light blue and olive-green	7·00	16·00
		g. Dot to left of chapel	£250	£325
		h. Dot by flagstaff	£350	
144		1s. slate and purple	7·00	15·00
		h. Dot by flagstaff	£325	£400
		i. Dash by turret	£500	£600
141/4 *Set of 4*			18·00	40·00
141s/4s Perf "SPECIMEN" *Set of 4*			£140	

For illustrations of plate varieties see Omnibus section following Zanzibar.

19 Greater Flamingos in flight   **20** King George VI

(Recess Waterlow)

1935 (22 May). Wmk Mult Script CA. P 12½.

145	**19**	8d. ultramarine and scarlet	9·00	3·75
		s. Perf "SPECIMEN"	80·00	

1937 (12 May). Coronation. As Nos. 95/7 of Antigua. P 14.

146		½d. green	15	15
147		1½d. yellow-brown	40	1·10
148		2½d. bright blue	55	1·10
146/8 *Set of 3*			1·00	2·10
146s/8s Perf "SPECIMEN" *Set of 3*			£120	

½d. Accent flaw (right pane R. 1/5) (1938 ptg only)   **2d.** Short "T" in "TWO" (right pane R. 3/6) (Retouched on No. 152*c*, although bottom of letter is still pointed)

3d. "RENCE" flaw (Right pane R. 9/3. Later corrected.

(Typo D.L.R.)

1938 (11 Mar)–**52**. Wmk Mult Script CA. Chalk-surfaced paper (1s. to £1). P 14.

149	**20**	½d. green	3·50	1·25
		a. Elongated "E"	£180	£225
		b. Accent flaw	£550	£275
		c. Bluish green (11.9.42)	3·75	3·50
		ca. Elongated "E"	£225	
		d. Myrtle-green (11.12.46)	12·00	13·00
		da. Elongated "E"	£425	
149*e*		½d. brown-purple (18.2.52)	1·00	3·75
		ea. Error. Crown missing	£15000	
		eb. Error. St Edward's Crown	£4250	£3250
		ec. Elongated "E"	£180	£300
150		1d. carmine	8·50	1·50
150*a*		1d. olive-grey (17.9.41)	3·50	3·50
		ab. Pale slate (11.9.42)	60	70
151		1½d. red-brown (19.4.38)	1·50	1·25
		a. Pale red-brown (19.4.48)	11·00	3·00
152		2d. pale slate (19.4.38)	19·00	3·50
		a. Short "T"	£950	£375
152*b*		2d. scarlet (17.9.41)	1·00	65
		ba. Short "T"	£140	£120
		bb. "TWO PENCE" printed double...	†	£17000
		bc. Dull rose-red (19.4.48)	8·00	3·25
152*c*		2d. green (1.5.51)	2·25	80
153		2½d. ultramarine	3·25	1·50
153*a*		2½d. violet (1.7.43)	1·25	1·75
		ab. "2½ PENNY" printed double	£6000	
154		3d. violet (19.4.38)	16·00	3·00
154*a*		3d. blue (4.43)	2·50	1·25
		aa. "RENCE" flaw	£3750	
		ab. Bright ultramarine (19.4.48)	10·00	6·50
154*b*		3d. scarlet (1.2.52)	2·75	3·25
154*c*		10d. yellow-orange (18.11.46)	2·50	20
155		1s. grey-black and carmine (*thick paper*) (15.9.38)	35·00	6·50
		a. Brownish grey and scarlet (*thin striated paper*) (4.42)	£1000	£100
		b. Ordinary paper. *Black and carmine* (9.42)	28·00	7·00
		c. Ordinary paper. *Grey-black and bright crimson* (6.3.44)	20·00	75
		d. Pale brownish grey and crimson (19.4.48)	20·00	1·50
156		5s. lilac and blue (*thick paper*) (19.4.38)	£170	£100

		a. Reddish-lilac and blue (thin striated paper) (4.42)	£5000	£700
		b. Ordinary paper. Purple and blue (9.42)	40·00	25·00
		c. Ordinary paper. Dull mauve and deep blue (11.46)	£130	75·00
		d. Brown-purple and deep bright blue (19.4.48)	45·00	19·00
		e. Red-purple and deep bright blue (8.51)	24·00	24·00
157		£1 deep grey-green and black (*thick paper*) (15.9.38)	£250	£150
		a. Ordinary paper. *Blue-green and black* (13.4.43)	60·00	55·00
		b. Ordinary paper. *Grey-green and black* (3.44)	£200	£140
149/57*a Set of 17*			£150	85·00
149s/57s Perf "SPECIMEN" *Set of 14*			£600	

Nos. 149/50*a* exist in coils, constructed from normal sheets.

No. 149eb occurs on a row in the watermark in which the crowns and letters "CA" alternate.

The thick chalk-surfaced paper, used for the initial printing of the 1s., 5s. and £1, was usually toned and had streaky gum. The April 1942 printing for the 1s. and 5s., which was mostly used for the "LANDFALL" overprints, was on thin striated paper. Printings of the three values between September 1942 and November 1946 were on a thick, smooth, opaque ordinary paper.

21 Sea Garden, Nassau   **22** Fort Charlotte

23 Greater Flamingos in flight

3d. (24)

(Recess Waterlow)

1938 (1 July). Wmk Mult Script CA. P 12½.

158	**21**	4d. light blue and red-orange	1·25	1·00
159	**22**	6d. olive-green and light blue	1·25	1·00
160	**23**	8d. ultramarine and scarlet	16·00	3·75
158/60 *Set of 3*			17·00	5·25
158s/60s Perf "SPECIMEN" *Set of 3*			£150	

1940 (28 Nov). No. 153 surcharged with T **24** by *The Nassau Guardian*.

161	**20**	3d. on 2½d. blue	1·50	3·25

1 4 9 2
LANDFALL
OF
COLUMBUS
1 9 4 2
(25)

Broken "OF" and "US" (R. 2/6, late printing)

1942 (12 Oct). 450th Anniv of Landing of Columbus in New World. Optd as T **25** by *The Nassau Guardian*.

162	**20**	½d. bluish green	30	60
		a. Elongated "E"	80·00	
		b. Opt double	£2250	
		c. Accent flaw	£600	
163		1d. pale slate	30	60
164		1½d. red-brown	40	60
165		2d. scarlet	50	65
		a. Short "T"	£130	
166		2½d. ultramarine	50	65
167		3d. ultramarine	30	65
		a. "RENCE" flaw	£3500	
		sa. Opt double, Perf "SPECIMEN"	£950	
168	**21**	4d. light blue and red-orange	40	90
		a. "COIUMBUS" (R. 5/2)	£1200	£1400
169	**22**	6d. olive-green and light blue	40	1·50
		a. "COIUMBUS" (R. 5/2)	£1200	£1500
170	**23**	8d. ultramarine and scarlet	3·50	70
		a. "COIUMBUS" (R. 5/2)	£13000	£4250
171	**20**	1s. brownish grey and scarlet (thin striated paper)	12·00	5·00
		a. Ordinary paper. Black and carmine	12·00	16·00
		b. Ordinary paper. Grey-black and bright crimson	24·00	16·00
		c. Broken "OF" and "US"	£300	
172	**18**	2s. slate-purple and indigo	21·00	29·00
		a. Brownish black and indigo	9·00	10·00
		b. Brownish black and steel-blue...	42·00	35·00
		c. Stop after "COLUMBUS" (R. 2/12)	£5000	£5000
173		3s. slate-purple and myrtle-green...	10·00	6·50
		a. Brownish black and green	55·00	50·00
		b. Stop after "COLUMBUS" (R. 2/12)	£2500	
174	**20**	5s. reddish lilac and blue (thin striated paper)	50·00	25·00
		a. Ordinary paper. Purple and blue	23·00	15·00

175		*b.* Broken "OF" and "US"	£700	
		£1 deep grey-green and blk (*thick paper*)	80·00	£150
		a. Ordinary paper. Grey-green and black	30·00	25·00
		b. Broken "OF" and "US"	£950	
162/75*a Set of 14*			80·00	60·00
162s/75s Perf "SPECIMEN" *Set of 14*			£600	

These stamps replaced the definitive series for a period of six months. Initially stocks of existing printings were used, but when further supplies were required for overprinting a number of new printings were produced, some of which, including the new colour of the 3d., did not appear without overprint until much later.

1946 (11 Nov). Victory. As Nos. 110/11 of Antigua.

176		1½d. brown	10	60
177		3d. blue	10	60
176s/7s Perf "SPECIMEN" *Set of 2*			90·00	

26 Infant Welfare Clinic   **27** Agriculture (combine harvester)

28 Sisal   **29** Straw work

30 Dairy farm   **31** Fishing fleet

32 Hatchet Bay, Eleuthera   **33** Tuna fishing

34 Paradise Beach   **35** Modern hotels

36 Yacht racing   **37** Watersports—skiing

38 Shipbuilding   **39** Transportation

40 Salt production   **41** Parliament buildings

(Recess C.B.N.)

1948 (11 Oct). Tercentenary of Settlement of Island of Eleuthera. T **26/41**. P 12.

178	**26**	½d. orange	40	1·75
179	**27**	1d. sage-green	40	35
180	**28**	1½d. yellow	40	80
181	**29**	2d. scarlet	40	40
182	**30**	2½d. brown-lake	70	75
183	**31**	3d. ultramarine	2·50	85
184	**32**	4d. black	60	70
185	**33**	6d. emerald-green	2·50	80
186	**34**	8d. violet	1·25	70
187	**35**	10d. carmine	1·25	55
188	**36**	1s. sepia	3·00	50
189	**37**	2s. magenta	5·00	8·50
190	**38**	3s. blue	13·00	8·50
191	**39**	5s. mauve	20·00	5·50
192	**40**	10s. grey	17·00	13·00
193	**41**	£1 vermilion	17·00	17·00
178/93 *Set of 16*			75·00	55·00

1948 (1 Dec). Royal Silver Wedding. As Nos. 112/13 of Antigua.
194	1½d. red-brown	20	25
195	£1 slate-green	45·00	32·00

1949 (10 Oct). 75th Anniv of Universal Postal Union. As Nos. 114/17 of Antigua.
196	2½d. violet	35	75
197	3d. deep blue	2·25	3·50
198	6d. greenish blue	55	3·25
199	1s. carmine	55	75
196/9	Set of 4	3·25	7·50

(Des and eng B.W. Recess D.L.R.)

1953 (3 June). Coronation. As No. 120 of Antigua.
200	6d. black and pale blue	1·75	60

42 Infant Welfare Clinic

43 Queen Elizabeth II

(Recess B.W.)

1954 (1 Jan)–**63**. Designs previously used for King George VI issue, but bicoloured with portrait of Queen Elizabeth II as in T **42**, and commemorative inscr omitted. Wmk Mult Script CA. P 11×11½.
201	42	½d. black and red-orange	10	1·50
202	27	1d. olive-green and brown	10	30
203	32	1½d. blue and black	15	80
204	29	2d. yellow-brown and myrtle-green	15	30
		a. Yellow-brown and deep myrtle-green (23.1.62)	13·00	12·00
205	31	3d. black and carmine-red	65	1·25
206	37	4d. turquoise-green and deep reddish purple	30	30
		a. Turquoise-blue and deep reddish purple (23.1.62)	28·00	24·00
207	30	5d. red-brown and deep bright blue	1·40	2·25
208	39	6d. light blue and black	2·50	20
		w. Wmk inverted	—	£1200
209	34	8d. black and reddish lilac	1·75	40
		a. Black and deep reddish lilac (21.11.56)	9·00	2·75
210	35	10d. black and ultramarine	30	10
		a. Black and deep ultramarine (8.1.63)	8·50	2·75
211	36	1s. ultramarine and olive-brown	2·50	10
		a. Ultramarine and deep olive-sepia (19.2.58)	8·50	1·00
212	28	2s. orange-brown and black	5·00	70
		a. Chestnut and black (19.2.58)	19·00	2·00
213	38	2s.6d. black and deep blue	3·50	1·50
214	33	5s. bright emerald and orange	23·00	75
		a. Bright emerald and reddish orange (14.1.59)	90·00	11·00
215	40	10s. black and slate-black	40·00	2·50
216	41	£1 slate-black and violet	32·00	8·50
201/16		Set of 16	£100	19·00

Nos. 201/2, 205, 208 and 211 exist in coils, constructed from normal sheets.
See also No. 246.

(Recess Waterlow)

1959 (10 June). Centenary of First Bahamas Postage Stamp. W w **12**. P 13½.
217	43	1d. black and scarlet	50	20
218		2d. black and blue-green	50	1·00
219		6d. black and blue	60	40
220		10d. black and chocolate	60	1·00
217/20	Set of 4		2·00	2·40

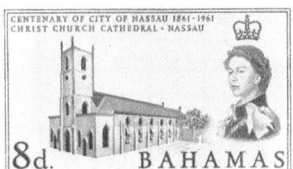
44 Christ Church Cathedral

(Photo Enschedé)

1962 (30 Jan). Nassau Centenary. T **44** and similar horiz design. P 14×13.
221	8d. green	65	55
222	10d. bluish violet	65	25

Design:—10d. Nassau Public Library.

1963 (4 June). Freedom from Hunger. As No. 146 of Antigua.
223	8d. sepia	40	40
	a. Name and value omitted	£1200	£2000

BAHAMAS TALKS 1962
(46)

NEW CONSTITUTION 1964
(47)

1963 (15 July). Bahamas Talks, 1962. Nos. 209/10 optd with T **46**.
224	8d. black and reddish lilac	65	75
225	10d. black and deep ultramarine	65	75

1963 (2 Sept). Red Cross Centenary. As Nos. 147/8 of Antigua.
226	1d. red and black	40	75
227	10d. red and blue	85	2·50

SELF GOVERNMENT

1964 (7 Jan). New Constitution. As Nos. 201/16 but W w **12**, optd with T **47**, by B.W.
228	½d. black and red-orange	15	1·50
229	1d. olive-green and brown	15	15
230	1½d. blue and black	70	1·50
231	2d. yellow-brown and deep myrtle-green	15	20
232	3d. black and carmine-red	2·00	1·75
233	4d. turquoise-blue and deep reddish purple	70	55
234	5d. red-brown and deep bright blue	70	1·50
235	6d. light blue and black	3·50	35
236	8d. black and reddish lilac	70	30
237	10d. black and deep ultramarine	30	15
238	1s. ultramarine and olive-brown	1·50	15
239	2s. chestnut and black	2·00	1·75
240	2s.6d. black and deep blue	3·00	3·00
241	5s. bright emerald and orange	7·00	3·25
242	10s. black and slate black	7·00	5·50
243	£1 slate-black and violet	7·50	27·00
228/243	Set of 16	32·00	42·00

1964 (23 Apr). 400th Birth Anniv of William Shakespeare. As No. 164 of Antigua.
244	6d. turquoise	30	10
	w. Wmk inverted	65·00	

(48)

1964 (1 Oct). Olympic Games, Tokyo. As No. 211 but W w **12**, surch with T **48**.
245	8d. on 1s. ultramarine and olive-brown	45	15

1964 (6 Oct). As No. 204a, but wmk w **12**.
246	2d. yellow-brown and deep myrtle-green	1·50	30

49 Colony's Badge

50 Out Island regatta

51 Hospital

52 High School

53 Greater Flamingo

54 RMS *Queen Elizabeth*

55 "Development"

56 Yachting

57 Public square

58 Sea Gardens

59 Old cannons at Fort Charlotte

60 Sikorsky S-38 flying boat, 1929 and Boeing 707 airliner

61 Williamson Film Project, 1914 and Undersea Post Office, 1939

62 Queen or Pink Conch

63 Columbus's flagship

(Queen's portrait by Anthony Buckley. Litho and recess (portrait and "BAHAMAS") B.W.)

1965 (7 Jan–14 Sept). Horiz designs as T **49/63**. W w **12**. P 13½.
247	49	½d. multicoloured	15	2·50
248	50	1d. slate, light blue and orange	80	1·25
249	51	1½d. red, green and brown	15	4·00
250	52	2d. slate, green and turquoise-blue	15	10
251	53	3d. red, light blue and purple	4·50	30
252	54	4d. green, blue and orange-brown	5·00	3·75
253	55	6d. dull green, light blue and rose	1·50	10
254	56	8d. reddish purple, light blue and bronze green	50	30
255	57	10d. orange-brown, green and violet	25	10
256	58	1s. red, yellow, turquoise-blue and deep emerald	2·50	20
		a. Red, yellow, dull blue and emerald (14.9.65)	2·00	10
257	59	2s. brown, light blue and emerald	1·00	1·25
258	60	2s.6d. yellow-olive, blue and carmine	2·50	3·00
259	61	5s. orange-brown, ultramarine and green	2·75	1·00
260	62	10s. rose, blue and chocolate	16·00	3·50
261	63	£1 chestnut, blue and rose-red	22·00	11·00
247/261	Set of 15		50·00	28·00

Nos. 247/8, 251, 253 and 256 exist in coils, constructed from normal sheets.

1965 (17 May). ITU Centenary. As Nos. 166/7 of Antigua.
262	1d. light emerald and orange	15	25
	w. Wmk inverted	£120	
263	2s. purple and yellow-olive	65	1·40
	w. Wmk inverted	16·00	

(64)

1965 (12 July). No. 254 surch with T **64**.
264	9d. on 8d. reddish purple, light blue and bronze-green	30	15

1965 (25 Oct). International Co-operation Year. As Nos. 168/9 of Antigua.
265	½d. reddish purple and turquoise-green	10	1·60
266	1s. deep bluish green and lavender	30	40

1966 (24 Jan). Churchill Commemoration. As Nos. 170/3 of Antigua.
267	½d. new blue	10	75
	w. Wmk inverted	60·00	
268	2d. deep green	50	30
269	10d. brown	85	85
270	1s. bluish violet	85	1·40
267/70	Set of 4	2·00	3·00

1966 (4 Feb). Royal Visit. As Nos. 174/5 of Antigua, but inscr "to the Caribbean" omitted.
271	6d. red and ultramarine	1·00	50
272	1s. black and magenta	1·25	1·25

(New Currency. 100 cents = 1 Bahamas dollar)

(65) (66)

1966 (25 May). Decimal Currency. Nos. 247/61 variously surch as T **65/6**, by B.W.
273	1c. on ½d. multicoloured	10	30
274	2c. on 1d. slate, light blue and orange	75	30
275	3c. on 2d. slate, green and turquoise-blue	10	10
276	4c. on 3d. red, light blue and purple	2·00	20
277	5c. on 4d. green, blue and orange-brown	2·00	3·00
	a. Surch omitted (vert strip of 10)	£3250	
278	8c. on 6d. dull green, light blue and rose	20	20
279	10c. on 8d. reddish purple, light blue and bronze-green	30	75
280	11c. on 1½d. rose-red, green and brown	15	30
281	12c. on 10d. orange-brown, green and violet	15	10
282	15c. on 1s. multicoloured	25	10
283	22c. on 2s. brown, light blue and emerald	60	1·25
284	50c. on 2s.6d. yellow-olive, blue and carmine	1·00	1·40
285	$1 on 5s. orange-brown, ultramarine and green	1·75	1·50
286	$2 on 10s. rose, blue and chocolate	7·50	4·50
287	$3 on £1 chestnut, blue and rose-red	7·50	4·50
273/287	Set of 15	22·00	16·00

The above were made on new printings, some of which vary slightly in shade, and in No. 273 the shield appears as vermilion and green instead of carmine and blue-green due to a different combination of the printing colours.

No. 277a. One sheet exists and the stamp can be distinguished from No. 252 when in a vertical strip of ten as these were printed in sheets of 100 whereas No. 252 was printed in sheets of 60 (six rows of ten across).

1966 (1 July). World Cup Football Championship. As Nos. 176/7 of Antigua.
288	8c. violet, yellow-green, lake and yellow-brown	35	15
289	15c. chocolate, blue-green, lake and yellow-brown	40	25

1966 (20 Sept). Inauguration of WHO Headquarters, Geneva. As Nos. 178/9 of Antigua.
290	11c. black, yellow-green and light blue	50	90
291	15c. black, light purple and yellow-brown	50	50

1966 (1 Dec). 20th Anniv of UNESCO As Nos. 196/8 of Antigua.
292	3c. slate-violet, red, yellow and orange	10	10
293	15c. orange-yellow, violet and deep olive	35	20
294	$1 black, bright purple and orange	1·10	2·00
292/4	Set of 3	1·40	2·00

67 Oceanic

68 Conch Shell

(Portrait by Anthony Buckley. Litho and recess (portrait, "BAHAMAS" and value), B.W.)

1967 (25 May)–**71**. As T **49**/**63** and additional design (T **67**) but values in decimal currency, as T **68** and colours changed. Toned paper. W w **12**. P 13½.

295	**49**	1c. multicoloured (as ½d.)	10	3·25
		a. Whiter paper (1970)	45	4·50
296	**50**	2c. slate, light blue and deep emerald (as 1d.)	50	60
		a. Whiter paper (1970)	1·40	12·00
297	**52**	3c. slate, green and violet (as 2d.)...	10	10
		a. Whiter paper (1970)	42·00	5·00
298	**53**	4c. red, light blue and ultramarine (as 3d.)	4·75	50
		a. Whiter paper (1970)	10·00	18·00
299	**67**	5c. black, greenish blue and purple	1·00	3·50
		a. Whiter paper (1970)	2·25	11·00
300	**55**	8c. dull green, light blue and sepia (as 6d.)	3·25	10
		a. Whiter paper (1970)	£160	20·00
301	**56**	10c. reddish purple, greenish blue and carmine (as 8d.)	30	70
		a. Whiter paper (1970)	1·00	4·50
302	**51**	11c. rose-red, green and blue (as 1½d.)	25	80
		a. Whiter paper (1970)	1·00	2·50
303	**57**	12c. orange-brown green and olive (as 10d.)	25	10
		a. Whiter paper (4.71)	12·00	29·00
304	**58**	15c. red, yellow, turquoise-blue and carmine (as 1s.)	55	10
		a. Whiter paper (1970)	£250	27·00
305	**59**	22c. brown, new blue and rose-red (as 2s.)	70	65
		a. Whiter paper (1970)	1·50	11·00
306	**60**	50c. yellow-olive, new blue and emerald (as 2s.6d.)	3·00	1·00
		a. Whiter paper (1970)	2·25	7·00
307	**61**	$1 orange-brown ultramarine and slate-purple (as 5s.)	2·00	60
		a. Whiter paper (4.71)	20·00	85·00
308	**68**	$2 multicoloured	13·00	3·00
		a. Whiter paper (4.71)	35·00	£100
309	**63**	$3 chestnut, new blue and purple (as £1)	3·75	2·00
		a. Whiter paper (4.71)	35·00	£100
295/309 *Set of 15*			30·00	15·00
295a/309a *Set of 15* (whiter paper)			£500	£375

*This is the earliest known date recorded in the Bahamas.
The 3c. has the value at right instead of at left as on No. 250.
The 1970–71 printings on whiter paper were released as needed, the 12c., $1, $2 and $3 only a week or two before the issue was withdrawn. Due to the marked difference in paper and the use of some new plates there are marked differences in shade in nearly all values.

69 Bahamas Crest

(Des R. Granger Barrett. Photo Enschedé)

1967 (1 Sept). Diamond Jubilee of World Scouting. T **69** and similar horiz design. Multicoloured. W w **12** (sideways*). P 14×13.

310		3c. Type **69**	35	15
		w. Wmk Crown to left of CA	42·00	
311		15c. Scout badge	40	15

*The normal sideways watermark shows Crown to right of CA, *as seen from the back of the stamp*.

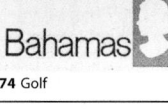

71 Globe and Emblem   **74** Golf

(Des R. Granger Barrett, Litho D.L.R.)

1968 (13 May). Human Rights Year. T **71** and similar horiz designs. Multicoloured. W w **12** (sideways*). P 14×13½.

312		3c. Type **71**	10	10
313		12c. Scales of Justice and emblem............	20	10
314		$1 Bahamas Crest and emblem............	70	80
312/14 *Set of 3*			90	85

*The normal sideways watermark shows Crown to right of CA on the 12c. and Crown to left of CA on the others, *each when seen from the back of the stamp*.

(Litho B.W.)

1968 (20 Aug). Tourism. T **74** and similar vert designs. Multicoloured. P 13.

315		5c. Type **74**	1·50	1·50
316		11c. Yachting	1·00	40
317		15c. Horse-racing	1·50	40
318		50c. Water-skiing	2·00	6·50
315/18 *Set of 4*			5·50	8·00

78 Racing Yacht and Olympic Monument

(Photo Harrison)

1968 (29 Sept). Olympic Games, Mexico City. T **78** and similar horiz designs. No wmk. P 14½×13½.

319		5c. red-brown, orange-yellow and blue-green	40	60
320		11c. multicoloured	40	15
321		50c. multicoloured	60	60
322		$1 olive-grey, greenish blue and violet	2·00	1·50
319/22 *Set of 4*			3·00	2·50

Designs:—11c. Long-jumping and Olympic Monument; 50c. Running and Olympic Monument; $1 Type **78**.

It is understood that the above were released by the Philatelic Agency in the USA on 1st September.

81 Legislative Building

(Des J. Cooter, Litho Format)

1968 (1 Nov). 14th Commonwealth Parliamentary Conference. T **81** and similar multicoloured designs. P 14.

323		3c. Type **81**	10	30
324		10c. Bahamas Mace and Westminster Clock Tower (*vert*)	15	30
325		12c. Local straw market (*vert*)	15	25
326		15c. Horse-drawn Surrey	20	35
323/6 *Set of 4*			55	1·10

85 Obverse and reverse of $100 Gold Coin

(Recess D.L.R.)

1968 (2 Dec). Gold Coins commemorating the first General Election under the New Constitution. T **85** and similar "boomerang" shaped designs. P 13½.

327		3c. red/*gold*	40	40
328		12c. blue-green/*gold*	45	50
329		15c. dull purple/*gold*	50	60
330		$1 black/*gold*	1·25	5·00
327/30 *Set of 4*			2·40	6·00

Designs:—12c. Obverse and reverse of $50 gold coin; 15c. Obverse and reverse of $20 gold coin; $1 Obverse and reverse of $10 gold coin.

89 First Flight Postcard of 1919

90 Sikorsky S-38 Flying Boat of 1929

(Des V. Whiteley. Litho Format)

1969 (30 Jan). 50th Anniv of Bahamas Airmail Service. P 14.

331	**89**	12c. multicoloured	50	50
332	**90**	15c. multicoloured	60	1·75

91 Game-fishing Boats   **92** The Adoration of the Shepherds (Louis le Nain)

(Des J. Cooter. Litho Format)

1969 (26 Aug). Tourism. One Millionth Visitor to Bahamas. T **91** and similar horiz designs. Multicoloured. W w **12** (sideways). P 14½.

333		3c. Type **91**	25	10
334		11c. Paradise Beach	35	15
335		12c. "Sunfish" sailing boats	35	15
336		15c. Rawson Square and Parade	45	25
333/6 *Set of 4*			1·25	60
MS337 130×96 mm. Nos. 333/6			2·75	4·00

(Des G. Drummond. Litho D.L.R.)

1969 (15 Oct). Christmas. T **92** and similar vert designs. W w **12**. P 12.

338		3c. Type **92**	20	20
339		11c. *The Adoration of the Shepherds* (Poussin)	30	30
340		12c. *The Adoration of the Kings* (Gerard David)	30	20
341		15c. *The Adoration of the Kings* (Vincenzo Foppa)	30	65
338/41 *Set of 4*			1·00	1·25

93 Badge of Girl Guides

(Des Mrs. R. Sands. Litho Harrison)

1970 (23 Feb). Girl Guides Diamond Jubilee. T **93** and similar designs. Multicoloured. W w **12**. P 14½.

342		3c. Type **93**	30	30
		w. Wmk inverted		
343		12c. Badge of Brownies	45	40
344		15c. Badge of Rangers	50	50
		w. Wmk inverted	17·00	
342/4 *Set of 3*			1·10	1·10

94 UPU Headquarters and Emblem

(Des L. Curtis, Litho J.W.)

1970 (20 May). New UPU Headquarters Building. W w **12** (sideways). P 14.

345	**94**	3c. multicoloured	10	40
346		15c. multicoloured	20	60

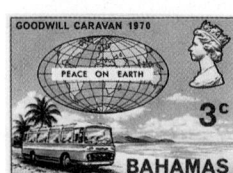

95 Coach and Globe

(Des G. Drummond. Litho B.W.)

1970 (14 July). "Goodwill Caravan". T **95** and similar horiz designs. Multicoloured. W w **12** (sideways*). P 13½×13.

347		3c. Type **95**	85	20
		w. Wmk Crown to right of CA		
348		11c. Diesel train and globe	1·60	60
349		12c. *Canberra* (liner), yacht and globe......	1·60	60
		w. Wmk Crown to right of CA		
350		15c. BAC One Eleven airliner and globe..	1·60	1·75
347/50 *Set of 4*			5·00	2·75
MS351 165×125 mm. Nos. 347/50			9·50	17·00

*The normal sideways watermark shows Crown to left of CA, *as seen from the back of the stamp*.

96 Nurse, Patients and Greater Flamingo

97 The Nativity (detail, Pittoni)

(Photo Harrison)

1970 (1 Sept). Centenary of British Red Cross. T **96** and similar horiz design. Multicoloured. W w **12** (sideways*). P 14½.

352	3c. Type **96**	1·00	50
	a. Gold ("EIIR", etc) omitted	£750	
	w. Wmk Crown to right of CA	35·00	
353	15c. Hospital and Blue Marlin	1·00	1·75
	w. Wmk Crown to right of CA	—	£150

*The normal sideways watermark shows Crown to left of CA, as seen from the back of the stamp.

(Des G. Drummond. Litho D.L.R.)

1970 (3 Nov). Christmas. T **97** and similar vert designs. Multicoloured. W w **12**. P 13.

354	3c. Type **97**	15	15
355	11c. The Holy Family (detail, Anton Raphael Mengs)	20	25
356	12c. The Adoration of the Shepherds (detail, Giorgione)	20	20
357	15c. The Adoration of the Shepherds (detail, School of Seville)	30	75
354/7 Set of 4		75	1·25
MS358 114×140 mm. Nos. 354/7 plus two labels....		1·40	4·25

STAMP BOOKLETS

1938. Black on pink cover with map and "BAHAMAS ISLES OF JUNE" on reverse. Stapled.

SB1	2s. booklet containing 12×1d. (No. 150) in blocks of 6 and 8×1½d. (No. 151) in folded block of 8........	£11000

1961. (15 Aug). Brown-purple cover (3s.) or green cover (6s.) Stitched.

SB2	3s. booklet containing eight each of 1d., 1½d. and 2d. (Nos. 202/4) in blocks of 4........	28·00
SB3	6s. booklet containing four of each of 4d., 6d. and 8d. (Nos. 206, 208/9) in blocks of 4........	35·00

1965. (23 Mar). Pink cover (3s.) or green cover (6s.).

SB4	3s. booklet containing eight each of 1d., 1½d. and 2d. (Nos. 248/50) in blocks of 4........	19·00
SB5	6s. booklet containing four each of 4d., 6d. and 8d. (Nos. 252/4) in blocks of 4........	19·00

SPECIAL DELIVERY STAMPS

SPECIAL DELIVERY

(S **1**)

1916 (1 May). No. 59 optd with Type S **1** by The Nassau Guardian.

S1	**6**	5d. black and orange	7·50	45·00
		a. Opt double	£800	£1200
		b. Opt double, one inverted	£950	£1300
		c. Opt inverted	£1300	£1400
		d. Pair, one without opt	£27000	£35000
		x. Wmk reversed	£850	

No. S1 was issued as a result of a reciprocal arrangement between the Bahamas and Canadian Post Offices, whereby the application of a special delivery stamp from the country of destination would ensure special treatment on arrival. Canadian special delivery stamps were supplied to the Bahamas Post Office but, there being no equivalent in Bahamas, the current 5d. definitive was overprinted "SPECIAL DELIVERY" and sent to Canada.

There were three printings from similar settings of 30 (6×5), and each sheet had to pass through the press twice. The first printing of 600 was on sale from March 1916 at four post offices in Canada; Ottawa, Toronto, Westmount (Montreal) and Winnipeg; and was used in combination with Canadian stamps and cancelled in Canada. Towards the end of 1916, however, the Canadian authorities decided to leave the Bahamas stamps to be cancelled on arrival in Nassau.

The second printing of 6000 was released in February 1917 and the third, estimated to be 1200 to 1800, in March the same year. They were both on sale only in the Bahamas. In August 1917 the Canadian Post Office became aware of the later printings and ordered all remaining stocks at the four offices in Canada to be sold off, bringing the facility to an end.

It is not possible to identify the three printings with certainty without plating both the basic stamp and the overprint. The first printing was applied to stamps from vignette plate 1 only, while the second and third were applied to stamps from both plate 1 and plate 2. In general, the word "SPECIAL" is further to the right in relation to "DELIVERY" in the second printing than the first or third, but this alone should not be considered conclusive.

Our prices for No. S1 are for the second printing and any stamps which can be positively identified as being from the first or third would be worth about ten times (first) or four times (third) as much, either unused or used. Examples on cover, posted at one of the four eligible Canadian offices and with the special delivery stamp cancelled in Canada, are very scarce.

All the errors appear to be from the second printing.

SPECIAL DELIVERY

(S **2**)

SPECIAL DELIVERY

(S **3**)

1917 (2 July). As No. 59, but Wmk Mult Crown CA. Optd with Type S **2** by D.L.R.

S2	**6**	5d. black and orange	60	10·00
		s. Optd "SPECIMEN"	70·00	

1918. No. 78 optd with Type S **3** by D.L.R.

S3	**6**	5d. black and mauve (R.)	40	4·25
		s. Optd "SPECIMEN"	70·00	

Nos. S2/3 were only on sale in the Bahamas.

Bahrain

An independent sheikhdom, with an Indian postal administration from 1884. A British postal administration operated from 1 April 1948 to 31 December 1965.

The first, and for 62 years the only, post office in Bahrain opened at the capital, Manama, on 1 August 1884 as a sub-office of the Indian Post Office at Bushire (Iran), both being part of the Bombay Postal Circle.

Unoverprinted postage stamps of India were supplied to the new office, continuing on sale there until 1933.

Stamps of INDIA cancelled with Type Z **1** (this was normally struck elsewhere on the envelope with the stamps obliterated with "B" enclosed in a circular background of horizontal bars) (1884–86)

1882–90. Queen Victoria (Nos. 84/101).

Z1	½a. deep blue-green	£600
Z2	2a. pale blue	£600

Stamps of INDIA cancelled with Type Z **2** (squared-circle) (1886–1909)

1882–90. Queen Victoria (Nos. 84/101).

Z5	½a. deep blue-green	15·00
Z5a	½a. blue-green	16·00
Z6	1a. brown-purple	17·00
Z6a	1a. plum	17·00
Z7	1a.6p. sepia	60·00
Z8	2a. pale blue	23·00
Z8a	2a. blue	24·00
Z9	3a. orange	65·00
Z9a	3a. brown-orange	25·00
Z10	4a. olive-green	50·00
Z10a	4a. slate-green	48·00
Z11	8a. dull mauve	75·00
Z11a	8a. magenta	70·00

1891. Surch on Queen Victoria (No. 102).

Z12	2½a. on 4a.6p. yellow-green	50·00

1892–97. Queen Victoria (Nos. 103/6).

Z13	2a.6p. yellow-green	18·00
Z13a	2a.6p. pale blue-green	20·00
Z14	1r. green and aniline carmine	95·00

1900–02. Queen Victoria (Nos. 112/18).

Z15	½a. pale yellow-green	21·00
Z15a	½a. yellow-green	23·00
Z16	1a. carmine	22·00
Z17	2½a. ultramarine	42·00

OFFICIAL STAMPS

1883–99. Queen Victoria (Nos. O37a/48).

Z18	½a. blue-green	90·00
Z19	1a. brown-purple	95·00

Stamps of INDIA cancelled with Type Z **3** (single circle, principally intended for use as a backstamp) (1897–1920)

1882–90. Queen Victoria (Nos. 84/101).

Z21	½a. blue-green	40·00
Z22	3a. brown-orange	45·00

1892–97. Queen Victoria (Nos. 103/6).

Z23	1r. green and aniline carmine	£110

1899. Queen Victoria (No. 111).

Z24	3p. aniline carmine	42·00

1900–02. Queen Victoria (Nos. 112/18).

Z24a	3p. grey	£120
Z25	½a. pale yellow-green	32·00
Z25a	½a. yellow-green	35·00
Z26	1a. carmine	32·00
Z26a	2a. pale violet	80·00
Z27	2a.6p. ultramarine	55·00

1902–11. King Edward VII (Nos. 119/47).

Z28	½a. green	30·00
Z29	2a. mauve	35·00
Z30	2a.6p. ultramarine	25·00

1906–07. King Edward VII (Nos. 149/50).

Z31	½a. green	18·00
Z32	1a. carmine	20·00

1911–22. King George V. Wmk Star (Nos. 151/91).

Z33	3p. grey	25·00
Z34	½a. light green	20·00
Z35	2a. purple	42·00
Z36	2a.6p. ultramarine (No. 171)	42·00

OFFICIAL STAMPS

1902–09. King Edward VII (Nos. O54/65).

Z37	2a. mauve	95·00

1906–07. King Edward VII (Nos. O66/7).

Z38	2a. mauve	90·00

Stamps of INDIA cancelled with Type Z **4** (double circle with date band and black lines in centre) (1902–24)

1876. Queen Victoria (Nos. 80/2).

Z40	6a. pale brown	90·00

1882–90. Queen Victoria (Nos. 84/101).

Z40a	½a. blue-green	28·00
Z41	3a. brown-orange	40·00
Z42	4a. slate-green	48·00
Z43	8a. dull mauve	65·00
Z44	12a. purple/red	£120

1892–97. Queen Victoria (Nos. 103/6).

Z44b	1r. green and aniline carmine	£130

1895. Queen Victoria (Nos. 107/9).

Z45	2r. carmine and yellow-brown	£400
Z45a	3r. brown and green	£425
Z46	5r. ultramarine and violet	£425

1899. Queen Victoria (No. 111).

Z47	3p. aniline carmine	22·00

1900–02. Queen Victoria (Nos. 112/18).

Z48	½a. pale yellow-green	18·00
Z48a	½a. yellow-green	20·00
Z49	1a. carmine	22·00
Z50	2a. pale violet	60·00
Z51	2a.6p. ultramarine	45·00

1902–11. King Edward VII (Nos. 119/47).

Z52	3p. grey	14·00
Z52a	3p. slate-grey	16·00
Z53	½a. yellow-green	9·00
Z53a	½a. green	9·00
Z54	1a. carmine	11·00
Z55	2a. violet	25·00
Z55a	2a. mauve	25·00
Z56	2a.6p. ultramarine	14·00
Z57	3a. orange-brown	32·00
Z58	4a. olive	38·00
Z59	6a. olive-bistre	60·00
Z60	8a. purple	80·00
Z60a	12a. purple/red	£130
Z60b	1r. green and carmine	£110
Z61	2r. rose-red and yellow-brown	£250

1905. Surcharged on King Edward VII (No. 148).

Z62	¼a. on ½a. green	38·00

1906–07. King Edward VII (Nos. 149/50).

Z63	½a. green	11·00
Z64	1a. carmine	18·00

1911–22. King George V. Wmk Star (Nos. 151/91).

Z65	3p. grey	20·00
Z66	½a. light green	11·00
Z67	1a. carmine	13·00
Z67a	1a. rose-carmine	13·00
Z68	1½a. chocolate (Type A)	48·00
Z69	2a. purple	28·00
Z70	2a.6p. ultramarine (No. 171)	20·00
Z71	3a. orange	38·00
Z72	6a. yellow-bistre	50·00

1922–26. King George V. Wmk Star (Nos. 197/200).

Z73	1a. chocolate	23·00
Z73b	3a. ultramarine	65·00

OFFICIAL STAMPS

1902–09. King Edward VII (Nos. O54/65).

Z74	2a. mauve	70·00
Z74a	4a. olive	£130

1906. King Edward VII (Nos. O66/7).

Z75	1a. carmine	55·00

1912–13. King George V (No. O85).

Z77	1a. carmine	50·00

1921. King George V (No. O97).

Z78	9p. on 1a. rose-carmine	80·00

Stamps of INDIA cancelled with type Z **5** (double circle without arc) (previously intended for use as a backstamp) (1915–33)

1911–22. King George V. Wmk Star (Nos. 151/91).

Z79	3p. grey	28·00
Z80	½a. light green	18·00
Z80a	½a. emerald	19·00
Z81	1a. aniline carmine	21·00
Z81a	1a. pale rose-carmine	22·00
Z82	1½a. chocolate (Type A)	65·00

Z83		2a. purple	30·00	
Z83a		2a. reddish purple	30·00	
Z83b		2a. bright reddish violet	30·00	
Z84		2a.6p. ultramarine (No. 171)	23·00	
Z85		3a. orange	45·00	
Z86		6a. yellow-bistre	65·00	
Z87		1r. brown and green (shades)	90·00	

1922–26. King George V. Wmk Star (Nos. 197/200).

Z88	1a. chocolate	27·00	
Z89	2a. ultramarine	50·00	

1926–33. King George V. Wmk Multiple Star (Nos. 201/19).

Z90	3p. slate	14·00	
Z91	½a. green	13·00	
Z92	1a. chocolate	11·00	
Z93	2a. bright purple (No. 205)	80·00	
Z94	2a. purple (No. 206)	23·00	
Z95	3a. ultramarine	42·00	
Z95a	3a. blue	38·00	
Z96	4a. sage-green (No. 211)	28·00	
Z97	8a. reddish purple	45·00	
Z98	1r. chocolate and green	55·00	
Z99	2r. carmine and orange	£100	
Z100	5r. ultramarine and purple	£180	

The 1a. is known with inverted watermark.

1929. Air (Nos. 220/5).

Z101	2a. deep blue-green	38·00	
Z102	3a. blue	35·00	
Z103	4a. olive-green	40·00	
Z104	6a. bistre	50·00	

1931. Inauguration of New Delhi (Nos. 226/31).

Z105	¼a. olive-green and orange-brown	55·00	
Z105a	¼a. violet and green	45·00	
Z106	1a. mauve and chocolate	32·00	

Nos. Z101/6 come with watermark sideways to left or right.

OFFICIAL STAMPS

1902–09. King Edward VII (Nos. O54/65).

Z107	2a. mauve	70·00	

1912–13. King George V. Wmk Star (Nos. O73/96).

Z108	½a. light green	40·00	
Z109	1a. rose-carmine	40·00	
Z110	2a. reddish purple	55·00	

Z 6

Stamps of INDIA cancelled with Type Z 6 (double circle with black arc in lower segment) (1924–33)

1911–22. King George V. Wmk Star (Nos. 151/91).

Z115	3p. grey	26·00	
Z116	½a. light green	16·00	
Z117	1a. aniline carmine	18·00	
Z118	2a. purple	28·00	
Z119	6a. yellow-bistre	42·00	

1921. King George V. (No. 192).

Z119a	9p. on 1a. rose-carmine	55·00	

1922–26. King George V. Wmk Star (Nos. 197/200).

Z120	1a. chocolate	17·00	
Z120a	2½a. orange	55·00	
Z121	3a. ultramarine	35·00	

1926–33. King George V. Wmk Multiple Star (Nos. 201/19).

Z122	3p. slate	8·50	
Z123	½a. green	9·50	
Z124	1a. chocolate	8·50	
	a. Tête-bêche (pair)		
Z125	1½a. rose-carmine	55·00	
Z126	2a. bright purple (No. 205)	60·00	
Z127	2a. purple (No. 206)	15·00	
Z128	3a. blue	18·00	
Z130	4a. sage-green (No. 211)	21·00	
Z131	8a. reddish purple	32·00	
Z131a	12a. claret	70·00	
Z131b	1r. chocolate and green	55·00	

The ½a. and 1a. are known with watermark inverted.

1929. Air (Nos. 220/5).

Z132	2a. deep blue-green	22·00	
Z133	3a. blue	23·00	
Z134	4a. olive-green	27·00	
Z135	6a. bistre	30·00	

1931. Inauguration of New Delhi (Nos. 226/31).

Z136	½a. violet and green	35·00	
Z137	2a. green and blue	40·00	
Z137a	3a. chocolate and carmine	38·00	

Nos. Z132/5 and Z136/7a exist with watermark showing stars pointing left or right.

1932–36. King George V. Wmk Multiple Star (Nos. 232/9).

Z138	1a. chocolate	21·00	
Z139	1a.3p. mauve	18·00	
Z140	2a. vermilion	32·00	
Z141	3a. carmine	38·00	

OFFICIAL STAMPS

1926–31. King George V (Nos. O109/20).

Z145	1a. chocolate	50·00	

PRICES FOR STAMPS ON COVER TO 1945	
Nos. 1/14	from × 5
Nos. 15/19	from × 6
Nos. 20/37	from × 2
Nos. 38/50	from × 6

(Currency. 12 pies = 1 anna; 16 annas = 1 rupee)

BAHRAIN
(1)

BAHRAIN
(2)

Stamps of India overprinted with T 1 or T 2 (rupee values).

1933 (10 Aug)–37. King George V. Wmk Mult Star. T **69**.

1	55	3p. slate (11.33)	4·00	45
2	56	½a. green	8·00	6·00
		w. Wmk inverted	80·00	48·00
3	80	9p. deep green (litho)	4·75	6·00
		a. Typo ptg (1937)	24·00	23·00
4	57	1a. chocolate	13·00	3·75
		w. Wmk inverted	48·00	12·00
5	82	1a.3p. mauve	18·00	4·50
		w. Wmk inverted	18·00	4·50
6	70	2a. vermilion	10·00	21·00
		w. Wmk inverted	22·00	21·00
7	62	3a. blue	19·00	75·00
8	83	3a.6p. ultramarine	3·75	40
		w. Wmk inverted	21·00	60
9	71	4a. sage-green	19·00	75·00
10	65	8a. reddish purple	6·00	30
		w. Wmk inverted	†	£130
11	66	12a. claret	7·50	3·50
		w. Wmk inverted	†	£130
12	67	1r. chocolate and green	16·00	15·00
13		2r. carmine and orange	35·00	45·00
14		5r. ultramarine and purple	£300	£250
1/14w Set of 14			£170	£190
			£300	£400

1934–37. King George V. Wmk Mult Star. T **69**.

15	79	½a. green (1935)	12·00	3·25
		w. Wmk inverted	20·00	2·75
16	81	1a. chocolate	13·00	40
		w. Wmk inverted (from booklets)	35·00	70·00
17	59	2a. vermilion (1935)	50·00	7·50
17a		2a. vermilion (small die) (1937)	£100	25
18	62	3a. carmine	6·50	60
19	63	4a. sage-green (1935)	6·50	40
15/19 Set of 6			£170	10·50

1938–41. King George VI.

20	91	3p. slate (5.38)	23·00	9·00
21		½a. red-brown (5.38)	11·00	20
22		9p. green (5.38)	18·00	17·00
23		1a. carmine (5.38)	19·00	20
24	92	2a. vermilion (1939)	5·00	8·50
26	94	3a. yellow-green (1941)	12·00	17·00
27	95	3a.6p. bright blue (7.38)	6·00	15·00
28	96	4a. brown (1941)	£190	75·00
30	98	8a. slate-violet (1940)	£325	35·00
31	99	12a. lake (1940)	£170	55·00
32	100	1r. grey and red-brown (1940)	10·00	3·25
33		2r. purple and brown (1940)	22·00	12·00
34		5r. green and blue (1940)	15·00	13·00
35		10r. purple and claret (1941)	95·00	70·00
36		15r. brown and green (1941)	£325	£350
		w. Wmk inverted	90·00	90·00
37		25r. slate-violet and purple (1941)	£130	£110
20/37 Set of 16			£1000	£450

1942–45. King George VI on white background.

38	100a	3p. slate	3·50	2·50
39		½a. purple	5·50	5·50
40		9p. green	18·00	26·00
41		1a. carmine	8·00	1·00
42	101	1a.3p. bistre	10·00	24·00
43		1½a. dull violet	7·00	8·00
44		2a. vermilion	7·00	1·50
45		3a. bright violet	22·00	7·50
46		3½a. bright blue	6·50	25·00
47	102	4a. brown	11·00	2·00
48		6a. turquoise-green	20·00	12·00
49		8a. slate-violet	16·00	8·50
50		12a. lake	23·00	9·50
38/50 Set of 13			£140	£110

Unoverprinted India Victory stamps, Nos. 278/81, were placed on sale in Bahrain on 2 January 1946 (½a. and 3½a.) and 8 February (9p. and 12a.).

Although the stamps of Pakistan were never placed on sale in Bahrain examples of the 1947 "PAKISTAN" overprints on India can be found cancelled in Bahrain from air mail originating at Dubai or Sharjah.

Stamps of Great Britain surcharged

For similar surcharges without the name of the country, see BRITISH POSTAL AGENCIES IN EASTERN ARABIA.

BAHRAIN
1
ANNA
(3)

BAHRAIN
5 RUPEES
(4)

1948 (1 Apr)–49. Surch as T **3**, **4** (2r. and 5r.) or similar surch with bars at foot (10r.).

51	128	½a. on ½d. pale green	50	1·25
52		1a. on 1d. pale scarlet	50	3·50
53		1½a. on 1½d. pale red-brown	50	5·50
54		2a. on 2d. pale orange	50	20
55		2½a. on 2½d. light ultramarine	50	6·00
56		3a. on 3d. pale violet	50	10
57	129	6a. on 6d. purple	50	10
58	130	1r. on 1s. bistre-brown	1·25	10
59	131	2r. on 2s.6d. yellow-green	5·50	5·50
60		5r. on 5s. red	5·50	5·50
60a	132	10r. on 10s. ultramarine (4.7.49)	95·00	80·00
51/60a Set of 11			£100	95·00

BAHRAIN 2½ ANNAS
(5)

BAHRAIN 15 RUPEES
(6)

1948 (26 Apr). Silver Wedding, surch as T **5** or **6**.

61	137	2½a. on 2½d. ultramarine	1·00	2·75
62	138	15r. on £1 blue	32·00	50·00

1948 (29 July). Olympic Games, surch as T **5**, but in one line (6a.) or two lines (others); the 1r. also has a square of dots as T **7**.

63	139	2½a. on 2½d. ultramarine	1·50	4·75
		a. Surch double	£3500	£4250
64	140	3a. on 3d. violet	1·00	4·25
65	141	6a. on 6d. bright purple	1·50	4·25
66	142	1r. on 1s. brown	2·75	4·25
63/6 Set of 4			6·00	16·00

15 used examples of No. 63a are known, of which 13, including a block of 4, were postmarked at Experimental P.O. K-121 (Muharraq), one on cover from F.P.O. 756 (Shaibah) on 25 October 1948 and one apparently cancelled-to-order at Bahrain on 10 October 1949.

BAHRAIN 3 ANNAS

(7)

1949 (10 Oct). 75th Anniv of UPU, surch as T **7**, in one line (2½a.) or in two lines (others).

67	143	2½a. on 2½d. ultramarine	60	3·00
		a. Lake in India	£150	£250
68	144	3a. on 3d. violet	70	5·50
69	145	6a. on 6d. bright purple	60	3·00
70	146	1r. on 1s. brown	1·25	4·00
67/70 Set of 4			2·75	14·00

BAHRAIN
(7a) Type I

BAHRAIN
Type II

2 RUPEES

2 RUPEES

BAHRAIN
5r. Extra bar (R. 6/1)

Three Types of 2r.:

Type I. As Type **7a** showing "2" level with "RUPEES" and "BAHRAIN" sharp. 15 mm between "BAHRAIN" and "2 RUPEES".

Type II. "2" raised. "BAHRAIN" worn. 15 mm between "BAHRAIN" and "2 RUPEES".

Type III. As Type II, but 16 mm between "BAHRAIN" and "2 RUPEES". Value is set more to the left of "BAHRAIN".

1950 (2 Oct)–55. Surch as T **3** or **7a** (rupee values).

71	128	½a. on ½d. pale orange (3.5.51)	2·50	4·00
72		1a. on 1d. light ultramarine (3.5.51)	3·25	20
73		1½a. on 1½d. pale green (3.5.51)	4·50	13·00
74		2a. on 2d. pale red-brown (3.5.51)	1·50	30
75		2½a. on 2½d. pale scarlet (3.5.51)	4·50	18·00
76	129	4a. on 4d. light ultramarine	5·50	1·50
77	147	2r. on 2s.6d. yellow-green (3.5.51)	45·00	17·00
		a. Surch Type II (1953)	£160	55·00
		b. Surch Type III (1955)	£1700	£140
		ba. "I" inverted and raised (R. 2/1)	£9000	£1000
78	148	5r. on 5s. red (3.5.51)	16·00	7·50
		a. Extra bar	£900	£700
79	149	10r. on 10s. ultramarine (3.5.51)	42·00	11·00
71/79 Set of 9			£110	60·00

1952 (5 Dec)–54. Q.E. II (W **153**), surch as T **3** (in two lines on 2½ and 6a.).

80	154	½a. on ½d. orange-red (31.8.53)	10	1·00
		a. Fraction "½" omitted	£200	£400
81		1a. on 1d. ultramarine (31.8.53)	15	10
82		1½a. on 1½d. green	10	10
83		2a. on 2d. red-brown (31.8.53)	30	10
84	155	2½a. on 2½d. carmine-red	20	1·75
85		3a. on 3d. deep lilac (B.) (18.1.54)	3·00	10
86	156	4a. on 4d. ultramarine (2.11.53)	18·00	30
87	157	6a. on 6d. reddish purple (18.1.54)	3·75	10
88	160	12a. on 1s.3d. green (2.11.53)	3·25	10
89	159	1r. on 1s.6d. grey-blue (2.11.53)	3·25	10
80/89 Set of 10			29·00	3·25

The word BAHRAIN is in taller letters on the 1½a., 2½a., 3a. and 6a.

In early printings of No. 80 the "½" was printed in a separate operation to "BAHRAIN" and "ANNA". Later printings of the ½a. and all printings of other values were printed in a single operation.

2½ BAHRAIN ANNAS

(8)

1953 (3 June). Coronation. Surch as T **8**, or similarly.

90	**161**	2½a. on 2½d. carmine-red	1·25	75
91	**162**	4a. on 4d. ultramarine	2·25	8·00
92	**163**	12a. on 1s.3d. deep yellow-green	6·00	6·50
93	**164**	1r. on 1s.6d. deep grey-blue	7·50	50
90/3		*Set of 4*	15·00	14·00

BAHRAIN 2 RUPEES

(9) I

BAHRAIN 2 RUPEES

(9) II

BAHRAIN 2 RUPEES

(9) III

BAHRAIN 5 RUPEES

(10) I

BAHRAIN 5 RUPEES

(10) II

BAHRAIN 10 RUPEES

(11) I

BAHRAIN 10 RUPEES

(11) II

TYPE I (T **9/11**). Type-set surch by Waterlow. Bold thick letters with sharp corners and straight edges.

TYPE II (T **9/11**). Plate-printed surch by Harrison. Thinner letters, rounded corners and rough edges. Bars wider apart.

TYPE III (T **9**). Plate-printed surch by Harrison. Similar to Type II as regards the position of the bars on all 40 stamps of the sheet, but the letters are thinner and with more rounded corners than in II, while the ink of the surcharge is less black.

The general characteristics of Type II of the 2r. are less pronounced than in the other values, but a distinguishing test is in the relative position of the bars and the "U" of "RUPEES". In Type II (except for the 1st stamp, 5th row) the bars start immediately beneath the left-hand edge of the "U". In Type I they start more to the right.

In the 10r. the "1" and the "0" are spaced 0.9 mm in Type I and only 0.6 mm in Type II.

1955 (23 Sept)–**60**. T **166/8** (Waterlow ptgs) surch as T **9/11**.

94		2r. on 2s.6d. black-brown (Type I)	5·50	2·25
		a. Type II (13.5.58)	14·00	21·00
		b. Type III (No. 536a, D.L.R.) (29.1.60)	26·00	70·00
95		5r. on 5s. rose-red (Type I)	20·00	2·75
		a. Type II (19.8.57)	8·00	7·00
96		10r. on 10s. ultramarine (Type I)	20·00	2·75
		a. Type II (13.5.58)	50·00	£120
		ab. Type II. Surch on No. 538a (D.L.R. ptg) (1960)		£120
94/6		*Set of 3*	40·00	7·00
94a/6a		*Set of 3*	65·00	£130

Designs:—No. 94, Carrickfergus Castle; No. 95, Caernarvon Castle; No. 96, Edinburgh Castle.

1956–57. Q.E. II (W **165**), surch as T **3** (in two lines on 6a.).

97	**154**	½ a. on ½d. orange-red (20.3.57)	10	15
98	**156**	4a. on 4d. ultramarine (8.6.56)	5·50	24·00
99	**155**	6a. on 6d. reddish purple (5.12.56)	50	75
100	**160**	12a. on 1s.3d. green (2.8.56)	7·50	11·00
101	**159**	1r. on 1s.6d. grey-blue (1.4.57)	11·00	10
		a. Surch double	†	£5000
97/101		*Set of 5*	22·00	32·00

The two surcharges on No. 101a are almost coincident.

New Currency. 100 naye paise = 1 rupee.

BAHRAIN BAHRAIN BAHRAIN

NP 1 NP	3 NP	75 NP
(12)	(13)	(14)

1957 (1 Apr)–**59**. Q.E. II (W **165**), surch as T **12** (1n.p., 15n.p., 25n.p., 40n.p., and 50n.p.), T **14** (75n.p.) or T **13** (others).

102	**157**	1n.p. on 5d. brown	10	10
103	**154**	3n.p. on ½d. orange-red	75	3·00

104		6n.p. on 1d. ultramarine	75	3·00
105		9n.p. on 1½d. green	50	3·25
106		12n.p. on 2d. light red-brown	30	70
107	**155**	15n.p. on 2½d. carmine-red (Type I)	30	15
		a. Type II (1959)	1·00	5·50
108		20n.p. on 3d. deep lilac (B.)	30	10
109	**156**	25n.p. on 4d. ultramarine	1·25	2·50
110	**157**	40n.p. on 6d. reddish purple	40	10
		a. Deep claret (1959)	65	10
111	**158**	50n.p. on 9d. bronze-green	3·75	4·50
112	**160**	75n.p. on 1s.3d. green	2·50	50
102/112		*Set of 11*	9·75	16·00

BAHRAIN 15 NP

(15)

1957 (1 Aug). World Scout Jubilee Jamboree. Surch in two lines as T **15** (15n.p.), or in three lines (others).

113	**170**	15n.p. on 2½d. carmine-red	35	35
114	**171**	25n.p. on 4d. ultramarine	35	35
115	**172**	75n.p. on 1s.3d. green	40	45
113/15		*Set of 3*	1·00	1·00

1960 (24 May). Q.E. II (W **179**), surch as T **12**.

116	**155**	15n.p. on 2½d. carmine-red (Type II)	2·25	8·00

16 Sheikh Salman bin Hamed al-Khalifa

17

(Des M. Farrar Bell. Photo Harrison (T **16**). Des O. C. Meronti. Recess D.L.R. (T **17**))

1960 (1 July). P 15×14 (T **16**) or 13½×13 (T **17**).

117	**16**	5n.p. bright blue	20	10
118		15n.p. red-orange	20	10
119		20n.p. reddish violet	20	10
120		30n.p. bistre-brown	20	10
121		40n.p. grey	20	10
122		50n.p. emerald-green	20	10
123		75n.p. chocolate	30	15
124	**17**	1r. black	3·00	30
125		2r. rose-red	3·00	2·50
126		5r. deep blue	5·00	3·50
127		10r. bronze-green	15·00	6·00
117/127		*Set of 11*	25·00	11·00

Sheikh Isa bin Salman al-Khalifa
2 November 1961–6 March 1999

18 Sheikh Isa bin Salman al-Khalifa

19 Air Terminal, Muharraq

20 Deep Water Harbour

(Des M. Farrar Bell. Photo Harrison (5 to 75n.p.). Des D. C. Rivett. Recess B.W. (others))

1964 (22 Feb). P 15×14 (T **18**) or 13½×13 (T **19/20**).

128	**18**	5n.p. bright blue	10	10
129		15n.p. orange red	15	1·00
130		20n.p. reddish violet	15	10
131		30n.p. olive-brown	15	10
132		40n.p. slate	15	10
133		50n.p. emerald-green	15	1·50
134		75n.p. brown	25	10
135	**19**	1r. black	11·00	2·25
136		2r. carmine-red	11·00	6·00
137	**20**	5r. ultramarine	15·00	21·00
138		10r. myrtle-green	15·00	21·00
128/138		*Set of 11*	48·00	48·00

LOCAL STAMPS

The following stamps were issued primarily for postage within Bahrain, but apparently also had franking value when used on external mail.

L **1** Sheikh Salman bin Hamed al-Khalifa

L **2** Sheikh Salman bin Hamed al-Khalifa

(Types L **1/2**. Recess De La Rue)

1953–56. P 12×12½.

L1	L **1**	½a. deep green (1.10.56)	3·25	1·00
L2		1a. deep blue (1.10.56)	3·25	1·00
L3		1½a. carmine (15.2.53)	50	3·25
L1/3		*Set of 3*	6·25	4·75

1957 (16 Oct). As Nos. L1/3 but values in new currency.

L4	3p. deep green	3·00	1·25
L5	5p. carmine	3·00	1·25
L6	9p. deep blue	3·00	1·25
L4/6	*Set of 3*	8·00	3·25

1961 (20 Mar). L **2**. P 12×12½.

L7	5p. green	1·25	30
L8	10p. carmine-red	3·75	30
L9	15p. grey	1·50	25
L10	20p. blue	2·50	25
L11	30p. sepia	2·00	25
L12	40p. ultramarine	9·50	30
L7/12	*Set of 6*	18·00	1·50

STAMP BOOKLET

1934. Red and black on tan cover. Mysore Sandal Soap advertisement on front.

SB1   1r. booklet containing 16×1a. (Nos. 16 and/or 16w) in blocks of 4 .... £2500

The Bahrain Post Department took over the postal services on 1 January 1966. Later stamp issues will be found in Stanley Gibbons *Arabia Catalogue*.

Barbados

Regular mails between Barbados and Great Britain were established at an early date in the island's development and it is believed that the British Mail Packet Agency at Bridgetown was opened in 1688 as part of the considerable expansion of the Packet Service in that year.

From 1 August 1851 the colonial authorities were responsible for the internal post system, but the British GPO did not relinquish control of the overseas post until 1858.

For illustrations of the handstamp types see BRITISH POST OFFICES ABROAD notes, following GREAT BRITAIN.

CROWNED-CIRCLE HANDSTAMPS

CC1   CC **1** *BARBADOES (3.10.1849) (R.)...... Price on cover*   £475
Combination covers exist with the local postage paid by a Barbados 1d. stamp and the overseas fee by an example of No. CC1.

During shortages of ½d. stamps in 1893 (17 February to 15 March) and of the ¼d. in 1896 (23 January to 4 May) No. CC1 was utilised, struck in black, on local mail. *Price on cover from* £100.

PRICES FOR STAMPS ON COVER TO 1945	
Nos. 1/35	*from* × 5
Nos. 43/63	*from* × 4
Nos. 64/6	*from* × 10
Nos. 67/83	*from* × 5
Nos. 86/8	*from* × 3
Nos. 89/103	*from* × 4
No. 104	*from* × 20
Nos. 105/15	*from* × 4
Nos. 116/24	*from* × 8
Nos. 125/33	*from* × 5
Nos. 135/44	*from* × 4
Nos. 145/52	*from* × 6
No. 153	*from* × 8
Nos. 158/62	*from* × 5
Nos. 163/9	*from* × 3
Nos. 170/96	*from* × 4
Nos. 197/8	*from* × 10
Nos. 199/212	*from* × 6
Nos. 213/39	*from* × 3
No. 240	*from* × 10
Nos. 241/4	*from* × 5
Nos. 245/7	*from* × 6
Nos. 248/56a	*from* × 4
Nos. 257/61	*from* × 5
Nos. D1/3	*from* × 25

PERKINS BACON "CANCELLED". For notes on these handstamps, showing "CANCELLED" between horizontal bars forming an oval, see Catalogue Introduction.

CROWN COLONY

1 Britannia   **2** Britannia

(Recess Perkins Bacon & Co)

1852 (15 Apr)–**55**. Paper blued. No wmk. Imperf.

1	**1**	(½d.) yellow-green (1855)	—	£700
2		(½d.) deep green	£150	£325
3		(1d.) blue	60·00	£190
4		(1d.) deep blue	42·00	70·00
4a		(2d.) greyish slate	£300	£1400
		b. Bisected (1d.) (*on cover*) (1854)	†	£8500
5		(4d.) brownish red (1855)	£120	£275

The bisect, No. 4b was authorised for use between 4 August and 21 September 1854 during a shortage of 1d. stamps.

Prepared for use but not issued.

5a	**1**	(No value), slate-blue (*shades*)	28·00
5b		(No value), deep slate	£250

Nos. 5a/b were never sent to Barbados and come from the Perkins Bacon remainders sold in the 1880's.

Apart from the shade, which is distinctly paler, No. 4a can be distinguished from No. 5b by the smooth even gum, the gum of No. 5b being yellow and patchy, giving a mottled appearance to the back of the stamp. No. 5a also has the latter gum.

1855–58. White paper. No wmk. Imperf.

7	**1**	(½d.) yellow-green (1857)	£500	£110
8		(½d.) green (*shades*) (1858)	£190	£150
9		(1d.) pale blue	£170	70·00
10		(1d.) deep blue (H/S "CANCELLED" in oval £12000)	£100	60·00

No. 8 exists in a yellowish green shade which should not be confused with No. 7.

1858 (10 Nov). No wmk. Imperf.

11	**2**	6d. pale rose-red	£750	£120
11a		6d. deep rose-red	£750	£180
12		1s. brown-black	£250	£110
12a		1s. black	£225	75·00

BISECTS. The various 1d. bisects recorded between Nos. 14a and 73a were principally used for the ½d. inland rate, covering newspapers from 1854 onwards. Prices for Nos. 24a, 52a, 66a and 73a are for examples on dated piece, undated pieces being worth considerably less. Nos. 14a, 15a and 19a are only known on undated piece and the prices for these bisects are for items in this condition.

1860. No wmk.

(a) Pin-perf 14

13	**1**	(½d.) yellow-green	£2750	£425
14		(1d.) pale blue	£2250	£150
		a. Bisected (½d.) (*on piece*)	†	£750
15		(1d.) deep blue	£2500	£180
		a. Bisected (½d.) (*on piece*)	†	£750

(b) Pin-perf 12½

16	**1**	(½d.) yellow-green	£9000	£650
16a		(1d.) blue	—	£1600

(c) Pin-perf 14×12½

16b	**1**	(½d.) yellow-green	—	£7500

1861. No wmk. Clean-cut perf 14 to 16.

17	**1**	(½d.) deep green (H/S "CANCELLED" in oval £12000)	£180	22·00
18		(1d.) pale blue	£750	85·00
19		(1d.) deep blue	£850	90·00
		a. Bisected (½d.) (*on piece*)	†	£550

1861–70. No wmk.

(a) Rough perf 14 to 16

20	**1**	(½d.) deep green	35·00	48·00
21		(½d.) green	29·00	35·00
21a		(½d.) blue-green	55·00	75·00
		b. Imperf (pair)	£750	
22		(½d.) grass-green	42·00	48·00
		a. Imperf (pair)	£850	
23		(1d.) blue (1861)	80·00	2·25
		a. Imperf (pair) (pale blue, worn plate)	£800	
24		(1d.) deep blue	75·00	4·00
		a. Bisected diag (½d.) (*on piece*) (1863)	†	£500
25		(4d.) dull rose-red (1861)	£160	70·00
		a. Imperf (pair)	£1100	
26		(4d.) dull brown-red (1865)	£190	80·00
		a. Imperf (pair)	£1600	
27		(4d.) lake-rose (1868)	£190	£100
		a. Imperf (pair)	£1700	
28		(4d.) dull vermilion (1869)	£350	£110
		a. Imperf (pair)	£1500	
29	**2**	6d. rose-red (1861) (Handstamped "CANCELLED" in oval £12000)	£375	24·00
30		6d. orange-red (1864)	£180	32·00
31		6d. bright orange-vermilion (1868)	£160	35·00
32		6d. dull orange-vermilion (1870)	£180	29·00
		a. Imperf (pair)	£750	
33		6d. orange (1870)	£200	50·00
34		1s. brown-black (1863)	75·00	11·00
		a. Error. Blue	£18000	
35		1s. black (1866)	65·00	11·00
		a. Imperf between (horiz pair)	£9000	

(b) Prepared for use, but not issued. P 11 to 12½

36	**1**	(½d.) grass-green	£15000	
37		(1d.) blue	£2000	

The (1d.) deep blue No. 24, also exists imperforate, from a new plate introduced in 1867, but examples cannot readily be distinguished from No. 10.

The bisect, No. 24a, was first authorised for use in April 1863 and further examples have been reported up to January 1869 during shortages of ½d. stamps.

No. 34a was an error on the part of the printer who supplied the first requisition of the 1s. value in the colour of the 1d. The 1s. blue stamps were never placed on sale, but the Barbados Colonial Secretary circulated some samples which were defaced by a manuscript corner-to-corner cross. A number of these samples subsequently had the cross removed.

Nos. 36/7 were never sent to Barbados and come from the Perkins Bacon remainders. It is believed that the imperforate pairs came from the same source.

1870. Wmk Large Star, Type w **1**. Rough perf 14 to 16.

43	**1**	(½d.) green	£170	10·00
43b		(½d.) yellow-green	£225	50·00
44		(1d.) blue	£2500	70·00
		a. Blue paper	£4500	£140
		b. Wmk sideways	†	£1400
45		(4d.) dull vermilion	£1600	£120
46	**2**	6d. orange-vermilion	£1000	90·00
47		1s. black	£450	19·00

No. 43 exists imperforate (*Price* £1300, *unused pair*).

1871. Wmk Small Star, Type w **2**. Rough perf 14 to 16.

48	**1**	(1d.) blue	£180	4·25
49		(4d.) dull rose-red	£1300	70·00
50	**2**	6d. orange-vermilion	£700	28·00
51		1s. black	£250	18·00

1872. Wmk Small Star, Type w **2**.

(a) Clean-cut perf 14½ to 15½

52	**1**	(1d.) blue	£325	3·00
		a. Bisected diag (½d.) (*on piece*)	†	£750
53	**2**	6d. orange-vermilion	£950	90·00
54		1s. black	£190	18·00

(b) P 11 to 13×14½ to 15½

56	**1**	(½d.) green	£375	65·00
57		(4d.) dull vermilion	£800	£110

1873. Wmk Large Star, Type w **1**.

(a) Clean-cut perf 14½ to 15½

58	**1**	(½d.) green	£450	28·00
59		(4d.) dull rose-red	£1400	£250
60	**2**	6d. orange-vermilion	£900	95·00
		a. Imperf between (horiz pair)	£10000	
		b. Imperf (pair)	£100	
61		1s. black	£150	23·00
		a. Imperf between (horiz pair)	£10000	

(b) Prepared for use, but not issued. P 11 to 12

62	**2**	6d. orange-vermilion	£10000	

Only eight mint examples, in two strips of four, are known of No. 62. Two used singles of No. 60b have been seen.

1873 (June). Wmk Small Star, Type w **2** (sideways = two points upwards). P 14.

63	**2**	3d. brown-purple	£325	£110

3

1873 (June). Wmk Small Star, Type w **2** (sideways). P 15½×15.

64	**3**	5s. dull rose	£950	£300
		s. Handstamped "SPECIMEN"	£375	

1874 (May)–**75**. Wmk Large Star, Type w **1**.

(a) Perf 14

65	**2**	½d. deep green	60·00	18·00
66		1d. deep blue	£140	5·50
		a. Bisected (½d.) (*on piece*) (5.75)	†	£600

(b) Clean-cut perf 14½ to 15½

66b	**2**	1d. deep blue	†	£25000
		c. Imperf (pair)		

(Recess D.L.R.)

1875–81. Wmk Crown CC (sideways* on 6d., 1s.).

(a) P 12½

67	**2**	½d. bright green	90·00	9·00
		x. Wmk reversed	£110	13·00
		y. Wmk inverted and reversed		
68		4d. deep red	£350	27·00
		w. Wmk inverted	£475	55·00
		x. Wmk reversed	£350	29·00
69		6d. bright yellow (aniline)	£950	£100
70		6d. chrome-yellow	£650	90·00
		a. Wmk upright	†	£3000
		w. Wmk Crown to right of CC	£750	80·00
		x. Wmk sideways reversed		
71		1s. violet (aniline)	£500	4·50
		x. Wmk sideways reversed	£500	4·00
		y. Wmk sideways inverted and reversed	—	13·00

(b) P 14

72	**2**	½d. bright green (1876)	27·00	50
		s. Handstamped "SPECIMEN" in red	£110	
		sa. Handstamped "SPECIMEN" in black	£130	
		w. Wmk inverted	—	25·00
		x. Wmk reversed	27·00	75
		y. Wmk inverted and reversed	£180	
73		1d. dull blue	£140	2·00
		a. Bisected (½d.) (*on piece*) (3.77)	†	£300
		s. Handstamped "SPECIMEN" in red	£110	
		sa. Handstamped "SPECIMEN" in black	£140	
		w. Wmk inverted	£150	2·50
		x. Wmk reversed	£140	1·50
74		1d. grey-blue	£140	1·50
		a. Wmk sideways	†	£750
		w. Wmk inverted	£225	30·00
		x. Wmk reversed	£150	1·75
		y. Wmk inverted and reversed	—	55·00
75		3d. mauve-lilac (*shades*) (1878)	£170	16·00
		s. Handstamped "SPECIMEN" in black	£150	
		w. Wmk inverted	†	£140
76		4d. red (1878)	£150	14·00
		s. Handstamped "SPECIMEN" in black	£150	
		x. Wmk reversed	£180	18·00
77		4d. carmine (1879)	£225	4·25
		w. Wmk inverted	†	95·00
		x. Wmk reversed	£225	6·50
78		4d. crimson-lake (1881)	£500	4·25
79		6d. chrome-yellow (1876)	£150	2·25
		s. Handstamped "SPECIMEN" in black	£150	
		w. Wmk Crown to right of CC	£160	3·00
		x. Wmk sideways reversed	£190	3·00
80		6d. yellow (1878)	£350	12·00
		w. Wmk Crown to right of CC	—	15·00
81		1s. purple (4.78)	£170	8·50
		s. Handstamped "SPECIMEN" in red	£150	
		w. Wmk Crown to right of CC	£150	8·50
		x. Wmk sideways reversed	—	12·00
82		1s. violet (aniline) (1876)	£4250	40·00
		w. Wmk Crown to right of CC	—	40·00
		x. Wmk sideways reversed	—	45·00
83		1s. dull mauve (1879)	£500	5·50
		a. Bisected (6d.) (*on piece*) (1.80)	†	
		x. Wmk sideways reversed	—	13·00

(c) P 14×12½

84	**2**	4d. red	£5000	

*The normal sideways watermark shows Crown to left of CC, *as seen from the back of the stamp.*

Only two examples, both used, of No. 70a have been reported.
Nos. 72sa/3sa were from postal stationery and are without gum.
About 20 examples of No. 84 have been found unused and only one used example is known.

$1^{D.}$ $1^{D.}$ $1^{D.}$
(3a)   **(3b)**   **(3c)**

1878 (28 Mar). No. 64 surch by *West Indian Press* with T **3a/c** sideways twice on each stamp and then divided vertically by 11½ to 13 perforations. The lower label, showing the original face value, was removed before use.

*(a) With T **3a**. Large numeral "1", 7 mm high with curved serif, and large letter "D", 2¾ mm high*

86	**3**	1d. on half 5s. dull rose	£5000	£650
		a. No stop after "D"	£16000	£2000
		b. Unsevered pair (both No. 86)	£26000	£2500
		c. Ditto, Nos. 86 and 87	—	£2500
		ca. Pair without dividing perf	†	£40000
		d. Ditto, Nos. 86 and 88	£42000	£8500

*(b) With T **3b**. As last, but numeral with straight serif*

87	**3**	1d. on half 5s. dull rose	£7500	£950
		a. Unsevered pair	—	£4250

*(c) With T **3c**. Smaller numeral "1", 6 mm high and smaller "D", 2½ mm high*

88	**3**	1d. on half 5s. dull rose	£9000	£1000
		a. Unsevered pair	£38000	£5000

All types of the surcharge were applied reading upwards and downwards in equal quantities, and there are minor varieties of the type.

4   **(5)**

HALF-PENNY

(Typo D.L.R.)

1882 (28 Aug)–**86**. Wmk Crown CA. P 14.

89	**4**	½d. dull green (1882)	35·00	2·00
		w. Wmk inverted	†	£250
90		½d. green	40·00	2·00
91		1d. rose (1882)	90·00	2·50
		a. Bisected (½d.) (on cover)	†	£2250
		w. Wmk inverted	†	£225
92		1d. carmine	60·00	1·25
93		2½d. ultramarine (1882)	£120	1·50
		w. Wmk inverted	—	£140
94		2½d. deep blue (1882)	£140	1·50
95		3d. deep purple (1885)	£120	50·00
96		3d. reddish purple	9·50	32·00
97		4d. grey (1882)	£350	4·50
		a. Value doubly printed	†	£4500
98		4d. pale brown (1885)	32·00	5·00
		w. Wmk inverted	—	£140
		x. Wmk reversed	†	£275
		y. Wmk inverted and reversed	†	£425
99		4d. deep brown	17·00	2·00
100		6d. olive-black (1886)	75·00	48·00
102		1s. chestnut (1886)	29·00	21·00
103		5s. bistre (1886)	£170	£200
89/103 Set of 9			£750	£275
96s/103s (ex 4d. grey) Optd "SPECIMEN" Set of 5			£475	

1892 (July). No. 99 surch with T **5** by West Indian Press.

104	**4**	½d. on 4d. deep brown	2·25	6·00
		a. No hyphen	20·00	40·00
		b. Surch double (R.+Bk.)	£900	£1200
		ba. Surch double (R.+Bk.) both without hyphen	£3500	£4000
		c. Surch double, one albino		
		d. Surch "PENNY HALF"	£375	£225

Nos. 104b/ba come from a sheet with a trial surcharge in red which was subsequently surcharged again in black and put back into stock.

No. 104c is known in a horizontal pair (Price, £2500, unused) with the left hand stamp showing the first two letters of the second impression inked. The right hand stamp shows a complete albino surcharge.

The 'No hyphen' variety occurs in several positions in the setting of 60.

6 Seal of Colony

7

(Typo D.L.R.)

1892 (July)–**1903**. Wmk Crown CA. P 14.

105	**6**	¼d. slate-grey and carmine (5.5.96)	2·50	10
		w. Wmk inverted		
106		½d. dull green	2·50	10
		w. Wmk inverted	£150	£150
107		1d. carmine	4·75	10
108		2d. slate-black and orange (5.99)	14·00	75
109		2½d. ultramarine	17·00	20
110		5d. grey-olive	7·50	4·50
111		6d. mauve and carmine	17·00	2·25
112		8d. orange and ultramarine	4·75	32·00
113		10d. dull blue-green and carmine	12·00	10·00
114		2s.6d. blue-black and orange	48·00	65·00
		w. Wmk inverted	£170	£200
115		2s.6d. violet and green (29.5.03)	£150	£300
105/15 Set of 11			£250	£375
105s/15s Optd "SPECIMEN" Set of 11			£275	

See also Nos. 135/44 and 163/9.

(Typo D.L.R.)

1897 (16 Nov)–**98**. Diamond Jubilee. T **7**. Wmk Crown CC. P 14.

(a) White paper

116		¼d. grey and carmine	10·00	1·00
		sa. Opt "SPECIMEN" double	£300	
117		½d. dull green	10·00	60
118		1d. rose	14·00	60
119		2½d. ultramarine	17·00	1·50
		w. Wmk inverted	—	£200
120		5d. olive-brown	40·00	20·00
121		6d. mauve and carmine	48·00	25·00
122		8d. orange and ultramarine	24·00	27·00
123		10d. blue-green and carmine	75·00	55·00
124		2s.6d. blue-black and orange	£110	65·00
		w. Wmk inverted		
116/24 Set of 9			£300	£170
116s/24s Optd "SPECIMEN" Set of 9			£250	

(b) Paper blued

125		¼d. grey and carmine	30·00	30·00
126		½d. dull green	30·00	30·00
127		1d. carmine	40·00	40·00
128		2½d. ultramarine	42·00	45·00
129		5d. olive-brown	£225	£250
130		6d. mauve and carmine	£140	£140
131		8d. orange and ultramarine	£140	£140
132		10d. dull green and carmine	£200	£225
133		2s.6d. blue-black and orange	£150	£150

1905. Wmk Mult Crown CA. P 14.

135	**6**	¼d. slate-grey and carmine	13·00	3·00
136		½d. green (shades)	28·00	10
137		1d. carmine	29·00	10

139		2½d. blue (shades)	32·00	15
141		6d. mauve and carmine	45·00	35·00
142		8d. orange and ultramarine	65·00	£130
144		2s.6d. violet and green	65·00	£150
135/144 Set of 7			£225	£275

See also Nos. 163/9.

8 Nelson Monument

(Des Mrs. G. Goodman. Recess D.L.R.)

1906 (1 Mar). Nelson Centenary. Wmk Crown CC. P 14.

145	**8**	¼d. black and grey	18·00	1·75
		w. Wmk inverted	55·00	65·00
146		½d. black and pale green	11·00	15
		w. Wmk inverted	£100	
		x. Wmk reversed	£225	£120
		y. Wmk inverted and reversed	£300	
147		1d. black and red	12·00	15
		w. Wmk inverted	£100	£100
		x. Wmk reversed	†	£120
148		2d. black and yellow	3·75	4·50
149		2½d. black and bright blue	4·25	1·25
		w. Wmk inverted	£350	£300
150		6d. black and mauve	19·00	28·00
151		1s. black and rose	23·00	50·00
145/51 Set of 7			75·00	75·00
145s/51s Optd "SPECIMEN" Set of 7			£160	

Two sets may be made of the above: one on thick, opaque, creamy white paper; the other on thin, rather transparent, bluish white paper. See also Nos. 158/62a.

9 Olive Blossom, 1605   **(10)**

(Des Lady Carter. Recess D.L.R.)

1906 (15 Aug). Tercentenary of Annexation. Wmk Multiple Crown CA (sideways). P 14.

152	**9**	1d. black, blue and green	19·00	25
		s. Optd "SPECIMEN"	70·00	

1907 (25 Jan–25 Feb). Kingston Relief Fund. No. 108 surch with T **10** by T. E. King & Co., Barbados.

153	**6**	1d. on 2d. slate-black and orange (R.)	9·50	16·00
		a. Surch inverted (25.2.07)	1·75	6·50
		b. Surch double	£850	£950
		c. Surch double, both inverted	£850	
		d. Surch tête-bêche (vert pair)	£1800	
		e. No stop after "1d."	70·00	£110
		ea. Do., surch inverted (25.2.07)	42·00	£100
		eb. Do., surch double	—	£2250
		f. Vert pair, one normal, one surch double		£1200

The above stamp was sold for 2d. of which 1d. was retained for the postal revenue, and the other 1d. given to a fund for the relief of the sufferers from the earthquake in Jamaica.

An entire printing as No. 153a was created after a sheet of inverted surcharges was found in the initial supply.

1907 (6 July). Nelson Centenary. Wmk Mult Crown CA. P 14.

158	**8**	¼d. black and grey	6·00	13·00
161		2d. black and yellow	32·00	48·00
		x. Wmk reversed	£325	
162		2½d. black and bright blue	8·00	50·00
		a. Black and indigo	£700	£800
158/62 Set of 3			42·00	£100

1909 (July)–**10**. Wmk Mult Crown CA. P 14.

163	**6**	¼d. brown	11·00	30
165		1d. red	30·00	10
166		2d. greyish slate (8.10)	12·00	24·00
168		6d. dull and bright purple (1910)	28·00	40·00
169		1s. black/green (8.10)	19·00	20·00
163/9 Set of 5			90·00	75·00
163s/9s Optd "SPECIMEN" Set of 5			£140	

11

12

13

(Typo D.L.R.)

1912 (23 July)–**16**. Wmk Mult Crown CA. P 14.

170	**11**	¼d. brown	2·25	1·50
		a. Pale brown (1916)	4·25	3·50
		aw. Wmk inverted		
171		½d. green	3·75	10
		a. Wmk sideways	†	£2000
172		1d. red (13.8.12)	11·00	10
		a. Scarlet (1915)	42·00	4·00
173		2d. greyish slate (13.8.12)	7·50	24·00

174		2½d. bright blue (13.8.12)	1·75	1·50
175	**12**	3d. purple/yellow (13.8.12)	2·75	14·00
176		4d. black and red/yellow (13.8.12)	5·00	26·00
177		6d. dull purple and purple (13.8.12)	12·00	12·00
178	**13**	1s. black/green (13.8.12)	17·00	28·00
179		2s. purple and blue/blue (13.8.12)	65·00	65·00
180		3s. green and violet (13.8.12)	£120	£120
170/80 Set of 11			£225	£250
170s/80s Optd "SPECIMEN" Set of 11			£180	

14   **(15)**

WAR TAX

(Recess D.L.R.)

1916 (16 June)–**19**. Wmk Mult Crown CA. P 14.

181	**14**	¼d. deep brown	75	40
		a. Chestnut-brown (9.17)	1·50	35
		b. Sepia-brown (4.18)	4·25	3·00
		w. Wmk inverted	17·00	18·00
		y. Wmk inverted and reversed	50·00	60·00
182		½d. green	4·00	15
		a. Deep green (9.17)	1·60	15
		b. Pale green (4.18)	2·25	80
		w. Wmk inverted	40·00	
		x. Wmk reversed		
		y. Wmk inverted and reversed	75·00	75·00
183		1d. deep red	17·00	6·00
		a. Bright carmine-red (4.17)	2·50	15
		b. Pale carmine-red (9.17)	6·00	65
		w. Wmk inverted	42·00	50·00
		x. Wmk reversed	£130	
		y. Wmk inverted and reversed	45·00	55·00
184		2d. grey	15·00	40·00
		a. Grey-black (9.19)	60·00	80·00
		x. Wmk reversed	—	£750
		y. Wmk inverted and reversed		
185		2½d. deep ultramarine	8·00	3·50
		a. Royal blue (11.17)	13·00	4·50
		w. Wmk inverted		
		y. Wmk inverted and reversed	50·00	50·00
186		3d. purple/yellow (thin paper)	14·00	18·00
		a. Dp purple/yell (thick paper) (9.19)	45·00	60·00
187		4d. red/yellow	1·50	14·00
188		6d. purple	14·00	9·50
189		1s. black/green	16·00	12·00
190		2s. purple/blue	21·00	7·50
		y. Wmk inverted and reversed	£250	
191		3s. deep violet	75·00	£180
		w. Wmk inverted		
		y. Wmk inverted and reversed	£1700	£2250
181/91 Set of 11			£140	£250
181s/91s Optd "SPECIMEN" Set of 11			£275	

Dates quoted for shades are those of despatch from Great Britain.

Examples of the ½d. and 1d. values can be found perforated either by line or by comb machines.

See also Nos. 199/200a.

1917 (10 Oct)–**18**. War Tax. Optd in London with T **15**.

197	**11**	1d. bright red	50	15
		s. Optd "SPECIMEN"	55·00	
		w. Wmk inverted	—	£225
198		1d. pale red (thicker bluish paper) (4.18)	7·50	70

1918 (18 Feb)–**20**. Colours changed. Wmk Mult Crown CA. P 14.

199	**14**	4d. black and red	2·25	4·00
		x. Wmk reversed	£325	
		y. Wmk inverted and reversed	†	£500
200		3s. green and deep violet	30·00	£110
		a. Green and bright violet (1920)	£250	£375
199s/200s Optd "SPECIMEN" Set of 2			£130	

The centres of these are from a new die having no circular border line.

16 Winged Victory from the Louvre

17 Victory from Victoria Memorial, London

(Recess D.L.R.)

1920 (9 Sept)–**21**. Victory. P 14.

(a) Wmk Mult Crown CA (sideways on T **17**)*

201	**16**	¼d. black and bistre-brown	30	70
		a. "C" of "CA" missing from wmk	£400	
		b. Substituted crown in wmk	£450	£450
		w. Wmk inverted	£160	
		x. Wmk reversed	75·00	
		y. Wmk inverted and reversed	80·00	
202		½d. black and bright yellow-green	2·25	15
		a. "C" of "CA" missing from wmk	£450	£400
		b. "A" of "CA" missing from wmk	£450	
		c. Substituted crown in wmk	£650	
		w. Wmk inverted	£200	£170
		x. Wmk reversed	£160	
		y. Wmk inverted and reversed	£150	£150
203		1d. black and vermilion	4·00	10
		a. "A" of "CA" missing from wmk	£600	£500
		b. "C" of "CA" missing from wmk	£600	
		c. Substituted crown in wmk	†	£500

	w. Wmk inverted	55·00	65·00
	wa. Substituted crown in wmk.	£1200	
	x. Wmk reversed	£200	
	y. Wmk inverted and reversed	£150	£150
204	2d. black and grey	2·75	18·00
	a. "C" of "CA" missing from wmk.	£500	
205	2½d. indigo and ultramarine	2·75	28·00
	a. "C" of "CA" missing from wmk.	£500	
	b. "A" of "CA" missing from wmk.	£500	
	w. Wmk inverted	—	£180
	y. Wmk inverted and reversed	£160	£180
206	3d. black and purple	4·00	6·50
	a. "C" of "CA" missing from wmk.	£500	
	w. Wmk inverted	35·00	55·00
207	4d. black and blue-green	4·00	7·00
208	6d. black and brown-orange	6·00	26·00
	w. Wmk inverted	80·00	£150
	wa. "C" of "CA" missing from wmk.	£1800	
	wb. Substituted crown in wmk.	£1800	
209 **17**	1s. black and bright green	21·00	55·00
	a. "C" of "CA" missing from wmk.	£1300	
	w. Wmk Crown to left of CA	£150	
	x. Wmk sideways reversed	£225	
	y. Wmk sideways inverted and reversed	£250	£350
210	2s. black and brown	50·00	75·00
	w. Wmk Crown to left of CA	80·00	£160
	x. Wmk sideways reversed	£250	
	y. Wmk sideways inverted and reversed	£225	
211	3s. black and dull orange	55·00	95·00
	a. "C" of "CA" missing from wmk.	£1500	£1500
	c. Substituted crown in wmk	£1500	
	w. Wmk Crown to left of CA	£160	
	x. Wmk sideways reversed	£300	£300
	y. Wmk sideways inverted and reversed		

(b) Wmk Mult Script CA

212 **16**	1d. black and vermilion (22.8.21)	17·00	30
201/12 *Set of 12*		£150	£275
201s/12s Optd "SPECIMEN" *Set of 12*		£275	

*The normal sideways watermark on Nos. 209/11 shows Crown to right of CA, *as seen from the back of the stamp.*

For illustration of the substituted watermark crown see Catalogue Introduction.

18   **19**

(Recess D.L.R.)

1921 (14 Nov)–**24**. P 14.

(a) Wmk Mult Crown CA

213 **18**	3d. purple/*pale yellow*	2·00	13·00
	a. "A" of "CA" missing from wmk.	†	£600
	x. Wmk reversed	£325	£325
214	4d. red/*pale yellow*	1·75	26·00
215	1s. black/*emerald*	7·00	24·00
	w. Wmk inverted	†	£475
	x. Wmk reversed	£425	£375

(b) Wmk Mult Script CA

217 **18**	¼d. brown	25	10
	x. Wmk reversed	30·00	
	y. Wmk inverted and reversed	70·00	£100
219	½d. green	1·50	10
220	1d. red	80	10
	aw. Wmk inverted	25·00	32·00
	ax. Wmk reversed	—	£180
	ay. Wmk inverted and reversed	—	£180
	b. *Bright rose-carmine*	9·50	1·00
	bw. Wmk inverted	27·00	
221	2d. grey	1·75	20
	y. Wmk inverted and reversed	†	£500
222	2½d. ultramarine	1·50	9·00
225	6d. reddish purple	3·50	8·50
226	1s. black/*emerald* (18.9.24)	55·00	£150
	sa. Opt "SPECIMEN" double	£200	
227	2s. purple/*blue*	10·00	25·00
228	3s. deep violet	29·00	85·00
	y. Wmk inverted and reversed		
213/28 *Set of 12*		£100	£300
213s/28s Optd "SPECIMEN" *Set of 12*		£225	

1925 (1 Apr)–**35**. Wmk Mult Script CA. P 14.

229 **19**	¼d. brown	25	10
230	½d. green	60	10
	a. Perf 13½×12½ (2.32)	11·00	10
231	1d. scarlet	60	10
	a. "A" of "CA" missing from wmk.	†	£1000
	bx. Wmk inverted	†	£500
	c. Perf 13½×12½ (2.32)	14·00	50
231d	1½d. orange (1933)	15·00	3·25
	da. Perf 13½×12½ (15.8.32)	8·00	1·00
232	2d. grey	75	3·25
233	2½d. blue	50	80
	a. *Bright ultramarine* (1933)	21·00	2·50
	ab. Perf 13½×12½ (2.32)	21·00	10·00
234	3d. purple/*pale yellow*	1·25	45
	a. *Reddish purple/yellow* (1935)	6·50	7·50
235	4d. red/*pale yellow*	75	1·50
236	6d. purple	1·00	90
237	1s. black/*emerald*	3·00	8·50
	a. Perf 13½×12½ (8.32)	70·00	
	b. *Brownish black/bright yellow-green* (1934)	8·50	10·00
238	2s. purple/*blue*	7·00	9·50
238a	2s.6d. carmine/blue (1.9.32)	30·00	50·00
239	3s. deep violet	11·00	23·00
229/39 *Set of 13*		55·00	90·00
229s/39s Optd or Perf (1½d., 2s.6d.) "SPECIMEN" *Set of 13*		£225	

Nos. 230/1 exist in coils constructed from normal sheets.

20 King Charles I and King George V   **21** Badge of the Colony

(Recess B.W.)

1927 (17 Feb). Tercentenary of Settlement of Barbados. Wmk Mult Script CA. P 12½.

240 **20**	1d. carmine	1·75	80
	a. Perf 12×12½	4·50	3·50
	s. Optd "SPECIMEN"	55·00	

1935 (6 May). Silver Jubilee. As Nos. 91/4 of Antigua, but ptd by Waterlow. P 11×12.

241	1d. deep blue and scarlet	2·50	20
	j. Damaged turret	£700	£375
242	1½d. ultramarine and grey	5·50	8·50
	j. Damaged turret	£850	
243	2½d. brown and deep blue	3·00	6·50
	m. "Bird" by turret	£300	£400
244	1s. slate and purple	25·00	35·00
	l. Kite and horizontal log	£750	£800
241/4 *Set of 4*		32·00	45·00
241s/4s Perf "SPECIMEN" *Set of 4*		£140	

For illustrations of plate varieties see Omnibus section following Zanzibar.

1937 (14 May). Coronation. As Nos. 95/7 of Antigua, but printed by D.L.R. P 14.

245	1d. scarlet	30	15
246	1½d. yellow-brown	1·00	75
247	2½d. bright blue	1·40	75
245/7 *Set of 3*		2·40	1·50
245s/7s Perf "SPECIMEN" *Set of 3*		90·00	

½d. Recut line (R. 10/6)

2d. Extra frame line (R. 11/9)   **2½d.** Mark on central ornament (R. 1/3, 2/3, 3/3)   **3d.** Vertical line over horse's head (R. 4/10) (corrected on Dec 1947 ptg)

4d. "Flying mane" (R. 4/1) (corrected on Dec 1947 ptg)   **4d.** Curved line at top right (R. 7/8) (corrected on Dec 1947 ptg)   **4d.** Scratched plate (extends to top right ornament) (R. 6/10)

(Recess D.L.R.)

1938 (3 Jan)–**47**. Wmk Mult Script CA. P 13½×13.

248 **21**	½d. green	6·00	15
	a. Recut line	£150	40·00
	b. Perf 14 (8.42)	70·00	2·00
	ba. Recut line	£650	95·00
248c	½d. yellow-bistre (16.10.42)	15	30
	ca. "A" of "CA" missing from wmk.	£1100	
	cb. Recut line	23·00	35·00
249	1d. scarlet (9.39)	£275	5·00
	a. Perf 14 (3.1.38)	18·00	10
249b	1d. blue-green (16.10.42)	5·00	1·50
	c. Perf 14 (16.10.42)	15	10
	ca. "A" of "CA" missing from wmk.	£1100	£1100
	cb. Printed double, one albino	£900	£1000
250	1½d. orange	20	40
	a. "A" of "CA" missing from wmk.	£1100	
	b. Perf 14 (11.41)	9·00	1·00
250c	2d. claret (3.6.41)	1·50	2·50
	ca. Extra frame line	80·00	£140
250d	2d. carmine (20.9.43)	1·75	70
	da. Extra frame line	60·00	65·00
	db. "A" of "CA" missing from wmk.	†	—
	e. Perf 14 (11.9.44)	60	2·00
	ea. Extra frame line	50·00	£120
251	2½d. ultramarine	1·00	60
	a. Mark on central ornament	55·00	55·00
	b. *Blue* (17.2.44)	2·50	6·00
	ba. "A" of "CA" missing from wmk.	£1000	
	bb. Mark on central ornament	85·00	£160
252	3d. brown	2·00	4·25

	a. Vertical line over horse's head	£150	£275
	ab. "A" of "CA" missing from wmk.	£1000	
	b. Perf 14 (4.41)	30	60
	ba. Vertical line over horse's head	£110	£140
252c	3d. blue (1.4.47)	1·00	1·75
	ca. Vertical line over horse's head	£130	£170
253	4d. black	30	10
	a. Flying mane	£160	70·00
	b. Curved line at top right	£140	70·00
	c. Scratched plate	£160	80·00
	d. Perf 14 (11.9.44)	1·75	6·50
	da. Flying mane	£180	£375
	db. Curved line at top right	£170	£375
	dc. Scratched plate	£150	£375
254	6d. violet	1·00	40
254a	8d. magenta (9.12.46)	1·00	2·00
	ab. "A" of "CA" missing from wmk.	£1200	
255	1s. olive-green	16·00	50
	a. *Deep brown-olive* (19.11.45)	2·00	10
256	2s.6d. purple	12·00	1·50
256a	5s. indigo (3.6.41)	12·00	14·00
	ab. "A" of "CA" missing from wmk.	£2250	
248/56a *Set of 16*		50·00	22·00
248s/56as Perf "SPECIMEN" *Set of 16*		£450	

No. 249a was perforated by two machines, one gauging 13.8×14.1 line (1938), the other 14.1 comb (October 1940).

Nos. 248/c and 249/c exist in coils constructed from normal sheets.

22 Kings Charles I, George VI, Assembly Chamber and Mace

(Recess D.L.R.)

1939 (27 June). Tercentenary of General Assembly. Wmk Mult Script CA. P 13½×14.

257 **22**	½d. green	3·00	1·00
258	1d. scarlet	3·00	1·25
259	1½d. orange	3·25	60
260	2½d. bright ultramarine	5·00	8·50
261	3d. brown	5·00	5·50
257/61 *Set of 5*		17·00	15·00
257s/61s Perf "SPECIMEN" *Set of 5*		£180	

1½d. Two flags on tug (R. 5/2)

3d. "Kite" (R.10/4)

1946 (18 Sept). Victory. As Nos. 110/11 of Antigua.

262	1½d. red-orange	15	50
	a. Two flags on tug	27·00	42·00
263	3d. brown	15	50
	a. Kite flaw	42·00	55·00
262s/3s Perf "SPECIMEN" *Set of 2*		85·00	

ONE PENNY
(23)

NY PEN

Short "Y" (R. 6/2)   Broken "E" (R. 7/4 and 11/4)

ONE PENNY

Broken "N"s (R. 2/8, later sheets only)

(Surch by Barbados Advocate Co.)

1947 (21 Apr). Surch with T **23**.

(a) P 14

264 **21**	1d. on 2d. carmine (No. 250e)	2·25	6·50
	a. Extra frame line	£110	£190
	b. Broken "N"s	£180	
	c. Short "Y"	£110	£190
	d. Broken "E"	70·00	£110

(b) P 13½×13

264e **21**	1d. on 2d. carmine (No. 250d)	3·00	8·00
	ea. Extra frame line	£200	£325
	eb. Broken "N"s	£325	£600
	ec. Short "Y"	£200	£325
	ed. Broken "E"	£140	£225
	f. Surch double	£3000	

The relationship of the two words in the surcharge differs on each position of the sheet.

1948 (24 Nov). Royal Silver Wedding. As Nos. 112/13 of Antigua.
265		1½d. orange	30	50
266		5s. indigo	17·00	14·00

1949 (10 Oct). 75th Anniv of Universal Postal Union. As Nos. 114/17 of Antigua.
267		1½d. red-orange	50	2·00
268		3d. deep blue	2·75	7·50
269		4d. grey	50	3·75
270		1s. olive	50	1·25
267/70	*Set of 4*		3·75	13·00

(New Currency. 100 cents = 1 West Indian, later Barbados, dollar)

24 Dover Fort

25 Sugar cane breeding

26 Public buildings

27 Statue of Nelson

28 Casting net

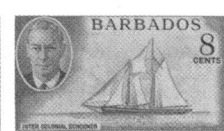

29 *Frances W. Smith* (schooner)

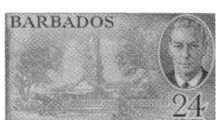

30 Four-winged Flying Fish   **31** Old Main Guard Garrison

32 St. Michael's Cathedral

33 Careenage

34 Map of Barbados and wireless mast

35 Seal of Barbados

(Recess B.W.)

1950 (1 May). T **24/35**. Wmk Mult Script CA. P 11×11½ (horiz), 13½ (vert).
271	**24**	1c. indigo	35	4·50
272	**25**	2c. emerald-green	15	3·00
273	**26**	3c. reddish brown and blue-green	1·25	4·00
274	**27**	4c. carmine	15	40
275	**28**	6c. light blue	15	2·25
276	**29**	8c. bright blue and purple-brown	2·50	3·75
277	**30**	12c. greenish blue and brown-olive	1·00	1·75
278	**31**	24c. scarlet and black	1·00	50
279	**32**	48c. violet	12·00	7·00
280	**33**	60c. green and claret	11·00	14·00
281	**34**	$1.20 carmine and olive-green	13·00	4·75
282	**35**	$2.40 black	26·00	42·00
271/282	*Set of 12*		55·00	75·00

1951 (16 Feb). Inauguration of B.W.I. University College. As Nos. 118/19 of Antigua.
283		3c. brown and blue-green	30	40
284		12c. blue-green and brown-olive	1·25	2·25

36 King George VI and Stamp of 1852

(Recess Waterlow)

1952 (15 Apr). Barbados Stamp Centenary. Wmk Mult Script CA. P 13½.
285	**36**	3c. green and slate-green	40	40
286		4c. blue and carmine	40	1·40
287		12c. slate-green and bright green	40	1·00
288		24c. red-brown and brownish black	50	55
285/8	*Set of 4*		1·50	3·00

37 Harbour Police

(Recess B.W.)

1953 (13 Apr)–**61**. Designs previously used for King George VI issue, but with portrait or cypher ($2.40) of Queen Elizabeth II, as in T **37**. Wmk Mult Script CA. P 11×11½ (horiz) or 13½ (vert).
289	**24**	1c. indigo	10	80
290	**25**	2c. orange and deep turquoise (15.4.54)	15	1·50
291	**26**	3c. black and emerald (15.4.54)	1·00	1·00
292	**27**	4c. black and orange (15.4.54)	20	20
		a. Black and reddish orange (18.3.59)	5·50	2·25
293	**37**	5c. blue and deep carmine-red (4.1.54)	1·00	60
294	**28**	6c. red-brown (15.4.54)	3·25	60
		w. Wmk inverted		
295	**29**	8c. black and blue (15.4.54)	2·00	40
296	**30**	12c. turquoise-blue and brown-olive (15.4.54)	1·00	10
		a. Turquoise-green and brown-olive (18.3.59)	17·00	3·00
		b. Turquoise-blue and bronze-green (13.6.61)	19·00	2·00
297	**31**	24c. rose-red and black (2.3.56)	1·25	10
298	**32**	48c. deep violet (2.3.56)	8·00	1·00
299	**33**	60c. blue-green and brown-purple (3.4.56)	40·00	5·50
		a. Blue-green and pale maroon (17.5.60)	70·00	11·00
300	**34**	$1.20 carmine and bronze-green (3.4.56)	19·00	6·50
301	**35**	$2.40 black (1.2.57)	7·50	1·75
289/301	*Set of 13*		75·00	18·00

See also Nos. 312/19.

1953 (4 June). Coronation. As No. 120 of Antigua.
302		4c. black and red-orange	1·00	20

1958 (23 Apr). Inauguration of British Caribbean Federation. As Nos. 135/7 of Antigua.
303		3c. deep green	75	20
304		6c. blue	90	2·25
305		12c. scarlet	90	30
303/5	*Set of 3*		2·25	2·50

38 Deep Water Harbour, Bridgetown

(Recess B.W.)

1961 (6 May). Opening of Deep Water Harbour, Bridgetown. W w **12**. P 11×12.
306	**38**	4c. black and red-orange	55	50
307		6c. black and blue	55	60
308		24c. carmine-red and black	60	60
306/8	*Set of 3*		1·50	1·50

SELF-GOVERNMENT

39 Scout Badge and Map of Barbados

(Recess B.W.)

1962 (9 Mar). Golden Jubilee of Barbados Boy Scout Association. W w **12**. P 11½×11.
309	**39**	4c. black and orange	85	10
310		12c. blue and olive-brown	1·40	15
311		$1.20 carmine and olive-green	2·00	3·75
309/11	*Set of 3*		3·75	3·75

1964 (14 Jan)–**65**. As Nos. 289, etc., but wmk w **12**.
312	**24**	1c. indigo (6.10.64)	50	6·00
313	**27**	4c. black and orange	30	50
314	**29**	8c. black and blue (29.6.65)	70	35
315	**30**	12c. turquoise-blue and brown-olive (29.6.65)	50	50
316	**31**	24c. rose-red and black (6.10.64)	2·25	70
317	**32**	48c. deep violet	6·00	1·50
318	**33**	60c. blue-green and brown-purple (6.10.64)	10·00	4·00
319	**35**	$2.40 black (29.6.65)	1·25	1·75
312/19	*Set of 8*		19·00	14·00

The above dates are for Crown Agents releases. The 14.1.64 printings were not released in Barbados until April 1964, the 6.10.64 printings until December 1964 and of the stamps released in London on 29 June 1965 the 8c. and $2.40 were released from about 15 June 1965, but the 12c. value was never put on sale in Barbados.

1965 (17 May). ITU Centenary. As Nos. 166/7 of Antigua.
320		2c. lilac and red	20	40
321		48c. yellow and grey-brown	45	1·00

40 Deep Sea Coral

41 Lobster

42 Lined Seahorse

43 Sea Urchin

44 Staghorn Coral   **45** Spot-finned Butterflyfish

46 Rough File Shell   **47** Porcupinefish ("Balloon Fish")

48 Grey Angelfish   **49** Brain Coral

50 Brittle Star

51 Four-winged Flyingfish

52 Queen or Pink Conch Shell

53 Fiddler Crab

(Des V. Whiteley, from drawings by Mrs. J. Walker. Photo Harrison)

1965 (15 July). Marine Life. T **40/53**. W w **12** (upright). P 14×13½.
322	**40**	1c. black, pink and blue	20	30
323	**41**	2c. olive-brown, yellow and magenta	20	15
324	**42**	3c. olive-brown and orange	45	60
325	**43**	4c. deep blue and olive-green	15	10
		a. Imperf (pair)	£325	£250
		w. Wmk inverted	—	24·00
326	**44**	5c. sepia, rose and lilac	30	20
327	**45**	6c. multicoloured	45	20
		w. Wmk inverted	1·25	1·00
328	**46**	8c. multicoloured	25	10
		w. Wmk inverted	5·50	
329	**47**	12c. multicoloured	35	10
		a. Grey printing double	65·00	
		w. Wmk inverted	†	£160
330	**48**	15c. black, greenish yellow and red	4·00	30
331	**49**	25c. ultramarine and yellow-ochre	1·00	30
332	**50**	35c. brown-red and deep green	1·50	15
		w. Wmk inverted	†	85·00
333	**51**	50c. bright blue and apple-green	2·00	40
334	**52**	$1 multicoloured	3·50	2·00
335	**53**	$2.50 multicoloured	2·75	8·50
322/35	*Set of 14*		15·00	12·00

The 3c. value is wrongly inscribed "Hippocanpus", the correct spelling "Hippocampus" was used for subsequent printings, see No. 344.

See also Nos. 342, etc.

1966 (24 Jan). Churchill Commemoration. As Nos. 170/3 of Antigua.
336		1c. new blue	10	3·75
		w. Wmk inverted	40·00	
337		4c. deep green	60	10
338		25c. brown	1·50	50
339		35c. bluish violet	1·50	70
336/9	*Set of 4*		3·25	4·50

1966 (4 Feb). Royal Visit. As Nos. 174/5 of Antigua.
340		3c. black and ultramarine	75	1·00
341		35c. black and magenta	2·25	1·00

53a Dolphin Fish

54 Arms of Barbados

1966 (15 Mar)–**69**. As Nos. 322/35 but wmk w **12** (sideways*). New value and design (as T **53a**).
342	40	1c. black, pink and blue	10	20
		w. Wmk Crown to right of CA		
343	41	2c. olive-brown, yellow and magenta (16.5.67)	30	80
344	42	3c. olive-brown and orange (4.12.67)	30	2·75
345	43	4c. deep blue and olive-green	50	10
		w. Wmk Crown to right of CA	70·00	
346	44	5c. sepia, rose and lilac (23.8.66)	45	10
347	45	6c. multicoloured (31.1.67)	70	10
348	46	8c. multicoloured (19.9.67)	75	10
349	47	12c. multicoloured (31.1.67)	45	10
350	48	15c. black, greenish yellow and red	2·25	10
351	49	25c. ultramarine and yellow-ochre	2·25	40
		aw. Wmk Crown to right of CA	9·50	9·50
		b. Deep ultramarine and yellow-ochre (26.9.66)	12·00	2·25
352	50	35c. brown-red and deep green (23.8.66)	4·50	65
		a. Chestnut and deep green (26.11.68)	18·00	3·50
353	51	50c. bright blue and apple-green	1·75	4·25
		w. Wmk Crown to right of CA	85·00	
354	52	$1 multicoloured (23.8.66)	6·00	1·00
355	53	$2·50 multicoloured (23.8.66)	7·00	3·00
355a	53a	$5 multicoloured (9.1.69)	21·00	19·00
342/55a Set of 15			42·00	29·00

*The normal sideways watermark shows Crown to left of CA, as seen from the back of the stamp.

The 3c. value is correctly inscribed "Hippocampus".

All values except the 50c. exist with PVA gum as well as gum arabic but the $5 exists with PVA gum only.

The $5 was released by the Crown Agents on 6 January but was not put on sale locally until 9 January.

INDEPENDENT

(Des V. Whiteley. Photo Harrison)

1966 (2 Dec). Independence. T **54** and similar multicoloured designs. P 14.
356		4c. Type **54**	10	10
357		15c. Hilton Hotel (horiz)	15	10
358		35c. G. Sobers (Test cricketer)	1·50	65
359		50c. Pine Hill Dairy (horiz)	70	1·10
356/9 Set of 4			2·25	1·75

1967 (6 Jan). 20th Anniv of UNESCO As Nos. 196/8 of Antigua.
360		4c. slate-violet, red, yellow and orange	20	10
361		12c. orange-yellow, violet and deep olive	45	50
362		25c. black, bright purple and orange	75	1·25
360/2 Set of 3			1·25	1·60

58 Policeman and Anchor

62 Governor-General Sir Winston Scott, G.C.M.G.

(Des V. Whiteley. Litho D.L.R.)

1967 (16 Oct). Centenary of Harbour Police. T **58** and similar multicoloured designs. P 14.
363		4c. Type **58**	25	10
364		25c. Policeman with telescope	40	15
365		35c. BP1 (police launch) (horiz)	45	15
366		50c. Policeman outside HQ	60	1·60
363/6 Set of 4			1·50	1·75

(Des V. Whiteley. Photo Harrison)

1967 (4 Dec). First Anniv of Independence. T **62** and similar multicoloured designs. P 14½×14 (4c.) or 14×14½ (others).
367		4c. Type **62**	15	10
368		25c. Independence Arch (horiz)	25	10
369		35c. Treasury Building (horiz)	30	10
370		50c. Parliament Building (horiz)	40	90
367/70 Set of 4			1·00	1·00

66 UN Building, Santiago, Chile

67 Radar Antenna

(Des G. Vasarhelyi. Photo Harrison)

1968 (27 Feb). 20th Anniv of the Economic Commission for Latin America. P 14½.
371	66	15c. multicoloured	10	10

(Des G. Vasarhelyi. Photo Harrison)

1968 (4 June). World Meteorological Day. T **67** and similar multicoloured designs. P 14×14½ (25c.) or 14½×14 (others).
372		3c. Type **67**	10	10
373		25c. Meteorological Institute (horiz)	25	10
374		50c. Harp Gun and Coat of Arms	30	90
372/4 Set of 3			55	1·00

70 Lady Baden-Powell, and Guide at Camp Fire

(Des V. Whiteley (from local designs). Photo Harrison)

1968 (29 Aug). 50th Anniv of Girl Guiding in Barbados. T **70** and similar horiz designs. P 14.
375		3c. ultramarine, black and gold	20	60
376		25c. turquoise-blue, black and gold	30	60
377		35c. orange-yellow, black and gold	35	60
375/7 Set of 3			75	1·60

Designs:—25c. Lady Baden-Powell and Pax Hill; 35c. Lady Baden-Powell and Guide Badge.

73 Hands breaking Chain, and Human Rights Emblem

(Des V. Whiteley. Litho B.W.)

1968 (10 Dec*). Human Rights Year. T **73** and similar horiz designs. P 11×12.
378		4c. violet, brown and light green	10	20
379		25c. black, blue and orange-yellow	10	25
380		35c. multicoloured	15	25
378/80 Set of 3			30	60

Designs:—25c. Human Rights emblem and family enchained; 35c. Shadows of refugees beyond opening fence.

*This was the local release date but the Crown Agents issued the stamps on 29 October.

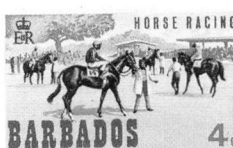

76 Racehorses in the Paddock

(Des J. Cooter. Litho Format)

1969 (20 Mar*). Horse-Racing. T **76** and similar horiz designs. Multicoloured. P 14.
381		4c. Type **76**	25	15
382		25c. Starting-gate	25	15
383		35c. On the flat	30	15
384		50c. Winning post	35	2·40
381/4 Set of 4			1·00	2·50
MS385 117×85 mm. Nos. 381/4			2·00	2·75

*This was the local release date but the Crown Agents issued the stamps on 15 March.

80 Map showing CARIFTA Countries

81 "Strength in Unity"

(Des J. Cooter. Photo Harrison)

1969 (6 May). First Anniv of CARIFTA (Caribbean Free Trade Area). W w **12** (sideways on T **80**). P 14.
386	80	5c. multicoloured	10	10
387	81	12c. multicoloured	10	10
388	80	25c. multicoloured	10	10
389	81	50c. multicoloured	15	20
386/9 Set of 4			30	30

82 ILO Emblem and "1919–1969". **(83)**

(Des Sylvia Goaman. Litho Enschedé)

1969 (12 Aug). 50th Anniv of International Labour Organisation. P 14×13.
390	82	4c. black, emerald and turquoise-blue	10	10
391		25c. black, cerise and brown-red	20	10

Although released by the Crown Agents on 5 August, the above were not put on sale in Barbados until 12 August.

1969 (30 Aug). No. 363 surch with T **83**.
392		1c. on 4c. Type **58**	10	10
		a. Surch double	£100	

84 National Scout Badge

(Des J. Cooter. Litho Enschedé)

1969 (16 Dec). Independence of Barbados Boy Scouts Association and 50th Anniv of Barbados Sea Scouts. T **84** and similar horiz designs. Multicoloured. P 13×13½.
393	84	5c. Type **84**	15	10
394		25c. Sea Scouts rowing	30	10
395		35c. Scouts around camp fire	35	10
396		50c. Scouts and National Scout Headquarters	60	1·25
393/6 Set of 4			1·25	1·40
MS397 155×115 mm. Nos. 393/6			15·00	13·00

4 x (88)

89 Lion at Gun Hill

1970 (11 Mar). No. 346 surch locally with T **88**.
398		4c. on 5c. sepia, rose and lilac	10	10
		a. Vert pair, one without surch	60·00	70·00
		b. Surch double	30·00	38·00
		c. Vert pair, one normal, one surch double	85·00	95·00
		d. Surch triple	£300	£160
		e. Surch normal on front, inverted on back	22·00	
		f. Surch omitted on front, inverted on back	30·00	

(Des J.W. Photo D.L.R.)

1970 (4 May)–**71**. Multicoloured designs as T **89**. W w **12** (sideways on 12c. to $5). Chalk-surfaced paper. P 12½.
399		1c. Type **89**	10	2·50
		a. Glazed, ordinary paper (15.3.71)	10	1·50
400		2c. Trafalgar Fountain	30	1·25
		a. Glazed, ordinary paper (15.3.71)	10	1·75
401		3c. Montefiore Drinking Fountain	1·50	1·00
		a. Glazed, ordinary paper (15.3.71)	10	1·75
		aw. Wmk inverted	9·50	
402		4c. St. James' Monument	1·00	15
		a. Glazed, ordinary paper (15.3.71)	30	10
403		5c. St. Anne's Fort	10	10
		a. Glazed, ordinary paper (15.3.71)	10	10
404		6c. Old Sugar Mill, Morgan Lewis	35	3·00
		a. Glazed, ordinary paper (15.3.71)	10	10
405		8c. Cenotaph	10	10
		a. Glazed, ordinary paper (15.3.71)	10	10
406		10c. South Point Lighthouse	3·50	50
		a. Glazed, ordinary paper (15.3.71)	1·25	15
407		12c. Barbados Museum (horiz)	1·75	10
		a. Glazed, ordinary paper (13.12.71)	9·00	30
408		15c. Sharon Moravian Church (horiz)	30	15
		a. Glazed, ordinary paper (13.12.71)	2·75	30
409		25c. George Washington House (horiz)	25	15
		a. Glazed, ordinary paper (15.3.71)	50	35
410		35c. Nicholas Abbey (horiz)	30	85
		a. Glazed, ordinary paper (15.3.71)	45	70
411		50c. Bowmanston Pumping Station (horiz)	40	1·00
		a. Glazed, ordinary paper (15.3.71)	70	4·50
412		$1 Queen Elizabeth Hospital (horiz)	70	2·50
		a. Glazed, ordinary paper (15.3.71)	4·00	11·00

413		$2.50 Modern sugar factory (*horiz*)		1·50	4·00
	a.	Glazed, ordinary paper (13.12.71)		32·00	16·00
414		$5 Seawell International Airport (*horiz*)		6·00	11·00
	a.	Glazed, ordinary paper (15.3.71)		13·00	15·00
399/414 *Set of 16*				14·00	24·00
399a/414a *Set of 15*				55·00	48·00

Stamps in this set were re-issued between 1972 and 1974 with watermark *w* **12** sideways on 4c. to 10c.; upright on 12c. to $5.

105 Primary Schoolgirl

(Des V. Whiteley. Litho J.W.)

1970 (26 June). 25th Anniv of United Nations. T **105** and similar horiz designs. Multicoloured. W *w* **12**. P 14.

415	4c. Type **108**		10	10
416	5c. Secondary Schoolboy		10	10
417	40c. Technical Student		40	10
418	50c. University Buildings		55	1·50
415/18 *Set of 4*			1·00	1·60

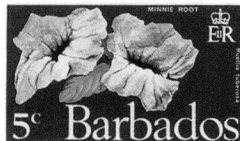

106 Minnie Root

(Des and litho J.W.)

1970 (24 Aug). Flowers of Barbados. T **106** and similar designs. Multicoloured. W *w* **12** (sideways on horiz designs). P 14½.

419	1c. Barbados Easter Lily (*vert*)		10	3·25
420	5c. Type **106**		30	10
421	10c. Eyelash Orchid		1·60	30
422	25c. Pride of Barbados (*vert*)		1·00	75
423	35c. Christmas Hope		1·00	85
419/23 *Set of 5*			3·50	4·75
MS424	162×101 mm. Nos. 419/23. Imperf		2·00	6·50

STAMP BOOKLETS

1906 (Feb).
SB1   2s.0½d. booklet containing 24×1d. (No. 137) in blocks of 6

1909. Black on red cover. Stapled.
SB1a   1s.6d. booklet containing 18×1d. (No. 165) in blocks of 6

1913 (June). Black on red cover. Stapled.
SB2   2s. booklet containing 12×½d. and 18×1d. (Nos. 171/2) in blocks of 6 .... £3000

1916 (16 June). Black on red cover. Stapled.
SB3   2s. booklet containing 12×½d. and 18×1d. (Nos. 182/3) in pairs £1000

1920 (Sept). Black on red cover. Stapled.
SB4   2s. booklet containing 12×½d. and 18×1d. (Nos. 202/3) in pairs £3000

1932 (12 Nov). Black on pale green cover. Austin Cars and Post Office Guide advertisements on front. Stapled.
SB5   2s. booklet containing ½d. and 1d. (Nos. 230a, 231a) each in block of 10 and 1½d. (No. 231da) in block of 6 .... £2250

1933 (4 Dec). Black on pale green cover. Advocate Co. Ltd. advertisement on front. Stapled.
SB6   2s. booklet containing ½d. and 1d. (Nos. 230/1) each in block of 10 and 1½d. (No. 231d) in block of 6 .... £2500

1938 (3 Jan). Black on light blue cover. Advocate Co. Ltd. advertisement on front. Stapled.
SB7   2s. booklet containing ½d. and 1d. (Nos. 248, 249a) each in block of 10 and 1½d. (No. 250) in block of 6 .... £2750

POSTAGE DUE STAMPS

D **1**   Missing top serif on "c" (R. 2/4)

(Typo D.L.R.)

1934 (2 Jan)–**47**. Wmk Mult Script CA. P 14.

D1	D **1**	½d. green (10.2.35)		1·25	9·50
D2		1d. black		2·25	1·25
	a.	Bisected (½d.) (*on cover*)		†	£1800
D3		3d. carmine (11.3.47)		20·00	24·00
D1/3 *Set of 3*				21·00	32·00
D1s/3s Perf "SPECIMEN" *Set of 3*				£110	

The bisected 1d. was officially authorised for use between March 1934 and February 1935. Some examples had the value "½d." written across the half stamp in red or black ink (*Price on cover* £2250).

(Typo D.L.R.)

1950 (8 Dec)–**53**. Values in cents. Wmk Mult Script CA. Ordinary paper. P 14.

D4	D **1**	1c. green		5·00	45·00
	a.	Chalk-surfaced paper. *Deep green* (29.11.51)		30	3·00
	ab.	Error. Crown missing, W **9a**		£900	
	ac.	Error. St. Edward's Crown, W **9b**		£450	£650
D5		2c. black		7·00	20·00
	a.	Chalk-surfaced paper (20.1.53)		1·00	6·50
	ac.	Error. St. Edward's Crown, W **9b**		£800	
D6		6c. carmine		23·00	23·00
	a.	Chalk-surfaced paper (20.1.53)		1·00	8·50
	ab.	Error. Crown missing, W **9a**		£325	
	ac.	Error. St. Edward's Crown, W **9b**		£180	
D4/6 *Set of 3*				32·00	80·00
D4a/6a *Set of 3*				2·10	16·00

The 1c. has no dot below "c".

1965 (3 Aug)–**68**. As Nos. D4/6 but wmk *w* **12** (upright). Chalk-surfaced paper.

D7	D **1**	1c. deep green		30	4·00
	a.	Missing top serif on "C" (R. 2/4).		8·00	
	b.	*Green*		3·00	8·50
	c.	Centre inverted		£26000	
D8		2c. black		30	5·00
D9		6c. carmine		50	7·00
	a.	*Carmine-red* (14.5.68)		1·40	12·00
D7/9 *Set of 3*				1·00	13·50

Barbuda (*see after* Antigua)

Basutoland

Stamps of CAPE OF GOOD HOPE were used in Basutoland from about 1876, initially cancelled by upright oval with framed number type postmarks of that colony. Cancellation numbers known to have been used in Basutoland are 133 (Quthing), 156 (Mafeteng), 210 (Mohaleshoek), 277 (Morija), 281 (Maseru), 317 (Thlotse Heights) and 688 (Teyateyaneng).

From 1910 until 1933 the stamps of SOUTH AFRICA were in use. Stamps of the Union provinces are also known used in Basutoland during the early years of this period and can also be found cancelled-to-order during 1932–33.

The following post offices and postal agencies existed in Basutoland before December 1933. Stamps of Cape of Good Hope or South Africa with recognisable postmarks from them are worth a premium. For a few of the smaller offices or agencies there are, as yet, no actual examples recorded. Dates given are those generally accepted as the year in which the office was first opened.

Bokong (1931)	Motsekuoa (1915)
Butha Buthe (1907)	Mount Morosi (1918)
Jonathan's (1927)	Mphotos (1914)
Khabos (1927)	Peka (1908)
Khetisas (1930)	Phamong (1932)
Khukhune (1933)	Pitseng (1921)
Kolonyama (1914)	Qachasnek (1895)
Kueneng (1914)	Qalo (1923?)
Leribe (1890)	Quthing (1882)
Mafeteng (1874)	Rankakalas (1933)
Majara (1912)	Roma Mission (1913)
Makhoa (1932)	Sebapala (1930)
Makoalis (1927)	Seforong (1924)
Mamathes (1919)	Sehlabathebe (1921)
Mapoteng (1925)	Sekake (1931)
Marakabeis (1932)	Teyateyaneng (1886)
Maseru (1872)	Thaba Bosigo (1913)
Maseru Rail (1915?)	Thabana Morena (1922)
Mashai (1929)	Thabaneng (1914)
Matsaile (1930)	Thaba Tseka (1929)
Mekading (1914)	Thlotse Heights (1872)
Mofokas (1915)	Tsepo (1923)
Mohaleshoek (1873)	Tsoelike (1927)
Mokhotlong (1921)	Tsoloane (1918)
Morija (1884)	

For further details of the postal history of Basutoland see *The Cancellations and Postal Markings of Basutoland/Lesotho* by A. H. Scott, published by Collectors Mail Auctions (Pty) Ltd, Cape Town, from which the above has been, with permission, extracted.

PRICES FOR STAMPS ON COVER TO 1945	
Nos. 1/19	*from* × 5
Nos. 11/14	*from* × 6
Nos. 15/17	*from* × 10
Nos. 18/28	*from* × 6
Nos. 29/31	*from* × 10
Nos. O1/4	*from* × 4
Nos. D1/2	*from* × 25

CROWN COLONY

1 King George V, Nile Crocodile and Mountains

(Recess Waterlow)

1933 (1 Dec). Wmk Mult Script CA. P 12½.

1	**1**	½d. emerald		1·00	1·75
2		1d. scarlet		1·25	1·25
3		2d. bright purple		1·25	80
4		3d. bright blue		1·25	1·25
5		4d. grey		3·25	7·50
6		6d. orange-yellow		2·25	1·75
7		1s. red-orange		4·00	4·50
8		2s.6d. sepia		45·00	55·00
9		5s. violet		80·00	95·00
10		10s. olive-green		£225	£250
1/10 *Set of 10*				£325	£375
1s/10s Perf "SPECIMEN" *Set of 10*				£350	

1935 (4 May). Silver Jubilee. As Nos. 91/4 of Antigua. P 13½×14.

11		1d. deep blue and carmine		1·00	3·50
	f.	Diagonal line by turret		£180	£275
	h.	Dot by flagstaff		—	£700
12		2d. ultramarine and grey		1·00	3·75
	f.	Diagonal line by turret		£180	£275
	g.	Dot to left of chapel		£350	£400
	i.	Dash by turret		£425	
13		3d. brown and deep blue		4·25	8·00
	g.	Dot to left of chapel		£375	£450
	h.	Dot by flagstaff		£450	
	i.	Dash by turret		£550	
14		6d. slate and purple		4·25	8·00
	g.	Dot to left of chapel		£650	
	h.	Dot by flagstaff		£425	£475
	i.	Dash by turret		£600	£700
11/14 *Set of 4*				9·50	21·00
11s/14s Perf "SPECIMEN" *Set of 4*				£150	

For illustrations of plate varieties see Omnibus section following Zanzibar.

1937 (12 May). Coronation. As Nos. 95/7 of Antigua, but printed by D.L.R. P 14.

15	1d. scarlet	35	1·25
16	2d. bright purple	50	1·25
17	3d. bright blue	60	1·25
15/17 Set of 3		1·25	3·25
15s/17s Perf "SPECIMEN" Set of 3		£130	

2 King George VI, Nile Crocodile and Mountains | **1d.** Tower flaw (R. 2/4)

(Recess Waterlow)

1938 (1 Apr). Wmk Mult Script CA. P 12½.

18	2	½d. green	30	1·25
19		1d. scarlet	1·50	70
		a. Tower flaw	£170	£250
20		1½d. light blue	75	50
21		2d. bright purple	75	60
22		3d. bright blue	75	1·25
23		4d. grey	3·00	3·75
24		6d. orange-yellow	3·50	1·50
25		1s. red-orange	3·50	1·00
26		2s.6d. sepia	20·00	8·50
27		5s. violet	45·00	9·50
28		10s. olive-green	48·00	24·00
18/28 Set of 11			£110	45·00
18s/28s Perf "SPECIMEN" Set of 11			£375	

Basutoland
(3)

1945 (3 Dec). Victory. Stamps of South Africa, optd with T **3**, inscr alternately in English and Afrikaans.

			Un pair	Used pair	Used single
29	**55**	1d. brown and carmine	50	80	10
		a. Barbed wire flaw	15·00		
30	**56**	2d. slate-blue and violet	50	60	10
31	**57**	3d. deep blue and blue	50	85	15
29/31 Set of 3			1·40	2·00	30

4 King George VI | **5** King George VI and Queen Elizabeth

6 Queen Elizabeth II as Princess, and Princess Margaret | **7** The Royal Family

(Recess Waterlow)

1947 (17 Feb). Royal Visit. Wmk Mult Script CA. P 12½.

32	4	1d. scarlet	10	10
33	5	2d. green	10	10
34	6	3d. ultramarine	10	10
35	7	1s. mauve	15	10
32/5 Set of 4			40	30
32s/5s Perf "SPECIMEN" Set of 4			£140	

1948 (1 Dec). Royal Silver Wedding. As Nos. 112/13 of Antigua.

36	1½d. ultramarine	20	10
37	10s. grey-olive	50·00	50·00

1949 (10 Oct). 75th Anniv of Universal Postal Union. As Nos. 114/17 of Antigua.

38	1½d. blue	20	1·50
39	3d. deep blue	2·00	2·00
40	6d. orange	1·00	5·50
41	1s. red-brown	50	1·40
38/41 Set of 4		3·25	9·50

1953 (3 June). Coronation. As No. 120 of Antigua.

42	2d. black and reddish purple	65	40

8 Qiloane | **9** Orange River

10 Mosuto horseman | **11** Basuto household

12 Maletsunyane Falls | **13** Herd-boy playing lesiba

14 Pastoral scene | **15** Aeroplane over Lancers Gap

16 Old Fort, Leribe | **17** Mission Cave House

18 Mohair (Shearing Angora Goats)

(Recess D.L.R.)

1954 (18 Oct)–**58**. T **8/18** Wmk Mult Script CA. P 11½ (10s.) or 13½ (others).

43	8	½d. grey-black and sepia	65	10
44	9	1d. grey-black and bluish green	60	10
45	10	2d. deep bright blue and orange	1·25	10
46	11	3d. yellow-green and deep rose-red	2·25	30
		a. Yellow-green and rose (27.11.58)	17·00	2·50
47	12	4½d. indigo and deep ultramarine	1·50	15
48	13	6d. chestnut and deep grey-green	2·75	15
49	14	1s. bronze-green and purple	2·50	30
50	15	1s.3d. brown and turquoise-green	28·00	9·50
51	16	2s.6d. deep ultramarine and crimson	30·00	15·00
		a. Bright ultramarine and crimson-lake (27.11.58)	£110	27·00
52	17	5s. black and carmine-red	15·00	15·00
53	18	10s. black and maroon	40·00	30·00
43/53 Set of 11			£110	60·00

½d. ▆
(19)

1959 (1 Aug). No. 45 surch with T **19**, by South African Govt Ptr, Pretoria.

54	½d. on 2d. deep bright blue and orange.	35	20

20 Chief Moshoeshoe I (engraving by Delangle)

21 Council house | **22** Mosuto horseman

(Des from drawings by James Walton. Recess Waterlow)

1959 (15 Dec). Basutoland National Council. T **20**/2. W w **12**. P 13×13½.

55	3d. black and yellow-olive	75	20
56	1s. carmine and yellow-green	75	80
57	1s.3d. ultramarine and red-orange	1·00	70
55/7 Set of 3		2·25	1·50

(New Currency. 100 cents = 1 rand)

½c. (23) | 1c. (24) | 2c (25)
2½c (I) | 2½c (II) | 3½c (I) | 3½c (II)
5c (I) | 5c (II) | 10c (I) | 10c (II)
12½c (I) | 12½c (II) | 50c (I) | 50c (II)
25c (I) | 25c (II) | 25c (III)
R1 (I) | R1 (II) | R1 (III)

1961 (14 Feb). Nos. 43/53 surch with T **23** (½c.), **24** (1c.) or as T **25** (others) by South African Govt Printer, Pretoria.

58	½c. on ½d. grey-black and sepia	10	30
	a. Surch double	£900	
	b. Surch omitted		
59	1c. on 1d. grey-black and bluish green	30	10
60	2c. on 2d. deep bright blue and orange	1·50	2·00
	a. Surch inverted	£250	
61	2½c. on 3d. yellow-green and rose (Type I)	15	10
	a. Type II (central on vignette)	15	10
	ab. Type II (higher to left, fraction dropped)	30	15
	b. Type II inverted	†	£4750
62	3½c. on 4½d. indigo and deep ultramarine (Type I)	45	20
	a. Type II	5·00	12·00
63	5c. on 6d. chestnut and deep grey-green (Type I)	1·00	10
	a. Type II	50	10
64	10c. on 1s. bronze-green and purple (Type I)	50	10
	a. Type II	£200	£250
65	12½c. on 1s.3d. brown and turquoise-green (Type I)	17·00	6·50
	a. Type II	7·00	2·50
66	25c. on 2s.6d. bright ultramarine and crimson-lake (Type I)	2·25	1·00
	a. Type II	75·00	19·00
	b. Type III	2·75	3·50
67	50c. on 5s. black and carmine-red (Type I)	11·00	8·00
	a. Type II	6·00	8·00
68	1r. on 10s. black and maroon (Type I)	75·00	32·00
	a. Type II	38·00	75·00
	b. Type III	38·00	32·00
58/68b Set of 11 (cheapest)		50·00	42·00

Examples of the 2c. surcharge are known in a fount similar to Type **24** (Price £300 unused).

No. 58b was caused by a paper fold affecting a single sheet.

All known examples of No. 61b are postmarked Mokhotlong on 2 or 3 July 1962.

26 Basuto Household

(Recess D.L.R.)

1961–63. As Nos. 43/53 but values in cents as in T **26**. Wmk Mult Script CA. P 13½ or 11½ (1r.).

69	½c. grey-black and sepia (as ½d.) (25.9.62)	50	20
	a. Imperf (pair)	£425	
70	1c. grey-black and bluish green (as 1d.) (25.9.62)	1·25	40
71	2c. deep bright blue and orange (as 2d.) (25.9.62)	3·00	2·00
72	2½c. yellow-green and deep rose-red (14.2.61)	2·00	1·00
	a. Pale yellow-green and rose-red (22.5.62)	20·00	2·00
73	3½c. indigo and deep ultramarine (as 4½d.) (25.9.62)	1·00	2·25
74	5c. chestnut and deep grey-green (as 6d.) (10.8.62)	70	75
75	10c. bronze-green and purple (as 1s.) (22.10.62)	50	40
76	12½c. brown and turquoise-green (as 1s.3d.) (17.12.62)	26·00	15·00
77	25c. deep ultramarine and crimson (as 2s.6d.) (25.9.62)	6·50	6·50
78	50c. black and carmine-red (as 5s.) (22.10.62)	22·00	28·00
79	1r. black and maroon (as 10s.) (4.2.63)	55·00	32·00
	a. Black and light maroon (16.12.63)	90·00	50·00
69/79 Set of 11		£100	75·00

1963 (4 June). Freedom from Hunger. As No. 146 of Antigua.

80	12½c. reddish violet	40	15

1963 (2 Sept). Red Cross Centenary. As Nos. 147/8 of Antigua.

81	2½c. red and black	30	10
82	12½c. red and blue	80	90

1964 (10 Mar–10 Nov). As Nos. 70, 72, 74, 76 and 78, but W w **12**.

84	1c. grey-black and bluish green (11.8.64)		10	20
86	2½c. pale yellow-green and rose-red (10.3.64)		25	25
88	5c. chestnut and deep grey-green (10.11.64)		40	50
90	12½c. brown and turquoise-green (10.11.64)		16·00	3·50
92	50c. black and carmine-red (29.9.64)		7·25	18·00
84/92 *Set of 5*			22·00	20·00

SELF-GOVERNMENT

28 Mosotho Woman and Child   **29** Maseru Border Post

1965 (10 May). New Constitution. T **28/9** and similar horiz designs. Multicoloured. W w **12**. P 14×13½.

94	2½c. Type **28**		45	10
	w. Wmk inverted		95·00	50·00
95	3½c. Type **29**		80	50
96	5c. Mountain scene		80	50
	w. Wmk inverted		30·00	22·00
97	12½c. Legislative Buildings		80	1·00
94/7 *Set of 4*			2·50	1·90

1965 (17 May). ITU Centenary. As Nos. 166/7 of Antigua.

98	1c. orange-red and bright purple		15	10
99	20c. light blue and orange-brown		50	30

1965 (25 Oct). International Co-operation Year. As Nos. 168/9 of Antigua.

100	½c. reddish purple and turquoise-green		10	1·75
101	12½c. deep bluish green and lavender		45	35

1966 (24 Jan). Churchill Commemoration. Printed in black, cerise, gold and background in colours stated. As Nos. 170/3 of Antigua.

102	1c. new blue		15	2·25
103	2½c. deep green		75	10
104	10c. brown		1·10	60
105	22½c. bluish violet		1·75	1·75
102/5 *Set of 4*			3·25	4·25

OFFICIAL STAMPS

OFFICIAL

(O **1**)

1934 (Feb). Nos. 1/3 and 6 optd with Type O **1**, by Govt printer, Pretoria.

O1	**1**	½d. emerald	£16000	£8000
O2		1d. scarlet	£6000	£4000
O3		2d. bright purple	£6500	£1400
O4		6d. orange-yellow	£6000	£5000
O1/4 *Set of 4*			£40000	£17000

Collectors are advised to buy these stamps only from reliable sources. They were not sold to the public.

300 of each value were supplied in January 1934 for use by the Secretariat in Maseru. Limited usage is recorded between 28 Feb 1934 and 8 June 1934. The issue was then withdrawn and the remainders destroyed. Only the following numbers appear to have been issued: ½d. 24, 1d. 34, 2d. 54, 6d. 27, from which a maximum of ten mint sets exist.

POSTAGE DUE STAMPS

D **1**

Normal

Large "d." (R. 9/6, 10/6)

2d. Serif on "d" (R. 1/6)

(Typo D.L.R.)

1933 (1 Dec)–**52**. Ordinary paper. Wmk Mult Script CA. P 14.

D1	D **1**	1d. carmine	4·25	17·00
		a. Scarlet (1938)	50·00	60·00
		b. Chalk-surfaced paper. *Deep carmine* (24.10.51)	2·25	10·00
		ba. Error. Crown missing, W **9a**	£425	
		bb. Error. St. Edward's Crown, W **9b**	£170	
D2		2d. violet	12·00	25·00
		aa. Large "d"	70·00	
		a. Chalk-surfaced paper (6.11.52)	30	25·00
		ab. Error. Crown missing, W **9a**	£450	
		ac. Error. St. Edward's Crown, W **9b**	£180	
		ad. Large "d"	8·50	£120
		ae. Serif on "d"	12·00	
D1s/2s Perf "SPECIMEN" *Set of 2*			75·00	

D **2**

(Typo D.L.R.)

1956 (1 Dec). Wmk Mult Script CA. P 14.

D3	D **2**	1d. carmine	30	3·00
D4		2d. deep reddish violet	30	6·00

(I)   (II)

1961 (14 Feb). Surch as T **24**, but without stop.

D5	D **2**	1c. on 1d. carmine	10	35
D6		1c. on 2d. deep reddish violet	10	1·25
D7		5c. on 2d. deep reddish violet (Type I)	15	45
		a. Type II	16·00	60·00
D5/7 *Set of 3*			30	1·90

1961 (1 June). No. D2a surch as T **24** (without stop).

D8	D **1**	5c. on 2d. violet	1·00	7·50
		a. Error. Missing Crown, W **9a**	£2000	
		b. Error. St. Edward's Crown, W **9b**	£375	
		c. Large "d"	22·00	

1964. As No. D3/4 but values in cents and W w **12** (sideways on 1c.).

D9	D **2**	1c. carmine	4·75	26·00
D10		5c. deep reddish violet	5·50	26·00

POSTAL FISCAL

In July 1961 the 10s. stamp, T **9**, surcharged "R1 Revenue", was used for postage at one post office at least, but such usage was officially unauthorised.

Basutoland attained independence on 4 October 1966 as the Kingdom of Lesotho.

Batum

Batum, the outlet port on the Black Sea for the Russian Transcaucasian oilfields, was occupied by the Turks on 15 April 1918.

Under the terms of the armistice signed at Mudros on 30 October 1918 the Turks were to withdraw and be replaced by an Allied occupation of Batum, the Baku oilfields and the connecting Transcaucasia Railway. British forces arrived off Batum in early December and the oblast, or district, was declared a British military governorship on 25 December 1918. The Turkish withdrawal was complete five days later.

The provision of a civilian postal service was initially the responsibility of the Batum Town Council. Some form of mail service was in operation by February 1919 with the postage prepaid in cash. Letters are known showing a framed oblong handstamp, in Russian, to this effect. The Town Council was responsible for the production of the first issue, Nos. 1/6, but shortly after these stamps were placed on sale a strike by Council employees against the British military governor led to the postal service being placed under British Army control.

SURCHARGES. Types **2** and **4/8** were all applied by handstamp. Most values from No. 19 to 40 are known showing the surcharge inverted, surcharge double or in pairs with surcharge *tête-bêche*. Inverted surcharges are worth from 2×normal, *tête-bêche* pairs from four times the price of a single stamp.

FORGERIES. Collectors are warned that all the stamps, overprints and surcharges of Batum have been extensively forged. Even the Type **1** stamps should be purchased with caution, and rarities should not be acquired without a reliable guarantee.

BRITISH OCCUPATION
(Currency. 100 kopeks = 1 rouble)

PRICES FOR STAMPS ON COVER	
Nos. 1/6	*from* × 50
Nos. 7/10	*from* × 15
Nos. 11/18	*from* × 50
Nos. 19/20	*from* × 15
Nos. 21/44	—
Nos. 45/53	*from* × 75

1 Aloe Tree

БАТУМ. ОБ.

Руб **10** Руб.

(**2**)

1919 (4 Apr). Litho. Imperf.

1	**1**	5k. green	7·50	27·00
2		10k. ultramarine	9·50	27·00
3		50k. yellow	9·00	15·00
4		1r. chocolate	13·00	9·50
5		3r. violet	11·00	20·00
6		5r. brown	10·00	45·00
1/6 *Set of 6*			55·00	£130

Nos. 1/6 were printed in sheets of 198 (18×11).

1919 (13 Apr). Russian stamps (Arms types) handstamped with T **2**.

7		10r. on 1k. orange (imperf)	80·00	90·00
8		10r. on 3k. carmine-red (imperf)	35·00	42·00
9		10r. on 5k. brown-lilac (perf)	£500	£600
10		10r. on 10 on 7k. deep blue (perf)	£650	£750

A similar handstamped surcharge, showing the capital letters without serifs, is bogus.

BRITISH OCCUPATION

(**3**)

1919 (10 Nov). Colours changed and new values. Optd with T **3**.

11	**1**	5k. yellow-green	32·00	18·00
12		10k. bright blue	16·00	23·00
13		25k. orange-yellow	32·00	26·00
14		1r. pale blue	9·50	24·00
15		2r. pink	1·00	8·50
16		3r. bright violet	1·00	10·00
17		5r. brown	1·25	10·00
		a. "CCUPATION" (R. 5/1)	£400	
18		7r. brownish red	7·00	14·00
11/18 *Set of 8*			90·00	£120

Nos. 11/18 were printed in sheets of 432 (18×24).

БАТУМ BRITISH

Р **10** Р.   Р. **15** Р.

BRITISH OCCUPATION   OCCUPATION О БЛ.

(**4**)   (**5**)

1919 (27 Nov)–**20**. Russian stamps (Arms types) handstamped with T **4** or **5**. Imperf.

19		10r. on 3k. carmine-red	30·00	32·00
20		15r. on 1k. orange	£100	£110
		a. Red surch	85·00	90·00
		b. Violet surch (10.3.20)	£120	£150

Nos. 20a/b have the handstamp in soluble ink.

1920 (12 Jan). Russian stamps (Arms types) handstamped as T **4**.

(a) *Imperf*

21		50r. on 1k. orange	£650	£800
22		50r. on 2k. yellow-green (R.)	£900	£1100

ANDREW PROMOTING PHILATELY ON
THE ALAN TITCHMARSH SHOW ITV

Selling Your Stamps?

Summary Tip #19:
5 Different Ways to Sell your Stamps: Choose with Care

by Andrew McGavin

Dear Colleague,

Following the first article (page 42) in the 'Selling your Stamps?' series we present the advantages and disadvantages inherent in each of the 5 different ways to sell your stamps.

1. Direct Sale: To a Dealer – or Stamp Auction buying on their own account.

The merits of 'direct sale' are often under-estimated by collectors. Direct sale, intelligently handled, may yield considerable benefits. For example we recently purchased a modest collection at a major London auction which was estimated at £4,000 to £5,000. Remember in our last article #18 when we talked about 'know the strength of your collection' ... this collection was the kind that no public auction house could afford to 'break' on behalf of the owner – so it was offered intact as one lot. Inevitably no collector would purchase such a diverse collection – so the 'trade' was bidding against each other in order to purchase. Finally we purchased the collection for £8,158 including 20% buyer's premium. The collection actually sold for £6,800. The auction's commission charged to the buyer was £1,358.

But that's not the end of the story. Did the seller receive £6,800? ... NO. The seller received £6,800 less the seller's commission which unless specially negotiated was a further 17.62% inclusive of VAT. That's a further £1,198 to be deducted from the £6,800 sale price. The owner will have received £5,602 upon a collection sold to us for which we paid £8,158 !

I can hear you saying that Auctions exist so that buyers compete to pay more for your stamps – it's true – but some collections simply are not suited to being sold via public auction. All you are doing is paying an auction to ensure

that dealers compete to purchase your collection ...

45% MORE was paid for the public auction to sell the collection to a stamp dealer. £2,556 more was paid that the collector did not receive.

BUT – there are imaginative ways that you can obtain more from dealers without going to auction – and have the benefit of certainty too, whilst not waiting up to 6 months for your money ... for example – ... a valuable collection was offered to us earlier this year. We're allowed to write what happened without revealing any confidences. Unfortunately the Father had died leaving one of his two Daughters £25,000 and the other Daughter his Stamp Collection – a very difficult situation as you might imagine. Believing the collection may be valuable, unusually, 3 different dealers visited to value it. All 3 dealers incurred costs – in our case 6 travelling hours and 260 miles – so none was happy to leave an offer on the 'table' for the next dealer to pay £50 more and purchase the collection – what was the client to do allowing fair play to all? We suggested an 'auction' monitored by the owner of the collection – not hard to conduct in the age of landline and mobile phones... and opened the bidding with a £20,000 bid.

The 3rd Dealer dropped out – the 2nd dealer had just finished viewing the collection so was actually on the client's premises. He bid £21,000, we bid £22,000 ... and so it went on until bidding 'narrowed' to £500 increments and finally we purchased the collection for £27,500 and travelled 260 miles again to collect it and pay for it. The client thanked the 2nd dealer for his time

and participation with a small ex-gratia payment. Fortunately a happy ending for the client – amazingly, more than her Sister ... it could so easily have been a different outcome.

But what if that collection had been auctioned as one lot or 7 volumes + residue? For the client to have been better off – the trade would have had to pay more than £40,000 ... an unlikely scenario. The moral – know the strength of your collection and 'pick' the right people to participate in its purchase.

In our next article we'll discuss alternatives

Happy collecting from us all,

Andrew

PS. If you find this 'tip' interesting please forward it to a philatelic friend.

Andrew McGavin
Managing Director: Universal Philatelic Auctions, Omniphil & Avon Approvals, Avon Mixtures, Universal Philatelic (Ebay)

To read the rest of this series 'SELLING YOUR STAMPS?' see the relevant pages listed below:

Summary Tip 18 – page 42 (Australia)
Summary Tip 19 – page 98 (Bechuanaland)
Summary Tip 20 – page 210 (Egypt)
Summary Tip 21 – page 272 (India)

To read the final instalment, Summary Tip 22 – 'Selling via Online Auction' simply e-mail and request to: *info@upastampauctions.co.uk*

Also, at the back of this catalogue to see how UPA can pay you upto 36% more for your collection

Column 1 (Batum continued)

	(b) Perf		
23	50r. on 2k. yellow-green	£850	£1000
24	50r. on 3k. carmine-red	£1500	£1600
25	50r. on 4k. red	£1000	£1100
26	50r. on 5k. brown-lilac	£450	£600
27	50r. on 10k. deep blue (R.)	£3250	£3250
28	50r. on 15k. blue and red-brown	£850	£1100

(6)

1920 (30 Jan–21 Feb). Russian stamps (Arms types) handstamped as T **6**.

	(a) Perf		
29	25r. on 5k. brown-lilac (21.2)	55·00	75·00
	a. Blue surch	55·00	70·00
30	25r. on 10 on 7k. blue (21.2)	£150	£160
	a. Blue surch	90·00	£110
31	25r. on 20 on 14k. deep carmine and blue (21.2)	£100	£130
	a. Blue surch	£100	£130
32	25r. on 25k. deep violet and light green (21.2)	£180	£200
	a. Blue surch	£120	£150
33	25r. on 50k. green and copper-red (21.2)	£130	£140
	a. Blue surch	95·00	£130
34	50r. on 2k. yellow-green	£140	£190
35	50r. on 3k. carmine-red	£140	£190
36	50r. on 4k. red	£130	£160
37	50r. on 5k. brown-lilac	£100	£140
	(b) Imperf		
38	50r. on 2k. yellow-green	£450	£500
39	50r. on 3k. carmine-red	£550	£650
40	50r. on 5k. brown-lilac	£1800	£1900

1920 (10 Mar). Romanov issue, as T **25** of Russia, handstamped with T **6**.

41	50r. on 4k. rose-carmine (B.)	£140	£170

(7)   (8)

1920 (1 Apr). Nos. 3, 11 and 13 handstamped with T **7** (Nos. 42/3) or **8** (No. 44).

42	25r. on 5k. yellow-green	55·00	75·00
	a. Blue surch	75·00	£100
43	25r. on 25k. orange-yellow	42·00	45·00
	a. Blue surch	£170	£190
44	50r. on 50k. yellow	35·00	42·00
	a. "50" cut	23·00	26·00
	b. Blue surch	£120	£150
	ba. "50" cut	£275	£325

Nos. 44a and 44ba show the figures broken by intentional file cuts applied as a protection against forgery. The "5" is cut at the base and on the right side of the loop. The "0" is chipped at top and foot, and has both vertical lines severed.

1920 (19 June). Colours changed and new values. Optd with T **3**. Imperf.

45	**1**	1r. chestnut	2·25	18·00
		a. "BPITISH"	90·00	
46		2r. pale blue	2·25	18·00
		a. "BPITISH"	£110	
47		3r. pink	2·25	18·00
		a. "BPITISH"	£110	
48		5r. black-brown	2·25	18·00
		a. "BPITISH"	£110	
49		7r. yellow	2·25	18·00
		a. "BPITISH"	£110	
50		10r. myrtle-green	2·25	18·00
		a. "BPITISH"	£110	
51		15r. violet	2·75	23·00
		a. "BPITISH"	£250	
52		25r. scarlet	2·50	22·00
		a. "BPITISH"	£190	
53		50r. deep blue	2·75	25·00
		a. "BPITISH"	£425	
45/53		*Set of 9*	19·00	£160

Nos. 45/53 were printed in sheets of 308 (22×14). The "BPITISH" error occurs on R. 1/19 of the overprint.

POSTCARD STAMPS

When Nos. 7/10 were issued on 13 April 1919 a similar 35k. surcharge was applied to stocks of various Russian postcards held by the post office. The majority of these had stamp impressions printed directly on to the card, but there were also a few cards, originally intended for overseas mail, on which Russia 4k. stamps had been affixed.

PRICES. Those in the left-hand column are for unused examples on complete postcard; those on the right for used examples off card. Examples used on postcard are worth more.

1919 (13 Apr). Russian stamps handstamped as T **2**.

P1	35k. on 4k. red (Arms type)	£10000	£10000
P2	35k. on 4k. carmine-red (Romanov issue)	£18000	£18000

Batum was handed over to the National Republic of Georgia on 7 July 1920.

Bechuanaland

Before the 1880s the only Europeans in the area which became Bechuanaland were scattered hunters and traders, together with the missionaries who were established at Kuruman as early as 1816.

Tribal conflicts in the early years of the decade led to the intervention of Boers from the Transvaal who established the independent republics of Goshen and Stellaland.

STELLALAND

The Boer republic of Stellaland was proclaimed towards the end of 1882. A postal service was organised from the capital, Vryburg, and stamps were ordered from a firm in Cape Town. These were only valid within the republic. Until June 1885 mail to other parts of South Africa was sent through Christiana, in the Transvaal, and was franked with both Stellaland and Transvaal stamps.

No date stamps or obliterators were used by the Stellaland Post Office. Stamps were initially pen-cancelled with the date only and from August 1884 to May 1885 by the date and the postmaster's initials. After May 1885 they were generally cancelled by a pen stroke or cross or left uncancelled. Postmarks found on Stellaland stamps were applied in transit; those known being '3' (Rustenburg), '6' (Christiana) and '8' (Zeerust) of Transvaal, '27' (Hoopstad, Orange Free State) or '232' (Barkly West, Cape Colony).

> **PRICES FOR STAMPS ON COVER**
>
> The issues of Stellaland are very rare on cover.

1 Arms of the Republic

(Litho by Van der Sandt, de Villiers & Co., Cape Town)

1884 (29 Feb). P 12.

1	**1**	1d. red	£225	£325
		a. Imperf between (horiz pair)	£4500	
		b. Imperf between (vert pair)	£5000	
2		3d. orange	38·00	£375
		a. Imperf between (horiz pair)	£1000	
		b. Imperf between (vert pair)	£2250	
		c. Imperf vert (horiz pair)	£1400	
3		4d. olive-grey	32·00	£400
		a. Imperf between (horiz pair)	£800	
		b. Imperf between (vert pair)	£2500	
4		6d. lilac-mauve	38·00	£400
		a. Imperf between (horiz pair)	£1700	
		b. Imperf between (vert pair)	£1900	
5		1s. green	90·00	£800
		a. Imperf between (vert pair)		

In 1884 the British Government, following appeals from local chiefs for protection, decided to annex both Goshen and Stellaland. A force under Sir Charles Warren from the Cape reached Vryburg on 7 February 1885 and continued to Mafeking, the principal town of Goshen.

On 30 September 1885 Stellaland and other territory to the south of the Molopo River was constituted the Crown Colony of British Bechuanaland. A protectorate was also proclaimed over a vast tract of land to the north of the Molopo.

Stellaland stamps continued to be used until 2 December 1885 with external mail, franked with Stellaland and Cape of Good Hope stamps, postmarked at Barkly West and Kimberley in Griqualand West.

1885 (Oct). Handstamped "*Three*" sideways in violet-lake.

6	**1**	2d. on 4d. olive-grey	£3500

On 2 December 1885 Cape of Good Hope stamps overprinted "British Bechuanaland" were placed on sale at the Vryburg post office.

BRITISH BECHUANALAND

CROWN COLONY

> **PRICES FOR STAMPS ON COVER**
>
> | Nos. 1/8 | *from × 12* |
> |---|---|
> | No. 9 | *from × 80* |
> | Nos. 10/21 | *from × 8* |
> | Nos. 22/8 | *from × 10* |
> | No. 29 | *from × 10* |
> | No. 30 | *from × 10* |
> | Nos. 31/2 | *from × 12* |
> | Nos. 33/7 | *from × 20* |
> | Nos. 38/9 | *from × 25* |

BRITISH

British
Bechuanaland
(1)

BECHUANALAND
(2)

1885 (2 Dec)–**87**. Stamps of Cape of Good Hope ("Hope" seated) optd with T **1**, by A. Richards & Sons, Cape Town.

		(a) Wmk Crown CC (No. 3) or Crown CA (others)		
1		½d. grey-black (No. 40a) (R.)	35·00	45·00
		a. Opt in lake	£5000	£5500
		b. Opt double (Lake+Black)	£750	

2		3d. pale claret (No. 43)	60·00	70·00
		a. No dot to 1st "i" of "British"	£800	
3		4d. dull blue (No. 30) (2.6.87)	95·00	85·00
		*(b) Wmk Anchor (Cape of Good Hope Type **13**)*		
4		½d. grey-black (No. 48a) (24.12.86)	16·00	30·00
		a. Error. "ritish"	£2750	
		b. Opt double	£3500	
		w. Wmk inverted		
5		1d. rose-red (No. 49)	27·00	9·00
		a. Error. "ritish"	£4250	£2250
		b. No dot to 1st "i" of "British"	£475	£2250
		c. Opt double	†	£2250
6		2d. pale bistre (No. 50)	55·00	6·00
		a. Error. "ritish"	£8000	£4000
		b. No dot to 1st "i" of "British"	£850	£275
		c. Opt double	†	£2250
		w. Wmk inverted	†	£800
7		6d. reddish purple (No. 52)	£200	38·00
		a. No dot to 1st "i" of "British"	£2250	£750
8		1s. green (No. 53) (26.11.86)	£375	£190
		a. Error. "ritish"	£24000	£15000

Nos. 1/8 were overprinted from settings of 120. The missing "B" errors are believed to have occurred on one position for one of these settings only. The 'No dot to 1st "i"' variety occurs on R. 10/3 on the left pane.

Overprints with stop after "Bechuanaland" are forged, as are overprints on the 1s. Wmk Crown CC and the 5s. Cape of Good Hope stamps.

1888 (19 Jan). No. 197 of Great Britain optd with T **2**, by D.L.R.

9	½d. vermilion	2·50	1·50
	a. Opt double	£2500	
	s. Handstamped "SPECIMEN"	85·00	

3   4   5

(Typo D.L.R.)

1888 (19 Jan).

		*(a) Wmk Orb (Great Britain Type **48**). P 14*		
10	**3**	1d. lilac and black	27·00	4·50
11		2d. lilac and black	£120	2·25
		a. Pale dull lilac and black	£120	25·00
12		3d. lilac and black	8·50	8·00
		a. Pale reddish lilac and black	80·00	25·00
13		4d. lilac and black	65·00	2·50
14		6d. lilac and black	80·00	2·50
		(b) Wmk Script "V R" (sideways, reading up). P 13½		
15	**4**	1s. green and black	30·00	12·00
16		2s. green and black	70·00	60·00
17		2s.6d. green and black	80·00	80·00
18		5s. green and black	£130	£170
19		10s. green and black	£275	£400
		(c) Two Orbs (sideways). P 14×13½		
20	**5**	£1 lilac and black (f.c. £50)	£900	£800
21		£5 lilac and black (f.c. £200)	£4000	£1700
10s/21s	H/S "SPECIMEN" *Set of 12*		£1000	

Nos. 10/21 were produced by overprinting a series of "Unappropriated Die" designs originally produced by the Board of Inland Revenue for use as Great Britain fiscal stamps.

Several values are known on blued paper. No. 11a is the first printing of the 2d. (on safety paper?) and has a faded appearance.

When purchasing Nos. 20/21 in used condition beware of copies with fiscal cancellations cleaned off and bearing forged postmarks.

For No. 15 surcharged "£5" see No. F2.

1d.   **1s.**
(6)   (7)

2d.
Curved foot to "2"

1888 (Sept–20 Nov). Nos. 10/11 and 13/15 surch as T **6** or **7**, by P. Townshend & Co., Vryburg.

22	**3**	1d. on 1d. lilac and black	8·00	8·00
23		2d. on 2d. lilac and black (R.)	65·00	4·00
		a. Pale dull lilac and black (No. 11a)	£150	65·00
		b. Curved foot to "2"	£350	£150
		c. Surch in green	†	£4000
25		4d. on 4d. lilac and black (R.) (20.11)	£425	£600
26		6d. on 6d. lilac and black (R.)	£150	12·00
		a. Surch in blue	†	£13000
28	**4**	1s. on 1s. green and black	£250	90·00

Nos. 23c and 26a are from two sheets of surcharge trials subsequently put into stock and used at Vryburg (2d.) or Mafeking (6d.) during 1888–89.

It should be noted that, in addition to its curved foot, the "2" on No. 23b is distinctly shorter than the "d".

A single example of No. 23c with the 'curved foot to "2"' variety has been recorded (*Price, £18,000, used*).

One Half-Penny
(8)

1888 (8 Dec). No. 12a surch with T **8**, by P. Townshend & Co, Vryburg.

29	**3**	½d. on 3d. pale reddish lilac and black	£275	£325
		a. Broken "f" in "Half"	£17000	

No. 29 was produced from a setting of 60 (12×5).

No. 29a shows the letter "f" almost completely missing and occurs on R. 5/11 of the setting. Five examples are known, one being in the Royal Collection.

Errors of spelling on this surcharge are bogus. The normal surcharge has also been extensively forged.

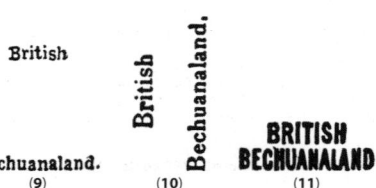

British		**BRITISH**
		BECHUANALAND
Bechuanaland.		
(9)	**(10)**	**(11)**

1888 (27 Dec). No. 48a of Cape of Good Hope (wmk Anchor) optd with T **9**, by P. Townshend & Co, Vryburg.
30		½d. grey-black (G.)............................	3·25	35·00
		a. Opt "Bechuanaland British"..............	£3000	
		ab. "British" omitted.........................	£7000	
		b. Opt double, one inverted, inverted		
		opt "Bechuanaland British".........	£3000	
		ba. Opt double, one inverted, inverted		
		"British" omitted......................	£7500	
		c. Opt double, one vertical	£850	
		ca. Se-tenant with stamp without opt ...	£10000	

No. 30 was produced using a setting of 30 (6×5).

The overprint was misplaced upwards on at least one pane, giving the overprint "Bechuanaland British" (No. 30a) on rows 1 to 4 and "British" omitted on row 5 (No. 30ab). "British" was also omitted on R. 5/1 of the setting on some sheets only.

On one pane on which the overprint was applied double, one inverted, the inverted overprint was misplaced downwards, giving No. 30b on rows 7 to 10 and "British" omitted (No. 30ba) on row 6.

n n

Normal "n"   Inverted "u"

1891 (Nov). Nos. 49a/50 of Cape of Good Hope (wmk Anchor), optd with T **10**, reading upwards.
31		1d. carmine-red...............................	13·00	20·00
		a. Horiz pair, one without opt.........	£26000	
		b. Optd "Bechuanaland. British"..........	£3500	
		c. "Bechuanaland" omitted	£3500	
		d. Inverted "u" for 2nd "n"..............	£225	£275
32		2d. bistre (shades)............................	8·00	2·25
		a. No stop after "Bechuanaland".......	£350	£350
		b. Inverted "u" for 2nd "n".............	£300	£300
	31s/2s H/S "SPECIMEN" Set of 2..................	£130	

The overprint on Nos. 31 and 32 was of 120 impressions in two panes of 60 (6×10). No. 32 was applied both by a stereo plate and by a forme made up from loose type. No. 31 was overprinted only with the latter. No. 32a is from the stereo overprinting (left pane, R. 3/3), 31d and 32b are from the typeset overprinting (left pane, R. 10/4).

A single example of No. 31 with "British" omitted is known; it is in the Royal Philatelic Collection.

See also Nos. 38 and 39.

1891 (1 Dec)–**1904**. Nos. 172, 200, 205, 208 and 211 of Great Britain optd with T **11**, by D.L.R.
33		1d. lilac...	7·00	1·50
34		2d. grey-green and carmine................	24·00	4·00
35		4d. green and purple-brown...............	4·50	60
		a. Bisected (2d.) (on cover) (11.99)...	†	£2500
36		6d. purple/rose-red..........................	9·00	2·25
37		1s. dull green (7.94)........................	13·00	19·00
		a. Bisected (6d.) (on cover) (12.04)...	†	—
	33/7 Set of 5...	50·00	25·00
	33s/6s H/S "SPECIMEN" Set of 4..................	£170	

No. 35a was used at Palapye Station and No. 37a at Kanye, both in the Protectorate.

1893 (Dec)–**95**. As Nos. 31/2, but T **10** reads downwards.
38		1d. carmine-red...............................	4·50	2·25
		b. "British" omitted.........................	£4250	£4250
		c. Optd "Bechuanaland. British"..........	£1500	£1600
		d. Inverted "u" for 2nd "n"..............	£160	£160
		e. No dots to "i" of "British"..........	£160	£160
		f. "s" omitted...............................	£700	£700
		g. Opt reading up, no dots to "i" of		
		"British"...............................	£4500	
39		2d. bistre (12.3.95).........................	15·00	3·75
		a. Opt double...............................	£1400	£700
		b. "British" omitted.........................	£850	£500
		c. "Bechuanaland" omitted	—	£700
		d. Optd "Bechuanaland. British"..........	£500	£300
		e. Inverted "u" for 2nd "n"..............	£275	£170
		f. No dots to "i" of "British"..........	£275	£170
		g. Opt reading up, no dots to "i" of		
		"British"...............................	£4750	

The same typeset overprint was used for Nos. 38 and 39 as had been employed for Nos. 31 and 32 but applied the other way up; the inverted "u" thus falling on the right pane, R. 1/3. The no dots to "i" variety only occurs on this printing (right pane, R. 1/4). Some sheets of both values were overprinted the wrong way up, resulting in Nos. 38g. and 39g.

No. 38f. developed gradually on right pane R. 10/8. The variety is not known on Nos. 31, 32 or 39.

On 16 November 1895 British Bechuanaland was annexed to the Cape of Good Hope and ceased to have its own stamps, but they remained in use in the Protectorate until superseded in 1897. The Postmaster-General of Cape Colony had assumed control of the Bechuanaland postal service on 1 April 1893 and the Cape, and subsequently the South African, postal authorities continued to be responsible for the postal affairs of the Bechuanaland Protectorate until 1963.

BECHUANALAND PROTECTORATE

PRICES FOR STAMPS ON COVER TO 1945		
Nos. 40/51	*from* × 10	
Nos. 52/71	*from* × 6	
Nos. 72/82	*from* × 5	
Nos. 83/98	*from* × 4	
Nos. 99/110	*from* × 6	
Nos. 111/17	*from* × 10	
Nos. 118/28	*from* × 4	
Nos. 129/31	*from* × 10	
Nos. D1/3	*from* × 50	
Nos. D4/6	*from* × 60	
No. F1	*from* × 5	
No. F2	—	
No. F3	*from* × 5	

This large area north of the Molopo River was proclaimed a British Protectorate on 30 September 1885 at the request of the native chiefs.

A postal service using runners was inaugurated on 9 August 1888 and Nos. 40 to 55 were issued as a temporary measure with the object of assessing the cost of this service.

 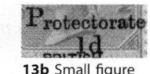

Protectorate		**Protectorate 1d**
(12) 15½ mm		**(13)**

13a Small figure "1" (R. 7/2)   **13b** Small figure "1" (R. 10/2)

2   2

Normal "2"   Curved foot to "2" (42b)

1888 (Aug). No. 9 optd with T **12** and Nos. 10/19 surch or optd only as T **13** by P. Townshend & Co. Vryburg.
40	–	½d. vermilion...............................	13·00	55·00
		a. "Protectorate" double	£350	
		s. Handstamped "SPECIMEN"	90·00	
41	**3**	1d. on 1d. lilac and black................	20·00	16·00
		a. Small figure "1" (R. 7/2, 10/2)	£425	£500
		b. Space between "1" and "d"		
		(R. 10/9)...............................	£650	
42		2d. on 2d. lilac and black................	48·00	18·00
		b. Curved foot to "2"...................	£950	£550
43		3d. on 3d. pale reddish lilac and		
		black..	£200	£275
44		4d. on 4d. lilac and black................	£475	£500
		a. Small figure "4" (R. 7/12)	£6000	£6000
45		6d. on 6d. lilac and black................	£120	55·00
46	**4**	1s. green and black........................	£140	60·00
		a. First "o" omitted.......................	£6500	£3750
		s. Handstamped "SPECIMEN"	£130	
47		2s. green and black........................	£750	£1200
		a. First "o" omitted.......................	£18000	
48		2s.6d. green and black.....................	£600	£950
		a. First "o" omitted.......................	£20000	
49		5s. green and black........................	£1300	£2250
		a. First "o" omitted.......................	£25000	
50		10s. green and black.......................	£5000	£7500

Nos. 40/5 were produced from a basic setting of 120 (12×10) on which a faulty first "o" in "Protectorate" occurred on R. 5/12. For Nos. 46/50 the setting was reduced to 84 (12×7) and on many sheets the first "o" on R. 5/12 failed to print.

There were two distinct printings made of No. 40, the first in 1888 and the second in 1889. The overprint setting used for the first printing was broken up and had to be remade for the second. The first printing used a matt ink which produces a cleaner impression than the second, which is printed with a black glossy ink giving a distinctly muddy appearance.

There are a number of smaller than normal "1"s in the setting, usually identifiable by the upper serif of the "1" which is pointed and slopes sharply downwards at the left. R. 7/2 and 10/2 are quite distinct and are as shown.

The normal space between "1" and "d" measures 1 mm. On No. 41b it is 1.7 mm.

It should be noted that, like No. 23b, the "2" on No. 42b is distinctly shorter than the "d" and has a distinctive curl to the upper part of the "2", not present on No. 23.

The height of the "4" on No. 44a is 2.15 mm, as opposed to 2.4-2.5 mm for the normal surcharge. Other identifying features of the genuine variety are the "4" positioned below the first "t" of "Protectorate" and the top of the surcharge "t" being missing.

A single example of No. 50 with the first "o" omitted is known; it is in the Royal Philatelic Collection.

Nos. 40/50 were first placed on sale in Vryburg on 23 June 1888. The August issue date refers to the start of the Runner Post.

See also Nos. 54/5.

1888 (10 Dec). No. 25 optd with T **12** by P. Townshend & Co., Vryburg.
51	**3**	4d. on 4d. lilac and black................	£150	60·00
		a. Opt (T **12**) double.....................	†	£2750

Bechuanaland		
Protectorate		**Fourpence**
Proteotorate		
(14)		**(15)**

1888 (27 Dec). No. 48a of Cape of Good Hope (wmk Anchor), optd with T **14** by P. Townshend & Co., Vryburg.
52		½d. grey-black (G.)........................	6·50	55·00
		a. Opt double...............................	£500	£750
		ab. Ditto, one reading "Protectorate		
		Bechuanaland"..........................	£1200	

		ac. Ditto, one reading "Bechuanaland"		
		only..................................	£2500	
		b. "Bechuanaland" omitted	£2000	
		c. Optd "Protectorate Bechuanaland"...	£1100	£1100

1889 (Mar). No. 9 surch with T **15** by P. Townshend & Co., Vryburg.
53		4d. on ½d. vermilion.......................	48·00	6·00
		a. "rpence" omitted (R. 9/2)..............	†	£6000
		b. "ourpence" omitted (R. 9/2)..........	£10000	
		c. Surch (T **15**) inverted................	†	£4000
		cb. Ditto. "ourpence" omitted	†	£17000
		s. Handstamped "SPECIMEN"	£150	

The lines of the surcharge are normally 6 mm apart, but 5 mm and 4.5 mm spacings are known.

Examples of No. 53c are postmarked "679" (Tati).

The surcharge is known printed in green, due to faulty cleaning of the inking roller. All examples known were cancelled at Shoshong. (Price £1500 used).

Protectorate	**Protectorate**
(16) 15 mm	**(17)** 19 mm

1890. No. 9 optd.
54	**16**	½d. vermilion..................................	£225	£250
		a. Type **16** inverted.....................	85·00	£120
		b. Type **16** double........................	£130	£180
		c. Type **16** double and inverted.......	£750	£850
		d. Optd "Portectorate" inverted	£20000	
		w. Wmk inverted...........................		
55	**17**	½d. vermilion..................................	£275	£450
		a. Type **17** double........................	£1600	£1700
		b. Optd "Portectorate"...................	£5000	
		c. Optd "Protectorrte" double	£20000	

These were trial printings made in June 1888 (No. 55) and subsequently (No. 54) which were later issued.

The 15 mm measurement of the overprint on No. 54 should not be relied on as a sole diagnostic, since the overprint on a few positions within the setting of No. 40 similarly measure 15 mm. No. 54 is a cleaner, more even overprint and the out of line letters so frquently encountered on No. 40, especially the raised 'P' of 'Protectorate' and its consequent greater separation from the first 'r' are not found on this stamp.

In June 1890 the Bechuanaland Protectorate and the Colony of British Bechuanaland came under one postal administration and the stamps of British Bechuanaland were used in the Protectorate until 1897.

BRITISH	**BECHUANALAND**
BECHUANALAND	**PROTECTORATE**
(18)	**(19)**

1897. No. 61 of Cape of Good Hope (wmk Anchor), optd as T **18**.

(a) Lines 13 mm apart, bottom line 16 mm long, by Taylor & Marshall, Cape Town
56		½d. yellow-green (7.97?)....................	2·50	20·00

(b) Lines 13½ mm apart bottom line 15 mm long, by P. Townshend & Co, Vryburg
57		½d. yellow-green (4.97)......................	42·00	£110

(c) Lines 10½ mm apart, bottom line 15 mm long, by W. A. Richards & Sons, Cape Govt Printers
58		½d. yellow-green (7.97?)....................	19·00	75·00

Although issued only in the Protectorate, the above were presumably overprinted "BRITISH BECHUANALAND" because stamps bearing this inscription were in use there at the time.

Examples of No.57 are known with an addional reversed albino overprint due to the sheet having been folded through overprinting.

1897 (Oct)–**1902**. Nos. 172, 197, 200, 202, 205 and 208 of Great Britain (Queen Victoria) optd with T **19** by D.L.R.
59		½d. vermilion..................................	2·75	2·25
60		½d. blue-green (25.2.02)....................	1·40	3·50
61		1d. lilac...	4·00	75
62		2d. grey-green and carmine................	15·00	3·50
63		3d. purple/yellow (12.97)..................	6·00	14·00
64		4d. green and purple-brown...............	28·00	25·00
65		6d. purple/rose-red..........................	24·00	15·00
	59/65 Set of 7......................................	70·00	55·00
	59s/65s Optd or H/S (No. 60s) "SPECIMEN" Set of 7....	£275	

BECHUANALAND	**PROTECTORATE**	
		BECHUANALAND PROTECTORATE
(20)		**(21)**

1904 (29 Nov)–**13**. Nos. 216, 218/19, 230 and 313/14 (Somerset House ptgs) of Great Britain (King Edward VII) optd with T **20**, by D.L.R.
66		½d. blue-green (3.06)........................	2·75	4·00
67		½d. yellowish green (11.08).................	3·75	3·75
68		1d. scarlet (4.05).............................	11·00	30
		s. Optd "SPECIMEN".....................	65·00	
69		2½d. ultramarine.............................	12·00	10·00
		a. Stop after "P" in "PROTECTORATE"....	£1000	£1300
70		1s. deep green and scarlet (10.12)......	55·00	£170
		a. Opt double, one albino	£225	
71		1s. green and carmine (1913)	60·00	£140
		s. Optd "SPECIMEN".....................	£110	

No. 69a occurs on R. 5/9 of the lower pane.

1912 (Sept)–**14**. No. 342 of Great Britain (King George V, wmk Crown) optd with T **20**.
72		1d. scarlet.....................................	3·75	60
		a. No cross on crown......................	£150	75·00
		b. Aniline scarlet (No. 343) (1914).....	£190	95·00

1913 (1 July)–**24**. Stamps of Great Britain (King George V) optd.

(a) Nos. 351, 357, 362, 367, 370/1, 376, 379, 385 and 395
*(wmk Simple Cypher, T **100**) optd with T **20***

73	½d. green (*shades*)		1·25	1·50
74	1d. scarlet (*shades*) (4.15)		2·75	75
	a. Carmine-red (1922)		40·00	4·00
75	1½d. red-brown (12.20)		7·00	2·50
	a. Opt double, one albino		£325	
76	2d. reddish orange (Die I)		13·00	3·25
	a. Orange (Die I) (1921)		25·00	3·00
	aw. Wmk inverted			
77	2d. orange (Die II) (1924)		50·00	2·75
78	2½d. cobalt-blue		3·50	30·00
	a. Blue (1915)		27·00	25·00
79	3d. bluish violet		6·00	18·00
80	4d. grey-black		6·50	40·00
81	6d. reddish purple (*shades*)		9·50	28·00
	a. Opt double, one albino		£325	
82	1s. bistre		23·00	45·00
	a. Bistre-brown (1923)		55·00	32·00
	b. Opt double, albino		£350	
	s. Optd "SPECIMEN"		£100	
73/82 *Set of 9*			65·00	£130

*(b) With T **21***

(i) Waterlow printings (Nos. 399 and 401) (1914–15)

83	2s.6d. deep sepia-brown (1.15)		£140	£275
	a. Re-entry (R. 2/1)		£1400	£2000
	b. Opt double, one albino		£300	
84	5s. rose-carmine (1914)		£160	£375
	a. Opt double, one albino		£375	
83s/4s Optd "SPECIMEN" *Set of 2*			£275	

(ii) D.L.R. printings (Nos. 407/8 and 409) (1916–19)

85	2s.6d. pale brown (7.16)		£120	£250
	a. Re-entry (R. 2/1)		£1200	£1800
86	2s.6d. sepia (1917)		£130	£225
	a. Opt treble, two albino		£1400	£1700
	b. Re-entry (R. 2/1)			
87	5s. bright carmine (8.19)		£300	£425
	a. Opt double, one albino		£450	

(iii) B.W. printings (Nos. 414 and 416) (1920–23)

88	2s.6d. chocolate-brown (7.23)		90·00	£160
	a. Major re-entry (R. 1/2)		£2500	
	b. Opt treble, two albino		£550	
	c. Opt treble, one albino		£550	
89	5s. rose-carmine (7.20)		£110	£275
	a. Opt treble, two albino		£375	

Examples of Nos. 83/9 are known showing a forged Lobatsi postmark dated "6 MAY 35" or "6 MAY 39".

1925 (July)–**27**. Nos. 418/19, 421, 423/4, 426/*a* and 429 of Great Britain (wmk Block Cypher, T **111**) optd with T **20**.

91	½d. green (1927)		1·50	1·75
92	1d. scarlet (8.25)		2·00	70
	w. Wmk inverted		£400	
93	2d. orange (Die II)		2·25	1·00
94	3d. violet (10.26)		4·75	29·00
	a. Opt double, one albino		£200	
	w. Wmk inverted		£200	
95	4d. grey-green (10.26)		9·00	55·00
	a. Printed on the gummed side			
96	6d. reddish purple (*chalk-surfaced paper*) (12.25)		75·00	£110
97	6d. purple (*ordinary paper*) (1926)		50·00	55·00
98	1s. bistre-brown (10.26)		9·00	26·00
	w. Wmk inverted		£350	£300
91/8 *Set of 8*			£140	£250

No. 94w. also usually shows the variety, opt double, one albino.

22 King George V, Baobab Tree and Cattle

23 King George VI, Baobab Tree and Cattle

(Des from photo by Resident Commissioner, Ngamiland, Recess Waterlow)

1932 (12 Dec). Wmk Mult Script CA. P 12½.

99	**22**	½d. green	2·75	50
		a. Imperf between (horiz pair)	£35000	
100		1d. scarlet	2·50	40
101		2d. brown	2·50	45
102		3d. ultramarine	5·00	5·50
103		4d. orange	5·00	14·00
104		6d. purple	7·50	9·50
105		1s. black and olive-green	6·50	9·50
106		2s. black and orange	27·00	75·00
107		2s.6d. black and scarlet	27·00	55·00
108		3s. black and purple	48·00	65·00
109		5s. black and ultramarine	£130	£130
110		10s. black and brown	£325	£325
99/110 *Set of 12*			£500	£600
99s/110s Perf "SPECIMEN" *Set of 12*			£450	

Examples of most values are known showing a forged Lobatsi postmark dated "6 MAY 35" or "6 MAY 39".

1935 (4 May). Silver Jubilee. As Nos. 91/4 of Antigua but ptd by B.W. P 11×12.

111	1d. deep blue and scarlet		1·75	7·00
	a. Extra flagstaff		£275	£500
	b. Short extra flagstaff		£550	
	c. Lightning conductor		£400	
	d. Flagstaff on right-hand turret		£650	
	e. Double flagstaff		£650	£700
112	2d. ultramarine and grey-black		3·50	6·50
	a. Extra flagstaff		£140	£225
	b. Short extra flagstaff		£200	£300
	c. Lightning conductor		£170	£275

113	3d. brown and deep blue		4·25	12·00
	a. Extra flagstaff		£180	£350
	b. Short extra flagstaff		£275	
	c. Lightning conductor		£200	£350
114	6d. slate and purple		9·50	13·00
	a. Extra flagstaff		£200	£300
	b. Short extra flagstaff		£250	
	c. Lightning conductor		£225	£300
111/14 *Set of 4*			17·00	35·00
111s/14s Perf "SPECIMEN" *Set of 4*			£140	

For illustrations of plate varieties see Omnibus section following Zanzibar.

1937 (12 May). Coronation. As Nos. 95/7 of Antigua, but printed by D.L.R. P 14.

115	1d. scarlet		45	40
116	2d. yellow-brown		60	1·00
117	3d. bright blue		60	1·25
115/17 *Set of 3*			1·50	2·40
115s/17s Perf "SPECIMEN" *Set of 3*			£140	

(Recess Waterlow)

1938 (1 Apr)–**52**. Wmk Mult Script CA. P 12½.

118	**23**	½d. green	4·25	3·75
		a. Light yellowish green (1941)	15·00	13·00
		b. Yellowish green (4.43)	19·00	6·00
		c. Deep green (4.49)	5·00	14·00
119		1d. scarlet	75	50
120		1½d. dull blue	16·00	2·50
		a. Light blue (4.43)	1·00	1·00
121		2d. chocolate-brown	75	50
122		3d. deep ultramarine	1·00	2·50
123		4d. orange	2·00	3·50
124		6d. reddish purple	11·00	3·00
		a. Purple (1944)	6·00	2·50
		ab. "A" of "CA" missing from wmk	†	—
125		1s. black and brown-olive	5·50	9·50
		a. Grey-black and olive-green (21.5.52)	28·00	50·00
126		2s.6d. black and scarlet	14·00	20·00
127		5s. black and deep ultramarine	48·00	32·00
		a. Grey-black and deep ultramarine (10.46)	90·00	75·00
128		10s. black and red-brown	30·00	40·00
118/28 *Set of 11*			£110	£100
118s/28s Perf "SPECIMEN" *Set of 11*			£375	

Bechuanaland
(**24**)

1945 (3 Dec). Victory. Stamps of South Africa optd with T **24**. Inscr alternately in English and Afrikaans.

			Un pair	Used pair	Used single
129	**55**	1d. brown and carmine	75	1·50	10
		a. Barbed wire flaw	15·00		
130	**56**	2d. slate-blue and violet	50	1·50	10
131	**57**	3d. deep blue and blue	50	1·75	10
		a. Opt omitted (in vert pair with normal)	£17000		
129/31 *Set of 3*			1·60	4·25	25

No. 131a comes from a sheet on which the overprint was displaced downwards so that it is omitted from stamps in the top row and shown on the sheet margin at foot.

(Recess Waterlow)

1947 (17 Feb). Royal Visit. As Nos. 32/5 of Basutoland. Wmk Mult Script CA. P 12½.

132	1d. scarlet		10	10
133	2d. green		10	10
134	3d. ultramarine		10	10
135	1s. mauve		10	10
132/5 *Set of 4*			35	30
132s/5s Perf "SPECIMEN" *Set of 4*			£150	

1948 (1 Dec). Royal Silver Wedding. As Nos. 112/13 of Antigua.

136	1½d. ultramarine		30	10
137	10s. black		42·00	50·00

1949 (10 Oct). 75th Anniv of Universal Postal Union. As Nos. 114/17 of Antigua.

138	1½d. blue		30	1·25
139	3d. deep blue		1·50	2·50
140	6d. magenta		60	4·75
141	1s. olive		60	1·50
138/41 *Set of 4*			2·75	9·00

1953 (3 June). Coronation. As No. 120 of Antigua.

142	2d. black and brown		1·50	30

25 Queen Elizabeth II, Baobab Tree and Cattle

26 Queen Victoria, Queen Elizabeth II and Landscape

(Des from photo by Resident Commissioner, Ngamiland. Recess Waterlow)

1955 (3 Jan)–**58**. Wmk Mult Script CA. P 13½×14.

143	**25**	½d. green	50	30
144		1d. rose-red	80	10
145		2d. red-brown	1·25	30
146		3d. ultramarine	3·00	2·50
		a. Bright ultramarine (16.1.57)	19·00	5·50
146b		4d. red-orange (1.12.58)	13·00	15·00
147		4½d. blackish blue	1·50	35

148	6d. purple		1·25	60
149	1s. black and brown-olive		1·25	1·00
150	1s.3d. black and lilac		18·00	9·50
151	2s.6d. black and rose-red		13·00	10·00
152	5s. black and violet-blue		20·00	20·00
153	10s. black and red-brown		45·00	20·00
143/53 *Set of 12*			£100	70·00

(Photo Harrison)

1960 (21 Jan). 75th Anniv of Bechuanaland Protectorate. W w **12**. P 14½×14.

154	**26**	1d. sepia and black	50	50
155		3d. magenta and black	50	30
156		6d. bright blue and black	55	50
154/6 *Set of 3*			1·40	1·10

(New Currency. 100 cents = 1 rand)

1c	1c	1c	2½c	2½c
(**27**)	(I)	(II)	(I)	(II)

3	3	3	5c	5c	R1	R1
(I)	(II)	(III)	(I)	(II)	(I)	(II)

2½c
Spaced "c"
(R. 10/3)

3½c — Normal

3½c — Bold "c"

The Bold "c" variety occurs on the Type II surcharge (R. 9/3) and Type III (R. 7/3).

1961 (14 Feb–26 July). Nos. 144/6*a* and 148/53 surch as T **27** by South African Govt Printer, Pretoria.

157	**25**	1c. on 1d. rose-red (Type I)	30	10
		a. Type II (6.6)	40	10
158		2c. on 2d. red-brown	30	10
159		2½c. on 2d. red-brown (Type I)	30	10
		a. Type II (26.7)	2·25	3·50
		b. Vert pair, one without surch	£16000	
160		2½c. on 3d. bright ultramarine	12·00	16·00
		a. Spaced "c" (R. 10/3)	£250	
161		3½c. on 4d. red-orange (Type I)	50	4·00
		a. Wide surch (I)	18·00	48·00
		b. Type II	3·00	16·00
		ba. Bold "c" (Type II)	£120	£180
		c. Wide surch (II)	65·00	£100
		d. Type III (6.6)	20	60
		da. Bold "c" (Type III)	10·00	19·00
162		5c. on 6d. purple (Type I)	2·25	3·25
		a. Type II (12.5)	20	10
163		10c. on 1s. black and brown-olive	20	10
		a. Horiz pair, righthand stamp without surch	£13000	
164		12½c. on 1s.3d. black and lilac	65	20
165		25c. on 2s.6d. black and rose-red	1·50	1·00
166		50c. on 5s. black and violet-blue	2·00	3·50
167		1r. on 10s. black and red-brown (Type I)		
		a. Type II (surch at bottom left) (17.3)	£300	£170
		b. Type II (surch at foot, either to right or central) (4.61)	32·00	45·00
			29·00	25·00
157/67b *Set of 11* (*cheapest*)			42·00	42·00

Nos. 161/c occur from the same printing, each sheet containing 33 examples of Type I, five of Type I with wide spacing, 19 of Type II and three of Type II with wide spacing. The wide surcharge measures 9½ mm overall (with "C" spaced 1½ mm from "½") and comes on eight of the ten stamps in the last vertical row. The surcharge on the remainder of the sheet varies between 8½ and 9½ mm.

No. 163a was caused by a shift of the surcharge so that the last vertical row on the sheet is without "10 c".

A later printing of the 12½c. on 1s.3d. was from a fresh setting of type, but is insufficiently different for separate listing. Later printings of the 10c. and 25c. were identical to the originals.

Examples of No.167 with the surcharge central at foot are believed to originate from the Botswana Post archive.

28 African Golden Oriole	**29** Hoopoe	**30** Scarlet-chested Sunbird
31 Yellow-rumped Bishop	**32** Swallow-tailed Bee-eater	**33** African Grey Hornbill

Come and Visit us at 399 Strand

1856　　　　1896　　　　1936　　　　1976　　　2017

- Get advice from our experienced and knowledgeable staff
- See first hand our superb range of top quality stamps, albums and accessories
- Get insider tips on how to enhance and expand your collection
- Ask for guidance on techniques for care and storage of your stamps and covers
- View our specialist material
- All Stanley Gibbons stamps come with a lifetime guarantee of authenticity from our stamp specialists.

Everything for the stamp collector.

399 Strand opening hours
- Mon-Fri 9am-5.30pm　• Sat 9:30am-5.30pm
- Sun Closed

For more information visit
stanleygibbons.com

BY APPOINTMENT TO
HER MAJESTY THE QUEEN
PHILATELISTS
STANLEY GIBBONS LTD
LONDON

STANLEY GIBBONS
LONDON 1856

399 Strand, WC2R 0LX, London
Phone: +44 1425 472 363 | Email: support@stanleygibbons.com
www.stanleygibbons.com

34 Red-headed Weaver **35** Brown-hooded Kingfisher **36** Woman Musician

37 Baobab Tree

38 Woman grinding maize **39** Bechuana Ox

40 Lion **41** Police Camel Patrol

(Des P. Jones (1c. to 12½c.). Photo Harrison)

1961 (2 Oct). T **28/41**. W w **12**. P 14½×14 (25c., 50c.) or 14×14½ (others).

168	28	1c. yellow, red, black and lilac	1·50	50
169	29	2c. orange, black and yellow-olive	2·00	4·50
170	30	2½c. carmine, green, black and bistre	1·75	10
171	31	3½c. yellow, black, sepia and pink	2·50	5·00
172	32	5c. yellow, blue, black and buff	3·25	1·00
173	33	7½c. brown, red, black and apple-green	2·25	2·25
174	34	10c. red, yellow, sepia and turquoise-green	2·25	60
175	35	12½c. buff, blue, red and grey-black	18·00	6·00
176	36	20c. yellow-brown and drab	4·50	4·75
177	37	25c. deep brown and lemon	5·00	2·75
178	38	35c. deep blue and orange	4·50	6·50
179	39	50c. sepia and olive	3·50	2·75
180	40	1r. black and cinnamon	11·00	2·75
181	41	2r. brown and turquoise-blue	32·00	17·00
168/81		Set of 14	80·00	50·00

1963 (4 June). Freedom from Hunger. As No. 146 of Antigua.

182	12½c. bluish green	30	15

1963 (2 Sept). Red Cross Centenary. As Nos. 147/8 of Antigua.

183	2½c. red and black	30	10
184	12½c. red and blue	70	50

1964 (23 Apr). 400th Birth Anniv of William Shakespeare. As No. 164 of Antigua.

185	12½c. light brown	15	15

INTERNAL SELF-GOVERNMENT

42 Map and Gaberones Dam

Bay flaw (R. 4/1) Lake flaw (R. 5/5)

(Des Mrs. M. Townsend, adapted V. Whiteley. Photo Harrison)

1965 (1 Mar). New Constitution. W w **12**. P 14½×14.

186	42	2½c. red and gold	35	10
		a. Bay flaw	12·00	10·00
		b. Lake flaw	12·00	10·00
		w. Wmk inverted	24·00	2·50
187		5c. ultramarine and gold	35	40
		a. Bay flaw	12·00	13·00
		b. Lake flaw	12·00	13·00

188		12½c. brown and gold	45	40
		a. Bay flaw	14·00	14·00
		b. Lake flaw	14·00	14·00
189		25c. green and gold	50	55
		a. Bay flaw	15·00	16·00
		b. Lake flaw	15·00	16·00
186/9		Set of 4	1·50	1·25

1965 (17 May). ITU Centenary. As Nos. 166/7 of Antigua.

190	2½c. red and bistre-yellow	20	10
191	12½c. mauve and brown	45	30

1965 (25 Oct). International Co-operation Year. As Nos. 168/9 of Antigua.

192	1c. reddish purple and turquoise-green	10	1·00
193	12½c. deep bluish green and lavender	60	55

1966 (24 Jan). Churchill Commemoration. As Nos. 170/3 of Antigua.

194	1c. new blue	30	3·00
195	2½c. deep green	40	10
196	12½c. brown	75	35
197	20c. bluish violet	75	55
194/7	Set of 4	2·00	3·50

43 Haslar Smoke Generator

(Des V. Whiteley. Photo Harrison)

1966 (1 June). Bechuanaland Royal Pioneer Corps. T **43** and similar horiz designs. W w **12**. P 14½.

198	2½c. Prussian blue, red and light emerald	25	10
199	5c. brown and light blue	30	20
200	15c. Prussian blue, rosine and emerald	1·75	25
201	35c. buff, blackish brown, red and green	30	1·75
198/201	Set of 4	2·40	2·00

Designs:—5c. Bugler; 15c. Gun-site; 35c. Regimental cap badge.

POSTAGE DUE STAMPS

(D **1**) (D **2**)

1926 (1 Jan). Nos. D9/10 and D13 of Great Britain, optd with Types D **1** or D **2** (2d.).

D1	½d. emerald (wmk sideways - inverted)	15·00	£130
D2	1d. carmine	15·00	80·00
D3	2d. agate	15·00	90·00
D1/3	Set of 3	40·00	£275

The watermark shows Crown to the left of GvR on D1 and to the right of GvR of D2/3, *as seen from the back of the stamp.*

D **3** Normal Large "d." (R. 9/6, 10/6)

2d. Serif on "d" (R. 1/6)

(Typo D.L.R.)

1932 (12 Dec)–**58**. Ordinary paper. Wmk Mult Script CA. P 14.

D4	D **3**	½d. sage-green	6·00	48·00
D5		1d. carmine	7·00	9·00
		a. Chalk-surfaced paper (27.11.58)	1·50	30·00
D6		2d. violet	9·00	48·00
		a. Large "d"	£160	£225
		b. Serif on "d"	£250	
		c. Chalk-surfaced paper (27.11.58)	1·75	22·00
		ca. Large "d"	50·00	
		cb. Serif on "d"	70·00	
D4/6c	Set of 3 (cheapest)		8·50	70·00
D4s/6s	Perf "SPECIMEN" Set of 3		£110	

Nos. D6a/b first occurred on the 1947 printing.

1c **1c** **c**
I (Small) II (Large) Narrow "C" (R.3/6)

1961 (14 Feb–Apr). Surch as T **27**. Chalk-surfaced paper (Nos. D7/8).

D7	D **3**	1c. on 1d. (Type I)	25	50
		a. Type II (4.61)	15	1·75
		ab. Double surch	£375	
		ac. Ordinary paper	21·00	65·00
		ad. Narrow "c"	12·00	

D8		2c. on 2d. (Type I)	25	1·50
		a. Large "d"	12·00	
		b. Serif on "d"	22·00	
		c. Type II	15	2·00
		ca. Large "d"	8·50	26·00
		cb. Serif on "d"	16·00	
		d. Ordinary paper. Type II	£180	£200
		da. Large "d"	£800	
D9		5c. on ½d.	20	60
D7/9	Set of 3		45	2·40

Normal **1c.** Bold "c" and larger dot (R. 2/6)

1961 (15 Nov). As Type D **3** but values in cents. Chalk-surfaced paper. Wmk Mult Script CA. P 14.

D10	1c. carmine	30	2·00
	a. Bold "c" and larger dot	12·00	
D11	2c. violet	30	2·00
D12	5c. green	50	2·00
D10/12	Set of 3	1·00	5·50

POSTAL FISCAL STAMPS

The following stamps issued for fiscal purposes were each allowed to be used for postal purposes for a short time. No. F2 was used by the public because the word "POSTAGE" had not been obliterated and No. F3 because the overprint did not include the words "Revenue only" as did the contemporary fiscal overprints for Basutoland and Swaziland.

Bechuanaland

Bechuanaland Protectorate (F **1**) **£5** (F **2**) Bechuanaland Protectorate. (F **3**)

1910 (July). No. 266a of Transvaal optd with Type F **1** by Transvaal Govt Ptg Wks, Pretoria.

F1	6d. black and brown-orange (Bl-Blk)	£190	£375

No. F1 was supplied to Assistant Commissioners in January 1907 for revenue purposes. The "POSTAGE" inscription was not obliterated, however, and the stamp is known postally used for a period of a year from July 1910.

1918. No. 15 surch with Type F **2** at top.

F2	4	£5 on 1s. green and black (F.C. £1000)	£60000

1921. No. 4b of South Africa optd with Type F **3**, in varying positions.

F3	1d. scarlet	50·00	£150
	a. Opt double, one albino	£180	

Bechuanaland became the independent republic of Botswana, within the Commonwealth, on 30 September 1966.

MILITARY TELEGRAPH STAMPS

Military Telegraph Stamps were provided for the pre-payment of non-official messages sent via the army telegraph system. They were used by army personnel for private communications, newspaper reporters and the local population when the army was in control of the telegraph system. They were supplied to the Bechuanaland Expedition in late November 1884.

T **1** T **2** T **3**

(Typo D.L.R.)

1884.

(a) Wmk Orb. P 14

MT1	T **1**	1d. lilac and black	95·00	£275
MT2		3d. lilac and brown	95·00	£275
MT3		6d. lilac and green	95·00	£275

(b) Wmk script "VR", sideways reading up. P 13½

MT4	T **2**	1s. green and black	95·00	£450
MT5		2s. green and blue	£140	£550
MT6		5s. green and mauve	£190	£700
MT7		10s. green and red	£350	£800

(c) Wmk Two Orbs (sideways). P 14×13½

MT8	T **3**	£1 lilac and black	£650	£1300

For use of Nos. MT1/8 in Egypt and Sudan see Egypt (British Forces) Nos. MT1/8.

For similar stamps inscribed "ARMY TELEGRAPHS" see South Africa (VIII, British Army Field Offices During South African War) Nos. AT3/15.

The stamps were either cancelled in manuscript or by an "ARMY TELEGRAPHS" datestamp incorporating a code letter at either end of the date to identify the office of despatch. The codes used were:

B L Barkley	**B K** Bank's Drift	**B R** Brussels Farm
D H Dry Hartz	**G C** Groot Choing	**G L** Barkley West
G U Gunning's Store	**L P** Leeuw Pan	**M F** Mafeking
M L Muller's Store	**M Z** Maritzani	**S A** Saanies
S H Setlagoli	**T S** Taungs	**V R** Vryburg

Military

Telegraphs

(T **4**)

1885. Nos 52 and 26 of Cape of Good Hope optd with Type T **4**.

MT9	6d. purple	65·00	32·00
MT10	1s. green	80·00	38·00

The above were overprinted in Cape Town for use in Vryburg, following its occupation by Sir Charles Warren's forces on 7 February 1885.

MT9/10 can be found with or without stop after "Telegraphs".

1885. (July–Aug). Nos. MT1, MT7, MT6 and MT8 surch in manuscript.

MT11	"6d" on 1d. lilac and black	†	—
MT12	"6d" on 10s. green and red	†	—
MT13	"1/-" on 5s. green and mauve	†	—
MT14	"1/-" on £1 lilac and black	†	—

Bermuda

The first internal postal system for Bermuda was organised by Joseph Stockdale, the proprietor of the *Bermuda Gazette*, in January 1784. This service competed with that of the colonial post office, set up in May 1812, until 1818.

Control of the overseas postal services passed to the British GPO in 1818. The internal delivery system was discontinued between 1821 and 1830. The overseas posts became a colonial responsibility in September 1859.

For illustrations of the handstamp types see BRITISH POST OFFICES ABROAD notes, following GREAT BRITAIN.

CROWNED-CIRCLE HANDSTAMPS

CC1	CC **1** ST. GEORGES BERMUDA (R.) (1.8.1845)		
		Price on cover	£8500
CC2	IRELAND ISLE BERMUDA (R.) (1.8.1845)		
		Price on cover	£7500
CC3	HAMILTON BERMUDA (R.) (13.11.1846)		
		Price on cover	£4000

For Nos. CC1 and CC3 used as adhesive Postmasters' Stamps see Nos. O7 and O6.

PRICES FOR STAMPS ON COVER TO 1945	
Nos. 1/11	from × 5
Nos. 12/17	from × 10
Nos. 19/29a	from × 8
Nos. 30/a	from × 10
Nos. 31/4	from × 4
Nos. 34/55	from × 3
Nos. 56/8	from × 10
Nos. 59/76	from × 4
Nos. 76a/93	from × 3
Nos. 94/7	from × 4
Nos. 98/106	from × 3
Nos. 107/15	from × 4
Nos. 116/21	from × 5
No. 122	from × 20

COLONY

O **1**   O **2**

1848–61. Postmasters' Stamps. Adhesives prepared and issued by the postmasters at Hamilton and St. Georges. Dated as given in brackets.

(a) By W. B. Perot at Hamilton

O1	O **1**	1d. black/*bluish grey* (1848)	—	£180000
O2		1d. black/*bluish grey* (1849)	—	£200000
O3		1d. red/*thick white* (1853)	—	£180000
O4		1d. red/*bluish wove* (1854)	—	£400000
O5		1d. red/*bluish wove* (1856)	—	£250000
O6	O **2**	(1d.) carmine-red/*bluish laid* (1861)	£140000	£100000

*(b) By J. H. Thies at St. Georges. As Type O **2** but inscr "ST. GEORGES"*

O7	–	(1d.) carmine-red/*buff* (1860)	†	£85000

Stamps of Type O **1** bear manuscript value and signature, the dates being those shown on the 11 known examples. The stamps are distributed between the dates as follows: 1848 three examples, 1849 two examples, 1853 three examples, 1854 two examples, 1856 one example.

It is believed that the franking value of Nos. O6/7 was 1d., although this is not shown on the actual stamps. Four examples are known of this type used from Hamilton, from March 1861 (and one unused), and five used from St. Georges between July 1860 and January 1863, both issues being cancelled by pen.

Prices shown reflect our estimation of value based on known copies. For instance of the two copies known of No. O4, one is in the Royal collection and the other is on entire.

It is possible that a fourth postmaster's provisional was used by Robert Ward at Hamilton in late 1862 when two examples of Type O **2** on laid paper are known cancelled by blue crayon.

1   2   3

4   5

(Typo D.L.R.)

1865–1903. Wmk Crown CC.

(a) P 14

1	**1**	1d. rose-red (25.9.65)	£100	1·25
		a. Imperf	£75000	£27000
		w. Wmk inverted	£550	£200
2		1d. pale rose	£140	7·50
		w. Wmk inverted	£600	£275

3	**2**	2d. dull blue (14.3.66)	£475	40·00
		w. Wmk inverted	£1800	£700
4		2d. bright blue (1877)	£475	21·00
		w. Wmk inverted	£1800	£700
5	**3**	3d. orange (10.3.73)	£2250	£170
5a		3d. yellow-buff (1875)	£475	65·00
		aw. Wmk inverted	£1400	£325
		ax. Wmk reversed	£2500	£1200
6	**4**	6d. dull purple (25.9.65)	£1000	75·00
		w. Wmk inverted	—	£1600
7		6d. dull mauve (2.7.74)	23·00	12·00
		w. Wmk inverted	£180	£275
8	**5**	1s. green (25.9.65)	£350	70·00
		w. Wmk inverted	£900	£350

(b) P 14×12½

10	**3**	3d. yellow-buff (12.81)	£180	60·00
10a	**4**	6d. bright mauve (1903)	17·00	22·00
		w. Wmk inverted	£1500	£1600
11	**5**	1s. green (11.93)	17·00	£120
		a. Imperf between (vert strip of 3)	£12000	
		w. Wmk inverted	—	£1400

No. 11a occurs from Rows 8, 9, and 10 of four panes, possibly from a single sheet. Some of the stamps have become partially separated. One *used* vertical pair is known (*Price* £18000).

Although they arrived in Bermuda in March 1880, stamps perforated 14×12½ were not issued until the dates given above.

(6)   (6a)

(7)   (8)

1874 (12 Mar–19 May). Nos. 1 and 8 surch diagonally.

*(a) With T **6** ("P" and "R" different type)*

12	**1**	3d. on 1d. rose-red	£18000
13	**5**	3d. on 1s. green	£2500	£850

*(b) With T **6a** ("P" same type as "R")*

13b	**5**	3d. on 1s. green	£2000	£800

*(c) With T **7** (19 May)*

14	**5**	3d. on 1s. green	£1500	£650

The 3d. on 1d. was a trial surcharge which was not regularly issued, though a few examples were postally used before 1879. Nos. 13, 13b and 14, being handstamped, are found with double or partial double surcharges.

(Surch by Queens Printer, Donald McPhee Lee)

1875 (March–May). Surch with T **8**.

15	**2**	1d. on 2d. (No. 3) (23.4)	£700	£375
		a. No stop after "Penny"	£25000	£13000
16	**3**	1d. on 3d. (No. 5a) (8.5)	£450	£350
17	**5**	1d. on 1s. (No. 8) (11.3)	£500	£250
		a. Surch inverted	—	£50000
		b. No stop after "Penny"	£40000	£18000

It is emphasised that the prices quoted for Nos. 12/17 are for fine examples. The many stamps from these provisional issues which are in inferior condition are worth much less.

9   10   11

(Typo D.L.R.)

1880 (25 Mar). Wmk Crown CC. P 14.

19	**9**	½d. stone	8·50	4·75
		w. Wmk inverted	£130	£225
		y. Wmk inverted and reversed	£2250	
20	**10**	4d. orange-red	20·00	1·75
		w. Wmk inverted	—	£1600
		x. Wmk reversed		

(Typo D.L.R.)

1883–1904. Wmk Crown CA. P 14.

21	**9**	½d. dull green (10.92)	9·00	4·50
21a		½d. deep grey-green (1893)	5·00	80
22	**1**	1d. dull rose (12.83)	£170	4·75
		w. Wmk inverted	£750	£400
23		1d. rose-red	90·00	3·25
		w. Wmk inverted	—	£375
24		1d. carmine-rose (3.86)	60·00	1·00
		w. Wmk inverted	—	£375
24a		1d. aniline carmine (1889)	21·00	20
		aw. Wmk inverted	£500	£200
25	**2**	2d. blue (12.86)	75·00	7·50
		x. Wmk reversed	†	£1400
26		2d. aniline purple (7.93)	17·00	5·50
26a		2d. brown purple (1898)	6·00	2·50
27	**11**	2½d. deep ultramarine (10.11.84)	38·00	3·75
		aw. Wmk inverted	£1000	£300
27b		2½d. pale ultramarine	24·00	40
		bw. Wmk inverted	£600	£250
28	**3**	3d. grey (20.1.86)	23·00	11·00
28a	**10**	4d. orange-brown (18.1.04)	35·00	60·00
		ax. Wmk reversed	£500	£750
29	**5**	1s. yellow-brown (1893)	24·00	24·00
		ax. Wmk reversed	£1800	£1100
29b		1s. olive-brown	14·00	24·00
		bx. Wmk reversed	£1800	£1200
21/9b	Set of 8 (cheapest)		£180	95·00
21s, 26s & 29s	Optd "SPECIMEN" Set of 3		£375	

1893 PROVISIONAL POSTCARD. Following the reduction of the overseas postcard rate to 1d. in 1893 existing stocks of postal stationery postcards, including some from the September 1880 issue franked with Nos. 19 and 22, were surcharged "One Penny". This surcharge was applied by the *Royal Gazette* press. It is generally believed that an individual in the Post Office acquired all the examples showing Nos. 19 and 22, but provisional postcards are known used to Europe or locally (*Price from* £600 *unused*, £1600 *used*).

Purves Philatelics

PTS

For all your British Commonwealth philatelic requirements (1840-1970)

We are one of the **leading online and mail-order philatelic dealers in the world**, with a reputation for service and quality that is second to none.

We have a **huge stock** with items priced from a few pounds to several thousands so we cater for all pockets and collection needs. Our worldwide client base tell us that we have one of the very best philatelic websites so why note visit the fully interactive site today and see for yourself. There you can place orders, **sign up to our regular newsletter** and be one of the first to hear about new additions to stock. Or, if you can't find what you're looking for you can **create your own online 'wants list'**.

Even if you don't have a computer we can still help you as we produce free monthly catalogues each containing thousands of sets and single items.

Contact us today and receive **20% off your first order***! If you register online you will need to enter the promo code 'NEWREG' on the registration page.

www.purvesphilatelics.co.uk
info@purvesphilatelics.co.uk
☎ **01892 724896**

Purves Philatelics, PO Box 95, Tonbridge, Kent TN12 7PX, UK

All major credit and debit cards accepted.

20% OFF your first order*

For online registrations please enter the promo code 'NEWREG' on the registration page.

ONE FARTHING

| (12) | 13 Dry Dock | 14 |

1901. As Nos. 29/b but colour changed, surch with T **12** by D.L.R.
30	**5**	¼d. on 1s. dull grey (11.1.01)	5·00	1·00
		as. Optd "SPECIMEN"	80·00	
30b		¼d. on 1s. bluish grey (18.3.01)	5·50	1·50
		ba. "F" in "FARTHING" inserted by handstamp	£8000	£10000

Ten examples of No. 30ba are known, eight unused (one being in the Royal Philatelic Collection) and two used (one on postcard). It would appear that the "F" in position 1 of an unspecified horizontal row was damaged and an additional impression of the letter was then inserted by a separate handstamp.

(Typo D.L.R.)
1902 (Nov)–**03.** Wmk Crown CA. P 14.
31	**13**	½d. black and green (12.03)	14·00	4·50
32		1d. brown and carmine	8·00	10
33		3d. magenta and sage-green (9.03)	6·00	2·50
31/3 Set of 3			25·00	6·25
31s/3s Optd "SPECIMEN" Set of 3			£150	

1906–10. Wmk Mult Crown CA. P 14.
34	**13**	¼d. brown and violet (9.08)	1·75	1·50
35		½d. black and green (12.06)	21·00	65
36		½d. green (3.09)	27·00	5·00
37		1d. brown and carmine (4.06)	45·00	20
		w. Wmk inverted	£700	£350
		y. Wmk inverted and reversed	£1200	
38		1d. red (5.08)	26·00	10
39		2d. grey and orange (10.07)	7·50	10·00
40		2½d. brown and ultramarine (12.06)	35·00	7·00
41		2½d. blue (14.2.10)	28·00	9·50
42		4d. blue and chocolate (11.09)	3·00	16·00
34/42 Set of 9			£170	45·00
34s, 36s, 38s/42s Optd "SPECIMEN" Set of 7			£400	

"Flag" flaw (R. 1/8)

(Recess D.L.R.)
1910–25. Wmk Mult Crown CA. P 14.
44	**14**	¼d. brown (26.3.12)	1·75	2·00
		a. Pale brown	2·50	1·50
45		½d. green (4.6.10)	3·75	25
		a. Deep green (1918)	15·00	1·25
		w. Wmk inverted	†	—
		x. Wmk reversed	£1000	£550
46		1d. red (I) (15.10.10)	20·00	30
		a. Rose-red (1916)	26·00	30
		b. Carmine (12.19)	60·00	8·00
		ba. "Flag" flaw	£400	85·00
		w. Wmk inverted	£750	£500
		x. Wmk reversed	£1300	£950
		y. Wmk inverted and reversed	£850	£850
47		2d. grey (1.13)	6·50	21·00
48		2½d. blue (27.3.12)	3·50	60
		w. Wmk inverted	£700	£550
		x. Wmk reversed	—	£600
		y. Wmk inverted and reversed	£475	£325
49		3d. purple/yellow (1.13)	3·50	6·00
49a		4d. red/yellow (1.9.19)	14·00	17·00
50		6d. purple (26.3.12)	19·00	20·00
		a. Pale claret (2.6.24)	11·00	8·50
51		1s. black/green (26.3.12)	6·50	4·75
		a. Jet black/olive (1925)	6·50	23·00
		ax. Wmk reversed	£1700	
44/51 Set of 9			60·00	50·00
44s/51s Optd "SPECIMEN" Set of 9			£475	

Nos. 44 to 51a are comb-perforated 13.8×14 or 14. No. 45 exists also line-perforated 14 probably from the printing dispatched to Bermuda on 13 March 1911.

See also Nos. 77/87a.

15

HIGH VALUE KEY TYPES. The reign of King Edward VII saw the appearance of the first in a new series of "key type" designs, initially for Nyasaland, to be used for high value denominations where a smaller design was felt to be inappropriate. The system was extended during the reign of King George V, using the portrait as Bermuda Type **15**, to cover Bermuda, Ceylon, Leeward Islands, Malaya — Straits Settlements, Malta and Nyasaland. A number of these territories continued to use the key type concept for high value King George VI stamps and one, Leeward Islands, for stamps of Queen Elizabeth II.

In each instance the King George V issues were printed in sheets of 60 (12×5) on various coloured papers. The system utilised a common "head" plate used with individual "duty" plates which printed the territory name and face value.

Many of the major plate flaws on the King George V head plate occur in different states, having been repaired and then damaged once again, perhaps on several occasions. Later printings of R. 1/12 show additional damage to the crown and upper scrolls. The prices quoted in the listings are for examples approximately as illustrated.

Break in scroll (R. 1/12)   Broken crown and scroll (R. 2/12)

Nick in top right scroll (R. 3/12) (Some printings from 1920 onwards show attempts at repair)   Break through scroll (R. 1/9. Ptgs from June 1929. Some show attempts at repair)

Break in lines below left scroll (R. 4/9. Ptgs from May 1920)   Damaged leaf at bottom right (R. 5/6. Ptgs from April 1918)

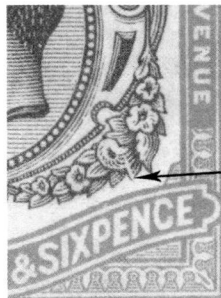

Gash in fruit and leaf (R. 5/12. Ptgs from November 1928)

(Typo D.L.R.)
1918 (1 Apr)–**22.** Wmk Mult Crown CA. Chalk-surfaced paper. P 14.
51b	**15**	2s. purple and blue/blue (19.6.20)	22·00	55·00
		ba. Break in scroll	£275	£350
		bb. Broken crown and scroll	£225	£350
		bc. Nick in top right scroll	£275	
		be. Break in lines below left scroll	£275	£400
		bf. Damaged leaf at bottom right	£275	
		bx. Wmk reversed	£2000	£2500
52		2s.6d. black and red/blue	38·00	80·00
		a. Break in scroll	£325	£400
52b		4s. black and carmine (19.6.20)	60·00	£160
		ba. Break in scroll	£300	£650
		bb. Broken crown and scroll	£300	£650
		bc. Nick in top right scroll	£325	£650
		be. Break in lines below left scroll	£350	£650
		bf. Damaged leaf at bottom right	£350	
53		5s. deep green and deep red/yellow	75·00	£140
		a. Break in scroll	£425	
		c. Nick in top right scroll	£425	£550
		d. Green and carmine-red/pale yellow (1920)	60·00	£120
		da. Break in scroll	£375	£550
		db. Broken crown and scroll	£375	£550
		de. Break in lines below left scroll	£400	
		df. Damaged leaf at bottom right	£400	
		dw. Wmk inverted	£475	£650
		dx. Wmk reversed	£8000	
		dy. Wmk inverted and reversed	£6000	
54		10s. green and carmine/pale bluish green	£180	£350
		a. Break in scroll	£750	
		c. Green and red/pale bluish green (10.22)	£275	£425

55		ca. Break in scroll	£950	
		cb. Broken crown and scroll	£950	
		ce. Break in lines below left scroll	£1000	
		cf. Damaged leaf at bottom right	£1000	
		cw. Wmk inverted	†	—
		£1 purple and black/red	£325	£550
		a. Break in scroll	£850	
		b. Broken crown and scroll	£1000	
		c. Nick in top right scroll	£1000	
		d. Break through scroll	£2250	
		e. Break in lines below left scroll	£1600	
		f. Damaged leaf at bottom right	£1200	
		g. Gash in fruit and leaf	£2250	
		w. Wmk inverted	£2000	£2750
51b/5 Set of 6			£600	£1100
51bs/5s Optd "SPECIMEN" Set of 6			£900	

Beware of cleaned copies of the 10s. with faked postmarks.
Examples of Nos. 51b/5 are known showing a forged Hamilton double ring postmark dated "22 JAN 13".
See also Nos. 88/93.

WAR TAX   WAR TAX

(16)   (17)

1918 (4 May). Nos. 46 and 46a optd with T **16** by the Bermuda Press.
56	**14**	1d. red	50	1·25
		a. Rose-red	1·25	2·00
		ay. Wmk inverted and reversed	£3000	£2000

1920 (5 Feb). No. 46b optd with T **17** by the Bermuda Press.
| 58 | **14** | 1d. carmine | 4·00 | 3·50 |
| | | a. "Flag" flaw | £140 | £180 |

The War Tax stamps represented a compulsory levy on letters to Great Britain and often Empire Countries in addition to normal postal fees until 31 Dec 1920. Subsequently they were valid for ordinary postage.

18   19

(Des by the Governor (Gen. Sir James Willcocks). Typo D.L.R.)
1920 (11 Nov)–**21.** Tercentenary of Representative Institutions (1st issue). Chalk-surfaced paper (3d. to 1s.). P 14.
(a) Wmk Mult Crown CA (sideways*) (19.1.21)
59	**18**	¼d. brown	3·50	28·00
		a. "C" of "CA" missing from wmk	£800	
		b. "A" of "CA" missing from wmk	£800	
		w. Wmk Crown to right of CA	£300	£350
		x. Wmk sideways reversed	£400	£450
		y. Wmk sideways inverted and reversed	£450	£600
60		½d. green	9·50	19·00
		a. "C" of "CA" missing from wmk	£1100	
		b. "A" of "CA" missing from wmk	£1300	
		w. Wmk Crown to right of CA	£450	£500
		x. Wmk sideways reversed	£475	£500
		y. Wmk sideways inverted and reversed	£550	£550
61		2d. grey	18·00	55·00
		a. "C" of "CA" missing from wmk	£1100	
		w. Wmk Crown to right of CA	£650	
		y. Wmk sideways inverted and reversed	£850	£900
62		3d. dull and deep purple/pale yellow	12·00	55·00
		w. Wmk Crown to right of CA	£1100	
		x. Wmk sideways reversed	£1200	£1200
63		4d. black and red/pale yellow	12·00	40·00
		a. "C" of "CA" missing from wmk	£1800	
		x. Wmk sideways reversed	£1100	
64		1s. black/blue-green	18·00	48·00
(b) Wmk Mult Script CA (sideways*)
65	**18**	1d. carmine	4·50	30
		w. Wmk Crown to right of CA	†	£750
		y. Wmk sideways inverted and reversed	†	£750
66		2½d. bright blue	19·00	20·00
67		6d. dull and bright purple (19.1.21)	30·00	95·00
59/67 Set of 9			£110	£325
59s/67s Optd "SPECIMEN" Set of 9			£375	

*The normal sideways watermark shows Crown to left of CA, as seen from the back of the stamp.

(Des J. H. Dale. Recess D.L.R.)
1921 (12 May). Tercentenary of Representative Institutions (2nd issue). P 14.
(a) Wmk Mult Crown CA (sideways*)
68	**19**	2d. slate-grey	12·00	55·00
		a. "C" of "CA" missing from wmk	£1000	£1000
		w. Wmk Crown to left of CA	£750	
69		2½d. bright ultramarine	15·00	7·00
		a. "C" of "CA" missing from wmk	£1000	
		b. "A" of "CA" missing from wmk	£1000	
		w. Wmk Crown to left of CA	—	£750
		x. Wmk sideways reversed	£1100	£700
70		3d. purple/pale yellow	5·50	20·00
		w. Wmk Crown to left of CA		
71		4d. red/pale yellow	19·00	42·00
		x. Wmk sideways reversed	£300	£425
72		6d. purple	19·00	65·00
		a. "C" of "CA" missing from wmk	£1400	
		b. "A" of "CA" missing from wmk	£1500	
		c. Substituted crown in wmk	†	£2750
73		1s. black/green	25·00	65·00
(b) Wmk Mult Script CA (sideways*)
74	**19**	¼d. brown	4·25	4·00
		w. Wmk Crown to right of CA	£550	£550
		x. Wmk sideways reversed	£750	£700
		y. Wmk sideways inverted and reversed	—	£750
75		½d. green	3·50	9·00
		w. Wmk Crown to left of CA	£250	£325
		x. Wmk sideways reversed	£750	£950

	y. Wmk sideways inverted and reversed	£475		
	ys. Optd "SPECIMEN"	£225		
76	1d. deep carmine	12·00	35	
	a. "C" of "CA" missing from wmk.	£750		
	w. Wmk Crown to left of CA	£700	£600	
	x. Wmk sideways reversed	£500	£650	
	y. Wmk sideways inverted and reversed	£1000	£700	

68/76 *Set of 9* £100 £225
68s/76s Optd "SPECIMEN" *Set of 9* £350

*The normal sideways watermark shows Crown to right of CA, *as seen from the back of the stamp.*

For illustration of the substituted watermark crown see Catalogue Introduction.

Examples of most values of Nos. 59/76 are known showing part strikes of the forged Hamilton postmark mentioned below Nos. 51b/5.

Three Types of the 1d.

I. Scroll at top left very weak and figure "1" has pointed serifs.
II. Scroll weak. "1" has square serifs and "1d" is heavy.
III. Redrawn. Scroll is completed by a strong line and "1" is thinner with long square serifs.

I II

Two Types of the 2½d.

I. Short, thick figures, especially of the "1", small "d".
II. Figures taller and thinner, "d" larger.

1922–34. Wmk Mult Script CA. P 14.

77	14	¼d. brown (7.28)	1·50	3·00
77a		½d. green (11.22)	1·50	15
		aw. Wmk inverted	£850	£500
		ax. Wmk reversed	£900	£500
78		1d. scarlet (I) (11.22)	17·00	60
		aa. "Flag" flaw	£180	42·00
		a. Carmine (7.24)	18·00	60
		ab. "Flag" flaw	£180	42·00
		bx. Wmk reversed	£600	£500
78c		1d. carmine (II) (12.25)	55·00	8·50
		d. Scarlet (8.27)	35·00	4·25
79		1d. scarlet (III) (10.28)	17·00	30
		a. Carmine-lake (1934)	25·00	2·25
79b		1½d. red-brown (27.3.34)	10·00	35
80		2d. grey (12.23)	1·50	1·50
		x. Wmk reversed	75·00	£150
81		2½d. pale sage-green (12.22)	3·75	1·50
		a. Deep sage-green (1924)	3·75	1·50
		aw. Wmk inverted	—	£750
		ax. Wmk inverted	£800	£500
		ay. Wmk inverted and reversed	£800	£500
82		2½d. ultramarine (I) (1.12.26)	5·50	50
		aw. Wmk inverted	£300	£325
82b		2½d. ultramarine (II) (3.32)	2·00	70
83		3d. ultramarine (12.24)	19·00	26·00
		w. Wmk reversed	£160	£200
84		3d. purple/yellow (10.26)	4·00	1·00
		sa. Opt "SPECIMEN" double, one albino	£250	
85		4d. red/yellow (8.24)	2·50	1·00
		x. Wmk reversed	£550	£600
86		6d. purple (8.24)	1·50	1·00
87		1s. black/emerald (10.27)	9·00	9·00
		a. Brownish black/yellow-green (1934)	35·00	50·00

77/87 *Set of 12* .... 65·00 40·00
77s/87s Optd or Perf (1½d.) "SPECIMEN" *Set of 12* ... £650
Both comb and line perforations occur on Nos. 77/87a.

Detailed gauges are as follows:
13.7×13.9 comb — Nos. 77a, 78/a, 80, 81/a, 83, 84, 85, 86, 87
13.75 line — Nos. 77a, 77, 78c/d, 79/a, 79b, 80, 82, 82b, 84, 85, 86, 87/a
13.75×14 line — Nos. 77a, 78c/d, 79b, 80, 82b, 86, 87/a
14×13.75 line — Nos. 79/a
14 line — Nos. 81/a

Breaks in scrolls at right (R. 1/3. Ptgs of 12s.6d. from July 1932)

1924–32. Wmk Mult Script CA. Chalk-surfaced paper. P 14.

88	15	2s. purple and bright blue/pale blue (1.9.27)	50·00	75·00
		a. Break in scroll	£250	
		b. Broken crown and scroll	£250	£350
		c. Nick in top right scroll	£275	
		e. Break in lines below left scroll...	£275	
		f. Damaged leaf at bottom right...	£275	
		g. Purple and blue/grey-blue (1931)	65·00	85·00
		ga. Break in scroll	£300	£500
		gb. Broken crown and scroll	£300	
		gd. Break through scroll	£350	£550
		ge. Break in lines below left scroll...	£350	
		gf. Damaged leaf at bottom right...	£350	
		gg. Gash in fruit and leaf	£350	
89		2s.6d. black and carmine/pale blue (4.27)	60·00	£100
		a. Break in scroll	£300	
		b. Broken crown and scroll	£300	
		d. Break through scroll	£450	
		e. Break in lines below left scroll	£350	
		f. Damaged leaf at bottom right...	£350	
		g. Black and red/blue to deep blue (6.29)	75·00	£110
		ga. Break in scroll	£350	
		gb. Broken crown and scroll	£350	
		gd. Break through scroll	£400	
		ge. Break in lines below left scroll...	£400	
		gf. Damaged leaf at bottom right...	£400	
		gg. Gash in fruit and leaf	£400	
		h. Grey-black and pale orange-vermilion/grey-blue (3.30)	£2750	£2750
		ha. Break in scroll	£5500	
		hb. Broken crown and scroll	£5500	
		hd. Break through scroll	£5500	
		he. Break in lines below left scroll	£5500	
		hf. Damaged leaf at bottom right...	£5500	
		hg. Gash in fruit and leaf	£5500	
		i. Black and carmine-red/deep grey-blue (8.30)	£100	£140
		ia. Break in scroll	£500	
		ib. Broken crown and scroll	£500	
		id. Break through scroll	£600	
		ie. Break in lines below left scroll...	£600	
		if. Damaged leaf at bottom right...	£600	
		ig. Gash in fruit and leaf	£600	
		j. Black and scarlet-vermilion/deep blue (9.31)	90·00	£130
		ja. Break in scroll	£450	
		jb. Broken crown and scroll	£450	
		jc. Nick in top right scroll	£500	£600
		jd. Break through scroll	£550	
		je. Break in lines below left scroll	£550	
		jf. Damaged leaf at bottom right...	£550	
		jg. Gash in fruit and leaf	£550	
		k. Black and brt orange-vermilion/deep blue (8.32)	£3250	£3000
		kb. Broken crown and scroll	£6000	
		kc. Nick in top right scroll	£6000	
		kd. Break through scroll	£6000	
		ke. Break in lines below left scroll...	£6000	
		kf. Damaged leaf at bottom right...	£6000	
		kg. Gash in fruit and leaf	£6000	
92		10s. green and red/pale emerald (12.24)	£140	£250
		a. Break in scroll	£800	£1000
		b. Broken crown and scroll	£700	£1000
		e. Break in lines below left scroll...	£800	
		f. Damaged leaf at bottom right...	£800	
		g. Green and red/deep emerald (1930)	£150	£275
		ga. Break in scroll	£800	£1000
		gb. Broken crown and scroll	£700	£900
		gc. Nick in top right scroll	£750	
		gd. Break through scroll	£850	£1000
		ge. Break in lines below left scroll	£850	
		gf. Damaged leaf at bottom right	£750	
		gg. Gash in fruit and leaf	£750	
93		12s.6d. grey and orange (8.32)	£250	£375
		a. Break in scroll	£700	£900
		b. Broken crown and scroll	£750	£950
		c. Nick in top right scroll	£800	£950
		d. Break through scroll	£900	
		e. Break in lines below left scroll	£900	
		f. Damaged leaf at bottom right...	£900	
		g. Gash in fruit and leaf	£800	
		h. Break in scrolls at right	£900	£1100
		i. Error. Ordinary paper		

88/93 *Set of 4* £450 £700
88s/93s Optd or Perf (12s.6d) "SPECIMEN" *Set of 4* ... £600
The true No. 89h is the only stamp on grey-blue paper, other deeper orange-vermilion shades exist on different papers. No. 89k was despatched to Bermuda in July/August 1932, but is not known used before 1937.

Beware of fiscally used 2s.6d. 10s. and 12s.6d. stamps cleaned and bearing faked postmarks. Large quantities were used for a "head tax" levied on travellers leaving the country.

For 12s.6d. design inscribed "Revenue" at both sides see No. F1 under POSTAL FISCAL.

1935 (6 May). Silver Jubilee. As Nos. 91/4 of Antigua, but ptd by Waterlow. P 11×12.

94		1d. deep blue and scarlet	1·25	2·50
		j. Damaged turret	£1000	
		m. "Bird" by turret	£200	£225
95		1½d. ultramarine and grey	1·25	3·50
		m. "Bird" by turret	£200	£275
96		2½d. brown and deep blue	1·50	2·50
		m. "Bird" by turret	£275	£325
97		1s. slate and purple	22·00	50·00
		k. Kite and vertical log	£275	£425
		l. Kite and horizontal log	£700	£850

94/7 *Set of 4* .... 23·00 50·00
94s/7s Perf "SPECIMEN" *Set of 4* £225
For illustrations of plate varieties see Omnibus section following Zanzibar.

---

20 Red Hole, Paget   **21** South Shore

22 *Lucie* (yacht)   **23** Grape Bay, Paget Parish

24 Point House, Warwick Parish   **25** Gardener's Cottage, Par-la-Ville, Hamilton

(Recess B.W.)

1936 (14 Apr)–**47.** T **12.** Wmk Mult Script CA (sideways on horiz designs).

98	20	½d. bright green	10	10
99	21	1d. black and scarlet	65	30
100		1½d. black and chocolate	1·25	50
101	22	2d. black and pale blue	5·00	1·75
102	23	2½d. light and deep blue	1·00	25
103	24	3d. black and scarlet	7·00	2·75
104	25	6d. carmine-lake and violet	80	10
		a. Claret and dull violet (6.47)	8·00	2·75
105	23	1s. green	21·00	23·00
106	20	1s.6d. brown	50	10

98/106 *Set of 9* .... 32·00 25·00
98s/106s Perf "SPECIMEN" *Set of 9* £325
All are line-perf 11.9, except printings of the 6d. from July 1951 onwards, which are comb-perf 11.9×11.75.

1937 (14 May). Coronation. As Nos. 95/7 of Antigua, but printed by D.L.R. P 14.

107		1d. scarlet	90	1·50
108		1½d. yellow-brown	60	1·75
109		2½d. bright blue	70	1·75

107/9 *Set of 3* .... 2·00 4·50
107s/9s Perf "SPECIMEN" *Set of 3* £225

26 Ships in Hamilton Harbour   **27** St. David's Lighthouse

28 White-tailed Tropic Bird, Arms of Bermuda and Native Flower   **29** King George VI

(Des Miss Higginbotham (T **28**). Recess B.W.)

1938 (20 Jan)–**52.** T **22, T 23** (but with portrait of King George VI) and T **26** to **28**. Wmk Mult Script CA. P 12.

110	26	1d. black and red (a) (b)	2·75	20
111		1½d. deep blue and purple-brown (a) (b)	12·00	1·50
		a. Blue and brown (a) (3.43)	19·00	9·50
		b. light blue and purple-brown (a) (b) (9.45)	2·75	2·00
		ba. "A" of "CA" missing from wmk....	£1800	
112	22	2d. light blue and sepia (a)	50·00	10·00
112a		2d. ultramarine and scarlet (a) (b) (8.11.40)	3·75	2·25
113	23	2½d. light and deep blue (a)	13·00	1·25
113a		2½d. light blue and sepia-black (a) (18.12.41)	6·00	6·50
		b. Pale blue and sepia-black (a) (3.43)	4·50	4·00
		c. Bright blue and deep sepia-black (b) (23.9.52)	6·00	9·00
114	27	3d. black and rose-red (a)	50·00	6·00
114a		3d. black and deep blue (a) (b) (16.7.41)	3·50	40
114b	28	7½d. black, blue and bright green (a) (18.12.41)	12·00	4·75
		c. Black, blue and yellow-green (a) (3.43)	8·50	2·75

115 **23** 1s. green (*a*) (*b*) .... 2·25 50
    a. Bluish green (*b*) (20.6.52) .... 14·00 7·50

Perforations. Two different perforating machines were used on the various printings of these stamps: (*a*) the original 11.9 line perforation; (*b*) 11.9×11.75 comb perforation, introduced in July 1950. These perforations occur as indicated above.

Shading omitted from top right scroll (R. 1/1. March 1943 ptgs of 2s. and £1)

Lower right scroll with broken tail (R. 2/10. Line perforated printings only)

Broken top right scroll (R. 5/11. Line perforated ptgs only. A retouched state of the flaw is visible in later ptgs up to March 1943)

Broken lower right scroll (R. 5/12. Occurs on printings made between May 1941 and March 1943)

Gash in chin (R. 2/5. Ptgs between May 1941 and March 1943)

Missing pearl (R. 5/1, Nov 1945 ptg of 5s. only)

"ER" joined (R. 1/2. Occurs in its complete state on 1938 ptg only. Subsequent ptgs show it incomplete)

Damaged left value tablet (R. 1/11. Part of 1951 ptg only)

(Typo D.L.R.)

1938 (20 Jan)–**53**. T **29**. Wmk Mult Crown CA (£1) or Mult Script CA (others). Chalk-surfaced paper. P 14 (comb).
116 2s. deep purple and ultramarine/*grey-blue* .... £110 18·00
  a. Deep reddish purple and ultramarine/grey-blue (21.11.40)* ..... £350 50·00
  b. Perf 14¼ line. Deep purple and ultramarine/grey-blue (14.11.41)* £350 £100
  bc. Lower right scroll with broken tail ... £4000 £1800
  bd. Broken top right scroll £2000 £900
  be. Broken lower right scroll £2000 £900
  bf. Gash in chin £2750 £1300
  c. Ordinary paper. Purple and blue/ deep blue (7.6.42) .... 11·00 1·50
  ce. Broken lower right scroll £225 £120
  cf. Gash in chin £325 £150
  d. Ordinary paper. Purple and deep blue/pale blue (5.3.43) .... 15·00 2·00
  db. Shading omitted from top right scroll £2000 £2000
  de. Broken lower right scroll £700 £700
  df. Gash in chin £850 £850

  e. Perf 13. Ordinary paper. Dull purple and blue/pale blue (15.2.50) .... 14·00 18·00
  f. Perf 13. Ordinary paper. Reddish purple and blue/pale blue (10.10.50) .... 18·00 38·00
117 2s.6d. black and red/*grey-blue* .... 70·00 14·00
  a. Perf 14¼ line. Black and red/grey-blue (21.2.42)* £600 £120
  ac. Lower right scroll with broken tail ... £4250 £1900
  ad. Broken top right scroll £2750 £1100
  ae. Broken lower right scroll £2750 £1100
  af. Gash in chin £3250 £1500
  b. Ordinary paper. Black and red/pale blue (5.3.43) .... 22·00 13·00
  be. Broken lower right scroll £650 £650
  bf. Gash in chin £850 £750
  c. Perf 13. Ordinary paper. Black and orange-red/pale blue (10.10.50) .... 17·00 11·00
  d. Perf 13. Ordinary paper. Black and red/pale blue (18.6.52) .... 16·00 25·00
118 5s. green and red/*yellow* .... £150 48·00
  a. Pale green and red/yellow (14.3.39)* .... £375 85·00
  b. Perf 14¼ line. Dull yellow-green and red/yellow (11.10.42)* .... £300 40·00
  bc. Lower right scroll with broken tail ... £3500 £1100
  bd. Broken top right scroll £1300 £550
  be. Broken lower right scroll £1300 £550
  bf. Gash in chin £1600 £750
  c. Ordinary paper. Bronze-green and carmine-red/pale yellow (5.42)* £1500 £180
  ce. Broken lower right scroll £9000 £2750
  cf. Gash in chin £9500 £2750
  d. Ordinary paper. Pale bluish green and carmine-red/pale yellow (5.3.43) ..... £100 50·00
  de. Broken lower right scroll £1100 £800
  df. Gash in chin £1200 £800
  e. Ordinary paper. Green and red/pale yellow (5.45)* .... 50·00 27·00
  ea. Missing pearl £1000
  f. Perf 13. Ordinary paper. Yellow-green and red/pale yellow (15.2.50) ... 35·00 38·00
  g. Perf 13. Green and scarlet/yellow (chalk-surfaced) (10.10.50) .... 60·00 75·00
119 10s. green and deep lake/*pale emerald* ... £450 £325
  a. Bluish green and deep red/green (8.39)* £225 £130
  b. Perf 14¼ line. Ordinary paper. Yellow green and carmine/green (1942)* £550 £130
  bc. Lower right scroll with broken tail ... £5000 £2250
  bd. Broken top right scroll £2500 £1300
  be. Broken lower right scroll £2500 £1300
  bf. Gash in chin £3250 £1400
  c. Ordinary paper. Yellowish green and deep carmine-red/green (5.3.43) .... 70·00 65·00
  ce. Broken lower right scroll £2750
  cf. Gash in chin £3000
  d. Ordinary paper. Deep green and dull red/green (emerald back) (11.12.46) ... 85·00 70·00
  e. Perf 13. Ordinary paper. Green and vermilion/green (19.9.51) .... 48·00 50·00
  f. Perf 13. Ordinary paper. Green and dull red/green (16.4.53) .... 50·00 65·00
120 12s.6d. deep grey and brownish orange £550 £450
  a. Grey and brownish orange (shades) .... £225 75·00
  b. Grey and pale orange (9.11.40)* .... £110 55·00
  c. Ordinary paper (2.3.44)* .... £120 70·00
  ce. Broken lower right scroll £2250 £2500
  cf. Gash in chin £2500
  d. Ordinary paper. Grey and yellow† (17.9.47)* £700 £500
  e. Perf 13. Grey and pale orange (chalk surfaced) (10.10.50) .... £100 85·00
121 £1 purple and black/*red* £275 £100
  a. "ER" joined £1100 £600
  b. Pale purple and black/pale red (13.5.43)* .... 90·00 80·00
  ba. "ER" joined £700 £600
  be. Broken lower right scroll £2000 £1500
  bf. Gash in chin £2250 £1700
  c. Deep reddish purple and black/pale red (5.3.43)* .... 60·00 75·00
  ca. "ER" joined £650 £700
  cb. Shading omitted from top right scroll £4000
  ce. Broken lower right scroll £1800 £1500
  cf. Gash in chin £2000
  d. Perf 13. Violet and black/scarlet (7.12.51) .... 55·00 85·00
  da. Damaged left value tablet £4500
  e. Perf 13. Bright violet and black/ scarlet (10.12.52) £180 £300
110/21d *Set of 16* £350 £225
110s/21s Perf "SPECIMEN" *Set of 16* £2000

Following extensive damage to their printing works on 29 December 1940 much of De La Rue's work was transferred to other firms operating under their supervision. It is understood that Williams Lea & Co produced those new printings ordered for the Bermuda high value stamps during 1941. The first batch of these printings showed the emergency use, by Williams Lea, of a 14¼ line perforating machine (exact gauge 14.15) instead of the comb perforation (exact gauge 13.9×13.8).

Dates marked * are those of earliest known use.

In No. 116*c* the coloured surfacing of the paper is mottled with white specks sometimes accompanied by very close horizontal lines. In Nos. 116*d*, 117*b* and 118*c/d* the surfacing is the same colour as the back, sometimes applied in widely spaced horizontal lines giving the appearance of laid paper.

†No. 120*d* is the so-called "lemon" shade.

HALF PENNY

X   X
  30

31 Postmaster Perot's Stamp

1940 (20 Dec). No. 110 surch with T **30** by Royal Gazette, Hamilton.
122 **26** ½d. on 1d. black and red (*shades*) .... 1·75 3·75
The spacing between "PENNY" and "X" varies from 12½ mm to 14 mm.

1946 (6 Nov). Victory. As Nos. 110/11 of Antigua.
123 1½d. brown 15 15
124 3d. blue 40 65
123s/4s Perf "SPECIMEN" Set of 2 .... £170

1948 (1 Dec). Royal Silver Wedding. As Nos. 112/13 of Antigua.
125 1½d. red-brown 30 50
126 £1 carmine .... 45·00 55·00

(Recess B.W.)

1949 (11 Apr). Centenary of Postmaster Perot's Stamp. Wmk Mult Script CA. P 13½.
127 **31** 2½d. blue and brown 35 35
128 3d. black and blue 35 15
129 6d. violet and green 40 15
127/9 *Set of 3* .... 1·00 60

1949 (10 Oct). 75th Anniv of Universal Postal Union. As Nos. 114/17 of Antigua.
130 2½d. blue-black .... 30 2·25
  a. "C" of "CA" missing from watermark ... £1200
131 3d. deep blue .... 2·25 1·50
132 6d. purple .... 40 1·00
133 1s. blue-green .... 60 1·75
130/3 *Set of 4* .... 3·25 6·00

1953 (4 June). Coronation. As No. 200 of Bahamas, but ptd by B. W.
134 1½d. black and blue .... 1·25 60

32 Easter Lilies

33 Postmaster Perot's stamp

34 Easter Lily

35 *Victory II* (racing dinghy)

36 Sir George Somers and *Sea Venture*

37 Map of Bermuda

38 *Sea Venture* (galleon), coin and Perot stamp

39 White-tailed Tropic Bird

40 Early Bermudan coinage

41 Arms of St. Georges

42 Warwick Fort

43 1 tog coin

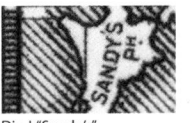
44 Obverse and reverse of 1 tog coin

45 Arms of Bermuda

Die I "Sandy's"   Die II "Sandys"

(Des C. Deakins (½d., 3d., 1s.3d., 5s.), J. Berry (1d., 1½d., 2½d., 4d., 1s.). B. Brown (2d., 6d., 8d.), D. Haig (4½d., 9d.), Pamela Braley-Smith (2s.6d.) and E. C. Leslie (10s.) all adapted by W. Harrington Recess (except £1, centre typo), B.W.)

1953 (9 Nov)–**62**. T **32/45**. Wmk Mult Script CA. P 13½.

135	**32**	½d. olive-green	1·00	5·00
		a. Yellow-olive (19.5.54)	40	2·75
136	**33**	1d. black and red	2·25	75
		a. Black and deep red (19.5.54)	9·00	1·50
137	**34**	1½d. green	30	10
138	**35**	2d. ultramarine and brown-red	50	40
139	**36**	2½d. rose-red	2·00	50
140	**37**	3d. deep purple (I)	30	10
140a		3d. deep purple (II) (2.1.57)	1·00	20
141	**33**	4d. black and bright blue	55	1·75
142	**38**	4½d. emerald	1·75	1·00
143	**39**	6d. black and deep turquoise	6·50	60
143a		8d. black and red (16.5.55)	3·25	30
143b	**38**	9d. violet (6.1.58)	14·00	2·50
144	**40**	1s. orange	50	15
145	**37**	1s.3d. blue (I)	3·75	30
		a. Greenish blue (21.9.54)	14·00	1·50
145b		1s.3d. blue (II) (2.1.57)	7·00	50
		bc. Bright blue (14.8.62)	25·00	9·00
146	**41**	2s. brown	4·00	85
147	**42**	2s.6d. scarlet	11·00	45
148	**43**	5s. carmine	23·00	1·00
149	**44**	10s. deep ultramarine	22·00	9·50
		a. Ultramarine (13.2.57)	80·00	19·00
150	**45**	£1 brown, blue, red, green and bronze-green	48·00	21·00
135/150 Set of 18			£130	40·00

Nos. 136, 138 and 143 exist in coils, constructed from normal sheets.

1953 (26 Nov). Royal Visit. As No. 143 but inscr "ROYAL VISIT 1953" in top left corner.

151		6d. black and deep turquoise	1·25	20

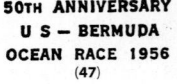

Three Power Talks December, 1953.
(46)

Three Power Talks December, 1953.
(46a)

First setting (Type **46**). First line 24½ mm long.
Second setting (Type **46a**). First line 25¼ mm long.

1953 (8 Dec). Three Power Talks. Nos. 140 and 145 optd with T **46** by Royal Gazette, Hamilton.

152	**37**	3d. deep purple (Type **46**) (B.)	20	10
		a. Optd with Type **46a**	2·00	30
153		1s.3d. blue (Type **46**) (R.)	20	10
		a. Optd with Type **46a**	9·00	8·00

50TH ANNIVERSARY U S – BERMUDA OCEAN RACE 1956
(47)

48 Perot's Post Office

1956 (22 June). 50th Anniv of United States–Bermuda Yacht Race. Nos. 143a and 145a optd with T **47** by the Bermuda Press.

154		8d. black and red (Bk.)	30	45
155		1s.3d. greenish blue (R.)	30	55

(Des W. Harrington. Recess B.W.)

1959 (1 Jan). Wmk Mult Script CA. P 13½.

156	**48**	6d. black and deep mauve	1·75	15

49 Arms of King James I and Queen Elizabeth II

3d. and **8d.** A horizontal red registration line shows in the SW section of the right garter (R. 4/8)

(Des W. Harrington. Recess; arms litho D.L.R.)

1959 (29 July). 350th Anniv of First Settlement. Arms, red, yellow and blue; frame colours below. W w **12**. P 13.

157	**49**	1½d. grey-blue	35	10
158		3d. drab-grey	40	50
		a. Registration line	25·00	
159		4d. reddish purple	45	55
160		8d. slate-violet	45	15
		a. Registration line	25·00	
161		9d. olive-green	45	1·25
162		1s.3d. brown	45	30
157/162 Set of 6			2·25	2·50

50 The Old Rectory, St. George's, circa 1730

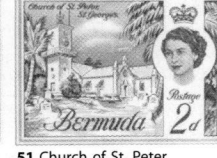

51 Church of St. Peter, St. George's

52 Government House, 1892

53 The Cathedral, Hamilton, 1894

54 HM Dockyard, 1811

55 Perot's Post Office, 1848

56 GPO Hamilton, 1869

57 Library, Par-la-Ville

58 Bermuda cottage, circa 1705

59 Christ Church, Warwick, 1719

60 City Hall Hamilton, 1960

61 Town of St. George

62 Bermuda house, circa 1710

63 Bermuda house, early 18th-century

64 Colonial Secretariat, 1833

65 Old Post Office, Somerset, 1890

66 The House of Assembly, 1815

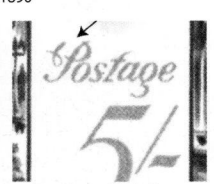

5s. Top loop of "P" of "Postage" broken. (Pl. 1A-1A, R. 1/1). Corrected on No. 246

(Des W. Harrington. Photo Harrison)

1962 (26 Oct)–**68**. T **50/66**. W w **12** (upright). P 12½.

163	**50**	1d. reddish purple, black and orange	10	75
		w. Wmk inverted	—	£750
164	**51**	2d. lilac, indigo, yellow and green	1·00	35
		a. Lilac omitted	£1000	£1000
		b. Green omitted	†	£7500
		c. Imperf (pair)	£2250	

---

		d. Pale lilac, indigo, yellow and green (22.10.68)	8·50	4·25
		w. Wmk inverted	—	£325
165	**52**	3d. yellow-brown and light blue	10	10
166	**53**	4d. red-brown and magenta	20	40
167	**54**	5d. grey-blue and rose	1·25	3·25
168	**55**	6d. grey-blue, emerald and light blue	30	30
		w. Wmk inverted	£225	£225
169	**56**	8d. bright blue, bright green and orange	30	35
170	**57**	9d. light blue and brown	30	60
170a	**58**	10d. violet and ochre (8.2.65)	15·00	2·25
		w. Wmk inverted	£1500	£1100
171	**59**	1s. black, emerald, bright blue and orange	30	10
172	**60**	1s.3d. lake, grey and bistre	75	15
		w. Wmk inverted	†	£2500
173	**58**	1s.6d. violet and ochre	75	1·00
174	**61**	2s. red-brown and orange	3·00	1·25
175	**62**	2s.3d. bistre-brown and yellow-green	1·00	7·00
176	**63**	2s.6d. bistre-brown, bluish green and olive-yellow	55	50
177	**64**	5s. brown-purple and blue-green	1·25	1·50
		a. Broken "P"	35·00	
		w. Wmk inverted	£325	£325
178	**65**	10s. magenta, deep bluish green and buff	5·00	7·00
		w. Wmk inverted	£700	£750
179	**66**	£1 black, yellow-olive and yellow-orange	14·00	14·00
163/79 Set of 18			40·00	35·00

Three examples of No. 164b are known, all used on piece. The 3d. value with the yellow-brown omitted, previously No. 165a, is no longer listed as this is believed to be a dry print. All reported examples show traces of the yellow-brown.

See also Nos. 195/200 and 246a.

1963 (4 June). Freedom from Hunger. As No. 146 of Antigua.

180		1s.3d. sepia	60	40

1963 (2 Sept). Red Cross Centenary. As Nos. 147/8 of Antigua.

181		3d. red and black	50	25
182		1s.3d. red and blue	1·00	2·50

67 Tsotsi in the Bundu (Finn class dinghy)

(Des V. Whiteley. Photo D.L.R.)

1964 (28 Sept). Olympic Games, Tokyo. W w **12**. P 14×13½.

183	**67**	3d. red, violet and blue	10	10

1965 (17 May). ITU Centenary. As Nos. 166/7 of Antigua.

184		3d. light blue and emerald	35	25
185		2s. yellow and ultramarine	65	1·50

68 Scout Badge and St. Edward's Crown

(Des W. Harrington. Photo Harrison)

1965 (24 July). 50th Anniv of Bermuda Boy Scouts Association. W w **12**. P 12½.

186	**68**	2s. multicoloured	50	50
		w. Wmk inverted	55·00	65·00

1965 (25 Oct). International Co-operation Year. As Nos. 168/9 of Antigua.

187		4d. reddish purple and turquoise-green	40	20
188		2s.6d. deep bluish green and lavender	60	80

1966 (24 Jan). Churchill Commemoration. As Nos. 170/3 of Antigua.

189		3d. new blue	30	20
190		6d. deep green	70	1·25
191		10d. brown	80	75
192		1s.3d. bluish violet	1·00	2·50
189/92 Set of 4			2·50	4·25

1966 (1 July). World Cup Football Championship. As Nos. 176/7 of Antigua.

193		10d. violet, yellow-green, lake and yellow-brown	40	15
194		2s.6d. chocolate, blue-green, lake and yellow-brown	60	1·25

1966 (25 Oct)–**69**. Designs as Nos. 164, 167 (1s.6d.), 169, 170a/1 and 174 but W w **12** (sideways*).

195	**51**	2d. lilac, indigo, yellow and green (20.5.69)	6·50	8·00
		w. Wmk Crown to right of CA	—	£375
196	**56**	8d. bright blue, bright green and orange (14.2.67)	50	1·50
197	**58**	10d. violet and ochre (1.11.66)	1·00	60
		w. Wmk Crown to right of CA	£1400	£1400
198	**59**	1s. black, emerald, bright blue and orange (14.2.67)	1·50	1·40

199	**54**	1s.6d. grey-blue and rose (1.11.66)		1·00	30
		w. Wmk Crown to right of CA		£140	£150
200	**61**	2s. red-brown and orange		1·25	60
195/200 *Set of 6*				10·50	11·00

*The normal sideways watermark shows Crown to left of CA, *as seen from the back of the stamp.*

The 2d. value exists with PVA gum only, and the 8d. exists with PVA gum as well as gum arabic.

1966 (1 Dec). 20th Anniv of UNESCO As Nos. 196/8 of Antigua.

201		4d. slate-violet, red, yellow and orange		35	15
202		1s.3d. orange-yellow, violet and deep olive		60	65
203		2s. black, bright purple and orange		75	1·40
201/3 *Set of 3*				1·50	2·00

69 GPO Building

(Des G. Vasarhelyi. Photo Harrison)

1967 (23 June). Opening of New General Post Office, Hamilton. W w **12**. P 14½.

204	**69**	3d. multicoloured		10	10
205		1s. multicoloured		15	10
206		1s.6d. multicoloured		30	25
207		2s.6d. multicoloured		35	1·00
204/7 *Set of 4*				75	1·25

70 *Mercury* (cable ship) and Chain Links

1s. Broken cable above "R" of "BERMUDA" (R. 12/1)

(Des V. Whiteley. Photo Harrison)

1967 (14 Sept). Inauguration of Bermuda–Tortola Telephone Service. T **70** and similar horiz designs. Multicoloured. W w **12**. P 14½×14.

208		3d. Type **70**		15	10
209		1s. Map, telephone and microphone		25	10
		a. Broken cable		12·00	
210		1s.6d. Telecommunications media		25	25
211		2s.6d. *Mercury* (cable ship) and marine fauna		40	1·00
208/11 *Set of 4*				1·00	1·25

74 Human Rights Emblem and Doves

(Des M. Farrar Bell. Litho Harrison)

1968 (1 Feb). Human Rights Year. W w **12**. P 14×14½.

212	**74**	3d. indigo, blue and dull green		10	10
213		1s. yellow-brown, blue and light blue		10	10
214		1s.6d. black, blue and rose		10	15
215		2s.6d. grey-green, blue and yellow		15	25
212/15 *Set of 4*				30	55

REPRESENTATIVE GOVERNMENT

75 Mace and Queen's Profile

(Des R. Granger Barrett. Photo Harrison)

1968 (1 July). New Constitution. T **75** and similar horiz design. W w **12**. P 14.

216	**75**	3d. multicoloured		10	10
217		1s. multicoloured		10	10
218	–	1s.6d. greenish yellow, black and turquoise-blue		10	20
219	–	2s.6d. lilac, black and orange-yellow		15	75
216/19 *Set of 4*				30	1·00

Design:—1s.6d., 2s.6d. Houses of Parliament and House of Assembly, Bermuda.

77 Football, Athletics and Yachting

(Des V. Whiteley. Photo Harrison)

1968 (24 Sept). Olympic Games, Mexico. W w **12**. P 12½.

220	**77**	3d. multicoloured		15	10
		a. Red-brown ("BERMUDA" and value) omitted		£4750	£5000
221		1s. multicoloured		25	10
222		1s.6d. multicoloured		50	30
223		2s.6d. multicoloured		50	1·40
220/3 *Set of 4*				1·25	1·75

78 Brownie and Guide

80 Emerald-studded Gold Cross and Seaweed

(Des Harrison. Litho Format)

1969 (17 Feb). 50th Anniv of Bermuda Girl Guides. P 14.

224	**78**	3d. multicoloured		10	10
225		1s. multicoloured		20	10
226	–	1s.6d. multicoloured		25	40
227	–	2s.6d. multicoloured		35	1·40
224/7 *Set of 4*				80	1·75

Design:—1s.6d., 2s.6d. Guides and badge.

(Des K. Giles adapted by V. Whiteley. Photo Harrison)

1969 (29 Sept). Underwater Treasure. T **80** and similar vert design. Multicoloured. W w **12** (sideways). P 14½×14.

228		4d. Type **80**		20	10
229		1s.3d. Emerald-studded gold cross and seabed		35	15
		a. Green (jewels) omitted			
230		2s. Type **80**		45	90
231		2s.6d. As 1s.3d		45	1·75
228/31 *Set of 4*				1·25	2·50

(New Currency. 100 cents = 1 Bermuda dollar)

1c

(**82**)   **2c**   Tall "2" (Pl 1A. R. 2/2)

1970 (6 Feb). Decimal Currency. As Nos. 163, 165/6, 168, 170, 172, 175/9 and 195/200 surch as T **82**. W w **12** (sideways* on 2, 5, 10, 12, 15, 18, 24, 30, 60c., \$1.20 and \$2.40).

232		1c. on 1d. reddish purple, black and orange		10	1·75
		w. Wmk inverted		50·00	50·00
233		2c. on 2d. lilac, indigo, yellow and green		10	10
		a. Lilac omitted		£1000	
		b. Vert pair, one without surch		£7500	
		c. Tall "2"		10·00	
		d. Surch double, one albino			
		ew. Wmk Crown to right of CA		£130	£160
		f. Wmk upright (No. 164)		3·00	7·00
		fa. Tall "2"		45·00	
		g. Wmk upright (No. 164d)		7·00	9·00
		ga. Tall "2"		75·00	
234		3c. on 3d. yellow-brown and light blue		10	30
235		4c. on 4d. red-brown and magenta (Br.)		10	10
236		5c. on 8d. bright blue, bright green and orange		15	2·25
237		6c. on 6d. grey-blue, emerald and light blue		15	1·75
		a. Horiz pair, one with albino surch, the other with albino bar		£5500	
		w. Wmk inverted		£325	£190
238		9c. on 9d. light blue and brown (Br.)		30	2·75
239		10c. on 10d. violet and ochre		30	25
240		12c. on 1s. black, emerald, bright blue and orange		30	1·25
241		15c. on 1s.3d. lake, grey and bistre		2·00	1·75
242		18c. on 1s.6d. grey-blue and rose		80	65
243		24c. on 2s. red-brown and orange		85	4·50
		w. Wmk Crown to right of CA		£170	£225
244		30c. on 2s.6d. bistre-brown, bluish green and olive-yellow		1·00	3·00
245		36c. on 2s.3d. bistre-brown and yellow-green		1·75	8·00
246		60c. on 5s. brown-purple and blue-green		2·25	4·00
		a. Surch omitted †		£1500	
247		\$1.20 on 10s. magenta, deep bluish green and buff		4·50	12·00
248		\$2.40 on £1 black, yellow-olive and yellow-orange		5·50	15·00
232/48 *Set of 17*				18·00	50·00

*The normal sideways watermark shows Crown to left of CA, *as seen from the back of the stamp.*

†No. 246a differs from the normal No. 177 by its watermark, which is sideways, and its gum, which is PVA.

The surcharge was applied typo on the 1c., 2c., 3c., 6c. and 36c. and photo on the remaining values.

83 *Spathiphyllum*

(Des W. Harrington. Photo D.L.R.)

1970 (6 July)–**75**. Flowers. Multicoloured designs as T **83**. W w **12** (sideways on horiz designs). P 14.

249		1c. Type **83**		10	20
250		2c. Bottlebrush		20	25
251		3c. Oleander (*vert*)		15	10
252		4c. Bermudiana		15	10
253		5c. Poinsettia		2·75	20
254		6c. Hibiscus		30	30
255		9c. Cereus		20	45
256		10c. Bougainvillea (*vert*)		20	15
257		12c. Jacaranda		60	60
258		15c. Passion-Flower		90	1·00
258a		17c. As 15c. (2.6.75)		2·75	5·50
259		18c. Coralita		1·75	1·00
259a		20c. As 18c. (2.6.75)		2·75	4·50
260		24c. Morning Glory		1·50	5·00
260a		25c. As 24c. (2.6.75)		2·75	4·50
261		30c. Tecoma		1·00	1·00
262		36c. Angel's Trumpet		1·00	1·25
262a		40c. As 36c. (2.6.75)		2·75	5·50
263		60c. Plumbago		1·50	1·25
263a		\$1 As 60c. (2.6.75)		3·25	6·50
264		\$1.20 Bird of Paradise flower		1·75	1·25
264a		\$2 As \$1.20 (2.6.75)		11·00	10·00
265		\$2.40 Chalice Cup		4·00	1·50
265a		\$3 As \$2.40 (2.6.75)		13·00	11·00
249/65a *Set of 24*				50·00	50·00

84 The State House, St. George's

(Des G. Drummond. Litho Questa)

1970 (12 Oct). 350th Anniv of Bermuda Parliament. T **84** and similar horiz designs. Multicoloured. W w **12** (sideways). P 14.

266		4c. Type **84**		10	10
267		15c. The Sessions House, Hamilton		30	20
268		18c. St. Peter's Church, St. George's		30	25
269		24c. Town Hall, Hamilton		40	1·00
266/9 *Set of 4*				1·00	1·40
MS270 131×95 mm. Nos. 266/9				1·10	1·50

STAMP BOOKLETS

1948 (5 Apr–10 May). Pink (No. SB1), or light blue (No. SB2) covers. Stapled.

SB1	5s. booklet containing six of each 1d., 1½d., 2d., 2½d. and 3d. (Nos. 110, 111b, 112a, 113b, 114a) in blocks of 6 (10.5)		£140
SB2	10s.6d. booklet containing 6×3d. and 18×6d. (Nos. 114a, 104) in blocks of 6 with twelve air mail labels		£150

POSTAL FISCAL

1937 (1 Feb). As T **15**, but inscr "REVENUE" at each side. Wmk Mult Script CA. Chalk-surfaced paper. P 14

F1	12s.6d. grey and orange		£1100	£1500
	a. Break in scroll (R. 1/12)		£4250	£6500
	b. Broken crown and scroll (R. 2/12)		£4250	
	d. Break through scroll (R. 1/9)		£4250	
	e. Break in lines below left scroll		£4250	
	f. Damaged leaf at bottom right		£4250	
	g. Gash in fruit and leaf		£4250	
	h. Breaks in scrolls at right (R. 1/3)		£4250	

No. F1 was issued for fiscal purposes towards the end of 1936. Its use as a postage stamp was authorised from 1 February to April 1937. The used price quoted above is for examples postmarked during this period. Later in the same year postmarks with other dates were obtained by favour.

For illustrations of No. F1a/h see above Nos. 51b and 88.

Botswana

INDEPENDENCE

47 National Assembly Building

(Des R. Granger Barrett. Photo Harrison)

1966 (30 Sept). Independence. T **47** and similar horiz designs. Multicoloured. P 14½.

202	2½c. Type **47**	15	10
	a. Imperf (pair)		£450
203	5c. Abattoir Lobatsi	20	10
204	15c. National Airways Douglas DC-3	65	20
205	35c. State House, Gaberones	40	30
202/5 Set of 4		1·25	55

REPUBLIC OF BOTSWANA

(51)

52 Golden Oriole

1966 (30 Sept). Nos. 168/81 of Bechuanaland optd as T **51**.

206	1c. yellow, red, black and lilac	25	10
207	2c. orange, black and yellow-olive	30	1·75
208	2½c. carmine, green, black and bistre	30	10
209	3½c. yellow, black, sepia and pink	1·50	40
	a. Yellow, black, sepia and flesh	12·00	2·25
210	5c. yellow, blue, black and buff	1·75	1·50
211	7½c. brown, red, black and apple-green	50	1·75
	a. Yellow background	—	£1000
212	10c. red, yellow, sepia and turquoise-green	1·00	20
213	12½c. buff, blue, red and grey-black	2·00	3·75
214	20c. yellow-brown and drab	20	1·00
215	25c. deep brown and lemon	20	2·00
216	35c. deep blue and orange	30	2·75
217	50c. sepia and olive	20	70
218	1r. black and cinnamon	40	1·25
219	2r. brown and turquoise-blue	1·00	3·50
206/19 Set of 14		9·00	19·00

No. 209a was a special printing produced to make up quantities. It does not exist without the overprint.

No. 211a shows the background in yellow instead of apple-green and may have come from a trial printing. Most known examples come from first day covers but 8 unused examples have also been reported.

(Des D. M. Reid-Henry. Photo Harrison)

1967 (3 Jan). Birds. Vert designs as T **52**. Multicoloured. P 14×14.

220	1c. Type **52**	30	15
	a. Error. Wmk **105** of Malta	†	£800
221	2c. Hoopoe	60	70
222	3c. Groundscraper Thrush	55	10
223	4c. Cordon-bleu ("Blue Waxbill")	55	10
224	5c. Secretary Bird	55	10
225	7c. Yellow-billed Hornbill	60	1·00
226	10c. Burchell's Gonolek ("Crimson-breasted Shrike")	60	15
227	15c. Malachite Kingfisher	8·50	3·25
228	20c. African Fish Eagle	8·50	2·25
229	25c. Go-away Bird ("Grey Loerie")	4·00	1·50
230	35c. Scimitar-bill	6·00	3·75
231	50c. Comb Duck	2·75	2·75
232	1r. Levaillant's Barbet	5·00	3·50
233	2r. Didric Cuckoo	7·00	17·00
220/33 Set of 14		40·00	32·00

A used copy of the 20c. has been seen with the pale brown colour missing, resulting in the value (normally shown in white) being omitted.

The 1, 2, 4, 7 and 10c. values exist with PVA gum as well as gum arabic.

66 Students and University

(Des V. Whiteley. Photo Harrison)

1967 (7 Apr). First Conferment of University Degrees. P 14×14½.

234	**66**	3c. sepia, ultramarine and light orange-yellow	10	10
235		7c. sepia, ultram and lt greenish bl	10	10
236		15c. sepia, ultramarine and rose	10	10
237		35c. sepia, ultramarine and light violet	20	20
234/7 Set of 4			30	30

67 Bushbuck

(Des G. Vasarhelyi. Photo Harrison)

1967 (2 Oct). Chobe Game Reserve. T **67** and similar horiz designs. Multicoloured. P 14.

238	3c. Type **67**	10	20
239	7c. Sale Antelope	15	30
240	35c. Fishing on Chobe River	90	1·10
238/40 Set of 3		1·00	1·40

70 Arms of Botswana and Human Rights Emblem

(Litho D.L.R.)

1968 (8 Apr). Human Rights Year. T **70** and similar horiz designs showing Anniv of Botswana and Human Rights emblem arranged differently. P 13½×13.

241	3c. multicoloured	10	10
242	15c. multicoloured	25	45
243	25c. multicoloured	25	60
241/3 Set of 3		50	1·00

73 Eland and Giraffe Rock Paintings, Tsodilo Hills

75 Baobab Trees (Thomas Baines)

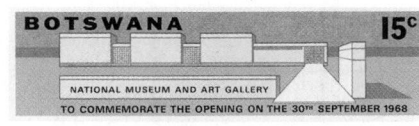

76 National Museum and Art Gallery

(Litho D.L.R.)

1968 (30 Sept). Opening of National Museum and Art Gallery. T **73/6** and similar multicoloured design. P 12½ (7c.), 12½×13½ (15c.), or 13×13½ (others).

244	3c. Type **73**	20	20
245	7c. Girl wearing ceremonial beads (30×48 mm)	25	40
246	10c. Type **75**	25	30
247	35c. Type **76**	40	1·50
244/7 Set of 4		1·00	2·25
MS248 132×82 mm. Nos. 244/7. P 13		1·00	2·25

77 African Family, and Star over Village

(Des Mrs M. E. Townsend, adapted J. Cooter. Litho Enschedé)

1968 (11 Nov). Christmas. P 13×14.

249	**77**	1c. multicoloured	10	25
250		2c. multicoloured	10	25
251		5c. multicoloured	10	10
252		25c. multicoloured	15	50
249/52 Set of 4			30	1·00

78 Scout, Lion and Badge in Frame

(Des D.L.R. Litho Format)

1969 (21 Aug). 22nd World Scout Conference, Helsinki. T **78** and similar multicoloured designs. P 13½.

253	3c. Type **78**	35	30
254	15c. Scouts cooking over open fire (vert)	35	1·00
255	25c. Scouts around camp fire	40	1·00
253/5 Set of 3		1·00	2·00

81 Woman, Child and Christmas Star

82 Diamond Treatment Plant, Orapa

(Des A. Vale, adapted V. Whiteley. Litho Harrison)

1969 (6 Nov). Christmas. P 14½×14.

256	**81**	1c. pale blue and chocolate	10	20
257		2c. pale yellow-olive and chocolate	10	20
258		4c. yellow and chocolate	10	10
259		35c. chocolate and bluish violet	35	20
256/9 Set of 4			50	60
MS260 86×128 mm. Nos. 256/9. P 14½ (shades)		1·00	1·10

(Des J.W. Litho Harrison)

1970 (23 Mar). Developing Botswana. T **82** and similar designs. Multicoloured. P 14½×14 (3c., 7c.) or 14×14½ (others).

261	3c. Type **82**	80	20
262	7c. Copper-nickel mining	1·00	20
263	10c. Copper-nickel mine, Selebi–Pikwe (horiz)	1·25	15
264	35c. Orapa diamond mine, and diamonds (horiz)	3·00	1·25
261/4 Set of 4		5·50	1·60

83 Mr. Micawber (David Copperfield)

(Des V. Whiteley. Litho Walsall)

1970 (6 July). Death Centenary of Charles Dickens. T **83** and similar horiz designs. Multicoloured. P 11.

265	3c. Type **83**	25	10
266	7c. Scrooge (A Christmas Carol)	25	10
267	15c. Fagin (Oliver Twist)	45	40
268	25c. Bill Sykes (Oliver Twist)	70	60
265/8 Set of 4		1·50	1·00
MS269 114×81 mm. Nos. 265/8		2·75	4·00

84 UN Building and Emblem

(Des J. Cooter. Litho Walsall)

1970 (24 Oct). 25th Anniv of United Nations. P 11.

270	**84**	15c. bright blue, chestnut and silver	70	50

85 Crocodile

(Des A. Vale. Litho Questa)

1970 (3 Nov). Christmas. T **85** and similar horiz designs. Multicoloured. P 14.

271	1c. Type **85**	10	10
272	2c. Giraffe	10	10
273	7c. Elephant	15	15
274	25c. Rhinoceros	60	80
271/4 Set of 4		80	1·00
MS275 128×90 mm. Nos. 271/4		1·00	3·00

POSTAGE DUE STAMPS

REPUBLIC OF

BOTSWANA

(D **4**)

1967 (1 Mar). Nos. D10/12 of Bechuanaland optd with Type D **4**.

D13	1c. carmine	15	1·75
	a. Bold "c" and larger dot	8·00	
D14	2c. violet	15	1·75
D15	5c. green	20	1·75
D13/15 Set of 3		45	4·75

British Antarctic Territory

1963. 12 pence (d.) = 1 shilling; 20 shillings = £1
1971. 100 pence (p.) = £1

For use at the following bases:

Adelaide Island (Graham Land) *(closed* 1977)
Argentine Islands ("Faraday" *from* 1981), (Graham Land) *(closed* 8 February 1996 *and transferred to Ukraine)*
Brabant Island (Graham Land) *(opened* 1984, *closed* 1985)
Deception Island (South Shetlands) *(closed* December 1967, *opened* 4 December 1968, *closed* 23 February 1969)
Halley Bay (Coats Land)
Hope Bay (Graham Land) *(closed* 12 February 1964)
Port Lockroy (Graham Land) *(opened* 25 November 1996)
Rothera Point (Graham Land) *(opened* 1977)
Signy Island (South Orkneys)
Stonington Island (Graham Land) *(closed* February 1975)

1 MV *Kista Dan*

2 Manhauling

3 Muskeg (tractor)

4 Skiing

5 de Havilland DHC-2 Beaver

6 RRS *John Biscoe II*

7 Camp scene

8 HMS *Protector*

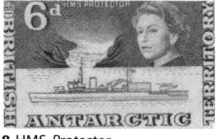

9 Sledging

10 de Havilland DHC-3 Otter

11 Huskies

12 Westland Whirlwind

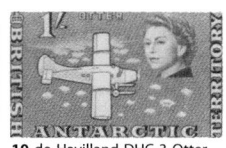

13 Snocat

14 RRS *Shackleton*

15 Antarctic map

16 HMS *Endurance*

(Des B.W. (No. 15*a*), M. Goaman (others). Recess B.W.)

1963 (1 Feb)–**69**. Horiz designs as T **1**. W w **12**. P 11×11½.

1	1	½d. deep blue	1·25	1·75
2	2	1d. brown	1·25	80
3	3	1½d. orange-red and brown-purple..	1·25	1·50
4	4	2d. purple	1·50	80
5	5	2½d. myrtle-green	2·50	1·25
6	6	3d. deep blue	3·00	1·50
7	7	4d. sepia	2·25	1·50
8	8	6d. olive and deep ultramarine	5·00	2·50
9	9	9d. olive-green	3·00	2·00
10	10	1s. deep turquoise-blue	3·25	1·50
11	11	2s. deep violet and orange-sepia ...	20·00	10·00

12	12	2s.6d. blue	22·00	15·00
13	13	5s. red-orange and rose-red	22·00	19·00
14	14	10s. deep ultramarine and emerald..	45·00	26·00
15	15	£1 black and light blue	48·00	48·00
15*a*	16	£1 red and brownish black (1.12.69)	£130	£120
1/15*a* Set of 16			£275	£225

1966 (24 Jan). Churchill Commemoration. As Nos. 223/6 of Falkland Islands.

16		½d. new blue	80	3·25
17		1d. deep green	3·25	3·25
18		1s. brown	16·00	5·00
19		2s. bluish violet	17·00	5·50
16/19 Set of 4			32·00	15·00

17 Lemaire Channel and Icebergs

(Des R. Granger Barrett. Litho Format)

1969 (6 Feb). 25th Anniv of Continuous Scientific Work. T **17** and similar horiz designs. W w **12** (sideways). P 14.

20		3½d. black, pale blue and ultramarine	2·50	2·50
21		6d. multicoloured	75	1·75
22		1s. black, pale blue and vermilion	75	1·50
23		2s. black, orange and turquoise-blue	75	2·25
20/3 Set of 4			4·25	7·25

Designs:—6d. Radio Sonde balloon; 1s. Muskeg pulling tent equipment; 2s. Surveyors with theodolite.

British Columbia and Vancouver Island *see* Canada

British East Africa *see* Kenya, Uganda and Tanganyika

British Guiana

The postal service from what was to become British Guiana dates from 1796, being placed on a more regular basis after the final British occupation.

An inland postal system was organised in 1850, using the adhesive stamps of British Guiana, but, until 1 May 1860, overseas mails continued to be the province of the British GPO. The stamps of Great Britain were supplied for use on such letters from 11 May 1858 and examples of their use in combination with British Guiana issues have been recorded.

For illustration of the handstamp and postmark type see BRITISH POST OFFICES ABROAD notes, following GREAT BRITAIN.

CROWNED-CIRCLE HANDSTAMPS

The provision of a handstamp, probably as Type CC **1**, inscribed "DEMERARA", is recorded in the GPO proof book under 1 March 1856. No examples have been reported. A further handstamp, as Type CC **6**, recorded in the proof book on 17 February 1866, is known used as a cancellation in at least three instances, including one on cover dated 8 November 1868.

GEORGETOWN (DEMERARA)

Stamps of GREAT BRITAIN cancelled "A 03" as Type **2**.

1858–60.

Z1	1d. rose-red (1857), perf 14		£350
Z2	4d. rose (1857)		£180
Z3	6d. lilac (1856)		£120
	a. Azure paper		
Z4	1s. green (1856)		£1800

NEW AMSTERDAM (BERBICE)

Stamps of GREAT BRITAIN cancelled "A 04" as Type **2**.

1858–60.

Z5	1d. rose-red (1857), perf 14		£850
Z6	2d. blue (1858) (Plate Nos. 7, 8)		£1300
Z7	4d. rose (1857)		£450
Z8	6d. lilac (1856)		£325
Z9	1s. green (1856)		£2250

PRICES FOR STAMPS ON COVER TO 1945	
No. 1	*from* × 1
Nos. 2/8	*from* × 4
Nos. 9/21	*from* × 3
No. 23	†
Nos. 24/7	*from* × 3
Nos. 29/115	*from* × 5
Nos. 116/24	*from* × 20
Nos. 126/36	*from* × 7
Nos. 137/59	*from* × 8
Nos. 162/5	*from* × 15
Nos. 170/4	*from* × 8
Nos. 175/89	*from* × 10
No. 192	*from* × 30
Nos. 193/210	*from* × 5
Nos. 213/15	*from* × 8
Nos. 216/21	*from* × 5
Nos. 222/4	*from* × 10
Nos. 233/50	*from* × 4
No. 251	—
Nos. 252/7	*from* × 4
Nos. 259/82	*from* × 5
Nos. 283/7	*from* × 8
Nos. 288/300	*from* × 5
Nos. 301/4	*from* × 6
Nos. 305/7	*from* × 8
Nos. 308/19	*from* × 5
Nos. D1/4	*from* × 15
Nos. O1/12	—

CROWN COLONY
(Currency. 100 cents = 1 dollar)

1   **2**

(Set up and printed at the office of the *Royal Gazette*, Georgetown, British Guiana)

1850 (1 July)–**51**. Type-set. Black impression.

*(a) Medium wove paper. Prices are for—*I. Cut square. II. Cut round

			I Used	II Used
1	1	2c. rose (1.3.51)	—	£325000
2		4c. orange	£100000	£16000
3		4c. lemon-yellow (1851)	£130000	£24000
4		8c. green	£70000	£16000
5		12c. blue	£35000	£11000
6		12c. indigo	£45000	£13000
7		12c. pale blue (1851)	£40000	£13000
		a. "2" of "12" with straight foot..	£110000	£25000
		b. "1" of "12" omitted	†	£250000
		(b) Pelure paper (1851)		
8	1	4c. pale yellow	£130000	£24000

These stamps were usually initialled by the postmaster, or the Post Office clerks, before they were issued. The initials are—E. T. E. D(alton), E. D. W(ight), J. B. S(mith), H. A. K(illikelly), and W. H. L(ortimer). There are several types of each value and it seems likely that the setting contained one horizontal row of four slightly different impressions.

Ten examples of No. 1 have been recorded, including three pairs on separate covers.

(Litho Waterlow)

1852 (1 Jan). Surface-coloured paper. Imperf.

9	**2**	1c. black/*magenta*		£15000	£5500
10		4c. black/*deep blue*		£25000	£12000

There are two types of each value, which can be distinguished by differences in the waves at left, and in the outline of the upper sail. A sub-type of the 1c. exists without stop after "CENT".

Reprints on thicker paper, and perf 12½, were made in 1865 (*Price £24 either value*).

Such reprints with the perforations removed are sometimes offered as genuine originals.

CONDITION. Prices for Nos. 9 to 27 are for fine copies. Poor to medium specimens can be supplied when in stock at much lower rates.

3   4   5

(Dies eng and stamps litho Waterlow)

1853–59. Imperf.

(a) Original printing

11	**3**	1c. vermilion		£7500	£1700

This 1c. in *reddish brown* is probably a proof (*Price £1700*).

     A   B

     C   D

A. "O" large and 1 mm from left corner.
B. "O" small and ¾ mm from left corner.
C. "O" small and ¾ mm from left corner. "NT" widely spaced.
D. "ONE" close together, "O" 1¼ mm from left corner.

(b) Fresh lithographic transfers from the 4c. with varying labels of value. White line above value (1857–59).

12	**3**	1c. dull red (A)		£7500	£2000
13		1c. brownish red (A)		£15000	£2500
14		1c. dull red (B)		£8500	£2250
15		1c. brownish red (B)		£16000	£2750
16		1c. dull red (C)		£10000	£2500
16a		1c. brownish red (C)		—	£3500
17		1c. dull red (D)		†	£25000

The four types (A to D) occurred within the same sheet and exist *se-tenant* (Prices, for *se-tenant* pair from £26000 unused, £7500 used).

1853–55. Imperf.

18	**4**	4c. deep blue		£5500	£1100
		a. Retouched		£8000	£1600
19		4c. blue (1854)		£3000	£800
		a. Retouched		£4500	£1000
20		4c. pale blue (1855)		£2250	£700
		a. Retouched		£3250	£1000

The 4c. value was produced from transfers from the original 1c., with the bottom inscription removed, teamed with a new face value. The join often shows as a white line or traces of it above the label of value and lower corner figures. In some stamps on the sheet this line is missing, owing to having been retouched, and in these cases a line of colour usually appears in its place.

The 1c. and 4c. stamps were reprinted in 1865 from fresh transfers of five varieties. These are on thin paper and perf 12½ (*Price £21 each unused*).

1860 (May). Figures in corners framed. Imperf

21	**5**	4c. blue		£7000	£800

6

(Type-set and printed at the *Official Gazette* by Baum and Dallas, Georgetown).

1856.

(a) Surface-coloured paper

23	**6**	1c. black/*magenta*		*	—
24		4c. black/*magenta* (1.56)		£100000	£25000
25		4c. black/*rose-carmine* (8.56)		†	£40000
26		4c. black/*blue* (9.56)		†	£150000

(b) Paper coloured through

27		4c. black/*deep blue* (8.56)		†	£225000

Since only one example of No. 23 is known, no market price can be given. This celebrated stamp, frequently termed "the world's rarest", was last sold in New York in June 2014 for nearly £6 million. It is initialled by E. D. Wight and postmarked at Demerara on 4 April 1856.

These stamps, like those of the first issue, were initialled before being issued; the initials are—E.T.E.D.(alton), E.D.W.(ight), C.A.W.(atson), and W.H.L.(ortimer). C.A.W. only appears on stamps postmarked between 14 March and 4 April and also 16–20 May. E.T.E.D. is only known on stamps between 1–5 July and on 1 August. All examples on the rose-carmine or blue papers show E.D.W.

Stamps as Type **6** were printed in sheets of four (2×2) each stamp differing slightly in the position of the inscriptions. There is evidence that the setting was re-arranged at some point before August, *possibly* to accommodate the production of the 1c.

PAPERMAKERS' WATERMARKS. Seven different papermakers' watermarks were used in the period 1860 to 1875 and stamps bearing portions of these are worth a premium.

7

   A   B

   C   D

   E   F

(Dies eng and litho Waterlow)

1860 (July)**–63.** Tablets of value as illustrated. Thick paper. P 12.

29	**7**	1c. pale rose		£3500	£275
30		2c. deep orange (8.60)		£325	55·00
31		2c. pale orange		£350	60·00
32		4c. deep blue (8.60)		£850	£120
33		4c. blue		£475	75·00
34		8c. brownish rose		£1200	£160
35		8c. pink		£850	90·00
36		12c. lilac		£950	50·00
37		12c. grey-lilac		£800	50·00
38		24c. deep green (6.63)		£2500	£150
39		24c. green		£1700	80·00

The 1c. was reprinted in 1865 on *thin* paper, P 12½–13, and in a different shade. *Price £22.*

The 12c. in both shades is frequently surcharged with a large "5d" in *red*; this is to denote the proportion of postage repayable by the colony to Great Britain for overseas letters.

1861 (3 Aug*). Colour changed. Thick paper. P 12.

40	**7**	1c. reddish brown		£500	£110

*Earliest known postmark date.

1862–65.

(a) Thin paper. P 12

41	**7**	1c. brown		£950	£250
42		1c. black (1863)		£170	60·00
43		2c. orange		£160	60·00
44		4c. blue		£180	50·00
45		4c. pale blue		£160	38·00
46		8c. pink (1863)		£325	85·00
47		12c. dull purple (1863)		£400	35·00
48		12c. purple		£425	40·00
49		12c. lilac		£425	50·00
50		24c. green		£1800	£100

(b) Thin paper. P 12½–13 (1863)

51	**7**	1c. black		80·00	24·00
52		2c. orange		95·00	26·00
53		4c. blue		£100	18·00
54		8c. pink		£375	90·00
55		12c. brownish lilac		£1300	£140
56		24c. green		£850	65·00

Copies are found on *pelure* paper.

(c) Medium paper. P 12½–13

57	**7**	1c. black		70·00	50·00
58		2c. deep orange (1864)		90·00	29·00
59		2c. orange		95·00	27·00
60		4c. greyish blue (1864)		£110	22·00
61		4c. blue		£130	30·00
62		8c. pink (1864)		£325	75·00
63		12c. brownish lilac (1865)		£1100	£130
64		24c. green (1864)		£425	50·00
65		24c. deep green		£500	£100

(d) Medium paper. P 10 (Nov. 1865)

65a	**7**	12c. grey-lilac		£850	90·00

8   9

   G   H

   I   K

New transfers for the 1c., 2c., 8c., and 12c. with the spaces between values and the word "CENTS" about 1 mm.

1863–76. Medium paper.

(a) P 12½–13 (1863–68)

66	**8**	1c. black (1866)		90·00	38·00
67		2c. orange-red (1865)		95·00	9·50
68		2c. orange		95·00	9·50
69	**9**	6c. blue (1865)		£225	65·00
70		6c. greenish blue		£225	70·00
71		6c. deep blue		£300	£100
72		6c. milky blue		£225	65·00
73	**8**	8c. pink (1868)		£450	25·00
74		8c. carmine		£550	27·00
75		12c. grey-lilac (1867)		£650	48·00
76		12c. brownish purple		£750	50·00
77	**9**	24c. green (perf 12)		£350	21·00
78		24c. yellow-green (perf 12)		£275	13·00
79		24c. yellow-green (perf 12½–13)		£250	13·00
80		24c. green (perf 12½–13) (1864)		£275	13·00

81		24c. blue-green (perf 12½–13)		£375	22·00
82		48c. pale red		£375	75·00
83		48c. deep red		£425	75·00
84		48c. carmine-rose		£425	75·00

The 4c. corresponding to this issue can only be distinguished from that of the previous issue by minor plating flaws.

There is a variety of the 6c. with stop before "VICISSIM".

Varieties of most of the values of issues of 1863–64 and 1866 are to be found on both very thin and thick papers.

(b) P 10 (1866–71)

85	**8**	1c. black (1869)		26·00	8·00
86		1c. grey-black		28·00	16·00
87		2c. orange (1868)		65·00	4·75
88		2c. reddish orange		85·00	6·50
89		4c. slate-blue		£160	13·00
90		4c. blue		£140	9·00
		a. Bisected (on cover)		†	£7500
		b. Ditto. Imperf (on cover)		†	
91		4c. pale blue		£120	9·50
92	**9**	6c. milky blue (1867)		£200	35·00
93		6c. ultramarine		£250	60·00
94		6c. dull blue		£200	38·00
95	**8**	8c. pink (5.71)		£300	42·00
96		8c. brownish pink		£375	50·00
96a		8c. carmine		£475	55·00
97		12c. pale lilac (1867)		£350	26·00
98		12c. grey-lilac		£325	25·00
99		12c. brownish grey		£325	27·00
100		12c. lilac		£325	27·00
101	**9**	24c. deep green		£375	9·50
102		24c. bluish green		£350	8·00
103		24c. yellow-green		£300	7·50
104		48c. crimson (1867)		£450	48·00
		s. Handstamped "SPECIMEN"		£350	
		as. Perf "SPECIMEN"		£300	
105		48c. red		£425	40·00

(c) P 15 (1875–76)

106	**8**	1c. black		65·00	7·50
107		2c. orange-red		£190	16·00
108		2c. orange		£190	16·00
109		4c. bright blue		£325	£100
111	**9**	6c. ultramarine		£1100	£150
112	**8**	8c. deep rose (1876)		£375	£110
113		12c. lilac		£900	95·00
114	**9**	24c. yellow-green		£700	35·00
115		24c. deep green		£700	£120

There is a variety of the 48c. with stop after "P" in "PETIMUSQUE".

Imperforate stamps of this and of the previous issue are considered to be proofs, although examples of the 24c. imperforate from the 1869–73 period are known commercially used.

NOTE: Prices for stamps of the 1862 issue are for good average copies. Copies with roulettes on all sides very seldom occur and do not exist in marginal positions.

10   11   12

13   14   15

(Type-set and printed at the Office of the *Royal Gazette*, Georgetown)

1862 (Sept). Black on coloured paper. Roul 6.

116	**10**	1c. *rose*		£5500	£850
		a. Unsigned		£700	
		b. Wrong ornament (as T **13**) at left (R. 1/1)		—	£1300
		c. "1" for "I" in "BRITISH" (R. 1/5)		—	£1300
		d. Wrong ornament (as T **13**) at right (R. 2/6)		£9500	£1300
117	**11**	1c. *rose*		£7000	£1000
		a. Unsigned		£800	
		b. Narrow "T" in "CENT" (R. 3/1)		—	£1300
		c. Wrong ornament (as T **15**) at top (R. 3/3)		—	£1300
		d. "1" for "I" in "BRITISH" and italic "S" in "POSTAGE" (R. 3/5)		—	£1300
118	**12**	1c. *rose*		£9500	£1400
		a. Unsigned		£1300	
		b. "1" for "I" in "GUIANA" (R. 4/4)		—	£1400
		c. Wrong ornament (as T **15**) at left (R. 4/5)		—	£1400
		d. "C" for "O" in "POSTAGE" (R. 4/6)		—	£1400
119	**10**	2c. *yellow*		£5500	£450
		a. Unsigned		£2500	
		b. Wrong ornament (as T **13**) at left (R. 1/1)		—	£800
		c. "1" for "I" in "BRITISH" (R. 1/5)		—	£800
120	**11**	2c. *yellow*		£7000	£550
		a. Unsigned		£2750	
		b. "C" for "O" in "TWO" and narrow "T" in "CENTS" (R. 3/1)		—	£800
		c. Wrong ornament (as T **15**) at top (R. 3/3)		—	£800
		d. Italic "S" in "CENTS" (R. 3/4)		£8500	£800
		e. "1" for "I" in "BRITISH" and italic "S" in "POSTAGE" (R. 3/5)		£8500	£800
		f. Italic "T" in "TWO" (R. 3/6)		—	£800
121	**12**	2c. *yellow*		£9500	£900
		a. Unsigned		£3500	
		b. "1" for "I" in "GUIANA" (R. 4/4)		—	£900
		c. Wrong ornament (as T **15**) at left (R. 4/5)		—	£900
		d. "C" for "O" in "POSTAGE" (R. 4/6)		—	£900
122	**13**	4c. *blue*		£6000	£950
		a. Unsigned		£1200	
		b. Wrong ornament (as T **15**) at left (R. 1/6)		£8000	£1600

		c. Wrong ornament (as T **15**) at top and italic "S" in "CENTS" (R. 2/2)	—	£1600
		d. Ornament omitted at right (R. 2/4)	—	£1600
123	**14**	4c. *blue*	£8000	£1400
		a. Unsigned	£1300	
		b. With inner frame lines (as in T **10/13**) (R. 2/5–6)	£11000	£1900
		ba. "1" for "I" in "BRITISH" (R. 2/5)	£11000	£1900
		c. "1" for "I" in "BRITISH" and "GUIANA" (R. 4/1)	—	£1600
124	**15**	4c. *blue*	£8000	£1400
		a. Unsigned	£1400	
		b. Wrong ornament (as T **12**) at foot (R. 3/1)	—	£1600
		c. Italic "S" in "CENTS" (R. 3/2)	—	£1600
		d. Italic "S" in "BRITISH" (R. 3/3)	—	£1600

Stamps were initialled across the centre before use by the Acting Receiver-General, Robert Mather. Black was used on the 1c., red for the 2c. and an ink which appears white for the 4c.

The three values of this provisional were each printed in sheets of 24 (6×4). The 1c. and 2c. were produced from the same setting of the border ornaments which contained 12 examples as Type **10** (Rows 1 and 2), eight as Type **11** (R. 3/1 to R. 4/2) and four as Type **12** (R. 4/3–6).

The setting of the 4c. contained ten examples as Type **13** (R. 1/1 to R. 2/4), eight as Type **14** (R. 2/5–6 and Row 4) and six as Type **15** (Row 3).

16	(**17**)

(Typo D.L.R.)

1876 (1 July)–79. Wmk Crown CC.

(a) P 14

126	**16**	1c. slate	2·75	1·40
		w. Wmk inverted	£250	£250
127		2c. orange	85·00	4·00
		w. Wmk inverted	†	£300
128		4c. blue	£140	9·00
129		6c. brown	£100	13·00
		w. Wmk inverted	†	£400
130		8c. rose	£150	75
		w. Wmk inverted	†	£300
131		12c. pale violet	75·00	2·50
		w. Wmk inverted	†	£550
132		24c. emerald-green	80·00	3·50
		w. Wmk inverted	†	£550
133		48c. red-brown	£150	45·00
134		96c. olive-bistre	£475	£250
126/34	Set of 9		£1100	£275
126s/32s, 134s Handstamped "SPECIMEN" Set of 8			£1200	
131sa/2sa Perf "SPECIMEN" Set of 2			£300	

(b) P 12½ (1877)

135	**16**	4c. blue	£1200	£200

(c) Perf compound of 14×12½ (1879)

136	**16**	1c. slate	—	£200

1878. Provisionals. Various stamps with old values ruled through with thick bars, the bars varying in depth of colour.

(a) With two horiz bars (17 Apr)

137	**16**	(1c.) on 6c. brown	50·00	£130

(b) Official stamps with horiz bars across "OFFICIAL" (end Aug)

138	**8**	1c. black	£300	80·00
		a. Imperf between (horiz pair)		£30000
139	**16**	1c. slate	£200	75·00
140		2c. orange	£450	75·00

*(c) With horiz and vert bars as T **17** (6 Nov)*

141	**9**	(1c.) on 6c. ultramarine (No.93)	£225	75·00
142	**16**	(1c.) on 6c. brown	£425	£110
		a. Optd without "SPECIMEN"		£8500

(d) Official stamps with bars across "OFFICIAL" (23 Nov)

(i) With two horiz bars and one vert

144	**16**	(1c.) on 4c. blue	£400	£110
145	**16**	(1c.) on 4c. blue	£700	£110
146	**8**	(2c.) on 8c. rose	£5000	£400

(ii) With one horiz bar and one vert

147	**16**	(1c.) on 4c. blue	†	£5500
148		(2c.) on 8c. rose	£550	£140

1	**2**	**2**
(**18**)	(**19**)	(**20**)

1881 (21 Dec). No. 134 with old value ruled through with bar in black ink and surch.

149	**18**	1 on 96c. olive-bistre	5·50	13·00
		a. Bar in red		
		b. Bar omitted		
150	**19**	2 on 96c. olive-bistre	23·00	27·00
		a. Bar in red		
		b. Bar omitted		
151	**20**	2 on 96c. olive-bistre	85·00	£160
		a. Bar in red		

In the setting of 60 Type **19** occurs on the first five vertical rows and Type **20** on the sixth.

1	**2**	**2**
(**21**)	(**23**)	(**24**)

1881 (28 Dec). Various stamps with old value ruled with bar and surch.

(a) On No. 105

152	**21**	1 on 48c. red	50·00	5·50
		a. Bar omitted	—	£600

*(b) On Official stamps (including unissued 48c. optd with Type O **2**)*

153	**21**	1 on 12c. brownish purple (No.O4)	£140	75·00
154		1 on 48c. red-brown	£200	£130
155	**23**	2 on 12c. pale violet (No.O11)	90·00	50·00
		a. Pair. Nos. 155/6	£1600	£1800
		b. Surch double	£850	£475
		c. Surch double (T **23 + 24**)	£6000	£3750
		d. Extra bar through "OFFICIAL"		
156	**24**	2 on 12c. pale violet (No.O11)	£700	£475
157	**23**	2 on 24c. emerald-green (No.O12)	£100	65·00
		a. Pair. Nos. 157/8	£1900	£2000
		b. Surch double	£1100	
158	**24**	2 on 24c. emerald-green (No.O12)	£900	£900
159	**19**	2 on 24c. green (No.O5)	£375	£180

On Nos. 149/59 the bar is found in various thicknesses ranging from 1 to 4 mm.

It is believed that the same composite surcharge setting of 60 (6×10) was used for Nos. 155/6 and 157/8. Type **24** occurs on R. 7/2, 4-6 and R. 8/1.

26	**27**

(Type-set, Baldwin & Co. Georgetown)

1882 (9 Jan). Black impression. P 12. Perforated with the word "SPECIMEN" diagonally.

162	**26**	1c. magenta	75·00	30·00
		a. Imperf between (horiz pair)	†	—
		b. Without "SPECIMEN"	£1500	£550
		c. "1" with foot	£180	85·00
163		2c. yellow	£110	55·00
		a. Without "SPECIMEN"	£1300	£700
		b. Small "2"	£110	55·00
164	**27**	1c. magenta	75·00	30·00
		a. Without "SPECIMEN"	£1500	£550
		b. "1" with foot	£275	£110
		c. Imperf between (horiz pair)	†	£10000
165		2c. yellow	95·00	50·00
		a. Bisected diagonally (1c.) (on cover)	†	—
		b. Without "SPECIMEN"	£1300	£700
		c. Small "2"	£180	£100

These stamps were perforated "SPECIMEN" as a precaution against fraud. The letters may be upright, inverted, reversed or inverted and reversed and stamps are known with "SPECIMEN" double or treble.

The 2c. is known printed double, one albino.

The 1c. and 2c. stamps were printed in separate sheets, but utilising the same clichés, these being altered according to the face value required. Two settings were used, common to both values:—

First setting. Four rows of three, T **26** being Nos. 5, 6, 7, 8, 11 and 12, and T **27** the remainder.

From this setting there were two printings of the 2c., but only one of the 1c.

Second setting. Six rows of two, T **26** being Nos. 3, 7, 8, 9, 11 and 12, and T **27** the remainder.

There were two printings of each value from this setting.

Se-tenant pairs are worth about 20% more.

The "1" with foot occurs on T **27** on No. 9 in the first setting and on T **26** on No. 7 in the first printing only of the second setting.

The small "2" appears on T **26** in the first setting on Nos. 6, 7, 8 and 12 in the first printing and on Nos. 7, 8 and 12 only in the second printing: in the second setting it comes on Nos. 3, 9 and 12 in the first printing and on Nos. 9, 11 and 12 in the second printing. On T **27** the variety occurs in the first setting on No. 9 of the second printing only and in the second setting on No. 10 in both printings.

(Typo D.L.R.)

1882. Wmk Crown CA. P 14.

170	**16**	1c. slate (27.1)	19·00	30
		w. Wmk inverted		
		x. Wmk reversed	—	£275
171		2c. orange (27.1)	60·00	15
		a. Value doubly printed	†	£9500
		w. Wmk inverted	£400	£325
		x. Wmk reversed	—	£325
172		4c. blue	£110	5·00
173		6c. brown	5·00	6·50
		w. Wmk inverted		
174		8c. rose	£140	40
		x. Wmk reversed		£300
170/4	Set of 5		£300	11·00
170s/4s Perf "SPECIMEN" Set of 5			£500	

I N L A N D

2 CENTS
R E V E N U E
(**28**)

4 CENTS **4 CENTS**
(*a*) (*b*)

Two types of "4"

6 **6**
(*c*) (*d*)

Two types of "6"

1888–89. T **16** (without lower label) optd "INLAND REVENUE", and surch with value as T **28**, by D.L.R. Wmk Crown CA. P 14.

175		1c. dull purple (8.89)	2·75	20
176		2c. dull purple (25.5.89)	3·25	20
177		3c. dull purple	2·25	20
178		4c. dull purple (a)	12·00	30
		a. Larger figure "4" (b)	21·00	6·50

179		6c. dull purple (c)	17·00	7·50
		a. Figure 6 with straight top (d)	21·00	10·00
180		8c. dull purple (8.89)	2·50	1·00
181		10c. dull purple	8·00	2·50
182		20c. dull purple	27·00	25·00
183		40c. dull purple	50·00	40·00
184		72c. dull purple (1.10.88)	80·00	65·00
185		$1 green (1.10.88)	£500	£600
186		$2 green (1.10.88)	£250	£300
187		$3 green (1.10.88)	£250	£300
188		$4 green (a) (1.10.88)	£600	£700
		a. Larger figure "4" (b)	£2250	£2750
189		$5 green (1.10.88)	£375	£425
175/89	Set of 15		£1900	£2000

Nos. 175/89 were surcharged in settings of 60 (6×10). No. 178a occurs on all stamps in the third vertical column, No. 179a in the fourth and sixth vertical columns and No. 188a in the second vertical column.

2		
(**29**)	**30**	(**31**)

1889 (6 June). No. 176 surch with T **29** in red by Official Gazette.

192		"2" on 2c. dull purple	7·00	1·00

The varieties with figure "2" inverted or double were made privately by a postal employee in Demerara.

1889 (Sept). Wmk Crown CA. P 14.

193	**30**	1c. dull purple and slate-grey	10·00	3·50
194		2c. dull purple and orange	8·00	10
		w. Wmk inverted	—	£300
195		4c. dull purple and ultramarine	4·50	3·75
		w. Wmk inverted	£300	
196		4c. dull purple and cobalt	21·00	3·75
197		6c. dull purple and brown	35·00	29·00
198		6c. dull purple and maroon	7·50	27·00
199		8c. dull purple and rose	23·00	4·00
		w. Wmk inverted	—	£300
200		12c. dull purple and bright purple	18·00	4·50
200a		12c. dull purple and mauve	8·50	4·00
201		24c. dull purple and green	6·00	3·75
202		48c. dull purple and orange-red	40·00	12·00
		w. Wmk inverted	£750	
		x. Wmk reversed	£700	
		xs. Ditto. Optd "SPECIMEN"	£275	
203		72c. dull purple and red-brown	28·00	50·00
204		72c. dull purple and yellow-brown	65·00	75·00
205		96c. dull purple and carmine	65·00	70·00
		x. Wmk reversed	£650	£650
206		96c. dull purple and rosine	75·00	80·00
193/205	Set of 10		£170	£150
193s/205s Optd "SPECIMEN" Set of 10			£200	

1890 (15 July). Stamps of 1888-89 surch locally "One Cent", in red, as in T **31**.

207		1c. on $1 (No. 185)	3·25	35
		a. Surch double	£275	£150
208		1c. on $2 (No. 186)	2·25	1·25
		a. Surch double	£110	
209		1c. on $3 (No. 187)	3·75	1·25
		a. Surch double	£150	
210		1c. on $4 (No. 188)	7·00	15·00
		a. Surch double	£140	
		b. Larger figure "4" (b)	15·00	48·00
207/10	Set of 4		14·50	16·00

1890–91. Colours changed. Wmk Crown CA. P 14

213	**30**	1c. sea-green (12.90)	1·00	10
		w. Wmk inverted	†	£225
214		5c. ultramarine (1.91)	5·50	10
215		8c. dull purple and greenish black (10.90)	12·00	3·00
213/15	Set of 3		17·00	3·00
213s/15s Optd "SPECIMEN" Set of 3			85·00	

32 Mount Roraima	**33** Kaieteur Falls

(Recess D.L.R.)

1898 (18 July). Queen Victoria's Jubilee. Wmk Crown CC (sideways* on T **32**). P 14.

216	**32**	1c. blue-black and carmine-red	9·50	2·25
		w. Wmk Crown to left of CC	11·00	2·50
		x. Wmk sideways reversed		
		y. Wmk sideways inverted and reversed		
217	**33**	2c. brown and indigo	35·00	4·25
		a. Imperf between (horiz pair)	£16000	
		w. Wmk inverted	£500	
		x. Wmk reversed	£425	£225
		y. Wmk inverted and reversed	£475	
218		2c. brown and blue	42·00	4·25
219	**32**	5c. deep green and sepia	55·00	6·00
		a. Imperf between (horiz pair)		
		w. Wmk Crown to left of CC	48·00	5·00
220	**33**	10c. blue-black and brown-red	27·00	30·00
		x. Wmk reversed	£650	
221	**32**	15c. red-brown and blue	32·00	27·00
		x. Wmk sideways reversed	£700	
216/21	Set of 5		£130	60·00
216s/21s Optd "SPECIMEN" Set of 5			£160	

*The normal sideways watermark on Type **32** shows Crown to right of CC, *as seen from the back of the stamp.*

A second plate was later used for the 1c. on which the lines of shading on the mountains in the background are strengthened, and those along the ridge show distinct from each other, whereas, in the original, they are more or less blurred. In the second plate the shading of the sky is less pronounced.

TWO CENTS.

(34)   Shaved "E"   **35**

(Surch at Printing Office of *The Daily Chronicle*, Georgetown)

1899 (24 Feb–15 June). Surch with T **34**.

222	**32**	2c. on 5c. (No. 219) (15.6)...............	4·50	4·25
		a. No stop after "CENTS".................	£180	£160
		b. Comma after "CENTS" (R. 7/2)...	75·00	
		c. "CINTS" (R. 4/1).........................	£180	£200
		d. Shaved "E" (R. 6/2).....................	70·00	70·00
		w. Wmk Crown to left of CC...........	5·50	4·25
223	**33**	2c. on 10c. (No. 220).......................	4·25	2·25
		a. No stop after "CENTS" (R. 5/5 or 2/9)...	22·00	60·00
		b. "GENTS" for "CENTS" (R. 5/7)......	65·00	£100
		c. Surch inverted............................	£700	£800
		ca. Surch inverted and stop omitted...	£7500	
		d. Shaved "E" (R. 4/2 or 3/8)............	42·00	
		x. Wmk reversed..............................	£200	
		y. Wmk inverted and reversed........	£350	
224	**32**	2c. on 15c. (No. 221).......................	4·75	1·25
		a. No stop after "CENTS" (R. 9/2)....	75·00	75·00
		b. Surch double..............................	£1000	£1300
		ba. Surch double, one without stop...	£12000	
		d. Surch inverted............................	£800	£950
		da. Surch inverted and stop omitted......................................	£10000	
		f. Shaved "E" (R. 6/2).....................	60·00	
		222/4 *Set of 3*	12·00	7·00

No. 222c was caused by damage to the first "E" of "CENTS" which developed during surcharging. The listing is for an example with only the upright stroke of the letter visible.

There were two settings of No. 223 with the no stop and shaved "E" varieties occurring on R. 5/5 and R. 4/2 of the first and on R. 2/9 and R. 3/8 of the second.

No. 224b occurred on the first five vertical columns of one sheet, the surcharges on the right hand vertical column being normal. Only two examples of No. 224ba are known.

There is only one known example of No. 224da.

1900–03. Wmk Crown CA. P. 14.

233	**30**	1c. grey-green (1902).......................	2·00	6·50
234		2c. dull purple and carmine............	3·25	30
		x. Wmk reversed..............................	—	£325
235		2c. dull purple and black/*red* (1901)...	3·25	10
		w. Wmk inverted..............................	—	£150
236		6c. grey-black and ultramarine (1902)...	7·50	11·00
237		48c. grey and purple-brown (1901)..	50·00	50·00
		a. Brownish grey and brown............	35·00	32·00
238		60c. green and rosine (1903)	70·00	£250
		233/8 *Set of 6*	£110	£275
		233s/8s Optd "SPECIMEN" *Set of 6*	£140	

No. 233 is a reissue of No. 213 in non-fugitive ink.

1905–07. Wmk Multiple Crown CA. Ordinary paper (1c. to 60c.) or chalk-surfaced paper (72, 96c.).

240	**30**	1c. grey-green.................................	10·00	30
		aw. Wmk inverted..............................	—	£250
		b. Chalk-surfaced paper...................	12·00	1·25
		c. Blue-green (1907).......................	16·00	2·75
241		2c. purple and black/*red*..............	21·00	10
		a. Chalk-surfaced paper...................	8·00	10
242		4c. dull purple and ultramarine......	19·00	24·00
		a. Chalk-surfaced paper...................	8·00	14·00
243		5c. dull purple and blue/*blue* (1.5.05)..	25·00	26·00
		a. Chalk-surfaced paper...................	3·50	8·00
		s. Optd "SPECIMEN"........................	27·00	
244		6c. grey-black and ultramarine.......	24·00	48·00
		aw. Wmk inverted..............................	£400	£350
		b. Chalk-surfaced paper...................	15·00	42·00
		bw. Wmk inverted..............................		
245		12c. dull and bright purple................	35·00	48·00
		a. Chalk-surfaced paper...................	22·00	50·00
246		24c. dull purple and green (1906)......	16·00	23·00
		a. Chalk-surfaced paper...................	3·75	6·50
247		48c. grey and purple-brown..............	38·00	48·00
		a. Chalk-surfaced paper...................	14·00	25·00
248		60c. green and rosine.......................	26·00	£110
		a. Chalk-surfaced paper...................	14·00	95·00
249		72c. purple and orange-brown (1907)...	42·00	75·00
250		96c. black and vermilion/*yellow* (20.11.05).....................................	35·00	50·00
		s. Optd "SPECIMEN"........................	40·00	
		240/50 *Set of 11*	£150	£325

1905. Optd "POSTAGE AND REVENUE". Wmk Multiple Crown CA. Chalk-surfaced paper. P. 14.

251	**35**	$2.40, green and violet....................	£190	£450
		s. Optd "SPECIMEN"........................	85·00	

No. 253

No. 253a

1907–10. Colours changed. Wmk Mult Crown CA. P 14.

253	**30**	2c. rose-red....................................	22·00	1·00
		a. Redrawn (1910)...........................	8·50	10

254		4c. brown and purple.......................	6·50	1·50
255		5c. ultramarine...............................	21·00	7·00
256		6c. grey and black............................	13·00	7·00
257		12c. orange and mauve.....................	4·00	6·00
		253a/7 *Set of 5*	48·00	19·00
		253s/7s Optd "SPECIMEN" *Set of 5*	£110	

In No. 253a the flag at the main truck is close to the mast, whereas in the original type it appears to be flying loose from halyards. There are two background lines above the value "2 CENTS" instead of three and the "S" is further away from the end of the tablet.

War Tax

37   (38)

(Typo D.L.R.)

1913–21. Wmk Mult Crown CA. Chalk-surfaced paper (4c. and 48c. to 96c.). P. 14.

259	**37**	1c. yellow-green.............................	5·50	80
		a. Blue-green (1917).......................	2·75	25
		ay. Wmk inverted and reversed.......	†	£375
		w. Wmk inverted..............................	†	£450
260		2c. carmine.....................................	1·50	10
		a. Scarlet (1916).............................	3·50	10
		b. Wmk sideways............................	†	£3000
		w. Wmk inverted..............................	†	£475
261		4c. brown and bright purple (1914)...	8·50	25
		aw. Wmk inverted..............................	£275	
		b. Deep brown and purple..............	3·75	25
262		5c. bright blue.................................	2·00	1·00
263		6c. grey and black............................	3·75	3·50
264		12c. orange and violet.......................	1·50	1·00
265		24c. dull purple and green (1915)......	3·25	6·00
266		48c. grey and purple-brown (1914)...	23·00	17·00
267		60c. green and rosine (1915)	17·00	65·00
268		72c. purple and orange-brown (1915)...	55·00	£100
269		96c. black and vermilion/*yellow* (1915)...	30·00	60·00
		a. White back (1913).......................	28·00	50·00
		b. On lemon (1916)..........................	20·00	50·00
		bs. Optd "SPECIMEN"........................	38·00	
		c. On pale yellow (1921).................	23·00	60·00
		cs. Optd "SPECIMEN"........................	40·00	
		259/69a *Set of 11*	£120	£225
		259s/69as Optd "SPECIMEN" *Set of 11*..	£250	

Examples of Nos. 267/9c are known with part strikes of forged postmarks of Grove dated "29 OCT 1909" and of Georgetown dated "30 OCT 1909".

1918 (4 Jan). No. 260a optd with T **38**, by *The Daily Chronicle*, Georgetown.

271	**37**	2c. scarlet.......................................	1·50	15

The relative position of the words "WAR" and "TAX" vary considerably in the sheet.

1921–27. Wmk Mult Script CA. Chalk-surfaced paper (24c. to 96c.). P. 14.

272	**37**	1c. green (1922)..............................	4·75	30
273		2c. rose-carmine.............................	7·00	20
		w. Wmk inverted..............................	†	£375
274		2c. bright violet (1923)....................	2·50	10
275		4c. brown and bright purple (1922)...	4·75	10
276		6c. bright blue (1922)......................	3·00	30
277		12c. orange and violet (1922)............	2·75	1·50
278		24c. dull purple and green................	2·00	4·50
279		48c. black and purple (1926).............	9·50	3·50
280		60c. green and rosine (1926).............	10·00	60·00
281		72c. dull purple and orange-brown (1923)...	38·00	80·00
282		96c. black and red/*yellow* (1927)	32·00	50·00
		272/82 *Set of 11*	£100	£180
		272s/82s Optd "SPECIMEN" *Set of 11* ...	£250	

39 Ploughing a Rice Field

40 Indian shooting Fish

41 Kaieteur Falls

42 Public buildings, Georgetown

(Recess Waterlow)

1931 (21 July). Centenary of County Union. T **39/42**. Wmk Mult Script CA. P. 12½.

283	**39**	1c. emerald-green............................	2·50	1·25
284	**40**	2c. brown..	2·00	10
285	**41**	4c. carmine.....................................	2·50	45
286	**42**	6c. blue..	2·50	1·25
287	**41**	$1 violet..	55·00	65·00
		283/7 *Set of 5*	60·00	65·00
		283s/7s Perf "SPECIMEN" *Set of 5*	£140	

---

43 Ploughing a Rice Field

44 Gold Mining

45 Shooting logs over falls

46 Stabroek Market

47 Sugar canes in punts

48 Forest road

49 *Victoria Regia* Lilies

50 Mount Roraima

51 Sir Walter Raleigh and his son

52 Botanical Gardens

(Recess Waterlow)

1934 (1 Oct)–**51**. T **40** (without dates at top of frame) and **43/52**. Wmk Mult Script CA (sideways on horiz designs). P. 12½.

288	**43**	1c. green...	60	2·00
289	**40**	2c. red-brown..................................	1·50	1·75
290	**44**	3c. scarlet.......................................	30	10
		aa. Wmk error. Crown missing..........	£4000	£2500
		a. Perf 12½×13½ (30.12.43)............	1·00	1·00
		b. Perf 13×14 (28.4.49)...................	1·75	70
291	**41**	4c. slate-violet................................	2·00	3·50
		a. Imperf between (vert pair)	†	£40000
		b. Imperf horiz (vert pair)...............	£21000	£22000
292	**45**	6c. deep ultramarine.......................	7·50	7·00
293	**46**	12c. red-orange.................................	45	20
		a. Perf 14×13 (16.4.51)...................	50	1·00
294	**47**	24c. purple.......................................	3·75	14·00
295	**48**	48c. black...	12·00	10·00
296	**49**	50c. green...	17·00	24·00
297	**49**	60c. red-brown..................................	28·00	32·00
298	**50**	72c. purple.......................................	2·00	3·00
299	**51**	96c. black...	40·00	45·00
300	**52**	$1 bright violet...............................	50·00	50·00
		288/300 *Set of 13*	£140	£170
		288s/300s Perf "SPECIMEN" *Set of 13* ...	£250	

Examples of Nos. 295/300 are known with forged Georgetown postmarks dated "24 JY 31" or "6 MY 35".

1935 (6 May). Silver Jubilee. As Nos. 91/4 of Antigua.

301		2c. ultramarine and grey.................	40	20
		f. Diagonal line by turret................	50·00	40·00
		g. Dot to left of chapel...................	—	£180
		h. Dot by flagstaff..........................	£130	£130
		i. Dash by turret.............................	£200	
302		6c. brown and deep blue.................	2·00	5·00
		f. Diagonal line by turret................	£120	
		g. Dot to left of chapel...................	£140	£190
		h. Dot by flagstaff..........................	£180	
303		12c. green and indigo........................	9·50	9·50
		f. Diagonal line by turret................	£160	£180
		g. Dot to left of chapel...................	£350	
		h. Dot by flagstaff..........................	£300	£325
		i. Dash by turret.............................	£375	
304		24c. slate and purple........................	15·00	22·00
		h. Dot by flagstaff..........................	£325	£400
		i. Dash by turret.............................	£450	£550
		301/4 *Set of 4*	24·00	32·00
		301s/4s Perf "SPECIMEN" *Set of 4*	£130	

For illustrations of plate varieties see Omnibus section following Zanzibar.

1937 (12 May). Coronation. As Nos. 95/7 of Antigua, but ptd by D.L.R. P 14.

305		2c. yellow-brown.............................	15	10
306		4c. carmine.....................................	60	1·00
307		6c. bright blue.................................	75	2·00
		305/7 *Set of 3*	1·40	2·75
		305s/7s Perf "SPECIMEN" *Set of 3*	£120	

53 South America

54 *Victoria Regia*, water-lilies

(Recess Waterlow)

1938 (1 Feb)–**52.** As earlier types but with portrait of King George VI as in T **53/4**. Wmk Mult Script CA. P 12½

308	43	1c. yellow-green	23·00	1·50
		a. Green (1940)	30	10
		ab. "A" of "CA" missing from Wmk	—	£1200
		b. Perf 14×13 (1949)	1·50	80
309	41	2c. slate-violet	60	10
		a. Perf 13×14 (28.4.49)	55	10
310	53	4c. scarlet and black	70	30
		a. Imperf horiz (vert pair)	£40000	£32000
		b. Perf 13×14 (1952)	1·50	15
311	40	6c. deep ultramarine	2·75	10
		a. Perf 13×14 (24.10.49)	3·00	30
312	47	24c. blue-green	26·00	10·00
		a. Wmk sideways	4·25	
313	41	36c. bright violet (7.3.38)	7·00	20
		a. Perf 13×14 (13.12.51)	3·00	30
314	48	48c. orange	2·25	50
		a. Perf 14×13 (8.5.51*)	2·00	3·00
315	45	60c. red-brown	22·00	9·50
316	51	96c. purple	17·00	2·75
		a. Perf 12½×13½ (1944)	17·00	17·00
		b. Perf 13×14 (8.2.51)	6·50	13·00
317	52	$1 bright violet	28·00	35
		a. Perf 14×13 (1951)	£550	£600
318	50	$2 purple (11.6.45)	22·00	27·00
		a. Perf 14×13 (9.8.50)	27·00	42·00
319	54	$3 red-brown (2.7.45)	38·00	45·00
		a. Bright red-brown (12.46)	60·00	32·00
		b. Perf 14×13. Red-brown (29.10.52)	42·00	50·00
308a/19 Set of 12			£110	65·00
308s/19s Perf "SPECIMEN" Set of 12			£375	

*Earliest known postmark date.

1946 (21 Oct). Victory. As Nos. 110/11 of Antigua.

320	3c. carmine	25	40
321	6c. blue	75	85
320s/1s Perf "SPECIMEN" Set of 2		£100	

1948 (20 Dec). Royal Silver Wedding. As Nos. 112/13 of Antigua, but $3 in recess.

322	3c. scarlet	10	40
323	$3 red-brown	22·00	29·00

1949 (10 Oct). 75th Anniv of Universal Postal Union. As Nos. 114/17 of Antigua.

324	4c. carmine	20	60
325	6c. deep blue	1·75	2·00
326	12c. orange	30	75
327	24c. blue-green	30	70
324/7 Set of 4		2·25	3·50

1951 (16 Feb). University College of B.W.I. As Nos. 118/19 of Antigua.

328	3c. black and carmine	50	50
329	6c. black and blue	50	65

1953 (2 June). Coronation. As No. 120 of Antigua.

330	4c. black and scarlet	60	10

55 GPO, Georgetown

56 Botanical Gardens

57 *Victoria Regia* Water-lilies

58 Amerindian shooting fish

59 Map of Caribbean

60 Rice combine harvester

61 Sugar cane entering factory

62 Felling Greenheart

63 Mining for bauxite

64 Mount Roraima

65 Kaieteur Falls

66 Arapaima

67 Channel-billed Toucan

68 Dredging gold

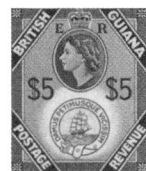

69 Arms of British Guiana

3c. Green flaw on lily below second "I" of "BRITISH" resembling weed (R. 3/10)

3c. Green spot on claw of right-hand bird appearing as clubbed foot (R. 4/1)

(Centre litho, frame recess ($1); recess (others). Waterlow (until 1961), then D.L.R.)

1954 (1 Dec)–**63.** T **55/69**. Wmk Mult Script CA. P 12½×13* (horiz) or 13 (vert).

331	55	1c. black	20	10
332	56	2c. myrtle-green	20	10
333	57	3c. brown-olive and red-brown	4·00	20
		a. "Weed" flaw	65·00	
		b. "Clubbed foot"	65·00	
		w. Wmk inverted		
334	58	4c. violet	1·75	10
		a. D.L.R. ptg (5.12.61)	13·00	4·00
		ab. Deep violet (3.1.63)	25·00	4·50
335	59	5c. scarlet and black	1·75	10
		w. Wmk inverted		
336	60	6c. yellow-green	1·50	10
		a. D.L.R. ptg. Green (22.5.62)	4·75	5·00
337	61	8c. ultramarine	1·50	20
		a. D.L.R. ptg. Blue (19.9.61)	20·00	2·50
338	62	12c. black and reddish brown	1·50	40
		a. Black and light brown (13.6.56)	1·50	10
		b. D.L.R. ptg. Black and brown (11.7.61)	40·00	4·25
339	63	24c. black and brownish orange	5·00	10
		a. Black and orange (13.6.56)	9·00	10
340	64	36c. rose-carmine and black	12·00	1·25
		w. Wmk inverted		
341	65	48c. ultramarine and brown-lake	2·00	1·00
		a. Bright ultramarine and pale brown-lake (13.6.56)	1·75	1·00
		ab. D.L.R. ptg (19.9.61)	42·00	28·00
342	66	72c. carmine and emerald	22·00	2·75
		a. D.L.R. ptg (17.7.62)	18·00	25·00
343	67	$1 pink. yellow. green and black	20·00	4·00
344	68	$2 deep mauve	35·00	9·00
		a. D.L.R. ptg. Reddish mauve (11.7.61)	75·00	15·00
345	69	$5 ultramarine and black	27·00	38·00
		a. D.L.R. ptg (19.9.61)	50·00	50·00
331/45 Set of 15			£110	50·00

On the Waterlow printings there is *always* a single wide-tooth perforation on each side at the top of the stamps. For the De La Rue stamps these teeth can occur *either* at the top or the bottom and, where not distinguishable by shade, can be identified by the quality of the printing, which is characterised by finer lines of shading and less intense colour than the Waterlow versions. Those listed De La Rue printings, which do not differ in shade, are for examples with the wide-tooth perforation at the bottom.

*All the Waterlow printings and early De La Rue printings of the horizontal designs are perforated 12.3×12.8, but De La Rue printings from 22 May 1962 (including those on the Block CA watermark) are perf 12.3×12.6.

The 1c. and 2c., printed by Waterlow, exist in coils constructed from normal sheets.

See also Nos. 354/65.

SELF-GOVERNMENT

70

71 Weightlifting

(Photo Harrison)

1961 (23 Oct). History and Culture Week. W w **12**. P 14½×14.

346	70	5c. sepia and orange-red	20	10
347		6c. sepia and blue-green	20	15
348		30c. sepia and yellow-orange	45	45
346/8 Set of 3			75	60

1963 (14 July). Freedom from Hunger. As No. 146 of Antigua.

349	20c. reddish violet	30	60

1963 (2 Sept). Red Cross Centenary. As Nos. 147/8 of Antigua.

350	5c. red and black	20	20
351	20c. red and blue	55	35

1963–65. As Nos. 333/44, but wmk w **12**.

354	57	3c. brown-olive and red-brown (12.65)	5·00	2·00
356	59	5c. scarlet and black (28.5.64)	1·25	10
		w. Wmk inverted		
359	62	12c. black and yellowish brown (6.10.64)	2·50	10
360	63	24c. black and bright orange (10.12.63)	4·00	10
361	64	36c. rose-carmine and black (10.12.63)	1·75	60
362	65	48c. bright ultramarine and Venetian red (25.11.63)	2·75	1·50
		w. Wmk inverted		
363	66	72c. carmine and emerald (25.11.63)	5·00	25·00
364	67	$1 pink, yellow, green and black (10.12.63)	10·00	1·00
365	68	$2 reddish mauve (10.12.63)	17·00	14·00
354/65 Set of 9			45·00	40·00

There was no London release of No. 354.

The 5c. exists in coils constructed from normal sheets.

For 1c. value with wmk w **12**, see Guyana No. 429a (error opt omitted).

(Photo D.L.R.)

1964 (1 Oct). Olympic Games, Tokyo. W w **12**. P 13×13½.

367	71	5c. orange	10	10
368		8c. blue	15	35
369		25c. magenta	25	40
367/9 Set of 3			45	75

1965 (17 May). ITU Centenary. As Nos. 166/7 of Antigua.

370	5c. emerald and yellow-olive	10	15
371	25c. light blue and magenta	20	15

1965 (25 Oct). International Co-operation Year. As Nos. 168/9 of Antigua.

372	5c. reddish purple and turquoise-green	15	10
373	25c. deep bluish green and lavender	30	20

72 St. George's Cathedral, Georgetown

(Des Jennifer Toombs, Photo Harrison)

1966 (24 Jan). Churchill Commemoration. W w **12**. P 14×14½.

374	72	5c. black, crimson and gold	1·25	10
375		25c. black, blue and gold	2·75	50

1966 (3 Feb). Royal Visit. As Nos. 174/5 of Antigua.

376	3c. black and ultramarine	75	15
377	25c. black and magenta	1·50	60

STAMP BOOKLETS

1909 (14 June). Black on pink cover without face value. Stapled.

SB1	49c. booklet containing 12×1c. and 18×2c. (Nos. 252/3) in blocks of 6	£2750

1923. Black on pink cover without face value. Stapled.

SB2	30c. booklet containing 6×1c. and 12×2c. (Nos. 272, 274) in blocks of 6.	

1923. Black on pink without face value. Stapled.

SB3	48c. booklet containing 12×1c. and 18×2c. (Nos. 272, 274) in blocks of 6.	£2000
	a. With face value on front cover.	

1923. Black on red cover without face value. Stapled.

SB4	72c. booklet containing 12×1c., 6×2c. and 12×4c. (Nos. 272, 274/5) in blocks of 6	£3000

1934. Black on orange cover. Stitched.
SB5   24c. booklet containing 8×1c. and 8×2c.
          (Nos. 288/9) in blocks of 4 ....

1934. Black on orange cover. Stitched.
SB6   36c. booklet containing 4×1c., 8×2c. and 4×4c.
          (Nos. 288/9, 291) in blocks of 4 ....

1938. Black on orange cover. Stitched.
SB7   36c. booklet containing 4×1c., 8×2c. and 4×4c.
          (Nos. 308/10) in blocks of 4 .... £850

1944. Black on red cover. Stitched.
SB8   24c. booklet containing 8×1c. and 8×2c.
          (Nos. 308a/9) in blocks of 4 .... £600

1945–49. Black on red cover. Stitched.
SB9   24c. booklet containing 1c., 2c. and 3c., each in
          block of 4
        a. Containing Nos. 290, 308a, 309 .... 70·00
        b. Containing Nos. 290, 308a, 309a .... 70·00
        c. Containing Nos. 290a, 308a, 309 .... 75·00
        d. Containing Nos. 290b, 308a, 309 .... 95·00
        e. Containing Nos. 290b, 308a, 309a .... 90·00
        f. Containing Nos. 290b, 308b, 309a £110

POSTAGE DUE STAMPS

D **1**

(Typo D.L.R.)

1940 (Mar)**–55.** Wmk Mult Script CA. Chalk-surfaced paper (4c.).
P 14.
D1   D **1**   1c. green .... 6·50   15·00
        a. Chalk-surfaced paper. *Deep*
          green, (30.4.52) .... 2·00   22·00
        ab. W **9a** (Crown missing) £600
        ac. W **9b** (St. Edward's Crown) £150
D2   2c. black .... 28·00   2·00
        a. Chalk-surfaced paper (30.4.52).. 4·50   12·00
        ab. W **9a** (Crown missing) £425
        ac. W **9b** (St. Edward's Crown) £160
D3   4c. bright blue (1.5.52) 40   14·00
        a. W **9a** (Crown missing) £400
        b. W **9b** (St. Edward's Crown) £160
D4   12c. scarlet .... 38·00   7·50
        a. Chalk-surfaced paper (19.7.55)... 20·00   48·00
D1, D2, D4 *Set of 3* .... 65·00   22·00
D1a/4a *Set of 4* .... 24·00   85·00
D1s, D2s and D4s Perf "SPECIMEN" *Set of 3* £100

OFFICIAL STAMPS

OFFICIAL   OFFICIAL   OFFICIAL
  (O **1**)   (O **1a**)   (O **2**)

1875. Optd with Type O **1** (1c.) or O **1a** (others) by litho. P 10.
O1   **8**   1c. black (R.) .... 75·00   27·00
        a. Imperf between (horiz pair)..... †   £30000
O2   2c. orange .... £475   14·00
O3   8c. rose £375   150
O4   **7**   12c. brownish purple £3500   £500
O5   **9**   24c. green £2750   £275
    Two types of the word "OFFICIAL" are found on each value. On the
1c. the word is either 16 or 17 mm long. On the other values the chief
difference is in the shape and position of the letter "o" in "OFFICIAL". In
one case the "o" is upright, in the other it slants to the left.

1877. Optd with Type O **2** by typo. Wmk Crown CC. P 14.
O6   **16**   1c. slate .... £375   65·00
        a. Imperf between (vert pair) .... †   £30000
O7   2c. orange .... £180   15·00
O8   4c. blue .... £150   28·00
O9   6c. brown £5500   £600
O10   8c. rose £2000   £450

Prepared for use, but not issued.
O11   **16**   12c. pale violet £1800
O12   24c. green £2250

The "OFFICIAL" overprints have been extensively forged.
The use of Official stamps was discontinued in June 1878.
British Guiana became independent as Guyana on 25 May 1966.

British Honduras

It is recorded that the first local post office was established by the
inhabitants in 1809, but Belize did not become a regular packet port
of call until December 1829. The post office came under the control
of the British GPO in April 1844 and the stamps of Great Britain were
supplied for use on overseas mail from May 1858.
    The colonial authorities took over the postal service on 1 April 1860,
the Great Britain stamps being withdrawn at the end of the month.
There was no inland postal service until 1862.
    For illustrations of the handstamp and postmark types see BRITISH
POST OFFICES ABROAD notes, following GREAT BRITAIN.

BELIZE
CROWNED-CIRCLE HANDSTAMPS
CC1   CC **1** BELIZE (R.) (13.11.1841) .... *Price on cover* £4000

Stamps of GREAT BRITAIN cancelled "A 06" as Type **2**.
1858–60.
Z1   1d. rose-red (1857), *perf* 14 .... £1200
Z2   4d. rose (1857) £425
Z3   6d. lilac (1856) £375
Z4   1s. green (1856) £2500

PRICES FOR STAMPS ON COVER TO 1945	
Nos. 1/4	from × 50
Nos. 5/16	from × 30
Nos. 17/22	from × 20
Nos. 23/6	from × 10
Nos. 27/30	from × 15
Nos. 35/42	from × 20
Nos. 43/4	from × 30
Nos. 49/50	from × 25
Nos. 51/69	from × 15
Nos. 80/100	from × 6
Nos. 101/10	from × 5
Nos. 111/20	from × 15
Nos. 121/2	from × 8
No. 123	from × 10
Nos. 124/37	from × 6
Nos. 138/42	from × 10
Nos. 143/9	from × 8
Nos. 150/61	from × 5
Nos. D1/3	from × 30

CROWN COLONY

1

(Typo D.L.R.)

1865 (1 Dec). No wmk. P 14.
1   **1**   1d. pale blue .... 70·00   65·00
        a. Imperf between (pair) ....
2   1d. blue .... £100   75·00
3   6d. rose £425   £170
4   1s. green £400   £130
        a. In horiz pair with 6d. £50000
        b. In vert pair with 1d. £65000
    In the first printing all three values were printed in the same
sheet separated by horizontal and vertical gutter margins. The sheet
comprised two panes of 60 of the 1d. at the top with a pane of 60
of the 1s. at bottom left and another of 6d. at bottom right. Copies
of 1d. *se-tenant* with the 6d. are not known. There were two later
printings of the 1d. but they were in sheets without the 6d. and 1s.

1872–79. Wmk Crown CC.
        (a) P 12½
5   **1**   1d. pale blue .... 95·00   35·00
        w. Wmk inverted £350
        y. Wmk inverted and reversed....... £450
6   1d. deep blue (1874) .... £120   30·00
7   3d. red-brown (1874) .... £170   80·00
8   3d. chocolate (1874) £190   £100
9   6d. rose .... £450   55·00
9a   6d. bright rose-carmine (1874) ...... £600   65·00
10   1s. green .... £700   48·00
10a   1s. deep green (1874) .... £550   30·00
        b. Imperf between (horiz pair)....... †   £26000
        w. Wmk inverted .... —   £250
        (b) P 14 (1877–79)
11   **1**   1d. pale blue (1878) .... 85·00   32·00
12   1d. blue (1878) .... 90·00   26·00
        a. Imperf between (horiz strip of
          3) £28000
13   3d. chestnut .... £170   32·00
14   4d. mauve (1879) .... £300   9·50
        x. Wmk reversed ....
15   6d. rose (1878) £475   £200
        w. Wmk inverted .... —   £550
16   1s. green .... £325   14·00
        a. Imperf between (pair) ....

1882–87. Wmk Crown CA. P 14.
17   **1**   1d. blue (4.84) .... 75·00   25·00
18   1d. rose (1884) .... 23·00   16·00
        a. Bisected (½d.) (*on cover*) .... †   —
        s. Optd "SPECIMEN" £275
19   1d. carmine (1887) .... 60·00   32·00
20   4d. mauve (7.82) .... 95·00   4·75
        w. Wmk inverted .... —   £200
21   6d. yellow (1885) £275   £225
22   1s. grey (1.87) £250   £160
        s. Optd "SPECIMEN" .... 75·00

(New Currency. 100 cents = 1 British Honduras dollar)

2   **2**   **2**
CENTS   TWO   CENTS
  (2)   (3)   (4)

1888 (1 Jan). Stamps of 1872–79 (wmk Crown CC), surch locally
as T **2**.
        (a) P 12½
23   **1**   2c. on 6d. rose £350   £275
24   3c. on 3d. chocolate £18000   £6000
        (b) P 14
25   **1**   2c. on 6d. rose £190   £170
        a. Surch double £2500
        b. Bisected (1c.) (*on cover*) .... †   £300
        c. Slanting "2" with curved foot.... £3250
        w. Wmk inverted .... —   £650
26   3c. on 3d. chestnut £110   £110
    There are very dangerous forgeries of these surcharges, particularly
of No. 24.
    No. 25c may be a trial.

1888. Stamps of 1882–87 (wmk Crown CA), surch locally as T **2**,
P 14.
27   **1**   2c. on 1d. rose .... 14·00   48·00
        a. Surch inverted £7500   £5500
        b. Surch double £900   £900
        c. Bisected (1c.) (*on cover*) .... †   £200
28   10c. on 4d. mauve .... 70·00   19·00
29   20c. on 6d. yellow .... 30·00   50·00
30   50c. on 1s. grey £475   £700
        a. Error. "5" for "50" £17000
    Various settings were used for the surcharges on Nos. 23/30, the
most common of which was of 36 (6×6) impressions. For No. 29 this
setting was so applied that an albino surcharge occurs in the margin
above each stamp in the first horizontal row.
    The same setting was subsequently amended, by altering the "2"
to "1", to surcharge the 4d. value. As this was in sheets of 30 it was only
necessary to alter the values on the bottom five rows of the setting.
Albino surcharges once again occur in the top margin of the sheet,
but, as the type in the first horizontal row remained unaltered, these
read "20 CENTS" rather than the "10 CENTS" on the actual stamps.

1888 (Mar). No. 30 further surch locally with T **3**.
35   **1**   "TWO" on 50c. on 1s. grey (R.) .... 60·00   £100
        a. Bisected (1c.) (*on cover*) .... †   £300
        b. Surch in black £16000   £15000
        c. Surch double (R.+Blk.) £16000   £16000

1888 (July)**–91.** Surch in London as T **4.** Wmk Crown CA. P 14.
36   **1**   1c. on 1d. dull green (?12.91) ..... 1·00   1·50
37   2c. on 1d. carmine 75   2·25
        a. Bisected (1c.) (*on cover*) .... †   £110
        w. Wmk inverted £325
38   3c. on 3d. red-brown .... 6·00   1·40
39   6c. on 3d. ultramarine (?4.91) ..... 7·00   26·00
40   10c. on 4d. mauve .... 27·00   50
        a. Surch double £3250
41   20c. on 6d. yellow (2.89) .... 19·00   14·00
42   50c. on 1s. grey (11.88) .... 38·00   85·00
36/42 *Set of 7* .... 85·00   £110
36s/42s Optd "SPECIMEN" *Set of 7* £375

CENTS
  (5)

FIVE   **15**
  (6)   (7)

1891. Stamps of 1888–9 surch locally.
        *(a) With T **5** (May)*
43   **1**   6c. on 10c. on 4d. mauve (R.) ...... 1·50   2·25
        a. "6" and bar inverted £600   £600
        b. "6" only inverted .... †   £6500
44   6c. on 10c. on 4d. mauve (Blk.) ..... 3·50   1·50
        a. "6" and bar inverted £4500   £1100
        b. "6" only inverted .... †   £6500
    Of variety (b) only six copies of each can exist, as one of each of
these errors came in the first six sheets, and the mistake was then
corrected. Of variety (a) more copies exist.
    Essays are known with "SIX" in place of "6" both with and without
bars (*price* £140 *and* £550 *respectively*). Although not issued we
mention them, as three contemporary covers franked with them
are known.
        *(b) With T **6/7** (23 Oct)*
49   **1**   5c. on 3c. on 3d. red-brown .... 1·25   1·40
        a. Wide space between "I" and "V".. 60·00   75·00
        b. "FIVE" and bar double £375   £425
50   15c. on 6c. on 3d. ultramarine (R.) .. 18·00   28·00

8   **9**

10   **11**

| Normal | Malformed "S" | Repaired "S" |

The Malformed and Repaired "S" occur on R. 7/3 of the left pane from Key Plate 2.

(Typo D.L.R.)

1891 (July)–**1901**. Wmk Crown CA. P 14.

51	8	1c. dull green (4.95)	2·75	2·00
		a. Malformed "S"	£400	£250
		w. Wmk inverted	†	£300
52		2c. carmine-rose	4·25	20
		a. Malformed "S"	£450	£180
		b. Repaired "S"	£375	£150
53		3c. brown	10·00	4·75
		w. Wmk inverted	£300	
54		5c. ultramarine (4.95)	12·00	1·50
		a. Malformed "S"	£650	£225
55	11	5c. grey-black and ultramarine/*blue* (10.00)	23·00	4·00
56	8	6c. ultramarine	15·00	2·00
57	9	10c. mauve and green (4.95)	14·00	21·00
58	10	10c. dull purple and green (1901)	12·00	11·00
59	9	12c. reddish lilac and green	2·50	4·25
60		24c. yellow and blue	7·00	25·00
		a. *Orange and blue*	30·00	55·00
61		25c. red-brown and green (3.98)	95·00	£150
62	10	50c. green and carmine (3.98)	30·00	75·00
63	11	$1 green and carmine (12.99)	95·00	£160
64		$2 green and ultramarine (12.99)	£150	£225
65		$5 green and black (12.99)	£325	£475
51/65 *Set of 15*			£700	£1000
51s/65s Optd "SPECIMEN" *Set of 15*			£400	

Most values are known with a forged Belize postmark dated "OC 23 09".

1899 (1 July). Optd "REVENUE" 12 mm long.

66	8	5c. ultramarine	28·00	3·25
		a. "BEVENUE"	£180	£180
		b. Malformed "S" at right	£700	£350
		d. Opt 11 mm long	35·00	12·00
67	9	10c. mauve and green	21·00	24·00
		a. "BEVENUE"	£350	£425
		b. "REVENU"	£700	
		c. Opt 11 mm long	25·00	50·00
		cb. "REVENU"	£800	£900
68		25c. red-brown and green	5·00	42·00
		a. "BEVENUE"	£200	£425
		b. "REVE UE"	£2500	
		c. Repaired "S" at right	£750	
		d. Opt 11 mm long	6·50	65·00
69	1	50c. on 1s. grey	£275	£425
		a. "BEVENUE"	£5500	£6500
		c. Opt 11 mm long	£425	£650

Two minor varieties, a small "U" and a tall, narrow "U" are found in the word "REVENUE".

The overprint setting of 60 (6×10) contained 43 examples of the 12 mm size and 17 of the 11 mm. The smaller size overprints occur on R. 8/1, R. 8/3 to 6 and on all positions in Rows 9 and 10.

The "BEVENUE" error appears on R. 6/4 and, it is believed, "REVE UE" comes from R. 6/6. Both occur on parts of the printing only. The missing "E" developed during the overprinting and damage to this letter can be observed on at least eight positions in the setting.

| 14 | 15 |

(Typo D.L.R.)

1902 (10 Oct)–**04**. Wmk Crown CA. P 14.

80	14	1c. grey-green and green (28.4.04)	2·75	28·00
81		2c. purple and black/*red* (18.3.03)	3·25	25
		w. Wmk inverted	£200	£110
82		5c. grey-black and blue/*blue*	21·00	30
		w. Wmk inverted	£170	
83	15	20c. dull and bright purple (28.4.04)	15·00	19·00
80/3 *Set of 4*			38·00	42·00
80s/3s Optd "SPECIMEN" *Set of 4*			80·00	

1904 (Dec)–**07**. Wmk Mult Crown CA. Ordinary paper (1, 2c.) or chalk-surfaced paper (others). P 14.

84	14	1c. grey-green and green (8.05)	21·00	21·00
		a. Chalk-surfaced paper (1906)	5·00	2·50
85		2c. purple and black/*red*	3·50	30
		a. Chalk-surfaced paper (1906)	3·50	20
86		5c. grey-black and blue/*blue* (5.2.06)	2·50	20
87	15	10c. dull purple and emerald-green (20.9.07)	4·00	20·00
89		25c. dull purple and orange (20.9.07)	12·00	60·00
90		50c. grey-green and carmine (20.9.07)	35·00	£110
91	14	$1 grey-green and carmine (20.9.07)	80·00	£130
92		$2 grey-green and blue (20.9.07)	£160	£275
93		$5 grey-green and black (20.9.07)	£375	£450
84a/93 *Set of 9*			£600	£900
87s/93s Optd "SPECIMEN" *Set of 6*			£250	

Examples of most values are known showing a forged Belize postmark dated "OC 23 09".

1908 (7 Dec)–**11**. Colours changed. Wmk Mult Crown CA. Chalk-surfaced paper (25c.). P 14.

95	14	1c. blue-green (1.7.10)	23·00	50
96		2c. carmine	19·00	10
		w. Wmk inverted		
97		5c. ultramarine (1.6.09)	4·00	10
100	15	25c. black/*green* (14.10.11)	9·00	48·00
95/100 *Set of 4*			50·00	48·00
96s/100s Optd "SPECIMEN" *Set of 3*			95·00	

  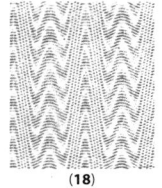

| 16 | 17 | (18) |

1913–21. Wmk Mult Crown CA. Chalk-surfaced paper (10c. to $5). P 14.

101	16	1c. blue-green	6·50	1·50
		a. *Yellow-green* (13.3.17)	13·00	2·75
		w. Wmk inverted	£275	
102		2c. red	7·00	1·00
		a. *Bright scarlet* (1915)	12·00	1·00
		b. *Dull scarlet* (8.17)	8·50	1·50
		c. *Red/bluish*	15·00	8·00
		w. Wmk inverted	†	£400
103		3c. orange (16.4.17)	2·50	20
104		5c. bright blue	4·00	85
105	17	10c. dull purple and yellow-green	7·50	6·50
		a. *Dull purple and bright green* (1917)	26·00	25·00
		ax. *Wmk reversed*	£550	
106		25c. black/*green*	2·00	12·00
		a. *On blue-green, olive back* (8.17)	5·00	11·00
		b. *On emerald back* (1921)	2·00	35·00
107		50c. purple and blue/*blue*	32·00	16·00
108	16	$1 black and carmine	35·00	70·00
109		$2 purple and green	90·00	£130
110		$5 purple and black/*red*	£275	£350
101/10 *Set of 10*			£400	£500
101s/10s Optd "SPECIMEN" *Set of 10*			£275	

1915–16. Optd with T **18**, in violet.

111	16	1c. green (30.12.15)	4·75	25·00
		a. *Yellow-green* (6.6.16)	50	22·00
112		2c. scarlet (3.11.15)	3·50	50
113		5c. bright blue (29.7.15)	30	6·00
111s/13s Optd "SPECIMEN" *Set of 3*			£140	

These stamps were shipped early in the 1914–18 war, and were thus overprinted, so that if seized by the enemy, they could be distinguished and rendered invalid.

| WAR | WAR | 21 |
| (19) | (20) | |

1916 (23 Aug). No. 111 optd locally with T **19**.

114	16	1c. green	10	3·00
		a. Opt inverted	£300	£350

1917–18. Nos. 101 and 103 optd with T **19**.

116	16	1c. blue-green (6.17)	1·50	9·00
		aw. Wmk inverted	£250	
		ax. Wmk reversed	£300	
		b. *Yellow-green* (3.3.17)	20	5·00
118		3c. orange (12.3.18)	5·50	18·00
		a. Opt double	£400	

1918. Nos. 101 and 103 optd with T **20**.

119	16	1c. blue-green (25.4.18)	20	40
		a. *Yellow-green*	4·50	6·50
120		3c. orange (9.18)	80	4·25
		y. Wmk inverted and reversed	£225	
119s/20s Optd "SPECIMEN" *Set of 2*			£120	

(Recess D.L.R.)

1921 (28 Apr). Peace Commemoration. Wmk Mult Crown CA (sideways). P 14.

121	21	2c. rose-red	6·50	50
		a. "C" of "CA" missing from wmk	£400	
		s. Optd "SPECIMEN"	60·00	

1921 (26 Nov). Wmk Mult Script CA. P 14.

122	16	1c. green	9·50	13·00
		s. Optd "SPECIMEN"	55·00	

1922 (4 Jan). As T **21** but with words "PEACE" omitted. Wmk Mult Script CA (sideways). P 14.

123		4c. slate	14·00	50
		s. Optd "SPECIMEN"	50·00	

| 22 | (23) |

(Typo D.L.R.)

1922 (1 Aug)–**33**. Ordinary paper (1c. to 5c.) or chalk-surfaced paper (others). P 14.

(a) Wmk Mult Crown CA

124	22	25c. black/*emerald*	9·50	50·00
125		$5 purple and black/*red* (1.10.24)	£225	£300

(b) Wmk Mult Script CA

126	22	1c. green (2.1.29)	20·00	6·50
127		2c. brown (1.3.23)	1·50	1·50
128		2c. rose-carmine (10.12.26)	12·00	1·50
129		3c. orange (1933)	38·00	4·00
130		4c. grey (1.10.29)	22·00	85
131		5c. ultramarine	1·75	55
		a. *Milky blue* (1923)	5·50	4·25
132		10c. dull purple and sage-green (1.12.22)	4·25	30
133		25c. black/*emerald* (1.10.24)	3·25	8·50
134		50c. purple and blue/*blue* (1.11.23)	8·00	16·00
136		$1 black and scarlet (2.1.25)	23·00	38·00
137		$2 yellow-green and bright purple	50·00	£130
124/37 *Set of 13*			£350	£500
124s/37s Optd or Perf (1c., 3c., 4c.) "SPECIMEN" *Set of 13*			£375	

1932 (2 May). Belize Relief Fund. Surch as T **23**. Wmk Mult Script CA. P 14.

138	22	1c.+1c. green	3·00	17·00
139		2c.+2c. rose-carmine	3·00	17·00
140		3c.+3c. orange	3·50	35·00
141		4c.+4c. grey (R.)	18·00	38·00
142		5c.+5c. ultramarine	9·50	14·00
138/42 *Set of 5*			32·00	£110
138s/42s Perf "SPECIMEN" *Set of 5*			£150	

1935 (6 May). Silver Jubilee. As Nos. 91/4 of Antigua, but ptd by B.W. & Co. P 11×12.

143		3c. ultramarine and grey-black	2·25	1·00
		a. Extra flagstaff	80·00	£100
		b. Short extra flagstaff	£140	£170
		c. Lightning conductor	90·00	£110
		d. Flagstaff on right-hand turret	£250	
		e. Double flagstaff	£275	
144		4c. green and indigo	5·00	4·75
		a. Extra flagstaff	£180	£225
		c. Lightning conductor	£200	£225
		d. Flagstaff on right-hand turret	£375	
		e. Double flagstaff	£400	£425
145		5c. brown and deep blue	2·50	3·25
146		25c. slate and purple	12·00	16·00
		a. Extra flagstaff	£250	£350
		b. Short extra flagstaff	£500	
		c. Lightning conductor	£325	£400
		d. Flagstaff on right-hand turret	£450	
		e. Double flagstaff	£475	
143/6 *Set of 4*			20·00	22·00
143s/6s Perf "SPECIMEN" *Set of 4*			£120	

For illustrations of plate varieties see Omnibus section following Zanzibar.

1937 (12 May). Coronation. As Nos. 95/7 of Antigua, but printed by D.L.R. P 14.

147		3c. orange	30	30
148		4c. grey-black	70	30
149		5c. bright blue	80	1·90
147/9 *Set of 3*			1·60	2·25
147s/9s Perf "SPECIMEN" *Set of 3*			95·00	

24 Maya Figures   **25** Chicle Tapping

26 Cohune palm   **27** Local products

28 Grapefruit   **29** Mahogany logs in river

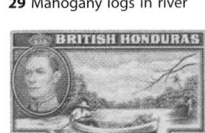

30 Sergeant's Cay   **31** Dorey

32 Chicle industry   **33** Court House Belize

34 Mahogany felling   **35** Arms of Colony

(Recess B.W.)

1938 (10 Jan)–**47**. T **24/35**. Wmk Mult Script CA (sideways on horizontal stamps). P 11½×11 (horiz designs) or 11×11½ (vert designs).

150	**24**	1c. bright magenta and green (14.2.38)	70	1·50
151	**25**	2c. black and scarlet (14.2.38)	1·50	1·00
		a. Perf 12 (1947)	3·75	1·50
152	**26**	3c. purple and brown	2·25	1·75
153	**27**	4c. black and green	2·00	70
154	**28**	5c. mauve and dull blue	3·50	1·75
155	**29**	10c. green and reddish brown (14.2.38)	4·50	60
156	**30**	15c. brown and light blue (14.2.38)	8·50	1·50
157	**31**	25c. blue and green (14.2.38)	5·00	2·00
158	**32**	50c. black and purple (14.2.38)	38·00	4·75
159	**33**	$1 scarlet and olive (28.2.38)	50·00	10·00
160	**34**	$2 deep blue and maroon (28.2.38)	55·00	40·00
161	**35**	$5 scarlet and brown (28.2.38)	50·00	60·00
150/61 *Set of 12*			£190	£110
150s/61s Perf "SPECIMEN" *Set of 12*			£300	

1946 (9 Sept). Victory. As Nos. 110/11 of Antigua.

162		3c. brown	10	20
163		5c. blue	10	20
162s/3s Perf "SPECIMEN" *Set of 2*			95·00	

1948 (1 Oct). Royal Silver Wedding. As Nos. 112/13 of Antigua.

164		4c. green	15	60
165		$5 brown	27·00	50·00

36 Island of St. George's Cay   **37** HMS *Merlin*

(Recess Waterlow)

1949 (10 Jan). 150th Anniv of Battle of St. George's Cay. Wmk Mult Script CA. P 12½.

166	**36**	1c. ultramarine and green	20	1·25
167		3c. blue and yellow-brown	20	1·50
168		4c. olive and violet	20	1·75
169	**37**	5c. brown and deep blue	2·25	75
170		10c. green and red-brown	2·25	30
171		15c. emerald and ultramarine	2·25	30
166/71 *Set of 6*			6·75	5·50

1949 (10 Oct). 75th Anniv of UPU As Nos. 114/17 of Antigua.

172		4c. blue-green	30	1·25
173		5c. deep blue	1·50	50
174		10c. red-brown	40	3·75
175		25c. blue	35	50
172/5 *Set of 4*			2·25	5·50

1951 (16 Feb). Inauguration of B.W.I. University College. As Nos. 118/19 of Antigua.

176		3c. reddish violet and brown	45	1·75
177		10c. green and brown	45	30

1953 (2 June). Coronation. As No. 120 of Antigua.

178		4c. black and green	75	30

38 Arms of British Honduras   **39** Baird's Tapir ("Mountain Cow")

40 Mace and Legislative Council Chamber   **41** Pine industry

42 Spiny Lobster   **43** Stanley Field Airport

44 Maya frieze, Xunantunich   **45** *Morpho peleides*

---

46 Maya Indian   **47** Nine-banded Armadillo

48 Hawkesworth Bridge   **49** Mountain Orchid

(Recess Waterlow (until 20.6.1961), then D.L.R.)

1953 (2 Sept)–**62**. T **38/39**. Wmk Mult Script CA. P 13½.

179	**38**	1c. green and black	10	40
		a. Perf 13½×13 (3.10.61)	3·25	2·50
180	**39**	2c. yellow-brown and black	1·75	3·00
		a. Perf 14 (18.9.57)	2·75	65
		b. Perf 13½×13 (20.6.61)	3·25	2·00
181	**40**	3c. reddish violet and bright purple	45	45
		a. Perf 14 (18.9.57)	20	10
		b. Perf 13½×13 (20.6.61)	15·00	27·00
		ba. *Reddish lilac and pale magenta* (19.1.62)	2·75	3·50
182	**41**	4c. brown and green	1·50	30
183	**42**	5c. deep olive-green and scarlet	1·00	20
		a. Perf 14 (15.5.57)	2·50	10
		ab. D.L.R. ptg (3.10.61)	15·00	27·00
		aba. Imperf three sides (horiz pair)	£9000	
184	**43**	10c. slate and bright blue	2·00	10
		a. Perf 13½×13 (19.1.62)	2·00	10
185	**44**	15c. green and violet	65	10
186	**45**	25c. bright blue and yellow-brown	7·50	3·75
187	**46**	50c. yellow-brown and reddish purple	20·00	4·00
		a. *Pale yellow-brown and pale purple* (22.3.60)	70·00	15·00
188	**47**	$1 slate-blue and red-brown	11·00	5·00
189	**48**	$2 scarlet and grey	11·00	4·00
190	**49**	$5 purple and slate	48·00	17·00
179/90 *Set of 12*			90·00	30·00

Nos. 179/90 were released a day earlier by the Crown Agents in London.

Stamps from the Waterlow printings perforated 13½×13 or 14 have a very fine perforation tooth at the *top* of each vertical side. On the De La Rue printings this tooth is at the *bottom*. Stamps perforated 13½ have "normal" perforation teeth at top and bottom.

50 *Belize from Fort George, 1842* (C. J. Hullmandel)   **51** Public Seals, 1860 and 1960

52 Tamarind Tree, Newtown Barracks

(Recess B.W.)

1960 (1 July). Post Office Centenary. W w **12**. P 11½×11.

191	**50**	2c. green	75	1·25
192	**51**	10c. deep carmine	75	10
193	**52**	15c. blue	75	35
191/3 *Set of 3*			2·00	1·50

NEW CONSTITUTION 1960 (53)   **HURRICANE HATTIE** (54)

1961 (1 Mar). New Constitution. Nos. 180a, 181a and 184/5 optd with T **53** by Waterlow.

194		2c. yellow-brown and black	25	40
195		3c. reddish violet and bright purple	30	40
196		10c. slate and bright blue	30	30
197		15c. green and violet	30	20
194/7 *Set of 4*			1·00	1·00

1962 (15 Jan). Hurricane Hattie Relief Fund. Nos. 179a, 184a, 186 and 187 optd with T **54** by D.L.R.

198		1c. green and black	10	1·60
199		10c. slate and bright blue	30	10
200		25c. bright blue and yellow-brown	1·75	80
201		50c. yellow-brown and reddish purple	75	1·60
198/201 *Set of 4*			2·50	3·50

---

55 Great Curassow

(Des D. R. Eckelberry. Photo Harrison)

1962 (2 Apr). Horiz designs on T **55**. Multicoloured. W w **12** (upright). P 14×14½.

202		1c. Type 55	1·50	75
		a. Orange-yellow (knob) omitted	£800	
		w. Wmk inverted		
203		2c. Red-legged Honey-creeper	2·00	10
		a. Turquoise-blue (bird's head) omitted	£800	
204		3c. Northern Jacana	4·50	3·25
		a. Blue-green (legs) omitted	£700	
205		4c. Great Kiskadee	3·75	4·25
206		5c. Scarlet-rumped Tanager	2·75	10
		w. Wmk inverted		
207		10c. Scarlet Macaw	4·50	10
		a. Blue omitted	£850	
		w. Wmk inverted	†	—
208		15c. Slaty-tailed Trogon	1·50	10
		w. Wmk inverted	45·00	17·00
209		25c. Red-footed Booby	4·50	30
		w. Wmk inverted		
210		50c. Keel-billed Toucan	6·00	35
		a. Pale blue (claw and beak) omitted	£1200	£1200
211		$1 Magnificent Frigate Bird	9·00	2·25
212		$2 Rufous-tailed Jacamar	24·00	7·50
		a. *Shade**	70·00	20·00
		w. Wmk inverted	£140	
213		$5 Montezuma Oropendola	28·00	20·00
202/13 *Set of 12*			80·00	35·00

*On No. 212a, the bird is myrtle-green and red-brown instead of yellow-green and orange-brown.

Nos. 202, 206 and 207 exist in coils, constructed from normal sheets. See also Nos. 239/45.

1963 (4 June). Freedom from Hunger. As No. 146 of Antigua.

214		22c. bluish green	30	15

1963 (2 Sept). Red Cross Centenary. As Nos. 147/8 of Antigua.

215		4c. red and black	20	1·40
216		22c. red and blue	40	1·40

SELF-GOVERNMENT

SELF GOVERNMENT 1964 (56)   **DEDICATION OF SITE NEW CAPITAL 9th OCTOBER 1965** (57)

1964. New Constitution. Nos. 202, 204/5, 207 and 209 optd with T **56**.

217		1c. Type 55 (20.4)	10	30
		a. Opt inverted	£800	
		b. Orange-yellow (knob) omitted	£275	
218		3c. Northern Jacana (20.4)	45	30
219		4c. Great Kiskadee (3.2)	45	30
220		10c. Scarlet Macaw (20.4)	45	10
221		25c. Red-footed Booby (3.2)	55	30
217/21 *Set of 5*			1·75	1·10

1965 (17 May). ITU Centenary. As Nos. 166/7 of Antigua.

222		2c. orange-red and light green	10	10
223		50c. yellow and light purple	35	25

1965 (25 Oct). International Co-operation Year. As Nos. 168/9 of Antigua.

224		1c. reddish purple and turquoise-green	10	15
225		22c. deep bluish green and lavender	20	15

1966 (24 Jan). Churchill Commemoration. As Nos. 170/3 of Antigua.

226		1c. new blue	10	75
227		4c. deep green	70	10
228		22c. brown	1·10	10
229		25c. bluish violet	1·25	45
226/9 *Set of 4*			2·75	1·10

1966 (1 July). Dedication of New Capital Site. As Nos. 202, 204/5, 207 and 209, but wmk sideways, optd with T **57** by Harrison.

230		1c. Type 55	15	40
		a. Orange-yellow (knob) omitted	£375	
		w. Wmk Crown to right of CA	70	
231		3c. Northern Jacana	60	40
232		4c. Great Kiskadee	60	40
233		10c. Scarlet Macaw	60	10
234		25c. Red-footed Booby	85	35
230/4 *Set of 5*			2·50	1·50

*The normal sideways watermark shows Crown to left of CA, *as seen from the back of the stamp.*

58 Citrus Grove

(Des V. Whiteley. Photo Harrison)

1966 (1 Oct). Stamp Centenary. T **58** and similar horiz designs. Multicoloured. W w **12**. P 14×14½.

235		5c. Type 58	10	10
236		10c. Half Moon Cay	10	10
237		22c. Hidden Valley Falls	10	10
238		25c. Maya Ruins, Xunantunich	15	45
235/8 *Set of 4*			30	65

1967. As Nos. 202, etc, but W w **12** (sideways).

239		1c. Type 55 (16.2)	10	50
240		2c. Red-legged Honey-creeper (28.11)	30	1·00
241		4c. Great Kiskadee (16.2)	3·50	3·00

242	5c. Scarlet-rumped Tanager (16.2)		60	10
243	10c. Scarlet Macaw (28.11)		40	10
244	15c. Slaty-tailed Trogon (28.11)		40	10
245	50c. Keel-billed Toucan (16.2)		2·50	3·50
239/45 *Set of 7*			7·00	7·50

The 15c. value exists with PVA gum as well as gum arabic.

59 Sailfish

60 *Schomburgkia tibicinis*

(Des R. Granger Barrett. Photo Harrison)

1967 (1 Dec). International Tourist Year. T **59** and similar horiz designs. W w **12**. P 12½.

246	5c. deep violet-blue black and light yellow		20	30
247	10c. brown, black and orange-red		20	10
248	22c. yellow-orange, black and bright green		35	10
249	25c. light greenish blue, black and greenish yellow		35	60
246/9 *Set of 4*			1·00	1·00

Designs:—10c. Red Brocket; 22c. Jaguar; 25c. Atlantic Tarpon.

(Des Sylvia Goaman. Photo Harrison)

1968 (16 Apr). 20th Anniv of Economic Commission for Latin America. T **60** and similar vert designs showing orchids. Multicoloured. W w **12** (sideways). P 14½×14.

250	5c. Type **60**		20	15
251	10c. *Muxillaria tenuifolia*		25	10
252	22c. *Bletia purpurea*		30	10
253	25c. *Sobralia macrantha*		40	20
250/3 *Set of 4*			1·10	40

61 Monument to Belizean Patriots

62 Monument at Site of New Capital

(Des G. Vasarhelyi. Litho B.W.)

1968 (15 July). Human Rights Year. W w **12**. P 13½.

254	**61**	22c. multicoloured	15	10
255	**62**	50c. multicoloured	15	20

63 Spotted Jewfish

(Des J. W. Litho D.L.R.)

1968 (15 Oct). Wildlife. Horiz designs as T **63**. Multicoloured. No wmk. P 13×12½.

256	1c. Type **63**		30	10
257	2c. White-Tipped Peccary ("Warree")		10	10
258	3c. Misty Grouper		20	10
259	4c. Collared Anteater		15	1·25
260	5c. Bonefish		15	1·25
261	10c. Para ("Gibnut")		15	10
262	15c. Dolphinfish		2·00	20
263	25c. Kinkajou ("Night Walker")		30	20
264	50c. Mutton Snapper		70	1·25
265	$1 Tayra ("Bush Dog")		2·50	1·25
266	$2 Great Barracuda		2·50	2·00
267	$5 Puma		14·00	6·50
256/67 *Set of 12*			21·00	12·00

See also Nos. 276/8.

The 3c., 5c. and 10c. were re-issued in 1972 with watermark W **12** upright.

64 *Rhyncholaelia digbyana*

65 Ziricote Tree

(Des Sylvia Goaman. Photo Harrison)

1969 (9 Apr). Orchids of Belize (1st series). T **64** and similar vert designs. Multicoloured. W w **12** (sideways). P 14½×14.

268	5c. Type **64**		60	20
269	10c. *Cattleya bowringiana*		65	15
270	22c. *Lycaste cochleatum*		95	15
271	25c. *Coryanthes speciosum*		1·10	1·10
268/71 *Set of 4*			3·00	1·40

See also Nos. 287/90.

(Des V. Whiteley. Litho D.L.R.)

1969 (1 Sept). Indigenous Hardwoods (1st series). T **65** and similar vert designs. Multicoloured. W w **12**. P 14.

272	5c. Type **65**		10	50
273	10c. Rosewood		10	10
274	22c. Mayflower		20	20
275	25c. Mahogany		20	85
272/5 *Set of 4*			45	1·50

See also Nos. 291/4.

1969–72. As Nos. 257/8, 261, 267 and new value and design (½ c.), but W w **12** (sideways*).

276	½c. Mozambique Mouthbrooder ("Crana") (ultramarine background) (1.9.69)		10	30
277	½c. Mozambique Mouthbrooder ("Crana") (yellow-olive background) (1.2.71)		2·50	3·00
	a. Black (inscr and value) omitted		£500	
	bw. Wmk Crown to right of CA		4·00	
277c	2c. White-tipped Peccary (5.5.72)		7·00	6·00
277d	3c. Misty Grouper (5.5.72)		7·00	6·00
277e	10c. Paca (5.5.72)		7·00	6·00
278	$5 Puma (12.5.70)		2·50	10·00
276/8 *Set of 6*			23·00	28·00

*The normal sideways watermark shows Crown to left of CA, *as seen from the back of the stamp.*

66 *The Virgin and Child* (Bellini)

POPULATION CENSUS 1970

(68)

(Des adapted by G. Drummond. Litho Format)

1969 (1 Nov). Christmas. Paintings. T **66** and similar vert design. Multicoloured. W w **12**. P 14×14½.

279	5c. Type **66**		10	10
280	15c. Type **66**		10	10
281	22c. *The Adoration of the Kings* (Veronese)		10	10
282	25c. As 22c.		10	20
279/82 *Set of 4*			30	30

Although released by the Crown Agents on 1 October this issue was not put on sale locally until 1 November.

1970 (2 Feb). Population Census. As Nos. 260 and 262/3 but W w **12** (sideways) and No. 277e optd with T **68**.

283	5c. Bonefish		10	10
284	10c. Paca		15	10
285	15c. Dolphinfish		20	10
286	25c. Kinkajou		20	15
283/6 *Set of 4*			55	30

(Des G. Drummond. Litho Format)

1970 (2 Apr). Orchids of Belize (2nd series). As T **64**. Multicoloured. W w **12**. P 14.

287	5c. Black Orchid		35	15
288	15c. White Butterfly Orchid		50	10
289	22c. Swan Orchid		70	10
290	25c. Butterfly Orchid		70	40
287/90 *Set of 4*			2·00	60

69 Santa Maria

70 *The Nativity* (A. Hughes)

(Des Jennifer Toombs, Litho Questa)

1970 (7 Sept). Indigenous Hardwoods (2nd series). T **69** and similar vert designs. Multicoloured. W w **12** (sideways). P 14×14½.

291	5c. Type **69**		25	10
292	15c. Nargusta		40	10
293	22c. Cedar		45	10
294	25c. Sapodilla		45	35
291/4 *Set of 4*			1·40	55

(Des J. Cooter Litho J.W.)

1970 (7 Nov*). Christmas. T **70** and similar vert design. Multicoloured. W w **12**. P 14.

295	½c. Type **70**		10	10
296	5c. *The Mystic Nativity* (Botticelli)		10	10
297	10c. Type **70**		15	10
298	15c. As 5c.		25	10
299	22c. Type **70**		30	10
300	50c. As 5c.		40	85
295/300 *Set of 6*			1·00	1·10

*These stamps were released by the Crown Agents in London on 2 November.

STAMP BOOKLETS

1920. Black on pink cover inscr "British Honduras–100–Two Cent Stamps". Stapled.

SB1	$2 booklet containing 100×2c. (No. 102b) in blocks of 10 (5×2)		£4000

1920. Grey-blue cover inscr "British Honduras–100–Three Cent Stamps". Stapled.

SB2	$3 booklet containing 100×3c. (No. 103) in blocks of 10 (5×2)		

1923. Black on pink cover inscr "British Honduras–100–Two Cent Stamps". Stapled.

SB3	$2 booklet containing 100×2c. brown (No. 127) in blocks of 10 (5×2)		£5000

1927. Black on pink cover inscr "British Honduras–100–Two Cent Stamps". Stapled.

SB4	$2 booklet containing 100×2c. rose-carmine (No. 128) in blocks of 10 (5×2)		

POSTAGE DUE STAMPS

D 1

(Typo D.L.R.)

1923–64. Wmk Mult Script CA. Ordinary paper. P 14.

D1	D **1**	1c. black		2·25	13·00
		a. Chalk-surfaced paper (25.9.56)		50	27·00
		b. White uncoated paper (9.4.64)		18·00	42·00
D2		2c. black		2·25	7·50
		a. Chalk-surfaced paper (25.9.56)		50	22·00
D3		4c. black		1·25	6·00
		a. Missing top serif on "C" (R. 6/6)		55·00	
		bw. Wmk inverted		£300	
		c. Chalk-surfaced paper (25.9.56)		1·00	22·00
		ca. Missing top serif on "C" (R. 6/6)		45·00	
D1/3 *Set of 3*				5·25	24·00
D1a/3c *Set of 3*				1·75	65·00
D1s/3s Optd "SPECIMEN" *Set of 3*				85·00	

The early ordinary paper printings were yellowish and quite distinct from No. D1b.

1965 (3 Aug)–**72**. As Nos. D2a and D3c, but Wmk w **12** (sideways on 2c.). P 13½×13 (2c.) or 13½×14 (4c.).

D4	D **1**	2c. black (10.1.72)		3·75	9·50
D5		4c. black		2·25	9·50

The missing top serif on "C" variety of R. 6/6 was corrected before No. D5 was printed.

Although the design size is the same, No. D4 measures 22×26 mm, while D2/a and D5 are 21×24½ mm.

British Indian Ocean Territory

This Crown Colony was created on 8 November 1965 when it comprised the Chagos Archipelago, previously administered by Mauritius, together with the islands of Aldabra, Farquhar and Desroches, previously administered by Seychelles.

(Currency. 100 cents = 1 rupee).

B.I.O.T.
(1)

1968 (17 Jan). As Nos. 196/200, 202/4 and 206/12 of Seychelles, optd with T **1**. W w **12** (sideways* on 5, 10, 15, 20, 25, 50, 75c. and 10r.).

1	5c. multicoloured	1·00	1·50
	a. No stop after "I"	19·00	22·00
	b. No stop after "O"	6·50	10·00
	w. Wmk Crown to right of CA	85·00	
2	10c. multicoloured	10	15
	a. No stop after "I"	40·00	38·00
	b. No stop after "O"	5·50	13·00
3	15c. multicoloured	25	20
	a. No stop after "I"	16·00	19·00
	b. No stop after "O"	5·50	9·50
4	20c. multicoloured	20	15
	a. No stop after "I"	17·00	17·00
	b. No stop after "O"	7·00	8·50
5	25c. multicoloured	20	15
	a. No stop after "I"	12·00	17·00
	b. No stop after "O"	5·50	10·00
6	40c. multicoloured	20	20
	a. No stop after "I"	20·00	20·00
	b. No stop after "O"	8·50	13·00
7	45c. multicoloured	20	30
	a. No stop after "I"	24·00	18·00
	b. No stop after "B"	45·00	27·00
	c. No stop after "O"	80·00	55·00
8	50c. multicoloured	20	30
	a. No stop after "I"	20·00	19·00
	b. No stop after "O"	7·50	9·50
9	75c. multicoloured	3·00	35
10	1r. multicoloured	2·00	35
	a. No stop after "I"	27·00	24·00
	b. No stop after "O"	8·00	11·00
11	1r.50 multicoloured	2·00	1·50
	a. No stop after "I"	50·00	50·00
	b. No stop after "O"	28·00	17·00
12	2r.25 multicoloured	3·00	3·75
	a. No stop after "I"	£110	£120
	b. No stop after "O"	80·00	80·00
13	3r.50 multicoloured	3·00	4·50
	a. No stop after "1"	£100	£100
	b. No stop after "O"	45·00	42·00
14	5r. multicoloured	10·00	6·50
	a. No stop after "I"	£150	£140
	b. No stop after "O"	60·00	55·00
15	10r. multicoloured	20·00	15·00
	a. No stop after "B"	£190	£180
	b. No stop after "I"	£250	£250
	c. No stop after "O"	£110	£110
1/15 *Set of* 15		40·00	30·00

*The normal sideways watermark shows Crown to left of CA, *as seen from the back of the stamp.*

These were issued by the Crown Agents on 15 January but owing to shipping delays they were not put on sale locally until 17 January.

The positions of the "no stop" varieties are as follows:

After "I": R. 2/4 on horiz stamps except 45c. where it occurs on R. 3/3, and R. 8/5 on vert stamps except 10r. where it occurs on R. 4/3.

After "O": R. 3/2 and 5/1 on vert stamps, R. 2/1 and 4/4 on horiz stamps (only occurs on R. 2/1 for 45c.), and R. 2/7 and 5/9 on 10r. value.

After "B": R. 10/4 (45c.) or R. 1/8 (10r.).

As sheets of all values from 5c. to 50c. are known with all stops in place the no stop varieties either developed during printing or their omission was discovered and replacements inserted.

2 Lascar

(Des G. Drummond, based on drawings by Mrs. W. Veevers-Cartor. Litho D.L.R.)

1968 (23 Oct)–**70**. Marine Life. Multicoloured designs as T **2**. White paper (Nos. 20a, 23a, 24a) or cream paper (others). W w **12** (sideways on horiz, inverted on vert designs). P 14.

16	5c. Type **2**	1·00	2·50
17	10c. Smooth Hammerhead (*vert*)	30	1·25
18	15c. Tiger Shark	30	1·75
19	20c. Spotted Eagle Ray ("Bat Ray")	30	1·00
20	25c. Yellow-finned Butterflyfish and Earspotted Angelfish (*vert*)	80	1·00
20a	30c. Robber Crab (7.12.70)	3·00	2·75
21	40c. Blue-finned Trevally ("Caranx")	2·25	40
22	45c. Crocodile Needlefish ("Garfish") (*vert*)	2·25	2·50
23	50c. Pickhandle Barracuda	2·25	30
23a	60c. Spotted Pebble Crab (7.12.70)	3·00	4·00
24	75c. Indian Ocean Steep-headed Parrotfish	2·50	2·25
24a	85c. Rainbow Runner ("Dorado") (7.12.70)	3·50	3·00
	b. Magenta omitted	£1100	
25	1r. Giant Hermit Crab	1·75	35
26	1r.50 Parrotfish ("Humphead")	2·50	3·00

27	2r.25 Yellow-edged Lyretail and Areolate Grouper ("Rock Cod")	7·00	10·00
28	3r.50 Black Marlin	3·50	3·75
29	5r. black, blue-green and greenish blue (Whale Shark) (*vert*)	24·00	16·00
30	10r. Lionfish	5·00	6·50
	a. Imperf (pair)	£1100	
16/30 *Set of* 18		55·00	50·00

The 5c. was re-issued in 1973 on white paper with watermark w **12** upright.

3 Sacred Ibis and Aldabra Coral Atoll

(Des and litho D.L.R.)

1969 (10 July). Coral Atolls. W w **12** (sideways). P 13½×13.

31	**3** 2r.25 multicoloured	1·50	1·00

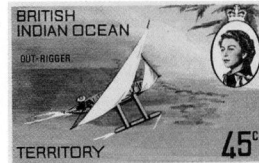

4 Outrigger Canoe

(Des Mrs. M. Hayward adapted by V. Whiteley. Litho D.L.R.)

1969 (15 Dec). Ships of the Islands. T **4** and similar horiz designs. Multicoloured. W w **12** (sideways). P 13½×14.

32	45c. Type **4**	45	75
33	75c. Pirogue	45	80
34	1r. MV *Nordvaer*	50	90
35	1r.50 *Isle of Farquhar*	55	1·00
32/5 *Set of* 4		1·75	3·00

British Levant

The term "British Levant" is used by stamp collectors to describe the issues made by various British Post Offices within the former Turkish Empire.

Arrangements for the first such service were included amongst the terms of a commercial treaty between the two countries in 1832, but the system did not start operations until September 1857 when a post office for civilian use was opened in Constantinople, replacing the Army Post Office which had existed there since June 1854.

Eventually the number of British Post Offices grew to five:

Beyrout (Beirut, Lebanon). Opened March 1873, closed 30 September 1914.

Constantinople (Istanbul). Opened 1 July 1857, closed 30 September 1914, re-opened 4 February 1919, finally closed 27 September 1923.

Salonica (Thessalonika, Greece). Opened 1 May 1900, closed October 1914. The city was captured by Greek troops on 7 November 1912 and incorporated into Greece by the Treaty of London (July 1913).

Smyrna (Izmir). Opened December 1872, closed 30 September 1914, re-opened 1 March 1919, finally closed 13 September 1922. Between 15 May 1919 and 8 September 1922 the city was under Greek occupation.

Stamboul (a sub-office of Constantinople). Opened April 1885, closed 25 August 1896, re-opened 10 February 1908, finally closed 30 September 1914.

Stamps from the two British Post Offices in Egypt still technically part of the Turkish Empire, are listed under EGYPT.

A. BRITISH POST OFFICES IN TURKISH EMPIRE, 1857–1914

From 1 August 1885 letter and registered charges were prepaid with surcharged stamps (No. 1 onwards). Until 14 August 1905 postcards and parcels continued to be franked with unoverprinted Great Britain stamps. Only a limited range of values were stocked for this purpose and these are listed. Other values exist with Levant postmarks, but these stamps did not originate from the local post offices.

After 15 August 1905 the post offices were supplied with Great Britain stamps overprinted "LEVANT". Subsequent examples of unoverprinted stamps with Levant postmarks are omitted from the listing. Such stamps used during 1919–22 at Constantinople and Smyrna are listed as Z176/201 and Z282/95.

BEYROUT (BEIRUT)

Between 1873 and 1876 much of the mail from the British Post Office in Beyrout sent to European addresses was forwarded through the French or Italian Post Offices at Alexandria. Such covers show Great Britain stamps used in combination with those of French or Italian P.O's in the Turkish Empire.

Stamps of GREAT BRITAIN cancelled "G 06" Type Z **4** or with circular postmark inscr "BEYROUT" as Types Z **6** or Z **8**.

1873–81.

Z1	½d. rose-red (1870–79)	*From*	65·00	
	Plate Nos. 12, 13, 14, 19, 20.			
Z2	1d. rose-red (1864–79)	*From*	27·00	
	Plate Nos. 107, 118, 130, 140, 145, 148, 155, 157, 162, 167, 177, 179, 180, 184, 185, 186, 187, 195, 198, 200, 203, 204, 211, 213, 215, 218, 220, 222.			

Z3	1½d. lake-red (1870–74) (Plate 3)	£400
Z4	2d. blue (1858–69) ... From	30·00
	Plate Nos. 13, 14, 15.	
Z5	2½d. rosy mauve (1875) (blued paper)	80·00
	Plate No. 1.	
Z6	2½d. rosy mauve (1875–76) ... From	35·00
	Plate Nos. 1, 2, 3.	
Z7	2½d. rosy mauve (1876–79) ... From	26·00
	Plate Nos. 3, 4, 5, 6, 7, 8, 9, 10, 11, 12, 13, 14, 15, 16, 17.	
Z8	2½d. blue (1880) ... From	16·00
	Plate Nos. 17, 18, 19, 20.	
Z9	2½d. blue (1881) ... From	12·00
	Plate Nos. 21, 22, 23.	
Z10	3d. rose (1867–73) (Plate No. 10)	65·00
Z11	3d. rose (1873–76)	
	Plate Nos. 12, 15, 16, 18, 19, 20.	
Z12	3d. rose (1881) (Plate Nos. 20, 21)	
Z13	4d. vermilion (1865–73) ... From	48·00
	Plate Nos. 11, 12, 13, 14.	
Z14	4d. vermilion (1876) (Plate No. 15)	£190
Z15	4d. sage-green (1877)	£130
	Plate Nos. 15, 16.	
Z16	4d. grey-brown (1880) wmk Large Garter (Plate No. 17)	
Z17	4d. grey-brown (1880) wmk Crown	75·00
	Plate Nos. 17, 18.	
Z18	6d. mauve (1870) (Plate Nos. 8, 9)	
Z19	6d. buff (1872–73) ... From	95·00
	Plate Nos. 11, 12.	
Z20	6d. chestnut (1872) (Plate No. 11)	50·00
Z21	6d. grey (1873) (Plate No. 12)	£160
Z22	6d. grey (1874–80)	42·00
	Plate Nos. 13, 14, 15, 16, 17.	
Z23	8d. orange (1876)	£550
Z24	10d. red-brown (1867)	£170
Z25	1s. green (1867–73)	48·00
	Plate Nos. 6, 7.	
Z26	1s. green (1873–77) ... From	65·00
	Plate Nos. 8, 9, 10, 12, 13.	
Z27	1s. orange-brown (1880) (Plate No. 13)	
Z28	1s. orange-brown (1881)	90·00
	Plate Nos. 13, 14.	
Z29	2s. blue (1867)	£180
Z30	5s. rose (1867) (Plate Nos. 1, 2) ... From	£800

1880.

Z31	½d. deep green	16·00
Z32	½d. pale green	17·00
Z33	1d. Venetian red	26·00
Z34	1½d. Venetian red	£250
Z35	2d. pale rose	80·00
Z36	2d. deep rose	80·00
Z37	5d. indigo	£140

1881.

Z38	1d. lilac (14 dots)	
Z39	1d. lilac (16 dots)	7·50

1884.

Z40	½d. slate-blue	23·00
Z41	1½d. lilac	£140
Z42	2d. lilac	£100
Z43	2½d. lilac	12·00
Z44	4d. dull green	£275
Z45	5d. dull green	£120
Z46	1s. dull green	£450

1887–92.

Z47	½d. vermilion	11·00
Z48	1½d. dull purple and green	
Z51	3d. purple/yellow	
Z54	6d. purple/rose-red	30·00
Z55	1s. dull green	£225

1900.

Z56	½d. blue-green	13·00
Z57	1s. green and carmine	£225

1902–04. De La Rue ptgs.

Z58	½d. blue-green	6·00
Z59	½d. yellowish green	6·50
Z60	1d. scarlet	5·50
Z61	1½d. dull purple and green	
Z62	3d. dull purple/yellow	
Z63	6d. pale dull purple	
Z64	1s. dull green and carmine	48·00

CONSTANTINOPLE

Stamps of GREAT BRITAIN cancelled "C" or circular postmark, Types Z **1/2**, as Type Z **3** or Type Z **7**.

1857–83.

Z68	½d. rose-red (1870–79) ... From	28·00
	Plate Nos. 4, 5, 6, 10, 11, 12, 13, 14, 15, 20.	
Z69	1d. red-brown (1854), Die I, wmk Small Crown, perf 16.	
Z70	1d. red-brown (1855), Die II, wmk Small Crown, perf 14.	
Z71	1d. red-brown, (1855), Die II, wmk Large Crown, perf 14.	22·00
Z72	1d. rose-red (1857)	8·50
Z73	1d. rose-red (1861) Alphabet IV	
Z74	1d. rose-red (1864–79)	12·00
	Plate Nos. 71, 72, 73, 74, 76, 78, 79, 80, 81, 83, 85, 87, 89, 90, 92, 93, 94, 95, 96, 97, 99, 101, 102, 105, 106, 108, 109, 110, 111, 113, 116, 118, 119, 120, 121, 122, 123, 124, 125, 127, 129, 130, 131, 134, 135, 136, 137, 138, 140, 141, 143, 144, 145, 146, 147, 148, 149, 150, 151, 152, 155, 156, 157, 158, 159, 160, 161, 162, 163, 164, 165, 166, 167, 170, 171, 172, 173, 174, 175, 176, 177, 178, 179, 180, 181, 183, 184, 186, 187, 188, 189, 190, 191, 192, 193, 194, 195, 196, 197, 198, 199, 200, 201, 203, 204, 205, 206, 207, 208, 210, 211, 212, 214, 215, 216, 220, 222, 224.	
Z75	1½d. rose-red (1870) (Plate 1)	£250
Z76	2d. blue (1855), wmk Large Crown, perf 14. (Plate Nos. 5, 6)	

Z77	2d. blue (1858–69) ... From	15·00
	Plate Nos. 7, 8, 9, 12, 13, 14, 15.	
Z78	2½d. rosy mauve (1875–76) (blued paper) (Plate Nos. 1, 2) ... From	60·00
Z79	2½d. rosy mauve (1875–76) ... From	32·00
	Plate Nos. 1, 2, 3.	
Z80	2½d. rosy mauve (Error of Lettering)	
Z81	2½d. rosy mauve (1876–79) ... From	24·00
	Plate Nos. 3 to 17.	
Z82	2½d. blue (1880–81) ... From	12·00
	Plate Nos. 17, 18, 19, 20.	
Z83	2½d. blue (1881) (Plate Nos. 21, 22, 23)	8·00
Z84	3d. carmine-rose (1862) (Plate No. 2)	£150
Z85	3d. rose (1865) (Plate No. 4)	90·00
Z86	3d. rose (1867–73) (Plate No. 4 to 10)	85·00
Z87	3d. rose (1873–76)	30·00
	Plate Nos. 11, 12, 15, 16, 17, 18, 19.	
Z88	3d. rose (1881) (Plate No. 21)	
Z89	3d. on 3d. lilac (1883) (Plate No. 21)	
Z90	4d. rose (1857)	48·00
	a. Rose-carmine	
Z91	4d. red (1862) (Plate Nos. 3, 4) ... From	40·00
Z92	4d. vermilion (1865–73) ... From	27·00
	Plate Nos. 7 to 14.	
Z93	4d. vermilion (1876) (Plate No. 15)	£160
Z94	4d. sage-green (1877)	£110
	Plate Nos. 15, 16.	
Z95	4d. grey-brown (1880) wmk Large Garter (Plate No. 17)	
Z96	4d. grey-brown (1880) wmk Crown (Plate Nos. 17, 18) ... From	60·00
Z97	6d. lilac (1856)	65·00
Z98	6d. lilac (1862) (Plate Nos. 3, 4)	40·00
Z99	6d. lilac (1865–67)	38·00
	Plate Nos. 5, 6.	
Z100	6d. lilac (1867) (Plate No. 6)	42·00
Z101	6d. violet (1867–70) ... From	35·00
	Plate Nos. 6, 8, 9.	
Z102	6d. buff (1872–73)	60·00
	Plate Nos. 11, 12.	
Z103	6d. chestnut (1872) (Plate No. 11)	32·00
Z104	6d. grey (1873) (Plate No. 12)	80·00
Z105	6d. grey (1874–76) ... From	35·00
	Plate Nos. 13, 14, 15, 16, 17.	
Z106	6d. grey (1881–82) (Plate Nos. 17, 18)	42·00
Z107	6d. on 6d. lilac (1883)	£100
	a. Dots slanting (Letters MI or SJ)	£225
Z108	8d. orange (1876)	£500
Z109	10d. red-brown (1867), wmk Emblems	£35000
Z110	10d. red-brown (1867)	£170
Z111	1s. green (1856)	£120
Z112	1s. green (1862)	65·00
Z113	1s. green (1862) ("K" variety)	
Z114	1s. green (1862) (thick paper)	
Z115	1s. green (1865) (Plate No. 4)	70·00
Z116	1s. green (1867–73) ... From	22·00
	Plate Nos. 4, 5, 6, 7.	
Z117	1s. green (1873–77) ... From	32·00
	Plate Nos. 8, 9, 10, 11, 12, 13.	
Z118	1s. orange-brown (1880) (Plate No. 13)	£200
Z119	1s. orange-brown (1881) ... From	55·00
	Plate Nos. 13, 14.	
Z120	2s. blue (1867)	£100
Z121	5s. rose (1867–74) ... From	£275
	Plate Nos. 1, 2.	
Z122	5s. rose (1882) (white paper)	£900
Z123	5s. rose (1882) (blued paper)	£1600

1880.

Z124	½d. deep green	10·00
Z125	½d. pale green	12·00
Z126	1d. Venetian red	17·00
Z127	2d. pale rose	48·00
Z128	2d. deep rose	48·00
Z129	5d. indigo	

1881.

Z130	1d. lilac (14 dots)	
Z131	1d. lilac (16 dots)	3·00

1883–84.

Z132	½d. slate-blue	10·00
Z133	1½d. lilac	£150
Z134	2d. lilac	80·00
Z135	2½d. lilac	7·50
Z136	3d. lilac	£200
Z137	4d. dull green	£300
Z138	5d. dull green	95·00
Z139	6d. dull green	£250
Z140	9d. dull green	£550
Z141	1s. dull green	£350
Z142	2s.6d. lilac (blued paper)	£750
Z143	2s.6d. lilac (white paper)	95·00
Z144	5s. rose (blued paper)	
Z145	5s. rose (white paper)	

1887–92.

Z146	½d. vermilion	3·75
Z147	1½d. dull purple and green	
Z148	2d. grey-green and carmine	
Z150	3d. purple/yellow	
Z154	6d. purple/rose-red	15·00
Z157	1s. dull green	£120

1900.

Z158	½d. blue-green	7·00
Z159	1s. green and carmine	£180

1902–04. De La Rue ptgs.

Z160	½d. blue-green	3·50
Z161	½d. yellowish green	4·00
Z162	1d. scarlet	3·00
Z163	1½d. dull purple and green	
Z166	3d. purple/yellow	
Z169	6d. purple	15·00
Z172	1s. green and carmine	25·00
Z173	2s.6d. lilac	
Z174	5s. carmine	

POSTAL FISCALS

Z175	1d. purple (wmk Anchor) (1868)	
Z175a	1d. purple (wmk Orb) (1881)	£600

SALONICA

Stamps of GREAT BRITAIN cancelled with circular postmark as in Type Z **6** or double-circle datestamp.

1881.

Z202	½d. vermilion (1887)	26·00
Z203	½d. blue-green (1900)	28·00
Z204	1d. lilac (1881)	26·00
Z205	6d. purple/red (1887)	42·00
Z206	1s. green and carmine (1900)	£300
Z207	5s. rose (white paper) (1883)	£1300

1902.

Z208	½d. blue-green	30·00
Z209	½d. yellow-green	24·00
Z209a	1d. scarlet	24·00
Z209c	1s. green and carmine	75·00

SMYRNA (IZMIR)

Stamps of GREAT BRITAIN cancelled "F 87" or circular postmark as Types Z **4**, Z **5** or Z **6**.

1858–83.

Z210	½d. rose-red (1870–79) ... From	38·00
	Plates 11, 12, 13, 14, 15.	
Z211	1d. rose-red (1864–79) ... From	17·00
	Plate Nos. 120, 124, 134, 137, 138, 139, 140, 142, 143, 145, 146, 148, 149, 150, 151, 152, 153, 155, 156, 157, 158, 159, 160, 161, 162, 163, 164, 166, 167, 168, 169, 170, 171, 172, 173, 174, 175, 176, 177, 178, 183, 184, 185, 186, 187, 188, 191, 193, 194, 195, 196, 198, 200, 201, 204, 210, 212, 215, 217, 218.	
Z212	1½d. lake-red (1870–74) (Plate Nos. 1, 3)	£275
Z214	2d. blue (1858–69) ... From	20·00
	Plate Nos. 13, 14, 15.	
Z215	2½d. rosy mauve (1875) (blued paper)	65·00
	Plate No. 1.	
Z216	2½d. rosy mauve (1875–76) ... From	29·00
	Plate Nos. 1, 2, 3.	
Z217	2½d. rosy mauve (Error of lettering)	
Z218	2½d. rosy mauve (1876–79) ... From	23·00
	Plate Nos. 3, 4, 5, 6, 7, 8, 9, 10, 11, 12, 13, 14, 15, 16, 17.	
Z219	2½d. blue (1880) ... From	12·00
	Plate Nos. 17, 18, 19, 20.	
Z220	2½d. blue (1881)	10·00
	Plate Nos. 21, 22, 23.	
Z221	3d. rose (1867–73)	55·00
	Plate Nos. 5, 7, 9, 10.	
Z222	3d. rose (1873–76) (Plate No. 14)	
Z223	4d. vermilion (1865–73)	28·00
	Plate Nos. 12, 13, 14.	
Z224	4d. vermilion (1876) (Plate No. 15)	£160
Z225	4d. sage-green (1877)	£100
	Plate Nos. 15, 16.	
Z226	4d. grey-brown (1880) wmk Large Garter (Plate No. 17)	
Z227	4d. grey-brown (1880) wmk Crown (Plate Nos. 17, 18) ... From	50·00
Z228	6d. buff (1872–73)	75·00
	Plate Nos. 11, 12.	
Z229	6d. chestnut (1872) (Plate No. 11)	
Z230	6d. grey (1873) (Plate No. 12)	80·00
Z231	6d. grey (1874–80) ... From	28·00
	Plate Nos. 13, 14, 15, 16, 17.	
Z232	6d. grey (1881–82) (Plate Nos. 17, 18)	65·00
Z233	6d. on 6d. lilac (1883)	£130
Z234	8d. orange (1876)	
Z235	9d. straw (1867)	£450
Z236	10d. red-brown (1867)	£160
Z237	1s. green (1867–73) (Plate Nos. 6, 7)	
Z238	1s. green (1873–77) ... From	40·00
	Plate Nos. 8, 9, 10, 11, 12, 13.	
Z239	1s. orange-brown (1880) (Plate No. 13)	£200
Z240	1s. orange-brown (1881) (Plate Nos. 13, 14)	60·00
Z241	5s. rose (1867–74) (Plate No. 2)	

1880.

Z242	½d. deep green	12·00
Z243	½d. pale green	12·00
Z244	1d. Venetian red	19·00
Z245	1½d. Venetian red	£150
Z246	2d. pale rose	50·00
Z247	2d. deep rose	50·00
Z248	5d. indigo	90·00

1881.

Z249	1d. lilac (16 dots)	5·00

1884.

Z250	½d. slate-blue	20·00
Z251	2d. lilac	95·00
Z252	2½d. lilac	11·00
Z253	4d. dull green	
Z254	5d. dull green	£110
Z255	1s. dull green	£450

1887.

Z256	½d. vermilion	7·00
Z257	1½d. dull purple and green	
Z260	3d. purple/yellow	
Z263	6d. purple/rose-red	21·00
Z263a	9d. purple and blue	
Z264	1s. dull green	£160

1900.

Z265	½d. blue-green	9·00
Z266	1s. green and carmine	

1902–04. De La Rue ptgs.

Z267	½d. blue-green	5·00
Z268	½d. yellowish green	6·00

Z269		1d. scarlet		4·50
Z270		1½d. dull purple and green		
Z273		3d. purple/*yellow*		
Z276		6d. purple		18·00
Z279		1s. green and carmine		35·00
Z280		2s.6d. purple		
Z281		5s. carmine		

STAMBOUL (CONSTANTINOPLE)

Stamps of GREAT BRITAIN cancelled "S" as Type **3**, or circular postmarks inscribed either "BRITISH POST OFFICE CONSTANTINOPLE S" or "BRITISH POST OFFICE STAMBOUL" as Type Z **6**.

1884.

Z296		½d. slate-blue		30·00
Z297		1d. lilac		13·00
Z298		2d. lilac		
Z299		2½d. lilac		16·00
Z300		5d. dull green		£160

1887–92.

Z306		½d. vermilion		16·00
Z314		6d. purple/*rose-red*		38·00
Z317		1s. dull green		

The "S" cancellation was in use from 1885 to 1891 and the "Stamboul" mark from 1892 to 1896, when the office was closed, and from its reopening in 1908 to 1914. The "CONSTANTINOPLE S" handstamp was normally used as a back stamp, but can be found cancelling stamps in the period 1885 to 1892.

PRICES FOR STAMPS ON COVER	
Nos. 1/3a	from × 8
Nos. 4/6a	from × 5
Nos. 7/40	from × 3
Nos. L1/10	from × 6
Nos. L11/17	from × 3

I. TURKISH CURRENCY
(40 paras = 1 piastre)

Following the depreciation of the Turkish piastre against sterling in 1884 it was decided to issue stamps surcharged in Turkish currency to avoid speculation. During the early period unsurcharged stamps of Great Britain remained on sale from the British Post Offices at the current rate of exchange until replaced by "LEVANT" overprints.

80 PARAS 4 PIASTRES 12 PIASTRES
(1)   (2)   (3)

PRINTERS. Nos. 1/24 were surcharged or overprinted by De La Rue, *unless otherwise stated.*

Stamps of Great Britain (Queen Victoria) surch as T **1** to **3**

1885 (1 Aug)–88.

1	**64**	40pa. on 2½d. lilac	£140	1·25
2	**62**	80pa. on 5d. lilac	£225	9·50
3	**58**	12pi. on 2s.6d. lilac/*bluish*	£550	£300
		a. On white paper (4.88)	65·00	26·00

Nos. 3, 11 and 33 were surcharged from a horizontal setting of eight clichés of which three showed a small final 'S'.

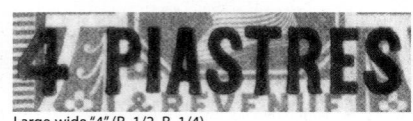

Large wide "4" (R. 1/2, R. 1/4)

1887 (June)–96.

4	**74**	40pa. on 2½d. purple/*blue*	21·00	10
		a. Surch double	£1900	£2500
5	**78**	80pa. on 5d. purple and blue (7.90)	18·00	30
		a. Small "0" in "80"	£375	95·00
		w. Wmk inverted	—	£650
6	**81**	4pi. on 10d. dull purple and carmine (10.10.96)	45·00	8·50
		a. Dull purple and deep bright carmine	45·00	11·00
		b. Large, wide "4" (R. 1/2, 1/4)	£225	70·00

No. 5a first appeared on the June 1895 printing when the size of the surcharge plate was increased from 60 to 120. On the Victorian stamp the variety comes on R. 4/1 and 4/7. The same setting was used for the first printing of the Edward VII surcharge, but here the sheet size was further increased to 240 so that No. 9a occurs on R. 4/1, 4/7, 14/1 and 14/7.

1893 (25 Feb). Roughly handstamped at Constantinople, as T **1**.

7	**71**	40pa. on ½d. vermilion	£425	£100

This provisional was in use for five days only at the Constantinople and Stamboul offices. As fraudulent copies were made with the original handstamp, and can be found "used" on piece cancelled by fraudulent use of the usual canceller, this stamp should only be purchased from undoubted sources.

The handstamp became damaged during use so that by 1 March the top of the "S" was broken. Used examples dated 25 or 26 February showing the broken "S" *must* be fraudulent. It is also known with genuine handstamp inverted (*Price £850 unused, £325 used*).

1902–05. Stamps of King Edward VII surch as T **1** to **3**.

8	**86**	40pa. on 2½d. ultramarine (3.02)	24·00	10
		a. Pale ultramarine	26·00	10
		ab. Surch double	†	£2500
9	**89**	80pa. on 5d. dull purple and ultramarine (5.6.02)	18·00	2·00
		a. Small "0" in "80"	£325	£200
10	**92**	4pi. on 10d. dull purple and carmine (6.9.02)	26·00	4·50
		a. No cross on crown	£180	90·00
		b. Chalk-surfaced paper	6·00	10·00
		ba. Chalk-surfaced paper. No cross on crown	£100	£120

11	**94**	12pi. on 2s.6d. lilac (29.8.03)	42·00	38·00
		a. Chalk-surfaced paper. *Pale dull purple*	75·00	80·00
		b. Chalk-surfaced paper. *Dull purple*	42·00	38·00
12	**95**	24pi. on 5s. bright carmine (15.8.05)	32·00	42·00
8/12 *Set of 5*			£110	75·00
9s/11s Optd "SPECIMEN" *Set of 3*				£160

No. 9a only occurs on the first printing of 80pa. on 5d.

1 PIASTRE
(4)

1905–08. Surch in "PIASTRES" instead of "PARAS" as T **4** and **2**.

13	**86**	1pi. on 2½d. ultramarine (17.4.06)	32·00	10
		a. Surch double	†	£2000
		w. Wmk inverted	£750	£750
14	**89**	2pi. on 5d. dull purple and ultramarine (11.11.05)	50·00	2·50
		a. Chalk-surfaced paper (1.08)	30·00	5·00
		ab. *Slate-purple and ultramarine*	50·00	9·50

1 PIASTRE
ɪ Piastre   10 PARAS
(5)   (6)

1906 (2 July). Issued at Beyrout. No. L4 surch with T **5** by American Press, Beyrout.

15	**85**	1pi. on 2d. grey-green and carmine	£1500	£700

1909 (16 Nov–Dec). Stamps of King Edward VII surch as T **1** (30pa.) **6**, and **2** (5pi). Ordinary paper (No. 19) or chalk-surfaced paper (others).

16	**84**	30pa. on 1½d. pale dull purple and green	20·00	1·25
		a. Surch double, one albino		
17	**87**	1pi.10pa. on 3d. dull purple/*orange-yellow*	12·00	50·00
18	**88**	1pi.30pa. on 4d. green and chocolate-brown	5·00	20·00
19		1pi.30pa. on 4d. brown-orange (16.12.09)	22·00	70·00
20	**83**	2pi.20pa. on 6d. dull purple	26·00	70·00
21	**93**	5pi. on 1s. dull green and carmine	4·25	17·00
		s. Optd "SPECIMEN"	80·00	
16/21 *Set of 6*			75·00	£200

Examples of Nos. 17/21 are known showing forged Constantinople postmarks dated "MR 1 10", "AP 1 10" and "AP 18 10", or a forged Smyrna registered oval dated "24 OC 10".

1¾
PIASTRE   4   4
(7)   Normal "4"   Pointed "4"

1910 (24 Jan). Stamps of King Edward VII surch as T **7**. Chalk-surfaced paper (Nos. 22 and 24).

22	**87**	1¼pi. on 3d. dull purple/*orange-yellow*	1·00	1·00
23	**88**	1¾pi. on 4d. pale orange	50	60
		a. Orange-red	7·00	7·50
		b. Thin, pointed "4" in fraction	5·50	26·00
24	**83**	2½pi. on 6d. dull purple	4·00	65
22/4 *Set of 3*			5·00	2·00

No. 23b occurs in the first and seventh vertical rows of the sheet. The variety also occurs on No. 38, but not on No. 38b.

1 PIASTRE   1 PIASTRE
(8)   (9)

TYPE DIFFERENCES. In T **4** the letters are tall and narrow and the space enclosed by the upper part of the "A" is small.

In T **8** the opening of the "A" is similar but the letters are shorter and broader, the "P" and the "E" being particularly noticeable.

In T **9** the letters are short and broad, but the "A" is thin and open.

1911–13. Stamps of King Edward VII, Harrison or Somerset House ptgs, surch at Somerset House.

		*(a) Surch with T **4** (20 July)*		
25	**86**	1pi. on 2½d. bright blue (perf 14)	26·00	11·00
		a. Surch double, one albino	£225	
26		1pi. on 2½d. bright blue (perf 15×14) (14.10.11)	40·00	4·50
		a. Dull blue	32·00	4·00
		b. Surch double, one albino		
		*(b) Surch with T **8***		
27	**86**	1pi. on 2½d. bright blue (perf 15×14) (3.12)	27·00	6·50
		a. Dull blue	32·00	7·00
		*(c) Surch with T **9***		
28	**86**	1pi. on 2½d. bright blue (perf 15×14)	90·00	75
		a. Dull blue	90·00	75
		*(d) Surch with T **1** to **3** (1911–13)*		
29	**84**	30pa. on 1½d. reddish purple and bright green (22.8.11)	6·50	75
		a. Slate-purple and green	12·00	2·50
		b. Surch double, one albino	55·00	
30	**89**	2pi. on 5d. dull reddish purple and bright blue (13.5.12)	27·00	3·25
		a. Deep dull reddish purple and bright blue	30·00	3·25
31	**92**	4pi. on 10d. dull purple and scarlet (26.6.12)	60·00	26·00
		a. Dull reddish purple and aniline pink	£325	£140
		b. Dull reddish purple and carmine	19·00	11·00
		c. No cross on crown		
32	**93**	5pi. on 1s. green and carmine (2.13)	23·00	12·00
		a. Surch double, one albino	£250	
33	**94**	12pi. on 2s.6d. reddish purple (3.2.12)	65·00	38·00
		a. Dull greyish purple	65·00	38·00
34	**95**	24pi. on 5s. carmine (1912)	80·00	£100
		a. Surch double, one albino	£325	
29/34 *Set of 6*			£200	£140

1913 (Apr)–14. Stamps of King George V, wmk Royal Cypher, surch as T **1** (30pa.), **9** (1pi.) **7** or **2** (4 and 5pi.).

35	**105**	30pa. on 1½d. red-brown (4.13)	3·50	14·00
		a. Surch double, one albino	£120	
36	**104**	1pi. on 2½d. cobalt-blue (6.13)	16·00	10
		a. Bright blue	14·00	15
37	**106**	1¼pi. on 3d. dull reddish violet (9.13)	9·00	4·25
		a. Violet	14·00	7·50
		b. Surch double, one albino	£300	
38		1¾pi. on 4d. deep grey-green (7.13)	4·50	8·50
		a. Thin, pointed "4" in fraction	45·00	90·00
		b. Grey-green	14·00	7·00
39	**108**	4pi. on 10d. turquoise-blue (12.13)	13·00	29·00
40		5pi. on 1s. bistre-brown (1.14)	48·00	75·00
35/40 *Set of 6*			80·00	£120

II. BRITISH CURRENCY

Stamps overprinted "LEVANT" were for use on parcels, with the ½d. and 1d. principally used for printed paper and post cards. They replaced unoverprinted Great Britain stamps, Nos. Z58/64, Z160/74, Z208/9c and Z267/81, which had previously been used for these purposes.

From October 1907 the three lowest values were also used for certain other amended postal rates until Nos. 16/21 were introduced.

LEVANT
(L **1**)

1905 (15 Aug)–12. Stamps of King Edward VII optd with Type L **1**.

		(a) De La Rue ptgs		
L1	**83**	½d. pale yellowish green	8·50	15
		a. Yellowish green	8·50	15
L2		1d. scarlet	14·00	15
		a. Bright scarlet	14·00	90
L3	**84**	1½d. dull purple and green	6·50	2·50
		a. Chalk-surfaced paper. Pale dull purple and green	24·00	3·50
L4	**85**	2d. grey-green and carmine-red	18·00	50·00
		a. Chalk-surfaced paper. Pale grey-green and carmine-red	4·25	8·50
		ab. Dull blue-green and carmine	4·25	8·50
L5	**86**	2½d. ultramarine	8·50	20·00
L6	**87**	3d. dull purple/*orange-yellow*	7·00	12·00
L7	**88**	4d. green and grey-brown	10·00	70·00
		a. Green and chocolate-brown	26·00	75·00
L8	**89**	5d. dull purple and ultramarine	16·00	38·00
L9	**83**	6d. slate-purple	12·00	25·00
L10	**93**	1s. dull green and carmine	42·00	55·00
		a. Chalk-surfaced paper	42·00	55·00
L1/10 *Set of 10*			£110	£200
		(b) Harrison ptgs optd at Somerset House		
L11	**83**	½d. dull yellow-green (P 14) (1.12)	50·00	50·00
		a. Dull green	50·00	50·00
		b. Deep dull green	65·00	55·00

On 28 December 1909 all values, except for the ½d., 1d. and 2d. were withdrawn from sale. Subsequently dated cancellations on the withdrawn values are philatelic, being worth much less than the used prices quoted.

ANT
Distorted "N" (R. 2/12, 12/12)

1911–13. Stamps of King George V optd with Type L **1** at Somerset House.

		(a) Die A. Wmk Crown		
L12	**98**	½d. green (No. 322) (12.9.11)	3·25	4·50
		a. Distorted "N"	50·00	
L13	**99**	1d. carmine-red (No. 327) (1.1.12)	75	8·50
		a. No cross on crown	£150	
		b. Opt double, one albino	£100	
		c. Distorted "N"	21·00	
		(b) Redrawn types. Wmk Crown		
L14	**101**	½d. green (No. 339) (19.3.12)	3·75	20
		a. Yellow-green	4·75	1·25
		b. Distorted "N"	42·00	
L15	**102**	1d. bright scarlet (No. 341) (24.2.12)	3·25	1·60
		a. Scarlet (No. 342)	3·25	1·60
		b. Opt triple, two albino	45·00	
		c. Distorted "N"	40·00	
		(c) New types. Wmk Royal Cypher (7.13)		
L16	**105**	½d. green (No. 351)	2·25	3·50
		a. Yellow-green	4·50	4·75
		b. Distorted "N"	30·00	
L17	**104**	1d. scarlet (No. 357)	40	7·50
		a. Vermilion	22·00	21·00
		b. Distorted "N"	18·00	

Similar overprints were issued when the British Post Offices reopened in 1919, and are listed below.

B. BRITISH POST OFFICES IN CONSTANTINOPLE AND SMYRNA, 1919–1923

CONSTANTINOPLE

Following the occupation of Constantinople by Allied forces a British Military Post Office was opened for civilian use on 4 February 1919. During the period of its existence stamps of Great Britain with face values to 10s. were available and such use can be identified by the following cancellations:

"FIELD POST OFFICE H12" (4 February 1919 to 18 March 1919)
"ARMY POST OFFICE Y" (20 March 1919 to June 1920)
"ARMY POST OFFICE S.X.3" (March 1919 to April 1920)
"British A.P.O. CONSTANTINOPLE" (July 1919 to July 1920).
Of these four marks the first two types were also used for military mail.

The office reverted to civilian control on 29 July 1920, Nos. 41/50 and L18/24 being intended for its use.

Z 9   Z 10

Z 11   Z 12

1919–20. Used at the Army Post Office. Stamps of GREAT BRITAIN cancelled with Types Z **9**, Z **10**, Z **11**, Z **12**.

Z176	½d. green		2·50
Z177	1d. scarlet		2·50
Z178	1½d. brown		3·75
Z179	2d. orange (Die I)		3·00
Z180	2½d. blue		4·50
Z181	4d. grey-green		12·00
Z181a	5d. yellow-brown		
Z182	6d. purple		6·50
Z183	9d. agate		30·00
Z184	1s. bistre		7·00
Z185	2s.6d. brown		70·00
Z186	5s. rose-carmine		£110
Z187	10s. dull grey-blue		£190

1920–21. Used at the Civilian Post Office. Stamps of GREAT BRITAIN cancelled as Type Z **7** or double-circle datestamp.

Z188	½d. green		2·50
Z189	1d. scarlet		2·50
Z190	1½d. brown		3·75
Z191	2d. orange (Die I)		3·00
Z192	2½d. blue		4·50
Z193	3d. violet		8·50
Z194	4d. grey-green		12·00
Z195	5d. brown		18·00
Z196	6d. purple		6·50
Z197	10d. turquoise-blue		30·00
Z198	1s. bistre		7·00
Z199	2s.6d. brown		70·00
Z200	5s. rose-carmine		£110
Z201	10s. dull grey-blue		£190

PRICES FOR STAMPS ON COVER	
Nos. 41/50	from × 2
Nos. L18/24	from × 5

Stamps of Great Britain surch at Somerset House

I. TURKISH CURRENCY

(10)   (11)

Short fraction bar (R. 4/12, 14/12)

1921 (Aug). Stamps of King George V, wmk Royal Cypher, surch as T **1** (30pa.), **10** and **11** (15 and 18¾pi.).

41	105	30pa. on ½d. green	75	17·00
		a. Yellow-green	4·75	19·00
42	104	1½pi. on 1d. bright scarlet	1·75	2·00
		a. Vermilion	25·00	8·50
		b. Scarlet-vermilion	22·00	9·50
43		3¾pi. on 2½d. blue	1·25	25
		a. Dull Prussian blue	60·00	40·00
44	106	4½pi. on 3d. violet	2·00	3·75
		a. Bluish violet	8·00	3·75
45	107	7½pi. on 5d. brown	50	10
		a. Yellow-brown	3·50	50
46	108	15pi. on 10d. turquoise-blue	70	15
47		18¾pi. on 1s. bistre-brown	4·25	5·00
		a. Short fraction bar	65·00	
		b. Olive-bistre	10·00	7·00
		ba. Short fraction bar	£110	

No. 41 is known with inverted surcharge, but the status of this variety is uncertain.

45 PIASTRES   **45**

(12)   Joined figures (second stamp in each horiz row)

1921. Stamps of King George V (Bradbury Wilkinson printing) surch as T **12**.

48	109	45pi. on 2s.6d. chocolate-brown	22·00	45·00
		a. Joined figures	35·00	70·00
		b. Olive-brown	55·00	65·00

---

		ba. Joined figures	75·00	95·00
		c. Pale brown	£250	£250
49		90pi. on 5s. rose-carmine	25·00	30·00
		a. Surch double, one albino	£250	
50		180pi. on 10s. dull grey-blue	45·00	40·00
		a. Surch double, one albino	£250	
41/50		Set of 10	90·00	£130
47s/50s		Optd "SPECIMEN" Set of 4	£275	

II. BRITISH CURRENCY

1921. Stamps of King George V optd as Type L **1**.

L18	106	2d. reddish orange (Die I)	2·75	45·00
		a. Bright orange	2·25	45·00
L19		3d. bluish violet	7·50	10·00
L20		4d. grey-green	5·00	27·00
L21	107	5d. yellow-brown	12·00	28·00
L22		6d. dull purple (chalk-surfaced paper)	24·00	42·00
		a. Reddish purple	42·00	8·50
L23	108	1s. bistre-brown	21·00	8·50
		a. Olive-bistre	21·00	8·50
		s. Optd "SPECIMEN"	80·00	
L24	109	2s.6d. chocolate-brown	38·00	£100
		a. Olive-brown	65·00	£130
		b. Pale brown	£250	£150
		s. Optd "SPECIMEN"	£140	
L18/24		Set of 7	£100	£200

On No. L24 the letters of the overprint are shorter, being only 3 mm high.

Nos. 41/50 and L18/24 were used at the Constantinople office only.

SMYRNA

When the office re-opened on 1 March 1919 existing stocks of surcharged or overprinted issues were utilised until they were exhausted in mid-1920. During this period examples of Nos. 24, 29a, 30a, 33a/7, 39/40, L4ab, L14/17 are known with commercial postmarks. These stamps were supplemented and finally replaced in mid-1920 by ordinary stamps of Great Britain.

1919–22. Stamps of GREAT BRITAIN cancelled with circular postmark as Type Z **7** or with "REGISTERED" oval.

Z282	½d. green		3·00
Z283	1d. scarlet		3·00
Z284	1½d. brown		4·00
Z285	2d. orange (Die I)		3·50
Z286	2d. orange (Die II)		35·00
Z287	2½d. blue (shades)		5·50
Z288	2½d. dull Prussian blue		£500
Z289	4d. grey-green		13·00
Z290	6d. purple		9·00
Z290a	8d. black/yellow-buff		
Z291	10d. turquoise-blue		42·00
Z292	1s. bistre		10·00
Z293	2s.6d. brown		£110
Z294	5s. rose-carmine		£180
Z295	10s. dull grey-blue		£325

Turkish forces entered Smyrna on 9 September 1922 and the British postal service was suspended shortly afterwards.

C. BRITISH FIELD OFFICE IN SALONICA

These overprints were originally prepared for use by a civilian post office to be set up on Mt. Athos, Northern Greece. When the project was abandoned they were placed on sale at the Army Field Office in Salonica.

PRICES FOR STAMPS ON COVER	
Nos. S1/8	from × 3

Levant
(S **1**)

1916 (end Feb–9 Mar). Stamps of Gt. Britain, optd with Type S **1** by Army Printing Office, Salonica.

S1	105	½d. green	70·00	£325
		a. Opt double	£4500	£5000
		b. Vert pair, one without opt	£2250	£3000
S2	104	1d. scarlet	70·00	£325
		a. Opt double	£3000	£3500
S3	106	2d. reddish orange (Die I)	£200	£475
S4		3d. bluish violet	£160	£475
S5		4d. grey-green	£190	£475
S6	107	6d. reddish purple (chalk-surfaced paper)	£110	£400
		a. Vert pair, one without opt	£2250	£3250
S7	108	9d. agate	£400	£750
		a. Opt double	£17000	£12000
S8		1s. bistre-brown	£350	£650
S1/8		Set of 8	£1400	£3500

There are numerous forgeries of this overprint.

All values can be found with an additional albino overprint, inverted on the gummed side. These are worth a 25% premium.

British New Guinea
*see **Papua** after **Australia***

British Occupation of Iraq *see **Iraq***

British Occupation of Italian Colonies

PRICES FOR STAMPS ON COVER TO 1945		
Nos. M1/21		from × 4
Nos. MD1/5		from × 10
Nos. S1/9		from × 4

The above prices refer to covers from the territories concerned, not examples used in Great Britain.

MIDDLE EAST FORCES

For use in territory occupied by British Forces in Eritrea (1942), Italian Somaliland (from 13 April 1942), Cyrenaica (1943), Tripolitania (1943), and some of the Dodecanese Islands (1945).

PRICES. Our prices for used stamps with "M.E.F." overprints are for examples with identifiable postmarks of the territories in which they were issued. These stamps were also used in the United Kingdom with official sanction, from the summer of 1950 onwards, and with U.K. postmarks are worth considerably less.

PRINTERS. Considerable research has been undertaken to discover the origins of Nos. M1/10. It is now suggested that Nos. M1/5, previously assigned to Harrison and Sons, were produced by the Army Printing Services, Cairo, and that the smaller printing, Nos. M6/10, previously identified as the work of the Army Printing Services, Cairo, was from GHQ, Middle East Land Forces, Nairobi.

M.E.F. M.E.F.

(M **1**) Opt. 14 mm long. Regular lettering and upright oblong stops.

(M **2**) Opt. 13½ mm long. Regular lettering and square stops.

M.E.F. M.E.F.

(M **2a**) Opt. 13½ mm long. Rough lettering and round stops.

Sliced "M" (R. 6/10)

(Illustrations twice actual size)

1942 (2 Mar). Stamps of Great Britain optd. W **127**. P 15×14.

		*(a) With Type M **1***		
M1	128	1d. scarlet (No. 463)	3·50	4·75
		a. Sliced "M"	£170	£200
M2		2d. orange (No. 465)	3·00	6·00
		a. Sliced "M"	£120	
M3		2½d. ultramarine (No. 466)	3·00	2·00
		a. Sliced "M"	£170	£190
M4		3d. violet (No. 467)	2·75	30
		a. Sliced "M"		
M5	129	5d. brown	2·75	1·00
		a. Sliced "M"	£160	£170
		*(b) With Type M **2***		
M6	128	1d. scarlet (No. 463)	55·00	26·00
		a. Optd with Type M **2a**	48·00	18·00
		b. Nos. M6/a se-tenant vert	£200	£160
M7		2d. orange (No. 465)	90·00	£160
		a. Optd with Type M **2a**	80·00	£140
		b. Nos. M7/a se-tenant vert	£425	£700
M8		2½d. ultramarine (No. 466)	70·00	12·00
		a. Optd with Type M **2a**	65·00	9·50
		b. Nos. M8/a se-tenant vert	£325	95·00
M9		3d. violet (No. 467)	£140	60·00
		aa. Opt double	†	£6500
		a. Optd with Type M **2a**	£130	55·00
		ab. Opt double	†	£6500
		b. Nos. M9/a se-tenant vert	£600	£350
M10	129	5d. brown	£500	£130
		a. Optd with Type M **2a**	£450	£110
		b. Nos. M10/a se-tenant vert	£1800	£1000

See note after No. M21.

Nos. M6/10 were issued in panes of 60 (6×10), rows 2, 3, and 7 being overprinted with Type M **2** and the other seven rows with Type M **2a**.

M.E.F.

(M **3**) Optd 13½ mm long. Regular lettering and upright oblong stops.

(Illustration twice actual size)

1943 (1 Jan)–**47.** Stamps of Great Britain optd with Type M **3** by Harrison & Sons. W **127**, P 15×14 (1d. to 1s.); W **133**, P 14 (others).

M11	128	1d. pale scarlet (No. 486)	1·50	10
M12		2d. pale orange (No. 488)	2·25	1·25
M13		2½d. light ultramarine (No. 489)	2·25	10
M14		3d. pale violet (No. 490)	1·50	10
M15	129	5d. brown	4·00	10
M16		6d. purple	65	10
M17	130	9d. deep olive-green	85	10
M18		1s. bistre-brown	50	10
M19	131	2s.6d. yellow-green	7·00	10
M20		5s. red (27.1.47)	32·00	17·00
M21	132	10s. ultramarine (27.1.47)	45·00	10·00
M11/21		Set of 11	85·00	27·00
M18s/21s		Optd "SPECIMEN" Set of 4	£650	

The overprint on No. M15 should not be confused with the other overprints on the 5d. value. It can be distinguished from No. M5 by the ½ mm difference in length; and from No. M10 by the more intense colour, thicker lettering and larger stops.

POSTAGE DUE STAMPS
M.E.F.
(MD 1)

1942 (2 Mar). Postage Due stamps of Great Britain Nos. D27/30 and D33 optd with Type MD 1, in blue-black.

MD1	D 1	½d. emerald	40	13·00
MD2		1d. carmine	40	1·75
		w. Wmk sideways inverted*	—	£110
MD3		2d. agate	2·00	1·25
MD4		3d. violet	50	4·25
MD5		1s. deep blue	4·00	13·00
		s. Optd "SPECIMEN"	£190	
MD1/5 Set of 5			6·50	30·00

*No. MD2w shows the Crown pointing to the left, as seen from the back of the stamp.

CYRENAICA

In June 1949 the British authorities recognised the leader of the Senussi, Amir Mohammed Idris Al-Senussi, as Amir of Cyrenaica with autonomy in internal affairs.

(Currency. 10 millièmes = 1 piastre, 100 piastres = 1 Egyptian pound)

24 Mounted Warrior	25 Mounted Warrior

(Recess Waterlow)

1950 (16 Jan). P 12½.

136	24	1m. brown	5·50	10·00
137		2m. carmine	5·50	10·00
138		3m. orange-yellow	5·50	7·50
139		4m. blue-green	5·50	10·00
140		5m. grey-black	5·50	10·00
141		8m. orange	5·50	4·75
142		10m. violet	5·50	2·75
143		12m. scarlet	5·50	4·25
144		20m. blue	5·50	2·75
145	25	50m. ultramarine and purple-brown	22·00	11·00
146		100m. carmine and black	35·00	13·00
147		200m. violet and deep blue	45·00	48·00
148		500m. orange-yellow and green	70·00	£110
136/148 Set of 13			£190	£225

POSTAGE DUE STAMPS

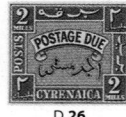

D 26

(Recess Waterlow)

1950 (16 Jan). P 12½.

D149	D 26	2m. brown	60·00	£110
D150		4m. blue-green	60·00	£110
D151		8m. scarlet	60·00	£120
D152		10m. orange	60·00	£120
D153		20m. orange-yellow	60·00	£140
D154		40m. blue	60·00	£180
D155		100m. grey-brown	60·00	£200
D149/155 Set of 7			£375	£900

On 24 December 1951 Cyrenaica united with Tripolitania, Fezzan and Ghadames to form the independent Kingdom of Libya, whose issues are listed in our Part 13 (Africa since Independence F—M) catalogue.

ERITREA

From early 1950 examples of Nos. E1/32 exist precancelled in manuscript by a black or blue horizontal line for use on non-concession rate mail.

BRITISH MILITARY ADMINISTRATION
(Currency. 100 cents = 1 shilling)

B.M.A. ERITREA	B.M.A. ERITREA
10 CENTS	5 SHILLINGS
(E 1)	(E 2)

SH. 50 SH .50

Normal	Misplaced Stop

Two settings of the 5s. on 5s.
I 1.8mm between obliterating bars
II 1mm between obliterating bars

1948 (27 May)–**49**. Stamps of Great Britain surch as Types E 1 or E 2.

E1	128	5c. on ½d. pale green	2·75	65
E2		10c. on 1d. pale scarlet	2·00	2·50

E3		20c. on 2d. pale orange	3·00	2·25
E4		25c. on 2½d. light ultramarine	2·00	60
E5		30c. pale violet	2·50	4·50
E6	129	40c. on 5d. brown	2·75	4·25
E7		50c. on 6d. purple	2·25	1·00
E7a	130	65c. on 8d. bright carmine (1.2.49)	7·00	2·00
E8		75c. on 9d. deep olive-green	3·75	75
E9		1s. on 1s. bistre-brown	2·50	50
E10	131	2s.50c. on 2s.6d. yellow-green	13·00	12·00
		a. Misplaced stop (R. 4/7)	£180	£225
E11		5s. on 5s. red	14·00	24·00
		a. Second setting (1.49)	£250	
E12	132	10s. on 10s. ultramarine	30·00	24·00
E1/12 Set of 13			75·00	70·00

BRITISH ADMINISTRATION

1950 (6 Feb). As Nos. E1/12, but surch "B.A. ERITREA" and new values instead of "B.M.A." etc.

E13	128	5c. on ½d. pale green	1·50	8·00
E14		10c. on 1d. pale scarlet	40	3·00
E15		20c. on 2d. pale orange	1·50	80
E16		25c. on 2½d. light ultramarine	1·00	60
E17		30c. on 3d. pale violet	40	2·25
E18	129	40c. on 5d. brown	3·00	1·75
E19		50c. on 6d. purple	40	20
E20	130	65c. on 8d. bright carmine	6·50	1·50
E21		75c. on 9d. deep olive-green	2·00	25
E22		1s. on 1s. bistre-brown	40	15
E23	131	2s.50c. on 2s.6d. yellow-green	10·00	5·50
E24		5s. on 5s. red	10·00	12·00
E25	132	10s. on 10s. ultramarine	80·00	70·00
E13/25 Set of 13			£100	95·00

1951 (28 May*). Nos. 503/4, 506/7 and 509/11 of Great Britain surch "B.A. ERITREA" and new values.

E26	128	5c. on ½d. pale orange	3·50	5·50
E27		10c. on 1d. light ultramarine	2·75	75
E28		20c. on 2d. pale red-brown	3·50	30
E29		25c. on 2½d. pale scarlet	3·50	30
E30	147	2s.50c. on 2s.6d. yellow-green	22·00	32·00
E31	148	5s. on 5s. red	23·00	40·00
E32		10s. on 10s. ultramarine	30·00	40·00
E26/32 Set of 7			75·00	£100

*This is the local release date. The stamps were placed on sale in London on 3 May.

POSTAGE DUE STAMPS
B.M.A. ERITREA
10 CENTS
(ED 1)

1948 (27 May). Postage Due stamps of Great Britain Nos. D27/30 and D33 surch as Type ED 1.

ED1	D 1	5c. on ½d. emerald	10·00	22·00
		a. No stop after "A"	—	£475
ED2		10c. on 1d. carmine	10·00	24·00
		a. No stop after "B" (R. 1/9)	£190	£375
ED3		20c. on 2d. agate	17·00	16·00
		a. No stop after "A"	70·00	
		b. No stop after "B" (R. 1/9)	£225	£300
ED4		30c. on 3d. violet	13·00	17·00
ED5		1s. on 1s. deep blue	21·00	32·00
		a. No stop after "A"	—	£650
ED1/5 Set of 5			65·00	£100

1950 (6 Feb). As Nos. ED1/5, but surch "B.A. ERITREA" and new values instead of "B.M.A." etc.

ED6	D 1	5c. on ½d. emerald	16·00	65·00
ED7		10c. on 1d. carmine	16·00	22·00
		a. "C" of "CENTS" omitted	£5000	
		ab. "C" omitted and vertical oblong for "E" of "CENTS"	£8500	
ED8		20c. on 2d. agate	16·00	25·00
		a. No stop after "A"	£450	
ED9		30c. on 3d. violet	20·00	50·00
		w. Wmk sideways-inverted*	—	75·00
ED10		1s. on 1s. deep blue	21·00	50·00
		a. No stop after "A" (R. 2/13)	£650	
ED6/10 Set of 5			80·00	£180

No. ED7a, and probably No. ED7ab, occurred on R. 7/17, but the error was quickly corrected.

*No. ED9w shows the Crowns pointing to the left, as seen from the back of the stamp.

Stamps of Ethiopia were used in Eritrea after 15 September 1952 following federation with Ethiopia.

SOMALIA
BRITISH OCCUPATION
E.A.F.
(S 1 "East Africa Forces")

1943 (15 Jan)–**46**. Stamps of Great Britain optd with Type S 1, in blue.

S1	128	1d. pale scarlet	1·50	2·75
S2		2d. pale orange	1·75	1·75
S3		2½d. light ultramarine	2·00	3·50
S4		3d. pale violet	1·75	15
S5	129	5d. brown	2·50	40
S6		6d. purple	2·25	1·50
S7	130	9d. deep olive-green	2·75	4·25
S8		1s. bistre-brown	3·75	15
S9	131	2s.6d. yellow-green (14.1.46)	42·00	14·00
S1/9 Set of 9			55·00	25·00
S8s/9s Optd "SPECIMEN" Set of 2			£350	

The note re used prices above Type M 1 of Middle East Forces also applies to the above issue.

BRITISH MILITARY ADMINISTRATION
(Currency. 100 cents = 1 shilling)

1948 (27 May). Stamps of Great Britain surch "B.M.A./SOMALIA" and new values, as Types E 1 and E 2 of Eritrea.

S10	128	5c. on ½d. pale green	1·25	2·75
S11		15c. on 1½d. pale red-brown	1·75	15·00
S12		20c. on 2d. pale orange	3·00	7·00
S13		25c. on 2½d. light ultramarine	2·25	4·50
S14		30c. on 3d. pale violet	2·25	9·00
S15	129	40c. on 5d. brown	1·25	20
S16		50c. on 6d. purple	50	2·00
S17	130	75c. on 9d. deep olive-green	2·00	28·00
S18		1s. on 1s. bistre-brown	1·25	20
S19	131	2s.50c. on 2s.6d. yellow-green	11·00	25·00
		a. Misplaced stop (R. 4/7)	£140	£300
S20		5s. on 5s. red	22·00	65·00
S10/20 Set of 11			42·00	£140

For illustration of No. S19a, see above No. E1 of Eritrea.

BRITISH ADMINISTRATION

1950 (2 Jan). As Nos. S10/20, but surch "B.A./SOMALIA" and new values, instead of "B.M.A." etc.

S21	128	5c. on ½d. pale green	20	3·50
S22		15c. on 1½d. pale red-brown	75	17·00
S23		20c. on 2d. pale orange	75	7·50
S24		25c. on 2½d. light ultramarine	50	14·00
S25		30c. on 3d. pale violet	1·25	11·00
S26	129	40c. on 5d. brown	60	3·00
S27		50c. on 6d. purple	60	1·00
S28	130	75c. on 9d. deep olive-green	2·00	14·00
S29		1s. on 1s. bistre-brown	70	2·00
S30	131	2s.50c. on 2s.6d. yellow-green	8·50	38·00
S31		5s. on 5s. red	23·00	55·00
S21/31 Set of 11			35·00	£140

Somalia reverted to Italian Administration on 1 April 1950 later becoming independent. Later issues will be found listed in our Part 8 (Italy and Switzerland) catalogue.

TRIPOLITANIA
BRITISH MILITARY ADMINISTRATION
(Currency. 100 centesimi = 1 Military Administration lira)

4 M.A.L.   4 M.A.L.

Normal	Misaligned surcharge (R. 8/8, 18/8)

1948 (1 July). Stamps of Great Britain surch "B.M.A./TRIPOLITANIA" and new values, as Types E 1 and E 2 of Eritrea, but expressed in M(ilitary) A(dministration) L(ire).

T1	128	1l. on ½d. pale green	1·00	5·50
T2		2l. on 1d. pale scarlet	50	15
T3		3l. on 1½d. pale red-brown	50	50
		a. Misaligned surch	65·00	75·00
T4		4l. on 2d. pale orange	50	70
		a. Misaligned surch	65·00	85·00
T5		5l. on 2½d. light ultramarine	50	20
T6		6l. on 3d. pale violet	50	40
T7	129	10l. on 5d. brown	50	15
T8		12l. on 6d. purple	50	20
T9	130	18l. on 9d. deep olive-green	1·50	1·75
T10		24l. on 1s. bistre-brown	2·50	3·00
T11	131	60l. on 2s.6d. yellow-green	9·50	17·00
T12		120l. on 5s. red	29·00	30·00
T13	132	240l. on 10s. ultramarine	32·00	£150
T1/13 Set of 13			70·00	£180

BRITISH ADMINISTRATION

1950 (6 Feb). As Nos. T1/13, but surch "B.A. TRIPOLITANIA" and new values, instead of "B.M.A." etc.

T14	128	1l. on ½d. pale green	6·00	13·00
T15		2l. on 1d. pale scarlet	5·00	40
T16		3l. on 1½d. pale red-brown	4·25	13·00
		a. Misaligned surch	£140	£350
T17		4l. on 2d. pale orange	4·25	4·50
		a. Misaligned surch	£150	£180
T18		5l. on 2½d. light ultramarine	2·25	70
T19		6l. on 3d. pale violet	3·75	3·25
T20	129	10l. on 5d. brown	3·75	4·00
T21		12l. on 6d. purple	5·00	50
T22	130	18l. on 9d. deep olive-green	8·00	2·75
T23		24l. on 1s. bistre-brown	7·50	3·75
T24	131	60l. on 2s.6d. yellow-green	20·00	12·00
T25		120l. on 5s. red	40·00	48·00
T26	132	240l. on 10s. ultramarine	55·00	90·00
T14/26 Set of 13			£140	£170

1951 (3 May). Nos. 503/7 and 509/11 of Great Britain surch "B.A. TRIPOLITANIA" and new values.

T27	128	1l. on ½d. pale orange	55	10·00
T28		2l. on 1d. light ultramarine	55	1·00
T29		3l. on 1½d. pale red-brown	55	8·00
T30		4l. on 2d. pale red-brown	55	1·25
T31		5l. on 2½d. pale scarlet	1·00	7·50
T32	147	60l. on 2s.6d. yellow-green	21·00	40·00
T33	148	120l. on 5s. red	21·00	45·00
T34	149	240l. on 10s. ultramarine	50·00	85·00
T27/34 Set of 8			80·00	£170

POSTAGE DUE STAMPS

1948 (1 July). Postage Due stamps of Great Britain Nos. D27/30 and D33 surch "B.M.A./TRIPOLITANIA" and new values, as Type ED 1 of Eritrea, but expressed in M(ilitary) A(dministration) L(ire).

TD1	D 1	1l. on ½d. emerald	6·00	65·00
		a. No stop after "A"	90·00	

TD2	2l. on 1d. carmine		2·50	55·00
	a. No stop after "A"		50·00	
	b. No stop after "M" (R. 1/17)		£160	
TD3	4l. on 2d. agate		13·00	50·00
	a. No stop after "A" (R. 2/12, R. 3/8)		£170	
	b. No stop after "M" (R. 1/17)		£325	
TD4	6l. on 3d. violet		7·50	27·00
TD5	24l. on 1s. deep blue		29·00	£110
TD1/5 Set of 5			50·00	£275

1950 (6 Feb). As Nos. TD1/5, but surch "B.A. TRIPOLITANIA" and new values, instead of "B.M.A." etc.

TD6	D 1	1l. on ½d. emerald	16·00	£110
		a. No stop after "B"	£250	
TD7		2l. on 1d. carmine	10·00	38·00
		a. No stop after "A" (R.11/2)	£250	
		b. No stop after "B" (R. 11/10)	£130	
TD8		4l. on 2d. agate	12·00	50·00
		a. No stop after "B" (R. 11/10)	£140	
TD9		6l. on 3d. violet	19·00	80·00
		a. No stop after "B" (R. 11/10)	£275	
		w. Wmk sideways-inverted*	35·00	£150
TD10		24l. on 1s. deep blue	55·00	£180
		a. No stop after "A" (R. 11/2)	£700	
		b. No stop after "B" (R. 11/10)	£700	
TD6/10 Set of 5			£100	£400

*No. TD9w shows the Crowns pointing to the left, *as seen from the back of the stamp.*

Tripolitania became part of the independent kingdom of Libya on 24 December 1951.

British P.Os in Crete

BRITISH ADMINISTRATION OF CANDIA PROVINCE (HERAKLEION)

Crete, formerly part of the Turkish Empire, was made autonomous, under Turkish suzerainty, in November 1898 with British, French, Italian and Russian troops stationed in separate zones to keep the peace.

Overseas mail franked with Nos. B1/5 was forwarded through the Austrian post office at Canea, being additionally franked with stamps of the Austro-Hungarian Post Offices in the Turkish Empire.

(Currency. 40 paras = 1 piastre)

PRICES FOR STAMPS ON COVER	
No. B1	*from* × 8
Nos. B2/5	—

B **1**

B **2**

1898 (25 Nov). Handstruck locally. Imperf.

B1	B **1**	20pa. bright violet	£450	£225

1898 (3 Dec). Litho by M. Grundmann, Athens. P 11½.

B2	B **2**	10pa. blue	11·00	25·00
		a. Imperf (pair)	£250	
B3		20pa. green	20·00	23·00
		a. Imperf (pair)	£250	

1899. P 11½.

B4	B **2**	10pa. brown	11·00	35·00
		a. Imperf (pair)	£250	
B5		20pa. rose	20·00	19·00
		a. Imperf (pair)	£250	

Forgeries exist of Nos. B1/5. Note that genuine examples of type B **2** show a full circle in the ornament above the figures of value. Forgeries with a broken circle in this position are frequently met with.

The British postal service closed at the end of 1899.

British P.O. in Siam
(Bangkok)

An overseas postal service for foreign residents was operated by the British Consulate at Bangkok from 1858. Mail was despatched by steamer to Singapore and from 1876 onwards was increasingly franked with Straits Settlements stamps. These were initially cancelled on arrival at Singapore, but later an oval postmark inscribed "BRITISH CONSULATE BANGKOK" was used. In 1883 a circular "BANGKOK" datestamp was introduced for use with Nos. 1/23. Both cancellations can also be found used on Hong Kong stamps between 1881 and 1885.

(Currency. 100 cents = 1 Straits dollar)

Stamps of Straits Settlements (see Malaysia) cancelled with oval postmark inscribed "BRITISH CONSULATE BANGKOK" around Royal Arms.

1882. Wmk Crown CC (Nos. 11/15, 33, 35).

Z1	2c. brown	£450
Z2	4c. rose	£500
Z3	6c. dull lilac	£500
Z4	8c. orange-yellow	£450
Z5	10c. on 30c. claret (thin "0") (No. 33)	£1300
Z6	10c. on 30c. claret (thick "10") (No. 34)	£1300
Z7	10c. on 30c. claret (thin "1", thick "0") (No. 35)	£1600
Z8	12c. blue	£700

Subsequent Straits Settlements values to 8c. watermarked Crown CA are known used at Bangkok in 1883 and 1884. During this period the stamps overprinted "B" were on sale at the British Post Office.

PRICES FOR STAMPS ON COVER
The issues of the British Post Offices in Siam are worth *from* × 100 the prices quoted for used stamps when on cover.

B B

(**1**) (**2**)

1882 (May)–**85**. Stamps of Straits Settlements optd with T **1**.

(a) On No. 9 of 1867

1	32c. on 2a. yellow (1885)	£35000	

(b) On Nos. 11/13, 14a, 15/17 and 19 of 1867–72 and Nos. 48/9 of 1882. Wmk Crown CC

2	2c. brown	£4000	£1600
3	4c. rose	£3750	£1400
	a. Opt double	—	£7500
4	5c. purple-brown	£475	£550
5	6c. lilac	£325	£150
	a. Opt Type 2	†	£1800
6	8c. orange	£3750	£275
7	10c. slate	£750	£200
	a. Opt double	†	£4750
	b. Opt Type 2	†	£1700
8	12c. blue	£1500	£550
	a. Opt Type 2	†	£1000
9	24c. green	£800	£170
	a. Opt Type 2	†	£1500
10	30c. claret	£45000	£30000
11	96c. grey	£7500	£3000

(c) On Nos. 59/60 of April 1883

12	2c. on 32c. pale red (*Wide* "S")	£3250	£3250
13	2c. on 32c. pale red (*Wide* "E")	£4250	£4250

(d) On Nos. 50/3 of 1882 and Nos. 63/7 of 1883–84. Wmk Crown CA

14	2c. brown	£750	£400
	a. Opt Type 2	†	£1600
15	2c. pale rose (1883)	75·00	55·00
	a. Opt inverted	†	£16000
	b. Opt double	£2750	£2750
	c. Opt treble	£10000	
16	4c. rose (1883)	£900	£375
	a. Opt Type 2	†	£1500
17	4c. pale brown (1883)	£100	85·00
	a. Opt double	£3500	
	b. Broken oval	£1800	£1600
18	5c. blue (1884)	£400	£200
19	6c. lilac (1884)	£325	£160
20	8c. orange (1883)	£250	75·00
	a. Opt inverted	£30000	£16000
	b. Opt Type 2	†	£1400
	c. Opt double	†	£4250
21	10c. slate (1883)	£250	95·00
22	12c. brown-purple (1883)	£425	£180
23	24c. yellow-green (1884?)	£8000	£3250

B B

(**1**) (**2**)

Opt Type **2** differs from Type **1** in having the two loops of the "B" almost equal in size with wider internal dimensions. The Type **2** overprints are generally placed higher than Type **1**. It is believed that the two types were both supplied to Bangkok in May 1882.

The prices quoted for the overprint double errors, Nos. 3a, 15b, 17a and 20c, are for stamps showing two clear impressions of the overprint. Examples showing partial doubling, on these and other values, are worth a small premium over the price quoted for normal stamps.

No. 17b shows the edge of the central oval broken above the "O" of "POSTAGE". It occurs on R. 10/5 of the lower right pane.

The use of these stamps ceased on 30 June 1885. Siam joined the Universal Postal Union on 1 July 1885.

British Postal Agencies in Eastern Arabia

Certain Arab States in Eastern Arabia, whilst remaining independent, had British postal administrations replacing Bahrain, and subsequently Indian, post offices at Dubai and Muscat.

Bahrain and Kuwait (from 1948) and Qatar (from 1957) used British stamps overprinted and surcharged in local currency. Abu Dhabi (from 1964) and Trucial States (from 1961 and used only in Dubai) had definitive issues made under the auspices of the British Agencies.

In addition, British stamps were surcharged with value only for use in Muscat and certain other states. They were formerly listed under Muscat as they were first put on sale there, but in view of their more extended use, the list has been transferred here, retaining the same numbering.

The stamps were used in Muscat from 1 April 1948 to 29 April 1966; in Dubai from 1 April 1948 to 6 January 1961; in Qatar: Doha from August 1950, Umm Said from February 1956, to 31 March 1957; and in Abu Dhabi from 30 March 1963 (Das Island from December 1960) to 29 March 1964.

Nos. 21/2 were placed on sale in Kuwait Post Offices in April and May 1951 and from February to November 1953 due to shortages of stamps with "KUWAIT" overprint. Isolated examples of other values can be found commercially used from Bahrain or Kuwait.

(Currency. 12 pies = 1 anna; 16 annas = 1 rupee)
Stamps of Great Britain surcharged

1	**2 RUPEES**	
ANNA		
(3)	**(4)**	

1½	**1½**
I	II

Two types of 1½a. surcharge:
I. "1" 3¼ mm high and aligns with top of "2" in "½" (Rows 1 to 10).
II. "1" 3½ mm high with foot of figure below top of "2" (Rows 11 to 20).

1948 (1 Apr). Surch with T **3** (½a. to 1r.) or **4** (2r.).

16	**128**	½a. on ½d. pale green	3·00	9·50
17		1a. on 1d. pale scarlet	3·00	30
18		1½a. pale red-brown (I)	21·00	11·00
		a. 1½a. on 1½d. pale Type II	21·00	11·00
		b. Vert pair. Nos. 18/a	£550	
19		2a. on 2d. pale orange	2·25	3·25
20		2½a. on 2½d. light ultramarine	3·50	10·00
21		3a. on 3d. pale violet	3·50	10
22	**129**	6a. on 6d. purple	5·00	10
23	**130**	1r. on 1s. bistre-brown	7·00	1·50
24	**131**	2r. on 2s.6d. yellow-green	13·00	50·00
16/24		Set of 9	55·00	75·00

One example of No. 22 is known with the surcharge almost completely omitted from position R. 20/2 in the sheet.

2½		**15**
ANNAS		**RUPEES**
(5)		**(6)**

1948 (26 Apr). Royal Silver Wedding. Nos. 493/4 surch with T **5** or **6**.

25	**137**	2½a. on 2½d. ultramarine	2·75	5·50
26	**138**	15r. on £1 blue	25·00	35·00

1948 (29 July). Olympic Games. Nos. 495/8 surch with new values in "ANNAS" or "1 RUPEE", as T **5/6**, but in one line on 2½a. (vert.) or 6a. and 1r. (horiz) and grills obliterating former values of all except 2½a.

27	**139**	2½a. on 2½d. ultramarine	45	2·50
28	**140**	3a. on 3d. violet	55	2·50
		a. Crown flaw	£100	
29	**141**	6a. on 6d. bright purple	65	2·75
30	**142**	1r. on 1s. brown	1·40	5·00
		a. Surch double	£1800	
27/30		Set of 4	2·75	11·50

1949 (10 Oct). 75th Anniv of Universal Postal Union. Nos. 499/502 surch with new values in "ANNAS" or "1 RUPEE" as T **3/4**, but all in one line, with grills obliterating former values.

31	**143**	2½a. on 2½d. ultramarine	60	3·25
		a. Lake in India	£120	
32	**144**	3a. on 3d. violet	60	4·25
33	**145**	6a. on 6d. bright purple	60	2·75
34	**146**	1r. on 1s. brown	2·25	7·50
31/4		Set of 4	3·50	16·00

2 RUPEES		**2 RUPEES**
(6a)		**(6b)**

Type **6a**. "2" and "RUPEES" level and in line with lower of the two bars.
Type **6b**. "2" raised in relation to "RUPEES" and whole surcharge below the lower bar.

1950 (2 Oct)–**55**. Nos. 503/8 surch as T **3** and No. 509 with T **6a**.

35	**128**	½a. on ½d. pale orange (3.5.51)	1·00	9·00
36		1a. on 1d. light ultramarine (3.5.51)	40	7·50

37		1½a. on 1½d. pale green (I) (3.5.51)	19·00	48·00
		a. Type II	19·00	48·00
		b. Vert pair. Nos. 37/a	£500	
38		2a. on 2d. pale red-brown (3.5.51)	40	8·50
39		2½a. on 2½d. pale scarlet (3.5.51)	40	16·00
40	**129**	4a. on 4d. light ultramarine	1·25	3·50
41	**147**	2r. on 2s.6d. yellow-green (3.5.51)	50·00	8·50
		a. Surch with Type 6b (1955)	£400	65·00
35/41		Set of 7	65·00	90·00

1952 (5 Dec)–**54**. Stamps of Queen Elizabeth II. Wmk Tudor Crown, surch as T **3** (in one line on 2½a. and 6a.).

42		½a. on ½d. orange-red (31.8.53)	10	3·25
43		1a. on 1d. ultramarine (31.8.53)	20	2·25
44		1½a. on 1½d. green	10	2·25
45		2a. on 2d. red-brown (31.8.53)	20	10
46		2½a. on 2½d. carmine-red	10	10
47		3a. on 3d. deep lilac (B.) (13.1.54)	20	1·25
48		4a. on 4d. ultramarine (2.11.53)	3·00	4·00
49		6a. on 6d. reddish purple (18.1.54)	35	10
50		12a. on 1s.3d. green (2.11.53)	9·00	30
51		1r. on 1s.6d. grey-blue (2.11.53)	2·25	10
42/51		Set of 10	14·00	11·50

In early printings of No. 42 the "½" was printed in a separate operation to "ANNA". Later printings and all printings of other values were printed in a single operation.

1953 (10 June). Coronation. Nos. 532/5 surch with new values.

52		2½a. on 2½d. carmine-red	1·75	5·00
53		4a. on 4d. ultramarine	1·75	1·25
54		12a. on 1s.3d. deep yellow-green	4·75	4·00
55		1r. on 1s.6d. deep grey-blue	5·00	50
52/5		Set of 4	12·00	7·00

2 RUPEES	
2 RUPEES	
2 RUPEES	
(7)	
5 RUPEES	
5 RUPEES	
(8)	

Types of surcharges

2 rupees.
Type I. On *Waterlow ptg*. Top of "R" level with top of "2" and other letters of "RUPEES". Bars 7 mm long.
Type II. On *Waterlow ptg* by Harrison: "R" dropped out of alignment with 2" and other letters of RUPEES". Bars 6½ mm long.
Type III. On *De La Rue ptg* by Harrison. Top of "R" below level of top of "2". Bars 7–7¼ mm long and with left sides aligned with "S".

5 rupees.
Type I. On *Waterlow ptg* by Harrison. Ends of letters square and sharp. There were two printings made in March and May 1957.
Type II. On *De La Rue ptg* by Harrison. Type is thicker and ends of letters are relatively rounded.

For differences between Waterlow and De La Rue printings of the basic stamps see notes in Great Britain after No. 539.

1955–60. T **166/7** (Waterlow ptgs) (W **165**, St. Edward's Crown) surch with T **7/8**.

56		2r. on 2s.6d. black-brown (Type I) (23.9.55)	10·00	70
		a. Type II (2.57)	10·00	5·50
		b. Type III (No. 536a D.L.R.) (6.60)	28·00	80·00
57		5r. on 5s. rose-red (Type I) (1.3.57)	10·00	2·25
		a. Wide surcharge	£550	£425
		b. Type II (No. 537a D.L.R.) (27.11.60)	20·00	65·00

Designs:—No. 56, Carrickfergus Castle; No. 57, Caernarvon Castle. No. 57a ("5" and "R" spaced 2¼ mm instead of 1¼ mm) occurred on R. 8/4 of the first surcharging of No. 57 only.

1956–57. Stamps of Queen Elizabeth II, W **165**, St. Edward's Crown, surch as T **3** (in one line on 2½a and 6a.).

58		1a. on 1d. ultramarine (20.3.57)	35	1·00
58a		1½a. on 1½d. green (1956)	£8000	£1200
59		2a. on 2d. red-brown (8.6.56)	70	2·50
60		2½a. on 2½d. carmine-red (8.6.56)	80	7·50
61		3a. on 3d. deep lilac (B.) (3.2.57)	1·00	11·00
62		4a. on 4d. ultramarine (9.12.56)	7·00	24·00
63		6a. on 6d. red-purple (10.2.57)	1·25	7·00
64		1r. on 1s.6d. grey-blue (2.8.56)	18·00	15
58/64		(ex 58a) Set of 7	26·00	48·00

No. 58a came from a few sheets of the St. Edward's Crown watermark included, in error, with a printing of No. 44. Most examples were used in Dubai, but two are known from Muscat, a pair and a single on separate covers from Bahrain and a single postmarked F.P.O. 936 (Sharjah). A single mint example also exists.

NP **1**	**NP**	**3** **NP**	**NP**	**75** **NP**
(9)	**(10)**		**(11)**	

1957 (1 Apr)–**59**. Value in naye paise. Stamps of Queen Elizabeth II, W **165**, St. Edward's Crown, surch as T **9** (1, 15, 25, 40, 50n.p.), **11** (75n.p.) or **10** (others).

65		1n.p. on 5d. brown	10	1·00
66		3n.p. on ½d. orange-red	20	2·50

67		6n.p. on 1d. ultramarine	20	2·75
68		9n.p. on 1½d. green	1·25	2·50
69		12n.p. on 2d. light red-brown	30	2·75
70		15n.p. on 2½d. carmine-red (Type I)	30	10
		a. Type II (4.59)	30	4·00
71		20n.p. on 3d. deep lilac (B.)	20	10
72		25n.p. on 4d. ultramarine	70	12·00
73		40n.p. on 6d. reddish purple	30	10
		a. Deep claret (3.59)	35	10
74		50n.p. on 9d. bronze-green	1·25	2·75
75		75n.p. on 1s.3d. green	3·75	40
65/75		Set of 11	7·75	24·00

15 NP

(12)

1957 (1 Aug). World Scout Jubilee Jamboree. Nos. 557/9 surch in one line as T **12** (15np.) or in two lines (others).

76		15n.p. on 2½d. carmine-red	35	85
77		4a. on 4d. ultramarine	35	85
78		75n.p. on 1s.3d. green	40	85
76/8		Set of 3	1·00	2·25

Designs:—No. 76, Scout badge and "Rolling Hitch"; No. 77, "Scouts coming to Britain"; No. 78, Globe within a compass.

1960 (26 Apr)–**61**. Stamps of Queen Elizabeth II. W **179**, Mult Crown, surch as T **9** (1, 15, 30, 40, 50n.p.), **11** (75n.p.), **3** (1r.), **7** (2r., 5r.) or **10** (others).

79		1n.p. on 5d. brown (30.8.60)	10	20
80		3n.p. on ½d. orange-red (21.6.60)	55	80
81		5n.p. on 1d. ultramarine (8.4.61)	2·50	6·00
82		6n.p. on 1d. ultramarine (21.6.60)	1·25	1·00
83		10n.p. on 1½d. green (8.4.61)	1·50	3·00
84		12n.p. on 2d. light red-brown (21.6.60)	2·00	2·50
85		15n.p. on 2½d. carmine-red (Type II)	25	10
86		20n.p. on 3d. deep lilac (B.) (28.9.60)	25	10
87		30n.p. on 4½d. chestnut (8.4.61)	40	65
88		40n.p. on 6d. deep claret (28.9.60)	45	10
89		50n.p. on 9d. bronze-green (8.4.61)	1·25	2·50
90		75n.p. on 1s.3d. green (8.4.61)	5·50	2·00
91		1r. on 1s.6d. grey-blue (8.4.61)	35·00	11·00
92		2r. on 2s.6d. black-brown (No. 595) (8.4.61)	16·00	55·00
93		5r. on 5s. rose-red (No. 596) (8.4.61)	32·00	70·00
79/93		Set of 15	85·00	£140

Designs:—Nos. 79/91, Queen Elizabeth II; No. 92, Carrickfergus Castle; No. 93, Caernarvon Castle.

The "5" on No. 93 differs from that on Nos. 57/b, being the same height as "RUPEES".

British Solomon Islands

The first British Resident Commissioner, Charles Woodford, was appointed in 1896 and an administrative centre established at Tulagi.

Mail was initially sent unstamped by sealed bag to Sydney where New South Wales stamps were applied and cancelled. Later the Resident Commissioner kept a stock of New South Wales stamps which were still not cancelled until arrival at Sydney. From April 1906 Mr. Woodford used a vertical oblong "BRITISH SOLOMON ISLANDS PAID" handstamp in place of New South Wales stamps which were then added to many of the covers by the postal authorities in Sydney.

PRICES FOR STAMPS ON COVER TO 1945	
Nos. 1/7	from × 12
Nos. 8/17	from × 25
Nos. 18/36	from × 6
Nos. 37/8	—
Nos. 39/51	from × 6
No. 52	—
Nos. 53/6	from × 2
Nos. 57/9	from × 6
Nos. 60/72	from × 2
Nos. D1/8	from × 5

BRITISH PROTECTORATE

1   **2**

(Des C. M. Woodford. Litho W. E. Smith & Co. Sydney)

1907 (14 Feb). No wmk. P 11.
1	1	½d. ultramarine	9·00	14·00
2		1d. rose-carmine	23·00	25·00
3		2d. indigo	48·00	32·00
		a. Imperf between (horiz pair)	£15000	
4		2½d. orange-yellow	32·00	50·00
		a. Imperf between (vert pair)	£7500	
		b. Imperf between (horiz pair)	£12000	£7000
5		5d. emerald-green	60·00	70·00
6		6d. chocolate	55·00	70·00
		a. Imperf between (vert pair)	£7000	
7		1s. bright purple	80·00	85·00
1/7 Set of 7			£275	£300

Nos. 1/7 did not become valid for international postage until early September 1907. Overseas covers before that date show additional New South Wales values.

Three types exist of the ½d. and 2½d., and six each of the other values, differing in minor details.

Forgeries of Nos. 1/7 show different perforations and have the boat paddle touching the shore. Genuine stamps show a gap between the paddle and the shore.

(Recess D.L.R.)

1908 (1 Nov)–**11**. Wmk Mult Crown CA (sideways). P 14.
8	2	½d. green	1·50	1·00
9		1d. red	1·25	1·25
10		2d. greyish slate	1·25	1·00
11		2½d. ultramarine	3·75	2·00
11a		4d. red/yellow (6.3.11)	3·50	9·00
12		5d. olive	10·00	5·00
13		6d. claret	10·00	5·50
14		1s. black/green	8·50	5·00
15		2s. purple/blue (7.3.10)	50·00	55·00
16		2s.6d. red/blue (7.3.10)	60·00	70·00
17		5s. green/yellow (7.3.10)	90·00	£110
8/17 Set of 11			£200	£225
8s/17s Optd "SPECIMEN" Set of 11			£325	

The ½d. and 1d. were issued in 1913 on rather thinner paper and with brownish gum.

3   **4**

(T **3** and **4**. Typo D.L.R.)

1913. Inscribed "POSTAGE POSTAGE". Wmk Mult Crown CA. P 14.
18	3	½d. green (1.4)	1·00	3·50
19		1d. red (1.4)	8·00	19·00
20		3d. purple/yellow (27.2)	1·75	4·00
		a. On orange-buff	12·00	24·00
21		11d. dull purple and scarlet (27.2)	38·00	12·00
18/21 Set of 4			12·50	35·00
18s/21s Optd "SPECIMEN" Set of 4			85·00	

1914 (Mar)–**23**. Inscribed "POSTAGE REVENUE". Chalk-surfaced paper (3d. to £1). Wmk Mult Crown CA. P 14.
22	4	½d. green	2·25	12·00
23		½d. yellow-green (1917)	6·50	20·00
24		1d. carmine-red	1·75	1·25
25		1d. scarlet (1917)	7·50	6·50
26		2d. grey (7.14)	4·50	9·00
27		2½d. ultramarine (7.14)	4·75	4·00
28		3d. purple/pale yellow (3.23)	30·00	£140
29		4d. black and red/yellow (7.14)	2·00	2·50
30		5d. dull purple and olive-green (7.14)	24·00	30·00

31		5d. brown-purple and olive-green (7.14)	24·00	30·00
32		6d. dull and bright purple (7.14)	6·00	12·00
33		1s. black/green (7.14)	4·75	7·00
		a. On blue-green, olive back (1923)	7·50	22·00
34		2s. purple and blue/blue (7.14)	9·50	10·00
35		2s.6d. black and red/blue (7.14)	9·50	15·00
36		5s. green and red/yellow (7.14)	48·00	48·00
		a. On orange-buff (1920)	55·00	70·00
37		10s. green and red/green (7.14)	95·00	65·00
38		£1 purple and black/red (7.14)	£250	£120
22/38 Set of 14			£425	£425
22s/38s Optd "SPECIMEN" Set of 14			£425	

Variations in the coloured papers are mostly due to climate and do not indicate separate printings.

1922–31. Chalk-surfaced paper (4d. and 5d. to 10s). Wmk Mult Script CA. P 14.
39	4	½d. green (10.22)	50	3·50
40		1d. scarlet (4.23)	6·00	11·00
41		1d. dull violet (2.27)	1·00	7·50
42	3	1½d. bright scarlet (7.24)	2·25	60
43	4	2d. slate-grey (4.23)	6·00	15·00
44		3d. pale ultramarine (11.23)	70	4·50
45		4d. black and red/yellow (7.27)	3·50	25·00
45a		4½d. red-brown (1931)	3·00	20·00
46		5d. dull purple and olive-green (12.27)	3·25	30·00
47		6d. dull and bright purple (12.27)	3·75	30·00
48		1s. black/emerald (12.27)	2·75	12·00
49		2s. purple and blue/blue (2.27)	28·00	55·00
50		2s.6d. black and red/blue (12.27)	9·00	60·00
51		5s. green and red/pale yellow (12.27)	42·00	60·00
52		10s. green and red/emerald (1.25)	£140	£110
39/52 Set of 15			£200	£375
39s/52s Optd or Perf (4½d.) "SPECIMEN" Set of 16			£425	

1935 (6 May). Silver Jubilee. As Nos. 91/4 of Antigua. P 13½×14.
53		1½d. deep blue and carmine	1·00	1·00
		a. Frame printed double, one albino		
		f. Diagonal line by turret	90·00	£100
		h. Dot by flagstaff	£180	
		i. Dash by turret	£300	
54		3d. brown and deep blue	6·50	7·50
		f. Diagonal line by turret	£160	£200
		h. Dot by flagstaff	£300	£350
55		6d. light blue and olive-green	16·00	12·00
		a. Frame printed double, one albino		
		b. Frame printed triple, two albino	£1300	
		h. Dot by flagstaff	£425	£425
		i. Dash by turret	£650	
56		1s. slate and purple	7·50	26·00
		a. Frame printed double, one albino	£1800	
		f. Diagonal line by turret	£300	
		h. Dot by flagstaff	£425	£550
		i. Dash by turret	£600	
53/6 Set of 4			28·00	42·00
53s/6s Perf "SPECIMEN" Set of 4			£130	

The second albino impression on No. 55b is sometimes almost co-incidental with the inked impression of the frame.

For illustrations of plate varieties see Omnibus section following Zanzibar.

1937 (13 May). Coronation. As Nos. 95/7 of Antigua. P 11×11½.
57		1d. violet	30	1·25
58		1½d. carmine	30	60
59		3d. blue	50	50
57/9 Set of 3			1·00	2·10
57s/9s Perf "SPECIMEN" Set of 3			£120	

5 Spears and Shield

6 Native Constable and Chief

7 Artificial Island, Malaita

8 Canoe House

9 Roviana Canoe

10 Roviana Canoes

11 Native House, Reef Islands

12 Coconut Plantation

13 Breadfruit

14 Tinakula Volcano

15 Bismarck Scrub Fowl   **16** Malaita Canoe

(Recess D.L.R. (2d., 3d., 2s. and 2s.6d.), Waterlow (others))

1939 (1 Feb)–**51**. T **5/16**. Wmk Mult Script CA. P 13½ (2d., 3d., 2s. and 2s.6d.) or 12½ (others).
60	5	½d. blue and blue-green	15	1·50
61	6	1d. brown and deep violet	30	1·50
62	7	1½d. blue-green and carmine	2·25	1·75
63	8	2d. orange-brown and black	3·75	2·00
		a. Perf 12 (7.11.51)	75	1·50
64	9	2½d. magenta and sage-green	4·00	2·25
		a. Imperf horiz (vert pair)	£26000	
65	10	3d. black and ultramarine	3·50	2·00
		a. Perf 12 (29.11.51)	1·50	2·50
66	11	4½d. green and chocolate	5·50	13·00
67	12	6d. deep violet and reddish purple	2·75	1·00
68	13	1s. green and black	2·50	1·00
		a. "A" of "CA" missing from wmk	£1200	
69	14	2s. black and orange	14·00	6·50
70	15	2s.6d. black and violet	32·00	4·50
71	16	5s. emerald-green and scarlet	32·00	13·00
72	10	10s. sage-green and magenta (27.4.42)	4·00	8·50
60/72 Set of 13			90·00	50·00
60s/72s Perf "SPECIMEN" Set of 13			£500	

Examples of No. 64a from the first two rows of the only known sheet are perforated between stamp and top margin.

1946 (15 Oct). Victory. As Nos. 110/1 of Antigua.
73		1½d. carmine	15	1·25
74		3d. blue	15	20
73s/4s Perf "SPECIMEN" Set of 2			£110	

Pocket handkerchief flaw (R. 1/6)

1949 (14 Mar). Royal Silver Wedding. As Nos. 112/3 of Antigua.
75		2d. black	50	50
		a. Pocket handkerchief flaw	60·00	60·00
76		10s. magenta	9·00	9·00

1949 (10 Oct). 75th Anniv of UPU As Nos. 114/7 of Antigua.
77		2d. red-brown	50	1·00
78		3d. deep blue	2·25	2·00
79		5d. deep blue-green	50	1·75
80		1s. blue-black	50	1·75
77/80 Set of 4			3·25	6·00

1953 (2 June). Coronation. As No. 120 of Antigua.
81		2d. black and grey-black	1·50	1·25

17 Ysabel Canoe

18 Roviana Canoe

19 Map

20 Miena (schooner)

21 Henderson Airfield   **22** Voyage of HMS Swallow

23 Mendaña and *Todos los Santos*

24 Native Constable and Malaita Chief

25 Arms of the Protectorate

(Des Miss I. R. Stinson (½d.), R. Bailey (2½d.), R. A. Sweet (5d., 1s., 1s.3d.), Capt. J. Brett Hilder (6d., 8d., 9d., 5s.). Recess B.W. (½d., 2½d., 5d., 6d., 8d., 9d., 1s., 1s.3d., 5s.), D.L.R. (1d., 2d., 2s.), Waterlow (1½d., 3d., 2s.6d., 10s., £1), until 1962, then D.L.R.)

1956 (1 Mar)–**63**. T **17/25** and similar horiz designs. Wmk Mult Script CA. P 12 (1d., 2d., 2s.), 13 (1½d., 3d., 2s.6d., 10s., £1) or 11½ (others).

82	**17**	½d. orange and purple	15	50
83	**10**	1d. yellow-green and red-brown	15	15
84	**7**	1½d. slate-green and carmine-red	15	1·25
		a. Slate-green and brown-red (31.7.63)	4·00	75
85	**8**	2d. deep brown and dull green	30	30
86	**18**	2½d. black and blue	1·50	60
87	**16**	3d. blue-green and red	85	15
88	**19**	5d. black and blue	60	55
89	**20**	6d. black and turquoise-green	60	25
90	**21**	8d. bright blue and black	1·50	30
90a		9d. emerald and black (28.1.60)	3·25	80
91	**22**	1s. slate and yellow-brown	3·00	50
		a. Slate and orange-brown (13.6.61)	10·00	3·75
91b	**19**	1s.3d. black and blue (28.1.60)	6·00	1·75
		ba. Black and pale ultramarine (11.12.62)	15·00	3·75
92	**14**	2s. black and carmine	15·00	7·00
93	**11**	2s.6d. emerald and bright purple	7·50	45
		a. Emerald and reddish purple (19.2.63)	27·00	4·00
94	**23**	5s. red-brown	15·00	5·50
95	**24**	10s. sepia	26·00	9·00
96	**25**	£1 black and blue (5.11.58)	32·00	40·00
82/96 *Set of 17*			£100	60·00

See also Nos. 103/11.

LEGISLATIVE COUNCIL

32 Great Frigate Bird

(Litho Enschedé)

1961 (19 Jan). New Constitution, 1960. W w **12** (sideways*). P 13×12½.

97	**32**	2d. black and turquoise-green	10	30
		w. Wmk Crown to right of CA	10	30
98		3d. black and rose-carmine	10	10
		w. Wmk Crown to right of CA	10	10
99		9d. black and reddish purple	15	30
		w. Wmk Crown to right of CA	15	30
97/9 *Set of 3*			30	60

*This issue with watermark sideways exists in almost equal quantities with the watermark showing Crown to left or right of CA.

1963 (4 June). Freedom from Hunger. As No. 146 of Antigua.

100		1s.3d. ultramarine	75	35

1963 (2 Sept). Red Cross Centenary. As Nos. 147/8 of Antigua.

101		2d. red and black	25	20
102		9d. red and black	50	1·50

1963–64. As Nos. 83/5, 87, 89, 90a and 91a/3, but wmk w **12**.

103	**10**	1d. yellow-green and red-brown (9.7.64)	25	30
104	**7**	1½d. slate-green and red (9.7.64)	3·00	1·00
105	**8**	2d. deep brown and dull green (9.7.64)	25	20
106	**16**	3d. light blue-green and scarlet (16.11.63)	2·75	15
		a. Yellowish green and red (9.7.64)	5·50	4·00
107	**20**	6d. black and turquoise (7.7.64)	60	40
108	**21**	9d. emerald and black (7.7.64)	1·25	35
109	**19**	1s.3d. black and blue (7.7.64)	60	70
110	**14**	2s. black and carmine (9.7.64)	1·00	5·50
111	**11**	2s.6d. emerald and reddish purple (9.7.64)	16·00	15·00
103/11 *Set of 9*			23·00	21·00

33 Makira Food Bowl

(48)

(Des M. Farrar-Bell. Litho D.L.R.)

1965 (24 May). Horiz designs as T **33**. W w **12**. P 13×12½.

112		½d. black, deep slate-blue and light blue	10	1·40
113		1d. black, orange and yellow	70	60
114		1½d. black, blue and yellow-green	35	65
115		2d. black, ultramarine and light blue	60	1·75
116		2½d. black, light brown and pale yellow-brown	10	1·25
117		3d. black, green and light green	10	10
118		6d. black, magenta and yellow-orange	35	80
119		9d. brownish black, deep bluish green and pale yellow	40	15
120		1s. black, chocolate and magenta	1·00	15
121		1s.3d. black and rose-red	4·50	2·25
122		2s. black, bright purple and lilac	7·50	2·75
123		2s.6d. black, olive-brown and light brown	1·00	70
124		5s. black, ultramarine and violet	13·00	4·50
125		10s. black, olive-green and yellow	17·00	3·00
126		£1 black, deep reddish violet and pink	11·00	4·50
112/126 *Set of 15*			50·00	22·00

Designs:—1d. *Dendrobium veratrifolium* (orchid); 1½d. Chiragra Spider Conch; 2d. Blyth's Hornbill; 2½d. Ysabel shield; 3d. Rennellese club; 6d. Moorish Idol; 9d. Lesser Frigate Bird; 1s. *Dendrobium macrophyllum* (orchid); 1s.3d. *Dendrobium spectabilis* (orchid); 2s. Sanford's Sea Eagle; 2s.6d. Malaita belt; 5s. *Ornithoptera victoreae* (butterfly); 10s. Ducorp's Cockatoo; £1, Western canoe figurehead.

1965 (28 June). ITU Centenary. As Nos. 166/7 of Antigua.

127		2d. orange-red and turquoise-blue	20	15
128		2d. turquoise-blue and olive-brown	20	15

1965 (25 Oct). International Co-operation Year. As Nos. 168/9 of Antigua.

129		1d. reddish purple and turquoise-green	10	30
130		2s.6d. deep bluish green and lavender	45	70

1966 (24 Jan). Churchill Commemoration. As Nos. 170/3 of Antigua.

131		2d. new blue	15	10
132		9d. deep green	25	10
133		1s.3d. brown	35	10
134		2s.6d. bluish violet	40	55
131/4 *Set of 4*			1·00	70

(New Currency. 100 cents = 1 Australian, later Solomon Islands dollar)

8 c.
Normal "8"

8 c.
Inverted "8" (No. 142Aa) (R. 9/2. Later corrected)

1966 (14 Feb)–**67**. Decimal Currency. Nos. 112/26 variously surch as T **48** by De La Rue.

A. Wmk upright

135A		1c. on ½d. black, deep slate-blue and light blue	10	10
136A		2c. on 1d. black, orange and yellow	10	10
137A		3c. on 1½d. black, blue and yellow-green	10	10
138A		4c. on 2d. black, ultramarine and light blue	15	10
139A		5c. on 6d. black, magenta and yellow-orange	15	10
140A		6c. on 2½d. black, light brown and pale yellow-brown	15	10
141A		7c. on 3d. black, green and light green	15	10
142A		8c. on 9d. brownish black, deep bluish green and pale yellow	25	10
		a. Inverted "8"	55·00	20·00
		b. Surch omitted (vert pair with normal)	£5000	
143A		10c. on 1s. black, chocolate and magenta	30	10
145A		13c. on 1s.3d. black and rose-red	2·50	15
147A		20c. on 2s. black, bright purple and lilac	2·50	25
148A		25c. on 2s.6d. black, olive-brown and light brown	60	40
150A		50c. on 5s. black, ultramarine and violet (R.)	4·50	1·50
151A		$1 on 10s. black, olive-green and yellow	3·00	1·50
152A		$2 on £1 black, deep reddish violet and pink	2·25	3·00
135A/52A *Set of 15*			15·00	7·00

B. Wmk sideways

135B		1c. on ½d. black, deep slate-blue and light blue (6.66)	10	10
136B		2c. on 1d. black, orange and yellow (6.66)	10	10
137B		3c. on 1½d. black, blue and yellow-green (6.66)	15	10
138B		4c. on 2d. black, ultramarine and light blue (6.66)	15	10
139B		5c. on 6d. black, magenta and yellow-orange (6.66)	15	10
140B		6c. on 2½d. black, light brown and pale yellow-brown (6.66)	10	10
141B		7c. on 3d. black, green and light green (6.66)	10	10
142B		8c. on 9d. brownish black, deep bluish green and pale yellow (6.66)	15	10
143B		10c. on 1s. black, chocolate and magenta (6.66)	40	10
144B		12c. on 1s.3d. black and rose-red (1.3.67)	65	10
145B		13c. on 1s.3d. black and rose-red (6.66)	4·50	1·75
146B		14c. on 2d. black, green and light green (1.3.67)	40	10
147B		20c. on 2s. black, bright purple and lilac (6.66)	3·25	30
148B		25c. on 2s.6d. black, olive-brown and light brown (6.66)	2·50	35
149B		35c. on 2d. black, ultramarine and light blue (1.3.67)	2·50	25
		a. Surch omitted (horiz pair with normal)	£4250	
		b. Surch value only omitted		

150B		50c. on 5s. black, ultramarine and violet (R.) (6.66)	12·00	4·00
151B		$1 on 10s. black, olive-green and yellow (6.66)	9·00	1·25
152B		$2 on £1 black, deep reddish violet and pink (6.66)	9·00	2·00
135B/52B *Set of 18*			40·00	9·00

The positions of the bars in the surcharge vary considerably from stamp to stamp within the sheets.

The stamps with sideways watermark are all from new printings and in some instances there are marked shade variations from Nos. 112/26 which were used for making Nos. 135A/152A.

No. 142Ab comes from the bottom left-hand corner of the sheet and was covered by a paper fold. The bottom stamp in the pair is completely without surcharge and the upper has the surcharge value and one bar missing.

1966 (1 July). World Cup Football Championship. As Nos. 176/7 of Antigua.

153		8c. violet, yellow-green, lake and yellow-brown	15	15
154		35c. chocolate, blue-green, lake and yellow-brown	30	15

1966 (20 Sept). Inauguration of WHO Headquarters, Geneva. As Nos. 178/9 of Antigua.

155		3c. black, yellow-green and light blue	20	10
156		50c. black, light purple and yellow-brown	60	20

1966 (1 Dec). 20th Anniv of UNESCO As Nos. 196/8 of Antigua.

157		3c. slate-violet, red, yellow and orange	15	10
158		25c. orange-yellow, violet and deep olive	30	15
159		$1 black, bright purple and orange	75	70
157/9 *Set of 3*			1·10	85

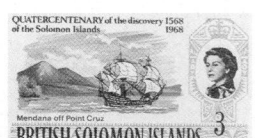

49 Henderson Field

(Des V. Whiteley. Photo Harrison)

1967 (28 Aug). 25th Anniv of Guadalcanal Campaign (Pacific War). T **49** and similar horiz design. Multicoloured. W w **12**. P 14×14½.

160		8c. Type **49**	15	15
161		35c. Red Beach landings	15	15

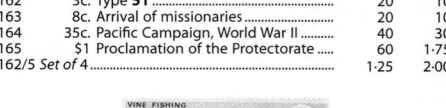

51 Mendaña's *Todos los Santos* off Point Cruz

(Des V. Whiteley. Photo Harrison)

1968 (7 Feb). Quatercentenary of the Discovery of Solomon Is. T **51** and similar horiz designs. Multicoloured. W w **12**. P 14.

162		3c. Type **51**	20	10
163		8c. Arrival of missionaries	20	10
164		35c. Pacific Campaign, World War II	40	30
165		$1 Proclamation of the Protectorate	60	1·75
162/5 *Set of 4*			1·25	2·00

55 Vine Fishing

(Des R. Granger Barrett. Photo Harrison)

1968 (20 May)–**71**. Horiz designs as T **55**. Chalk-surfaced paper. W w **12**. P 14½.

166		1c. turquoise-blue, black and brown	10	10
		a. Glazed, ordinary paper (9.8.71)	1·00	1·00
		aw. Wmk inverted	1·00	
167		2c. apple-green, black and brown	10	10
		aw. Wmk inverted. Glazed, ordinary paper (9.8.71)	1·75	1·00
168		3c. green, myrtle-green and black	10	10
		a. Glazed, ordinary paper (9.8.71)	1·00	1·00
169		4c. bright purple, black and brown	15	10
		a. Glazed, ordinary paper (9.8.71)	1·00	1·00
170		6c. multicoloured	30	10
171		8c. multicoloured	25	10
172		12c. yellow-ochre, brown-red and black	50	50
		a. Glazed, ordinary paper (9.8.71)	2·25	2·50
		aw. Wmk inverted	3·50	
173		14c. orange-red, chocolate and black	2·00	3·50
174		15c. multicoloured	80	80
		a. Glazed, ordinary paper (9.8.71)	3·50	3·75
175		20c. bright blue, red and black	4·00	3·00
		a. Glazed, ordinary paper (9.8.71)	4·75	8·00
176		24c. rose-red, black and yellow	1·50	3·25
177		35c. multicoloured	1·50	30
178		45c. multicoloured	1·00	30
179		$1 violet-blue light green and black	2·00	1·50
180		$2 multicoloured	8·00	3·50
		w. Wmk inverted	£140	
166/80 *Set of 15*			20·00	15·00
166a/75a *Set of 8*			14·00	18·00

Designs:—2c. Kite fishing; 3c. Platform fishing; 4c. Net fishing; 6c. Gold Lip shell diving; 8c. Night fishing; 12c. Boat building; 14c. Cocoa; 15c. Road building; 20c. Geological survey; 24c. Hauling timber; 35c. Copra; 45c. Harvesting rice; $1, Honiara Port; $2, Internal air service.

The stamps on glazed, ordinary paper exist with PVA gum only. The 1c. to 12c. and 20c. on chalk-surfaced paper exist with PVA gum as well as gum arabic, but the others exist with gum arabic only.

70 Map of Australasia and Diagram   **71** Basketball Player

(Des R. Gates. Litho Enschedé)

1969 (10 Feb). Inaugural Year of the South Pacific University. P 12½×12.

181	**70**	3c. multicoloured	10	10
182		12c. multicoloured	10	10
183		35c. multicoloured	15	10
181/3		Set of 3	30	25

(Des J. Cooter. Photo Harrison)

1969 (13 Aug). Third South Pacific Games, Port Moresby. T **71** and similar vert designs. Multicoloured. W w **12** (sideways*). P 14½×14.

184		3c. Type **71**	10	10
		w. Wmk Crown to right of CA	65	80
185		8c. Footballer	10	10
186		14c. Sprinter	10	10
187		45c. Rugby player	20	15
184/7		Set of 4	45	40
MS188		126×120 mm. Nos. 184/7	2·75	8·00

*The normal sideways watermark shows Crown to left of CA, *as seen from the back of the stamp*.

Stamps from the miniature sheets differ slightly from those in the ordinary sheets, particularly the 14c. value, which has a shadow below the feet on the runner. The footballer and rugby player on the 8c. and 45c. values also have shadows below their feet, but these are more pronounced than on the stamps from the ordinary sheets.

75 South Sea Island with Star of Bethlehem   **76** Southern Cross, "PAX" and Frigatebird (stained glass window)

(Des L. Curtis. Photo Harrison)

1969 (21 Nov). Christmas. W w **12** (sideways). P 14½×14.

189	**75**	8c. black, violet and turquoise-green	10	10
190	**76**	35c. multicoloured	20	20

77 "Paid" Stamp, New South Wales 1896–1906 2d. Stamp and 1906–07 Tulagi Postmark

(Des G. Drummond. Litho B.W.)

1970 (15 Apr). Inauguration of New GPO Honiara. T **77** and similar horiz designs. W w **12** (sideways). P 13.

191		7c. light magenta, deep blue and black	15	15
192		14c. sage-green, deep blue and black	20	15
193		18c. multicoloured	15	15
194		23c. multicoloured	20	20
191/4		Set of 4	65	60

Designs:—14c. 1906–07 2d. stamp and C. M. Woodford; 18c. 1910–14 5s. stamp and Tulagi postmark, 1913; 23c. New GPO, Honiara.

81 Coat of Arms   **83** British Red Cross HQ, Honiara

(Des V. Whiteley. Photo Harrison)

1970 (15 June). New Constitution. T **81** and similar design. W w **12** (sideways on 18c.). P 14½×14 (18c.) or 14×14½ (35c.).

195		18c. multicoloured	15	10
196		35c. pale apple-green, deep blue and ochre	35	20

Design: Horiz—35c. Map.

(Des L. Curtis. Litho Questa)

1970 (17 Aug). Centenary of British Red Cross. T **83** and similar horiz design. W w **12** (sideways). P 14×14½.

197		3c. multicoloured	10	10
198		35c. blue, vermilion and black	25	20

Design:—35c. Wheelchair and map.

86 Reredos (Altar Screen)

(Des L. Curtis. Litho J.W.)

1970 (19 Oct). Christmas. T **86** and similar design. W w **12** (sideways on 45c.). P 14×13½ (8c.) or 13½×14 (45c.).

199		8c. ochre and bluish violet	10	10
200		45c. chestnut, yellow-orange and blackish brown	25	20

Design: Vert—8c. Carved angel.

STAMP BOOKLETS

1959 (1 Apr). Black on buff (No. SB1) or grey (No. SB2) covers. Stapled.

SB1	4s. booklet containing 8 of each 1d., 2d. and 3d. (Nos. 83, 85, 87) in blocks of 4		30·00
SB2	11s. booklet containing 8 of each 1d. and 8d., and four 3d. and 1s. (Nos. 83, 87, 90/1) in blocks of 4		40·00

1960 (1 May)–**64**. Black on green (No. SB3) or orange (No. SB4) covers. Stapled.

SB3	5s. booklet containing 8 of each 1d., 1½d., 2d. and 3d. (Nos. 83/5, 87) in blocks of 4		50·00
SB4	£1 booklet containing 8 of each 1d., 2d., 3d., 9d. and 1s.3d. (Nos. 83, 85, 87, 90a, 91a) in blocks of 4		80·00
	a. Contents as No. SB4, but Nos. 103, 85, 106a, 108/9 (1964)		

POSTAGE DUE STAMPS

D 1

(Typo B.W.)

1940 (1 Sept). Wmk Mult Script CA. P 12.

D1	D **1**	1d. emerald-green	6·50	7·00
D2		2d. scarlet	7·00	7·00
D3		3d. brown	7·00	11·00
D4		4d. blue	11·00	11·00
D5		5d. grey-green	12·00	21·00
D6		6d. purple	12·00	15·00
D7		1s. violet	14·00	29·00
D8		1s.6d. turquoise-green	38·00	48·00
D1/8		Set of 8	95·00	£130
D1s/8s		Perf "SPECIMEN" Set of 8	£250	

British Virgin Islands

CROWN COLONY

Apart from the 1951 Legislative Council issue, the word "BRITISH" did not appear regularly on the stamps until 1968 when it was introduced to avoid confusion with the nearby Virgin Islands of the United States (the former Danish West Indies).

Most mail from the early years of the islands' history was sent via the Danish island of St. Thomas.

It is not known exactly when the first post office, or agency, was established on Tortola, but an entry in a GPO account book suggest that it was operating by 1787 and the earliest letter postmarked "TORTOLA" dates from June of that year. The stamps of Great Britain were used from 1858 to May 1860, when the colonial authorities assumed responsibility for the overseas mails from the British GPO.

For illustrations of the handstamp and postmark types see BRITISH POST OFFICES ABROAD notes, following GREAT BRITAIN.

TORTOLA

CROWNED-CIRCLE HANDSTAMPS

CC1	CC **1** TORTOLA (R.) (15.12.1842)	Price on cover	£6500
CC2	CC **5** TORTOLA (R.) (21.6.1854)	Price on cover	£22000

No. CC2 is known used as an Official Paid mark during the years 1900 to 1918. Price on cover £750.

Stamps of GREAT BRITAIN cancelled "A 13" as Type **2**.

1858–60.

Z1	1d. rose-red (1857), perf 14		£4250
Z2	4d. rose (1857)		£5500
Z3	6d. lilac (1856)		£1800
Z4	1s. green (1856)		£1800

PRICES FOR STAMPS ON COVER TO 1945	
Nos. 1/7	from × 30
Nos. 8/9	from × 40
No. 10	—
No. 11	from × 10
No. 12	from × 30
No. 13	—
Nos. 14/b	from × 10
Nos. 15/17	from × 30
Nos. 18/19	from × 40
No. 20	—
Nos. 21/b	from × 20
Nos. 22/b	from × 30
Nos. 24/31	from × 25
Nos. 32/4	from × 50
Nos. 35/7	from × 30
Nos. 38/41	from × 15
No. 42	from × 30
Nos. 43/50	from × 8
Nos. 54/77	from × 6
Nos. 78/81	from × 6
Nos. 82/101	from × 3
Nos. 103/6	from × 4
Nos. 107/9	from × 6
Nos. 110/21	from × 2

1 St. Ursula   **2** St. Ursula

(Litho Nissen & Parker from original dies by Waterlow)

1866 (Dec). No wmk. P 12.

(a) White wove paper

1	**1**	1d. green	50·00	60·00
2		1d. deep green	55·00	65·00
3	**2**	6d. rose	90·00	£110
		a. Large "V" in "VIRGIN" (R. 2/1)	£375	£475
4		6d. deep rose	£130	£140
		a. Large "V" in "VIRGIN" (R. 2/1)	£425	£500

(b) Toned paper

5	**1**	1d. green	50·00	60·00
		a. Perf 15×12	£5500	£7000
6		1d. deep green	£100	£120
7	**2**	6d. rose-red	60·00	90·00
		a. Large "V" in "VIRGIN" (R. 2/1)	£275	£375

The above were printed in sheets of 25.

6d. stamps showing part of the papermaker's watermark ("A. Cowan & Sons Extra Superfine A. C. & S.") are worth 50% more.

Beware of fakes of No. 5a made from perf 12 stamps.

3   **4**

Normal   Variety

1s. Long-tailed "S" in "ISLANDS" (R. 3/1)

(Litho and typo (figure of the Virgin) (1s.) or litho (others) Nissen and Parker from original dies by Waterlow)

1867–70. No wmk. P 15. 1s. with double-lined frame.

(a) White wove paper

8	**1**	1d. yellow-green (1868)	80·00	80·00
9		1d. blue-green (1870)	65·00	70·00
10	**2**	6d. pale rose	£600	£600
11	**4**	1s. black and rose-carmine	275	£375
		a. Long-tailed "S"	£900	£1100

(b) Greyish (No. 14) or toned paper (others)

12	**1**	1d. yellow-green (1868)	85·00	80·00
13	**2**	6d. dull rose (1868)	£300	£350
14	**4**	1s. black and rose-carmine *(greyish paper)*	275	£375
14b		1s. black and rose-carmine *(toned paper)*	£325	£375
		ba. Long-tailed "S"	£900	£1100

(c) Pale rose paper

15	**3**	4d. lake-red	55·00	75·00

(d) Buff paper

16	**3**	4d. lake-red	45·00	60·00
17		4d. lake-brown	45·00	60·00

The thin lines of the frame on the 1s. are close together and sometimes merge into one.

The 1d. from the 1868 printing was in sheets of 20 (5×4) with narrow margins between the stamps. Later printings in sheets of 12 (3×4) with wider margins. The 4d. was in sheets of 25; and the remaining two values in sheets of 20 (5×4).

The greyish paper used for Nos. 14 and 20 often shows traces of blue.

1867. Nos. 11 and 14/b with crimson frames superimposed extending into margins. P 15.

18	**4**	1s. black and rose-carmine *(white paper)*	90·00	£100
		a. Long-tailed "S"	£300	£350
		b. Figure of Virgin omitted	£150000	
19		1s. black and rose-carmine *(toned paper)*	75·00	85·00
		a. Long-tailed "S"	£225	£275
20		1s. black and rose-carmine *(greyish paper)*	£750	£900
		a. Long-tailed "S"	£2000	£2250

1868. Nos. 11 and 14b with frame lines retouched so as to make them single lines. Margins remain white. P 15.

21	**4**	1s. black and rose-carmine *(white paper)*	£160	£190
		a. Long-tailed "S"	£500	£600
21b		1s. black and rose-carmine *(toned paper)*	£160	£190
		ba. Long-tailed "S"	£500	£600

(Litho D.L.R.)

1878. Wmk Crown CC (sideways). P 14.

22	**1**	1d. green	85·00	£100
		a. Yellow-green	£170	£130
		b. Wmk upright	£100	£130

6 (Die I)

(7)

(Typo D.L.R.)

1879–80. Wmk Crown CC. P 14.

24	**6**	1d. emerald-green (1880)	75·00	90·00
25		2½d. red-brown	£120	£130

1883 (June)**–84.** Wmk Crown CA. P 14.

26	**6**	½d. yellow-buff	85·00	85·00
		x. Wmk reversed		
27		½d. dull green *(shades)* (11.83)	6·50	17·00
		b. Top left triangle detached	£325	£475
29		1d. pale rose (15.9.83)	50·00	50·00
		a. Deep rose (1884)	65·00	70·00
31		2½d. ultramarine (9.84)	4·00	16·00
		b. Top left triangle detached	£300	
		w. Wmk inverted	£180	

For illustration of "top left triangle detached" variety see above No. 21 of Antigua.

(Litho D.L.R.)

1887–89. Wmk Crown CA. P 14.

32	**1**	1d. red (5.89)	3·75	9·00
		x. Wmk reversed	£225	
33		1d. rose-red	3·25	8·50
34		1d. rose	5·50	14·00
35	**3**	4d. chestnut	35·00	65·00
		x. Wmk reversed	£300	
36		4d. pale chestnut	35·00	65·00
37		4d. brown-red	45·00	70·00
38		6d. dull violet	19·00	50·00
39		6d. deep violet	19·00	50·00
40	**4**	1s. sepia (2.89)	80·00	£100
41		1s. brown *to* deep brown	45·00	70·00
34s/40s Optd "SPECIMEN" *Set of 4*			£130	

The De La Rue transfers of T 1 to 4 are new transfers and differ from those of Messrs. Nissen and Parker, particularly T **4**.

1888 (July). Nos. 18/19. Surch with T **7**, in violet, in Antigua.

42	**4**	4d. on 1s. black and rose-carmine *(toned paper)*	£140	£160
		a. Surch double	£8500	
		b. Surch inverted (in pair with normal)	£55000	
		c. Long-tailed "S"	£500	£600
42d		4d. on 1s. black and rose-carmine *(white paper)*	£180	£225
		dc. Long-tailed "S"	£600	£750

The special issues for Virgin Islands were superseded on 31 October 1890, by the general issue for Leeward Islands. In 1899, however, a new special issue, Nos. 43/50, appeared; it did not supersede the general issue for Leeward Islands, but was used concurrently, as were all subsequent issues, until 1 July 1956 when the general Leeward Islands stamps were withdrawn.

8   **9**   **10**

(Recess D.L.R.)

1899 (Jan). Wmk Crown CA. P 14.

43	**8**	½d. yellow-green	4·00	55
		a. Error."HALFPFNNY" (R. 10/1)	85·00	£120
		b. Error."HALFPENNY" (R. 8/2)	85·00	£120
		c. Imperf between (horiz pair)	£13000	
44		1d. brick-red	6·00	2·00
45		2½d. ultramarine	12·00	2·75
46		4d. brown	5·50	21·00
		a. Error."FOURPENCF" (R.10/3)	£750	£1100
47		6d. dull violet	8·00	3·00
48		7d. deep green	13·00	6·00
49		1s. brown-yellow	23·00	35·00
50		5s. indigo	80·00	90·00
43/50 *Set of 8*			£130	£140
43s/50s Optd "SPECIMEN" *Set of 8*			£190	

Nos. 43a/b and 46a were corrected after the first printing.

(Typo D.L.R.)

1904 (1 June). Wmk Mult Crown CA. P 14.

54	**9**	½d. dull purple and green	1·00	40
55		1d. dull purple and scarlet	2·50	35
56	**10**	2d. dull purple and ochre	7·50	3·50
57	**9**	2½d. dull purple and ultramarine	4·00	2·25
58	**10**	3d. dull purple and black	6·00	2·50
59	**9**	6d. dull purple and brown	4·50	2·50
60	**10**	1s. green and scarlet	7·50	7·00
61		2s.6d. green and black	40·00	55·00
62	**9**	5s. green and blue	50·00	70·00
54/62 *Set of 9*			£110	£130
54s/62s Optd "SPECIMEN" *Set of 9*			£160	

11   **12**

(Typo D.L.R.)

1913 (Feb)**–19.** Die I. Chalk-surfaced paper (3d. to 5s.). Wmk Mult Crown CA. P 14.

69	**11**	½d. green	4·00	6·50
		a. Yellow-green (8.16)	5·00	15·00
		b. Blue-green and deep green (3.19)	1·25	6·00
70		1d. deep red	9·00	11·00
		a. Deep red and carmine (10.17)	2·25	14·00
		b. Scarlet (10.17)	2·25	14·00
		c. Carmine-red (3.19)	50·00	27·00
71	**12**	2d. grey	8·00	30·00
		a. Slate-grey (1919)	9·00	45·00
72	**11**	2½d. bright blue	9·00	9·00
73	**12**	3d. purple/yellow	2·75	6·50
74	**11**	6d. dull and bright purple	10·00	21·00
75	**12**	1s. black/blue-green	3·25	10·00
76		2s.6d. black and red/blue	50·00	55·00
77	**11**	5s. green and red/yellow	45·00	£130
69/77 *Set of 9*			£110	£250
69s/77s Optd "SPECIMEN" *Set of 9*			£200	

Stock of the original printing of the ½d., No. 69 was exhausted by January 1916 and Leeward Islands ½d. stamps were used until the yellow-green printing, No. 69a, arrived in August 1916.

WAR STAMP

(13)   **14**

1916 (20 Oct)**–19.** Optd with T **13** by D.L.R.

78	**11**	1d. carmine	1·75	24·00
		a. Watermark sideways	£1100	
		b. Pale red/bluish	50	7·00
		bw. Wmk inverted	75·00	
		by. Wmk inverted and reversed	£150	
		c. Scarlet (11.3.19)	2·50	6·00
		d. Short opt (right pane R.10/1)	25·00	
79	**12**	3d. purple/yellow	7·00	35·00
		a. Purple/lemon (12.3.17)	8·00	22·00
		b. Purple/buff-yellow (11.3.19)	9·00	29·00
		bw. Wmk inverted	10·00	50·00
		by. Wmk inverted and reversed		
		c. Short opt (right pane R. 10/1)	60·00	
78s/9s Optd "SPECIMEN" *Set of 2*			75·00	

Nos. 78d and 79c show the overprint 2 mm high instead of 2½ mm. No. 78c is known with the "A" of the "CA" watermark sideways.

1921 (18 Nov). As 1913–19, but Die II and wmk Mult Script CA.

80	**11**	½d. green	16·00	60·00
		w. Wmk inverted		
81		1d. scarlet and deep carmine	10·00	35·00
80s/1s Optd "SPECIMEN" *Set of 2*			85·00	

(Typo D.L.R.)

1922 (Mar)**–28.** P 14.

(a) Wmk Mult Crown CA. Chalk surfaced paper

82	**14**	3d. purple/pale yellow (15.6.22)	65	17·00

83		1s. black/emerald (15.6.22)	75	17·00
84		2s.6d. black and red/blue (15.6.22)	5·50	11·00
85		5s. green and red/pale yellow (15.6.22)	48·00	£110
82/5 *Set of 4*			50·00	£140
82s/5s Optd "SPECIMEN" *Set of 4*			£100	

(b) Wmk Mult Script CA. Chalk-surfaced paper (5d. to 5s.)

86	**14**	½d. dull green	85	2·75
87		1d. rose-carmine	60	60
88		1d. bright violet (1.27)	1·75	7·00
89		1d. scarlet (12.28)	27·00	14·00
90		1½d. carmine-red (1.27)	1·75	3·00
91		1½d. Venetian red (11.28)	2·50	1·50
92		2d. grey	1·25	6·00
93		2½d. pale bright blue	6·50	23·00
94		2½d. dull orange (1.9.23)	1·25	2·50
95		2½d. bright blue (1.27)	18·00	3·50
96		3d. purple/pale yellow (2.28)	2·25	11·00
97		5d. dull purple and olive (6.22)	5·50	48·00
98		6d. dull and bright purple (6.22)	1·75	6·50
99		1s. black/emerald (2.28)	2·50	17·00
100		2s.6d. black and red/blue (2.28)	19·00	55·00
101		5s. green and red/yellow (1.9.23)	23·00	75·00
86/101 *Set of 16*			£100	£225
86s/101s Optd or Perf (Nos. 89, 91) "SPECIMEN" *Set of 16*			£350	

In the 1½d. stamps the value is in colour on a white ground.

1935 (6 May). Silver Jubilee. As Nos. 91/4 of Antigua but printed by Waterlow. P 11×12.

103		1d. deep blue and scarlet	1·25	9·00
		k. Kite and vertical log	£160	
		l. Kite and horizontal log	£160	£275
104		1½d. ultramarine and grey	1·25	7·50
		k. Kite and vertical log	£170	
		l. Kite and horizontal log	£170	£275
		m. "Bird" by turret	£200	£300
105		2½d. brown and deep blue	4·75	8·00
		k. Kite and vertical log	£190	
		l. Kite and horizontal log	£200	£275
106		1s. slate and purple	21·00	40·00
		k. Kite and vertical log	£425	
		l. Kite and horizontal log	£400	£500
103/6 *Set of 4*			25·00	55·00
103s/6s Perf "SPECIMEN" *Set of 4*			£140	

For illustrations of plate varieties see Omnibus section following Zanzibar.

1937 (12 May). Coronation. As Nos. 95/7 of Antigua. P 11×11½.

107		1d. carmine	1·00	3·75
108		1½d. yellow-brown	75	3·00
109		2½d. blue	60	1·50
107/9 *Set of 3*			2·10	7·50
107s/9s Perf "SPECIMEN" *Set of 3*			£110	

 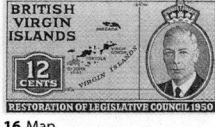

15 King George VI and Badge of Colony   **16** Map

(Photo Harrison)

1938 (1 Aug)**–47.** Chalk-surfaced paper. Wmk Mult Script CA. P 14.

110	**15**	½d. green	3·75	4·00
		a. Ordinary paper (10.43)	1·50	1·00
111		1d. scarlet	6·50	2·50
		a. Ordinary paper (10.43)	2·50	1·75
112		1½d. red-brown	8·00	8·00
		a. Ordinary paper (10.43)	3·25	1·75
		w. Wmk inverted	†	£2250
113		2d. grey	8·00	3·25
		a. Ordinary paper (10.43)	3·25	1·75
114		2½d. ultramarine	4·75	2·50
		a. Ordinary paper (10.43)	2·75	2·75
115		3d. orange	9·00	1·50
		a. Ordinary paper (10.43)	2·25	1·00
116		6d. mauve	14·00	3·50
		a. Ordinary paper (10.43)	6·00	2·25
117		1s. olive-brown	24·00	6·00
		a. Ordinary paper (8.42)	6·00	2·25
118		2s.6d. sepia	70·00	13·00
		a. Ordinary paper (8.42)	17·00	6·50
119		5s. carmine	70·00	15·00
		a. Ordinary paper (8.42)	20·00	7·50
120		10s. blue (1.12.47)	9·00	10·00
121		£1 black (1.12.47)	11·00	24·00
110a/21 *Set of 12*			75·00	55·00
110s/21s Perf "SPECIMEN" *Set of 12*			£400	

The ordinary paper, used as a substitute for the chalk-surfaced for printings between 1942 and 1945, is thick, smooth and opaque.

1946 (1 Nov). Victory. As Nos. 110/11 of Antigua.

122		1½d. lake-brown	10	10
123		3d. orange	10	60
122s/3s Perf "SPECIMEN" *Set of 2*			90·00	

1949 (3 Jan). Royal Silver Wedding. As Nos. 112/13 of Antigua.

124		2½d. ultramarine	10	10
125		£1 black	16·00	23·00

1949 (10 Oct). 75th Anniv of UPU As Nos. 114/17 of Antigua.

126		2½d. ultramarine	30	3·25
127		3d. orange	1·50	2·75
128		6d. magenta	45	75
129		1s. olive	35	50
126/9 *Set of 4*			2·40	6·50

(New Currency. 100 cents = 1 B.W.I. dollar)

1951 (16 Feb–10 Apr). Inauguration of B.W.I. University College. As Nos. 118/19 of Antigua.

130		3c. black and brown-red (10.4)	40	2·50
131		12c. black and reddish violet	60	1·75

Issue of the 3c. value was delayed when the supplies were sent to Puerto Rico by mistake.

(Recess Waterlow)
1951 (2 Apr). Restoration of Legislative Council. Wmk Mult Script CA. P 14½×14.

132	**16**	6c. orange	70	2·00
133		12c. purple	1·25	1·00
134		24c. olive	70	1·25
135		$1.20 carmine	3·50	1·75
132/5	*Set of 4*		5·50	5·50

17 Sombrero Lighthouse

18 Map of Jost Van Dyke

19 Sheep industry

20 Map of Anegada

21 Cattle industry

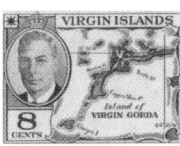
22 Map of Virgin Gorda

23 Map of Tortola

24 Badge of the Presidency

25 Dead Man's Chest

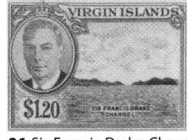
26 Sir Francis Drake Channel

27 Road Town

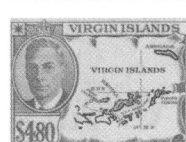
28 Map of Virgin Islands

(Recess D.L.R.)
1952 (15 Apr). T **17/28**. Wmk Mult Script CA. P 12½×13 (vert) or 13×12½ (horiz).

136	**17**	1c. black	80	4·00
137	**18**	2c. deep green	70	30
138	**19**	3c. black and brown	80	2·75
139	**20**	4c. carmine-red	70	3·00
140	**21**	5c. claret and black	1·50	50
141	**22**	8c. bright blue	1·00	2·25
142	**23**	12c. dull violet	1·00	2·25
143	**24**	24c. deep brown	70	50
144	**25**	60c. yellow-green and blue	6·50	11·00
145	**26**	$1.20 black and bright blue	5·50	12·00
146	**27**	$2.40 yellowish green and red-brown	17·00	19·00
147	**28**	$4.80 bright blue and carmine	22·00	21·00
136/47	*Set of 12*		50·00	65·00

1953 (2 June). Coronation. As No. 120 of Antigua.

148		2c. black and green	30	1·25

29 Map of Tortola

30 Virgin Islands sloop

31 Nelthrop Red Poll bull

32 Road Harbour

33 Mountain travel

35 Beach scene

37 White Cedar tree

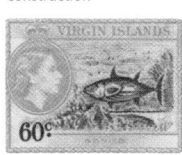
34 Badge of the Presidency

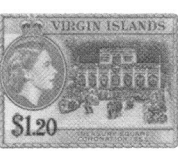
36 *New Idea* (sloop) under construction

38 Skipjack Tuna ("Bonito")

39 Coronation celebrations, Treasury Square

40 Brown Pelican

41 Magnificent Frigate Bird

(Recess D.L.R.)
1956 (1 Nov)–**62**. T **29/41**. Wmk Mult Script CA. P 13×12½ (½c. to $1.20) or 12×11½ ($2.40 and $4.80).

149	**29**	½c. black and reddish purple	1·25	30
		a. *Black and deep reddish purple* (19.4.60)	3·25	4·75
150	**30**	1c. turquoise-blue and slate	1·50	2·00
		a. *Turquoise and slate-violet* (26.11.62)	23·00	28·00
151	**31**	2c. vermilion and black	30	10
152	**32**	3c. blue and deep olive	30	30
153	**33**	4c. deep brown and turquoise-green	70	30
154	**34**	5c. grey-black	50	10
155	**35**	8c. yellow-orange and deep blue	2·25	40
156	**36**	12c. ultramarine and rose-red	4·00	75
157	**37**	24c. myrtle-green and brown-orange	1·00	65
158	**38**	60c. indigo and yellow-orange	8·50	8·00
159	**39**	$1.20 deep yellow-green and carmine-red	6·50	13·00
160	**40**	$2.40 lemon and deep dull purple	48·00	17·00
161	**41**	$4.80 blackish brown and turquoise-blue	48·00	17·00
149/61	*Set of 13*		£110	50·00

(New Currency. 100 cents = 1 U.S. dollar)

 1¢
(42)

1962 (10 Dec). As Nos. 149/53 and 155/61, but W w **12**, surch in US currency as T **42** by D.L.R.

162		1c. on ½c. black and deep reddish purple	30	20
163		2c. on 1c. turquoise and slate-violet	1·75	15
164		3c. on 2c. vermilion and black	70	15
165		4c. on 3c. black and deep olive	50	15
166		5c. on 4c. deep brown and turquoise-green	30	15
167		8c. on 8c. yellow-orange and deep blue	30	15
168		10c. on 12c. ultramarine and rose-red	2·00	15
169		12c. on 24c. myrtle-green and brown-orange	30	15
170		25c. on 60c. indigo and yellow-orange	2·75	45
171		70c. on $1.20 deep yellow-green and carmine-red	35	45
		a. Stop to right of C in surcharge instead of beneath it (in pair with normal)	4·00	3·50
172		$1.40 on $2.40 lemon and deep dull purple	9·50	4·50
173		$2.80 on $4.80 blackish brown and turquoise-blue	9·50	4·50
162/73	*Set of 12*		25·00	10·00

No. 171a occurs on the first stamp on Rows 1 to 10.

1963 (4 June). Freedom from Hunger. As No. 146 of Antigua.

174		25c. reddish violet	20	10

1963 (2 Sept). Red Cross Centenary. As Nos. 147/8 of Antigua.

175		2c. red and black	15	1·40
176		25c. red and blue	50	20

1964 (23 Apr). 400th Birth Anniv of William Shakespeare. As No. 164 of Antigua.

177		10c. bright blue	20	10

43 Skipjack Tuna

44 Soper's Hole

45 Brown Pelican

46 Dead Man's Chest

47 Road Harbour

48 Fallen Jerusalem

49 The Baths, Virgin Gorda

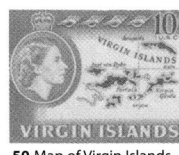
50 Map of Virgin Islands

51 *Youth of Tortola*, Tortola-St. Thomas ferry

52 The Towers, Tortola

53 Beef Island Airfield

54 Map of Tortola

55 Virgin Gorda

56 Yachts at anchor

57 Badge of the Colony

(Des and recess D.L.R.)
1964 (2 Nov)–**68**. T **43/57**. W w **12**. P 11½×12 ($2.80), 13×13½ (70c., $1, $1.40), or 13×12½ (others).

178	**43**	1c. blue and olive-green	30	2·25
179	**44**	2c. yellow-olive and rose-red	15	30
180	**45**	3c. sepia and turquoise-blue	4·75	2·75
181	**46**	4c. black and carmine-red	80	3·25
182	**47**	5c. black and deep bluish green	2·00	2·25
183	**48**	6c. black and brown-orange	30	85
184	**49**	8c. black and magenta	30	1·00
185	**50**	10c. lake and deep lilac	6·00	1·50
		a. *Bright lake and reddish lilac* (26.11.68)	20·00	4·25
186	**51**	12c. deep bluish green and deep violet-blue	2·50	3·50
187	**52**	15c. yellow-green and grey-black	50	2·75
188	**53**	25c. green and purple	13·00	2·50
189	**54**	70c. black and yellow-brown	4·25	8·50
190	**55**	$1 yellow-green and chestnut	4·00	3·50
191	**56**	$1.40 light blue and rose	24·00	14·00
192	**57**	$2.80 black and bright purple	28·00	15·00
178/92	*Set of 15*		80·00	55·00

1965 (17 May). ITU Centenary. As Nos. 166/7 of Antigua.
193	4c. yellow and turquoise		20	10
194	25c. light blue and orange-buff		45	20

1965 (25 Oct). International Co–operation Year. As Nos. 168/9 of Antigua.
195	1c. reddish purple and turquoise-green		10	15
196	25c. deep bluish green and lavender		30	15

1966 (24 Jan). Churchill Commemoration. As Nos. 170/3 of Antigua.
197	1c. new blue		10	40
198	2c. deep green		50	40
199	10c. brown		1·10	10
200	25c. bluish violet		1·50	25
197/200	Set of 4		2·75	1·00

1966 (22 Feb). Royal Visit. As Nos. 174/5 of Antigua.
201	4c. black and ultramarine		40	10
202	70c. black and magenta		1·40	45

58 *Atrato I* (paddle-steamer), 1866

(Des R. Granger Barrett. Litho B.W.)

1966 (25 Apr). Stamp Centenary. T **58** and similar horiz designs. W w **12** (sideways). P 13.
203	5c. black, red, yellow and emerald		35	10
204	10c. black, green and rose-red/*cream*		35	10
205	25c. black, rose-red and blue/*pale green*		55	10
206	60c. black, red and green/*pale blue*		1·00	2·50
203/6	Set of 4		2·00	2·50

Design:—10c. 1d. and 6d. stamps of 1866; 25c. Air mail transport, Beef Island, and 6d. stamp of 1866; 60c. Landing mail at Roadtown, 1866 and 1d. stamp of 1866.

50c.

(**62**)

1966 (15 Sept). As Nos. 189 and 191/2 but wmk sideways, surch as T **62**.
207	50c. on 70c. black and yellow-brown		1·25	90
208	$1.50 on $1.40 light blue and rose		2·25	2·00
209	$3 on $2.80 black and bright purple		2·25	2·75
207/9	Set of 3		5·00	5·00

1966 (1 Dec). 20th Anniv of UNESCO As Nos. 196/8 of Antigua.
210	2c. slate-violet, red, yellow and orange		10	10
211	12c. orange-yellow, violet and deep olive		40	10
212	60c. black, bright purple and orange		1·10	45
210/12	Set of 3		1·40	60

63 Map of Virgin Islands

(Des G. Vasarhelyi. Photo Harrison)

1967 (18 Apr). New Constitution. W w **12**. P 14½.
213	**63**	2c. multicoloured	10	10
214		10c. multicoloured	15	10
		w. Wmk inverted	24·00	
215		25c. multicoloured	15	10
		w. Wmk inverted	9·00	
216		$1 multicoloured	55	40
213/16	Set of 4		75	55

64 *Mercury* (cable ship) and Bermuda-Tortola Link

(Des G. Drummond, Photo Harrison)

1967 (14 Sept). Inauguration of Bermuda-Tortola Telephone Service. T **64** and similar horiz designs. Multicoloured. W w **12**. P 14½.
217	4c. Type **64**		30	10
218	10c. Chalwell Telecommunications Station		20	10
219	50c. *Mercury* (cable ship)		60	30
217/19	Set of 3		1·00	40

67 Blue Marlin

(Des V. Whiteley. Photo Enschedé)

1968 (2 Jan). Game Fishing. T **67** and similar horiz designs. W w **12** (sideways). P 12½×12.
220	2c. multicoloured		10	1·75
221	10c. multicoloured		25	10
222	25c. black, blue and bright violet		55	10
223	40c. multicoloured		85	85
220/3	Set of 4		1·60	2·50

Designs—10c. Cobia; 25c. Wahoo; 40c. Fishing launch and map.

1968 INTERNATIONAL YEAR FOR HUMAN RIGHTS (**71**)

72 Dr. Martin Luther King, Bible, Sword and Armour Gauntlet

1968 (29 July). Human Rights Year. Nos. 185 and 188 optd with T **71**.
224	10c. lake and deep lilac		20	10
225	25c. green and purple		30	40

29 July was the date of issue in the islands. The Crown Agents supplies went on sale in London on 1 July, the local consignment being delayed in transit.

(Des V. Whiteley. Litho Format)

1968 (15 Oct). Martin Luther King Commemoration. W w **12** (sideways). P 14.
226	**72**	4c. multicoloured	25	20
227		25c. multicoloured	40	40

73 de Havilland DHC-6 Twin Otter 100

(Des R. Granger Barrett. Litho Format)

1968 (16 Dec). Opening of Beef Island Airport Extension. T **73** and similar horiz designs. Multicoloured. P 14.
228	2c. Type **73**		25	1·50
229	10c. Hawker Siddeley H.S.748 airliner		30	10
230	25c. de Havilland DH.114 Heron 2		35	10
231	$1 Royal Engineers cap badge		35	2·00
228/31	Set of 4		1·10	3·25

77 Long John Silver and Jim Hawkins

78 Jim Hawkins escaping from the Pirates

(Des Jennifer Toombs. Photo Enschedé)

1969 (18 Mar). 75th Death Anniv of Robert Louis Stevenson. Scenes from *Treasure Island*. T **77/8** and similar designs. W w **12** (sideways on 10c., $1). P 13½×13 (4c., 40c.) or 13×13½ (others).
232	4c. indigo, pale yellow and carmine-red		20	15
233	10c. multicoloured		20	10
234	40c. brown, black and blue		25	30
235	$1 multicoloured		45	1·00
232/5	Set of 4		1·00	1·40

Designs: Vert—40c. The fight with Israel Hands. Horiz—$1 Treasure trove.

82 Yachts in Road Harbour, Tortola

(Des J. Cooter, Litho P.B.)

1969 (20 Oct). Tourism. T **82** and similar multicoloured designs. W w **12** (sideways on 2c., $1). P 12½.
236	2c. Tourist and Yellow-finned Grouper (fish) (*vert*)		15	50
237	10c. Type **82**		30	10
238	20c. Sun-bathing at Virgin Gorda National Park		40	20
239	$1 Tourist and Pipe Organ Cactus at Virgin Gorda (*vert*)		90	1·50
236/9	Set of 4		1·60	2·00

85 Carib Canoe

(Des and litho J.W.)

1970 (16 Feb)–**74**. Horiz designs as T **85**. W w **12** (sideways*). P 14.
240	½c. buff, red-brown and sepia		10	1·75
241	1c. new blue, apple-green and chalky blue		15	75
	a. Perf 13½ (12.11.74)		1·25	2·00
242	2c. yellow-orange, red-brown and slate		40	1·00
243	3c. orange-red, cobalt and sepia		30	1·25
244	4c. greenish blue, chalky blue and bistre-brown		30	50
	w. Wmk Crown to right of CA		£170	
245	5c. emerald, pink and black		30	10
246	6c. reddish violet mauve and myrtle-green		40	2·25
247	8c. apple-green, greenish yellow and sepia		50	6·00
248	10c. greenish blue, yellow-brown and red-brown		50	15
	a. Perf 13½ (12.11.74)		2·00	2·25
249	12c. yellow, crimson and brown		65	1·50
	a. Perf 13½ (12.11.74)		2·00	3·25
250	15c. turquoise-green, orange and bistre-brown		5·00	85
	a. Perf 13½ (12.11.74)		2·75	3·25
251	25c. grey-green, steel-blue and plum		3·50	1·75
252	50c. magenta, dull green and purple-brown		2·75	1·50
253	$1 salmon, olive-green and red-brown		3·50	3·75
254	$2 buff, slate and grey		7·50	7·00
255	$3 ochre, deep blue and sepia		2·25	4·50
256	$5 violet and grey		2·25	5·00
240/56	Set of 17		26·00	35·00

Designs:—1c. *Santa Maria*. (Columbus' flagship); 2c. *Elizabeth Bonaventure* (Drake's flagship); 3c. Dutch Buccaneer, *circa* 1660; 4c. *Thetis*, 1827 (after etching by E. W. Cooke); 5c. Henry Morgan's ship (17th-century); 6c. HMS *Boreas* (Captain Nelson, 1784); 8c. HMS *Eclair*, 1804; 10c. HMS *Formidable*, 1782; 12c. HMS *Nymph*, 1778; 15c. *Windsor Castle* (sailing packet) engaging *Jeune Richard* (French brig), 1807; 25c. HMS *Astrea*, 1808; 50c. Wreck of RMS *Rhone*, 1867; $1 Tortola sloop; $2 HMS *Frobisher*; $3 *Booker Viking* (cargo liner), 1967; $5 Hydrofoil *Sun Arrow*.

*The normal sideways watermark shows Crown to left of CA, *as seen from the back of the stamp*.

The ½c., 3c., 4c., 5c., 10c., and 12c. were reissued in 1973 with W w **12** upright.

102 *A Tale of Two Cities*

(Des W. G. Brown. Litho D.L.R.)

1970 (4 May). Death Centenary of Charles Dickens. T **102** and similar horiz designs showing original book illustrations. W w **12** (sideways). P 14.
257	5c. black, light rose and grey		30	1·00
258	10c. black, light blue and pale green		40	10
259	25c. black, light green and pale yellow		70	25
257/9	Set of 3		1·25	1·00

Designs:—10c. *Oliver Twist*; 25c. *Great Expectations*.

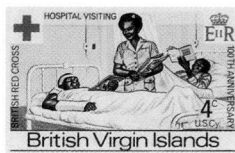

103 Hospital Visit

(Des R. Granger Barrett. Litho Questa)

1970 (10 Aug). Centenary of British Red Cross. T **103** and similar horiz designs. Multicoloured. W w **12** (sideways*). P 14.
260	4c. Type **103**		20	45
261	10c. First Aid Class		20	10
262	25c. Red Cross and Coat of Arms		50	55
	w. Wmk Crown to right of CA		75·00	
260/2	Set of 3		1·00	1·00

*The normal sideways watermark shows Crown to left of CA, *as seen from the back of the stamp*.

104 Mary Read

(Des and litho J.W.)

1970 (16 Nov). Pirates. T **104** and similar vert designs. Multicoloured. W w **12**. P 14×14½.
263	½c. Type **104**		10	15
264	10c. George Lowther		30	10
265	30c. Edward Teach (Blackbeard)		60	25
266	60c. Henry Morgan		80	1·00
263/6	Set of 4		1·50	1·40

Brunei

Sultan Hashim Jalil-ul-alam Akamudin, 1885–1906

(Currency. 100 cents = 1 Straits, later Malayan and Brunei, dollar)

For many years the status of the 1895 issue remained uncertain to such an extent that the 1906 provisionals on Labuan were taken to be the first issue of Brunei.

The 1895 "Star and Crescent" design stamps were, from their first appearance, considered bogus or, at best, as an issue made purely for philatelic purposes. Research into the background of the events surrounding the set led to the publication, in 1933, of the original agreement between Sultan Hashim and J. C. Robertson, dated 20 August 1894, which made clear that the stamps fulfilled a genuine postal purpose. Although Robertson and his partners intended to exploit the philatelic sales for their own benefit, the agreement testifies, as does other evidence, to the use of the stamps by the Sultan for his postal service. As Brunei did not, at that time, belong to any local or international postal union, the stamps were only valid within the state or on mail to Labuan or Sarawak. Items for further afield required franking with Labuan stamps in addition. Although most covers surviving are addressed to Robertson's associates, enough commercial covers and cards exist to show that there was, indeed, a postal service.

PRICES FOR STAMPS ON COVER TO 1945
Nos. 1/10 are rare used on cover.	
Nos. 11/22	from × 30
Nos. 23/33	from × 25
Nos. 34/50	from × 10
Nos. 51/9	from × 12
Nos. 60/78	from × 8

The Sarawak Government maintained a post office at the coal mining centre of Brooketon, and the stamps of SARAWAK were used there from 1893 until the office was handed over to Brunei in February 1907.

1 Star and Local Scene

(Litho in Glasgow)

1895 (22 July). P 13–13½.
1	**1**	½c. brown	8·00	22·00
2		1c. brown-lake	7·50	15·00
3		2c. black	4·50	20·00
4		3c. deep blue	7·00	14·00
5		5c. deep blue-green	6·50	22·00
6		8c. plum	6·50	50·00
7		10c. orange-red	8·00	50·00
		a. Imperf (pair)	£3000	
8		25c. turquoise-green	85·00	£100
9		50c. yellow-green	27·00	£100
10		$1 yellow-olive	28·00	£120
1/10 Set of 10			£170	£450

BRUNEI. **BRUNEI.** **TWO CENTS.** **25 CENTS.**
(2)   (3)   (4)

Line through "B" (R. 5/10)

(Optd by Govt Printer, Singapore)

1906 (1 Oct). Nos. 117, 119, 121 and 123/4 of Labuan (see North Borneo), optd with T **2**, or surch as T **3** or **4** (25c.), in red. P 13½ or 14 (1c.).
11		1c. black and purple	50·00	55·00
		a. Error. Opt in black	£2500	£3000
		b. Line through "B"	£900	
		c. Perf 13½–14, comp 12–13	£325	
12		2c. on 3c. black and sepia	7·00	22·00
		a. "BRUNEI" double	£3750	£2500
		b. "TWO CENTS" double	£5000	
		c. Line through "B"	£325	
13		2c. on 8c. black and vermilion	27·00	80·00
		a. "TWO CENTS" double	£14000	
		b. "TWO CENTS" omitted (in vert pair with normal)	£15000	
		c. Line through "B"	£800	
14		3c. black and sepia	38·00	85·00
		a. Line through "B"	£850	
15		4c. on 12c. black and yellow	8·50	5·00
		a. Line through "B"	£350	
16		5c. on 16c. green and brown	48·00	75·00
		a. Line through "B"	£950	

17		8c. black and vermilion	15·00	32·00
		a. Line through "B"	£500	
18		10c. on 16c. green and brown	7·00	22·00
		a. Line through "B"	£450	£600
19		25c. on 16c. green and brown	£110	£120
		a. Line through "B"	£1700	
20		30c. on 16c. green and brown	£120	£130
		a. Line through "B"	£1700	
21		50c. on 16c. green and brown	£120	£130
		a. Line through "B"	£1700	
22		$1 on 8c. black and vermilion	£120	£130
		a. Line through "B"	£1700	
11/22 Set of 12			£600	£800

Only one sheet of the 1c. received the black overprint.

The surcharges were applied in settings of 50. Nos. 13a/b occur from one sheet on which the surcharge from the second impression of the setting was misplaced to give two surcharges on row five and none on row ten.

Examples of all values are known showing a forged Brunei postmark dated "13 JUL".

Sultan Mohamed Jemal-ul-Alam, 1906–1924

PRINTERS. All Brunei stamps from Nos. 23 to 113 were recess-printed by De La Rue.

5 View on Brunei River

1907 (26 Feb)–**10**. Wmk Mult Crown CA. P 14.
23	**5**	1c. grey-black and pale green	2·25	11·00
		x. Wmk reversed	15·00	25·00
24		2c. grey-black and scarlet	2·50	3·25
		x. Wmk reversed	32·00	42·00
		xs. Ditto, opt "SPECIMEN"	50·00	
25		3c. grey-black and chocolate	10·00	22·00
		x. Wmk reversed	40·00	55·00
26		4c. grey-black and mauve	7·50	6·00
		a. Grey-black and reddish purple (1910)	50·00	40·00
		w. Wmk inverted	£300	
		x. Wmk reversed	85·00	£100
27		5c. grey-black and blue	50·00	95·00
		x. Wmk reversed	£120	£180
		y. Wmk inverted and reversed	£275	
28		8c. grey-black and orange	7·50	23·00
29		10c. grey-black and deep green	4·50	4·00
30		25c. pale blue and ochre-brown	32·00	48·00
31		30c. violet and black	29·00	20·00
		x. Wmk reversed	£425	
32		50c. green and deep brown	15·00	20·00
33		$1 red and grey	60·00	90·00
23/33 Set of 11			£200	£300
23xs/33s Optd "SPECIMEN" Set of 11			£300	

The 1c. "SPECIMEN" is normally found with wmk reversed.

I

II

I	Double plate. Lowest line of shading on water is dotted.
II	Single plate. Dotted line of shading removed.

Stamps printed in two colours are as I.

1908 (12 June)–**22**. Colours changed. Double or single plates. Wmk Mult Crown CA. P 14.
34	**5**	1c. green (I)	80	2·25
35		1c. green (II) (1911)	60	2·00
		a. "A" missing from wmk	£225	
		b. "C" missing from wmk	£225	
36		2c. black and brown (5.4.11)	4·25	1·25
		w. Wmk inverted	£130	
37		3c. scarlet (I)	8·00	1·25
		a. Substituted crown in wmk	£700	
38		3c. scarlet (II) (1916)	£130	38·00
39		4c. claret (II) (17.4.12)	8·00	75
40		5c. black and orange (1916)	7·00	7·00
41		8c. blue and indigo-blue (10.08)	7·00	11·00
42		10c. purple/yellow (11.12)	9·50	1·75
		a. On pale yellow (1922)	7·00	4·00
		as. Optd "SPECIMEN"	60·00	
		w. Wmk inverted	£225	
		x. Wmk reversed	£190	
		y. Wmk inverted and reversed	£450	£450
43		25c. deep lilac (II) (30.5.12)	11·00	30·00
		a. Deep dull purple (1920)	20·00	30·00
44		30c. purple and orange-yellow (18.3.12)	18·00	20·00
45		50c. black/green (II) (1912)	38·00	65·00
		a. On blue-green (1920)	11·00	42·00
46		$1 black and red/blue (18.3.12)	28·00	48·00
47		$5 carmine/green (I) (1910)	£190	£350
48		$25 black/red (I) (1910)	£650	£1300
34/47 Set of 12			£250	£450
34s/48s Optd "SPECIMEN" Set of 13			£650	

The used price for No. 48 is for a cancelled-by-favour example, dated before December 1941; there being no actual postal rate for which this value could be used. Examples dated after 1945 are worth much less.

For illustration of the substituted watermark crown see Catalogue Introduction.

MALAYA-BORNEO EXHIBITION, 1922.
(6)

Retouch   Normal

RETOUCHES. We list the very distinctive 5c. Retouch (top left value tablet, R. 1/8), but there are others of interest, notably in the clouds.

1916. Colours changed. Single plates. Wmk Mult Crown CA. P 14.
49	**5**	5c. orange	27·00	23·00
		a. "5c." retouch	£600	£700
50		8c. ultramarine	8·00	32·00
49s/50s Optd "SPECIMEN" Set of 2			£120	

MALAYA-BORNEO EXHIBITION OVERPRINTS. These were produced from a setting of 30 examples, applied twice to overprint the complete sheet of 60 stamps. Three prominent overprint flaws exist, each occurring on all the stamps in two vertical rows of the sheet.

H I Short "I" (all stamps in 2nd and 8th vertical rows)

E X Broken "E" (all stamps in 4th and 10th vertical rows)

N E Broken "N" (all stamps in 6th and 12th vertical rows)

(Optd by Govt Printer, Singapore)

1922 (31 Mar). Optd with T **6**, in black.
51	**5**	1c. green (II)	12·00	55·00
		a. Short "I"	15·00	75·00
		b. Broken "E"	15·00	75·00
		c. Broken "N"	15·00	75·00
52		2c. black and brown	13·00	50·00
		a. Short "I"	16·00	70·00
		b. Broken "E"	16·00	70·00
		c. Broken "N"	16·00	70·00
53		3c. scarlet (II)	14·00	60·00
		a. Short "I"	17·00	85·00
		b. Broken "E"	17·00	85·00
		c. Broken "N"	17·00	85·00
54		4c. claret (II)	20·00	55·00
		a. Short "I"	25·00	80·00
		b. Broken "E"	25·00	80·00
		c. Broken "N"	25·00	80·00
55		5c. orange (II)	26·00	65·00
		a. "5c." retouch (and short "I")	£600	£1100
		b. Short "I"	32·00	95·00
		c. Broken "E"	32·00	95·00
		d. Broken "N"	32·00	95·00
56		10c. purple/yellow (II)	11·00	60·00
		a. Short "I"	14·00	90·00
		b. Broken "E"	14·00	90·00
		c. Broken "N"	14·00	90·00
57		25c. deep dull purple (II)	14·00	80·00
		a. Short "I"	30·00	£130
		b. Broken "E"	30·00	£130
		c. Broken "N"	30·00	£130
		d. "C" of "CA" missing from wmk	£1300	
		x. Wmk reversed	£425	
58		50c. black/blue-green (II)	45·00	£150
		a. Short "I"	80·00	£225
		b. Broken "E"	80·00	£225
		c. Broken "N"	80·00	£225
59		$1 black and red/blue	75·00	£190
		a. Short "I"	£130	£275
		b. Broken "E"	£130	£275
		c. Broken "N"	£130	£275
51/9 Set of 9			£200	£700

Examples of all values are known showing a forged Brunei postmark dated "13 JUL".

Sultan Ahmed Tajudin Akhazul Khairi Wadin, 1924–1950

7 Native houses, Water Village

1924 (Feb)–**37**. Printed from single plates as Type II, except 30c. and $1 as Type I. Wmk Mult Script CA. P 14.
60	**5**	1c. black (9.26)	1·00	75
		a. "A" of "CA" missing from wmk	£800	
61		2c. brown (3.24)	1·25	11·00
62		2c. green (3.33)	2·00	1·00
63		3c. green (3.24)	1·75	6·50
64		4c. maroon (3.24)	3·50	1·25
65		4c. orange (1929)	2·00	1·00
66		5c. orange-yellow* (3.24)	16·00	2·00
		a. "5c." retouch	£325	£130
67		5c. grey (1931)	25·00	12·00
		a. "5c." retouch	£550	£425
68		5c. chocolate (1933)	25·00	1·00
		a. "5c." retouch	£325	70·00
69	**7**	6c. intense black** (3.24)	14·00	10·00
		x. Wmk reversed	£500	
70		6c. scarlet (1931)	12·00	11·00
71	**5**	8c. ultramarine (9.27)	6·00	5·00
72		8c. grey-black (1933)	16·00	75
73		10c. purple/yellow (3.37)	42·00	30·00
		a. Perf "SPECIMEN"†	£170	
74	**7**	12c. blue (shades)	4·50	9·00
75	**5**	25c. slate-purple (1931)	24·00	13·00
76		30c. purple and orange-yellow (1931)	25·00	16·00
77		50c. black/emerald (1931)	19·00	15·00
78		$1 black and red/blue (1931)	28·00	80·00
60/78 Set of 19			£225	£200
60s/78s Optd (Nos. 60/1, 63/4, 66, 69, 71, 74) or Perf "SPECIMEN" Set of 18			£600	

*For 5c, orange, see No. 82. No. 66 is a "Wet" printing and No. 82 a "Dry".

**For 6c. black, see No. 83. Apart from the difference in shade there is a variation in size, No. 69 being 37¾ mm long and No. 83 39 mm.

The 2c. orange and 3c. blue-green in Type **5**, and the 6c. greenish grey (Perf 14×11½), 8c. red and 15c. ultramarine in Type **7** were not issued without the Japanese Occupation overprint, although unoverprinted examples exist. It is believed that these 1941 printings were produced and possibly perforated, by other firms in Great Britain following bomb damage to the De La Rue works at the end of 1940 (*Prices* 2c., 8c., *each* £75, 15c. £100, 6c. £130, 3c. £250 *unused*).

During the life of this issue De La Rue changed the method of production from a "Wet" to a "Dry" process. Initially the stamps were printed on ungummed paper which was dampened before being put on the press. Once the paper had dried, and contracted in the process, the gum was then applied. "Dry" printings, introduced around 1934, were on pre-gummed paper. The contraction of the "Wet" printings was considerable and usually involves a difference of between 0.5 mm and 1 mm when compared with the larger "Dry" printings. The following stamps occur from both "Wet" and "Dry" versions: 1c., 2c. green, 4c. orange, 5c. chocolate, 6c. scarlet, 8c. grey-black, 10c. and 25c.

Stamps of this issue can be found either line or comb perforated.
† The 10c. perforated "SPECIMEN" (No 73s) is listed separately due to its later distribution by the UPU.

Brunei was occupied by the Japanese Army in January 1942 and remained under Japanese administration until liberated by the 9th Australian Division in June 1945.

After the cessation of hostilities with the Japanese, postal services were re-introduced by the British Military Administration. From 6 November, military post offices using Australian stamps were opened for civilian use, until offices under B.M.A. control were opened at Brunei Town and Kuala Belait on 17 December 1945 where B.M.A. overprints on the stamps of NORTH BORNEO and SARAWAK were used until the reappearance of Brunei issues on 2 January 1947.

Redrawn clouds (R. 1/1 of No. 80*ab* only)

1947 (2 Jan)–**51**. Colours changed and new values. Wmk Mult Script CA. P 14.

79	**5**	1c. chocolate	50	2·00
		a. "A" of "CA" missing from wmk.	£1200	
80		2c. grey	60	10·00
		a. Perf 14½×13½ (25.9.50)	2·00	4·75
		ab. Black (27.6.51)	2·00	6·50
		ac. Redrawn clouds	85·00	
81	**7**	3c. green	1·50	8·00
82	**5**	5c. orange*	80	2·00
		a. "5c." retouch	70·00	£100
		b. Perf 14½×13½ (25.9.50)	4·00	22·00
		c. Ditto "5c." retouch	£140	£275
83	**7**	6c. black*	1·25	7·00
84	**5**	8c. scarlet	50	2·50
		a. Perf 13 (25.1.51)	55	13·00
85		10c. violet	2·25	30
		a. Perf 14½×13½ (25.9.50)	3·75	5·50
86		15c. ultramarine	1·75	70
87		25c. deep claret	2·75	3·50
		a. "A" of "CA" missing from wmk.	—	£1200
		b. Perf 14½×13½ (25.1.51)	4·50	18·00
88		30c. black and orange	2·50	1·00
		aw. Wmk inverted	—	£1500
		b. Perf 14½×13½ (25.1.51)	3·25	23·00
89		50c. black	6·50	1·50
		a. Perf 13 (25.9.50)	1·90	24·00
90		$1 black and scarlet	28·00	2·75
91		$5 green and red-orange (2.2.48)	25·00	28·00
92		$10 black and purple (2.2.48)	£120	30·00
79/92 *Set of 14*			£160	80·00
79s/92s Perf "SPECIMEN" *Set of 14*			£350	

*See also Nos. 66 and 69.

The 1, 2, 3, 5, 6, 10 and 25c. values utilised the plates of the pre-war issue and were line perforated until the introduction of the 14½×13½ comb machine for some values in 1950–51. The 8, 15, 50c., $1, $5 and $10 were from new plates with the sheets comb perforated. The 30c. was initially a pre-war plate, but it is believed that a new plate was introduced in 1951.

8 Sultan Ahmed Tajudin and Water Village

1949 (22 Sept). Sultan's Silver Jubilee. Wmk Mult Script CA. P 13.

93	**8**	8c. black and carmine	1·40	1·25
94		25c. purple and red-orange	1·40	1·60
95		50c. black and blue	1·40	1·60
93/5 *Set of 3*			3·75	4·00

1949 (10 Oct). 75th Anniv of Universal Postal Union. As Nos. 114/17 of Antigua.

96		8c. carmine	1·00	2·50
97		15c. deep blue	3·50	1·50
98		25c. magenta	1·00	1·50
99		50c. blue-black	1·00	1·25
96/9 *Set of 4*			6·00	6·00

Sultan Sir Omar Ali Saifuddin-Wasa'adul Khairi Wadin, 1950-1967

9 Sultan Omar Ali Saifuddin **10** Native houses, Water Village

1952 (1 Mar)–**58**. Wmk Mult Script CA. P 13.

100	**9**	1c. black	10	50
101		2c. black and orange	15	50
102		3c. black and lake-brown	25	30
103		4c. black and green	30	20
104		6c. black and grey	2·50	10
105		8c. black and crimson	1·25	60
		a. Black and crimson-lake (15.2.56)	19·00	20
106		10c. black and sepia	30	10
107		12c. black and violet	6·00	10
108		15c. black and pale blue	5·00	10
109		25c. black and purple	2·50	10
		a. Black and reddish purple (8.10.53)	11·00	1·00
110		50c. black and ultramarine	6·00	10
		a. Black and blue (22.6.55)	16·00	10
111	**10**	$1 black and green	5·50	1·60
		a. Black and bronze-green (23.7.58)	12·00	3·50
112		$2 black and scarlet	7·00	3·00
113		$5 black and maroon	38·00	12·00
		a. Black and brown-purple (15.2.56)	55·00	13·00
100/13 *Set of 14*			65·00	16·00

No. 106 exists in coils constructed from normal sheets.
See also Nos. 118/31.

11 Brunei Mosque and Sultan Omar

(Recess B.W.)

1958 (24 Sept). Opening of Brunei Mosque. W w **12**. P 13½.

114	**11**	8c. black and myrtle-green	20	65
115		15c. black and carmine	25	15
116		35c. black and deep lilac	30	90
114/16 *Set of 3*			65	1·50

12 "Protein Foods"

(Des M. Goaman. Photo Harrison)

1963 (4 June). Freedom from Hunger. W w **12**. P 14×14½.

117	**12**	12c. sepia	2·75	1·00

1964–**72**. As Nos. 100/13, but W w **12**. Glazed paper ($2, 5) or ordinary paper (others).

118	**9**	1c. black (17.3.64)	50	70
		a. Glazed paper. Grey (28.11.69)	2·75	4·50
		ab. Slate grey (30.6.72)	15	2·75
119		2c. black and orange (17.3.64)	1·50	20
		a. Glazed paper (27.5.70)	2·50	10
120		3c. black and lake-brown (10.11.64)	1·50	60
		a. Glazed paper (27.5.70)	2·50	10
121		4c. black and green (12.5.64)	40	10
		a. Glazed paper (6.3.70)	50	10
		ab. Black and emerald (19.11.71)	2·50	4·00
122		6c. black and grey (12.5.64)	3·75	10
		a. Black (28.11.69)	11·00	11·00
		b. Glazed paper (28.11.69)	50	30
		ba. Light grey (19.11.71)	2·00	3·75
123		8c. black and crimson-lake (12.5.64)	1·50	10
		a. Glazed paper (27.5.70)	1·00	15
		ab. Black and brown-red (19.11.71)	5·00	4·50
124		10c. black and sepia (12.5.64)	1·25	10
		a. Glazed paper (31.3.70)	2·75	10
		ab. Grey and pale brown (coil) (11.10.71)	4·00	6·50
125		12c. black and violet (12.5.64)	1·50	10
		a. Glazed paper (5.11.70)	15·00	1·00
126		15c. black and pale blue (12.5.64)	55	10
		a. Glazed paper (28.11.69)	65	20
127		25c. black and purple (12.5.64)	7·50	10
		a. Glazed paper (18.5.70)	14·00	9·00
		ab. Glazed paper. Black and reddish violet (30.4.71)	17·00	1·25
128		50c. black and ultramarine (10.11.64)	2·50	10
		a. Black and bright ultramarine (17.3.69)	8·50	2·25
		b. Glazed paper (5.11.70)	19·00	4·00
		ba. Grey and indigo (21.12.71)	22·00	6·50
129	**10**	$1 black and bronze-green (14.5.68)	3·00	6·00
		a. Glazed paper (5.11.70)	9·00	7·00

130		$2 black and scarlet (5.11.70)	45·00	20·00
131		$5 black and maroon (5.11.70)	45·00	35·00
118/29 *Set of 12*			23·00	7·00
118ab/29a, 130/1 *Set of 14*			£140	65·00

Printings of the 6 and 15c. issued on 28 November 1969 were on both ordinary and glazed paper, the 6c. on ordinary producing a distinct shade.

No. 124a exists in coils constructed from normal sheets.

The 2c., 3c., 4c., 6c., 8c., 10c., 12c. and 15c. were reissued between 1972 and 1974 with W w **12** sideways.

13 ITU Emblem

(Des M. Goaman. Litho Enschedé)

1965 (17 May). ITU Centenary. W w **12**. P 11×11½.

132	**13**	4c. mauve and orange-brown	35	10
133		75c. orange-yellow and light emerald	1·00	75

14 ICY Emblem

(Des V. Whiteley. Litho Harrison)

1965 (25 Oct). International Co-operation Year. W w **12**. P 14.

134	**14**	4c. reddish purple and turquoise-green	20	10
135		15c. deep bluish green and lavender	55	35

15 Sir Winston Churchill and St. Paul's Cathedral in Wartime

(Des Jennifer Toombs. Photo Harrison)

1966 (24 Jan). Churchill Commemoration. W w **12**. P 14.

136	**15**	3c. black, cerise, gold and new blue	30	2·75
137		10c. black, cerise, gold and deep green	1·25	20
138		15c. black, cerise, gold and brown	1·50	35
139		75c. black, cerise, gold and bluish violet	3·75	5·00
136/9 *Set of 4*			6·00	7·50

16 Footballer's Legs, Ball and Jules Rimet Cup

(Des V. Whiteley. Litho Harrison)

1966 (4 July). World Cup Football Championship. W w **12** (sideways). P 14.

140	**16**	4c. violet, yellow-green, lake and yellow-brown	20	15
141		75c. chocolate, blue-green, lake and yellow-brown	80	60

17 WHO Building

(Des M. Goaman. Litho Harrison)

1966 (20 Sept). Inauguration of WHO Headquarters, Geneva. W w **12** (sideways). P 14.

142	**17**	12c. black, yellow-green and light blue	40	65
143		25c. black, light purple and yellow-brown	60	1·50

18 "Education"

19 "Science"

20 "Culture"

(Des Jennifer Toombs. Litho Harrison)

1966 (1 Dec). 20th Anniv of UNESCO W w **12** (sideways). P 14.

144	**18**	4c. slate-violet, red, yellow and orange	35	10
145	**19**	15c. orange-yellow, violet and deep olive	75	50
146	**20**	75c. black, bright purple and orange	2·50	6·50
144/6 *Set of 3*			3·25	6·50

Sultan Sir Hassanal Bolkiah Mu'izzadin Waddaulah, 1967

21 Religious Headquarters Building

(Des and photo Harrison)

1967 (19 Dec). 1400th Anniv of Revelation of the Koran. W w **12** (sideways). P 12½.

147	**21**	4c. multicoloured	10	10
148		10c. multicoloured	15	10
149	–	25c. multicoloured	20	30
150	–	50c. multicoloured	35	1·50
147/50 *Set of 4*			70	1·75

Nos. 149/50 are as T **21** but have sprigs of laurel flanking the main design (which has a smaller circle) in place of flagpoles.

22 Sultan of Brunei, Mosque and Flags

(Des V. Whiteley. Photo Enschedé)

1968 (9 July). Installation of Y.T.M. Seri Paduka Duli Pengiran Temenggong. T **22** and similar multicoloured design. P 14×13 (12c.) or 13×14 (others).

151		4c. Type **22**	15	80
152		12c. Sultan of Brunei, Mosque and Flags (*horiz*)	40	1·60
153		25c. Type **22**	55	2·00
151/3 *Set of 3*			1·00	4·00

23 Sultan of Brunei   **24** Sultan of Brunei

(Des V. Whiteley. Litho D.L.R.)

1968 (15 July). Sultan's Birthday. W w **12** (sideways). P 12.

154	**23**	4c. multicoloured	10	50
155		12c. multicoloured	20	85
156		25c. multicoloured	30	1·40
154/6 *Set of 3*			55	2·50

(Des V. Whiteley. Photo Harrison)

1968 (1 Aug). Coronation of the Sultan of Brunei. W w **12** (sideways). P 14½×14.

157	**24**	4c. multicoloured	15	25
158		12c. multicoloured	25	50
159		25c. multicoloured	40	75
157/9 *Set of 3*			70	1·40

25 New Building and Sultan's Portrait

26 New Building and Sultan's Portrait

(Photo Enschedé)

1968 (29 Sept). Opening of Language and Literature Bureau. W w **12** (sideways). P 13½ (10c.) or 12½×13½ (others).

160	**25**	10c. multicoloured	20	1·75
		a. *Tête-bêche* (pair)	40	3·50
161	**26**	15c. multicoloured	20	35
162		30c. multicoloured	45	90
160/2 *Set of 3*			75	2·75

The above were scheduled for release in 1967, and when finally issued had the year altered by overprinting.

27 Human Rights Emblem and struggling Man

28 Sultan of Brunei and WHO Emblem

(Des V. Whiteley. Litho Harrison)

1968 (16 Dec). Human Rights Year. W w **12**. P 14.

163	**27**	12c. black, yellow and green	10	20
164		25c. black, yellow and blue	15	25
165		75c. black, yellow and dull purple	45	1·75
163/5 *Set of 3*			65	2·00

(Des V. Whiteley. Litho Format)

1968 (19 Dec). 20th Anniv of World Health Organization. P 14.

166	**28**	4c. yellow, black and cobalt	30	1·25
167		15c. yellow, black and deep bluish violet	55	65
168		25c. yellow, black and pale yellow-olive	65	1·25
166/8 *Set of 3*			1·40	2·75

29 Deep Sea Oil-Rig, Sultan of Brunei and inset portrait of Pengiran Di-Gadong

(Des adapted by V. Whiteley. Photo Enschedé)

1969 (10 July). Installation (9th May, 1968) of Pengiran Shahbandar as Y.T.M. Seri Paduka Duli Pengiran Di-Gadong Sahibol Mal. W w **12**. P 14×13.

169	**29**	12c. multicoloured	85	50
170		40c. multicoloured	1·25	2·25
171		50c. multicoloured	1·25	2·25
169/71 *Set of 3*			3·00	4·50

30 Aerial View of Parliament Buildings

(Des Harrison. Litho D.L.R.)

1969 (23 Sept). Opening of Royal Audience Hall and Legislative Council Chamber. P 15.

172	**30**	12c. multicoloured	20	25
173		30c. multicoloured	30	45
174	–	50c. rose-red and bluish violet	60	3·50
172/4 *Set of 3*			1·00	3·75

Design:—50c. Elevation of new buildings.

32 Youth Centre and Sultan's Portrait

(Des V. Whiteley. Litho D.L.R.)

1969 (20 Dec). Opening of the New Youth Centre. W w **12**. P 15×14½.

175	**32**	6c. flesh, slate-lilac and black	20	1·00
176		10c. olive-yellow, grey-green and blackish brown	25	10
177		30c. yellow-olive, yellow-brown and black	70	1·00
175/7 *Set of 3*			1·00	1·90

JAPANESE OCCUPATION OF BRUNEI

Japanese forces landed in Northern Borneo on 15 December 1941 and the whole of Brunei had been occupied by 6 January 1942.

Brunei, North Borneo, Sarawak and, after a short period, Labuan, were administered as a single territory by the Japanese. Until September-October 1942, previous stamp issues, without overprint, continued to be used in conjunction with existing postmarks. From the Autumn of 1942 onwards unoverprinted stamps of Japan were made available and examples can be found used from the area for much of the remainder of the War. Japanese Occupation issues for Brunei, North Borneo and Sarawak were equally valid throughout the combined territory but not, in practice, equally available.

PRICES FOR STAMPS ON COVER	
Nos. J1/16	*from* × 8
Nos. J17/20	—

(**1**) ("Imperial Japanese Government")

(**2**) ("Imperial Japanese Postal Service $3")

1942 (Oct)–**44**. Stamps of Brunei handstamped with T **1** in violet to blue. Wmk Mult Script CA (except Nos. J18/19, Mult Crown CA). P 14.

J1	**5**	1c. black	10·00	23·00
		a. Red opt	£225	£250
J2		2c. green	50·00	£110
J3		2c. orange (1943)	6·00	9·00
J4		3c. blue-green	32·00	75·00
		a. Opt omitted (in pair with normal)	£4250	
J5		4c. orange	4·00	13·00
J6		5c. chocolate	6·50	13·00
		a. "5c." retouch	£160	£375
J7	**7**	6c. greenish grey (P 14×11½) (1944)	40·00	£325
J8		6c. scarlet	£600	£600
J9	**5**	8c. grey-black	£850	£900
J10	**7**	8c. red	10·00	12·00
		a. Opt omitted (in pair with normal)	£2750	
J11	**5**	10c. purple/*yellow*	10·00	26·00
J12	**7**	12c. blue	35·00	26·00
		a. Red opt	£650	£750
J13		15c. ultramarine (1944)	25·00	26·00
J14	**5**	25c. slate-purple	26·00	50·00
		a. Red opt	£800	£950
J15		30c. purple and orange-yellow	95·00	£180
J16		50c. black/*emerald*	38·00	60·00
		a. Red opt	£850	
J17	**7**	$1 black and red/*blue* (1944)	55·00	70·00
		a. Red opt	—	£1800
J18	**5**	$5 carmine/*green* (1944)	£1000	£3500
J19		$25 black/*red* (1944)	£1000	£3500

The overprint varies in shade from violet to blue, and being handstamped, exists inverted, double, double one inverted and treble. Nos. J3, J4, J7, J10 and J13 were not issued without the overprint (See footnote below Brunei No. 78).

1944 (11 May). No. J1 surch with T **2** in orange-red.

J20	**5**	$3 on 1c. black	£9000	£10000
		a. Surch on No. 60 of Brunei	£11000	

Three separate handstamps were used to apply Type **2**, one for the top line, one for the bottom and the third for the two central characters.

Burma

(Currency. 12 pies = 1 anna; 16 annas = 1 rupee)

Stamps of India were used in Burma from 1854 and, after 1856, individual examples can be identified by the use of the concentric octagonal postmarks of the Bengal Postal Circle of which the following were supplied to Burmese post offices:

Type A No. B156 (Rangoon)

Type B No. B5 (Akyab)

B5	Akyab	B146	Pegu
B12*	Bassein	B150	Prome
B22	Nga Thine Khyoung	B156*	Rangoon
B56	Amherst	B159	Sandoway
B108	Kyouk Phyoo	B165	Sarawah (to 1860)
B111	Meeaday	B165	Henzada (from 1861)
B112	Mengyee	B171	Shoay Gyeen
B127	Moulmein	B173	Sittang
B128	Mergui	B179	Thayetmyo
B129	Tavoy	B181	Toungoo
B133	Myanoung	B227	Port Blair
B136	Namayan		

Exists in black or blue. Remainder in black only.

Akyab, Moulmein and Rangoon used postmarks as both Type A and Type B, Port Blair as Type B only and the remainder as Type A only.

From 1860 various types of duplex cancellations were introduced and Burmese examples can be identified when sufficient of the left-hand portion is visible on the stamp. Such marks were issued for the following offices:

Akyab	Rangoon
Bassein	Rangoon C.R.H. (Cantonment
Mandalay	Receiving House)
Moulmein	Thayetmyo
Port Blair	Toungoo
Prome	

1862 Duplex from Toungoo

1865 Duplex from Akyab

During 1875, a further series of duplex marks was introduced in which the right-hand portion of the cancellation included the office code number, prefixed by the letter "R" for Rangoon:

R–1	Rangoon	R–9	Myanoung
R–1/1	Rangoon Cantonment	R–10	Port Blair
R–2	Akyab	1/R–10	Nancowry
R–3	Bassein	R–11	Prome
R–4	Henzada	R–12	Sandoway
R–5	Kyouk Phyoo	R–13	Shwegyeen
R–6	Mandalay	R–14	Tavoy
R–7	Mergui	R–15	Thayetmyo
R–8	Moulmein	R–16	Toughoo
1/R–8	Amherst		

1875 type from Rangoon

1875 type from Rangoon Cantonment Receiving House

From 1886 the whole of Burma was united under the Crown and the post offices were supplied with circular date stamps giving the name of the town.

Most Indian stamps, both postage and official, issued during the period were supplied to post offices in Burma. None of the imperforates printed by De La Rue have been seen however, and from the later issues the following have not been recorded with Burma postmarks:

Nos. 39a, 66a, 68, 85a, 92a, 110a/b, 148a, 155a, 165, 192a/c, 195a/b, O15, O38, O40b, O50a/b, O74a, O101a, O102, O103/a, O104/5 and O142.

The value of most Indian stamps used in Burma coincides proportionally with the used prices quoted for India, but some, especially the provisional surcharges, are extremely rare with Burmese postmarks. Stamps of the face value of 2r. and above from the reigns of Victoria and Edward VII are more common with telegraph cancellations than with those of the postal service.

PRICES FOR STAMPS ON COVER TO 1945	
Nos. 1/18	from × 6
Nos. 18a/33	from × 4
No. 34	from × 5
Nos. 35/50	from × 8
Nos. O1/27	from × 15

BRITISH ADMINISTRATION

From 1 January 1886 Burma was a province of the Indian Empire but was separated from India and came under direct British administration on 1 April 1937.

BURMA   BURMA
(1)   **(1a)**

1937 (1 Apr). Stamps of India. (King George V inscr "INDIA POSTAGE") optd with T **1** or **1a** (rupee values). W **69**. P 14.

1		3p. slate	2·50	10
		w. Wmk inverted	22·00	3·25
2		½a. green	1·00	10
		w. Wmk inverted	20·00	3·25
3		9p. deep green (typo)	1·25	10
		w. Wmk inverted	14·00	3·25
4		1a. chocolate	5·00	10
		w. Wmk inverted	16·00	3·25
5		2a. vermilion (small die)	1·00	10
6		2½a. orange	75	10
		w. Wmk inverted	17·00	3·25
7		3a. carmine	5·00	30
		w. Wmk inverted	35·00	4·25
8		3½a. deep blue	9·00	10
		aw. Wmk inverted	10·00	30
		b. Dull blue	29·00	14·00
		bw. Wmk inverted	20·00	4·00
9		4a. sage-green	1·25	10
		w. Wmk inverted	—	£130
10		6a. bistre	1·50	35
		w. Wmk inverted	£200	£130
11		8a. reddish purple	4·25	10
		w. Wmk inverted	£200	
12		12a. claret	19·00	4·25
		w. Wmk inverted	42·00	9·50
13		1r. chocolate and green	70·00	6·50
14		2r. carmine and orange	50·00	27·00
		w. Wmk inverted	80·00	38·00
15		5r. ultramarine and purple	70·00	38·00
		w. Wmk inverted	—	£325
16		10r. green and scarlet	£275	£100
			†	
17		15r. blue and olive (wmk inverted)	£800	£275
18		25r. orange and blue	£1600	£600
		aw. Wmk inverted	£1600	£600
1/18		Set of 18	£2500	£900

The opt is at top on all values except the 3a.

The 1a. has been seen used from Yenangyaung on 22 Mar 1937.
It is necessary to emphasis that the unused prices quoted for Nos. 1/18 are for unmounted examples, as they were issued within the reign of King George VI.

2 King George VI and "Chinthes"

3 King George VI and "Nagas"

4 Karaweik (royal barge)

5 Burma teak

6 Burma rice

7 River Irrawaddy

8 King George VI and Peacock

9 King George VI and "Nats"

10 Elephants' Heads

6p. "Medallion" flaw (R. 14/3)

2a.6p. "Birds over trees at left (R. 15/3)

3a.6p. Extra trees flaw (R. 11/8)

3a.6p. "Tick bird" flaw (R. 9/5)

(Des Maung Kyi (2a.6p.), Maung Hline (3a.), Maung Ohn Pe (3a.6p.) and N. K. D. Naigamwalla (8a.). Litho Security Ptg Press, Nasik)

1938 (15 Nov)–**40**. T **2/9**. W **10**. P 14 (vert) or 13½ × 13 (horiz).

18b	**2**	1p. red-orange (1.8.40)	3·50	2·50
19		3p. bright violet	30	3·00
20		6p. bright blue	2·00	10
		a. Medallion flaw	80·00	24·00
21		9p. yellow-green	3·25	2·50

22	**3**	1a. purple-brown		30	10
23		1½a. turquoise-green		2·75	4·00
24		2a. carmine		4·25	1·00
25	**4**	2a.6p. claret		17·00	3·75
		a. Birds over trees		£300	95·00
26	**5**	3a. dull violet		21·00	4·00
27	**6**	3a.6p. light blue and blue		4·50	9·50
		a. Extra trees flaw		£160	£190
		b. Tick bird flaw		£160	£190
28	**3**	4a. greenish blue		4·50	20
29	**7**	8a. myrtle-green		4·00	55
30	**8**	1r. purple and blue		4·00	1·00
31		2r. brown and purple		27·00	7·00
32	**9**	5r. violet and scarlet		80·00	70·00
33	**9**	10r. brown and myrtle		85·00	£100
18b/33 Set of 16				£225	£180

The 1a. exists lithographed or typographed, the latter having a "Jubilee" line in the sheet margin.

COMMEMORATION POSTAGE STAMP 6th MAY 1840

(11)

Broken bar (R. 7/8)

1940 (6 May). Centenary of First Adhesive Postage Stamps. No. 25 surch with T **11**.

34	**4**	1a. on 2a.6p. claret		4·25	2·00
		a. Birds over trees		90·00	80·00
		b. Broken bar		90·00	80·00

For stamps issued in 1942–45 see under Japanese Occupation.

CHIN HILLS DISTRICT. This area, in the far north-west of the country, remained in British hands when the Japanese overran Burma in May 1942.

During the period July to December 1942 the local officials were authorised to produce provisional stamps and the letters "OHMS" are known overprinted by typewriter on Nos. 3, 20, 22/4, 28/9 and 31 of Burma or handstamped, in violet, on Nos. 25, 27 and 29. The two types can also occur together or in combination with a handstamped "SERVICE".

From early in 1943 ordinary postage stamps of India were used from the Chin Hills post offices of Falam, Haka, Fort White and Tiddim, this expedient continuing until the fall of Falam to the Japanese on 7 November 1943.

The provisional stamps should only be collected on Official cover (*Price, from* £2250) where dates and the sender's handwriting can be authenticated.

BRITISH MILITARY ADMINISTRATION

Preparations for the liberation of Burma commenced in February 1943 when the Civil Affairs Service (Burma) (CAS(B)) was set up at Delhi as part of the proposed military administration structure. One of the specific tasks assigned to CAS(B) was the operation of a postal service for the civilian population.

Operations against the Japanese intensified during the second half of 1944. The port of Akyab in the Arakan was reoccupied in January 1945. The 14th Army took Mandalay on 29 March and Rangoon was liberated from the sea on 3 May.

Postal services for the civilian population started in Akyab on 13 April 1945, while post offices in the Magwe Division around Meiktila were operating from 4 March. Mandalay post offices opened on 8 June and those in Rangoon on 16 June, but the full network was only completed in December 1945, just before the military administration was wound up.

MILY ADMN (12)   MILY ADMN (13)

1945 (from 11 Apr). Nos. 18b to 33 optd with T **12** (small stamps) or **13** (others) by Security Printing Press, Nasik.

35	**2**	1p. red-orange		10	10
		a. Opt omitted (in pair with normal)		£1600	
36		3p. bright violet		20	2·00
37		6p. bright blue		20	30
		a. Medallion flaw		35·00	40·00
38		9p. yellow-green		30	2·00
39	**3**	1a. purple-brown (16.6)		20	10
40		1½a. turquoise-green (16.6)		20	15
41		2a. carmine		20	15
42	**4**	2a.6p. claret		2·25	3·75
		a. Birds over trees		70·00	90·00
43	**5**	3a. dull violet		1·50	30
44	**6**	3a.6p. light blue and blue		20	1·00
		a. Extra trees flaw		40·00	
45	**3**	4a. greenish blue		20	70
46	**7**	8a. myrtle-green		20	2·00
47	**8**	1r. purple and blue		50	50
48		2r. brown and purple		50	1·50
49	**9**	5r. violet and scarlet		50	1·50
50		10r. brown and myrtle		50	1·50
35/50 Set of 16				7·00	16·00

Only the typographed version of the 1a., No. 22, received this overprint.

The missing overprints on the 1p. occur on the stamps from the bottom row of one sheet. A further block with two examples of the variety caused by a paper fold also exists.

The exact dates of issue for Nos. 35/50 are difficult to establish.

The initial stock of overprints is known to have reached CAS(B) headquarters, Imphal, at the beginning of April 1945. Postal directives issued on 11 April refer to the use of the overprints in Akyab and in the Magwe Division where surcharged pre-war postal stationery envelopes had previously been in use. The 6p., 1a., 1½a. and 2a.values were placed on sale at Mandalay on 8 June and the 1a. and 2a. at Rangoon on 16 June. It has been suggested that only a limited service was initially available in Rangoon. All values were on sale by 9 August 1945.

BRITISH CIVIL ADMINISTRATION

3a.6p. Curved plough handle (R. 8/4)

1946 (1 Jan). As Nos. 19/33, but colours changed.

51	**2**	3p. brown		15	4·00
52		6p. deep blue		1·25	30
		a. Medallion flaw			
53		9p. green		1·75	7·00
54	**3**	1a. blue		1·25	20
55		1½a. orange		1·25	10
56		2a. claret		60	50
57	**4**	2a.6p. greenish blue		2·75	9·50
		aa. Birds over trees		80·00	£100
57a	**5**	3a. blue-violet		6·50	13·00
57b	**6**	3a.6p. black and ultramarine		4·50	6·00
		ba. Curved plough handle		£120	
58	**3**	4a. purple		70	1·50
59	**7**	8a. maroon		1·75	7·50
60	**8**	1r. violet and maroon		3·25	3·75
61		2r. brown and orange		10·00	9·00
62	**9**	5r. green and brown		12·00	32·00
63		10r. claret and violet		25·00	45·00
51/63 Set of 15				60·00	£120

No. 54 was printed in typography only.

14 Burman

(Des A. G. I. McGeogh. Litho Nasik)

1946 (2 May). Victory. T **14** and similar vert designs. W **10** (sideways). P 13.

64		9p. turquoise-green		20	40
65		1½a. violet		20	15
66		2a. carmine		20	15
67		3a.6p. ultramarine		1·00	40
64/7 Set of 4				1·40	1·00

Designs:—1½a. Burmese woman; 2a. Chinthe; 3a.6p. Elephant.

INTERIM BURMESE GOVERNMENT

ကြားဖြတ်	၁။ဖြတ်ကြ	တ်ကြားဖြ
အစိုးရ။	အစိုးရ။	အစိုးရ။
(18 Trans. "Interim Government")	18a	18b

Type **18a** shows the first character transposed to the end of the top line (R. 6/15).

Type **18b** shows the last two characters transposed to the front of the top line (R. 14/14).

Some sheets of the 3p. show both errors corrected by a handstamp as Type **18**.

1947 (1 Oct). Stamps of 1946 optd with T **18** (small stamps) or larger opt (others).

68	**2**	3p. brown		1·75	70
		a. Opt Type **18a**		75·00	
		ab. Corrected by handstamp as Type **18**		£200	
		b. Opt Type **18b**		80·00	
		ba. Corrected by handstamp as Type **18**		£200	
69		6p. deep violet		20	30
		a. Opt Type **18a**		65·00	
		b. Medallion flaw		40·00	
70		9p. yellow-green		20	30
		a. Opt inverted		25·00	38·00
71	**3**	1a. blue		40	30
		a. Vert pair, one with opt omitted		£1600	
72		1½a. orange		3·00	10

73		2a. claret		40	15
		a. Horiz pair, one with opt omitted		£1700	
		b. Opt Type **18a**		90·00	
74	**4**	2a.6p. greenish blue		1·75	1·00
		a. Birds over trees		60·00	60·00
75	**5**	3a. blue-violet		2·75	1·75
76	**6**	3a.6p. black and ultramarine		2·75	3·75
77	**3**	4a. purple		1·75	30
78	**7**	8a. maroon		1·75	3·50
79	**8**	1r. violet and maroon		9·50	4·00
80		2r. brown and orange		11·00	11·00
81	**9**	5r. green and brown		11·00	11·00
82		10r. claret and violet		10·00	11·00
68/82 Set of 15				50·00	45·00

The 3p, 6p, 2a, 2a.6p, 3a.6p. and 1r. are also known with overprint inverted.

OFFICIAL STAMPS

BURMA   **BURMA**

SERVICE (O 1)   **SERVICE** (O 1a)

1937 (Apr–June). Stamps of India. (King George V inscr "INDIA POSTAGE") optd with Type O **1** or O **1a** (rupee values). W **69**. P 14.

O1		3p. slate		4·50	10
		w. Wmk inverted		£150	50·00
O2		½a. green		19·00	10
		w. Wmk inverted		†	£120
O3		9p. deep green		5·00	2·75
O4		1a. chocolate		9·50	10
O5		2a. vermilion (small die)		20·00	45
		w. Wmk inverted		—	55·00
O6		2½a. orange		12·00	5·00
O7		4a. sage-green		12·00	10
O8		6a. bistre		10·00	22·00
O9		8a. reddish purple (1.4.37)		12·00	4·75
O10		12a. claret (1.4.37)		13·00	22·00
O11		1r. chocolate and green (1.4.37)		38·00	14·00
		w. Wmk inverted		£250	
O12		2r. carmine and orange		55·00	85·00
		w. Wmk inverted		55·00	85·00
O13		5r. ultramarine and purple		£225	95·00
O14		10r. green and scarlet		£600	£325
O1/14 Set of 4				£900	£500

For the above issue the stamps were either overprinted "BURMA" and "SERVICE" at one operation or had the two words applied separately. Research has yet to establish if all values exist with both forms of overprinting.

An example of the 4a. in orange is known cancelled at Moulmein.

SERVICE (O 2)   **SERVICE** (O 3)

1939 (1 Apr). Nos. 19/24 and 28 optd with Type O **2** (typo) and Nos. 25 and 29/33 optd with Type O **3** (litho).

O15	**2**	3p. bright violet		20	20
O16		6p. bright blue		20	20
		a. Medallion flaw		42·00	42·00
O17		9p. yellow-green		4·00	7·50
O18	**3**	1a. purple-brown		20	15
O19		1½a. turquoise-green		3·50	3·75
O20		2a. carmine		2·25	20
O21	**4**	2a.6p. claret		35·00	26·00
		a. Birds over trees		£425	£300
O22	**3**	4a. greenish blue		4·50	2·50
O23	**7**	8a. myrtle-green		23·00	4·25
O24	**8**	1r. purple and blue		16·00	5·50
O25		2r. brown and purple		35·00	23·00
O26	**9**	5r. violet and scarlet		26·00	50·00
O27		10r. brown and myrtle		£140	55·00
O15/27 Set of 13				£250	£150

Both versions of the 1a. value exist with this overprint.

1946 (1 Jan). British Civil Administration. Nos. 51/6 and 58 optd with Type O **2** (typo) and Nos. 57 and 59/63 optd with Type O **3** (litho).

O28	**2**	3p. brown		4·25	8·50
O29		6p. deep violet		3·25	2·25
O30		9p. green		2·75	9·00
O31	**3**	1a. blue		40	2·00
O32		1½a. orange		3·00	20
O33		2a. claret		40	2·00
O34	**4**	2a.6p. greenish blue		4·25	16·00
		a. Birds over trees		85·00	
O35	**3**	4a. purple		1·75	70
O36	**7**	8a. maroon		6·50	19·00
O37	**8**	1r. violet and maroon		4·25	13·00
O38		2r. brown and orange		8·50	55·00
O39	**9**	5r. green and brown		23·00	70·00
O40		10r. claret and violet		23·00	80·00
O28/40 Set of 13				75·00	£250

1947 (1 Oct). Interim Burmese Government. Nos. O28/40 optd with T **18** (small stamps) or larger opt (others).

O41	**2**	3p. brown		4·00	40
O42		6p. deep violet		6·50	15
O43		9p. green		9·00	90
O44	**3**	1a. blue		9·00	80
O45		1½a. orange		16·00	30
O46		2a. claret		9·50	15
O47	**4**	2a.6p. greenish blue		42·00	25·00
		a. Birds over trees		£425	£275
O48	**3**	4a. purple		29·00	4·00
O49	**7**	8a. maroon		29·00	5·00
O50	**8**	1r. violet and maroon		18·00	4·75
O51		2r. brown and orange		21·00	25·00
O52	**9**	5r. green and brown		22·00	27·00
O53		10r. claret and violet		22·00	45·00
O41/53 Set of 13				£200	£120

TELEGRAPH STAMPS

Indian telegraph stamps were used in Burma up to 1910 and subsequently Indian and then Burmese postage stamps, prior to the issue of the first Burmese telegraph stamps in 1946.

T 1

(Litho Nasik)

1946 (1 Oct?). T **T 1**. W **10**. P 14.

T 1	**1**	1a. carmine-red	3·00	40·00
T 2		2a. deep dull blue	3·00	40·00
T 3		8a. grey-green	4·00	
T 4		12a. bluish grey	5·00	
T 5		1r. brown	6·00	50·00
T 6		2r. deep dull purple	7·00	50·00
T 7		10r. turquoise-blue	8·00	
T1/7 Set of 7			32·00	

Nos. T 1/7 also exist with a one-line "Service" overprint in Burmese script, for official use (*Price, £75, for set of 7, unused*). Their date of issue is unknown.

Later stamp issues will be found listed in Part 21 (*South-East Asia*) of this catalogue.

JAPANESE OCCUPATION OF BURMA

PRICES FOR STAMPS ON COVER	
Nos. J1/44	
Nos. J45/6	from × 6
Nos. J47/56	from × 8
No. J56g	
Nos. J57/72	from × 6
Nos. J73/5	from × 25
No. J76	from × 8
No. J77	from × 20
Nos. J78/81	from × 25
Nos. J82/4	from × 10
Nos. J85/7	from × 40
No. J88	from × 12
Nos. J89/97	from × 30
Nos. J98/104	from × 50
Nos. J105/111	from × 30

BURMA INDEPENDENCE ARMY ADMINISTRATION

The Burma Independence Army, formed by Aung San in 1941, took control of the Delta area of the Irrawaddy in May 1942. They reopened a postal service in the area and were authorised by the Japanese to overprint local stocks of stamps with the Burmese emblem of a peacock.

Postage and Official stamps with the peacock overprints or handstamps were used for ordinary postal purposes with the probable exception of No. J44.

DISTINGUISHING FEATURES. Type **1**. Body and head of Peacock always clearly outlined by broad uncoloured band. There are four slightly different sub-types of overprint Type **1**.

Type **2**. Peacock with slender neck and more delicately detailed tail. Clear spur on leg at right. Heavy fist-shaped blob of ink below and parallel to beak and neck.

Type **4**. No basic curve. Each feather separately outlined. Straight, short legs.

Type **5**. Much fine detail in wings and tail in clearly printed overprints. Thin, long legs ending in claws which, with the basic arc, enclose clear white spaces in well printed copies. Blob of colour below beak shows shaded detail and never has the heavy fist-like appearance of this portion in Type **2**.

Two sub-types may be distinguished in Type **5**, the basic arc of one having a chord of 14–15 mm and the other 12½–13 mm.

Type **6**. Similar to Type **5**, but with arc deeply curved and reaching nearly to the top of the wings. Single diagonal line parallel to neck below beak.

Collectors are warned against forgeries of these overprints, often in the wrong colours or on the wrong values.

(1)

(2)

(3)

1942 (May). Stamps of Burma overprinted with the national device of a Peacock.

I. Overprinted at Myaungmya

*A. With Type **1** in black*

On Postage Stamps of King George V.

J1		9p. deep green (No. 3)	£110
J2		3½a. deep blue (No. 8)	80·00

J3		6a. bistre (No. O8)	80·00	

On Official Stamp of King George V

On Postage Stamps of King George VI

J4	**2**	9p. yellow-green	£150	
J5	**3**	1a. purple-brown	£550	
J6		4a. greenish blue (opt black on red)	£160	
		a. Triple opt, black on double red	£450	

On Official Stamps of King George VI

J7	**2**	3p. bright violet	42·00	90·00
J8		6p. bright blue	27·00	65·00
J9	**3**	1a. purple-brown	28·00	55·00
J9a		1½a. turquoise-green	£900	£1300
J10		2a. carmine	40·00	£100
J11		4a. greenish blue	40·00	80·00

The overprint on No. J6 was apparently first done in red in error, and then corrected in black. Some stamps have the black overprint so accurately superimposed that the red hardly shows. These are rare.

Nos. J5 and J9 exist with the Peacock overprint on both the typographed and the litho printings of the original stamps.

*B. With Types **2** or **3** (rupee values), in black*

On Postage Stamps of King George VI

J12	**2**	3p. bright violet	22·00	75·00
J13		6p. bright blue	50·00	£110
J14		9p. yellow-green	27·00	70·00
J15	**3**	1a. purple-brown	17·00	65·00
J16		2a. carmine	28·00	85·00
J17		4a. greenish blue	60·00	£120
		a. Opt double	£850	
		b. Opt inverted	£850	
		c. Opt double, one inverted	£475	
		d. Opt double, both inverted	£750	
J18	**8**	1r. purple and blue	£450	£750
J19		2r. brown and purple	£275	£550

The Myaungmya overprints (including No. J44) are usually clearly printed.

(4)

(5)

(6)

Type **5** generally shows the details of the peacock much less clearly and, due to heavy inking, or careless impression, sometimes appears as almost solid colour.

Type **6** was officially applied only to postal stationery. However, the handstamp remained in the possession of a postal official who used it on postage stamps after the war. These stamps are no longer listed.

*II. Handstamped (at Pyapon?) with T **4**, in black (so-called experimental type)*

On Postage Stamps of King George VI.

J19a	**2**	6p. bright blue	75·00	
J19b	**3**	1a. purple-brown	£100	£250
J20		2a. carmine	£130	£300
J21		4a. greenish blue	£700	£700

Unused specimens of Nos. J20/1 are usually in poor condition.

*III. Overprinted at Henzada with T **5** in blue, or blue-black*

On Postage Stamps of King George V

J22		3p. slate (No. 1)	4·00	23·00
		a. Opt double	10·00	55·00
J23		9p. deep green (No. 3)	27·00	70·00
		a. Opt double	80·00	
J24		2a. vermilion (No. 5)	£130	£225

On Postage Stamps of King George VI

J25	**2**	1p. red-orange	£225	£375
J26		3p. bright violet	48·00	80·00
J27		6p. bright blue	25·00	55·00
		a. Opt double	£100	£150
		b. Clear opt, on back and front	£350	
J28		9p. yellow-green	£1100	
J29	**3**	1a. purple-brown	9·00	42·00
		a. Opt inverted	£2500	£1200
J30		1½a. turquoise-green	23·00	70·00
		a. Opt omitted (in pair with normal)	£4250	
J31		2a. carmine	23·00	70·00
		a. Opt double	£2750	
J32		4a. greenish blue	45·00	£100
		a. Opt double	£250	
		b. Opt inverted	£3750	

On Official Stamps of King George VI

J33	**2**	3p. bright violet	£140	£275
J34		6p. bright blue	£160	£275
J35	**3**	1½a. turquoise-green	£180	£325
J35a		2a. carmine	£375	£450
J36		4a. greenish blue	£1000	

(6a) ("Yon Thon" = "Office use")

*V. Official Stamp of King George VI optd at Myaungmya with Type **6a** in black.*

J44	**7**	8a. myrtle-green	£110	£300

No. J44 was probably for official use.

There are two types of T **6a**, one with base of peacock 8 mm long and the other with base about 5 mm long. The neck and other details also vary. The two types are found *se-tenant* in the sheet. Stocks of the peacock types were withdrawn when the Japanese Directorate-General took control of the postal services in the Delta in August 1942.

JAPANESE ARMY ADMINISTRATION

7

8 Farmer

1942 (1 June). Impressed by hand. Thick yellowish paper. No gum. P 12×11.

J45	**7**	(1a.) red	50·00	70·00

This device was the personal seal of Yano Sitza, the Japanese official in charge of the Posts and Telegraphs department of the Japanese Army Administration. It was impressed on paper already perforated by a line machine. Some stamps show part of the papermaker's watermark, either "ABSORBO DUPLICATOR" or "ELEPHANT BRAND", each with an elephant.

Other impressions of this seal on different papers, and showing signs of wear, were not valid for postal purposes.

(Des T. Kato. Typo *Rangoon Gazette* Press)

1942 (15 June). Value in annas. P 11 or 11×11½. Laid bâtonné paper. No gum.

J46	**8**	1a. scarlet	23·00	25·00

Some stamps show part of the papermaker's watermark, either "ELEPHANT BRAND" or "TITAGHUR SUPERFINE", each with an elephant.

½A.   1R.

(9)   (10)

1942 (22 Sept).

*(a) Nos. 314/17, 320/2, 325, 327 and 396 of Japan surch as T **9/10**.*

J47	**9**	¼a. on 1s. chestnut (Rice harvesting)	50·00	50·00
		a. Surch inverted	£150	£150
		b. Surch double, one inverted	£190	
J48		½a. on 2s. bright scarlet (General Nogi)	55·00	50·00
		a. Surch inverted	£140	£150
		b. Surch double, one inverted	£150	
J49		¾a. on 3s. green (Power station)	80·00	80·00
		a. Surch inverted	£170	£170
		b. Surch double, one inverted	—	£200
J50		1a. on 5s. claret (Admiral Togo)	80·00	70·00
		a. Surch inverted	£250	£250
		b. Surch double, one inverted	£300	£275
		c. Surch omitted (in pair with normal)	£450	£400
J51		3a. on 7s. green (Diamond Mts)	£130	£150
		a. Surch inverted	£325	
J52		4a. on 4s. emerald (Togo)	60·00	65·00
		a. Surch inverted	£225	
J53		8a. on 8s. violet (Meiji Shrine)	£150	£150
		a. Surch inverted	£325	£325
		b. Surch double, one inverted	£425	
		c. Surch in red	£275	£300
		d. Red surch inverted	£450	
		e. Surch double (black and red)	£1100	
J54	**10**	1r. on 10s. deep carmine (Yomei Gate)	29·00	38·00
		a. Surch inverted	95·00	£110
		b. Surch double	80·00	£100
		c. Surch double (black and red)	£500	£500
		d. Surch omitted (in pair with normal)	£400	£400
		e. Surch omitted (in pair with inverted surch)	£550	
J55		2r. on 20s. ultramarine (Mt Fuji)	55·00	55·00
		a. Surch inverted	£150	£150
		b. Surch double, one inverted	£170	
		c. Surch omitted (in pair with normal black surch)	£275	£275
		d. Surch in red	55·00	55·00
		e. Red surch inverted	£150	£150
		f. Red surch double	£140	£140
		g. Surch omitted (in pair with normal red surch)	£350	£350
		ga. Surch omitted (in pair with double red surch)	£500	
		h. Surch double (black and red)	£500	
J56	**9**	5r. on 30s. turquoise (Torii Shrine)	19·00	27·00
		a. Surch inverted	90·00	
		b. Surch double	£120	
		c. Surch double, one inverted	£160	
		d. Surch omitted (in pair with normal surch)	£325	£325
		e. Surch omitted (in pair with inverted black surch)	£425	
		f. Surch in red	30·00	32·00
		fa. Red surch inverted	95·00	95·00
		fb. J56a and J56fa se-tenant	£650	£650
		fc. Surch omitted (in pair with normal red surch)	£325	£325

(b) No. 386 of Japan commemorating the fall of Singapore similarly surch

J56g	**9**	4a. on 4+2s. green and red	£180	£190
		h. Surch omitted (in pair with normal)	£750	
		ha. Surch omitted (in pair with inverted surch)	£800	
		i. Surch inverted	£450	

15 C. 15 C. 15 C.
(11)   (12)   (13)

1942 (15 Oct). Previous issues, with "anna" surcharges obliterated, handstamped with new value in cents, as T **11** or **12**. (No. J57 handstamped with new value only).

(a) On No. J46

J57	5c. on 1a. scarlet	26·00	30·00
	a. Surch omitted (in pair with normal)	£2000	

(b) On Nos. J47/53

J58	1c. on ¼a. on 1s. chestnut	55·00	55·00
	a. "1 c." omitted (in pair with normal) ..	£900	
	b. "¼ a." inverted	£275	
J59	2c. on ½a. on 2s. bright scarlet	55·00	55·00
J60	3c. on ¾a. on 3s. green	60·00	60·00
	a. Surch in blue	£225	
J61	5c. on 1a. on 5s. claret	85·00	65·00
J62	10c. on 3a. on 7s. green	£170	£140
J63	15c. on 4a. on 4s. emerald	50·00	55·00
J64	20c. on 8a. on 8s. violet	£900	£700
	a. Surch on No. J53c (surch in red)	£350	£170

The "anna" surcharges were obliterated by any means available, in some cases by a bar or bars, and in others by the butt of a pencil dipped in ink. In the case of the fractional surcharges, the letter "A" and one figure of the fraction, were sometimes barred out, leaving the remainder of the fraction to represent the new value, e.g. the "1" of "½" deleted to create the 2c. surcharge or the "4" of "¾" to create the 3c. surcharge.

1942. Nos. 314/17, 320/1 and 396 of Japan surcharged in cents only as T **13**.

J65	1c. on 1s. chestnut (Rice harvesting)	40·00	20·00
	a. Surch inverted	£140	£140
J66	2c. on 2s. brt scarlet (General Nogi)	60·00	45·00
J67	3c. on 3s. green (Power station)	£100	65·00
	a. Pair, with and without surch	—	£375
	b. Surch inverted	£170	
	c. Surch in blue	£110	£120
	d. Surch in blue inverted	£325	£350
J68	5c. on 5s. claret (Admiral Togo)	£100	55·00
	a. Pair, with and without surch	£450	
	b. Surch in violet	£180	£190
	ba. Surch inverted	—	£350
J69	10c. on 7s. green (Diamond Mts)	£140	80·00
J70	15c. on 4s. emerald (Togo)	29·00	29·00
	a. Surch inverted	£170	£180
	b. Pair, with and without surch	—	£350
J71	20c. on 8s. violet (Meiji Shrine)	£200	95·00
	a. Surch double	£425	

Nos. J67c and J68b were issued for use in the Shan States.

BURMESE GOVERNMENT

On 1 November 1942 the Japanese Army Administration handed over the control of the postal department to the Burmese Government. On 1 August 1943 Burma was declared by the Japanese to be independent.

14 Burma State Crest   **15** Farmer

(Des U Tun Tin and Maung Tin from drawing by U Ba Than. Typo Rangoon)

1943 (15 Feb). No gum. P 11.

J72	**14** 5c. scarlet	29·00	35·00
	a. Imperf	29·00	35·00
	ab. Printed on both sides	95·00	

No. J72 was usually sold affixed to envelopes, particularly those with the embossed 1a. King George VI stamp, which it covered. Unused specimens off cover are not often seen and blocks are scarce.

1943. Typo. No gum. P 11½.

J73	**15** 1c. orange (22.3)	6·00	9·00
	a. Brown-orange	5·00	10·00
J74	2c. yellow-green (24.3)	1·50	1·00
	a. "3" for "2" in face value (R. 2/10)	£350	
	b. Blue-green	15·00	
J75	3c. light blue (25.3)	5·00	1·00
	a. On laid paper	23·00	40·00
	b. Imperf between (horiz pair)	—	£350
J76	5c. carmine (small "c") (17.3)	32·00	21·00
J77	5c. carmine (large "C")	3·50	8·00
	a. Imperf (pair)	£110	
	b. "G" for "C" (R. 2/6)	£180	
J78	10c. grey-brown (25.3)	9·50	9·50
	a. Imperf (pair)	£110	
	b. Imperf between (horiz pair)	—	£350
J79	15c. magenta (26.3)	30	4·50
	b. On laid paper	6·00	23·00
	ba. Inverted "C" in value (R. 2/3)	£200	
J80	20c. grey-lilac (29.3)	30	1·00
J81	30c. deep blue-green (29.3)	1·25	3·00

The 1c., 2c. and 3c. have large "C" in value as illustrated. The 10c. and higher values have small "c". Nos. J73/81 had the face values inserted individually into the plate used for No. J46 with the original face value removed. There were a number of printings for each value, often showing differences such as missing stops, various founts of figures or "c", etc., in the value tablets.
The face value error, No. J74a, was later corrected.

Some sheets of No. J75a show a sheet watermark of Britannia seated within a crowned oval spread across 15 stamps in each sheet. This paper was manufactured by T. Edmonds and the other half of the sheet carried the watermark inscription "FOOLSCAP LEDGER". No stamps have been reported showing letters from this inscription, but a block of 25 is known on laid paper showing a different sheet watermark "HERTFORDSHIRE LEDGER MADE IN ENGLAND". Examples showing parts of these sheet watermarks are rare.
There are marked varieties of shade in this issue.

16 Soldier carving word "Independence"   **17** Rejoicing Peasant

18 Boy with National Flag

Normal   Skyline flaw (R. 5/6)

(Des Maung Ba Thit (**16**), Naung Ohn Maung (**17**), and Maung Soi Yi (**18**). Typo State Press, Rangoon)

1943 (1 Aug). Independence Day. No gum.

(a) P 11

J82	**16**	1c. orange	15·00	20·00
J83	**17**	3c. light blue	15·00	20·00
J84	**18**	5c. carmine	23·00	11·00
		a. Skyline flaw	£140	
J82/4 *Set of 3*			48·00	45·00

(b) Rouletted

J85	**16**	1c. orange	1·50	1·75
		b. Perf×roul	£150	£150
		c. Imperf (pair)	45·00	55·00
J86	**17**	3c. light blue	2·50	4·00
		b. Perf×roul	£120	£120
		c. Imperf (pair)	45·00	55·00
J87	**18**	5c. carmine	3·50	4·25
		b. Perf×roul	70·00	70·00
		c. Imperf (pair)	45·00	55·00
		d. Skyline flaw	32·00	38·00
J85/7 *Set of 3*			6·50	9·00

The stamps perf×rouletted may have one, two or three sides perforated.
The rouletted stamps often appear to be roughly perforated owing to failure to make clean cuts. These apparent perforations are very small and quite unlike the large, clean holes of the stamps perforated 11.
A few imperforate sets, mounted on a special card folder and cancelled with the commemorative postmark were presented to officials. These are rare.

19 Burmese Woman   **20** Elephant carrying Log

21 Watch Tower, Mandalay

(Litho G. Kolff & Co, Batavia)

1943 (1 Oct). P 12½.

J88	**19**	1c. red-orange	20·00	15·00
J89		2c. yellow-green	50	2·00
J90		3c. deep violet	50	2·25
		a. Bright violet	1·75	5·50
J91	**20**	5c. carmine	75	60
J92		10c. blue	2·25	1·10
J93		15c. red-orange	1·00	3·00
J94		20c. yellow-green	1·00	1·75
J95		30c. olive-brown	1·00	6·00
J96	**21**	1r. red-orange	30	2·00
J97		2r. bright violet	30	2·25
J88/97 *Set of 10*			26·00	29·00

22 Bullock Cart   **23** Shan Woman   (**24** "Burma State" and value)

(Litho G. Kolff & Co, Batavia)

1943 (1 Oct). Issue for Shan States. P 12½.

J98	**22**	1c. olive-brown	45·00	48·00
J99		2c. yellow-green	50·00	48·00
J100		3c. bright violet	8·00	14·00
J101		5c. ultramarine	3·50	8·50
J102	**23**	10c. blue	17·00	18·00
J103		20c. carmine	48·00	22·00
J104		30c. olive-brown	27·00	65·00
J98/104 *Set of 7*			£180	£200

The Shan States, except for the frontier area around Keng Tung which was ceded to Thailand on 20 August 1943, were placed under the administration of the Burmese Government on 24 December 1943, and these stamps were later overprinted as T **24** for use throughout Burma.

1944 (1 Nov). Optd as T **24** (the lower characters differ for each value).

J105	**22**	1c. olive-brown	5·00	10·00
J106		2c. yellow-green	60	6·50
		a. Opt inverted	£425	£700
J107		3c. bright violet	2·50	7·00
J108		5c. ultramarine	3·00	4·00
J109	**23**	10c. blue	3·25	2·25
J110		20c. carmine	65	1·50
J111		30c. olive-brown	1·50	1·75
J105/11 *Set of 7*			15·00	30·00

Bushire

BRITISH OCCUPATION

(Currency. 20 chahis = 1 kran; 10 kran = 1 toman)

Bushire, a seaport town of Persia, was occupied by the British on 8 August 1915. The Persian postal authorities resumed control on 18 October 1915. British forces returned to Bushire during 1916, but mail from this period was carried by Indian Army F.P.O. No. 319.

> **FORGERIES.** Collectors are warned that the Bushire type **1** opt has been extensively forged. These stamps should not be purchased without a reliable guarantee.

PRICES FOR STAMPS ON COVER	
Nos. 1/29	from × 5
No. 30	—

Types of Iran (Persia) overprinted

57 66

67 68

BUSHIRE
Under British
Occupation.
(1)

1915 (16 Aug). Nos. 361/3, 365, 367/70, 372, 374/6 and 378/9 of Iran optd with T **1** at the British Residency.

1	**57**	1ch. orange and green	85·00	85·00
		a. No stop	£275	£275
2		2ch. sepia and carmine	80·00	80·00
		a. No stop	£250	£275
3		3ch. green and grey	95·00	95·00
		a. No stop	£375	£400
4		5ch. carmine and brown	£650	£500
5		6ch. brown-lake and green	80·00	50·00
		a. No stop	£250	£190
		b. Opt double	†	£10000
6		9ch. indigo-lilac and brown	90·00	£100
		a. No stop	£350	£400
		b. Opt double		
7		10ch. brown and carmine	85·00	90·00
		a. No stop	£350	£375
8		12ch. blue and green	£100	90·00
		a. No stop	£425	£400
9		24ch. green and purple	£200	£110
		a. No stop	£700	£400
10		1kr. carmine and blue	£180	60·00
		a. Opt double	£10000	
		b. No stop	£650	£200
11		2kr. claret and green	£550	£325
		a. No stop	£1700	£850
12		3kr. black and lilac	£450	£425
		a. No stop	£1400	£1200
13		5kr. blue and red	£400	£275
		a. No stop	£1200	£850
14		10kr. rose and bistre-brown	£375	£250
		a. No stop	£1200	£750

Nos. 1/3 and 5/14 were overprinted in horizontal strips of ten and No. 4 in horizontal strips of five. Eight different settings are recognized with the "No stop" variety occurring on stamp 9 from four settings with 3 mm between "Under" and "British" and on stamp 10 from one setting where the gap is 2 mm.

1915 (11 Sept). Nos. 426/40 and 441 of Iran optd with T **1**.

15	**66**	1ch. deep blue and carmine	£900	£750
16		2ch. carmine and deep blue	£18000	£18000
17		3ch. deep green	£1000	£950
18		5ch. vermilion	£16000	£16000
19		6ch. carmine and green	£12000	£12000
20		9ch. deep violet and brown	£1700	£1300
21		10ch. brown and deep green	£3000	£3000
22		12ch. ultramarine	£3250	£3250
23		24ch. sepia and brown	£1300	£900
24	**67**	1kr. black, brown and silver	£1400	£1100
25		2kr. carmine, slate and silver	£1400	£1200
26		3kr. sepia, dull lilac and silver	£1500	£1300
27		5kr. slate, sepia and silver	£1400	£1400
		a. Opt inverted	—	£26000
28	**68**	1kr. black, violet and gold	£1200	£1200
29		3t. red, crimson and gold	£9000	£7500

Nos. 15/29 were overprinted in strips of five.

1915. No. 414 of Iran ("1 CH 1915" provisional) optd with T **1**.

30	**57**	1ch. on 5ch. carmine and brown	£15000	

Cameroon

Allied operations against the German protectorate of Kamerun commenced in September 1914 and were completed in 18 February 1916. The territory was divided, under an Anglo-French agreement, on 31 March 1916, with the British administering the area in the west along the Nigerian border. League of Nations mandates were issued for the two sections of Cameroon on 20 July 1922, which were converted into United Nations trusteeships in 1946.

Supplies of Kamerun stamps were found on the German steamer *Professor Woermann*, captured at Freetown, and these were surcharged, probably at Duala, and issued by the Cameroons Expeditionary Force in Duala in July 1915.

A French post office opened in Duala on 10 November 1915 using stamps of Gabon overprinted "Corps Expeditionnaire Franco Anglais Cameroun". Although under the overall control of the British combined force commander, this office remained part of the French postal system.

PRICES FOR STAMPS ON COVER
The stamps of British Occupation of Cameroons are rare used on cover.

I. CAMEROONS EXPEDITIONARY FORCE

A B

C.E.F.   C.E.F.
1d.   1s.
(1)   (2)

SETTINGS. Nos. B1/3 were surcharged from a setting of 100 (10×10) with the face value changed for the 1d.

Nos. B4 and B6/9 were surcharged from a common setting of 50 (5×10) with the face value amended.

No. B5 was surcharged from a setting of ten in a vertical strip repeated across the sheet. The figures of the surcharge on this are in a different style from the remainder of the pence stamps.

Nos. B10/13 were surcharged from a common setting of 20 (4×5) with the face value amended.

Normal

Different fount
"d" (R. 2/10, 6/9, 10/10)

"1" with thin serifs
(R. 5/1)

Short "4" (R. 10/2, 10/7)

5s 5s.

"s" broken at top   "s" inverted (R. 3/4)

1915 (12 July). Stamps of German Kamerun. Types A and B, surch as T **1** (Nos. B1/9) or **2** (Nos. B10/13) in black or blue.

B1	A	½d. on 3pf. brown (No. K7) (B.)	13·00	55·00
		a. Different fount "d"	£180	£425
B2		½d. on 5pf. green (No. K21 wmk lozenges) (B.)	7·00	10·00
		a. Different fount "d"	85·00	£140
		b. Surch double	†	£1000
		ba. Surch double, one albino	£400	
B3		1d. on 10pf. carmine (No. K22 wmk lozenges) (B.)	1·25	9·50
		a. "1" with thin serifs	13·00	70·00
		b. Surch double	£425	
		ba. Surch double, one albino	£160	
		c. "1d." only double	£2000	
		d. Surch triple, two albino	£400	
		e. "1" in black	12·00	55·00
		ea. "1" with thin serifs	£275	
B4		2d. on 20pf. ultramarine (No. K23 wmk lozenges) (B.)	3·50	22·00
		a. Surch double, one albino	£400	
B5		2½d. on 25pf. black and red/*yellow* (No. K11)	20·00	55·00
		a. Surch double	£13000	
		ab. Surch double, one albino	£1500	
B6		3d. on 30pf. black and orange/*buff* (No. K12)	13·00	60·00
		a. Large "3" (R. 3/5, 3/10)	£1500	
		b. Surch triple, two albino	£475	
B7		4d. on 40pf. black and carmine (No. K13)	14·00	60·00
		a. Short "4"	£1000	£1800
		b. Surch triple, two albino	£375	
		c. Surch quadruple, three albino	£1500	
B8		6d. on 50pf. black and purple/*buff* (No. K14)	13·00	60·00
		a. Surch double, one albino	£375	
B9		8d. on 80pf. black and carmine/*rose* (No. K15)	13·00	60·00
		a. Surch triple, two albino	£1600	
B10	B	1s. on 1m. carmine (No. K16)	£200	£900
		a. "s" inverted	£1000	£3750
B11		2s. on 2m. blue (No. K17)	£225	£1000
		a. "s" inverted	£1000	£3750
		b. Surch double, one albino	£2750	
B12		3s. on 3m. violet-black (No. K18)	£225	£1000
		a. "s" inverted	£1000	£4000
		b. "s" broken at top	£900	
		c. Surch double	£15000	
		ca. Surch triple, two albino	£2750	
B13		5s. on 5m. carmine and black (No. K25a wmk lozenges)	£275	£1100
		a. "s" inverted	£1300	£4500
		b. "s" broken at top	£1200	
B1/13 *Set of 13*			£900	£4000

The 1d. on 10pf. was previously listed with "C.E.F." omitted. This was due to misplacement, so that all stamps (except for a pair in the Royal Collection) from the bottom row show traces of the overprint on the top perforations.

Examples of all values exist showing a forged Duala, Kamerun postmark dated "11 10 15". Another forged cancel dated "16 11 15" is also known. This can be identified by the lack of a serif on the index letter "b".

The stamps of Nigeria were subsequently used in British Cameroons and the area was administered as part of Nigeria from February 1924.

For issues of Cameroun under French administration see Stanley Gibbons *French Colonies Catalogue*.

II. CAMEROONS TRUST TERRITORY

Following the independence of the French Trust Territory of Cameroun on 1 January 1960 the United Nations directed that a plebiscite should be held in the British Trust Territory whose postal service continued, for the time being, to be run by Nigeria. The northern area voted to join Nigeria, but the southern part of the territory decided to join the Cameroun Republic.

The following issue, although ordered by the Southern Cameroons authorities, was also on sale in Northern Cameroons, until the latter joined Nigeria on 1 June 1961. The stamps therefore can be found with Nigerian postmarks.

CAMEROONS
U.K.T.T.
(1)

6d. Major re-touch consisting of heavy diagonal shading (Pl. 2-1, R. 2/10)

1960 (1 Oct)–**61**. Nos. 69/71, 72*cd/f* and 73/80 of Nigeria optd with T **1**, in red.

T1	**18**	½d. black and orange	10	2·75
T2	–	1d. black and bronze-green	10	70
		a. Grey-black and dull bronze-green (19.9.61)	1·00	2·25
T3	–	1½d. blue-green	10	20
T4	**21**	2d. grey (Type B)	75	3·75
		a. Slate-blue (Type A)	£1100	£400
		b. Bluish grey (Type B)	95·00	29·00
		c. Pale grey (Type B) (19.9.61)	3·25	5·50
T5	–	3d. black and deep lilac	20	10
T6	–	4d. black and blue	30	3·00
T7	**24**	6d. orange-brown and black (P 14)	40	20
		a. Perf 13×13½ (19.9.61)	30	2·50
		ab. Major retouch	35·00	
T8	–	1s. black and maroon	40	10
T9	**26**	2s.6d. black and green	2·50	1·00
T10	–	5s. black and red-orange	3·50	
T11	–	10s. black and red-brown	4·50	7·50
T12	**29**	£1 black and violet	21·00	38·00
T1/12 *Set of 12*			30·00	55·00

Nos. T2 and T4/b were overprinted on stamps printed by Waterlows' subsidiary, Imprimerie Belge de Securité.

Nos. T2a, T4c and T7a were from new printings produced by De La Rue instead of Waterlow.

As well as being a paler shade, No. T4c is much less deeply engraved than T4/b, clearly evident in the shading in the hills and sky.

The above stamps were withdrawn on 30 September 1961, when Southern Cameroons became part of the Cameroun Republic, although some post offices had been using unoverprinted Nigerian stamps for some months previously.

Looking for that Elusive Stamp?

Canada

Separate stamp issues appeared for British Columbia and Vancouver Island, Canada, New Brunswick, Newfoundland, Nova Scotia and Prince Edward Island before these colonies joined the Dominion of Canada.

BRITISH COLUMBIA & VANCOUVER ISLAND

Vancouver Island was organised as a Crown Colony in 1849 and the mainland territory was proclaimed a separate colony as British Columbia in 1858. The two colonies combined, as British Columbia, on 19 November 1866.

PRICES FOR STAMPS ON COVER	
Nos. 2/3	from × 6
Nos. 11/12	from × 2
Nos. 13/14	from × 6
Nos. 21/2	from × 10
Nos. 23/7	from × 6
Nos. 28/9	from × 10
No. 30	—
No. 31	from × 10
Nos. 32/3	—

1

(Typo D.L.R.)

1860. No wmk. P 14.

2	1	2½d. deep reddish rose	£425	£200
3		2½d. pale reddish rose	£425	£200

When Vancouver Island adopted the dollar currency in 1862 the 2½d. was sold at 5c. From 18 May until 1 November 1865 examples of Nos. 2/3 were used to prepay mail from Vancouver Island to British Columbia at the price of 15 cents a pair.

From 20 June 1864 to 1 November 1865, the 2½d. was sold in British Columbia for 3d. and was subsequently used for the same purpose during a shortage of 3d. stamps in 1867.

Imperforate plate proofs exist in pale dull red (*Price* £10,000 *un*).

VANCOUVER ISLAND

(New Currency. 100 cents = 1 dollar)

2

3

(Typo D.L.R.)

1865 (19 Sept). Wmk Crown CC.

(a) Imperf (1866)

11	2	5c. rose	£32000	£9000
12	3	10c. blue	£2000	£900

(b) P 14

13	2	5c. rose	£350	£200
		w. Wmk inverted	£1900	£900
		x. Wmk reversed	†	£1100
14	3	10c. blue	£250	£170
		w. Wmk inverted	£800	£600

Medium or poor examples of Nos. 11 and 12 can be supplied at much lower prices, when in stock.

After the two colonies combined Nos. 13/14 were also used in British Columbia.

BRITISH COLUMBIA

4

(Typo D.L.R.)

1865 (1 Nov)–67. Wmk Crown CC. P 14.

21	4	3d. deep blue	£120	85·00
22		3d. pale blue (19.7.67)	£110	85·00
		w. Wmk inverted	£500	£275
		y. Wmk inverted and reversed	†	£550

British Columbia changed to the dollar currency on 1 January 1866. Remaining stocks of No. 21 and the supply of No. 22, when it finally arrived, were sold at 12½c. a pair.

(New Currency. 100 cents = 1 dollar)

TWO CENTS (5) **5.CENTS.5** (6)

1868–71. T **4** in various colours. Surch as T **5** or **6**. Wmk Crown CC.

(a) P 12½ (3.69)

23	5c. red (Bk.)	£1600	£1200
24	10c. lake (B.)	£900	£700
25	25c. yellow (V.)	£600	£600
26	50c. mauve (R.)	£850	£700
27	$1 green (G.)	£1300	£1400

(b) P 14

28	2c. brown (Bk.) (1.68)	£170	£140
29	5c. pale red (Bk.) (5.69)	£250	£160
30	10c. lake (B.)	£1400	
31	25c. yellow (V.) (21.7.69)	£250	£160
	w. Wmk inverted	†	£1200
32	50c. mauve (R.) (23.2.71)	£650	£1100
	w. Wmk inverted		£1100
33	$1 green (G.)		£1100

Nos. 30 and 33 were not issued.

British Columbia joined the Dominion of Canada on 20 July 1871.

COLONY OF CANADA

The first British post offices in what was to become the Colony of Canada were opened at Quebec, Montreal and Trois Rivières during 1763. These, and subsequent, offices remained part of the British GPO system until 6 April 1851.

The two provinces of Upper Canada (Ontario) and Lower Canada (Quebec) were united in 1840.

For illustration of the handstamp types see BRITISH POST OFFICES ABROAD notes, following GREAT BRITAIN.

QUEBEC

CROWNED-CIRCLE HANDSTAMPS

CC1	CC **1**	QUEBEC L.C. (R.) (13.1.1842)… *Price on cover*		£160

PRICES FOR STAMPS ON COVER	
Nos. 1/23	from × 2
Nos. 25/8	from × 3
Nos. 29/43a	from × 3
Nos. 44/5	from × 8

1 American Beaver (Designed by Sir Sandford Fleming)

2 Prince Albert

3

Major re-entry: Line through "EE PEN" (Upper pane R. 5/7)

(T **1/6**. Eng and recess Rawdon, Wright, Hatch and Edson, New York)

1851. Laid paper. Imperf.

1	1	3d. red (23.4)	£38000	£1100
1a		3d. orange-vermilion	£38000	£1100
		b. Major re-entry	—	£3750
2	2	6d. slate-violet (15.5)	£50000	£1300
3		6d. brown-purple	£50000	£1400
		a. Bisected (3d.) *on cover*	†	£38000
4	3	12d. black (14.6)	£200000	£100000

There are several re-entries on the plate of the 3d. in addition to the major re-entry listed. All re-entries occur in this stamp on all papers.

Forgeries of the 3d. are known without the full stop after "PENCE". They also omit the foliage in the corners, as do similar forgeries of the 6d.

4

5

6 Jacques Cartier

Re-entry (R. 10/12)

1852–57. Imperf.

A. Handmade wove paper, varying in thickness (1852–57)

5	1	3d. red	£2750	£225
		a. Bisected (1½d.) *on cover* (1856)	†	£38000
6		3d. deep red	£3000	£275
7		3d. scarlet-vermilion	£3500	£275
8		3d. brown-red	£3000	£275
		a. Bisected (1½d.) *on cover* (1856).	†	£38000
		b. Major re-entry (*all shades*) *from*	£7500	£950
9	2	6d. slate-violet	£45000	£1100
		a. Bisected (3d.) *on cover*	†	£20000
10		6d. greenish grey	£45000	£1200
11		6d. brownish grey	£48000	£1400
12	5	7½d. yellow-green (*shades*) (2.6.57)	£13000	£2500
13	6	10d. bright blue (1.55)	£14000	£1800
14		10d. dull blue	£13000	£1700
15		10d. blue to deep blue	£14000	£1800
		a. Major re-entry (*all shades*) *from*	—	£3250
16	3	12d. black		† £150000

B. Machine-made medium to thick wove paper of a more even hard texture with more visible mesh. Clearer impressions (1857)

17	4	½d. deep rose (1.8.57)	£1000	£600
		a. Re-entry	£3250	£1500
18	1	3d. red	£3500	£450
		a. Bisected (1½d.) *on cover*	†	£38000
		b. Major re-entry	—	£1500

19	2	6d. grey-lilac	£48000	£2500
20	6	10d. blue to deep blue	£16000	£2250
		a. Major re-entry	£27000	£3500

C. Thin soft horizontally ribbed paper (1857)

21	4	½d. deep rose	£9500	£2250
		a. Vertically ribbed paper	£10000	£3250
22	1	3d. red	£4750	£450
		a. Major re-entry	—	£1600

D. Very thick soft wove paper (1857)

23	2	6d. reddish purple	£48000	£4000
		a. Bisected (3d.) *on cover*	†	£35000

Bisected examples of the 3d. value were used to make up the 7½d. Canadian Packet rate to England from May 1856 until the introduction of the 7½d. value on 2 June 1857.

The 7½d. and 10d. values can be found in wide and narrow versions. These differences are due to shrinkage of the paper, which was wetted before printing and then contracted unevenly during drying. The width of these stamps varies between 17 and 18 mm.

The listed major re-entry on the 10d. occurs on R. 3/5 and shows strong doubling of the top frame line and the left-hand "8d. stg." with a line through the lower parts of "ANAD" and "ENCE". Smaller re-entries occur on all values.

Examples of the 12d. on wove paper come from a proof sheet used for postal purposes by the postal authorities.

The 3d. is known perforated 14 and also *percé en scie* 13. Both are contemporary, but were unofficial.

1858–59. P 11¾.

A. Machine-made medium to thick wove paper with a more even hard texture

25	4	½d. deep rose (12.58)	£4750	£950
		a. Lilac-rose	£4750	£1000
		b. Re-entry (R. 10/10)	£8500	£2250
26	1	3d. red (1.59)	£13000	£375
		a. Major re-entry	—	£1500
27	2	6d. brownish grey (1.59)	£18000	£4250
		a. Slate-violet	£18000	£4000

B. Thin soft horizontally ribbed paper

27b	4	½d. deep rose-red		£4500
28	1	3d. red	—	£1800
		a. Major re-entry		

The re-entry on the imperforate and perforated ½d. sheets was the same, but occurred on R. 10/10 of the perforated sheets because the two left-hand vertical rows were removed prior to perforation.

(New Currency. 100 cents = 1 dollar)

7

8 American Beaver

9 Prince Albert

10

11 Jacques Cartier

5c. Major re-entry showing as doubling of oval frame lines and lettering, particularly at the left of the design (R. 3/8)

(On 1 May 1858, Messrs. Rawdon, Wright, Hatch and Edson joined with eight other firms to form "The American Bank Note Co" and the "imprint" on sheets of the following stamps has the new title of the firm with "New York" added.)

(Recess A.B.N. Co)

1859 (1 July). P 12.

29	7	1c. pale rose (*to* rose-red)	£425	50·00
30		1c. deep rose (*to* carmine-rose)	£500	70·00
		a. Imperf (*pair*)	£4750	
		b. Imperf×perf		
31	8	5c. pale red	£450	20·00
32		5c. deep red	£450	22·00
		a. Re-entry* (R.3/8)	£4000	£450
		b. Imperf (*pair*)	£18000	
		c. Bisected (2½c.) with 10c. *on cover*	†	£7500
33	9	10c. black-brown	£18000	£2500
		a. Bisected (5c.), *on cover*	†	£12000
33b		10c. deep red-purple	£4250	£700
		ba. Bisected (5c.), *on cover*	†	£7000
34		10c. purple (*shades*)	£1500	80·00
		a. Bisected (5c.), *on cover*	†	£6500

35		10c. brownish purple	£1400	85·00
36		10c. brown (*to pale*)	£1400	80·00
		a. Bisected (5c.), on cover	†	£7500
37		10c. dull violet	£1500	85·00
38		10c. bright red-purple	£1500	80·00
		a. Imperf (pair)	£15000	
39	10	12½c. deep yellow-green	£1300	70·00
40		12½c. pale yellow-green	£1200	70·00
41		12½c. blue-green	£1500	85·00
		a. Imperf (pair)	£7000	
		b. Imperf between (vert pair)		
42	11	17c. deep blue	£1600	95·00
		a. Imperf (pair)	£6500	
43		17c. slate-blue	£1900	£130
43*a*		17c. indigo	£1800	£100

*Slighter re-entries are worth from £40 upwards in used condition.

As there were numerous PO Dept. orders for the 10c., 12½c. and 17c. and some of these were executed by more than one separate printing, with no special care to ensure uniformity of colour, there is a wide range of shade, especially in the 10c., and some shades recur at intervals after periods during which other shades predominated. The colour-names given in the above list therefore represent groups only.

It has been proved by leading Canadian specialists that the perforations may be an aid to the approximate dating of a particular stamp, the gauge used measuring 11¾×11¾ from mid-July 1859 to mid-1863, 12×11¾ from March 1863 to mid-1865 and 12×12 from April 1865 to 1868. Exceptionally, in the 5c. value many sheets were perforated 12×12 between May and October, 1862, whilst the last printings of the 12½c. and 17c. perf 11¾×11¾ were in July 1863, the perf 12×11¾ starting towards the end of 1863.

12

(Recess A.B.N. Co)

1864 (1 Aug). P 12.

44	12	2c. rose-red	£600	£170
45		2c. bright rose	£600	£170
		a. Imperf (pair)	£3500	

The Colony of Canada became part of the Dominion of Canada on 1 July 1867.

NEW BRUNSWICK

New Brunswick, previously part of Nova Scotia, became a separate colony in June 1784. The colony became responsible for its postal service on 6 July 1851.

PRICES FOR STAMPS ON COVER	
Nos. 1/4	*from* × 2
Nos. 5/6	*from* × 3
Nos. 7/9	*from* × 10
Nos. 10/12	*from* × 30
No. 13	—
Nos. 14/17	*from* × 2
No. 18	*from* × 5
No. 19	*from* × 100

1 Royal Crown and Heraldic
Flowers of the United Kingdom

(Recess P.B.)

1851 (5 Sept)–60. Blue paper. Imperf.

1	1	3d. bright red	£4000	£425
2		3d. dull red	£3500	£350
		a. Bisected (1½d.) (1854) (on cover)	†	£3000
2*b*		6d. mustard-yellow	£7500	£1500
3		6d. yellow	£5000	£900
4		6d. olive-yellow	£5000	£800
		a. Bisected (3d.) (1854) (on cover)	†	£3000
		b. Quartered (1½d.) (1860) (on cover)	†	£42000
5		1s. reddish mauve	£18000	£4500
6		1s. dull mauve	£21000	£5000
		a. Bisected (6d.) (1855) (on cover)	†	£24000
		b. Quartered (3d.) (1860) (on cover)	†	£38000

Reprints of all three values were made in 1890 on thin, hard, white paper. The 3d. is bright orange, the 6d. and 1s. violet-black.

Nos. 2a and 4b were to make up the 7½d. rate to Great Britain, introduced on 1 August 1854.

(New Currency. 100 cents = 1 dollar)

2 Locomotive   **3**   **3a** Charles
Connell

---

6 Paddle-steamer   **7** King Edward VII
Washington   when Prince
of Wales

(Recess A.B.N. Co)

1860 (15 May)–63. No wmk. P 12.

7	2	1c. brown-purple	85·00	60·00
8		1c. purple	70·00	50·00
9		1c. dull claret	70·00	50·00
		a. Imperf vert (horiz pair)	£650	
10	3	2c. orange (1863)	35·00	29·00
11		2c. orange-yellow	42·00	29·00
12		2c. deep orange	45·00	29·00
		a. Imperf horiz (vert pair)	£475	
13	3a	5c. brown	£10000	
14	4	5c. yellow-green	28·00	18·00
15		5c. deep green	28·00	18·00
16		5c. sap-green (deep yellowish green)	£300	40·00
17	5	10c. red	65·00	75·00
		a. Bisected (5c.) (on cover) (1860)	†	£600
18	6	12½c. indigo	70·00	42·00
19	7	17c. black	42·00	90·00

Beware of forged cancellations.

No. 13 was not issued due to objections to the design showing Charles Connell, the Postmaster-General. Most of the printing was destroyed.

New Brunswick joined the Dominion of Canada on 1 July 1867 and its stamps were withdrawn in March of the following year.

NEWFOUNDLAND

Newfoundland became a self-governing colony in 1855 and a Dominion in 1917. In 1934 the adverse financial situation led to the suspension of the constitution.

The first local postmaster, at St. John's, was appointed in 1805, the overseas mails being routed via Halifax, Nova Scotia. A regular packet service was established between these two ports in 1840, the British GPO assuming control of the overseas mails at the same time.

The responsibility for the overseas postal service reverted to the colonial administration on 1 July 1851.

ST. JOHN'S

CROWNED-CIRCLE HANDSTAMPS

CC **1a**

CC1	CC **1a**	ST. JOHN'S NEWFOUNDLAND (R.) (27.6.1846)	*Price on cover*	£1000

PRICES FOR STAMPS ON COVER TO 1945	
No. 1	*from* × 30
Nos. 2/4	*from* × 3
No. 5	*from* × 20
No. 6	*from* × 10
No. 7	*from* × 3
No. 8	*from* × 30
No. 9	*from* × 8
No. 10	—
No. 11	*from* × 8
No. 12	*from* × 3
Nos. 13/14	*from* × 20
Nos. 15/17	—
Nos. 18/20	*from* × 20
No. 21	*from* × 15
Nos. 22/3	—
No. 25	*from* × 30
No. 26	*from* × 5
No. 27	*from* × 8
No. 28	*from* × 3
Nos. 29/30	*from* × 10
No. 31	*from* × 30
No. 32	*from* × 8
No. 33	*from* × 5
Nos. 34/9	*from* × 8
Nos. 40/1	*from* × 5
Nos. 42/3	*from* × 8
Nos. 44/8	*from* × 8
No. 49	*from* × 50
Nos. 50/3	*from* × 10
No. 54	*from* × 4
Nos. 55/8b	*from* × 8
No. 59	*from* × 100
No. 59a	*from* × 10
Nos. 60/1	*from* × 4
Nos. 62/5	*from* × 8

PRICES FOR STAMPS ON COVER TO 1945	
Nos. 65a/79	*from* × 3
Nos. 83/90	*from* × 10
Nos. 91/3	*from* × 2
No. 94	*from* × 50
Nos. 95/141	*from* × 3
Nos. 142/a	*from* × 1½
No. 143	*from* × 8
Nos. 144/8f	*from* × 2
Nos. 149/62	*from* × 3
No. 163	*from* × 1½
Nos. 164/78	*from* × 2
Nos. 179/90	*from* × 3
No. 191	*from* × 1½
Nos. 192/220	*from* × 2
No. 221	*from* × 1½
Nos. 222/9	*from* × 3
Nos. 230/4	*from* × 2
No. 235	*from* × 1½
Nos. 236/91	*from* × 2
Nos. D1/6	*from* × 10

1   **2**

3

4   **5**

Royal Crown and Heraldic flowers of the United Kingdom

(Recess P.B.)

1857 (1 Jan)–64. Thick, machine-made paper with a distinct mesh. No wmk. Imperf.

1	1	1d. brown-purple	£160	£250
		a. Bisected (½d.) (1864) (on cover)	†	£40000
2	2	2d. scarlet-vermilion (15.2)	£25000	£6500
3	3	3d. yellowish green (H/S "CANCELLED" in oval £12000)	£2000	£425
4	4	4d. scarlet-vermilion	£15000	£3500
5	1	5d. brown-purple	£350	£500
6	4	6d. scarlet-vermilion	£28000	£4750
7	5	6½d. scarlet-vermilion	£4500	£4750
8	4	8d. scarlet-vermilion	£400	£950
		a. Bisected (4d.) (1859) (on cover)	†	£4250
9	2	1s. scarlet-vermilion	£27000	£9000
		a. Bisected (6d.) (1860) (on cover)	†	£17000

The 6d. and 8d. differ from the 4d. in many details, as does also the 1s. from the 2d.

PERKINS BACON "CANCELLED". For notes on these handstamps, showing "CANCELLED" between horizontal bars forming an oval, see Catalogue Introduction.

1860 (15 Aug–Dec). Medium, hand-made paper without mesh. Imperf.

10	2	2d. orange-vermilion	£600	£700
11	3	3d. green to deep green* (H/S "CANCELLED" in oval £11000)	£110	£190
12	4	4d. orange-vermilion (H/S "CANCELLED" in oval £14000)	£4500	£1100
		a. Bisected (2d.) (12.60) (on cover)	†	£20000
13	1	5d. Venetian red (H/S "CANCELLED" in oval £13000)	£140	£400
14	4	6d. orange-vermilion (H/S "CANCELLED" in oval £13000)	£5000	£800
15	2	1s. orange-vermilion (H/S "CANCELLED" in oval £17000)	£35000	£11000
		a. Bisected (6d.) (12.60) (on cover)	†	£45000

*No. 11 includes stamps from the July and November 1861 printings which are very difficult to distinguish.

The 1s. on horizontally or vertically *laid* paper is now considered to be a proof (*Price* £21000).

Stamps of this and the following issue may be found with part of the paper-maker's watermark "STACEY WISE 1858".

BISECTS. Collectors are warned against buying bisected stamps of these issues without a reliable guarantee.

1862–64. New colours. Hand-made paper without mesh. Imperf.

16	1	1d. chocolate-brown	£350	£450
		a. Red-brown	£8500	
17	2	2d. rose-lake	£300	£500
18	4	4d. rose-lake (H/S "CANCELLED" in oval £13000)	50·00	£110
		a. Bisected (2d.) (1864) (on cover)	†	£38000
19	1	5d. chocolate-brown (shades)	£100	£325
		a. Red-brown (shades)	90·00	£200
20	4	6d. rose-lake (H/S "CANCELLED" in oval £11000)	35·00	£100
		a. Bisected (3d.) (1863) (on cover)	†	£9500
21	5	6½d. rose-lake (H/S "CANCELLED" in oval £11000)	£100	£450

22	**4**	8d. rose-lake	£130	£650
23	**2**	1s. rose-lake (H/S "CANCELLED" in oval £12000)	50·00	£300
		a. Bisected (6d.) (1863) (*on cover*).	†	£22000

Nos. 16/23 come from printings made in July (2d., 4d., 6d., 6½d., and 1s. only) or November 1861 (all values), which were received in Newfoundland in January 1862. The paper used was from the same manufacturer as that for Nos. 10/15, but was of more variable thickness and texture, ranging from a relatively soft medium paper, which can be quite opaque, to a thin hard transparent paper. The rose-lake stamps also show a considerable variation in shade ranging from pale to deep. The extensive remainders of this issue were predominantly in pale shades on thin hard paper, but it is not possible to distinguish between stamps from the two printings with any certainty. Deep shades of the 2d., 4d., 6d., 6½d. and 1s. on soft opaque paper do, however, command a considerable premium.

Beware of buying used examples of the stamps which are worth much less in unused condition, as many unused stamps have been provided with faked postmarks. A guarantee should be obtained.

(New Currency. 100 cents = 1 dollar)

6 Atlantic Cod

7 Common Seal on Ice-floe

8 Prince Consort

9 Queen Victoria

10 Schooner

11 Queen Victoria

(Recess A.B.N. Co, New York)

1865 (15 Nov)–70. P 12.

		(a) Thin yellowish paper		
25	**6**	2c. yellowish green	£170	£110
		a. Bisected (1c.) (*on cover*) (1870)..	†	£8500
26	**7**	5c. brown	£600	£180
		a. Bisected (2½c.) (*on cover*)	†	£10000
27	**8**	10c. black	£375	£110
		a. Bisected (5c.) (*on cover*) (1869)...	†	£7000
28	**9**	12c. red-brown	£650	£150
		a. Bisected (6c.) (*on cover*) (1869)...	†	£5000
29	**10**	12c. orange-yellow	£120	£140
30	**11**	24c. blue	50·00	38·00
		(b) Medium white paper		
31	**6**	2c. bluish green (to deep) (1870)....	£120	50·00
32	**8**	10c. black (1870)	£275	48·00
33	**9**	12c. chestnut (1870)	60·00	48·00

The inland postage rate was reduced to 3c. on 8 May, 1870. Until the 3c. value became available examples of No. 25 were bisected to provide 1c. stamps.

For the 12c. value in deep brown, see No. 61.

12 King Edward VII when Prince of Wales

14 Queen Victoria

I

II

In Type II the white oval frame line is unbroken by the scroll containing the words "ONE CENT", the letters "N.F." are smaller and closer to the scroll, and there are other minor differences.

(Recess National Bank Note Co, New York)

1868 (Nov). P 12.

34	**12**	1c. dull purple (I)	75·00	60·00

(Recess A.B.N. Co)

1868 (Nov)–73. P 12.

35	**12**	1c. brown-purple (II) (3.71)	£130	70·00
36	**14**	3c. vermilion (7.70)	£300	£100

37		3c. blue (1.4.73)	£275	27·00
38	**7**	5c. black	£325	£110
39	**14**	5c. rose (7.70)	17·00	30·00

1876–79. Rouletted.

40	**12**	1c. lake-purple (II) (1877)	£120	55·00
41	**6**	2c. bluish green (1879)	£170	50·00
42	**14**	3c. blue (1877)	£325	6·00
43	**7**	5c. blue	£200	4·00
		a. Imperf (pair)		

15 King Edward VII when Prince of Wales

16 Atlantic Cod

17

18 Common Seal on Ice-floe

(Recess British American Bank Note Co, Montreal)

1880–82. P 12.

44	**15**	1c. dull grey-brown	50·00	17·00
		a. Dull brown	50·00	17·00
		b. Red-brown	55·00	20·00
46	**16**	2c. yellow-green (1882)	60·00	32·00
47	**17**	3c. pale dull blue	£150	9·50
		a. Bright blue	85·00	6·50
48	**18**	5c. pale dull blue	£350	10·00

19 Newfoundland Dog

20 Atlantic Brigantine

21 Queen Victoria

(Recess British American Bank Note Co, Montreal)

1887 (1 Nov). New colours and values. P 12.

49	**19**	½c. rose-red	15·00	11·00
50	**15**	1c. blue-green	21·00	14·00
		a. Green	6·00	4·25
		b. Yellow-green	13·00	11·00
51	**16**	2c. orange-vermilion	27·00	7·50
		a. Imperf (pair)	£375	
52	**17**	3c. deep brown	85·00	2·75
53	**18**	5c. deep blue	£120	5·50
54	**20**	10c. black	75·00	75·00
49/54		Set of 6	£300	95·00

For reissues in similar colours, see Nos. 62/5a.

(Recess B.A.B.N. Co)

1890 (Nov). P 12.

55	**21**	3c. deep slate	55·00	3·50
		a. Imperf (pair)		
56		3c. slate-grey (to grey)	50·00	3·75
		a. Imperf horiz (vert pair)	£550	
57		3c. slate-violet	70·00	8·00
58		3c. grey-lilac	70·00	3·75
58a		3c. brown-grey	75·00	9·00
58b		3c. purple-grey	75·00	9·00

There is a very wide range of shades in this stamp, and those given only cover the main groups.

Stamps on pink paper are from a consignment recovered from the sea and which were affected by the salt water.

(Recess British American Bank Note Co, Montreal)

1894 (Aug–Dec). Changes of colour. P 12.

59	**19**	½c. black (11.94)	10·00	9·50
59a	**18**	5c. bright blue (12.94)	80·00	5·50
60	**14**	6c. crimson-lake (12.94)	32·00	27·00
61	**9**	12c. deep brown	90·00	90·00

The 6c. is printed from the old American Bank Note Company's plates.

1896 (Jan)–98. Reissues. P 12.

62	**19**	½c. orange-vermilion	65·00	55·00
63	**15**	1c. deep brown	90·00	55·00
63a		1c. deep green (1898)	32·00	26·00
64	**16**	2c. green	£120	70·00
65	**17**	3c. deep blue	90·00	30·00
65a		3c. chocolate-brown	£120	95·00
62/5a		Set of 6	£450	£300

The above were *reissued* for postal purposes. The colours are generally brighter than those of the original stamps.

22 Queen Victoria

23 John Cabot

24 Cape Bonavista

25 Caribou hunting

26 Mining

27 Logging

28 Fishing

29 *Matthew* (Cabot)

30 Willow Grouse

31 Group of Grey Seals

32 Salmon-fishing

33 Seal of the Colony

34 Iceberg off St. John's

35 Henry VII

(Des R. O. Smith. Recess A.B.N. Co)

1897 (24 June). 400th Anniv of Discovery of Newfoundland and 60th year of Queen Victoria's reign. P 12.

66	**22**	1c. green	8·50	12·00
67	**23**	2c. bright rose	2·75	2·75
		a. Bisected (1c.) *on cover*	†	£325
68	**24**	3c. bright blue	4·00	1·00
		a. Bisected (1½c.) *on cover.*	†	£325
69	**25**	4c. olive-green	13·00	9·00
70	**26**	5c. violet	14·00	4·50
71	**27**	6c. red-brown	9·50	3·25
		a. Bisected (3c.) *on cover*	†	£350
72	**28**	8c. orange	21·00	9·50
73	**29**	10c. sepia	42·00	15·00
74	**30**	12c. deep blue	40·00	12·00
75	**31**	15c. bright scarlet	26·00	25·00
76	**32**	24c. dull violet-blue	32·00	38·00
77	**33**	30c. slate-blue	55·00	£110
78	**34**	35c. red	70·00	95·00
79	**35**	60c. black	27·00	22·00
66/79		Set of 14.	£325	£325

The 60c. surcharged "TWO—2—CENTS" in three lines is an essay made in December 1918 (*Price* £450).

ONE CENT

(36)

ONE CENT

(37)

ONE CENT

(38)

1897 (19 Oct). T **21** surch with T **36/8** by *Royal Gazette*, St. John's, on stamps of various shades.

80	**36**	1c. on 3c. grey-purple	80·00	40·00
		a. Surch double, one diagonal	£1300	
		d. Vert pair, one without lower bar and "ONE CENT"	£4000	
81	**37**	1c. on 3c. grey-purple	£170	£120
82	**38**	1c. on 3c. grey-purple	£600	£500

Nos. 80/2 occur in the same setting of 50 (10×5) applied twice to each sheet. Type 36 appeared in the first four horizontal rows, Type 37 on R. 5/1–8 and Type 38 on R. 5/9 and 10.

Trial surcharges in red or red and black were not issued. (*Price:* Type **36** *in red* £1000, *in red and black* £1000: Type **37** *in red* £3000, *in red and black* £3000: Type **38** *in red* £7500, *in red and black* £8000).

These surcharges exist on stamps of various shades, but those on brown-grey are clandestine forgeries, having been produced by one of the printers at the *Royal Gazette*.

39 Prince Edward later Duke of Windsor

40 Queen Victoria

41 King Edward VII when Prince of Wales

42 Queen Alexandra when Princess of Wales

43 Queen Mary when Duchess of York

44 King George V when Duke of York

(Recess A.B.N. Co)

1897 (4 Dec)–**1918**. P 12.

83	39	½c. olive (8.98)	2·25	1·50
		a. Imperf (pair)	£650	
84	40	1c. carmine	7·50	8·50
85		1c. blue-green (6.98)	18·00	20
		a. Yellow-green	20·00	20
		b. Imperf horiz (vert pair)	£275	
86	41	2c. orange	10·00	9·50
		a. Imperf (pair)	—	£500
87		2c. scarlet (6.98)	22·00	75
		b. Imperf between (pair)	£650	
88	42	3c. orange (6.98)	30·00	30
		a. Imperf horiz (vert pair)	£450	
		b. Imperf (pair)	£375	£375
		c. Red-orange/bluish (6.18)	50·00	3·50
89	43	4c. violet (21.10.01)	35·00	11·00
		a. Imperf (pair)	£600	
90	44	5c. blue (6.99)	50·00	3·00
83/90		Set of 8	£150	30·00

No. 88c was an emergency war-time printing made by the American Bank Note Co from the old plate, pending receipt of the then current 3c. from England.

The imperforate errors of this issue are found used, but only as philatelic "by favour" items. It is possible that No. 86a only exists in this condition.

45 Map of Newfoundland

(Recess A.B.N. Co)

1908 (31 Aug). P 12.

94	45	2c. lake	29·00	1·00

46 King James I

47 Arms of Colonisation Co

48 John Guy

49 Endeavour (immigrant ship), 1610

50 Cupids

51 Sir Francis Bacon

52 View of Mosquito

53 Logging Camp, Red Indian Lake

54 Paper Mills, Grand Falls

55 King Edward VII

56 King George V

1c. "NFWFOUNDLAND" (Right pane, R. 5/1)

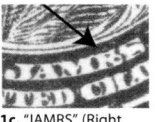
1c. "JAMRS" (Right pane, R. 5/2)

6c. (A) "Z" in "COLONIZATION" reversed. (B) "Z" correct.

(Litho Whitehead, Morris & Co Ltd)

1910 (15 Aug).

		(a) P 12		
95	46	1c. green	19·00	3·75
		a. "NFWFOUNDLAND"	85·00	£110
		b. "JAMRS"	85·00	£110
		c. Imperf between (horiz pair)	£350	£375
96	47	2c. rose-carmine	26·00	2·50
97	48	3c. olive	14·00	26·00
98	49	4c. violet	26·00	21·00
99	50	5c. bright blue	50·00	15·00
100	51	6c. claret (A)	60·00	£170
100a		6c. claret (B)	38·00	£110
101	52	8c. bistre-brown	70·00	£130
102	53	9c. olive-green	70·00	£110
103	54	10c. purple-slate	75·00	£140
104	55	12c. pale red-brown	70·00	£100
		a. Imperf (pair)	£325	
105	56	15c. black	70·00	£130
95/105		Set of 11	£475	£700
		(b) P 12×14		
106	46	1c. green	9·00	18·00
		a. "NFWFOUNDLAND"	70·00	£160
		b. "JAMRS"	70·00	£160
		c. Imperf between (horiz pair)	£700	£750
107	47	2c. rose-carmine	9·50	40
		a. Imperf between (horiz pair)	£700	
108	50	5c. bright blue (P 14×12)	12·00	3·00
		(c) P 12×11		
109	46	1c. green	3·25	30
		a. Imperf between (horiz pair)	£325	
		b. Imperf between (vert pair)	£375	
		c. "NFWFOUNDLAND"	45·00	60·00
		e. "JAMRS"	45·00	60·00
		(d) P 12×11½		
110	47	2c. rose-carmine	£450	£300

(Dies eng Macdonald & Sons. Recess A. Alexander & Sons, Ltd)

1911 (7 Feb). As T **51** to **56**, but recess printed. P 14.

111		6c. claret (B)	18·00	50·00
112		8c. yellow-brown	50·00	80·00
		a. Imperf between (horiz pair)	£1100	
113		9c. sage-green	50·00	£150
		a. Imperf between (horiz pair)	£1100	
114		10c. purple-black	90·00	£150
		a. Imperf between (horiz pair)	£1100	
115		12c. red-brown	70·00	70·00
116		15c. slate-green	65·00	£130
111/16		Set of 6	£300	£550

The 9c. and 15c. exist with papermaker's watermark "E. TOWGOOD FINE".
Nos. 111/16 exist imperforate. (Price £250, unused, for each pair).

57 Queen Mary

58 King George V

59 Duke of Windsor when Prince of Wales

60 King George VI when Prince Albert

61 Princess Mary, the Princess Royal

62 Prince Henry, Duke of Gloucester

63 Prince George, Duke of Kent

64 Prince John

65 Queen Alexandra

66 Duke of Connaught

67 Seal of Newfoundland

(1c. to 5c., 10c. eng and recess D.L.R.; others eng Macdonald & Co, recess A. Alexander & Sons)

1911 (19 June)–**16**. Coronation. P 13½×14 (comb) (1c. to 5c., 10c.) or 14 (line) (others).

117	57	1c. yellow-green	10·00	30
		a. Blue-green (1915)	25·00	30

118	58	2c. carmine	12·00	20
		a. Rose-red (blurred impression). Perf 14 (1916)	17·00	1·00
119	59	3c. red-brown	25·00	50·00
120	60	4c. purple	24·00	45·00
121	61	5c. ultramarine	8·00	2·25
122	62	6c. slate-grey	14·00	27·00
123	63	8c. aniline blue	60·00	85·00
		a. Greenish blue	95·00	£130
124	64	9c. violet-blue	32·00	55·00
125	65	10c. deep green	42·00	50·00
126	66	12c. plum	32·00	50·00
127	67	15c. lake	29·00	50·00
117/27		Set of 11	£250	£350

The 2c. rose-red, No. 118a is a poor war-time printing by Alexander & Sons.

Although No. 123 has a typical aniline appearance it is believed that the shade results from the thinning of non-aniline ink.

Nos. 117/18, 121 and 126/7 exist imperforate, without gum. (Prices for 1c., 2c., 5c., 12c., £250, for 15c. £75, unused, per pair).

68 Caribou

FIRST TRANS-ATLANTIC AIR POST April, 1919.

(69)

(Des J. H. Noonan. Recess D.L.R.)

1919 (2 Jan). Newfoundland Contingent, 1914–1918. P 14.

130	68	1c. green (a) (b)	3·75	20
131		2c. scarlet (a) (b)	3·75	85
		a. Carmine-red (b)	25·00	80
132		3c. brown (a) (b)	8·00	20
		a. Red-brown (b)	16·00	60
133		4c. mauve (a) (b)	13·00	80
		a. Purple (b)	28·00	50
134		5c. ultramarine (a) (b)	17·00	1·25
135		6c. slate-grey (a)	19·00	70·00
136		8c. bright magenta (a)	19·00	70·00
137		10c. deep grey-green (a)	8·50	8·00
138		12c. orange (a)	22·00	75·00
139		15c. indigo (a)	16·00	90·00
		a. Prussian blue (a)	£110	£150
140		24c. bistre-brown (a)	32·00	42·00
141		36c. sage-green (a)	24·00	50·00
130/41		Set of 12	£160	£350

Each value bears with "Trail of the Caribou" the name of a different action: 1c. Suvla Bay; 3c. Gueudecourt; 4c. Beaumont Hamel; 6c. Monchy; 10c. Steenbeck; 15c. Langemarck; 24c. Cambrai; 36c. Combles; 2c., 5c., 8c., and 12c. inscribed "Royal Naval Reserve-Ubique".

Perforations. Two perforating heads were used: (a) comb 14×13.9; (b) line 14.1×14.1.

Nos. 130/41 exist imperforate, without gum. (Price £350 unused, for each pair).

1919 (12 Apr). Air. No. 132 optd with T **69**, by Robinson & Co Ltd, at the offices of the *Daily News*.

142	68	3c. brown	£22000	£12000

These stamps franked correspondence carried by Lieut. H. Hawker on his Atlantic flight. 18 were damaged and destroyed, 95 used on letters, 11 given as presentation copies, and the remaining 76 were sold in aid of the Marine Disasters Fund.

1919 (19 Apr). Nos. 132 inscribed in MS. "Aerial Atlantic Mail. J.A.R.".

142a	68	3c. brown	£70000	£20000

This provisional was made by W. C. Campbell, the Secretary of the Postal Department, and the initials are those of the Postmaster, J. A. Robinson, for use on correspondence intended to be carried on the abortive Morgan-Raynham Trans-Atlantic flight. The mail was eventually delivered by sea.

In addition to the 25 to 30 used examples, one unused, no gum, example of No. 142a is known.

Single examples of a similar overprint on the 2c., (No. 131) and 5c. (No. 134) are known used on cover, the former with an unoverprinted example of the same value.

Trans-Atlantic AIR POST, 1919. ONE DOLLAR.
(70)

THREE CENTS
(71)

1919 (9 June). Air. No. 75 surch with T **70** by *Royal Gazette*, St. John's.

143	31	$1 on 15c. bright scarlet	£130	£150
		a. No comma after "AIR POST"	£160	£180
		b. As var a and no stop after "1919"	£375	£450
		c. As var a and "A" of "AIR" under "a" of "Trans"	£375	£450

These stamps were issued for use on the mail carried on the first successful flight across the Atlantic by Capt. J. Alcock and Lieut. A. Brown, and on other projected Trans-Atlantic flights (Alcock flown cover, Price £3000).

The surcharge was applied in a setting of which 16 were normal, 7 as No. 143a, 1 as No. 143b and 1 as No. 143c.

1920 (Sept). Nos. 75 and 77/8 surch as T **71**, by *Royal Gazette* (2c. with only one bar, at top of stamp).

A. Bars of surch 10½ mm apart. B. Bars 13½ mm apart.

144	33	2c. on 30c. slate-blue (24.9)	7·50	35·00
		a. Surch inverted	£1400	£1600
145	31	3c. on 15c. bright scarlet (A) (13.9)	£250	£275
		a. Surch inverted	£3000	
146		3c. on 15c. bright scarlet (B) (13.9)	38·00	40·00

147	34	3c. on 35c. red (15.9)	17·00	26·00
		a. Surch inverted	£2750	
		b. Lower bar omitted	£180	£225
		c. "THREE" omitted	£1200	

Our prices for Nos. 147b and 147c are for stamps with lower bar or "THREE" entirely missing. The bar may be found in all stages of incompleteness and stamps showing broken bar are not of much value.

On the other hand, stamps showing either only the top or bottom of the letters "THREE" are scarce, though not as rare as No. 147c.

The 6c. T **27** surcharged "THREE CENTS", in red or black, is an essay (*Price £950*). The 2c. on 30c. with red surcharge is a colour trial (*Price £1300*).

AIR MAIL
to Halifax, N.S.
1921.
(72)

1921 (16 Nov). Air. No. 78 optd with T **72** by *Royal Gazette*.

I. 2¾ mm between "AIR" and "MAIL"

148	34	35c. red	£150	£100
		a. No stop after "1921"	£130	90·00
		b. No stop and first "1" of "1921" below "f" of "Halifax"	£375	£275
		c. As No. 148, inverted	£7000	
		d. As No. 148a, inverted	£5000	
		e. As No. 148b, inverted	£27000	

II. 1½ mm between "AIR" and "MAIL"

148f	34	35c. red	£180	£120
		g. No stop after "1921"	£225	£150
		h. No stop and first "1" of "1921" below "f" of "Halifax"	£375	£275
		i. As No. 148f, inverted	£9000	
		k. As No. 148g, inverted	£16000	
		l. As No. 148h, inverted	£27000	

Type **72** was applied as a setting of 25 which contained ten stamps as No. 148a, seven as No. 148, four as No. 148f, two as No. 148g, one as No. 148b and one as No. 148h.

73 Twin Hills, Tor's Cove

74 South-West Arm, Trinity

75 Statue of the Fighting Newfoundlander St. John's

76 Humber River

77 Coast at Trinity

78 Upper Steadies, Humber River

79 Quidi Vidi, near St. John's

80 Caribou crossing lake

81 Humber River Canyon

82 Shell Bird Island

83 Mount Moriah, Bay of Islands

84 Humber River nr. Little Rapids

85 Placentia

86 Topsail Falls

(Recess D.L.R.)

1923 (9 July)–**24**. T **73/86**. P 14 (comb or line).

149	73	1c. green	2·25	20
150	74	2c. carmine	1·00	10
		a. Imperf (pair)	£170	
151	75	3c. brown	3·75	10
152	76	4c. deep purple	1·00	30
153	77	5c. ultramarine	6·50	1·75
154	78	6c. slate	11·00	19·00
155	79	8c. purple	18·00	4·25
156	80	9c. slate-green	21·00	38·00
157	81	10c. violet	17·00	11·00
		a. Purple	25·00	3·50
158	82	11c. sage-green	7·00	38·00
159	83	12c. lake	8·00	19·00
160	84	15c. Prussian blue	8·00	38·00
161	85	20c. chestnut (28.4.24)	32·00	21·00
162	86	24c. sepia (22.4.24)	70·00	£100
149/62 *Set of 14*			£180	£250

Perforations. Three perforating heads were used: comb 13.8×14 (all values); line 13.7 and 14, and combinations of these two (for all except 6, 8, 9 and 11c.).

Nos. 149 and 151/60 also exist imperforate, but these are usually without gum. (*Price per pair from £200, unused*)

Air Mail
DE PINEDO
1927
(87)

1927 (18 May). Air. No. 79 optd with T **87**, by Robinson & Co, Ltd.

163	35	60c. black (R.)	£42000	£13000

For the mail carried by De Pinedo to Europe 300 stamps were overprinted, 230 used on correspondence, 66 presented to De Pinedo, Government Officials, etc., and four damaged and destroyed. Stamps without overprint were also used.

88 Newfoundland and Labrador

89 SS *Caribou*

90 King George V and Queen Mary

91 Duke of Windsor when Prince of Wales

92 Express Train

93 Newfoundland Hotel, St. John's

94 Heart's Content

95 Cabot Tower, St. John's

96 War Memorial, St. John's

97 GPO, St. John's

98 Vickers Vimy Aircraft

99 Parliament House, St. John's

100 Grand Falls, Labrador

(Recess D.L.R.)

1928 (3 Jan)–**29**. Publicity issue. P 14 (1c.) 13½×13 (2, 3, 5, 6, 10, 14, 20c.), 13×13½ (4c.) (all comb), or 14–13½* (line) (others).

164	88	1c. deep green	4·75	1·50
165	89	2c. carmine	5·50	50
166	90	3c. brown	13·00	2·25
		a. Perf 14–13½ (line)	5·00	5·00
167	91	4c. mauve	7·50	4·25
		a. Rose-purple (1929)	14·00	14·00
168	92	5c. slate-grey	15·00	19·00
		a. Perf 14–13½ (line)	48·00	16·00
169	93	6c. ultramarine	15·00	55·00
		a. Perf 14–13½ (line)	35·00	50·00
170	94	8c. red-brown	11·00	55·00
171	95	9c. deep green	3·00	27·00
172	96	10c. deep violet	27·00	35·00
		a. Perf 14–13½ (line)	7·00	35·00
173	97	12c. carmine-lake	3·00	27·00
174	95	14c. brown-purple (8.28)	45·00	55·00
		a. Perf 14–13½ (line)	25·00	11·00
175	98	15c. deep blue	14·00	50·00
176	99	20c. grey-black	30·00	20·00
		a. Perf 14–13½ (line)	9·00	13·00
177	97	28c. deep green (11.28)	28·00	70·00
178	100	30c. sepia	8·00	25·00
164/78 (*cheapest*) *Set of 15*			£140	£350

*Exact gauges for the various perforations are: 14 comb = 14×13.9; 13½×13 comb = 13.5×12.75; 14–13½ line = 14–13.75.

See also Nos. 179/87 and 198/208.

Differences between De La Rue and Perkins Bacon Printings of Types **88-100**

De La Rue	Perkins Bacon
1c. "C. NORMAN" is below "C.BAULD"	**1c.** "C. NORMAN" is above "C.BAULD"
2c. Two wires to left of rear mast	**2c.** One wire to left of rear mast
3c. The jewels are in the band of the crown are colourless	**3c.** The jewels are represented by dark dashes
4c. The shading of the "4" is cross-hatched	**4c.** The "4" is shaded horizontally
5c. The tips of the leaves framing the value tablets are rounded	**5c.** The tips of the leaves are pointed
6c. The lower leaves in the corner ornaments do not curl upwards at the end. Full stop after "ST. JOHNS"	**6c.** The lower leaves curl upwards at the ends. No full stop after "ST. JOHNS"
10c. The torch at left is topped by a single flame. Full stop after "ST. JOHNS"	**10c.** The torch is topped by a double flame. No full stop after "ST. JOHNS"
15c. "L" of "LEAVING" under "AI" of "AIRPLANE" in inscription	**15c.** "L" of "LEAVING" under "T" of "FIRST"
20c. The points at the foot of the "W" of "NEWFOUNDLAND" are flattened	**20c.** The points of the "W" are sharp

There are many other differences between the work of the two printers.

1929 (10 Aug)–**31**. Perkins Bacon printing. Former types re-engraved. No wmk. P 14 (comb) (1c.), 13½ (comb) (2, 6c.), 14–13½ (line) (20c.) or 13½×14 (comb) (others)*.

179	**88**	1c. green (26.9.29)	7·50	1·50
		a. Perf 14–13½ (line)	8·00	30
		b. Imperf between (vert pair)	£225	
		c. Imperf (pair)	£160	
180	**89**	2c. scarlet	1·75	40
		a. Imperf (pair)	£170	
		b. Perf 14–13½ (line)	6·00	1·25
181	**90**	3c. red-brown	1·00	20
		a. Imperf (pair)	£160	
182	**91**	4c. reddish purple (26.8.29)	2·75	80
		a. Imperf (pair)	£180	
183	**92**	5c. deep green (14.9.29)	12·00	5·00
184	**93**	6c. ultramarine (8.11.29)	17·00	27·00
		a. Perf 14–13½ (line)	3·50	32·00
185	**96**	10c. violet (5.10.29)	9·50	5·50
186	**98**	15c. blue (1.30)	22·00	£100
187	**99**	20c. black (1.1.31)	65·00	60·00
179/87 *Set of 9*			£110	£170

*Exact gauges for the various perforations are: 14 comb = 14×13.9; 13½ comb = 13.6×13.5; 14–13½ line = 14–13.75; 13½ ×14 comb = 13.6×13.8.

THREE CENTS

(**101**)

(Surch by Messrs D. R. Thistle, St. John's)

1929 (23 Aug). No. 154 surch with T **101**.

188		3c. on 6c. slate (R.)	3·50	12·00
		a. Surch inverted	£950	£1400
		b. Surch in black	£1000	

The issued surcharge shows 3 mm. space between "CENTS" and the bar. The black surcharge also exists with 5 mm. space, from a trial setting (*Price*, £900).

Trans-Atlantic AIR MAIL By B. M. "Columbia" September 1930 Fifty Cents

(**102**)

1930 (25 Sept). Air. No. 141 surch with T **102** by Messrs D. R. Thistle.

191	**68**	50c. on 36c. sage-green	£6500	£6000

103 Aeroplane and Dog-team

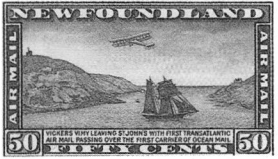

104 Vickers-Vimy Biplane and early Sailing Packet

105 Routes of historic Transatlantic Flights

106

(Des A. B. Perlin. Recess P.B.)

1931. Air. P 14.

(a) Without wmk (2.1.31)

192	**103**	15c. chocolate	9·00	18·00
		a. Imperf between (horiz pair)	£1000	
		b. Imperf between (vert pair)	£1200	
		c. Imperf (pair)	£550	
193	**104**	50c. green	38·00	55·00
		a. Imperf between (horiz pair)	£1300	£1200
		b. Imperf between (vert pair)	£1700	
		c. Imperf (pair)	£850	
194	**105**	$1 deep blue	50·00	95·00
		a. Imperf between (horiz pair)	£1300	
		b. Imperf between (vert pair)	£1400	
		c. Imperf (pair)	£900	
192/4 *Set of 3*			85·00	£150

*(b) Wmk W **106**, (sideways*) (13.3.31)*

195	**103**	15c. chocolate	13·00	32·00
		a. Pair, with and without wmk	42·00	

		b. Imperf between (horiz pair)	£1000	
		c. Imperf between (vert pair)	£1200	
		ca. Ditto, one without wmk (vert pair)	£1700	
		d. Imperf (pair)	£600	
		e. Wmk Cross (pair)	£160	
196	**104**	50c. green	35·00	75·00
		a. Imperf between (horiz pair)	£1100	
		b. Imperf between (vert pair)	£1600	
		c. Imperf (pair)	£850	
		d. Pair, with and without wmk	£550	
		w. Wmk top of shield to right	90·00	
197	**105**	$1 deep blue	80·00	£150
		a. Imperf between (horiz pair)	£1400	
		b. Imperf between (vert pair)	£1200	
		c. Imperf horiz (vert pair)	£800	
		d. Pair, with and without wmk	£900	
		e. Imperf (pair)	£800	
195/7 *Set of 3*			£110	£225

The normal sideways wmk on this issue shows the top of the shield to right on the 15c., but top of the shield to left on the 50c. and $1.

"WITH AND WITHOUT WMK" PAIRS listed in the issues from No. 195a onwards must have one stamp *completely* without any trace of watermark.

1931 (25 March–July). Perkins, Bacon printing (re-engraved types). W **106** (sideways on 1c., 4c., 30c.). P 13½ (1c.) or 13½×14 (others), both comb*.

198	**88**	1c. green (7.31)	17·00	3·00
		a. Imperf between (horiz pair)	£650	
199	**89**	2c. scarlet (7.31)	11·00	6·00
		w. Wmk inverted	75·00	
200	**90**	3c. red-brown (7.31)	8·00	4·50
		w. Wmk inverted	75·00	
201	**91**	4c. reddish purple (7.31)	8·00	1·25
202	**92**	5c. deep grey-green (7.31)	7·00	22·00
203	**93**	6c. ultramarine	7·00	38·00
		w. Wmk inverted	90·00	
204	**94**	8c. chestnut (1.4.31)	48·00	55·00
		w. Wmk inverted	95·00	£110
205	**96**	10c. violet (1.4.31)	38·00	45·00
206	**98**	15c. blue (1.7.31)	21·00	85·00
207	**99**	20c. black (1.7.31)	60·00	27·00
208	**100**	30c. sepia (1.7.31)	40·00	55·00
198/208 *Set of 11*			£225	£300

*Exact gauges for the two perforations are: 13½ = 13.6×13.5; 13½×14 = 13.6×13.8.

107 Atlantic Cod

108 King George V

109 Queen Mary

110 Duke of Windsor when Prince of Wales

111 Caribou

112 Queen Elizabeth II when Princess

113 Atlantic Salmon

114 Newfoundland Dog

115 Harp Seal

116 Cape Race

117 Sealing Fleet

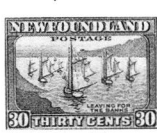

118 Fishing Fleet

(Recess P.B.)

1932 (2 Jan). W **106** (sideways* on vert designs). P 13½ (comb).

209	**107**	1c. green	3·50	30
		a. Imperf (pair)	£180	
		b. Perf 13 (line)	23·00	55·00
		ba. Imperf between (vert pair)	£130	
		w. Wmk top of shield to right	70·00	
210	**108**	2c. carmine	1·50	20
		a. Imperf (pair)	£180	
		c. Perf 13 (line)	23·00	45·00
		w. Wmk top of shield to right	70·00	
211	**109**	3c. orange-brown	1·50	20
		a. Imperf (pair)	£100	
		c. Perf 13 (line)	27·00	55·00
		ca. Imperf between (vert pair)	£250	
		d. Perf 14 (line). Small holes	35·00	55·00
		w. Wmk top of shield to right	70·00	

212	**110**	4c. bright violet	13·00	2·25
		w. Wmk top of shield to right		
213	**111**	5c. maroon	10·00	7·50
		a. Imperf (pair)	£180	
		w. Wmk top of shield to right	75·00	
214	**112**	6c. light blue	4·00	15·00
215	**113**	10c. black-brown	1·00	65
		a. Imperf (pair)	70·00	
		w. Wmk inverted	10·00	
216	**114**	14c. black	5·50	6·00
		a. Imperf (pair)	£160	
217	**115**	15c. claret	1·25	2·00
		a. Imperf (pair)	£180	
		b. Perf 14 (line)	8·00	11·00
218	**116**	20c. green	1·00	1·00
		a. Imperf (pair)	£180	
		b. Perf 14 (line)	£150	£150
		w. Wmk inverted	48·00	
219	**117**	25c. slate	2·00	2·25
		a. Imperf (pair)	£180	
		b. Perf 14 (line)	75·00	90·00
		c. Imperf between (vert pair)	£500	
220	**118**	30c. ultramarine	50·00	42·00
		a. Imperf (pair)	£600	
		b. Imperf between (vert pair)	£1600	
		c. Perf 14 (line)	£500	
209/20 *Set of 12*			80·00	70·00

The Caribou shown on T **111** is taken from the monument to the Royal Newfoundland Regiment, near Beaumont Hamel, France.

*The normal sideways watermark shows the top of the shield to left, *as seen from the back of the stamp.*

Nos. 209b, 210c and 211c were only issued in stamp booklets.

For similar stamps in different perforations see Nos. 222/8c and 276/89.

TRANS-ATLANTIC WEST TO EAST Per Dornier DO-X May, 1932. One Dollar and Fifty Cents

(**119**)

1932 (19 May). Air. No. 197 surch as T **119**, by Messrs. D. R. Thistle. P 14.

221	**105**	$1.50 on $1 deep blue (R.)	£250	£225
		a. Surch inverted	£21000	

120 Queen Mother, when Duchess of York

121 Corner Brook Paper Mills

122 Loading Iron Ore, Bell Island

(Recess P.B.)

1932 (15 Aug)–**38**. W **106** (sideways* on vert designs). P 13½ (comb).

222	**107**	1c. grey	3·25	10
		a. Imperf (pair)	48·00	
		c. Perf 14 (line)	8·50	22·00
		d. Perf 14 (line). Small holes	30·00	55·00
		e. Pair, with and without wmk	95·00	
		w. Wmk top of shield to right	65·00	50·00
223	**108**	2c. green	2·50	10
		a. Imperf (pair)	40·00	
		c. Perf 14 (line)	8·50	22·00
		ca. Imperf between (horiz pair)	£275	
		d. Perf 14 (line). Small holes	23·00	50·00
		e. Pair, with and without wmk	95·00	
		w. Wmk top of shield to right	50·00	
224	**110**	4c. carmine (21.7.34)	6·00	40
		a. Imperf (pair)	70·00	
		b. Perf 14 (line)	8·00	15·00
		ba. Imperf between (horiz pair)	£350	
		bb. Imperf between (vert pair)	£140	
		c. Pair, with and without wmk	£100	
		w. Wmk top of shield to right	70·00	
225	**111**	5c. violet (Die I)	6·00	1·75
		a. Imperf (pair)	75·00	
		b. Perf 14 (line). Small holes	27·00	55·00
		c. Die II	1·00	30
		ca. Imperf (pair)	70·00	
		cb. Perf 14 (line)	25·00	50·00
		cbw. Wmk top of shield to right	80·00	
		cc. Imperf between (horiz pair)	£275	
		cd. Pair, with and without wmk	£180	
		cw. Wmk top of shield to right	75·00	
226	**120**	7c. red-brown	3·00	4·00
		b. Perf 14 (line)	£250	
		ba. Imperf between (horiz pair)	£650	
		c. Imperf (pair)	£190	
		w. Wmk top of shield to right		
227	**121**	8c. brownish red	3·75	2·00
		a. Imperf (pair)	£110	
		w. Wmk inverted		
228	**122**	24c. bright blue	1·25	3·25
		a. Imperf (pair)	£350	
		b. Doubly printed	£1600	
		w. Wmk inverted	75·00	

228c	118	48c. red-brown (1.1.38)	13·00	10·00
		ca. Imperf (pair)	£140	
222/8c		*Set of 8*	30·00	18·00

*The normal sideways watermark shows the top of the shield to left, *as seen from the back of the stamp.*

No. 223. Two dies exist of the 2c., Die I was used for No. 210 and both dies for No. 223. The differences, though numerous, are very slight.

No. 225. There are also two dies of the 5c., Die I only being used for No. 213 and both dies for the violet stamp. In Die II the antler pointing to the "T" of "POSTAGE" is taller than the one pointing to the "S" and the individual hairs on the underside of the caribou's tail are distinct.

For similar stamps in a slightly larger size and perforated 12½ or 13½ (5c.) see Nos. 276/89.

(123) "L. & S."—Land and Sea

1933 (9 Feb). No. 195 optd with T **123** for ordinary postal use, by Messrs D. R. Thistle. W **106** (sideways top of shield to right from back). P 14.

229	103	15c. chocolate	6·00	22·00
		a. Pair, one without wmk	26·00	
		b. Opt reading up	£5000	
		c. Vertical pair, one without opt	£7000	

124 Put to Flight

126 Spotting the Herd

127 News from Home

125 Land of Heart's Delight

128 Labrador

(Des J. Scott. Recess P.B.)

1933 (9 June). Air. T **124/8** and similar horiz designs. W **106** (sideways*). P 14 (5c., 30c., 75c.) or 11½ (10c., 60c.).

230	124	5c. red-brown	22·00	22·00
		a. Imperf (pair)	£190	
		b. Imperf between (horiz pair)	£1000	
		c. Imperf between (vert pair)	£1200	
231	125	10c. orange-yellow	18·00	35·00
		a. Imperf (pair)	£160	
232	126	30c. light blue	40·00	50·00
		a. Imperf (pair)	£600	
233	127	60c. green	50·00	£120
		a. Imperf (pair)	£600	
234	128	75c. yellow-brown	50·00	£120
		a. Imperf (pair)	£550	
		b. Imperf between (horiz or vert pair)	£6000	
		w. Wmk top of shield to left	£150	
230/4		*Set of 5*	£160	£325

*The normal sideways watermark shows the top of the shield to right, *as seen from the back of the stamp.*

1933
GEN. BALBO
FLIGHT.
$4.50
(129)

(Surch by Robinson & Co, St. John's)

1933 (24 July). Air. Balbo Transatlantic Mass Formation Flight. No. 234 surch with T **129**. W **106**. P 14.

235		$4.50 on 75c. yellow-brown	£275	£350
		a. Surch inverted	£90000	
		b. Surch on 10c. (No. 231)	£75000	
		w. Wmk top of shield to left		

No. 235a. When this error was discovered the stamps were ordered to be officially destroyed but four copies which had been torn were recovered and skilfully repaired. In addition, four undamaged examples exist and the price quoted is for one of these (*Price for repaired example, £20000, unused*).

130 Sir Humphrey Gilbert

131 Compton Castle, Devon

132 Gilbert Coat of Arms

133 Eton College

134 Anchor token

135 Gilbert commissioned by Elizabeth I

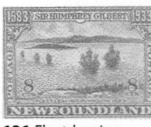

136 Fleet leaving Plymouth, 1583

137 Arrival at St. John's

138 Annexation, 5th August, 1583

139 Royal Arms

140 Gilbert in the *Squirrel*

141 Map of Newfoundland, 1626

142 Queen Elizabeth

143 Gilbert's statue at Truro

(Recess P.B.)

1933 (3 Aug). 350th Anniv of the Annexation by Sir Humphrey Gilbert. T **130/43**. W **106** (sideways* on vert designs). P 13½ (comb†).

236	130	1c. slate	1·25	1·50
		a. Imperf (pair)	60·00	
237	131	2c. green	2·00	70
		a. Imperf (pair)	50·00	
		b. Doubly printed	£500	
238	132	3c. chestnut	2·50	1·25
239	133	4c. carmine	1·00	50
		a. Imperf (pair)	55·00	
240	134	5c. violet	2·00	1·00
241	135	7c. greenish blue	17·00	23·00
		a. Perf 14 (line)	20·00	60·00
242	136	8c. vermilion	9·50	25·00
		a. Brownish red	£500	
		b. Bisected (4c.) (*on cover*)	†	£425
243	137	9c. ultramarine	7·00	26·00
		a. Imperf (pair)	£300	
		b. Perf 14 (line)	85·00	£110
244	138	10c. brown-lake	8·00	20·00
		a. Imperf (pair)	£300	
		b. Perf 14 (line)	£120	£150
245	139	14c. grey-black	22·00	50·00
		a. Perf 14 (line)	25·00	70·00
		aw. Wmk top of shield to right	£100	
246	140	15c. claret	26·00	50·00
		w. Wmk top of shield to right	9·00	35·00
247	141	20c. grey-green	19·00	25·00
		a. Perf 14 (line)	35·00	70·00
		w. Wmk inverted	90·00	
248	142	24c. maroon	22·00	35·00
		a. Imperf (pair)	£140	
		b. Perf 14 (line)	42·00	55·00
		w. Wmk top of shield to right	45·00	
249	143	32c. olive-black	19·00	75·00
		a. Perf 14 (line)	22·00	95·00
		w. Wmk top of shield to right	18·00	80·00
236/49		*Set of 14*	£110	£275

*The normal sideways watermark shows the top of the shield to left, *as seen from the back of the stamp.*

†Exact gauges for the two perforations are: 13½ comb = 13.4; 14 line = 13.8.

1935 (6 May). Silver Jubilee. As Nos. 91/4 of Antigua, but ptd by B.W. P 11×12.

250		4c. rosine	1·00	1·75
251		5c. bright violet	1·25	4·25
252		7c. blue	4·25	7·00
253		24c. olive-green	5·00	28·00
250/3		*Set of 4*	10·50	38·00
250s/3s		Perf "SPECIMEN" *Set of 4*	£190	

1937 (12 May). Coronation Issue. As Nos. 95/7 of Antigua, but name and value uncoloured on coloured background. P 11×11½.

254		2c. green	1·00	3·00
255		4c. carmine	1·60	4·00
256		5c. purple	3·00	4·00
254/6		*Set of 3*	5·00	10·00
254s/6s		Perf "SPECIMEN" *Set of 3*	£150	

144 Atlantic Cod

145 Map of Newfoundland

146 Caribou

147 Corner Brook Paper Mills

148 Atlantic Salmon

149 Newfoundland Dog

150 Harp Seal

151 Cape Race

152 Bell Island

153 Sealing Fleet

154 The Banks Fishing Fleet

Die I

Die II

No. 258. In Die II the shading of the King's face is heavier and dots have been added down the ridge of the nose. The top frame line is thicker and more uniform.

1c. Fish-hook flaw (R. 1/7 or 3/3)

7c. Re-entry to right of design (inscr oval, tree and value) (R. 4/8)

20c. Extra chimney (R. 6/5)

(Des and eng J. B. Dickinson & Co. Recess P.B.)

1937 (12 May). Additional Coronation Issue. T **144/54**. W **106**. P 14 (line)*.

257	144	1c. grey	3·50	30
		a. Pair, with and without wmk	32·00	
		b. Fish-hook flaw	32·00	20·00
		cw. Wmk inverted	70·00	
		d. Perf 13½ (line)	5·00	1·25
		da. Pair, with and without wmk	45·00	
		db. Fish-hook flaw	45·00	30·00
		e. Perf 13 (comb)	38·00	80·00
		ea. Pair, with and without wmk		
		eb. Fish-hook flaw	£200	£425

258	145	3c. orange-brown (I)	38·00	7·00
		a. Pair, with and without wmk	£250	
		b. Imperf between (horiz pair)	£500	
		c. Perf 13½ (line)	38·00	10·00
		ca. Imperf between (vert pair)	£250	
		cb. Imperf between (vert pair)	£650	
		d. Perf 13 (comb)	21·00	4·00
		e. Die II (P 14, line)	17·00	12·00
		ea. Pair, with and without wmk	£200	
		ec. Perf 13½ (line)	14·00	13·00
		eca. Pair, with and without wmk	£200	
		ecb. Imperf between (vert pair)	£750	
		ed. Perf 13 (comb)	9·50	4·75
		eda. Pair, with and without wmk	£180	
259	146	7c. bright ultramarine	4·00	1·25
		a. Pair, with and without wmk	£150	
		b. Re-entry at right	85·00	85·00
		c. Perf 13½ (line)	4·25	1·75
		ca. Pair, with and without wmk	£160	
		cb. Re-entry at right	85·00	
		d. Perf 13 (comb)	£700	£800
		db. Re-entry at right	£4000	
260	147	8c. scarlet	5·00	4·00
		a. Pair, with and without wmk	£130	
		b. Imperf between (horiz pair)	£1200	
		c. Imperf between (vert pair)	£1300	
		d. Imperf (pair)	£450	
		e. Perf 13½ (line)	7·00	8·00
		ea. Pair, with and without wmk	£160	
		eb. Imperf between (vert pair)		
		f. Perf 13 (comb)	23·00	29·00
261	148	10c. blackish brown	7·00	9·00
		a. Pair, with and without wmk	£170	
		b. Perf 13½ (line)	9·00	13·00
		ba. Pair, with and without wmk	£170	
		c. Perf 13 (comb)	3·25	20·00
		cw. Wmk inverted	£110	
262	149	14c. black	2·75	4·00
		a. Pair, with and without wmk	£150	
		b. Perf 13½ (line)	3·50	6·00
		ba. Pair, with and without wmk	£150	
		c. Perf 13 (comb)	£25000	£16000
263	150	15c. claret	21·00	9·00
		a. Pair, with and without wmk	£180	
		bw. Wmk inverted	£150	
		c. Perf 13½ (line)	26·00	13·00
		ca. Pair, with and without wmk	£200	
		cb. Imperf between (vert pair)	£1600	
		d. Perf 13 (comb)	48·00	75·00
		da. Pair, with and without wmk	£325	
264	151	20c. green	10·00	20·00
		a. Pair, with and without wmk	£160	
		c. Extra chimney	£130	
		dw. Wmk inverted	£180	
		e. Perf 13½ (line)	10·00	22·00
		ea. Pair, with and without wmk	£250	
		eb. Imperf between (vert pair)	£2500	
		ec. Extra chimney	£130	£200
		f. Perf 13 (comb)	7·00	10·00
		fc. Extra chimney	£120	
		fw. Wmk inverted	£275	
265	152	24c. light blue	2·75	3·00
		a. Pair, with and without wmk	£275	
		c. Perf 13½ (line)	2·75	3·00
		ca. Pair, with and without wmk	£275	
		cb. Imperf between (vert pair)	£4000	
		d. Perf 13 (comb)	50·00	70·00
266	153	25c. slate	5·00	4·50
		a. Pair, with and without wmk	£225	
		b. Perf 13½ (line)	8·00	6·00
		ba. Pair, with and without wmk	£250	
		c. Perf 13 (comb)	50·00	£120
267	154	48c. slate-purple	11·00	6·50
		a. Pair, with and without wmk	£350	
		b. Imperf between (vert pair)	£3750	
		c. Perf 13½ (line)	16·00	13·00
		ca. Pair, with and without wmk	£400	
		cb. Imperf between (vert pair)	£3750	
		cw. Wmk inverted	£350	
		d. Perf 13 (comb)	65·00	£150
257/67 *Set of 11*			60·00	50·00

The line perforations measure 14.1 (14) or 13.7 (13½). The comb perforation measures 13.3×13.2. The 1c., 7c. and 14c. values are known with compound perforations of 13½ and 14.

The paper used had the watermarks spaced for smaller format stamps. In consequence, the individual watermarks are out of alignment so that for instance stamps from the second vertical column or the bottom horizontal row were sometimes without watermark.

155 King George VI

156 Queen Mother

157 Queen Elizabeth II as princess

158 Queen Mary

(Recess P.B.)

1938 (12 May). T **155/8**. W **106** (sideways*). P 13½ (comb).

268	155	2c. green	5·00	1·75
		a. Pair, with and without wmk	£250	
		b. Imperf (pair)	£130	
		w. Wmk top of shield to right	£100	

269	156	3c. carmine	1·00	1·00
		a. Perf 14 (line)	£1000	£650
		b. Pair, with and without wmk	£375	
		c. Imperf (pair)	£130	
270	157	4c. light blue	4·00	1·00
		a. Pair, with and without wmk	£150	
		b. Imperf (pair)	£120	
		w. Wmk top of shield to right	£100	
271	158	7c. deep ultramarine	1·00	12·00
		a. Pair, with and without wmk	£225	
		b. Imperf (pair)	£190	
268/71 *Set of 4*.			10·00	14·00

* The normal sideways watermark shows the top of the shield to left, *as seen from the back of the stamp*.
For similar designs, perf 12½, see Nos. 277/81.

159 King George VI and Queen Elizabeth

(Recess B.W.)

1939 (17 June). Royal Visit. No wmk. P 13½.

272	159	5c. deep ultramarine	3·75	1·00

2
▲ CENTS ▲
(160)

"CENTL" (R. 5/3)

1939 (20 Nov). No. 272 surch as T **160**, at St. John's.

273	159	2c. on 5c. deep ultramarine (Br.)	2·50	50
274		4c. on 5c. deep ultramarine (C.)	2·00	2·00
		a. "CENTL"	50·00	50·00

161 Grenfell on the *Strathcona* (after painting by Gribble)

162 Memorial University College

(Recess C.B.N.)

1941 (1 Dec). 50th Anniv of Sir Wilfred Grenfell's Labrador Mission. P 12.

275	161	5c. blue	30	1·00

Damaged "A" (R. 5/9)

(Recess Waterlow)

1941 (Oct)–44. W **106** (sideways* on vert designs). P 12½ (line).

276	107	1c. grey (14.8.42)	20	2·75
		w. Wmk top of shield to right	75·00	
277	155	2c. green (11.41)	40	75
		w. Wmk top of shield to right	55·00	
278	156	3c. carmine (10.41)	40	30
		a. Pair, with and without wmk	£140	
		b. Damaged "A"	90·00	50·00
		w. Wmk top of shield to right	55·00	
279	157	4c. blue (As No. 270) (10.41)	4·50	40
		a. Pair, with and without wmk	£250	
		w. Wmk top of shield to right	70·00	
280	111	5c. violet (Die I) (P 13½ comb) (11.41)	£180	
		a. Perf 12½ (line) (6.42)	2·75	1·00
		ab. Pair, with and without wmk	£225	
		ac. Printed double	£750	
		ad. Imperf vert (horiz pair)	£650	
		b. Imperf (pair)	£225	
281	158	7c. deep ultramarine (As No. 271) (3.43)	14·00	29·00
		a. Pair, with and without wmk	£350	

282	121	8c. rose-red (9.42)	2·25	4·50
		a. Pair, with and without wmk	£225	
283	113	10c. black-brown (4.43)	1·75	2·25
284	114	14c. black (1.44)	9·00	14·00
285	115	15c. claret (7.43)	6·00	8·50
286	116	20c. green (1.44)	6·00	8·50
287	122	24c. blue (4.43)	3·25	25·00
		w. Wmk inverted	90·00	
288	117	25c. slate (4.43)	11·00	20·00
289	118	48c. red-brown (1.43)	5·00	9·50
276/89 *Set of 14*			55·00	£110

*The normal sideways watermark shows the top of the shield to left, *as seen from the back of the stamp*.
Nos. 276/89 are redrawn versions of previous designs with slightly larger dimensions; the 5c. for example, measures 21 mm in width as opposed to the 20.4 mm of the Perkins Bacon printings.
No. 280. For Die I see note relating to No. 225.

(Recess C.B.N.)

1943 (1 Jan). P 12.

290	162	30c. carmine	2·50	5·50

163 St. John's

TWO CENTS
(164)

(Recess C.B.N.)

1943 (1 June). Air. P 12.

291	163	7c. ultramarine	50	1·25

1946 (21 Mar). No. 290 surch locally with T **164**.

292	162	2c. on 30c. carmine	30	2·50

165 Queen Elizabeth II when Princess

166 Cabot off Cape Bonavista

(Recess Waterlow)

1947 (21 Apr). Princess Elizabeth's 21st Birthday. W **106** (sideways). P 12½.

293	165	4c. light blue	40	1·00
		a. Imperf vert (horiz pair)	£475	

(Recess Waterlow)

1947 (24 June). 450th Anniv of Cabot's Discovery of Newfoundland. W **106** (sideways). P 12½.

294	166	5c. mauve	50	1·00
		w. Wmk top of shield to right	50·00	

STAMP BOOKLETS

1926. Black on pink cover with Ayre and Sons advertisement on front. Stapled.

SB1	40c. booklet containing 8× 1c. and 16× 2c. (Nos. 149/50) in blocks of 8		£1900

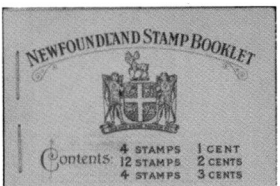

B **1**

1932 (2 Jan). Black on buff cover as Type B **1**. Stapled.

SB2	40c. booklet containing 4× 1c., 12× 2c. and 4× 3c. (Nos. 209b, 210c, 211c) in blocks of 4		£500
	a. Contents as No. SB2, but containing Nos. 209b, 210 and 211c		£550
	b. Contents as No. SB2, but containing Nos. 222d, 223d and 211d		£500

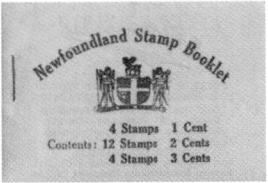

B **2**

1932. Black on cream cover as Type B **2**. Stapled.

SB3	40c. booklet containing 4× 1c., 12× 2c. and 4× 3c. (Nos. 222, 223, 211) in blocks of 4		£500

POSTAGE DUE STAMPS

D **1**

"POSTAGE LUE" (R. 3/3 and 3/8)

Stop after "E" (R. 10/1 and 10/6)

(Litho John Dickinson & Co, Ltd)

1939 (1 May)–**49**. No Wmk. P 10.

D1	D **1**	1c. green	2·25	22·00
		a. Perf 11 (1949)	3·25	27·00
D2		2c. vermilion	19·00	8·50
		a. Perf 11×9 (1946)	14·00	28·00
D3		3c. ultramarine	5·00	40·00
		a. Perf 11×9 (1949)	13·00	65·00
		b. Perf 9	£4750	
D4		4c. orange	9·00	30·00
		a. Perf 11×9 (5.48)	15·00	70·00
D5		5c. brown	12·00	42·00
D6		10c. violet	13·00	30·00
		a. Perf 11 (W **106**) (1949)	18·00	£100
		ab. Ditto. Imperf between (vert pair)	£1400	
		ac. "POSTAGE LUE"	£150	£475
		ad. Stop after "E"	£150	£475
D1/6 *Set of 6*			48·00	£150

Newfoundland joined the Dominion of Canada on 31 March 1949.

NOVA SCOTIA

Organised postal services in Nova Scotia date from April 1754 when the first of a series of Deputy Postmasters was appointed, under the authority of the British GPO. This arrangement continued until 6 July 1851 when the colony assumed responsibility for its postal affairs.

For illustrations of the handstamp types see BRITISH POST OFFICES ABROAD notes, following GREAT BRITAIN.

AMHERST
CROWNED-CIRCLE HANDSTAMPS

CC1 CC **1** AMHERST. N.S.(R) (25.2.1845)...*Price on cover* £1000

ST. MARGARETS BAY
CROWNED-CIRCLE HANDSTAMPS

CC2 CC **1** ST. MARGARETS BAY. N.S.(R)
(30.6.1845) .... *Price on cover* £10000
Nos. CC1/2 were later used during temporary shortages of stamps, struck in red or black.

PRICES FOR STAMPS ON COVER	
No. 1	*from* × 5
Nos. 2/4	*from* × 2
Nos. 5/8	*from* × 4
Nos. 9/10	*from* × 10
Nos. 11/13	*from* × 2
Nos. 14/15	—
No. 16	*from* × 4
Nos. 17/19	*from* × 10
Nos. 20/5	*from* × 2
No. 26	*from* × 50
Nos. 27/8	*from* × 4
No. 29	*from* × 10

Crown and Heraldic Flowers of United Kingdom and Mayflower of Nova Scotia.

(Recess P.B.)

1851 (1 Sept)–**60**. Bluish paper. Imperf.

1	**1**	1d. red-brown (12.5.53)	£3000	£475
		a. Bisected (½d.) (on cover) (1857)	†	£50000
2	**2**	3d. deep blue	£1300	£170
		a. Bisected (1½d.) (on cover)	†	£2500
3		3d. bright blue	£1100	£150
		a. Bisected (1½d.) (on cover)	†	£2500
4		3d. pale blue (1857)	£1000	£150
		a. Bisected (1½d.) (on cover)	†	£2500
5		6d. yellow-green	£4750	£550
		a. Bisected (3d.) (on cover)	†	£3250
		b. Quartered (1½d.) (on cover) (1860)	†	£60000
6		6d. deep green (1857)	£10000	£1000
		a. Bisected (3d.) (on cover)	†	£5000
7		1s. cold violet	£25000	£5500
7c		1s. deep purple (1851)	£18000	£4000
		d. Watermarked	£25000	£6000

8		1s. purple (1857)	£18000	£3500
		a. Bisected (6d.) (on cover) (1860)	†	£38000
		b. Quartered (3d.) (on cover) (1858)	†	£90000

The watermark on No. 7d consists of the whole or part of a letter from the name "T. H. SAUNDERS" (the papermakers).

The stamps formerly catalogued on almost white paper are probably some from which the bluish paper has been discharged.

Reprints of all four values were made in 1890 on thin, hard, white paper. The 1d. is brown, the 3d. blue, the 6d. deep green, and the 1s. violet-black.

The 3d. bisects, which were authorised on 19 October 1854, are usually found used to make up the 7½d. rate.

(New Currency. 100 cents = 1 dollar)

3 **4** **5**

(Recess American Bank Note Co, New York)

1860–63. P 12.

		(a) Yellowish paper		
9	**3**	1c. jet black	4·25	18·00
		a. Bisected (½c.) (on cover)	†	£8000
10		1c. grey-black	4·25	18·00
11		2c. grey-purple	11·00	16·00
11a		2c. purple	17·00	15·00
12		5c. blue	£475	25·00
13		5c. deep blue	£475	25·00
14	**4**	8½c. deep green	5·00	65·00
15		8½c. yellow-green	4·00	65·00
16		10c. scarlet	25·00	42·00
17	**5**	12½c. black	38·00	30·00
17a		12½c. greyish black	—	30·00
		(b) White paper		
18	**3**	1c. black	4·25	21·00
		a. Imperf vert (horiz pair)	£170	
19		1c. grey	4·25	21·00
20		2c. dull purple	4·75	14·00
21		2c. purple	4·75	14·00
22		2c. grey-purple	4·75	14·00
		a. Bisected (1c.) (on cover)	†	£3500
23		2c. slate-purple	4·75	13·00
24		5c. blue	£550	29·00
25		5c. deep blue	£550	29·00
26	**4**	8½c. deep green	23·00	65·00
27		10c. scarlet	8·50	42·00
28		10c. vermilion	5·50	42·00
		a. Bisected (5c.) (on cover)	†	£750
29	**5**	12½c. black	60·00	32·00

Nova Scotia joined the Dominion of Canada on 1 July 1867.

PRINCE EDWARD ISLAND

Prince Edward Island, previously administered as part of Nova Scotia, became a separate colony in 1769.

PRICES FOR STAMPS ON COVER	
Nos. 1/4	*from* × 4
No. 5	—
No. 6	*from* × 5
Nos. 7/8	*from* × 10
Nos. 9/11	*from* × 8
Nos. 12/18	*from* × 6
Nos. 19/20	*from* × 10
Nos. 21/6	*from* × 4
Nos. 27/31	*from* × 8
Nos. 32/3	*from* × 40
Nos. 34/7	*from* × 8
No. 38	*from* × 30
Nos. 39/41	*from* × 20
No. 42	*from* × 50
Nos. 43/7	*from* × 8

1 **2** **3**

4 **5** **6**

Two Dies of 2d.:
Die I. Left-hand frame and circle merge at centre left (all stamps in the sheet of 60 (10×6) except R. 2/5)
Die II. Left-hand frame and circle separate at centre left (R. 2/5). There is also a break in the top frame line.

(Typo Charles Whiting, London)

1861 (1 Jan). Yellowish toned paper.

		(a) P 9		
1	**1**	2d. rose (I)	£500	£190
		a. Imperf between (horiz pair)	£11000	
		b. Imperf horiz (vert pair)		
		c. Bisected (1d.) (on cover)	†	£8000
		d. Die II		

2		2d. rose-carmine (I)	£550	£200
		a. Die II	—	£1000
3	**2**	3d. blue	£1100	£450
		a. Bisected (1½d.) (on cover)	†	£8000
		b. Double print	£4000	
4	**3**	6d. yellow-green	£1700	£750
		(b) Rouletted		
5	**1**	2d. rose (I)	†	£22000

The 2d. and 3d., perf 9, were authorised to be bisected and used for half their normal value.

1862–69. Yellowish toned paper.

		(a) P 11 (1862) or 11¼ (1869)		
6	**4**	1d. brown-orange	£120	90·00
6a		2d. rose (I) (1869)	†	£550
7	**6**	9d. bluish lilac (29.3.62)	£170	£100
8		9d. dull mauve	£170	£100
		(b) P 11½–12 (1863-69)		
9	**4**	1d. yellow-orange (1863)	55·00	70·00
		a. Bisected (½d.) (on cover)	†	£5500
		b. Imperf between (horiz pair)	£550	
10		1d. orange-buff	60·00	70·00
11		1d. yellow	70·00	70·00
12	**1**	2d. rose (I) (1863)	26·00	19·00
		a. Imperf between (horiz pair)		
		b. Bisected (1d.) (on cover)	†	£3750
		c. Die II	£110	£100
13		2d. deep rose (I)	28·00	23·00
		a. Die II	£120	£110
14	**2**	3d. blue (1863)	48·00	32·00
		a. Imperf horiz (vert pair)	†	
		b. Bisected (1½d.) (on cover)	†	—
15		3d. deep blue	48·00	32·00
16	**5**	4d. black (1869)	32·00	65·00
		a. Imperf vert (horiz pair)	£350	
		b. Bisected (2d.) (on cover)	†	£2000
		c. Imperf between (horiz strip of 3)	£550	
17	**3**	6d. yellow-green (15.12.66)	£170	£120
		a. Bisected (3d.) (on cover)	†	£6500
18		6d. blue-green (1868)	£170	£120
19	**6**	9d. lilac (1863)	£120	£100
20		9d. reddish mauve (1863)	£120	£100
		a. Imperf vert (horiz pair)	£950	
		b. Bisected (4½d.) (on cover)	†	£6000

A new perforator, gauging exactly 11¼, was introduced in 1869. Apart from No. 6a, it was used in compound with the perf 11½–12 machine.

		(c) Perf compound of 11 or 11¼ (1869) and 11½–12		
21	**4**	1d. yellow-orange	£250	90·00
22	**1**	2d. rose (I)	£225	70·00
		a. Die II		
23	**2**	3d. blue	£275	70·00
24	**5**	4d. black	£325	£250
25	**3**	6d. yellow-green	£375	£300
26	**6**	9d. reddish mauve	£475	£325

1870. Coarse, wove bluish white paper. P 11½–12.

27	**1**	2d. rose (I)	17·00	21·00
		a. Die II	95·00	£110
28		2d. rose-pink (I)	9·50	19·00
		a. Die II	70·00	85·00
		b. "TWC" (R. 6/4)	90·00	£130
		c. Imperf between (horiz pair)	£275	
		d. Imperf horiz (vert pair)	£275	
29	**2**	3d. pale blue	16·00	23·00
30		3d. blue	11·00	23·00
		a. Imperf between (horiz pair)	£375	
31	**5**	4d. black	7·00	45·00
		a. Imperf between (horiz pair)	£225	
		b. Bisected (2d.) (on cover)	†	£2000

(New Currency. 100 cents = 1 dollar)

7

(Recess British-American Bank Note Co., Montreal and Ottawa)

1870 (1 June).

32	**7**	4½d. (3d. stg), yellow-brown	75·00	85·00
33		4½d. (3d. stg), deep brown	75·00	95·00

8 **9** **10**

11 **12** **13**

(Typo Charles Whiting, London)

1872 (1 Jan).

		(a) P 11½–12		
34	**8**	1c. orange	10·00	35·00
35		1c. yellow-orange	13·00	30·00
36		1c. brown-orange	9·00	35·00
37	**10**	3c. rose	42·00	48·00
		a. Stop between "PRINCE. EDWARD"	85·00	£110
		b. Bisected (1½c.) (on cover)		
		c. Imperf horiz (vert pair)	£550	

(b) Perf 12 to 12¼ large holes

38	9	2c. blue	27·00	65·00
		a. Bisected (1c.) (*on cover*)	†	£4000
39	11	4c. yellow-green	12·00	38·00
40		4c. deep green	14·00	38·00
		a. Bisected (2c.) (*on cover*)	†	£4750
41	12	6c. black	8·50	38·00
		a. Bisected (3c.) (*on cover*)	†	£2000
		b. Imperf between (horiz pair)	£300	
		c. Imperf vert (horiz pair)		
42	13	12c. reddish mauve	10·00	85·00

(c) P 12½–13, smaller holes

43	8	1c. orange	24·00	
44		1c. brown-orange	9·50	40·00
45	10	3c. rose	40·00	50·00
		a. Stop between "PRINCE. EDWARD"	85·00	£130
45*b*	12	6c. black		£250

(d) Perf compound of (a) and (c) 11½–12×12½–13

46	8	1c. orange	90·00	65·00
47	10	3c. rose	£120	70·00
		a. Stop between "PRINCE. EDWARD"	£300	£275

The Stop between "PRINCE. EDWARD" variety listed as Nos. 37a, 45a, 47a occurred at R. 1/2 in the master block of ten clichés (5×2), which was repeated ten times to construct the plate of 100 (10×10). It therefore appears ten times in each sheet at R. 1/2, 1/7, 3/2, 3/7, 5/2, 5/7, 7/2, 7/7, 9/2 and 9/7.

Prince Edward Island joined the Dominion of Canada on 1 July 1873.

DOMINION OF CANADA

On 1 July 1867, Canada, Nova Scotia and New Brunswick were united to form the Dominion of Canada.

The provinces of Manitoba (1870), British Columbia (1871), Prince Edward Island (1873), Alberta (1905), Saskatchewan (1905), and Newfoundland (1949) were subsequently added, as were the Northwest Territories (1870) and Yukon Territory (1898).

PRICES FOR STAMPS ON COVER TO 1945	
Nos. 46/67	*from* × 2
Nos. 68/71	*from* × 10
Nos. 72/89	*from* × 3
Nos. 90/100	*from* × 2
Nos. 101/2	*from* × 5
Nos. 103/11	*from* × 3
Nos. 115/20	*from* × 6
Nos. 121/49	*from* × 3
Nos. 150/65	*from* × 2
Nos. 166/72	*from* × 3
Nos. 173/87	*from* × 5
Nos. 188/95	*from* × 2
Nos. 196/215	*from* × 3
Nos. 219/224*b*	*from* × 4
Nos. 225/45	*from* × 2
Nos. 246/55	*from* × 8
Nos. 256/310	*from* × 2
No. 312	*from* × 20
No. 313	*from* × 10
Nos. 315/18	*from* × 2
Nos. 319/28	*from* × 3
Nos. 329/40	*from* × 2
Nos. 341/400	*from* × 1
Nos. R1/7a	*from* × 5
Nos. R8/9	*from* × 50
Nos. R10/11	*from* × 20
Nos. S1/3	*from* × 8
No. S4	*from* × 6
No. S5	*from* × 5
Nos. S6/11	*from* × 3
Nos. S12/14	*from* × 5
Nos. D1/8	*from* × 4
Nos. D9/13	*from* × 5
Nos. D14/24	*from* × 4

13   **14**   **15**

Large types

PRINTERS. Nos. 46/120 were recess-printed by the British American Bank Note Co at Ottawa or Montreal.

1868 (1 Apr)**–90**. As T **13/15** (various frames).
I. Ottawa printings. P 12
(a) Thin rather transparent crisp paper

46	13	½c. black (1.4.68)	£120	85·00
47	14	1c. red-brown (1.4.68)	£750	85·00
48		2c. grass-green (1.4.68)	£850	65·00
49		3c. red-brown (1.4.68)	£1600	38·00
50		6c. blackish brown (1.4.68)	£1800	£170
51		12½c. bright blue (1.4.68)	£1200	£130
52		15c. deep reddish purple (1.4.68)	£1300	£180

In these first printings the impression is generally blurred and the lines of the background are less clearly defined than in later printings.

(b) Medium to stout wove paper (1868–71)

53	13	½c. black	80·00	70·00
54		½c. grey-black	80·00	70·00
		a. Imperf between (pair)		
		b. Watermarked	£25000	£9500
55	14	1c. red-brown	£550	65·00
		a. Laid paper	£25000	£4000
		b. Watermarked (1868)	£2750	£325
56		1c. deep orange (1.1869)	£1600	£130
56*a*		1c. orange-yellow (5(?).1869)	£1100	£100
56*b*		1c. pale orange-yellow	£1200	£110
		ba. Imperf		

57		2c. deep green	£750	55·00
57*a*		2c. pale emerald-green (1871)	£950	85·00
		ab. Bisected (1c. with 2c. to make 3c. rate) *on cover*	†	£5500
		ac. Laid paper	†	£150000
57*d*		2c. bluish green	£800	55·00
		da. Watermarked (1868)	£2750	£300
58		3c. brown-red	£1300	25·00
		a. Laid paper	£16000	£600
		b. Watermarked (1868)	£3750	£250
59		6c. blackish brown (to chocolate)	£1400	75·00
		a. Watermarked (1868)	£9500	£1300
59*b*		6c. yellow-brown (1870)	£1300	65·00
		ba. Bisected (3c.), *on cover*	†	£3250
60		12½c. bright blue	£950	60·00
		a. Imperf horiz (vert pair)	†	£25000
		b. Watermarked (1868)	£5000	£300
60*c*		12½c. pale dull blue (milky)	£1000	75·00
61		15c. deep reddish purple	£850	70·00
61*a*		15c. pale reddish purple	£650	65·00
		ab. Watermarked (1868)	—	£1400
61*b*		15c. dull violet-grey	£250	35·00
		ba. Watermarked (1868)	£5500	£800
61*c*		15c. dull grey-purple	£325	35·00

The official date of issue was 1 April 1868. Scattered examples of most values can be found used in the second half of March.

The watermark on the stout paper stamps consists of the words "E & G BOTHWELL CLUTHA MILLS," in large double-lined capitals which can be found upright, inverted or reversed. Portions of one or two letters only may be found on these stamps, which occur in the early printings of 1868.

The paper may, in most cases, be easily divided if the stamps are laid face downwards and carefully compared. The thin hard paper is more or less transparent and shows the design through the stamp; the thicker paper is softer to the feel and more opaque.

Of the 2c. laid paper No. 57ac three examples only are known. No. 60a is only known as a vertical strip of five.

II. Montreal printings. Medium to stout wove paper
(a) P 11½×12 or 11¾×12

62	13	½c. black (1873)	£110	85·00
63	15	5c. olive-green (28.9.75)	£850	85·00
		a. Perf 12	£6000	£800
64	14	15c. dull grey-purple (1874)	£1200	£225
65		15c. lilac-grey (3.77)	£1300	£225
		a. Script watermark	£24000	£3750
		b. "BOTHWELL" watermark	†	£850
66		15c. slate	£1300	£300

(b) P 12

67	14	15c. clear deep violet (*thick paper*) (1879)	£4000	£700
68		15c. deep slate (1881)	£160	35·00
69		15c. slaty blue (1887)	£180	35·00
70		15c. slate-purple (*shades*) (7.88–92)	75·00	20·00

No. 63a gauges 12 or above on all four sides.

The watermark on No. 65a is part of "Alexr Pirie & Sons" which appeared diagonally as script letters once per sheet in a small batch of the paper used for the 1877 printing. For a description of the sheet watermark on No. 65b, see note after No. 61c.

Several used examples of the 12½c. have been reported perforated 11½×12 or 11¾×12.

The last printing of the 15c. slate-purple, No. 70, took place at Ottawa.

III. Ottawa printings. Thinnish paper of poor quality, often toned grey or yellowish. P 12

71	14	15c. slate-violet (*shades*) (5.90)	75·00	22·00
		a. Imperf (pair). *Brown-purple*	£1400	

Examples of No. 71 are generally found with yellowish streaky gum.

21 *Small type*

1c. Strand of hair

5c. Straw in hair

6c. Major re-entry (Pl. A, R. 7/7)

1870–90. As T **21** (various frames). Ottawa (1870–73) and Montreal printings. P 12 (or slightly under).

Papers	(a)	1870–80. Medium to stout wove.
	(b)	1870–72. Thin, soft, very white.
	(c)	1878–97. Thinner and poorer quality.

72	21	1c. bright orange (*a, b*) (2.1870–73)	£225	45·00
		a. Thick soft paper (1871)	£800	£160
73		1c. orange-yellow (*a*) (1876–79)	90·00	7·00
74		1c. pale dull yellow (*a*) (1877–79)	65·00	4·75
75		1c. bright yellow (*a, c*) (1878–97)	48·00	2·25
		a. Imperf (pair) (*c*)	£600	
		b. Bisected (½c.) (on *Railway News*)	†	£4500
		c. Printed both sides	£2000	
		d. Strand of hair	£1000	£325
76		1c. lemon-yellow (*c*) (1880)	£110	20·00
77		2c. deep green (*a, b*) (2.72–73 and 1876–78)	90·00	6·00
78		2c. grass-green (*c*) (1878–88)	60·00	2·50
		a. Imperf (pair)	£700	
		b. Bisected (1c.) *on cover*	†	£2500
		c. Stamp doubly printed	†	£5000
79		3c. Indian red (*a*) (1.70)	£1100	50·00
		a. Perf 12½ (2.70)	£8000	£700
80		3c. pale rose-red (*a*) (9.70)	£350	17·00
81		3c. deep rose-red (*a*) (1870–73)	£375	17·00
		a. Thick soft paper (1.71)	£2000	£150
82		3c. dull red (*a, c*) (1876–88)	£100	3·50
83		3c. orange-red (*shades*) (*a, c*) (1876–88)	75·00	3·00
84		3c. rose-carmine (*a, c*) (1876–88)	£375	18·00
85		5c. olive-green (*a, c*) (2.76–88)	£425	17·00
		a. Straw in hair	£2000	£650
86		6c. yellowish brown (*a, b, c*) (1.72–73 and 1876–90)	£350	24·00
		a. Major re-entry	£1300	£300
		b. Bisected (3c.) *on cover*	†	£1400
		c. Perf 12×11½* (1873)	†	—
		d. Perf 12×12½	†	£2500
87		10c. pale lilac-magenta (*a*) (1876–?)	£700	55·00
88		10c. deep lilac-magenta (*a, c*) (3.76–88)	£800	65·00
89		10c. lilac-pink (3.88)	£350	50·00

Nos. 75 and 78 were printed in the same shades during the second Ottawa period. Nos. 75a and 78a date from *circa* 1894–95.

There are four variants of the Strand of Hair, with the strand in the same position but varying in length. R. 2/13 and R. 3/16 have been identified. The illustration shows the "Long Strand".

Examples of paper (*a*) can often be found showing traces of ribbing, especially on the 2c. value.

No. 79a was issued in New Brunswick and Nova Scotia.

*The exact perforation measurement on No. 86c is 11.85×11.6.

6c. Neck flaw ("A" Plate, R. 5/1)   **27**

1873–79. Montreal printings. Medium to stout wove paper. P 11½×12 or 11¾×12.

90	21	1c. bright orange	£300	50·00
91		1c. orange-yellow (1873–79)	£250	17·00
92		1c. pale dull yellow (1877–79)	£250	21·00
93		1c. lemon-yellow (1879)	£300	21·00
94		2c. deep green (1873–78)	£400	24·00
95		3c. dull red (1875–79)	£300	24·00
96		3c. orange-red (1873–79)	£300	24·00
97		5c. olive-green (1.2.76–79)	£650	38·00
98		6c. yellowish brown (1873–79)	£550	55·00
		a. Neck flaw	£1800	£275
99		10c. very pale lilac-magenta (11.74)	£1500	£350
100		10c. deep lilac-magenta (1876–79)	£1100	£200

1882–97. Montreal (to March 1889) and Ottawa printings. Thinnish paper of poor quality. P 12.

101	27	½c. black (7.82–97)	22·00	13·00
102		½c. grey-black	22·00	13·00
		ab. Imperf (pair) (1891–93?)	£700	
		ac. Imperf between (horiz pair)	£950	

2c. Latent entries (R. 9, above, R. 10/8, below)

3c. "Vampire bite"

5c. on **6c.** re-entry (R. 3/5)

6c. Major re-entry (Pane B, R. 9/7)

1889–97. Ottawa printings. Thinnish paper of poor quality, often toned grey or yellowish. P 12.

103	21	2c. dull sea-green	75·00	2·50
104		2c. blue-green (7.89–91)	60·00	3·50
		a. Latent entries	£750	£250
105		3c. bright vermilion (4.89–97)	55·00	1·50
		a. Vampire bite	£550	£180
		b. Imperf (pair) (1891–93?)	£550	
106		5c. brownish grey (5.89)	£110	1·75
		a. Imperf (pair) (1891–93?)	£700	
107		6c. deep chestnut (10.90)	50·00	20·00
		"Sc." re-entry*	£4500	£1800
		b. Major re-entry	£500	£150
		c. Imperf (pair) (1891–93?)	£750	
108		6c. pale chestnut	65·00	20·00
109		10c. salmon-pink	£325	£110
110		10c. carmine-pink (4.90)	£275	45·00
		a. Imperf (pair) (1891–93?)	£850	
111		10c. brownish red (1894?)	£250	42·00
		a. Imperf (pair)	£750	

On No. 107a the top portion of the 5c. design cuts across "CANADA POSTAGE", the white circle surrounding the head, and can be seen on the top of the head itself. Lesser re-entries are visible on R. 2/10 and R. 3/1 from another plate.

There are two latent entries recognised on the 2c. The stamp with the partial image in the upper margin has been identified as being R. 10/8, that with the image in the lower margin is from a position in row 9. The plates are not known.

The 1c. showed no change in the Ottawa printings, so is not included. The 2c. reverted to its previous grass-green shade in 1891.

28   **29**

(Recess B.A.B.N.)

1893 (17 Feb). P 12.

115	28	20c. vermilion	£250	65·00
		a. Imperf (pair)	£1700	
116		50c. blue	£275	45·00
		a. Imperf (*Prussian blue*) (pair)	£1800	

1893 (1 Aug). P 12.

117	29	8c. pale bluish grey	£180	9·50
		a. Imperf (pair)	£950	
118		8c. bluish slate	£150	9·50
119		8c. slate-purple	£130	9·50
120		8c. blackish purple	£110	9·50
		a. Imperf (pair)	£900	

PRINTERS. The following stamps to No. 287 were recess-printed by the American Bank Note Co, Ottawa, which in 1923 became the Canadian Bank Note Co.

30

(Des L. Pereira and F. Brownell)

1897 (19 June). Jubilee issue. P 12.

121	30	½c. black	75·00	75·00
122		1c. orange	13·00	6·50
123		1c. orange-yellow	13·00	6·50
		a. Bisected (½c.) (on *Railway News*)	†	£5500
124		2c. green	26·00	11·00
125		2c. deep green	26·00	11·00
126		3c. carmine	12·00	2·25
127		5c. slate-blue	55·00	20·00
128		5c. deep blue	55·00	20·00
129		6c. brown	£140	£140

130		8c. slate-violet	55·00	40·00
131		10c. purple	90·00	70·00
132		15c. slate	£140	£120
133		20c. vermilion	£140	£100
134		50c. pale ultramarine	£190	£110
135		50c. bright ultramarine	£200	£120
136		$1 lake	£550	£550
137		$2 deep violet	£1000	£425
138		$3 bistre	£1500	£800
139		$4 violet	£1400	£700
140		$5 olive-green	£1400	£700
121/40	*Set of 16*		£6000	£3500
133s/40s	Handstamped "SPECIMEN" *Set of 7*		£2500	

No. 123a was used on issues of the *Railway News* of 5, 6 and 8 November 1897 and must be on a large part of the original newspaper with New Glasgow postmark.

31   **32**

(From photograph by W. & D. Downey, London)

1897–98. P 12.

141	31	½c. grey-black (9.11.97)	18·00	7·50
142		½c. black	15·00	5·00
		a. Imperf (pair)	£475	
143		1c. blue-green (12.97)	30·00	1·00
		a. Imperf (pair)	£450	
144		2c. violet (12.97)	26·00	2·00
		a. Imperf (pair)	£475	
145		3c. carmine (1.98)	55·00	2·25
		a. Imperf (pair)	£800	
146		5c. deep blue/*bluish* (12.97)	70·00	3·00
		a. Imperf (pair)	£475	
147		6c. brown (12.97)	60·00	35·00
		a. Imperf (pair)	£750	
148		8c. orange (12.97)	85·00	11·00
		a. Imperf (pair)	£475	
149		10c. brownish purple (1.98)	£140	55·00
		a. Imperf (pair)	£550	
141/9	*Set of 8*		£425	£100

BOOKLET PANES. Most definitive booklets issued from 1900 onwards had either the two horizontal sides or all three outer edges imperforate. Stamps from the panes show one side or two adjacent sides imperforate.

Two types of the 2c.

Die Ia. Frame consists of four fine lines.

Die Ib. Frame has one thick line between two fine lines.

The die was retouched in 1900 for Plates 11 and 12, producing weak vertical frame lines and then retouched again in 1902 for Plates 15 to 20 resulting in much thicker frame lines. No. 155b covers both states of the retouching.

1898–1902. P 12.

150	32	½c. black (9.98)	8·00	1·10
		a. Imperf (pair)	£475	
151		1c. blue-green (6.98)	35·00	1·00
152		1c. deep green/*toned paper*	45·00	3·25
		a. Imperf (pair)	£1100	
153		2c. dull purple (Die Ia) (9.98)	48·00	65
		a. Thick paper (6.99)	£25	10·00
154		2c. violet (Die Ia)	30·00	30
154a		2c. reddish purple (Die Ia)	70·00	2·25
155		2c. rose-carmine (Die Ia) (20.8.99)	38·00	30
		a. Imperf (pair)	£475	
155b		2c. rose-carmine (Die Ib) (1900)	80·00	2·25
		ba. Booklet pane of 6 (11.6.00)	£750	
156		3c. rose-carmine (6.98)	80·00	1·00
157		5c. slate-blue/*bluish*	£110	4·00
		a. Imperf (pair)	£1000	
158		5c. Prussian blue/*bluish*	£120	4·00
159		6c. brown (9.98)	£100	65·00
		a. Imperf (pair)	£1000	
160		7c. greenish yellow (23.12.02)	70·00	25·00
161		8c. orange-yellow (10.98)	£130	45·00
162		8c. brownish orange	£120	45·00
		a. Imperf (pair)	£1000	
163		10c. pale brownish purple (11.98)	£170	15·00
164		10c. deep brownish purple	£170	15·00
		a. Imperf (pair)	£1000	
165		20c. olive-green (29.12.00)	£325	50·00
150/65	*Set of 11*		£950	£180

The 7c. and 20c. also exist imperforate, but unlike the values listed in this condition, they have no gum. (Price, 7c. £450, 20c. £3500 *pair, un*).

33

(Des R. Weir Crouch, G. Hahn, A. H. Howard and R. Holmes. Eng C. Skinner. Design recess, colours added by typo)

1898 (7 Dec). Imperial Penny Postage. Design in black. British possessions in red. Oceans in colours given. P 12.

166	33	2c. lavender	30·00	7·00
		a. Imperf (pair) (*no gum*)	£400	
167		2c. greenish blue	38·00	7·50
		a. Imperf (pair) (*no gum*)	£450	
168		2c. blue	42·00	7·50
		a. Imperf (pair) (*no gum*)	£475	

Forgeries of Type **33** are without horizontal lines across the continents and have a forged Montreal postmark dated 24.12.98.

1899 (4 Jan). Provisionals used at Port Hood, Nova Scotia. No. 156 divided vertically and handstamped.

169	32	"1" in blue, on ¹⁄₃ of 3c.	—	£3500
170		"2" in violet, on ²⁄₃ of 3c.	—	£3000

Nos. 169/70 were prepared by the local postmaster during a shortage of 2c. stamps caused by a change in postage rates.

2 CENTS
(34)

35 King Edward VII

1899. Surch with T **34**, by Public Printing Office.

171	31	2c. on 3c. carmine (8.8)	22·00	8·00
		a. Surch inverted	£350	
172	32	2c. on 3c. rose-carmine (28.7)	19·00	4·25
		a. Surch inverted	£350	

(Des King George V when Prince of Wales and J. A. Tilleard)

1903 (1 July)–**12**. P 12.

173	35	1c. pale green	42·00	50
174		1c. deep green	35·00	50
175		1c. green	35·00	50
176		2c. rose-carmine	20·00	50
		a. Booklet pane of 6	£800	£950
177		2c. pale rose-carmine	20·00	50
		a. Imperf (pair) (18.7.09)	30·00	45·00
178		5c. blue/*bluish*	90·00	2·75
179		5c. indigo/*bluish*	90·00	2·75
180		7c. yellow-olive	90·00	2·75
181		7c. greenish bistre	£110	2·75
181a		7c. straw (1.12)	£120	65·00
182		10c. brown-lilac	£160	26·00
183		10c. pale dull purple	£160	26·00
184		10c. dull purple	£160	26·00
185		20c. pale olive-green (27.9.04)	£300	38·00
186		20c. deep olive-green	£325	38·00
		s. Handstamped "SPECIMEN"	£110	
187		50c. deep violet (19.11.08)	£500	£130
173/87	*Set of 7*		£1100	£180

The 1c., 5c., 7c. and 10c. exist imperforate but are believed to be proofs. (*Prices per pair,* 1c. £550, 5c. £1000, 7c. £650, 10c. £1000, *without gum*).

IMPERFORATE AND PART-PERFORATED SHEETS. Prior to 1946 many Canadian issues exist imperforate, or with other perforation varieties, in the colours of the issued stamps and, usually, with gum. In the years before 1927 such examples are believed to come from imprimatur sheets, removed from the Canadian Post Office archives. From 1927 until 1946 it is known that the printers involved in the production of the various issues submitted several imperforate plate proof sheets of each stamp to the Post Office authorities for approval. Some of these sheets were retained for record purposes, but the remainder found their way on to the philatelic market.

Part-perforated sheets also occur from 1927–29 issues.

From 1908 until 1946 we now only list and price such varieties of this type which are known to be genuine errors, sold from post offices. Where other imperforate or similar varieties are known they are recorded in footnotes.

It is possible, and in some cases probable, that some imperforate varieties listed before 1908 may also have been removed from the archives as mentioned above, but it is far harder to be explicit over the status of this earlier material.

36 King George V and Queen Mary when Prince and Princess of Wales

37 Jacques Cartier and Samuel Champlain

Re-entry (R. 5/4)

38 King Edward VII and Queen Alexandra

39 Champlain's house in Quebec

40 Generals Montcalm and Wolfe

41 Quebec in 1700

42 Champlain's departure for the West

43 Cartier's arrival before Quebec

(Des Machado)

1908 (16 July). Quebec Tercentenary. T **36/43**. P 12.

188	36	½c. sepia	6·00	3·50
		a. Re-entry	75·00	75·00
189	37	1c. blue-green	38·00	3·00
190	38	2c. carmine	28·00	1·00
191	39	5c. indigo	65·00	40·00
192	40	7c. olive-green	90·00	65·00
193	41	10c. violet	£100	85·00

194	**42**	15c. brown-orange	£120	95·00
195	**43**	20c. dull brown	£160	130
188/95 Set of 8			£550	£375

Some values exist on both toned and white papers.
Nos. 188/95 exist imperforate. (*Price £650, un, for each pair*).

WET AND DRY PRINTINGS. Until the end of December 1922 all Canadian stamps were produced by the "wet" method of recess-printing in which the paper was dampened before printing, dried and then gummed.

In late December 1922 the Canadian Bank Note Co. began to use the "dry" process in which the paper was gummed before printing. Late printings of the 3c. brown were the first stamps to be produced by this method, but the changeover was not completed until January 1926.

"Dry" printings have a sharper appearance and can often be found with a degree of embossing showing on the reverse. Stamps from "wet" printings shrink during drying and are narrower than "dry" examples. In many cases the difference can be as great as 0.5 mm. On some early booklet panes the difference is in the vertical, rather than the horizontal, measurement.

On Nos. 196/215 all values only exist from "wet" printings, except the 3c., 20c. and 50c. which come from both types of printing.

44 King George V

1c. Major re-entry

1911–22. P 12.

196	**44**	1c. yellow-green (22.12.11)	14·00	75
197		1c. bluish green	5·50	50
		a. Major re-entry	£5000	£1500
		b. Booklet pane of 6 (1.5.13)	50·00	
198		1c. deep bluish green	8·00	50
		a. With fine horiz lines across stamp	50·00	10·00
199		1c. deep yellow-green	8·00	1·00
		a. Booklet pane of 6	18·00	
200		2c. rose-red (15.12.11)	11·00	50
201		2c. deep rose-red	6·50	50
		a. Booklet pane of 6 (1.12)	32·00	
202		2c. pale rose-red	8·50	50
		a. With fine horiz lines across stamp	26·00	18·00
203		2c. carmine	10·00	50
204		3c. brown (6.8.18)	7·50	50
205		3c. deep brown	7·50	50
		a. Booklet pane of 4+2 labels (2.22)	55·00	
205b		5c. deep blue (17.1.12)	70·00	75
206		5c. indigo	£120	9·50
206a		5c. grey-blue	£110	5·00
206b		7c. straw (12.1.12)	95·00	20·00
207		7c. pale sage-green (1914)	£275	55·00
208		7c. olive-yellow (1915)	26·00	4·25
209		7c. yellow-ochre (1916)	26·00	4·25
210		10c. brownish purple (12.1.12)	£100	2·75
211		10c. reddish purple	£140	7·00
212		20c. olive-green (23.1.12)	45·00	1·50
213		20c. olive	45·00	1·75
214		50c. grey-black (26.1.12)	£140	12·00
215		50c. sepia	50·00	3·75
196/215 Set of 8			£275	12·00

The 20c. and 50c. values exist imperforate (*Price £3500 un, for each pair*).

The major re-entry on the 1c. (No. 197a) shows as a distinct doubling of the lower right corner of the stamp on Plate 12, lower right pane, R. 4/5.

1912 (Oct)**–21.** For use in coil-machines.

(a) P 12×imperf

216	**44**	1c. yellow-green (1914)	3·50	16·00
217		1c. blue-green (1914)	28·00	28·00
		a. Two large holes at top and bottom (vert pair) (7.18)	80·00	90·00
218		2c. deep rose-red (1914)	45·00	26·00
218a		3c. brown (1921)	5·00	10·00

No. 217a has two large holes about 3½ mm in diameter in the top and bottom margins. They were for experimental use in a vending machine at Toronto in July 1918 and were only in use for two days.

The 1c. and 2c. also exist with two small "V" shaped holes about 9.5 mm apart at top which are gripper marks due to modifications made in vending machines in 1917.

(b) Imperf×perf 8

219	**44**	1c. yellow-green (10.12)	25·00	8·00
220		1c. blue-green (10.12)	32·00	7·50
		a. With fine horiz lines across stamp	75·00	
221		2c. carmine (10.12)	23·00	2·00
222		2c. rose-red	24·00	2·50
223		2c. scarlet	48·00	6·50
224		3c. brown (8.18)	5·00	2·00

(c) P 8×imperf

224a	**44**	1c. blue-green (13.2.13)	65·00	50·00
224b		2c. carmine (15.2.13)	65·00	50·00

The stamps imperf×perf 8 were sold in coils over the counter; those perf 8×imperf were on sale in automatic machines. Varieties showing perf 12 on 2 or 3 adjacent sides and 1 or 2 sides imperf are from booklets, or the margins of sheets.

(45) 46 47

1915 (12 Feb). Optd with T **45**.

225	**44**	5c. blue	£130	£200
226		20c. olive-green	60·00	£100
227		50c. sepia (R.)	£140	£180
225/7 Set of 3			£300	£425

These stamps were intended for tax purposes, but owing to ambiguity in an official circular dated 16 April 1915, it was for a time believed that their use for postal purposes was authorised. The position was clarified by a further circular on 20 May 1916 which made clear that Nos. 225/7 were for fiscal use only.

1915. P 12.

228	**46**	1c. green (15.4.15)	7·00	50
229		2c. carmine (16.4.15)	28·00	3·25
230		2c. rose-carmine	35·00	4·50

Die I   Die II

In Die I there is a long horizontal coloured line under the foot of the "T", and a solid bar of colour runs upwards from the "1" to the "T".

In Die II this solid bar of colour is absent, and there is a short horizontal line under the left side of the "T", with two short vertical dashes and a number of dots under the right-hand side.

1916 (1 Jan). P 12.

231	**47**	2c. +1c. rose-red (Die I)	65·00	1·25
232		2c. +1c. bright carmine (Die I)	50·00	1·25
233		2c. +1c. scarlet (Die I)	60·00	2·25

1916 (Feb). Imperf×perf 8 (coils).

234	**47**	2c. +1c. rose-red (Die I)	70·00	12·00

1916 (July). P 12×8.

235	**47**	2c. +1c. carmine-red (Die I)	38·00	60·00
236		2c. +1c. bright rose-red (Die I)	45·00	60·00

1916 (Aug). P 12.

237	**47**	2c. +1c. carmine-red (Die II)	£170	27·00

1916 (Aug). Colour changed.

(a) P 12

238	**47**	2c. +1c. brown (Die I)	£375	26·00
239		2c. +1c. yellow-brown (Die II)	7·00	50
		a. Imperf (pair)	£1500	
240		2c. +1c. deep brown (Die II)	22·00	50

(b) Coil stamps. Imperf×perf 8

241	**47**	2c. +1c. brown (Die I)	£110	13·00
		a. Pair, 241 and 243	£350	
243		2c. +1c. deep brown (Die II)	60·00	4·75

No. 239a, which is a genuine error, should not be confused with ungummed proofs of the Die I stamp, No. 238 (*Price per pair, £140*).

This value also exists P 12×imperf or imperf×p 12, but was not issued with these perforations (*Price, in either instance, £350, un, per pair*).

48 Quebec Conference, 1864, from painting *The Fathers of Confederation*, by Robert Harris

1917 (15 Sept). 50th Anniv of Confederation. P 12.

244	**48**	3c. bistre-brown	24·00	3·50
245		3c. deep brown	26·00	4·25

No. 244 exists imperforate, without gum (*Price per pair, £500 un*).

Die I (top). Space between top of "N" and oval frame line and space between "CENT" and lower frame line.

Die II (bottom). "ONE CENT" appears larger so that "N" touches oval and "CENT" almost touches frame line. There are other differences but this is the most obvious one.

Die I (top). The lowest of the three horizontal lines of shading below the medals does not touch the three heavy diagonal lines; three complete white spaces over both "E's" of "THREE"; long centre bar to figures "3". Vertical spandrel lines fine.

Die II (bottom). The lowest horizontal line of shading touches the first of the three diagonal lines; two and a half spaces over first "E" and spaces over second "E" partly filled by stem of maple leaf; short centre bar to figures "3". Vertical spandrel lines thick. There are numerous other minor differences.

WET AND DRY PRINTINGS. See notes above No. 196.

On Nos. 246/63 all listed items occur from both "wet" and "dry" printings except Nos. 246aa/ab, 248aa, 256, 259, 260 and 262 which come "wet" only, and Nos. 246a, 248/a, 252/4a, 256b and 263 which are "dry" only.

1922–31. As T **44**.

(a) P 12

246	**44**	1c. chrome-yellow (7.6.22)	3·25	60
		aa. Booklet pane of 4+2 labels (7.22)	60·00	
		ab. Booklet pane of 6 (12.22)	40·00	
		a. Die II (1925)	9·00	30
247		2c. deep green (6.6.22)	2·25	10
		aa. Booklet pane of 4+2 labels (7.22)	55·00	
		ab. Booklet pane of 6 (12.22)	£325	
		b. Thin paper (9.24)	6·00	
248		3c. carmine (Die I) (18.12.23)	3·75	10
		aa. Booklet pane of 4+2 labels (12.23)	50·00	
		a. Die II (11.24)	45·00	80
249		4c. olive-yellow (7.7.22)	8·00	3·50
		a. Olive-ochre	8·00	3·50
250		5c. violet (2.2.22)	5·00	1·75
		a. Thin paper (9.24)	5·00	9·50
		b. Reddish violet (1925)	12·00	2·00
251		7c. red-brown (12.12.24)	12·00	9·00
		a. Thin paper	£170	50·00
252		8c. blue (1.9.25)	23·00	11·00
253		10c. blue (20.2.22)	15·00	3·25
254		10c. bistre-brown (1.8.25)	29·00	4·00
		a. Yellow-brown	18·00	5·00
255		$1 brown-orange (22.7.23)	55·00	9·50
246/55 Set of 10			£130	38·00

The $1 differs from T **44** in that the value tablets only.

Nos. 249/52 and 254/5 exist imperforate (*Prices per un pair* 4c. *to* 10c. £2500 *each*, $1 £3000).

(b) Coil stamps. Imperf×perf 8

256	**44**	1c. chrome-yellow (Die I) (1922)	4·00	11·00
		a. Imperf horiz (vert pair) (1924)	£180	
		b. Die II (1925)	4·50	7·00
		c. Do. Imperf horiz (vert pair) (1927)	8·00	27·00
257		2c. deep green (26.7.22)	7·00	2·25
		b. Imperf horiz (vert pair) (1927)	9·00	27·00
258		3c. carmine (Die I) (9.4.24)	80·00	18·00
		a. Imperf horiz (vert pair) (1924)	£250	
		b. Die II (1925)	£100	38·00
256/8 Set of 3			85·00	25·00

Nos. 256a, 256c, 257b and 258a come from coil printings sold in sheet form. Those issued in 1924 were from "wet" printings and those in 1927 from "dry". A "wet" printing of No. 257b, issued in 1924, also exists (*Price £180 mint*), but cannot be identified from that issued in 1927 except by the differences between "wet" and "dry" stamps.

(c) Imperf (pairs)

259	**44**	1c. chrome-yellow (Die I) (6.10.24)	50·00	70·00
260		2c. deep green (6.10.24)	50·00	70·00
261		3c. carmine (Die I) (31.12.23)†	32·00	55·00

(d) P 12×imperf

262	**44**	2c. deep green (9.24)	65·00	65·00

(e) P 12×8

263	**44**	3c. carmine (Die II) (24.6.31)	5·50	4·00

†Earliest known postmark.

Nos. 259 to 261 were on sale only at the Philatelic Branch, PO Dept, Ottawa.

No. 263 was produced by adding horizontal perforations to unused sheet stock of No. 258b. The stamps were then issued in 1931 pending the delivery of No. 293.

2 CENTS   **2 CENTS**
(49)   (50)

1926. No. 248 surch.

*(a) With T **49**, by the Govt Printing Bureau*

264	**44**	2c. on 3c. carmine (12.10.26)	50·00	65·00
		a. Pair, one without surch	£450	
		b. On Die II	£400	

*(b) With T **50**, by the Canadian Bank Note Co*

265	**44**	2c. on 3c. carmine (4.11.26)	19·00	32·00
		a. Surch double (partly treble)	£200	

51 Sir J. A. Macdonald   **52** *The Fathers of Confederation*

53 Parliament Buildings, Ottawa   **54** Sir W. Laurier

55 Canada, Map 1867–1927

1927 (29 June). 60th Anniv of Confederation. P 12.

I. Commemorative Issue. Inscr "1867–1927 CANADA CONFEDERATION"

266	**51**	1c. orange	2·50	1·50
267	**52**	2c. green	2·25	30
268	**53**	3c. carmine	11·00	5·00
269	**54**	5c. violet	7·00	4·50
270	**55**	12c. blue	35·00	7·50
266/70 *Set of 5*			50·00	17·00

Nos. 266/70 exist imperforate, imperf×perf or perf×imperf (*Prices from £120, un, per pair*).

56 Darcy McGee

57 Sir W. Laurier and Sir J. A. Macdonald

58 R. Baldwin and L. H. Lafontaine

II. Historical Issue

271	**56**	5c. violet	3·00	2·50
272	**57**	12c. green	17·00	17·00
273	**58**	20c. carmine	17·00	14·00
271/3 *Set of 3*			32·00	19·00

Nos. 271/3 exist imperforate, imperf×perf or perf×imperf (*Prices from £120, un, per pair*).

59

(Des H. Schwartz)

1928 (21 Sept). Air. P 12.

274	**59**	5c. olive-brown	8·00	6·50

No. 274 exists imperforate, imperf×perf or perf×imperf (*Price per pair, £275, un*).

60 King George V

61 Mt. Hurd and Indian Totem Poles

62 Quebec Bridge

63 Harvesting with Horses

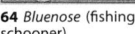

64 *Bluenose* (fishing schooner)

65 Parliament Buildings, Ottawa

1928–29.

		(a) P 12		
275	**60**	1c. orange (25.10.28)	2·75	3·00
		a. Booklet pane of 6	19·00	
276		2c. green (16.10.28)	1·25	20
		a. Booklet pane of 6	19·00	
277		3c. lake (12.12.28)	20·00	23·00
278		4c. olive-bistre (16.8.29)	13·00	13·00
279		5c. violet (12.12.28)	6·50	5·50
		a. Booklet pane of 6 (6.1.29)	£130	
280		8c. blue (21.12.28)	7·50	7·50
281	**61**	10c. green (5.12.28)	8·50	2·25
282	**62**	12c. grey-black (8.1.29)	26·00	20·00
283	**63**	20c. lake (8.1.29)	38·00	20·00
284	**64**	50c. blue (8.1.29)	£150	55·00
285	**65**	$1 olive-green (8.1.29)	£150	85·00
		a. Brown-olive	£225	£100
275/85 *Set of 11*			£375	£200

		(b) Coil stamps. Imperf×perf 8 (5.11.28)		
286	**60**	1c. orange	15·00	27·00
287		2c. green	20·00	9·00

Slight differences in the size of many Canadian stamps, due to paper shrinkage, are to be found.

Nos. 275/85 exist imperforate, imperf×perf or perf×imperf (*Prices per unused pair, 1c. to 8c., from £110, 10c. to 20c., from £200, 50c. and $1, from £650*). *Tête-bêche* horizontal pairs of the 1c., 2c. and 5c. are also known from uncut booklet sheets (*Prices per pair, £325, un*).

PRINTERS. The following stamps to No. 334 were recess-printed by the British American Bank Note Co, Ottawa.

66 King George V

67 Parliamentary Library, Ottawa

68 The Old Citadel, Quebec

69 Harvesting with Tractor

70 Acadian Memorial Church and Statue of *Evangeline*, Grand Pre, Nova Scotia

71 Mt. Edith Cavell, Canadian Rockies

Die I — Die II — Die I — Die II

1c. — **2c.**

1c. Die I. Three thick coloured lines and one thin between "P" and ornament, at right. Curved line in ball-ornament short.

Die II. Four thick lines. Curved line longer.

2c. Die I. Three thick coloured lines between "P" and ornament, at left. Short line in ball.

Die II. Four thick lines. Curved line longer.

2c. "Cockeyed King"

1930–31.

		(a) P 11		
288	**66**	1c. orange (I) (17.7.30)	1·75	1·50
289		1c. green (I) (6.12.30)	3·75	10
		b. Booklet pane of 6 (21.7.31)	35·00	
		d. Die II (8.31)	3·75	10
		da. Imperf (pair)	£2000	
		db. Booklet pane of 4+2 labels (13.11.31)	£100	
290		2c. green (I) (6.6.30)	1·75	10
		a. Booklet pane of 6 (17.6.30)	45·00	
291		2c. scarlet (I) (17.11.30)	3·00	3·50
		a. Booklet pane of 6 (17.11.30)	27·00	
		b. Die II	1·00	10
292		2c. deep brown (I) (4.7.31)	2·75	6·00
		a. Booklet pane of 6 (23.7.31)	55·00	
		b. Die II (4.7.31)	2·00	10
		ba. Booklet pane of 4+2 labels (13.11.31)	£140	
293		3c. scarlet (13.7.31)	2·50	10
		a. Booklet pane of 4+2 labels	55·00	
294		4c. yellow-bistre (5.11.30)	12·00	4·50
295		5c. violet (18.6.30)	2·75	8·00
296		5c. deep slate-blue (13.11.30)	5·50	20
		a. Dull blue	25·00	1·50
297		8c. blue (13.8.30)	11·00	16·00
298		8c. red-orange (5.11.30)	10·00	5·50
299	**67**	10c. olive-green (15.9.30)	23·00	2·00
		a. Imperf (pair)	£1800	
300	**68**	12c. grey-black (4.12.30)	14·00	6·50
301	**69**	20c. red (4.12.30)	22·00	2·25
302	**70**	50c. blue (4.12.30)	90·00	17·00
303	**71**	$1 olive-green (4.12.30)	£130	40·00
288/303 *Set of 16*			£275	90·00

		(b) Coil stamps. Imperf×perf 8½		
304	**66**	1c. orange (I) (14.7.30)	12·00	21·00
305		1c. green (I) (4.2.31)	6·00	7·00
306		2c. green (I) (27.6.30)	4·00	13·00
		a. Cockeyed King	65·00	95·00
307		2c. scarlet (I) (19.11.30)	4·50	11·00
		a. Cockeyed King	70·00	95·00
308		2c. deep brown (I) (4.7.31)	9·00	1·50
		a. Cockeyed King	80·00	65·00
309		3c. scarlet (13.7.31)	14·00	2·00
304/9 *Set of 6*			45·00	50·00

Nos. 300/3 exist imperforate (*Prices per unused pair, 12c. £900, 20c. £900, 50c. £950, $1 £1000*).

Some low values in the above and subsequent issues have been printed by both Rotary and "Flat plate" processes. The former can be distinguished by the gum, which has a striped appearance.

For 13c. bright violet, T **68**, see No. 325.

---

72 Mercury and Western Hemisphere

73 Sir Georges Étienne Cartier

(Des H. Schwartz)

1930 (4 Dec). Air. P 11.

310	**72**	5c. deep brown	26·00	26·00

1931 (30 Sept). P 11.

312	**73**	10c. olive-green	14·00	20

No. 312 exists imperforate (*Price per pair, £500, un*).

(74) — (75)

1932 (22 Feb). Air. No. 274 surch with T **74**.

313	**59**	6c. on 5c. olive-brown	3·00	2·75

Examples of this stamp with surcharge inverted, surcharge double, surcharge triple or surcharge omitted in pair with normal are not now believed to have been regularly issued. Such "errors" have also been forged and collectors are warned against forged examples, some of which bear unauthorized markings which purport to be the guarantee of Stanley Gibbons Ltd.

1932 (21 June). Nos. 291/b surch with T **75**.

314	**66**	3c. on 2c. scarlet (I)	5·50	4·75
		a. Die II	1·00	60

76 King George V

77 Duke of Windsor when Prince of Wales

78 Allegory of British Empire

OTTAWA CONFERENCE 1932

(79)

1932 (12 July). Ottawa Conference. P 11.

		(a) Postage stamps		
315	**76**	3c. scarlet	1·00	80
316	**77**	5c. blue	14·00	5·50
317	**78**	13c. green	13·00	6·00

		(b) Air. No. 310 surch with T 79		
318	**72**	6c. on 5c. deep brown (B.)	16·00	24·00
315/18 *Set of 4*			40·00	32·00

80 King George V

"3" level Die I — "3" raised Die II

1932 (1 Dec)–**33.**

		(a) P 11		
319	**80**	1c. green	60	10
		a. Booklet pane of 6 (28.12.33)	16·00	
		b. Booklet pane of 4+2 labels (19.9.33)	85·00	
320		2c. sepia	70	10
		a. Booklet pane of 6 (7.9.33)	22·00	
		b. Booklet pane of 4+2 labels (19.9.33)	95·00	
321		3c. scarlet (Die I)	2·75	10
		a. Booklet pane of 4+2 labels (22.8.33)	60·00	
		b. Die II (29.11.32)	85	10
		ba. Booklet pane of 4+2 labels (19.9.33)	45·00	
322		4c. yellow-brown	50·00	15·00
323		5c. blue	13·00	10
		a. Imperf vert (horiz pair)	£1800	
324		8c. red-orange	45·00	4·25
325	**68**	13c. bright violet	85·00	6·00
319/25 *Set of 7*			£170	20·00

Nos. 319/25 exist imperforate (*Prices per unused pair, 1c. to 8c., £225, 13c. £800*).

		(b) Coil stamps. Imperf×perf 8½ (1933)		
326	**80**	1c. green (3.11.33)	24·00	6·50
327		2c. sepia (15.8.33)	24·00	5·50
328		3c. scarlet (Die II) (16.8.33)	12·00	3·25
326/8 *Set of 3*			55·00	15·00

81 Parliament Buildings, Ottawa

1933 (18 May). UPU Congress Preliminary Meeting. P 11.
329   **81** 5c. blue............................13·00 4·00
No. 329 exists imperforate (*Price per pair £850, un*).

**WORLD'S
GRAIN EXHIBITION &
CONFERENCE**

REGINA 1933
(82)

1933 (24 July). World's Grain Exhibition and Conference, Regina. No. 301 optd with T **82** in blue.
330   **69** 20c. red...........................22·00 14·00
No. 330 exists imperforate (*Price per pair £850, un*).

83 SS *Royal William* (after S. Skillett)
84 Jacques Cartier approaching Land

1933 (17 Aug). Centenary of First Trans-Atlantic Steamboat Crossing. P 11.
331   **83** 5c. blue............................20·00 5·00
No. 331 exists imperforate (*Price per pair £850, un*).

1934 (1 July). 400th Anniversary of Discovery of Canada. P 11.
332   **84** 3c. blue............................7·50 1·50
No. 332 exists imperforate (*Price per pair £800, un*).

85 UEL Statue, Hamilton
86 Seal of New Brunswick

1934 (1 July). 150th Anniv of Arrival of United Empire Loyalists. P 11.
333   **85** 10c. olive-green.................16·00 11·00
No. 333 exists imperforate (*Price per pair £1600, un*).

1934 (16 Aug). 150th Anniv of Province of New Brunswick. P 11.
334   **86** 2c. red-brown.....................1·50 3·50
No. 334 exists imperforate (*Price per pair £850, un*).

PRINTERS. The following stamps were recess-printed (except where otherwise stated) by the Canadian Bank Note Co, Ottawa, until No. 616.

87 Queen Elizabeth II when Princess
88 King George VI when Duke of York

89 King George V and Queen Mary
90 King Edward VIII when Prince of Wales

91 Windsor Castle
92 Royal Yacht *Britannia*

"Weeping Princess" (Pl 1 upper right pane R. 3/1)
"Shilling mark" (Pl 1 upper right pane R. 8/8)

1935 (4 May). Silver Jubilee. T **87/92**. P 12.
335 **87** 1c. green............................1·50 80
      a. Weeping Princess............£160 £100
336 **88** 2c. brown..........................1·00 80
337 **89** 3c. carmine-red..................4·25 2·00
338 **90** 5c. blue............................8·00 9·00
339 **91** 10c. green.........................13·00 10·00
340 **92** 13c. blue..........................15·00 10·00
      a. Shilling mark.................£500 £500
335/40 *Set of 6*............................38·00 29·00
Nos. 335/40 exist imperforate (*Prices per unused pair*, 1c to 5c. *each* £300, 10c. and 13c. *each* £350).

93 King George V
94 Royal Canadian Mounted Policeman

95 Confederation Conference, Charlottetown, 1864
96 Niagara Falls

97 Parliament Buildings, Victoria, British Columbia
98 Champlain Monument, Quebec

99 Daedalus

10c. Broken leg (Pl. 1, R. 5/8)

50c. Major re-entry (Pl. 1 upper right pane, R. 5/5)

1c. Normal
1c. Narrow "1"

6c. Moulting wing (Pl. 1, lower right pane, R. 3/4)

1935 (1 June–16 Nov). T **93/99**.

(*a*) *Postage*
(*i*) *P 12*
341 **93** 1c. green.......................1·75 10
    a. Booklet pane of 6 (19.8.35)........28·00
    b. Booklet pane of 4+2 labels (22.7.35)..........70·00
342   2c. brown....................1·75 10
    a. Booklet pane of 6 (16.11.35).....29·00
    b. Booklet pane of 4+2 labels (22.7.35)..........70·00
343   3c. scarlet...................1·75 10
    a. Booklet pane of 4+2 labels........42·00
    b. Printed on the gummed side....£325
344   4c. yellow....................3·50 2·75
345   5c. blue......................3·50 10
    a. Imperf vert (horiz pair)........£225
346   8c. orange...................4·25 5·00
347 **94** 10c. carmine................6·50 50
    a. Broken leg..............£1900 £1400
348 **95** 13c. purple.................7·50 65
349 **96** 20c. olive-green...........25·00 1·75
350 **97** 50c. deep violet...........26·00 8·00
    a. Major re-entry...........£140 £85·00
351 **98** $1 bright blue............42·00 11·00
341/51 *Set of 11*.......................£110 26·00

(*ii*) *Coil stamps. Imperf×perf 8*
352 **93** 1c. green (5.11.35)........21·00 15·00
    a. Narrow "1".................80·00 65·00
353   2c. brown (14.10.35)........14·00 6·50
354   3c. scarlet (20.7.35)........9·00 1·75
352/4 *Set of 3*..........................40·00 21·00

(*b*) *Air. P 12*
355 **99** 6c. red-brown..............4·25 1·00
    a. Imperf vert (horiz pair)......£8500
    b. Moulting wing.............£110 70·00
Nos. 341/51 (*Prices per pair*, 1c. to 8c. *each* £170, 10c. to 50c. *each* £300, $1 £350, *un*) and 355 (*Price per pair* £750, *un*) exist imperforate.

100 King George VI and Queen Elizabeth

1937 (10 May). Coronation. P 12.
356 **100** 3c. carmine................1·75 1·50
No. 356 exists imperforate (*Price per pair £900, un*).

101 King George VI
102 Memorial Chamber, Parliament Buildings, Ottawa

103 Entrance to Halifax Harbour
104 Fort Garry Gate, Winnipeg

105 Entrance, Vancouver Harbour
106 Château de Ramezay, Montréal

107 Fairchild 45-80 Sekani Seaplane over *Distributor* on River Mackenzie
Crease on collar (Pl 2 upper right pane R. 9/5)

(T **101**. Photograph by Bertram Park)

1937–38. T **101/107**.

(*a*) *Postage*
(*i*) *P 12*
357 **101** 1c. green (1.4.37)........2·50 10
    a. Booklet pane of 4+2 labels (14.4.37)..........30·00
    b. Booklet pane of 6 (18.5.37)........8·50
358   2c. brown (1.4.37)........3·25 10
    a. Booklet pane of 4+2 labels (14.4.37)..........60·00
    b. Booklet pane of 6 (3.5.38)........11·00

359		3c. scarlet (1.4.37)	1·75	10
		a. Booklet pane of 4+2 labels (14.4.37)	4·25	
		b. Crease on collar	£100	40·00
360		4c. yellow (10.5.37)	5·50	1·75
361		5c. blue (10.5.37)	7·50	10
362		8c. orange (10.5.37)	6·50	3·75
363	102	10c. rose-carmine (15.6.38)	6·00	60
		a. Red	5·00	10
364	103	13c. blue (15.11.38)	35·00	3·00
365	104	20c. red-brown (15.6.38)	25·00	2·75
366	105	50c. green (15.6.38)	50·00	16·00
367	106	$1 violet (15.6.38)	65·00	16·00
		a. Imperf horiz (vert pair)	£7500	
357/67		*Set of 11*	£180	40·00

Nos. 357/67 exist imperforate (*Prices per pair 1c. to 8c. each £375, 10c. to 50c. each £700, $1 £900, un*).

(ii) Coil stamps. Imperf×perf 8

368	101	1c. green (1.4.37)	4·50	7·00
369		2c. brown (18.6.37)	3·75	6·50
370		3c. scarlet (15.4.37)	35·00	2·50
368/70		*Set of 3*	38·00	14·50

(b) Air. P 12

371	107	6c. blue (15.6.38)	20·00	2·25

No. 371 exists imperforate (*Price per pair £850, un*).

108 Queen Elizabeth II when Princess and Princess Margaret

109 National War Memorial   **110** King George VI and Queen Elizabeth

1939 (15 May). Royal Visit. P 12.

372	108	1c. black and green	2·50	25
373	109	2c. black and brown	3·00	2·00
374	110	3c. black and carmine	2·00	25
372/4		*Set of 3*	6·75	2·25

Nos. 372/4 exist imperforate (*Price £850, un, for each pair*).

111 King George VI in Naval uniform   **112** King George VI in Military uniform   **113** King George VI in Air Force uniform

114 Grain Elevator   **115** Farm Scene

116 Parliament Buildings   **117** Ram Tank

118 Launching of Corvette HMCS *La Malbaie*, Sorel   **119** Munitions Factory

120 HMS *Cossack* (destroyer)   **121** Air Training Camp

1942 (1 July)–**48**. War Effort. T **111/121** and similar designs.

(a) Postage

(i) P 12

375	111	1c. green	1·50	10
		a. Booklet pane of 4+2 labels (12.9.42)	35·00	
		b. Booklet pane of 6 (24.11.42)	2·50	
376	112	2c. brown	1·75	10
		a. Booklet pane of 4+2 labels (12.9.42)	42·00	
		b. Booklet pane of 6 (6.10.42)	32·00	
377	113	3c. carmine-lake	1·25	60
		a. Booklet pane of 4+2 labels (20.8.42)	4·25	
378		3c. purple (30.6.43)	1·75	10
		a. Booklet pane of 4+2 labels (28.8.43)	6·50	
		b. Booklet pane of 6 (24.11.47)	16·00	
379	114	4c. slate	5·50	3·50
380	112	4c. carmine-lake (9.4.43)	70	10
		a. Booklet pane of 6 (3.5.43)	3·50	
381	111	5c. blue	3·50	10
382	115	8c. red-brown	5·50	1·25
383	116	10c. brown	16·00	10
384	117	13c. dull green	12·00	12·00
385		14c. dull green (16.4.43)	29·00	1·00
386	118	20c. chocolate	22·00	45
387	119	50c. violet	26·00	7·00
388	120	$1 blue	50·00	14·00
375/88		*Set of 14*	£150	35·00

Nos. 375/88 exist imperforate (*Prices per pair 1c. to 8c. each £375, 10c. to 20c. each £750, 50c. and $1 each £850, un*).

(ii) Coil stamps. Imperf×perf 8

389	111	1c. green (9.2.43)	1·00	1·50
390	112	2c. brown (24.11.42)	2·25	3·25
391	113	3c. carmine-lake (23.9.42)	2·00	11·00
392		3c. purple (19.8.43)	12·00	11·00
393	112	4c. carmine-lake (13.5.43)	13·00	2·25
389/93		*Set of 5*	27·00	26·00

(iii) Booklet stamps. Imperf×perf 12 (1.9.43)

394	111	1c. green	6·50	1·25
		a. Booklet pane of 3	17·00	
395	113	3c. purple	6·50	1·75
		a. Booklet pane of 3	17·00	
396	112	4c. carmine-lake	6·50	2·25
		a. Booklet pane of 3	17·00	
394/6		*Set of 3*	17·00	4·75

Nos. 394/6 are from booklets in which the stamps are in strips of three, imperforate at top and bottom and right-hand end.

(iv) Coil stamps. Imperf×perf 9½

397	111	1c. green (13.7.48)	4·75	5·00
397a	112	2c. brown (1.10.48)	10·00	19·00
398	113	3c. purple (2.7.48)	5·00	6·00
398a	112	4c. carmine-lake (22.7.48)	11·00	7·00
397/8a		*Set of 4*	28·00	32·00

(b) Air. P 12

399	121	6c. blue (1.7.42)	32·00	13·00
400		7c. blue (16.4.43)	5·50	50

Nos. 399/400 exist imperforate (*Price £1000, un, for each pair*).

122 Ontario Farm Scene   **123** Great Bear Lake

124 St. Maurice River Power Station   **125** Combine Harvester

126 Lumbering in British Columbia   **127** *Abegweit* (train ferry), Prince Edward Is.

128 Canada Geese in Flight   **129** Alexander Graham Bell and "Fame"

1946 (16 Sept)–**47**. Peace Re-conversion. T **122/128**. P 12.

(a) Postage

401	122	8c. brown	3·25	2·75
402	123	10c. olive-green	2·75	10
403	124	14c. sepia	6·50	3·25
404	125	20c. slate	5·00	10
405	126	50c. green	16·00	6·50
406	127	$1 purple	27·00	6·50

(b) Air

407	128	7c. blue	6·00	40
		a. Booklet pane of 4 (24.11.47)	9·00	
401/7		*Set of 7*	55·00	17·00

1947 (3 Mar). Birth Centenary of Bell (inventor of telephone). P 12.

408	129	4c. blue	15	50

130 "Canadian Citizenship"   **131** Queen Elizabeth II when Princess

1947 (1 July). Advent of Canadian Citizenship and 18th Anniv of Confederation. P 12.

409	130	4c. blue	10	40

(From photograph by Dorothy Wilding)

1948 (16 Feb). Princess Elizabeth's Marriage. P 12.

410	131	4c. blue	15	25

132 Queen Victoria, Parliament Building, Ottawa, and King George VI   **133** Cabot's Ship *Matthew*

1948 (1 Oct). 100 Years of Responsible Government. P 12.

411	132	4c. grey	10	10

1949 (1 Apr). Entry of Newfoundland into Canadian Confederation. P 12.

412	133	4c. green	30	10

134 *Founding of Halifax, 1749* (C. W. Jefferys)

1949 (21 June). Bicentenary of Halifax, Nova Scotia. P 12.

413	134	4c. violet	45	10

135   **136**   **137**

138 King George VI   **139** King George VI

(From photographs by Dorothy Wilding)

1949 (15 Nov)–**51**.

(i) P 12

414	135	1c. green	50	10
415	136	2c. sepia	2·25	45
415a		2c. olive-green (25.7.51)	1·75	10
416	137	3c. purple	30	10
		a. Booklet pane of 4+2 labels (12.4.50)	2·25	
417	138	4c. carmine-lake	20	10
		a. Booklet pane of 6 (5.5.50)	22·00	
417b		4c. vermilion (2.6.51)	60	10
		ba. Booklet pane of 6	6·00	
418	139	5c. blue	1·75	60
414/18		*Set of 7*	6·50	1·00

(ii) Coil stamps. Imperf×perf 9½

419	135	1c. green (18.5.50)	3·00	3·25
420	136	2c. sepia (18.5.50)	9·50	6·00
420a		2c. olive-green (9.10.51)	1·75	5·00
421	137	3c. purple (18.5.50)	2·25	3·75
422	138	4c. carmine-lake (20.4.50)	14·00	11·00
422a		4c. vermilion (27.11.51)	3·25	2·75
419/22a		*Set of 6*	30·00	29·00

(iii) Booklet stamps. Imperf×perf 12

422b	135	1c. green (18.5.50)	1·25	3·25
		ba. Booklet pane of 3	3·25	
423	137	3c. purple (18.5.50)	1·40	1·00
		a. Booklet pane of 3	3·75	
423b	138	4c. carmine-lake (18.5.50)	18·00	12·00
		ba. Booklet pane of 6	50·00	
423c		4c. vermilion (25.10.51)	13·00	11·00
		a. Booklet pane of 6	35·00	
422b/3c		*Set of 4*	29·00	24·00

These booklet panes are imperforate at top, bottom and right-hand end.

140 King
George VI

141 Oil Wells in Alberta

(From photograph by Dorothy Wilding)

1950 (19 Jan). As T **135/9** but without "POSTES POSTAGE", as T **140**.

(i) P 12

424	1c. green		70	2·00
425	2c. sepia		1·00	5·00
426	3c. purple		70	65
427	4c. carmine-lake		70	20
428	5c. blue		70	3·50
424/8 *Set of 5*			3·50	10·00

(ii) Imperf×perf 9½ (coil stamps)

429	1c. green		30	1·50
430	3c. purple		80	2·50

1950 (1 Mar). P 12.

431	**141**	50c. green	7·50	1·00

142 Drying Furs

143 Fisherman

1950 (2 Oct). P 12.

432	**142**	10c. brown-purple	4·00	10

1951 (1 Feb). P 12.

433	**143**	$1 ultramarine	40·00	6·00

144 Sir R. L.
Borden

145 W. L.
Mackenzie King

1951 (25 June). Prime Ministers (1st issue). P 12.

434	**144**	3c. blue-green	30	1·50
435	**145**	4c. rose-carmine	80	15

See also Nos. 444/5, 475/6 and 483/4.

146 Mail Trains, 1851 and
1951

147 SS *City of Toronto* and
SS *Prince George*

148 Mail Coach and DC-4M
North Star

149 Reproduction
of 3d., 1851

1951 (24 Sept). Canadian Stamp Centenary. P 12.

436	**146**	4c. black	75	10
437	**147**	5c. violet	2·00	3·25
438	**148**	7c. blue	75	1·75
439	**149**	15c. scarlet	1·60	10
436/9 *Set of 4*			4·50	4·75

150 Queen Elizabeth II
when Princess and Duke of
Edinburgh

151 Forestry Products

1951 (26 Oct). Royal Visit. P 12.

440	**150**	4c. violet	20	30

(Des A. L. Pollock)

1952 (1 Apr). P 12.

441	**151**	20c. grey	2·75	10

152 Red Cross Emblem

1952 (26 July). 18th International Red Cross Conference, Toronto. Design recess; cross litho. P 12.

442	**152**	4c. scarlet and blue	15	10

153 Canada Goose

154 Pacific Coast
Indian House and
Totem Pole

(Des E. Hahn)

1952 (3 Nov). P 12.

443	**153**	7c. blue	1·25	10

1952 (3 Nov). Prime Ministers (2nd issue). Various portraits as T **144**. P 12.

444		3c. reddish purple	35	75
445		4c. orange-red	25	35

Portraits:—3c. Sir John J. C. Abbott; 4c. A. Mackenzie.

(Des E. Hahn)

1953 (2 Feb). P 12.

446	**154**	$1 black	3·25	20

155 Polar Bear

156 Elk

157 American
Bighorn

(Des J. Crosby (2c.), E. Hahn (others))

1953 (1 Apr). National Wild Life Week. P 12.

447	**155**	2c. blue	15	10
448	**156**	3c. sepia	15	70
449	**157**	4c. slate	15	10
447/9 *Set of 3*			40	70

158 Queen
Elizabeth II

159 Queen
Elizabeth II

(From photograph by Karsh, Ottawa)

1953 (1 May–3 Sept).

(a) Sheet stamps. P 12

450	**158**	1c. purple-brown	10	10
451		2c. green	15	10
452		3c. carmine	15	15
		a. Booklet pane of 4+2 labels (17.7)	1·90	
453		4c. violet	20	10
		a. Booklet pane of 6 (6.7)	5·00	
454		5c. ultramarine	25	10
450/4 *Set of 5*			75	30

(b) Coil stamps. Imperf×perf 9½

455	**158**	2c. green (30.7)	2·25	1·60
456		3c. carmine (27.7)	2·25	1·00
457		4c. violet (3.9)	2·25	1·25
455/7 *Set of 3*			6·00	3·50

(c) Booklet stamps. Imperf×perf 12

458	**158**	1c. purple-brown (12.8)	2·25	1·50
		a. Booklet pane of 3	6·00	
459		3c. carmine (17.7)	2·25	1·50
		a. Booklet pane of 3	6·00	
460		4c. violet (6.7)	2·25	1·50
		a. Booklet pane of 3	6·00	
458/60 *Set of 3*			6·00	4·00

These booklet stamps have top and bottom or top, bottom and right-hand sides imperforate.

(Des E. Hahn)

1953 (1 June). Coronation. P 12.

461	**159**	4c. violet	10	10

160 Textile Industry

161 Queen
Elizabeth II

(Des A. L. Pollock)

1953 (2 Nov). P 12.

462	**160**	50c. deep bluish green	1·75	10

(From photograph by Dorothy Wilding)

1954–62.

(i) P 12

463	**161**	1c. purple-brown (10.6.54)	10	10
		a. Booklet pane. 5 stamps plus printed label (1.6.56)	1·50	
		p. 2 phosphor bands (13.1.62)	1·00	3·75
464		2c. green (10.6.54)	20	10
		a. Pack. 2 blocks of 25 (12.61)	9·00	
		p. 2 phosphor bands (13.1.62)	1·00	4·50
465		3c. carmine (10.6.54)	10	10
		a. Imperf vert (horiz pair)	£1800	
		p. 2 phosphor bands (13.1.62)	1·50	3·50

466		4c. violet (10.6.54)	30	10
		a. Booklet pane of 6 (7.7.55)	4·75	
		b. Booklet pane. 5 stamps plus printed label (1.6.56)	2·25	
		p. 1 phosphor band (13.1.62)	2·25	11·00
467		5c. bright blue (1.4.54)	30	10
		a. Booklet pane. 5 stamps plus printed label (14.7.54)	2·75	
		b. Pack. 1 block of 20 (12.61)	6·00	
		c. Imperf vert (horiz pair)*	£6000	
		p. 2 phosphor bands (13.1.62)	3·50	8·00
468		6c. red-orange (10.6.54)	1·75	55
463/8 *Set of 6*			3·25	70
463p/7p *Set of 5*			8·25	27·00

(ii) Coil stamps. Imperf×perf 9½

469	**161**	2c. green (9.9.54)	1·50	75
470		4c. violet (23.8.54)	55	1·60
471		5c. bright blue (6.7.54)	1·75	45
469/71 *Set of 3*			3·50	2·50

*No. 467c is from the left side of a sheet and shows perforations between the stamps and the sheet margin.

Nos. 464a and 467b are blocks with the outer edges imperf. These come from "One Dollar Plastic Packages" sold at post offices.

WINNIPEG PHOSPHOR BANDS. In 1962 facer-cancelling machines were introduced in Winnipeg which were activated by phosphor bands on the stamps. Under long or short wave ultra-violet light the phosphor glows and there is also a short after-glow when the lamp is turned off. This should not be confused with the fluorescent bands introduced in Ottawa in 1971.

162 Walrus

163 American
Beaver

164 Northern
Gannet

(Des E. Hahn)

1954 (1 Apr). National Wild Life Week. P 12.

472	**162**	4c. slate-black	45	30
473	**163**	5c. ultramarine	35	10
		a. Booklet pane. 5 stamps plus 1 printed label	2·00	

(Des L. Hyde)

1954 (1 Apr). P 12.

474	**164**	15c. black	1·50	10

1954 (1 Nov). Prime Ministers (3rd issue). Various portraits as T **144**. P 12.

475		4c. violet	20	1·00
476		5c. bright blue	20	60

Portraits:—4c. Sir John Thompson; 5c. Sir Mackenzie Bowell.

165 Eskimo Hunter

(Des H. Beament)

1955 (21 Feb). P 12.

477	**165**	10c. purple-brown	1·25	10

166 Musk Ox

167 Whooping Cranes

(Des E. Hahn (4c.), Dr. W. Rowan (5c.))

1955 (4 Apr). National Wild Life Week. P 12.

478	**166**	4c. violet	30	10
479	**167**	5c. ultramarine	1·00	20

168 Dove and Torch

169 Pioneer Settlers

(Des W. Lohse)

1955 (1 June). Tenth Anniv of International Civil Aviation Organisation. P 12.

480	**168**	5c. ultramarine	40	20

(Des L. Hyde)

1955 (30 June). 50th Anniv of Alberta and Saskatchewan Provinces. P 12.

481	**169**	5c. ultramarine	20	30

170 Scout Badge and Globe

173 Ice-hockey Players

(Des L. Hyde)
1955 (20 Aug). Eighth World Scout Jamboree, Niagara-on-the-Lake. P 12.
482	**170**	5c. orange-brown and green............	30	10

1955 (8 Nov). Prime Ministers (4th issue). Various portraits as T **144**. P 12.
483	4c. violet...........................	25	70
484	5c. bright blue.....................	25	10

Portraits:—4c. R. B. Bennett; 5c. Sir Charles Tupper.

(Des J. Simpkins)
1956 (23 Jan). Ice-hockey Commemoration. P 12.
485	**173**	5c. ultramarine....................	20	20

174 Reindeer

175 Mountain Goat

(Des E. Hahn)
1956 (12 Apr). National Wild Life Week. P 12.
486	**174**	4c. violet.........................	20	15
487	**175**	5c. bright blue...................	20	10

176 Pulp and Paper Industry

177 Chemical Industry

(Des A. J. Casson (20c.), A. L. Pollock (25c.))
1956 (7 June). P 12.
488	**176**	20c. green.........................	75	10
489	**177**	25c. red...........................	75	10

178

(Des A. Price)
1956 (9 Oct). Fire Prevention Week. P 12.
490	**178**	5c. red and black.................	30	10

179 Fishing

180 Swimming

(Des L. Hyde)
1957 (7 Mar). Outdoor Recreation. T **179/180** and similar horiz designs. P 12.
491	**179**	5c. ultramarine....................	40	15
		a. Block of 4. Nos. 491/4..........	1·40	1·50
492	**180**	5c. ultramarine....................	40	15
493	–	5c. ultramarine....................	40	15
494	–	5c. ultramarine....................	40	15
491/4 *Set of 4*			1·40	55

Designs:—No. 493, Hunting. No. 494, Skiing.
Nos. 491/4 are printed together in sheets of 50 (5×10). In the first, second, fourth and fifth vertical rows the four different designs are arranged in *se-tenant* blocks, whilst the central row is made up as follows (reading downwards):—Nos. 491/4, 491/2 (or 493/4), 491/4.

183 White-billed Diver

184 Thompson with Sextant, and North American Map

(Des L. Hyde)
1957 (10 Apr). National Wild Life Week. P 12.
495	**183**	5c. black..........................	50	20

(Des G. A. Gundersen)
1957 (5 June). Death Centenary of David Thompson (explorer). P 12.
496	**184**	5c. ultramarine....................	45	30

185 Parliament Buildings, Ottawa

186 Globe within Posthorn

(Des Carl Mangold)
1957 (14 Aug). 14th UPU Congress, Ottawa. P 12.
497	**185**	5c. grey-blue.....................	15	10
498	**186**	15c. blackish blue.................	55	1·75

187 Miner

188 Queen Elizabeth II and Duke of Edinburgh

(Des A. J. Casson)
1957 (5 Sept). Mining Industry. P 12.
499	**187**	5c. black..........................	35	20

(From photographs by Karsh, Ottawa)
1957 (10 Oct). Royal Visit. P 12.
500	**188**	5c. black..........................	30	10

189 "A Free Press"

190 Microscope

(Des A. L. Pollock)
1958 (22 Jan). The Canadian Press. P 12.
501	**189**	5c. black..........................	20	70

(Des A. L. Pollock)
1958 (5 Mar). International Geophysical Year. P 12.
502	**190**	5c. blue...........................	20	10

191 Miner panning for Gold

192 La Vérendrye (statue)

(Des J. Harman)
1958 (8 May). Centenary of British Columbia. P 12.
503	**191**	5c. deep turquoise-green..........	20	10

(Des G. Trottier)
1958 (4 June). La Vérendrye (explorer) Commemoration. P 12.
504	**192**	5c. ultramarine....................	20	10

193 Samuel de Champlain and the Heights of Québec

194 Nurse

(Des G. Trottier)
1958 (26 June). 350th Anniv of Founding of Québec. P 12.
505	**193**	5c. brown-ochre and deep green...	30	10

(Des G. Trottier)
1958 (30 July). National Health. P 12.
506	**194**	5c. reddish purple................	30	10

195 "Petroleum 1858–1958"

196 Speaker's Chair and Mace

(Des A. L. Pollock)
1958 (10 Sept). Centenary of Canadian Oil Industry. P 12.
507	**195**	5c. scarlet and olive.............	30	10

(Des G. Trottier and C. Dair)
1958 (2 Oct). Bicentenary of First Elected Assembly. P 12.
508	**196**	5c. deep slate....................	30	10

197 John McCurdy's *Silver Dart* Biplane

198 Globe showing NATO Countries

1959 (23 Feb). 50th Anniv of First Flight of the *Silver Dart* in Canada. P 12.
509	**197**	5c. black and ultramarine........	30	10

(Des P. Weiss)
1959 (2 Apr). Tenth Anniv of North Atlantic Treaty Organisation. P 12.
510	**198**	5c. ultramarine...................	40	10

199

200 Queen Elizabeth II

(Des Helen Fitzgerald)
1959 (13 May). "Associated Country Women of the World" Commemoration. P 12.
511	**199**	5c. black and yellow-olive.......	15	10

(Des after painting by Annigoni)
1959 (18 June). Royal Visit. P 12.
512	**200**	5c. lake-red......................	30	10

201 Maple Leaf linked with American Eagle

202 Maple Leaves

(Des A. L. Pollock, G. Trottier (of Canada); W. H. Buckley, A. J. Copeland, E. Metzl (of the United States))
1959 (26 June). Opening of St. Lawrence Seaway. P 12.
513	**201**	5c. ultramarine and red..........	20	10
		a. Centre inverted...............	£9000	£6500

It is believed that No. 513a occurred on two printer's sheets, each of 200 stamps. About 230 examples have been discovered, but many have slight imperfections. The prices quoted are for examples in very fine condition.

(Des P. Weiss)
1959 (10 Sept). Bicentenary of Battle of Plains of Abraham (Québec). P 12.
514	**202**	5c. deep green and red...........	30	10

203

204 Dollard des Ormeaux

(Des Helen Fitzgerald)
1960 (20 Apr). Golden Jubilee of Canadian Girl Guides Movement. P 12.
515	**203**	5c. ultramarine and orange-brown	20	10

(Des P. Weiss)
1960 (19 May). Tercentenary of Battle of the Long Sault. P 12.
516	**204**	5c. ultramarine and light brown..	20	10

205 Surveyor, Bulldozer and Compass Rose

206 E. Pauline Johnson

(Des B. J. Reddie)
1961 (8 Feb). Northern Development. P 12.
517	**205**	5c. emerald and red..............	15	10

(Des B. J. Reddie)
1961 (10 Mar). Birth Centenary of E. Pauline Johnson (Mohawk poetess). P 12.
518	**206**	5c. green and red................	15	10

207 Arthur Meighen (statesman)

208 Engineers and Dam

1961 (19 Apr). Arthur Meighen Commemoration. P 12.
519	**207**	5c. ultramarine...................	15	10

(Des B. J. Reddie)
1961 (28 June). Tenth Anniv of Colombo Plan. P 12.
520	**208**	5c. blue and brown...............	30	10

209 "Resources for Tomorrow"

210 "Education"

(Des A. L. Pollock)

1961 (12 Oct). Natural Resources. P 12.
521 **209** 5c. blue-green and brown 15 10

(Des Helen Fitzgerald)

1962 (28 Feb). Education Year. P 12.
522 **210** 5c. black and orange-brown 15 10

211 Lord Selkirk and Farmer

212 Talon bestowing Gifts on Married Couple

(Des Phillips-Gutkin Ltd)

1962 (3 May). 150th Anniv of Red River Settlement. P 12.
523 **211** 5c. chocolate and green 20 10

(Des P. Weiss)

1962 (13 June). Jean Talon Commemoration. P 12.
524 **212** 5c. blue 20 10

213 Br. Columbia & Vancouver Is. 2½d. stamp of 1860, and Parliament Buildings, B.C.

214 Highway (map version) and Provincial Arms

(Des Helen Bacon)

1962 (22 Aug). Centenary of Victoria, B.C. P 12.
525 **213** 5c. red and black 30 10

(Des A. L. Pollock)

1962 (31 Aug). Opening of Trans-Canada Highway. P 12.
526 **214** 5c. black and orange-brown 15 20

215 Queen Elizabeth II and Wheat (agriculture) Symbol

216 Sir Casimir Gzowski

(From drawing by Ernst Roch)

1962–64. Horiz designs as T **215** showing Queen Elizabeth II and industry symbols.

(i) P 12
527 1c. chocolate (4.2.63) 10 10
   a. Booklet pane. 5 stamps plus 1
    printed label (15.5.63) .... 5·00
   p. 2 phosphor bands (15.5.63) 15 55
528 2c. green (2.5.63) 15 20
   a. Pack. 2 blocks of 25 .... 11·00
   p. 2 phosphor bands (15.5.63) ..... 40 2·75
529 3c. reddish violet† (2.5.63) 15 10
   p. 2 phosphor bands (15.5.63) ..... 40 1·00
530 4c. carmine-red (4.2.63) 20 10
   a. Booklet pane. 5 stamps plus 1
    printed label (15.5.63) .... 5·00
   b. Pack. 1 block of 25 .... 10·00
   p. 1 centre phosphor band (narrow)*
    (2.63) .... 50 3·25
   pa. 1 centre phosphor band (wide)
    (8.64) .... 6·00 13·00
   pb. 1 side phosphor band (12.64) ... 1·50 6·00
531 5c. ultramarine (3.10.62) 50 10
   a. Booklet pane. 5 stamps plus 1
    printed label (5.63) .... 7·50
   b. Pack. 1 block of 20 .... 13·00
   c. Imperf horiz (vert pair) £3250 £750
   p. 2 phosphor bands (31.1.63?) ... 50 1·50
   pa. Pack. 1 block of 20 .... 17·00
   pb. Imperf (pair) £3250
527/31 *Set of 5* .... 1·00 25
527p/31p *Set of 5* .... 1·75 8·00

(ii) Coil stamps. P 9½×imperf
532 2c. green (2.5.63) .... 8·00 9·50
532a 3c. reddish violet (2.5.63) .... 4·75 3·50
533 4c. carmine-red (4.4.63) .... 3·00 3·50
   a. Imperf (vert pair) £3250

534 5c. ultramarine (3.10.62) .... 4·50 1·50
532/4 *Set of 4* .... 18·00 16·00
Symbols:—1c. Crystals (Mining); 2c. Tree (Forestry); 3c. Fish (Fisheries); 4c. Electricity pylon (Industrial power).
Nos. 528a, 530b, 531b and 531pa are blocks with the outer edges imperf. These come from "One Dollar Plastic Packages" sold at post offices.
†This is a fugitive colour which tends to become reddish on drying. In successive printings the violet colour became more and more reddish as the printer tried to match the shade of each previous printing instead of referring back to the original shade. A deep reddish violet is also known from Plate 3. As there is such a range of shades it is not practical to list them.
*On No. 530p the band is 4 mm wide as against 8 mm on No. 530pa. No. 530pb exists with the band at either left or right side of the stamp, the bands being applied across alternate vertical perforations.
Postal forgeries are known of the 4c. showing a coarser background and lack of shading on the Queen's face.

(Des P. Weiss)

1963 (5 Mar). 150th Birth Anniv of Sir Casimir Gzowski (engineer). P 12.
535 **216** 5c. reddish purple 15 10

217 "Export Trade"

218 Frobisher and barque *Gabriel*

(Des A. L. Pollock)

1963 (14 June). P 12.
536 **217** $1 carmine .... 4·25 1·50

(Des P. Weiss)

1963 (21 Aug). Sir Martin Frobisher Commemoration. P 12.
537 **218** 5c. ultramarine 30 10

219 Horseman and Map

220 Canada Geese

(Des B. J. Reddie)

1963 (25 Sept). Bicentenary of Quebec–Trois-Rivieres–Montreal Postal Service. P 12.
538 **219** 5c. red-brown and deep green 20 25

(Des A. Short and P. Arthur)

1963 (30 Oct). P 12.
539 **220** 15c. blue .... 1·00 10

221 Douglas DC-9 Airliner and Uplands Airport, Ottawa

222 "Peace on Earth"

1964. P 12.
540 **221** 7c. blue (11.3) 35 80
540a 8c. blue (18.11) 50 50

1964 (8 Apr). "Peace". Litho and recess. P 12.
541 **222** 5c. ochre, blue and turquoise-blue . 15 10

223 Maple Leaves

1964 (14 May). "Canadian Unity". P 12.
542 **223** 5c. lake-red and light blue 10 10

224 White Trillium and Arms of Ontario

225 Madonna Lily and Arms of Quebec

226 Purple Violet and Arms of New Brunswick

227 Mayflower and Arms of Nova Scotia

228 Dogwood and Arms of British Columbia

229 Prairie Crocus and Arms of Manitoba

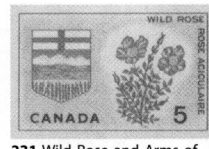
230 Lady's Slipper and Arms of Prince Edward Island

231 Wild Rose and Arms of Alberta

232 Prairie Lily and Arms of Saskatchewan

233 Pitcher Plant and Arms of Newfoundland

234 Mountain Avens and Arms of Northwest Territories

235 Fireweed and Arms of Yukon Territory

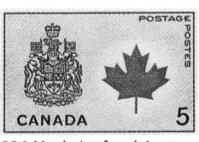
236 Maple Leaf and Arms of Canada

1964–66. Provincial Emblems. T **224/236.** Recess (No. 555) or litho and recess (others). P 12.
543 5c. green, brown and orange (30.6.64).. 35 20
544 5c. green, orange-brown and yellow
   (30.6.64) 35 20
545 5c. carmine-red, green and bluish
   violet (3.2.65) 25 20
546 5c. blue, red and green (3.2.65) 25 20
547 5c. purple, green and yellow-brown
   (28.4.65) 25 20
548 5c. red-brown, deep bluish green and
   mauve (28.4.65) 25 20
549 5c. slate-lilac, green and light reddish
   purple (21.7.65) 40 20
550 5c. green, yellow and rose-red (19.1.66) 25 20
551 5c. sepia, orange and green (19.1.66) 25 20
552 5c. black, green and red (23.2.66) ... 25 20
553 5c. drab, green and yellow (23.3.66) 25 20
554 5c. blue, green and rose-red (23.3.66) ... 25 20
555 5c. red and blue (30.6.66) 25 20
543/55 *Set of 13* .... 3·25 2·40

(237)
238 Fathers of the Confederation Memorial, Charlottetown

1964 (15 July). No. 540 surch with T **237.**
556 **221** 8c. on 7c. blue 25 30
   a. Surch omitted (left-hand
    stamp of horiz pair) £11000

(Des P. Weiss)

1964 (29 July). Centenary of Charlottetown Conference. P 12.
557 **238** 5c. black 10 10

239 Maple Leaf and Hand with Quill Pen

240 Queen Elizabeth II

(Des P. Weiss)

1964 (9 Sept). Centenary of Quebec Conference. P 12.
558 **239** 5c. light red and chocolate 15 10

(Portrait by Anthony Buckley)

1964 (5 Oct). Royal Visit. P 12.
559 **240** 5c. reddish purple 15 10

241 "Canadian Family" **242** "Co-operation"

1964 (14 Oct). Christmas. P 12.
560	**241**	3c. scarlet	10	10
		a. Pack. 2 blocks of 25	7·00	
		p. 2 phosphor bands	60	2·50
		pa. Pack. 2 blocks of 25	16·00	
561		5c. ultramarine	10	10
		p. 2 phosphor bands	90	5·00

Nos. 560a and 560pa are blocks with the outer edges imperf. These come from "$1.50 Plastic Packages" sold at post offices.

1965 (3 Mar). International Co-operation Year. P 12.
562	**242**	5c. grey-green	35	10

243 Sir W. Grenfell **244** National Flag

1965 (9 June). Birth Centenary of Sir Wilfred Grenfell (missionary). P 12.
563	**243**	5c. deep bluish green	20	10

1965 (30 June). Inauguration of National Flag. P 12.
564	**244**	5c. red and blue	15	10

245 Sir Winston Churchill **246** Peace Tower, Parliament Buildings, Ottawa

(Des P. Weiss from photo by Karsh. Litho)

1965 (12 Aug). Churchill Commemoration. P 12.
565	**245**	5c. purple-brown	15	10

(Des Philips-Gutkin)

1965 (8 Sept). Inter-Parliamentary Union Conference, Ottawa. P 12.
566	**246**	5c. deep green	10	10

247 Parliament Buildings, Ottawa, 1865 **248** "Gold, Frankincense and Myrrh"

(Des G. Trottier)

1965 (8 Sept). Centenary of Proclamation of Ottawa as Capital. P 12.
567	**247**	5c. brown	10	10

(Des Helen Fitzgerald)

1965 (13 Oct). Christmas. P 12.
568	**248**	3c. olive-green	10	10
		a. Pack. 2 blocks of 25	5·00	
		p. 2 phosphor bands	10	2·00
		pa. Pack. 2 blocks of 25	6·50	
569		5c. ultramarine	10	10
		p. 2 phosphor bands	30	50

Nos. 568a and 568pa are blocks with the outer edges imperf. These come from "$1.50 Plastic Packages" sold at post offices.

249 Alouette 2 over Canada **250** La Salle

1966 (5 Jan). Launching of Canadian Satellite, Alouette 2. P 12.
570	**249**	5c. ultramarine	15	10

(Des Brigdens Ltd., Toronto)

1966 (13 Apr). 300th Anniv of La Salle's Arrival in Canada. P 12.
571	**250**	5c. deep bluish green	15	10

251 Road Signs **252** Canadian Delegation and Houses of Parliament

(Des Helen Fitzgerald)

1966 (2 May). Highway Safety. Invisible gum. P 12.
572	**251**	5c. yellow, blue and black	15	10

(Des P. Pederson (Brigdens Ltd.))

1966 (26 May). London Conference Centenary. P 12.
573	**252**	5c. red-brown	10	10

253 Douglas Point Nuclear Power Station **254** Parliamentary Library, Ottawa

(Des A. L. Pollock)

1966 (27 July). Peaceful Uses of Atomic Energy. P 12.
574	**253**	5c. ultramarine	10	10

(Des Brigdens Ltd.)

1966 (8 Sept). Commonwealth Parliamentary Association Conference, Ottawa. P 12.
575	**254**	5c. purple	10	10

255 Praying Hands, after Dürer **256** Flag and Canada on Globe

(Des G. Holloway)

1966 (12 Oct). Christmas. P 12.
576	**255**	3c. carmine	10	10
		a. Pack. 2 blocks of 25	4·50	
		p. 2 phosphor bands	1·25	1·25
		pa. Pack. 2 blocks of 25	8·00	
577		5c. orange	10	10
		p. 2 phosphor bands	1·25	1·25

Nos. 576a and 576pa are blocks with the outer edges imperf. These come from "$1.50 Plastic Packages" sold at post offices.

(Des Brigdens Ltd.)

1967 (11 Jan). Canadian Centennial. Invisible gum. P 12.
578	**256**	5c. scarlet and blue	10	10
		p. 2 phosphor bands	40	2·00

257 Northern Lights and Dog-team **258** Totem pole **259** Combine-harvester and oil derrick

260 Ship in lock **261** Harbour scene **261a** "Transport"

262 Alaska Highway (A.Y. Jackson) **263** The Jack Pine (T. Thomson)

 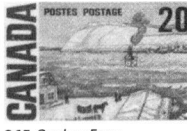

264 Bylot Island (L. Harris) **265** Quebec Ferry (J. W. Morrice)

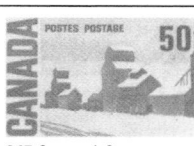

266 The Solemn Land (J. E. H. MacDonald) **267** Summer's Stores (grain elevators) (J. Ensor)

268 Oilfield (near Edmonton) (H. G. Glyde) **268a** Library of Parliament

1967 (8 Feb)–**73**. T **257/268a**.

A. Recess C.B.N.

(i) P 12
579	1c. brown	10	10
	a. Booklet pane. 5 stamps plus 1 printed label (2.67)	1·25	
	b. Printed on the gummed side	£850	
	c. White paper (10.71)	10	
	ca. White fluorescent paper (6.71)	1·00	
	p. 2 phosphor bands	60	1·00
	pa. Centre phosphor band (12.68)	30	2·00
	pac. Centre phosphor band, white paper (9.71)	30	
	paca. Centre phosphor band, white fluorescent paper (10.71)	3·00	
	q. 2 fluorescent bands (11.71)	60	75
580	2c. green	10	20
	a. Glazed fluorescent paper (booklets) (26.10.70)	25	
	b. Booklet pane. No. 580a×4 se-tenant with No. 581a×4 with gutter margin between	1·75	
	c. White paper (3.72)	10	
	p. 2 phosphor bands	1·25	3·50
	pa. Centre phosphor band (12.68)	30	1·00
	pac. Centre phosphor band, white paper (3.72)	60	
	q. 2 fluorescent bands (12.72)	75	1·00
581	3c. slate-purple	30	50
	a. Glazed fluorescent paper (booklets) (26.10.70)	25	
	p. 2 phosphor bands	30	3·00
	q. 2 fluorescent bands (1972?)	2·00	3·50
582	4c. red	20	10
	a. Booklet pane. 5 stamps plus 1 printed label (2.67)	1·75	
	b. Pack. 1 block of 25 (8.2.67)	13·00	
	c. White paper (5.72)	20	
	p. 1 side phosphor band	1·25	4·00
	pa. Centre phosphor band (3.69)	30	1·00
	pac. Centre phosphor band, white paper (5.72)	50	
	paca. Centre phosphor band, white fluorescent paper (1972)	2·00	
	q. 2 fluorescent bands (4.73)	55	1·50
583	5c. blue	20	10
	a. Booklet pane. 5 stamps plus 1 printed label (3.67)	6·00	
	b. Pack. 1 block of 20 (2.67)	22·00	
	c. White paper (12.71?)	40	
	ca. White fluorescent paper (12.71)	1·00	
	p. 2 phosphor bands	75	3·25
	pa. Pack. 1 block of 20 (8.2.67)	35·00	
	pb. Centre phosphor band (12.68)	30	2·50
	pbc. Centre phosphor band, white paper (4.72)	1·00	
	pbca. Centre phosphor band, white fluorescent paper (12.71)	1·00	
583r	6c. black (white paper) (1.72)	2·25	30
	ra. Printed on the gummed side	12·00	
	rp. Centre phosphor band (1.72)	4·75	6·00
	rq. 2 fluorescent bands (1.72)	1·00	1·50
584	8c. purple-brown	25	1·00
	c. White fluorescent paper (7.71)	12·00	
585	10c. olive-green	25	10
	c. White paper (3.71)	80	
	ca. White fluorescent paper (12.71)	80	
	p. 2 phosphor bands (9.12.69)	1·50	3·50
	pc. 2 phosphor bands, white paper (11.72)	1·00	
	pca. 2 phosphor bands, white fluorescent paper (1.72)	4·50	
	q. 2 fluorescent bands (1.72)	1·00	1·00
	qa. 2 fluorescent bands, white fluorescent paper (2.72)	4·50	
586	15c. dull purple	30	10
	c. White paper (3.72)	65	
	ca. White fluorescent paper (3.71)	2·00	
	p. 2 phosphor bands (9.12.69)	1·50	2·75
	pc. 2 phosphor bands, white paper (3.72)	2·00	
	q. 2 fluorescent bands (2.72)	1·00	1·75
587	20c. deep blue	2·00	10
	c. White paper (5.72)	1·60	
	ca. White fluorescent paper (8.71)	2·00	
	p. 2 phosphor bands (9.12.69)	2·50	5·50
	pc. 2 phosphor bands, white paper (5.72)	2·00	
588	25c. myrtle-green	2·00	10
	ca. White fluorescent paper (10.71)	2·25	
	p. 2 phosphor bands (9.12.69)	4·25	8·00
	pca. 2 phosphor bands, white fluorescent paper (12.71)	16·00	
589	50c. cinnamon	2·00	10
	c. White paper (12.71)	2·50	
	ca. White fluorescent paper (3.71)	2·75	

590	$1 scarlet	1·50	1·25
	c. White paper (12.71)	3·00	
	ca. White fluorescent paper (3.71)	3·00	
579/590 *Set of 13*		8·50	3·00
579pa/588p *Set of 10*		13·50	29·00

(ii) Coil stamps. Perf 9½×imperf

591	3c. slate-purple (3.67)	2·00	5·00
592	4c. red (3.67)	2·00	2·50
593	5c. blue (2.67)	2·00	3·75

(iii) Coil stamps. Perf 10×imperf

594	6c. orange-red (1.69)	90	35
	a. Imperf (vert pair)	£225	
	c. White fluorescent paper (12.69)	11·00	
	ca. Imperf (vert pair)	£2000	
595	6c. black (*white fluorescent paper*) (8.70)	35	3·00
	a. Imperf (vert pair)	£2000	
596	7c. green (*white fluorescent paper*) (30.6.71)	40	2·75
	a. Imperf (vert pair)	£850	
597	8c. black (*white paper*) (30.12.71)	1·75	2·75
	a. Imperf (vert pair)	£425	
	q. 2 fluorescent bands (7.72)	40	40
	qa. 2 fluorescent bands, white fluorescent paper	1·00	
	qb. Imperf (vert pair)	£800	

B. Recess B.A.B.N.

(i) P 10 (sheets (601/p) or booklets)

598	1c. brown (9.68)	30	2·50
	a. Booklet pane. No. 598×5 *se-tenant* with No. 599×5 (9.68)	1·75	
	b. Booklet pane. No. 601×4 *se-tenant* with No. 598 plus one printed label (10.68)	2·00	
	c. White fluorescent paper (11.69)	10·00	
	cb. Booklet pane. No. 601c×4 *se-tenant* with No. 598c plus 1 printed label (11.69)	16·00	
599	4c. red (9.68)	20	2·50
	a. Booklet pane. 25 stamps plus 2 printed labels	6·50	
600	5c. blue (9.68)	30	2·50
	a. Booklet pane of 20	4·50	
601	6c. orange-red (10.68)	45	90
	a. Booklet pane. 25 stamps plus 2 printed labels (10.68)	10·00	
	c. White fluorescent paper (11.69)	1·50	
	p. 2 phosphor bands (1.11.68)	1·00	1·00
602	6c. black (1.70)	1·00	2·25
	a. Booklet pane. 25 stamps plus 2 printed labels	16·00	
	c. White fluorescent paper (11.69)	60·00	
	ca. Booklet pane. 25 stamps plus 2 printed labels	£1200	
603	6c. black (*re-engraved die*) (8.70)	3·50	4·25
	a. Booklet pane of 4	12·00	

(ii) P 12½×12 (sheets (606/10) or booklets)

604	1c. brown (30.6.71)	50	3·00
	a. Booklet pane. Nos. 604×4, 605×4 and 609×12 *se-tenant*	13·00	
	b. Booklet pane. Nos. 604/5 and 609×3 *se-tenant* plus 1 printed label	4·00	
	c. Booklet pane. Nos. 604×3, 608 and 610×2 *se-tenant* (30.12.71)	1·50	
	d. Booklet pane. Nos. 604×6, 608 and 610×11 *se-tenant* (30.12.71)	6·50	
	e. Booklet pane. Nos. 604×4, 608 and 610×5 *se-tenant* (8.72)	4·50	
	f. White fluorescent paper (30.12.71)	40	75
	fa. Booklet pane. No. 604f×4, 608 and 610×5 *se-tenant* (30.12.71)	1·75	
	q. 2 fluorescent bands (30.12.71)	40	2·25
	qc. Booklet pane. Nos. 604q×3, 608q and 610q×2 *se-tenant*	2·00	
	qd. Booklet pane. Nos. 604q×6, 608q and 610q×11 *se-tenant*	5·00	
	qe. Booklet pane. Nos. 604q×4, 608q and 610q×5 *se-tenant* (8.72)	4·50	
	qf. 2 fluorescent bands, white fluorescent paper (30.12.71)	40	
	qfa. Booklet pane. No. 604qfa×4, 608 and 610×5 *se-tenant* (30.12.71)	2·50	
605	3c. slate-purple (30.6.71)	4·50	7·50
606	6c. orange-red (3.69)	60	1·00
	f. White fluorescent paper (12.69)	17·00	
	p. 2 phosphor bands (4.69)	2·00	2·00
	pf. 2 phosphor bands, white fluorescent paper (12.69)	£850	
607	6c. black (7.1.70)	30	10
	a. Booklet pane. 25 stamps plus 2 printed labels (8.70)	18·00	
	f. White fluorescent paper (1.70)	14·00	
	p. 2 phosphor bands (1.70)	2·50	3·25
608	6c. black (*re-engraved die*) (9.70)	1·00	10
	a. Booklet pane of 4 (11.70)	4·00	
	f. White fluorescent paper	1·25	
	p. One centre phosphor band (9.71)	3·75	4·75
	q. 2 fluorescent bands (30.12.71)	1·75	45
	qf. 2 fluorescent bands, white fluorescent paper (12.71)	1·00	
609	7c. myrtle-green (30.6.71)	30	1·00
	p. 2 phosphor bands	1·00	3·50
610	8c. slate-black (30.12.71)	30	10
	c. White paper (7.72)	30	
	cf. White fluorescent paper (11.72)	2·75	
	p. 2 phosphor bands	60	1·00
	pf. 2 phosphor bands, white paper (7.72)	50	
	pfa. 2 phosphor bands, white fluorescent paper (11.72)	4·50	
	q. 2 fluorescent bands (30.12.71)	45	15
	qf. 2 fluorescent bands, white paper	75	
	qfa. 2 fluorescent bands, white fluorescent paper (12.72)	1·50	

No. 581q only exists as a pre-cancel.
Nos. 582b, 583b, 583pa are blocks with the outer edges imperf. These come from "One Dollar Plastic Packages" sold at post offices.

No. 582p comes with the band to the left or right of the stamp, the phosphor having been applied across alternate vertical perforations. Postal forgeries exist of the 6c. orange printed in lithography and perforated 12½.

Normal

Re-engraved

When the basic postal rate was changed to 6c. the C.B.N. lent their die to B.A.B.N. who made a duplicate die from it by transfer. Parts of this proved to be weak, but it was used for Nos. 601/2 and 606/7. B.A.B.N. later re-engraved their die to make fresh plates which were used for Nos. 603 and 608. No. 608 first appeared on sheets from Plate 4.

There are no records of dates of issue of the booklets, packs and coils, but supplies of these were distributed to depots in the months indicated.

IMPERF BETWEEN PAIRS FROM COIL STAMPS. Nos. 594/7 are known in blocks or horizontal pairs imperf between vertically. Coils are supplied to post offices in batches of ten coils held together by roulettes between every fourth stamp so that they can easily be split apart. If two or more unsplit coils are purchased it is possible to obtain blocks or pairs imperf between vertically.

Vertical coil stamps are also known imperf between horizontally or with some stamps apparently completely imperf. These can result from blind perforations identifiable by slight indentations.

WHITE PAPERS. Original printings of the sheet and coil stamps were made on toned paper. From the later part of 1969 experimental printings were made on white fluorescent paper, as referred to in the note below No. 620; this paper is distinct from the glazed type used for the "Opal" booklet (see Nos. 580a and 581a).

During 1971 a further type of paper, white but non-fluorescent, was introduced. This later white (non-fluorescent) paper typically has PVA gum, readily distinguishable from the shiny 'Dextrine' gum of the white fluorescent paper. Exceptions are 582paca and 610/qfa, which have PVA gum. Identification of fluorescent papers can be confirmed with the use of a UV lamp. Particular care is needed in the cases of Nos. 602c/ca and 606pf, where the listings refer to examples on the "hybrite" paper.

FLUORESCENT BANDS. During the second half of 1971 new sorting machines were installed in the Ottawa area which were activated by stamps bearing fluorescent bands. These differ from the Winnipeg phosphor bands in that they react green and have no after-glow. To the naked eye the fluorescent bands appear shiny when compared with the remainder of the stamp when looking along its surface. Winnipeg phosphor bands appear matt.

The experiments were successful and what was at first called "Ottawa tagging" has since come into more general use and the Winnipeg phosphor was phased out. However, the substance at first used (known as OP-4) was found to migrate to envelopes, documents, album pages, etc. as well as to adjoining stamps. Late in 1972 this fault was cured by using another substance (called OP-2). The migrating bands were used on early printings of Nos. 604q, 608q and 610q as well as certain stamps referred to in a footnote after No. 692. It is therefore advisable to use plastic mounts for housing stamps with migrating bands or else clear acetate should be affixed to the album leaves.

269 Canadian Pavilion | **270** Allegory of "Womanhood" on Ballot-box

(Des C.B.N.)

1967 (28 Apr). World Fair, Montreal. P 12.

611	**269**	5c. blue and red	10	10

(Des Helen Fitzgerald. Litho)

1967 (24 May). 50th Anniv of Women's Franchise. P 12.

612	**270**	5c. reddish purple and black	10	10

271 Queen Elizabeth II and Centennial Emblem | **272** Athlete

(Portrait from photo by Anthony Buckley)

1967 (30 June). Royal Visit. P 12.

613	**271**	5c. plum and orange-brown	15	10

(Des Brigdens Ltd.)

1967 (19 July). Fifth Pan-American Games, Winnipeg. P 12.

614	**272**	5c. rose-red	10	10

273 "World News" | **274** Governor-General Vanier

(Des W. McLauchlan)

1967 (31 Aug). 50th Anniv of the Canadian Press. P 12.

615	**273**	5c. blue	10	10

(Des from photo by Karsh)

1967 (15 Sept). Vanier Commemoration. P 12.

616	**274**	5c. black	10	10

PRINTERS. The following were printed either by the Canadian Bank Note Co, Ottawa (C.B.N.) or the British American Bank Note Co, Ottawa (B.A.B.N.), *except where otherwise stated.*

275 People of 1867 and Toronto, 1967 | **276** Carol Singers

(Des and recess C.B.N.)

1967 (28 Sept). Centenary of Toronto as Capital City of Ontario. P 12.

617	**275**	5c. myrtle-green and vermilion	10	10

(Des and recess B.A.B.N.)

1967 (11 Oct). Christmas. P 12.

618	**276**	3c. scarlet	10	10
		a. Pack. 2 blocks of 25	4·50	
		p. 2 phosphor bands	20	1·75
		pa. Pack. 2 blocks of 25	5·50	
619		5c. emerald-green	10	10
		p. 2 phosphor bands	70	1·50

Nos. 618a and 618pa are blocks with the outer edges imperf. These come from "$1.50 Plastic Packs" sold at post offices.

277 Grey Jays | **278** Weather Map and Instruments

(Des M. G. Loates. Litho C.B.N.)

1968 (15 Feb). Wild Life. P 12.

620	**277**	5c. multicoloured	30	10

See also Nos. 638/40.

WHITE FLUORESCENT PAPER. Different papers with varying degrees of whiteness have been used for Canadian stamps and it is understood that much of the paper contained a high percentage of recycled pulp. The fluorescent content of this paper varies, but during 1968–70 a distinctive very white and highly fluorescent paper was used known by the trade-name "hybrite"; this fluoresces on the back and front. Some issues were wholly printed on this paper, and these can be used for distinguishing those which appeared on ordinary paper as well, both being listed.

See also notes following No. 610qfa.

(Des and litho B.A.B.N.)

1968 (13 Mar). Bicentenary of First Meteorological Readings. P 11.

621	**278**	5c. multicoloured	15	10
		a. White fluorescent paper	1·00	

279 Narwhal | **280** Globe, Maple Leaf and Rain Gauge

(Des J. A. Crosby. Litho B.A.B.N.)

1968 (10 Apr). Wildlife. White fluorescent paper. P 11.

622	**279**	5c. multicoloured	15	10
		a. Ordinary paper	2·00	

No. 622 has a background of yellow-green and pale blue but copies are known with the yellow-green apparently missing. This "yellow-green" is produced by an overlay of yellow on the blue but we have not come across any examples where the yellow is completely missing and the wide range of colour variation is due to technical difficulties in maintaining an exact blend of the two colours.

(Des I. von Mosdossy. Litho B.A.B.N.)

1968 (8 May). International Hydrological Decade. P 11.

623	**280**	5c. multicoloured	15	10
		a. White fluorescent paper	40	

IMPERF EDGES. On Nos. 624/54, 657 and 659 (stamps printed by the B.A.B.N. Co.) the outer edges of the sheets were guillotined to remove the imprints for PO stock so that single stamps may, therefore, be found with either one, or two adjacent sides imperforate.

281 *Nonsuch*   **282** Lacrosse Players

(Recess and photo B.A.B.N.)

1968 (5 June). 300th Anniv of Voyage of the *Nonsuch*. P 10.
624 **281** 5c. multicoloured 20 20

(Des J. E. Aldridge. Recess and photo B.A.B.N.)
1968 (3 July). Lacrosse. P 10.
625 **282** 5c. black, red and lemon.................. 15 10

283 Front Page of *The Globe*, George Brown and Legislative Building   **284** H. Bourassa

(Des N. Sabolotny. Recess and photo B.A.B.N.)
1968 (21 Aug). 150th Birth Anniv of George Brown (politician and journalist). P 10.
626 **283** 5c. multicoloured 10 10

(Des, recess and litho C.B.N.)
1968 (4 Sept). Birth Centenary of Henri Bourassa (journalist and politician). White fluorescent paper. P 12.
627 **284** 5c. black, red and pale cream 10 10

285 John McCrae, Battlefield and First Lines of *In Flanders Fields*   **286** Armistice Monument, Vimy

(Des I. von Mosdossy. Litho C.B.N.)
1968 (15 Oct). 50th Death Anniv of John McCrae (soldier and poet). White fluorescent paper. P 12.
628 **285** 5c. multicoloured 10 10

(Des and recess C.B.N.)
1968 (15 Oct). 50th Anniversary of 1918 Armistice. P 12.
629 **286** 15c. slate-black.................................. 30 50

287 Eskimo Family (carving)   **288** Mother and Child (carving)

(Designs from Eskimo carvings by Munamee (6c.) and unknown carver (5c.). Photo C.B.N.)
1968. Christmas. White fluorescent paper. P 12.
630 **287** 5c. black and new blue (1.11.68) 10 10
    a. Booklet pane of 10 (15.11.68) ..... 2·25
    p. 1 centre phosphor band............. 10 1·75
    pa. Booklet pane of 10 (15.11.68) ... 3·00
631 **288** 6c. black and ochre (15.11.68) 10 10
    p. 2 phosphor bands........................ 20 2·00

289 Curling   **290** Vincent Massey

(Des D. Eales. Recess and photo B.A.B.N.)
1969 (15 Jan). Curling. P 10.
632 **289** 6c. black, new blue and scarlet 15 25

(Des I. von Mosdossy. Recess and litho C.B.N.)
1969 (20 Feb). Vincent Massey, First Canadian-born Governor-General. White fluorescent paper. P 12.
633 **290** 6c. sepia and yellow-ochre.............. 10 10

291 *Return from the Harvest Field* (Suzor-Côté)   **292** Globe and Tools

(Photo C.B.N.)
1969 (14 Mar). Birth Centenary of Marc Aurèle de Foy Suzor-Côté (painter). White fluorescent paper. P 12.
634 **291** 50c. multicoloured .... 1·50 3·25

(Des J. Hébert. Recess B.A.B.N.)
1969 (21 May). 50th Anniv of International Labour Organisation. White fluorescent paper. P 12½×12.
635 **292** 6c. bronze-green 10 10
    a. Ordinary paper.............................. 1·00

293 Vickers FB-27 Vimy Aircraft over Atlantic Ocean   **294** *Sir William Osler* (J. S. Sargent)

(Des R. W. Bradford. Recess and photo B.A.B.N.)
1969 (13 June). 50th Anniv of First Non-stop Transatlantic Flight. White fluorescent paper. P 12×12½.
636 **293** 15c. chocolate, bright green and pale blue........................... 40 1·50

(Des, recess and photo B.A.B.N.)
1969 (23 June). 50th Death Anniv of Sir William Osler (physician). P 12½×12.
637 **294** 6c. deep blue, light blue and chestnut.................... 20 10
    a. White fluorescent paper.............. 80

295 White-throated Sparrows   **298** Flags of Winter and Summer Games

(Des M. G. Loates. Litho C.B.N.)
1969 (23 July). Birds. T **295** and similar multicoloured designs. White fluorescent paper. P 12.
638 6c. Type **295**............................... 25 10
639 10c. Savannah Sparrow ("Ipswich Sparrow") (*horiz*) .... 35 1·25
640 25c. Hermit Thrush (*horiz*) .... 1·10 3·75
638/40 *Set of 3*.. 1·50 4·50

(Des C. McDiarmid. Recess and litho C.B.N.)
1969 (15 Aug). Canadian Games. White fluorescent paper. P 12.
641 **298** 6c. emerald, scarlet and blue 10 10

299 Outline of Prince Edward Island showing Charlottetown   **300** Sir Isaac Brock and Memorial Column

(Des L. Fitzgerald. Recess and photo B.A.B.N.)
1969 (15 Aug). Bicentenary of Charlottetown as Capital of Prince Edward Island. White fluorescent paper. P 12½×12.
642 **299** 6c. yellow-brown, black and blue... 20 20
    a. Ordinary paper.............................. 80

(Des I. von Mosdossy. Recess and litho C.B.N.)
1969 (12 Sept). Birth Bicentenary of Sir Isaac Brock. P 12.
643 **300** 6c. orange, bistre and bistre-brown 10 10

301 Children of the World in Prayer   **302** Stephen Butler Leacock, Mask and "Mariposa"

(Des Rapid Grip and Batten Ltd. Litho C.B.N.)
1969 (8 Oct). Christmas. White fluorescent paper. P 12.
644 **301** 5c. multicoloured 10 10
    a. Booklet pane of 10 .... 1·50
    p. 1 centre phosphor band............. 10 1·75
    pa. Booklet pane of 10 .... 2·50
645 6c. multicoloured 10 10
    a. Black (inscr, value and frame omitted) £1700 £1300
    p. 2 phosphor bands........................ 20 1·75

(Des, recess and photo B.A.B.N.)
1969 (12 Nov). Birth Centenary of Stephen Butler Leacock (humorist). P 12×12½.
646 **302** 6c. multicoloured 10 10

303 Symbolic Cross-roads   **304** "Enchanted Owl" (Kenojuak)

(Des K. C. Lochhead. Litho C.B.N.)
1970 (27 Jan). Centenary of Manitoba. P 12.
647 **303** 6c. ultramarine, lemon and vermilion 15 10
    p. 2 phosphor bands........................ 15 1·75

(Des N. E. Hallendy and Miss S. Van Raalte. Recess C.B.N.)
1970 (27 Jan). Centenary of Northwest Territories. White fluorescent paper. P 12.
648 **304** 6c. carmine, red and black................ 10 10

305 Microscopic View of Inside of Leaf   **306** Expo 67 Emblem and Stylized Cherry Blossom

(Des I. Charney. Recess and photo B.A.B.N.)
1970 (18 Feb). International Biological Programme. P 12×12½.
649 **305** 6c. emerald, orange-yellow and ultramarine 15 10

(Des E. R. C. Bethune. Litho C.B.N.)
1970 (18 Mar). World Fair, Osaka. T **306** and similar horiz designs. Multicoloured; colour of Cherry Blossom given. P 12.
650 25c. red .... 1·50 2·25
    a. Block of 4. Nos. 650/3 .... 5·50 8·00
    p. 2 phosphor bands........................ 1·50 2·75
    pa. Block of 4. Nos. 650p/3p............ 5·50 10·00
651 25c. violet .... 1·50 2·25
    p. 2 phosphor bands........................ 1·50 2·75
652 25c. green .... 1·50 2·25
    p. 2 phosphor bands........................ 1·50 2·75
653 25c. blue .... 1·50 2·25
    p. 2 phosphor bands........................ 1·50 2·75
650/3 *Set of 4* .... 5·50 8·00
650p/3p *Set of 4* .... 5·50 10·00

Designs:—No. 650, Type **306**; No. 651, Dogwood and stylized cherry blossom; No. 652, White Trillium and stylized cherry blossom; No. 653, White Garden Lily and stylized cherry blossom.
Nos. 650/3 and 650p/3p are printed together in sheets of 50 (5×10). In the first, second, fourth and fifth vertical rows the four different designs are arranged in *se-tenant* blocks, whilst the centre row is composed as follows (reading downwards:—650(p)/3(p), 650(p)×2, 653(p), 651(p), 652(p) and 650(p).

310 Henry Kelsey   **311** "Towards Unification"

(Des D. Burton. Recess and photo B.A.B.N.)
1970 (15 Apr). 300th Birth Anniv of Henry Kelsey (explorer). P 12×12½.
654 **310** 6c. multicoloured 10 10

(Des B. Fisher. Litho B.A.B.N.)
1970 (13 May). 25th Anniv of United Nations. P 11.
655 **311** 10c. blue .... 40 1·50
    p. 2 phosphor bands........................ 60 3·25
656 15c. magenta and bluish lilac 40 50
    p. 2 phosphor bands........................ 60 3·00

312 Louis Riel
(Métis leader)

313 Mackenzie's
Inscription, Dean
Channel

(Des R. Derreth. Photo B.A.B.N.)

1970 (19 June). Louis Riel Commemoration. P 12½×12.

657	**312**	6c. greenish blue and vermilion......	10	10

(Design from Government Archives photo. Recess C.B.N.)

1970 (25 June). Sir Alexander Mackenzie (explorer). White fluorescent paper. P 12×11½.

658	**313**	6c. bistre-brown	15	10

314 Sir Oliver Mowat
(statesman)

315 Isles of Spruce
(A. Lismer)

(Des E. Roch. Recess and photo B.A.B.N.)

1970 (12 Aug). Sir Oliver Mowat Commemoration. P 12×12½.

659	**314**	6c. vermilion and black.......................	10	10

(Litho Ashton-Potter)

1970 (18 Sept). 50th Anniv of "Group of Seven" (artists). P 11.

660	**315**	6c. multicoloured.......................	10	10

316 Horse-drawn Sleigh
(D. Niskala)

317 Christ in Manger
(C. Fortier)

(Des from children's drawings. Litho C.B.N.)

1970 (7 Oct). Christmas. Horiz designs as T **316/17**, showing children's drawings. Multicoloured. White fluorescent paper. P 12.

661		5c. Type **316**............................	30	20
	a.	Strip of 5. Nos. 661/5	1·40	2·50
	p.	1 centre phosphor band............	55	1·25
	pa.	Strip of 5. Nos. 661p/5p........	2·50	5·00
662		5c. Stable and Star of Bethlehem		
		(L. Wilson) (26×21 mm)............	30	20
	p.	1 centre phosphor band............	55	1·25
663		5c. Snowmen (M. Lecompte) (26×21		
		mm)..................................	30	20
	p.	1 centre phosphor band............	55	1·25
664		5c. Skiing (D. Durham) (26×21 mm).......	30	20
	p.	1 centre phosphor band............	55	1·25
665		5c. Santa Claus (A. Martin)		
		(26×21 mm)........................	30	20
	p.	1 centre phosphor band............	55	1·25
666		6c. Santa Claus (E. Bhattacharya)		
		(26×21 mm)........................	30	20
	a.	Strip of 5. Nos. 666/70........	1·40	2·50
	p.	2 phosphor bands................	55	1·25
	pa.	Strip of 5. Nos. 666p/70p........	2·50	5·00
667		6c. Christ in Manger (J. McKinney)		
		(26×21 mm)........................	30	20
	p.	2 phosphor bands................	55	1·25
668		6c. Toy Shop (N. Whateley) (26×21 mm)......	30	20
	p.	2 phosphor bands................	55	1·25
669		6c. Christmas Tree (J. Pomperleau)		
		(26×21 mm)........................	30	20
	p.	2 phosphor bands................	55	1·25
670		6c. Church (J. McMillan) (26×21 mm)......	30	20
	p.	2 phosphor bands................	55	1·25
671		10c. Type **317**.......................	25	30
	p.	2 phosphor bands................	45	1·25
672		15c. Trees and Sledge (J. Dojcak)		
		(35×24 mm)........................	35	60
	p.	2 phosphor bands................	55	1·75
661/72		Set of 12	3·25	2·50
661p/672p		Set of 12	6·00	12·50

The designs of the 5c. and 6c. were each issued with the various designs se-tenant in a diamond-shaped arrangement within the sheet. This generally results in se-tenant pairs both vert and horiz, but due to the sheet arrangement vert and horiz pairs of the same design exist from the two centre vert and horiz rows.

328 Sir Donald
A. Smith

(Des Dora de Pédery-Hunt. Litho C.B.N.)

1970 (4 Nov). 150th Birth Anniv of Sir Donald Alexander Smith. P 12.

673	**328**	6c. yellow, brown and bronze-green...	15	10

STAMP BOOKLETS

Booklet Nos. SB1/60 are stapled.

All booklets up to and including No. SB41 contain panes consisting of two rows of three (3×2).

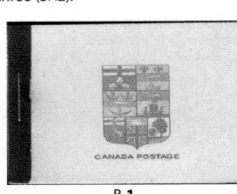

B 1

1900 (11 June). Red on pink cover. Two panes of 6× 2c. (No. 155ba).

SB1	25c. booklet. Cover as Type B **1** with English text......................................	£2000

1903 (1 July). Red on pink cover. Two panes of 6× 2c. (No. 176a).

SB2	25c. booklet. Cover as Type B **1** with English text	£2500

1912 (Jan)–**16**. Red on pink cover. Two panes of 6× 2c. (No. 201a).

SB3	25c. booklet. Cover as Type B **1** with English text......................................	65·00
	a. Cover handstamped "NOTICE Change in Postal Rates For New Rates See Postmaster".	65·00
	b. French text (4.16)........................	£160
	ba. Cover handstamped "AVIS Changement des tarifs Postaux Pour les nouveaux tarifs consulter le maitre de poste".................	£120

1913 (1 May)–**16**. Green on pale green cover. Four panes of 6× 1c. (No. 197a).

SB4	25c. booklet. Cover as Type B **1** with English text	£450
	a. Containing pane No. 199a.....................	90·00
	ab. Cover handstamped "NOTICE Change in Postal Rates For New Rates See Postmaster".	90·00
	b. French text (28.4.16)........................	£700
	ba. Containing pane No. 199a..................	£225
	bb. Cover handstamped "AVIS Changement des tarifs Postaux Pour les nouveaux tarifs consulter le maitre de poste".................	£750

1922 (Mar). Black on brown cover. Two panes of 4× 3c. and two labels (No. 205a).

SB5	25c. booklet. Cover as Type B **1** with English text	£350
	a. French text................................	£700

1922 (July–Dec). Black on blue cover. Panes of 4× 1c., 2c. and 3c each. (Nos. 246aa, 247aa, 205a) and two labels.

SB6	25c. booklet. Cover as Type B **1** with English text	£350
	a. French text (12.22)........................	£650

1922 (Dec). Black on orange cover. Four panes of 6× 1c. (No. 246ab).

SB7	25c. booklet. Cover as Type B **1** with English text	£140
	a. French text................................	£170

1922 (Dec). Black on green cover. Two panes of 6× 2c. (No. 247ab).

SB8	25c. booklet. Cover as Type B **1** with English text	£600
	a. French text................................	£700

1923 (Dec). Black on blue cover. Panes of 4× 1c., 2c. and 3c each. (Nos. 246aa, 247aa, 248aa) and 2 labels.

SB9	25c. booklet. Cover as Type B **1** with English text	£250
	a. French text................................	£650

1923 (Dec)–**24**. Black on brown cover. Two panes of 4× 3c. (No. 248aa) and two labels.

SB10	25c. booklet. Cover as Type B **1** with English text	£200
	a. French text (5.24)........................	£375

B 2

1928 (16 Oct). Black on green cover. Two panes of 6× 2c. (No. 276a).

SB11	25c. booklet. Cover as Type B **2** with English text	65·00
	a. French text................................	£150

1928 (25 Oct). Black on orange cover. Four panes of 6× 1c. (No. 275a).

SB12	25c. booklet. Cover as Type B **2** with English text	£120
	a. French text................................	£300

1929 (6 Jan). Plain manilla cover. Three panes of 6× 1c., two panes of 6× 2c. and one pane of 6× 5c. (Nos. 275a, 276a, 279a).

SB13	72c. booklet. Plain cover......................	£400
	a. With "Philatelic Div., Fin. Br. P.O. Dept., Ottawa" circular cachet on front cover........	£1400
	b. With "1928" in the centre of the circular cachet......................................	£1500

1930 (17 June). Black on green cover. Two panes of 6× 2c. (No. 290a).

SB14	25c. booklet. Cover as Type B **2** with English text	£110
	a. French text................................	£200

1930 (17 Nov). Black on red cover. Two panes of 6× 2c. (No. 291a).

SB15	25c. booklet. Cover as Type B **2** with English text	65·00
	a. French text................................	£160

1931 (13 July). Black on red cover. Two panes of 4× 3c. (No. 293a) and two labels.

SB16	25c. booklet. Cover as Type B **2** with English text	85·00
	a. French text................................	£130

1931 (21 July). Black on green cover. Four panes of 6× 1c. (No. 289b).

SB17	25c. booklet. Cover as Type B **2** with English text	£130
	a. French text................................	£200

1931 (23 July). Black on brown cover. Two panes of 6× 2c. (No. 292a).

SB18	25c. booklet. Cover as Type B **2** with English text	£140
	a. French text................................	£450

1931 (13 Nov). Black on blue cover. Panes of 4× 1c., 2c. and 3c each. (Nos. 289db, 292ba, 293a) and 2 labels.

SB19	25c. booklet. Cover as Type B **2** with English text	£300
	a. French text................................	£500

1933 (22 Aug–13 Nov). Black on red cover. Two panes of 4× 3c. (No. 321a) and two labels.

SB20	25c. booklet. Cover as Type B **2** with English text (13 Nov)........................	90·00
	a. French text (22.8)........................	£170

1933 (7 Sept). Black on brown cover. Two panes of 6× 2c. (No. 320a).

SB21	25c. booklet. Cover as Type B **2** with English text	£225
	a. French text................................	£450

1933 (19 Sept–5 Dec). Black on blue cover. Panes of 4× 1c., 2c. and 3c each. (Nos. 319b, 320b, 321ba) and two labels.

SB22	25c. booklet. Cover as Type B **2** with English text	£200
	a. French text (5.12)........................	£300

1933 (28 Dec)–**34**. Black on green cover. Four panes of 6× 1c. (No. 319a).

SB23	25c. booklet. Cover as Type B **2** with English text	£150
	a. French text (26.3.34)........................	£225

B 3

1935 (1 June–8 Aug). Red on white cover. Two panes of 4× 3c. (No. 343a) and two labels.

SB24	25c. booklet. Cover as Type B **3** with English text (8.8)................................	65·00
	a. French text (1.6)........................	£110

1935 (22 July–1 Sept). Blue on white cover. Panes of 4× 1c., 2c. and 3c each. (Nos. 341b, 342b, 343a) and two labels.

SB25	25c. booklet. Cover as Type B **3** with English text	£150
	a. French text (.9)........................	£190

1935 (19 Aug–18 Oct). Green on white cover. Four panes of 6× 1c. (No. 341a).

SB26	25c. booklet. Cover as Type B **3** with English text	90·00
	a. French text (18.10)........................	£130

1935 (16–18 Mar). Brown on white cover. Two panes of 6× 2c. (No. 342a).

SB27	25c. booklet. Cover as Type B **3** with English text	70·00
	a. French text (18.3)........................	£120

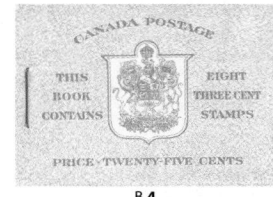

B 4

1937 (14 Apr)–**38**. Blue and white cover. Panes of 4× 1c., 2c. and 3c each. (Nos. 357a, 358a, 359a) and two labels.

SB28	25c. booklet. Cover as Type B **3** with English text	85·00
	a. French text (4.1.38)........................	£150
SB29	25c. booklet. Cover as Type B **4** with English text 57 mm wide	70·00
	a. English text 63 mm wide....................	£120
	b. French text 57 mm wide (4.1.38)............	95·00
	ba. French text 63 mm wide....................	£190

1937 (23–27 Apr). Red and white cover. Two panes of 4× 3c. (No. 359a) and two labels.

SB30	25c. booklet. Cover as Type B **3** with English text (27.4)................................	50·00
	a. French text (23.4)........................	65·00
SB31	25c. booklet. Cover as Type B **4** with English text 57 mm wide (27.4)........................	10·00
	a. English text 63 mm wide....................	65·00
	b. French text 57 mm wide (23.4)............	13·00
	ba. French text 63 mm wide....................	£180

1937 (18 May)–**38**. Green and white cover. Four panes of 6× 1c. (No. 357b).

SB32	25c. booklet. Cover as Type B **3** with English text	60·00
	a. French text (14.10.38)........................	75·00
SB33	25c. booklet. Cover as Type B **4** with English text 57 mm wide	40·00
	a. English text 63 mm wide....................	75·00
	b. French text 57 mm wide (14.10.38)........	22·00
	ba. French text 63 mm wide....................	£170

1938 (3 May)–**39**. Brown and white cover. Two panes of 6× 2c. (No. 358b).

SB34	25c. booklet. Cover as Type B **3** with English text	60·00
	a. French text (3.3.39)........................	85·00
SB35	25c. booklet. Cover as Type B **4** with English text 57 mm wide	26·00
	a. English text 63 mm wide....................	85·00
	b. French text 57 mm wide....................	35·00
	ba. French text 63 mm wide....................	£120

1942 (20–29 Aug). Red and white cover. Two panes of 4× 3c. (No. 377a) and two labels.
SB36 25c. booklet. Cover as Type B **4** with English text ...... 8·50
   a. French text (29.8) .... 12·00

1942 (12–14 Sept). Violet and white cover. Panes of 4× 1c., 2c. and 3c each. (Nos. 375a, 376a, 377a), each with two labels.
SB37 25c. booklet. Cover as Type B **4** with English text (14.9) .... 48·00
   a. French text (12.9) .... 90·00

1942 (6 Oct)–**43**. Brown and white cover. Two panes of 6× 2c. (No. 376b).
SB38 25c. booklet. Cover as Type B **4** with English text ...... 55·00
   a. French text (6.4.43) .... 70·00

1942 (24 Nov)–**46**. Green and white cover. Four panes of 6× 1c. (No. 375b).
SB39 25c. booklet. Cover as Type B **4** with English text ...... 11·00
   a. French text (16.2.43) .... 17·00
   b. Bilingual text (8.1.46) .... 42·00

1943 (3 May)–**46**. Orange and white cover. One pane of 6× 4c. (No. 380a).
SB40 25c. booklet. Cover as Type B **4** with English text ...... 4·00
   a. French text (12.5.43) .... 15·00
   b. Bilingual text (8.1.46) .... 18·00

1943 (28 Aug)–**46**. Purple and white cover. Two panes of 4× 3c. (No. 378a) and two labels.
SB41 25c. booklet. Cover as Type B **4** with English text ...... 10·00
   a. French text (7.9.43) .... 28·00
   b. Bilingual text (8.1.46) .... 22·00

B **5**

1943 (1 Sept)–**46**. Black and white cover. Panes of 3× 1c., 3c. and 4c each. (Nos. 394a, 395a, 396a) (3×1).
SB42 25c. booklet. Cover as Type B **5** with English text ...... 55·00
   a. French text (18.9.43) .... 70·00
   c. Bilingual text (23.1.46) .... 65·00

B **6**

1947 (24 Nov). Brown on orange cover. Panes of 6× 3c. and 4c each. (3×2) and two panes of 4× 7c. (2×2) (Nos. 378b, 380a, 407a).
SB43 $1 booklet. Cover as Type B **6** with English text ...... 25·00
   a. French text .... 40·00

1950 (12 Apr–18 May). Purple and white cover. Two panes of 4× 3c. (No. 416a) and two labels (3×2).
SB44 25c. booklet. Cover as Type B **4** with English text ...... 5·00
   a. Bilingual text (18.5) .... 5·00

1950 (5–10 May). Orange and white cover. One pane of 6× 4c. (No. 417a) (3×2).
SB45 25c. booklet. Cover as Type B **4** with English text ...... 35·00
   a. Stitched .... 60·00
   b. Bilingual text (10.5) .... 55·00

1950 (18 May). Black and white cover. Panes of 3× 1c., 3c. and 4c. each (Nos. 422ba, 423a, 423ba) (3×1).
SB46 25c. booklet. Cover as Type B **5** with English text ...... 55·00
   a. Bilingual text .... 75·00

1951 (2 June). Orange and white cover. One pane of 6× 4c. (No. 417b) (3×2).
SB47 25c. booklet. Cover as Type B **4** with English text ...... 6·00
   a. Stitched .... 12·00
   b. Bilingual text .... 12·00

1951 (25 Oct)–**52**. Black and white cover. Panes of 3× 1c., 3c. and 4c. each (Nos. 422ba, 423a, 423ca) (3×1).
SB48 25c. booklet. Cover as Type B **5** with English text ...... 55·00
   a. Bilingual text (9.7.52) .... 70·00

1953 (6 July–19 Aug). Orange cover. One pane of 6× 4c. (No. 453a) (3×2).
SB49 25c. booklet. Cover as Type B **4** with English text ...... 5·00
   a. Bilingual text (19.8) .... 11·00

1953 (17 July–20 Oct). Purple cover. Two panes of 4× 3c. (No. 452a) and two labels (3×2).
SB50 25c. booklet. Cover as Type B **4** with English text ...... 4·50
   a. Bilingual text (20.10) .... 18·00

1953 (12 Aug). Grey cover. Panes of 3× 1c., 3c. and 4c. each (Nos. 458a, 459a, 460a) (3×1).
SB51 25c. booklet. Cover as Type B **5** with English text ...... 17·00
   a. Bilingual text .... 40·00

All the following booklets are bilingual

1954 (1 Apr–Nov). Blue cover as Type B **4**.
SB52 25c. booklet containing pane of 5× 5c. and one label (No. 473a) (3×2) .... 2·25
   a. Stitched (11.54) .... 3·25

1954 (14 July–Nov). Blue cover as Type B **4**.
SB53 25c. booklet containing pane of 5× 5c. and one label (No. 467a) (3×2) .... 2·75
   a. Stitched (11.54) .... 6·00

1955 (7 July). Violet cover as Type B **4**.
SB54 25c. booklet containing pane of 6× 4c. (No. 466a) (3×2) .... 4·75

B **7**

1956 (1 June). Red and white cover as Type B **7**.
SB55 25c. booklet containing two panes of 5× 1c. and 5× 4c., each with one label (Nos. 463a, 466a) (3×2) .... 3·50

1956 (July). Blue and white cover as Type B **7**.
SB56 25c. booklet containing pane of 5× 5c. and one label (No. 467a) (3×2) .... 2·75

B **8**

1963 (May)–**67**. Blue and white cover as Type B **7**.
SB57 25c. booklet containing pane of 5× 5c. and one label (No. 531a) (2×3) .... 7·50
   a. Cover Type B **8** (1.67) .... 48·00

1963 (15 May). Red and white cover as Type B **7**.
SB58 25c. booklet containing two panes of 5× 1c. and 5× 4c., each with one label (Nos. 527a, 530a) (2×3) .... 10·00

1967 (Feb). Red cover as Type B **8**.
SB59 25c. booklet containing two panes of 5× 1c. and 5× 4c., each with one label (Nos. 579a, 582a) (2×3) .... 3·00

1967 (Mar). Blue cover as Type B **8**.
SB60 25c. booklet containing pane of 5× 5c. and one label (No. 583a) (2×3) .... 6·00

B **9**

1968 (Sept). Brown and cream cover, 70×48 mm, as Type B **9**.
SB61 25c. booklet containing se-tenant pane of 5× 1c. and 5× 4c. (No. 598a) (2×5) .... 1·75

1968 (Sept). Red and cream cover as Type B **9**.
SB62 $1 booklet containing pane of 25× 4c. and two labels (No. 599a) (3×9) .... 6·50

1968 (Sept). Blue and cream cover, 82×48 mm, as Type B **9**.
SB63 $1 booklet containing pane of 20× 5c. (No. 600a) (2×10) .... 4·50

1968 (Oct). Orange and cream cover, 70×48 mm, as Type B **9**, but without border.
SB64 25c. booklet containing se-tenant pane of 1× 1c., 4 6c. and one label (No. 598b) (2×3) .... 2·00

B **10** (Illustration reduced. Actual size 128×60 mm)

1968 (15 Nov). Christmas. Red and green cover as Type B **10**.
SB65 $1 booklet containing two panes of 10× 5c. (No. 630a) (5×2) .... 4·50
   p. Phosphor (No. 630pa) .... 6·00
Nos. SB65/p exist with left or right opening (i.e. with selvedge at left or right of pane).

1969 (Jan). Orange-red on cream cover as Type B **9**, but without border.
SB66 $1.50, booklet containing pane of 25× 6c. and two labels (No. 601a) (3×9) .... 10·00

1969 (8 Oct). Christmas. Red cover size as Type B **10**.
SB67 $1 booklet containing two panes of 10× 5c. (No. 644a) (5×2) .... 3·00
   p. Phosphor (No. 644pa) .... 5·00

1970 (Jan). Black on cream cover as Type B **9**, but without border.
SB68 $1.50 booklet containing pane of 25× 6c. and two labels (No. 602a) (3×9) .... 16·00

1970 (Aug). Black on cream cover, 70×48 mm, as Type B **9**, but without border.
SB69 25c. booklet containing pane of 4× 6c. (No. 603a) (2×2) .... 12·00

1970 (Aug). Black on cream cover as Type B **9**, but without border.
SB70 $1.50 booklet containing pane of 25× 6c. and two labels (No. 607a) (3×9) .... 18·00

1970 (26 Oct). Indigo on cream cover, 70×50mm. Inscr "CANADIAN POSTAGE STAMPS ... MADE EXPRESSLY FOR OPAL MANUFACTURING CO. LIMITED".
SB71 25c. booklet containing 4× 2c. and 4× 3c. (No. 580b) (2×2) with gutter margin between ...... 1·75
No. SB71 was produced by the Canadian Bank Note Co for use in the private stamp-vending machines owned by the Opal Manufacturing Co Ltd, Toronto. To cover the cost of manufacture and installation these booklets were sold at 25c. each. They were not available from the Canadian Post Office.

1970 (Nov). Black on cream cover, 70×48 mm, as Type B **9**, but without border.
SB72 25c. booklet containing pane of 4× 6c. (No. 608a) (2×2) .... 4·00

REGISTRATION STAMPS

R **1**

(Eng and recess-printed British-American Bank Note Co, Montreal and Ottawa)

1875 (15 Nov)–**92**. White wove paper.

(a) P 12 (or slightly under)

R1	R **1**	2c. orange (1876)	65·00	1·00
R2		2c. orange-red (1889)	75·00	6·00
R3		2c. vermilion (1889)	90·00	10·00
		a. Imperf (pair)	†	£4500
R4		2c. rose-carmine (1888)	£150	55·00
R5		5c. yellow-green (12.1.76)	£120	1·50
R6		5c. deep green	90·00	1·25
		a. Imperf (pair)	£950	
R7		5c. blue-green (1889)	95·00	1·50
R7a		5c. dull sea-green (1892)	£150	3·50
R8		8c. bright blue	£450	£300
R9		8c. dull blue	£425	£275

(b) P 12×11½ or 12×11¾

R10	R **1**	2c. orange	£350	60·00
R11		5c. green (shades)	£1000	£150

SPECIAL DELIVERY STAMPS

PRINTERS. The following Special Delivery and Postage Due Stamps were recess-printed by the American Bank Note Co (to 1928), the British American Bank Note Co (to 1934), and the Canadian Bank Note Co (1935 onwards).

S **1**

1898–1920. P 12.

S1	S **1**	10c. blue-green (28.6.98)	90·00	16·00
S2		10c. deep green (12.13)	60·00	16·00
S3		10c. yellowish green (8.20)	70·00	18·00

The differences between Types I and II (figures "10" with and without shading) formerly illustrated were due to wear of the plate. There was only one die.

S **2**   S **3** Mail-carrying, 1867 and 1927

1922 (21 Aug). P 12.

S4	S **2**	20c. carmine-red	40·00	6·50

No. S4 exists in two slightly different sizes due to the use of "wet" or "dry" printing processes. See note below No. 195.

1927 (29 June). 60th Anniversary of Confederation. P 12.

S5	S **3**	20c. orange	13·00	20·00

No. S5 exists imperforate, imperf×perf or perf×imperf (Price, in each instance, £190 per pair, un).

S 4

1930 (2 Sept). P 11.
S6   S **4**   20c. brown-red .... 42·00   10·00

1932 (24 Dec). Type as S **4**, but inscr "CENTS" in place of "TWENTY CENTS". P 11.
S7   20c. brown-red .... 45·00   20·00
     No. S7 exists imperforate (*Price per pair £700, un*).

S **5** Allegory of Progress

(Des A. Foringer)

1935 (1 June). P 12.
S8   S **5**   20c. scarlet .... 5·00   5·00
     No. S8 exists imperforate (*Price per pair £750, un*).

S **6** Canadian Coat of Arms

1938–39. P 12.
S9   S **6**   10c. green (1.4.39) .... 24·00   4·00
S10   20c. scarlet (15.6.38) .... 42·00   28·00
     Nos. S9/10 exist imperforate (*Price £800, un, for each pair*).

(S **7**)

1939 (1 Mar). Surch with Type S **7**.
S11   S **6**   10c. on 20c. scarlet .... 10·00   20·00

S **8** Coat of Arms and Flags

S **9** Lockheed L.18 Lodestar

1942 (1 July)–**43**. War Effort. P 12.

(a) Postage
S12   S **8**   10c. green .... 13·00   60

(b) Air
S13   S **9**   16c. ultramarine .... 6·00   45
S14   17c. ultramarine (1.4.43) .... 4·50   55
     Nos. S12/14 exist imperforate (*Prices un pair 10c. £750, 16c. £900, 17c. £900*).

S **10** Arms of Canada and Peace Symbols

1946 (16 Sept–5 Dec). P 12.

(a) Postage
S15   S **10**   10c. green .... 12·00   1·75

(b) Air

(i) Circumflex accent in "EXPRÊS"
S16   S **11**   17c. ultramarine .... 4·50   9·50

(ii) Grave accent in "EXPRÈS"
S17   S **11**   17c. ultramarine (5.12.46) ...... 12·00   7·50

POSTAGE DUE STAMPS

PRINTERS. See note under "Special Delivery Stamps".

D **1**   D **2**

1906 (1 July)–**28**. P 12.
D1   D **1**   1c. dull violet .... 10·00   2·75
D2   1c. red-violet (1916) .... 18·00   4·25
D3   a. Thin paper (10.24) .... 16·00   23·00
D3   2c. dull violet .... 38·00   1·00
D4   2c. red-violet (1917) .... 35·00   2·25
       a. Thin paper (10.24) .... 32·00   23·00
D5   4c. violet (3.7.28) .... 50·00   65·00
D6   5c. dull violet .... 40·00   4·25
D7   5c. red-violet (1917) .... 50·00   5·50
       a. Thin paper (10.24) .... 20·00   40·00
D8   10c. violet (3.7.28) .... 32·00   26·00
D1/8 *Set of 5* .... £130   90·00
     The 1c., 2c. and 5c. values exist imperforate, without gum (*Price £375 for each un pair*).
     Printings up to October 1924 used the "wet" method, those from mid 1925 onwards the "dry". For details of the differences between these two methods, see above No. 196.

1930–32. P 11.
D9   D **2**   1c. bright violet (14.7.30) .... 8·50   11·00
D10   2c. bright violet (21.8.30) .... 7·50   2·25
D11   4c. bright violet (14.10.30) ...... 15·00   6·50
D12   5c. bright violet (12.12.31) ...... 16·00   42·00
D13   10c. bright violet (24.8.32) ...... 65·00   45·00
D9/13 *Set of 5* .... £100   95·00
     No. D13 exists imperf×perf (*Price for vertical pair £1200, un*).

D **3**   D **4**

1933–34. P 11.
D14   D **3**   1c. violet (5.5.34) .... 14·00   19·00
D15   2c. violet (20.12.33) .... 9·00   5·50
D16   4c. violet (12.12.33) .... 17·00   15·00
D17   10c. violet (20.12.33) .... 30·00   48·00
D14/17 *Set of 4* .... 60·00   80·00
     No. D14 exists imperforate (*Price per pair £400, un*).

1935–65. P 12.
D18   D **4**   1c. violet (14.10.35) 80   10
D19   2c. violet (9.9.35) .... 3·75   10
D20   3c. violet (4.65) .... 6·00   5·00
D21   4c. violet (2.7.35) .... 1·50   10
D22   5c. violet (12.48) .... 6·00   6·00
D23   6c. violet (1957) .... 2·00   1·75
D24   10c. violet (16.9.35) 70   10
D18/24 *Set of 7* .... 19·00   11·50
     The 1c., 2c., 4c. and 10c. exist imperforate (*Price £225 for each un pair*).

D **5**

1967–78. Litho. P 12½×12 (20c., 24c., 50c.) or 12 (others).

(a) Size 20×17½ mm
D25   D **5**   1c. scarlet (3.67) .... 2·00   6·00
D26   2c. scarlet (3.67) .... 1·50   1·00
D27   3c. scarlet (3.67) .... 2·75   7·00
D28   4c. scarlet (2.67) .... 2·75   1·25
D29   5c. scarlet (3.67) .... 4·25   7·50
D30   6c. scarlet (2.67) .... 1·60   3·75
D31   10c. scarlet (1.67) .... 2·00   2·50
D25/31 *Set of 7* .... 15·00   26·00

(b) Size 19½×16 mm
D32   D **5**   1c. scarlet (12.69) .... 2·00   1·00
       a. White paper (1.74) 75   1·50
       b. White fluorescent paper ...... 4·00
       c. Perf 12½×12 (*white paper*) (9.12.77) 15   2·00
D33   2c. scarlet (*white paper*) (1973) .... 1·00   3·00
       a. White fluorescent paper ...... 7·50
D34   3c. scarlet (*white paper*) (1.74) .... 3·50   6·50
       a. White fluorescent paper ...... 5·00
D35   4c. scarlet (4.69) .... 2·00   60
       a. White paper (1.74) 60   60
       b. White fluorescent paper 60
       ba. Printed on the gummed side £750
       c. Perf 12½×12 (*white paper*) (9.12.77) 30   1·00
D36   5c. scarlet (2.69) .... 25·00   35·00
       c. Perf 12½×12 (*white paper*) (9.12.77) 30   2·00
D37   6c. scarlet (*white paper*) (1973) ...... 2·75   3·75
       a. White fluorescent paper ...... 5·00
D38   8c. scarlet (1.69) 30   45
       a. White paper (1.74) 60   45
       b. White fluorescent paper 75

---

       c. Perf 12½×12 (*white paper*) (28.6.78) 75   1·40
D39   10c. scarlet (4.69) .... 1·75   45
       a. White paper (1973) 40   45
       b. Perf 12½×12 (*white paper*) (9.77) 40   60
D40   12c. scarlet (1.69) 30   50
       a. White paper (1973) 30   1·00
       b. White fluorescent paper ...... 1·00
       c. Perf 12½×12 (*white paper*) (9.77) 80   1·50
D41   16c. scarlet (*white paper*) (1.74) ...... 5·50   6·50
D42   20c. scarlet (*white paper*) (9.12.77) 30   1·25
D43   24c. scarlet (*white paper*) (9.12.77) 30   1·50
D44   50c. scarlet (*white paper*) (9.12.77) 40   2·00
D32/44 *Set of 13* .... 14·00   27·00
     There are no records of dates of issue of the above but supplies were distributed to depots in the months indicated.
     The original 1969 printings of the 1, 4, 5, 8, 10 and 12c. on ordinary paper, and the 8c. and 12c. on white fluorescent paper (Nos. D38b, 40b), have shiny "Dextrine" gum. Later issues on white and white fluorescent ("hybrite") papers have PVA gum.

OFFICIAL STAMPS

Stamps perforated "O H M S" were introduced in May 1923 for use by the Receiver General's department in Ottawa and by the Assistant Receiver Generals' offices in provincial cities. From 1 July 1939 this use was extended to all departments of the federal government and such stamps continued to be produced until replaced by the "O.H.M.S." overprinted issue of 1949.

The perforated initials can appear either upright, inverted or sideways on individual stamps. The prices quoted are for the cheapest version. Stamps perforated with Type O **1** are only priced used. Only isolated examples are known mint and these are very rare.

A number of forged examples of the perforated "O.H.M.S." are known, in particular of Type O **1**. Many of these forged perforated initials were applied to stamps which had already been used and this can aid their detection. Genuine examples, postmarked after the perforated initials were applied, often show the cancellation ink bleeding into the holes.

(O **1**) (Five holes in vertical bars of "H")   (O **2**) (Four holes in vertical bars of "H")

1923 (May). Nos. 196/215 punctured as Type O **1**.
O1   **44**   1c. yellow-green .... —   50·00
O2   2c. carmine .... —   40·00
O3   3c. deep brown .... —   35·00
O4   5c. deep blue .... —   45·00
O5   7c. yellow-ochre .... —   70·00
O6   10c. reddish purple .... —   60·00
O7   20c. olive .... —   50·00
O8   50c. sepia .... —   75·00
O1/8 *Set of 8* .... —   £375

1923 (May). 50th Anniv of Confederation. No. 244 punctured as Type O **1**.
O9   **48**   3c. bistre-brown .... —   £275

1923 (May)–**31**. Nos. 246/55 and 263 punctured as Type O **1**.

(a) P 12
O10   **44**   1c. chrome-yellow (Die I) ...... —   40·00
       a. Die II (1925) .... —   40·00
O11   2c. deep green .... —   32·00
O12   3c. carmine (Die I) (12.23) .... —   32·00
       a. Die II (1924) .... —   35·00
O13   4c. olive-yellow .... —   48·00
O14   5c. violet .... —   42·00
       a. Thin paper (1924) .... —   48·00
O15   7c. red-brown (1924) .... —   50·00
O16   8c. blue (1925) .... —   65·00
O17   10c. blue .... —   48·00
O18   10c. bistre-brown (1925) ...... —   35·00
O19 $1 brown-orange (7.23) .... —   £110
O10/19 *Set of 10* .... —   £450

(b) P 12×8
O20   **44**   3c. carmine (Die II) (1931) .... —   90·00

1927 (29 June). 60th Anniv of Confederation. Nos. 266/73 punctured as Type O **1**.

(a) Commemorative issue
O21   **51**   1c. orange .... —   75·00
O22   **52**   2c. green .... —   85·00
O23   **53**   3c. carmine .... —   £100
O24   **54**   5c. violet .... —   65·00
O25   **55**   12c. blue .... —   £275
O21/5 *Set of 5* .... —   £550

(b) Historical issue
O26   **56**   5c. violet .... —   70·00
O27   **57**   12c. green .... —   £250
O28   **58**   20c. carmine .... —   £180
O26/8 *Set of 3* .... —   £450

1928 (21 Sept). Air. No. 274 punctured as Type O **1**.
O29   **59**   5c. olive-brown .... —   £190

1928–29. Nos. 275/85 punctured as Type O **1**.
O30   **60**   1c. orange .... —   42·00
O31   2c. green .... —   30·00
O32   3c. lake .... —   75·00
O33   4c. olive-bistre .... —   £100
O34   5c. violet .... —   35·00
O35   8c. blue .... —   85·00
O36   **61**   10c. green .... —   28·00
O37   **62**   12c. grey-black .... —   £275
O38   **63**   20c. lake .... —   75·00
O39   **64**   50c. blue .... —   £450
O40   **65** $1 olive-green .... —   £375
O30/40 *Set of 11* .... —   £1400

1930–31. Nos. 288/97 and 300/5 punctured as Type O **1**.
O41   **66**   1c. orange (Die I) .... —   45·00
O42   1c. green (Die I) .... —   26·00
       a. Die II .... —   24·00
O43   2c. green (Die I) .... —   £110

O44		2c. scarlet (Die I)	—	35·00
		a. Die II	—	30·00
O45		2c. deep brown (Die I)	—	35·00
		a. Die II	—	32·00
O46		3c. scarlet	—	24·00
O47		4c. yellow-bistre	—	75·00
O48		5c. violet	—	50·00
O49		5c. deep slate-blue	—	42·00
O50		8c. blue	—	90·00
O51		8c. red-orange	—	65·00
O52	67	10c. olive-green	—	35·00
O53	68	12c. grey-black	—	£200
O54	69	20c. red	—	90·00
O55	70	50c. blue	—	£140
O56	71	$1 olive-green	—	£275
O41/56 Set of 15			—	£1100

1930 (4 Dec). Air. No. 310 punctured as Type O **1**.

O57		5c. deep brown	—	£275

1931 (30 Sept). No. 312 punctured as Type O **1**.

O58	73	10c. olive-green	—	48·00

1932 (22 Feb). Air. No. 313 punctured as Type O **1**.

O59	59	6c. on 5c. olive-brown	—	£200

1932 (21 June). Nos. 314/a punctured as Type O **1**.

O60	66	3c. on 2c. scarlet (Die I)	—	48·00
		a. Die II	—	40·00

1932 (12 July). Ottawa Conference. Nos. 315/18 punctured as Type O **1**.

(a) Postage

O61	76	3c. scarlet	—	35·00
O62	77	5c. blue	—	75·00
O63	78	13c. green	—	£300

(b) Air

O64	72	6c. on 5c. deep brown	—	£250
O61/4 Set of 4			—	£600

1932–33. Nos. 319/25 punctured as Type O **1**.

O65	80	1c. green	—	24·00
O66		2c. sepia	—	24·00
O67		3c. scarlet	—	24·00
O68		4c. yellow-brown	—	£100
O69		5c. blue	—	45·00
O70		8c. red-orange	—	£100
O71	68	13c. bright violet	—	90·00
O65/71 Set of 7			—	£375

1933 (18 May). UPU Congress Preliminary Meeting. No. 329 punctured as Type O **1**.

O72	81	5c. blue	—	£100

1933 (24 July). World's Grain Exhibition and Conference, Regina. No. 330 punctured as Type O **1**.

O73	69	20c. red	—	£130

1933 (17 Aug). Centenary of First Trans-Atlantic Steamboat Crossing. No. 331 punctured as Type O **1**.

O74	83	5c. blue	—	£100

1934 (1 July). Fourth Centenary of Discovery of Canada. No. 332 punctured as Type O **1**.

O75	84	3c. blue	—	£110

1934 (1 July). 150th Anniv of Arrival of United Empire Loyalists. No. 333 punctured as Type O **1**.

O76	85	10c. olive-green	—	£140

1934 (16 Aug). 150th Anniv of Province of New Brunswick. No. 334 punctured as Type O **1**.

O77	86	2c. red-brown	—	£140

1935 (4 May). Silver Jubilee. Nos. 335/40 punctured as Type O **1**.

O78	87	1c. green	—	75·00
O79	88	2c. brown	—	90·00
O80	89	3c. carmine-red	—	£100
O81	90	5c. blue	—	£120
O82	91	10c. green	—	£250
O83	92	13c. blue	—	£275
O78/83 Set of 6			—	£850

1935. Nos. 341/51 and 355 punctured as Type O **1**.

(a) Postage

O84	93	1c. green	—	28·00
O85		2c. brown	—	50·00
O86		3c. scarlet	—	48·00
O87		4c. yellow	—	90·00
O88		5c. blue	—	55·00
O89		8c. orange	—	90·00
O90	94	10c. carmine	—	75·00
O91	95	13c. purple	—	80·00
O92	96	20c. olive-green	—	90·00
O93	97	50c. deep violet	—	60·00
O94	98	$1 bright blue	—	£180

(b) Air

O95	99	6c. red-brown	—	£200
O84/95 Set of 12			—	£950

1937 (10 May). Coronation. No. 356 punctured as Type O **1**.

O96	100	3c. carmine	—	£100

1937–38. Nos. 357/67, 370 and 371 punctured as Type O **1**.

(a) Postage

O97	101	1c. green	—	5·00
O98		2c. brown	—	6·00
O99		3c. scarlet	—	8·00
O100		4c. yellow	—	20·00
O101		5c. blue	—	14·00
O102		8c. orange	—	35·00
O103	102	10c. rose-carmine	—	40·00
		a. Red	—	45·00
O104	103	13c. blue	—	55·00
O105	104	20c. red-brown	—	65·00
O106	105	50c. green	—	£130
O107	106	$1 violet	—	£225
O97/107 Set of 11			—	£550

(b) Coil stamp

O108	101	3c. scarlet	—	£130

(c) Air

O109	107	6c. blue	—	60·00

1939 (15 May). Royal Visit. Nos. 372/4 punctured as Type O **1**.

O110	108	1c. black and green	—	90·00
O111	109	2c. black and brown	—	95·00
O112	110	3c. black and carmine	—	90·00
O110/12 Set of 3			—	£250

1939 (1 July). Air. No. 274 punctured as Type O **2**.

O113	59	5c. olive-brown	32·00	22·00

1939 (1 July). Nos. 347/50 and 355 punctured as Type O **2**.

(a) Postage

O114	94	10c. carmine	£120	55·00
O115	95	13c. purple	£130	55·00
O116	96	20c. olive-green	£140	65·00
O117	97	50c. deep violet	£130	55·00

(b) Air

O118	99	6c. red-brown	£110	90·00
O114/18 Set of 5			£550	£275

1939 (1 July). Coronation. No. 356 punctured as Type O **2**.

O119	100	3c. carmine	£110	70·00

1939 (1 July). Nos. 357/67, 369/70 and 371 punctured as Type O **2**.

(a) Postage

O120	101	1c. green	3·25	1·00
O121		2c. brown	4·00	1·00
O122		3c. scarlet	4·25	1·00
O123		4c. yellow	9·50	5·50
O124		5c. blue	6·00	1·50
O125		8c. orange	23·00	7·50
O126	102	10c. rose-carmine	75·00	3·75
		a. Red	17·00	1·00
O127	103	13c. blue	30·00	3·25
O128	104	20c. red-brown	50·00	4·00
O129	105	50c. green	75·00	13·00
O130	106	$1 violet	£150	48·00
O120/30 Set of 11			£325	75·00

(b) Coil stamps

O131	101	2c. brown	£100	65·00
O132		3c. scarlet	£100	65·00

(c) Air

O133	107	6c. blue	5·50	2·00

1939 (1 July). Royal Visit. Nos. 372/4 punctured as Type O **2**.

O134	108	1c. black and green	£130	60·00
O135	109	2c. black and brown	£130	60·00
O136	110	3c. black and carmine	£130	60·00
O134/6 Set of 3			£350	£160

1942–43. War Effort. Nos. 375/88 and 399/400 punctured as Type O **2**.

(a) Postage

O137	111	1c. green	2·00	50
O138	112	2c. brown	2·00	50
O139	113	3c. carmine-lake	4·50	2·50
O140		3c. purple	3·50	30
O141	114	4c. slate	13·00	4·00
O142	112	4c. carmine-lake	2·50	30
O143	111	5c. blue	4·00	1·25
O144	–	8c. red-brown	16·00	4·00
O145	116	8c. red-brown	11·00	30
O146	117	13c. dull green	17·00	14·00
O147		14c. dull green	18·00	2·50
O148	118	20c. chocolate	25·00	2·00
O149	119	50c. violet	55·00	8·50
O150	120	$1 blue	£120	35·00

(b) Air

O151	121	6c. blue	7·00	8·50
O152		7c. blue	7·00	2·00
O137/52 Set of 16			£250	75·00

1946. Peace Re-conversion. Nos. 401/7 punctured as Type O **2**.

(a) Postage

O153	122	8c. brown	48·00	8·00
O154	123	10c. olive-green	5·00	20
O155	124	14c. sepia	17·00	3·00
O156	125	20c. slate	17·00	75
O157	126	50c. green	50·00	19·00
O158	127	$1 purple	85·00	25·00

(b) Air

O159	128	7c. blue	5·50	3·75
O153/9 Set of 7			£200	50·00

1949. Nos. 415 and 416 punctured as Type O **2**.

O160	136	2c. sepia	4·00	6·50
O161	137	3c. purple	4·00	6·00

O.H.M.S.

(O **3**)

1949. Nos. 375/6, 378, 380 and 402/7 optd as Type O **3** by typography.

(a) Postage

O162	111	1c. green	6·50	9·00
		a. Missing stop after "S"	£250	£150
O163	112	2c. brown	12·00	12·00
		a. Missing stop after "S"	£225	£150
O164	113	3c. purple	5·50	6·00
O165	112	4c. carmine-lake	6·50	5·50
O166	123	10c. olive-green	9·00	20
		a. Missing stop after "S"	£200	85·00
O167	124	14c. sepia	19·00	9·00
		a. Missing stop after "S"	£275	£150
O168	125	20c. slate	14·00	1·75
		a. Missing stop after "S"	£250	£110
O169	126	50c. green	£180	£170
		a. Missing stop after "S"	£1300	£1100
O170	127	$1 purple	45·00	70·00
		a. Missing stop after "S"	£6500	£6500

(b) Air

O171	128	7c. blue	24·00	15·00
		a. Missing stop after "S"	£275	£140
O162/71 Set of 10			£275	£275

Forgeries exist of this overprint. Genuine examples are 2.3×15 mm and show the tops of all letters aligned, as are the stops. The serifs are well defined and, in the case of the "S", they are vertical. The crossbar of the "H" is slightly above centre. Overprints applied by lithography are forgeries.

Only a few sheets of the $1 showed the variety, No. O170a.

MISSING STOP VARIETIES. These occur on R. 6/2 of the lower left pane (Nos. O162a, O163a, O175a and O176a). No. 176a occurs on R. 10/2 of the lower left pane (O166a, O167a, O168a, O169a, O170a and O171a). No. O176a also occurs on R. 8/8 of the upper left pane in addition to R. 6/2 of the lower left pane.

1949–50. Nos. 414/15, 416/17, 418 and 431 optd as Type O **3** by typography.

O172	135	1c. green	6·00	4·00
O173	136	2c. sepia	3·50	6·00
O174	137	3c. purple	2·75	3·75
O175	138	4c. carmine-lake	2·75	50
		a. Missing stop after "S"	£250	£150
O176	139	5c. blue (1949)	8·00	3·75
		a. Missing stop after "S"	£150	75·00
O177	141	50c. green (1950)	48·00	55·00
O172/7 Set of 6			65·00	65·00

G   G   G

(O **4**)   (O **5**)   (O **6**)

Variations in thickness are known in Type O **4** these are due to wear and subsequent cleaning of the plate. All are produced by typography. Examples showing the "G" applied by lithography are forgeries.

1950 (2 Oct)–**52.** Nos. 402/4, 406/7, 414/18 and 431 optd with Type O **4** (1 to 5c.) or O **5** (7c. to $1).

(a) Postage

O178	135	1c. green	1·50	10
O179	136	2c. sepia	7·00	8·00
O180		2c. olive-green (11.51)	1·75	10
O181	137	3c. purple	2·25	10
O182	138	4c. carmine-lake	8·00	2·00
O183		4c. vermilion (1.5.52)	3·00	60
O184	139	5c. blue	8·00	10
O185	123	10c. olive-green	3·00	10
O186	124	14c. sepia	23·00	14·00
O187	125	20c. slate	60·00	2·00
O188	126	50c. green	20·00	27·00
O189	127	$1 purple	80·00	85·00

(b) Air

O190	–	7c. blue	24·00	15·00
O178/90 Set of 13			£200	£130

1950–51. Nos. 432/3 optd with Type O **5**.

O191	142	10c. brown-purple	4·00	1·00
		a. Opt omitted in pair with normal	£950	£650
O192	143	$1 ultramarine	80·00	90·00

On a small number of sheets of 10c. the opt was omitted from R7/1.

1952–53. Nos. 441, 443 and 446 optd with Type O **5**.

O193	153	7c. blue (3.11.52)	2·00	3·50
O194	151	20c. grey (1.4.52)	3·00	20
O195	154	$1 black (2.2.53)	5·50	13·00
O193/5 Set of 3			9·50	5·50

1953 (1 Sept)–**61.** Nos. 450/4 and 462 optd with Type O **4** (1 to 5c.) or O **5** (50c.).

O196	158	1c. purple-brown	15	10
O197		2c. green	20	10
O198		3c. carmine	20	10
O199		4c. violet	30	10
O200		5c. ultramarine	30	10
O201	160	50c. deep bluish green (2.11.53)	3·25	6·00
		a. Opt Type O **6** (24.4.61*)	2·50	7·00
O196/201 Set of 6			3·25	6·00

*Earliest recorded date.

1955–56. Nos. 463/4 and 466/7 optd with Type O **4**.

O202	161	1c. purple-brown (12.11.56)	65	20
O203		2c. green (19.1.56)	15	20
O204		4c. violet (23.7.56)	40	1·00
O205		5c. bright blue (11.1.55)	15	10
O202/5 Set of 4			1·25	1·25

1955–62. Nos. 477 and 488 optd with Type O **5**.

O206	165	10c. purple-brown (21.2.55)	70	80
		a. Opt Type O **6** (28.3.62*)	40	2·75
O207	176	20c. green (4.12.56)	3·25	30
		a. Opt Type O **6** (10.4.62*)	5·50	2·50

*Earliest recorded date.

1963 (15 May). Nos. 527/8 and 530/1 optd as Type O **4**.

O208		1c. chocolate	50	6·50
		a. Opt double	£750	
O209		2c. green	1·00	6·50
		a. Type O **4** omitted (vert pair with normal)	£900	
O210		4c. carmine-red	60	2·25
O211		5c. ultramarine	50	16·00
O208/11 Set of 4			2·40	16·00

No. O209a comes from the top row of an upper pane on which the overprint was misplaced downwards by one row. Owing to the margin between the panes the top row of the bottom pane had the overprint at the top of the stamp.

OFFICIAL SPECIAL DELIVERY STAMPS

1923 (May). Nos. S3/4 punctured as Type O **1**.

OS1	S 1	10c. yellowish green	—	£300
OS2	S 2	20c. carmine-red	—	£300

1927 (29 June). 60th Anniv of Confederation. No. S5 punctured as Type O **1**.

OS3	S 3	20c. orange	—	£300

1930 (2 Sept). Inscr "TWENTY CENTS" at foot. No. S6 punctured as Type O **1**.

OS4	S 4	20c. brown-red	—	£250

1932 (24 Dec). Inscr "CENTS" at foot. No. S7 punctured as Type O **1**.

OS5	S 4	20c. brown-red	—	£225

1935 (1 June). No. S8 punctured as Type O **1**.

OS6	S 5	20c. scarlet	—	£225

1938–39. Nos. S9/10 punctured as Type O **1**.

OS7	S 6	10c. green	—	80·00
OS8		20c. scarlet	—	£150

1939 (1 Mar). No. S11 punctured as Type O **1**.
OS9   S **6**   10c. on 20c. scarlet.................................   —   £140

1939 (1 July). Inscr "CENTS" at foot. No. S7 punctured as Type O **2**.
OS10   S **4**   20c. brown-red.....................................   £300   £150

1939 (1 July). No. S8 punctured as Type O **2**.
OS11   S **5**   20c. scarlet...   £150   65·00

1939 (1 July). No. S9 punctured as Type O **2**.
OS12   S **6**   10c. green...   14·00   14·00

1939 (1 July). No. S11 punctured as Type O **2**.
OS13   S **6**   10c. on 20c. scarlet..............................   £180   75·00

1942–43. Nos. S12/14 punctured as Type O **2**.
(a) Postage
OS14   S **8**   10c. green...   17·00   15·00
(b) Air
OS15   S **9**   16c. ultramarine...................................   26·00   32·00
OS16   17c. ultramarine...................................   20·00   18·00

1946–47. Nos. S15/17 punctured as Type O **2**.
(a) Postage
OS17   S **10**   10c. green..   16·00   11·00
(b) Air
OS18   S **11**   17c. ultramarine (circumflex accent)   60·00   45·00
OS19   17c. ultramarine (grave accent)........   95·00   85·00

1950. No. S15 optd as Type O **3**, but larger.
OS20   S **10**   10c. green..   15·00   40·00

1950 (2 Oct). No. S15 optd as Type O **4**, but larger.
OS21   S **10**   10c. green..   26·00   30·00

The use of official stamps was discontinued on 31 December 1963.

Cape of Good Hope *see* South Africa

Cayman Islands

The first post office was opened at Georgetown in April 1889. The stamps of Jamaica with the following cancellations were used until 19 February 1901. At some stage, probably around 1891, a supply of the Jamaica 1889 1d., No. 27, was overprinted "CAYMAN ISLANDS", but these stamps were never issued. Two surviving examples are known, one unused and the other cancelled at Richmond in Jamaica.

Types of Jamaica

    2   **3**   **4**

    8   **11**

13

PRICES OF NOS. Z1/27. These are for a single stamp showing a clear impression of the postmark. Nos. Z1, 2, 6/8, 11/13, 18, 22, 25 and 26 are known used on cover and these are worth considerably more.

GEORGETOWN, GRAND CAYMAN

Z **1**

Z **2**   Z **3**

Stamps of JAMAICA cancelled with Type Z **1** in purple.
1889–94.
Z1	**8**	½d. yellow-green (No. 16)		£600
Z2	**11**	1d. purple and mauve (No. 27)		£600
Z2a	**2**	2d. slate (No. 20*a*)		£7500
Z3	**11**	2d. green (No. 28)		£950
Z4		2½d. dull purple and blue (No. 29)		£1300
Z5	**4**	4d. red-brown (No. 22*b*)		£4250

Stamps of JAMAICA cancelled with Type Z **2** in purple or black.
1895–98.
Z6	**8**	½d. yellow-green (No. 16)	£700
Z7	**11**	1d. purple and mauve (No. 27)	£600
Z8		2½d. dull purple and blue (No. 29)	£1000
Z9	**3**	3d. sage-green (No 21)	£6500

Stamps of JAMAICA cancelled with Type Z **3**
1898–1901.
Z10	**8**	½d. yellow-green (No. 16)	£600
		a. Green (No. 16*a*)	£600
Z11	**11**	1d. purple and mauve (No. 27)	£600
Z12	**13**	1d. red (No. 31) (1900)	£650
Z13	**11**	2½d. dull purple and blue (No. 29)	£850

OFFICIAL STAMPS

Stamps of JAMAICA cancelled with Type Z **1** in purple.
1890–94.
Z14	**8**	½d. green (No. O1) (*opt 17–17½ mm long*)...		£1400
Z15		½d. green (No. O3) (*opt 16 mm long*) (1893)		£3750
Z16	**11**	1d. rose (No. O4)		£1500
Z17		2d. grey (No. O5)		£6500

Stamps of JAMAICA cancelled with Type Z **2** in purple or black.
1895–98.
Z18	**8**	½d. green (No. O3)	£4250
Z19	**11**	1d. rose (No. O4)	£6500
Z20		2d. grey (No. O5)	£7500

STAKE BAY, CAYMAN BRAC

Z **4**

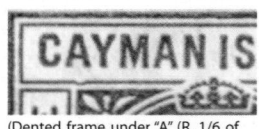

Z **5**

Stamps of JAMAICA cancelled with Type Z **4**.
1898–1900.
Z21	**8**	½d. yellow-green (No. 16)	£4500
Z22	**11**	1d. purple and mauve (No. 27)	£4250
Z23		2d. green (No. 28)	£7500
Z24		2½d. dull purple and blue (No. 29)	£4250

Stamps of JAMAICA cancelled with Type Z **5**.
1900–01.
Z25	**8**	½d. yellow-green (No. 16)	£5500
Z26	**11**	1d. purple and mauve (No. 27)	£5500
Z27	**13**	1d. red (No. 31)	£6000
Z28	**11**	2½d. dull purple and blue (No. 29)	£5500

PRICES FOR STAMPS ON COVER TO 1945	
Nos. 1/2	*from × 25*
Nos. 3/12	*from × 5*
Nos. 13/16	*from × 4*
Nos. 17/19	*from × 12*
Nos. 25/34	*from × 5*
Nos. 35/52b	*from × 4*
Nos. 53/67	*from × 5*
Nos. 69/83	*from × 4*
Nos. 84/95	*from × 6*
Nos. 96/9	*from × 5*
Nos. 100/11	*from × 4*
Nos. 112/14	*from × 6*
Nos. 115/26	*from × 2*

DEPENDENCY OF JAMAICA

    1   **2**   **3**

(T **1/3**, **8/9** and **12/13** typo D.L.R.)

1900 (1 Nov). Wmk Crown CA. P 14.
1	**1**	½d. deep green	21·00	27·00
		a. Pale green	15·00	23·00
2		1d. rose-carmine	17·00	4·50
		a. Pale carmine	21·00	16·00
1s/2s Optd "SPECIMEN" *Set of 2*			£170	

(Dented frame under "A" (R. 1/6 of left pane). (The variety is believed to have occurred at some point between 9 January and 9 April 1902 and is then present on all subsequent printings of the "POSTAGE POSTAGE" design)

1902 (1 Jan)–**03**. Wmk Crown CA. P 14.
3	**2**	½d. green (15.9.02)	6·00	28·00
		a. Dented frame	£300	
4		1d. carmine (6.3.03)	10·00	13·00
		a. Dented frame	£375	£400
5		2½d. bright blue	11·00	21·00
		a. Dented frame	£425	
6		6d. brown	35·00	70·00
		a. Dented frame	£750	£1100
7	**3**	1s. orange	60·00	£120
		a. Dented frame	£950	£1400
3/7 *Set of 5*			£110	£225
3s/7s Optd "SPECIMEN" *Set of 5*			£250	

1905 (Feb–Oct). Wmk Mult Crown CA. P 14.
8	**2**	½d. green	12·00	18·00
		a. Dented frame	£375	£425
9		1d. carmine (18.10)	24·00	17·00
		a. Dented frame	£550	£500
10		2½d. bright blue	12·00	5·50
		a. Dented frame	£375	£350
11		6d. brown	19·00	40·00
		a. Dented frame	£450	£600
12	**3**	1s. orange	29·00	48·00
		a. Dented frame	£650	
8/12 *Set of 5*			85·00	£110

1907 (13 Mar). Wmk Mult Crown CA. P 14.
13	**3**	4d. brown and blue	40·00	60·00
		a. Dented frame	£800	£1000

14	**2**	6d. olive and rose	45·00	75·00
		a. Dented frame	£800	£1000
15	**3**	1s. violet and green	60·00	90·00
		a. Dented frame	£950	
16		5s. salmon and green	£200	£325
		a. Dented frame	£5000	£6000
13/16 *Set of 4*			£300	£500
13s/16s Optd "SPECIMEN" *Set of 4*			£225	

One Halfpenny.
(4) (5) (6)

1907 (30 Aug). No. 9 surch at Govt Printing Office, Kingston, with T **4**.

17	**2**	½d. on 1d. carmine	60·00	85·00
		a. Dented frame	£1100	£1400

1907 (Nov). No. 16 handstamped at Georgetown PO with T **5** or **6**.

18	**3**	½d. on 5s. salmon and green (25.11)	£300	£450
		a. Surch inverted	£100000	
		b. Surch double	£12000	£11000
		c. Surch double, one inverted		
		d. Surch omitted (in pair with normal)	£100000	
19		1d. on 5s. salmon and green (23.11)	£275	£400
		a. Surch double	£22000	
		b. Surch inverted	£150000	
		c. Dented frame	£5000	£6000

The ½d. on 5s. may be found with the figures "1" or "2" omitted, owing to defective handstamping.

8   9   2½D (10)

1907 (27 Dec)–**09**. Chalk-surfaced paper (3d. to 10s.). P 14.

(a) Wmk Mult Crown CA

25	**8**	½d. green	5·00	4·00
26		1d. carmine	1·75	75
27		2½d. ultramarine (30.3.08)	7·00	2·50
28	**9**	3d. purple/yellow (30.3.08)	3·25	2·75
29		4d. black and red/yellow (30.3.08)	60·00	80·00
30	**8**	6d. dull purple and violet purple (2.10.08)	27·00	35·00
		a. Dull and bright purple	32·00	55·00
31	**9**	1s. black/green (5.4.09)	9·00	22·00
32		5s. green and red/yellow (30.3.08)	40·00	75·00

(b) Wmk Crown CA (30.3.08)

33	**9**	1s. black/green	65·00	£100
34	**8**	10s. green and red/green	£180	£250
25/34 *Set of 9*			£350	£500
25s/30s, 32s/4s Optd "SPECIMEN" *Set of 9*			£350	

1908 (12 Feb). No. 13 handstamped by J. H. O'Sullivan, Inspector of Police, with T **10**.

35	**3**	2½d. on 4d. brown and blue	£1800	£3500
		a. Surch double	£50000	£30000
		b. Dented frame	£24000	

No. 35 should only be purchased when accompanied by an expert committee's certificate or similar form of guarantee.

MANUSCRIPT PROVISIONALS. During May and June 1908 supplies of ½d. and 1d. stamps became exhausted, and the payment of postage was indicated by the postmistress, Miss Gwendolyn Parsons, using a manuscript endorsement. Such endorsements were in use from 12 May to 1 June.

MP1	"(Postage Paid G.A.P.)" (12.5 to 1.6)	£6000
MP1a	"(Postage Paid G.A.P.)1½" (23.5 to 1.6)	£8500
MP1b	"(Postage Paid G.A.P.)1" (23.5 to 1.6)	£7500

In October of the same year there was a further shortage of ¼d. stamps and the manuscript endorsements were again applied by either the new Postmaster, William Graham McCausland or by Miss Parsons who remained as his assistant.

MP2	"Pd ¼d.W.G. McC" (4.10 to 27.10)	£250
MP2a	¼d. Pd. W.G. McC" (14.10)	£1500
MP2b	"Pd ¼d.W.G. McC" (6.10)	£2000
MP3	"Paid" (7.10)	£13000
MP4	"Pd ¼d." (8.10)	£8500
MP5	"Paid ¼d/ GAP. asst." (15.10)	£11000

No. MP2 exists in different inks and formats. Nos. MP2 and MP2a show the endorsement in two lines, whereas it is in one line on No. MP2b.

Manuscript endorsement for the 2½d. rate is also known, but this is thought to have been done by oversight.

A 1d. surcharge on 4d. (No. 29), issued in mid-May, was intended as a revenue stamp and was never authorised for postal use (*price £250 un.*). Used examples were either cancelled by favour or passed through the post in error. Exists with surcharge inverted (*price £2000 un.*), surcharge double (*price £2750 un.*) or surcharge double, both inverted (*price £3000 un.*).

11   12   13

1908 (30 June)–**09**. Wmk Mult Crown CA. Litho. P 14.

38	**11**	¼d. brown	5·50	60
		a. Grey-brown (2.09)	7·00	1·00
		s. Optd "SPECIMEN"	95·00	

1912 (24 Apr)–**20**. Die I. Wmk Mult Crown CA. Chalk-surfaced paper (3d. to 10s.). P 14.

40	**13**	¼d. brown (10.2.13)	1·00	40
41	**12**	½d. green	2·75	5·00
		w. Wmk inverted	†	£1400
42		1d. red (25.2.13)	3·25	2·50
43	**13**	2d. pale grey	1·00	10·00
44	**12**	2½d. bright blue (26.8.14)	6·00	7·50
		a. Deep bright blue (9.11.17)	14·00	25·00
45	**13**	3d. purple/yellow (26.11.14)	15·00	45·00
		a. White back (19.11.13)	3·50	8·00
		b. On lemon (12.3.18)	4·00	18·00
		bs. Optd "SPECIMEN"	70·00	
		c. On orange-buff (1920)	10·00	32·00
		d. On buff (1920)		
		e. On pale yellow (1920)	4·50	30·00
46		4d. black and red/yellow (25.2.13)	1·00	10·00
47	**12**	6d. dull and bright purple (25.2.13)	5·00	8·00
48	**13**	1s. black/green (15.5.16)	3·50	27·00
		as. Optd "SPECIMEN"	65·00	
		b. White back (19.11.13)	3·50	3·50
49		2s. purple and bright blue/blue	15·00	65·00
50		3s. green and violet	19·00	75·00
51		5s. green and red/yellow (26.8.14)	85·00	£170
52	**12**	10s. deep green and red/green (26.11.14)	£150	£250
		as. Optd "SPECIMEN"	£110	
		b. White back (19.11.13)	£130	£190
		c. Deep olive-green, olive back (5.10.18)	£120	£250
40/52b *Set of 13*			£225	£500
40s/4s, 45as, 46s/7s, 48bs, 49s/51s, 52bs Optd "SPECIMEN" *Set of 13*			£425	

WAR STAMP. 1½d (14)   WAR STAMP. 1½d (15)   1½d Straight serif (Left-hand pane R. 10/2)

1917 (26 Feb). T **12** surch with T **14** or **15** at Kingston, Jamaica.

53	**14**	1½d. on 2½d. deep blue	20·00	26·00
		a. No fraction bar	£275	£300
		b. Missing stop after "STAMP" (R. 1/4)	£850	
54	**15**	1½d. on 2½d. deep blue	1·75	6·00
		a. No fraction bar	75·00	£140
		b. Straight serif	95·00	£180

On No. 53 "WAR STAMP" and "1½d." were applied separately.

WAR STAMP 1½d (16)   WAR STAMP 1½a (17)   WAR STAMP 1½d. (18)

1917 (4 Sept). T **12** surch with T **16** or **17** by D.L.R.

55	**16**	1½d. on 2½d. deep blue	£750	£2000
56	**17**	1½d. on 2½d. deep blue	30	60
		s. Optd "SPECIMEN"	£120	
		x. Wmk reversed		£170

De La Rue replaced surcharge Type **16** by Type **17** after only a few sheets as it did not adequately obliterate the original face value. A small quantity, said to be 3½ sheets, of Type **16** was included in the consignment in error.

1919–20. T **12** and **13** (2½d. special printing), optd only, or surch in addition at Kingston (No. **58**) or by D.L.R. (others).

57		½d. green (4.2.19)	60	2·50
		a. Short opt (right pane R. 10/1)	27·00	
58	**18**	1½d. on 2d. grey (10.3.20)	5·00	9·00
59	**17**	1½d. on 2½d. orange (4.2.19)	80	1·25
57s, 59s Optd "Specimen" *Set of 2*			£120	

No. 57 was overprinted with T **13** of British Virgin Islands.

The ½d. stamps on *buff* paper, and later consignments of the 2d. T **13** on *pinkish*, derived their colour from the paper in which they were packed for despatch from England.

No. 57a shows the overprint 2 mm high instead of 2½ mm.

A further surcharge as No. **58**, but in red, was prepared in Jamaica during April 1920, but these were not issued.

19   20 King William IV and King George V

1921 (4 Apr)–**26**. P 14.

(a) Wmk Mult Crown CA

60	**19**	3d. purple/orange-buff	1·50	8·00
		aw. Wmk inverted	£250	£325
		ay. Wmk inverted and reversed	£160	£200
		b. Purple/pale yellow	45·00	60·00
		bw. Wmk inverted	£375	
62		4d. red/yellow (1.4.22)	1·00	6·50
63		1s. black/green	1·25	10·00
		x. Wmk reversed	£550	
64		5s. yellow-green/pale yellow	16·00	70·00
		a. Deep green/pale yellow	£100	£160
		b. Blue-green/pale yellow	£110	£180
		c. Deep green/orange-buff (19.11.21)	£160	£225
67		10s. carmine/green (19.11.21)	75·00	£120
60/7 *Set of 5*			85·00	£190
60s/7s Optd "SPECIMEN" *Set of 5*			£225	

(b) Wmk Mult Script CA

69	**19**	¼d. yellow-brown (1.4.22)	50	1·50
		y. Wmk inverted and reversed	£325	
70		½d. pale grey-green (1.4.22)	50	30
		w. Wmk inverted		
		y. Wmk inverted and reversed	£500	
71		1d. deep carmine-red (1.4.22)	1·75	85
72		1½d. orange-brown (1.4.22)	1·75	30
73		2d. slate-grey (1.4.22)	1·75	4·50
74		2½d. bright blue (1.4.22)	50	30
		x. Wmk reversed	£500	
75		3d. purple/yellow (29.6.23)	3·75	5·50
		y. Wmk inverted and reversed	£500	
76		4½d. sage-green (29.6.23)	4·25	3·25
77		6d. claret (1.4.22)	5·50	35·00
		a. Deep claret	19·00	40·00
79		1s. black/green (15.5.25)	9·50	32·00
80		2s. violet/blue (1.4.22)	14·00	35·00
81		3s. violet (1.4.22)	23·00	16·00
82		5s. green/yellow (15.2.25)	30·00	55·00
83		10s. carmine/green (5.9.26)	70·00	£100
69/83 *Set of 14*			£140	£250
69s/83s Optd "SPECIMEN" *Set of 14*			£450	

An example of the 4d., No. 62, is known with the 'C' missing from the watermark in the top sheet margin.

"A.S.R." PROVISIONAL. On the night of 9/10 November 1932 the Cayman Brac Post Office at Stake Bay, and its contents, was destroyed by a hurricane. Pending the arrival of replacement stamp stocks and cancellation the Postmaster, Mr A. S. Rutty, initialled covers to indicate that postage had been paid. Those destined for overseas addresses additionally received a "Postage Paid" machine postmark in red when they passed through Kingston, Jamaica.

MP6	Endorsed "A.S.R." in manuscript	£11000
MP7	Endorsed "A.S.R." in manuscript and "Postage Paid" machine postmark in red	£16000

These emergency arrangements lasted until 19 December.

(Recess Waterlow)

1932 (5 Dec). Centenary of the "Assembly of Justices and Vestry". Wmk Mult Script CA. P 12½.

84	**20**	¼d. brown	1·50	1·00
		a. "A" of "CA" missing from wmk	£1500	£1500
85		½d. green	2·75	11·00
		a. "A" of "CA" reversed in wmk	£1600	
86		1d. scarlet	2·75	15·00
87		1½d. red-orange	2·75	2·75
		a. "A" of "CA" missing from wmk	£1800	
88		2d. grey	2·75	3·50
89		2½d. ultramarine	2·75	1·50
90		3d. olive-green	8·50	6·50
91		6d. purple	14·00	24·00
92		1s. black and brown	17·00	32·00
93		2s. black and ultramarine	50·00	85·00
94		5s. black and green	£100	£160
95		10s. black and scarlet	£350	£450
84/95 *Set of 12*			£500	£750
84s/95s Perf "SPECIMEN" *Set of 12*			£600	

The design of Nos. 92/5 differs slightly from Type **20**.

No. 85a shows one "A" of the watermark reversed so that its head points to right when seen from the back. It is believed that this stamp may also exist with "A" missing.

Examples of all values are known showing a forged George Town postmark dated "DE 31 1932".

21 Cayman Islands   22 Cat Boat

23 Red-footed Booby   24 Queen or Pink Conch Shells

25 Hawksbill Turtles

(Recess Waterlow)

1935 (1 May). T **21/5**. Wmk Mult Script CA. P 12½.

96	**21**	¼d. black and brown	50	1·00
97	**22**	½d. ultramarine and yellow-green	1·00	1·00
98	**23**	1d. ultramarine and scarlet	4·00	2·25
99	**24**	1½d. black and orange	1·50	1·75
100	**22**	2d. ultramarine and purple	3·75	1·10
101	**25**	2½d. blue and black	3·25	1·25
102	**21**	3d. black and olive-green	2·50	3·00
103	**25**	6d. bright purple and black	8·50	4·75
104	**22**	1s. ultramarine and orange	6·00	6·50
105	**23**	2s. ultramarine and black	50·00	38·00
106	**25**	5s. green and black	65·00	65·00
107	**24**	10s. black and scarlet	£100	£100
96/107 *Set of 12*			£200	£200
96s/107s Perf "SPECIMEN" *Set of 12*			£350	

Examples of all values are known showing a forged George Town postmark dated "AU 23 1936".

1935 (6 May). Silver Jubilee. As Nos. 91/4 of Antigua.

108	½d. black and green		15	1·00
	f. Diagonal line by turret		70·00	95·00
	g. Dot to left of chapel		£160	
	h. Dot by flagstaff		£130	
	i. Dash by turret		£160	
109	2½d. brown and deep blue		7·00	1·00
110	6d. light blue and olive-green		1·75	10·00
	h. Dot by flagstaff		£350	£450
	i. Dash by turret		£400	
111	1s. slate and purple		13·00	10·00
	h. Dot by flagstaff		£450	£450
	i. Dash by turret		£650	
108/11 Set of 4			20·00	20·00
108s/11s Perf "SPECIMEN" Set of 4			£160	

For illustrations of plate varieties see Omnibus section following Zanzibar.

1937 (13 May). Coronation Issue. As Nos. 95/7 of Antigua.

112	½d. green		30	1·90
113	1d. carmine		50	20
114	2½d. blue		95	40
112/14 Set of 3			1·60	2·25
112s/14s Perf "SPECIMEN" Set of 3			£150	

26 Beach View

27 Dolphinfish (*Coryphaena hippurus*)

28 Cayman Islands map

29 Hawksbill Turtles

30 *Rembro* (schooner)

(Recess D.L.R. (½d., 2d., 6d., 1s., 10s.), Waterlow (others))

1938 (5 May)–**48**. T **26/7** and similar designs. Wmk Mult Script CA (sideways on ¼d., 1d., 1½d., 2½d., 3d., 2s., 5s.). Various perfs.

115	26	¼d. red-orange (P 12½)	70	55
		a. Perf 13½×12½ (16.7.43)	10	1·50
116	27	½d. green (P 13×11½)	1·00	55
		a. Perf 14 (16.7.43)	2·50	1·40
		ab. "A" of "CA" missing from wmk.	£1700	
117	28	1d. scarlet (P 12½)	30	75
118	26	1½d. black (P 12½)	30	10
119	29	2d. violet (P 11½×13)	3·00	40
		a. Perf 14 (16.7.43)	60	30
120	30	2½d. bright blue (P 12½)	40	20
120a		2½d. orange (P 12½) (25.8.47)	3·50	50
121	28	3d. orange (P 12½)	40	15
121a		3d. bright blue (P 12½) (25.8.47)	3·00	30
122	29	6d. olive-green (P 11½×13)	15·00	4·50
		a. Perf 14 (16.7.43)	3·25	1·25
		b. Brownish olive (P 11½×13) (8.7.47)	3·00	1·50
123	27	1s. red-brown (P 13×11½)	6·50	2·00
		a. Perf 14 (16.7.43)	7·00	2·00
		ab. "A" of "CA" missing from wmk.	£2500	
124	26	2s. yellow-green (shades) (P 12½)	55·00	14·00
		a. Deep green (16.7.43)	25·00	9·00
125	30	5s. carmine-lake (P 12½)	42·00	15·00
		a. Crimson (1948)	75·00	27·00
126	29	10s. chocolate (P 11½×13)	38·00	9·00
		a. Perf 14 (16.7.43)	30·00	9·00
		aw. Wmk inverted		
115/26a Set of 14			£100	35·00
115s/26s Perf "SPECIMEN" Set of 14			£500	

3d. Stop after "1946" (Plate B1 R. 2/1)

1946 (26 Aug). Victory. As Nos. 110/11 of Antigua.

127	1½d. black		65	40
128	3d. orange-yellow		65	40
	a. Stop after "1946"		40·00	50·00
127s/8s Perf "SPECIMEN" Set of 2			£130	

1948 (29 Nov). Royal Silver Wedding. As Nos. 112/13 of Antigua.

129	½d. green		10	1·00
130	10s. violet-blue		24·00	32·00

1949 (10 Oct). 75th Anniv of Universal Postal Union. As Nos. 114/17 of Antigua.

131	2½d. violet		30	1·50
132	3d. deep blue		1·50	3·50
133	6d. olive		60	3·50
134	1s. red-brown		60	70
131/4 Set of 4			2·75	8·25

31 Cat Boat

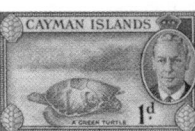

32 Coconut Grove, Cayman Brac

33 Green Turtle

34 Thatch Rope Industry

35 Cayman Seamen

36 Map of Cayman Islands

37 Parrotfish

38 Bluff, Cayman Brac

39 Georgetown Harbour

40 Turtle in "crawl"

41 *Ziroma* (schooner)

42 Boat-building

43 Government Offices, Grand Cayman

(Recess B.W.)

1950 (2 Oct). T **31/2** and similar horiz designs. Wmk Mult Script CA. P 11½ × 11.

135	31	¼d. bright blue and pale scarlet	15	60
136	32	½d. reddish violet and emerald-green	15	1·50
137	33	1d. olive-green and deep blue	60	1·00
138	34	1½d. green and brown	40	75
139	35	2d. reddish violet and rose-carmine	1·25	1·50
140	36	2½d. turquoise and black	1·25	60
141	37	3d. bright green and light blue	1·40	1·50
142	38	6d. red-brown and blue	2·00	1·25
143	39	9d. scarlet and grey-green	13·00	2·00
144	40	1s. brown and orange	3·25	2·75
145	41	2s. violet and reddish purple	14·00	11·00
146	42	5s. olive-green and violet	24·00	7·50
147	43	10s. black and scarlet	29·00	25·00
135/47 Set of 13			80·00	50·00

44 South Sound Lighthouse, Grand Cayman

45 Queen Elizabeth II

1953 (2 Mar)–**62**. Designs previously used for King George VI issue but with portrait of Queen Elizabeth II as in T **44/5**. Wmk Mult Script CA. P 11½×11 or 11×11½ (4d., £1).

148	31	¼d. deep bright blue and rose-red (21.2.55)	1·00	60
		a. Bright blue and bright rose-red (5.12.56)	4·75	2·50
149	32	½d. purple and bluish green (7.7.54)	75	50
150	33	1d. brown-olive and indigo (7.7.54)	70	40
151	34	1½d. deep green and red-brown (7.7.54)	60	20
152	35	2d. reddish violet and cerise (2.6.54)	3·00	85
153	36	2½d. turquoise-blue and black (2.6.54)	3·50	80
154	37	3d. bright green and blue (21.2.55)	4·00	60
155	44	4d. black and deep blue	2·00	40
		a. Black and greenish blue (13.10.54)	27·00	24·00
		b. Black and deep bright blue (10.7.62)	15·00	15·00
156	38	6d. lake-brown and deep blue (7.7.54)	1·75	30
157	39	9d. scarlet and bluish green (2.6.54)	7·50	30
158	40	1s. brown and red-orange (21.2.55)	3·75	20
159	41	2s. slate-violet and reddish purple (21.2.55)	13·00	9·00
160	42	5s. olive-green and slate-violet (21.2.55)	15·00	10·00
161	43	10s. brown and rose-red (21.2.55)	24·00	10·00
161a	45	£1 blue (6.1.59)	45·00	16·00
148/61a Set of 15			£110	42·00

1953 (2 June). Coronation. As No. 120 of Antigua, but printed by B.W.

162	1d. black and emerald		30	2·00

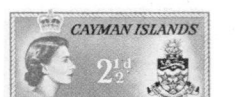

46 Arms of the Cayman Islands

(Photo D.L.R.)

1959 (4 July). New Constitution. Wmk Mult Script CA. P 12.

163	46	2½d. black and light blue	45	2·50
164		1s. black and orange	55	50

CROWN COLONY

47 Cuban Amazon

48 Cat Boat

49 *Schomburgkia thomsoniana* (orchid)

50 Map of Cayman Islands

51 Fisherman casting net

52 West Bay Beach

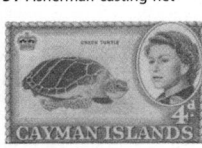

53 Green Turtle

54 *Kirk B* (schooner)

55 Angler with King Mackerel

56 Iguana

57 Swimming pool, Cayman Brac

58 Water sports

59 Fort George

60 Coat of Arms

61 Queen Elizabeth II

(Recess B.W.)

1962 (28 Nov)–64. T **47/61**. W w **12**. P 11×11½ (vert) or 11½×11 (horiz).

165	**47**	¼d. emerald and red	55	2·25
		a. *Emerald and rose* (18.2.64)	4·00	6·00
166	**48**	1d. black and yellow-olive	80	20
167	**49**	1½d. yellow and purple	2·75	80
168	**50**	2d. blue and deep brown	1·50	30
169	**51**	2½d. violet and bluish green	85	1·00
170	**52**	3d. bright blue and carmine	30	10
171	**53**	4d. deep green and purple	3·75	60
172	**54**	6d. bluish green and sepia	3·25	30
173	**55**	9d. ultramarine and purple	4·00	40
174	**56**	1s. sepia and rose-red	2·00	10
175	**57**	1s.3d. bluish green and orange-brown	7·00	3·50
176	**58**	1s.9d. deep turquoise and violet	20·00	1·25
177	**59**	5s. plum and deep green	13·00	17·00
178	**60**	10s. olive and blue	22·00	17·00
179	**61**	£1 carmine and black	22·00	30·00
165/79 *Set of 15*			90·00	60·00

1963 (4 June). Freedom from Hunger. As No. 146 of Antigua.

180	1s.9d. carmine	30	15

1963 (2 Sept). Red Cross Centenary. As Nos. 147/8 of Antigua.

181	1d. red and black	30	1·25
182	1s.9d. red and blue	70	1·75

1964 (23 Apr). 400th Birth Anniv of William Shakespeare. As No. 164 of Antigua.

183	6d. magenta	20	10

1965 (17 May). ITU Centenary. As Nos. 166/7 of Antigua.

184	1d. blue and light purple	15	30
185	1s.3d. bright purple and green	55	70

1965 (25 Oct). International Co-operation Year. As Nos. 168/9 of Antigua.

186	1d. reddish purple and turquoise-green	20	10
187	1s. deep bluish green and lavender	80	25

1966 (24 Jan). Churchill Commemoration. As Nos. 170/3 of Antigua.

188	¼d. new blue	10	2·25
	w. Wmk inverted	60·00	
189	1d. deep green	60	15
190	1s. brown	1·00	15
	w. Wmk inverted	2·00	3·75
191	1s.9d. bluish violet	1·00	75
188/91 *Set of 4*		2·40	3·00

1966 (4 Feb). Royal Visit. As Nos. 174/5 of Antigua.

192	1d. black and ultramarine	50	35
193	1s.9d. black and magenta	2·00	1·50

1966 (1 July). World Cup Football Championships. As Nos. 176/7 of Antigua.

194	1½d. violet, yellow-green, lake and yellow-brown	25	10
195	1s.9d. chocolate, blue-green, lake and yellow-brown	1·00	25

1966 (20 Sept). Inauguration of WHO Headquarters, Geneva. As Nos. 178/9 of Antigua.

196	2d. black, yellow-green and light blue	75	15
197	1s.3d. black, light purple and yellow-brown	1·75	60

62 Telephone and Map

(Des V. Whiteley. Litho Harrison)

1966 (5 Dec). International Telephone Links. W w **12**. P 14½×14.

198	**62**	4d. red, black, greenish blue and olive-green	20	20
199		9d. violet-blue, black, brown-red and light green	20	30

1966 (12 Dec*). 20th Anniv of UNESCO. As Nos. 196/8 of Antigua.

200	1d. slate-violet, red, yellow and orange	15	10
201	1s.9d. orange-yellow, violet and deep olive	60	10
202	5s. black, bright purple and orange	1·50	1·00
200/2 *Set of 3*		2·00	1·10

*This is the local date of issue; the Crown Agents released the stamps on 1 December.

63 BAC One Eleven 200/400 Airliner over *Ziroma* (Cayman schooner)

(Des V. Whiteley. Photo Harrison)

1966 (17 Dec). Opening of Cayman Jet Service. W w **12**. P 14½.

203	**63**	1s. black, new blue and olive-green	35	30
204		1s.9d. deep purple-brown, ultramarine and emerald	40	35

64 Water-skiing

(Des G. Vasarhelyi. Photo Harrison)

1967 (1 Dec). International Tourist Year. T **64** and similar horiz designs. Multicoloured. W w **12**. P 14½×14.

205		4d. Type **64**	35	10
		a. Gold omitted	£375	£325
206		6d. Skin diving	35	30
207		1s. Sport fishing	35	30
208		1s.9d. Sailing	40	1·25
205/8 *Set of 4*			1·25	1·25

A used copy of No. 207 is known with yellow omitted.

68 Former Slaves and Emblem

(Des and photo Harrison)

1968 (3 June). Human Rights Year. W w **12**. P 14½×14.

209	**68**	3d. deep bluish green, black and gold	10	10
		w. Wmk inverted	60	80
210		9d. brown, gold and myrtle-green	10	10
211		5s. ultramarine, gold and myrtle-green	30	90
209/11 *Set of 3*			40	1·00

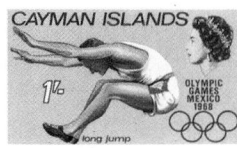
69 Long jumping

(Des R. Granger Barrett. Litho P.B.)

1968 (1 Oct). Olympic Games, Mexico. T **69** and similar multicoloured designs. W w **12**. P 13½.

212		1s. Type **69**	15	10
213		1s.3d. High jumping	20	25
214		2s. Pole vaulting (*vert*)	20	75
212/14 *Set of 3*			50	1·00

72 The Adoration of the Shepherds (Fabritius)

1968–69. Christmas. T **72** and similar horiz design. Centres multicoloured; country name and frames in gold; value and background in colours given. P 14×14½.

(a) W w **12**. (18.11.68)

215	**72**	¼d. brown	10	20
		a. Gold omitted	£275	
216	–	1d. bluish violet	10	10
217	**72**	6d. bright blue	20	10
218	–	8d. cerise	20	15
219	**72**	1s.3d. bright green	25	25
220	–	2s. grey	30	35

(b) No wmk (8.1.69)

221	**72**	¼d. bright purple	10	20
215/21 *Set of 7*			1·00	1·10

Design:—1d., 8d., 2s. *The Adoration of the Shepherds* (Rembrandt).

(Des G. Vasarhelyi. Litho Format)

1969 (5 June). Designs as T **74** and T **76** in black, ochre and red (£1) or multicoloured (others). No wmk. P 14.

222	¼d. Type **74**		10	75
223	1d. Brahmin Cattle		10	10
224	2d. Blowholes on the coast (*horiz*)		10	10
225	2½d. Map of Grand Cayman (*horiz*)		15	10
226	3d. Georgetown scene (*horiz*)		10	10
227	4d. Royal Poinciana (*horiz*)		15	10
228	6d. Cayman Brac and Little Cayman on Chart (*horiz*)		20	10
229	8d. Motor vessels at berth (*horiz*)		25	10
230	1s. Basket-making (*horiz*)		15	10
231	1s.3d. Beach scene (*horiz*)		35	1·00
232	1s.6d. Straw-rope making (*horiz*)		35	1·00
233	2s. Great Barracuda (*horiz*)		1·25	80
234	4s. Government House (*horiz*)		35	80
235	10s. Type **76**		1·00	1·50
236	£1 Queen Elizabeth II (*vert*)		1·25	2·00
222/36 *Set of 15*			5·00	7·00

1969 (11 Aug). As No. 222, but wmk w **12** (sideways).

237	**74**	¼d. multicoloured	30	65

(New Currency. 100 cents = 1 dollar.)

(89)

1969 (8 Sept). Decimal Currency. No. 237, and as Nos. 223/36, but wmk w **12** (sideways on horiz designs), surch as T **89**.

238	¼c. on ¼d. Type **74**		10	75
239	1c. on 1d. Brahmin Cattle		10	10
240	2c. on 2d. Blowholes on the coast		10	10
241	3c. on 4d. Royal Poinciana		10	10
242	4c. on 2½d. Map of Grand Cayman		10	10
243	5c. on 6d. Cayman Brac and Little Cayman on Chart		10	10
244	7c. on 8d. Motor vessels at berth		10	10
245	8c. on 3d. Georgetown scene		15	10
246	10c. on 1s. Basket-making		25	10
247	12c. on 1s.3d. Beach scene		35	1·75
248	15c. on 1s.6d. Straw-rope making		45	2·00
249	20c. on 2s. Great Barracuda		1·25	1·75
250	40c. on 4s. Government House		45	85
251	$1 on 10s. Type **76**		1·50	2·50
	w. Wmk inverted		£400	
252	$2 on £1 Queen Elizabeth II		1·50	3·25
238/52 *Set of 15*			5·50	11·00

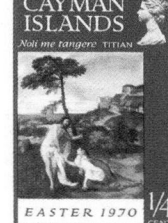
90 *Virgin and Child* (Vivarini)

92 *Noli me tangere* (Titian)

(Des adapted by G. Drummond. Photo Harrison)

1969 (14 Nov*). Christmas. Multicoloured; background colours given. W w **12** (sideways on 1, 7 and 20c.). P 14½.

253	**90**	¼c. orange-red	10	10
		w. Wmk inverted	2·75	7·00
254		¼c. magenta	10	10
		w. Wmk inverted	2·75	7·00
255		¼c. emerald	10	10
		a. Gold frame omitted	£250	
		w. Wmk inverted	1·00	2·00
256		¼c. new blue	10	10
		w. Wmk inverted	2·75	7·00
257	–	1c. ultramarine	10	10
258	**90**	5c. orange-red	10	10
259	–	7c. myrtle-green	10	10
260	**90**	12c. emerald	15	15
261	–	20c. brown-purple	20	25
253/61 *Set of 9*			45	45

Design:—1, 7, 20c. *The Adoration of the Kings* (Gossaert).

*This is the local release date. The Crown Agents released the stamps on 4 November.

(Des L. Curtis. Litho D.L.R.)

1970 (23 Mar). Easter. Paintings multicoloured; frame colours given. P 14.

262	**92**	¼c. carmine-red	10	10
263		¼c. deep green	10	10
264		¼c. yellow-brown	10	10
265		¼c. pale violet	10	10
266		10c. chalky blue	30	10
267		12c. chestnut	30	10
268		40c. plum	40	60
262/8 *Set of 7*			1·00	75

74 Grand Cayman Thrush

76 Arms of the Cayman Islands

93 Barnaby (*Barnaby Rudge*)

97 Grand Cayman Thrush

(Des Jennifer Toombs. Photo Harrison)

1970 (17 June). Death Centenary of Charles Dickens. T **93** and similar vert designs. W w **12** (sideways*). P 14½×14.

269		1c. black, olive-green and greenish yellow	10	10
		w. Wmk Crown to right of CA	—	2·25
270		12c. black, lake-brown and red	40	15
271		20c. black, ochre-brown and gold	45	15
272		40c. black, bright ultramarine and new blue	55	35
269/72 *Set of 4*			1·25	65

Designs:—12c. Sairey Gamp (*Martin Chuzzlewit*); 20c. Mr. Micawber and David (*David Copperfield*); 40c. The "Marchioness" (*The Old Curiosity Shop*).
*The normal sideways watermark shows Crown to left of CA, *as seen from the back of the stamp.*

1970 (8 Sept). Decimal Currency. Designs as Nos. 223/37, but with values inscr in decimal currency as T **97**. W w **12** (sideways*) on cent values).

273	**97**	¼c. Type **97**	65	1·50
274		1c. Brahmin Cattle	10	10
275		2c. Blowholes on the coast	10	10
276		3c. Royal Poinciana	20	10
277		4c. Map of Grand Cayman	20	10
278		5c. Cayman Brac and Little Cayman on Chart	35	10
		w. Wmk Crown to right of CA	20·00	
279		7c. Motor vessels at berth	30	10
280		8c. Georgetown scene	30	10
281		10c. Basket-making	30	10
282		12c. Beach scene	90	1·25
283		15c. Straw-rope making	1·25	4·00
284		20c. Great Barracuda	3·25	1·25
285		40c. Government House	85	75
286		$1 Type **76**	1·25	4·75
		w. Wmk inverted	11·00	9·00
287		$2 Queen Elizabeth II	2·25	4·75
273/87 *Set of 15*			10·50	17·00

*The normal sideways watermark shows Crown to left of CA, *as seen from the back of the stamp.*

98 The Three Wise Men

(Des G. Drummond. Litho Format)

1970 (8 Oct). Christmas. T **98** and similar horiz design. W w **12** (sideways*). P 14.

288	**98**	¼c. apple-green, grey and emerald	10	85
		w. Wmk Crown to right of CA	4·00	5·50
289	–	1c. black, lemon and turquoise-green	10	10
290	**98**	5c. grey, red-orange and crimson	10	10
291	–	10c. black, lemon and orange-red	10	10
292	**98**	12c. grey, pale turquoise and ultramarine	15	10
293	–	20c. black, lemon and green	20	15
288/93 *Set of 6*			55	1·25

Design:—1, 10, 20c. Nativity scene and Globe.
*The normal sideways watermark shows Crown to left of CA, *as seen from the back of the stamp.*

Ceylon

PRICES FOR STAMPS ON COVER TO 1945

No. 1	from × 5
Nos. 2/12	from × 4
Nos. 16/17	from × 5
Nos. 18/59	from × 8
Nos. 60/2	from × 15
Nos. 63/72	from × 8
Nos. 121/38	from × 6
Nos. 139/41	†
Nos. 142/3	from × 10
Nos. 146/51	from × 6
Nos. 151a/2	†
Nos. 153/93	from × 8
Nos. 195/201	from × 12
Nos. 202/43	from × 6
Nos. 245/9	from × 4
Nos. 250/5	from × 5
Nos. 256/64	from × 4
Nos. 265/76	from × 3
Nos. 277/88	from × 4
Nos. 289/300	from × 8
Nos. 301/18	from × 2
Nos. 319/23	—
Nos. 330/7b	from × 4
Nos. 338/56	from × 2
Nos. 357/60	—
Nos. 361/2	from × 5
Nos. 363/7	from × 3
Nos. 368/78	from × 2
Nos. 379/82	from × 4
Nos. 383/5	from × 3
Nos. 386/97	from × 2
Nos. 398/9	from × 8
Nos. O1/7	†
Nos. O11/27	from × 30

CROWN COLONY

PRICES. The prices of the imperf stamps of Ceylon vary greatly according to condition. The following prices are for fine copies with four margins.

Poor to medium specimens can be supplied at much lower prices.

1   **2**   **3**

NOTE. Beware of stamps of Type **2** which are often offered with corners added.

(Recess P.B.)

1857 (1 Apr). Blued paper. Wmk Star W w **1**. Imperf.

1	**1**	6d. purple-brown	£12000	£450

Collectors should beware of proofs with faked watermark, often offered as originals.

PERKINS BACON "CANCELLED". For notes on these handstamps, showing "CANCELLED" between horizontal bars forming an oval, see Catalogue Introduction.

1857 (2 July)–**59**. Wmk Star, W w **1**. White paper.

(a) Imperf

2	**1**	1d. deep turquoise-blue (24.8.57)	£1100	45·00
		a. Blue	£1200	80·00
		b. Blued paper	—	£225
3		2d. green (shades) (24.8.57)	£200	65·00
		a. Yellowish green	£500	90·00
4	**2**	4d. dull rose (23.4.59)	£70000	£4500
5	**1**	5d. chestnut	£1600	£150
6		6d. purple-brown (1859)	£2750	£140
		a. Brown	£11000	£550
		b. Deep brown	£12000	£1000
		c. Light brown		£1500
7	**2**	8d. brown (23.4.59)	£28000	£1500
8		9d. purple-brown (23.4.59)	£60000	£900
9	**3**	10d. dull vermilion	£900	£325
10		1s. slate-violet	£5500	£200
11	**2**	1s.9d. green (H/S "CANCELLED" in oval £9500)	£800	£800
		a. Yellow-green	£5500	£3000
12		2s. dull blue (23.4.59)	£6500	£1300

(b) Unofficial perf 7½ (1s.9d.) or roul (others)

13	**1**	1d. blue	£10000	
14		5d. chestnut	£5000	£2750
15	**2**	1s.9d. green	£16000	

Nos. 13/15 were privately produced, probably by commercial firms for their own convenience.
The 10d. also exists with "CANCELLED" in oval, but no examples are believed to be in private hands.

4

(Typo D.L.R.)

1857 (Oct)–**64**. No wmk. Glazed paper.

(a) Imperf

16	**4**	½d. reddish lilac (blued paper)	£4250	£650

17		½d. dull mauve (1858)	£190	£250
		a. Private roul	£8000	

(b) P 12½

18	**4**	½d. dull mauve (1864)	£225	£180

(Recess P.B.)

1861–64. Wmk Star, W w **1**.

(a) Clean-cut and intermediate perf 14 to 15½

19	**1**	1d. light blue	£2500	£300
		a. Dull blue (H/S "CANCELLED" in oval £11000)	£200	15·00
20		2d. green (shades)	£275	28·00
		a. Imperf between (vert pair)	†	
		b. Yellowish green (H/S "CANCELLED" in oval £12000)	£275	25·00
21	**2**	4d. dull rose (H/S "CANCELLED" in oval £12000)	£2250	£325
22	**1**	5d. chestnut (H/S "CANCELLED" in oval £8000)	£120	8·50
23		6d. brown (H/S "CANCELLED" in oval £9000)	£3000	£180
		a. Bistre-brown	—	£275
24	**2**	8d. brown (H/S "CANCELLED" in oval £10000)	£2500	£500
25		9d. purple-brown	£15000	£250
26	**3**	1s. slate-violet (H/S "CANCELLED" in oval £11000)	£140	13·00
27	**2**	2s. dull blue	£4750	£900

(b) Rough perf 14 to 15½

28		1d. dull blue	£160	13·00
		a. Blued paper	£800	27·00
29		2d. green	£475	85·00
30	**2**	4d. rose-red	£600	£130
		a. Deep rose-red	£700	£160
31	**1**	6d. deep brown	£1300	£130
		a. Light brown	£2250	£200
		b. Olive-sepia	£1200	£120
32	**2**	8d. brown	£1700	£650
		a. Yellow-brown	£1600	£425
33		9d. deep brown (H/S "CANCELLED" in oval £9000)	£150	£120
		a. Light brown	£1300	£130
		b. Olive-sepia	£850	85·00
34	**3**	10d. dull vermilion	£300	28·00
		a. Imperf vert (horiz pair)	†	—
35		1s. slate-violet	£225	18·00
36	**2**	1s.9d. light green (prepared for use, but not issued)	£750	
37		2s. dull blue (H/S "CANCELLED" in oval £11000)	£750	£160
		a. Deep dull blue	£1100	£200

(c) P 12½ by D.L.R.

38	**3**	10d. dull vermilion (9.64)	£325	22·00

The line machine used for Nos. 19/37 produced perforations of variable quality due to wear, poor cleaning and faulty servicing, but it is generally accepted that the clean-cut and intermediate versions occurred on stamps perforated up to March 1861 and the rough variety when the machine was used after that date.

(Recess D.L.R.)

1862. No wmk. Smooth paper.

(a) P 13

39	**1**	1d. dull blue	£180	7·00
40		5d. lake-brown	£1800	£150
41		6d. brown	£200	29·00
		a. Deep brown	£200	29·00
42	**2**	9d. brown	£1300	£120
43	**3**	1s. slate-violet	£1800	£100

(b) P 11½, 12

44	**1**	1d. dull blue	£1800	£130
		a. Imperf between (horiz pair)	†	£18000

Nos. 39/44 were printed on paper showing a papermaker's watermark of "T H SAUNDERS 1862", parts of which can be found on individual stamps. Examples are rare and command a premium.
The 1s. is known imperforate, but was not issued in this condition (*Price, £4000, unused*).

5 (23 mm high. "CC" oval)   **6** (21½ mm high. "CC" round and smaller)

(Typo (½d.) or recess (others) D.L.R.)

1863–66. W **5**. Paper medium thin and slightly soft.

(a) P 11½, 12

45	**1**	1d. deep blue	£3500	£325
		x. Wmk reversed	£4750	£550

(b) P 13

46	**1**	6d. sepia	£2750	£250
		x. Wmk reversed	£3250	£300
		y. Wmk inverted and reversed	£4000	£700
47	**2**	9d. sepia	£6500	£1000

(c) P 12½

48	**4**	½d. dull mauve (1864)	80·00	50·00
		aw. Wmk inverted	£500	£180
		b. Reddish lilac	90·00	65·00
		c. Mauve	55·00	55·00
49	**1**	1d. deep blue	£180	9·00
		a. Imperf		
		w. Wmk inverted	†	65·00
		x. Wmk reversed	£250	9·50
		y. Wmk inverted and reversed	†	£100
50		2d. grey-green (1864)	£100	15·00
		a. Imperf	†	£5000
		bw. Wmk inverted	£400	£110
		by. Wmk inverted and reversed	†	£225
		c. Bottle-green	†	£4000
		d. Yellowish green	£9000	£400

	dx. Wmk reversed		†	£1100
	e. Emerald (wmk reversed)		£190	£110
	ew. Wmk inverted		£950	£500
51	2d. ochre (wmk reversed) (1866)		£325	£275
	w. Wmk inverted		£950	£800
	y. Wmk inverted and reversed		£850	£600
52	2	4d. rose-carmine (1865)	£900	£275
	ax. Wmk reversed		£1300	
	b. Rose		£550	£130
	bx. Wmk reversed		£750	£170
53	1	5d. red-brown (shades) (1865)	£325	£110
	w. Wmk inverted		†	£325
	x. Wmk reversed		£450	80·00
54		5d. grey-olive (1866)	£2000	£425
	ax. Wmk reversed		£1600	£350
	b. Yellow-olive		£900	£275
	bx. Wmk reversed		£850	£300
55		6d. sepia	£250	4·50
	aw. Wmk inverted		†	£120
	ax. Wmk reversed			
	b. Reddish brown		£350	15·00
	c. Blackish brown		£300	11·00
	ca. Double print		†	£4250
	cw. Wmk inverted		£450	£110
	cx. Wmk reversed		£375	75·00
	cy. Wmk inverted and reversed		†	£225
56	2	8d. reddish brown (shades) (1864)	£150	80·00
	x. Wmk reversed		£275	£130
	y. Wmk inverted and reversed		£600	£200
57		9d. sepia	£350	50·00
	x. Wmk reversed		£850	£130
58	3	10d. vermilion (1866)	£5000	70·00
	ax. Wmk reversed		†	£170
	b. Orange-red		£7500	£450
	bx. Wmk reversed		†	£650
59	2	2s. steel-blue (shades) (1864)	£375	40·00
	x. Wmk reversed		£750	£130
	y. Wmk inverted and reversed		£1000	£350

Watermarks as Type **5** were arranged in four panes, each of 60, with the words "CROWN COLONIES" between the panes. Parts of this marginal watermark often appear on the stamps.

De La Rue had considerable difficulty matching the standard Crown CC watermark to the plates received from Perkins Bacon with the result that the watermark W **5** is frequently found misplaced.

A further aid to identifying the two watermarks is the distance between the top of the cross and the foot of "CC", which measures 2 mm on W **5** and 6.5 mm on W **6**.

The ½d. dull mauve, 2d. ochre and 5d. grey-olive with this watermark also exist imperforate, but are not known used. The 6d. sepia and 2s. steel-blue also exist imperforate on wove paper without watermark.

One used example of the 2d. grey-green is known showing private roulettes added to an imperforate stamp (Price £5000).

7 **8**

(Typo D.L.R.)

1866–68. Wmk Crown CC.

(a) P 12½

60	7	3d. rose	£275	£100

(b) P 14

61	8	1d. blue (shades) (1868)	26·00	13·00
	w. Wmk inverted		†	£250
62	7	3d. carmine-rose (1867)	90·00	50·00
	a. Bright rose		95·00	55·00

Nos. 60/1 exist imperforate.

(Recess D.L.R.)

1867–70. W **6**. Specially produced hand-made paper. P 12½.

63	1	1d. dull blue	£325	18·00
	aw. Wmk inverted		£700	£160
	ax. Wmk reversed		£325	18·00
	ay. Wmk inverted and reversed		†	£275
	b. Deep blue		£275	17·00
	bw. Wmk inverted		—	£170
	bx. Wmk reversed		£450	45·00
64		2d. ochre	£170	14·00
	aw. Wmk inverted			
	ax. Wmk reversed		£300	45·00
	b. Bistre		95·00	9·50
	bw. Wmk inverted		£160	
	c. Olive-bistre		£170	20·00
	cw. Wmk inverted		£170	
	d. Yellow		£130	8·50
	dx. Wmk reversed		85·00	21·00
65	2	4d. rose	£300	55·00
	ax. Wmk reversed		£275	45·00
	b. Rose-carmine		85·00	23·00
	bw. Wmk inverted		†	£150
	bx. Wmk reversed		£110	25·00
	by. Wmk inverted and reversed		£700	£225
66	1	5d. yellow-olive	£160	24·00
	ax. Wmk reversed		£150	27·00
	ay. Wmk inverted and reversed		†	£150
	b. Olive-green		£150	28·00
	bx. Wmk reversed		†	75·00
	c. Bronze-green		65·00	60·00
67		6d. deep brown (1869)	£140	12·00
	ax. Wmk reversed		£250	
	b. Blackish brown		£190	9·50
	bw. Wmk inverted		†	£170
	bx. Wmk reversed		£225	19·00
	c. Red-brown		60·00	42·00
68	2	8d. chocolate	£130	80·00
	ax. Wmk reversed		—	£150
	b. Lake-brown		£140	85·00
	bx. Wmk reversed		£325	£150
69		9d. bistre-brown (12.68)	£950	38·00
	ax. Wmk reversed		£500	25·00
	b. Blackish brown		70·00	8·00
70	3	10d. dull vermilion (wmk reversed)	£6000	£150
	ay. Wmk inverted and reversed		†	£350
	b. Red-orange		90·00	18·00
	bx. Wmk reversed		£190	18·00

	by. Wmk inverted and reversed		£1000	
	c. Orange		£150	19·00
71		1s. reddish lilac (1870)	£300	30·00
	ax. Wmk reversed		£500	85·00
	b. Reddish violet		£150	13·00
	bw. Wmk inverted		†	£250
	ax. Wmk reversed		£450	85·00
72	2	2s. steel-blue	£275	22·00
	ax. Wmk reversed		†	55·00
	b. Deep blue		£170	18·00
	bx. Wmk reversed		£200	24·00

Watermarks as Type **6** were arranged in one pane of 240 (12×20) with the words "CROWN COLONIES" twice in each side margin.

Unused examples of the 1d. dull blue, 1d. deep blue, 5d. yellow-olive, 6d. deep brown, 9d. blackish brown and 10d. red orange with this watermark exist imperforate.

Nos. 73 to 120 are vacant.

> **PRINTERS.** All stamps from No. 121 to 367 were typographed by De La Rue & Co. Ltd, London.
> A wide variety of shades may be found on stamps of this period. We only list the most significant.

(New Currency. 100 cents = 1 rupee)

9	10	11
12	**13**	**14**
15	**16**	**17**
18	**19**	

1872–80. Wmk Crown CC.

(a) P 14

121	9	2c. pale brown (shades)	38·00	4·25
	w. Wmk inverted		£190	£100
122	10	4c. grey	55·00	2·00
	w. Wmk inverted		£450	£100
123		4c. rosy-mauve (1880)	80·00	1·50
	w. Wmk inverted		£400	£225
124	11	8c. orange-yellow	65·00	7·00
	a. Yellow		50·00	8·00
	w. Wmk inverted		†	£250
126	12	16c. pale violet	£150	2·75
	w. Wmk inverted		†	£225
127	13	24c. green	85·00	2·25
	w. Wmk inverted		†	£180
128	14	32c. slate (1877)	£190	15·00
	w. Wmk inverted		£600	£200
129	15	36c. blue	£200	30·00
	x. Wmk reversed		£425	£170
130	16	48c. rose	£110	9·50
	w. Wmk inverted		—	90·00
131	17	64c. red-brown (1877)	£300	75·00
132	18	96c. drab	£275	30·00
	w. Wmk inverted		—	£250
121/32	Set of 11		£1300	£150

(b) P 14×12½

133	9	2c. brown	£425	70·00
134	10	4c. grey	£2500	40·00
135	11	8c. orange-yellow	£475	55·00
	w. Wmk inverted		†	£400

(c) P 12½

136	9	2c. brown	£4500	£250
	w. Wmk inverted		†	£650
137	10	4c. grey	£3000	£325

(d) P 12½×14

138	19	2r.50 dull-rose (1879)	£800	£425

(e) Prepared for use and sent out to Ceylon, but not issued unsurcharged

139	14	32c. slate (P 14×12½)	£1400	
140	17	64c. red-brown (P 14×12½)	£1600	
141	19	2r.50 dull rose (P 12½)	£3250	

FORGERIES—Beware of forged overprint and surcharge varieties on Victorian issues.

SIXTEEN

16

CENTS

(20)

1882 (Oct). Nos. 127 and 131 surch as T **20** by Govt Printer.

142	13	16c. on 24c. green	45·00	9·50
	a. Surch inverted			
143	17	20c. on 64c. red-brown	14·00	9·00
	a. Surch double		†	£1800

1883–98. Wmk Crown CA.

(a) P 14

146	9	2c. pale brown	75·00	3·75
147		2c. dull green (1884)	3·50	15
	s. Optd "SPECIMEN"		£475	
	w. Wmk inverted		£275	£120
148	10	4c. rosy mauve	7·00	50
	w. Wmk inverted		†	£275
	x. Wmk reversed		†	£400
149		4c. rose (1884)	7·50	13·00
	s. Optd "SPECIMEN"		£475	
150	11	8c. orange-yellow	8·50	14·00
	a. Yellow (1898)		6·00	12·00
151	12	16c. pale violet	£2000	£180

(b) Trial perforation. P 12

151a	9	2c. dull green	£7000	
151b	10	4c. rose	£7000	
151c	13	24c. brown-purple	£7500	

(c) Prepared for use and sent out to Ceylon, but not issued unsurcharged. P 14

152	13	24c. brown-purple	£1700	
	s. Optd "SPECIMEN"		£800	

Although delivered in 1884 it is believed that the 4c. rose, No. 149, was not used until the early 1890s.

See also Nos. 246, 256 and 258 for the 2c. and 4c. in different colours.

Postage &

FIVE CENTS Revenue **(21)**

TEN CENTS **(22)**

Twenty Cents **(23)**

One Rupee Twelve Cents **(24)**

1885 (1 Jan–Mar). T **10/19** surch locally as T **21/24**.

I. Wmk Crown CC

(a) P 14

153	21	5c. on 16c. pale violet	†	£3000
154		5c. on 24c. green	£6500	£110
155		5c. on 32c. slate	70·00	15·00
	a. Surch inverted		†	£2750
	b. Dark grey		£225	48·00
156		5c. on 36c. blue	£300	13·00
	a. Surch inverted		†	£2750
	x. Wmk reversed		†	£190
157		5c. on 48c. rose	£2500	70·00
158		5c. on 64c. red-brown	£140	13·00
	a. Surch double		†	£3500
159		5c. on 96c. drab	£550	70·00
161	22	10c. on 16c. pale violet	£12000	£3000
162		10c. on 24c. green	£500	£140
163		10c. on 36c. blue	£475	£275
164		10c. on 64c. red-brown	£450	£225
165		20c. on 24c. green	85·00	32·00
166	23	20c. on 32c. slate	95·00	80·00
	a. Dark grey		£120	65·00
	aw. Wmk inverted		£450	
167		25c. on 32c. slate	28·00	10·00
	a. Dark grey		30·00	11·00
168		28c. on 48c. rose	40·00	£30
	a. Surch double		†	£3000
	w. Wmk inverted		†	£425
169	22	30c. on 36c. blue	26·00	18·00
	x. Wmk reversed		18·00	14·00
	xa. Surch inverted		£325	£150
170		56c. on 96c. drab	35·00	27·00

(b) P 14×12½

172	21	5c. on 32c. slate	£850	55·00
173		5c. on 64c. red-brown	£950	55·00
	w. Wmk inverted		†	£650
174	22	10c. on 64c. red-brown	95·00	£170
	a. Imperf between (vert pair)		£7000	
175	24	1r.12 on 2r.50 dull rose (P 12½)	£700	£110
176		1r.12 on 2r.50 dull rose (P 12½×14)	£110	50·00

II. Wmk Crown CA. P 14

178	21	5c. on 4c. rose (3.85)	27·00	5·50
	a. Surch inverted		†	£325
179		5c. on 8c. orange-yellow	95·00	11·00
	a. Surch double		†	£3750
	b. Surch inverted		†	£4250
180		5c. on 16c. pale violet	£190	19·00
	a. Surch inverted		†	£250
182		5c. on 48c. brown-purple		£500
184	22	10c. on 16c. pale violet	£13000	£1700
185		10c. on 24c. brown-purple	19·00	12·00
186		10c. on 16c. pale violet	16·00	11·00

The 5c. on 4c. rosy mauve and 5c. on 24c. green, both watermarked Crown CA, previously catalogued are now known to be forgeries.

REVENUE AND POSTAGE

5 CENTS **(25)** 10 CENTS **(26)** 1 R. 12 C. **(27)**

1885. T **11/15**, **18** and **19** surch with T **25/7** by D.L.R. P 14.

(a) Wmk Crown CA

187	**25**	5c. on 8c. lilac	28·00	1·50
		w. Wmk inverted	†	£160
		x. Wmk reversed	£425	£375
188	**26**	10c. on 24c. brown-purple	15·00	8·50
189		15c. on 16c. orange-yellow	60·00	15·00
190		28c. on 32c. slate	28·00	2·50
191		30c. on 36c. olive-green	29·00	16·00
192		56c. on 96c. drab	50·00	17·00

(b) Wmk Crown CC (sideways)

193	**27**	1r.12 on 2r.50 dull rose	60·00	£140
187/93	*Set of 7*		£225	£180
187s/93s	Optd "SPECIMEN" *Set of 7*		£1300	

28   **29**

1886. Wmk Crown CA. P 14.

195	**28**	5c. dull purple	3·75	10
		w. Wmk inverted	£275	£160
196	**29**	15c. sage-green	9·00	2·50
		w. Wmk inverted	£350	£275
197		15c. olive-green	11·00	2·75
198		25c. yellow-brown	7·00	2·00
		a. Value in yellow	£150	90·00
199		28c. slate	26·00	1·75
195s, 197s/9s	Optd "SPECIMEN" *Set of 4*		£300	

Six plates were used for the 5c., No. 195, between 1885 and 1901, each being replaced by its successor as it became worn. Examples from the worn plates show thicker lines in the background and masses of solid colour under the chin, in front of the throat, at the back of the neck and at the base.

30

1887. Wmk Crown CC (sideways). White or blued paper. P 14.

201	**30**	1r.12 dull rose	35·00	35·00
		aw. Wmk Crown to left of CC	£120	£120
		b. Wmk upright	70·00	80·00
		bw. Wmk inverted	£750	£375
		s. Optd "SPECIMEN"	£200	

The normal sideways watermark shows Crown to right of CC, *as seen from the back of the stamp.*

Two CENTS   **Two**
(31)   **(32)**

2 Cents
(33)

Two Cents
(34)

2 Cents
(35)

1888–90. Nos. 148/9 surch with T **31/5**.

202	**31**	2c. on 4c. rosy mauve	1·50	80
		a. Surch inverted	26·00	24·00
		b. Surch double, one inverted	—	£400
203		2c. on 4c. rose	2·50	40
		a. Surch inverted	21·00	22·00
		b. Surch double	—	£425
204	**32**	2(c). on 4c. rosy mauve	1·00	30
		a. Surch inverted	45·00	45·00
		b. Surch double	£130	£140
		c. Surch double, one inverted	£100	£100
205		2(c). on 4c. rose	9·00	20
		a. Surch inverted	£450	
		b. Surch double	£120	£140
		c. Surch double, one inverted	£120	£140
206	**33**	2c. on 4c. rosy mauve	85·00	32·00
		a. Surch inverted	£180	42·00
		b. Surch double, one inverted	£250	
207		2c. on 4c. rose	4·50	75
		a. Surch inverted	19·00	10·00
		b. Surch double	£200	£160
		c. Surch double, one inverted	8·50	15·00
		w. Wmk inverted	£225	
208	**34**	2c. on 4c. rosy mauve	65·00	28·00
		a. Surch inverted	£200	30·00
209		2c. on 4c. rose	3·00	1·10
		a. Surch inverted	20·00	10·00
		b. Surch double	£160	£150
		c. Surch double, one inverted	20·00	13·00
210	**35**	2c. on 4c. rosy mauve	70·00	38·00
		a. Surch inverted	£100	42·00
		b. Surch double, one inverted	£150	£120
		c. Surch double	—	£450
		d. "s" of "Cents" inverted (R. 3/5)	—	£750
211		2c. on 4c. rose	15·00	1·00
		a. Surch inverted	25·00	9·00
		b. Surch double, one inverted	£150	£150
		c. Surch double, one inverted	26·00	16·00
		d. "s" of "Cents" inverted (R. 3/5)	£650	£375
		x. Wmk reversed	†	£400
209s, 211s	Optd "SPECIMEN" *Set of 2*		65·00	

The 4c. rose and the 4c. rosy mauve are found surcharged "Postal Commission 3 (or "Three") Cents". They denote the extra commission charged by the Post Office on postal orders which had not been cashed within three months of the date of issue. For a short time the Post Office did not object to the use of these stamps on letters.

POSTAGE

Five Cents   **FIFTEEN**
REVENUE   **CENTS**
(36)   **(37)**

1890. No. 197 surch locally with T **36**.

233		5c. on 15c. olive-green	4·25	2·75
		a. Surch inverted	65·00	75·00
		b. Surch double	£120	£140
		c. "Flve" for "Five" (R. 1/1)	£140	95·00
		d. Variety as c, inverted	—	£1800
		e. "REVENUE" omitted	£225	£200
		f. Inverted "s" in "Cents" (R. 10/2)	£140	£120
		g. Variety as f, and whole surch inverted	£2250	
		h. "REVENUE" omitted and inverted "s" in "Cents"	£1800	
		i. "POSTAGE" spaced between "T" and "A" (R. 1/5)	90·00	90·00
		j. Variety as i, and whole surch inverted	£2250	£1800
		s. Optd "SPECIMEN"	35·00	

1891. Nos. 198/9 surch locally with T **37**.

239	**29**	15c. on 25c. yellow-brown	20·00	20·00
240		15c. on 28c. slate	21·00	9·00
		w. Wmk inverted	†	£350

3 Cents
(38)   **39**

1892. Nos. 148/9 and 199 surch locally with T **38**.

241	**10**	3c. on 4c. rosy mauve	2·00	3·25
242		3c. on 4c. rose	9·00	13·00
		s. Optd "SPECIMEN"	42·00	
		w. Wmk inverted	£200	
		ws. Optd "SPECIMEN"	£150	
243	**29**	3c. on 28c. slate	6·50	6·50
		a. Surch double	£170	
241/3	*Set of 3*		16·00	20·00

1893–99. Wmk Crown CA. P 14.

245	**39**	3c. terracotta and blue-green	7·00	45
246	**10**	4c. carmine-rose (1898)	13·00	16·00
247	**29**	30c. brown and green	5·00	3·25
		a. Bright mauve and chestnut	6·50	3·50
249	**19**	2r.50 purple/red (1899)	42·00	70·00
245/9	*Set of 4*		60·00	80·00
245s, 247s/9s	Optd "SPECIMEN" *Set of 3*		80·00	

Six Cents   **2 R. 25 C.**
(40)   **(41)**

1898 (Dec)–**99.**

*(a) No. 196 surch locally with T **40***

250	**29**	6c. on 15c. sage-green	1·25	75

*(b) As No. 138, but colour changed and perf 14, surch as T **41** by D.L.R. (1899)*

254	**19**	1r.50 on 2r.50 slate	21·00	55·00
		w. Wmk inverted	£325	£400
255		2r.25 on 2r.50 yellow	50·00	85·00
250s/5s	Optd "Specimen" (Nos. 250s) or "SPECIMEN" *Set of 3*		80·00	

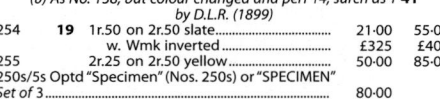

43

1899–1900. Wmk Crown CA (1r.50, 2r.25 wmk Crown CC). P 14.

256	**9**	2c. pale orange-brown	5·00	30
257	**39**	3c. deep green	5·00	55
258	**10**	4c. yellow	4·25	3·75
259	**29**	6c. rose and black	3·25	45
		w. Wmk inverted	†	£300
260	**39**	12c. sage-green and rose (1900)	6·00	9·50
261	**29**	15c. blue	8·50	1·25
262	**39**	75c. black and red-brown	11·00	10·00
263	**43**	1r.50 rose	35·00	55·00
		w. Wmk inverted	£425	£425
264		2r.25 dull blue	38·00	55·00
256/64	*Set of 9*		£100	£120
256s/64s	Optd "SPECIMEN" *Set of 9*		£225	

44   **45**   **46**

47   **48**

1903 (29 May)–**05.** Wmk Crown CA. P 14.

265	**44**	2c. red-brown (21.7.03)	2·00	20
266	**45**	3c. green (11.6.03)	2·25	1·00
267		4c. orange-yellow and blue	2·25	6·00
268	**46**	5c. dull purple (2.7.03)	3·00	60
		sa. Opt "SPECIMEN" double, one albino	£225	
269	**47**	6c. carmine (5.11.03)	9·50	1·50
		w. Wmk inverted	£140	£150
270	**45**	12c. sage-green and rosine (13.8.03)	5·00	11·00
271	**48**	15c. blue (2.7.03)	6·50	3·50
272		25c. bistre (11.8.03)	6·00	12·00
273		30c. dull violet and green	3·25	4·00
274	**45**	75c. dull blue and orange (31.3.05)	4·25	24·00
275	**48**	1r.50 greyish slate (7.4.04)	65·00	70·00
276		2r.25 brown and green (12.4.04)	95·00	65·00
265/76	*Set of 12*		£180	£180
265s/76s	Optd "SPECIMEN" *Set of 12*		£180	

1904 (13 Sept)–**05.** Wmk Mult Crown CA. Ordinary paper. P 14.

277	**44**	2c. red-brown (17.11.04)	2·50	10
278	**45**	3c. green (17.11.04)	1·75	15
279		4c. orange and ultramarine	3·00	1·50
		w. Wmk inverted	—	£275
280	**46**	5c. dull purple (29.11.04)	3·75	1·25
		a. Chalk-surfaced paper (5.10.05)	7·50	70
		ay. Wmk inverted and reversed	—	£350
281	**47**	6c. carmine (11.10.04)	5·50	15
		w. Wmk inverted	†	£325
282	**45**	12c. sage-green and rosine (29.9.04)	1·75	1·75
283	**48**	15c. blue (1.12.04)	3·75	60
284		25c. bistre (5.1.05)	6·00	3·75
		w. Wmk inverted	†	£375
285		30c. violet and green (7.9.05)	2·50	3·00
286	**45**	75c. dull blue and orange (25.5.05)	5·25	8·00
287	**48**	1r.50 grey (5.1.05)	32·00	14·00
288		2r.25 brown and green (22.12.04)	22·00	32·00
277/88	*Set of 12*		80·00	55·00

50   **51**

1908. Wmk Mult Crown CA. P 14.

289	**50**	5c. deep purple (26.5)	7·50	10
290		5c. dull purple	9·50	30
291	**51**	6c. carmine (6.6)	3·50	10
289s, 291s	Optd "SPECIMEN" *Set of 2*		70·00	

1910 (1 Aug)–**11.** Wmk Mult Crown CA. P 14.

292	**44**	2c. brown-orange (20.5.11)	1·50	50
293	**48**	3c. green (5.7.11)	1·00	75
294		10c. sage-green and maroon	2·50	3·50
295		25c. grey	2·50	2·00
296		50c. chocolate	4·00	7·50
297		1r. purple/yellow	8·50	13·00
298		2r. red/yellow	15·00	30·00
299		5r. black/green	48·00	£120
300		10r. black/red	£140	£300
292/300	*Set of 9*		£200	£425
292s/300s	Optd "SPECIMEN" *Set of 9*		£275	

Examples of Nos. 298/300 are known showing a forged Colombo registered postmark dated '27.1.10'.

52   **53**

(A)   **(B)**

Most values in Type **52** were produced by two printing operations, using "Key" and "Duty" plates. Differences in the two Dies of the Key plate are described in the introduction to this catalogue.

In the Ceylon series, however, the 1c. and 5c. values, together with later printings of the 3c. and 6c., were printed from special plates at one operation. These plates can be identified by the large "C" in the value tablet (see illustration A). Examples of these values from Key and Duty plates printing have value tablet as illustration B. The 3c. and 5c. stamps from the single plates *resemble* Die I, and the 1c. and 6c. Die II, although in the latter case the inner top corners of the side panels are square and not curved.

1912–25. Wmk Mult Crown CA. Chalk-surfaced paper (30c. to 100r.). P 14.

(a) Printed from single plates. Value tablet as A

301	**52**	1c. brown (1919)	1·00	10
		w. Wmk inverted	24·00	
302		3c. blue-green (1919)	5·50	45
		w. Wmk inverted	21·00	45·00
		y. Wmk inverted and reversed	28·00	65·00
303		5c. purple	12·00	2·75
		a. Wmk sideways (Crown to right of CA)	£500	
		x. Wmk reversed	†	£300
		y. Wmk inverted and reversed	£140	
304		5c. bright magenta	1·00	60

305		w. Wmk inverted	£180	£150
		6c. pale scarlet (1919)	14·00	85
		a. Wmk sideways (Crown to left of CA)	45·00	£100
		w. Wmk inverted	32·00	60·00
306		6c. carmine	19·00	1·25
		a. Wmk sideways (Crown to right of CA)	55·00	
		aw. Wmk sideways (Crown to left of CA)	95·00	
		w. Wmk inverted	70·00	
		y. Wmk inverted and reversed	50·00	

(b) Printed from Key and Duty plates. Die I. 3c. and 6c. have value tablet as B

307	52	2c. brown-orange	40	30
		a. Deep orange-brown	30	20
308		3c. yellow-green	6·50	2·25
		a. Deep green (1917)	4·50	1·10
309		6c. scarlet (shades)	1·10	50
		a. Deep bright blue	†	—
310		10c. sage-green	3·00	1·75
		a. Deep sage-green (1917)	7·00	2·50
		w. Wmk inverted	£200	
311		15c. deep bright blue	3·25	1·25
		a. Ultramarine (1918)	1·75	1·25
		aw. Wmk inverted	25·00	
312		25c. orange and blue	8·00	4·50
		a. Yellow and blue (1917)	1·75	1·75
		aw. Wmk inverted	£200	£200
313		30c. blue-green and violet	4·00	3·25
		a. Yellow-green and violet (1915)	7·00	4·00
		ab. Wmk sideways (Crown to right of CA)	35·00	
		abw. Wmk Crown to left of CA	35·00	
		aw. Wmk inverted	55·00	
		awa. Ditto. Duty plate ("CEYLON" and "30c") printed double, one albino and inverted	£375	
314		50c. black and scarlet	1·75	1·75
		w. Wmk inverted	20·00	45·00
315		1r. purple/yellow	6·00	4·50
		a. White back (1913)	6·00	5·00
		as. Optd "SPECIMEN"	50·00	
		b. On lemon (1915)	4·25	8·00
		bs. Optd "SPECIMEN"	45·00	
		c. On orange-buff (1918)	28·00	35·00
		cw. Wmk inverted	80·00	
		d. On pale yellow (1922)	6·00	10·00
		ds. Optd "SPECIMEN"	45·00	
316		2r. black and red/yellow	4·25	16·00
		a. White back (1913)	2·75	16·00
		as. Optd "SPECIMEN"	50·00	
		b. On lemon (1915)	28·00	30·00
		bs. Optd "SPECIMEN"	45·00	
		c. On orange-buff (1919)	45·00	48·00
		cw. Wmk inverted	65·00	
		d. On pale yellow (1921)	45·00	45·00
317		5r. black/green	20·00	48·00
		a. White back (1914)	25·00	42·00
		as. Optd "SPECIMEN"	48·00	
		b. On blue-grn (olive back) (1917)	26·00	48·00
		bs. Optd "SPECIMEN"	£100	
		bw. Wmk inverted	£100	£150
		c. Die II. On emerald back (1923)	48·00	£120
		cs. Optd "SPECIMEN"	65·00	
318		10r. purple and black/red	70·00	90·00
		aw. Wmk inverted	£300	
		b. Die II (1923)	90·00	£180
		bw. Wmk inverted	£750	
319		20r. black and red/blue	£150	£160
320	53	50r. dull purple (f.c. £60)	£650	£1400
		a. Break in scroll	£1800	
		b. Broken crown and scroll	£1800	
		f. Damaged leaf at bottom right	£1800	
		s. Optd "SPECIMEN"	£225	
321		100r. grey-black (f.c. £120)	£3000	
		a. Break in scroll	£5500	
		b. Broken crown and scroll	£5500	
		f. Damaged leaf at bottom right	£5500	
		s. Optd "SPECIMEN"	£425	
		w. Wmk inverted	£7000	
322		500r. dull green (f.c. £350)	£8000	
		a. Break in scroll	£16000	
		b. Broken crown and scroll	£16000	
		f. Damaged leaf at bottom right		
		s. Optd "SPECIMEN"	£700	
323		1000r. purple/red (1925) (f.c. £3000)	£35000	
		b. Broken crown and scroll	£48000	
		e. Break in lines below left scroll		
		f. Damaged leaf at bottom right		
		s. Optd "SPECIMEN"	£1500	
301/18 Set of 14			£100	£140
301s/19s Optd "SPECIMEN" Set of 15			£425	

For illustrations of the varieties on Nos. 320/3 see above No. 51b of Bermuda.

The 2c. and 5c. exist in coils, constructed from normal sheets, used in stamp-affixing machines introduced in 1915.

Sideways watermark varieties are described *as seen from the back of the stamp.*

The "substituted crown" watermark variety is known on the sheet margin of the 1c., No. 301.

An example of the 1000r. optd "SPECIMEN" is known with the break in scroll variety (R. 1/12).

```
WAR                    WAR
STAMP                  STAMP
WAR          ONE CENT
STAMP
  (54)              (55)
```

1918 (18 Nov)–**19**.

(a) Optd with T 54 by Govt Printer, Colombo

330	52	2c. brown-orange	20	40
		a. Opt inverted	70·00	80·00
		b. Opt double	32·00	45·00
331		3c. blue-green (No. 302) (1919)	3·75	40
		a. Opt double	£140	
332		3c. deep green (No. 308a)	20	50
		a. Opt double	£100	£120
		aw. Wmk inverted	†	£200

333		5c. purple	50	30
		a. Opt double	70·00	80·00
		w. Wmk inverted	£120	
334		5c. bright magenta	4·50	3·25
		a. Opt inverted	70·00	80·00
		b. Opt double	50·00	60·00

(b) Surch with T 55

335	52	1c. on 5c. purple	50	40
		w. Wmk inverted	£160	
		y. Wmk inverted and reversed	£120	
336		1c. on 5c. bright magenta	3·25	20
330s, 332s/3s, 335s Optd "SPECIMEN" Set of 4			£130	

Collectors are warned against forgeries of the errors in the "WAR STAMP" overprints.

1918. Surch as T **55**, but without "WAR STAMP".

337	52	1c. on 5c. purple	15	25
		a. Surch double	£200	
		bs. Optd "SPECIMEN"	42·00	
		by. Wmk inverted and reversed	£160	
337c		1c. on 5c. bright magenta	3·25	4·25

1921–32. Wmk Mult Script CA. Chalk-surfaced paper (30c. to 100r.). P 14.

(a) Printed from single plates. Value tablet as A

338	52	1c. brown (1927)	1·00	35
339		3c. green (5.5.22)	5·50	75
		w. Wmk inverted	20·00	50·00
340		3c. slate-grey (1923)	75	20
		a. Wmk sideways	£1700	
		w. Wmk inverted	45·00	
341		5c. purple (1927)	60	15
342		6c. carmine-red (3.8.21)	4·00	75
		w. Wmk inverted	22·00	50·00
		y. Wmk inverted and reversed	75·00	
343		6c. bright violet (1922)	2·75	15
		w. Wmk inverted	48·00	
		y. Wmk inverted and reversed	75·00	

(b) Printed from Key and Duty plates

344	52	2c. brown-orange (Die II) (1927)	70	25
345		9c. red/pale yellow (Die II) (1926)	3·00	30
346		10c. sage-green (Die I) (16.9.21)	1·40	40
		aw. Wmk inverted	50·00	
		ay. Wmk inverted and reversed	42·00	70·00
		b. Die II (1924)	1·75	60
		c. Vert gutter pair. Die I and Die II. Nos. 346 and 346b	£375	
347		12c. rose-scarlet (Die I) (1925)	10·00	5·50
		a. Die II	1·25	2·25
		as. Optd "SPECIMEN"	£110	
		b. Vert gutter pair. Die I and Die II. Nos. 347 and 347a	£160	
348		15c. ultramarine (Die I) (30.5.22)	3·75	21·00
349		15c. green/pale yellow (Die I) (1923)	5·50	1·25
		a. Die II (1924)	4·75	1·00
		aw. Wmk inverted	48·00	
		b. Vert gutter pair. Die I and Die II. Nos. 349 and 349a	£325	
350		20c. bright blue (Die I) (1922)	6·00	6·00
		aw. Wmk inverted	70·00	
		b. Die II (1924)	3·50	45
		c. Vert gutter pair. Die I and Die II. Nos. 350 and 350b	£375	
351		25c. orange-yellow and blue (Die I) (17.10.21)	3·00	1·90
		aw. Wmk inverted	75·00	
		b. Die II (1924)	5·50	1·25
		c. Vert gutter pair. Die I and Die II. Nos. 351 and 351b	£190	
352		30c. yellow-green and violet (Die I) (15.3.22)	1·60	6·50
		a. Die II (1924)	6·00	1·25
		b. Vert gutter pair. Die I and Die II. Nos. 352 and 352a	£750	
353		50c. black and scarlet (Die II) (1922)	2·00	80
		a. Die I (1932)	60·00	95·00
354		1r. purple/pale yellow (Die I) (1923)	15·00	50·00
		a. Die II (1925)	25·00	42·00
		b. Vert gutter pair. Die I and Die II. Nos. 354 and 354a	£400	
355		2r. black and red/pale yellow (Die II) (1923)	7·00	14·00
356		5r. black/emerald (Die II) (1924)	50·00	95·00
357		20r. black and red/blue (Die II) (1924)	£325	£400
358	53	50r. dull purple (1924) (f.c. £70)	£800	£1400
		a. Break in scroll	£1500	
		b. Broken crown and scroll	£1500	
		e. Break in lines below left scroll	£1500	
		f. Damaged leaf at bottom right	£1500	
		g. Gash in fruit and leaf	£1500	
		s. Optd "SPECIMEN"	£200	
359		100r. brownish grey (1924) (f.c. £140)	£3000	
		a. Break in scroll	£5000	
		b. Broken crown and scroll	£5000	
		c. Nick in top right scroll	£5000	
		e. Break in lines below left scroll	£5000	
		f. Damaged leaf at bottom right	£5000	
		h. Grey-black	£3000	
		ha. Break in scroll	£5000	
		hb. Broken crown and scroll	£5000	
		he. Break in lines below left scroll	£5000	
		hf. Damaged leaf at bottom right	£5000	
		s. Optd "SPECIMEN"	£475	
360		100r. dull purple and blue (24.10.27) (f.c. £180)	£2500	
		a. Break in scroll	£4500	
		b. Broken crown and scroll	£4500	
		e. Break in lines below left scroll	£4500	
		f. Damaged leaf at bottom right	£4500	
		g. Gash in fruit and leaf	£4500	
		s. Optd "SPECIMEN"	£500	
338/56 Set of 19			£100	£160
338s/57s Optd "SPECIMEN" Set of 20			£650	

The 2c. to 30c. and 1r. values produced from Key and Duty plates were printed in sheets of 240 using two plates one above the other. Nos. 346c, 347b, 349b, 350c, 351c, 352b and 354b come from printings in 1924 and 1925 which combined Key Plate 7 (Die I) with Key Plate 12 (Die II).

No. 353a, from Key Plate 23, was a mistake; the "retired" Die I being issued in error when it became necessary to replace Key Plate 21.

For illustrations of the varieties on Nos. 358/60 see above No. 51b of Bermuda.

2 Cents.

(56)   57

(Surch at Ceylon Govt Printing Works)

1926 (27 Nov). Surch as T **56**.

361	52	2c. on 3c. slate-grey	3·25	1·00
		a. Surch double	70·00	
		b. Bar omitted	80·00	90·00
362		5c. on 6c. bright violet	1·00	40
361s/2s Optd "SPECIMEN" Set of 2			80·00	

No. 361b comes from the bottom horizontal row of the sheet which was often partially obscured by the selvedge during surcharging.

1927 (27 Nov)–**29**. Wmk Mult Script CA. Chalk-surfaced paper. P 14.

363	57	1r. dull and bright purple (1928)	2·50	1·25
364		2r. green and carmine (1929)	3·75	2·75
365		5r. green and dull purple (1928)	17·00	30·00
366		10r. green and brown-orange	70·00	£160
367		20r. dull purple and blue	£300	£450
363/7 Set of 5			£350	£550
363s/7s Optd "SPECIMEN" Set of 5			£275	

No. 364. Collectors are warned against faked 2r. stamps, showing what purports to be a double centre.

58 Tapping Rubber

59 Adam's Peak

60 Colombo Harbour

61 Plucking tea

62 Hill paddy (rice)

63 River scene

64 Coconut Palms

65 Temple of the Tooth, Kandy

66 Ancient irrigation tank

67 Wild elephants

68 Trincomalee

(Recess D.L.R. (2, 3, 20, 50c.), B.W. (others))

1935 (1 May)–**36**. T **58**/**68**. Wmk Mult Script CA (sideways on 10, 15, 25, 30c. and 1r.). Various perfs.

368	58	2c. black and carmine (P 12×13)	30	40
		a. Perf 14	9·00	40
369	59	3c. black and olive-green (P 13×12) (1.10.35)	1·25	40
		a. Perf 14	40·00	35
370	60	6c. black and blue (P 11×11½) (1.1.36)	30	30
371	61	9c. green and orange (P 11×11½) (1.6.35)	1·50	65
372	62	10c. black and purple (P 11½×11) (1.6.35)	1·25	3·00
373	63	15c. red-brown and green (P 11½×11)	2·25	50
374	64	20c. black and grey-blue (P 12×13) (1.1.36)	2·75	3·50

375	65	25c. deep blue and chocolate (P 11½×11)	2·00	1·50
376	66	30c. carmine and green (P 11½×11) (1.8.35)	2·75	3·50
377	67	50c. black and mauve (P 14) (1.1.36)	17·00	1·75
378	68	1r. violet-blue and chocolate (P 11½×11) (1.7.35)	40·00	30·00
368/78 Set of 11			60·00	40·00
368s/78s Perf "SPECIMEN" Set of 11			£350	

1935 (6 May). Silver Jubilee. As Nos. 91/4 of Antigua. P 13½×14.

379		6c. ultramarine and grey	75	30
		f. Diagonal line by turret	80·00	32·00
		g. Dot to left of chapel	£130	50·00
		h. Dot by flagstaff	£110	50·00
		i. Dash by turret	£180	90·00
380		9c. green and indigo	75	2·75
		f. Diagonal line by turret	95·00	£130
		g. Dot to left of chapel	£200	£225
		h. Dot by flagstaff	£170	£200
381		20c. brown and deep blue	4·25	2·75
		f. Diagonal line by turret	£200	£130
		g. Dot to left of chapel	£350	£200
382		50c. slate and purple	5·25	16·00
		f. Diagonal line by turret	£400	£450
		h. Dot by flagstaff	£400	£450
379/82 Set of 4			10·00	20·00
379s/82s Perf "SPECIMEN" Set of 4			£140	

For illustrations of plate varieties, see Omnibus section following Zanzibar.

1937 (12 May). Coronation. As Nos. 95/7 of Antigua. P 11×11½.

383		6c. carmine	65	1·00
384		9c. green	2·50	4·50
385		20c. blue	3·50	4·00
383/5 Set of 3			6·00	8·50
383s/5s Perf "SPECIMEN" Set of 3			£120	

69 Tapping Rubber

70 Sigiriya (Lion Rock)

71 Ancient Guard-stone, Anuradhapura

72 King George VI

Comma flaw (Pl 2A R. 5/6)

5c. Apostrophe flaw (Frame Pl 1A R. 6/6) (ptg of 1 Jan 1943 only)

(Recess B.W. (6, 10, 15, 20, 25, 30c., 1r., 2r. (both)), D.L.R (others) T **72** typo D.L.R.)

1938–49. T **69/72** and designs as 1935–36, but with portrait of King George VI instead of King George V, "POSTAGE & REVENUE" omitted and some redrawn. Wmk Mult Script CA (sideways on 10, 15, 25, 30c. and 1r.). Chalk-surfaced paper (5r.). P 11×11½ (6, 20c., 2r. (both)), 11½×11 (10, 15, 25, 30c., 1r.), 11½×13 (2c.), 13×11½ (3, 50c.), 13½ (5c.) or 14 (5r.).

386	69	2c. black and carmine (25.4.38)	25·00	3·75
		aa. Comma flaw	£550	£160
		a. Perf 13½×13 (1938)	£120	1·75
		ab. Comma flaw	£1500	£140
		b. Perf 13½ (25.4.38)	3·75	10
		ba. Comma flaw	£170	80·00
		c. Perf 11×11½ (17.2.44)	1·50	2·00
		cw. Wmk inverted	—	£1600
		d. Perf 12 (22.4.49)	2·50	6·00

387	59	3c. black and deep blue-green (21.3.38)	12·00	3·50
		a. Perf 13×13½ (1938)	£275	17·00
		b. Perf 13½ (21.3.38)	7·00	10
		c. Perf 14 (line) (7.41)	£150	1·00
		d. Perf 11½×11 (14.5.42)	1·00	10
		da. "A" of "CA" missing from wmk	£1300	£1300
		dw. Wmk inverted	†	£1800
		e. Perf 12 (14.1.46)	1·50	85
387f	64	5c. sage-green and orange (1.1.43)	30	10
		fa. Apostrophe flaw	£100	50·00
		fb. "A" of "CA" missing from wmk	†	£1500
		g. Perf 12 (1947)	2·25	30
388	60	6c. black and blue (1.1.38)	1·00	10
		a. "A" of "CA" missing from wmk	†	£1300
389	70	10c. black and light blue (1.2.38)	4·00	20
		a. Wmk upright (1.6.44)	2·50	50
390	63	15c. green and red-brown (1.1.38)	2·00	20
		a. Wmk upright (23.7.45)	2·75	60
391	61	20c. black and grey-blue (15.1.38)	3·25	20
392	65	25c. deep blue and chocolate (15.1.38)	5·00	30
		a. Wmk upright (1944)	4·25	20
393	66	30c. carmine and green (1.2.38)	12·00	3·50
		a. "A" of "CA" missing from wmk	†	£1400
		b. Wmk upright (16.4.45)	13·00	7·00
394	67	50c. black and mauve (25.4.38)	£160	50·00
		a. Perf 13×13½ (25.4.38)	£450	2·75
		b. Perf 13½ (25.4.38)	27·00	1·00
		c. Perf 14 (line) (4.42)	£110	27·00
		d. Perf 11½×11 (14.5.42)	8·50	4·75
		da. "A" of "CA" missing from wmk	£1500	
		e. Perf 12 (14.1.46)	9·50	20
395	68	1r. blue-violet and chocolate (1.2.38)	24·00	1·75
		a. Wmk upright (1944)	19·00	2·25
396	71	2r. black and carmine (1.2.38)	19·00	4·75
		a. "A" of "CA" missing from wmk	£1700	
396b		2r. black and violet (15.3.47)	4·25	3·00
397	72	5r. green and purple (1.7.38)	55·00	22·00
		a. Ordinary paper. *Green and pale purple* (19.2.43)	45·00	19·00
386/97a (cheapest) Set of 14			£100	30·00
386s/97s Perf "SPECIMEN" Set of 14			£650	

Printings of the 2c., 3c. and 50c. perforated 11×11½ or 11½×11 were produced by Bradbury Wilkinson after the De La Rue works had been bombed in December 1940.

3 CENTS

(73)   (74)

1940–41. Nos. 388 and 391 surch by Govt Ptg Office, Colombo.

398	73	3c. on 6c. black and blue (10.5.41)	1·25	10
399	74	3c. on 20c. black and grey-blue (5.11.40)	6·00	4·00

1946 (10 Dec). Victory. As Nos. 110/11 of Antigua.

400		6c. blue	30	35
401		15c. brown	30	1·75
400s/1s Perf "SPECIMEN" Set of 2			£110	

75 Parliament Building

77 Temple of the Tooth

76 Adam's Peak

78 Anuradhapura

(Des R. Tenison and M. S. V. Rodrigo. Recess B.W.)

1947 (25 Nov). Inauguration of New Constitution. T **75/8**. Wmk Mult Script CA. P 11×12 (horiz) or 12×11 (vert).

402	75	6c. black and blue	40	15
403	76	10c. black, orange and carmine	35	40
404	77	15c. green and purple	35	80
405	78	25c. ochre and emerald-green	35	1·75
402/5 Set of 4			1·25	2·75
402s/5s Perf "SPECIMEN" Set of 4			£130	

DOMINION

79 Lion Flag of Dominion

80 D. S. Senanayake

81 Lotus Flowers and Sinhalese Letters "Sri"

4c. Normal

4c. "Short rope" (Pl 1 R. 10/9)

(Recess (flag typo) B.W.)

1949 (4 Feb–5 Apr). First Anniv of Independence.

(a) Wmk Mult Script CA (sideways on 4c.). P 12½×12 (4c.) or 12×12½ (5c.)

406	79	4c. yellow, carmine and brown	20	20
		a. "Short rope"	30·00	25·00
407	80	5c. brown and green	10	10

*(b) W **81** (sideways on 15c.). P 13×12½ (15c.) or 12×12½ (25c.) (5 Apr)*

408	79	15c. yellow, carmine and vermilion	1·00	1·50
409	80	25c. brown and blue	15	1·00
406/9 Set of 4			1·25	2·50

The 15c. is larger, measuring 28×12 mm.

82 Globe and Forms of Transport

83   **84**

(Recess D.L.R.)

1949 (10 Oct). 75th Anniv of Universal Postal Union. W **81**. P 13 (25c.) or 12 (others).

410	82	5c. brown and bluish green	75	10
411	83	15c. black and carmine	1·10	2·75
412	84	25c. black and ultramarine	1·10	1·10
410/12 Set of 3			2·75	3·50

85 Kandyan Dancer

86 Kiri Vehera Polonnaruwa

87 Vesak Orchid

88 Sigiriya (Lion Rock)

89 Octagon Library, Temple of the Tooth

90 Ruins at Madirigiriya

(Recess B.W.)

1950 (4 Feb). T **85/90**. W **81**. P 11×11½ (75c.), 11½×11 (1r.), 12×12½ (others).

413	**85**	4c. purple and scarlet	15	10
414	**86**	5c. green	15	10
415	**87**	15c. blue-green and violet	3·00	50
416	**88**	30c. carmine and yellow	30	70
417	**89**	75c. ultramarine and orange	9·50	20
418	**90**	1r. deep blue and brown	1·75	30
413/18 *Set of 6*			13·50	1·50

These stamps were issued with redrawn inscriptions in 1958/9. See Nos. 448/65.

91 Sambars, Ruhuna National Park

92 Ancient Guard-stone, Anuradhapura

93 Harvesting rice

94 Coconut trees

95 Sigiriya fresco

96 Star Orchid

97 Rubber Plantation

98 Outrigger canoe

99 Tea Plantation

100 River Gal Dam

101 Bas-relief, Anuradhapura

102 Harvesting rice

35c. I. No. 424

35c. II. No. 424a (Dot added)

(Photo Courvoisier)

1951 (1 Aug)–**54**. T **91/102**. No wmk. P 11½.

419	**91**	2c. brown and blue-green (15.5.54)	10	1·25
420	**92**	3c. black and slate-violet (15.5.54)	10	1·00
421	**93**	6c. brown-black and yellow-green (15.5.54)	15	30
422	**94**	10c. green and blue-grey	1·00	65
423	**95**	25c. orange-brown and bright blue (15.3.54)	20	20

424	**96**	35c. red and deep green (I) (1.2.52)	1·50	1·50
		a. Type II (1954)	7·00	60
425	**97**	40c. deep brown (15.5.54)	5·00	1·00
426	**98**	50c. indigo and slate-grey (15.3.54)	30	50
427	**99**	85c. black and deep blue-green (15.5.54)	3·00	30
428	**100**	2r. blue and deep brown (15.5.54)	12·00	1·50
429	**101**	5r. brown and orange (15.3.54)	17·00	1·75
430	**102**	10r. red-brown and buff (15.3.54)	60·00	27·00
419/30 *Set of 12*			85·00	32·00

Nos. 413/30 (except 422) were reissued in 1958–62, redrawn with 'CEYLON' much smaller and other inscriptions in Sinhalese. See Nos. 448/65.

103 Ceylon Mace and symbols of Progress

(Photo Harrison)

1952 (23 Feb). Colombo Plan Exhibition. Chalk-surfaced paper. W **81** (sideways). P 14½×14.

431	**103**	5c. green	30	10
432		15c. ultramarine	30	60

104 Queen Elizabeth II

105 Ceremonial Procession

(Recess B.W.)

1953 (2 June). Coronation. W **81**. P 12×13.

433	**104**	5c. green	1·75	10

(Recess D.L.R.)

1954 (10 Apr). Royal Visit. W **81** (sideways). P 13×12½.

434	**105**	10c. deep blue	1·50	10

106 King Coconuts

107 Farm Produce

(Photo Courvoisier)

1954 (1 Dec). No wmk. P 11½.

435	**106**	10c. orange, bistre-brown and buff..	50	10

For this design with redrawn inscription see No. 453.

(Photo Harrison)

1955 (10 Dec). Royal Agricultural and Food Exhibition. W **81** (sideways). P 14×14½.

436	**107**	10c. brown and orange	10	10

108 Sir John Kotelawala and House of Representatives

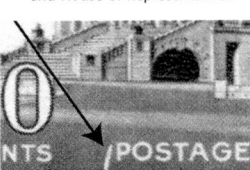

White stroke to left of "POSTAGE" (R. 2/6)

(Photo Courvoisier)

1956 (26 Mar). Prime Minister's 25 Years of Public Service. P 11½.

437	**108**	10c. deep bluish green	10	10
		a. White stroke		1·50

109 Arrival of Vijaya in Ceylon

110 Lampstand and Dharmachakra

---

111 Hand of Peace and Dharmachakra

112 Dharmachakra encircling the Globe

(Photo Courvoisier)

1956. Buddha Jayanti. P 11½.

438	**109**	3c. blue and brownish grey (23.5)	70	15
439	**110**	4c. +2c. greenish yellow and deep blue (10.5)	20	75
440	**111**	10c. +5c. carmine, yellow and grey (10.5)	20	1·00
441	**112**	15c. bright blue (23.5)	25	10
438/41 *Set of 4*			1·25	1·75

113 Mail Transport

114 Stamp of 1857

(Photo Enschedé (4c., 10c.), Courvoisier (others))

1957 (1 Apr). Centenary of First Ceylon Postage Stamp. P 12½×13 (4c., 10c.) or 11½ (others).

442	**113**	4c. orange-red and deep bluish green	60	50
443		10c. vermilion and blue	60	10
444	**114**	35c. brown, yellow and blue	30	35
445		85c. brown, yellow and grey-green	60	1·25
442/5 *Set of 4*			1·90	2·00

(115)   (116)

117 Kandyan Dancer

1958 (15 Jan). Nos. 439/40 with premium obliterated as T **115** (4c.) or T **116** (10c.).

446	**110**	4c. greenish yellow and deep blue .	10	10
		a. Opt inverted	20·00	35·00
		b. Opt double	32·00	50·00
447	**111**	10c. carmine, yellow and grey	10	10
		a. Opt inverted	14·00	19·00
		b. Narrower square (R. 2/3 and R. 10/1)		1·25

The 4c. exists with opt misplaced to right so that some stamps show the vertical bar on the left (*Price £20 un*.).

On No. 447b the obliterating square is 3 mm. wide instead of 4 mm.

(Recess B.W. (4c., 5c., 15c., 30c., 75c., 1r.). Photo Courvoisier (others))

1958 (14 May)–**62**. As earlier types, but inscriptions redrawn as in T **117**. W **81** (4, 5, 15, 30, 75c., 1r.) or no wmk (others). P 11×11½ (75c.), 11½×11 (1r.), 12×12½ (4, 5, 15, 30c.), or 11½ (others).

448	**91**	2c. brown and blue-green	10	50
449	**92**	3c. black and slate-violet	10	70
450	**117**	4c. purple and scarlet	10	10
451	**86**	5c. green (1.10.58)	10	1·60
		a. Yellow-green (13.6.61)	1·00	2·50
		b. Deep green (19.6.62)	9·00	4·00
452	**93**	6c. brown-black and yellow-green..	50	1·00
453	**106**	10c. orange, bistre-brown and buff (1.10.58)	10	10
454	**87**	15c. blue-green and violet (1.10.58)..	3·00	1·00
455	**95**	25c. orange-brown and bright blue .	25	10
456	**88**	30c. carmine and yellow (1.5.59)	25	1·40
457	**96**	35c. red and deep green (II) (15.7.58)	2·00	30
459	**98**	50c. indigo and slate-grey (15.7.58).	30	10
460	**89**	75c. ultramarine and orange (1.5.59)	9·00	5·50
		a. Ultramarine and brown-orange (3.4.62)	12·00	4·00
461	**99**	85c. black and deep blue-green (1.5.59)	3·75	13·00
462	**90**	1r. deep blue and brown (1.10.58)..	60	10
463	**100**	2r. blue and deep brown	8·50	30
464	**101**	5r. brown and orange	19·00	30
465	**102**	10r. red-brown and buff	19·00	1·00
448/65 *Set of 17*			60·00	22·00

118 "Human Rights"

119 Portraits of Founders and University Buildings

(Photo Enschedé)

1958 (10 Dec). Tenth Anniv of Declaration of Human Rights.
P 13×12½.

| 466 | **118** | 10c. vermilion and dull purple | 10 | 10 |
| 467 | | 85c. vermilion and deep blue-green | 30 | 1·25 |

(Photo Enschedé)

1959 (31 Dec). Institution of Pirivena Universities. P 13×12½.

| 468 | **119** | 10c. red-orange and ultramarine | 10 | 10 |

120 Uprooted Tree **121** S. W. R. D. Bandaranaike

(Des W. A. Ariyasena. Photo Courvoisier)

1960 (7 Apr). World Refugee Year. P 11½.

| 469 | **120** | 4c. red-brown and gold | 10 | 85 |
| 470 | | 25c. blackish violet and gold | 10 | 15 |

(Photo Courvoisier)

1961 (8 Jan). Prime Minister Bandaranaike Commemoration. P 11½.

| 471 | **121** | 10c. deep blue and greenish blue | 10 | 10 |
| | | a. Portrait redrawn (15.6.61)* | 10 | 10 |

*Earliest known postmark date.

No. 471a can be identified by Mr. Bandaranaike's dark hair at temples.

122 Ceylon Scout Badge **123** Campaign Emblem

(Des W. A. Ariyasena. Photo Courvoisier)

1962 (26 Feb). Golden Jubilee of Ceylon Boy Scouts Association. P 11½.

| 472 | **122** | 35c. buff and blue | 15 | 10 |

(Photo Harrison)

1962 (7 Apr). Malaria Eradication. W **81**. P 14½×14.

| 473 | **123** | 25c. red-orange and sepia | 10 | 10 |

124 de Havilland DH.85 Leopard Moth and Hawker Siddeley Comet 4 **125** "Produce" and Campaign Emblem

(Photo Courvoisier)

1963 (28 Feb). 25th Anniv of Airmail. P 11½.

| 474 | **124** | 50c. black and light blue | 50 | 50 |

(Photo Courvoisier)

1963 (21 Mar). Freedom from Hunger. P 11½.

| 475 | **125** | 5c. vermilion and blue | 1·50 | 2·00 |
| 476 | | 25c. brown and yellow-olive | 3·50 | 30 |

(126) **127** "Rural Life"

1963 (1 June). No. 450 surch with T **126**.

477	**117**	2c. on 4c. purple and scarlet	10	10
		a. Surch inverted	17·00	
		b. Surch double	50·00	
		c. Surch omitted (in pair with normal)	£300	

(Photo Harrison)

1963 (5 July). Golden Jubilee of Ceylon Co-operative Movement (1962). W **81**. P 14×14½.

| 478 | **127** | 60c. rose-red and black | 1·50 | 50 |

128 S. W. R. D. Bandaranaike **129** Terrain, Elephant and Tree

(Recess Courvoisier)

1963 (26 Sept). P 11½.

| 479 | **128** | 10c. light blue | 10 | 10 |

(Photo Harrison)

1963 (9 Dec). National Conservation Week. W **81** (sideways). P 14×14½.

| 480 | **129** | 5c. sepia and blue | 60 | 40 |

130 S. W. R. D. Bandaranaike **131** Anagarika Dharmapala (Buddhist missionary)

(T **130/1**. Photo Courvoisier)

1964 (1 July). P 11½

| 481 | **130** | 10c. deep violet-blue and greenish grey | 10 | 10 |

1964 (16 Sept). Birth Centenary of Anagarika Dharmapala (founder of Maha Bodhi Society). P 11½.

| 482 | **131** | 25c. sepia and olive-yellow | 10 | 10 |

134 Southern Grackle **135** D. S. Senanayake

136 **137** Common Peafowl

138 Ruins at Madirigiriya **139** Ceylon Junglefowl

140 Asian Black-headed Oriole **146** Tea Plantation

147 Girls transplanting rice **149** Map of Ceylon

(Des A. Dharmasiri (5r.); P. A. Miththapala (10r.). Photo Courvoisier (10c. (486), 20c.), Harrison (10c. (487), 60c., 1r., 5r., 10r.), D.L.R. (others incl sheet))

1964 (1 Oct)–72. T **134/140**, **146**, **149** and similar designs. No wmk (Nos. 486, 489). W **81** (others; sideways on Nos. 487, 494 499). P 11½ (Nos. 486, 489), 14½×14 (No. 494) or 14 (others).

485	**134**	5c. multicoloured (5.2.66)	2·00	1·00
486	**135**	10c. myrtle-green (22.3.66)	80	10
487	**136**	10c. myrtle-green (23.9.68)	10	10
		a. Imperf (pair)	48·00	
		b. Horiz pair, one stamp imperf 3 sides	£150	
488	**137**	15c. multicoloured (5.2.66)	4·50	30
489	**138**	20c. brown-purple and buff	30	25
494	**139**	60c. multicoloured (5.2.66)	5·50	1·25
		a. Red omitted	55·00	
		b. Blue and green omitted*	45·00	
495	**140**	75c. multicoloured (5.2.66)	3·00	70
		a. No wmk (8.6.72)	12·00	16·00
497	**146**	1r. brown and bluish green	1·50	30
		a. Brown (tea picker, etc) omitted	£1400	
		b. Bluish green omitted	£1500	
499	**147**	5r. multicoloured (15.8.69)	12·00	11·00
500	**149**	10r. multicoloured (1.10.69)	29·00	3·00
485/500 Set of 10			50·00	16·00
MS500a 148×174 mm. As Nos. 485, 488, 494 and 495.			8·00	14·00

*Actually only the blue printing is omitted on this sheet, but where this was printed over the yellow to form the leaves it appeared as green.

The 5c., 75c. and 1r. exist with PVA gum as well as gum arabic.

No. 487b comes from a sheet which showed stamps in the third vertical row imperforate at top, bottom and at right.

In the miniature sheet the inscriptions on the 60c. have been rearranged to conform with the style of the other values.

150 Exhibition Buildings and Cogwheels **151** Trains of 1864 and 1964

(Photo State Printing Works, Budapest)

1964 (1 Dec). Industrial Exhibition. T **150** and similar horiz design. No wmk. P 11.

501	**150**	5c. multicoloured	10	75
		a. Pair. Nos. 501/2	35	2·50
502		5c. multicoloured	10	75

No. 501 is inscribed "INDUSTRIAL EXHIBITION" in Sinhala and Tamil, No. 502 in Sinhala and English. The stamps were issued together se-tenant in alternate vertical rows, producing horizontal pairs.

(Photo Harrison)

1964 (21 Dec). Centenary of Ceylon Railways. T **151** and similar horiz design. W **81** (sideways). P 14×14½.

503	**151**	60c. blue, reddish purple and yellow-green	2·75	40
		a. Vert pair. Nos. 503/4	5·50	5·50
504		60c. blue, reddish purple and yellow-green	2·75	40

No. 503 is inscribed "RAILWAY CENTENARY" in Sinhala and Tamil, No. 504 in Sinhala and English. The stamps were issued together se-tenant in alternate horizontal rows, producing vertical pairs.

152 ITU Emblem and Symbols **153** ICY Emblem

(Photo Harrison)

1965 (17 May). ITU Centenary. W **81** (sideways). P 14½.

505	**152**	2c. bright blue and red	1·00	1·10
506		30c. brown and red	3·25	45
		a. Value omitted	£190	

No. 506a was caused by the misplacement of the red.

(Photo Courvoisier)

1965 (26 June). International Co-operation Year. T **153** and similar horiz design. P 11½.

| 507 | | 3c. deep blue and rose-carmine | 1·25 | 1·00 |
| 508 | | 50c. black, rose-carmine and gold | 3·25 | 50 |

No. 508 is similar to T **153** but has the multilingual inscription "CEYLON" rearranged.

154 Town Hall, Colombo (**155**)

(Photo Courvoisier)

1965 (29 Oct). Centenary of Colombo Municipal Council. P 11×11½.

| 509 | **154** | 25c. myrtle-green and sepia | 40 | 30 |

1965 (18 Dec). No. 481 surch with T **155**.

| 510 | **130** | 5c. on 10c. deep violet-blue and greenish grey | 10 | 2·00 |

157 Kandy and Council Crest **158** WHO Building

(Photo Harrison)

1966 (15 June). Kandy Municipal Council Centenary. W **81**. P 14×13½.

| 512 | **157** | 25c. multicoloured | 20 | 20 |

(Litho D.L.R.)

1966 (8 Oct). Inauguration of WHO Headquarters. Geneva. P 14.

| 513 | **158** | 4c. multicoloured | 3·50 | 3·00 |
| 514 | | 1r. multicoloured | 8·50 | 1·50 |

159 Rice Paddy and Map of Ceylon **160** Rice Paddy and Globe

(Photo Courvoisier)

1966 (25 Oct). International Rice Year. P 11½.
515	**159**	6c. multicoloured	20	1·00
516	**160**	30c. multicoloured	30	15

161 UNESCO Emblem **162** Water-resources Map

(Litho State Ptg Wks, Vienna)

1966 (3 Nov). 20th Anniv of UNESCO. P 12.
517	**161**	3c. multicoloured	2·75	3·75
518		50c. multicoloured	8·00	50

(Litho D.L.R.)

1966 (1 Dec). International Hydrological Decade. P 14.
519	**162**	2c. orange-brown, greenish yellow and blue	30	85
520		2r. orange-brown, greenish yellow, blue and yellow-green	2·25	2·25

163 Devotees at Buddhist Temple **167** Galle Fort and Clock Tower

(Photo State Ptg Wks, Vienna)

1967 (2 Jan). Poya Holiday System. T **163** and similar horiz designs. Multicoloured. P 12.
521	5c. Type **163**	20	60
522	20c. Mihintale	30	10
523	35c. Sacred Bo-tree, Anuradhapura	30	15
524	60c. Adam's Peak	30	10
521/4	*Set of 4*	1·00	85

(Litho Rosenbaum Brothers, Vienna)

1967 (5 Jan). Centenary of Galle Municipal Council. P 13½.
525	**167**	25c. multicoloured	70	20

168 Field Research

(Litho Rosenbaum Bros, Vienna)

1967 (1 Aug). Centenary of Ceylon Tea Industry. T **168** and similar horiz designs. Multicoloured. P 13½.
526	4c. Type **168**	50	80
527	40c. Tea-tasting equipment	1·00	1·50
528	50c. Leaves and bud	1·00	20
529	1r. Shipping tea	1·00	10
526/9	*Set of 4*	3·25	2·25

169 Elephant Ride **170** Ranger, Jubilee Emblem and Flag

(Litho Rosenbaum Bros, Vienna)

1967 (15 Aug). International Tourist Year. P 13½.
530	**169**	45c. multicoloured	2·25	80

1967 (16 Sept). First National Stamp Exhibition. No. **MS**500*a* optd "FIRST NATIONAL STAMP EXHIBITION 1967".
MS531	148×174 mm. Nos. 485, 488, 494/5. Imperf	4·75	6·00

(Litho D.L.R.)

1967 (19 Sept). Golden Jubilee of Ceylon Girl Guides Association. P 12½×13.
532	**170**	3c. multicoloured	50	20
533		25c. multicoloured	75	10

171 Col. Olcott and Buddhist Flag

(Litho Rosenbaum Bros, Vienna)

1967 (8 Dec). 60th Death Anniv of Colonel H. S. Olcott (theosophist). P 13½.
534	**171**	15c. multicoloured	30	20

172 Independence Hall **173** Lion Flag and Sceptre

(Photo Harrison)

1968 (2 Feb). 20th Anniv of Independence. W **81** (sideways). P 14.
535	**172**	5c. multicoloured	10	55
536	**173**	1r. multicoloured	50	10

174 Sir D. B. Jayatilleke **175** Institute of Hygiene

(Litho D.L.R.)

1968 (14 Feb). Birth Centenary of Sir Baron Jayatilleke (scholar and statesman). P 14.
537	**174**	25c. yellow-brown and sepia	10	10

(Litho B.W.)

1968 (7 Apr). 20th Anniv of World Health Organization. W **81**. P 12.
538	**175**	50c. multicoloured	10	10

176 Vickers Super VC-10 Aircraft over Terminal Building **177** Open Koran and "1400"

(Des and litho B.W.)

1968 (5 Aug). Opening of Colombo Airport. W **81**. P 13½.
539	**176**	60c. grey-blue, chestnut, red and yellow	1·00	10

(Des M. I. M. Mohideen. Photo Harrison)

1968 (14 Oct). 1400th Anniv of the Holy Koran. W **81**. P 14.
541	**177**	25c. multicoloured	10	10

178 Human Rights Emblem **179** All Ceylon Buddhist Congress Headquarters

(Photo Pakistan Security Printing Corp)

1968 (10 Dec). Human Rights Year. P 12½×13½.
542	**178**	2c. multicoloured	10	30
543		20c. multicoloured	10	10
544		40c. multicoloured	10	10
545		2r. multicoloured	80	4·75
542/5	*Set of 4*	1·00	4·75

(Des A. Dharmasiri. Litho Rosenbaum Bros, Vienna)

1968 (19 Dec). Golden Jubilee of All Ceylon Buddhist Congress. P 13½.
546	**179**	5c. multicoloured	10	50

A 50c. value showing a footprint was prepared but its release was stopped the day before it was due for issue. However, some are known to have been released in error at rural offices (*Price £38 mint*).

180 E. W. Perera (patriot) **181** Symbols of Strength in Savings

(Photo Harrison)

1969 (17 Feb). E. W. Perera Commemoration. W **81**. P 14×13½.
547	**180**	60c. brown	10	30

(Des A. Dharmasiri. Photo Harrison)

1969 (20 Mar). Silver Jubilee of National Savings Movement. W **81**. P 14.
548	**181**	3c. multicoloured	10	30

---

182 Seat of Enlightenment under Sacred Bodhi Tree **183** Buduresmala (Six fold Buddha-Rays)

(Des L. T. P. Manjusree. Litho D.L.R.)

1969 (10 Apr). Vesak Day (inscr "Wesak"). W **81** (sideways). P 15.
549	**182**	4c. multicoloured	10	50
550	**183**	6c. multicoloured	10	50
551	**182**	35c. multicoloured	10	10
549/51	*Set of 3*	25	1·00

No. 549 exists with the gold apparently omitted. Normally the gold appears (without a seperate plate number) over an underlay of olive-green on carmine. In one sheet we have seen, the gold only shows as tiny specks under a strong magnifying glass and as there may be intermediate stages of faint printing we do not list this.

184 A. E. Goonesinghe **185** ILO Emblem

(Des and photo Harrison)

1969 (29 Apr). Commemoration of Goonesinghe (founder of Labour Movement in Ceylon). W **81**. P 14.
552	**184**	15c. multicoloured	10	10

(Photo Harrison)

1969 (4 May). 50th Anniv of International Labour Organisation. W **81** (sideways). P 14.
553	**185**	5c. black and turquoise-blue	10	10
554		25c. black and carmine-red	10	10

186 Convocation Hall, University of Ceylon **187** Uranium Atom

(Des Ahangama Edward (35c.); L. D. P. Jayawardena (50 c.); A. Dharmasiri (60c.); 4c. from photograph. Litho Rosenbaum Bros, Vienna)

1969 (1 Aug). Educational Centenary. T **186**, **187** and similar multicoloured designs. P 13½.
555	4c. Type **186**	10	80
556	35c. Lamp of Learning, Globe and flags (*horiz*)	20	10
557	50c. Type **187**	20	10
558	60c. Symbols of Scientific education	30	10
555/8	*Set of 4*	70	1·00

188 Ath Pana (Elephant Lamp) **189** Rock Fortress of Sigiriya

(Des from photographs. Litho Rosenbaum Bros, Vienna)

1969 (1 Aug). Archaeological Centenary. P 13½.
559	**188**	6c. multicoloured	25	1·50
560	**189**	1r. multicoloured	25	10

A 50c. stamp showing the footprint of Buddha was due to be issued on 19 December 1969 in commemoration of the 50th anniversary of the All Ceylon Buddhist Congress. Following objections from religious leaders, the stamp was withdrawn before issue date; nevertheless, examples are known on first day cover.

190 Leopard **191** Emblem and Symbols

(Litho Rosenbaum Bros, Vienna)

1970 (11 May). Wildlife Conservation. T **190** and similar horiz designs. Multicoloured. P 13½.
561	5c. Water Buffalo	1·25	1·25
	a. Magenta omitted	£160	

562		15c. Slender Loris	2·00	1·25
	a.	Magenta omitted	£200	
563		50c. Spotted Deer	1·40	1·25
	a.	Imperf (in vert pair with stamp perf 3 sides)	£600	
564		1r. Type **190**	1·40	1·75
561/4	*Set of 4*		5·50	5·00

In No. 561a the Buffalo are predominantly green instead of brown and in No. 562a the sky is blue instead of violet and the animal is in green and yellow only.

(Des A. Dharmasiri. Litho Rosenbaum Bros, Vienna)

1970 (17 June). Asian Productivity Year. P 13½.

565	**191**	60c. multicoloured	10	10

192 New UPU HQ Building   **193** Oil Lamp and Caduceus

(Litho Rosenbaum Bros, Vienna)

1970 (14 Aug). New UPU Headquarters Building. P 13½.

566	**192**	50c. yellow-orange, black and new blue	50	10
	a.	New blue (Building) omitted	£200	
567		1r.10 vermilion, black and new blue	4·00	40

(Des A. Dharmasiri. Litho Rosenbaum Bros, Vienna)

1970 (1 Sept). Centenary of Colombo Medical School. P 13½.

568	**193**	5c. multicoloured	1·25	80
	a.	Vert pair, bottom stamp imperf	£500	
569		45c. multicoloured	1·50	60

194 Victory March and S. W. R. D. Bandaranaike   **195** UN Emblem and Dove of Peace

(Des A. Dharmasiri. Litho D.L.R.)

1970 (25 Sept). Definitive issue marking establishment of United Front Government. P 13½.

570	**194**	10c. multicoloured	10	10

(Des A. Dharmasiri. Photo Pakistan Security Printing Corp)

1970 (24 Oct). 25th Anniv of United Nations. P 12½×13½.

571	**195**	2r. multicoloured	2·00	4·25

196 Keppetipola Dissawa   **197** Ola Leaf Manuscript

(Des A. Dharmasiri. Litho Harrison)

1970 (26 Nov). 152nd Death Anniv of Keppetipola Dissawa (Kandyan patriot). P 14×14½.

572	**196**	25c. multicoloured	10	10

(Des A. Dharmasiri. Photo Pakistan Security Printing Corp)

1970 (21 Dec). International Education Year. P 13.

573	**197**	15c. multicoloured	2·75	1·25

STAMP BOOKLETS

1905 (Oct). Black on grey (No. SB1) or black on buff (No. SB1a) covers. Stapled.

SB1	1r.21, booklet containing 24× 5c. (No. 280) in blocks of 12		
SB1a	1r.45, booklet containing 24× 6c. (No. 281) in blocks of 6		£5000

1908. Black on grey cover. Advertisement on back cover. Stapled.

SB2	1r.20, booklet containing 24× 5c. (No. 289) in blocks of 12		

1912. Black on grey cover. Advertisement on back cover, Stapled.

SB2a	1r.20, booklet containing 24× 5c. (No. 304) in blocks of 12		

1919. Black on orange covers. Telegraph details on back cover. Stapled.

SB3	1r.44, booklet containing 24× 6c. (No. 309) in blocks of 6		
	a. Black on grey cover. Advertisement on back cover		
SB4	1r.44, booklet containing 24× 3c. and 12× 6c. (Nos. 308/9) in blocks of 6		
	a. Advertisement on back cover		

1919 (?). Black on cream cover. Advertisement on back. Stapled.

SB4b	1r.45, booklet containing 24× 3c. (No. 302) and 12× 6c. (No. 305)		

1922. Black on green covers. "Fiat" advertisement on back cover. Stapled.

SB5	1r.44, booklet containing 24× 6c. (No. 343) in blocks of 6		
SB6	1r.46, booklet containing 24× 6c. (No. 343) in blocks of 6		£3750
SB6a	1r.46, booklet containing 24×r 3c. and 12× 6c. (Nos. 340/3) in blocks of 6		£4000
	b. Black on orange cover. "Colombo Jewelry Store" advertisement on back cover		

1926. Black on green covers. Kennedy & Co. (No. SB7) or Fiat (No. SB8) advertisements on back cover. Stapled.

SB7	2r.06, booklet containing 12× 3c., 5c. on 6c. and 9c. each (Nos. 340, 362 and 345) in blocks of 6		£3500
SB8	2r.16, booklet containing 24× 9c. (No. 345) in blocks of 6		

1932. Black on green covers. Stapled.

SB9	1r.80, booklet containing 30× 6c. (No. 343) in blocks of 6 and pane of three airmail labels		£1600
SB10	2r.70, booklet containing 30× 9c. (No. 345) in blocks of 6 and pane of three airmail labels		£2000

1935 (May). Silver Jubilee of King George V. Black on light blue (No. SB11) or light green (No. SB12) covers. Stapled.

SB11	1r.80, booklet containing 30× 6c. (No. 379) in blocks of 6		£1400
SB12	2r.70, booklet containing 30× 9c. (No. 380) in blocks of 6		£1800

1935 (Dec)–**36**. Black on blue (No. SB13) or green (No. SB14) covers. Stapled.

SB13	1r.80, booklet containing 30× 6c. (No. 370) in blocks of 6 and pane of four airmail labels		£900
	a. Stamps in blocks of 10		£900
SB14	2r.70, booklet containing 30× 9c. (No. 371) in blocks of 6 and pane of four airmail labels		£1100
	a. Stamps in blocks of 10 (1936)		£1100

1937 (May). Coronation of King George VI. Black on blue (No. SB15) or olive-green (No. SB16) covers. Stapled.

SB15	1r.80, booklet containing 30× 6c. (No. 383) in blocks of 10 and pane of four airmail labels		£1200
SB16	2r.70, booklet containing 30× 9c. (No. 384) in blocks of 10 and pane of four airmail labels		£1300

1938. Black on blue (No. SB17) or grey (No. SB18) covers. Stapled.

SB17	1r.80, booklet containing 30× 6c. (No. 388) in blocks of 10 and pane of four airmail labels		£1400
SB18	3r. booklet containing 15× 20c. (No. 391) in blocks of 5 or 10 and pane of four airmail labels		£1500

1941. Black on pink cover, with contents amended in manuscript. Stapled.

SB19	1r.80, booklet containing 60× 3c. on 6c. (No. 398) in blocks of 10		
	a. Black on blue cover		

1951 (5 Dec). Black on buff cover. Stitched.

SB20	1r. booklet containing 20× 5c. (No. 414) in blocks of four and pane of airmail labels		20·00
	a. Containing two blocks of 10× 5c. stamps and no airmail labels		50·00

1952 (21 Jan). Black on green cover. Stitched.

SB21	6r. booklet containing 8× 75c. (No. 417) in blocks of 4 and two panes of four airmail labels		20·00

OFFICIAL STAMPS

1869. Issues of 1867–68 overprinted "SERVICE" in block letters. Although these stamps were prepared for use and sent out to the colony, they were never issued.

SERVICE

Type O **1**

Optd with Type O **1** by D.L.R. Wmk **6**. P 12½.

O1	**1**	2d. yellow	75·00
		x. Wmk reversed	£225
O2		6d. deep brown (R.)	75·00
O3	**2**	8d. chocolate	75·00
O4	**1**	1s. pale lilac	£170
O5	**2**	2s. deep blue	£120
		a. Imperf	£1100

SERVICE

Type O **2**

Optd with Type O **2** by D.L.R. Wmk Crown CC. P 14.

O6	**8**	1d. blue	75·00
O7	**7**	3d. carmine-rose	£150

Until 1 October 1895 all Official mail was carried free. After that date postage was paid on Official letters to the general public, on certain interdepartmental mail and on all packets over 1lb in weight. Nos. O11/27 were provided for this purpose.

On Service

(O **3**)

1895. Optd with Type O **3** by the Govt Printer, Colombo.

O11	**9**	2c. green (No. 147)	20·00	70
		w. Wmk inverted	†	£400

O12	**39**	3c. terracotta and blue-green	12·00	2·75
O13	**28**	5c. dull purple (No. 195)	5·50	30
O14	**29**	15c. sage-green (No. 196)	24·00	65
		x. Wmk reversed	†	£350
O15		25c. yellow-brown (No. 198)	13·00	3·25
O16		30c. bright mauve and chestnut (No. 247)	13·00	60
O17	**30**	1r.12 dull rose (*wmk sideways*)	95·00	65·00
		a. Opt double, one albino	£300	
		b. Wmk upright	£100	80·00
O11/17	*Set of 7*		£160	65·00

1899 (June)–**1900**. Nos. 256/7 and 261/2 optd with Type O **3**.

O18	**9**	2c. pale orange-brown (3.00)	12·00	60
O19	**39**	3c. deep green (9.00)	13·00	4·75
O20	**29**	15c. blue (9.00)	27·00	60
O21	**39**	75c. black and red-brown (R.)	10·00	10·00
O18/21	*Set of 4*		55·00	14·00

1903 (26 Nov)–**04**. Nos. 265/6, 268 and 271/3 optd with Type O **3**.

O22	**44**	2c. red-brown (4.1.04)	23·00	1·00
O23	**45**	3c. green	16·00	2·00
O24	**46**	5c. dull purple	32·00	1·50
O25	**48**	15c. blue	42·00	2·50
O26		25c. bistre (15.7.04)	38·00	18·00
O27		30c. dull violet and green (14.3.04)	21·00	1·50
O22/27	*Set of 6*		£150	25·00

Stamps overprinted "On Service" were withdrawn on 1 October 1904.

POSTAL FISCAL

1952 (1 Dec). As T **72** but inscr "REVENUE" at sides. Chalk-surfaced paper.

F1		10r. dull green and yellow-orange	£100	50·00

This revenue stamp was on sale for postal use from 1 December 1952 until 14 March 1954. Earlier printings were on ordinary paper. Used price for stamp with identifiable postal cancellation.

TELEGRAPH STAMPS

Telegraph Stamps of INDIA used in Ceylon

1869 (1 July)–**78**. Telegraph stamps of India (Nos. T5/20) used in Ceylon.

ZT1	2a. maroon		6·00
ZT2	4a. blue		4·50
ZT3	8a. brown		3·50
	a. Imperf (10.78)		£1000
ZT4	1r. grey (Die I)		80·00
ZT5	1r. grey (Die II)		3·00
ZT6	2r.8a. orange-yellow (Die I)		5·50
ZT7	2r.8a. orange (Die II) (1878)		48·00
ZT8	5r. orange-brown		6·00
ZT9	10r. green (Die I)		5·50
ZT10	10r. green (Die II) (1878)		35·00
ZT11	14r.4a. lilac (1870)		45·00
ZT12	25r. violet (Die I)		15·00
ZT13	25r. violet (Die II) (1878)		35·00
ZT14	28r.8a. yellow-green (1870)		45·00
ZT15	50r. rose (Die I)		45·00

The prices quoted above are for used upper halves with clearly identifiable cancels of offices in Ceylon. The large block letters used in these straight-line cancels are such that only three or four letters usually appear on a single stamp, and multiples or examples on piece may be needed to confirm identification. Usage is recorded at the following offices, with Colombo being the most frequently seen : ANURADHAPURA, BADULLA, BATTICALOA, COLOMBO, GALLE, GAMPOLA, JAFFNA (or JAFFRA, in error), KALATURA, KANDY, MANAAR, MATALLE, NAWALAPITYA, NEWARAELIYA or NEWARAELLYA, PANADURE and TRINCOMALEE.

The Tapling Collection (British Library) includes a pair of the India 1a yellow-green (No. T4) used at Colombo.

The use of Indian telegraph stamps in Ceylon ceased with the release of the following optd issue (Nos. T1/9).

PRICES. For Nos. T1/164 prices are quoted for unused whole stamps and used upper halves. Used lower halves (often with punched holes) are worth from ×2. Used whole stamps are rare and for many issues unknown.

(T **1**)

1880 (1 July). Telegraph stamps of India (1869–78 issue) optd with Type T **1** twice (on upper and lower halves).

T1	2a. maroon	†	60·00
T2	4a. blue	£1400	48·00
T3	8a. brown	†	24·00
T4	1r. grey (Die I)	†	15·00
T5	2r.8a. orange (Die II)	†	40·00
T6	5r. orange-brown	†	50·00
T7	10r. green (Die II)	†	35·00
T8	25r. violet (Die II)	—	45·00
T9	50r. rose-carmine (Die II)	†	£700

The Type T **1** opt has been extensively forged.

T 2	T 3	T 4

T 5	T 6	T 7

T 8	T 9	T 10

T 11	T 12	T 13

T 14 ("CA" in narrow letters)

(Typo, De La Rue)

1881 (14 Feb)–**82**. W T **14**. Perf 14.

T10	T **2**	12c. bistre	20·00	1·00
		w. Wmk inverted	75·00	11·00
T11	T **3**	25c. blue-green	£325	25·00
T12	T **4**	25c. green (3.82)	20·00	50
		w. Wmk inverted	—	50·00
T13	T **5**	50c. blue	22·00	50
		w. Wmk inverted	75·00	12·00
T14	T **6**	1r. red-brown	£180	7·50

T15	T **7**	1r. red-brown (3.82)	20·00	50
		w. Wmk inverted	£120	35·00
T16	T **8**	2r.50c. grey	40·00	1·00
		w. Wmk inverted	—	38·00
T17	T **9**	5r. orange	90·00	1·25
		w. Wmk inverted	—	42·00
T18	T **10**	10r. reddish lilac	£375	16·00
T19	T **11**	10r. rose-lilac (3.82)		3·00
		a. Claret	£375	3·00
		b. Reddish purple	£275	2·25
T20	T **12**	25r. bright rose	£1100	2·25
		a. Carmine	£1100	2·25
		w. Wmk inverted	—	42·00
T21	T **13**	50r. brown-rose	£1600	6·50
		a. Brown-lilac	£1600	6·00

The original types of the 25c. (T **3**), 1r. (T **6**) and 10r. (T **10**) were withdrawn and replaced after it was found that the face value could become difficult to determine after horizontal bisection in use. In the other designs the face value was clearly stated on both top and bottom halves.

For later printings in these types, but wmk T **129**, see Nos. T139/47.

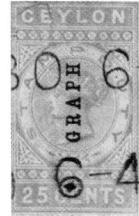

(T **15**)

1882 (7 Feb). Fiscal stamp inscr "STAMP DUTY" opt as Type T **15**. Wmk T **14**. Perf 14.

T22	T **15**	25c. lilac	†	£800

Alternate horizontal rows were optd "TELE" and "GRAPH", to provide vertical pairs for separation. No unused examples, or used examples with "TELE", have been reported.

(T **16**)	(T **17**)	(T **18**)

(T **19**)	(T **20**)

(T **21**)	(T **22**)

1882 (1 Jan)–**94**. Nos. T 12/17 and T 19/21 surch with new values by Ceylon Govt Printer, as Types T **16/121**.

(a) Surch 12c.

T23	T **16**	12c. on 25c. green (20.4.87)	£325	60·00
T24	T **17**	12c. on 25c. green (16.1.89)	£375	22·00
		a. Small "12", "2" with straight foot (Type T **18**)	—	65·00
T25	T **19**	12c. on 50c. blue (20.4.87)	£130	5·00
T26	T **20**	12c. on 50c. blue (7.5.88)	70·00	5·00
T27	T **21**	12c. on 50c. blue (16.1.89)	—	28·00
		a. Small "12", "2" with straight foot (Type T **22**)	—	75·00

(T **23**)	(T **24**)	(T **25**)

(T **26**)	(T **27**)	(T **28**)

(T **29**)	(T **30**)

(T **31**)	(T **32**)

(b) Surch 20c.

T28	T **23**	20c. on 25c. green (9.7.86)	£150	6·00
		a. Surch double	†	£500
T29	T **24**	20c. on 25c. green (7.4.87)	£150	6·50
T30	T **25**	20c. on 25c. green (13.4.88)	95·00	10·00
T31	T **26**	20c. on 25c. green (1.4.92)	£180	15·00
		a. "2" in upper "20 cents" with straight foot	†	85·00
T32	T **27**	20c. on 50c. blue (7.4.87)	£130	5·00
		a. Surch double	†	£550
		w. Wmk inverted	—	65·00
T33	T **28**	20c. on 50c. blue (16.1.89)	95·00	5·50
T34	T **29**	20c. on 50c. blue (2.8.89)	95·00	5·00
T35	T **30**	20c. on 50c. blue (18.1.90)	80·00	5·50
T36	T **31**	20c. on 50c. blue (26.9.90)	75·00	5·50
T37	T **32**	20c. on 1r. red-brown (2.92)	£140	6·00

(T **33**)	(T **34**)

(T 35)

(c) Surch 25c.

T38	T **33**	25c. on 50c. blue (20.1.92)	—	65·00
T39	T **34**	25c. on 1r. red-brown (T **7**)		
		(3.2.92)..	—	85·00
T40	T **35**	25c. on 50r. brown-lilac (26.2.92)...	£2750	80·00

(T 36)   (T 37)   (T 38)

T **39** is as T **50** but surcharged in black.

(T 40)   (T 41)   (T 42)

(T 43)   (T 44) (14½ mm   (T 45)
                    between words
                    and figures)

Type **46** is as Type **44** but with 18 mm between words and figures.

(T 47)   (T 48) (single bar)   (T 49) (double bar)

(T 50)   (T 51)   (T 52)

(T 53)   (T 54)

(d) Surch 40c.

T41	T **36**	40c. on 50c. blue (23.12.81)............	—	75·00
		a. Surch double..............................	†	£550
T42	T **37**	40c. on 50c. blue (10.1.82).............	£225	22·00
T43	T **38**	40c. on 50c. blue (6.3.82)...............	£225	28·00
T44	T **39**	40c. on 50c. blue (1883?)................		
T45	T **40**	40c. on 50c. blue (9.7.86)...............	70·00	5·00
		a. Surch double..............................		
T46	T **41**	40c. on 50c. blue (14.11.87)...........	55·00	4·00
T47	T **42**	40c. on 50c. blue (16.1.89).............	£100	5·00
T48	T **43**	40c. on 50c. blue (23.7.89).............	70·00	4·00
T49	T **44**	40c. on 50c. blue (18.1.90).............	55·00	5·00
T50	T **45**	40c. on 50c. blue (26.8.90).............	55·00	7·50
T51	T **46**	40c. on 50c. blue (24.6.91).............	—	11·00
T52	T **47**	40c. on 50c. blue (1.4.92)...............	—	16·00
T53	T **48**	40c. on 50c. blue (R.) (5.2.83).........	70·00	7·00
		a. Inverted "s" in "cents" in lower		
		half.......................................		£300
T54	T **49**	40c. on 50c. blue (R.) (20.7.83)........	75·00	6·00
T55	T **50**	40c. on 50c. blue (R.) (23.4.84)........	£170	11·00
T56	T **51**	40c. on 50c. blue (R.) (2.3.85).........	£150	4·50
		a. Surch T **51** in red and as T **40**		
		in black................................		
T57	T **52**	40c. on 1r. red-brown (T **7**) (26.9.90)	70·00	5·00
T58	T **53**	40c. on 1r. red-brown (T **7**) (2.92)..	£110	6·00
T59	T **54**	40c. on 2r.50c. grey (18.1.82)...........	—	£100

(T 55)

(e) Surch 50c.

T60	T **55**	50c. on 2r.50c. grey (16.2.82)..........	—	£190

(T 56)   (T 57)   (T 58)

T **59** is surcharged "60 cents" as T **56/8** but at top *and* centre.

(T 60)   (T 61)   (T 62)

(T 63)   (T 64)   (T 65)

(T 66)   (T 67)   (T 68)

(T 69)   (T 70)   (T 71)

(T 72)   (T 73)   (T 74)

(T 75)   (T 76)   (T 77)

(T 78)   (T 79)

(f) Surch 60c.

T61	T **56**	60c. on 1r. red-brown (T **6**) (23.12.81)............................	—	17·00
T62	T **57**	60c. on 1r. red-brown (T **7**) (6.3.82)	£170	11·00
		a. Surch inverted............................	†	£750
		w. Wmk inverted	†	85·00
T63	T **58**	60c. on 1r. red-brown (T **7**) (18.10.82)	—	12·00
T64	T **59**	60c. on 1r. red-brown (T **7**) (1883?)		
T65	T **60**	60c. on 1r. red-brown (T **7**) (2.3.85)	—	18·00
		w. Wmk inverted	—	70·00
T66	T **61**	60c. on 1r. red-brown (T **7**) (6.7.85)	£170	7·00
		w. Wmk inverted	†	85·00
T67	T **62**	60c. on 1r. red-brown (T **7**) (9.7.86)	—	10·00
		a. Surch double, one inverted....		
		b. Surch double............................	†	£700
T68	T **63**	60c. on 1r. red-brown (T **7**) (7.4.87)	£150	11·00
T69	T **64**	60c. on 1r. red-brown (T **7**) (10.8.87)	—	16·00
T70	T **65**	60c. on 1r. red-brown (T **7**) (21.12.87)	£140	6·00
T71	T **66**	60c. on 1r. red-brown (T **7**) (13.4.88)	85·00	7·00
T72	T **67**	60c. on 1r. red-brown (T **7**) (16.1.89)	65·00	4·50
		w. Wmk inverted	—	65·00
T73	T **68**	60c. on 1r. red-brown (T **7**) (12.12.89)	70·00	6·00
T74	T **69**	60c. on 1r. red-brown (T **7**) (26.9.90)	75·00	6·50
T75	T **70**	60c. on 1r. red-brown (T **7**) (24.6.91)	75·00	5·00
T76	T **71**	60c. on 1r. red-brown (T **7**) (2.92)	£120	7·50
		w. Wmk inverted	†	85·00
T77	T **72**	60c. on 2r.50c. grey (16.2.82)........	—	£110
T78	T **73**	60c. on 2r.50c. grey (25.2.87)	£130	7·00
T79	T **74**	60c. on 2r.50c. grey (10.8.87)	—	35·00
T80	T **75**	60c. on 2r.50c. grey (29.10.88)	—	12·00
T81	T **76**	60c. on 2r.50c. grey (R.) (20.7.83)...	75·00	6·00
		a. Inverted "s" in "cents" in lower half		£325
T82	T **77**	60c. on 2r.50c. grey (R.) (23.4.84)	80·00	8·50
T83	T **78**	60c. on 50r. brown-lilac (5.2.83)	80·00	12·00
T84	T **79**	60c. on 50r. brown-lilac (1883?).....	—	£190

(T **80**) (T **81**) (T **82**)

(T **83**) (T **84**) (T **85**)

(T **86**) (T **87**) (T **88**)

(T **89**) (T **90**) (T **91**)

(T **92**) (T **93**) (T **94**)

(T **95**) (T **96**) (T **97**)

(T **98**) (T **99**) (T **100**)

(T **101**) (T **102**) (T **103**)

(T **104**)

T **105** is surcharged "80 Cents" similar to T **87**, but at top *and* centre.

(T **106**) (T **107**) (T **108**)

(T **109**) (T **110**) (T **111**)

(T **112**) (T **113**) (T **114**)

(T **115**) (T **116**) (T **117**)

(T **118**) (T **119**)

(g) Surch 80c.

T85	T **80**	80c. on 1r. red-brown (T **6**) (10.1.82)	—	14·00
T86	T **81**	80c. on 1r. red-brown (T **7**) (6.3.82)	£225	18·00
T87	T **82**	80c. on 1r. red-brown (T **7**) (18.10.82)	£110	16·00
T88	T **83**	80c. on 1r. red-brown (T **7**) (6.7.85)	£170	6·00
		a. Surch double	†	£500
T89	T **84**	80c. on 1r. red-brown (T **7**) (13.4.88)	90·00	8·00
T90	T **85**	80c. on 1r. red-brown (T **7**) (16.1.89)	85·00	7·00
		w. Wmk inverted	£160	30·00
T91	T **86**	80c. on 1r. red-brown (T **7**) (16.1.89)	—	17·00
T92	T **87**	80c. on 1r. red-brown (T **7**) (2.8.89)	—	11·00
		a. "s" in upper "Cents" inverted	†	75·00
T93	T **88**	80c. on 1r. red-brown (T **7**) (18.1.90)	90·00	4·50
T94	T **89**	80c. on 1r. red-brown (T **7**) (3.92)	£120	13·00
T95	T **90**	80c. on 2r.50c. grey (2.3.85)	£225	25·00
T96	T **91**	80c. on 2r.50c. grey (9.7.86)	£160	6·00
		a. Surch double	†	£425
T97	T **92**	80c. on 2r.50c. grey (26.9.88)	—	8·00
		a. "S" in upper "CENTS" inverted ...	†	65·00
T98	T **93**	80c. on 2r.50c. grey (16.1.89)	£150	10·00
T99	T **94**	80c. on 2r.50c. grey (18.1.90)	95·00	8·00

T100	T **95**	80c. on 2r.50c. grey (16.9.90)	£350	10·00
T101	T **96**	80c. on 2r.50c. grey (3.2.92)	—	16·00
T102	T **97**	80c. on 5r. orange (3.9.84)	—	48·00
T103	T **98**	80c. on 5r. orange (7.4.87)	£225	35·00
		w. Wmk inverted	†	85·00
T104	T **99**	80c. on 5r. orange (10.8.87)	—	40·00
		w. Wmk inverted	—	40·00
T105	T **100**	80c. on 5r. orange (21.12.87)	—	22·00
T106	T **101**	80c. on 5r. orange (26.9.90)	£160	12·00
		a. "00" for "80"	£5500	£375
T107	T **102**	80c. on 10r. rose-lilac (T **11**) (3.9.84)	—	85·00
T108	T **103**	80c. on 10r. rose-lilac (T **11**) (7.4.87)	—	11·00
		w. Wmk inverted	£350	
T109	T **104**	80c. on 10r. rose-lilac (T **11**) (10.8.87)	—	22·00
T110	T **105**	80c. on 10r. rose-lilac (T **11**) (1887?)	—	
T111	T **106**	80c. on 10r. rose-lilac (T **11**) (21.12.87)	£190	21·00
T112	T **107**	80c. on 10r. reddish purple (T **11**) (26.9.90)	£150	12·00
		a. "00" for "80"	£6000	£450
T113	T **108**	80c. on 25r. bright rose (5.2.83)	90·00	13·00
		a. Inverted "s" in "80 cents" on lower half	£350	
T114	T **109**	80c. on 25r. bright rose (20.7.83)	£190	19·00
T115	T **110**	80c. on 25r. bright rose (23.4.84)	£140	16·00
T116	T **111**	80c. on 25r. bright rose (10.8.87)	£200	21·00
T117	T **112**	80c. on 25r. bright rose (21.12.87)	—	15·00
T118	T **113**	80c. on 25r. carmine (26.9.90)	—	16·00
T119	T **114**	80c. on 25r. carmine (3.92)	—	45·00
T120	T **115**	80c. on 50r. brown-rose (20.7.83)	—	40·00
T121	T **116**	80c. on 50r. brown-lilac (3.9.84)	—	£110
T122	T **117**	80c. on 50r. brown-lilac (7.4.87)	—	£160
T123	T **118**	80c. on 50r. brown-lilac (21.12.87)	—	20·00
T124	T **119**	80c. on 50r. brown-lilac (3.92)	—	55·00

(T **120**)

(T **121**)

(h) Surch 5r.

T125	T **120**	5r. on 25r. carmine (1.4.92)	£325	11·00
		a. Small "s" in "RUPEES" on upper half	—	75·00
T126	T **121**	5r. on 50r. brown-lilac (13.8.94)	—	£200

The dates quoted above for Nos. T23/126 refer to printing dates, where known. For stamps similar to Nos. T125/6, but wmk T **129**, see Nos. T148/49.

T **122**

T **123**

T **124**

T **125**

T **126**   T **127**

T **128**

T **129** ("CA" in wide letters)

(Typo, Govt Printer, Colombo)

1892 (1 Apr)–**1903**. T **122/8** (different frame ornaments for each value). No wmk. Date and control figures in black. Perf 12.

(a) Date numerals separated by oblique lines. Large control figures

T127	T **122**	20c. green (1/4/92)	—	12·00
		a. Small control figures	£375	4·00
T128	T **123**	40c. blue (1/4/92)	—	8·50
		a. Small control figures	£375	4·00
T129	T **124**	60c. brown (1/4/92)	—	12·00
		a. Small control figures	£400	4·00
T130	T **125**	80c. olive (1/4/92)	—	12·00
		a. Small control figures	£375	4·00

The 80c. exists imperforate, with date "1/4/92", and the 40c. and 80c. also imperforate with date "1/5/92" but the latter were not issued.

(b) Date numerals separated by dashes

T131	T **126**	5c. lilac-rose (1-4-97)	85·00	3·00
		a. Date 1-11-97	75·00	3·00
		b. Date 1-7-98	—	5·00
		c. Date 1-12-98	80·00	3·00
		d. Date 1-12-99	95·00	2·50
T132		5c. deep purple (1-12-00)	75·00	2·50
		a. Date 1-12-01	80·00	3·00
		b. Date 1-12-02	—	3·00
		c. Bluish paper. Date 18-5-03	—	6·00
T133	T **127**	10c. yellow (1-4-97)	95·00	3·00
		a. Date 1-11-97	90·00	3·00
		b. Date 1-12-98	—	3·00
		c. Date 1-12-99	90·00	2·50
		d. Date 1-12-00	£110	3·00
		e. Date 1-12-01	85·00	3·00
		f. Bluish paper. Date 18-5-03	—	6·00
T134	T **122**	20c. green (1-9-92)	90·00	5·00
		a. Date 9-1-93	95·00	3·00
		b. Date 1-5-94	85·00	3·00
		c. Date 1-11-94	80·00	3·00
		d. Date 1-11-95	—	3·00
		e. Date 1-9-96	—	3·00
		f. Date 1-11-97	80·00	2·50
		g. Date 1-12-98	£200	3·00
		h. Date 1-12-99	75·00	3·00
		i. Date 1-12-00	95·00	4·50
		j. Date 1-12-01	85·00	4·50
		k. Bluish paper. Date 18-5-03	—	6·00
T135	T **128**	25c. deep olive (1-12-97. Date in black without control figures)	£450	8·00
T136	T **123**	40c. blue (1-9-92)	95·00	3·00
		a. Date 9-1-93	85·00	3·00
		b. Date 1-5-94	75·00	2·50
		c. Date 1-11-94	85·00	2·00
		d. Date 1-11-95	—	3·00
		e. Date 1-9-96	70·00	2·00
		f. Date 1-12-99	—	6·00
		g. Date 1-12-00	£100	4·50
		h. Date 1-12-01	£100	6·00
		i. Bluish paper. Date 18-5-03	—	7·00
T137	T **124**	60c. dark brown (1-9-92)	90·00	5·00
		a. Date 9-1-93	—	3·00
		b. Date 1-5-94	£160	8·00
		c. Date 1-11-94	85·00	3·00
		d. Date 1-11-95	—	3·00
		e. Date 1-9-96	85·00	3·00
		f. Date 1-7-98	75·00	3·00
		g. Date 1-12-98	—	8·00
		h. Date 1-12-99	—	6·00
		i. Date 1-12-00	—	5·00
		j. Date 1-12-01	£100	5·00
		k. Date 1-12-02	—	6·00
		l. Bluish paper. Date 18-5-03	—	6·00
T138	T **125**	80c. olive (1-9-92)	95·00	5·00
		a. Date 9-1-93	—	3·00
		b. Date 1-5-94	—	3·50
		c. Date 1-11-94	80·00	3·00
		d. Date 1-11-95	—	3·00
		e. Date 1-9-96	90·00	2·50
		f. Date 1-7-98	90·00	3·00
		g. Date 1-12-98	—	12·00
		h. Date 1-12-99	—	6·00
		i. Date 1-12-00	90·00	5·00
		j. Date 1-12-01	90·00	4·00
		k. Date 1-12-02	—	6·00
		l. Bluish paper. Date 18-5-03	—	8·00

The plates used to print the 5c., 10c. and 25c. values (Nos. T131/3, 135) each included two different 'dies', which can be found in *se-tenant* pairs.

1894. Typo, De La Rue. As Nos. T10, T12/13, T15/17, T19/21, but wmk T **129**. Perf 14.

T139	T **2**	12c. olive-bistre	22·00	1·25
T140	T **4**	25c. green	22·00	75
T141	T **5**	50c. blue	22·00	1·00
T142	T **7**	1r. red-brown	25·00	75
T143	T **8**	2r.50c. slate	48·00	1·00
T144		5r. orange	75·00	1·25
T145	T **11**	10r. purple	£250	2·50
		a. Claret	—	2·50
		b. Dull magenta	—	2·50
T146	T **12**	25r. carmine	£1100	2·00
T147	T **13**	50r. lake	£1600	15·00

(T **130**)

T **131**

T **132**

1894. Nos. T146/7 surch with new values as T **121** and T **130** by Ceylon Govt Printer, Colombo.

T148	T **130**	5r. on 25r. carmine (26.11.94)	—	42·00
T149	T **121**	5r. on 50r. lake (13.8.94)	—	24·00

(Typo, De La Rue)

1903 (June)–**04**. T **131** or T **132** (25c.). Wmk T **129**. Perf 14.

T150	T **131**	5c. brown and green	£140	2·50
T151		10c. bluish green and ochre	£140	3·50
T152		12c. olive-bistre and green (1.04)	£225	7·00
T153		20c. drab and purple	£140	4·00
T154	T **132**	25c. green (1.04)	£140	2·50
		w. Wmk inverted	†	45·00
T155	T **131**	40c. purple and brown	£140	5·00
T156		50c. blue and purple	£140	3·00
T157		60c. olive and ochre	£140	4·00
T158		75c. pale blue and blue	£140	3·00
T159		1r. red-brown	£140	1·00
T160		2r.50c. slate and ochre	£375	5·00
T161		5r. orange and carmine	£375	8·00
T162		10r. reddish purple and green	£600	15·00
T163		25r. carmine and scarlet	£1800	10·00
T164		50r. claret and blue	£3000	80·00

1905. As Nos. T150/64, but Wmk Mult Crown CA (sideways)*.

			Unused	Used whole	Used upper half
T165	T **131**	5c. brown and green	12·00	2·50	50
T166		10c. bluish green and ochre	16·00	3·00	50
T167		12c. olive-bistre and green	15·00	10·00	75
T168		20c. drab and purple	14·00	5·50	75
T169	T **132**	25c. green	17·00	3·00	50
T170	T **131**	40c. purple and brown	15·00	8·50	60
T171		50c. blue and purple	20·00	7·00	75
T172		60c. olive and ochre	18·00	7·50	75
T173		75c. pale blue and blue	19·00	7·50	75
T174		1r. red-brown	18·00	4·00	75
T175		2r.50c. slate and ochre	35·00	8·00	1·00
		w. Wmk Crown to right of CA	†	—	65·00
T176		5r. orange and carmine	£100	11·00	1·00
T177		10r. reddish purple and green	£180	15·00	1·50
T178		25r. carmine and scarlet	£650	£110	5·00
T179		50r. claret and blue	£950	£300	35·00

*The normal sideways watermark shows Crown to left of CA, *as seen from the back of the stamp.*

During the currency of Nos. T165/79 changes in administrative practice meant that horizontal bisection of the stamps largely ceased. Prices are accordingly quoted both for used whole stamps and used upper halves.

(T **133**)

(T **134**)

1910 (May–July). Nos T167, T169 and T174 surch with new values in words as T **133** or T **134** (No. T181) by Ceylon Govt Printer, Colombo.

T180	T **133**	20c. on 12c. olive-bistre and green		85·00
T181	T **134**	20c. on 25c. green (7.10)		85·00
T182	T **133**	40c. on 12c. olive-bistre and green		85·00
T183		40c. on 1r. red-brown (7.10)		85·00
T184		60c. on 12c. olive-bistre and green		85·00
T185		5r. on 12c. olive-bistre and green		£3750
T186		5r. on 1r. red-brown (7.10)		£3750
T187		10r. on 12c. olive-bistre and green		£3750

No used examples of Nos. T180/7 have been seen. Forged surcharges exist.

The telegraph stamps of Ceylon were withdrawn from use on 1 August 1910.

Cook Islands

COOK ISLANDS

A British Protectorate was declared over this group of fifteen islands by the local Vice-Consul on 20 September 1888.

Before the introduction of the Cook Islands Post Office, mail was forwarded via Auckland, New Zealand.

PRICES FOR STAMPS ON COVER TO 1945	
Nos. 1/4	from × 5
Nos. 5/74	from × 4
Nos. 75/145	from × 3

BRITISH PROTECTORATE

1	**2** Queen Makea Takau	**3** White Tern or Torea

(Des F. Moss. Typo Govt Printing Office, Wellington)

1892 (19 Apr). No wmk. Toned or white paper. P 12½.
1	1	1d. black	35·00	26·00
		a. Imperf between (vert pair)	£10000	
2		1½d. mauve	48·00	38·00
		a. Imperf (pair)	£17000	
3		2½d. blue	48·00	38·00
4		10d. carmine	£140	£130
1/4 *Set of 4*			£225	£200

Nos. 1/4 were printed in sheets of 60 (6×10) from plates constructed from a matrix of six slightly different types.

(Eng A. E. Cousins. Typo Govt Printing Office, Wellington)

1893 (28 July)–**1900**. W **12b** of New Zealand (N Z and Star wide apart) (sideways on T **3**).

(a) P 12×11½
5	2	1d. brown	50·00	55·00
6		1d. blue (3.4.94)	13·00	2·00
		a. Perf 12×11½ and 12½ mixed	†	£2250
7		1½d. mauve	19·00	7·00
8		2½d. rose	55·00	23·00
		a. Rose-carmine	65·00	48·00
		ab. Perf 12×11½ and 12½ mixed	£3000	
9		5d. olive-black	23·00	15·00
10		10d. green	85·00	50·00
5/10 *Set of 6*			£200	£130

(b) P 11 *(July 1896–1900)*
11	3	½d. steel blue (1st setting) (11.99)...	35·00	48·00
		a. Upper right "d" omitted	£1500	
		b. Second setting	23·00	23·00
		ba. Deep blue (1900)	5·50	15·00
12	2	1d. blue	5·00	5·50
13		1d. deep brown/cream (4.99)	30·00	21·00
		a. Wmk sideways	£1600	
		b. Bistre-brown (1900)	30·00	23·00
14		1½d. deep lilac	18·00	7·00
		a. Deep mauve (1900)	12·00	7·00
15	3	2d. brown/thin toned (7.98)	18·00	6·50
		a. Deep brown (1900)	15·00	8·50
16	2	2½d. pale rose	55·00	38·00
		a. Deep rose (1900)	25·00	14·00
17		5d. olive-black	29·00	19·00
18	3	6d. purple/thin toned (7.98)	42·00	40·00
		a. Bright purple (1900)	23·00	27·00
19	2	10d. green	18·00	55·00
20	3	1s. red/thin toned (7.98)	65·00	75·00
		a. Deep carmine (1900)	48·00	48·00
11ba/20a *Set of 10*			£190	£200

Examples of the 1d., 1½d., 2½d. and 5d. perforated 11 and on laid paper are perforation trials. On the first setting of the ½d. the face values are misplaced in each corner. As corrected in the second setting the face values are correctly positioned in each corner.

ONE HALF PENNY
(4)

1899 (24 Apr). No. 12 surch with T **4** by Govt Printer, Rarotonga.
21	2	½d. on 1d. blue	32·00	48·00
		a. Surch inverted	£850	£900
		b. Surch double	£1000	£900

NEW ZEALAND TERRITORY

On 8 and 9 October 1900 the chiefs of all the main islands, except Aitutaki, ceded their territory to the British Crown. On 11 June 1901 all the islands, including Aitutaki, were transferred by Great Britain to New Zealand control.

1901 (8 Oct). No. 13 optd with T **5** by Govt Printer, Rarotonga.
22	2	1d. brown	£180	£140
		a. Crown inverted	£2250	£1700
		c. Optd with crown twice	£1600	£1600

1902. No wmk. P 11.
(a) Medium white Cowan paper (Feb)
23	3	½d. blue-green	9·50	9·50
		a. Imperf horiz (vert pair)	£1300	
24	2	1d. dull rose	15·00	21·00
(b) Thick white Pirie paper (May)
25	3	½d. yellow-green	10·00	4·25
26	2	1d. rose-red	19·00	11·00
		a. Rose-lake	18·00	6·50
27		2½d. dull blue	13·00	21·00

NEW ZEALAND WATERMARKS. In W **43** the wmk units are in vertical columns widely spaced and the sheet margins are unwatermarked or wmkd "NEW ZEALAND POSTAGE" in large letters.

In W **98** the wmk units are arranged alternately in horizontal rows closely spaced and are continued into the sheet margins. Stamps with W **98** sideways show the star to the left of NZ, *as seen from the back.* Sideways inverted varieties have the star to the right, *as seen from the back.*

1902 (Sept). W **43** of New Zealand (single-lined NZ and Star, close together; sideways on T **2**). P 11.
28	3	½d. yellow-green	4·75	3·25
		a. Grey-green	30·00	70·00
29	2	1d. rose-pink	4·00	3·00
30		1½d. deep mauve	5·00	8·50
31	3	2d. deep brown	10·00	10·00
		a. No figures of value	£2250	£3500
		b. Perf 11×14	£2500	
32	2	2½d. deep blue	3·75	7·00
33		5d. olive-black	35·00	48·00
34	3	6d. purple	35·00	28·00
35	2	10d. green	50·00	£110
36	3	1s. carmine	50·00	80·00
		a. Perf 11×14	£3000	
28/36 *Set of 9*			£170	£275

Stamps in Type **3** were printed from a master plate with the value added by a series of separate duty plates. One sheet of the 2d. missed this second pass through the press and was issued without value.

For Nos. 28/36 Type **3** exists with the watermark in equal quantities either upright or inverted and for Type **2**, on which the watermark is sideways, in equal quantities with the star to the right or left of NZ.

1909–11. W **43** of New Zealand.
37	3	½d. green (P 14½×14) (1911)	12·00	8·00
38	2	1d. deep red (P 14)	42·00	32·00
		a. Wmk sideways (24.12.09)	14·00	2·50

For Nos. 37/8 the watermark is either upright or inverted. For No. 38a it is sideways, either with star to right or left of NZ.

1913–19. W **43** of New Zealand (sideways on T **3**). Chalk-surfaced paper.
39	3	½d. deep green (P 14) (1915)	11·00	15·00
		a. Wmk upright	15·00	25·00
40	2	1d. red (P 14) (7.13)	13·00	4·50
41		1d. red (P 14×14½) (1914)	11·00	6·00
42		1½d. deep mauve (P 14) (1915)	90·00	18·00
43		1½d. deep mauve (P 14×15) (1916)	20·00	4·00
44	3	2d. deep brown (P 15×14) (1919)	5·00	48·00
45	2	10d. green (P 14×15) (1918)	38·00	£120
46	3	1s. carmine (P 15×14) (1919)	27·00	£110
39/46 *Set of 6*			£100	£275

RAROTONGA

APA PENE
(8)

1919 (Apr–July). Stamps of New Zealand surch as T **8**.
(a) T 53. W 43. De La Rue chalk-surfaced paper. P 14×15
47		1d. carmine (No. 405) (B.) (6.19)	1·50	5·00
(b) T 60 (recess). W 43. Cowan unsurfaced paper. P 14×13½
48		2½d. blue (No. 419) (R.) (6.19)	2·50	6·50
		a. Perf 14×14½	2·00	2·25
		b. Vert pair. Nos. 48/a	20·00	50·00
49		3d. chocolate (No. 420) (B.)	3·50	8·00
		a. Perf 14×14½	3·50	4·00
		b. Vert pair. Nos. 49/a	22·00	60·00
50		4d. bright violet (No. 422) (B.)	2·00	5·50
		a. Re-entry (Pl 20 R. 1/6)	60·00	
		b. Re-entry (Pl 20 R. 4/10)	60·00	
		c. Perf 14×14½	1·75	4·25
		d. Vert pair (Nos. 50 and 50c)	20·00	65·00
51		4½d. deep green (No. 423) (B.)	3·00	7·50
		a. Perf 14×14½	1·75	8·00
		b. Vert pair. Nos. 51/a	20·00	75·00
52		6d. carmine (No. 425) (B.) (6.19)	4·25	8·50
		a. Perf 14×14½	1·75	5·50
		b. Vert pair. Nos. 52/a	38·00	90·00
53		7½d. red-brown (No. 426a) (B.)	1·50	5·50
54		9d. sage-green (No. 429) (R.)	4·00	15·00
		a. Perf 14×14½	3·00	15·00
		b. Vert pair. Nos. 54/a	40·00	£120
55		1s. vermilion (No. 430) (B.) (6.19)	12·00	30·00
		a. Perf 14×14½	2·75	28·00
		b. Vert pair. Nos. 55/a	48·00	£140
(c) T 61 (typo). W 43. De La Rue chalk-surfaced paper. P 14×15
56		½d. green (No. 435) (R.)(6.19)	40	1·00
57		1½d. orange-brown (No. 438) (R.) (6.19)	50	75
58		2d. yellow (No. 439) (R.)	1·75	2·00
59		3d. chocolate (No. 440) (B.) (7.19)	2·75	13·00
47/59 *Set of 13*			23·00	80·00

9 Capt. Cook landing

10 Wharf at Avarua

11 Capt. Cook (Dance)

12 Palm Tree

---

13 Huts at Arorangi   **14** Avarua Harbour

R. 2/8	R. 3/6 Double derrick flaws	R. 5/2

(Des, eng and recess Perkins Bacon & Co)

1920 (23 Aug). No wmk. P 14.
70	9	½d. black and green	4·00	28·00
71	10	1d. black and carmine-red	4·75	28·00
		a. Double derrick flaw (R. 2/8, 3/6 or 5/2)	13·00	
72	11	1½d. black and dull blue	8·50	8·50
73	12	3d. black and chocolate	2·25	5·50
74	13	6d. brown and yellow-orange	4·50	8·50
75	14	1s. black and violet	8·50	17·00
70/5 *Set of 6.*			29·00	85·00

Examples of the 1d. and 1s. with centre inverted were not supplied to the Post Office (*Price £850 each, unused*).

RAROTONGA
(15)

RAROTONGA
Trimmed overprint (R. 1/6 and R. 3/7)

1921 (Oct)–**23**. Postal Fiscal stamps as Type F **4** of New Zealand optd with T **15**. W **43** (sideways). Chalk-surfaced "De La Rue" paper. P 14½×14.
76		2s. deep blue (No. F111) (R.)	27·00	55·00
		a. Trimmed opt	£120	
		b. Carmine opt (1923)	£200	£225
		ba. Trimmed opt	£600	£650
		c. Optd on "Jones" chalk-surfaced paper	—	£650
77		2s.6d. grey-brown (No. F112) (B.)	19·00	50·00
		a. Trimmed opt	90·00	
78		5s. yellow-green (No. F115) (R.)	28·00	70·00
		a. Trimmed opt	£120	
79		10s. maroon (No. F120) (B.)	85·00	£140
		a. Trimmed opt	£275	
80		£1 rose-carmine (No. F123) (B.)	£140	£200
		a. Trimmed opt	£375	
76/80 *Set of 5*			£275	£500

For details of the "Jones" paper, see below No. 385 of New Zealand. See also Nos. 85/9.

16 Te Po, Rarotongan Chief	**17** Harbour, Rarotonga and Mt. Ikurangi

(2½d. from a print; 4d. des A. H. Messenger. Plates by P.B. Recess Govt Ptg Office, Wellington)

1924–27. W **43** of New Zealand (sideways on 4d.). P 14.
81	9	½d. black and green (13.5.26)	4·50	8·50
82	10	1d. black and deep carmine (10.11.24)	6·00	2·25
		a. Double derrick flaw (R. 2/8, 3/6 or 5/2)	16·00	10·00
		x. Wmk reversed	£225	
83	16	2½d. red-brown and steel blue (15.10.27)	12·00	35·00
84	17	4d. green and violet (15.10.27)	19·00	16·00
81/4 *Set of 4*			38·00	55·00

1926 (Feb–May). As Nos. 76/80, but on thick, opaque white chalk-surfaced "Cowan" paper.
85		2s. blue (No. F131) (C.)	£200	£325
		a. Trimmed opt	£600	
86		2s.6d. deep grey-brown (No. F132) (B.)	95·00	£180
87		5s. yellow-green (No. F135) (R.) (5.26)	£110	£180
		a. Trimmed opt	£325	
88		10s. brown-red (No. F139) (B.) (5.26)	£140	£250
		a. Trimmed opt	£350	
89		£1 rose-pink (No. F142) (B.) (5.26)	£190	£375
		a. Trimmed opt	£550	
85/9 *Set of 5*			£650	£1200

1926 (Oct)–**28**. T **72** of New Zealand, overprinted with T **15**.
(a) Jones chalk-surfaced paper
90		2s. deep blue (No. 466) (R.)	10·00	40·00
		w. Wmk inverted		
(b) Cowan thick, opaque chalk-surfaced paper
91		2s. light blue (No. 469) (R.) (18.6.27)	19·00	40·00
92		3s. pale mauve (No. 470) (R.) (30.1.28)	16·00	50·00
90/2 *Set of 3*			40·00	£120

TWO PENCE   COOK ISLANDS.
(18)   **(19)**

1931 (1 Mar). Surch with T **18**. P 14.

(a) No wmk

93	**11**	2d. on 1½d. black and blue (R.).......	9·50	4·50

*(b) W **43** of New Zealand*

94	**11**	2d. on 1½d. black and blue (R.).......	4·75	11·00

1931 (12 Nov)–**32**. Postal Fiscal stamps as Type F **6** of New Zealand. W **43**. Thick, opaque, white chalk-surfaced "Cowan" paper. P 14.

*(a) Optd with T **15***

95		2s.6d. deep brown (No. F147) (B.)......	15·00	22·00
96		5s. green (No. F149) (R.).................	26·00	55·00
97		10s. carmine-lake (No. F155) (B.)......	38·00	£110
98		£1 pink (No. F158) (B.)..................	£120	£190

*(b) Optd with T **19** (3.32)*

98a		£3 green (No. F164) (R.).................	£500	£900
98b		£5 indigo-blue (No. F168) (R.)..........	£250	£400

The £3 and £5 values were mainly used for fiscal purposes.

20 Capt. Cook landing

21 Capt. Cook

22 Double Maori Canoe

23 Natives working Cargo

24 Port of Avarua   **25** RMS *Monowai*

26 King George V

(Des L. C. Mitchell. Recess P.B.)

1932 (15 Mar–2 May). No wmk. P 13.

99	**20**	½d. black and deep green	3·50	16·00
		a. Perf 14..............................	28·00	95·00
100	**21**	1d. black and lake......................	9·50	4·50
		a. Centre inverted.....................	£8500	£8500
		b. Perf compound of 13 and 14	£225	£275
		c. Perf 14..............................	15·00	32·00
101	**22**	2d. black and brown...................	3·00	8·50
		a. Perf 14..............................	9·00	20·00
102	**23**	2½d. black and deep blue.............	25·00	60·00
		a. Perf 14..............................	19·00	60·00
103	**24**	4d. black and bright blue............	32·00	70·00
		a. Perf 14..............................	11·00	55·00
		b. Perf 14×13.........................	30·00	£110
		c. Perf compound of 14 and 13 ...	50·00	£120
104	**25**	6d. black and orange..................	29·00	48·00
		a. Perf 14..............................	4·25	15·00
105	**26**	1s. black and violet (P 14) (2.5).......	23·00	23·00
99/105		*Set of 7*..........................	65·00	£160

Nos. 100b and 103c come from sheets reperforated 14 on arrival at Wellington. No. 100b comes from the first vertical column of a sheet and has 14 at left and No. 103c from the third or fourth vertical column with 13 at left or right.

Other major errors exist on this issue, but these are not listed as they originated from printer's waste which appeared on the market in 1935. They include the ½d. in vertical pair, imperforate horizontally (*price* £425, *unused*), and the ½d. 2d. and 2½d. with centre inverted (*prices ½d.* £950, *2d.* £500 *and 2½d.* £300, *unused*).

(Recess from P.B. plates at Govt Printing Office, Wellington)

1933–36. W **43** of New Zealand (Single N Z and Star). P 14.

106	**20**	½d. black and deep green	1·25	4·50
		w. Wmk inverted......................	—	£120
107	**21**	1d. black and scarlet (1935).........	1·50	2·00
		y. Wmk inverted and reversed.......		
108	**22**	2d. black and brown (1936)..........	1·50	50
		w. Wmk inverted......................	—	£425
109	**23**	2½d. black and deep blue............	1·50	2·25
110	**24**	4d. black and bright blue............	1·50	50
111	**25**	6d. black and orange-yellow (1936)...	1·75	2·25
112	**26**	1s. black and violet (1936)..........	22·00	42·00
106/12		*Set of 7*..........................	28·00	48·00

SILVER JUBILEE OF KING GEORGE V. 1910–1935.

(27)

Normal Letters: **B K E N**

Narrow Letters: **B K E N**

1935 (7 May). Silver Jubilee. Optd with T **27** (wider vertical spacing on 6d.). Colours changed. W **43** of New Zealand. P 14.

113	**21**	1d. red-brown and lake...............	60	1·40
		a. Narrow "K" in "KING"............	2·75	5·50
		b. Narrow "B" in "JUBILEE"........	19·00	22·00
114	**23**	2½d. dull and deep blue (R.)........	3·75	3·50
		a. Narrow first "E" in "GEORGE"	3·75	6·50
115	**25**	6d. green and orange.................	9·50	6·50
		a. Narrow "N" in KING..............	11·00	20·00
113/15		*Set of 3*..........................	12·50	10·00

1936 (15 July)–**44**. Stamps of New Zealand optd with T **19**. W **43**. P 14.

*(a) T **72**. Cowan thick, opaque chalk-surfaced paper*

116		2s. light blue (No. 469).............	14·00	45·00
117		3s. pale mauve (No. 470)...........	15·00	70·00

*(b) Type F **6**. Cowan thick, opaque chalk-surfaced paper*

118		2s.6d. deep brown (No. F147) (R.)...	48·00	£110
119		5s. green (No. F149) (R.)............	50·00	£130
120		10s. carmine-lake (No. F155) (R.)...	90·00	£250
121		£1 pink (No. F158)...................	£120	£275
118/21		*Set of 4*..........................	£225	£700

*(c) Type F **6**. Thin, hard, chalk-surfaced Wiggins Teape paper*

122		2s.6d. dull brown (No. F170) (12.40)...	£180	£160
123		5s. green (No. F172) (R.) (10.40)......	£600	£500
123a		10s. pale carmine-lake (No. F177) (11.44)	£150	£200
123b		£3 green (No. F183) (R.) (date?)......	£450	£700
122/3b		*Set of 4*..........................	£1200	£1400

COOK IS'DS.

(28)

IS'DS.

Small second "S" (R. 1/2 and R. 8/4, first printing, and R. 6/10, second printing)

1937 (1 June). Coronation. Nos. 599/601 of New Zealand (inscr "12th MAY 1937") optd with T **28**.

124		1d. carmine............................	40	80
		a. Small second "S".................	16·00	18·00
125		2½d. Prussian blue...................	80	1·40
		a. Small second "S".................	27·00	30·00
126		6d. red-orange........................	80	60
		a. Small second "S".................	27·00	27·00
124/6		*Set of 3*..........................	1·75	2·50

The "Small second 'S'" was corrected for the third printing.

29 King George VI

30 Native Village

31 Native Canoe

32 Tropical Landscape

(Des J. Berry (2s., 3s., and frame of 1s.). Eng B.W. Recess Govt Ptg. Office, Wellington)

1938 (2 May). W **43** of New Zealand. P 14.

127	**29**	1s. black and violet...................	9·00	13·00
128	**30**	2s. black and red-brown..............	22·00	13·00
		w. Wmk inverted......................		
129	**31**	3s. greenish blue and green..........	65·00	55·00
127/9		*Set of 3*..........................	85·00	70·00

(Recess B.W.)

1940 (2 Sept). Surch as in T **32**. W **98** of New Zealand. P 13½×14.

130	**32**	3d. on 1½d. black and purple	75	60

Type **32** was not issued without surcharge but archival examples exist (*Price*, £250, *unused*).

1943–54. Postal Fiscal stamps as Type F **6** of New Zealand optd with T **19**. W **98**. Wiggins Teape chalk-surfaced paper. P 14.

131		2s.6d. dull brown (No. F193) (3.46)........	£140	£140
		w. Wmk inverted......................	50·00	50·00
132		5s. green (No. F195) (R.) (11.43)......	19·00	38·00
		w. Wmk inverted (5.54)...............	65·00	65·00
133		10s. pale carmine-lake (No. F201) (10.48)	£110	£150
		w. Wmk inverted (10.51).............	80·00	£120
134		£1 pink (No. F203) (11.47)...........	75·00	£130
		w. Wmk inverted (19.5.54)...........	£140	£190
135		£3 green (No. F208) (R.) (1946?)......	£1700	£1800
		w. Wmk inverted (28.5.53)...........	70·00	£180
136		£5 indigo-blue (No. F211) (R.) (25.10.50)	£375	£500
		w. Wmk inverted (19.5.54)...........	£325	£425
131w/6w		*Set of 6*..........................	£550	£850

The £3 and £5 were mainly used for fiscal purposes.

(Recess Govt Ptg Office, Wellington)

1944–46. W **98** of New Zealand (sideways on ½d. 1d., 1s., and 2s.). P 14.

137	**20**	½d. black and deep green (11.44)....	1·75	4·00
		w. Wmk sideways inverted............	6·50	11·00
138	**21**	1d. black and scarlet (3.45).........	2·00	2·50
		w. Wmk sideways inverted............	9·00	4·00
		x. Wmk sideways reversed............		
139	**22**	2d. black and brown (2.46)...........	4·50	19·00
140	**23**	2½d. black and deep blue (5.45)......	1·25	3·75
141	**24**	4d. black and blue (4.44)............	6·00	27·00
		y. Wmk inverted and reversed........	42·00	80·00
142	**25**	6d. black and orange (6.44).........	4·75	4·00
143	**29**	1s. black and violet (9.44)..........	5·50	4·50
144	**30**	2s. black and red-brown (8.45)......	38·00	60·00
145	**31**	3s. greenish blue and green (6.45)...	42·00	35·00
		w. Wmk inverted......................	£130	
137/45		*Set of 9*..........................	95·00	£140

The normal sideways watermark shows the star to the left of NZ as seen from the back of the stamp.

COOK ISLANDS

(33)

1946 (4 June). Peace. Nos. 668, 670, 674/5 of New Zealand optd with T **33** (reading up and down at sides on 2d.).

146		1d. green (Parliament House)	30	10
147		2d. purple (Royal Family) (B.)........	30	50
148		6d. chocolate and vermilion (Coat of Arms, foundry and farm).......	1·00	1·25
149		8d. black and carmine ("St. George") (B.)...................	60	1·25
146/9		*Set of 4*..........................	2·00	2·75

34 Ngatangiia Channel, Rarotonga

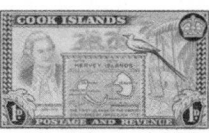

35 Capt. Cook and map of Hervey Islands

36 Raratonga and Revd. John Williams

37 Aitutaki and palm trees

38 Rarotonga Airfield

39 Penrhyn village

40 Native hut

41 Map and Statue of Capt. Cook

42 Native hut and palms   **43** *Matua* (inter-island freighter)

(Des J. Berry. Recess Waterlow)

1949 (1 Aug)–**61**. T **34/43**. W **98** of New Zealand (sideways on shilling values). P 13½×13 (horiz) or 13×13½ (vert).

150	**34**	½d. violet and brown.................	10	1·50
151	**35**	1d. chestnut and green..............	3·50	3·75
152	**36**	2d. reddish brown and scarlet......	2·00	3·75
153	**37**	3d. green and ultramarine...........	6·50	2·00
		aw. Wmk inverted.....................	£100	
		b. Wmk sideways (white opaque paper) (22.5.61).................	7·50	3·75
154	**38**	5d. emerald-green and violet........	8·00	1·50
155	**39**	6d. black and carmine..............	5·50	2·75
156	**40**	8d. olive-green and orange..........	70	3·75
		w. Wmk inverted......................	£150	80·00
157	**41**	1s. light blue and chocolate.........	4·25	3·75
158	**42**	2s. yellow-brown and carmine.......	7·50	13·00
		w. Wmk sideways inverted............		
159	**43**	3s. light blue and bluish green......	21·00	32·00
150/9		*Set of 10*.........................	50·00	60·00

43a Queen Elizabeth II

(Des J. Berry. Photo Harrison)

1953 (25 May). Coronation. T **43a** and similar vert design. W **98**. P 14×14½.

160		3d. brown.............................	1·50	85
161		6d. slate-grey........................	1·50	1·50

Design:—6d. Westminster Abbey.

IMPERFORATE STAMPS: Imperforate examples of many Cook Islands stamps formerly in the Islands' philatelic archives, were put on sale from mid-2013. These include Nos. 160/1 and numerous issues from 1966 onwards. Such material is outside the scope of this catalogue.

1/6

(44)

1960 (1 Apr). No. 154 surch with T **44**.
162   1s.6d. on 5d. emerald-green and violet 75   1·00

45 Tiare Maori   46 Fishing God

47 Frangipani   48 White Tern

49 Hibiscus   50 Long-tailed Tuna

51 Oranges   52 Queen Elizabeth II

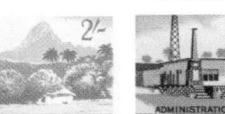

53 Island Scene   54 Administration Centre, Mangaia

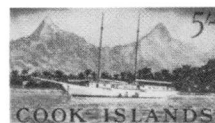

55 Rarotonga

(Des J. Berry. Recess (1s.6d.), litho (others) B.W.)

1963 (4 June). T **45**/**55**. W **98** of New Zealand (sideways). P 13½×13 (1d., 2d., 8d.), 13×13½ (3d., 5d., 6d., 1s.) or 13½ (others).
163	45	1d. emerald-green and yellow	75	75
164	46	2d. brown-red and yellow	30	65
165	47	3d. yellow, yellow-green and reddish violet	70	75
166	48	5d. blue and black............................	8·00	2·25
167	49	6d. red, yellow and green................	1·00	60
168	50	8d. black and blue............................	4·25	1·50
169	51	1s. orange-yellow and yellow-green..	1·00	1·00
170	52	1s.6d. bluish violet	2·75	2·00
171	53	2s. bistre-brown and grey-blue	2·75	1·50
172	54	3s. black and yellow-green	2·00	3·25
173	55	5s. bistre-brown and blue	20·00	8·00
163/73 *Set of 11*			40·00	20·00

56 Eclipse and Palm   57 N.Z. Ensign and Map

(Des L. C. Mitchell. Litho B.W.)

1965 (31 May). Solar Eclipse Observation, Manuae Island. W **98** of New Zealand. P 13½.
174   **56**   6d. black, yellow and light blue....... 20   10

The Cook Islands became a self-governing territory in "free association" with New Zealand on 16 September 1965.

SELF-GOVERNMENT

(Des R. M. Conly (4d.), L. C. Mitchell (10d., 1s.), J. Berry (1s.9d.). Litho B.W.)
1965 (16 Sept). Internal Self-Government. T **57** and similar horiz designs. W **98** of New Zealand (sideways). P 13½.
175	4d. red and blue..................................	45	10
176	10d. multicoloured..............................	20	15
177	1s. multicoloured................................	20	15
178	1s.9d. multicoloured............................	50	1·25
175/8 *Set of 4*		1·25	1·50

Designs:—10d. London Missionary Society Church; 1s. Proclamation of Cession, 1900; 1s.9d. Nikao School.

In Memoriam
Sɪʀ Wɪɴsᴛᴏɴ Cʜᴜʀᴄʜɪʟʟ
1874 - 1965
(61)

Airmail
(62)

1966 (24 Jan). Churchill Commemoration. Nos. 171/3 and 175/7 optd with T **61**, in red.
179	4d. red and blue	1·50	30
	a. "I" for "1" in "1874"	14·00	
180	10d. multicoloured..............................	2·50	80
	a. Opt inverted	£225	
	b. "I" for "1" in "1874"	16·00	
181	1s. multicoloured................................	2·75	1·25
	a. Opt inverted	£170	
	b. "I" for "1" in "1874"	16·00	
182	2s. bistre-brown and grey-blue................	2·75	2·25
	a. "I" for "1" in "1874"	8·00	
183	3s. black and yellow-green..................	2·75	2·25
	a. "I" for "1" in "1874"	8·00	
184	5s. bistre-brown and blue	3·00	2·25
	a. "I" for "1" in "1874"	11·00	
179/84 *Set of 6*..		13·50	8·25

The lower case "I" for "1" in "1874" occurred on R. 6/5 for all values and additionally on R. 12/5 for the 2s., 3s. and 5s.

1966 (22 Apr). Air. Various stamps optd with T **62** or surch also.
185	6d. red, yellow and green (No. 167)	1·25	20
186	7d. on 8d. black and blue (No. 168)	2·00	25
187	10d. on 3d. yellow, yellow-green and reddish violet (No. 165)............	1·00	15
188	1s. orange-yellow and yellow-green (No. 169)	1·00	15
189	1s.6d. bluish violet (No. 170)	2·00	1·25
190	2s.3d. on 3s. black and yellow-green (No. 172)	1·00	65
191	5s. bistre-brown and blue (No. 173).......	1·75	1·50
192	10s. on 2s. bistre-brown and grey-blue (No. 171)	1·75	14·00
193	£1 pink (No. 134)	13·00	19·00
	a. Aeroplane omitted	35·00	55·00
	w. Wmk inverted	17·00	22·00
	wa. Aeroplane omitted	38·00	60·00
185/93 *Set of 9*..		22·00	32·00

No. 193a occurred in all stamps of the last vertical row as insufficient aeroplane symbols were available. There are also numerous other varieties on all values, notably aeroplanes of different sizes and broken first "i" with dot missing owing to damaged type.

PRINTERS. The following stamps were printed by Heraclio Fournier, Spain except *where otherwise stated*. The process used was photogravure.

63 *Adoration of the Magi* (Fra Angelico)

1966 (28 Nov). Christmas. T **63** and similar multicoloured designs. P 13×12 (horiz) or 12×13 (vert).
194	1d. Type **63**	50	1·00
	a. Perf 13×14½	10	10
195	2d. *The Nativity* (Memling) (vert)............	13·00	23·00
	a. Perf 14½×13	20	10
196	4d. *Adoration of the Magi* (Velazquez)	1·00	1·00
	a. Perf 13×14½	30	15
197	10d. *Adoration of the Magi* (Bosch)............	2·00	7·00
	a. Perf 13×14½	30	20
198	1s.6d. *Adoration of the Shepherds* (J. de Ribera) (vert)............................	45·00	10·00
	a. Perf 14½×13	40	35
194/8 *Set of 5*		55·00	38·00
194a/8a *Set of 5*		1·10	80

68 Tennis, and Queen Elizabeth II

(Des V. Whiteley)

1967 (12 Jan). Second South Pacific Games, Nouméa. T **68** and similar horiz designs in orange-brown, black and new blue (1d.) or multicoloured (others). P 13½.

(a) Postage
199	½d. Type **68**	10	10
200	1d. Netball and Games emblem..........	10	10
201	4d. Boxing and Cook Islands' team badge	10	10
202	7d. Football and Queen Elizabeth II........	20	15

(b) Air
203	10d. Running and Games emblem	20	15
204	2s.3d. Running and Cook Islands' team badge	25	65
199/204 *Set of 6*		70	1·00

(New Currency, 100 cents = 1 dollar)

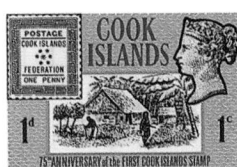

1967 (3 Apr–6 June). Decimal Currency. Nos. 134, 135w, 136, 163/70 and 172/5 surch as T **74** by the Government Printer. Sterling values obliterated except No. 218.
205	1c. on 1d. emerald-green and yellow (4.5.67)	45	1·50
	a. Condensed "c" (R. 2/4, 3/8, 6/2, 8/4)	3·50	
	b. Thin "c" (R. 3/5, 8/1)......................	4·50	
	c. Thin "1" (R. 3/6, 8/2)	4·50	
	d. Thin "1c" (R. 3/7, 8/3)	4·50	
206	2c. on 2d. brown-red and yellow..........	10	10
	a. Thin "2c" (R. 2/1, 8/8)	2·00	
	b. Condensed "c" (R. 4/8, 8/1)	2·00	
207	2½c. on 3d. yellow, yellow-green and reddish violet (I)	20	10
	a. Horiz pair. Nos. 207/8....................	60	75
	b. Thin "2½c" (R. 6/5)	4·00	
208	2½c. on 3d. yellow, yellow-green and reddish violet (II)............................	20	10
	a. Thin "2½c" and stop to left (R. 3/4).	4·00	
	b. Thin "2½c" and stop to right (R. 9/2)..	4·00	
209	3c. on 4d. red and blue......................	15	10
	a. Thin "3c" (R. 3/6, 4/10, 5/7, 6/3)......	2·00	
210	4c. on 5d. blue and black (4.5.67)........	12·00	30
	a. Thin "4c" (R. 5/4, 7/5)....................	45·00	
	b. Thin "4c" and stop (R. 2/8)............	75·00	
211	5c. on 6d. red, yellow and green............	15	10
	a. Thin "5c" (R. 2/8, 8/7)....................	3·00	
	b. Thin "5c" and stop (R. 6/4)............	6·50	
212	5c. on 6d. black, yellow and light blue......................................	5·00	2·75
	a. Thin "5c" (R. 5/10, 6/6)................	25·00	
	b. Thin "5c" and stop (R. 4/5)............	45·00	
	c. Condensed "c" (R. 2/4, 3/9)............	25·00	
213	7c. on 8d. black and blue....................	30	10
	a. Thin "7c" (R.7/1, 8/5)....................	5·00	
	b. Thin "7c" and stop (R. 3/8, 6/4)......	5·00	
214	10c. on 1s. orange-yellow and yellow-green	15	10
	a. Thin "10c" (R. 3/4, 5/5, 9/8)............	5·00	
215	15c. on 1s.6d. bluish violet (R.) (4.5.67)	2·00	1·00
216	30c. on 3s. black and yellow-green (R.) (4.5.67)	32·00	9·00
	a. Thin "30c" (R. 3/10)......................	85·00	
217	50c. on 5s. bistre-brown and blue (R.) (4.5.67)	4·00	3·00
	a. Thin "50c" (R. 2/1, 3/7, 5/4, 4/10)	13·00	
218	$1 and 10s. on 10d. mult (4.5.67)........	19·00	5·50
219	$2 on £1 pink (R.) (6.6.67)................	65·00	85·00
220	$6 on £3 green (R.) (6.6.67)................	£120	£160
221	$10 on £5 blue (R.) (6.6.67)................	£170	£200
	w. Wmk inverted	£150	£200
205/18 *Set of 14*		65·00	21·00

The two types of the 2½c. occur on alternate vertical rows within the sheet.

The surcharge on No. 218 is $1 and its equivalent 10s. in the old currency. The "10d." is obliterated by three bars.

75 Village Scene. Cook Islands 1d. Stamp of 1892 and Queen Victoria (from "Penny Black")

(Des V. Whiteley)

1967 (3 July). 75th Anniv of First Cook Islands Stamps. T **75** and similar horiz designs. Multicoloured. P 13½.
222	1c. (1d.) Type **75**	10	35
223	3c. (4d.) Post Office, Avarua, Rarotonga and Queen Elizabeth II..................	15	10
224	8c. (10d.) Avarua, Rarotonga and Cook Islands 10d. stamp of 1892..............	30	15
225	18c. (1s.9d.) *Moana Roo* (inter-island ship), Douglas DC-3 aircraft, map and Captain Cook	1·40	1·25
222/5 *Set of 4*		1·75	1·75
MS226 134×109 mm. Nos. 222/5		1·75	2·75

The face values are expressed in decimal currency and in the sterling equivalent.

Each value was issued in sheets of eight stamps and one label.

79 Hibiscus   80 Queen Elizabeth II

81 Queen Elizabeth and Flowers

Two types of $4

I. Value 32½ mm long. Coarse screen.
II. Value 33½ mm long. Finer screen.

(Floral designs from paintings by Kay Billings)

1967 (31 July)–**71**. Multicoloured designs as T **79/81**. P 14×13½.

A. Without fluorescent security markings

227A	½c. Typa **79**		10	10
228A	1c. *Hibiscus syriacus* (27×37 mm)		10	10
229A	2c. *Frangipani* (27×37 mm)		10	10
230A	2½c. *Clitoria ternatea* (27×37 mm)		20	10
231A	3c. "*Suva Queen*" (27×37 mm)		55	10
232A	4c. Water Lily ("WALTER LILY") (27×37 mm)		70	1·00
233A	4c. Water Lily (27×37 mm)		2·00	2·00
234A	5c. *Bauhinia bipinata rosea* (27×37 mm)		35	10
235A	6c. Hibiscus (27×37 mm)		40	10
236A	8c. *Aliamanda cathartica* (27×37 mm)		40	10
237A	9c. Stephanotis (27×37 mm)		40	10
238A	10c. *Poinciana regia flamboyant* (27×37 mm)		40	10
239A	15c. Frangipani (27×37 mm) (11.8.67)		40	10
240A	20c. Thunbergia (27×37 mm) (11.8.67)		4·50	1·50
241A	25c. Canna Lily (27×37 mm) (11.8.67)		80	30
242A	30c. *Euphorbia pulcherrima poinsettia* (27×37 mm) (11.8.67)		65	10
243A	50c. *Gardenia taitensis* (27×37 mm) (11.8.67)		1·00	55
244A	$1 Type **80** (31.8.67)		2·25	80
245A	$2 Type **80** (31.8.67)		4·75	1·50
246A	$4 Type **81** (I) (30.4.68)		1·50	4·25
247A	$6 Type **81** (30.4.68)		1·75	7·00
247cA	$8 Type **81** (21.4.69)		5·00	17·00
248A	$10 Type **81** (12.7.68)		3·25	14·00
227A/48A	*Set of 22*		26·00	42·00

B. With fluorescent security markings

227B	½c. Type **78** (9.2.70)		20	10
228B	1c. Type **79** (27×37 mm) (9.2.70)		20	10
229B	2c. Frangipani (27×37 mm) (9.2.70)		20	10
230B	2½c. *Clitoria ternatea* (27×37 mm) (9.2.70)		20	10
231B	3c. "*Suva Queen*" (27×37 mm) (9.2.70)		40	10
233B	4c. Water Lily (27×37 mm) (9.2.70)		2·50	10
234B	5c. *Bauhinia bipirsnata roses* (27×37 mm)		30	10
235B	6c. Hibiscus (27×37 mm) (9.2.70)		30	10
236B	8c. *Allemanda cathartica* (27×37 mm) (9.2.70)		30	10
237B	9c. Stephanotis (27×37 mm) (9.2.70)		30	10
238B	10c. *Poinciana regia flamboyant* (27×37 mm) (9.2.70)		30	10
239B	15c. Frangipani (27×37 mm) (9.2.70)		40	10
240B	20c. Thunbergia (27×37 mm) (9.2.70)		3·50	1·75
241B	25c. Canna Lily (27×37 mm) (9.2.70)		1·00	15
242B	30c. *Euphorbia pulcherrima poinsettia* (27×37 mm) (9.2.70)		1·25	40
243B	50c. *Gardenia taitensis* (27×37 mm) (9.2.70)		1·25	40
244B	$1 Type **80** (12.10.70)		1·25	80
245B	$2 Type **80** (12.10.70)		2·25	2·25
246B	$4 Type **81** (I) (11.11.70)		35·00	55·00
	a. Type II (14.7.71)		5·50	8·50
247B	$6 Type **81** (12.2.71)		11·00	6·00
247cB	$8 Type **81** (3.5.71)		12·00	10·00
248B	$10 Type **81** (14.6.71)		16·00	12·00
227B/48B	*Set of 22*		38·00	

The "WALTER" spelling error occurred on all stamps in one of the four post office sheets which went to make up the printing sheet and this was corrected in later supplies.

FLUORESCENT PAPER. This is on paper treated with fluorescent security markings, in the form of faint multiple Coats of Arms. Stamps exist with these markings inverted. In addition an invisible synthetic gum has been used which prevents curling and is suitable for use in the tropics without interleaving the sheets.

Some of the above are known with these markings omitted and can be distinguished when in unused condition from the original printings without markings by their synthetic invisible gum.

97 "*Ia Oraria Maria*"

1967 (24 Oct). Gauguin's Polynesian Paintings. T **97** and similar designs. Multicoloured. P 13.

249	1c. Type **97**		10	10
250	3c. *Riders on the Beach*		10	10
251	5c. *Still Life with Flowers*		15	10
252	8c. *Whispered Words*		20	10
253	15c. *Maternity*		30	15
254	22c. *Why are you angry?*		35	20
249/54	*Set of 6*		1·00	65
MS255	156×132 mm. Nos. 249/54		1·40	1·50

The 5c. includes an inset portrait of Queen Elizabeth.

---

98 *The Holy Family* (Rubens)

HURRICANE RELIEF PLUS 5c

(99)

1967 (4 Dec). Christmas. Renaissance Paintings. T **98** and similar designs. Multicoloured. P 12×13.

256	1c. Type **98**		10	10
257	3c. Adoration of the Magi (Dürer)		10	10
258	4c. *The Lucca Madonna* (J. van Eyck)		10	10
259	8c. *The Adoration of the Shepherds* (J. da Bassano)		20	15
260	15c. *Adoration of the Shepherds* (El Greco)		35	15
261	25c. *Madonna and Child* (Correggio)		40	15
256/61	*Set of 6*		1·10	65

1968 (12 Feb). Hurricane Relief. Nos. 231A, 233A, 251, 238A, 241A and 243/4A suroh as T **99** by Govt Printer, Rarotonga.

262	3c. +1c. "*Suva Queen*"		15	20
263	4c. +1c. Water Lily		15	20
264	5c. +2c. "*Still Life with Flowers*"		15	20
	a. Black surch albino			
265	10c. +2c. *Poinciana regia flamboyant*		15	20
266	25c. +5c. Canna Lily		20	25
267	50c. +10c. *Gardenia taitensis*		25	40
268	$1 +10c. Type **80**		35	60
262/8	*Set of 7*		1·25	1·75

The surcharge on No. 268 is as T **99**, but with seriffed letters. On No. 264 silver blocking obliterates the design area around the lettering.

100 *Matavai Bay, Tahiti* (J. Barralet)

101 *Resolution and Discovery* (J. Webber)

(Des J. Berry)

1968 (12 Sept). Bicentenary of Captain Cook's First Voyage of Discovery. Multicoloured. Invisible gum. P 13.

*(a) Postage. Vert designs as T **100***

269	½c. Type **100**		10	20
270	1c. *Island of Huaheine* (John Cleveley)		15	20
271	2c. *Town of St. Peter and St. Paul, Kamchatka* (J. Webber)		25	25
272	4c. *The Ice Islands* (Antarctica: W. Hodges)		35	20

*(b) Air. Horiz designs as T **101***

273	6c. Type **101**		35	25
274	10c. *The Island of Tahiti* (W. Hodges)		35	25
275	15c. *Karakakooa, Hawaii* (J. Webber)		35	35
276	25c. *The Landing at Middleburg* (J. Shemin)		45	55
269/76	*Set of 8*		2·00	2·00

Each value was issued in sheets of ten stamps and two labels.

FLUORESCENT PAPER. From No. 277, *unless otherwise stated*, all issues are printed on paper treated with fluorescent security markings with invisible synthetic gum. These markings may be inverted or omitted in error.

102 Dinghy-sailing

103 *Madonna and Child* (Titian)

1968 (21 Oct). Olympic Games, Mexico. T **102** and similar horiz designs. Multicoloured. P 13.

277	1c. Type **102**		10	10
278	5c. Gymnastics		10	10
279	15c. High jumping		15	10

280	20c. High-diving		15	10
281	30c. Cycling		60	10
282	50c. Hurdling		35	25
277/82	*Set of 6*		1·25	75

Each value was issued in sheets of ten stamps and two labels.

1968 (2 Dec). Christmas. Paintings. T **103** and similar vert designs. Multicoloured. P 13½.

283	1c. Type **103**		10	10
284	4c. *The Holy Family with Lamb* (Raphael)		15	10
285	10c. *The Virgin of the Rosary* (Murillo)		20	10
286	20c. *Adoration of the Kings* (Memling)		30	10
287	30c. *Adoration of the Magi* (Ghirlandaio)		40	10
283/7	*Set of 5*		1·00	45
MS288	114×177 mm. Nos. 283/7 plus label		1·25	1·60

104 Camp-fire Cooking

1969 (6 Feb). Diamond Jubilee of New Zealand Scout Movement and Fifth National (New Zealand) Jamboree. T **104** and similar square designs. Multicoloured. P 13½.

289	½c. Type **104**		10	10
290	1c. Descent by rope		10	10
291	5c. Semaphore		15	10
292	10c. Tree-planting		20	10
293	20c. Constructing a shelter		25	15
294	30c. Lord Baden-Powell and island scene		45	25
289/94	*Set of 6*		1·00	50

Each value was issued in sheets of ten stamps and two labels.

105 High Jumping

1969 (7 July). Third South Pacific Games, Port Moresby. T **105** and similar triangular designs. Multicoloured. Without fluorescent security markings. P 13×13½.

295	½c. Type **105**		10	40
296	½c. Footballer		10	40
297	1c. Basketball		50	40
298	1c. Weightlifter		50	40
299	4c. Tennis-player		50	50
300	4c. Hurdler		50	50
301	10c. Javelin-thrower		55	50
302	10c. Runner		55	50
303	15c. Golfer		1·75	1·50
304	15c. Boxer		1·75	1·50
295/304	*Set of 10*		6·00	5·75
MS305	174×129 mm. Nos. 295/304 plus two labels		8·00	7·00

Each value was issued in sheets containing five *se-tenant* pairs of both designs and two labels.

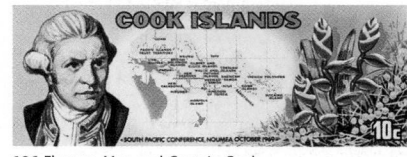

106 Flowers, Map and Captain Cook

1969 (8 Oct). South Pacific Conference, Nouméa. T **106** and similar horiz designs. Multicoloured. Without fluorescent security markings. P 13.

306	5c. Flowers, map and Premier Albert Henry		20	20
307	10c. Type **106**		80	40
308	25c. Flowers, map and N.Z. Arms		30	40
309	30c. Queen Elizabeth II, map and flowers		30	40
306/9	*Set of 4*		1·40	1·25

107 *Virgin and Child with Saints Jerome and Dominic* (Lippi)

108 *The Resurrection of Christ* (Raphael)

1969 (21 Nov). Christmas. Paintings. T **107** and similar designs. Multicoloured. Without fluorescent security markings. P 13.

310	1c. Type **107**		10	10
311	4c. "*The Holy Family*" (Fra Bartolomeo)		10	10

312	10c.	*The Adoration of the Shepherds* (A. Mengs)	15	10
313	20c.	*Madonna and Child with Saints* (R. Campin)	25	20
314	30c.	*The Madonna of the Basket* (Correggio)	25	30
310/14	*Set of 5*		75	70
MS315	132×97 mm. Nos. 310/14		1·00	1·50

Each value was issued in sheets of nine stamps and one label.

1970 (12 Mar). Easter. Paintings. T **108** and similar perf designs showing *The Resurrection of Christ* by the artists named. Multicoloured. P 13.

316	4c.	Type **108**	10	10
317	8c.	Dirk Bouts	10	10
318	20c.	Altdorfer	15	10
319	25c.	Murillo	20	10
316/19	*Set of 4*		50	35
MS320	132×162 mm. Nos. 316/19		1·25	1·25

Each value was issued in sheets of eight stamps and one label.

KIA ORANA
APOLLO 13
ASTRONAUTS
Te Atua to
Tatou Irinakianga
(109)

1970 (17–30 Apr). *Apollo 13*. Nos. 233, 236, 239/40, 242 and 245/6 optd with T **109** (4c. to $2) or with first three lines only in larger type ($4), by Govt Printer. Without fluorescent security markings.

321	4c.	Water Lily	10	15
	a.	Opt albino	26·00	
322	8c.	*Allamanda cathartics*	10	15
323	15c.	Frangipani	10	15
324	20c.	Thunbergia	40	20
325	30c.	*Euphorbia pulcherrima poinsettia*	20	25
326	$2	Type **80**	50	1·00
327	$4	Type **81** (30.4)	29·00	45·00
	a.	With fluorescent security markings	1·25	2·75
	ab.	Opt double, one albino	†	—
321/7a	*Set of 7*		2·25	4·25

110 The Royal Family

(Des V. Whiteley (5c.), J. Berry ($1))

1970 (12 June). Royal Visit to New Zealand. T **110** and similar horiz designs. Multicoloured. P 13.

328	5c.	Type **110**	75	30
329	30c.	Captain Cook and HMS *Endeavour*	1·75	1·75
330	$1	Royal Visit commemorative coin	2·25	3·00
328/30	*Set of 3*		4·25	4·50
MS331	145×97 mm. Nos. 328/30		8·50	10·00

Each value was issued in sheets of eight stamps and one label.

FOUR DOLLARS

FIFTH ANNIVERSARY SELF-GOVERNMENT AUGUST 1970 **$4.00**
(113) (114)

1970 (27 Aug). Fifth Anniv of Self-Government. Nos. 328/30 optd with T **113** (30c. and $1), or in single line in silver around frame of stamp (5c.).

332	5c.	Type **110**	40	15
333	30c.	Captain Cook and HMS *Endeavour*	80	35
334	$1	Royal Visit commemorative coin	1·00	90
332/4	*Set of 3*		2·00	1·25

1970 (11 Nov). Nos. 247c and 248 surch with T **114** by Govt Printer, Rarotonga. Without fluorescent security markings.

335	**81**	$4 on $8 multicoloured	32·00	28·00
	a.	With fluorescent security markings	1·25	1·75
336		$4 on $10 multicoloured	32·00	48·00
	a.	With fluorescent security markings	1·25	1·50

There are variations in the setting of this surcharge and also in the rule.

115 Mary, Joseph and Christ in Manger

(Des from De Lisle Psalter)

1970 (30 Nov). Christmas. T **115** and similar square designs. Multicoloured. P 13.

337	1c.	Type **115**	10	10
338	4c.	Shepherds and Apparition of the Angel	20	10
339	10c.	Mary showing Child to Joseph	25	10
340	20c.	The Wise Men bearing Gifts	30	20
341	30c.	Parents wrapping Child in swaddling clothes	30	35
337/41	*Set of 5*		1·00	75
MS342	100×139 mm. Nos. 337/41 plus label		1·00	1·50

Each value was issued in sheets of five stamps and one label. Stamps from the miniature sheet are smaller, since they do not have the buff parchment border as on the stamps from the sheets.

AITUTAKI

The island of Aitutaki, under British protection from 1888, was annexed by New Zealand on 11 June 1901.

NEW ZEALAND DEPENDENCY

Stamps of COOK ISLANDS were used in Aitutaki from 1892 until 1903.

PRICES FOR STAMPS ON COVER TO 1945	
Nos. 1/7	from × 4
Nos. 9/14	from × 3
Nos. 15/29	from × 4
Nos. 30/2	from × 6

Stamps of New Zealand overprinted or surcharged. For illustrations of watermarks and definitive types see New Zealand.

AITUTAKI. **Ava Pene.**
(1) (2) ½d.

Tai Pene. **Rua Pene Ma Te Ava.**
(3) 1d. (4) 2½d.

Toru Pene. **Ono Pene.** **Tai Tiringi.**
(5) 3d. (6) 6d. (7) 1s.

1903 (29 June)–11. T **23**, **27/8**, **31**, **34** and **42** surch with T **1** at top and T **2** to **7** at foot. Thin, hard "Cowan" paper. W **43**.

(a) P 14

1	½d. green (No. 302) (R.)		4·75	6·50
2	1d. carmine (No. 303) (B.)		5·00	5·50
3	2½d. deep blue (No. 320a) (R.) (9.11)		8·00	18·00
	a. "Ava" without stop		£150	£250
1/3	*Set of 3*		16·00	27·00

(b) P 11

4	2½d. blue (No. 308) (R.)		19·00	12·00
5	3d. yellow-brown (No. 309) (B.)		18·00	15·00
6	6d. rose-red (No. 312a) (B.)		30·00	25·00
7	1s. bright red (No. 315a) (B.)		55·00	90·00
	a. "Tiringi" without stop (R. 7/12)		£650	£950
	b. *Orange-red*		70·00	£100
	ba. "Tiringi" without stop (R. 7/12)		£850	£1100
4/7	*Set of 4*		£110	£130

Nos. 1/2 and 4/7 were placed on sale in Auckland on 12 June 1903. There were four states of the overprint used for No. 3. On the first the "no stop" variety (No. 3a) occurs on R. 6/8, on the second it appears on R. 1/4, 2/4 and 6/8, on the third on R. 5/8 and 6/8, and on the fourth all stops are present.

AITUTAKI.

Ono Pene.
(8)

1911–16. T **51** and **53** surch with T **1** at top and T **2** or **3** at foot and T **52** surch as T **8**. P 14×15 (½d., 1d.) or 14×14½ (others).

9	½d. green (No. 387) (R.) (9.11)		1·00	8·50
10	1d. carmine (No. 405) (B.) (2.13)		3·00	13·00
11	6d. carmine (No. 392) (B.) (23.5.16)		50·00	£140
12	1s. vermilion (No. 394) (B.) (9.14)		60·00	£150
9/12	*Set of 4*		£100	£275

1916–17. T **60** (recess) surch as T **8**. W **43**. P 14×13½.

13	6d. carmine (No. 425) (B.) (6.6.16)		9·00	50·00
	a. Perf 14×14½		7·50	28·00
	b. Vert pair. Nos. 13/13a		50·00	£180
14	1s. vermilion (No. 430) (B.) (3.17)		10·00	90·00
	a. Perf 14×14½		12·00	90·00
	ab. "Tai" without dot (R. 8/9, 9/12, 10/12)		£225	£750
	ac. "Tiringi" without dot on second "i" (R. 8/12, 10/7)		£300	£850
	ad. "Tiringi" without dot on third "i" (R. 8/11)		£425	£1100
	b. Vert pair. Nos. 14/14a		£100	£400

1917–18. T **60** (recess) optd "AITUTAKI" only, as in T **8**. W **43**. P 14×13½.

15	2½d. blue (No. 419) (R.) (12.18)		2·00	18·00
	a. Perf 14×14½		1·75	16·00
	b. Vert pair. Nos. 15/15a		30·00	£150
16	3d. chocolate (No. 420) (B.) (1.18)		1·75	40·00
	a. Perf 14×14½		1·50	32·00
	b. Vert pair. Nos. 16/16a		30·00	£170
17	6d. carmine (No. 425) (B.) (11.17)		6·00	22·00
	a. Perf 14×14½		4·75	21·00
	b. Vert pair. Nos. 17/17a		40·00	£150
18	1s. vermilion (No. 430) (B.) (11.17)		14·00	48·00
	a. Perf 14×14½		10·00	32·00
	b. Vert pair. Nos. 18/18a		65·00	£225
15/18	*Set of 4*		21·00	£120
15a/18a	*Set of 4*		16·00	90·00

1917–20. T **53** and **61** (typo) optd "AITUTAKI" only, as in T **8**. W **43**. P 14×15.

19	½d. green (No. 435) (R.) (2.20)		1·00	6·00
20	1d. carmine (No. 405) (B.) (5.20)		5·50	35·00
21	1½d. slate (No. 437) (R.) (11.17)		4·50	30·00
22	1½d. orange-brown (No. 438) (R.) (2.19)		80	7·00
23	3d. chocolate (No. 440) (B.) (6.19)		3·50	21·00
19/23	*Set of 5*		14·00	90·00

(Des and recess Perkins, Bacon & Co)

1920 (23 Aug). T **9/14** of Cook Islands, but inscr "AITUTAKI". No wmk. P 14.

24	½d. black and green		3·50	25·00
25	1d. black and dull carmine		3·50	17·00
	a. Double derrick flaw (R. 2/8, 3/6 or 5/2)		11·00	
26	1½d. black and sepia		6·00	12·00
27	3d. black and deep blue		2·50	14·00
28	6d. red-brown and slate		5·50	14·00
29	1s. black and purple		9·50	16·00
24/9	*Set of 6*		27·00	90·00

Examples of the 6d. with centre inverted (*price £900, unused*) and the 1s. with frame printed double (*price £225, unused*) come from printer's waste and were not issued.

(Recess Govt Printing Office, Wellington)

1924–27. T **9/10** and **16** of Cook Islands, but inscr "AITUTAKI". W **43** of New Zealand. P 14.

30	½d. black and green (5.27)		2·00	23·00
31	1d. black and deep carmine (10.24)		6·00	14·00
	a. Double derrick flaw (R. 2/8, 3/6 or 5/2)		16·00	28·00
32	2½d. black and dull blue (10.27)		7·50	80·00
30/2	*Set of 3*		14·00	£100

Cook Islands stamps superseded those of Aitutaki on 15 March 1932.

PENRHYN ISLAND

Stamps of COOK ISLANDS were used on Penrhyn Island from late 1901 until the issue of the surcharged stamps in May 1902.

PRICES FOR STAMPS ON COVER TO 1945	
No. 1	from × 25
No. 3	—
Nos. 4/5	from × 25
Nos. 6/8	—
Nos. 9/10	from × 50
Nos. 11/13	—
Nos. 14/18	from × 3
Nos. 19/23	from × 2
Nos. 24/37	from × 3
Nos. 38/40	from × 5

NEW ZEALAND DEPENDENCY The island of Penrhyn, under British protection from 20 September 1888, was annexed by New Zealand on 11 June 1901.

Stamps of New Zealand overprinted or surcharged. For illustrations of New Zealand watermarks and definitive types see New Zealand.

PENRHYN ISLAND.
$\frac{1}{2}$ **PENI.**
(1)

PENRHYN ISLAND.
TAI PENI.
(2) 1d.

PENRHYN ISLAND.
$2\frac{1}{2}$ **PENI.**
(3)

1902 (5 May). T **23**, **27** and **42** surch with T **1**, **2** and **3**.

(a) Thick, soft Pirie paper. No wmk. P 11

1	2½d. blue (No. 260) (R.)		14·00	14·00
	a. "½" and "P" spaced (all stamps in 8th vert row)		30·00	32·00

*(b) Thin, hard Basted Mills paper. W **38** of New Zealand*

(i) P 11

3	1d. carmine (No. 286) (Br.)		£850	£1200

(ii) P 14

4	½d. green (No. 287) (R.)		1·00	14·00
	a. No stop after "ISLAND"		£150	£325
5	1d. carmine (No. 288) (Br.)		3·25	28·00

(iii) Perf compound of 11 and 14

6	1d. carmine (No. 290) (Br.)		£1200	£1400

(iv) Mixed perfs

7	½d. green (No. 291) (R.)		£2250	
8	1d. carmine (No. 292) (Br.)		£2500	

*(c) Thin, hard Cowan paper. W **43** of New Zealand*

(i) P 14

9	½d. green (No. 302) (R.)		4·50	15·00
	a. No stop after "ISLAND" (R. 10/6)		£180	£375
10	1d. carmine (No. 303) (B.)		1·25	9·50
	a. No stop after "ISLAND" (R. 10/6)		60·00	£170

(ii) Perf compound of 11 and 14

11	1d. carmine (No. 305) (B.)		£15000	

(iii) Mixed perfs

12	½d. green (No. 306) (R.)		£2250	£2500
13	1d. carmine (No. 307) (B.)		£800	£1000

PENRHYN ISLAND.
(4)

Toru Pene.
(5) 3d.

Ono Pene.
(6) 6d.

Tahi Silingi.
(7) 1s.

1903 (28 Feb). T **28**, **31** and **34** surch with name at top, T **4**, and values at foot, T **5/7**. Thin, hard "Cowan" paper. W **43** (sideways) of New Zealand. P 11.

14	3d. yellow-brown (No. 309) (B.)		10·00	42·00
15	6d. rose-red (No. 312a) (B.)		15·00	80·00

16	1s. brown-red (No. 315) (B.)		60·00	60·00
	a. *Bright red*		42·00	42·00
	b. *Orange-red*		65·00	65·00
14/16a	Set of 3		60·00	£120

1914 (May)–**15.** T **51/2** surch with T **1** (½d.) or optd with T **4** at top and surch with T **6/7** at foot.

19	½d. yellow-green (No. 387) (C.) (5.14)		80	12·00
	a. No stop after "ISLAND"		25·00	£110
	b. No stop after "PENI" (R. 3/17)		£110	£350
	c. *Vermilion opt (1.15)*		80	8·00
	ca. No stop after "ISLAND"		10·00	75·00
	cb. No stop after "PENI" (R. 3/5, 3/17)		55·00	£190
22	6d. carmine (No. 393) (B.) (8.14)		23·00	75·00
23	1s. vermilion (No. 394) (B.) (8.14)		50·00	£100
19/23	Set of 3		65·00	£160

The "no stop after ISLAND" variety occurs on R. 1/4, 1/10, 1/16, 1/22, 6/4, 6/10, 6/16 and 6/22 of the carmine surcharge, No. 19, and on these positions plus R. 1/12, 1/24, 6/12 and 6/24 for the vermilion, No. 19c.

PENRHYN ISLAND. **PENRHYN ISLAND.**

Normal. Narrow spacing.

1917 (Nov)–**20.** Optd as T **4.**

(a) T **60** (recess). W **43** of New Zealand. P 14×13½

24	2½d. blue (No. 419) (R.) (10.20)		3·00	17·00
	a. Perf 14×14½		2·00	11·00
	ab. No stop after "ISLAND" (R. 10/8)		£190	£500
	b. Vert pair. Nos. 24/24a		45·00	£110
25	3d. chocolate (No. 420) (B.) (6.18)		12·00	70·00
	a. Perf 14×14½		9·50	70·00
	b. Vert pair. Nos. 25/25a		70·00	£275
26	6d. carmine (No. 425) (B.) (1.18)		8·00	26·00
	a. Perf 14×14½		5·00	21·00
	ab. No stop after "ISLAND" (R. 10/8)		£450	£900
	b. Vert pair. Nos. 26/26a		55·00	£160
27	1s. vermilion (No. 430) (B.) (12.17)		15·00	45·00
	a. Perf 14×14½		12·00	35·00
	ab. No stop after "ISLAND" (R. 10/8)		£550	£1000
	b. Vert pair. Nos. 27/27a		£100	£275
24/7	Set of 4		35·00	£140
24a/7a	Set of 4		26·00	£120

(b) T **61** (typo). W **43** of New Zealand. P 14×15

28	½d. green (No. 435) (R.) (2.20)		1·00	2·00
	a. No stop after "ISLAND" (R. 2/24)		£150	£225
	b. Narrow spacing		7·50	16·00
29	1½d. slate (No. 437) (R.)		7·00	28·00
	a. Narrow spacing		18·00	65·00
30	1½d. orange-brown (No. 438) (R.) (2.19)		1·00	28·00
	a. Narrow spacing		7·50	65·00
31	3d. chocolate (No. 440) (B.) (6.19)		4·00	45·00
	a. Narrow spacing		17·00	£100
28/31	Set of 4		11·50	90·00

The narrow spacing variety occurs on R. 1/5–8, 4/21–4, 7/5–8 and 9/21–4.

(Recess P.B.)

1920 (23 Aug). As T **9/14** of Cook Islands, but inscr "PENRHYN". No wmk. P. 14.

32	½d. black and emerald		1·50	24·00
	a. Part imperf block of 4		£1500	
33	1d. black and deep red		1·50	16·00
	a. Double derrick flaw (R. 2/8, 3/6 or 5/2)		5·50	48·00
34	1½d. black and deep violet		6·50	19·00
35	3d. black and red		2·50	18·00
36	6d. red-brown and sepia		3·25	20·00
37	1s. black and slate-blue		10·00	27·00
32/7	Set of 6		22·00	£110

No. 32a comes from sheets on which two rows were imperforate between horizontally and the second row additionally imperforate vertically.

Examples of the ½d. and 1d. with centre inverted were not supplied to the Post Office (*Price* £1000 *each, unused*).

(Recess Govt Printing Office, Wellington)

1927–29. As T **9/10** and **16** of Cook Islands, but inscr "PENRHYN". W **43.** P. 14.

38	½d. black and green (5.29)		5·50	24·00
39	1d. black and deep carmine (14.3.28)		5·50	24·00
	a. Double derrick flaw (R. 2/8, 3/6 or 5/2)		16·00	
40	2½d. red-brown and dull blue (10.27)		18·00	48·00
38/40	Set of 3		26·00	85·00

Cook Islands stamps superseded those of Penrhyn Island on 15 March 1932.

Cyprus

Cyprus was part of the Turkish Ottoman Empire from 1571.

The first records of an organised postal service date from 1871 when a post office was opened at Nicosia (Lefkosa) under the jurisdiction of the Damascus Head Post Office. Various stamps of Turkey from the 1868 issue onwards are known used from this office, cancelled "KIBRIS", in Arabic, within a double-lined oblong. Manuscript cancellations have also been reported. The records report the opening of a further office at Larnaca (Tuzla) in 1873, but no cancellation for this office has been identified.

To provide an overseas postal service the Austrian Empire opened a post office in Larnaca during 1845. Stamps of Austria and the Austrian Post Offices in the Turkish Empire were placed on sale there from 1 June 1864 and were cancelled with an unframed straight-line mark or circular date stamp. This Austrian post office closed on 6 August 1878.

BRITISH ADMINISTRATION

Following the convention with Turkey, Great Britain assumed the administration of Cyprus on 11 July 1878 and the first post office, as part of the British GPO. system, was opened at Larnaca on 27 July 1878. Further offices at Famagusta, Kyrenia, Limassol, Nicosia and Paphos followed in September 1878.

The stamps of Great Britain were supplied to the various offices as they opened and continued to be used until the Cyprus Administration assumed responsibility for the postal service on 1 April 1880. With the exception of "969" (Nicosia) similar numeral cancellations had previously been used at offices in Great Britain.

Numeral postmarks for Headquarters Camp, Nicosia ("D48") and Polymedia (Polemidhia) Camp, Limassol ("D47") were supplied by the GPO in London during January 1881. These cancellations had three bars above and three bars below the numeral. Similar marks, but with four bars above and below, had previously been used in London on newspapers and bulk mail.

Although both three bar cancellations subsequently occur on Cyprus issues only, isolated examples have been found on loose Great Britain stamps and there are no known covers or pieces which confirm such usage in Cyprus.

For illustrations of the postmark types see BRITISH POST OFFICES ABROAD notes, following GREAT BRITAIN.

FAMAGUSTA

Stamps of GREAT BRITAIN cancelled "982" as Type **9.**

1878–80.

Z1	½d. rose-red (1870–79) (Plate Nos. 11, 13)		£750
Z2	1d. rose-red (1864–79)		£600
	Plate Nos. 145, 174, 181, 193, 202, 204, 206, 215, 217.		
Z3	2d. blue (1858–69) (Plate Nos. 13, 15)		£1200
Z4	2½d. rosy mauve (1876) (Plate Nos. 13, 16)		£1300
Z5	6d. grey (1874–80) (Plate No. 15)		£3250
Z6	1s. green (1873–77) (Plate No. 12)		

KYRENIA

Stamps of GREAT BRITAIN cancelled "974" as Type **9.**

1878–80.

Z8	½d. rose-red (1870–79) (Plate No. 13)		£1100
Z9	1d. rose-red (1864–79) *From*		£700
	Plate Nos. 168, 171, 193, 196, 206, 207, 209, 220.		
Z10	2d. blue (1858–69) (Plate Nos. 13, 15)		£1200
Z11	2½d. rosy mauve (1876–79) (Plate Nos. 12, 13, 14, 15) *From*		£1200
Z12	4d. sage-green (1877) (Plate No. 16)		
Z13	6d. grey (1874–80) (Plate No. 16)		

LARNACA

Stamps of GREAT BRITAIN cancelled "942" as Type **9.**

1878–80.

Z14	½d. rose-red (1870–79) *From*		£250
	Plate Nos. 11, 12, 13, 14, 15, 19, 20.		
Z15	1d. rose-red (1864–79) *From*		£180
	Plate Nos. 129, 131, 146, 154, 170, 171, 174, 175, 176, 177, 178, 179, 181, 182, 183, 184, 187, 188, 190, 191, 192, 193, 194, 195, 196, 197, 198, 199, 200, 201, 202, 203, 204, 205, 206, 207, 208, 209, 210, 212, 213, 214, 215, 216, 217, 218, 220, 221, 222, 225.		
Z16	1½d. lake-red (1870) (Plate No. 3)		£2250
Z17	2d. blue (1858–69) (Plate Nos. 9, 13, 14, 15)		£300
Z18	2½d. rosy mauve (1876–79) *From*		75·00
	Plate Nos. 4, 5, 6, 8, 9, 10, 11, 12, 13, 14, 15, 16, 17.		
Z19	2½d. blue (1880) (Plate Nos. 17, 18)		£500
Z21	4d. sage-green (1877) (Plate Nos. 15, 16)		£550
Z22	6d. grey (1874–76) (Plate Nos. 15, 16, 17)		£600
Z23	6d. pale buff (1872–73) (Plate No. 11)		£3500
Z24	8d. orange (1876)		£8000
Z25	1s. green (1873–77) (Plate Nos. 12, 13)		£1000
Z27	5s. rose (1874) (Plate No. 2)		£8000

LIMASSOL

Stamps of GREAT BRITAIN cancelled "975" as Type **9.**

1878–80.

Z28	½d. rose-red (1870–79) (Plate Nos. 11, 13, 15, 19)		£450
Z29	1d. rose-red (1864–79) *From*		£300
	Plate Nos. 159, 160, 171, 173, 174, 177, 179, 184, 187, 190, 193, 195, 196, 197, 198, 200, 202, 206, 207, 208, 209, 210, 213, 215, 216, 218, 220, 221, 222, 225.		
Z30	1½d. lake-red (1870–74) (Plate No. 3)		£2750
Z31	2d. blue (1858–69) (Plate Nos. 14, 15) *From*		£550
Z32	2½d. rosy-mauve (1876–80) *From*		£250
	Plate Nos. 11, 12, 13, 14, 15, 16.		
Z33	2½d. blue (1880) (Plate No. 17)		£1200
Z34	4d. sage-green (Plate No. 16)		£1100

NICOSIA

Stamps of GREAT BRITAIN cancelled "969" as Type **9.**

1878–80.

Z35	½d. rose-red (1870–79)		£475
	Plate Nos. 12, 13, 14, 15, 20.		
Z36	1d. rose-red (1864–79) *From*		£300
	Plate Nos. 170, 171, 174, 189, 190, 192, 193, 195, 196, 198, 200, 202, 203, 205, 206, 207, 210, 212, 214, 215, 218, 221, 222, 225.		
Z36a	1½d. lake red (1870) (Plate No. 3)		£3250
Z37	2d. blue (1858–69) (Plate Nos. 14, 15)		£550
Z38	2½d. rosy mauve (1876–79) *From*		£200
	Plate Nos. 10, 11, 12, 13, 14, 15, 16.		
Z39	2½d. blue (1880) (Plate No. 17)		£800
Z42	4d. sage-green (1877) (Plate No. 16)		£850
Z43	6d. grey (1873) (Plate No. 16)		£1000

PAPHOS

Stamps of GREAT BRITAIN cancelled "981" as Type **9.**

1878–80.

Z44	½d. rose-red (1870–79) (Plate Nos. 13, 15)		
Z45	1d. rose-red (1864–79) *From*		£700
	Plate Nos. 196, 201, 202, 204, 206, 213, 217..		
Z46	2d. blue (1858–69) (Plate No. 15)		£1200
Z47	2½d. rosy mauve (1876–79) *From*		£650
	Plate Nos. 13, 14, 15, 16.		

PRICES FOR STAMPS ON COVER TO 1945	
Nos. 1/4	*from* × 50
Nos. 5/6	—
Nos. 7/10	*from* × 100
Nos. 11/15	*from* × 12
No. 16	—
Nos. 16a/22	*from* × 20
Nos. 23/5	*from* × 100
No. 26	—
No. 27	*from* × 25
No. 28	—
No. 29	*from* × 200
Nos. 31/5a	*from* × 10
Nos. 36/7	—
Nos. 40/9	*from* × 8
Nos. 50/71	*from* × 5
Nos. 74/99	*from* × 4
Nos. 100/2	—
Nos. 103/17	*from* × 4
No. 117a	—
Nos. 118/31	*from* × 8
No. 132	—
Nos. 133/43	*from* × 5
Nos. 144/7	*from* × 6
Nos. 148/63	*from* × 5

PERFORATION. Nos. 1/122 are perf 14.

Stamps of Great Britain overprinted

CYPRUS **CYPRUS**
(1) **(2)**

(Optd by D.L.R.)

1880 (1 Apr).

1	**1**	½d. rose		£120	£110
		a. Opt double (Plate 15)		†	£45000

Plate No.	Un.	Used.	Plate No.	Un.	Used
12.	£225	£250	19.	£5000	£700
15.	£120	£110			

2	**2**	1d. red		23·00	45·00
		a. Opt double (Plate 208)		£27000	†
		aa. Opt double (Plate 218)		£4250	†
		b. Vert pair, top stamp without opt (Plate 208)		£27000	†

Plate No.	Un.	Used.	Plate No.	Un.	Used
174.	£1400	£1400	208.	£130	55·00
181.	£500	£190	215.	23·00	60·00
184.	£20000	£3500	216.	24·00	45·00
193.	£800	†	217.	24·00	65·00
196.	£700	†	218.	30·00	70·00
201.	27·00	55·00	220.	£350	£375
205.	90·00	55·00			

3	**2**	2½d. rosy mauve		4·50	18·00
		a. Large thin "C" (Plate 14) (BK, JK)		£110	£375
		b. Large thin "C" (Plate 15) (BK, JK)		£200	£950
		w. Wmk inverted (Plate 15)		£650	

Plate No.	Un.	Used.	Plate No.	Un.	Used
14.	4·50	18·00	15.	8·00	50·00

4	**2**	4d. sage-green (Plate 16)		£140	£225
		a. Opt double, one albino		£1500	
5		6d. grey (Plate 16)		£500	£650
6		1s. green (Plate 13)		£850	£475

HALF·PENNY **HALF·PENNY**
(3) 18 mm **(4)** 16 or 16½ mm

HALF·PENNY **HALF·PENNY** **30 PARAS**
(4a) 17 mm **(5)** 13 mm **(6)**

(Optd by Govt Ptg Office, Nicosia)

1881 (Feb–June). No. 2 surch.

7	**3**	½d. on 1d. red (2.81)		80·00	90·00
		a. "HALFPENN" (BG, LG) (all plates) *From*		£3000	£2750
		b. Surch double (Plate 220)		£2750	

Plate No.	Un.	Used	Plate No.	Un.	Used
174.	£250	£375	215.	£800	£950
181.	£225	£250	216.	80·00	95·00
201.	£110	£130	217.	£900	£850
205.	80·00	90·00	218.	£500	£650
208.	£200	£350	220.	£325	£400

			Un.	Used
8	4	½d. on 1d. red (2.81)	£130	£160
		a. Surch double (Plates 201 and 216)	£3500	£2500

Plate No.	Un.	Used.	Plate No.	Un.	Used
201.	£130	£160	218.	—	£15000
216.	£350	£425			

			Un.	Used
8b	4a	½d. on 1d. red (2.81)	—	£750

Plate No.	Un.	Used	Plate No.	Un.	Used
201.	—	£750	216.	—	£1000

The most noticeable difference between type **4** (16½ mm) and type **4a** (17 mm) is the space between the "F" of "HALF" and the "P" of "PENNY". This measures 1 mm on type **4**, but 2 mm on type **4a**.

			Un.	Used
9	5	½d. on 1d. red (1 June)	50·00	70·00
		aa. Surch double (Plate 205)	£800	
		ab. Surch double (Plate 215)	£450	£650
		b. Surch treble (Plate 205)	£4500	
		ba. Surch treble (Plate 215)	£800	
		bc. Surch treble (Plate 218)	£4500	
		c. Surch quadruple (Plate 205)	£7000	
		ca. Surch quadruple (Plate 215)	£7000	

Plate No.	Un.	Used.	Plate No.	Un.	Used
205.	£400		217.	£160	£110
215.	50·00	70·00	218.	90·00	£120

The surcharges on Nos. 8 and 8b were handstamped; the others were applied by lithography.

(New Currency: 40 paras = 1 piastre, 180 piastres = £1)

1881 (June). No. 2 surch with T **6** by lithography.

			Un.	Used
10	6	30 paras on 1d. red	£150	90·00
		a. Surch double, one invtd (Plate 216)	£7500	
		aa. Surch double, one invtd (Plate 220)	£1900	£1400

Plate No.	Un.	Used.	Plate No.	Un.	Used
201.	£180	£110	217.	£200	£200
216.	£150	90·00	220.	£170	£180

7

"US" damaged at foot (R. 5/5 of both panes)

(Typo D.L.R.)

1881 (1 July). Die I. Wmk Crown CC.

			Un.	Used
11	7	½pi. emerald-green	£180	45·00
		w. Wmk inverted	£1200	£650
12		1pi. rose	£375	32·00
13		2pi. blue	£450	35·00
		w. Wmk inverted	—	£1800
14		4pi. pale olive-green	£950	£275
15		6pi. olive-grey	£1800	£475

Stamps of Queen Victoria initialled "J.A.B." or overprinted "POSTAL SURCHARGE" with or without the same initials were employed for accounting purposes between the Chief Post Office and sub-offices, the initials are those of the then Postmaster, Mr. J. A. Bulmer.

1882 (May)–**86**. Die I*. Wmk Crown CA.

			Un.	Used
16	7	½pi. emerald-green (5.82)	£5000	£500
		a. Dull green (4.83)	24·00	3·00
		ab. Top left triangle detached	£1400	£275
17		30pa. pale mauve (7.6.82)	80·00	28·00
		a. Top left triangle detached	£2500	£1000
		b. Damaged "US"	£1300	£500
18		1pi. rose (3.83)	£110	4·25
		a. Top left triangle detached	—	£325
19		2pi. blue (4.83)	£160	3·75
		a. Top left triangle detached	—	£375
20		4pi. pale olive-green (10.83)	£350	38·00
		a. Deep olive-green	£550	50·00
		b. Top left triangle detached	£5000	£1100
21		6pi. olive-grey (7.82)	75·00	17·00
		a. Top left triangle detached	—	£1100
22		12pi. orange-brown (1886)	£200	42·00
		s. Optd "SPECIMEN"	£2250	
16a/22 Set of 7			£900	£120

*For description and illustrations of Dies I and II see Introduction.

For illustration of "top left triangle detached" variety see above No. 21 of Antigua.

No. 21 with manuscript "Specimen" endorsement is known with "CYPRUS" and value double.

See also Nos. 31/7.

(8) (9)

Spur on "1" (position 3 in setting)

(Surch litho by Govt Ptg Office, Nicosia)

1882. Surch with T **8/9.**

(a) Wmk Crown CC

			Un.	Used
23	7	½ on ½pi. emerald-green (6.82)	£700	75·00
		c. Spur on "1"	£1500	£140
		w. Wmk inverted	£1600	
24		30pa. on 1pi. rose (22.5.82)	£1600	£110

(b) Wmk Crown CA

			Un.	Used
25	7	½ on ½pi. emerald-green (22.5.82)	£170	9·00
		a. Surch double	†	£2750
		b. "½" inserted by hand	†	£5000
		c. Spur on "1"	£325	16·00

Nos. 23 and 25 were surcharged by a setting of six arranged as a horizontal row.

No. 25b shows an additional handstamped "½" applied to examples on which the surcharge was so misplaced as to almost omit one of the original "½"s.

(10)
11

Varieties of numerals:

1 Normal 1 Large 1 Small

2 Normal 2 Large

1886 (Apr). Surch with T **10** (fractions approx 6 mm apart) in typography.

(a) Wmk Crown CC

			Un.	Used
26	7	½ on ½pi. emerald-green	£22000	†

(b) Wmk Crown CA

			Un.	Used
27	7	½ on ½pi. emerald-green	£300	70·00
		a. Large "2" at right	£3000	£750

No. 27a occured at R. 10/1 and another unknown position in the setting of 60.

1886 (27 May–June). Surch with T **10** (fractions approx 8 mm apart) in typography.

(a) Wmk Crown CC

			Un.	Used
28	7	½ on ½pi. emerald-green	£8000	£425
		a. Large "1" at left	—	£1900
		b. Small "1" at right	£16000	£2250
		c. Large "2" at left	—	£2250
		d. Large "2" at right	†	£2250

(b) Wmk Crown CA

			Un.	Used
29	7	½ on ½pi. emerald-green (1 June)	£550	17·00
		a. Large "1" at left	£4000	£275
		b. Small "1" at right	£3500	£275
		c. Large "2" at left	£4000	£350
		d. Large "2" at right	£4000	£350

Nos. 28/9 were surcharged in a setting of 60. The large "1" at left occurs at R. 4/4, the large "2" at left at R. 2/5 and the large "2" at right at R. 3/4. The position of the small "1" at right (as illustrated) may be R. 1/2, but this awaits confirmation.

A third type of this surcharge is known with the fractions spaced approximately 10 mm apart on CA paper with postmarks from August 1886. This may be due to the shifting of type.

1892–94. Die II. Wmk Crown CA.

			Un.	Used
31	7	½pi. green	15·00	2·50
		w. Wmk inverted		
32		30pa. mauve	11·00	14·00
		a. Damaged "US"	£350	£350
33		1pi. carmine	15·00	9·50
34		2pi. ultramarine	14·00	1·75
35		4pi. olive-green	50·00	50·00
		a. Pale olive-green	18·00	40·00
36		6pi. olive-grey (1894)	£250	£750
37		12pi. orange brown (1893)	£190	£450
31/7 Set of 7			£450	£1100

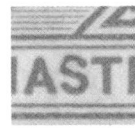

Large "S" in "PIASTRE"

1894 (14 Aug)–**96.** Colours changed and new values. Die II. Wmk Crown CA.

			Un.	Used
40	7	½pi. green and carmine (1896)	4·25	1·25
		a. Large "S" in "PIASTRE"	£180	85·00
		w. Wmk inverted	†	£2500
41		30pa. bright mauve and green (1896)	4·75	5·00
		a. Damaged "US"	£200	£200
42		1pi. carmine and blue (1896)	8·50	1·75
43		2pi. blue and purple (1896)	17·00	1·25
44		4pi. sage-green and purple (1896)	22·00	16·00
45		6pi. sepia and green (1896)	22·00	40·00
46		9pi. brown and carmine	28·00	38·00
47		12pi. orange-brown and black (1896)	24·00	70·00
48		18pi. greyish slate and brown	55·00	65·00
49		45pi. grey-purple and blue	£120	£160
40/9 Set of 10			£250	£325
40s/9s Optd "SPECIMEN" Set of 10			£350	

The large "S" in "PIASTRE" was a retouch to correct a damaged letter (R. 1/4, both panes). It was corrected when a new duty plate (120-set) was introduced in 1905.

LIMASSOL FLOOD HANDSTAMP. Following a flood on 14 November 1894, which destroyed the local stamp stocks, the postmaster of Limassol produced a temporary handstamp showing "½C.P." which was applied to local letters with the usual c.d.s.

(Typo D.L.R.)

1902–04. Wmk Crown CA.

			Un.	Used
50	11	½pi. green and carmine (12.02)	14·00	1·25
		a. Large "S" in "PIASTRE"	£200	60·00
		w. Wmk inverted	£160	90·00

			Un.	Used
51		30pa. violet and green (2.03)	25·00	5·00
		a. Mauve and green	30·00	10·00
		b. Damaged "US"	£450	£160
52		1pi. carmine and blue (9.03)	40·00	7·50
53		2pi. blue and purple (2.03)	85·00	15·00
54		4pi. olive-green and purple (9.03)	60·00	26·00
55		6pi. sepia and green (9.03)	50·00	£150
56		9pi. brown and carmine (5.04)	£120	£275
57		12pi. chestnut and black (4.03)	25·00	85·00
58		18pi. black and brown (5.04)	90·00	£170
59		45pi. dull purple and ultramarine (10.03)	£200	£500
50/9 Set of 10			£600	£1100
50sw/9s Optd "SPECIMEN" Set of 10			£450	

The ½pi "SPECIMEN" is only known with watermark inverted.

Broken top left triangle (Left pane R. 7/5)

1904–10. Wmk Mult Crown CA.

			Un.	Used
60	11	5pa. bistre and black (14.1.08)	1·00	2·00
		a. Broken top left triangle	95·00	£150
		w. Wmk inverted	£1900	
61		10pa. orange and green (12.06)	6·00	1·75
		aw. Wmk inverted	—	£160
		b. Orange-yellow and green	45·00	5·50
		bw. Wmk inverted	—	£180
		c. Broken top left triangle	£170	80·00
62		½pi. green and carmine (1.7.04)	11·00	1·50
		a. Broken top left triangle	£225	60·00
		b. Large "S" in "PIASTRE"	£275	75·00
		w. Wmk inverted	£225	£150
		y. Wmk inverted and reversed	†	£1700
63		30pa. purple and green (1.7.04)	20·00	2·50
		a. Violet and green (1910)	27·00	2·50
		b. Broken top left triangle	£400	£120
		c. Damaged "US"	£325	90·00
		w. Wmk inverted	†	£1800
64		1pi. carmine and blue (11.04)	16·00	1·00
		a. Broken top left triangle	£300	85·00
65		2pi. blue and purple (11.04)	21·00	1·75
		a. Broken top left triangle	£375	£110
66		4pi. olive-green and purple (2.05)	30·00	19·00
		a. Broken top left triangle	£475	£325
67		6pi. sepia and green (17.7.04)	32·00	15·00
		a. Broken top left triangle	£475	£375
68		9pi. brown and carmine (30.5.04)	50·00	9·00
		a. Yellow-brown and carmine	60·00	24·00
		aw. Wmk inverted	£325	£120
		b. Broken top left triangle	£750	£325
69		12pi. chestnut and black (4.06)	38·00	65·00
		a. Broken top left triangle	£750	£950
70		18pi. black and brown (16.6.04)	55·00	14·00
		a. Broken top left triangle	£850	£375
71		45pi. dull purple and ultram (15.6.04)	£120	£160
		a. Broken top left triangle	£1800	
60/71 Set of 12			£350	£250
60s/1s Optd "SPECIMEN" Set of 2			£130	

12   13

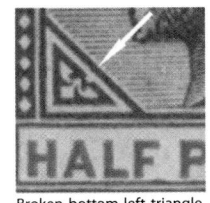

Broken bottom left triangle (Right pane R. 10/6)

(Typo D.L.R.)

1912 (July)–**15.** Wmk Mult Crown CA.

			Un.	Used
74	12	10pa. orange and green (11.12)	7·50	2·50
		a. Wmk sideways	†	£3500
		b. Broken bottom left triangle	£200	85·00
		c. Orange-yellow and bright green (8.15)	2·25	1·25
		ca. Broken bottom left triangle	£130	65·00
75		½pi. green and carmine	4·25	30
		a. Broken bottom left triangle	£160	75·00
		b. Yellow-green and carmine	7·50	1·90
		ba. Broken bottom left triangle	£200	90·00
		w. Wmk inverted	†	£2000
76		30pa. violet and green (12.12)	3·00	2·25
		a. Broken bottom left triangle	£150	75·00
		w. Wmk inverted		
77		1pi. rose-red and blue (9.12)	8·50	1·75
		a. Broken bottom left triangle	£225	80·00
		b. Carmine and blue (1.15?)	15·00	4·25
		ba. Broken bottom left triangle	£375	£120
78		2pi. blue and purple (7.13)	6·50	9·00
		a. Broken bottom left triangle	£225	85·00

79		4pi. olive-green and purple	4·50	6·00
		a. Broken bottom left triangle	£190	£225
80		6pi. sepia and green	8·00	11·00
		a. Broken bottom left triangle	£275	£325
81		9pi. brown and carmine (3.15)	42·00	27·00
		a. Yellow-brown and carmine	48·00	38·00
		b. Broken bottom left triangle	£750	£600
82		12pi. chestnut and black (7.13)	25·00	55·00
		b. Broken bottom left triangle	£450	£750
83		18pi. black and brown (12.14)	50·00	50·00
		a. Broken bottom left triangle	£750	£750
84		45pi. dull purple and ultramarine (3.15)	£130	£160
		a. Broken bottom left triangle	£1800	£2000
74/84 Set of 11			£250	£275
74s/84s Optd "SPECIMEN" Set of 11			£550	

1921–23.

(a) Wmk Mult Script CA

85	**12**	10pa. orange and green	15·00	18·00
		a. Broken bottom left triangle	£300	£350
		w. Wmk inverted	£3250	£3250
86		10pa. grey and yellow (1923)	15·00	10·00
		a. Broken bottom left triangle	£275	£190
87		30pa. violet and green	3·75	2·75
		a. Broken bottom left triangle	£160	85·00
		w. Wmk inverted	£3000	£3000
		y. Wmk inverted and reversed	†	£2750
88		30pa. green (1923)	7·50	1·75
		a. Broken bottom left triangle	£200	75·00
		w. Wmk inverted	†	£2500
89		1pi. carmine and blue	25·00	50·00
		a. Broken bottom left triangle	£375	
90		1pi. violet and red (1922)	3·50	4·00
		a. Broken bottom left triangle	£160	£180
91		1½pi. yellow and black (1922)	13·00	10·00
		a. Broken bottom left triangle	£250	£200
92		2pi. blue and purple	32·00	30·00
		a. Broken bottom left triangle	£475	£425
93		2pi. carmine and blue (1922)	15·00	27·00
		a. Broken bottom left triangle	£325	£550
94		2¾pi. blue and purple (1922)	11·00	9·00
		a. Broken bottom left triangle	£250	£275
95		4pi. olive-green and purple	18·00	25·00
		a. Broken bottom left triangle	£350	£450
		w. Wmk inverted	†	£2750
96		6pi. sepia and green (1923)	38·00	95·00
		a. Broken bottom left triangle	£475	
97		9pi. brown and carmine (1922)	50·00	95·00
		a. Yellow-brown and carmine	£120	£160
		b. Broken bottom left triangle	£695	£950
98		18pi. black and brown (1923)	90·00	£180
		a. Broken bottom left triangle	£1000	
99		45pi. dull purple and ultramarine (1923)	£275	£275
		a. Broken bottom left triangle	£2500	£2750
85/99 Set of 15			£550	£750
85s/99s Optd "SPECIMEN" Set of 15			£700	

A ½pi. black was prepared for use but not issued. One example exists, opt "SPECIMEN".

(b) Wmk Mult Crown CA (1923)

100	**12**	10s. green and red/*pale yellow*	£400	£900
		a. Broken bottom left triangle	£4750	
101		£1 purple and black/*red*	£1400	£3250
		a. Broken bottom left triangle	£8500	£14000
100s/1s Optd "SPECIMEN" Set of 2			£600	

Examples of Nos. 96/101 are known showing a forged Limassol postmark dated "14 MR 25".

1924–28. Chalk-surfaced paper.

(a) Wmk Mult Crown CA

102	**13**	£1 purple and black/*red*	£300	£850

(b) Wmk Mult Script CA

103	**13**	¼pi. grey and chestnut	2·00	50
		w. Wmk inverted	†	£2500
104		½pi. brownish black and black	6·00	14·00
105		¾pi. green	4·00	1·00
106		1pi. purple and chestnut	3·00	1·50
107		1½pi. orange and black	6·00	18·00
108		2pi. carmine and green	6·00	23·00
109		2¾pi. bright blue and purple	3·25	5·00
110		4pi. sage-green and purple	5·00	5·00
111		4½pi. black and orange/*emerald*	3·50	5·00
112		6pi. olive-brown and green	5·00	12·00
113		9pi. brown and purple	9·00	5·50
114		12pi. chestnut and black	17·00	65·00
115		18pi. black and orange	32·00	5·00
116		45pi. purple and blue	70·00	48·00
117		90pi. green and red/*yellow*	£130	£275
117a		£5 black/*yellow* (1928) (F.C. £350)	£3750	£8000
		as. Optd "SPECIMEN"	£1000	

Examples of No. 102 are known showing a forged Limassol postmark dated "14 MR 25" and of No. 117a showing a forged Registered Nicosia postmark dated "6 MAY 35".

CROWN COLONY

1925. Wmk Mult Script CA. Chalk-surfaced paper (½, ¾ and 2pi.).

118	**13**	½pi. green	4·50	1·00
119		¾pi. brownish black and black	6·00	1·00
120		1½pi. scarlet	9·50	1·50
121		2pi. yellow and black	15·00	3·25
122		2½pi. bright blue	10·00	1·75
102/22 (ex £5) Set of 21			£550	£1200
102/22s (ex £5) Optd "SPECIMEN" Set of 21			£1100	

In the above set the fraction bar in the value is horizontal. In Nos. 91, 94, 107 and 109 it is diagonal.

14 Silver Coin of Amathus, 6th-cent BC

15 Zeno (philosopher)

16 Map of Cyprus

17 Discovery of body of St. Barnabas

18 Cloister, Abbey of Bellapaise

19 Badge of Cyprus

20 Tekke of Umm Haram

21 Statue of Richard I, Westminster

22 St. Nicholas Cathedral (now Lala Mustafa Pasha Mosque), Famagusta

23 King George V

(Recess B.W.)

1928 (1 Feb). 50th Anniv of British Rule. T **14/23**. Wmk Mult Script CA. P 12.

123	**14**	¾pi. deep dull purple	3·75	1·50
124	**15**	1pi. black and greenish blue	4·00	1·50
125	**16**	1½pi. scarlet	8·00	2·00
126	**17**	2½pi. light blue	4·00	2·25
127	**18**	4pi. deep brown	11·00	11·00
128	**19**	6pi. blue	14·00	40·00
129	**20**	9pi. maroon	11·00	19·00
130	**21**	18pi. black and brown	30·00	45·00
131	**22**	45pi. violet and blue	42·00	50·00
132	**23**	£1 blue and bistre-brown	£225	£300
123/32 Set of 10			£300	£400
123s/32s Optd "SPECIMEN" Set of 10			£700	

24 Ruins of Vouni Palace

25 Small Marble Forum, Salamis

26 Church of St. Barnabas and St. Hilarion, Peristerona

27 Roman Theatre, Soli

28 Kyrenia Harbour

29 Kolossi Castle

30 St. Sophia Cathedral, Nicosia (now Selimiye Mosque)

31 Bayraktar Mosque, Nicosia

32 Queen's window, St. Hilarion Castle

33 Buyuk Khan, Nicosia

34 Forest scene, Troodos

(Recess Waterlow)

1934 (1 Dec). T **24/34**. Wmk Mult Script CA (sideways on ½pi., 1½pi., 2½pi., 4½pi., 6pi., 9pi. and 18pi.). P 12½.

133	**24**	¼pi. ultramarine and orange-brown	1·75	1·00
		a. Imperf between (vert pair)	£55000	£32000
134	**25**	½pi. green	3·50	1·00
		a. Imperf between (vert pair)	£18000	£20000
135	**26**	¾pi. black and violet	3·75	40
		a. Imperf between (vert pair)	£60000	
136	**27**	1pi. black and red-brown	4·75	2·25
		a. Imperf between (vert pair)	£25000	£25000
		b. Imperf between (horiz pair)	£21000	
137	**28**	1½pi. carmine	5·50	2·00
138	**29**	2½pi. ultramarine	6·50	1·75
139	**30**	4½pi. black and crimson	8·00	6·50
140	**31**	6pi. black and blue	12·00	23·00
141	**32**	9pi. sepia and violet	22·00	8·50
142	**33**	18pi. black and olive-green	55·00	55·00
143	**34**	45pi. green and black	£120	90·00
133/43 Set of 11			£200	£170
133s/43s Perf "SPECIMEN" Set of 11			£650	

1935 (6 May). Silver Jubilee. As Nos. 91/4 of Antigua, but ptd by Waterlow & Sons. P 11×12.

144	¾pi. ultramarine and grey	4·00	1·50
145	1½pi. deep blue and scarlet	6·00	2·75
	l. Kite and horizontal log	£650	£475
146	2½pi. brown and deep blue	5·00	2·00
147	9pi. slate and purple	23·00	29·00
144/7 Set of 4		35·00	32·00
144s/7s Perf "SPECIMEN" Set of 4		£200	

For illustration of plate variety see Omnibus section following Zanzibar.

1937 (12 May). Coronation. As Nos. 95/7 of Antigua. P 11×11½.

148	¾pi. grey	3·00	1·00
149	1½pi. carmine	3·50	2·50
150	2½pi. blue	3·50	3·00
148/50 Set of 3		9·00	6·00
148s/50s Perf "SPECIMEN" Set of 3		£225	

35 Vouni Palace

36 Map of Cyprus

37 Othello's Tower, Famagusta

38 King George VI

(Recess Waterlow)

1938 (12 May)–**51**. T **35** to **38** and other designs as 1934, but with portrait of King George VI. Wmk Mult Script CA. P 12½.

151	**35**	¼pi. ultramarine and orange-brown	1·75	60
152	**25**	½pi. green	2·75	50
152a		½pi. violet (2.7.51)	4·25	75
153	**26**	¾pi. black and violet	22·00	1·75
154	**27**	1pi. orange	3·25	40
		a. Perf 13½×12½ (4.44)	£550	27·00
155	**28**	1½pi. carmine	6·00	1·50
155a		1½pi. violet (15.3.43)	3·00	75
155ab		1½pi. carmine (2.7.51)	7·00	1·25
155b	**26**	2pi. black and carmine (2.2.42)	3·25	40
		c. Perf 12½×13½ (10.44)	4·00	16·00
156	**29**	2½pi. ultramarine	45·00	2·50
156a		3pi. ultramarine (2.2.42)	3·50	60
156b		4pi. ultramarine (2.7.51)	7·00	1·25
157	**30**	4½pi. grey	3·00	40
158	**31**	6pi. black and blue	4·25	1·00
159	**37**	9pi. black and purple	5·50	75
160	**33**	18pi. black and olive-green	16·00	1·75
		a. Black and sage-green (19.8.47)	24·00	2·50
161	**34**	45pi. green and black	55·00	4·75
162	**38**	90pi. mauve and black	38·00	8·50
163		£1 scarlet and indigo	65·00	32·00
151/63 Set of 19			£250	55·00
151s/63s Perf "SPECIMEN" Set of 16			£800	

Dot between "1"
and "½" in right-
hand value tablet
(Pl B1 R. 7/1)

Extra decoration
(R. 3/5)

1946 (21 Oct). Victory. As Nos. 110/11 of Antigua.
164	1½pi. deep violet	50	10
	a. Dot between "1" and "½"	70·00	60·00
165	3pi. blue	50	40
164s/5s Perf "SPECIMEN" *Set of 2*		£190	

1948 (20 Dec). Royal Silver Wedding. As Nos. 112/13 of Antigua.
166	1½pi. violet	1·50	50
	a. Extra decoration	55·00	65·00
167	£1 indigo	60·00	75·00

1949 (10 Oct). 75th Anniv of Universal Postal Union. As Nos. 114/17 of Antigua but inscr "CYPRUS" (recess).
168	1½pi. violet	60	1·50
169	2pi. carmine-red	1·50	1·50
	a. "C" of "CA" missing from wmk	£1600	
170	3pi. deep blue	1·00	1·50
171	9pi. purple	1·00	6·00
168/71 *Set of 4*		3·50	9·50

1953 (2 June). Coronation. As No. 120 of Antigua.
172	1½pi. black and emerald	2·00	10

(New Currency = 1000 mils = £1)

39 Carobs   **40** Grapes

41 Oranges   **42** Mavrovouni Copper Pyrites Mine

43 Troodos Forest   **44** Beach of Aphrodite

45 5th-century BC coin of Paphos   **46** Kyrenia

47 Harvest in Mesaoria   **48** Famagusta Harbour

49 St. Hilarion Castle   **50** Hala Sultan Tekke

51 Kanakaria Church   **52** Coins of Salamis, Paphos, Citium and Idalium

53 Arms of Byzantium, Lusignan, Ottoman Empire and Venice

1955 (1 Aug)–**60**. T **39/53**. Wmk Mult Script CA. P 13½ (Nos. 183/5) or 11½ (others).
173	**39**	2m. blackish brown	1·00	40
174	**40**	3m. blue-violet	65	15
175	**41**	5m. brown-orange	3·25	10
		a. Orange-brown (17.9.58)	13·00	1·00
176	**42**	10m. deep brown and deep green	3·25	10
177	**43**	15m. olive-green and indigo	5·00	45
		aa. Yellow-olive and indigo (17.9.58)	40·00	5·50
		a. Bistre and indigo (14.6.60)	32·00	16·00
178	**44**	20m. brown and deep bright blue	2·25	15
179	**45**	25m. deep turquoise-blue	5·00	60
		a. Greenish blue (17.9.58)	29·00	5·50
180	**46**	30m. black and carmine-lake	3·75	10
181	**47**	35m. orange-brown and deep turquoise-blue	3·25	40
182	**48**	40m. deep green and sepia	3·25	60
183	**49**	50m. turquoise-blue and reddish brown	3·25	30
184	**50**	100m. mauve and bluish green	13·00	60
185	**51**	250m. deep grey-blue and brown	16·00	13·00
186	**52**	500m. slate and purple	38·00	15·00
187	**53**	£1 brown-lake and slate	30·00	55·00
173/87 *Set of 15*			£110	75·00

(**54** "Cyprus Republic")   **55** Map of Cyprus

(Recess B.W.)

1960 (16 Aug)–**61**. Nos. 173/87 optd as T **54** in blue by B.W. Opt larger on Nos. 191/7 and in two lines on Nos 198/202.
188	2m. blackish brown	20	75
189	3m. blue-violet	20	15
190	5m. brown-orange	2·25	10
	a. Orange-brown (15.8.61)	10·00	1·00
191	10m. deep brown and deep green	1·00	10
192	15m. yellow-bistre and indigo	3·25	40
	a. Olive-green and indigo	£160	85·00
	b. Brownish bistre and deep indigo (10.10.61)	20·00	5·50
193	20m. brown and deep bright blue	1·75	1·50
	a. Opt double	†	£12000
194	25m. deep turquoise-blue	1·75	1·75
	a. Greenish blue (7.2.61)	50·00	16·00
195	30m. black and carmine-lake	1·75	30
	a. Opt double	†	£45000
196	35m. orange-brown and deep turquoise-blue	1·75	70
197	40m. deep green and sepia	2·00	2·50
198	50m. turquoise-blue and reddish brown	2·00	60
199	100m. mauve and bluish green	9·00	2·50
200	250m. deep grey-blue and brown	30·00	5·50
201	500m. slate and purple	45·00	27·00
202	£1 brown-lake and slate	48·00	65·00
188/202 *Set of 15*		£130	95·00

Only three used examples of No. 195a are known.

(Recess B.W.)

1960 (16 Aug). Constitution of Republic. W w **12**. P 11½.
203	**55**	10m. sepia and deep green	25	10
204		30m. ultramarine and deep brown	50	10
205		100m. purple and deep slate	1·75	2·00
203/5 *Set of 3*			2·25	2·00

> **PRINTERS.** All the following stamps were designed by A. Tassos and lithographed by Aspioti-Elka, Athens, unless otherwise stated.

56 Doves

(Des T. Kurpershoek)

1962 (19 Mar). Europa. P 14×13.
206	**56**	10m. purple and mauve	10	10
207		40m. ultramarine and cobalt	20	15
208		100m. emerald and pale green	20	20
206/8 *Set of 3*			45	40

57 Campaign Emblem

1962 (14 May). Malaria. Eradication. P 14×13½.
209	**57**	10m. black and olive-green	15	15
210		30m. black and brown	30	15

58 Mult K C K Δ and Map

WATERMARK VARIETIES. The issues printed by Aspioti-Elka with W **58** are known with the vertical stamps having the watermark normal or inverted and the horizontal stamps with the watermark reading upwards or downwards. Such varieties are not given separate listing.

59 Iron Age Jug   **60** Grapes   **61** Bronze head of Apollo

62 Selimiye Mosque, Nicosia   **63** St. Barnabas's Church

64 Temple of Apollo, Hylates   **65** Head of Aphrodite

66 Skiing, Troodos   **67** Salamis Gymnasium

68 Hala Sultan Tekke   **69** Bellapaise Abbey

70 Mouflon   **71** St. Hilarion Castle

1962 (17 Sept). T **59/71**. W **58** (sideways) on 25, 30, 40, 50, 250m., £1). P 13½×14 (vert) or 14×13½ (horiz).
211	**59**	3m. deep brown and orange-brown	10	30
212	**60**	5m. purple and grey-green	10	10
213	**61**	10m. black and yellow-green	15	10
214	**62**	15m. black and reddish purple	50	15
215	**63**	25m. deep brown and chestnut	60	20
216	**64**	30m. deep blue and light blue	20	10
217	**65**	35m. light green and blue	35	10
218	**66**	40m. black and violet-blue	1·25	1·75

219	**67**	50m. bronze-green and bistre.............	50	10
220	**68**	100m. deep brown and yellow-brown...	3·50	30
221	**69**	250m. black and cinnamon..............	17·00	1·75
222	**70**	500m. deep brown and light green.....	22·00	9·00
223	**71**	£1 bronze-green and grey................	15·00	28·00
211/23 *Set of 13*			55·00	38·00

72 Europa "Tree"

(Des L. Weyer)

1963 (28 Jan). Europa. W **58** (sideways). P 14×13½.

224	**72**	10m. bright blue and black.................	1·50	20
225		40m. carmine-red and black...............	4·50	1·50
226		150m. emerald-green and black...........	13·00	5·00
224/6 *Set of 3*			17·00	6·00

73 Harvester   **75** Wolf Cub in Camp

1963 (21 Mar). Freedom from Hunger. T **73** and similar vert design. W **58**. P 13½×14.

227		25m. ochre, sepia and bright blue..............	75	25
228		75m. grey, black and lake...................	2·50	2·25
Design:—75m. Demeter, Goddess of Corn.				

1963 (21 Aug). 50th Anniv of Cyprus Scout Movement and Third Commonwealth Scout Conference, Platres. T **75** and similar vert designs. Multicoloured. W **58**. P 13½×14.

229		3m. Type **75**...................................	10	20
230		20m. Sea Scout...............................	35	30
231		150m. Scout with Mouflon..................	1·00	2·50
229/31 *Set of 3*			1·25	2·50
MS231*a* 110×90 mm. Nos. 229/31 (*sold at 250m.*).				
Imperf...			£110	£180

78 Nurse tending Child   **79** Children's Centre, Kyrenia

1963 (9 Sept). Centenary of Red Cross. W **58** (sideways on 100m.). P 13½×14 (10m.) or 14×13½ (100m.).

232	**78**	10m. red, blue, grey-blue, chestnut and black..........................	50	15
233	**79**	100m. red, green, black and blue..........	3·00	4·25

80 "Co-operation" (emblem)   (**81**)

(Des A. Holm)

1963 (4 Nov). Europa. W **58** (sideways). P 14×13½.

234	**80**	20m. buff, blue and violet...................	1·75	40
235		30m. grey, yellow and blue.................	1·75	40
236		150m. buff, blue and orange-brown........	15·00	9·00
234/6 *Set of 3*			17·00	9·00

1964 (5 May). UN Security Council's Cyprus Resolutions, March, 1964. Nos. 213, 216, 218/20 optd with T **81** in blue by Govt Printing Office, Nicosia.

237	**61**	10m. black and yellow-green...............	15	10
238	**64**	30m. deep blue and light blue.............	20	10
239	**66**	40m. black and violet-blue.................	25	30
240	**67**	50m. bronze-green and bistre.............	25	10
241	**68**	100m. deep brown and yellow-brown......	25	50
237/41 *Set of 5*			1·00	1·00

82 Soli Theatre

1964 (15 June). 400th Birth Anniv of Shakespeare. T **82** and similar horiz designs. Multicoloured. W **58**. P 13½×13.

242	**82**	15m. Type **82**................................	90	15
243		35m. Curium Theatre........................	90	15

244		50m. Salamis Theatre.......................	90	15
245		100m. Othello Tower and scene from Othello.................................	1·50	2·25
242/5 *Set of 4*			3·75	2·50

86 Running   **89** Europa "Flower"

10m. Brown flaw covering face of right-hand runner gives the appearance of a mask (R. 9/2).

As these stamps were printed in sheets of 400, divided into four post office sheets of 100, the variety was only constant on one sheet in four. Moreover, it was quickly discovered and many were removed from the sheets by post office clerks.

1964 (6 July). Olympic Games, Tokyo. T **86** and similar designs. W **58** (sideways, 25m., 75m.). P 13½×14 (10m.) or 14×13½ (others).

246		10m. brown, black and yellow..............	10	10
		a. Blind runner........................	£850	
247		25m. brown, blue and blue-grey...........	20	10
248		75m. brown, black and orange-red.........	35	65
246/8 *Set of 3*			60	75
MS248*a* 110×90 mm. Nos. 246/8 (*sold at 250m.*).				
Imperf...			4·75	15·00
Designs: Horiz—25m. Boxing; 75m. Charioteers.				

(Des G. Bétemps)

1964 (14 Sept). Europa. W **58** (sideways). P 13½×14.

249	**89**	20m. chestnut and light ochre.............	1·25	10
250		30m. ultramarine and light blue..........	1·25	10
251		150m. olive and light blue-green...........	9·00	4·75
249/51 *Set of 3*			10·00	4·75

90 Dionysus and Acme   **91** Silenus (satyr)

1964 (26 Oct). Cyprus Wines. T **90/1** and similar multicoloured designs. W **58** (sideways, 10m. or 100m.). P 14×13½ (horiz) or 13½×14 (vert).

252		10m. Type **90**................................	30	10
253		40m. Type **91**................................	65	75
254		50m. Commandaria Wine (*vert*)...........	65	10
255		100m. Wine factory (*horiz*).................	1·50	2·00
252/5 *Set of 4*			2·75	2·50

94 President Kennedy

1965 (16 Feb). President Kennedy Commemoration. W **58** (sideways). P 14×13½.

256	**94**	10m. ultramarine.............................	10	10
257		40m. green....................................	25	35
258		100m. carmine-lake...........................	30	35
256/8 *Set of 3*			60	70
MS258*a* 110×90 mm. Nos. 256/8 (*sold at 250m.*).				
Imperf...			2·25	7·00

95 "Old Age"   **96** "Maternity"

1965 (12 Apr). Introduction of Social Insurance Law. T **95/6** and similar design. W **58**. P 13½×12 (75m.) or 13½×14 (others).

259		30m. drab and dull green....................	15	10
260		45m. light grey-green, blue and deep ultramarine............................	20	10
261		75m. red-brown and flesh...................	1·25	1·50
259/61 *Set of 3*			1·40	1·50
Design: Vert as T **95**—45m. "Accident".				

98 ITU Emblem and Symbols

1965 (17 May). ITU Centenary. W **58** (sideways). P 14×13½.

262	**98**	15m. black, brown and yellow.............	75	20
263		60m. black, green and light green........	6·50	3·25
264		75m. black, indigo and light blue.........	7·50	4·75
262/4 *Set of 3*			13·00	7·25

99 ICY. Emblem

1965 (17 May). International Co-operation Year. W **58** (sideways). P 14×13½.

265	**99**	50m. brown, deep green and light yellow-brown.........................	75	10
266		100m. purple, deep green and light purple.................................	1·25	50

100 Europa "Sprig"   U. N. Resolution on Cyprus 18 Dec. 1965

(**101**)

(Des H. Karlsson)

1965 (27 Sept). Europa. W **58** (sideways). P 14×13½.

267	**100**	5m. black, orange-brown and orange..................................	50	10
268		45m. black, orange-brown and light emerald................................	3·00	2·00
269		150m. black, orange-brown and light grey....................................	7·50	4·50
267/9 *Set of 3*			10·00	6·00

1966 (31 Jan). UN General Assembly's Cyprus Resolution, 18 December 1965. Nos. 211, 213, 216 and 221 optd with T **101** in blue by Govt Printing Office, Nicosia.

270	**59**	3m. deep brown and orange-brown......	10	50
271	**61**	10m. black and yellow-green...............	10	10
272	**64**	30m. deep blue and light blue.............	15	15
273	**69**	250m. black and cinnamon..................	80	2·25
270/3 *Set of 4*			1·00	2·75

102 Discovery of St. Barnabas's Body   **104** St. Barnabas (icon)

103 St. Barnabas's Chapel

105 "Privileges of Cyprus Church" (*Actual size 102×82 mm*)

1966 (25 Apr). 1900th Death Anniv of St. Barnabas. W **58** (sideways on 15m., 100m., 250m.). P 14×13 (25m.) or 13×14 (others).
274	**102**	15m. multicoloured	10	10
275	**103**	25m. drab, black and blue	15	10
276	**104**	100m. multicoloured	45	2·00
274/6 Set of 3			60	2·00
MS277 110×91 mm. Type **105** 250m. mult. Imperf			2·25	10·00

5 M

(106)

107 General K. S. Thimayya and UN Emblem

1966 (30 May). No. 211 surch with T **106** by Govt Printing Office, Nicosia.
278		5m. on 3m. deep brown and orange-brown	10	10

1966 (6 June). General Thimayya Commemoration. W **58** (sideways). P 14×13.
279	**107**	50m. black and light orange-brown	30	10

108 Europa "Ship"

(Des G. and J. Bender)

1966 (26 Sept). Europa. W **58**. P 13½×14.
280	**108**	20m. green and blue	30	10
281		30m. bright purple and blue	30	10
282		150m. bistre and blue	2·25	2·50
280/2 Set of 3			2·50	2·50

110 Church of St. James, Trikomo

119 Vase of 7th-Century BC

120 Bronze Ingot-stand

1966 (21 Nov)–**69**. T **110**, **119/20** and similar designs. W **58** (sideways on 3, 15, 25, 50, 250, 500m., £1. P 12×13 (3m.), 13×12 (5, 10m.), 14×13½ (15, 25, 50m.), 13½×14 (20, 30, 35, 40, 100m.) or 13×14 (others).
283		3m. grey-green, buff, black and light blue	40	10
284		5m. bistre, black and steel-blue	10	10
		a. Brownish bistre, black and steel-blue (18.4.69)	75	20
285		10m. black and bistre	15	10
286		15m. black, chestnut and light orange-brown	15	10
287		20m. black, slate and brown	1·25	1·00
288		25m. black, drab and lake-brown	30	10
289		30m. black, yellow-ochre and turquoise	50	20
290		35m. yellow, black and carmine-red	50	30
291		40m. black, grey and new blue	70	30
		a. Grey (background) omitted		
292		50m. black, slate and brown	90	10
293		100m. black, red, pale buff and grey	4·00	15
294		250m. olive-green, black and light yellow-ochre	1·00	40
295		500m. multicoloured	2·75	70
296		£1 black, drab and slate	2·25	6·50
283/96 Set of 14			13·00	8·50

Designs: Horiz (as T **110**)—3m. Stavrouni Monastery. (As T **119**)—15m. "Minoan wine ship of 700 BC "(painting); 25m. Sleeping Eros (marble statue); 50m. Silver coin of Alexander the Great. Vert (as T **110**)—10m. Zeno of Cibium (marble bust). (As T **119**)—20m. Silver coin of Evagoras I; 30m. St. Nicholas Cathedral, Famagusta; 35m. Gold sceptre from Curium; 40m. Silver dish from 7th-century. (As T **120**)—500m. The Rape of Ganymede (mosaic); £1 Aphrodite (marble statue).

123 Power Station, Limassol

124 Cogwheels

1967 (10 Apr). First Development Programme. T **123** and similar designs but horiz. Multicoloured. W **58** (sideways on 15 to 100m.). P 13½×14 (10m.) or 14×13½ (others).
297		10m. Type **123**	10	10
298		15m. Arghaka-Maghounda Dam	15	10
299		35m. Troodos Highway	30	10
300		50m. Hilton Hotel, Nicosia	20	10
301		100m. Famagusta Harbour	35	1·10
297/301 Set of 5			1·00	1·25

(Des O. Bonnevalle)

1967 (2 May). Europa. W **58**. P 13½×14.
302	**124**	20m. olive-green, green and pale yellow-green	25	10
303		30m. reddish violet, lilac and pale lilac	25	10
304		150m. brown, light reddish brown and pale yellow-brown	1·75	2·25
302/4 Set of 3			2·00	2·25

125 Throwing the Javelin

126 Running (amphora) and Map of Eastern Mediterranean (Actual size 97×77 mm)

1967 (4 Sept). Athletic Games, Nicosia. T **125** and similar designs and T **126**. Multicoloured. W **58**. P 13½×13.
305		15m. Type **125**	20	10
306		35m. Running	20	35
307		100m. High jumping	30	1·00
305/7 Set of 3			60	1·25
MS308 110×90 mm. Type **126**. 250m. (wmk sideways). Imperf			1·25	6·50

127 Ancient Monuments

128 St. Andrew Mosaic

1967 (16 Oct). International Tourist Year. T **127** and similar horiz designs. Multicoloured. W **58**. P 13×13½.
309		10m. Type **127**	10	10
310		40m. Famagusta Beach	20	90
311		50m. Hawker Siddeley Comet 4 at Nicosia Airport	40	10
312		100m. Skier and youth hostel	45	95
309/12 Set of 4			1·00	1·75

1967 (8 Nov). Centenary of St. Andrew's Monastery. W **58** (sideways). P 13×13½.
313	**128**	25m. multicoloured	10	10

129 The Crucifixion (icon)

130 The Three Magi

(Photo French Govt Ptg Wks, Paris)
1967 (8 Nov). Cyprus Art Exhibition, Paris. P 12½×13½.
314	**129**	50m. multicoloured	10	10

1967 (8 Nov). 20th Anniv of UNESCO W **58** (sideways). P 13×13½.
315	**130**	75m. multicoloured	20	20

131 Human Rights Emblem over Stars

132 Human Rights and U.N. Emblems

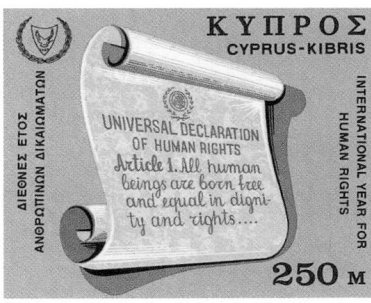
133 Scroll of Declaration (Actual size 95×75½ mm)

1968 (18 Mar). Human Rights Year. W **58**. P 13×14.
316	**131**	50m. multicoloured	10	10
317	**132**	90m. multicoloured	30	70
MS318 95×75½ mm. Type **133** 250m. multicoloured. W **58** (sideways). Imperf			60	4·75

134 Europa "Key"

(Des H. Schwarzenbach)

1968 (29 Apr). Europa. W **58** (sideways). P 14×13.
319	**134**	20m. multicoloured	25	10
320		30m. multicoloured	25	10
321		150m. multicoloured	1·00	2·25
319/21 Set of 3			1·40	2·25

135 U.N. Children's Fund Symbol and Boy drinking Milk

136 Aesculapius

1968 (2 Sept). 21st Anniv of UNICEF W **58** (sideways). P 14×13.
322	**135**	35m. yellow-brown, carmine-red and black	10	10

1968 (2 Sept). 20th Anniv of WHO W **58**. P 13×14.
323	**136**	50m. black, green and light olive	10	10

137 Throwing the Discus

138 ILO Emblem

1968 (24 Oct). Olympic Games, Mexico. T **137** and similar designs. Multicoloured. W **58** (sideways on 100m.). P 14×13 (100m.) or 13×14 (others).
324		10m. Type **137**	10	10
325		25m. Sprint finish	10	10
326		100m. Olympic Stadium (horiz)	20	1·25
324/6 Set of 3			35	1·25

1969 (3 Mar). 50th Anniv of International Labour Organization. W **58**. P 12×13½.
327	**138**	50m. yellow-brown, blue and light blue	15	10
328		90m. yellow-brown, black and pale grey	15	55

139 Mercator's Map of Cyprus, 1554

140 Blaeu's Map of Cyprus, 1635

1969 (7 Apr). First International Congress of Cypriot Studies. W **58** (sideways). P 14×14½.

329	**139**	35m. multicoloured	20	30
330	**140**	50m. multicoloured	20	10
		a. Wmk upright	5·00	2·75
		ab. Grey (shading on boats and cartouche) omitted	£450	

141 Europa Emblem **142** European Roller

(Des L. Gasbarra and G. Belli)

1969 (28 Apr). Europa. W **58** (sideways). P 14×13½.

331	**141**	20m. multicoloured	30	10
332		30m. multicoloured	30	10
333		150m. multicoloured	1·00	2·00
331/3	*Set of 3*		1·40	2·00

1969 (7 July). Birds of Cyprus. T **142** and similar designs. Multicoloured. W **58** (sideways on horiz designs). P 13½×12 (horiz designs) or 12×13½ (vert designs).

334		5m. Type **142**	35	15
335		15m. Audouin's Gull	40	15
336		20m. Cyprus Warbler	40	15
337		30m. Jay (*vert*)	40	15
338		40m. Hoopoe (*vert*)	45	30
339		90m. Eleanora's Falcon (*vert*)	80	3·50
334/9	*Set of 6*		2·50	4·00

The above were printed on glazed Samuel Jones paper with very faint watermark.

143 The Nativity (12th-century Wall Painting)

145 Virgin and Child between Archangels Michael and Gabriel (6th–7th-century Mosaic) (*Actual size* 102×81 *mm*)

1969 (24 Nov). Christmas. T **143** and similar horiz design, and T **145**. Multicoloured. W **58** (sideways). P 13½×13.

340		20m. Type **143**	15	10
341		45m. The Nativity (14th-century wall painting)	15	20
MS342	110×90 mm. Type **145**. 250m. Imperf	3·00	12·00
	a. Grey and light brown omitted	£3500	

146 Mahatma Gandhi

1970 (26 Jan). Birth Centenary of Mahatma Gandhi. W **58** (sideways). P 14×13½.

343	**146**	25m. ultramarine, drab and black	50	10
344		75m. yellow-brown, drab and black	75	65

147 "Flaming Sun" **148** Gladioli

(Des L. le Brocquy)

1970 (4 May). Europa. W **58** (sideways). P 14×13.

345	**147**	20m. brown, greenish yellow and orange	30	10
346		30m. new blue, greenish yellow and orange	30	10
347		150m. bright purple, greenish yellow and orange	1·00	2·50
345/7	*Set of 3*		1·40	2·50

1970 (3 Aug). European Conservation Year. T **148** and similar vert designs. Multicoloured. W **58**. P 13×13½.

348		10m. Type **148**	10	10
349		50m. Poppies	15	10
350		90m. Giant Fennel	50	1·10
348/50	*Set of 3*		65	1·10

149 IEY Emblem **150** Mosaic

151 Globe, Dove and UN Emblem

(Des G. Simonis (75m.))

1970 (7 Sept). Anniversaries and Events. W **58** (sideways on horiz designs). P 13×14 (5m.) or 14×13 (others).

351	**149**	5m. black, red-brown and light yellow-brown	10	10
352	**150**	15m. multicoloured	10	10
353	**151**	75m. multicoloured	15	75
351/3	*Set of 3*		30	85

Events:—5m. International Education Year; 15m. 50th General Assembly of International Vine and Wine Office; 75m. 25th anniv of United Nations.

152 Virgin and Child

(Photo Harrison)

1970 (23 Nov). Christmas. Wall-painting from Church of Panayia Podhythou, Galata. T **152** and similar multicoloured designs. P 14×14½.

354		25m. Archangel (facing right)	15	20
		a. Horiz strip of 3. Nos. 354/6	40	55
355		25m. Type **152**	15	20
356		25m. Archangel (facing left)	15	20
357		75m. Virgin and Child between Archangels	15	30
354/7	*Set of 4*		55	80

The 75m. is horiz, size 42×30 mm, and the 25m. values are vert, size as T **152**.

Nos. 354/6 were issued in *se-tenant* strips of three, throughout the sheet. The triptych thus formed is depicted in its entirety on the 75m. value.

STAMP BOOKLETS

Booklet vending machines, originally fitted to provide stamps to the value of 50m., were introduced by the Cyprus Post Office in 1962.

The stamps contained in these booklets were a haphazard selection of low values to the required amount, attached by their sheet margins to the cardboard covers. From 1968 these covers carried commercial advertising and details of postage rates.

Dominica

CROWN COLONY

A British packet agency was operating on Dominica from about 1778, the date of the earliest known use of a postal marking. This was replaced by a branch office of the British GPO which opened at Roseau on 8 May 1858. The stamps of Great Britain were used from that date until 1 May 1860, after which the colonial authorities assumed responsibility for the postal service. Until the introduction of Nos. 1/3 in 1874 No. CC1 and later handstamps were utilised.

For illustrations of handstamp and postmark types see BRITISH POST OFFICES ABROAD notes, following GREAT BRITAIN.

ROSEAU

CROWNED/CIRCLE HANDSTAMPS

CC1	CC **1**	DOMINICA (Black or R.) (17.5.1845)	
		Price on cover	£550

No. CC1 is also known struck in black on various adhesive stamps as late as 1883.

Stamps of GREAT BRITAIN cancelled "A 07" as Type **2**.

1858–60.

Z1	1d. rose-red (1857), *perf* 14	£350
Z2	2d. blue (1858) (Plate No. 7)	£1100
Z3	4d. rose (1857)	£325
Z4	6d. lilac (1856)	£300
Z5	1s. green	£2000

PRICES FOR STAMPS ON COVER TO 1945	
Nos. 1/3	from × 25
No. 4	from × 40
No. 5	from × 100
No. 6	from × 40
Nos. 7/8	from × 100
No. 9	from × 40
Nos. 10/12	from × 15
Nos. 13/15	from × 100
No. 17	from × 50
Nos. 18/a	—
No. 19	from × 40
Nos. 20/5	from × 30
No. 26	—
Nos. 27/90	from × 5
No. 91	—
Nos. 92/8	from × 10
Nos. 99/109	from × 3
Nos. R1/3	from × 15
No. R4	from × 50
No. R6	from × 3

1   **1**½   **2**   **HALF PENNY**

(2)   (3)   (4)

(Typo D.L.R.)

1874 (4 May). Wmk Crown CC. P 12½.

1	**1**	1d. lilac	£150	55·00
		a. Bisected vert (½d.) (on cover)	†	£9000
2		6d. green	£550	£100
3		1s. dull magenta	£325	70·00

NCE   **NCE**

Normal   Malformed "CE" (R. 10/6)

1877–79. Wmk Crown CC. P 14.

4	**1**	½d. olive-yellow (1879)	19·00	60·00
5		1d. lilac	21·00	3·75
		a. Bisected vert or diag (½d.) (on cover or card)	†	£2500
		w. Wmk inverted	£130	
6		2½d. red-brown (1879)	£250	42·00
		w. Wmk inverted	†	£180
7		4d. blue (1879)	£130	3·00
		a. Malformed "CE" in "PENCE"	£1600	£130
8		6d. green	£170	20·00
9		1s. magenta	£130	50·00

1882 (25 Nov)–**83**. No. 5 bisected vertically and surch.

10	**2**	½(d.), in *black*, on half 1d.	£225	55·00
		a. Surch inverted	£1100	£800
		b. Surcharges *tête-bêche* (pair)	£2500	
11	**3**	½(d.), in *red*, on half 1d. (12.82)	35·00	19·00
		a. Surch inverted	£1100	£475
		c. Surch double	£1600	£650
12	**4**	½d. in *black*, on half 1d. (3.83)	70·00	40·00
		b. Surch double	£800	

Type **4** is found reading up or down.

1883–86. Wmk Crown CA. P 14.

13	**1**	½d. olive-yellow	7·00	11·00
14		1d. lilac (1886)	60·00	15·00
		a. Bisected (½d.) (on cover)	†	£2250
15		2½d. red-brown (1884)	£140	4·50
		w. Wmk inverted	£500	

Half Penny   **One Penny**

(5)   (6)

1886 (1 Mar). Nos. 8 and 9 surch locally.

17	**5**	½d. on 6d. green	12·00	13·00
		w. Wmk inverted	†	£450
18	**6**	1d. on 6d. green	£35000	£10000
		a. Thick bar (approx 1 mm)	†	£18000
19		1d. on 1s. magenta	23·00	20·00
		a. Surch double	£11000	£4000

It is believed that only two sheets of the 1d. on 6d. were surcharged. On one of these sheets the six stamps in the top row showed the thick bar variety, No. 18a.

1886–90. Wmk Crown CA. P 14.

20	**1**	½d. dull green	5·00	5·50
22		1d. rose (1887)	17·00	26·00
		a. Deep carmine (1889)	5·50	15·00
		b. Bisected (½d.) (on cover)	†	£1900
		w. Wmk inverted	£200	£200
23		2½d. ultramarine (1888)	4·00	8·00
24		4d. grey	8·00	7·50
		a. Malformed "CE" in "PENCE"	£160	£275
25		6d. orange (1888)	22·00	90·00
26		1s. dull magenta (1890)	£200	£400
20/6 Set of 6			£200	£475
20s/5s Optd "SPECIMEN" Set of 5			£225	

The stamps of Dominica were superseded by the general issue for Leeward Islands on 31 October 1890, but the sets following were in concurrent use with the stamps inscribed "LEEWARD ISLANDS" until 31 December 1939, when the island came under the administration of the Windward Islands.

9 Roseau from the Sea (Lt. Caddy)　　　**10**

(T **9** to **11** typo D.L.R.)

1903 (1 Sept)–**07**. Wmk Crown CC (sideways* on T **9**). Ordinary paper. P 14.

27	**9**	½d. green and grey-green	4·50	4·50
		a. Chalk-surfaced paper (1906)	27·00	25·00
28		1d. grey and red	16·00	75
		a. Chalk-surfaced paper (1906)	50·00	8·00
29		2d. green and brown	6·00	8·00
		a. Chalk-surfaced paper (1906)	48·00	55·00
30		2½d. grey and bright blue	12·00	4·00
		a. Chalk-surfaced paper (3.9.07)	32·00	60·00
31		3d. dull purple and grey-black	11·00	3·25
		ay. Wmk sideways inverted and reversed	£275	
		b. Chalk-surfaced paper (1906)	50·00	38·00
32		6d. grey and chestnut	14·00	18·00
33		1s. magenta and grey-green	40·00	50·00
		a. Chalk-surfaced paper (1906)	75·00	£150
34		2s. grey-black and purple	40·00	32·00
		ws. Wmk Crown to left of CC, optd "SPECIMEN"	£120	
35		2s.6d. grey-green and maize	19·00	75·00
		w. Wmk Crown to left of CC		
36	**10**	5s. black and brown	£110	£170
27/36 Set of 10			£225	£325
27s/36s Optd "SPECIMEN" Set of 10			£180	

*The normal sideways watermark shows Crown to right of CC, as seen from the back of the stamp.

1907–08. Wmk Mult Crown CA (sideways* on T **9**). Chalk-surfaced paper. P 14.

37	**9**	½d. green	14·00	10·00
		x. Wmk sideways reversed	£200	
38		1d. grey and red	2·25	40
39		2d. green and brown	15·00	23·00
40		2½d. grey and bright blue	5·50	21·00
41		3d. dull purple and grey-black	4·00	19·00
42		6d. black and chestnut	55·00	85·00
43		1s. magenta and grey-green (1908)	3·75	55·00
44		2s. black and purple (1908)	38·00	32·00
45		2s.6d. grey-green and maize (1908)	29·00	70·00
46	**10**	5s. black and brown (1908)	75·00	75·00
37/46 Set of 10			£200	£350

*The normal sideways watermark shows Crown to right of CA, as seen from the back of the stamp.

Examples of Nos. 27/36 and 37/46 are known showing a forged Gen. Post Office Dominica postmark dated "JU 1 11".

WAR TAX

ONE HALFPENNY

11　　　　　(12)

1908–20. Wmk Mult Crown CA (sideways* on T **9**). Chalk-surfaced paper (3d., 6d., 1s.). P 14.

47	**9**	½d. blue-green	14·00	10·00
		aw. Wmk Crown to left of CA	7·00	4·50
		ay. Wmk sideways inverted and reversed		
		b. Deep green (wmk Crown to left of CA)	3·50	2·25
		by. Wmk sideways inverted and reversed		
48		1d. carmine-red	3·00	30
		aw. Wmk Crown to left of CA	6·50	40
		b. Scarlet (1916)	1·50	40
		bw. Wmk Crown to left of CA	2·75	70

49		2d. grey (1909)	4·75	5·00
		aw. Wmk Crown to left of CA	5·50	16·00
		b. Slate (wmk Crown to left of CA) (1918)	3·50	12·00
50		2½d. blue	8·50	3·50
		aw. Wmk Crown to left of CA	9·00	9·00
		b. Bright blue (1918)	5·00	9·00
		bw. Wmk Crown to left of CA	12·00	16·00
51		3d. purple/yellow (1909)	3·00	2·50
		a. Ordinary paper (wmk Crown to left of CA) (1912)	3·00	4·00
		ab. On pale yellow (1920)	8·50	19·00
52		6d. dull and bright purple (1909)	10·00	6·00
		a. Ordinary paper. Dull purple (wmk Crown to left of CA) (1915)	4·50	18·00
53		1s. black/green (1910)	4·00	2·75
		a. Ordinary paper (wmk Crown to left of CA) (1912)	5·00	4·00
		as. Optd "SPECIMEN" in red	70·00	
53b		2s. purple and deep blue/blue (wmk Crown to left of CA) (1919)	26·00	90·00
53c		2s.6d. black and red/blue (wmk Crown to left of CA) (1920)	26·00	£100
54	**11**	5s. red and green/yellow (1914)	60·00	£100
47/54 Set of 10			£120	£275
48s/54s Optd "SPECIMEN" (1s. optd in blk) Set of 9			£200	

The watermark orientation differs according to the printings. Unless otherwise stated the watermark shows the Crown to right of CA as seen from the back of the stamp.

1916 (Sept). No. 47b surch with T **12** by De La Rue.

55	**9**	½d. on 1d. deep green (R.)	3·75	75
		a. Small "O" in "ONE"	7·50	9·50
		x. Wmk sideways reversed	£150	

No. 55a occurs on ten stamps within each sheet of 60.

1918 (18 Mar). No. 47b optd with T **12** locally, from D.L.R. plate, but with "ONE HALF-PENNY" blanked out.

56	**9**	½d. deep green (Blk.)	9·00	6·00
		w. Wmk Crown to right of CA	£160	

The blanking out of the surcharge was not completely successful so that it almost always appears as an albino to a greater or lesser extent.

WAR TAX

(14)

1918 (1 June)–**19**. Nos. 47b and 51a optd with T **14** by De La Rue.

57	**9**	½d. deep green	15	50
		w. Wmk Crown to right of CA	£150	
		x. Wmk sideways reversed	£160	
		y. Wmk sideways inverted and reversed	£150	
58		3d. purple/yellow (R.) (1919)	5·50	4·00

WAR TAX
= 1½D. =

(15)

1 ½ **D.**

Short Fraction Bar (R. 6/4)

1919. As No. 50aw, but colour changed, surch with T **15** by De La Rue.

59	**9**	1½d. on 2½d. orange (R.)	15	55
		a. Short fraction bar	9·00	38·00
		b. "C" and "A" missing from wmk	£550	

No. 59b shows the "C" omitted from one impression with the "A" missing from the next one to the left (as seen from the back of the stamp). The "C" is badly distorted in the second watermark.

1920 (1 June). As No. 59, but without "WAR TAX".

60	**9**	1½d. on 2½d. orange (Blk.)	8·00	4·50
		a. Short fraction bar	60·00	70·00
		b. "A" of "CA" missing from wmk	£600	
55s/60s Optd "SPECIMEN" or "Specimen." (Nos. 56s) Set of 6			£200	

An example of No. 60 is known with "C" of "CA" missing from wmk in the sheet margin.

1921–22. Wmk Mult Script CA (sideways*). Chalk-surfaced paper (6d.). P 14.

62	**9**	½d. blue-green	2·50	24·00
63		1d. carmine-red	3·00	3·75
		w. Wmk Crown to right of CA	—	55·00
64		1½d. orange	3·00	20·00
65		2d. grey	2·75	3·25
66		2½d. bright blue	3·25	17·00
67		6d. purple	5·00	48·00
69		2s. purple and blue/blue (1922)	50·00	£150
70		2s.6d. black and red/blue	42·00	£160
62/70 Set of 8			£100	£375
62s/70s Optd "SPECIMEN" Set of 8			£160	

*The normal sideways watermark shows Crown to left of CA, as seen from the back of the stamp.

The 1½d. has figures of value in the lower corner and no ornamentation below words of value.

Examples of some values are known showing a forged GPO Dominica postmark dated "MY 19 27".

16

(Typo D.L.R.)

1923 (1 Mar)–**33**. Chalk-surfaced paper. P 14.

(a) Wmk Mult Script CA (sideways)*

71	**16**	½d. black and green	1·75	60
72		1d. black and bright violet	7·00	1·75
73		1d. black and scarlet (1933)	17·00	1·00
74		1½d. black and scarlet	6·50	65

75		1½d. black and red-brown (1933)	15·00	70
76		2d. black and grey	4·25	50
77		2½d. black and orange-yellow	4·00	9·00
78		2½d. black and ultramarine (1927)	7·50	2·00
79		3d. black and ultramarine	4·25	18·00
80		3d. black and red/yellow (1927)	4·50	1·00
81		4d. black and brown	4·75	5·50
82		6d. black and bright magenta	5·50	7·00
83		1s. black/emerald	3·50	4·00
84		2s. black and blue/blue	25·00	38·00
85		2s.6d. black and red/blue	27·00	38·00
86		3s. black and purple/yellow (1927)	4·50	14·00
		sa. Opt "SPECIMEN" double	£450	
87		4s. black and red/emerald	22·00	38·00
88		5s. black and green/yellow (1927)	40·00	60·00
		(b) Wmk Mult Crown CA (sideways)*		
89	**16**	3s. black and purple/yellow	4·25	70·00
90		5s. black and green/yellow	9·00	55·00
91		£1 black and purple/red	£225	£350
71/91 Set of 21			£375	£600
71s/91s Optd or Perf (Nos. 73s, 75s) "SPECIMEN" Set of 21			£425	

*The normal sideways watermark shows Crown to left of CA, as seen from the back of the stamp.

Examples of most values are known showing a forged GPO Dominica postmark dated "MY 19 27".

1935 (6 May). Silver Jubilee. As Nos. 91/4 of Antigua.

92		1d. deep blue and carmine	1·50	30
		f. Diagonal line by turret	70·00	50·00
		g. Dot to left of chapel	£100	
		h. Dot by flagstaff	£110	70·00
		i. Dash by turret	£150	
93		1½d. ultramarine and grey	6·00	3·50
		f. Diagonal line by turret	95·00	£120
		h. Dot by flagstaff	£130	£160
94		2½d. brown and deep blue	7·00	5·50
95		1s. slate and purple	7·00	14·00
		h. Dot by flagstaff	£160	£275
		i. Dash by turret	£300	£400
92/5 Set of 4			20·00	21·00
92s/5s Perf "SPECIMEN" Set of 4			£110	

For illustrations of plate varieties see Omnibus section following Zanzibar.

1937 (12 May). Coronation. As Nos. 95/7 of Antigua. P 11×11½.

96		1d. carmine	40	10
97		1½d. yellow-brown	60	10
98		2½d. blue	1·00	1·75
96/8 Set of 3			1·75	1·75
96s/8s Perf "SPECIMEN" Set of 3			£100	

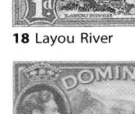

17 Fresh Water Lake　　　**18** Layou River

19 Picking limes　　　**20** Boiling Lake

(Recess Waterlow)

1938 (15 Aug)–**47**. T **17/20**. Wmk Mult Script CA. P 12½.

99	**17**	½d. brown and green	10	15
100	**18**	1d. grey and scarlet	25	25
101	**19**	1½d. green and purple	1·00	70
102	**19**	2d. carmine and grey-black	50	2·25
103	**19**	2½d. purple and bright blue	5·50	1·75
		a. Purple and bright ultramarine (8.42)	30	2·25
104	**18**	3d. olive-green and brown	30	50
104a	**19**	3½d. ultramarine and purple (15.10.47)	2·75	2·50
105	**17**	6d. emerald-green and violet	1·75	1·50
105a		7d. green and yellow-brown (15.10.47)	2·25	1·50
106	**20**	1s. violet and olive-green	6·00	1·50
106a	**18**	2s. slate and purple (15.10.47)	10·00	16·00
107	**17**	2s.6d. black and vermilion	23·00	5·50
108	**18**	5s. light blue and sepia	18·00	13·00
108a	**20**	10s. black and brown-orange (15.10.47)	22·00	25·00

21 King George VI

(Photo Harrison)

1940 (15 Apr)–**42**. Wmk Mult Script CA. Chalk-surfaced paper. P 15×14.

109	**21**	¼d. chocolate	1·25	70
		a. Ordinary paper (1942)	25	2·00
99/109a Set of 15			75·00	65·00
99s/109s Perf "SPECIMEN" Set of 15			£350	

1946 (14 Oct). Victory. As Nos. 110/11 of Antigua.

110		1d. carmine	30	10
111		3½d. blue	30	10
110s/11s Perf "SPECIMEN" Set of 2			80·00	

1948 (1 Dec). Royal Silver Wedding. As Nos. 112/13 of Antigua.

112		1d. scarlet	15	10
113		10s. red-brown	25·00	42·00

(New Currency. 100 cents = 1 B.W.I., later East Caribbean dollar)

1949 (10 Oct). 75th Anniv of Universal Postal Union. As Nos. 114/17 of Antigua.

114	5c. blue		20	15
115	6c. brown		1·25	2·75
116	12c. purple		45	2·75
	a. "A" of "CA" missing from wmk		—	£750
117	24c. olive		30	30
114/17 Set of 4			2·00	5·50

1951 (16 Feb). Inauguration of B.W.I. University College. As Nos. 118/19 of Antigua.

118	3c. yellow-green and reddish violet		50	1·25
119	12c. deep green and carmine		75	40

22 King George VI

23 Drying Cocoa

24 Making Carib baskets

25 Lime plantation

26 Picking oranges

27 Bananas

28 Botanical Gardens

29 Drying vanilla beans

30 Fresh Water Lake

31 Layou River

32 Boiling Lake

33 Picking oranges

(Photo Harrison (½c.). Recess B.W. (others))

1951 (1 July). T **22/33**. Wmk Mult Script CA. Chalk-surfaced paper (½c.). P 15×14 (½c.), 13½×13 ($2.40), 13×13½ (others).

120	**22**	½c. chocolate	10	30
121	**23**	1c. black and vermilion	10	30
		b. "A" of "CA" missing from wmk	£400	
		c. "JA" for "CA" in wmk	£450	
122	**24**	2c. red-brown and deep green	15	1·25
		a. "C" of "CA" missing from wmk	£450	£475
		b. "A" of "CA" missing from wmk	£450	
		c. "JA" for "CA" in wmk	—	£475
123	**25**	3c. green and reddish violet	25	3·50
		a. "C" of "CA" missing from wmk	£425	
		c. "JA" for "CA" in wmk	£450	
124	**26**	4c. brown-orange and sepia	70	4·00
		a. "C" of "CA" missing from wmk	£475	£475
		b. "A" of "CA" missing from wmk	£475	
125	**27**	5c. black and carmine	85	30
		a. "C" of "CA" missing from wmk	£600	
		b. "A" of "CA" missing from wmk	£600	
		c. "JA" for "CA" in wmk	£650	
126	**28**	6c. olive and chestnut	1·00	30
		a. "C" of "CA" missing from wmk	£475	
		b. "A" of "CA" missing from wmk	£600	
127	**29**	8c. blue-green and blue	3·25	2·25
128	**30**	12c. black and bright green	70	1·25
		a. "C" of "CA" missing from wmk	£950	
129	**31**	14c. blue and violet	1·25	3·50
		a. "C" of "CA" missing from wmk	£1000	
		b. "A" of "CA" missing from wmk	—	£650
		c. "JA" for "CA" in wmk	£850	
130	**32**	24c. reddish violet and rose-carmine	75	40
		a. "C" of "CA" missing from wmk	£1000	£850
131	**25**	48c. bright green and red-orange	7·00	16·00
		a. "C" of "CA" missing from wmk	£1000	
		b. "A" of "CA" missing from wmk	£1000	
		c. "JA" for "CA" in wmk	£1000	
132	**24**	60c. carmine and black	4·50	11·00
		c. "JA" for "CA" in wmk	£800	

133	30	$1.20 emerald and black	9·00	8·00
		a. "C" of "CA" missing from wmk	£1200	
		b. "A" of "CA" missing from wmk	£1200	
134	33	$2.40 orange and black	30·00	55·00
120/34 Set of 15			50·00	95·00

Nos. 121b, 122b, 124b, 125b, 126b, 127b, 129b, 131b and 133b must show no trace of the letter "A". Examples with part of the left leg of the "A" still present are worth much less.
Nos. 121c, 122c, 123c, 125c, 129c, 131c and 132c may represent an attempt to repair the missing "C" variety.

**NEW
CONSTITUTION
1951
(34)**

1951 (15 Oct). New Constitution. Nos. 123, 125, 127 and 129 optd with T **34** by B.W.

135	**25**	3c. green and reddish violet	25	70
		a. "C" of "CA" missing from wmk	£475	£500
		c. "JA" for "CA" in watermark	£475	
136	**27**	5c. black and carmine	25	2·00
		a. "JA" for "CA" in wmk	£550	£650
137	**29**	8c. blue-green and blue (R.)	25	20
		a. "JA" for "CA" in wmk	£600	
138	**31**	14c. blue and violet (R.)	2·50	1·50
		a. "C" of "CA" missing from wmk		
		b. "A" of "CA" missing from wmk	£750	
135/8 Set of 4			3·00	4·00

1953 (2 June). Coronation. As No. 120 of Antigua.

139		2c. black and deep green	30	10

35 Queen Elizabeth II

36 Mat Making

37 Canoe Making

38 Cutting bananas

(Photo Harrison (½c.). Recess B.W. (others))

1954 (1 Oct)–**62**. Designs previously used for King George VI issue, but with portrait of Queen Elizabeth II as in T **35/8**. Wmk Mult Script CA. P 15×14 (½c.), 13½×13 ($2.40), 13×13½ (others).

140	**35**	½c. brown	10	1·75
141	**23**	1c. black and vermilion	30	20
142	**24**	2c. chocolate and myrtle-green	1·25	2·75
		a. Chocolate and grey-green (13.3.62)	16·00	15·00
143	**25**	3c. green and purple	1·50	40
144	**36**	3c. black and carmine (15.10.57)	6·00	2·50
145	**26**	4c. brown-orange and sepia	30	10
146	**27**	5c. black and carmine-red	3·50	1·00
147	**37**	5c. light blue and sepia-brown (15.10.57)	16·00	1·75
		a. Blue and sepia (13.3.62)	45·00	10·00
148	**28**	6c. bronze-green and red-brown	50	10
149	**29**	8c. deep green and deep blue	1·75	10
150	**38**	10c. green and brown (15.10.57)	8·50	3·50
		a. Green and deep brown (17.7.62)	20·00	9·00
151	**30**	12c. black and emerald	60	10
152	**31**	14c. blue and purple	60	10
153	**32**	24c. purple and carmine	60	10
154	**25**	48c. green and red-orange	3·50	19·00
155	**36**	48c. deep brown and violet (15.10.57)	5·00	3·75
156	**24**	60c. rose-red and black	4·50	1·00
157	**30**	$1.20 emerald and black	22·00	8·50
158	**33**	$2.40 yellow-orange and black	22·00	14·00
140/58 Set of 19			85·00	50·00

1958 (22 Apr). Inauguration of British Caribbean Federation. As Nos. 135/7 of Antigua.

159		3c. deep green	80	10
160		6c. blue	95	1·50
161		12c. scarlet	1·10	15
159/61 Set of 3			2·50	1·60

40 Seashore at Rosalie

41 Queen Elizabeth II

42 Sailing canoe

43 Sulphur springs

44 Road-making

45 Dug-out canoe

46 Crapaud (Toad)

47 Scott's Head

48 Traditional Costume

49 Bananas

50 Imperial Amazon

51 Goodwill

52 Cocoa tree

53 Coat of Arms

54 Trafalgar Falls

55 Coconut Palm

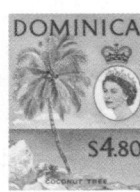

Two types of 14c.

I. Eyes of model looking straight ahead.
II. Eyes looking to her right.

(Des S. Scott. Photo Harrison)

1963 (16 May)–**65**. T **40/55**. W w **12** (upright). P 14×14½ (vert) or 14½×14 (horiz).

162	**40**	1c. green, blue and sepia	10	85
163	**41**	2c. bright blue	30	10
		w. Wmk inverted	—	18·00
164	**42**	3c. blackish brown and blue	1·75	1·25
165	**43**	4c. green, sepia and slate-violet	10	10
166	**41**	5c. magenta	30	10
167	**44**	6c. green, bistre and violet	15	80
168	**45**	8c. green, sepia and black	30	20
169	**46**	10c. sepia and pink	20	20
170	**47**	12c. green, blue and blackish brown	1·00	10
171	**48**	14c. multicoloured (I)	1·00	10
171a		14c. multicoloured (II) (1.4.65)	2·50	1·75
172	**49**	15c. yellow, green and brown	1·50	10
		w. Wmk inverted	—	30·00
173	**50**	24c. multicoloured	9·00	20
174	**51**	48c. green and black	1·00	1·50
175	**52**	60c. orange, green and black	1·00	70
176	**53**	$1.20 multicoloured	6·50	2·00
177	**54**	$2.40 blue, turquoise and brown	6·00	4·75
178	**55**	$4.80 green, blue and brown	27·00	38·00
162/78 Set of 17			50·00	45·00

See also Nos. 200/4.

1963 (4 June). Freedom from Hunger. As No. 146 of Antigua.

179		15c. reddish violet	15	10

1963 (2 Sept). Red Cross Centenary. As Nos. 147/8 of Antigua.

180		5c. black and red	20	40
181		15c. red and blue	40	60

1964 (23 Apr). 400th Birth Anniv of William Shakespeare. As No. 164 of Antigua.

182		15c. bright purple	10	10
		w. Wmk inverted	1·00	

1965 (17 May). ITU Centenary. As Nos. 166/7 of Antigua.

183		2c. light emerald and blue	10	10
184		48c. turquoise-blue and grey	45	20

1965 (25 Oct). International Co-operation Year. As Nos. 168/9 of Antigua.

185		1c. reddish purple and turquoise-green	10	20
186		15c. deep bluish green and lavender	75	10

1966 (24 Jan). Churchill Commemoration. As Nos. 170/3 of Antigua.

187	1c. new blue		10	1·60
	a. Gold omitted		£2500	
188	5c. deep green		45	10
189	15c. brown		95	10
190	24c. bluish violet		1·00	20
	w. Wmk inverted		£160	
187/90 *Set of 4*			2·25	1·75

No. 187a occurred on five stamps in the bottom two rows of one sheet.

An example of the 1c. is known showing the gold face value printed double.

1966 (4 Feb). Royal Visit. As Nos. 174/5 of Antigua.

191	5c. black and ultramarine		75	40
192	15c. black and magenta		1·00	60

1966 (1 July). World Cup Football Championship. As Nos. 176/7 of Antigua.

193	5c. violet, yellow-green, lake and yellow-brown		25	15
194	24c. chocolate, blue-green, lake and yellow-brown		85	15

1966 (20 Sept). Inauguration of WHO Headquarters, Geneva. As Nos. 178/9 of Antigua.

195	5c. black, yellow-green and light blue		15	15
196	24c. black, light purple and yellow-brown		30	15

1966 (1 Dec). 20th Anniv of UNESCO As Nos. 196/8 of Antigua.

197	5c. slate-violet, red, yellow and orange		20	15
198	15c. orange-yellow, violet and deep olive		50	10
199	24c. black, bright purple and orange		60	15
197/9 *Set of 3*			1·10	30

1966 (30 Dec)–**67**. As Nos. 165, 167/9 and 172 but wmk w **12** sideways.

200	**43**	4c. green, sepia and slate-violet (16.5.67)		1·00	90
201	**44**	6c. green, bistre and violet		20	15
202	**45**	8c. green, sepia and black		40	10
203	**46**	10c. sepia and pink (16.5.67)		50	10
204	**49**	15c. yellow, green and brown (16.5.67)		50	10
200/4 *Set of 5*				2·40	1·25

ASSOCIATED STATEHOOD

56 Children of Three Races

(Des and photo Harrison)

1967 (2 Nov). National Day. T **56** and similar horiz designs. Multicoloured. W w **12**. P 14½.

205	5c. Type **56**		10	10
206	10c. The *Santa Maria* and motto		40	15
207	15c. Hands holding motto ribbon		15	15
208	24c. Belaire dancing		15	20
205/8 *Set of 4*			70	45

57 John F. Kennedy

(Des G. Vasarhelyi. Litho D.L.R.)

1968 (20 Apr). Human Rights Year. T **57** and similar horiz designs. Multicoloured. W w **12** (sideways). P 14×13½.

209	1c. Type **57**		10	30
210	10c. Cecil A. E. Rawle		10	10
	a. Imperf (pair)		90·00	
211	12c. Pope John XXIII		45	15
212	48c. Florence Nightingale		20	25
213	60c. Albert Schweitzer		35	30
209/13 *Set of 5*			1·00	1·00

ASSOCIATED STATEHOOD (**58**) **NATIONAL DAY 3 NOVEMBER 1968** (**59**)

1968 (8 July). Associated Statehood. As Nos. 162, 170 and 174, but wmk sideways, or Nos. 163/4, 166, 170, 171a, 173, 175/8 and 200/4 optd with T **58**.

214	**40**	1c. green, blue and sepia (Sil.)		10	10
215	**41**	2c. bright blue (Sil.)		10	10
216	**42**	3c. blackish brown and blue (Sil.)..		10	10
217	**43**	4c. green, sepia and slate-violet (Sil.)..		10	10
218	**41**	5c. magenta (Sil.)		10	10
219	**44**	6c. green, bistre and violet		10	10
220	**45**	8c. green, sepia and black		10	10
221	**46**	10c. sepia and pink (Sil.)		55	10
222	**47**	12c. green, blue and blackish brown (wmk sideways)		10	60
		a. Wmk upright		10	10
224	**48**	14c. multicoloured (II) (Sil.)		10	10
225	**49**	15c. yellow, green and brown (Sil.)..		10	10
226	**50**	24c. multicoloured (Sil.)		4·50	10
227	**51**	48c. green, blue and black (Sil.) (wmk sideways)		55	3·00
		a. Wmk upright		65	1·00
228	**52**	60c. orange, green and black		1·00	70
229	**53**	$1.20 multicoloured		1·60	3·25
230	**54**	$2.40 blue, turquoise and brown (Sil.)..		1·00	2·50

231	**55**	$4.80 green, blue and brown (Sil.)		1·25	9·00
214/31 *Set of 17*				9·00	15·00

The 2, 5, 6, 8 and 10c. values exist with PVA gum as well as gum arabic.

1968 (3 Nov). National Day. Nos. 162/4, 171 and 176 optd with T **59**.

232	**40**	1c. green, blue and sepia		10	10
		a. Opt inverted		48·00	
		b. Opt double			
233	**41**	2c. bright blue		10	10
		a. Opt double		32·00	
234	**42**	3c. blackish brown and blue		10	10
		a. Opt double		32·00	
235	**48**	14c. multicoloured (I)		10	10
		a. Opt double		75·00	
236	**53**	$1.20 multicoloured		55	40
		a. Opt double		32·00	
		b. Vert pair, one opt omitted, other opt double		£160	
232/6 *Set of 5*				60	40

The above set was put on sale by the New York Agency on 1 November but not sold locally until the 3 November.

60 Forward shooting at Goal

(Des M. Shamir (1c., 60c.), K. Plowitz (5c., 48c.). Litho B.W.)

1968 (25 Nov). Olympic Games, Mexico. T **60** and similar horiz designs. Multicoloured. P 11½×11.

237	1c. Type **60**		10	10
	a. Horiz pair. Nos. 237/8		10	10
238	1c. Goalkeeper trying to save goal		10	10
239	5c. Swimmers about to dive		10	10
	a. Horiz pair. Nos. 239/40		10	10
240	5c. Swimmers diving		10	10
241	48c. Javelin-throwing		15	15
	a. Horiz pair. Nos. 241/2		30	30
242	48c. Hurdling		15	15
243	60c. Basketball		90	25
	a. Horiz pair. Nos. 243/4		1·75	50
244	60c. Basketball players		90	25
237/44 *Set of 8*			2·00	85

Nos. 237/44 were issued in sheets of 40 containing two panes of *se-tenant* pairs.

61 *The Small Cowper Madonna* (Raphael)   **62** *Venus and Adonis* (Rubens)

(Photo Delrieu, Paris)

1968 (23 Dec). Christmas. P 12½×12.

245	**61**	5c. multicoloured	10	50

Three other values were issued: 12c. *Madonna of the Chair* (Raphael); 24c. *Madonna and Child* (Italo-Byzantine, XVI-century); $1.20 *Madonna and Child* (Byzantine, XIII-century). Sizes as T **61**.

These only come from miniature sheets, containing two *se-tenant* strips of each value.

(Litho D.L.R.)

1969 (30 Jan). 20th Anniv of World Health Organisation. Paintings. T **62** and similar vert designs. Multicoloured. W w **12**. P 15.

246	5c. Type **62**		20	10
247	15c. *The Death of Socrates* (J.-L. David)		30	10
248	24c. *Christ and the Pilgrims of Emmaus* (Velázquez)		30	10
249	50c. *Pilate washing his Hands* (Rembrandt)		50	40
246/9 *Set of 4*			1·10	50

66 Picking Oranges   **67** "Strength in Unity" Emblem and Fruit Trees

(Des K. Plowitz. Litho Harrison)

1969 (10 Mar). Tourism. T **66** and similar horiz designs. Multicoloured. W w **12**. P 14½.

250	10c. Type **66**		15	10
	a. Horiz pair. Nos. 250/1		30	15
251	10c. Woman, child and ocean scene		15	10
252	12c. Fort Yeoung Hotel		50	10
	a. Horiz pair. Nos. 252/3		1·00	20
253	12c. Red-necked Amazons		50	10
254	24c. Calypso band		30	15
	a. Horiz pair. Nos. 254/5		60	30
	w. Wmk inverted		45·00	
255	24c. Women dancing		30	15
	w. Wmk inverted		45·00	

256	48c. Underwater life		30	25
	a. Horiz pair. Nos. 256/7		60	50
257	48c. Skin-diver and Turtle		30	25
250/7 *Set of 8*			2·25	1·00

Each denomination was printed *se-tenant* throughout the sheet. The 12c. values are on cream coloured paper.

(Litho B.W.)

1969 (July). First Anniv of CARIFTA (Caribbean Free Trade Area). T **67** and similar horiz designs. Multicoloured. P 13½×13.

258	5c. Type **67**		10	10
259	8c. Hawker Siddeley H.S.748 aircraft, emblem and island		30	20
260	12c. Chart of Caribbean Sea and emblem		30	25
261	24c. Steamship unloading, tug and emblem		40	25
258/61 *Set of 4*			1·00	70

71 *Spinning*   **72** Mahatma Gandhi Weaving and Clock Tower, Westminster

(Litho B.W.)

1969 (10 July). 50th Anniv of International Labour Organisation. T **71** and similar vert designs showing paintings of people at work by J. Millet, bordered by flags of member-nations of the ILO Multicoloured. No wmk. P 13×13½.

262	15c. Type **71**		10	10
263	30c. *Threshing*		15	15
264	38c. *Flax-pulling*		15	15
262/4 *Set of 3*			30	30

(Des G. Vasarhelyi. Litho Format)

1969 (20 Oct). Birth Centenary of Mahatma Gandhi. T **72** and similar horiz designs. Multicoloured. P 14½.

265	6c. Type **72**		45	10
266	38c. Gandhi, Nehru and Mausoleum		65	15
267	$1.20 Gandhi and Taj Mahal		1·00	1·00
265/7 *Set of 3*			1·90	1·00

Nos. 265/7 are incorrectly inscribed "Ghandi".

75 *Saint Joseph*

(Des G. Vasarhelyi. Litho Govt Printer, Jerusalem)

1969 (3 Nov). National Day. Stained Glass Windows. T **75** and similar vert designs. Multicoloured. P 14.

268	6c. Type **75**		10	10
269	8c. *Saint John*		10	10
270	12c. *Saint Peter*		10	10
271	30c. *Saint Paul*		30	50
268/71 *Set of 4*			40	60

Nos. 268/71 were printed in sheets of 16 (4×4) containing 12 stamps and four printed labels in the top row. The labels each contain two lines of a patriotic poem by W. O. M. Pond, the first letter from each line spelling "DOMINICA".

79 Queen Elizabeth II   **80** Purple-throated Carib and Flower

81 Government Headquarters

82 Coat of Arms

(Photo D.L.R.)

1969 (26 Nov)–**72**. T **79/82** and similar horiz designs. Multicoloured. W **41** of Singapore (Half-check Pattern) (60c. to $4.80) or no wmk (others). Chalk-surfaced paper. P 13½×14 (½c.), 14×13½ (1 to 50c.) or 14 (60c. to $4.80).

272	½c. Type **79**		10	2·75
	a. Glazed paper (1972)		75	2·50
273	1c. Type **80**		1·00	3·00
	a. Glazed paper (1972)		1·50	1·50
274	2c. Poinsettia		15	10
	a. Glazed paper (1972)		50	40
275	3c. Red-necked Pigeon		3·00	3·25
	a. Glazed paper (1972)		4·25	1·50
276	4c. Imperial Amazon		3·00	3·25
	a. Glazed paper (1972)		4·25	1·50
277	5c. *Battus polydamas* (butterfly)		2·75	3·00
	a. Glazed paper (1972)		2·75	1·75
278	6c. *Dryas julia* (butterfly)		2·75	4·25
	a. Glazed paper (1972)		2·75	2·75
279	8c. Shipping Bananas		20	10
	a. Glazed paper (1972)		40	50
280	10c. Portsmouth Harbour		20	10
	a. Glazed paper (1972)		35	20
281	12c. Copra processing plant		20	10
	a. Glazed paper (1972)		35	20
282	15c. Straw workers		20	10
	a. Glazed paper (1972)		35	25
283	25c. Timber plant		30	10
	a. Glazed paper (1972)		40	25
284	30c. Pumice mine		1·50	90
	a. Glazed paper (1972)		1·50	70
285	38c. Grammar school and playing field		13·00	1·75
	a. Glazed paper (1972)		8·50	15·00
286	50c. Roseau Cathedral		50	45
	a. Glazed paper (1972)		80	1·00
287	60c. Type **81**		55	1·50
288	$1.20 Melville Hall Airport (40×27 *mm*)		1·50	1·75
289	$2.40 Type **82**		1·00	4·00
290	$4.80 Type **79** (26×39 *mm*)		1·75	7·00
272/90 *Set of 19*			29·00	32·00
272a/86a *Set of 15*			25·00	27·00

99 *Virgin and Child with St. John (Perugino)*

101 *Astronaut's First Step onto the Moon*

(Des G. Vasarhelyi. Litho B.W.)

1969 (19 Dec). Christmas. Paintings. T **99** and similar perf designs. Multicoloured. P 14½×14½.

291	6c. *Virgin and Child with St. John* (Lippi)	10	10
292	10c. *Holy Family with the Lamb* (Raphael)	10	10
293	15c. Type **99**	10	10
294	$1.20 *Madonna of the Rose Hedge* (Botticelli)	35	40
291/4 *Set of 4*		35	40
MS295 89×76 mm. Nos. 293/4. Imperf		75	1·00

(Des G. Vasarhelyi. Photo Banknote Printing Office, Helsinki)

1970 (6 Feb*). Moon Landing. T **101** and similar horiz designs. Multicoloured. P 12½.

296	½c. Type **101**	10	10
297	5c. Scientific Experiment on the Moon, and Flag	15	10
298	8c. Astronauts collecting Rocks	15	10
299	30c. Module over the Moon	20	15
300	50c. Moon Plaque	30	25
301	60c. Astronauts	30	30
296/301 *Set of 6*		1·00	80
MS302 116×112 mm. Nos. 298/301. Imperf		1·75	2·25

*This is the date of release in Dominica, but the above were released by the Philatelic Agency in the USA on 2 February.

107 *Giant Green Turtle*

(Des G. Drummond. Litho Kyodo Printing Co, Tokyo)

1970 (7 Sept). Flora and Fauna. T **107** and similar horiz designs. Multicoloured. P 13.

303	6c. Type **107**	30	20
304	24c. Atlantic Flyingfish	35	45
305	38c. Anthurium Lily	40	65
306	60c. Imperial and Red-necked Amazons	4·25	5·50
303/6 *Set of 4*		4·75	6·00
MS307 160×111 mm. Nos. 303/6		5·50	8·00

108 *18th-Century National Costume*

(Des G. Drummond from local designs. Litho Questa)

1970 (30 Oct). National Day. T **108** and similar horiz designs. Multicoloured. P 14.

308	5c. Type **108**	10	10
309	8c. Carib Basketry	10	10
310	$1 Flag and Chart of Dominica	30	40
308/10 *Set of 3*		30	40
MS311 150×85 mm. Nos. 308/10 plus three labels.		50	1·75

109 *Scrooge and Marley's Ghost*

(Des R. Granger Barrett. Litho Questa)

1970 (23 Nov). Christmas and Charles Dickens' Death Centenary. T **109** and similar vert designs showing scenes from *A Christmas Carol*. Multicoloured. P 14×14½.

312	2c. Type **109**	10	10
313	15c. Fezziwig's Ball	25	10
314	24c. Scrooge and his Nephew's Party	25	10
315	$1.20 Scrooge and the Ghost of Christmas Present	80	90
312/15 *Set of 4*		1·25	1·00
MS316 142×87 mm. Nos. 312/15		1·25	3·75

110 *The Doctor (Sir Luke Fildes)*

(Des G. Vasarhelyi. Litho Questa)

1970 (28 Dec). Centenary of British Red Cross. T **110** and similar horiz designs. Multicoloured. P 14½×14.

317	8c. Type **110**	10	10
318	10c. Hands and Red Cross	10	10
319	15c. Flag of Dominica and Red Cross Emblem	15	10
320	50c. *The Sick Child* (E. Munch)	50	85
317/20 *Set of 4*		75	1·00
MS321 108×76 mm. Nos. 317/20		1·00	3·00

POSTAL FISCALS

REVENUE **Revenue**
(R **1**) (R **2**)

1879–**88**. Optd with Type R **1** by De La Rue. P 14.

(a) Wmk Crown CC

R1	**1**	1d. lilac	80·00	8·00
		a. Bisected vert (½d.) on cover	†	£2750
R2		6d. green	3·00	24·00
		w. Wmk inverted	£130	
R3		1s. magenta	16·00	16·00
R1/3 *Set of 3*			85·00	42·00

(b) Wmk Crown CA

R4	**1**	1d. lilac (1888)	6·50	9·50

1888. Optd with Type R **2** locally. Wmk Crown CA.

R6	**1**	1d. rose	£250	70·00

East Africa (G.E.A.) *see* **Tanganyika**

East Africa and Uganda Protectorates *see* **Kenya, Uganda and Tanganyika**

Egypt

TURKISH SUZERAINTY

In 1517 Sultan Selim I added Egypt to the Ottoman Empire, and it stayed more or less under Turkish rule until 1805, when Mohammed Ali became governor. He established a dynasty of governors owing nominal allegiance to the Sultan of Turkey until 1914.

Khedive Ismail
18 January 1863–26 June 1879

He obtained the honorific title of Khedive (viceroy) from the Sultan in 1867.

The operations of British Consular Post Offices in Egypt date from August 1839 when the first packet agency, at Alexandria, was opened. Further agencies at Suez (1 January 1847) and Cairo (1856) followed. Alexandria became a post office on 17 March 1858 with Cairo following on 23 February 1859 and Suez on 1 January 1861.

Great Britain stamps were issued to Alexandria in March 1858 and to the other two offices in August/September 1859. "B 01" cancellations as Type **2** were issued to both Alexandria and Cairo. Cancellations with this number as Types **8**, **12** and **15** were only used at Alexandria.

Before 1 July 1873 combination covers showing Great Britain stamps and the first issue of Egypt exist with the latter paying the internal postage to the British Post Office at Alexandria.

The Cairo office closed on 30 June 1873 and the other two on 30 March 1878. Suez continued to function as a transit office for a number of years.

Stamps issued after 1877 can be found with the Egyptian cancellation "Port Said", but these are on letters posted from British ships.

For cancellations used during the 1882 and 1885 campaigns, see BRITISH FORCES IN EGYPT at the end of the listing.

For illustrations of the handstamp and postmark types see BRITISH POST OFFICES ABROAD notes following GREAT BRITAIN.

ALEXANDRIA

CROWNED-CIRCLE HANDSTAMPS

CC1	CC **1b**	ALEXANDRIA (R.) (13.5.1843) *Price on cover*		£3250

Stamps of GREAT BRITAIN cancelled "B 01" as in Types **2** (also used at Cairo), **8**, **12** and **15**.

1858 (Mar)–**79**.

Z1	½d. rose-red (1870–79)	*From*	22·00
	Plate Nos. 5, 6, 8, 10, 13, 14, 15, 19, 20.		
Z2	1d. rose-red (1857)		7·50
Z3	1d. rose-red (1861) (Alph IV)		
Z4	1d. rose-red (1864–79)	*From*	11·00
	Plate Nos. 71, 72, 73, 74, 76, 78, 79, 80, 81, 82, 83, 84, 85, 86, 87, 88, 89, 90, 91, 92, 93, 94, 95, 96, 97, 98, 99, 100, 101, 102, 103, 104, 106, 107, 108, 109, 110, 111, 112, 113, 114, 115, 117, 118, 119, 120, 121, 122, 123, 124, 125, 127, 129, 130, 131, 133, 134, 136, 137, 138, 139, 140, 142, 143, 144, 145, 146, 147, 148, 149, 150, 152, 154, 156, 157, 158, 159, 160, 162, 163, 165, 168, 169, 170, 171, 172, 174, 175, 177, 179, 180, 181, 183, 185, 188, 190, 198, 200, 203, 206, 210, 220.		
Z5	2d. blue (1858–69)	*From*	11·00
	Plate Nos. 7, 8, 9, 13, 14, 15.		
Z6	2½d. rosy mauve (1875) (blued *paper*)	*From*	65·00
	Plate Nos. 1, 2, 3.		
Z7	2½d. rosy mauve (1875–6) (Plate Nos. 1, 2, 3)		35·00
Z8	2½d. rosy mauve (*Error of Lettering*)		£1800
Z9	2½d. rosy mauve (1876–79)	*From*	25·00
	Plate Nos. 3, 4, 5, 6, 7, 8, 9.		
Z10	3d. carmine-rose (1862)		£120
Z11	3d. rose (1865) (Plate No. 4)		60·00
Z12	3d. rose (1867–73)		25·00
	Plate Nos. 4, 5, 6, 7, 8, 9.		
Z13	3d. rose (1873–76)	*From*	27·00
	Plate Nos. 11, 12, 14, 15, 16, 18, 19.		
Z15	4d. rose (1857)		42·00
Z16	4d. red (1862) (Plate Nos. 3, 4)		42·00
Z17	4d. vermilion (1865–73)	*From*	29·00
	Plate Nos. 7, 8, 9, 10, 11, 12, 13, 14.		
Z18	4d. vermilion (1876) (Plate No. 15)		£160
Z19	4d. sage-green (1877) (Plate No. 15)		£110
Z20	6d. lilac (1856)		50·00
Z21	6d. lilac (1862) (Plate Nos. 3, 4)		45·00
Z22	6d. lilac (1865–67) (Plate Nos. 5, 6)	*From*	32·00
Z23	6d. lilac (1867) (Plate No. 6)		42·00
Z24	6d. violet (1867–70) (Plate Nos. 6, 8, 9)	*From*	38·00
	a. Imperf (Plate No. 8)		£4500
Z25	6d. buff (1872–73) (Plate Nos. 11, 12)	*From*	55·00
Z26	6d. chestnut (1872) (Plate No. 11)		27·00
Z27	6d. grey (1873) (Plate No. 12)		80·00
Z28	6d. grey (1874–76) Plate Nos. 13, 14, 15	*From*	24·00
Z29	9d. straw (1862)		£160
Z30	9d. bistre (1862)		
Z31	9d. straw (1865)		
Z32	9d. straw (1867)		
Z33	10d. red-brown (1867)		£140
Z34	1s. green (1856)		£130
Z35	1s. green (1862)		75·00
Z36	1s. green (1862) ("K" variety)		
Z37	1s. green (1865) (Plate No. 4)		35·00
Z38	1s. green (1867–73) Plate Nos. 4, 5, 6, 7	*From*	18·00
Z39	1s. green (1873–77)	*From*	30·00
	Plate Nos. 8, 9, 10, 11, 12, 13.		
Z40	2s. blue (1867)		£110
Z41	5s. rose (1867–74) (Plate Nos. 1, 2)	*From*	£250

CAIRO

CROWNED-CIRCLE HANDSTAMPS

CC2	CC **6**	CAIRO (R. or Blk.) (23.3.1859) *Price on cover*		£5000

Cancellation "B 01" as Type **2** (also issued at Alexandria) was used to cancel mail franked with Great Britain stamps between April 1859 and June 1873.

SUEZ
CROWNED-CIRCLE HANDSTAMPS

CC3   CC **1**   SUEZ (B. or Black) (16.7.1847) *Price on cover* £6000

Stamps of GREAT BRITAIN cancelled "B 02" as in Types **2** and **8**, or with circular date stamp as Type **5**.

1859 (Aug)–**79**.

Z42	½d. rose-red (1870–79)		38·00
	Plate Nos. 6, 10, 11, 12, 13, 14.		
Z43	1d. rose-red (1857)		12·00
Z44	1d. rose-red (1864–79)	*From*	15·00
	Plate Nos. 73, 74, 78, 79, 80, 81, 83, 84, 86,		
	87, 90, 91, 93, 94, 96, 97, 100, 101, 106, 107,		
	108, 110, 113, 118, 119, 120, 121, 122, 123,		
	124, 125, 129, 130, 131, 134, 136, 137, 138,		
	140, 142, 143, 144, 145, 147, 148, 149, 150,		
	151, 152, 153, 154, 156, 158, 159, 160, 161,		
	162, 163, 164, 165, 166, 167, 168, 170, 174,		
	176, 177, 178, 179, 180, 181, 182, 184, 185,		
	186, 187, 189, 190, 205.		
Z45	2d. blue (1858–69)	*From*	18·00
	Plate Nos. 8, 9, 13, 14, 15.		
Z46	2½d. rosy mauve (1875) (blued *paper*) .... *From*		75·00
	Plate Nos. 1, 2, 3.		
Z47	2½d. rosy mauve (1875–76)	*From*	40·00
	Plate Nos. 1, 2, 3.		
Z48	2½d. rosy mauve (*Error of Lettering*)		£2250
Z49	2½d. rosy mauve (1876–79)	*From*	30·00
	Plate Nos. 3, 4, 5, 6, 7, 8, 9, 10.		
Z50	3d. carmine-rose (1862)		£150
Z51	3d. rose (1865) (Plate No. 4)		80·00
Z52	3d. rose (1867–73) (Plate Nos. 5, 6, 7, 8, 10)		
Z53	3d. rose (1873–76) (Plate Nos. 12, 16)	*From*	32·00
Z54	4d. rose (1857)		65·00
Z55	4d. red (1862) (Plate Nos. 3, 4)	*From*	55·00
Z56	4d. vermilion (1865–73)	*From*	32·00
	Plate Nos. 7, 8, 9, 10, 11, 12, 13, 14.		
Z57	4d. vermilion (1876) (Plate No. 15).		
Z58	4d. sage-green (1877) (Plate No. 15)		£150
Z59	6d. lilac (1856)		65·00
Z60	6d. lilac (1862) (Plate Nos. 3, 4)	*From*	50·00
Z61	6d. lilac (1865–67) (Plate Nos. 5, 6)	*From*	42·00
Z62	6d. lilac (1867) (Plate No. 6)		55·00
Z63	6d. violet (1867–70) (Plate Nos. 6, 8, 9)	*From*	42·00
Z64	6d. buff (1872–73) (Plate Nos. 11, 12)	*From*	70·00
Z65	6d. pale chestnut (Plate No. 12) (1872)		£3000
Z66	6d. chestnut (1872) (Plate No. 11)		38·00
Z67	6d. grey (1873) (Plate No. 12)		£100
Z68	6d. grey (1874–76)	*From*	32·00
	Plate Nos, 13, 14, 15, 16.		
Z69	8d. orange (1876)		
Z70	9d. straw (1862)		£250
	a. Thick paper.		
Z71	9d. bistre (1862)		
Z72	9d. straw (1867)		
Z73	10d. red-brown (1867)		£225
Z74	1s. green (1856)		£170
Z75	1s. green (1862)		95·00
Z76	1s. green (1862) ("K" *variety*)		
Z77	1s. green (1865) (Plate No. 4)		55·00
Z78	1s. green (1867–73) Plate Nos. 4, 5, 6, 7	*From*	26·00
Z79	1s. green (1873–77)	*From*	38·00
	Plate Nos. 8, 9, 10, 11, 12.		
Z80	2s. blue (1867)		£190
Z81	5s. rose (1867–74) (Plate Nos. 1, 2)	*From*	£375

PRICES FOR STAMPS ON COVER

Nos. 1/41	*from × 10*
Nos. 42/3	*from × 1000*
Nos. 44/83	*from × 5*
Nos. 84/97	*from × 2*
Nos. D57/70	*from × 20*
Nos. D71/76	*from × 50*
Nos. D84/103	*from × 10*
Nos. O64/87	*from × 5*
Nos. O88/101	*from × 2*

(Currency: 40 paras = 1 piastre)

1   **2**   (**3**)

(Typo (1pi) or litho (others) Pellas Brothers, Genoa. Inscr (T **3**) applied typo (1, 2pi.) or litho (others))

1866 (1 Jan). Various designs as T **1** with black inscriptions as T **3**. The lowest group of characters indicates the value. 1pi. no wmk, others W **2** (inverted). P 12½.

1	5pa. grey	60·00	35·00
	a. Greenish grey	60·00	35·00
	b. Imperf (pair)	£225	
	c. Imperf between (pair)	£400	
	d. Perf 12½×13 and compound	80·00	60·00
	e. Perf 13	£350	£400
	w. Wmk upright	£450	£275
2	10pa. brown	70·00	35·00
	a. Imperf (pair)	£200	
	b. Imperf between (pair)	£500	
	c. Perf 12½×13 and compound	£100	60·00
	d. Perf 12½×15	£300	£325
	e. Perf 13	£275	£300
	w. Wmk upright	90·00	38·00
3	20pa. pale blue	85·00	38·00
	a. Greenish blue	85·00	38·00
	b. Imperf (pair)	30·00	
	c. Imperf between (pair)	£500	

	d. Perf 12½×13 and compound	£130	80·00
	e. Perf 13	£550	£350
	w. Wmk upright	85·00	38·00
4	1pi. claret	75·00	5·00
	a. Imperf (pair)	£130	
	b. Imperf between (pair)	£500	
	c. Perf 12½×13 and compound	£110	20·00
	d. Perf 13	£425	£275
	e. Perf 12½×15	£350	
5	2pi. yellow	£110	50·00
	a. Orange-yellow	£110	50·00
	b. Imperf (pair)	£500	
	c. Imperf between (pair)	£600	£500
	d. Bisected diag (1pi.) (*on cover*)	†	£2750
	e. Perf 12½×13 and compound	£180	70·00
	f. Perf 12½×15	£200	
	w. Wmk upright	£110	50·00
6	5pi. rose	£300	£190
	a. Imperf (pair)	£2000	
	b. Imperf between (pair)	£1200	
	c. Perf 12½×13 and compound	£350	
	d. Error. Inscr 10pi., perf 12½×15 ...	£1000	£900
	da. Imperf.	£750	
	e. Perf 13	£800	
	w. Wmk upright	£300	£190
7	10pi. slate	£350	£300
	a. Imperf (pair)	£750	
	b. Imperf between (pair)	£2250	
	c. Perf 12½×13 and compound	£500	£475
	d. Perf 13	£1900	
	e. Perf 12½×15	£325	£300

The 2pi. bisected was authorised for use between 16 and 31 July 1867 at Alexandria or Cairo.

Stamps perforated 12½, 12½×13 and compound, and 13 occur in the same sheets with the 13 gauge usually used on the top, left-hand, right-hand or bottom rows. Each sheet of 200 contained one stamp perforated 13 all round, two 13 on three sides, one 13 on two adjacent sides, 18 13×12½, eight 12½×13, eight 13 on one side and 18 13 at top or bottom. So many sheets were received imperforate or part-perforated that some stock was passed to V. Penasson of Alexandria who applied the 12½×15 gauge.

The two halves of each background differ in minor details of the ornamentation. All values can be found with either half at the top.

Proofs of all values exist on smooth paper, without watermark. Beware of forgeries.

All values also exist with the watermark reversed (*same price as upright*) or inverted and reversed (*same price as inverted*).

4   **5**

6

(Des F. Hoff. Litho V. Penasson, Alexandria)

1867 (1 Aug)–**71**. W **6** (impressed on reverse). P 15×12½.

11	**4**	5pa. orange-yellow	50·00	8·50
		a. Imperf (pair)		
		b. Imperf between (horiz pair)	£200	
		x. Wmk impressed on face		
12		10pa. dull lilac	90·00	13·00
		b. Bright mauve (7.69)	65·00	9·00
		ba. Bisected diag (5pa.) (*on piece*) (17.11.71)	†	£750
		w. Wmk inverted	£300	£200
		x. Wmk impressed on face		
13		20pa. deep blue-green	£130	13·00
		a. Pale blue-green	£130	13·00
		b. Yellowish green (7.69)	£130	12·00
		x. Wmk impressed on face		
14	**5**	1pi. dull rose-red *to* rose	32·00	1·00
		a. Lake	£170	
		b. Imperf (pair)	£110	
		c. Imperf between (horiz pair)	£200	
		d. Bisected diag (20pa.) (*on piece*) ..	†	£750
		e. Rouletted	65·00	
		w. Wmk inverted	60·00	30·00
		x. Wmk impressed on face		
15		2pi. bright blue	£140	17·00
		a. Pale blue	£140	17·00
		b. Imperf (pair)	£650	
		c. Imperf between (pair)	£550	£750
		d. Bisected diag (1pi.) (*on cover*) ...	†	—
		e. Perf 12½	£250	
16		5pi. brown	£300	£180
		x. Wmk impressed on face		

Each value was engraved four times, the resulting blocks being used to form sheets of 200. There are therefore four types showing minor variations for each value.

No. 12ba was used on newspapers from Alexandria between 17 November 1871 and 20 January 1872.

Stamps printed both sides, both imperf and perf, come from printer's waste. The 1pi. rose without watermark is a proof.

7   **8** (Side panels transposed and inverted)

8a (I)   **8a (II)**

WATERMARK 8a. There are two types of this watermark which, as they are not always easy to distinguish, we do not list separately. Type II is slightly wider and less deep and the crescent is flatter than in Type I. The width measurement for Type I is generally about 14 mm and for Type II about 15 mm, but there is some variation within the sheets for both types.

Nos. 26/43, 45/7a, 49/a, 50/1 and 57 come with Type I only. Nos. 44a, 48/a, 52, 54b, 73/7 and 78 exist with both types of watermark (but No. 83 and official overprints on these stamps still require research); our prices are generally for Type II. Other watermarked issues between 1888 and 1907 have Type II watermarks only.

1872 (1 Jan)–**75**. T **7** (the so-called "Penasson" printing*). Thick opaque paper. W **8a**. P 12½×13½.

A. LITHOGRAPHED

26	**7**	20pa. blue (*shades*)	£180	65·00
		a. Imperf (pair)		
		b. Imperf between (pair)	—	£2250
		c. Perf 13½	£300	70·00
		w. Wmk inverted	£300	85·00
27		1pi. red (*shades*)	£325	18·00
		a. Perf 13½	£850	38·00
		w. Wmk inverted	£650	35·00

B. TYPOGRAPHED

28	**7**	5pa. brown (*shades*)	12·00	7·50
		a. Perf 13½	30·00	9·50
		w. Wmk inverted	£100	50·00
29		10pa. mauve	6·00	3·00
		a. Perf 13½	6·00	3·25
		w. Wmk inverted	40·00	25·00
30		20pa. blue (*shades*)	65·00	5·00
		a. Perf 13½	90·00	20·00
		w. Wmk inverted	60·00	30·00
31		1pi. rose-red	70·00	1·25
		a. Bisected (20pa.) (*on piece* with No. 31) (7.75)	†	£850
		b. Perf 13½	90·00	3·50
		w. Wmk inverted	65·00	25·00
32		2pi. chrome-yellow	90·00	4·00
		a. Bisected (1pi.) (*on piece*) (4.73). .	†	£950
		b. Perf 13½	25·00	5·00
33		2½pi. violet	90·00	27·00
		a. Perf 13½	£800	£200
		w. Wmk inverted	£100	32·00
34		5pi. yellow-green	£200	50·00
		a. Tête-bêche (pair)	£11000	
		b. Perf 13½	£300	60·00
		w. Wmk inverted	£225	90·00

*It is now accepted that stamps in both processes were printed by the Government Printing Works at Bûlâq, Cairo, although Penasson may have been involved in the production of these stamps.

The lithographed and typographed stamps each show the characteristic differences between these two processes:—

The typographed stamps show the coloured lines of the design impressed into the paper and an accumulation of ink along the margins of the lines.

The lithographed stamps are essentially flat in appearance, without the heaping of the ink. Many of the 20pa. show evidence of retouching, particularly of the outer frame lines.

The 1p. bisected was used at Gedda, on 5 July 1875, or Scio, and the 2pi. vertically bisected at Gallipoli or Scio. The price quoted for No. 31a is for usage at Scio, with usage at Gedda worth double.

See also footnote below No. 41.

1874 (Nov)–**75**. Typo from new stereos at Bûlâq, on thinner paper. W **8a**. P 12½.

35	**8**	5pa. brown (3.75)	35·00	3·75
		a. Tête-bêche (vert pair)	60·00	60·00
		b. Tête-bêche (horiz pair)	£275	£300
		c. Imperf (pair)	£110	£130
		d. Imperf between (pair)	£325	
		ew. Wmk inverted	35·00	3·75
		f. Perf 13½×12½	38·00	3·75
		fa. Tête-bêche (vert pair)	70·00	70·00
		fb. Tête-bêche (horiz pair)	£325	£350
		fw. Wmk inverted	38·00	3·75
36	**7**	10pa. grey-lilac (*shades*) (8.75)	17·00	5·00
		a. Tête-bêche (vert pair)	£150	£170
		b. Tête-bêche (horiz pair)		
		c. Imperf (pair)		
		dw. Wmk inverted	17·00	5·00
		e. Perf 13½×12½	48·00	4·25
		ea. Tête-bêche (vert pair)	£160	£180
		eb. Tête-bêche (horiz pair)		
		ew. Wmk inverted	48·00	4·50
37		20pa. grey-blue (*shades*) (2.75)	£110	3·00
		b. Bisected diag (10pa.) (*on cover*) .	†	
		cw. Wmk inverted	£110	3·00
		d. Perf 13½×12½	16·00	3·50
		da. Imperf between (pair)	£325	
		dw. Wmk inverted	16·00	3·50
38		1pi. rose (*shades*) (4.75)	11·00	65
		a. Tête-bêche (vert pair)	90·00	90·00
		b. Tête-bêche (horiz pair)	£300	£300
		c. Imperf (pair)	£200	
		d. Imperf between (pair)	£400	£400
		ew. Wmk inverted	13·00	1·50
		f. Perf 13½×12½	85·00	1·25
		fa. Tête-bêche (vert pair)	£450	£450
		fb. Tête-bêche (horiz pair)	—	£450
		fw. Wmk inverted	90·00	7·50
39		2pi. yellow (12.74)	85·00	4·75
		a. Tête-bêche (pair)	£400	£400
		bw. Wmk inverted	£100	7·50
		c. Perf 13½×12½	5·50	6·50
		ca. Tête-bêche (pair)	£450	£400
		cb. Bisected diag (1pi.) (*on cover*) (13.4.75)	†	£4500
		cw. Wmk inverted	7·50	7·00
		d. Perf 12½×13½	75·00	16·00
		da. Tête-bêche (pair)	£950	£650
		dw. Wmk inverted	95·00	19·00

40		2½pi. violet	8·50	7·50
	a.	Tête-bêche (pair)	£400	£400
	bw.	Wmk inverted	12·00	8·50
	c.	Perf 12½×13½	75·00	19·00
	ca.	Tête-bêche (pair)	£1000	£1000
	cw.	Wmk inverted	65·00	25·00
41		5pi. green	60·00	20·00
	a.	Imperf (pair)	†	—
	bw.	Wmk inverted	£100	50·00
	c.	Perf 12½×13½	£350	£275

The 2pi. bisected was used at Gedda and are all postmarked 13 April.

The 1872 printings have a thick line of colour in the top margin of the sheet and the other margins are all plain, an exception being the 5pa., which on the majority of the sheets has the line at the right-hand side of the sheet. The 1874–75 printings have a wide fancy border all round every sheet.

The 1872 printings are on thick opaque paper, with the impressions sharp and clear. The 1874–75 printings are on thinner paper, often semi-transparent and oily in appearance, and having the impressions very blurred and badly printed. These are only general distinctions and there are a number of exceptions.

The majority of the 1874–75 stamps have blind or defective perforations, while the 1872 stamps have clean-cut perfs.

The two printings of the 5pa. to 1pi. values can be identified by their perforation gauges, which are always different; the 5pa. also differs in the side panels (Types 7 and 8). Only the perf 12½×13½ varieties of the three higher values may need to be distinguished. As well as the general points noted above the following features are also helpful:

2pi. In the 1872 issue the left-hand Arabic character in the top inscription is one complete shape, resembling an inverted "V" with a horizontal line on top. In the 1874 issue the character has three separate components, a line with two dots below.

2½pi. There is a distinct thinning of the frame line in the top right-hand corner of the 1872 issue. This sometimes takes the form of a short white line within the frame.

5pi. In the 1872 issue the top frame line is split for its entire length; in the 1874 issue the line is solid for all or most of its length. The 1872 printing always has a white dot above the "P" of "PIASTRE"; this dot appears on only a few positions of the 1874 printing.

There seem to be many different compositions of the sheets containing the tête-bêche varieties, settings being known with one, three, nine and ten inverted stamps in various sheets. Sheets of the 5pa. are known with nine of the 20 horizontal rows inverted, giving vertical tête-bêche pairs; four stamps were inverted within their row giving four horizontal tête-bêche pairs.

Examples of some values exist without watermark due to the paper being misplaced on the press.

(9) (9a)

1878 (Dec). No. 40 surch as T **9** at Bûlâq. P 12½.

42	**7**	5pa. on 2½pi. violet	6·50	6·00
	a.	Surch inverted	70·00	70·00
	b.	Tête-bêche (pair)	£5000	
	c.	Imperf (pair)	£900	
	d.	Surch as 9a	£100	£120
	dw.	Wmk inverted	7·50	7·50
	e.	Perf 12½×13½	6·50	8·00
	ea.	Surch inverted	£140	£140
	eb.	Tête-bêche (pair)	£5000	
	ed.	Surch as Type 9a	£100	£120
	ew.	Wmk inverted	7·50	7·50
43		10pa. on 2½ pi. violet	11·00	10·00
	a.	Surch inverted	75·00	75·00
	b.	Tête-bêche (pair)	£2250	
	c.	Surch as Type 9a	£100	£120
	dw.	Wmk inverted	15·00	15·00
	e.	Perf 12½×13½	16·00	15·00
	ea.	Surch inverted	£110	£110
	eb.	Tête-bêche (pair)	£2750	
	ed.	Surch as Type 9a	£100	£120
	ew.	Wmk inverted	25·00	25·00

Surcharge Type 9a, with guide marks in the corners, is assumed to be from an early printing. Guide marks are also known on stamps with the surcharge inverted.

10 11 12

13 14 15

(Typo De La Rue)

1879 (1 Apr). Ordinary paper. W **8a** (inverted on 10pa.). P 14.

44	**10**	5pa. deep brown	6·00	2·25
	a.	Pale brown	6·00	2·25
	w.	Wmk inverted	£120	£100
45	**11**	10pa. reddish lilac	75·00	3·00
	w.	Wmk upright	†	£100
46	**12**	20pa. pale blue	80·00	3·00
	w.	Wmk inverted	95·00	15·00
47	**13**	1pi. rose	50·00	20
	a.	Pale rose	50·00	20
	w.	Wmk inverted	65·00	10·00
48	**14**	2pi. orange	50·00	50
	a.	Orange-yellow	50·00	1·25
	w.	Wmk inverted	50·00	2·00
49	**15**	5pi. green	70·00	18·00
	a.	Blue-green	70·00	17·00
	w.	Wmk inverted	65·00	18·00

See also Nos. 50/6.

Khedive Tewfik
26 June 1879–7 January 1892

British troops were landed in Egypt in 1882 to secure the Suez Canal against a nationalist movement led by Arabi Pasha. Arabi was defeated at Tel-el-Kebir and British troops remained in Egypt until 1954. A British resident and consul-general advised the Khedive. Holders of this post were Sir Evelyn Baring (Lord Cromer), 1883–1907; Sir Eldon Gorst, 1907–11; and Lord Kitchener, 1911–14.

1881–1902. Colours changed. Ordinary paper. W **8a** (inverted on No. 50). P 14.

50	**11**	10pa. claret (1.81)	70·00	14·00
51		10pa. bluish grey (25.1.82)	28·00	2·00
	w.	Wmk inverted	50·00	3·25
52		10pa. green (15.12.84)	4·00	3·25
	w.	Wmk inverted	30·00	10·00
53	**12**	20pa. rose-carmine (15.12.84)	30·00	1·00
	a.	Bright rose	30·00	1·00
	w.	Wmk inverted	42·00	7·00
54	**13**	1pi. blue (15.12.84)	15·00	1·00
	a.	Deep ultramarine	15·00	1·00
	b.	Pale ultramarine	8·00	70
	cw.	Wmk inverted	27·00	10·00
	d.	Chalk-surfaced paper. Ultramarine (1902)	3·00	10
	da.	Blue	3·00	10
	dw.	Wmk inverted	75·00	40·00
55	**14**	2pi. orange-brown (1.8.93)	12·00	30
	aw.	Wmk inverted	80·00	40·00
	b.	Chalk-surfaced paper (1902)	12·00	1·00
	ba.	Orange	23·00	1·25
	bw.	Wmk inverted	—	30·00
56	**15**	5pi. pale grey (15.12.84)	25·00	50
	a.	Slate	25·00	50
	bw.	Wmk inverted	—	—
	c.	Chalk-surfaced paper. Slate-grey (1902)	16·00	15
	cw.	Wmk inverted	—	£100

(17)

1884 (1 Feb). Surch with T **17** at Bûlâq.

57	**15**	20pa. on 5pi. green	7·50	2·25
	a.	Surch inverted	65·00	60·00
	w.	Wmk inverted	50·00	30·00

(New Currency: 1000 milliemes = 100 piastres = £1 Egyptian)

18 19 20

21 22

1888 (1 Jan)–**1909.** Ordinary paper. W **8a**. P 14.

58	**18**	1m. pale brown	3·75	10
	a.	Deep brown	3·75	10
	bw.	Wmk inverted	25·00	4·00
	c.	Chalk-surfaced paper. Pale brown (1902)	3·75	10
	ca.	Deep brown	3·75	10
	cw.	Wmk inverted	40·00	5·00
59	**19**	2m. blue-green	4·00	30
	a.	Green	1·75	10
	bw.	Wmk inverted	40·00	5·00
	c.	Chalk-surfaced paper. Green (1902)	1·75	10
	cw.	Wmk inverted	40·00	5·00
60	**20**	3m. maroon (1.1.92)	11·00	3·50
61		3m. yellow (1.8.93)	10·00	1·00
	a.	Orange-yellow	5·00	15
	bw.	Wmk inverted	45·00	15·00
	c.	Chalk-surfaced paper. Orange-yellow (1902)	4·00	10
	cw.	Wmk inverted	75·00	30·00
62	**21**	4m. vermilion (chalk-surfaced paper) (1906)	5·50	10
	a.	Bisected (2m.) (on cover) (11.09)	†	£2500
	w.	Wmk inverted	—	60·00
63		5m. rose-carmine	11·00	55
	a.	Bright rose	5·50	10
	b.	Aniline rose	5·50	10
	cw.	Wmk inverted	—	75·00
	d.	Chalk-surfaced paper. Rose (1902)	3·00	10
	da.	Deep aniline rose	6·00	35
64	**22**	10p. mauve (1.1.89)	15·00	1·75
	a.	Aniline mauve	18·00	1·75
	bw.	Wmk inverted	—	50·00
	c.	Chalk-surfaced paper. Mauve (1902)	22·00	50

No. 62a was used at Gizira in conjunction with the 1m. value and the Official, No. O64.

No. 63d exists in coils constructed from normal sheets.

Khedive Abbas Hilmi
7 January 1892–19 December 1914

A set of three values, in a common design showing Cleopatra and a Nile boat, was prepared in 1895 for the Nile Winter Fête, but not issued. Examples survive from the De La Rue archives.

29 Nile Feluccas **30** Cleopatra from Temple of Dendera **31** Ras-el-Tin Palace, Alexandria

32 Pyramids of Giza **33** Sphinx **34** Colossi of Amenophis III at Thebes

35 Archway of Ptolemy III, Karnak **36** Citadel, Cairo

37 Rock Temple of Abu Simbel **38** Aswân Dam

(Typo D.L.R.)

1914 (8 Jan). W **8a**. P 13½×14 (1m. to 10m.) or 14 (20m. to 200m.).

73	**29**	1m. sepia	1·50	40
	w.	Wmk inverted	—	75·00
74	**30**	2m. green	4·00	20
	w.	Wmk inverted	—	40·00
75	**31**	3m. yellow-orange	3·75	35
	a.	Double impression	—	
	w.	Wmk inverted	—	40·00
76	**32**	4m. vermilion	6·50	65
	w.	Wmk inverted	—	40·00
77	**33**	5m. lake	4·25	10
	a.	Wmk sideways star to right* (booklets)	10·00	26·00
	aw.	Wmk sideways star to left	10·00	26·00
	w.	Wmk inverted	15·00	10·00
78	**34**	10m. dull blue	9·50	10
	w.	Wmk inverted	25·00	25·00
79	**35**	20m. olive	9·50	30
	w.	Wmk inverted	60·00	40·00
80	**36**	50m. purple	26·00	2·25
	w.	Wmk inverted	—	50·00
81	**37**	100m. slate	26·00	2·00
82	**38**	200m. maroon	35·00	5·50
73/82		Set of 10	£110	10·50

*The normal sideways watermark shows the star to the right of the crescent, as seen from the back of the stamp.

All the above exist imperforate, but imperforate stamps without watermark are proofs.

See also Nos. 84/97.

BRITISH PROTECTORATE

On 18 December 1914, after war with Turkey had begun, Egypt was declared to be a British protectorate. Abbas Hilmi was deposed, and his uncle, Hussein Kamil, was proclaimed Sultan of Egypt.

Sultan Hussein Kamil
19 December 1914–9 October 1917

(39)

1915 (15 Oct). No. 75 surch with T **39**, at Bûlâq.

83	**31**	2m. on 3m. yellow-orange	1·00	2·50
	a.	Surch inverted	£225	£200
	b.	Surch double, one albino	£150	
	w.	Wmk inverted	—	75·00

Sultan Ahmed Fuad
9 October 1917–15 March 1922

40 (A) (B)

41 Statue of Rameses II, Luxor   **42**

(Typo Harrison)

1921–22. As Nos. 73/82 and new designs (15m.). W **40**. P 14 (20, 50, 100m.) or 13½×14 (others).

84	29	1m. sepia (A)	1·50	4·75
		a. Two dots omitted (B) (R. 10/10)	35·00	55·00
		w. Wmk inverted	10·00	8·50
85	30	2m. green	10·00	6·00
		a. Imperf between (pair)		
		w. Wmk inverted	16·00	10·00
86		2m. vermilion (1922)	7·50	3·25
		w. Wmk inverted	16·00	10·00
87	31	3m. yellow-orange	11·00	7·00
		w. Wmk inverted	17·00	10·00
88	32	4m. green (1922)	10·00	8·00
		w. Wmk inverted	—	
89	33	5m. lake (1.21)	8·50	2·25
		a. Imperf between (vert pair)		
		w. Wmk inverted	15·00	10·00
90		5m. pink (11.21)	17·00	20
		w. Wmk inverted	21·00	10·00
91	34	10m. dull blue	14·00	1·25
		w. Wmk inverted	—	10·00
92		10m. lake (9.22)	4·50	1·25
		w. Wmk inverted	—	10·00
93	41	15m. indigo (3.22)	13·00	20
		w. Wmk inverted	—	8·00
94	42	15m. indigo	55·00	6·50
		w. Wmk inverted	60·00	11·00
95	35	20m. olive	13·00	30
		w. Wmk inverted	21·00	10·00
96	36	50m. purple	13·00	1·75
		w. Wmk inverted	20·00	12·00
97	37	100m. slate (1922)	90·00	7·50
84/97		Set of 14	£225	45·00

The 15m. Type **42** was printed first; but because the Arabic inscription at right was felt to be unsuitable the stamps were withheld and the corrected Type **41** printed and issued. Type **42** was released later.

STAMP BOOKLETS

1903 (1 Jan). Black on pink cover inscr "Egyptian Post Office" in English and French. Stapled.
SB1   121m. booklet containing 24×5m. (No. 63/d) in blocks of 6 .... £5000

1903 (1 July). Black on blue cover inscr "Egyptian Post Office" in English and French. Stapled.
SB2   73m. booklet containing 24×3m. (No. 61/bw) in blocks of 6 .... £8500

1911 (1 July). Black on pink cover inscr "Egyptian Post Office" in English and Arabic. Stapled.
SB3   120m. Contents as No. SB1 .... £4500

1914 (8 Jan). Black on pink cover inscr "Egyptian Post Office" in English and Arabic. Stapled.
SB4   125m. booklet containing 24×5m. (No. 77a) in blocks of 6 .... £4500

1919 (1 Jan). Black on pink cover inscr "Egyptian Post Office" in English and Arabic. Stapled.
SB5   120m. Contents as No. SB4 .... £3250

1921 (12 June). Deep blue on pink cover inscr "POST OFFICE" in English and Arabic. Stapled.
SB6   120m. booklet containing 24×5m. (No. 89) in blocks of 6 .... £2500
   a. Stitched £2500

1921 (Nov). Deep blue or pink cover inscr "POST OFFICE" in English and Arabic. Stapled.
SB7   120m. booklet containing 24×5m. (No. 90) in blocks of 6 .... £2250

POSTAGE DUE STAMPS

D **16**   D **23**   D **24**

(Des L. Barkhausen. Litho V. Penasson, Alexandria)

1884 (1 Jan). W **6** (impressed on reverse). P 10½.

D57	D **16**	10pa. red	65·00	9·00
		a. Imperf (pair)	£120	
		b. Imperf between (pair)	£140	
		x. Wmk impressed on face		
D58		20pa. red	£130	48·00
		x. Wmk impressed on face		
D59		1pi. red	£150	50·00
		x. Wmk impressed on face		

D60		2pi. red	£225	12·00
		w. Wmk inverted	£325	22·00
		x. Wmk impressed on face		
D61		5pi. red	15·00	50·00
		x. Wmk impressed on face		

1886 (1 Aug)–**87**. No wmk. P 10½.

D62	D **16**	10pa. rose-red (1887)	80·00	23·00
		a. Imperf between (pair)	£120	
D63		20pa. rose-red	£250	50·00
		a. Imperf between (pair)		
D64		1pi. rose-red	42·00	12·00
		a. Imperf between (pair)	£150	£150
D65		2pi. rose-red	48·00	4·00
		a. Imperf between (pair)	£150	

Specialists distinguish four types of each value in both these issues.

(Litho V. Penasson, Alexandria)

1888 (1 Jan). No wmk. P 11½.

D66	D **23**	2m. green	29·00	38·00
		a. Imperf between (pair)	£225	£225
		b. Imperf (pair)		
D67		5m. rose-carmine	50·00	32·00
		a. Imperf (pair)		
D68		1p. blue	£150	35·00
		a. Imperf between (pair)	£200	
D69		2p. orange	£160	19·00
D70		5p. grey	£250	£225
		a. With stop after left-hand "PIASTRES"	£325	£250

Specialists distinguish four types of each value. No. D70a occurs on all examples of one of these types in the sheet except that on R. 2/1. Beware of forgeries of the 5p.

(Typo De La Rue)

1889 (Apr)–**1907**. Ordinary paper. W **8a**. P 14.

D71	D **24**	2m. green	13·00	50
		a. Bisected (1m.) (on cover with unbisected 2m.) (2.98)	†	£500
		bw. Wmk inverted	14·00	3·00
		c. Chalk-surfaced paper (1906)	19·00	50
D72		4m. maroon	7·00	50
		aw. Wmk inverted	7·50	1·00
		b. Chalk-surfaced paper (1906)	7·00	50
D73		1p. ultramarine	5·50	50
		aw. Wmk inverted	8·50	3·00
		b. Chalk-surfaced paper (1906)	6·50	50
D74		2p. orange	5·50	70
		bw. Wmk inverted	5·00	70
		c. Chalk-surfaced paper (1907)	5·00	70

No. D71a was authorised for use on Egyptian Army letters from the Sudan campaign which were only charged 3m. postage due. See also Nos. 84/6 for stamps with watermark sideways.

(D **26**)   (D **27**)

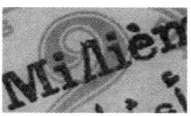

Slanting 'I' (R. 5/2)

Type D 26

The Arabic figure at right is less than 2 mm from the next character, which consists of a straight stroke only.

Type D 27

The distance is 3 mm and the straight character has a comma-like character above it. There are other minor differences.

1898 (7 May)–**1907**. No. D74 surch at Bûlâq. Ordinary paper.

(a) With Type D 26

D75	D **24**	3m. on 2p. orange	3·25	8·50
		a. Surch inverted	60·00	75·00
		b. Pair, one without surch	£200	
		c. Arabic "2" for "3"	60·00	
		d. Arabic "3" over "2"	£100	

No. D75c occurred in the first printing on positions 10, 20, 30, 40, 50 and 60 of the pane of 60 (the Arabic figure is the right-hand character of the second line—see illustration on page xxxi). In the second printing the correct figure was printed on top to form No. D75d. The error was corrected in subsequent printings.

(b) With Type D 27 (11.04)

D76	D **24**	3m. on 2p. orange	7·00	22·00
		a. Surch inverted	50·00	60·00
		b. Chalk-surfaced paper (1907)	7·00	22·00
		ba. Surch inverted	60·00	60·00
		bb. Surch double	£250	
		c. Slanting 'I'	50·00	

1914–15. As Nos. D71/3 but wmk sideways*.

D84	D **24**	2m. bright green (1915)	30·00	5·50
		w. Wmk star to left of crescent	40·00	16·00
D85		4m. maroon	30·00	24·00
		w. Wmk star to left of crescent	42·00	
D86		1p. dull ultramarine	45·00	14·00
		w. Wmk star to left of crescent	40·00	15·00

*The normal sideways watermark shows star to right of crescent, as seen from the back of the stamp.

D **43**   D **44**

(Typo Harrison)

1921 (Apr)–**22**. Chalk-surfaced paper. W **40** (sideways*). P 14×13½.

D98	D **43**	2m. green	4·00	9·50
		w. Wmk stars below crescents	13·00	9·50
D99		2m. scarlet (1922)	2·75	4·00
		w. Wmk stars below crescents	10·00	6·50
D100		4m. scarlet	9·00	26·00
D101		4m. green (1922)	9·50	3·50
		w. Wmk stars below crescents	16·00	8·00
D102	D **44**	10m. deep slate-blue (11.21)	15·00	35·00
D103		10m. lake (1922)	9·00	2·75
		w. Wmk stars below crescents	14·00	5·00
D98/103		Set of 6	45·00	70·00

*The normal sideways watermark shows the stars above the crescents.

OFFICIAL STAMPS

O **25**

O.H.H.S.
امیری

(O **28**)

"O.H.H.S."

(O **29**)

(Typo De La Rue)

1893 (1 Jan)–**1914**. Ordinary paper. W **8a**. P 14.

O64	O **25**	(–) chestnut	4·50	10
		a. Chalk-surfaced paper (1903)	7·00	50
		bw. Wmk inverted	9·50	
		c. Wmk sideways star to right.		
		Chalk-surfaced paper (1914)	12·00	12·00
		cw. Wmk sideways star to left.		

From January 1907 No. O64 was used on most official mail to addresses within Egypt. In 1907 it was replaced by Nos. O73/8, but the use of No. O64 for unregistered official mail to Egyptian addresses was resumed on 1 January 1909.

After No. O64c was withdrawn in 1915 the remaining stock was surcharged 1p., 2p., 3p. or 5p. for fiscal use.

1907 (1 Feb–Aug). Nos. 54da, 56c, 58c, 59c, 61c and 63d optd with Type O **28** by De La Rue.

O73	18	1m. pale brown	1·75	30
O74	19	2m. green	4·25	10
		a. Opt double		
O75	20	3m. orange-yellow	8·00	1·25
O76	21	5m. rose	15·00	10
O77	1	1p. blue	6·00	20
O78	15	5p. slate-grey (8.07)	16·00	12·00
O73/8		Set of 6	45·00	12·00

Nos. O73/8 were used on all official mail from February 1907 until 1 January 1909 after which their use was restricted to registered items and those sent to addresses overseas.

1913 (Nov). No. 63d optd at Bûlâq.

*(a) With Type O **29***

O79	21	5m. rose	—	£750
		a. Opt inverted	—	£6000

*(b) As Type O **29** but without inverted commas*

O80	21	5m. rose	13·00	70
		a. No stop after "S" (R. 11/10)	60·00	16·00
		b. Opt inverted	—	75·00

O.H.H.S.
امیری
(O **38**)

O.H.H.S.
أمیری
(O **39**)

O.H.H.S.
أمیری
(O **43**)

1914 (Dec)–**15**. Stamps of 1902–6 and 1914 optd with Type O **38** at Bûlâq.

O83	29	1m. sepia (1.15)	2·75	6·50
		a. No stop after "S" (R. 10/10)	15·00	30·00
		w. Wmk inverted	†	—
O84	19	2m. green (3.15)	8·00	15·00
		a. No stop after "S"	19·00	32·00
		b. Opt inverted	35·00	35·00
		c. Opt double	£500	
O85	31	3m. yellow-orange (3.15)	5·00	8·50
		a. No stop after "S" (R. 10/10)	16·00	30·00
O86	21	4m. vermilion (12.14)	11·00	8·00
		a. Opt inverted	£190	£140
		b. Pair, one without opt		
O87	33	5m. lake (1.15)	4·25	4·00
		a. No stop after "S" (R. 10/10)	16·00	23·00
O83/7		Set of 5	28·00	38·00

No. O84a occurs on three positions from the first printing and on two different positions from the second. Nos. O83a, O85a and O87a usually show a faint trace of the stop.

1915 (Oct). Nos. 59c, 62 and 77 optd lithographically with Type O **39** at Bûlâq.

O88	19	2m. green	7·00	7·00
		a. Opt inverted	20·00	20·00
		b. Opt double	25·00	
O89	21	4m. vermilion	15·00	16·00
O90	33	5m. lake	19·00	2·25
		a. Pair, one without opt	£275	

1922. Nos. 84, etc optd lithographically with Type O **43** at Bûlâq.

O98	29	1m. sepia (A) (28.6)	3·50	21·00
		a. Two dots omitted (B)	£200	
		w. Wmk inverted		
O99	30	2m. vermilion (16.6)	14·00	30·00
O100	31	3m. yellow-orange (28.6)	65·00	£140
O101	33	5m. pink (13.3)	29·00	7·50

Egypt was declared to be an independent kingdom on 15 March 1922, and Sultan Ahmed Fuad became king.

Later stamp issues will be found listed in the Stanley Gibbons North-East Africa catalogue.

ANDREW PROMOTING PHILATELY ON THE ALAN TITCHMARSH SHOW ITV

Selling Your Stamps?

Summary Tip #20:
5 Different Ways to Sell your Stamps: Dealer 'runners'/ Private Treaty

by Andrew McGavin

Dear Colleague,

In Part 2 of 'Selling Your Stamps' (Page 98) we discussed the advantages of direct sale to dealers and how with careful handling and awareness of the 'strength of your collection' it is often possible to obtain more for your collection selling directly to dealers than by selling through auction.

In Part 4 of 'Selling your Stamps' we'll discuss the potential advantages and disadvantages of selling through auction on your own account .... but in this article we'll deal with two lesser known but nevertheless important aspects of selling your stamps .... the first being Dealers 'runners'.

Before you even start to try selling your stamps; preparation is all. Make some research:

1. Draw up a list of whom you consider as a possible target to sell / handle your collection. ..... then consider –

2. Why have I chosen those dealers/ organisations ?

Here's something to think about ... for the best part of 20 years I watched the same advertisements extolling the merits of selling to this or that particular dealer ... but try as I might – I never once saw an advertisement by those companies to sell stamps. This was in 'pre-internet' days ... nowadays people trade on the internet with all manner of weird and unusual trading names, sometimes to disguise who they actually are – but in those days traditional selling 'avenues' were shops, stamp fairs, auctions, approvals, and retail/mail-order lists ....

... so why was it impossible to find out how those dealers actually conducted their business? The answer was simple – they sold to other dealers – they rarely if ever sold to collectors – they were Dealers 'runners'. Now for you to part with your beloved collection to the first dealer that you contact does not necessarily mean that you have made a mistake ... but, if that dealer writes you out a cheque ... and almost before the ink has even dried on it – (probably before you have presented the cheque at your bank) ... he or she is at the nearest big dealer 50 miles away being paid a profit upon the price you sold your collection for – this is NOT in your best interest.

...but try as I might – I never once saw an advertisement by those companies to sell stamps.

So what should you be looking for? You should be looking for an organisation / dealer that you can see and understand how they conduct their business. Dealers that sell to other dealers are unlikely to be paying the best price.

Private Treaty: What is it?

The idea of Private Treaty is that collectors 'place' their collection with a dealer or auction that charges a small commission to sell their collection outright. Sometimes it is claimed that the Buyer will pay the commission so that the collector pays no charges whatsoever. Historically 'Private Treaty' has acquired notoriety as an excuse for the company handling the transaction to 'buy-in' the collection for themselves. Maybe collectors and dealers should forget the concept of private treaty in favour of an open approach whereby the dealer/auction explains that they are purchasing on their own account ... or will charge a small percentage for handling/ passing the collector/collection to a more appropriate buyer. In Part 4 of 'Selling your Stamps?' we'll discuss consigning your stamps for sale by auction.

Happy collecting from us all,

PS. If you find this 'tip' interesting please forward it to a philatelic friend.

Andrew McGavin
Managing Director: Universal Philatelic Auctions, Omniphil & Avon Approvals, Avon Mixtures, Universal Philatelic (Ebay)

To read the rest of this series 'SELLING YOUR STAMPS?' see the relevant pages listed below:

Summary Tip 18 – page 42 (Australia)
Summary Tip 19 – page 98 (Bechuanaland)
Summary Tip 20 – page 210 (Egypt)
Summary Tip 21 –page 272 (India)

To read the final instalment, Summary Tip 22 – 'Selling via Online Auction' simply e-mail and request to: *info@upastampauctions.co.uk*

Also, at the back of this catalogue to see how UPA can pay you upto 36% more for your collection

EGYPTIAN POST OFFICES ABROAD

From 1865 Egypt operated various post offices in foreign countries. No special stamps were issued for these offices and use in them of unoverprinted Egyptian stamps can only be identified by the cancellation. Stamps with such cancellations are worth more than the used prices quoted in the Egypt listings.

Such offices operated in the following countries. An * indicates that details will be found under that heading elsewhere in the catalogue.

ETHIOPIA

MASSAWA. *Open Nov 1867 to 5 Dec 1885. Postmark types* A (*also without* REGIE), B, C, D. An *Arabic seal type is also known on stampless covers.*

SENHIT (near Keren). *Open 1878 to April 1885. Only one cover, cancelled "Mouderie Senhit" in 1879, is known, together with one showing possible hand-drawn cancellation.*

A post office is also recorded at Harar in 1878, but no postal marking has so far been reported.

SOMALILAND*

Unoverprinted stamps of Egypt used from 1876 until 1884.

SUDAN*

Unoverprinted stamps of Egypt used from 1867 until 1897.

TURKISH EMPIRE

The offices are listed according to the spelling on the cancellation. The present-day name (if different) and country are given in brackets.

ALESSANDRETTA (Iskenderun, Turkey). *Open 14 July 1870 to Feb 1872. Postmark types* E, I.

BAIROUT (Beirut, Lebanon). *Open 14 July 1870 to Feb 1872. Postmark types* E, J.

CAVALA (Kavala, Greece). *Open 14 July 1870 to Feb 1872. Postmark type* E.

COSTANTINOPOLI (Istanbul, Turkey). *Open 13 June 1865 to 30 June 1881. Postmark types* E, F, O.

DARDANELLI (Canakkle, Turkey). *Open 10 June 1868 to 30 June 1881. Postmark types* H, K.

DJEDDAH, *see* GEDDA.

GALIPOLI (Gelibolu, Turkey). *Open 10 June 1868 to 30 June 1881. Postmark types* E, L.

GEDDA, DJEDDAH (Jeddah, Saudi Arabia). *Open 8 June 1865 to 30 June 1881. Postmark types* F, G (*also with year replacing solid half-circle*), O (*all spelt* GEDDA), D (*spelt* DJEDDAH).

JAFFA (Jaffa, Israel). *Open 14 July 1870 to Feb 1872. Postmark type* E.

LAGOS (Port Logo, Greece). *Open 14 July 1870 to Feb 1872. Postmark type* E.

LATAKIA (Syria). *Open 14 July 1870 to Feb 1872. Postmark type* E.

LEROS (Aegean Is.) *Open July 1873 to January 1874 and May to October 1874. Postmark type* E.

MERSINA (Mersin, Turkey). *Open 14 July 1870 to Feb 1872. Postmark type* E.

METELINO (Lesbos, Greece). *Open 14 July 1870 to 30 June 1881. Postmark types* E, M.

RODI (Rhodes, Greece). *Open 13 Aug 1872 to 30 June 1881. Postmark type* E.

SALONNICCHI (Thessaloniki, Greece). *Open 14 July 1870 to Feb 1872. Postmark type* E.

SCIO (Chios, Aegean Is.). *Open 14 July 1870 to 30 June 1881. Postmark types* E, N.

SMIRNE (Izmir, Turkey). *Open 14 Nov 1865 to 30 June 1881. Postmark types* E (*also without* "V. R."), F.

TENEDOS (Bozcaada, Turkey). *Open 14 July 1870 to March 1871. Postmark type* E.

TRIPOLI (Lebanon). *Open 14 July 1870 to Feb 1872. Postmark type* E.

VOLO (Volos, Greece). *Open 14 July 1870 to Feb 1872. Postmark type* E.

BRITISH FORCES IN EGYPT

Following the rise of a nationalist movement led by Arabi Pasha, and serious disturbances in Alexandria, British troops landed at Ismalia in August 1882 and defeated the nationalists at Tel-el-Kebir on 13 September. A British Army Post Office detachment landed at Alexandria on 21 August and provided a postal service for the troops, using Great Britain stamps, from various locations until it was withdrawn on 7 October.

During the Gordon Relief Expedition of 1884–85 a postal detachment was sent to Suakin on the Red Sea. This operated between 25 March and 30 May 1885 using Great Britain stamps.

ZA **1**

Stamps of GREAT BRITAIN cancelled with Type ZA **1**.

1882 (Aug–Oct).

ZA1	½d. rose-red (Plate No. 20)	
ZA2	½d. green (1880)	£300
ZA3	1d. Venetian red (1880)	£600
ZA4	1d. lilac (1881)	£175
ZA5	2½d. blue (1881) (Plate Nos. 21, 22, 23)	£100

1885. Used at Suakin.

ZA6	½d. slate-blue (1884)	£500
ZA7	1d. lilac (1881)	£300
ZA8	2½d. lilac (1884)	£225
ZA9	5d. dull green (1884)	£500

From 1 November 1932 to 29 February 1936 members of the British Forces in Egypt and their families were allowed to send letters to the British Isles at reduced rates. Special seals, which were on sale in booklets at NAAFI Institutes and Canteens, were used instead of Egyptian stamps. These seals were stuck on the back of the envelopes, letters bearing the seals being franked on the front with a hand-stamp inscribed "EGYPT POSTAGE PREPAID" in a double circle surmounted by a crown.

PRICES FOR STAMPS ON COVER

Nos. A1/9	from × 5
No. A10	from × 1·5
No. A11	from × 5
No. A12	from × 75
No. A13	from × 20
No. A14	from × 100
No. A15	from × 20

A **1**

A **2**

(Des Lt-Col. C. Fraser. Typo Hanbury, Tomsett & Co. Ltd, London)

1932 (1 Nov)–33. P 11.

(a) Inscr "POSTAL SEAL"

A1	A **1**	1p. deep blue and red	95·00	6·00

(b) Inscr "LETTER SEAL"

A2	A **1**	1p. deep blue and red (8.33)	50·00	1·25

(Des Sgt. W. F. Lait. Litho Walker & Co, Amalgamated Press, Cairo)

1932 (26 Nov)–**35**. Christmas Seals. P 11½.

A3	A **2**	3m. black/azure	50·00	70·00
A4		3m. brown-lake (13.11.33)	7·50	50·00
A5		3m. deep blue (17.11.34)	8·00	32·00
A6		3m. vermilion (23.11.35)	1·25	50·00
		a. Pale vermilion (19.12.35)	15·00	38·00

A **3**

(Des Miss Waugh. Photo Harrison)

1934 (1 June)–**35**.

(a) P 14½×14

A7	A **3**	1p. carmine	55·00	85
A8		1p. green (5.12.34)	8·50	8·00

(b) P 13½×14

A9	A **3**	1p. carmine (24.4.35)	7·50	5·50

(A **4**)

1935 (6 May). Silver Jubilee. As No. A9, but colour changed and optd with Type A **4**, in red.

A10	A **3**	1p. ultramarine	£350	£180

Xmas 1935
3 Milliemes
(A **5**)

1935 (16 Dec). Provisional Christmas Seal. No. A9 surch with Type A **5**.

A11	A **3**	3m. on 1p. carmine	18·00	70·00

The seals and letter stamps were replaced by the following Army Post stamps issued by the Egyptian Postal Administration. No. A9 was accepted for postage until 15 March 1936.

A **6** King Fuad I

A **7** King Farouk

W **48** of Egypt

(Types A **6**/A **7**. Photo Survey Dept, Cairo)

1936. W **48** of Egypt. P 13½ × 14.

A12	A **6**	3m. green (1.12.36)	1·00	3·25
A13		10m. carmine (1.3.36)	9·00	10
		w. Wmk inverted		

1939 (16 Dec). W **48** of Egypt. P 13×13½.

A14	A **7**	3m. green	8·50	12·00
A15		10m. carmine	11·00	10
		w. Wmk inverted		

These stamps were withdrawn in April 1941 but the concession, without the use of special stamps, continued until October 1951 when the postal agreement was abrogated.

MILITARY TELEGRAPH STAMPS

Military Telegraph stamps were provided for the pre-payment of non-official messages sent by the army telegraph system. They were used by army personnel for private communications, newspaper reporters and the local population (when the army was in control of the telegraph system).

The 'unadopted die' stamps, (T T **1/3** of Bechuanaland inscribed "MILITARY TELEGRAPHS") were supplied for use in Bechuanaland, Egypt and Sudan.

Operations in Egypt commenced in 1884 and on 1 May 1885 the telegraph system in upper Egypt was transferred to military control.

1885. Nos. MT1/8 of Bechuanaland.

(a) Wmk Orb. P 14

MT1	1d. lilac and black	£300	
MT2	3d. lilac and brown		
MT3	6d. lilac and green		

(b) Wmk script "VR" (sideways). P 13½

MT4	1s. green and black	
MT5	2s. green and blue	
MT6	5s. green and mauve	
MT7	10s. green and red	£750

(c) Wmk Two Orbs (sideways). P 14×13½

MT8	£1 lilac and black	

The survival rate of unsurcharged military telegraph stamps used in Egypt is very low.

Used prices for Nos. MT1/8 are for stamps with identifiable Egypt cancellations. For usage in Sudan, see Sudan Nos. MT1/8. For mint prices see Bechuanaland Nos. MT1/8.

(MT **1**) (MT **2**)

(MT **3**) (MT **4**)

1886 (July). Nos. MT1/8 handstamped locally as T MT **1/4**.

MT9	MT **1**	"0.1 P.T." on 1d. lilac and black	£100
		a. bisected (0.05pt) (*on piece*)	† —
MT10		"0.25 P.T." on 3d. lilac and brown	£100
		a. bisected (0.125pt) (*on piece*)	† —
MT11	MT **2**	"ONE PIASTRE" on 6d. lilac and green	£100
MT12	MT **3**	"FIVE PIASTRES" on 1s. green and black	£100
MT13		"TEN PIASTRES" on 2s. green and blue	£275
MT14		"TWENTY FIVE PIASTRES" on 5s. green and mauve	£375
MT15		"FIFTY PIASTRES" on 10s. green and red	£750
MT16	MT **4**	"HUNDRED PIASTRES" on £1 lilac and black	£1600

TWENTY-FIVE

(MT **5**) (MT **6**)

ONE HUNDRED

PIASTRES

(MT **7**)

1887 (Feb). Nos. MT1/8 and additional values surch in London as T MT **5/7**.

MT17	MT **5**	"ONE DIME" on 1d. lilac and black	50·00
MT18		"TWO DIMES" on 2d. lilac and blue	50·00
MT19		"FIVE DIMES" on 3d. lilac and brown	50·00
MT20		"ONE PIASTRE" on 6d. lilac and green	75·00
MT21		"TWO PIASTRES" on 8d. lilac and carmine	75·00
MT22	MT **6**	"FIVE PIASTRES" on 1s. green and black	75·00
MT23		"TEN PIASTRES" on 2s. green and blue	£110
MT24		"TWENTY-FIVE PIASTRES" on 5s. green and mauve	£225
MT25		"FIFTY PIASTRES" on 10s. green and red	£375
MT26	MT **7**	"ONE HUNDRED PIASTRES" on £1 lilac and black	£650

Nos. MT 18 and 21 were surcharged on 2d and 8d values which were not issued without surcharge.

The London surcharges were withdrawn in Spring 1890. The usage was limited as nearly all the stamps were returned to England and destroyed.

SUEZ CANAL COMPANY

PRICES FOR STAMPS ON COVER	
Nos. 1/4	*from* × 25

100 Centimes = 1 Franc

On 30 November 1855 a concession to construct the Suez Canal was granted to Ferdinand de Lesseps and the Compagnie Universelle du Canal Maritime de Suez was formed. Work began in April 1859 and the canal was opened on 17 November 1869. In November 1875 the Khedive sold his shares in the company to the British Government, which then became the largest shareholder.

The company transported mail free of charge between Port Said and Suez from 1859 to 1867, when it was decided that payment should be made for the service and postage stamps were introduced in July 1868. Letters for destinations beyond Port Said or Suez required additional franking with Egyptian or French stamps.

The imposition of charges for the service was not welcomed by the public and in August the Egyptian Government agreed to take it over.

1

(Litho Chezaud, Aine & Tavernier, Paris)

1868 (8 July). Imperf.

1	**1**	1c. black	£250	£1500
2		5c. green	85·00	£1000
3		20c. blue	75·00	£500
4		40c. pink	£130	£1200

Shades of all values exist.

Stamps can be found showing parts of the papermaker's watermark "LA+–F" (La Croix Frères).

These stamps were withdrawn from sale on 16 August 1868 and demonetised on 31 August.

Many forgeries exist, unused and cancelled. The vast majority of these forgeries show vertical lines, instead of cross-hatching, between "POSTES" and the central oval. It is believed that other forgeries, which do show cross-hatching, originate from the plate of the 40c. value which is missing from the company's archives. These are, however, on thin, brittle paper with smooth shiny gum.

Falkland Islands

PRICES FOR STAMPS ON COVER TO 1945		
No.	1	*from* × 125
No.	2	*from* × 70
Nos.	3/4	*from* × 10
No.	5	—
Nos.	6/10	*from* × 30
Nos.	11/12	*from* × 15
Nos.	13/14	*from* × 20
Nos.	15/17	*from* × 20
Nos.	17b/c	*from* × 100
Nos.	18/21	*from* × 10
Nos.	22/b	*from* × 30
Nos.	23/4	*from* × 100
Nos.	25/6	*from* × 30
No.	27	*from* × 20
No.	28	*from* × 40
No.	29	*from* × 5
No.	30/b	*from* × 50
No.	30c	*from* × 15
No.	31	*from* × 5
Nos.	32/8	*from* × 15
Nos.	41/2	—
Nos.	43/8	*from* × 12
Nos.	49/50	—
Nos.	60/5	*from* × 10
Nos.	66/9	—
Nos.	70/1	*from* × 10
Nos.	72/b	—
Nos.	73/9	*from* × 4
No.	80	—
No.	115	*from* × 2
Nos.	116/19	*from* × 20
Nos.	120/2	*from* × 6
Nos.	123/6	—
Nos.	127/34	*from* × 5
Nos.	135/8	—
Nos.	139/45	*from* × 50
Nos.	146/63	*from* × 5

CROWN COLONY

1 **2**

1869–76. The Franks.

FR1	**1**	In black, *on cover*	£17000
FR2	**2**	In red, *on cover* (1876)	£26000

On piece, No. FR1 on white or coloured paper £110; No. FR2 on white £190.

The first recorded use of No. FR1 is on a cover to London date stamped 4 January 1869. The use of these franks ceased when the first stamps were issued.

3 (**4**)

In the ½d., 2d., 2½d. and 9d. the figures of value in the lower corners are replaced by small rosettes and the words of value are in colour.

NOTE. Nos. 1, 2, 3, 4, 8, 10, 11 and 12 exist with one or two sides imperf from the margin of the sheets.

(Recess B.W.)

1878–79. No wmk. P 14, 14½.

1	**3**	1d. claret (19.6.78)	£750	£425
2		4d. grey-black (9.79)	£1400	£150
		a. On wmkd paper	£3750	£500
3		6d. blue-green (19.6.78)	£120	80·00
4		1s. bistre-brown (1878)	85·00	70·00

No. 2a shows portions of the papermaker's watermark—"R. TURNER, CHAFFORD MILLS"—in ornate double-lined capitals.

NOTES. The dates shown for Nos. 5/12 and 15/38 are those on which the printer delivered the various printings to the Crown Agents. Several months could elapse before the stamps went on sale in the Colony, depending on the availability of shipping.

The plates used for these stamps did not fit the paper so that the watermark appears in all sorts of positions on the stamp. Well centred examples are scarce. Examples can also be found showing parts of the marginal watermarks, either "CROWN AGENTS" horizontally in letters 12 mm high or "CROWN AGENTS FOR THE COLONIES" vertically in 7 mm letters. Both are in double-lined capitals.

1882 (22 Nov). Wmk Crown CA (upright). P 14, 14½.

5	**3**	1d. dull claret	£325	£190
		a. Imperf vert (horiz pair)	£90000	
		x. Wmk reversed	£1400	
		y. Wmk inverted and reversed	£600	£475
6		4d. grey-black	£850	95·00
		w. Wmk inverted	£1600	£350

For later printings with upright wmk, in different shades, see Nos. 11/12, 18/24 and 31/2.

1885 (23 Mar)–**91**. Wmk Crown CA (sideways*). P 14, 14½.

7	**3**	1d. pale claret	95·00	65·00
		w. Wmk Crown to right of CA	£120	80·00
		x. Wmk sideways reversed	£300	£160
		y. Wmk Crown to right of CA and reversed	£275	£170
8		1d. brownish claret (3.10.87)	£120	55·00
		a. Bisected (on cover) (1.91)	†	£4000
		w. Wmk Crown to right of CA	£150	55·00
		x. Wmk sideways reversed	£350	£130
		y. Wmk Crown to right of CA and reversed	£350	£180
9		4d. pale grey-black	£850	85·00
		w. Wmk Crown to right of CA	£850	£120
		x. Wmk sideways reversed	£1000	£225
		y. Wmk Crown to right of CA and reversed	£900	£160
10		4d. grey-black (3.10.87)	£450	50·00
		w. Wmk Crown to right of CA	£450	55·00
		x. Wmk sideways reversed	£1300	£150
		y. Wmk Crown to right of CA and reversed	£1100	£120

*The normal sideways watermark shows Crown to left of CA, as seen from the back of the stamp.
For No. 8a see note below No. 14.

1889 (26 Sept)–**91**. Wmk Crown CA (upright). P 14, 14½.

11	**3**	1d. red-brown (21.5.91)	£350	90·00
		a. Bisected (on cover) (7.91)	†	£4500
		x. Wmk reversed	£800	£300
12		4d. olive grey-black	£200	60·00
		w. Wmk inverted	£1400	£475
		x. Wmk reversed	£500	£190

For No. 11a see note below No. 14.

1891 (Jan–11 July). Nos. 8 and 11 bisected diagonally and each half handstamped with T **4**.

13	**3**	½d. on half of 1d. brownish claret (No. 8)	£600	£300
		a. Unsevered pair	£4000	£1000
		b. Unsevered pair se-tenant with unsurcharged whole stamp	£40000	
		c. Bisect se-tenant with unsurcharged whole stamp	†	£2250
14		½d. on half of 1d. red-brown (No. 11) (11.7)	£700	£275
		a. Unsevered pair	£5000	£1600
		b. Bisect se-tenant with unsurcharged whole stamp	†	£2000

1891 PROVISIONALS. In 1891 the postage to the United Kingdom and Colonies was reduced from 4d. to 2½d. per half ounce. As no ½d. or 2½d. stamps were available the bisection of the 1d. was authorised from 1 January 1891. This authorisation was withdrawn on 11 January 1892, although bisects were accepted for postage until July of that year. The ½d. and 2½d. stamps were placed on sale from 10 September 1891.

Cork Cancel used in 1891

The Type **4** surcharge was not used regularly; unsurcharged bisects being employed far more frequently. Genuine bisects should be cancelled with the cork cancel illustrated above. The use of any other postmark, including a different cork cancel or an "F.I." obliterator, requires date evidence linked to known mail ship sailings to prove authenticity.

After 10 September 1891 the post office supplied "posthumous" examples of the surcharged bisects to collectors. These were without postal validity and differ from Type **4** by showing a large full stop, long fraction bar or curly tail to "2" (Prices from £50 each, unused or used). Some of the posthumous surcharges were applied to No. 18 which was not used for the original bisects. Examples are also known showing the surcharge double, inverted or sideways.

1891 (10 Sept)–**1902**. Wmk Crown CA (upright). P 14, 14½.

15	**3**	½d. blue-green (10.9–11.1891)	28·00	27·00
		x. Wmk reversed	£700	£650
		y. Wmk inverted and reversed	£750	£750
16		½d. green (20.5.92)	16·00	15·00
		ax. Wmk reversed	£325	£300
		ay. Wmk inverted and reversed	£550	£550
		b. Deep blue green (15.4.96)	40·00	30·00
17		½d. deep yellow-green (1894–95)	18·00	21·00
		ay. Wmk inverted and reversed	£325	£300
		b. Yellow-green (19.6.99)	3·25	3·25
		c. Dull yellowish green (13.1.1902)	7·50	4·75
		cx. Wmk reversed	£650	£600
18		1d. orange red-brown (14.10.91)	£130	85·00
		a. Brown	£180	90·00
		w. Wmk inverted	£1800	£750
		x. Wmk reversed	£375	£375
19		1d. reddish chestnut (20.4.92)	50·00	42·00
20		1d. orange-brown (wmk reversed) (18.1.94)	65·00	50·00
21		1d. claret (23.7.94)	£130	80·00
		x. Wmk reversed	85·00	50·00
22		1d. Venetian red (pale to deep) (1895–96)	25·00	17·00
		ax. Wmk reversed	13·00	12·00
		b. Venetian claret (1898?)	38·00	18·00
23		1d. pale red (19.6.99)	8·50	2·75
		x. Wmk reversed	£325	£500
24		1d. orange-red (13.1.1902)	17·00	4·25
25		2d. purple (pale to deep) (1895–98)	7·00	12·00
		x. Wmk reversed	£800	£800
		xs. Ditto, optd "SPECIMEN."	£750	
26		2d. reddish purple (15.4.96)	6·50	11·00
27		2½d. pale chalky ultramarine (10.9.91)	£275	55·00
28		2½d. dull blue (19.11.91)	£300	35·00
		x. Wmk reversed	£750	£500
29		2½d. Prussian blue (18.1.94)	£250	£130
30		2½d. ultramarine (1894–96)	50·00	13·00
		ax. Wmk reversed	£120	18·00

		ay. Wmk inverted and reversed	£1600	
		b. Pale ultramarine (10.6.98)	70·00	17·00
		bx. Wmk reversed	£150	75·00
		c. Deep ultramarine (18.9.1901)	50·00	42·00
		cx. Wmk reversed	£600	£600
31		4d. brownish black (wmk reversed) (18.1.94)	£800	£350
32		4d. olive-black (11.5.95)	16·00	21·00
33		6d. orange-yellow (19.11.91)	£325	£225
		x. Wmk reversed	85·00	55·00
34		6d. yellow (15.4.96)	55·00	48·00
35		9d. pale reddish orange (15.11.95)	60·00	60·00
		x. Wmk reversed	£700	£750
		y. Wmk inverted and reversed	£1000	£1000
36		9d. salmon (15.4.96)	65·00	65·00
		x. Wmk reversed	£700	£750
37		1s. grey-brown (15.11.95)	80·00	55·00
		x. Wmk reversed	£225	£225
38		1s. yellow-brown (15.4.96)	75·00	48·00
		x. Wmk reversed	£225	£225

17b/38 Set of 8 ... £225 £180
15s, 26s, 28s, 33s, 35s Optd "SPECIMEN." Set of 5 ... £700

The ½d. and 2½d. were first placed on sale in the Falkland Islands on 10 September 1891. Such stamps came from the August 1891 printing. The stock of the May printings sent to the Falkland Islands was lost at sea.

The 2½d. ultramarine printing can sometimes be found in a violet shade, but the reason for this is unknown.

5   **6**

(Recess B.W.)

1898 (5 Oct). Wmk Crown CC. P 14, 14½.

41	**5**	2s.6d. deep blue	£275	£275
42	**6**	5s. red	£250	£250

41s/2s Optd "SPECIMEN." Set of 2 ... £550

7   **8**

(Recess D.L.R.)

1904 (16 July)–**12**. Wmk Mult Crown CA. P 14.

43	**7**	½d. yellow-green	9·00	1·50
		aw. Wmk inverted	£700	£425
		ax. Wmk reversed	£1800	
		b. Pale yellow-green (on thick paper) (6.08)	21·00	7·50
		by. Wmk inverted and reversed	—	£2000
		c. Deep yellow-green (7.11)	17·00	3·00
44		1d. vermilion	17·00	1·50
		aw. Wmk inverted	£600	£400
		ax. Wmk reversed	£900	£650
		b. Wmk sideways (7.06)	1·50	4·25
		c. Thick paper (1908)	27·00	2·50
		cw. Wmk inverted	£850	£700
		cx. Wmk reversed	£1000	£750
		d. Dull coppery red (on thick paper) (3.08)	£200	30·00
		dx. Wmk reversed	£1600	£750
		e. Orange-vermilion (7.11)	40·00	2·75
		ex. Wmk reversed	£1100	£800
45		2d. purple (27.12.04)	25·00	21·00
		ax. Wmk reversed	£225	£225
		b. Reddish purple (13.1.12)	£225	£275
46		2½d. ultramarine (shades)	29·00	7·50
		aw. Wmk inverted	£750	£425
		aws. Ditto, optd "SPECIMEN"	£800	
		ay. Wmk inverted and reversed	£1600	£1400
		b. Deep blue (13.1.12)	£275	£150
47		6d. orange (27.12.04)	45·00	48·00
48		1s. brown (27.12.04)	45·00	32·00
49	**8**	3s. green	£180	£160
		aw. Wmk inverted	£4000	£3250
		axs. Wmk reversed, optd "SPECIMEN"	£3000	
		b. Deep green (4.07)	£150	£130
		bx. Wmk reversed	£4500	£3000
50		5s. red (27.12.04)	£225	£150

43/50 Set of 8 ... £475 £350
43s/50s Optd "SPECIMEN" Set of 8 ...

Examples of Nos. 41/50 and earlier issues are known with a forged Falkland Islands postmark dated "OCT 15 10".

> For details of South Georgia underprint, South Georgia provisional handstamps and Port Foster handstamp see under FALKLAND ISLANDS DEPENDENCIES.

9   **10**

(Des B. MacKennal. Eng J. A. C. Harrison. Recess D.L.R.)

1912 (3 July)–**20**. Wmk Mult Crown CA. P 13¾×14 (comb) (½d. to 1s.) or 14 (line) (3s. to £1).

60	**9**	½d. yellow-green	2·75	3·50
		a. Perf 14 (line). Deep yellow-green (1914)	18·00	38·00
		b. Perf 14 (line). Deep olive (1918)	24·00	£170
		c. Deep olive (4.19)	3·50	50·00
		ca. Printed both sides	†	£7000
		d. Dull yellowish green (on thick greyish paper) (1920)	4·50	40·00
61		1d. orange-red	5·00	2·50
		a. Perf 14 (line). Orange-vermilion (1914, 1916)	50·00	2·50
		b. Perf 14 (line). Vermilion (1918)	†	£900
		c. Orange-vermilion (4.19)	7·50	3·00
		d. Orange-vermilion (on thick greyish paper) (1920)	7·50	2·00
		dx. Wmk reversed	£425	£700
62		2d. maroon	30·00	23·00
		a. Perf 14 (line). Deep reddish purple (1914)	£375	£160
		b. Perf 14 (line). Maroon (4.18)	£400	£170
		c. Deep reddish purple (4.19)	8·50	16·00
63		2½d. deep bright blue	27·00	24·00
		a. Perf 14 (line). Deep bright blue (1914)	42·00	50·00
		b. Perf 14 (line). Deep blue (1916, 4.18)	50·00	60·00
		c. Deep blue (4.19)	7·00	17·00
64		6d. yellow-orange (6.7.12)	15·00	20·00
		aw. Wmk inverted	£1000	£800
		b. Brown-orange (4.19)	15·00	42·00
		by. Wmk inverted and reversed		
65		1s. light bistre-brown (6.7.12)	32·00	30·00
		a. Pale bistre-brown (4.19)	95·00	£130
		b. Brown (on thick greyish paper) (1920)	38·00	£160
66	**10**	3s. slate-green	95·00	95·00
67		5s. deep rose-red	£120	£120
		a. Reddish maroon (1914)	£300	£300
		b. Maroon (1916)	£130	£140
		bx. Wmk reversed	£7000	£5000
68		10s. red/green (11.2.14)	£190	£275
69		£1 black/red (11.2.14)	£550	£600

60/9 (inc 67b) Set of 11 ... £1000 £1200
60s/9s (inc both 67s and 67as) Optd "SPECIMEN" Set of 11 ... £1900

The exact measurement of the comb perforation used for Type **9** is 13.7×13.9. The line perforation, used for the 1914, 1916 and 1918 printings and for all the high values in Type **10**, measured 14.1×14.1.

It was previously believed that all examples of the 1d. in vermilion with the line perforation were overprinted to form No. 71, but it has now been established that some unoverprinted sheets of No. 61b were used during 1919.

Many of the sheets showed stamps from the left-hand side in a lighter shade than those from the right. It is believed that this was due to the weight of the impression. Such differences are particularly noticeable on the 2½d. 1916 and 1918 printings where the lighter shades, approaching milky blue in appearance, are scarce.

All 1919 printings show weak impressions of the background either side of the head caused by the poor paper quality.

Examples of all values are known with forged postmarks, including one of Falkland Islands dated "5 SP 19" and another of South Shetlands dated "20 MR 27".

WAR STAMP (11)   **2½D** (12)

1918 (22 Oct*)–**20**. Optd by Govt Printing Press, Stanley, with T **11**.

70	**9**	½d. deep olive (line perf) (No. 60b)	1·00	12·00
		a. Yellow-green (No. 60) (4.19)	30·00	£700
		ab. Albino opt	£2500	
		b. Deep olive (comb perf) (No. 60c) (4.19)	50	6·50
		c. Dull yellowish green (on thick greyish paper) (No. 60d) (5.20)	8·00	55·00
		cx. Wmk reversed	£550	
71		1d. vermilion (line perf) (No. 61b)	2·00	18·00
		a. Opt double, one albino	£425	
		b. Orange-vermilion (line perf) (No. 61a) (4.19)	32·00	†
		c. Orange-vermilion (comb perf) (No. 61c) (4.19)	50	3·75
		ca. Opt double	£4500	
		cx. Wmk reversed	£750	
		d. Orange-vermilion (on thick greyish paper) (No. 61d) (5.20)	£120	£200
72		1s. light bistre-brown (No. 65)	50·00	85·00
		a. Pale bistre-brown (No. 65a) (4.19)	4·50	50·00
		ab. Opt double, one albino	£2250	
		ac. Opt omitted (in pair with normal)	£20000	
		b. Brown (on thick greyish paper) (No. 65b) (5.20)	6·00	48·00
		ba. Opt double, one albino	£1900	
		bw. Wmk inverted	£425	£500
		bx. Wmk reversed	£3500	

*Earliest known postal use. Cancellations dated 8 October were applied much later.

There were five printings of the "WAR STAMP" overprint, but all, except that in May 1920, used the same setting. Composition of the five printings was as follows:

October 1918. Nos. 70, 71 and 72.
January 1919. Nos. 70, 71 and 72.
April 1919. Nos. 70/b, 71b/c and 72a.
October 1919. Nos. 70b, 71c and 72a.
May 1920. Nos. 70c, 71d and 72b.

It is believed that the entire stock of No. 70a was sold to stamp dealers. Only a handful of used examples are known which may have subsequently been returned to the colony for cancellation.

No. 71ca exists in a block of 12 (6×2) from the bottom of a sheet on which the first stamp in the bottom row shows a single overprint, but the remainder have overprint double.

Examples of Nos. 70/2 are known with a forged Falkland Islands postmark dated "5 SP 19".

1921–28. Wmk Mult Script CA. P 14.

73	**9**	½d. yellowish green	3·00	4·00
		a. Green (1925)	3·00	4·00
74		1d. dull vermilion (1924)	6·00	2·00
		aw. Wmk inverted	†	£4500
		ay. Wmk inverted and reversed	£850	
		b. Orange-vermilion (shades)		
		(1925)	5·50	1·25
75		2d. deep brown-purple (8.23)	26·00	8·00
		aw. Wmk inverted	—	£4500
		ax. Wmk reversed	£3750	
		b. Purple-brown (1927)	50·00	27·00
		c. Reddish maroon (1.28)	10·00	24·00
76		2½d. deep blue	24·00	16·00
		a. Indigo (28.4.27)	27·00	21·00
		b. Deep steel-blue (1.28)	16·00	16·00
77		2½d. deep purple/*pale yellow* (8.23)..	5·00	38·00
		a. Pale purple/pale yellow (1925)	5·00	38·00
		ay. Wmk inverted and reversed	£950	
78		6d. yellow-orange (1925)	11·00	38·00
		w. Wmk inverted	£600	
		x. Wmk reversed	£3750	
79		1s. deep ochre	23·00	48·00
80	**10**	3s. slate-green (8.23)	£100	£160
73/80 *Set of 8*			£150	£275
73s/80s *(inc both 76s and 76as)* Optd "SPECIMEN"				
Set of 9			£850	

Dates quoted above are those of despatch from Great Britain.
No. 76*b* includes the so-called "Prussian blue" shades (formerly listed as No. 76*c*) which formed part of a second printing in Oct 1928.

1928 (7 Feb). No. 75*b* surch with T **12.**

115	**9**	2½d. on 2d. purple-brown	£1300	£1300
		a. Surch double	£60000	

No. 115 was produced on South Georgia during a shortage of 2½d. stamps. The provisional was withdrawn on 22 February 1928.

13 Fin Whale and Gentoo Penguins   **14**

(Recess P.B.)

1929 (2 Sept)–**37**. P 14 (comb).

(a) Wmk Mult Script CA

116	**13**	½d. green	1·25	4·00
		a. Line perf (1936)	3·25	8·50
117		1d. scarlet	4·50	80
		a. Line perf. *Deep red* (1936)	8·00	14·00
118		2d. grey	6·00	4·00
119		2½d. blue	6·00	2·25
120	**14**	4d. orange (line perf) (18.2.32)	23·00	13·00
		a. Line perf 13½. *Deep orange*		
		(7.37)	£100	70·00
121	**13**	6d. purple	24·00	19·00
		a. Line perf. *Reddish purple* (1936)	50·00	25·00
122		1s. black/*emerald*	27·00	35·00
		a. Line perf. *On bright emerald*		
		(1936)	32·00	27·00
123		2s.6d. carmine/*blue*	70·00	70·00
124		5s. green/*yellow*	£100	£110
125		10s. carmine/*emerald*	£225	£275

(b) Wmk Mult Crown CA

126	**13**	£1 black/*red*	£325	£425
116/26 *Set of 11*			£700	£850
116s/26s Perf "SPECIMEN" *Set of 11*			£1000	

Three kinds of perforation exist:
A. Comb perf 13.9:—original values of 1929.
B. Line perf 13.9, 14.2 or compound (small holes)— 1931 printing of 4d. (Issued Feb 1932) and 1936 printings of ½d., 1d., 6d. and 1s. On some sheets of the former the last vertical row of perforations shows larger holes.
C. Line perf 13.7 (large holes) — 1937 printing of 4d.

Examples of most values are known with forged postmarks, including one of Port Stanley dated "14 JY 31" and another of South Georgia dated "AU 30 31".

15 Romney Marsh Ram   **16** Iceberg

17 Whale-catcher *Bransfield*   **18** Port Louis

19 Map of Falkland Islands   **20** South Georgia

21 Fin Whale   **22** Government House, Stanley

23 Battle Memorial   **24** King Penguin

25 Coat of Arms   **26** King George V

Thick serif to "1" at left (R. 1/3, first printing only)   1½d. Break in cloud (R. 9/3)

(Des (except 6d.) by G. Roberts. Eng and recess B.W.)

1933 (2 Jan–Apr). Centenary of British Administration. T **15/26.** Wmk Mult Script CA. P 12.

127	**15**	½d. black and green	4·00	13·00
128	**16**	1d. black and scarlet	3·50	2·75
		a. Thick serif to "1" at left	£475	£325
129	**17**	1½d. black and blue	21·00	26·00
		a. Break in cloud	£1500	£1600
130	**18**	2d. black and brown	17·00	30·00
131	**19**	3d. black and violet	28·00	35·00
132	**20**	4d. black and orange	25·00	28·00
133	**21**	6d. black and slate	75·00	95·00
134	**22**	1s. black and olive-green	70·00	£100
135	**23**	2s.6d. black and violet	£250	£400
136	**24**	5s. black and yellow	£950	£1500
		a. Black and yellow-orange (4.33)..	£3250	£3750
137	**25**	10s. black and chestnut	£850	£1500
138	**26**	£1 black and carmine	£2500	£3250
127/38 *Set of 12*			£4250	£6250
127s/38s Perf "SPECIMEN" *Set of 12*			£4250	

Examples of all values are known with forged Port Stanley postmarks dated "6 JA 33". Some values have also been seen with part strikes of the forged Falkland Islands postmark mentioned below Nos. 60/9 and 70/2.

(Des H. Fleury. Recess B.W.)

1935 (7 May). Silver Jubilee. As Nos. 91/4 of Antigua, but printed by B.W. P 11×12.

139		1d. deep blue and scarlet	3·25	40
		b. Short extra flagstaff	£1100	£1000
		d. Flagstaff on right-hand turret	£450	£350
		e. Double flagstaff	£550	£400
140		2½d. brown and deep blue	12·00	1·75
		b. Short extra flagstaff	£3500	£3500
		d. Flagstaff on right-hand turret	£500	£425
		e. Double flagstaff	£900	£500
		l. Re-entry on value tablet (R. 8/1)	£200	£110
141		4d. green and indigo	24·00	8·00
		b. Short extra flagstaff	£1200	£1000
		d. Flagstaff on right-hand turret	£850	£500
		e. Double flagstaff	£1000	£600
142		1s. slate and purple	15·00	3·75
		a. Extra flagstaff	£3500	£2500
		b. Short extra flagstaff	£900	£550
		c. Lightning conductor	£3500	£1800
		d. Flagstaff on right-hand turret	£1600	£850
		e. Double flagstaff	£1700	£900
139/42 *Set of 4*			48·00	12·50
139s/42s Perf "SPECIMEN" *Set of 4*			£500	

For illustrations of plate varieties see Omnibus section following Zanzibar.

1937 (12 May). Coronation. As Nos. 95/7 of Antigua. P 11×11½.

143		½d. green	30	10
144		1d. carmine	1·00	80
145		2½d. blue	1·50	1·40
143/5 *Set of 3*			2·50	1·75
143s/5s Perf "SPECIMEN" *Set of 3*			£425	

27 Whale's Jawbones   **28** Black-necked Swan

29 Battle Memorial   **30** Flock of sheep

31 Magellan Goose   **32** *Discovery II* (polar supply vessel)

33 *William Scoresby* (supply ship)   **34** Mount Sugar Top

34a Turkey Vultures   **35** Gentoo Penguins

36 Southern Sealion   **37** Deception Island

38 Arms of the Falkland Islands

(Des G. Roberts (Nos. 146, 148/9, 158 and 160/3), K. Lellman (No. 159). Recess B.W.)

1938 (3 Jan)–**50**. T **27/38.** Wmk Mult Script CA. P 12.

146	**27**	½d. black and green (*shades*)	30	75
147	**28**	1d. black and carmine	35·00	80
		a. Black and vermilion	3·75	85
148	**29**	1d. black and violet (14.7.41)	2·75	3·50
		a. Black and purple-violet	10·00	3·75
149		2d. black and deep violet	1·25	50
150	**28**	2d. black and carmine-red (14.7.41)	3·00	4·50
		a. Black and red	3·50	3·00
151	**30**	2½d. black and bright blue	1·25	30
152	**31**	2½d. black and blue (15.6.49)	8·50	8·00
153	**30**	3d. black and blue (14.7.41)	7·50	8·50
		a. Black and deep blue	17·00	4·75
154	**31**	4d. black and purple	3·25	2·00
155	**32**	6d. slate-black and deep brown	11·00	2·50
		a. Black and sepia (*shades*)	6·00	2·00
156		6d. black (15.6.49)	8·00	6·00
157	**33**	9d. black and grey-blue	28·00	6·00
158	**34**	1s. light dull blue	75·00	19·00
		a. Dull greenish blue	60·00	6·00
		b. Dull blue (greyish paper)	38·00	£160
		c. Deep dull blue (1948)	75·00	£130
159	**34a**	1s.3d. black and carmine-red (11.12.46)	2·75	1·60
160	**35**	2s.6d. slate	60·00	21·00
161	**36**	5s. blue and chestnut	£150	95·00
		b. Indigo and pale yellow-brown	£1100	90·00
		c. Dull blue and yellow brown		
		(greyish paper) (1949)	£120	£600
		d. Steel blue and buff-brown (thin		
		paper) (9.50)	£400	£500
162	**37**	10s. black and orange-brown	£200	65·00
		a. Black and orange (1942?)	£350	65·00
		b. Black and red-orange (greyish		
		paper) (1949)	£120	£600
		c. Black and deep reddish orange		
		(thin paper) (1950)	£800	£600
163	**38**	£1 black and violet	£130	60·00
146/63 *Set of 18*			£475	£225
146s/51s, 153s/5s, 157s/63s Perf "SPECIMEN" *Set of*				
16			£2500	

The 'thin paper' referred to will aid identification of Nos. 158*c*, 161*d* and 162*c*. It is more transparent than previous papers and has white gum.
Examples of values issued before 1946 are known with forged Port Stanley postmarks dated "14 JY 41" and "28 JY 43".

Crown flaw and re-entry (Pl 1, R. 8/5)

1946 (7 Oct). Victory. As Nos. 110/11 of Antigua. P 13½×14.

164		1d. dull violet	30	75
165		3d. blue	45	50
		a. Crown flaw and re-entry	65·00	70·00
164s/5s Perf "SPECIMEN" *Set of 2*			£400	

The re-entry, which shows as a doubling of the shadow lines to 'LANDS', the tower of Big Ben and the King's face, also exists without the Crown flaw and is scarcer in this form.

1948 (1 Nov). Royal Silver Wedding. As Nos. 112/13 of Antigua.

166	2½d. ultramarine	2·00	1·00
167	£1 mauve	90·00	60·00

1949 (10 Oct). 75th Anniv of Universal Postal Union. As Nos. 114/17 of Antigua.

168	1d. violet	1·75	1·00
169	3d. deep blue	5·00	6·00
170	1s.3d. deep blue-green	3·25	2·25
171	2s. blue	3·00	8·00
168/71	*Set of 4*	11·50	15·00

39 Sheep

40 *Fitzroy* (supply ship)

41 Magellan Goose

42 Map of Falkland Islands

43 Arms of the Colony

44 Auster Autocrat Aircraft

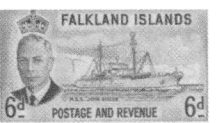

45 *John Biscoe* (research ship)

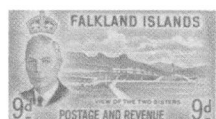

46 View of the Two Sisters

47 Gentoo Penguins

48 Kelp Goose and Gander

49 Sheep shearing

50 Battle Memorial

51 Southern Sealion and South American Fur Seal

52 Hulk of *Great Britain*

(Des from sketches by V. Spencer. Recess Waterlow)

1952 (2 Jan). T **39/52**. Wmk Mult Script CA. P 13×13½ (vert) or 13½×13 (horiz).

172	39	½d. green	1·25	70
173	40	1d. scarlet	2·50	40
174	41	2d. violet	4·50	2·50
175	42	2½d. black and light ultramarine	2·00	50
176	43	3d. deep ultramarine	2·25	1·00
177	44	4d. reddish purple	13·00	1·50
178	45	6d. bistre-brown	12·00	1·00
179	46	9d. orange-yellow	9·00	2·00
180	47	1s. black	24·00	1·00
181	48	1s.3d. orange	18·00	7·00
182	49	2s.6d. olive-green	22·00	12·00
183	50	5s. purple	20·00	11·00
184	51	10s. grey	30·00	20·00
185	52	£1 black	40·00	27·00
172/185	*Set of 14*		£180	75·00

1953 (4 June). Coronation. As No. 120 of Antigua.

186	1d. black and scarlet	80	1·50

53 Sheep

(Recess Waterlow)

1955–57. Designs previously used for King George VI issue but with portrait of Queen Elizabeth II as in T **53**. Wmk Mult Script CA. P 13×13½ (vert) or 13½×13 (horiz).

187	53	½d. green (2.9.57)	1·00	1·25
188	40	1d. scarlet (2.9.57)	1·25	1·25
189	41	2d. violet (4.9.56)	3·25	4·50
190	45	6d. deep yellow-brown (1.6.55)	11·00	60
191	46	9d. orange-yellow (2.9.57)	11·00	17·00
192	47	1s. black (15.7.55)	15·00	2·75
187/92	*Set of 6*		38·00	24·00

54 Austral Thrush

55 Southern Black-backed Gull

56 Gentoo Penguins

57 Long-tailed Meadowlark

58 Magellan Geese

59 Falkland Islands Flightless Steamer Ducks

60 Rockhopper Penguin

61 Black-browed Albatross

62 Silvery Grebe

63 Magellanic Oystercatchers

64 Chilean Teal

65 Kelp Geese

66 King Cormorants

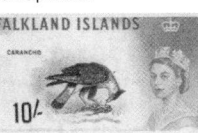

67 Common Caracara

68 Black-necked Swan

½d. Extended cross-bar to first "H" in "THRUSH" (D.L.R. Pl. 1 (black), R. 2/2).

variety	normal

½d., 1d., 2d., 2s. Weak entry under "FA" of "FALKLAND" (D.L.R. Pl. 2, R. 12/5).

(Des from sketches by S. Scott. Recess Waterlow, then D.L.R. (from 9.1.62 onwards))

1960 (10 Feb)–**66**. T **54/68**. W w **12** (upright). P 13½.

193	54	½d. black and myrtle-green	5·00	2·25
		a. Black and green (D.L.R.) (9.1.62).	12·00	7·50
		ab. Weak entry	80·00	55·00
		ac. "H" flaw	45·00	
		aw. Wmk inverted	£7500	£5500
194	55	1d. black and scarlet	4·50	2·00
		a. Black and carmine-red (D.L.R.) (15.7.63)	8·50	6·00
		ab. Weak entry	80·00	48·00
195	56	2d. black and blue	4·50	1·25
		a. Black and deep blue (D.L.R.) (25.10.66)	20·00	20·00
		ab. Weak entry	£130	£140
196	57	2½d. black and yellow-brown	2·50	1·00
197	58	3d. black and olive	1·25	50
198	59	4d. black and carmine	1·50	1·25
199	60	5½d. black and violet	3·25	2·50
200	61	6d. black and sepia	3·50	30
201	62	9d. black and orange-red	2·50	1·25
202	63	1s. black and maroon	1·25	40
203	64	1s.3d. black and ultramarine	13·00	14·00
204	65	2s. black and brown-red	32·00	2·50
		a. Black and lake-brown (D.L.R.) (25.10.66)	£225	70·00
		ab. Weak entry	£700	£325
205	66	5s. black and turquoise	28·00	11·00
206	67	10s. black and purple	48·00	24·00
207	68	£1 black and orange-yellow	48·00	27·00
193/207	*Set of 15*		£170	80·00

Waterlow	De La Rue

Waterlow printings were from frame plate 1 for all values except the 1d., 2½d., and 5s., where frame plate 2 was used. De La Rue used both frame plates for the ½d., 1d. and 6d. but only frame plate 2 for the 2d. and 2s. De La Rue printings can generally be distinguished by the finer lines of shading on the Queen's face (appearing as a white face), neck and shoulder and also the very faint cross-hatching left of the face. Typically the black vignette is also less intense on the De La Rue printings. The 6d. De La Rue shade varies little from the original, but for other values the shades are distinctive. The majority of the De La Rue 6d. stamps are from frame plate 1, plate 2 being rare. Perforation patterns and margin widths can also aid specialists in determining printers and printings.

Only one unused (without gum) and two used examples of No. 193aw have been reported.

For the ½d. watermark sideways see No. 227. An irreparable plate crack developed under R. 12/2 of the original vignette plate, so a new plate 2 had to be used for the final part of the 1968 printing.

69 Morse Key

70 One-valve Receiver

(Des M. Goaman. Photo Enschedé)

1962 (5 Oct). 50th Anniv of Establishment of Radio Communications. T **69/70** and similar vert design. W w **12**. P 11½×11.

208	69	6d. carmine-lake and orange	75	40
209	70	1s. deep bluish green and yellow-olive	80	40
210	–	2s. deep violet and ultramarine	90	1·75
		w. Wmk inverted	£140	£350
208/10	*Set of 3*		2·25	2·25

Design:—2s. Rotary Spark Transmitter.

1963 (4 June). Freedom from Hunger. As No. 146 of Antigua.

211	1s. ultramarine	7·00	1·50

1963 (2 Sept). Red Cross Centenary. As Nos. 147/8 of Antigua.

212	1d. red and black	2·00	75
213	1s. red and blue	8·00	5·00

1964 (23 Apr). 400th Birth Anniv of William Shakespeare. As No. 164 of Antigua.

214	6d. black	1·50	50

72 HMS *Glasgow*

73 HMS *Kent*

74 HMS *Invincible*

75 Battle Memorial

(Recess D.L.R.)

1964 (8 Dec). 50th Anniv of the Battle of the Falkland Islands.
T **72/75**. W w **12**. P 13×14 (2s.) or 13 (others).

215	2½d. black and red	9·00	3·75
216	6d. black and light blue	50	25
	a. Centre Type **72**	£40000	
217	1s. black and carmine-red	50	1·25
	w. Wmk inverted	£4000	
218	2s. black and blue	50	75
215/18 *Set of 4*		9·50	5·50

It is believed that No. 216a came from a sheet which was
first printed with the centre of the 2½d. and then accidentally
included among the supply of the 6d. value and thus received
the wrong frame. About 25 examples of the "Glasgow" error have
been recorded.

1965 (26 May). ITU Centenary. As Nos. 166/7 of Antigua.

219	1d. light blue and deep blue	50	30
	w. Wmk inverted	£3250	£3250
220	2s. lilac and bistre-yellow	2·50	1·75

1965 (25 Oct). International Co-operation Year. As Nos. 168/9 of
Antigua.

221	1d. reddish purple and turquoise-green	50	40
222	1s. deep bluish green and lavender	2·00	1·10

1966 (24 Jan). Churchill Commemoration. As Nos. 170/3 of
Antigua. Printed in black, cerise and gold with background in
colours stated. W w **12**. P 14.

223	½d. new blue	65	2·50
224	1d. deep green	1·75	30
	w. Wmk inverted	5·00	8·00
225	1s. brown	3·50	3·25
	w. Wmk inverted	£100	£100
226	2s. bluish violet	2·00	4·00
223/6 *Set of 4*		7·00	9·00

1966 (25 Oct). As No. 193a, but wmk w **12** sideways.

227	**54**	½d. black and green	30	40
		a. Weak entry	38·00	40·00
		b. "H" flaw	15·00	

76 Globe and Human Rights Emblem

(Des M. Farrar Bell. Photo Harrison)

1968 (4 July). Human Rights Year. W w **12**. P 14×14½.

228	**76**	2d. multicoloured	40	20
		a. Yellow omitted ("1968" white)	£2250	
229		6d. muticoloured	40	20
230		1s. multicoloured	50	20
231		2s. multicoloured	65	30
228/31 *Set of 4*			1·75	80

77 Dusty Miller

78 Pig Vine

79 Pale Maiden

80 Dog Orchid

81 Sea Cabbage

82 Vanilla Daisy

83 Arrowleaf Mangold

84 Diddle Dee

85 Scurvy Grass

86 Prickly Burr

87 Fachine

88 Lavender

89 Felton's Flower

90 Yellow Orchid

½**d.** Missing grey colour in diadem appears as a damaged crown
(Pl. 1A, R. 2/2).

(Des Sylvia Goaman. Photo Harrison)

1968 (9 Oct). Flowers. T **77/90**. Chalk-surfaced paper. W w **12**
(sideways on vert designs). P 14.

232	**77**	½d. multicoloured	15	1·75
		a. Crown damaged	9·00	
233	**78**	1½d. multicoloured	40	15
234	**79**	2d. multicoloured	50	15
235	**80**	3d. multicoloured	6·00	1·00
236	**81**	3½d. multicoloured	30	1·50
237	**82**	4½d. multicoloured	1·50	2·00
238	**83**	5½d. olive-green, brown and yellow-green	1·50	2·25
239	**84**	6d. carmine, black and yellow-green	75	20
240	**85**	1s. multicoloured	1·00	1·50
		w. Wmk inverted	£325	
241	**86**	1s.6d. multicoloured	8·00	16·00
242	**87**	2s. multicoloured	5·50	6·50
243	**88**	3s. multicoloured	9·50	8·00
244	**89**	5s. multicoloured	30·00	14·00
245	**90**	£1 multicoloured	12·00	3·75
232/45 *Set of 14*			65·00	48·00

A further printing of the £1 took place with the decimal
surcharges issued 15 February 1971. It was for some time believed
that stamps from this printing could be identified by the brown
shading which extended to the foot of the design, instead of
stopping short as on the original printing, but this test has now
been shown to be inconsistent.

91 de Havilland DHC-2 Beaver Seaplane

(Des V. Whiteley. Litho Format)

1969 (8 Apr). 21st Anniv of Government Air Services. T **91** and
similar horiz designs. Multicoloured. W w **12** (sideways). P 14.

246	2d. Type **91**	65	30
247	6d. Noorduyn Norseman V	65	35
248	1s. Auster Autocrat	65	35
249	2s. Falkland Islands Arms	1·00	2·00
246/9 *Set of 4*		2·75	2·75

92 Holy Trinity Church, 1869

(Des G. Drummond. Litho Format)

1969 (30 Oct). Centenary of Bishop Stirling's Consecration. T **92**
and similar horiz designs. W w **12** (sideways). P 14.

250	2d. black, grey and apple-green	40	60
251	6d. black, grey and orange-red	40	60
252	1s. black, grey and lilac	40	60
253	2s. multicoloured	50	75
250/3 *Set of 4*		1·50	2·25

Designs:—6d. Christ Church Cathedral, 1969; 1s. Bishop Stirling;
2s. Bishop's Mitre.

96 Mounted Volunteer

97 SS *Great Britain* (1843)

(Des R. Granger Barrett. Litho B.W.)

1970 (30 Apr). Golden Jubilee of Defence Force. T **96** and similar
designs. Multicoloured. W w **12** (sideways on 2d. and 1s.). P 13.

254	2d. Type **96**	1·00	70
255	6d. Defence Post (*horiz*)	1·00	70
256	1s. Corporal in Number One Dress Uniform	1·00	70
257	2s. Defence Force Badge (*horiz*)	1·00	75
254/7 *Set of 4*		3·50	2·50

(Des V. Whiteley. Litho J.W.)

1970 (30 Oct). Restoration of SS *Great Britain*. T **97** and views
of the ship at different dates. Multicoloured. W w **12**
(sideways*). P 14½×14.

258	2d. Type **97**	65	40
259	4d. In 1845	65	75
	w. Wmk Crown to right of CA	19·00	3·00
260	9d. In 1876	65	75
261	1s. In 1886	65	75
	w. Wmk Crown to right of CA	£1800	
262	2s. In 1970	1·00	75
258/62 *Set of 5*		3·25	3·00

*The normal sideways watermark shows Crown to left of CA, *as
seen from the back of the stamp.*

FALKLAND ISLANDS DEPENDENCIES

PRICES FOR STAMPS ON COVER TO 1945	
Nos. A1/D8	*from* × 20

A. GRAHAM LAND

For use at Port Lockroy (established 1 February 1944) and Hope Bay
(established 12 February 1945) bases.

Falkland Islands definitive stamps with face values of 1s.3d. and
above were valid for use from Graham Land in conjunction with Nos.
A1/8 and subsequently Nos. G1/16.

Z **1**

Z **2**

Stamps of FALKLAND ISLANDS cancelled as Type Z **1** or Z **2** at Port
Lockroy or Hope Bay with Graham Land circular datestamps
between 12 February 1944 and 31 January 1954. Further offices
were opened at Stonington Island (13.3.46–8.2.50) and Argentine
Islands (from 25.1.47).

1938–50. King George VI (Nos. 159/63).

Z1	1s.3d. black and carmine-red		£250
Z2	2s.6d. slate		90·00

Z3	5s. indigo and yellow-brown		£140
Z4	10s. black and orange		£100
Z5	£1 black and violet		£110

1952. King George VI (Nos. 181/5).

Z6	1s.3d. orange		£190
Z7	2s.6d. olive-green		£225
Z8	5s. purple		£225
Z9	10s. grey		£250
Z10	£1 black		£250

GRAHAM LAND

DEPENDENCY OF
(A **1**)

1944 (12 Feb)–**45**. Falkland Islands Nos. 146, 148, 150, 153/5, 157 and 158*a* optd with Type A **1**, in red, by B.W.

A1	½d. black and green	30	2·25
	a. Blue-black and green	£3000	£1100
A2	1d. black and violet	30	1·00
A3	2d. black and carmine-red	50	1·00
A4	3d. black and blue	50	1·00
A5	4d. black and purple	2·00	1·75
A6	6d. black and brown	18·00	2·25
	a. Blue-black and brown (24.9.45)	18·00	
A7	9d. black and grey-blue	2·50	1·50
A8	1s. deep blue	2·50	1·50
A1/8 *Set of 8*		24·00	11·00
A1s/8s *Perf "SPECIMEN" Set of 8*		£650	

B. SOUTH GEORGIA

The stamps of Falkland Islands were used at the Grytviken whaling station on South Georgia from 3 December 1909.

Mr. J. Innes Wilson, the Stipendary Magistrate whose duties included those of postmaster, was issued with a stock of stamps, values ½d. to 5s., together with an example of the current "FALKLAND ISLANDS" circular datestamp. This was used to cancel the stamps, but, as it gave no indication that mail had originated at South Georgia, a straight-line handstamp inscribed "SOUTH GEORGIA" was also supplied. A second handstamp, inscribed "South Georgia" was sent on 17 February 1910. It was intended that these should be struck directly on to each letter or card below the stamp, but they can sometimes be found struck across the stamp instead.

The use of the "South Georgia" handstamps continued after the introduction of the "SOUTH GEORGIA" circular datestamp in June 1910 apparently for philatelic purposes, but no example has been reported used after June 1912.

SOUTH GEORGIA.
Z **1**

South Georgia.
Z **2**

		On piece	On cover/ card
ZU1	Example of Type Z **1** used in conjunction with "FALKLAND ISLANDS" postmark (22 Dec 1909 to 30 March 1910). *Price from*	£2000	£10000
ZU2	Example of Type Z **2** used in conjunction with "FALKLAND ISLANDS" postmark (May 1910) .... *Price from*	£1300	£6000
ZU3	Example of Type Z **2** used in conjunction with "SOUTH GEORGIA" postmark (June 1910 to June 1912) .... *Price from*	£300	£1000

Stamps of FALKLAND ISLANDS cancelled at Grytviken with South Georgia circular datestamps between 27 June 1910 and 31 January 1954.

1891–1902. Queen Victoria (Nos. 17/38).

Z11	½d. yellow-green		£250
Z11*a*	1d. pale red		£200
Z11*b*	2d. purple		£325
Z11*c*	2½d. deep ultramarine		£400
Z12	4d. olive-black		£475
Z12*a*	6d. yellow		£475
Z12*b*	9d. salmon		£475
Z12*d*	1s. yellow-brown		£475

1898. Queen Victoria (No. 42).

Z13	5s. red		£1000

1904–12. King Edward VII (Nos. 43/50).

Z14	½d. green		24·00
Z15	1d. vermilion		23·00
	b. Wmk sideways		70·00
	d. Dull coppery red (on thick paper)		60·00
Z16	2d. purple		85·00
	b. Reddish purple		£325
Z17	2½d. ultramarine		35·00
	b. Deep blue		£200
Z18	6d. orange		£200
Z19	1s. brown		£200
Z20	3s. green		£550
Z21	5s. red		£650

SOUTH GEORGIA PROVISIONAL HANDSTAMPS

During October 1911 the arrival of the German South Polar Expedition at Grytviken, South Georgia, resulted in the local supply of stamps becoming exhausted. The Acting Magistrate, Mr. E. B. Binnie, who was also responsible for the postal facilities, produced a handstamp reading "Paid (at (or At) SOUTH GEORGIA" which, together with a manuscript indication of the postage paid and his signature, was used on mail from 18 October 1911 to January 1912, the handstamp being overstruck by the "SOUTH GEORGIA" double-ring datestamp. Further examples, signed by John Innes Wilson, are known from February 1912.

1911 (18 Oct)–**12**.

PH1	"Paid 1 at SOUTH GEORGIA EBB"...... *Price on cover* £9500
PH1*a*	"Paid 1 At SOUTH GEORGIA EBB" (16.12.11)
	.... *Price on cover* £8500
PH2	"Paid 2½ at SOUTH GEORGIA EBB"....... *Price on cover* £7500
PH2*a*	"Paid 2½ At SOUTH GEORGIA EBB" (16.12.11)
	.... *Price on cover* £9500

PH3	"Paid 1 At SOUTH GEORGIA JIW" (14.2.12)
	Price on cover £14000
PH4	"Paid 2½ At SOUTH GEORGIA JIW" (14.2.12)
	Price on cover £12000

1912–23. King George V. Wmk Mult Crown CA (Nos. 60/9).

Z22	½d. green	21·00
	a. Perf 14 (line). Deep yellow-green	38·00
	d. Dull yellowish green (on thick greyish paper)	50·00
Z23	1d. orange-red	14·00
	a. Perf 14 (line). Orange-vermilion	14·00
	d. Orange-vermilion	14·00
Z24	2d. maroon	65·00
Z25	2½d. deep bright blue	48·00
	c. Deep blue	45·00
Z26	6d. yellow-orange	90·00
	b. Brown-orange	£100
	ba. Bisected (diag) (3d.) (on cover) (3.23)	£25000
Z27	1s. light bistre-brown	£180
	a. Pale bistre-brown	£200
	b. Brown (on thick greyish paper)	£250
Z28	3s. slate-green	£350
Z29	5s. deep rose-red	£425
	a. Reddish maroon	£550
	b. Maroon	£500
Z30	10s. red/green	£700
Z31	£1 black/red	£1000

1918–20. "WAR STAMP" opts (Nos. 70/2).

Z32	½d. deep olive	32·00
Z33	1d. vermilion	32·00
Z34	1s. light bistre-brown	£160

1921–28. King George V. Wmk Mult Script CA (Nos. 73/80).

Z35	½d. yellowish green	8·50
Z36	1d. dull vermilion	7·00
Z37	2d. deep brown-purple	38·00
Z38	2½d. deep blue	32·00
	a. Bisected (diag) (1d.) (on cover) (3.23)	£18000
Z39	2½d. deep purple/pale yellow	65·00
Z40	6d. yellow-orange	75·00
Z41	1s. deep ochre	85·00
Z42	3s. slate-green	£325

1928 PROVISIONAL. For listing of the 2½d. on 2d. surcharge issued at Grytviken on 7 February 1928 see No. 115 of Falkland Islands.

1929–37. King George V. Whale and Penguins design (Nos. 116/26).

Z43	½d. green	9·00
Z44	1d. scarlet	7·50
Z45	2d. grey	18·00
	a. Bisected (diag) (1d.) (on postcard)	£15000
Z46	2½d. blue	9·00
Z47	4d. orange	38·00
Z48	6d. purple	55·00
Z49	1s. black/emerald	75·00
Z50	2s.6d. carmine/blue	£160
Z51	5s. green/yellow	£275
Z52	10s. carmine/emerald	£500
Z53	£1 black/red	£850

Examples of most values are known with forged postmarks dated "Au 30" in 1928, 1930 and 1931.

1933. Centenary of British Administration (Nos. 127/38).

Z54	½d. black and green	18·00
Z55	1d. black and scarlet	7·50
Z56	1½d. black and blue	48·00
Z57	2d. black and brown	55·00
Z58	3d. black and violet	60·00
Z59	4d. black and orange	45·00
Z60	6d. black and slate	£180
Z61	1s. black and olive-green	£200
Z62	2s.6d. black and blue	£700
Z63	5s. black and yellow	£2250
	a. Black and yellow-orange	£4750
Z64	10s. black and chestnut	£2250
Z65	£1 black and carmine	£4750

1935. Silver Jubilee (Nos. 139/42).

Z66	1d. deep blue and scarlet	8·00
Z67	2½d. brown and deep blue	9·00
Z68	4d. green and indigo	11·00
Z69	1s. slate and purple	11·00

1937. Coronation (Nos. 143/5).

Z70	½d. green	4·25
Z71	1d. carmine	4·25
Z72	2½d. blue	4·25

1938–50. King George VI (Nos. 146/63).

Z73	½d. black and green	8·00
Z74	1d. black and carmine	13·00
	a. Black and vermilion	7·00
Z75	1d. black and violet	15·00
Z76	2d. black and deep violet	14·00
Z77	2d. black and carmine-red	20·00
Z78	2½d. black and bright blue (No. 151)	7·50
Z79	3d. black and blue	22·00
Z80	4d. black and purple	16·00
Z81	6d. black and brown	18·00
Z82	9d. black and grey-blue	27·00
Z83	1s. light dull blue	70·00
	a. Dull greenish blue	75·00
Z84	1s.3d. black and carmine-red	85·00
Z85	2s.6d. slate	55·00
Z86	5s. blue and chestnut	£225
	a. Indigo and yellow-brown	£140
	b. Dull blue and yellow-brown	£850
	c. Steel blue and buff-brown	£650
Z87	10s. black and orange-brown	£180
	a. Black and orange	85·00
	b. Black and red-orange	£700
Z88	£1 black and violet	95·00

From 6 April 1944 the post office on South Georgia ceased to sell Falkland Islands stamps with values up to 1s. Stamps of 1s.3d. and above continued to be valid from South Georgia after the introduction of Nos. B1/8 and subsequently Nos. G1/16. Forged South Georgia postmarks exist dated "30 MR 49".

1952. King George VI (Nos. 181/5).

Z89	1s.3d. orange	£100
Z90	2s.6d. olive-green	£190

Z91	5s. purple		£190
Z92	10s. grey		£200
Z93	£1 black		£225

1944 (24 Feb)–**45**. Falkland Islands Nos. 146, 148, 150, 153/5, 157 and 158*a* optd "SOUTH GEORGIA/DEPENDENCY OF", in red, as Type A **1** of Graham Land.

B1	½d. black and green	30	2·25
	a. Wmk sideways	£4750	
B2	1d. black and violet	30	1·00
B3	2d. black and carmine-red	50	1·00
B4	3d. black and blue	50	1·00
B5	4d. black and purple	2·00	1·75
B6	6d. black and brown	18·00	2·25
	a. Blue-black and brown (24.9.45)	18·00	
B7	9d. black and grey-blue	2·50	1·50
B8	1s. deep blue	2·50	1·50
B1/8 *Set of 8*		24·00	11·00
B1s/8s *Perf "SPECIMEN" Set of 8*		£650	

C. SOUTH ORKNEYS

Used from the *Fitzroy* in February 1944 and at Laurie Island (established January 1946).

Falkland Islands definitive stamps with face values of 1s.3d. and above were valid for use from the South Orkneys in conjunction with Nos. C1/8 and subsequently Nos. G1/16.

Z **3**   Z **4**

Stamps of FALKLAND ISLANDS cancelled on the *Fitzroy*, at Laurie Island or at Signy Island with South Orkneys circular datestamps as Type Z **3** or Z **4** between 21 February 1944 and 31 January 1954.

1938–50. King George VI (Nos. 159/63).

Z94	1s.3d. black and carmine-red	£325
Z95	2s.6d. slate	90·00
Z96	5s. indigo and yellow-brown	£140
Z97	10s. black and orange	£100
Z98	£1 black and violet	£110

1952. King George VI (Nos. 181/5).

Z99	1s.3d. orange	£200
Z100	2s.6d. olive-green	£225
Z101	5s. purple	£225
Z102	10s. grey	£250
Z103	£1 black	£250

1944 (21 Feb)–**45**. Falkland Islands Nos. 146, 148, 150, 153/5, 157 and 158*a* optd "SOUTH ORKNEYS/DEPENDENCY OF", in red, as Type A **1** of Graham Land.

C1	½d. black and green	30	2·25
C2	1d. black and violet	30	1·00
	w. Wmk inverted	£8000	
C3	2d. black and carmine-red	50	1·00
C4	3d. black and blue	50	1·00
C5	4d. black and purple	2·00	1·75
C6	6d. black and brown	18·00	2·25
	a. Blue-black and brown (24.9.45)	18·00	
C7	9d. black and grey-blue	2·50	1·50
C8	1s. deep blue	2·50	1·50
C1/8 *Set of 8*		24·00	11·00
C1s/8s *Perf "SPECIMEN" Set of 8*		£650	

D. SOUTH SHETLANDS

Postal facilities were first provided at the Port Foster whaling station on Deception Island for the 1912–13 whaling season and were available each year between November and the following April until March 1931.

No postmark was provided for the 1912–13 season and the local postmaster was instructed to cancel stamps on cover with a straight-line "PORT FOSTER" handstamp. Most letters so cancelled subsequently received a "FALKLAND ISLANDS" circular postmark dated between 19 and 28 March 1913. It is known that only low value stamps were available at Port Foster. Higher values, often with other "FALKLAND ISLANDS" postmark dates, were, it is believed, subsequently "made to order".

Stamps of FALKLAND ISLANDS cancelled at Port Foster, Deception Island with part of "PORT FOSTER" straightline handstamp.

1904–12. King Edward VII (Nos. 43*c*, 44*e*).

Z104	½d. deep yellow-green	£1800
Z105	1d. orange-vermilion	£1800

1912. King George V. Wmk Mult Crown CA (Nos. 60/1).

Z106	½d. yellow-green	£1800
Z107	1d. orange-red	£1800

Stamps of FALKLAND ISLANDS cancelled at Port Foster with part of oval "DECEPTION ISLAND SOUTH SHETLANDS" postmark in black or violet between 1914 and 1927.

1904–12. King Edward VII (No. 43*c*).

Z108	½d. deep yellow-green	£550

1912–20. King George V. Wmk Mult Crown CA (Nos. 60/9).

Z110	½d. yellow-green	£170
Z111	1d. orange-red	£170
Z112	2d. maroon	£225
Z113	2½d. deep bright blue	£225
Z114	6d. yellow-orange	£325
Z115	1s. light bistre-brown	£400
	a. Brown (on thick greyish paper)	£475
Z116	3s. slate-green	£750
Z117	5s. maroon	£900
Z118	10s. red/green	£1200
Z119	£1 black/red	£1600

1918–20. "WAR STAMP" ovpts (Nos. 70/2).

Z120	½d. deep olive	£200
	a. Dull yellowish green (on thick greyish paper)	£225

Z121	1d. vermilion		£200
Z122	1s. light bistre-brown		£500

1921–28. King George V. Wmk Mult Script CA (Nos. 73/80).

Z123	½d. yellowish green		£200
Z126	2½d. deep blue		£250
Z129	1s. deep ochre		£350

Stamps of FALKLAND ISLANDS cancelled at Port Foster with "SOUTH SHETLANDS" circular datestamp between 1923 and March 1931.

1912–20. King George V. Wmk Mult Crown CA (Nos. 60/9).

Z129a	½d. dull yellowish green (on thick greyish paper)		£150
Z130	1d. orange-vermilion		£100
Z131	2d. deep reddish purple		£130
Z132	2½d. deep bright blue		£170
	c. Deep blue		£170
Z133	6d. brown-orange		£200
Z134	1s. bistre-brown		£300
Z135	3s. slate-green		£450
Z136	5s. maroon		£550
Z137	10s. red/green		£850
Z138	£1 black/red		£1400

Examples of all values are known with forged postmarks dated "20 MR 27".

1918–20. "WAR STAMP" ovpts (Nos. 70/2).

Z138a	½d. deep olive		£180
Z139	1d. vermilion		£160
Z140	1s. light bistre-brown		£400

1921–28. King George V. Wmk Mult Script CA (Nos. 73/80).

Z141	½d. yellowish green		55·00
Z142	1d. dull vermilion		55·00
Z143	2d. deep brown-purple		85·00
Z144	2½d. deep blue		80·00
Z145	2½d. deep purple/pale yellow		95·00
Z146	6d. yellow-orange		£150
Z147	1s. deep ochre		£160
Z148	3s. slate-green		£475

1929. King George V. Whale and Penguins design (Nos. 116/26).

Z149	½d. green		85·00
Z150	1d. scarlet		85·00
Z151	2d. grey		£130
Z152	2½d. blue		£110
Z153	6d. purple		£160
Z154	1s. black/emerald		£190
Z155	2s.6d. carmine/blue		£375
Z156	5s. green/yellow		£425
Z157	10s. carmine/emerald		£750
Z158	£1 black/red		£1300

The whaling station at Port Foster was abandoned at the end of the 1930–31 season.

It was reoccupied as a Falkland Islands Dependencies Survey base on 3 February 1944.

Falkland Islands definitive stamps with face values of 1s.3d. and above were valid for use from the South Shetlands in conjunction with Nos. D1/8 and subsequently Nos. G1/16.

Z 5　　　　　　Z 6

Stamps of FALKLAND ISLANDS cancelled at Port Foster (from 5.2.44) or Admiralty Bay (from 7.1.47) with South Shetlands circular datestamps as Type Z **5** or Z **6** between 5 February 1944 and 31 January 1954.

1938–50. King George VI (Nos. 159/63).

Z158a	1s.3d. black and carmine-red		£325
Z159	2s.6d. slate		90·00
Z160	5s. indigo and yellow-brown		£140
Z161	10s. black and orange		£100
Z162	£1 black and violet		£110

1952. King George VI (Nos. 181/5).

Z163	1s.3d. orange		£180
Z164	2s.6d. olive-green		£200
Z165	5s. purple		£200
Z166	10s. grey		£225
Z167	£1 black		£225

1944 (5 Feb)–**45.** Falkland Islands Nos. 146, 148, 150, 153/5, 157 and 158a optd "SOUTH SHETLANDS/DEPENDENCY OF", in red, as Type A **1** of Graham Land.

D1	½d. black and green	30	2·25
D2	1d. black and violet	30	1·00
D3	2d. black and carmine-red	50	1·00
D4	3d. black and blue	50	1·00
D5	4d. black and purple	2·00	1·75
D6	6d. black and brown	18·00	2·25
	a. Blue-black and brown (24.9.45)	18·00	
D7	9d. black and grey-blue	2·50	1·50
D8	1s. deep blue	2·50	1·50
D1/8	Set of 8	24·00	11·00
D1s/8s	Perf "SPECIMEN" Set of 8	£650	

From 12 July 1946 to 16 July 1963, Graham Land, South Georgia, South Orkneys and South Shetlands used FALKLAND ISLANDS DEPENDENCIES stamps.

E. FALKLAND ISLANDS DEPENDENCIES

For use at the following bases:

Admiralty Bay (South Shetlands) (*opened* January 1948, *closed* January 1961)

Argentine Islands (Graham Land) (*opened* 1947)

Deception Island (South Shetlands)

Grytviken (South Georgia)

Hope Bay (Graham Land) (*closed* 4 February 1949, *opened* February 1952)

Laurie Island (South Orkneys) (*closed* 1947)

Port Lockroy (Graham Land) (*closed* 16 January 1962)

Signy Island (South Orkneys) (*opened* 1946)

Stonington Island (Graham Land) (*opened* 1946, *closed* 1950, *opened* 1958, *closed* 1959, *opened* 1960)

G 1

Gap in 80th parallel (R. 1/4, 1/9, 3/4, 3/9, 5/4 and 5/9)

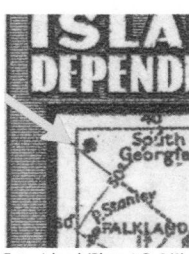

Extra island (Plate 1 R. 3/9)

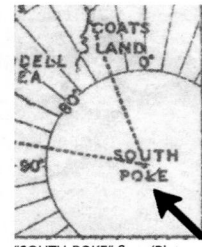

"SOUTH POKE" flaw (Plate 2 R. 6/8)

Missing "I" in "S. Shetland Is." (Plate 1 R. 1/2)

Extra dot by oval (Plate 1 R. 4/6)

3d. "Teardrop" flaw (Frame plate '1A', R. 6/7)

(Des. L.J. Newell. Map litho, frame recess D.L.R.)

1946 (12 July*)–**49.** Wmk Mult Script CA (sideways). P 12.

(a) Map thick and coarse

G1	G **1**	½d. black and green	1·00	3·50
		a. Gap in 80th parallel	3·00	10·00
		aa. Extra island	£325	£325
		b. Missing "I"	£325	£325
		c. "SOUTH POKE"	£225	£375
		d. Extra dot by oval	£325	£325
G2		1d. black and violet	1·25	2·00
		a. Gap in 80th parallel	3·50	6·50
		aa. Extra island	£170	£200
		b. Missing "I"	£170	£200
		d. Extra dot by oval	£180	£200
G3		2d. black and carmine	1·25	2·50
		a. Gap in 80th parallel	3·50	6·00
		aa. Extra island	£350	£350
		b. Missing "I"	£350	£350
		d. Extra dot by oval	£375	£375
G4		3d. black and blue	1·25	5·00
		a. Gap in 80th parallel	3·50	11·00
		aa. Extra island	£225	£350
		b. Missing "I"	£200	£325
		d. Extra dot by oval	£250	£375
		e. "Teardrop"	£110	£150

G5		4d. black and claret	2·25	4·75
		a. Gap in 80th parallel	6·50	14·00
		c. "SOUTH POKE"	£300	£375
G6		6d. black and orange	3·50	5·00
		a. Gap in 80th parallel	7·50	14·00
		aa. Extra island	£275	£325
		b. Missing "I"	£250	£325
		c. "SOUTH POKE"	£180	£375
		d. Extra dot by oval	£275	£325
		e. Black and ochre	55·00	95·00
		ea. Gap in 80th parallel	90·00	£160
		eaa. Extra island	£700	
		eb. Missing "I"	£700	
		ec. "SOUTH POKE"	£650	
		ed. Extra dot by oval	£700	£900
G7		9d. black and brown	2·00	3·75
		a. Gap in 80th parallel	5·50	12·00
		c. "SOUTH POKE"	£170	£275
G8		1s. black and purple	2·00	4·25
		a. Gap in 80th parallel	5·50	13·00
		c. "SOUTH POKE"	£150	£300
G1/8		Set of 8	13·00	27·00
G1s/8s		Perf "SPECIMEN" Set of 8	£1100	

*This is the date of issue for South Georgia. Nos. G1/8 were released in London on 11 February.

Nos. G1/8

Nos. G9/16

On Nos. G9 to G16 the map is redrawn; the "0°" meridian does not pass through the "S" of "COATS", the "n" of "Alexander" is not joined to the "L" of "Land" below, and the loops of letters "s" and "t" are generally more open.

Dot in "T" of "SOUTH" (R. 5/2, 5/4, 5/6, 5/8 and 5/10)

(b) Map thin and clear (16.2.48)

G9	G **1**	½d. black and green	2·25	18·00
		a. Recess frame printed double, one albino and inverted	£2500	
		b. Dot in "T"	7·50	50·00
G10		1d. black and violet	1·50	22·00
		a. Dot in "T"	6·50	65·00
G11		2d. black and carmine	2·75	28·00
		a. Dot in "T"	9·00	85·00
G11b		2½d. black and deep blue (6.3.49)	6·50	4·00
G12		3d. black and blue	2·75	4·00
		a. Dot in "T"	9·00	15·00
		b. "Teardrop"	£150	£180
G13		4d. black and claret	17·00	32·00
		a. Dot in "T"	45·00	95·00
G14		6d. black and orange	26·00	7·00
		a. Dot in "T"	55·00	23·00
G15		9d. black and brown	26·00	7·00
		a. Dot in "T"	55·00	23·00
G16		1s. black and purple	26·00	7·00
		a. Dot in "T"	55·00	23·00
G9/16		Set of 9	£100	£110

Nos. G11, G12 and G13 are known with the map apparently printed double. These are not true 'double prints', in that they were not the result of two impressions of the inked printing plate, but were caused by incorrect tension in the rubber 'blanket' which transferred ink from the cylinder to the paper. Such varieties are outside the scope of this catalogue.

1946 (4 Oct*). Victory. As Nos. 110/11 of Antigua.

G17	1d. deep violet	50	50
G18	3d. blue	75	50
G17s/18s	Perf "SPECIMEN" Set of 2	£375	

*This is the date of issue for South Georgia. The stamps were placed on sale from the South Orkneys on 17 January 1947, from the South Shetlands on 30 January and from Graham Land on 10 February 1947.

1948 (6 Dec). Royal Silver Wedding. As Nos. 112/13 of Antigua, but 1s. country name in recess.

G19	2½d. ultramarine	1·75	3·00
G20	1s. violet-blue	1·75	2·50

1949 (10 Oct). 75th Anniv of UPU As Nos. 114/17 of Antigua.
G21	1d. violet	1·00	4·00
G22	2d. carmine-red	5·00	4·00
G23	3d. deep blue	3·50	1·25
G24	6d. red-orange	4·00	3·00
G21/4 *Set of 4*		12·00	11·00

1953 (4 June). Coronation. As No. 120 of Antigua.
G25	1d. black and violet	1·10	1·25

G **2** *John Biscoe I*, 1947–52   G **3** *Trepassey*, 1945–47

G **4** *Wyatt Earp*, 1934–36   G **5** *Eagle*, 1944–45

G **6** *Penola*, 1934–37   G **7** *Discovery II*, 1929–37

G **8** *William Scoresby*, 1926–46   G **9** *Discovery*, 1925–27

G **10** *Endurance*, 1914–16   G **11** *Deutschland*, 1910–12

G **12** *Pourquoi-pas?*, 1908–10   G **13** *Français*, 1903–05

G **14** *Scotia*, 1902–04   G **15** *Antarctic*, 1901–03

G **16** *Belgica* 1897–99

Normal

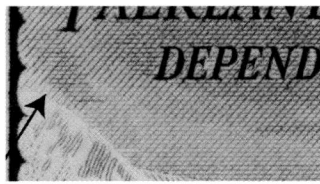

Retouch (R 12/1)

1d. There are a number of retouches of the cross-hatching in the clouds where lines have been deepened. The one illustrated is on left pane R. 12/1 and other prominent retouches occur on left pane R. 8/1 and R. 10/1 but there are other less marked ones.

(Recess Waterlow, then D.L.R. (from 27.3.62))
1954 (1 Feb)–**62**. Types G **2/16**. Wmk Mult Script CA. P 12½.
G26	G **2**	½d. black and bluish green	1·00	5·00
		a. Black and deep green (D.L.R.) (17.4.62)	10·00	42·00
G27	G **3**	1d. black and sepia-brown	1·75	3·00
		a. Retouches to cross-hatching .... *from*	12·00	
		b. Black and sepia (D.L.R.) (27.3.62)	17·00	42·00
		ba. Retouches to cross-hatching ....*from*	50·00	
G28	G **4**	1½d. black and olive	2·50	4·50
		a. Black and yellow-olive (D.L.R.) (21.9.62)	10·00	4·00
G29	G **5**	2d. black and rose-red	3·25	4·25
G30	G **6**	2½d. black and yellow-ochre	1·25	35
G31	G **7**	3d. black and deep bright blue	1·75	35
G32	G **8**	4d. black and bright reddish purple	6·00	3·75
G33	G **9**	6d. black and deep lilac	7·50	3·75
G34	G **10**	9d. black	6·50	5·00
G35	G **11**	1s. black and brown	5·00	4·00
G36	G **12**	2s. black and carmine	19·00	23·00
G37	G **13**	2s.6d. black and pale turquoise	24·00	12·00
G38	G **14**	5s. black and violet	42·00	14·00
G39	G **15**	10s. black and blue	65·00	28·00
G40	G **16**	£1 black	80·00	38·00
G26/40 *Set of 15*			£225	£130

TRANS-ANTARCTIC EXPEDITION 1955-1958
(G **17**)

1956 (30 Jan). Trans-Antarctic Expedition. Nos. G27, G30/1 and G33 optd with Type G **17**.
G41	1d. black and sepia-brown	10	35
	a. Retouches to cross-hatching.... *from*	10·00	
G42	2½d. black and yellow-ochre	50	60
G43	3d. black and deep bright blue	50	30
G44	6d. black and deep lilac	50	30
G41/4 *Set of 4*		1·40	1·40

The stamps of Falkland Islands Dependencies were withdrawn on 16 July 1963 after Coats Land, Graham Land, South Orkneys and South Shetlands had become a separate colony, known as British Antarctic Territory.

F. SOUTH GEORGIA

From 17 July 1963 South Georgia and South Sandwich Islands used stamps inscribed "South Georgia".

1 Reindeer   **2** South Sandwich Islands

3 Sperm Whale   **4** Chinstrap and King Penguins

5 South American Fur Seal   **6** Fin Whale

7 Southern Elephant-seal   **8** Light-mantled Sooty Albatross

9 *R2* (Whale catcher)   **10** Leopard Seal

11 Shackleton's Cross   **12** Wandering Albatross

13 Southern Elephant-seal and South American Fur Seal   **14** Plankton and Krill

15 Blue Whale   **16** King Penguins

(Des D.L.R. (No. 16), M. Goaman (others). Recess D.L.R.)
1963 (17 July)–**69**. T **1/16**. Ordinary or glazed paper (No. 16). W w **12**. P 15.
1	**1**	½d. brown-red	50	1·25
		a. Perf 14×15 (13.2.67)	70	1·50
2	**2**	1d. violet-blue	2·75	1·25
3	**3**	2d. turquoise-blue	1·25	1·25
4	**4**	2½d. black	6·00	2·50
5	**5**	3d. bistre	2·75	30
6	**6**	4d. bronze-green	5·50	1·50
7	**7**	5½d. deep violet	2·50	30
8	**8**	6d. orange	75	50
9	**9**	9d. blue	7·50	2·00
10	**10**	1s. purple	75	30
11	**11**	2s. yellow-olive and light blue	27·00	7·00
12	**12**	2s.6d. blue	25·00	4·00
13	**13**	5s. orange-brown	22·00	4·00
14	**14**	10s. magenta	48·00	15·00
15	**15**	£1 ultramarine	90·00	48·00
16	**16**	£1 grey-black (1.12.69)	8·00	13·00
1/16 *Set of 16*			£200	90·00

1970 (22 Jan). As No. 1, but wmk w **12** sideways and on glazed paper.
17		½d. brown-red	1·50	2·00

Faröe Islands
UNDER BRITISH OCCUPATION

The Faröe islands were under British administration from 12 April 1940 to 1945 to prevent their seizure by the Germans, who had occupied Denmark.

Types of Denmark overprinted

43   44

(1)   (1a)

(1b)

1940 (2 Nov)–**41**. T **44** of Denmark, surch with T **1** by H. N. Jacobsen, Tórshavn.

1	20ö. on 15ö. scarlet (II)	70·00	19·00
	a. Surcharge bar omitted (4.41)	—	£1400
	aa. Do. Surch double	—	£1400

No. 1a is from proof sheets (200 stamps), later sold over P.O. counter. Nearly all copies were used.

1940–**41**. T **43** of Denmark, surch by H. N. Jacobsen, Tórshavn, with T **1a** (No. 3) or as T **1b** (others).

2	20ö. on 1ö. blackish green (B.) (2.5.41)	50·00	95·00
3	20ö. on 5ö. maroon (B.) (17.3.41)	50·00	32·00
4	50ö. on 5ö. maroon (6.12.40)	£375	65·00
5	60ö. on 6ö. orange (21.12.40)	£150	£250

During a shortage of stamps in May and June 1941 circular post paid cancellations were used inscribed "FAERØERNE FRANCO-BETALT" and the value in the centre: 5, 10 or 20 ØRE and also with the centre blank and a higher value inserted by hand. These were mainly used on clippings from money order forms and are very rare on complete covers.

Fiji

PRICES FOR STAMPS ON COVER TO 1945

Nos. 1/9	from × 8
Nos. 10/34	from × 5
Nos. 35/59	from × 8
Nos. 60/3	—
Nos. 64/9	from × 20
Nos. 70/5	from × 5
Nos. 76/103	from × 8
Nos. 104/14	from × 5
Nos. 115/24	from × 4
Nos. 125/37	from × 3
Nos. 138/241	from × 4
Nos. 242/5	from × 3
Nos. 246/8	from × 8
Nos. 249/66b	from × 2
No. 267	from × 8
Nos. D1/5c	from × 6
Nos. D6/10	from × 20
Nos. D11/18	from × 15

King Cakobau 1852–Oct 1874

Christian missionaries reached Fiji in 1835 and early letters are known to and from their mission stations, sent via Sydney, Hobart or Auckland.

In 1852 Cakobau, the chief of the island of Bau, declared himself King of Fiji and converted to Christianity two years later. Internal problems and difficulties with the American government led the king to offer to cede Fiji to Great Britain. The offer was refused, but resulted in the appointment of a British Consul in 1858. A Consular Post Office operated from September 1858 until 1872 and franked mail with New South Wales stamps from 1863.

The destruction of plantations in the Confederacy during the American Civil War led to an increased demand for Fijian cotton and this upsurge in commercial activity encouraged *The Fiji Times* newspaper on Levuka to establish a postal service on 1 November 1870.

1

(Type-set and printed at the office of *The Fiji Times*, Levuka, Ovalau, Fiji)

1870 (1 Nov)–**71**. Rouletted in the printing.

(a) Thin Quadrillé paper

1	**1**	1d. black/*rose*	£4500	£4750
2		3d. black/*rose*	£5500	£5000
		a. Comma after "EXPRESS" (R. 4/4)	£8000	£8000
3		6d. black/*rose*	£3000	£3000
4		1s. black/*rose*	£2250	£2500

(b) Thin vertically ribbed paper (1871)

5	**1**	1d. black/*rose*	£1100	£2000
		a. Vert strip of 4. Nos. 5, 7/9	£45000	
6		3d. black/*rose*	£1800	£3250
7		6d. black/*rose*	£1500	£2000
8		9d. black/*rose*	£3250	£3750
		a. Comma after "EXPRESS" (R. 4/4)	£4250	
9		1s. black/*rose*	£1800	£1800

Nos. 1/4 were printed *se-tenant* as a sheet of 24 (6×4) with the 6d. stamps in the first horizontal row, the 1s. in the second, the 1d. in the third and the 3d. in the fourth. Nos. 5/9 were produced from the same plate on which three of the 3d. impressions had been replaced with three 9d. values.

The paper used for Nos. 1/4 shows a quadrillé watermark pattern comprising 3.7 mm squares. That used for Nos. 5/9 shows a pattern of vertical lines 1mm apart usually with thickened lines at 8.5 mm intervals. Stamps without the additional thickened lines are worth a premium.

The issued stamps showed the vertical frame lines continuous from top to bottom of the sheet with the horizontal rules broken and not touching the verticals. Used examples are cancelled in manuscript, by an Australian arrival mark or by the star cancellation used at Bua.

It should be noted that the initial rose colour of the papers has faded significantly in the majority of stamps found today.

There are no reprints of these stamps, but the 1d., 3d., 6d. and 1s. are known in the correct type on *yellow wove* paper and are believed to be proofs.

There are also three different sets of imitations made by the proprietors of *The Fiji Times* to meet the demands of collectors:—

The first was produced in 1876 on *white wove* paper, surfaced to simulate the appearance of vertically ribbed when viewed with light reflecting off its surface. Rouletted on dotted lines and arranged in sheets of 40 (5 rows of 8) comprising 1d., 3d., 6d., 9d. and 1s.; the horizontal frame lines are continuous and the vertical ones broken.

The second was produced before 1888 on *thick rosy mauve wove* paper, rouletted on dotted lines and arranged in sheets of 30 (5 rows of 6) comprising 1s., 9d., 6d., 3d. and 1d.; the vertical frame lines are continuous and the horizontal ones broken.

The third only came to light in the 1960s and is rare, only one complete sheet being recorded, which has since been destroyed. The sheet arrangement is the same as Nos. 1/4, which suggests that this was the first imitation to be produced. It is on *off-white wove* paper, rouletted on closely dotted or solid lines, with vertical frame lines continuous and the horizontal ones broken, as in the originals. These differ from the proofs mentioned above in that the lettering is slightly larger and the figures also differ.

King Cakobau established a formal government in June 1871 and stamps for the royal post office were ordered from Sydney. These arrived in October 1871 and the postal service was placed on a firm basis by the First Postal Act in December of that year. Under its terms *The Fiji Times* service closed on 17 January 1872 and the British Consular Post Office followed six months later.

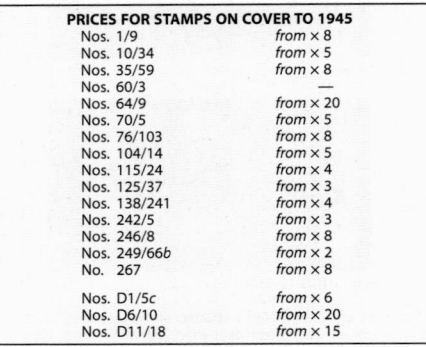

2   3   (4)

(Eng and electrotyped by A. L. Jackson. Typo Govt Printing Office, Sydney.)

1871 (Oct). Wove paper. Wmk impressed "FIJI POSTAGE" in small sans serif capitals across the middle row of stamps in the sheet. P 12½.

10	**2**	1d. blue	60·00	£120
11		3d. pale yellow-green	£120	£350
12	**3**	6d. rose	£160	£300

The 3d. differs from T **2** in having a white circle containing square dots surrounding the centre.

All three values are known *imperf*, but were not issued in that condition.

See notes after No. 33b.

1872 (13 Jan). Surch as T **4**, in local currency, by Govt Ptg Office, Sydney.

13	**2**	2c. on 1d. pale blue	60·00	65·00
		a. Deep blue	55·00	55·00
14		6c. on 3d. yellow-green	85·00	85·00
15	**3**	12c. on 6d. carmine-rose	£120	85·00

CROWN COLONY

King Cakobau renewed his offer to cede Fiji to Great Britain and this took place on 12 October 1874.

(5)   (6)   (7)

(Enlarged) Cross   Inverted "A"
pattée stop

Cross pattée stop after "R" (R. 3/6).
Round raised stop after "V" (R. 3/8).
Round raised stops after "V" and "R" (R. 3/9).
Inverted "A" for "V" (R. 3/10).
No stop after "R" (R. 2/3 on T **5**, R. 5/3 on T **6**).
Large stop after "R" (R. 5/10).

(Optd at *Polynesian Gazette* Office, Levuka)

1874 (21 Oct). Nos. 13/15 optd.

*(a) With T **5***

16	**2**	2c. on 1d. blue	£1100	£300
		a. No stop after "R"	£3250	£1000
		b. Cross pattée stop after "R"	£3250	£1000
		c. Round raised stop after "V"	£3250	£1000
		d. Round raised stops after "V" and "R"	£3250	£1000
		e. Inverted "A" for "V"	£3250	£1000
17		6c. on 3d. green	£2000	£700
		a. No stop after "R"	£5500	£1800
		b. Cross pattée stop after "R"	£5500	£1800
		c. Round raised stop after "V"	£5500	£1800
		d. Round raised stops after "V" and "R"	£5500	£1800
		e. Inverted "A" for "V"	£5500	£1800
		f. Vert pair. Nos. 17 and 20	£14000	
18	**3**	12c. on 6d. rose	£900	£250
		a. No stop after "R"	£3000	£1000
		b. Cross pattée stop after "R"	£3000	£1000
		c. Round raised stop after "V"	£3000	£1000
		d. Round raised stops after "V" and "R"	£3000	£1000
		e. Inverted "A" for "V"	£3000	£1000
		f. Opt inverted	—	£5500
		g. Vert pair. Nos. 18 and 21	£7500	

*(b) With T **6***

19	**2**	2c. on 1d. blue	£1200	£325
		a. No stop after "R"	£3250	£1000
		f. Large stop after "R"	—	£1000
20		6c. on 3d. green	£2500	£950
		a. No stop after "R"	£5500	£1800
21	**3**	12c. on 6d. rose	£1000	£275
		a. No stop after "R"	£3000	£1000
		b. Opt inverted	£7000	

Nos. 16/21 were produced in sheets of 50 (10×5) of which the top three rows were overprinted with Type **5** and the lower two with Type **6**.

1875. Stamps of 1874 surch at *Polynesian Gazette* Office, Levuka, with T **7**.

(a) In red (Apr)

22	**2**	2d. on 6c. on 3d. green (No. 17)	£750	£225
		a. No stop after "R"	£2250	£800
		b. Cross pattée stop after "R"	£2250	£800
		c. Round raised stop after "V"	£2250	£800
		d. Round raised stops after "V" and "R"	£2250	£800
		e. Inverted "A" for "V"	£2250	£800
		f. No stop after "2d" (R. 1/2)	£2250	£800
		g. Vert pair. Nos. 22/3	£6500	
23		2d. on 6c. on 3d. green (No. 20)	£900	£275
		a. No stop after "R"	£2250	£800
		b. Stop between "2" and "d" (R. 5/7)	£2250	£800

(b) In black (30 Sept)

24	**2**	2d. on 6c. on 3d. green (No. 17)	£1900	£600
		a. No stop after "R"	£4750	£1500
		b. Cross pattée stop after "R"	£4750	£1500
		c. Round raised stop after "V"	£4750	£1500
		d. Round raised stops after "V" and "R"	£4750	£1500
		e. Inverted "A" for "V"	£4750	£1500
		f. No stop after "2d" (R. 1/2)	£4750	£1500
		g. "V.R." double	£13000	
		h. Vert pair. Nos. 24/5	£13000	
25		2d. on 6c. on 3d. green (No. 20)	£2500	£800
		a. No stop after "R"	£4750	£1500

		b. Stop between "2" and "d" (R. 5/7)	£4750	£1500
		c. "V.R." double	£5500	£4500

1875 (20 Nov). No. 15 surch at *Polynesian Gazette* Office, Levuka, with T **7** and "V.R." at one operation.

*(a) "V.R." T **5***

26	3	2d. on 12c. on 6d. rose	£2750	£850
		a. No stop after "R"	—	£2250
		b. Round raised stop after "R"	—	£1600
		c. Inverted "A" for "V" (R. 1/3, 2/8, 4/4)	£4250	£1300
		d. Do. and round raised stop after "V" (R. 3/3, 3/6, 3/8, 3/10)	£4000	£1100
		e. As "c" and round raised stops after "R" and "V" (R. 3/2, 3/9)	£4500	£1400
		f. Surch double	—	£4750
		g. Vert pair. Nos. 26/7	£14000	

*(b) "V.R." T **6***

27	3	2d. on 6d. rose	£3000	£900
		a. Surch double	—	£5500

The setting used for Nos. 26/7 was similar to that of Nos. 16/21, but the fourth stamp in the fourth row had a Type **5** "V.R." instead of a Type **6**.

The position of No. 26b is not known.

(8)   (9)   Void corner (R. 2/1)

(Typo Govt Printing Office, Sydney, from plates of 1871)

1876–77. On paper previously lithographed "VR" as T **8**, the 3d. surch with T **9**. P 12½.

(a) Wove paper (31.1.76)

28	2	1d. grey-blue	55·00	55·00
		a. Dull blue	55·00	55·00
		b. Doubly printed	£550	
		c. Void corner	£750	£425
		d. Imperf vert (horiz pair)	£850	
29		2d. on 3d. pale green	60·00	60·00
		a. Deep green	55·00	60·00
30	3	6d. pale rose	70·00	70·00
		a. Dull rose	60·00	60·00
		b. Carmine-rose	60·00	60·00
		c. Doubly printed	£2500	

(b) Laid paper (5.1.77)

31	2	1d. blue	32·00	48·00
		a. Deep blue	32·00	48·00
		b. Void corner (R. 2/1)	£400	£350
		c. Imperf vert (horiz pair)	£700	
32		2d. on 3d. yellow-green	75·00	80·00
		a. Deep yellow-green	70·00	75·00
		b. Imperf between (pair)	£850	
		c. Perf 10	£375	
		ca. Imperf vert (horiz pair)	£950	
		d. Perf 11	£350	
33	3	6d. rose	55·00	38·00
		a. Carmine-rose	55·00	42·00
		b. Imperf vert (horiz pair)	£700	

The extent of the void area on Nos. 28c and 31b varies.

The 3d. *green* is known without the surcharge T **9** on wove paper and also without the surcharge and the monogram. In this latter condition it can only be distinguished from No. 11 by its colour, which is a fuller, deeper yellow-green.

Stamps on both wove and laid paper *imperf* are from printer's trial or waste sheets and were not issued.

All values are known on laid paper without the monogram "VR" and the 3d. stamp also without the surcharge but these are also believed to be from printer's trial sheets which were never issued for postal purposes. Being on laid paper they are easily distinguishable from Nos. 10/12.

1877 (12 Oct). Optd with T **8** and surch as T **9**. Laid paper. P 12½.

34	2	4d. on 3d. mauve	£100	26·00
		a. Imperf vert (horiz pair)	£1000	

10   11

Four Pence
A

Four Pence
B

Type A: Length 12½ mm
Type B: Length 14 mm
Note also the different shape of the two "e"s.

(Typo from new plates made from original dies of 1871 with "CR" altered to "VR" at Govt Printing Office, Sydney. 2d. and 4d. made from old 3d. die.)

1878–99. Surcharges as T **9** or as Types A or B for 4d. value. Wove unwatermarked paper, or with paper-maker's name "T. H. SAUNDERS", "E. D. & Co. SUPERFINE", "IMPERIAL LINEN" or "SANDERSON" in double-lined capitals extending over a varying number of stamps in each full sheet, the last being accompanied by an ornamental crown and shield.

(a) P 12½ (1878–80)

35	10	1d. pale ultramarine (19.2.79)	20·00	19·00
		a. Ultramarine	22·00	19·00
36		2d. on 3d. green (17.10.78)	12·00	42·00
37		2d. yellow-green (1.9.79)	45·00	20·00
		a. Blue-green	60·00	25·00

		b. Error. Ultramarine	£40000	
38	11	6d. rose (30.7.80)	£110	32·00

(b) P 10 (1881–90)

39	10	1d. dull blue (11.5.82)	60·00	3·00
		a. Ultramarine	32·00	3·00
		b. Cambridge blue (12.7.83)	60·00	4·25
40		2d. yellow-green (20.10.81)	45·00	1·00
		a. Blue-green	55·00	5·50
41		4d. on 1d. mauve (29.1.90)	75·00	55·00
42		4d. on 2d. pale mauve (A) (23.5.83)	90·00	15·00
		a. Dull purple	90·00	15·00
43		4d. on 2d. dull purple (B) (7.11.88)	—	£140
44		4d. mauve (13.9.90)	80·00	
		a. Deep purple	80·00	75·00
45	11	6d. pale rose (11.3.85)	75·00	32·00
		a. Bright rose	30·00	30·00

(c) P 10×12½ (1881–82)

46	10	1d. ultramarine (11.5.82)	£190	50·00
47		2d. green (20.10.81)	£160	60·00
48	11	6d. rose (20.10.81)	£350	55·00
		a. Pale rose	£350	55·00

(d) P 12½×10 (1888–90)

49	10	1d. ultramarine (1890)	—	£350
49a		2d. green (1888)		
49b		4d. on 2d. dull purple (A)	†	—

(e) P 10×11¾ (3.9.86)

50	10	1d. dull blue	£100	24·00
		a. Ultramarine		
51		2d. yellow-green	70·00	15·00

(f) P 11¾×10 (1886–88)

51a	10	1d. dull blue (7.11.88)	£225	55·00
		ab. Ultramarine		
51b		2d. yellow-green (3.9.86)	—	£550
52	11	6d. rose (1887)	†	£850

(g) P 11×10 (1892–93)

53	10	1d. ultramarine (18.8.92)	32·00	22·00
54		2d. pale mauve (18.8.92)	23·00	35·00
55	11	6d. pale rose (14.2.93)	25·00	22·00
		a. Rose	24·00	28·00

(h) P 11 (1897–99)

56	10	4d. mauve (14.7.96)	40·00	11·00
57	11	6d. dull rose (14.7.96)	50·00	60·00
		a. Printed both sides (12.99)	£2250	£1700
		b. Bright rose	75·00	80·00

(i) P 11×11¾ (1896)*

58	10	4d. deep purple (14.7.96)	60·00	
		a. Bright purple	15·00	7·00
59	11	6d. rose (23.7.96)	50·00	
		a. Bright rose	15·00	3·75

(j) Imperf (pairs) (1882–90)

60	10	1d. ultramarine		
61		2d. yellow-green		
62		4d. on 2d. pale mauve		
63	11	6d. rose	—	£1800

*Under this heading are included stamps from several perforating machines with a gauge varying between 11.6 and 12.

No. 37b was printed in the colour of the 1d. in error. Only four examples have been reported, one of which was subsequently destroyed.

In the absence of detailed information on dates of issue, printing dates are quoted for Nos. 35/63 and 76/103.

12   13

(Des T. Richards, Eng A. L. Jackson. Typo Govt Printing Office, Sydney)

1881–99. Paper-maker's name wmkd as previous issue.

(a) P 10 (19.10.81)

64	12	1s. pale brown	95·00	30·00
		a. Deep brown	95·00	32·00

(b) P 11×10 (1894)

65	12	1s. pale brown	60·00	55·00

(c) P 11 (1897)

66	12	1s. pale brown	55·00	15·00

(d) P 11×11¾ (5.99)

67	12	1s. pale brown	55·00	12·00
		a. Brown	55·00	12·00
		b. Deep brown	65·00	50·00

(e) P 11¾×11 (3.3.97)

68	12	1s. brown	70·00	55·00

Dates given of earliest known use.
Forgeries exist.

Red arc above "FIJI" (R. 1/4)

(Centre typo, frame litho Govt Printing Office, Sydney)

1882 (23 May). Toned paper wmkd with paper-maker's name "Cowan" in old English outline type once in each sheet. P 10.

69	13	5s. dull red and mauve	70·00	32·00
		a. Red arc above "FIJI"	£550	£250

An unknown quantity of the 1s. and 264 sheets (13,200 stamps) of the 5s., both perf 10 and imperf, were cancelled by the Fiji Post Office and sold as remainders. A number of different "SUVA" remainder cancellations have been recorded between "15 DEC 00" and "21 DE 1902".

An electrotyped plate was also produced for the frame of the 5s. This printing was not used for postal purposes but examples were included among the remainders, all cancelled "15 DEC 00". The electrotyped printing, in dull orange and black, is on paper watermarked "NEW SOUTH WALES GOVERNMENT", either upright or sideways in double-line capitals and perforated 11½ - 11¾. Apart from the colour of the medallion, it differs in a number of respects from the original, most notably in the circular frame surrounding the Queen's head, which is notably thicker than the litho printing. Examples are rare.

2½d. 2½d.
(14)   (15)

Types **14** (fraction bar 1 *mm* from "2") and **15** (fraction bar 2 *mm* from "2") are from the same setting of 50 (10×5) with Type **15** occurring on R. 1/2, 2/2, 3/2 and 4/2.

(Stamps typo in Sydney and surch at Govt Printing Office, Suva)

1891 (1 Jan). T **10** surch. P 10.

70	14	2½d. on 2d. green	50·00	50·00
71	15	2½d. on 2d. green	£130	£140

½d.   5ᵈ
(16)   (17)

FIVE   FIVE
PENCE   PENCE
(18) 2 mm spacing   (19) 3 mm spacing

1892 (1 Mar)–**93**. P 10.

*(a) Surch on T **10***

72	16	½d. on 1d. dull blue	60·00	80·00
		a. Ultramarine	60·00	75·00
73	17	5d. on 4d. deep purple (25.7.92)	60·00	75·00
		a. Dull purple	60·00	75·00

*(b) Surch on T **11***

74	18	5d. on 6d. brownish rose (30.11.92)	65·00	75·00
		a. Bright rose	60·00	70·00
		b. Perf 10×12½		
75	19	5d. on 6d. rose (4.1.93)	80·00	95·00
		a. Deep rose	70·00	85·00
		b. Brownish rose	75·00	

20   21 Native Canoe   22

(Typo in Sydney)

1891–8. Wmk in sheet, either "SANDERSON" or "NEW SOUTH WALES GOVERNMENT" in outline capitals.

(a) P 10 (1891–94)

76	20	½d. slate-grey (26.4.92)	6·50	10·00
77	21	1d. black (19.9.94)	30·00	6·00
78		2d. pale green (19.9.94)	£140	22·00
79	22	2½d. chocolate (8.6.91)	60·00	28·00
80	21	5d. ultramarine (14.2.93)	£120	60·00

(b) P 11×10 (1892–93)

81	20	½d. slate-grey (20.10.93)	16·00	32·00
82	21	1d. black (14.2.93)	20·00	8·50
83		2d. green (14.2.93)	35·00	10·00
84	22	2½d. chocolate (17.8.92)	32·00	48·00
		a. Brown	12·00	19·00
		b. Yellowish brown		
85	21	5d. ultramarine (14.2.93)	25·00	7·50

(c) P 11 (1893–96)

86	20	½d. slate-grey (2.6.96)	4·00	6·50
		a. Greenish slate	2·50	6·50
87	21	1d. black (31.10.95)	22·00	7·50
88		1d. pale mauve (2.6.96)	22·00	1·00
		a. Rosy mauve	23·00	1·00
89		2d. dull green (17.3.94)	8·50	80
		a. Emerald-green	12·00	2·00
90	22	2½d. brown (31.10.95)	55·00	19·00
		a. Yellowish brown	29·00	32·00
91	21	5d. ultramarine (14.2.93)	£170	

(d) P 10×11¾ (1893–94)

92	20	½d. greenish slate	£1000	£750
93	21	1d. black (20.7.93)	48·00	6·50
94		2d. dull green (19.9.94)	£800	£400

(e) P 11¾×10 (19.9.94)

94a	20	½d. greenish slate	—	£1000

(f) P 11¾ (1894–98)

95	20	½d. greenish slate (19.9.94)	3·50	12·00
		a. Grey	50·00	
96	21	1d. black (19.9.94)	£225	50·00
97		1d. rosy mauve (4.5.98)	17·00	8·00
98		2d. dull green (19.9.94)	£120	55·00

(g) P 11×11¾ (1895–97)

99	20	½d. greenish slate (8.10.97)	1·00	4·50
100	21	1d. black (31.10.95)	£3000	£1500
101		1d. rosy mauve (14.7.96)	12·00	1·00
		a. Pale rosy mauve	4·50	2·00
102		2d. dull green (26.7.97)	55·00	4·00
103	22	2½d. brown (26.7.97)	17·00	26·00
		a. Yellow-brown	8·50	5·00

(h) P 11¾×11 (1897–98)

103b	20	½d. greenish slate (8.10.97)	9·50	19·00
103c	21	1d. rosy mauve (10.2.97)	27·00	7·00
103d		2d. dull green (4.5.98) (shades)	£375	£100

The 2½d. brown is known doubly printed, but only occurs in the remainders and with the special obliteration (Price £180 *cancelled-to-order*). It was never issued for postal use.

23   **24**

(Typo D.L.R.)

1903 (1 Feb). Wmk Crown CA. P 14.

104	**23**	½d. green and pale green	3·00	2·25
105		1d. dull purple and black/*red*	19·00	55
106	**24**	2d. dull purple and orange	3·75	1·25
107	**23**	2½d. dull purple and blue/*blue*	14·00	1·50
108		3d. dull purple and purple	1·50	2·25
109	**24**	4d. dull purple and black	1·50	2·25
110	**23**	5d. dull purple and green	1·50	2·00
111	**24**	6d. dull purple and carmine	1·50	1·75
112	**23**	1s. green and carmine	18·00	80·00
113	**24**	5s. green and black	80·00	£160
114	**23**	£1 grey-black and ultramarine (*shades*)	£375	£475
104/14 *Set of 11*			£450	£650
104s/14s Optd *SPECIMEN" Set of 11*			£325	

1904–09. Wmk Mult Crown CA. Chalk-surfaced paper (1s.). P 14.

115	**23**	½d. green and pale green	18·00	3·00
116	**23**	1d. purple and black/*red*	38·00	10
117		1s. green and carmine (1909)	30·00	40·00
115/17 *Set of 3*			75·00	40·00

1906–12. Colours changed. Wmk Mult Crown CA. Chalk surfaced paper (6d. to £1). P 14.

118	**23**	½d. green (1908)	12·00	3·25
119		1d. red (1906)	23·00	10
		w. Wmk inverted	†	
120		2½d. bright blue (1910)	7·00	9·50
121	**24**	6d. dull purple (1910)	30·00	48·00
122	**23**	1s. black/*green* (1911)	11·00	16·00
123	**24**	5s. green and red/*yellow* (1911)	70·00	£100
124	**23**	£1 purple and black/*red* (1912)	£300	£275
118/24 *Set of 7*			£400	£400
119s/24s Optd "SPECIMEN" *Set of 6*			£300	

Nos. 112/14, 117 and 120/4 are known with a forged registered postmark of Suva dated "10 DEC 1909".

WAR STAMP

25   **26**   **(27)**

(Typo D.L.R.)

1912 (Oct)–**23.** Die I. Wmk Mult Crown CA. Chalk-surfaced paper (5d. to £1). P 14.

125	**26**	¼d. brown (21.3.16)	2·50	30
		a. *Deep brown* (1917)	1·50	40
		y. Wmk inverted and reversed		
126	**25**	½d. green	4·25	1·00
		a. *Yellow-green* (1916)	10·00	8·50
		b. *Blue-green* (1917)	4·25	50
		w. Wmk inverted	£225	
		y. Wmk inverted and reversed	£180	
127		1d. carmine	3·50	10
		a. *Bright scarlet* (1916)	2·25	75
		ax. Wmk reversed	†	
		b. *Deep rose* (1916)	12·00	2·00
		bw. Wmk inverted	†	
128	**26**	2d. greyish slate (5.14)	1·75	10
		a. Wmk sideways		
		b. "C" of "CA" missing from wmk	†	
		w. Wmk inverted	—	£350
129	**25**	2½d. bright blue (5.14)	3·00	3·50
130		3d. purple/*yellow* (5.14)	4·25	12·00
		a. Wmk sideways	£350	£500
		b. On lemon (1915)	2·25	8·50
		c. On pale yellow (1921)	3·50	20·00
		ca. "A" of "CA" missing from wmk		
		cw. Wmk inverted		
		d. Die II. On pale yellow (1922)	3·25	24·00
131	**26**	4d. black and red/*yellow* (5.14)	23·00	21·00
		a. On lemon	3·00	16·00
		b. On orange-buff (1920)	50·00	65·00
		c. On pale yellow (1921)	6·50	14·00
		cw. Wmk inverted	£475	
		d. Die II. On pale yellow (1922)	3·00	35·00
		ds. Optd "SPECIMEN"	50·00	
132	**25**	5d. dull purple and olive-green (5.14)	4·75	11·00
133	**26**	6d. dull and bright purple (5.14)	2·00	5·50
134	**25**	1s. black/*green*	1·25	14·00
		a. *White back* (4.14)	1·00	17·00
		b. On blue-green, olive back (1916)	3·00	10·00
		c. On emerald back (1921)	4·50	65·00
		cs. Optd SPECIMEN"	60·00	
		d. Die II. On emerald back (1922)	2·25	38·00
135	**26**	2s.6d. black and red/*blue* (19.1.16)	32·00	30·00
136		5s. green and red/*yellow*	32·00	35·00
137	**25**	£1 purple and black/*red* (5.14)	£275	£325
		a. Die II (1923)	£250	£325
125/37 *Set of 13*			£300	£400
125s/37s Optd "SPECIMEN" *Set of 13*			£500	

Bold "TA" (left pane, R. 5/4)

1915 (1 Dec)–**19.** Optd with T **27** by Govt Printer, Suva.

138	**25**	½d. green		
		a. *Yellow-green* (1916)	2·00	12·00
		b. *Blue-green* (1917)	1·50	5·50
		c. Opt inverted	£650	

		d. Opt double	£130	
		e. Bold "TA"	£130	
139		1d. carmine	42·00	26·00
		a. *Bright scarlet*	4·00	75
		ab. Horiz pair, one without opt	£6500	
		ac. Opt inverted	£700	
		d. *Deep rose* (1919)	8·50	3·25
		e. Bold "TA"	£250	£225
138s/9s H/S "SPECIMEN" *Set of 2*			£140	

No. 139ab occurred on one pane of 120 only, the overprint being so misplaced that all the stamps of the last vertical row escaped it entirely.

The bold "TA" variety only occurs on later printings of Nos. 138/9.

Nos. 140/227 are no longer used.

1922–27. Die II. Wmk Mult Script CA. Chalk-surfaced paper (1s. to 5s.). P 14.

228	**26**	¼d. deep brown (1923)	3·75	24·00
229	**25**	½d. green (1923)	1·00	1·00
		w. Wmk inverted		
230		1d. carmine-red	6·00	50
231		1d. violet (6.1.27)	1·25	10
232	**26**	1½d. scarlet (6.1.27)	4·00	1·00
233		2d. grey	1·25	10
		a. Face value omitted	£28000	
234	**25**	3d. bright blue (1924)	2·75	1·00
235	**26**	4d. black and red/*yellow* (1924)	15·00	5·50
236	**25**	5d. dull purple and sage-green (1927)	1·50	1·50
237	**26**	6d. dull and bright purple	2·25	1·25
238	**25**	1s. black/*emerald* (1924)	13·00	2·00
		w. Wmk inverted		
		y. Wmk inverted and reversed		
239	**26**	2s. purple and blue/*blue* (6.1.27)	25·00	70·00
240		2s.6d. black and red/*blue* (1925)	11·00	32·00
241		5s. green and red/*pale yellow* (1926)	55·00	90·00
228/41 *Set of 14*			£120	£200
228s/41s Optd "SPECIMEN" *Set of 14*			£120	

The 2d. imperforate with watermark Type **10** of Ireland came from a trial printing and was not issued.

Only one example of No. 233a is known. It was caused by an obstruction during the printing of the duty plate.

1935 (6 May). Silver Jubilee. As Nos. 91/4 of Antigua. P 13½×14.

242		1½d. deep blue and carmine	1·00	9·50
		a. *Deep blue and aniline red*	11·00	29·00
		ab. Frame printed double, one albino	£1000	
		f. Diagonal line by turret	£150	
		g. Dot to left of chapel	£350	
		h. Dot by flagstaff	£275	
		i. Dash by turret	£375	
243		2d. ultramarine and grey	1·50	35
		f. Diagonal line by turret	£120	£120
		g. Dot to left of chapel	£250	
244		3d. brown and deep blue	2·75	5·50
		f. Diagonal line by turret	£225	£275
		h. Dot by flagstaff	£425	£475
		i. Dash by turret	£500	£550
245		1s. slate and purple	14·00	18·00
		a. Frame printed double, one albino	£1600	
		f. Diagonal line by turret	£350	£400
		h. Dot by flagstaff	£500	
		i. Dash by turret	£700	
242/5 *Set of 4*			17·00	30·00
242s/5s Perf "SPECIMEN" *Set of 4*			£120	

For illustrations of plate varieties see Omnibus section following Zanzibar.

1937 (12 May). Coronation. As Nos. 95/7 of Antigua.

246		1d. purple	60	1·25
247		2d. grey-black	60	2·25
248		3d. Prussian blue	60	2·25
246/8 *Set of 3*			1·60	5·25
246s/8s Perf "SPECIMEN" *Set of 3*			£120	

28 Native sailing Canoe   **29** Native Village

30 Camakua (canoe)   **31** Map of Fiji Islands

Two Dies of Type **30**:

Die I Empty Canoe   Die II Native in Canoe

Two Dies of Type **31**:

 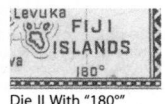

Die I Without "180°"   Die II With "180°"

32 Government Offices   **33** Canoe and Arms of Fiji

34 Sugar cane   **35** Arms of Fiji

36 Spearing fish by torchlight   **37** Suva Harbour

38 River scene   **39** Chief's hut

40 Paw-paw tree   **41** Police bugler

½**d.** Extra palm frond (R. 5/8)

Extra line (R. 10/2)

Scratch through value (R. 5/1)   **2d.** Scratched building (Pl. 1. R. 10/2)

2½**d.** Extra island (R. 10/5)

3d. Spur on Arms medallion (Pl 2 R. 4/2) (ptg of 26 Nov 1945)

(Des V. E. Ousey (½d., 1s., 2s.6d.), Miss C. D. Lovejoy (1d., 1½d., 5d.), Miss I. Stinson (3d.) and A. V. Guy (2d. (Nos. 253/4), 2½d., 6d., 2s.). Recess De La Rue (½d., 1½d., 2d., (Nos. 253/5a), 2½d., 6d., 8d., 1s.5d., 1s.6d.), Waterlow (others))

1938 (5 Apr)–**55.** T **28/41.** Wmk Mult Script CA. Various perfs.

249	28	½d. green (P 13½)	20	75
		a. Perf 14 (5.41)	23·00	6·50
		b. Perf 12 (8.48)	1·50	3·00
		ba. Extra palm frond	£140	£200
250	29	1d. brown and blue (P 12½)	65	20
251	30	1½d. carmine (Die I) (P 13½)	18·00	35
252		1½d. carmine (Die II) (P 13½) (1.10.40)	3·50	3·00
		a. Deep carmine (10.42)	6·50	1·00
		b. Perf 14 (6.42)	32·00	19·00
		c. Perf 12 (21.7.49)	3·75	1·25
253	31	2d. brown and green (Die I) (P 13½)	40	40
		a. Extra line	£1000	95·00
		b. Scratch through value	£1000	95·00
254		2d. brown and green (Die II) (P 13½) (1.10.40)	24·00	16·00
255	32	2d. green and magenta (P 13½) (19.5.42)	65	60
		aa. Scratched building	55·00	50·00
		a. Perf 12 (27.5.46)	2·50	70
		ab. Scratched building	90·00	60·00
256	31	2½d. brown and green (Die II) (P 14) (6.1.42)	4·00	1·00
		a. Extra island	£150	60·00
		b. Perf 13½ (6.1.42)	3·00	80
		ba. Extra island	£130	60·00
		c. Perf 12 (19.1.48)	2·50	50
		ca. Extra island	£110	40·00
257	33	3d. blue (P 12½)	2·25	30
		a. Spur on Arms medallion	£750	£300
258	34	5d. blue and scarlet (P 12½)	42·00	12·00
259		5d. yellow-green and scarlet (P 12½) (1.10.40)	20	30
260	31	6d. black (Die I) (P 13×12)	60·00	10·00
261		6d. black (Die II) (P 14) (1.10.40)	9·00	65
		a. Violet-black (1.44)	27·00	28·00
		b. Perf 12. Black (5.6.47)	4·25	1·00
261c	35	8d. carmine (P 14) (15.11.48)	3·50	3·50
		d. Perf 13 (7.6.50)	2·50	2·75
262	36	1s. black and yellow (P 12½)	3·00	70
263	35	1s.5d. black and carm (P 14) (13.6.40)	30	10
263a		1s.5d. ultramarine (P 14) (1.8.50)	4·00	2·00
		b. Perf 13 (16.2.55)	1·50	18·00
264	37	2s. violet and orange (P 12½)	4·25	40
265	38	2s.6d. green and brown (P 12½)	8·00	1·50
266	39	5s. green and purple (P 12½)	8·00	2·50
266a	40	10s. orange and emerald (P 12½) (13.3.50)	42·00	50·00
266b	41	£1 ultramarine and carmine (P 12½) (13.3.50)	55·00	60·00
249/66b Set of 22			£275	£140
249s/66s (excl 8d. and 1s.6d.) Perf "SPECIMEN" Set of 18			£800	

2½d.

(42)

1941 (10 Feb). No. 254 surch with T **42** by Govt Printer, Suva.

267	31	2½d. on 2d. brown and green	2·50	1·00

1946 (17 Aug). Victory. As Nos. 110/11 of Antigua.

268	2½d. green	20	1·50
	a. Printed double, one albino	£550	
269	3d. blue	60	10
268s/9s Perf "SPECIMEN" Set of 2		£110	

1948 (17 Dec). Royal Silver Wedding. As Nos. 112/13 of Antigua.

270	2½d. green	40	2·50
271	5s. violet-blue	14·00	8·00

1949 (10 Oct). 75th Anniv of Universal Postal Union. As Nos. 114/17 of Antigua.

272	2d. bright reddish purple	30	75
273	3d. deep blue	2·00	6·50
274	8d. carmine-red	30	4·25
275	1s.6d. blue	35	3·00
272/5 Set of 4		2·75	13·00

43 Children Bathing **44** Rugby Football

(Recess B.W.)

1951 (17 Sept). Health Stamps. Wmk Mult Script CA. P 13½.

276	43	1d. +1d. brown	10	1·50
277	44	2d. +1d. green	50	1·00

(Des and eng B.W. Recess D.L.R.)

1953 (2 June). Coronation. As No. 120 of Antigua.

278	2½d. black and green	2·00	50

45 Arms of Fiji

(Recess D.L.R.)

1953 (16 Dec). Royal Visit. Wmk Mult Script CA. P 13.

279	45	8d. deep carmine-red	40	15

46 Queen Elizabeth II (after Annigoni) **47** Government Offices

48 Loading Copra **49** Sugar Cane Train

50 Preparing Bananas for Export **51** Gold Industry

(Des V. E. Ousey (½d., 1s., 2s.6d.), A. V. Guy (6d.). Recess D.L.R. (½d., 2d., 6d., 8d.), Waterlow (1s., 2s.6d., 10s., £1) B.W. (others))

1954 (1 Feb)–**59.** T **46/51** and similar designs previously used for King George VI issue (but with portrait of Queen Elizabeth II as in T **47**). Wmk Mult Script CA. P 12 (2d.),13 (8d.), 12½ (1s., 2s.6d., 10s., £1), 11½×11 (3d., 1s.6d., 2s., 5s.) or 11½ (½d. 1d., 1½d., 2½d. 6d.).

280	28	½d. myrtle-green (1.7.54)	1·00	1·00
281	46	1d. turquoise-blue (1.6.56)	1·75	10
282		1½d. sepia (1.10.56)	2·75	65
283	47	2d. green and magenta	1·25	40
284	46	2½d. blue-violet (1.10.56)	3·00	10
285	48	3d. brown and reddish violet (1.10.56)	4·75	20
		a. Brown and deep reddish violet (10.11.59)	21·00	1·00
287	31	6d. black (1.7.54)	2·50	85
288	35	8d. deep carmine-red (1.7.54)	8·00	1·75
		a. Carmine-lake (6.3.58)	18·00	2·00
289	36	1s. black and yellow	3·00	10
290	49	1s.6d. blue and myrtle-green (1.10.56)	16·00	1·00
291	50	2s. black and carmine (1.10.56)	4·75	60
292	38	2s.6d. bluish green and brown	2·50	50
		a. Bluish green and red-brown (14.9.54)	1·75	10
293	51	5s. ochre and blue (1.10.56)	8·00	1·25
294	40	10s. orange and emerald (1.7.54)	7·50	14·00
295	41	£1 ultramarine and carmine (1.7.54)	32·00	10·00
280/95 Set of 15			85·00	29·00

52 River Scene **53** Cross of Lorraine

(Recess B.W.)

1954 (1 Apr). Health Stamps. Wmk Mult Script CA. P 11×11½.

296	52	1½d. +½d. bistre-brown and green	15	1·00
297	53	2½d. +½d. orange and black	15	20

54 Queen Elizabeth II (after Annigoni) **55** Fijian beating Lali

56 Hibiscus **57** Yaqona ceremony

58 Location Map **59** Nadi Airport

60 Red Shining Parrot **61** Cutting Sugar-cane

62 Arms of Fiji

(Des M. Goaman: Photo Harrison (8d., 4s.). Recess. B.W. (others))

1959–**63.** T **54/62.** Wmk Mult Script CA. P 11½ (T **46** and **54**), 11½×11 (6d., 10d., 1s., 2s.6d., 10s. £1), 14½×14 (8d.) or 14×14½ (4s.).

298	46	½d. emerald-green (14.11.61)	15	2·50
299	54	1d. deep ultramarine (3.12.62)	3·50	2·50
300		1½d. sepia (3.12.62)	3·50	2·50
301	46	2d. rose-red (14.11.61)	1·50	10
302		2½d. orange-brown (3.12.62)	3·00	4·75
303	55	6d. carmine and black (14.11.61)	1·75	10
304	56	8d. scarlet, yellow, green and black (1.8.61)	50	25
305	57	10d. brown and carmine (1.4.63)	2·50	60
306	58	1s. light blue and blue (14.11.61)	1·50	10
307	59	2s.6d. black and purple (14.11.61)	9·00	10
308	60	4s. red, green, blue and slate-green (13.7.59)	3·00	1·25
309	61	10s. emerald and deep sepia (14.11.61)	2·50	2·50
310	62	£1 black and orange (14.11.61)	5·50	3·50
298/310 Set of 13			32·00	16·00

Nos. 299 and 311 have turtles either side of "Fiji" instead of shells.

63 Queen Elizabeth II **64** International Dateline

65 White Orchid **66** Orange Dove

(Des M. Goaman. Photo Harrison (3d., 9d., 1s.6d., 2s., 4s., 5s.). Recess B.W. (others))

1962 (3 Dec)–**67.** W w **12** (upright). P 11½ (1d., 2d.), 12½ (3d.), 11½×11 (6d., 10d., 1s., 2s.6d., 10s., £1), 14½×14 (9d., 2s.) or 14×14½ (1s.6d., 4s., 5s.).

311	54	1d. deep ultramarine (14.1.64)	1·00	3·75
312	46	2d. rose-red (3.8.65)	50	10
313	63	3d. multicoloured	25	10
		w. Wmk inverted		
314	55	6d. carmine and black (9.6.64)	1·50	10
315	56	9d. scarlet, yellow, green and ultramarine (1.4.63)	90	65
316	57	10d. brown and carmine (14.1.64)	60	50
317	58	1s. light blue and blue (24.1.66*)	2·25	45
318	64	1s.6d. red, yellow, gold, black and blue	1·50	60
		a. Error. Wmk sideways	£1100	
319	65	2s. yellow-green, green and copper (16.5.67)	10·00	3·50
		a. Apple-green, green and copper	25·00	4·50
320	59	2s.6d. black and purple (3.8.65)	5·50	1·25
		a. Black and deep purple (8.67)	9·00	3·50
321	60	4s. red, yellow-green, blue and green (1.4.64)	7·50	2·00
322		4s. red, green, blue and slate-green (1.3.66)	6·00	2·50

323	**66**	5s. red, yellow and grey	10·00	35
		w. Wmk inverted	£200	£160
324	**61**	10s. emerald and deep sepia (14.1.64)	7·50	2·50
325	**62**	£1 black and orange (9.6.64)	14·00	7·00
311/25 *Set of 15*			55·00	22·00

*This is the earliest known used date in Fiji and it was not released by the Crown Agents until 1 November.

The 3d. value exists with PVA gum as well as gum arabic.

For 4s. with watermark sideways see No. 359.

ROYAL VISIT

1963

ROYAL VISIT 1963

(67) (68)

1963 (1 Feb). Royal Visit. Nos. 313 and 306 optd with T **67/8**.

326	**67**	3d. multicoloured	40	20
327	**68**	1s. light blue and blue	60	20

1963 (4 June). Freedom from Hunger. As No. 146 of Antigua.

328		2s. ultramarine	1·00	2·00

69 Running

(**73** CS *Retriever*.)

(Des M. Goaman. Photo Harrison)

1963 (6 Aug). First South Pacific Games, Suva. T **69** and similar designs. W w **12**. P 14½.

329		3d. red-brown, yellow and black	25	10
330		9d. red-brown, violet and black	25	1·50
331		1s. red-brown, green and black	25	10
332		2s.6d. red-brown, light blue and black	60	60
329/32 *Set of 4*			1·25	2·00

Designs: Vert—9d. Throwing the discus; 1s. Hockey. Horiz—2s.6d. High-jumping.

1963 (2 Sept). Red Cross Centenary. As Nos. 147/8 of Antigua.

333		2d. red and black	35	40
334		3d. red and blue	75	2·50

1963 (3 Dec). Opening of COMPAC (Trans-Pacific Telephone Cable). No. 317 optd with T **73** by B.W.

335		1s. light blue and blue	55	20

74 Jamborette Emblem   **75** Scouts of Three Races

1s. "Pocket in sulu" (R. 1/1)

(Des V. Whiteley assisted by Norman L. Joe Asst. D.C., Fiji Scouts for Jamboree emblem. Photo Harrison)

1964 (4 Aug). 50th Anniv of Fijian Scout Movement. W w **12**. P 12½.

336	**74**	3d. multicoloured	20	25
337	**75**	1s. violet and yellow-brown	20	30
		a. Pocket in sulu	9·00	

76 Flying-boat *Aotearoa*   **78** *Aotearoa* and Map

(Des V. Whiteley. Photo Harrison)

1964 (24 Oct). 25th Anniv of First Fiji-Tonga Airmail Service. T **76**, **78** and similar design. W w **12**. P 14½×14 (1s.) or 12½ (others).

338		3d. black and vermilion	50	10
339		6d. vermilion and bright blue	80	55
340		1s. black and turquoise-blue	80	55
338/40 *Set of 3*			1·90	1·10

Design: Vert (as T **76**)—6d. de Havilland DH.114 Heron 2.

1965 (17 May). ITU Centenary. As Nos. 166/7 of Antigua.

341		3d. blue and rose-carmine	20	10
342		2s. orange-yellow and bistre	50	25

1965 (25 Oct). International Co-operation Year. As Nos. 168/9 of Antigua.

343		2d. reddish purple and turquoise-green	20	20
344		2s.6d. deep bluish green and lavender	80	25

1966 (24 Jan). Churchill Commemoration. As Nos. 170/3 of Antigua.

345		3d. new blue	50	10
346		9d. deep green	75	85
347		1s. brown	75	10
348		2s.6d. bluish violet	1·00	85
345/8 *Set of 4*			2·75	1·60

1966 (1 July). World Cup Football Championship. As Nos. 176/7 of Antigua.

349		2d. violet, yellow-green, lake and yellow-brown	25	10
350		2s. chocolate, blue-green, lake and yellow-brown	1·25	30

79 HMS *Pandora* approaching Split Island, Rotuma

(Des V. Whiteley. Photo Enschedé)

1966 (29 Aug). 175th Anniv of Discovery of Rotuma. T **79** and similar horiz designs. Multicoloured. W w **12** (sideways). P 14×13.

351		3d. Type **79**	30	10
352		10d. Rotuma Chiefs	30	10
353		1s.6d. Rotumans welcoming HMS *Pandora*	50	1·00
351/3 *Set of 3*			1·00	1·00

1966 (20 Sept). Inauguration of WHO Headquarters, Geneva. As Nos. 178/9 of Antigua.

354		6d. black, yellow-green and light blue	1·25	25
355		2s.6d. black, light purple and yellow-brown	2·75	2·50

LEGISLATIVE ASSEMBLY

82 Running

(Des V. Whiteley. Photo Harrison)

1966 (5 Dec*). Second South Pacific Games, Nouméa. T **82** and similar designs. W w **12** (sideways on 9d.). P 14½×14 (9d.) or 14×14½ (others).

356		3d. black, chestnut and yellow-olive	10	10
357		9d. black, chestnut and greenish blue	15	15
358		1s. multicoloured	15	15
356/8 *Set of 3*			30	30

Designs: Vert—9d. Putting the shot. Horiz—1s. Diving.
*These were not released in London until 8.12.66.

1967 (16 Feb). As No. 321 but wmk w **12** sideways.

359	**60**	4s. red, yellow-green, blue and green	4·25	1·00

85 Military Forces Band

(Des G. Vasarhelyi. Photo Enschedé)

1967 (20 Oct). International Tourist Year. T **85** and similar horiz designs. Multicoloured. W w **12** (sideways). P 14×13.

360		3d. Type **85**	40	10
361		9d. Reef diving	15	10
362		1s. Beqa fire walkers	15	10
363		2s. *Oriana* (cruise liner) at Suva	40	15
360/3 *Set of 4*			1·00	30

89 Bligh (bust), HMS *Providence* and Chart   **91** Bligh's Tomb

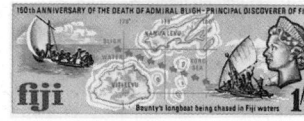

90 "*Bounty's* longboat being chased in Fiji waters"

(Des V. Whiteley. Photo Harrison)

1967 (11 Dec). 150th Death Anniv of Admiral Bligh. W w **12** (sideways on 1s.). P 12½×13 (1s.) or 15×14 (others).

364	**89**	4d. multicoloured	10	10
365	**90**	1s. multicoloured	20	10
366	**91**	2s.6d. multicoloured	20	15
364/6 *Set of 3*			45	30

92 Simmonds Spartan Seaplane

6d. White beacon on radio mast (R. 12/3)

(Des V. Whiteley. Photo Harrison)

1968 (5 June). 40th Anniv of Kingsford Smith's Pacific Flight via Fiji. T **92** and similar horiz designs. W w **12**. P 14×14½.

367		2d. black and green	15	10
368		6d. greenish blue, black and lake	15	10
		a. Radio mast flaw	9·00	
369		1s. deep violet and turquoise-green	20	10
370		2s. orange-brown and blue	30	15
367/70 *Set of 4*			70	30

Designs—6d. Hawker Siddeley H.S.748 and airline insignias; 1s. Fokker F.VIIa/3M *Southern Cross* and crew; 2s. Lockheed 8D Altair *Lady Southern Cross* monoplane.

96 Bure Huts   **97** Eastern Reef Heron (after Belcher)

98 Sea Snake   **99** Queen Elizabeth and Arms of Fiji

(Des G. Hamori (½d., 1d., 9d.), W. O. Cernohorsky (2d., 4s.) H. S. Robinson (4d., 10d.), W. Blair (6d., 5s.), P. D. Clarke (1s.), G. Vasarhelyi (2s.6d.), W. O. Cernohorsky and E. Jones (3s.), E. Jones and G. Hamori (10s.), E. Jones (£1) Adapted V. Whiteley. Photo D.L.R.)

1968 (15 July). T **96/9** and similar designs. W w **12** (sideways on all vert designs). P 14×13½ (2s., 2s.6d., 5s., £1), 13½×14 (3d., 1s., 1s.6d., 4s., 10s.) or 13½×13 (others).

371		½d. multicoloured	10	10
372		1d. deep greenish blue, red and yellow	10	10
373		2d. new blue, brown and ochre	10	10
374		3d. blackish green, blue and ochre	35	10
375		4d. multicoloured	80	2·00
376		6d. multicoloured	25	10
377		9d. multicoloured	15	2·00
378		10d. royal blue, orange and blackish brown	1·25	20
379		1s. Prussian blue and brown-red	20	10
380		1s.6d. multicoloured	4·50	4·50
381		2s. turquoise, black and rosine	75	2·00
382		2s.6d. multicoloured	75	30
383		3s. multicoloured	1·50	6·00
384		4s. yellow-ochre, black and olive	3·50	2·75
385		5s. multicoloured	2·00	1·50
386		10s. lake-brown, black and ochre	1·00	3·00
387		£1 multicoloured	1·25	3·00
371/87 *Set of 17*			16·00	24·00

Designs: Horiz (as T **96**)—1d. Passion Flowers; 2d. Chambered or Pearly Nautilus; 4d. *Psilogramma jordana* (moth); 6d. Pennant Coralfish; 9d. Bamboo raft; 10d. *Asota woodfordi* (moth); 3s. Golden Cowrie shell. Vert (as T **97**)—1s. Black Marlin; 1s.6d. Orange-breasted Honeyeaters (after Belcher); 4s. Mining industry; 10s. Ceremonial whale's tooth. Horiz (as T **98**)—2s.6d. Outrigger canoes; 5s. Bamboo Orchids.

113 Map of Fiji, WHO Emblem and Nurses

(Des V. Whiteley. Litho D.L.R.)

1968 (9 Dec). 20th Anniv of World Health Organization. T **113** and similar horiz designs. Multicoloured. W w **12** (sideways). P 14.

388		3d. Type **113**	15	10
389		9d. Transferring patient to Medical Ship *Vuniwai*	20	25
390		3s. Recreation	25	30
388/90 *Set of 3*			55	55

116 Passion Flowers **117** Fijian Soldiers overlooking the Solomon Islands

1969 (13 Jan)–**70**. Decimal Currency. Designs as Nos. 371/87, but with values inscr in decimal currency as T **116**. W w **12** (sideways on vert designs). Chalk-surfaced paper. P 14×13½ (20, 25, 50c. $2) 13½×14 (3, 10, 15, 40c., $1) or 13½×13 (others).

391	**116**	1c. deep greenish blue, red and yellow	10	10
392	–	2c. new blue, brown and ochre (as 2d.)	10	10
393	**97**	3c. blackish green, blue and ochre	1·25	1·00
394	–	4c. multicoloured (as 4d.)	1·50	1·00
395	–	5c. multicoloured (as 6d.)	20	10
396	**96**	6c. multicoloured	10	10
397	–	8c. multicoloured (as 9d.)	10	10
398	–	9c. royal blue, orange and blackish brown (as 10d.)	1·50	2·25
399	–	10c. Prussian blue and brown-red (as 1s.)	20	10
400		15c. multicoloured (as 1s.6d.)	6·50	6·00
401	**98**	20c. turquoise, black and rosine	1·25	80
402	–	25c. multicoloured (as 2s.6d.)	1·00	20
403	–	30c. multicoloured (as 3s.)	3·50	1·50
404	–	40c. yellow-ochre, black and olive (as 4s.)	7·50	4·00
405	–	50c. multicoloured (as 5s.)	2·00	20
		a. Glazed, ordinary paper (3.9.70)	8·00	1·50
406	–	$1 lake-brown, black and ochre (as 10s.)	1·50	40
		a. Glazed, ordinary paper (3.9.70)	2·00	2·75
407	**99**	$2 multicoloured	3·00	1·50
391/407		Set of 17	27·00	17·00

(Des G. Drummond. Photo Harrison)

1969 (23 June). 25th Anniv of Fijian Military Forces' Solomons Campaign. T **117** and similar horiz designs. W w **12**. P 14.

408		3c. yellow-brown, black and bright emerald	20	10
409		10c. multicoloured	25	10
410		25c. multicoloured	35	20
408/10		Set of 3	70	30

Designs:—10c. Regimental Flags and Soldiers in full dress and battledress; 25c. Cpl. Sefanaia Sukanaivalu and Victoria Cross.

120 Javelin Thrower **123** Map of South Pacific and "Mortar-board"

(Des L. Curtis. Photo Harrison)

1969 (18 Aug). Third South Pacific Games. Port Moresby. T **120** and similar vert designs. W w **12** (sideways*). P 14½×14.

411		4c. black, brown and vermilion	10	10
		w. Wmk Crown to right of CA	3·00	
412		8c. black, grey and new blue	10	10
413		20c. multicoloured	20	20
411/13		Set of 3	30	30

Designs:—8c. Sailing dinghy; 20c. Games medal and winners' rostrum.
*The normal sideways watermark shows Crown to left of CA, as seen from the back of the stamp.

(Des G. Drummond. Photo Harrison)

1969 (10 Nov). Inauguration of University of the South Pacific. T **123** and similar horiz designs. Multicoloured. W w **12**. P 14×15.

414		2c. Type **123**	10	15
415		8c. RNZAF badge and Short S.25 Sunderland flying boat over Laucala Bay (site of University)	15	10
416		25c. Science students at work	25	15
		w. Wmk inverted	2·00	1·50
414/16		Set of 3	45	30

ROYAL VISIT 1970

(126) **127** Chaulmugra Tree, Makogai

1970 (4 Mar). Royal Visit. Nos. 392, 399 and 402 optd with T **126**.

417		2c. new blue, brown and ochre	10	20
418		10c. Prussian blue and brown-red	10	10
419		25c. multicoloured	20	10
417/19		Set of 3	35	30

(Des G. Drummond. Photo Harrison)

1970 (25 May). Closing of Leprosy Hospital Makogai. T **127** and similar designs. W w **12** (sideways* on 10c.). P 14×14½.

420		2c. multicoloured	10	50
421		10c. pale turquoise-green and black	40	65
		a. Pair. Nos. 421/2	80	1·25
		w. Wmk Crown to right of CA	6·00	6·00
422		10c. turquoise-blue, black and magenta	40	65
		w. Wmk Crown to right of CA	6·00	6·00
423		30c. multicoloured	70	50
420/3		Set of 4	1·40	2·10

Designs:—Vert—No. 421, Cascade (Semisi Maya); No. 422, Sea Urchins (Semisi Maya). Horiz—No. 423, Makogai Hospital.
*The normal sideways watermark shows Crown to left of CA, as seen from the back of the stamp.
Nos. 421/2 were printed together, se-tenant, throughout the sheet.

131 Abel Tasman and Log, 1643

(Des V. Whiteley. Litho D.L.R.)

1970 (18 Aug). Explorers and Discoverers. T **131** and similar horiz designs. W w **12** (sideways*). P 13×12½.

424		2c. black, brown and turquoise	30	25
		w. Wmk Crown to right of CA	85·00	
425		3c. multicoloured	60	25
426		10c. multicoloured	60	15
427		25c. multicoloured	30	15
424/7		Set of 4	1·60	70

Designs:—3c. Captain Cook and HMS Endeavour, 1774; 8c. Captain Bligh and longboat, 1789; 25c. Fijian and ocean-going canoe.
*The normal sideways watermark shows Crown to left of CA, as seen from the back of the stamp.

INDEPENDENT

135 King Cakobau and Cession Stone **139** 1d. and 6d. Stamps of 1870

(Des J. W. Litho Format)

1970 (10 Oct). Independence. T **135** and similar horiz designs. Multicoloured. W w **12** (sideways). P 14.

428		2c. Type **135**	10	10
429		3c. Children of the World	10	10
430		10c. Prime Minister and Fijian flag	1·00	10
431		25c. Dancers in costume	25	20
428/31		Set of 4	1·25	30

The design for the 10c. value does not incorporate the Queen's head profile.

(Des V. Whiteley. Photo Harrison)

1970 (2 Nov). Stamp Centenary. T **139** and similar horiz designs. Multicoloured. W w **12** (sideways on 15c.). P 14½×14.

432		4c. Type **139**	15	10
433		15c. Fijian stamps of all reigns (61×21 mm)	40	15
434		20c. Fiji Times office and modern GPO	40	15
		w. Wmk inverted	80·00	
432/4		Set of 3	85	35

STAMP BOOKLETS

1909. Black and pink cover. Stapled.

SB1	2s. booklet containing 11×1½d. (No. 118) in blocks of 5 and 6, and 18×1d. (No. 119) in blocks of 6	£4000

1914. Black on red cover. Stapled.

SB2	2s. booklet containing 11×1½d. (No. 126) in blocks of 5 and 6, and 18×1d. (No. 127) in blocks of 6	£3500

1939 (10 Mar)–**40**. Black on deep green covers. No advertising pages. Stapled.

SB3	3s. booklet containing 8×½d. and 8×1d. (Nos. 249/50) in blocks of 8 and 12×2d. (No. 253) in blocks of 6	£1400
	a. Including four advertising pages (black on pale greenish buff cover) (1940)	£1200
SB4	5s.9d. booklet containing 10×½d. and 10×1d. (Nos. 249/50) in blocks of 10 and 27×2d. (No. 253) in blocks of 9	£4500
	a. Including four advertising pages (black on pink cover) (1940)	£4250

Nos. SB3/4 were produced locally and Nos. SB3a/4a by De La Rue.

1967 (23 Jan). Black on salmon cover. Stitched.

SB5	2s. booklet containing 8×3d. (No. 313) in blocks of four	9·50

The first printing was not released by the Crown Agents, but a second printing was released in London on 30.6.67. The first printing had 4d. as the surface-rate for letters to the British Commonwealth on the inside back cover (Price £12); in the second printing this was corrected to 3d.

1969 (27 Feb). Black on salmon cover. Stitched.

SB6	20c. booklet containing 10×2c. (No. 392) in two blocks of 4 and a vert pair	5·00

1970 (27 Oct). Black on salmon cover. Stitched.

SB7	20c. booklet containing 4×1c. and 8×2c. (Nos. 391/2) in blocks of 4	6·50

POSTAGE DUE STAMPS

D 1 **D 2**

(Typo Govt Printer, Suva)

1917 (1 Jan). Thick yellowish white laid paper with paper-maker's name "DANVERS" and an ornamental device incorporating a crown and the figure of Britannia. No gum. P 11.

D1	**D 1**	½d. black	£1400	£500
		a. Se-tenant strip of 4: 1d.+½d.+4d.+3d.	£10000	
D2		1d. black	£550	£140
D3		2d. black	£325	80·00
D4		3d. black	£650	£120
D5		4d. black	£1600	£550

Nos. D1/2 and D4/5 were printed, se-tenant, in sheets of 96 (8×12) with each horizontal row containing three 1d., one ½d., one 4d. and three 3d. in that order (Price for complete horizontal strip of 8, £18000, unused). Only 31 such sheets were issued. The 2d. was printed separately in sheets of 84 (7×12). On all these sheets marginal copies were imperforate on the outer edge.

1917 (21 Apr)–**18**. As Nos. D1/3 but narrower setting, value in ½d. as Type D **2**.

D5a		½d. black	£500	£300
D5b		1d. black	£350	£140
D5c		2d. black (5.4.18)	£650	£550

1d. and 2d. stamps must have wide margins (3½ to 4 mm) on the vertical sides to be Nos. D2 or D3. Stamps with narrow margins of approximately the same width on all four sides are Nos. D5b or D5c. Nos. D5a/c were printed in separate sheets of 84 (7×12). The marginal copies are perforated on all sides.

D 3 **D 4**

(Typo D.L.R.)

1918 (1 June). Wmk Mult Crown CA. P 14.

D6	**D 3**	½d. black	3·00	30·00
D7		1d. black	3·50	5·00
D8		2d. black	3·25	7·50
D9		3d. black	3·25	55·00
		sa. Wmk sideways, optd "SPECIMEN"	£750	
D10		4d. black	6·00	30·00
D6/10		Set of 5	17·00	£110
D6s/10s		Optd "SPECIMEN" Set of 5	£160	

No. D9sa shows Wmk Crown to right of CA as seen from the back of the stamp.
No postage due stamps were in use between 31 August 1931 and 3 July 1940.

(Typo Waterlow)

1940 (3 July). Wmk Mult Script CA. P 12½.

D11	**D 4**	1d. emerald-green	8·50	70·00
D12		2d. emerald-green	17·00	70·00
D13		3d. emerald-green	19·00	75·00
D14		4d. emerald-green	20·00	80·00
D15		5d. emerald-green	23·00	85·00
D16		6d. emerald-green	25·00	85·00
D17		1s. carmine-lake	25·00	£110
D18		1s.6d. carmine-lake	25·00	£160
D11/18		Set of 8	£140	£650
D11s/18s		Perf "SPECIMEN" Set of 8	£250	

All values are known with forged postmarks, including one of Levuka dated "8 APR 41" and others of Suva dated "12 AUG 42", "14 AU 42" or "20 MR 45".
The use of postage due stamps was discontinued on 30 April 1946.

Gambia

WEST AFRICAN SETTLEMENT

British traders were active in the River Gambia area from the beginning of the 17th-century, but it was not until 1808 that it was officially recognised as a Settlement. Administration passed from the merchants to the Governor of Freetown (Sierra Leone) in 1821 and in 1843 Gambia became a separate colony with a Protectorate declared over the banks of the river for 300 miles inland in 1857. A period of colonial retrenchment in 1865 saw a return to Settlement status under Sierra Leone, but Gambia once again became a Crown Colony in 1888. There was no government postal service before 1858.

PRICES. The prices of Nos. 1 to 8 are for fine copies, with good margins and embossing. Brilliant or poor examples can be supplied at prices consistent with their condition.

DOUBLE EMBOSSING. The majority of the stamps of T 1 with so-called "double embossing" are merely examples in which the printing and embossing do not register accurately and have no special value. We no longer list "twice embossed" or "twice embossed, once inverted" varieties as they are considered to be outside the scope of this catalogue.

1

(Typo and embossed by D.L.R.)

1869 (18 Mar)–72. No wmk. Imperf.

1	**1**	4d. brown	£600	£200
2		4d. pale brown (1871)	£500	£200
3		6d. deep blue	£550	£180
3a		6d. blue (shades)	£600	£180
4		6d. pale blue (17.2.72)	£3250	£1100

The 6d. pale blue shade, No. 4, is distinctive and rare. The date given is the earliest known postmark. It should not be confused with paler shades of the "blue" group (No. 3a).

1874 (Aug). Wmk Crown CC. Imperf.

5	**1**	4d. brown	£400	£200
		w. Wmk inverted	£850	£400
		x. Wmk reversed	£950	£475
		y. Wmk inverted and reversed	£1000	£500
6		4d. pale brown	£425	£225
7		6d. deep blue	£350	£225
		w. Wmk inverted	£700	£400
		x. Wmk reversed	£900	£500
		y. Wmk inverted and reversed	£850	£475
8		6d. blue	£350	£200
		a. Sloping label	£850	£450
		b. Wmk sideways	†	—
		w. Wmk inverted	£700	£400

R. 1/1   R. 1/5

SLOPING LABEL VARIETIES. Traces of this flaw first occur in the 6d. imperforate on R. 1/1 and R. 1/5. In the perforated printings the variety on R. 1/5 is much more pronounced and appears as illustrated above. Our listings are these examples from R.1/5, the less noticeable varieties of this type from R. 1/1 being worth less. These varieties continued to appear until the introduction of a new 6d. plate in 1893, used for No. 34.

1880–81. Wmk Crown CC. P 14*.

A. Wmk sideways†

10A	**1**	½d. orange	£550	£425
		w. Wmk Crown to left of CC	£850	
12A		1d. maroon	£1700	£1200
		w. Wmk Crown to left of CC	£2500	
13A		2d. rose	£250	£100
		w. Wmk Crown to left of CC		
14A		3d. bright ultramarine	£500	£500
		w. Wmk Crown to left of CC		
15A		4d. brown	£800	£120
		w. Wmk Crown to left of CC	£600	65·00
16A		4d. pale brown	£750	£110
		w. Wmk Crown to left of CC	£550	65·00
17A		6d. deep blue	£300	£120
		c. Sloping label	£750	£350
18A		6d. blue	£225	£100
		c. Sloping label	£650	£325
19A		1s. green	£500	£325

20A		1s. deep green	£650	£325
		w. Wmk Crown to left of CC	£900	
10A/20A	Set of 7		£3750	£2500

B. Wmk upright

10B	**1**	½d. orange	19·00	27·00
11B		½d. dull orange	20·00	27·00
		w. Wmk inverted	£150	
12B		1d. maroon	11·00	6·00
		w. Wmk inverted	£225	£160
13B		2d. rose	65·00	11·00
		w. Wmk inverted	£700	£400
14B		3d. bright ultramarine	£100	45·00
14cB		3d. pale dull ultramarine	70·00	32·00
		w. Wmk inverted	85·00	60·00
15B		4d. brown	£325	23·00
		w. Wmk inverted	†	£300
16B		4d. pale brown	£325	24·00
17B		6d. deep blue	£130	45·00
		c. Sloping label	£350	£150
18B		6d. blue	£130	45·00
		c. Sloping label	£350	£150
		w. Wmk inverted	†	£600
19B		1s. green	£275	£150
		w. Wmk inverted	—	£700
20B		1s. deep green	£375	£180
10B/20B	Set of 7		£800	£320

*There were three different printings of these stamps. The original supply, sent in June 1880 and covering all seven values, had watermark sideways and was perforated by a line machine. In October of the same year a further printing of the lowest five values had the watermark changed to upright, but was still with line perforation. The final printing, sent May 1881 and containing all values, also had watermark upright, but was perforated on a comb machine.

†The normal sideways watermark shows Crown to right of CC, as seen from the back of the stamp.

1886–93. Wmk Crown CA (sideways*). P 14.

21	**1**	½d. myrtle-green (1887)	6·00	2·25
		w. Wmk Crown to right of CA	£100	£150
22		½d. grey-green	5·00	3·25
23		1d. crimson (1887)	10·00	12·00
23a		1d. aniline crimson	8·50	14·00
23b		1d. pale carmine	8·50	14·00
24		2d. orange (1887)	14·00	5·00
25		2d. deep orange	4·50	10·00
		w. Wmk Crown to right of CA	†	£400
26		2½d. ultramarine (1887)	14·00	2·25
27		2½d. deep bright blue	12·00	2·00
		w. Wmk Crown to right of CA	£225	
28		3d. slate-grey (1886)	13·00	16·00
29		3d. grey	13·00	18·00
30		4d. brown (1887)	14·00	2·00
		w. Wmk Crown to right of CA	—	£150
31		4d. deep brown	12·00	2·25
		a. Wmk upright	†	£4250
		w. Wmk Crown to right of CA	£200	£140
32		6d. yellowish olive-green (1886)	£100	40·00
		a. Sloping label	£300	£100
		bw. Wmk Crown to right of CA	£425	
32d		6d. olive-green (1887)	80·00	70·00
		da. Sloping label	£250	£180
33		6d. bronze-green (1889)	45·00	70·00
		a. Sloping label	90·00	£170
		bw. Wmk Crown to right of CA	£425	
33c		6d. deep bronze-green (1889)	45·00	70·00
		ca. Sloping label	90·00	£170
34		6d. slate-green (1893)	19·00	65·00
35		1s. violet (1887)	4·25	19·00
36		1s. deep violet	10·00	22·00
36b		1s. aniline violet	£1100	
21/35	Set of 8		70·00	90·00
21s/4s, 32cs	Optd "SPECIMEN" Set of 4		£400	

*The normal sideways watermark shows Crown to left of CA, as seen from the back of the stamp.

The above were printed in panes of 15 on paper intended for larger panes. Hence the watermark is sometimes misplaced or omitted and letters from "CROWN AGENTS FOR THE COLONIES" from the margin may appear on the stamps.

All values with watermark Crown CA are known imperforate (price from £2250 each, unused).

The previously listed 3d. "pearl-grey" shade has been deleted as it is impossible to distinguish from other 3d. shades when it occurs on a single stamp. Sheets from this late printing can be identified by three coloured dots in the left sheet margin and one in the right, this being the reverse of the normal arrangement.

Only three used examples are known of the 4d. with upright watermark, No. 31a.

CROWN COLONY

2

Normal   Malformed "S"   Repaired "S"

The Malformed "S" occurs on R. 7/3 of the left pane from Key Plate 2. This was used to print the initial supply of all values. Printings of the ½d., 1d. and 2½d. despatched on 24 September 1898 had the "S" repaired as shown above. Subsequent printings of the ½d., 1d. and 3d. were from Key Plate 3.

(Typo D.L.R.)

1898 (2 May)–1902. Wmk Crown CA. P 14.

37	**2**	½d. dull green (shades)	2·75	1·75
		a. Malformed "S"	£400	
		b. Repaired "S"	£550	£400
38		1d. carmine (shades)	3·50	75
		a. Malformed "S"	£425	
		b. Repaired "S"	£550	£425
39		2d. orange and mauve	6·50	3·50
		a. Malformed "S"	£500	£500
40		2½d. ultramarine	5·50	2·50
		a. Malformed "S"	£475	£450
		b. Repaired "S"	£650	
41		3d. reddish purple and blue	48·00	12·00
		a. Malformed "S"	£750	£600
		b. Deep purple and ultramarine (1902)	£100	£100
42		4d. brown and blue	20·00	35·00
		a. Malformed "S"	£800	£850
43		6d. olive-green and carmine	18·00	48·00
		a. Malformed "S"	£800	£900
44		1s. violet and green	42·00	85·00
		a. Malformed "S"	£800	£1000
37/44	Set of 8		£130	£170
37s/44s	Optd "SPECIMEN" Set of 8		£200	

3   **4**

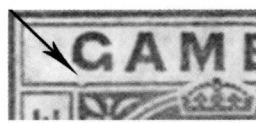

Dented frame (R. 1/6 of left pane)

1902 (13 Mar)–05. Wmk Crown CA. P 14.

45	**3**	½d. green (19.4.02)	7·00	2·50
		a. Dented frame	£180	£140
46		1d. carmine	15·00	1·00
		a. Dented frame	£275	£110
47		2d. orange and mauve (14.6.02)	3·25	2·00
		a. Dented frame	£225	£170
48		2½d. ultramarine (14.6.02)	50·00	18·00
		a. Dented frame	£650	£300
49		3d. purple and ultramarine (19.4.02)	23·00	3·50
		a. Dented frame	£450	£200
50		4d. brown and ultramarine (14.6.02)	10·00	42·00
		a. Dented frame	£300	
51		6d. pale sage-green and carmine (14.6.02)	19·00	14·00
		a. Dented frame	£375	£425
52		1s. violet and green (14.6.02)	48·00	90·00
		a. Dented frame	£700	
53	**4**	1s.6d. green and carmine/yellow (6.4.05)	13·00	26·00
		a. Dented frame	£400	£550
54		2s. deep slate and orange (14.6.02)	55·00	75·00
		a. Dented frame	£800	£1100
55		2s.6d. purple and brown/yellow (6.4.05)	15·00	70·00
		a. Dented frame	£500	
56		3s. carmine and green/yellow (6.4.05)	21·00	70·00
		a. Dented frame	£600	£1000
45/56	Set of 12		£250	£375
45s/56s	Optd "SPECIMEN" Set of 12		£250	

1904 (Aug)–06. Wmk Mult Crown CA. P 14.

57	**3**	½d. green (9.05)	4·50	30
		a. Dented frame	£170	95·00
58		1d. carmine	4·50	15
		a. Dented frame	£180	80·00
59		2d. orange and mauve (23.2.06)	13·00	2·25
		a. Dented frame	£375	£160
60		2½d. bright blue (8.05)	17·00	4·75
		a. Bright blue and ultramarine	25·00	26·00
		b. Dented frame	£350	£180
61		3d. purple and ultramarine (9.05)	20·00	2·00
		a. Dented frame	£350	£160
62		4d. brown and ultramarine (23.2.06)	25·00	48·00
		a. Dented frame	£550	
63	**4**	5d. grey and black (6.4.05)	19·00	30·00
		a. Dented frame	£475	£600
64	**3**	6d. olive-green and carmine (23.2.06)	26·00	70·00
		a. Dented frame	£550	
65	**4**	7½d. green and carmine (6.4.05)	21·00	60·00
		a. Dented frame	£475	
66		10d. olive and carmine (6.4.05)	32·00	50·00
		a. Dented frame	£550	£800
67	**3**	1s. violet and green (9.05)	42·00	65·00
		a. Dented frame	£700	
68	**4**	2s. deep slate and orange (7.05)	95·00	£120
		a. Dented frame	£1000	
57/68	Set of 12		£275	£400
63s, 65s/6s	Optd "SPECIMEN" Set of 3		75·00	

See also Nos. 72/85.

HALF PENNY

 ONE PENNY

(5)   (6)

1906 (10 Apr). Nos. 55 and 56 surch with T **5** or **6** by Govt Printer.

69		½d. on 2s.6d. purple and brown/yellow	55·00	65·00
		a. Dented frame	£900	£1000

70		1d. on 3s. carmine and green/*yellow*......	60·00	30·00
	a.	Surch double.................................	£1800	£5000
	b.	Dented frame................................	£1000	£1000

No. 69 was surcharged in a setting of 30 (6×5), the spacing between the words and the bars being 5 mm on rows 1, 2 and 5; and 4 mm on rows 3 and 4. Constant varieties occur on R. 2/1 (broken "E") and R. 5/1 (dropped "Y") of the setting.

No. 70 was surcharged in a setting of 60 (6×10) and a similar dropped "Y" variety occurs on R. 6/3 and R. 8/4, the latter in conjunction with a dropped "E".

Both values were withdrawn on 24 April when fresh supplies of ½d. and 1d. definitives were received from London.

1909 (1 Oct). Colours changed. Wmk Mult Crown CA. P 14.

72	**3**	½d. blue-green...........................	15·00	7·00
	a.	Dented frame...............................	£250	£190
73		1d. red.....................................	17·00	15
	a.	Dented frame...............................	£375	95·00
74		2d. greyish slate......................	2·25	11·00
	a.	Dented frame...............................	£200	£300
75		3d. purple/*yellow*....................	7·50	1·00
	a.	Purple/*lemon-yellow*.............	6·50	1·75
	b.	Dented frame...............................	£250	£160
76		4d. black and red/*yellow*.......	3·75	65
	a.	Dented frame...............................	£225	£150
77	**4**	5d. orange and purple..............	3·75	1·50
	a.	Dented frame...............................	£225	£200
78	**3**	6d. dull and bright purple........	3·50	1·50
	a.	Dented frame...............................	£250	£250
79	**4**	7½d. brown and blue.................	5·00	2·50
	a.	Dented frame...............................	£250	£275
80		10d. pale sage-green and carmine ...	7·00	7·00
	a.	Dented frame...............................	£300	£350
81	**3**	1s. black/*green*.....................	7·50	17·00
	a.	Dented frame...............................	£350	
82	**4**	1s.6d. violet and green.............	30·00	75·00
	a.	Dented frame...............................	£550	
83		2s. purple and bright blue/*blue*	15·00	20·00
	a.	Dented frame...............................	£450	
84		2s.6d. black and red/*blue*.......	25·00	20·00
	a.	Dented frame...............................	£550	
85		3s. yellow and green.................	48·00	48·00
	a.	Dented frame...............................	£750	£850
72/85		Set of 14..................................	£160	£190
73s/85s		Optd "SPECIMEN" Set of 13.......	£300	

Most values between Nos. 45 and 85 are known with forged postmarks. These include circular types of Bathurst, dated "JA 2 97", and Macarthy Island, dated "FE 17 10", and an oval registered Gambia postmark dated "22 JU 10".

POSTAGE

7 **8** Split "A" (R. 8/3 of left pane) (ptgs to 1918)

(Type D.L.R)

1912 (1 Sept)–**22**. Wmk Mult Crown CA. Chalk-surfaced paper (5s.) P 14.

86	**7**	½d. deep green........................	3·50	1·50
	a.	Green.......................................	3·75	45
	b.	Pale green (1916).....................	6·00	3·25
	c.	Split "A"...................................	£150	£140
87		1d. red.....................................	2·75	80
	a.	Rose-red...................................	4·50	30
	b.	Scarlet (1916)..........................	10·00	90
	c.	Split "A"...................................	£180	£130
88	**8**	1½d. olive-green and blue-green	75	30
	a.	Split "A"...................................	£180	£275
89	**7**	2d. greyish slate......................	75	2·75
	a.	Split "A"...................................	£170	£300
90		2½d. deep bright blue...............	6·50	3·50
	a.	Bright blue................................	4·50	2·50
	b.	Split "A"...................................	£300	£275
91		3d. purple/*yellow*....................	2·00	30
	a.	On lemon (1917).......................	14·00	18·00
	b.	On orange-buff (1920)..............	10·00	8·50
	c.	On pale yellow..........................	1·50	1·00
	d.	Split "A"...................................	£190	£190
92		4d. black and red/*yellow*.......	1·00	10·00
	a.	On lemon (1917).......................	3·75	7·50
	b.	On orange-buff (1920)..............	9·00	13·00
	c.	On pale yellow..........................	1·50	13·00
	d.	Split "A"...................................	£225	£500
	w.	Wmk inverted...........................	£225	
93	**8**	5d. orange and purple..............	1·75	2·00
	a.	Split "A"...................................	£225	£275
94	**7**	6d. dull and bright purple........	2·75	2·50
	a.	Split "A"...................................	£250	£275
95	**8**	7½d. brown and blue.................	6·00	16·00
	a.	Split "A"...................................	£350	£650
96		10d. pale sage-green and carmine	6·00	17·00
	a.	Deep sage-green and carmine ...	7·50	15·00
	b.	Split "A"...................................	£425	£550
97	**7**	1s. black/*green*.....................	4·25	1·00
	a.	On emerald back (1921)............	3·50	27·00
	b.	Split "A"...................................	£275	£275
98	**8**	1s.6d. violet and green.............	23·00	10·00
	a.	Split "A"...................................	£700	£550
99	**7**	2s. purple and blue/*blue*........	10·00	6·00
	a.	Split "A"...................................	£650	£475
100		2s.6d. black and red/*blue*.......	10·00	14·00
	a.	Split "A"...................................	£650	£750

101		3s. yellow and green.................	18·00	50·00
	a.	Split "A"...................................	£850	£1100
102		5s. green and red/*pale yellow* (1922)..................................	£130	£200
86/102		Set of 17..................................	£200	£300
86s/102s		Optd "SPECIMEN" Set of 17.......	£375	

1921–22. Wmk Mult Script CA. Chalk-surfaced paper (4s.). P 14.

108	**7**	½d. dull green........................	30	21·00
	x.	Wmk reversed..........................	£200	
109		1d. carmine-red.....................	2·50	10·00
	x.	Wmk reversed..........................	£150	£150
110	**8**	1½d. olive-green and blue-green	2·75	24·00
111	**7**	2d. grey...................................	1·50	3·00
	x.	Wmk reversed..........................	£170	
112		2½d. bright blue.......................	65	12·00
113	**8**	5d. orange and purple..............	1·75	26·00
	x.	Wmk reversed..........................	50·00	
114	**7**	6d. dull and bright purple........	3·25	21·00
	x.	Wmk reversed..........................	27·00	
115	**8**	7½d. brown and blue.................	3·00	55·00
	x.	Wmk reversed..........................	29·00	
116		10d. pale sage-green and carmine ...	11·00	26·00
	x.	Wmk reversed..........................	£120	
117		4s. black and red (1922)..........	£100	£200
	w.	Wmk inverted...........................	90·00	£225
108/17		Set of 10..................................	£110	£350
108s/17s		Optd "SPECIMEN" Set of 10.......	£225	

Forged postmarks of the types mentioned below No. 85 have also been seen on various values between No. 86 and 117. Collectors should beware of partial strikes which do not show the year date.

9 **10**

(Recess D.L.R.)

1922 (1 Sept)–**29**. Portrait and shield in black. P 14*.

(a) Wmk Mult Crown CA

118	**9**	4d. red/*yellow* (a).................	7·50	7·00
119		7½d. purple/*yellow* (a)............	9·50	11·00
120	**10**	1s. purple/*yellow* (a)............	42·00	50·00
	w.	Wmk inverted...........................	£190	£225
121		5s. green/*yellow* (c).............	75·00	£250
	w.	Wmk inverted...........................		
118/21		Set of 4...................................	£120	£275
118s/21s		Optd or H/S (5s.) "SPECIMEN" Set of 4	£180	

(b) Wmk Mult Script CA

122	**9**	½d. green (*abd*).....................	55	55
123		½d. deep green (*bd*)..............	8·50	2·25
124		1d. brown (*abd*)....................	1·00	30
	x.	Wmk reversed..........................	†	
125		1½d. bright rose-scarlet (*abd*)	1·00	30
	w.	Wmk inverted...........................	†	£750
126		2d. grey (*abd*).......................	2·00	5·00
127		2½d. orange-yellow (*b*)...........	3·25	14·00
	w.	Wmk inverted...........................	£200	
128		3d. bright blue (*abd*)............	1·00	20
	a.	"C" of "CA" missing from wmk...	£1100	
129		4d. red/*yellow* (*bd*) (1.3.27)	28·00	40·00
130		5d. sage-green (a)..................	4·50	18·00
131		6d. claret (*ad*)......................	1·25	1·00
132		7½d. purple/*yellow* (*ab*) (1927)	25·00	95·00
133		10d. blue (a)............................	7·50	23·00
134	**10**	1s. purple/*yellow* (*aef*) (9.24)	5·50	2·25
	a.	Blackish purple/*yellow-buff* (c) (1929)...............................	70·00	45·00
135		1s.6d. blue (*af*)....................	25·00	23·00
136		2s. purple/*blue* (*ac*)............	15·00	8·50
137		2s.6d. deep green (a)..............	16·00	13·00
138		3s. bright aniline violet (a).....	32·00	95·00
139		3s. slate-purple (c) (1928)......	£275	£450
140		4s. brown (*ace*)....................	18·00	25·00
141		5s. green/*yellow* (*acf*) (9.26)	50·00	80·00
142		10s. sage-green (*ce*).............	85·00	£150
122/42		Set of 19..................................	£275	£600
122s/42s		Optd "SPECIMEN" Set of 19.......	£550	

Perforations. A number of different perforating machines were used for the various printings of these stamps and the following varieties are known: (a) the original 14 line perforation; (b) 14×13.8 comb perforation used for Type **9**; (c) 13.8×13.7 comb perforation used for Type **10**; (d) 13.7 line perforation used for Type **9**; (e) 14×13.8 compound line perforation used for Type **9**; (f) 13.8×14 compound line perforation used for Type **10**. The occurrence of these perforations on the individual values is indicated by the letters shown after the colour descriptions above.

No. 139 has been faked, but note that this stamp is comb perf 13.8×13.7 whereas No. 138 is line perf 14 exactly. There are also shades of the slate-purple.

Most values of the above issue are known with a forged oval registered Gambia postmark dated "22 JU 10", often with the year date not shown. Collectors should exercise particular caution in buying used examples of No. 139.

1935 (6 May). Silver Jubilee. As Nos. 91/4 of Antigua, but printed by B.W. P 11×12.

143		1½d. deep blue and scarlet........	70	4·50
	a.	Extra flagstaff..........................	£350	£475
	b.	Short extra flagstaff.................	£350	£425
	c.	Lightning conductor..................	£500	
	d.	Flagstaff on right-hand turret....	£600	
	e.	Double flagstaff........................	£600	
144		3d. brown and deep blue.........	2·25	2·00
	a.	Extra flagstaff..........................	£200	£275
	b.	Short extra flagstaff.................	£275	£325
	c.	Lightning conductor..................	£275	
145		6d. light blue and olive-green...	3·75	8·00
	a.	Extra flagstaff..........................	£190	£350
	b.	Short extra flagstaff.................	£350	£400
	c.	Lightning conductor..................	£300	£350
	d.	Flagstaff on right-hand turret....	£900	
146		1s. slate and purple.................	15·00	15·00
	a.	Extra flagstaff..........................	£275	£325
	b.	Short extra flagstaff.................	£425	£500

	c.	Lightning conductor..................	£425	£475
	d.	Flagstaff on right-hand turret....	£1100	
143/6		Set of 4...................................	19·00	26·00
143s/6s		Perf "SPECIMEN" Set of 4.........	£130	

For illustrations of plate varieties see Omnibus section following Zanzibar.

Sheets from the second printing of the 6d. and 1s. in November 1935 had the extra flagstaff partially erased with a sharp point.

1937 (12 May). Coronation. As Nos. 95/7 of Antigua. P 11×11½

147		1d. yellow-brown......................	30	1·25
148		1½d. carmine...........................	30	1·25
149		3d. blue....................................	55	2·00
147/9		Set of 3...................................	1·00	4·00
147s/9s		Perf "SPECIMEN" Set of 3.........	£120	

11 Elephant (from Colony Badge)

(Recess B.W.)

1938 (1 Apr)–**46**. Wmk Mult Script CA. P 12.

150	**11**	½d. black and emerald-green....	15	70
151		1d. purple and brown...............	30	50
152		1½d. brown-lake and bright carmine	£275	18·00
	a.	Brown-lake and scarlet.............	8·00	4·00
	b.	Brown-lake and vermilion..........	50	2·00
152c		1½d. blue and black (2.1.45).....	30	1·50
153		2d. blue and black...................	15·00	3·25
153a		2d. lake and scarlet (1.10.43)...	1·60	2·25
154		3d. light blue and grey-blue.....	30	10
154a		5d. sage-green and purple-brown (13.3.41)...............................	75	50
155		6d. olive-green and claret........	3·25	35
156		1s. slate-blue and violet..........	5·00	20
156a		1s.3d. chocolate and light blue (28.11.46).............................	4·00	2·00
157		2s. carmine and blue...............	15·00	3·50
158		2s.6d. sepia and dull green......	19·00	2·75
159		4s. vermilion and purple..........	42·00	2·75
160		5s. blue and vermilion.............	42·00	4·00
161		10s. orange and black..............	42·00	12·00
150/61		Set of 16..................................	£170	35·00
150s/61s		Perf "SPECIMEN" Set of 16.......	£550	

1946 (6 Aug). Victory. As Nos. 110/11 of Antigua.

162		1½d. black................................	10	1·00
163		3d. blue....................................	10	40
162s/3s		Perf "SPECIMEN" Set of 2.........	£110	

1948 (24 Dec). Royal Silver Wedding. As Nos. 112/13 of Antigua.

164		1½d. black................................	25	10
165		£1 mauve.................................	21·00	25·00

1949 (10 Oct). 75th Anniv of Universal Postal Union. As Nos. 114/17 of Antigua.

166		1½d. blue-black.........................	30	1·50
167		3d. deep blue...........................	1·25	3·25
168		6d. magenta.............................	75	4·75
169		1s. violet..................................	45	60
166/9		Set of 4...................................	2·50	9·00

1953 (2 June). Coronation. As No. 120 of Antigua, but ptd by B. W.

170		1½d. black and deep bright blue	80	1·50

12 Tapping for Palm Wine   **13** Cutter

14 Wollof woman   **15** Barra canoe

16 SS *Lady Wright*   **17** James Island

18 Woman hoeing   **19** Elephant and Palm (from colony badge)

(Des Mrs O. W. Meronti. Recess D.L.R.)

1953 (2 Nov)–**59**. T **12/19**. Wmk Mult Script CA. P 13½.

171	**12**	½d. carmine-red and bluish green...	65	30
	a.	Carmine and bluish green (7.1.59)	5·50	4·50

172	13	1d. deep ultramarine and deep brown	2·00	50
		a. Deep ultramarine and chocolate (22.8.56)	4·25	2·50
173	14	1½d. deep brown and grey-black	20	1·00
174	15	2½d. black and carmine-red	60	70
175	16	3d. deep blue and slate-lilac	45	10
176	17	4d. black and deep blue	1·75	3·00
177	12	6d. brown and reddish purple	1·25	15
178	18	1s. yellow-brown and yellow-green	1·25	60
179	13	1s.3d. ultramarine and pale blue	18·00	60
		a. Ultramarine and light blue (22.2.56)	24·00	75
180	15	2s. indigo and carmine	8·50	6·00
181	13	2s.6d. deep bluish green and sepia	10·00	3·25
182	17	4s. grey-blue and Indian red	17·00	4·75
183	14	5s. chocolate and bright blue	7·00	4·25
184	16	10s. deep blue and myrtle-green	30·00	17·00
185	19	£1 green and black	30·00	17·00
171/85 Set of 15			£110	50·00

20 Queen Elizabeth II and Palm

21 Queen Elizabeth II and West African Map

(Des J. R. F. Ithier (T **20**), A. W. Morley (T **21**). Recess B.W.)

1961 (2 Dec). Royal Visit. W w **12**. P 11½.

186	20	2d. green and purple	30	40
187	21	3d. turquoise-blue and sepia	75	15
188		6d. blue and cerise	75	70
189	20	1s.3d. violet and myrtle-green	75	2·25
186/9 Set of 4			2·25	3·25

1963 (4 June). Freedom from Hunger. As No. 146 of Antigua.

190		1s.3d. carmine	55	15

1963 (2 Sept). Red Cross Centenary. As Nos. 147/8 of Antigua.

191		2d. red and black	20	50
192		1s.3d. red and blue	40	2·00

SELF-GOVERNMENT

22 Beautiful Sunbird

23 Yellow-mantled Whydah

24 Cattle Egret

25 Senegal Parrot

26 Rose-ringed Parakeet

27 Violet Starling

28 Village Weaver

29 Rufous-crowned Roller

30 Red-eyed Dove

31 Double-spurred Francolin

32 Palm-nut Vulture

33 Orange-cheeked Waxbill

Gambia £1   **SELF GOVERNMENT 1963**

34 African Emerald Cuckoo   (**35**)

(Des V. Whiteley. Photo Harrison)

1963 (4 Nov). Birds. Horiz designs as T **22/34**. Centres multicoloured, background colours given. W w **12**. P 12½×13.

193	22	½d. pale buff	75	1·50
194	23	1d. sage green	75	30
195	24	1½d. lilac	2·50	70
196	25	2d. pale yellow-ochre	2·50	70
197	26	3d. pale drab	2·50	1·00
198	27	4d. pale apple green	2·50	80
199	28	6d. pale turquoise-blue	2·50	10
200	29	1s. pale grey-green	2·50	10
201	30	1s.3d. pale blue	14·00	4·75
202	31	2s.6d. pale violet	9·00	2·50
203	32	5s. light blue	9·00	3·50
204	33	10s. pale grey-green	14·00	11·00
205	34	£1 pale rose-pink	35·00	14·00
193/205 Set of 13			85·00	35·00

1963 (7 Nov). New Constitution. Nos. 194, 197, 200/1 optd with T **35**.

206	23	1d. Yellow-mantled Whydah	15	70
207	26	3d. Rose-ringed Parakeet	35	55
208	29	1s. Rufous-crowned Roller	35	10
		a. Opt double	†	£5000
209	30	1s.3d. Red-eyed Dove	35	65
206/9 Set of 4			1·10	1·75

1964 (23 Apr). 400th Birth Anniv of William Shakespeare. As No. 164 of Antigua.

210		6d. bright blue	20	10
		w. Wmk inverted	50·00	55·00

INDEPENDENT

36 Gambia Flag and River

37 Arms

(Des V. Whiteley. Photo Harrison)

1965 (18 Feb). Independence. P 14½.

211	36	½d. multicoloured	10	40
212	37	2d. multicoloured	15	10
213	36	7½d. multicoloured	40	35
214	37	1s.6d. multicoloured	50	30
211/14 Set of 4			1·00	1·00

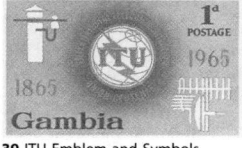

INDEPENDENCE 1965   (**38**)

39 ITU Emblem and Symbols

1965 (18 Feb). Nos. 193/205 optd with T **38** or with date centred (1d., 2d., 3d., 4d., 1s., 5s.).

215	22	½d. Beautiful Sunbird	30	1·00
216	23	1d. Yellow-mantled Whydah	40	20
217	24	1½d. Cattle Egret	60	1·00
218	25	2d. Senegal Parrot	70	30
219	26	3d. Rose-ringed Parakeet	70	15
220	27	4d. Violet Starling	70	1·75
221	28	6d. Village Weaver	70	10
222	29	1s. Rufous-crowned Roller	70	10
223	30	1s.3d. Red-eyed Dove	70	10
224	31	2s.6d. Double-spurred Francolin	70	60
225	32	5s. Palm-nut Vulture	70	75
226	33	10s. Orange-cheeked Waxbill	2·00	6·50
227	34	£1 African Emerald Cuckoo	11·00	9·00
215/27 Set of 13			18·00	19·00

(Des V. Whiteley. Photo Harrison)

1965 (17 May). ITU Centenary. P 14½.

228	39	1d. silver and Prussian blue	25	10
229		1s.6d. gold and bluish violet	1·00	40

THE GAMBIA. From this point onwards stamps are inscribed "The Gambia".

40 Sir Winston Churchill and Houses of Parliament

(Des Jennifer Toombs. Photo Harrison)

1966 (24 Jan). Churchill Commemoration. P 14×14½.

230	40	1d. multicoloured	15	40

231		6d. multicoloured	35	15
232		1s.6d. multicoloured	60	1·40
230/2 Set of 3			1·00	1·75

41 Red-cheeked Cordon Bleu

42 Pin-tailed Whydah

(Des V. Whiteley. Photo Harrison)

1966 (18 Feb). Birds. Horiz designs as T **41**, and T **42**. Multicoloured. P 14×14½ (£1) or 12×13 (others).

233		½d. Type **41**	90	40
234		1d. White-faced Whistling Duck	30	50
235		1½d. Red-throated Bee-eater	30	40
236		2d. Lesser Pied Kingfisher	5·50	75
237		3d. Golden Bishop	30	10
238		4d. African Fish Eagle	50	30
239		6d. Yellow-bellied Green Pigeon	30	10
240		1s. Blue-bellied Roller	30	10
241		1s.6d. African Pygmy Kingfisher	40	30
242		2s.6d. Spur-winged Goose	40	70
243		5s. Cardinal Woodpecker	50	75
244		10s. Violet Turaco	65	2·75
245		£1 Type **42**	1·00	7·00
233/45 Set of 13			10·00	12·50

The ½d., 1d. and 2d. to 1s. values exist with PVA gum as well as gum arabic.

54 Arms, Early Settlement and Modern Buildings

(Photo, Arms die-stamped Harrison)

1966 (24 June). 150th Anniv of Bathurst. P 14½×14.

246	54	1d. silver, brown and yellow-orange	10	10
247		2d. silver, brown and light blue	10	10
248		6d. silver, brown and light emerald	10	10
249		1s.6d. silver, brown and light magenta	15	15
		a. Silver omitted	†	£600
246/9 Set of 4			30	30

No. 249a shows an albino impression of the Arms.

55 ITY Emblem and Hotels

(Des and photo (emblem die-stamped) Harrison)

1967 (20 Dec). International Tourist Year. P 14½×14.

250	55	2d. silver, brown and apple-green	10	10
251		1s. silver, brown and orange	10	10
252		1s.6d. silver, brown and magenta	15	35
250/2 Set of 3			30	40

56 Handcuffs

(Des V. Whiteley. Photo Enschedé)

1968 (15 July). Human Rights Year. T **56** and similar horiz designs. Multicoloured. P 14×13.

253		1d. Type **56**	10	10
254		1s. Fort Bullen	10	10
255		5s. Methodist Church	30	1·00
253/5 Set of 3			35	1·00

59 Queen Victoria, Queen Elizabeth II and 4d. Stamp of 1869

(Des G. Drummond. Photo and embossing (cameo head) Harrison)

1969 (20 Jan). Gambia. Stamp Centenary. P 14½×13½.

256	59	4d. sepia and yellow-ochre	20	10
257		6d. Prussian blue and deep yellow-green	20	10
258	–	2s.6d. multicoloured	70	1·60
256/8 Set of 3			1·00	1·60

Design:—2s.6d. Queen Elizabeth II with 4d. and 6d. stamps of 1869. In the 6d. value the stamp illustrated is the 6d. of 1869.

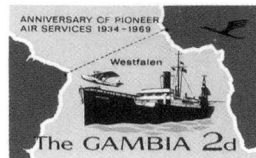

61 Catapult-Ship *Westfalen* launching Dornier DO-J II 10-t Wal

(Des L. Curtis. Litho Format)

1969 (15 Dec). 35th Anniv of Pioneer Air Services. T **61** and similar horiz designs showing various forms of transport, map of South Atlantic and Lufthansa emblem. Multicoloured. P 13½×14.

259		2d. Type **61**	60	20
260		1s. Dornier Do-J II 10-t Wal *Boreas* flying boat	60	20
261		1s.6d. Airship LZ-127 *Graf Zeppelin*	70	1·60
259/61 *Set of 3*			1·75	1·75

REPUBLIC

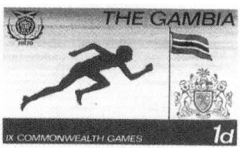

63 Athlete and Gambian Flag

(Des Jennifer Toombs. Litho Format)

1970 (16 July). Ninth British Commonwealth Games, Edinburgh. P 14.

262	**63**	1d. multicoloured	10	10
263		1s. multicoloured	10	10
264		5s. multicoloured	30	1·25
262/4 *Set of 3*			35	1·25

64 President Sir Dawda Kairaba Jawara and State House

(Des G. Vasarhelyi. Litho Questa)

1970 (2 Nov). Republic Day. T **64** and similar multicoloured designs. P 14.

265		2d. Type **64**	10	10
266		1s. President Sir Dawda Jawara	15	10
267		1s.6d. President and flag of Gambia	50	60
265/7 *Set of 3*			65	65

The 1s. and 1s.6d. are both vertical designs.

Ghana

DOMINION

*CANCELLED REMAINDERS. In 1961 remainders of some issues of 1957 to 1960 were put on the market cancelled-to-order in such a way as to be indistinguishable from genuine postally used copies for all practical purposes. Our used quotations which are indicated by an asterisk are the same for cancelled-to-order or postally used copies.

29 Dr. Kwame Nkrumah, Palm-nut Vulture and Map of Africa

GHANA INDEPENDENCE 6TH MARCH, 1957.

(30)

(Photo Harrison)

1957 (6 Mar). Independence. Wmk Mult Script CA. P 14×14½.

166	**29**	2d. scarlet	10	10
167		2½d. green	10	15
168		4d. brown	10	15
169		1s.3d. deep blue	15	15
166/9 *Set of 4*			40	45

1957 (6 Mar)–**58**. Nos. 153*a*/64 of Gold Coast optd as T **30**.

170		½d. bistre-brown and scarlet	10	10
		a. Olive-brown and scarlet	40	10
171		1d. deep blue (R.)	10	10
172		1½d. emerald-green	10	10
173		2d. chocolate (26.5.58)	30	30
174		2½d. scarlet (26.5.58)	1·00	1·75
175		3d. magenta	30	10
176		4d. blue (26.5.58)	6·50	13·00
177		6d. black and orange (R.)	10	10
		a. Opt double	†	£750
178		1s. black and orange-red	10	10
179		2s. brown-olive and carmine	60	10
180		5s. purple and black	3·50	10
181		10s. black and olive-green	3·50	70
170/81 *Set of 12*			14·50	14·00

Nos. 173/4 and 176 were officially issued on 26 May 1958 although, in error, small quantities were sold at certain post offices when the rest of the set appeared.

Nos. 170 and 171 exist in coils constructed from normal sheets.

31 Viking Ship

(Des W. Wind. Recess E. A. Wright Bank Note Co., Philadelphia)

1957 (27 Dec). Inauguration of Black Star Shipping Line. T **31** and similar horiz designs. No wmk. P 12.

182		2½d. emerald-green	35	20
		a. Imperf between (vert pair)	£600	
		b. Imperf between (horiz pair)	£600	
183		1s.3d. deep blue	40	1·25
		a. Imperf horiz (vert pair)	£800	
184		5s. bright purple	60	3·00
		a. Imperf vert (horiz pair)	£850	
182/4 *Set of 3*			1·25	4·00

Designs:—1s.3d. Galleon; 5s. MV *Volta River*.

PRINTERS. Nos. 185/**MS**568 were printed in photogravure by Harrison & Sons *except where otherwise stated*.

34 Ambassador Hotel, Accra **35** Ghana Coat of Arms

1958 (6 Mar). First Anniv of Independence. T **34/5** and similar designs. Wmk Mult Script CA. P 14½×14 (2s.) or 14×14½ (others).

185	**34**	½d. black, red, yellow, green and carmine	10	40
186	–	2½d. black, red, green and yellow	10	10
187	–	1s.3d. black, red, yellow, green and blue	30	10
188	**35**	2s. red, yellow, blue, green, brown and black	45	50
185/8 *Set of 4*			75	1·00

Designs: Horiz as T **34**—2½d. State Opening of Parliament; 1s.3d. National Monument.

38 Map showing the Independent African States

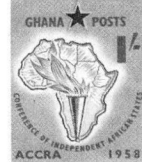

39 Map of Africa and Flaming Torch

(Des R. Milton)

1958 (15 Apr). First Conference of Independent African States, Accra. Wmk Mult Script CA. P 13½×14½ (2½d., 3d) or 14½×13½ (others).

189	**38**	2½d. black, bistre and bright carmine-red	10	10
190		3d. black, bistre, brown and bright green	10	10
191	**39**	1s. black, yellow, red and dull blue	20	10
192		2s.6d. black, yellow, red and dull violet	40	90
189/92 *Set of 4*			60	1·00

40 Palm-nut Vulture over Globe **41** Bristol 175 Britannia 309 Airliner

(Des M. Goaman (2½d., 2s.6d.), R. Milton (1s.3d.), W. Wind (2s.))

1958 (15 July). Inauguration of Ghana Airways. T **40/1** and similar designs. Wmk Mult Script CA. P 15×14 (2s.6d.) or 14×15 (others).

193	**40**	2½d. black, yellow-bistre and rose-carmine	35	10
194	**41**	1s.3d. multicoloured	55	20
195	–	2s. multicoloured	65	55
196	–	2s.6d. black and bistre	65	95
193/6 *Set of 4*			2·00	1·60

Designs: Horiz (as T **41**)—2s. Boeing 377 Stratocruiser and Yellow-nosed Albatross. (As T **40**)—2s.6d. Palm-nut Vulture and Vickers VC-10 aircraft.

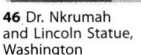

PRIME MINISTER'S VISIT, U.S.A. AND CANADA

(44) **45**

1958 (18 July). Prime Minister's Visit to the United States and Canada. Nos. 166/9 optd with T **44**.

197	**29**	2d. scarlet	10	40
198		2½d. green	10	30
199		4d. brown	10	50
200		1s.3d. deep blue	15	25
197/200 *Set of 4*			30	1·25

(Des W. Wind)

1958 (24 Oct). United Nations Day. Wmk Mult Script CA. P 14×14½.

201	**45**	2½d. purple-brown, green and black	10	10
202		1s.3d. purple-brown, blue and black	15	10
203		2s.6d. purple-brown, violet and black	15	35
201/3 *Set of 3*			30	40

46 Dr. Nkrumah and Lincoln Statue, Washington

47

(Des M. Goaman)

1959 (12 Feb). 150th Birth Anniv of Abraham Lincoln. W **47**. P 14×14½.

204	**46**	2½d. pink and deep purple	10	10
205		1s.3d. light blue and blue	10	10
206		2s.6d. orange-yellow and deep olive-green	15	35
204/6 *Set of 3*			30	45
MS206*a* 102×77 mm. Nos. 204/6. Imperf			65	2·25

48 Kente Cloth and Traditional Symbols

(Des Mrs. T. Sutherland (½d.), M. Karoly (2½d.), K. Antubam (1s.3d.), A. M. Medina (2s.))

1959 (6 Mar). Second Anniv of Independence. T **48** and similar multicoloured designs. W **47**. P 14½×14 (2s.) or 14×14½ (others).

207		½d. Type **48**	10	30

208	2½d. Talking drums and elephant-horn blower	10	10
209	1s.3d. "Symbol of Greeting" (vert)	15	10
210	2s. Map of Africa, Ghana flag and palms	30	1·40
207/10	Set of 4	50	1·60

52 Globe and Flags

(Des Mrs. H. Potter)

1959 (15 Apr). Africa Freedom Day. W **47** (sideways). P 14½×14.

211	**52**	2½d. multicoloured	15	10
212		8½d. multicoloured	15	20

53 "God's Omnipotence" **54** Nkrumah Statue, Accra

55 Ghana Timber **56** Volta River

 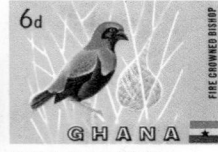

57 Cocoa bean **58** "God's Omnipotence"

59 Diamond and mine **60** Red-crowned Bishop

 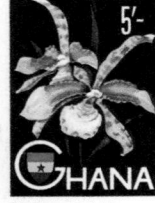

61 Golden Spider Lily **62** Shell Ginger

63 Great Blue Turaco **64** Tiger Orchid

65 Jewel Cichlid

65a Red-fronted Gazelle

66 Pennant-winged Nightjar **67** Crowned Cranes

Two Types of ½d. and 3d:

I. Inscr "GOD'S OMNIPOTENCE"
II. Inscr "GYE NYAME"

(Des Mrs. T. Sutherland (½d., 3d.), Ghana Information Bureau (source of 1d. and 2d.), O. Haulkland (1½d.), A. Medina (2½d., 4d.), M. Goaman (6d., 1s.3d., 2s.6d.), W. Wind (11d., 1s., 2s., 5s.), W. H. Brown (10s.), M. Shamir (£1))

1959 (5 Oct)–**61**. T **53/67**. W **47** (sideways on horiz designs). P 11½×12 (½d.), 12×11½ (1d.), 14×14½ (½d., 11d., 1s., 2s. and 5s.), 14×15 (10s.) or 14½×14 (others).

(a) Postage

213	**53**	½d. Multicoloured (I)	10	10
		a. Type II (29.4.61)	30	10
214	**54**	1d. Multicoloured	10	10
215	**55**	1½d. Multicoloured	10	10
216	**56**	2d. Multicoloured	10	10
217	**57**	2½d. Multicoloured	1·75	10
218	**58**	3d. Multicoloured (I)	10	10
		a. Type II (29.4.61)	30	10
219	**59**	4d. Multicoloured	4·00	65
220	**60**	6d. Multicoloured	2·50	10
		a. Green (flag) omitted	£160	£180
221	**61**	11d. Multicoloured	25	10
222	**62**	1s. Multicoloured	25	10
223	**63**	2s.6d. Multicoloured	1·75	15
224	**64**	5s. Multicoloured	2·00	65
225	**65**	10s. Multicoloured	75	70
225a	**65a**	£1 Multicoloured (29.4.61)	2·75	3·75

(b) Air

226	**66**	1s.3d. Multicoloured	1·75	10
227	**67**	2s. Multicoloured	1·50	10
213/27	Set of 16		17·00	5·00

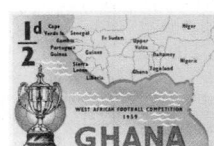

68 Gold Cup and West African Map

(Des K. Lehmann (½d., 3d.), M. & G. Shamir (1d.), W. Wind (8d.), and K. Antubam (2s.6d.))

1959 (15 Oct). West African Football Competition, T **68** and similar multicoloured designs. W **47** (sideways on horiz designs). P 14×14½ (1d., 2s.6d) or 14½×14 (others).

228	½d. Type **68**		10	10
229	1d. Footballers (vert)		10	10
230	3d. Goalkeeper saving ball		10	10
231	8d. Forward attacking goal		40	15
232	2s.6d. "Kwame Nkrumah" Gold Cup (vert)		50	15
228/32	Set of 5		1·00	40

73 The Duke of Edinburgh and Arms of Ghana

(Des A. S. B. New)

1959 (24 Nov). Visit of the Duke of Edinburgh to Ghana. W **47** (sideways). P 15×14.

233	**73**	3d. black and magenta	30	10

74 Ghana Flag and Talking Drums **75** Ghana Flag and UN Emblem

(Des K. Antubam (2e.6d.), A. Medina (others))

1959 (10 Nov). United Nations Trusteeship Council. T **74/5** and similar multicoloured designs. W **47** (sideways on 3d.). P 14½×14 (3d) or 14×14 (others).

234	3d. Type **74**		10	10
235	6d. Type **75**		10	10
236	1s.3d. Ghana flag and UN emblem (vert)		20	15
237	2s.6d. "Totem Pole" (vert)		25	15
234/7	Set of 4		55	45

78 Eagles in Flight **79** Fireworks

(Des A. Medina (½d.), M. Goaman (3d.), W. Wind (1s.3d., 2s.))

1960 (6 Mar). Third Anniv of Independence. T **78/9** and similar vert designs. Multicoloured. W **47**. P 14×14½.

238	½d. Type **78**		10	10
239	3d. Type **79**		10	10
240	1s.3d. "Third Anniversary"		30	10
241	2s. "Ship of State"		30	15
238/41	Set of 4		70	30

82 "A" of National Flags **85** President Nkrumah

(Des W. Wind)

1960 (15 Apr). Africa Freedom Day. T **82** and similar horiz designs. Multicoloured. W **47** (sideways). P 14½×14.

242	3d. Type **82**		10	10
243	6d. Letter "f"		20	10
244	1s. Letter "d"		20	10
242/4	Set of 3		40	20

REPUBLIC

(Des A. Medina (3d., 10s.), W. Wind (1s.3d., 2s))

1960 (1 July). Republic Day. T **85** and similar multicoloured designs. W **47**. P 14½×14 (10s) or 14×14½ (others).

245	3d. Type **85**		10	10
246	1s.3d. Ghana flag		30	10
247	2s. Torch of Freedom		20	20
248	10s. Arms of Ghana (horiz)		50	1·10
245/8	Set of 4		1·00	1·25
MS248a	102×77 mm. Nos. 245/8. Imperf.		40	1·50

 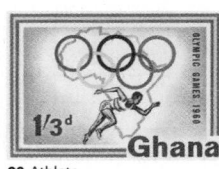

89 Olympic Torch **90** Athlete

(Des A. Medina (T **89**), W. Wind (T **90**))

1960 (15 Aug). Olympic Games. W **47** (sideways on T **90**). P 14×14½ (T **89**) or 14½×14 (T **90**).

249	**89**	3d. multicoloured	10	10
250		6d. multicoloured	15	10
251	**90**	1s.3d. multicoloured	25	15
252		2s.6d. multicoloured	35	1·10
249/52	Set of 4		70	1·25

91 President Nkrumah **94** UN Emblem and Ghana Flag

(Des M. Goaman (3d., 6d.), W. Wind (1s.3d.))

1960 (21 Sept). Founder's Day. T **91** and similar multicoloured designs. W **47** (sideways on 3d.). P 14½×14 (3d.) or 14×14½ (others).

253	3d. Type **91**		10	10
254	6d. President Nkrumah (vert)		10	15
255	1s.3d. Flag-draped column over map of Africa (vert)		20	30
253/5	Set of 3		30	45

(Des M. Goaman (3d., 1s.3d.), W. Wind (6d.))

1960 (10 Dec). Human Rights Day. T **94** and similar vert designs. W **47**. P 14×14½.

256	3d. multicoloured	10	10
257	6d. yellow, black and blue	15	15
258	1s.3d. multicoloured	25	55
256/8	Set of 3	40	65

Designs:—6d. UN emblem and Torch; 1s.3d. UN emblem.

97 Talking Drums

100 Eagle on Column

(Des M. Goaman (3d.), A. S. B. New (6d.), W. Wind (2s.))

1961 (15 Apr). Africa Freedom Day. T **97** and similar designs. W **47** (sideways on 2s.). P 14½×14 (2s.) or 14×14½ (others).

259	3d. multicoloured	10	10
260	6d. red, black and green	20	10
261	2s. multicoloured	50	45
259/61	Set of 3	70	50

Designs: Vert—6d. Map of Africa. Horiz—2s. Flags and map.

(Des A. S. B. New (3d.), M. Shamir (1s.3d.), W. Wind (2s.))

1961 (1 July). First Anniv of Republic. T **100** and similar vert designs. Multicoloured. W **47**. P 14×14½.

262	3d. Type **100**	10	10
263	1s.3d. "Flower"	10	10
264	2s. Ghana flags	20	1·25
262/4	Set of 3	30	1·25

103 Dove with Olive Branch

106 Pres. Nkrumah and Globe

(Des V. Whiteley)

1961 (1 Sept). Belgrade Conference. T **103** and similar designs. W **47** (sideways on 1s.3d., 5s.). P 14×14½ (3d.) or 14½×14 (others).

265	3d. yellow-green	10	10
266	1s.3d. deep blue	15	10
267	5s. bright reddish purple	40	1·25
265/7	Set of 3	50	1·25

Designs: Horiz—1s.3d. World map, chain and olive branch; 5s. Rostrum, conference room.

(Des A. Medina (3d.), M. Goaman (1s.3d.), Miriam Karoly (5s.))

1961 (21 Sept). Founder's Day. T **106** and similar multicoloured designs. W **47** (sideways on 3d.). P 14½×14 (3d.) or 14×14½ (others).

268	3d. Type **106**	10	10
269	1s.3d. President and Kente Cloth (vert)	20	10
270	5s. President in National Costume (vert)	65	2·50
268/70	Set of 3	75	2·50
MS270a	Three sheets 106×86 mm (3d.) or 86×106 mm (others) each with Nos. 268/70 in block of four. Imperf. Three sheets	2·50	14·00

The 1s.3d. Miniature Sheet is known with the brown colour omitted. (Price, £2750, unused).

109 Queen Elizabeth II and African Map

(Des M. Goaman)

1961 (9 Nov). Royal Visit. W **47**. P 14½×14.

271	**109** 3d. multicoloured	15	10
272	1s.3d. multicoloured	30	20
273	5s. multicoloured	65	4·00
271/3	Set of 3	1·00	4·00
MS273a	106×84 mm. No. 273 in block of four. Imperf	2·25	8·00

110 Ships in Tema Harbour

(Des C. Bottiau. Litho Enschedé & Sons)

1962 (10 Feb). Opening of Tema Harbour. T **110** and similar horiz designs. Multicoloured. No wmk. P 14×13.

(a) Postage

274	3d. Type **110**	15	10

(b) Air

112 Africa and Peace Dove

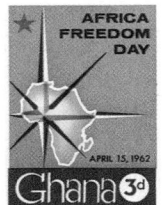

113 Compass over Africa

275	1s.3d. Douglas DC-8 aircraft and ships at Tema	65	15
276	2s.6d. As 1s.3d.	80	2·50
274/6	Set of 3	1·40	2·50

(Des R. Hegeman. Litho Enschedé)

1962 (6 Mar). First Anniv of Casablanca Conference. No wmk. P 13×14.

(a) Postage

277	**112** 3d. multicoloured	10	10

(b) Air

278	**112** 1s.3d. multicoloured	20	15
279	2s.6d. multicoloured	30	2·00
277/9	Set of 3	55	2·00

(Des R. Hegeman)

1962 (24 Apr). Africa Freedom Day. W **47**. P 14½×14.

280	**113** 3d. sepia, blue-green and reddish purple	10	10
281	6d. sepia, blue-green and orange-brown	10	15
282	1s.3d. sepia, blue-green and red	15	15
280/2	Set of 3	30	30

114 Ghana Star and "Five Continents"

115 Atomic Bomb-burst "Skull"

(Des M. Goaman (3d.), M. Shamir (6d.), W. Wind (1s.3d))

1962 (21 June). Accra Assembly, T **114/15** and similar vert design. W **47**. P 14×14½.

283	**114** 3d. black and lake-red	10	10
284	**115** 6d. black and scarlet	25	35
285	– 1s.3d. turquoise	30	50
283/5	Set of 3	55	80

Design:—1s.3d. Dove of Peace.

117 Patrice Lumumba

118 Star over Two Columns

(Des A. S. B. New)

1962 (30 June). First Death Anniv of Lumumba. W **47**. P 14½×14.

286	**117** 3d. black and orange-yellow	10	10
287	6d. black, green and lake	10	30
288	1s.3d. black, pink and black-green	15	35
286/8	Set of 3	30	60

(Des A. S. B. New (3d.), A. Medina (6d), M. Goaman (1s.3d) Litho Enschedé)

1962 (1 July). Second Anniv of Republic. T **118** and similar multicoloured designs. P 14×13½ (1s.3d) or 13½×14 (others).

289	3d. Type **118**	10	10
290	6d. Flaming torch	20	20
291	1s.3d. Eagle trailing flag (horiz)	40	40
289/91	Set of 3	60	60

121 President Nkrumah

125 Campaign Emblem

(Litho Enschedé)

1962 (21 Sept). Founder's Day. T **121** and similar vert designs. P 13×14½.

292	1d. multicoloured	10	10
293	3d. multicoloured	10	10

294	1s.3d. black and bright blue	30	15
295	2s. multicoloured	30	1·75
292/5	Set of 4	70	1·75

Designs:—3d. Nkrumah medallion; 1s.3d. President Nkrumah and Ghana Star; 2s. Laying "Ghana" Brick.

1962 (3 Dec). Malaria Eradication. W **47**. P 14×14½.

296	**125** 1d. cerise	10	10
297	4d. yellow-green	20	1·25
298	6d. bistre	20	30
299	1s.3d. bluish violet	25	90
296/9	Set of 4	65	2·25
MS299a	90×115 mm. Nos. 296/9. Imperf	75	1·50

126 Campaign Emblem

129 Map of Africa

1963 (21 Mar). Freedom from Hunger. T **126** and similar designs. W **47** (sideways on 4d., 1s.3d.). P 14×14½ (1d.) or 14½×14 (others).

300	1d. multicoloured	25	25
301	4d. sepia, yellow and orange	1·25	2·00
302	1s.3d. ochre, black and green	1·60	1·25
300/2	Set of 3	2·75	3·25

Designs: Horiz—4d. Emblem in hands; 1s.3d. World map and emblem.

1963 (15 Apr). Africa Freedom Day. T **129** and similar designs. W **47** (sideways on 4d.). P 14½×14 (4d.) or 14×14½ (others).

303	1d. gold and red	10	10
304	4d. red, black and yellow	10	10
305	1s.3d. multicoloured	20	10
306	2s.6d. multicoloured	35	1·25
303/6	Set of 4	65	1·40

Designs: Horiz—4d. Carved stool. Vert—1s.3d. Map and bowl of fire; 2s.6d. Topi (antelope) and flag.

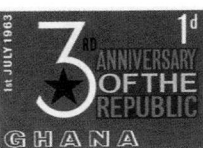

133 Red Cross

137 "3rd Anniversary"

(Des R. Hegeman (4d.), M. Shamir (others))

1963 (28 May). Red Cross Centenary. T **133** and similar multicoloured designs. W **47** (sideways on 1½d., 4d.). P 14½×14 (1d., 1s.3d.) or 14×14½ (others).

307	1d. Type **133**	50	15
308	1½d. Centenary emblem (horiz)	75	2·25
309	4d. Nurses and child (horiz)	1·25	20
310	1s.3d. Emblem, globe and laurel	1·75	2·00
307/10	Set of 4	3·75	4·25
MS310a	102×127 mm. Nos. 307/10. Imperf	2·75	12·00

(Des M. Goaman (1d., 4d.), R. Hegeman (others))

1963 (1 July). Third Anniv of Republic. T **137** and similar multicoloured designs. W **47** (sideways on 1d., 4d.). P 14½×14 (horiz) or 14×14½ (vert).

311	1d. Type **137**	10	10
312	4d. Three Ghanaian flags	30	25
	a. Black (stars on flag) omitted	†	£800
313	1s.3d. Map, flag and star (vert)	70	15
314	2s.6d. Flag and torch (vert)	70	2·50
311/14	Set of 4	1·60	2·75

141 President Nkrumah and Ghana Flag

145 Rameses II, Abu Simbel

(Des R. Hegeman (1d., 4d.), M. Shamir (1s.3d.), G. Rose (5s.))

1963 (21 Sept). Founder's Day. T **141** and similar designs. W **47** (sideways on 1s.3d., 5s.). P 14×14½ (vert) or 14½×14 (horiz).

315	1d. multicoloured	10	10
316	4d. multicoloured	15	10
317	1s.3d. multicoloured	30	10
	a. Green omitted	£400	
318	5s. yellow and bright reddish purple	65	90
315/18	Set of 4	1·00	1·00

Designs: Vert—4d. Nkrumah and flag. Horiz—1s.3d. Nkrumah and fireworks; 5s. Symbol of Wisdom.

(Des M. Farrar Bell and R. Hegeman. Litho (1½d., 2d.) or photo (others) Enschedé)

1963 (1 Nov). Nubian Monuments Preservation. T **145** and similar multicoloured designs. No wmk. P 11½×11 (vert) or 11×11½ (horiz).

319	1d. Type **145**	15	10
320	1½d. Rock paintings (horiz)	20	65

321		2d. Queen Nefertari (*horiz*)	20	10
322		4d. Sphinx, Selina	35	15
323		1s.3d. Rock Temple, Abu Simbel (*horiz*)	80	90
319/23	*Set of 5*		1·50	1·75

150 Class 248 Steam Locomotive and Diesel–electric Locomotive No. 1401

151 Eleanor Roosevelt and "Flame of Freedom"

(Des H. L. W. Stevens)

1963 (1 Dec). 60th Anniv of Ghana Railway. W **47** (sideways). P 14½×14.

324	**150**	1d. multicoloured	10	10
325		6d. multicoloured	40	10
326		1s.3d. multicoloured	45	40
327		2s.6d. multicoloured	75	1·90
324/7	*Set of 4*		1·50	2·25

(Des R. Hegeman and F. H. Savage. Photo Enschedé)

1963 (10 Dec). 15th Anniv of Declaration of Human Rights. T **151** and similar multicoloured designs. No wmk. P 11×11½ (1s.3d.) or 11½×11 (others).

328		1d. Type **151**	10	10
329		4d. Type **151**	10	30
330		6d. Eleanor Roosevelt	10	10
331		1s.3d. Eleanor Roosevelt and emblems (*horiz*)	15	15
328/31	*Set of 4*		30	50

No. 329 differs from No. 328 in the arrangement of the trailing "flame" and of the background within the circular emblem.

154 Sun and Globe Emblem

155 Harvesting Corn on State Farm

1964 (15 June). International Quiet Sun Years. W **47** (sideways). Each blue, yellow, red and green; background colours given. P 14½.

332	**154**	3d. pale brown	15	10
333		6d. pale grey	25	10
334		1s.3d. mauve	25	10
332/4	*Set of 3*		60	30
MS334*a*	90×90 mm. No. 334 in block of four. Imperf		75	2·50

Nos. 332/4 each exist in a miniature sheet of 12 in different colours (i.e. 3d. in colours of 6d.; 6d. in colours of 1s.3d.; 1s.3d. in colours of 3d.) but these were not generally available to the public.

(Des M. Shamir. Photo Govt Printer, Israel)

1964 (1 July). Fourth Anniv of Republic. T **155** and similar horiz designs. P 13×14.

335		3d. olive brown and yellow-olive	10	10
336		6d. bluish green, brown and turquoise-green	10	10
337		1s.3d. brown-red, brown and salmon-red	10	10
338		5s. multicoloured	40	2·00
335/8	*Set of 4*		55	2·00
MS338*a*	126×100 mm. Nos. 335/8. Imperf		85	2·00
	ab. Olive (central design and face value of 3d.) omitted		£1000	
	ac. Green (face value of 5s.) omitted		£1200	

Designs:—6d. Oil refinery, Tema; 1s.3d. "Communal Labour"; 5s. Procession headed by flag.

159 Globe and Dove

163 Pres. Nkrumah and Hibiscus Flowers

(Des M. Shamir. Litho Lewin-Epstein Ltd, Bat Yam, Israel)

1964 (15 July). First Anniv of African Unity Charter. T **159** and similar designs. P 14.

339		3d. multicoloured	10	10
340		6d. deep bronze-green and red	10	10
341		1s.3d. multicoloured	15	10
342		5s. multicoloured	45	1·00
339/42	*Set of 4*		65	1·00

Designs: Vert—6d. Map of Africa and quill pen; 5s. Planting flower. Horiz—1s.3d. Hitched rope on map of Africa.

1964 (21 Sept). Founder's Day. W **47** (sideways). P 14×14½.

343	**163**	3d. sepia, red, deep green and light blue	10	10
344		6d. sepia, red, deep green and yellow	15	10

345		1s.3d. sepia, red, deep green and grey	25	10
346		2s.6d. sepia, red, deep green and light emerald	40	1·00
343/6	*Set of 4*		75	1·10
MS346*a*	90×122 mm. No. 346 in block of four. Imperf		70	2·50
	ab. Deep green (face value) omitted		£1700	

IMPERFORATE STAMPS. Many issues, including miniature sheets, from here onwards exist imperforate, but these were not sold at post offices.

164 Hurdling

(Des A. S. B. New (No. 352))

1964 (25 Oct). Olympic Games, Tokyo. T **164** and similar multicoloured designs. W **47** (sideways on 1d., 2½d., 6d., 5s.). P 14½×14 (horiz) or 14×14½ (vert).

347	**164**	1d. Type **164**	10	10
348		2½d. Running	10	1·50
349		3d. Boxing (*vert*)	10	10
350		4d. Long-jumping (*vert*)	10	10
351		6d. Football (*vert*)	15	10
352		1s.3d. Athlete holding Olympic Torch (*vert*)	20	10
353		5s. Olympic Rings and flags	75	3·25
347/53	*Set of 7*		1·25	4·50
MS353*a*	128×102 mm. Nos. 351/3. Imperf		75	2·50
	ab. Brown omitted		£1000	

171 G. Washington Carver (botanist) and Plant

173 African Elephant

(Des M. Shamir)

1964 (7 Dec). UNESCO Week. W **47**. P 14½.

354	**171**	6d. deep blue and green	15	10
355		– 1s.3d. reddish purple and greenish blue	30	10
		w. Wmk inverted	11·00	
356	**171**	5s. sepia and orange-red	50	4·25
354/6	*Set of 3*		85	4·25
MS356*a*	127×77 mm. Nos. 354/6. Imperf		75	2·00

Design:—1s.3d. Albert Einstein (scientist) and atomic symbol.

(Des A. S. B. New (No. 360). Photo Enschedé)

1964 (14 Dec). Multicoloured designs as T **173**. P 11½×11 (vert) or 11×11½ (horiz).

357	**173**	1d. Type **173**	40	50
358		1½d. Secretary Bird (*horiz*)	50	2·25
359		2½d. Purple Wreath (flower)	15	2·25
360		3d. Grey Parrot	50	50
361		4d. Blue-naped Mousebird (*horiz*)	50	70
362		6d. African Tulip Tree (*horiz*)	15	30
363		1s.3d. Violet Starling (*horiz*)	60	85
364		2s.6d. Hippopotamus (*horiz*)	60	5·00
357/64	*Set of 8*		3·00	11·00
MS364*a*	(a) 150×86 mm. Nos. 357/9. (b) 150×110 mm. Nos. 360/4. Imperf *Set of 2 sheets*		3·00	14·00

181 ICY Emblem

(Litho Enschedé)

1965 (22 Feb). International Co-operation Year. P 14×12½.

365	**181**	1d. multicoloured	35	70
366		4d. multicoloured	1·00	2·00
367		6d. multicoloured	1·00	70
368		1s.3d. multicoloured	1·25	2·75
365/8	*Set of 4*		3·25	5·50
MS368*a*	100×100 mm. No. 368 in block of four. Imperf		2·75	5·00

182 ITU Emblem and Symbols

(Litho Enschedé)

1965 (12 Apr). ITU Centenary. P 13½.

369	**182**	1d. multicoloured	15	15
370		6d. multicoloured	30	15
371		1s.3d. multicoloured	55	25
372		5s. multicoloured	1·25	3·25
369/72	*Set of 4*		2·00	3·50
MS372*a*	132×115 mm. Nos. 369/72. Imperf		7·50	10·00

183 Lincoln's Home

(Des M. Farrar Bell (6d.), A. S. B. New (1s.3d., 5s.), R. Hegeman (2s.))

1965 (17 May). Death Centenary of Abraham Lincoln. T **183** and similar square-shaped designs. W **47** (sideways). P 12½.

373		6d. multicoloured	10	10
374		1s.3d. black, red and blue	15	15
375		2s. black, orange-brown and greenish yellow	15	35
376		5s. black and red	30	1·75
373/6	*Set of 4*		60	2·00
MS376*a*	115×115 mm. Nos. 373/6. Imperf		75	3·50
	ab. Green (part of flag on 6d.) omitted		£1100	

Designs:—1s.3d. Lincoln's Inaugural Address; 2s. Abraham Lincoln; 5s. Adaptation of US 90c Lincoln Stamp of 1899.

(New Currency. 100 pesewas = 1 cedi)

187 Obverse (Pres. Nkrumah) and Reverse of 5p. Coin

(Photo Enschedé)

1965 (19 July). Introduction of Decimal Currency. T **187** and similar horiz designs. Multicoloured. P 11×13 (5p., 10p.), 13×12½ (25p.) or 13½×14 (50p.).

377		5p. Type **187**	20	10
378		10p. As Type **187**	25	10
379		25p. Size 63×39 mm	55	1·00
380		50p. Size 71×43½ mm	1·00	3·00
377/80	*Set of 4*		1·75	3·75

The coins in Nos. 378/80 are all circular and express the same denominations as on the stamps.

₡2·40

Ghana New Currency 19th July. 1965.

(188)

1965 (19 July). Nos. 214, 216 and 218a/27 surch as T **188** diagonally upwards, (D) or horizontally, (H) by Govt Printer, Accra.

(a) Postage

381		1p. on 1d. multicoloured (R.) (D)	10	10
		a. Surch inverted	15·00	
		b. Surch double	70·00	
382		2p. on 2d. multicoloured (Ultram.) (H)	10	10
		a. Surch inverted	22·00	
		b. Surch double	17·00	
		c. Surch on back only	£200	
		d. Surch on front and back	£200	
		e. Red surch	28·00	
		f. Orange surch	35·00	
		g. Indigo surch	38·00	
		ga. Surch sideways	£200	
		gb. Ditto. Pair, one without surch	£200	
383		3p. on 3d. multicoloured (II) (Br.) (H)	1·00	7·00
		a. Surch inverted	22·00	
		b. Indigo surch		
384		4p. on 4d. multicoloured (B.) (H)	5·00	45
		a. Surch inverted	75·00	75·00
		b. Surch double	60·00	
		c. Vert pair, one without surch	£100	
		d. Red surch		
385		6p. on 6d. multicoloured (Blk.) (H)	50	10
		a. Surch inverted	8·50	10·00
		b. Surch double	16·00	
		c. Horiz pair, one without surch	£110	
		d. Green (flag) omitted	£275	
386		11p. on 11d. multicoloured (W.) (D)	25	10
		a. Surch inverted	13·00	9·00
387		12p. on 1s. multicoloured (B.) (D)	25	10
		a. Surch double	60·00	
		b. Surch double, one albino inverted		
		c. Pair, one without surch	£100	
		d. Black surch	15·00	10·00
		da. Surch inverted	14·00	7·00
388		30p. on 2s.6d. multicoloured (B.) (H)	6·00	11·00
389		60p. on 5s. multicoloured (B.) (D)	4·50	70
		a. Surch double (G.+B.)	55·00	
390		1c.20 on 10s. multicoloured (B.) (D)	75	2·25
		a. Surch double (G.+B.)	£170	
391		2c.40 on £1 multicoloured (B.) (D)	1·00	6·50
		a. Vert pair, one without surch	£170	

(b) Air

392		15p. on 1s.3d. multicoloured (W.) (H)	2·50	70
		a. Surch inverted		
393		24p. on 2s. multicoloured (G.) (D)	2·50	30
		a. Surch on front and back	42·00	
381/93	*Set of 13*		20·00	25·00

On the diagonal surcharges the values are horizontal.

The 30p. was not released in Ghana until 30 July and the 3p. sometime later.

Numerous minor varieties exist.

189 "OAU" and Flag

190 "OAU", Heads and Flag

191 "OAU" Emblem and Flag

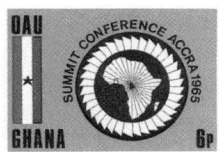

192 African Map and Flag

1965 (21 Oct). OAU Summit Conference, Accra. T **189/92** and similar horiz designs. Multicoloured. W **47** (sideways* except on 6p.). P 14 (T **189/91**) or 14½×14 (others).

394	1p. Type **189**	20	40
	a. Red (part of flag) omitted	£275	
395	2p. Type **190**	20	40
396	5p. Type **191**	30	40
397	6p. Type **192**	30	10
398	15p. "Sunburst", map and flag	40	30
399	24p. "OAU" on map, and flag	55	70
	w. Wmk top of G to left		
394/9 Set of 6		1·75	2·00

*The 1p. also exists with the watermark facing left or right, but positional blocks are required to show the two types. The normal sideways watermark has top of G to right, *as seen from the back of the stamp*.

195 Goalkeeper saving Ball

198 Pres. Kennedy and Grave Memorial

(Photo Enschedé)

1965 (15 Nov). African Soccer Cup Competition. T **195** and similar multicoloured designs. P 13×14 (15p.) or 14×13 (others).

400	6p. Type **195**	25	10
401	15p. Player with ball (vert)	40	30
402	24p. Players, ball and soccer cup	45	1·60
400/2 Set of 3		1·00	1·75

(Des A. S. B. New (No. 405))

1965 (15 Dec)–**66**. Second Anniv of President Kennedy's Death. T **198** and similar square-shaped designs. W **47** (sideways). P 12½.

403	6p. multicoloured	15	10
404	15p. violet, red and green	20	35
405	24p. black and reddish violet	20	60
406	30p. dull purple and black	25	1·25
403/6 Set of 4		70	2·00
MS407 114½×114 mm. Nos. 403/6. Imperf (21.3.66)		1·50	4·00

Designs:—15p. Pres. Kennedy and Eternal Flame; 24p. Pres. Kennedy and memorial inscription; 30p. President Kennedy.

202 Section of Dam and Generators   (206)

(Des A. S. B. New (No. 411). Photo Enschedé)

1966 (22 Jan). Volta River Project. T **202** and similar horiz designs. P 11×11½.

408	6p. multicoloured	15	10
409	15p. multicoloured	20	15
410	24p. multicoloured	25	20
411	30p. black and new blue	35	1·50
408/11 Set of 4		85	1·75

Designs:—15p. Dam and Lake Volta; 24p. Word "GHANA" as dam; 30p. "Fertility".

1966 (7 Feb). "Black Stars" Victory in African Soccer Cup Competition. Nos. 400/2 optd with T **206**, in black.

412	6p. Type **195**	50	20
	a. Green opt	22·00	
	b. Green opt double, one inverted	65·00	
	c. Stop after "Nov" omitted (R. 5/1)	13·00	13·00
413	15p. Player with ball	70	40
414	24p. Players, ball and cup	75	1·00
	a. Opt inverted*	32·00	
	ab. Vert pair, one without opt, the other with opt inverted	£170	
	b. Error. Opt for 15p. on 24p. inverted*	32·00	
	c. Stop after "Nov" omitted (R. 5/1)	17·00	
412/14 Set of 3		1·75	1·40

*In No. 414a the overprint reads downwards (top right to bottom left), but in No. 414b it reads upwards (bottom right to top left).

DATES OF ISSUE of miniature sheets are approximate as they are generally released some time after the related ordinary stamps, but it is known that the GPO sometimes applied first-day cancellations months after the dates shown on the cancellations.

207 WHO Building and Ghana Flag

1966 (1 July–Nov). Inauguration of WHO Headquarters, Geneva. T **207** and similar horiz design. Multicoloured. W **47**. P 14½×14.

415	6p. Type **207**	1·25	10
416	15p. Type **207**	2·00	65
417	24p. WHO Building and emblem	2·00	2·25
418	30p. As 24p.	2·00	6·50
415/18 Set of 4		6·50	8·50
MS419 120×101 mm. Nos. 415/18. Imperf (11.66)		24·00	22·00

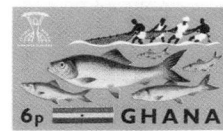

209 Atlantic Herring

(Des O. Hamann. Photo Enschedé)

1966 (10 Aug–Nov). Freedom from Hunger. T **209** and similar horiz designs. Multicoloured. P 14×13.

420	6p. Type **209**	20	10
421	15p. Turbot	40	15
422	24p. Spadefish	40	35
423	30p. Red Snapper	45	1·50
424	60p. Blue-finned Tuna	55	5·25
420/4 Set of 5		1·75	6·50
MS425 126×109 mm. No. 423 in block of four. Imperf (11.66)		6·50	13·00

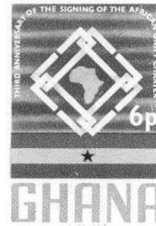

214 African "Links" and Ghana Flag

(Photo Enschedé)

1966 (11 Oct). Third Anniv of African Charter. T **214** and similar multicoloured designs. P 13½.

426	6p. Type **214**	15	10
427	15p. Flags as "Quill", and diamond (horiz)	35	55
428	24p. Ship's wheel, map and cocoa bean (horiz)	40	70
426/8 Set of 3		80	1·25

217 Player heading Ball, and Jules Rimet Cup

1966 (14 Nov). World Cup Football Championship, England. T **217** and similar horiz designs. Multicoloured. W **47**. P 14½×14.

429	5p. Type **217**	70	20
430	15p. Goalkeeper clearing ball	1·50	30
	w. Wmk inverted	1·60	1·60
431	24p. Player and Jules Rimet Cup (replica)	1·75	50
432	30p. Players and Jules Rimet Cup (replica)	2·00	1·75
433	60p. Players with ball	3·00	11·00
	w. Wmk inverted	12·00	
429/33 Set of 5		8·00	12·00
MS434 120×102 mm. 60p. (block of four). Imperf		24·00	26·00

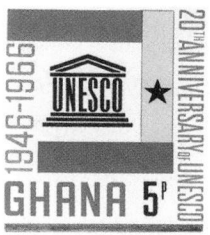

222 UNESCO Emblem

1966 (23 Dec). 20th Anniv of UNESCO. W **47** (sideways). P 14½.

435	**222** 5p. multicoloured	1·25	25
436	15p. multicoloured	2·50	60
437	24p. multicoloured	3·00	1·25
438	30p. multicoloured	3·00	3·75
439	60p. multicoloured	3·75	14·00
435/9 Set of 5		12·00	18·00
MS440 140×115 mm. Nos. 435/9. Imperf		25·00	28·00

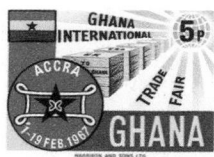

223 Fair Emblem and Crates

1967 (1 Feb). Ghana Trade Fair, Accra. T **223** and similar multicoloured designs. W **47** (sideways on 24p.). P 14×14½ (24p.) or 14½×14 (others).

441	5p. Type **223**	10	10
442	15p. Fair emblem and world map	15	20
443	24p. Shipping and flags (vert)	25	30
444	36p. Fair emblem and hand-held hoist	40	2·75
441/4 Set of 4		70	3·00

(New Currency. 100 new pesewae = 1 new cedi (1.2 old cedi))

1½Np (227)   N₵2.00 (228)

1967 (23 Feb). Nos. 216, 219/23, 225/6 and 393 surch as T **227/8**.

(a) Postage

445	1½n.p. on 2d. multicoloured (Blk.)	2·00	12·00
446	3½n.p. on 4d. multicoloured (R)	9·00	5·50
	a. Surch double, one sideways		
	b. Surch double	—	70·00
447	5n.p. on 6d. multicoloured (R.)	5·50	2·25
448	9n.p. on 11d. multicoloured (W)	30	1·00
449	10n.p. on 1s. multicoloured (W)	30	2·25
450	25n.p. on 2s.6d. multicoloured (R.)	3·50	10·00
451	1n.c. on 10s. multicoloured (R.)	2·50	16·00
452	2n.c. on £1 multicoloured (R.)	4·00	24·00

(b) Air

453	12½n.p. on 1s.3d. multicoloured (W.)	4·50	7·00
454	20n.p. on 24p. on 2s. multicoloured (R.1)	6·00	9·50
445/54 Set of 10		32·00	75·00

Inverted surcharges in a different type face on the 3½, 5 and 25n.p. are fakes.

229 Ghana Eagle and Flag

(Des M. Shamir)

1967 (24 Feb). First Anniv of February 24 Revolution. W **47** (sideways). P 14×14½.

455	**229** 1n.p. multicoloured	10	90
456	4n.p. multicoloured	10	10
457	12½n.p. multicoloured	35	60
458	25n.p. multicoloured	65	3·50
455/8 Set of 4		1·00	4·50
MS459 89×108 mm. Nos. 455/8. Perf or imperf		5·00	12·00

230 Maize

231 Forest Kingfisher

235 Rufous-crowned Roller
236 Akasombo Dam

1967 (1 June–Sept). T **230/1**, **235/6** and similar designs. W **47** (1½, 2, 4, 50n.p. and 1n.c.) or sideways (others). P 11½×12 (1, 8n.p.), 12×11½ (4n.p), 14×14½ (1½ 2, 2½, 20n.p., 2n.c. 50) or 14½×14 (others).

460	1n.p. multicoloured	10	10
	a. Salmon omitted**	£400	
461	1½n.p. multicoloured	1·00	2·75
	a. Blue omitted*	£275	
	b. Green printed double, once inverted†	†	£650
	c. Green omitted	†	£450
	d. Black omitted	†	£650
462	2n.p. multicoloured (4.9)	10	10
	a. Green (part of flag) omitted	£275	
	b. Gold (frame) omitted	£225	
	w. Wmk inverted	10·00	
463	2½n.p. multicoloured (4.9)	35	10
	a. Wmk upright	13·00	
	ab. Face value omitted	£450	
464	3n.p. multicoloured	20	40
	a. Green (part of flag) omitted	—	£700
465	4n.p. multicoloured	1·50	10
	a. Green (part of flag) omitted	£150	
	b. Red (part of flag) omitted	£700	
	c. Black (star, bird markings and shadow) omitted	£225	
466	6n.p. multicoloured	15	2·25
467	8n.p. multicoloured	15	1·00
468	9n.p. multicoloured (4.9)	75	10
469	10n.p. multicoloured	15	10
470	20n.p. deep blue and new blue (4.9)	20	10
471	50n.p. multicoloured	13·00	4·50
472	1n.c. multicoloured (4.9)	2·00	1·00
473	2n.c. multicoloured (4.9)	2·25	3·50
474	2n.c. 50 multicoloured	2·25	12·00
460/74 *Set of 15*		21·00	25·00

Designs:—Vert (as T **231**)—2n.p. The Ghana Mace; 2½n.p Commelina; 20n.p. Bush Hare; 2n.c. Frangipani; 2n.c. 50, Seat of State. Horiz (as T **236**)—3n.p. West African Lungfish; 9n.p. Chameleon; 10n.p Tema Harbour; 50n.p. Black-winged Stilt; 1n.c. Wooden Stool. (As T **230**)—8n.p. Adomi Bridge.

*In this stamp the blue not only affects the bird but is printed over the yellow background to give the value in green, so that its omission results in the value also being omitted.

**This affects the maize flowers, corn and foreground.

†This affects the feather-tips and the flag.

The 2n.p. and 20n.p. were officially issued on 4 September but small quanties of both were released in error on 1 June. The 2½ n.p. is also known to have been released in error in June.

245 Kumasi Fort

(Des O. Hamann)

1967 (1 July). Castles and Forts. T **245** and similar designs. Multicoloured. W **47** (diagonal). P 14½.

475	4n.p. Type **245**	25	10
476	12½n.p. Cristiansborg Castle and British galleon	60	1·00
477	20n.p. Elmina Castle and Portuguese galleon	75	3·00
478	25n.p. Cape Coast Castle and Spanish galleon	75	3·75
475/8 *Set of 4*		2·10	7·00

249 *Luna 10*

(Des M. Shamir. Photo Enschedé)

1967 (16 Aug). "Peaceful Use of Outer Space". T **249** and similar square designs. Multicoloured. P 13½×14.

479	4n.p. Type **249**	10	10

480	10n.p. *Orbiter 1*	10	60
481	12½n.p. Man in Space	20	90
479/81 *Set of 3*		35	1·40
MS482 140×90 mm. Nos. 479/81. Imperf		1·75	5·50

252 Scouts and Camp-fire

(Photo Enschedé)

1967 (18 Sept). 50th Anniv of Ghanaian Scout Movement. T **252** and similar horiz designs. multicoloured. P 14½×13.

483	4n.p. Type **252**	20	10
484	10n.p. Scout on march	40	50
485	12½n.p. Lord Baden-Powell	50	1·75
483/5 *Set of 3*		1·00	2·00
MS486 167×95 mm. Nos. 483/5. Imperf		2·50	10·00

255 UN Headquarters Building

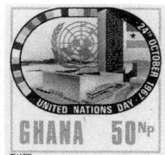
256 General View of UN HQ, Manhattan

(Litho D.L.R.)

1967 (20 Nov–4 Dec). United Nations Day (24 October). P 13½.

487	255	4n.p. multicoloured	10	10
488		10n.p. multicoloured	10	15
489	256	50n.p. multicoloured	20	70
490		2n.c.50 multicoloured	55	4·00
487/90 *Set of 4*			75	4·50
MS491 76×75 mm. No. 490. Imperf (4.12.67)			1·75	9·50

257 Leopard

1967 (28 Dec). International Tourist Year. T **257** and similar diamond-shaped designs. Multicoloured. W **47** (diagonal). P 12½.

492	4n.p. Type **257**	1·00	20
493	12½n.p. *Papilio demoducus* (butterfly)	2·50	1·50
494	20n.p. Carmine Bee-eater	3·50	3·75
495	50n.p. Waterbuck	2·50	9·00
492/5 *Set of 4*		8·50	13·00
MS496 126×126 mm. Nos. 493/5. Imperf		18·00	23·00

261 Revolutionaries entering Accra

(Litho D.L.R.)

1968 (24 Feb). Second Anniv of February Revolution. T **261** and similar horiz designs. Multicoloured. P 14.

497	4n.p. Type **261**	10	10
498	12½n.p. Marching troops	20	20
499	20n.p. Cheering people	30	40
500	40n.p. Victory celebrations	50	3·25
497/500 *Set of 4*		1·00	3·50

265 Microscope and Cocoa Beans

1968 (18 Mar). Cocoa Reseach. T **265** and similar horiz design. Multicoloured. W **47** (sideways). P 14½×14.

501	2½n.p. Type **265**	10	1·25
502	4n.p. Microscope and cocoa tree, beans and pods	10	10

503	10n.p. Type **265**	15	30
504	25n.p. As 4n.p.	60	1·75
501/4 *Set of 4*		80	3·00
MS505 102×102 mm. Nos. 501/4. Imperf		2·25	5·50

267 Kotoka and Flowers

271 Tobacco

(Des A. S. B. New (No. 508) and F. Mate (others) Litho D.L.R.)

1968 (17 Apr). First Death Anniv of Lt.-Gen. E. K. Kotoka. T **267** and similar multicoloured designs. P 14.

506	4n.p. Type **267**	10	10
507	12½n.p. Kotoka and wreath	20	30
508	20n.p. Kotoka in civilian clothes	35	75
509	40n.p. Lt.-Gen. Kotoka (*vert*)	50	3·00
506/9 *Set of 4*		1·00	3·75

(Des A. S. B. New (5n.p.))

1968 (19 Aug). Flora and Fauna. T **271** and similar vert designs. Multicoloured. W **47** (sideways). P 14×14½.

510	4n.p. Type **271**	15	10
511	5n.p. North African Crested Porcupine	15	1·25
512	12½n.p. Rubber	30	75
513	20n.p. *Cymothoe sangaris* (butterfly)	1·00	2·75
514	40n.p. *Charaxes ameliae* (butterfly)	1·25	5·00
510/14 *Set of 5*		2·50	8·50
MS515 88×114 mm. Nos. 510, 512/14. Imperf		2·50	9·00

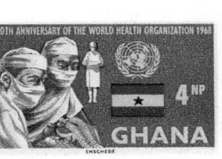
276 Surgeons, Flag and WHO Emblem

277 Hurdling

(Photo Enschedé)

1968 (11 Nov). 20th Anniv of World Health Organization. P 14×13.

516	276	4n.p. multicoloured	20	10
517		12½n.p. multicoloured	40	40
518		20n.p. multicoloured	60	1·25
519		40n.p. multicoloured	1·00	3·75
516/19 *Set of 4*			2·00	5·00
MS520 132×110 mm. Nos. 516/19. Imperf			2·00	6·50

1969 (10–17 Jan). Olympic Games, Mexico (1968). T **277** and similar vert designs. Multicoloured. W **47** (sideways). P 14×14½.

521	4n.p. Type **277**	10	10
522	12½n.p. Boxing	20	30
523	20n.p. Torch, Olympic Rings and flags	40	75
524	40n.p. Football	70	3·25
521/4 *Set of 4*		1·25	4·00
MS525 89×114 mm. Nos. 521/4 Imperf (17.1.69)		3·00	8·00

281 UN Building

(Litho D.L.R.)

1969 (1 Feb). United Nations Day (1968). T **281** and similar square-shaped designs. Multicoloured. P 13½.

526	4n.p. Type **281**	10	10
527	12½n.p. Native stool, staff and UN emblem	15	25
528	20n.p. UN building and emblem over Ghanaian flag	20	45
529	40n.p. UN emblem encircled by flags	40	2·75
526/9 *Set of 4*		75	3·25
MS530 127×117 mm. No. 526/9. Imperf		75	3·50

285 Dr. J. B. Danquah

1969 (7 Mar–17 Apr). Human Rights Year. T **285** and similar horiz design. Multicoloured. W **47** (sideways on MS535). P 14½×14.

531	4n.p. Type **285**	10	10
532	12½n.p. Dr. Martin Luther king	20	35
533	20n.p. As 12½n.p.	35	75
534	40n.p. Type **285**	50	3·00
531/4 *Set of 4*		1·00	3·75
MS535 116×50 mm. Nos. 531/4. Imperf (17.4.69)		80	4·25

287 Constituent Assembly Building

1969 (10 Sept). Third Anniv of the Revolution. T **287** and similar horiz design. W **47** (sideways on **MS**540). P 14½×14.

536	4n.p. Type **287**	10	10
537	12½n.p. Arms of Ghana	10	15
538	20n.p. Type **287**	15	20
539	40n.p. As 12½n.p.	20	75
536/9	*Set of 4*	40	1·00
MS540	114×89 mm. Nos. 536/9. Imperf	70	3·00

NEW CONSTITUTION
1969
(289)

1969 (1 Oct). New Constitution. Nos. 460/74 optd with T **289** in various positions by Government Press, Accra.

541	1n.p. multicoloured (*horiz*)	10	2·50
	a. Opt inverted	75·00	
542	1½n.p. multicoloured (*vert down*)	4·25	7·50
	aa. Opt omitted (*in horiz pair with normal*)	£325	
	a. Opt vert up	4·50	
	b. Horiz opt	27·00	
	ba. Opt omitted (*in vert pair with normal*)	£325	
543	2n.p. multicoloured (*vert up*)	10	4·00
	a. Opt vert up	5·00	
	b. Opt double	14·00	
544	2½n.p. multicoloured (*vert up*)	40	2·50
	a. Opt vert down	23·00	
	b. Opt omitted (*in horiz pair with normal*)	£225	
	c. Opt double, one diagonal	65·00	
545	3n.p. multicoloured (*horiz*)	1·50	2·75
	a. Opt inverted	18·00	
546	4n.p. multicoloured (Y.) (*vert down*)	3·00	1·25
	a. Black opt (*vert down*)	4·50	1·75
	b. Black opt (*vert up*)	23·00	
	c. Red opt (*vert down*)	20·00	
	d. Opt double (*White vert down+yellow vert up*)	30·00	
547	6n.p. multicoloured (*horiz*)	15	3·00
548	8n.p. multicoloured (*horiz*)	15	4·75
549	9n.p. multicoloured (*horiz*)	15	3·75
550	10n.p. multicoloured (*horiz*)	2·25	4·25
551	20n.p. deep blue and new blue (*vert up*)	2·50	2·75
	a. Opt vert down	24·00	
552	50n.p. multicoloured (*horiz*)	7·00	8·50
	a. Opt double	28·00	
553	1n.c. multicoloured (*horiz*)	1·50	9·50
554	2n.c. multicoloured (R.) (*vert up*)	1·50	9·50
	a. Opt double vert up and down	60·00	
	b. Opt triple (*Red vert up and yellow vert up*)	80·00	
555	2n.c. 50 multicoloured (*vert down*)	1·50	10·00
541/55	*Set of 15*	23·00	65·00

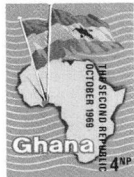

290 Map of Africa and Flags

(Litho D.L.R.)

1969 (4 Dec). Inauguration of Second Republic. T **290** and similar vert designs. Multicoloured. P 14.

556	4n.p. Type **290**	30	10
557	12½n.p. Figure "2", branch and Ghanaian colours	20	10
558	20n.p. Hands receiving egg	35	40
559	40n.p. Type **290**	90	1·75
556/9	*Set of 4*	1·60	2·00

293 ILO Emblem and Cog-wheels

1970 (5 Jan). 50th Anniv of International Labour Organisation. W **47** (sideways). P 14½×14.

560	**293**	4n.p. multicoloured	10	10
561		12½n.p. multicoloured	20	55
562		20n.p. multicoloured	30	1·25
560/2	*Set of 3*		55	1·60
MS563	117×89 mm. Nos. 560/2. Imperf		70	3·00

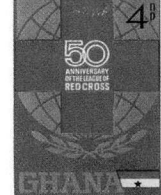

294 Red Cross and Globe

298 General Kotoka, Vickers VC-10 and Airport

1970 (2 Feb). 50th Anniv of League of Red Cross Societies. T **294** and similar multicoloured designs. W **47** (sideways on 4n.p.). P 14×14½ (4n.p) or 14½×14 (others).

564	4n.p. Type **294**	20	10
565	12½n.p. Henri Dunant and Red Cross emblem (*horiz*)	25	25
	w. Wmk inverted		
566	20n.p. Patient receiving medicine (*horiz*)	30	85
567	40n.p. Patient having arm bandaged (*horiz*)	35	3·25
564/7	*Set of 4*	1·00	4·00
MS568	114×89 mm. Nos. 564/7. Imperf	1·25	6·00

(Des G. Vasarhelyi. Litho D.L.R.)

1970 (17 Apr). Inauguration of Kotoka Airport. T **298** and similar horiz designs. Multicoloured. P 13×13½.

569	4n.p. Type **298**	15	10
570	12½n.p. Control tower and tail of Vickers VC-10	25	15
571	20n.p. Aerial view of airport	40	30
572	40n.p. Airport and flags	75	80
569/72	*Set of 4*	1·40	1·25

302 Lunar Module landing on Moon

306 Adult Education

(Des A. Medina (4n.p., 12½ n.p), G. Vasarhelyi (others). Litho D.L.R.)

1970 (15 June). Moon Landing. T **302** and similar multicoloured designs. P 12½.

573	4n.p. Type **302**	30	10
574	12½n.p. Astronaut's first step onto the Moon	35	60
575	20n.p. Astronaut with equipment on Moon (*horiz*)	45	1·40
576	40n.p. Astronauts (*horiz*)	55	3·25
573/6	*Set of 4*	1·50	4·75
MS577	142×142 mm. Nos. 573/6. Imperf (with or without simulated perfs)	2·00	12·00

On 18 September 1970 Nos. 573/6 were issued overprinted "PHILYMPIA LONDON 1970" but it is understood that only 900 sets were made available for sale in Ghana and we do not consider that this is sufficient to constitute normal postal use. The miniature sheet was also overprinted but not issued in Ghana.

(Litho D.L.R.)

1970 (10 Aug). International Education Year. T **306** and similar horiz designs. Multicoloured. P 13.

578	4n.p. Type **306**	10	10
579	12½n.p. International education	20	20
580	20n.p. "Ntesie" and IEY symbols	35	30
581	40n.p. Nursery schools	60	1·40
578/81	*Set of 4*	1·10	1·75

310 Saluting March-Past

(Litho D.L.R.)

1970 (1 Oct). First Anniv of the Second Republic. T **310** and similar horiz designs. Multicoloured. P 13×13½.

582	4n.p. Type **310**	20	10
583	12½n.p. Busia declaration	15	15
584	20n.p. Doves symbol	25	30
585	40n.p. Opening of Parliament	50	1·00
582/5	*Set of 4*	1·00	1·40

314 *Crinum ornatum*

(Des G. Vasarhelyi. Photo Harrison)

1970 (2 Nov). Flora and Fauna. T **314** and similar horiz designs. Multicoloured. W **47** (sideways). P 14½×14.

586	4n.p. Type **314**	1·75	25
	w. Wmk inverted	9·50	
587	12½n.p. Lioness	1·25	85
588	20n.p. *Ansellia africana* (flower)	1·25	1·50
589	40n.p. African Elephant	2·00	6·00
586/9	*Set of 4*	5·50	7·75

315 Kuduo Brass Casket

(Des G. Vasarhelyi. Photo Harrison)

1970 (7 Dec)–71. Monuments and Archaeological Sites in Ghana. T **315** and similar horiz designs. Multicoloured. W **47**. P 14½×14.

590	4n.p. Type **315**	15	10
	w. Wmk inverted	21·00	
591	12½n.p. Akan traditional house	30	20
592	20n.p. Larabanga Mosque	35	55
593	40n.p. Funerary clay head	50	2·50
590/3	*Set of 4*	1·10	3·00
MS594	89×71 mm. Nos. 590, 592 and 12½n.p. Basilica of Pompeii, 40n.p. Pistrinum of Pompeii (wmk sideways). Imperf (2.71)	2·50	9·00

STAMP BOOKLETS

1961. Red (No. SB2), yellow (No. SB3) or green (No. SB4) covers. Stitched.

SB2	3s. booklet containing 12×3d. (No. 218a) in blocks of 4		6·50
SB3	6s. booklet containing 8×3d. and 8×6d. (Nos. 218a, 220) in blocks of 4		8·00
SB4	10s. booklet containing 4×3d., 8×6d. and 4×1s.3d. (Nos. 218a, 220 and 226) in blocks of 4.		10·00

1963 (1 Jan). Black on red (No. SB5), black on yellow (No. SB6) or black on green (No. SB7) covers. Stitched.

SB5	4s. booklet containing 12×4d. (No. 219) in blocks of 4		
SB6	6s. booklet containing 12×4d. and 4×6d. (Nos. 219/20) in blocks of 4		
SB7	11s. booklet containing 12×4d., 4×6d. and 4×1s.3d. (Nos. 219/20, 226) in blocks of 4		
SB5/7	*Set of 3 booklets*		£350

POSTAGE DUE STAMPS

GHANA (D **2**) D **3**

1958 (25 June). Nos. D5/8 of Gold Coast and similar 1d. value optd with Type D **2** in red.

D9	D **1**	1d. black	10	30
D10		2d. black	10	30
		c. Large "d"	2·25	
D11		3d. black	10	30
		a. Missing serif	4·50	
D12		6d. black	15	65
D13		1s. black	20	1·50
		c. Upright stroke	1·50	
D9/13	*Set of 5*		50	2·75

(Typo De La Rue)

1958 (1 Dec). Chalk-surfaced paper. Wmk Mult Script CA. P 14.

D14	D **3**	1d. carmine	10	30
D15		2d. green	10	30
		c. Large "d"	2·25	
D16		3d. orange	10	30
		a. Missing serif	4·25	
D17		6d. bright ultramarine	10	50
D18		1s. reddish violet	15	2·00
		c. Upright stroke	1·50	
D14/18	*Set of 5*		45	3·00

3p.

Ghana New Currency 19th July, 1965. (D **4**)   **1½Np** (D **5**)

1965 (19 July). Nos. D14/18 surch as Type D **4** diagonally upwards (D) or horiz (H), by Govt Printer, Accra.

D19	D **3**	1p. on 1d. (D)	10	75
		a. Surch inverted	11·00	
		b. Surch double		
		c. Surch omitted (in horiz pair with normal)	£110	
D20		2p. on 2d. (B.) (H)	10	2·00
		a. Surch inverted	9·00	
		c. Large "d"	2·25	
		d. Surch omitted (in horiz pair with normal)	85·00	
D21		3p. on 3d. (indigo) (H)	10	2·00
		a. Surch inverted	12·00	
		b. Surch omitted (in horiz pair with normal)		
		c. Ultramarine surch	9·00	
		ca. Surch inverted	9·00	
		cb. Surch on front and back	15·00	
		d. Black surch		
		e. Missing serif	3·00	
D22		6p. on 6d. (R) (H)	10	3·25
		a. Surch inverted	14·00	
		b. Purple-brown surch	11·00	
		ba. Surch double	26·00	
		c. Green surch	14·00	

D23	12p. on 1s. (B) (D)		15	3·50
	c. Upright stroke		1·50	
D19/23	*Set of 5*		45	10·50

On the diagonal surcharges the figures of value are horizontal.
No. D21b occurs in the first or second vertical row of one sheet which shows the surcharges shifted progressively to the right.

1968 (1 Feb)–**70.** Nos. D20/2 additionally surch as Type D **5**, in red (1½n.p., 5n.p.), or black (2½n.p.).

D24	D **3** 1½p. on 2p. on 2d.		7·00	4·25
	a. Type D **5** double, one albino			
	b. Albino surch (Type D **4**)			
	c. Large "d"		23·00	
D25	2½n.p. on 3p. on 3d. (4.70?)		1·25	5·00
	a. Type D **5** double, one albino		5·50	
	b. Missing serif		5·50	
D26	5n.p. on 6p. on 6d. (1970)		3·25	
D24/6	*Set of 3*		10·50	

The above were three in a series of surcharges, the others being 1n.p on 1p. and 10n.p. on 12p, which were prepared, but owing to confusion due to the two surcharges in similar currency it was decided by the authorities not to issue the stamps, however, Nos. D24/6 were issued in error.

(Litho D.L.R.)

1970. Inscr in new currency. P 14½x14.

D27	D **3** 1n.p. carmine-red		1·75	6·50
D28	1½n.p. green		2·25	7·50
D29	2½n.p. yellow-orange		2·75	9·00
D30	5n.p. ultramarine		3·00	9·00
D31	10n.p. reddish violet		5·00	11·00
D27/31	*Set of 5*		13·00	38·00

Gibraltar

CROWN COLONY

Early details of postal arrangements in Gibraltar are hard to establish, although it is known that postal facilities were provided by the Civil Secretary's Office from 1749. Gibraltar became a packet port in July 1806, although the Civil Secretary's office continued to be responsible for other mail. The two services were amalgamated on 1 January 1857 as a Branch Office of the British GPO, the control of the postal services not reverting to Gibraltar until 1 January 1886.

Spanish stamps could be used at Gibraltar from their introduction in 1850 and, indeed, such franking was required on letters weighing over ½ oz. sent to Spain after 1 July 1854. From 1 July 1856 until 31 December 1875 all mail to Spain required postage to be prepaid by Spanish stamps and these issues were supplied by the Gibraltar postal authorities, acting as a Spanish Postal Agent. The mail forwarded under this system was cancelled at San Roque with a horizontal barred oval, later replaced by a cartwheel type mark showing numeral 63. From 1857 combination covers showing the 2d. ship mail fee paid in British stamps and the inland postage by Spanish issues exist.

Stamps of Great Britain were issued for use in Gibraltar from 3 September 1857 (earliest recorded cover is dated 7 September 1857) to the end of 1885.

The initial supply contained 1d., 4d. and 6d. values. No supplies of the 2d. or 1s. were sent until the consignment of October 1857. No other values were supplied until early 1862.

Stamps of GREAT BRITAIN cancelled "G" as Types Z **1** or Z **2** (3 Sept 1857 to 19 Feb 1859).

Z1	1d. red-brown (1841), *imperf*		£3250
Z1*a*	1d. red-brown (1854) Die I, *wmk* Small Crown, *perf* 16		£425
Z2	1d. red-brown (1855), Die II, *wmk* Small Crown, *perf* 16		£800
Z3	1d. red-brown (1855), Die II, *wmk* Small Crown *perf* 14		£375
Z4	1d. red-brown (1855), Die II, *wmk* Large Crown, *perf* 14		£100
Z5	1d. rose-red (1857), Die II, *wmk* Large Crown, *perf* 14		25·00
Z6	2d. blue (1855), *wmk* Small Crown, *perf* 14		£500
Z7	2d. blue (1855–58), *wmk* Large Crown, *perf* 16		£400
Z8	2d. blue (1855), *wmk* Large Crown, *perf* 14	*From*	75·00
	Plate Nos. 5, 6.		
Z9	2d. blue (1858) (Plate No. 7)		£350
Z10	4d. rose (1857)		60·00
	a. Thick glazed paper		
Z11	6d. lilac (1856)		42·00
Z12	6d. lilac (1856) (blued *paper*)		£850
Z13	1s. green (1856)		£130
	a. Thick paper		
Z14	1s. green (1856) (blued *paper*)		£1500

Stamps of GREAT BRITAIN cancelled "A 26" as in Types Z **3**, Z **4**, Z **5**, Z **6** or similar (20 Feb 1859 to 31 Dec 1885).

Z15	½d. rose-red (1870–79)	*From*	42·00
	Plate Nos. 4, 5, 6, 8, 10, 11, 12, 13, 14, 15, 19, 20		

Z16	1d. red-brown (1841), *imperf*		£2500
Z17	1d. red-brown (1855), *wmk* Large Crown, *perf* 14		£250
Z18	1d. rose-red (1857), *wmk* Large Crown, *perf* 14		14·00
Z19	1d. rose-red (1864–79)	*From*	24·00
	Plate Nos. 71, 72, 73, 74 ,76, 78, 79, 80, 81, 82, 83, 84, 85, 86, 87, 88, 89, 90, 91, 92, 93, 94, 95, 96, 97, 98, 99, 100, 101, 102, 103, 104, 105, 106, 107, 108, 109, 110, 111, 112, 113, 114, 115, 116, 117, 118, 119, 120, 121, 122, 123, 124, 125, 127, 129, 130, 131, 132, 133, 134, 135, 136, 137, 138, 139, 140, 141, 142, 143, 144, 145, 146, 147, 148, 149, 150, 151, 152, 153, 154, 155, 156, 157, 158, 159, 160, 161, 162, 163, 164, 165, 166, 167, 168, 169, 170, 171, 172, 173, 174, 175, 176, 177, 178, 179, 180, 181, 182, 183, 184, 185, 186, 187, 188, 189, 190, 191, 192, 193, 194, 195, 196, 197, 198, 199, 200, 201, 202, 203, 204, 205, 206, 207, 208, 209, 210, 211, 212, 213, 214, 215, 216, 217, 218, 219, 220, 221, 222, 223, 224, 225.		
Z20	1½d. lake-red (1870) (Plate No. 3)		£750
Z21	2d. blue (1855), *wmk* Large Crown, *perf* 14.		£160
	Plate No. 6.		
Z22	2d. blue (1858–69)	*From*	24·00
	Plate Nos. 7, 8, 9, 12, 13, 14, 15.		
Z23	2½d. rosy mauve (1875) (blued *paper*)	*From*	£100
	Plate Nos. 1, 2, 3.		
Z24	2½d. rosy mauve (1875–76)	*From*	32·00
	Plate Nos. 1, 2, 3.		
Z25	2½d. rosy mauve (*Error of Lettering*)		£3750
Z26	2½d. rosy mauve (1876–79)	*From*	21·00
	Plate Nos. 3, 4, 5, 6, 7, 8, 9, 10, 11, 12, 13, 14, 15, 16, 17.		
Z27	2½d. blue (1880–81)	*From*	13·00
	Plate Nos. 17, 18, 19, 20.		
Z28	2½d. blue (1881) (Plate Nos. 21, 22, 23)	*From*	10·00
Z29	3d. carmine-rose (1862)		£350
Z30	3d. rose (1865) (Plate No. 4)		90·00
Z31	3d. rose (1867–73)	*From*	65·00
	Plate Nos. 4, 5, 6, 7, 8, 9, 10.		
Z32	3d. rose (1873–76)	*From*	85·00
	Plate Nos. 11, 12, 14, 15, 16, 17, 18, 19, 20.		
Z33	3d. rose (1881) (Plate Nos. 20, 21)		£110
Z34	3d. lilac (1883) (3d. *on* 3d.)		£200
Z35	4d. rose (1857)		£110
Z36	4d. red (1862) (Plate Nos. 3, 4)	*From*	48·00
Z37	4d. vermilion (1865–73)	*From*	30·00
	Plate Nos. 7, 8, 9, 10, 11, 12, 13, 14.		
Z38	4d. vermilion (1876) (Plate No. 15)		£325
Z39	4d. sage-green (1877) (Plate Nos. 15, 16)		£140
Z40	4d. grey-brown (1880) *wmk* Large Garter		£425
	Plate No. 17.		
Z41	4d. grey-brown (1880) *wmk* Crown	*From*	75·00
	Plate Nos. 17, 18.		
Z42	6d. lilac (1856)		42·00
Z43	6d. lilac (1862) (Plate Nos. 3, 4)	*From*	40·00
Z44	6d. lilac (1865–67) (Plate Nos. 5, 6)	*From*	35·00
Z45	6d. lilac (1867) (Plate No. 6)		48·00
Z46	6d. violet (1867–70) (Plate Nos. 6, 8, 9)	*From*	32·00
Z47	6d. buff (1872–73) (Plate Nos. 11, 12)	*From*	£150
Z48	6d. chestnut (1872) (Plate No. 11)		38·00
Z49	6d. grey (1873) (Plate No. 12)		95·00
Z50	6d. grey (1874–80)	*From*	40·00
	Plate Nos. 13, 14, 15, 16, 17.		
Z51	6d. grey (1881) (Plate Nos. 17, 18)		£375
Z52	6d. lilac (1883) (6d. *on* 6d.)		£130
Z53	8d. orange (1876)		£750
Z54	9d. bistre (1862)		£450
Z55	9d. straw (1862)		£900
Z56	9d. straw (1865)		£850
Z57	9d. straw (1867)		£325
Z58	10d. red-brown (1867)		£150
Z59	1s. green (1856)		£110
Z60	1s. green (1862)		70·00
Z61	1s. green (1862) ("K" *variety*)		£2500
Z62	1s. green (1865) (Plate No. 4)		60·00
Z63	1s. green (1867–73) (Plate Nos. 4, 5, 6, 7)	*From*	40·00
Z64	1s. green (1873–77)	*From*	90·00
	Plate Nos. 8, 9, 10, 11, 12, 13.		
Z65	1s. orange-brown (1880) (Plate No. 13)		£475
Z66	1s. orange-brown (1881)	*From*	£130
	Plate Nos. 13, 14.		
Z67	2s. blue (1867)		£350
Z68	5s. rose (1867) (Plate No. 1)		£1000

1880.

Z69	½d. deep green		30·00
Z70	½d. pale green		30·00
Z71	1d. Venetian red		30·00
Z72	1½d. Venetian red		£400
Z73	2d. pale rose		75·00
Z74	2d. deep rose		75·00
Z75	5d. indigo		£160

1881.

Z76	1d. lilac (14 *dots*)		42·00
Z77	1d. lilac (16 *dots*)		11·00

1884.

Z78	½d. slate-blue		32·00
Z79	2d. lilac		£130
Z80	2½d. lilac		19·00
Z81	3d. lilac		
Z82	4d. dull green		£200
Z83	6d. dull green		

POSTAL FISCAL

Z83*a*	1d. purple (Die 4) (1878) *wmk* Small Anchor		£700
Z84	1d. purple (1881), *wmk* Orb		£1100

PRICES FOR STAMPS ON COVER TO 1945	
Nos. 1/2	*from* × 25
No. 3	*from* × 10
No. 4	*from* × 25
Nos. 5/6	*from* × 8
Nos. 7/33	*from* × 6

GIBRALTAR
(1)

1886 (1 Jan). Contemporary types of Bermuda optd with T **1** by D.L.R. Wmk Crown CA. P 14.

1	**9**	½d. dull green		23·00	12·00
2	**1**	1d. rose-red		85·00	6·00
3	**2**	2d. purple-brown		£140	85·00
		w. Wmk inverted			
4	**11**	2½d. ultramarine		£200	3·25
		a. Optd in blue-black		£500	£150
		w. Wmk inverted		—	£550
5	**10**	4d. orange-brown		£190	£110
6	**4**	6d. deep lilac		£300	£225
7	**5**	1s. yellow-brown		£450	£375
1/7 *Set of 7*				£1200	£700
1s/3s, 4as/7s Optd "SPECIMEN" *Set of 7*				£5500	

Nos. 1/7 were overprinted on special printings of the underlying Bermuda stamps. The ½d., 2d. and 1s. values were not issued in these colours in Bermuda until 1893, while the 4d. was not issued on CA paper in Bermuda until 1904. The 6d. does not exist without opt. Collectors should be aware of Bermuda stamps with forged "GIBRALTAR" overprints.

PRINTER. All Gibraltar stamps to No. 109 were typographed by De La Rue & Co, Ltd.

2   **3**

4   **5**

1886 (Nov)–**87**. Wmk Crown CA. P 14.

8	**2**	½d. dull green (1.87)		18·00	4·25
		w. Wmk inverted		†	£1000
9	**3**	1d. rose (2.87)		50·00	4·75
10	**4**	2d. brown-purple (12.86)		30·00	35·00
		w. Wmk inverted			£850
11	**5**	2½d. blue		85·00	3·00
		w. Wmk inverted		£400	90·00
12	**4**	4d. orange-brown (16.4.87)		85·00	85·00
13		6d. lilac (16.4.87)		£140	£140
14		1s. bistre (2.87)		£250	£200
		w. Wmk inverted			
8/14 *Set of 7*				£600	£400
8s/14s Optd "SPECIMEN" *Set of 7*				£500	

Examples of Nos. 3, 6/7 and 14 are known showing a forged Gibraltar postmark dated "JU-13 87".

See also Nos. 39/45.

5 CENTIMOS
(6)

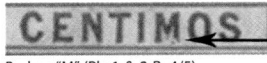

Normal

"5" with short foot (all stamps in 1st, 5th and 6th vertical columns (5c. on ½d.) or all stamps in 2nd vertical column (25c. on 2d., 25c. on 2½d., 50c. on 6d. and 75c. on 1s.)

1889 (1 Aug). Surch as T **6**.

15	**2**	5c. on ½d. green		13·00	32·00
		a. "5" with short foot		13·00	32·00
16	**3**	10c. on 1d. rose		14·00	19·00
17	**4**	25c. on 2d. brown-purple		4·75	11·00
		a. "5" with short foot		10·00	22·00
		ab. Small "I" (R. 6/2)		£100	£170
		b. Broken "N" (R. 10/5)		£100	£170
18	**5**	25c. on 2½d. bright blue		29·00	2·50
		a. "5" with short foot		55·00	5·00
		ab. Small "I" (R. 6/2)		£325	£100
		b. Broken "N" (R. 10/5)		£325	£100
19	**4**	40c. on 4d. orange-brown		55·00	75·00
20		50c. on 6d. bright lilac		55·00	80·00
		a. "5" with short foot		£140	£170
21		75c. on 1s. bistre		55·00	65·00
		a. "5" with short foot		£150	£160
15/21 *Set of 7*				£200	£250
15s/21s Optd "SPECIMEN" *Set of 7*				£375	

10c., 40c. and 50c. values from this issue and that of 1889–96 are known bisected and used for half their value from various post offices in Morocco (*price on cover from £500*). These bisects were never authorised by the Gibraltar Post Office.

Broken "M" (Pls 1 & 2 R. 4/5)

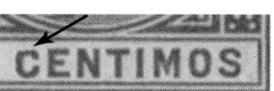

7   Flat top to "C" (Pl 2 R. 4/4)

1889 (8 Oct*)–**96**. Issue in Spanish currency. Wmk Crown CA. P 14.

22	**7**	5c. green		6·50	1·00
		a. Broken "M"		£190	85·00
		w. Wmk inverted		£300	£300
23		10c. carmine		4·50	50
		b. Value omitted		£7000	
24		20c. olive-green and brown (2.1.96)		30·00	24·00
		w. Wmk inverted		—	£850
25		20c. olive-green (8.7.96)		18·00	£100
		a. Flat top to "C"		£350	
26		25c. ultramarine		26·00	70
		a. Deep ultramarine		35·00	1·00
27		40c. orange-brown		3·75	4·75
28		50c. bright lilac (1890)		3·25	2·50
29		75c. olive-green (1890)		32·00	32·00
30		1p. bistre (11.89)		75·00	20·00
31		1p. bistre and ultramarine (6.95)		4·75	8·50
32		2p. black and carmine (2.1.96)		11·00	30·00
33		5p. slate-grey (12.89)		42·00	£100
22/33 *Set of 12*				£225	£300
22s/4s, 26s/33s Optd "SPECIMEN" *Set of 11*				£450	

*Earliest recorded postmark date.

1898 (1 Oct). Reissue in Sterling currency. Wmk Crown CA. P 14.

39	**2**	½d. grey-green		14·00	1·75
		w. Wmk inverted			
40	**3**	1d. carmine		14·00	50
		w. Wmk inverted		†	£1400
41	**4**	2d. brown-purple and ultramarine		29·00	2·25
42	**5**	2½d. bright ultramarine		45·00	50
		w. Wmk inverted		£350	90·00
43	**4**	4d. orange-brown and green		18·00	4·00
		a. "FOUR PENCE" trimmed at top (Pl 2 R. 6/4 and 5, R. 8/4-6)		£500	
44		6d. violet and red		45·00	22·00
45		1s. bistre and carmine		42·00	8·00
		w. Wmk inverted			
39/45 *Set of 7*				£180	35·00
39s/45s Optd "SPECIMEN" *Set of 7*				£275	

No. 39 is greyer than No. 8, No. 40 brighter and deeper than No. 9 and No. 42 much brighter than No. 11.

The degree of "trimming" on No. 43a varies, but is most prominent on R. 6/4 and 5.

8   **9**

Normal   Large "2"
2½d.

This occurs on R. 10/1 in each pane of 60. The diagonal stroke is also longer.

1903 (1 May). Wmk Crown CA. P 14.

46	**8**	½d. grey-green and green		14·00	10·00
47		1d. dull purple/*red*		35·00	60
48		2d. grey-green and carmine		30·00	42·00
49		2½d. dull purple and black/*blue*		8·50	60
		a. Large "2" in "½"		£325	£130
50		6d. dull purple and violet		38·00	21·00
51		1s. black and carmine		28·00	38·00
52	**9**	2s. green and blue		£200	£275
53		4s. dull purple and green		£150	£225
54		8s. dull purple and black/*blue*		£170	£200
55		£1 dull purple and black/*red*		£650	£750
46/55 *Set of 10*				£1200	£1400
46s/55s Optd "SPECIMEN" *Set of 10*				£550	

1904–08. Wmk Mult Crown CA. Ordinary paper (½d. to 2d. and 6d. to 2s.) or chalk-surfaced paper (others). P 14.

56	**8**	½d. dull and bright green (4.4.04*)		23·00	4·25
		a. Chalk-surfaced paper (10.05)		15·00	8·50
57		1d. dull purple/*red* (6.9.04*)		30·00	50
		a. Bisected (½d.) (*on card or cover*)		†	£1800
		bw. Wmk inverted		†	£950
		c. Chalk-surfaced paper (16.9.05)		8·00	85
58		2d. grey-green and carmine (9.1.05)		38·00	16·00
		a. Chalk-surfaced paper (2.07)		10·00	17·00
59		2½d. purple and black/*blue* (4.5.07)		35·00	90·00
		a. Large "2" in "½"		£600	£1000
60		6d. dull purple and violet (19.4.06)		50·00	40·00
		a. Chalk-surfaced paper (4.08)		32·00	22·00
61		1s. black and carmine (13.10.05)		65·00	24·00
		a. Chalk-surfaced paper (4.06)		55·00	24·00
62	**9**	2s. green and blue (2.2.05)		£120	£140
		a. Chalk-surfaced paper (10.07)		£120	£150
63		4s. deep purple and green (6.08)		£350	£425
64		£1 dull purple and black/*red* (15.3.08)		£650	£700
56/64 *Set of 9*				£1100	£1300

*Earliest known date of use.

1906 (Oct)–**11**. Colours changed. Wmk Mult Crown CA. Chalk-surfaced paper (6d. to 8s.). P 14.

66	**8**	½d. blue-green (1907)		15·00	1·75
		x. Wmk reversed		†	£2000
67		1d. carmine		5·50	60
		a. Wmk sideways		£3750	£3500
		w. Wmk inverted		†	£550
68		2d. greyish slate (5.10)		9·50	11·00
69		2½d. ultramarine (6.07)		8·50	1·75
		a. Large "2" in "½"		£300	£120
70		6d. dull and bright purple (4.12.11)*		£150	£375
71		1s. black/*green* (1910)		23·00	21·00
72	**9**	2s. purple and bright blue/*blue* (4.10)		65·00	48·00
73		4s. black and carmine (4.10)		£170	£190
		x. Wmk reversed		£1800	£2000
74		8s. purple and green (1911)		£250	£250
66/74 *Set of 9*				£600	£800
67s/74s Optd "SPECIMEN" *Set of 8*				£600	

*Earliest known date of use.

Examples of Nos. 54, 55, 64 and 73/4 are known showing a forged oval registered postmark dated "6 OC 10".

10   **11**

1912 (17 July)–**24**. Wmk Mult Crown CA. Ordinary paper (½d. to 2½d.) or chalk-surfaced paper (others). P 14.

76	**10**	½d. blue-green		3·25	70
		a. Yellow-green (4.17)		7·00	2·00
		w. Wmk inverted		†	£1200
		x. Wmk reversed		†	£1800
77		1d. carmine-red		4·50	75
		a. Scarlet (6.16)		9·00	1·25
		ay. Wmk inverted and reversed			
78		2d. greyish slate		20·00	1·50
79		2½d. deep bright blue		10·00	2·75
		a. Large "2" in "½"		£300	£160
		b. Pale ultramarine (1917)		11·00	2·75
		ba. Large "2" in "½"		£300	£160
80		6d. dull purple and mauve		9·00	17·00
81		1s. black/*green*		18·00	3·25
		a. Ordinary paper (8.18)		£900	
		b. On blue-green, olive back (1919)		28·00	26·00
		c. On emerald surface (12.23)		30·00	70·00
		d. On emerald back (3.24)		30·00	£110
		ds. Optd "SPECIMEN"		75·00	
82	**11**	2s. dull purple and blue/*blue* (shades)		29·00	4·25
		sa. Opt "SPECIMEN" double		£600	
83		4s. black and carmine		38·00	55·00
84		8s. dull purple and green		£100	£130
85		£1 dull purple and black/*red*		£140	£275
76/85 *Set of 10*				£325	£425
76s/85s Optd "SPECIMEN" *Set of 10*				£500	

WAR TAX
(12)

1918 (15 Apr). Optd with T **12** by Beanland, Malin & Co, Gibraltar.

86	**10**	½d. green		1·00	2·00
		a. Opt double		£900	
		w. Wmk inverted		£850	
		y. Wmk inverted and reversed		£550	

Two printings of this overprint exist, the second being in slightly heavier type on a deeper shade of green.

3 PENCE	THREE PENCE
(I)	(II)

1921–27. Wmk Mult Script CA. Chalk-surfaced paper (6d. to 8s.). P 14.

89	**10**	½d. green (25.4.27)		1·50	1·50
90		1d. carmine-red (2.21)		1·75	1·00
91		1½d. chestnut (1.12.22)		2·00	55
		a. Pale chestnut (7.24)		2·75	30
		w. Wmk inverted		†	£1300
93		2d. grey (17.2.21)		1·25	1·25
94		2½d. bright blue (2.21)		23·00	60·00
		a. Large "2" in "½"		£600	£850
95		3d. bright blue (I) (1.1.22)		3·50	4·50
		a. Ultramarine		2·50	1·50
97		6d. dull purple and mauve (1.23)		6·00	6·00
		a. Bright purple and magenta (22.7.26)		1·60	3·50
98		1s. black/*emerald* (20.6.24)		10·00	25·00
99	**11**	2s. grey-purple and blue/*blue* (20.6.24)		19·00	80·00
		a. Reddish purple and blue/*blue* (1925)		7·00	45·00
100		4s. black and carmine (20.6.24)		70·00	£130
101		8s. dull purple and green (20.6.24)		£325	£550
89/101 *Set of 11*				£400	£750
89s/101s Optd "SPECIMEN" *Set of 11*				£600	

The ½d. exists in coils, constructed from normal sheets, first issued in February 1937.

1925 (15 Oct)–**32**. New values and colours changed. Wmk Mult Script CA. Chalk-surfaced paper. P 14.

102	**10**	1s. sage-green and black (8.1.29)		14·00	40·00
		a. Olive and black (1932)		14·00	20·00
103	**11**	2s. red-brown and black (8.1.29)		10·00	40·00
104		2s.6d. green and black		10·00	29·00
105		4s. carmine and black		19·00	75·00
106		10s. deep ultramarine and black		32·00	80·00
107		£1 red-orange and black (16.11.27)		£190	£300
108		£5 violet and black		£1600	£6000
		s. Optd "SPECIMEN"		£800	

102/7 *Set of 6*			£250	£475
102s/7s Optd or Perf (1s., 2s.) "SPECIMEN" *Set of 6...*			£500	

Examples of Nos. 83/5, 99/101 and 102/8 are known showing forged oval registered postmarks dated "24 JA 25" or "6 MY 35".

1930 (11 Apr). T **10** inscribed "THREE PENCE". Wmk Mult Script CA. P 14.

109		3d. ultramarine (II)	8·00	2·25
	s.	Perf "SPECIMEN"	80·00	

13 The Rock of Gibraltar

(Des Capt. H. St. C. Garrood. Recess D.L.R.)

1931–33. Wmk Mult Script CA. P 14.

110	**13**	1d. scarlet (1.7.31)	2·50	2·50
	a.	Perf 13½×14	22·00	8·00
111		1½d. red-brown (1.7.31)	1·75	2·25
	a.	Perf 13½×14	17·00	4·00
112		2d. pale grey (1.11.32)	12·00	1·75
	a.	Perf 13½×14	24·00	4·25
113		3d. blue (1.6.33)	10·00	3·00
	a.	Perf 13½×14	42·00	42·00
110/13 *Set of 4*			23·00	8·50
110a/13a *Set of 4*			90·00	50·00
110s, 111as/3as Perf "SPECIMEN" *Set of 4*			£200	

Figures of value take the place of both corner ornaments at the base of the 2d. and 3d.

1935 (6 May). Silver Jubilee. As Nos. 91/4 of Antigua but ptd by B.W. P 11×12.

114		2d. ultramarine and grey-black	1·60	2·50
	a.	Extra flagstaff	75·00	£130
	b.	Short extra flagstaff	£160	£225
	c.	Lightning conductor	£110	£160
	d.	Flagstaff on right-hand turret	£425	£450
	e.	Double flagstaff	£425	£450
115		3d. brown and deep blue	3·75	5·00
	a.	Extra flagstaff	£325	£375
	b.	Short extra flagstaff	£325	£375
	c.	Lightning conductor	£350	£400
116		6d. green and indigo	14·00	19·00
	a.	Extra flagstaff	£275	£325
	b.	Short extra flagstaff	£500	£550
	c.	Lightning conductor	£300	£350
117		1s. slate and purple	18·00	28·00
	a.	Extra flagstaff	£225	£275
	b.	Short extra flagstaff	£550	£550
	c.	Lightning conductor	£275	£325
114/17 *Set of 4*			32·00	48·00
114s/17s Perf "SPECIMEN" *Set of 4*			£200	

For illustrations of plate varieties see Omnibus section following Zanzibar.

1937 (12 May). Coronation. As Nos. 95/7 of Antigua. P 11×11½.

118		½d. green	25	50
119		2d. grey-black	3·00	3·25
120		3d. blue	3·00	3·25
118/20 *Set of 3*			5·75	6·25
118s/20s Perf "SPECIMEN" *Set of 3*			£190	

14 King George VI   **15** Rock of Gibraltar

16 The Rock (North Side)   **17** Europa Point

18 Moorish Castle   **19** Southport Gate

20 Eliott Memorial   **21** Government House

22 Catalan Bay

2s. Bird on memorial (R. 9/3)

Broken second "R" in "GIBRALTAR" (Frame Pl 2 R. 9/4)

(Des Captain H. St. C. Garrood. Recess D.L.R.)

1938 (25 Feb)–**51**. T **14**/**22**. Mult Script CA.

121	**14**	½d. deep green (P 13½×14)	10	40
122	**15**	1d. yellow-brown (P 14)	30·00	2·25
	a.	Perf 13½ (1940)	30·00	2·25
	ab.	Perf 13½. Wmk sideways (1940)	6·50	7·00
	b.	Perf 13. Wmk sideways. *Red-brown* (1942)	2·00	60
	c.	Perf 13. Wmk sideways. *Deep brown* (1944)	3·00	3·50
	d.	Perf 13. *Red-brown* (1949)	6·00	1·50
123		1½d. carmine (P 14)	35·00	1·00
	a.	Perf 13½	£275	18·00
123b		1½d. slate-violet (P 13) (1.1.43)	75	1·50
124	**16**	2d. grey (P 14)	32·00	40
	aa.	Ape on rock	£650	£100
	a.	Perf 13½ (1940)	8·50	35
	ab.	Perf 13½. Wmk sideways (1940)	£800	45·00
	b.	Perf 13. Wmk sideways (1943)	4·00	3·00
	ba.	"A" of "CA" missing from wmk	£1700	
124c		2d. carmine (P 13) (*wmk sideways*) (15.7.44)	2·00	60
125	**17**	3d. light blue (P 13½)	42·00	1·00
	a.	Perf 14	£130	6·00
	b.	Perf 13 (1942)	4·50	30
	ba.	"A" of "CA" missing from wmk	£2000	
	bb.	*Greenish blue* (2.51)	8·00	1·00
125c		5d. red-orange (P 13) (1.10.47)	1·50	1·25
126	**18**	6d. carmine and grey-violet (P 13½) (16.3.38)	48·00	3·75
	a.	Perf 14	£120	1·25
	b.	Perf 13 (1942)	11·00	1·75
	c.	Perf 13. *Scarlet and grey-violet* (1945)	12·00	3·75
127	**19**	1s. black and green (P 14) (16.3.38)	45·00	35·00
	a.	Perf 13½	75·00	6·00
	b.	Perf 13 (1942)	3·25	4·25
	ba.	Broken "R"	£900	
128	**20**	2s. black and brown (P 14) (16.3.38)	65·00	23·00
	a.	Perf 13½	£130	50·00
	b.	Perf 13 (1942)	14·00	6·50
	ba.	Broken "R"	£1200	
	bb.	Bird on memorial	£650	£500
129	**21**	5s. black and carmine (P 14) (16.3.38)	£100	£170
	a.	Perf 13½	50·00	14·00
	b.	Perf 13 (1944)	42·00	17·00
	ba.	Broken "R"	£3750	
130	**22**	10s. black and blue (P 14) (16.3.38)	70·00	£130
	a.	Perf 13 (1943)	42·00	25·00
	ab.	Broken "R"	£4750	£3000
131	**14**	£1 orange (P 13½×14) (16.3.38)	42·00	55·00
121/31 *Set of 14*			£180	£100
121s/31s Perf "SPECIMEN" *Set of 14*			£850	

The ½d., 1d. and both colours of the 2d. exist in coils constructed from normal sheets. These were originally joined vertically, but, because of technical problems, the 1d. and 2d. grey were subsequently issued in horizontal coils. The 2d. carmine only exists in the horizontal version.

Examples of Nos. 129/31 are known showing forged oval registered postmarks dated "6 OC 43", "18 OC 43", "3 MR 44" and "4 AU 44".

1946 (12 Oct). Victory. As Nos. 110/11 of Antigua.

132		½d. green	30	1·50
133		3d. ultramarine	50	1·25
132s/3s Perf "SPECIMEN" *Set of 2*			£160	

1948 (1 Dec). Royal Silver Wedding. As Nos. 112/13 of Antigua.

134		½d. green	1·50	3·00
135		£1 brown-orange	60·00	80·00

1949 (10 Oct). 75th Anniv of Universal Postal Union. As Nos. 114/17 of Antigua.

136		2d. carmine	1·00	1·25
137		3d. deep blue	2·00	3·00
138		6d. purple	1·50	2·00
139		1s. blue-green	1·50	5·00
136/9 *Set of 4*			5·50	8·75

No. 139 is known with the "A" of "CA" almost completely missing from the watermark.

NEW CONSTITUTION 1950

(23)

1950 (1 Aug). Inauguration of Legislative Council. Nos. 124c, 125ba, 126b and 127b optd as T **23**.

140	**16**	2d. carmine	30	1·50
141	–	3d. greenish blue	65	1·00
142	–	6d. carmine and grey-violet	75	2·00
	a.	Opt double	£1000	£1300
143	–	1s. black and green (R.)	75	2·00
	a.	Broken "R"	£130	
140/3 *Set of 4*			2·25	6·00

Four sheets of No. 142 received double overprints. On some examples the two impressions are almost coincident.

Stop before "2" in "½" in right-hand value tablet (Pl. 1A–5A, R. 4/4)

1953 (2 June). Coronation. As No. 120 of Antigua.

144		½d. black and bronze-green	75	2·25
	a.	Stop before "2" in "½"	15·00	

24 Cargo and Passenger Wharves   **25** South View from Straits

26 Gibraltar Fish Canneries   **27** Southport Gate

28 Sailing in the Bay   **29** *Saturnia* (liner)

30 Coaling wharf   **31** Airport

32 Europa Point   **33** Straits from Buena Vista

34 Rosia Bay and Straits   **35** Main Entrance, Government House

36 Tower of Homage, Moorish Castle   **37** Arms of Gibraltar

5d. Major re-entry causing doubling of "ALTA" in "GIBRALTAR" (R. 4/6)

1s. Re-entry causing doubling of lines of sea wall and buildings (R. 6/3-5)

(Des N. Cummings. Recess (except £1, centre litho) De La Rue)
1953 (19 Oct)–**59**. T **24/37**. Wmk Mult Script CA. P 13.

145	**24**	½d. indigo and grey-green	15	30
146	**25**	1d. bluish green	1·50	1·00
		a. Deep bluish green (31.12.57)	4·25	1·50
147	**26**	1½d. black	1·00	2·25
148	**27**	2d. deep olive-brown	3·00	1·00
		a. Sepia (18.6.58)	5·00	1·25
149	**28**	2½d. carmine	4·75	1·25
		a. Deep carmine (11.9.56)	8·00	1·50
		aw. Wmk inverted	£600	
150	**29**	3d. light blue	4·75	20
		a. Deep greenish blue (8.6.55)	11·00	55
		b. Greenish blue (18.6.58)	26·00	2·50
151	**30**	4d. ultramarine	7·00	3·50
		a. Blue (17.6.59)	35·00	13·00
152	**31**	5d. maroon	1·75	1·50
		a. Major re-entry	55·00	
		b. Deep maroon (31.12.57)	4·50	2·50
		ba. Major re-entry	£100	
153	**32**	6d. black and pale blue	7·50	2·00
		a. Black and blue (24.4.57)	9·50	3·00
		b. Black and grey-blue (17.6.59)	18·00	10·00
154	**33**	1s. pale blue and red-brown	1·25	2·00
		a. Re-entry	27·00	
		b. Pale blue and deep red-brown (27.3.56)	1·00	2·25
		ba. Re-entry	27·00	
155	**34**	2s. orange and reddish violet	50·00	15·00
		a. Orange and violet (17.6.59)	32·00	8·00
156	**35**	5s. deep brown	40·00	17·00
157	**36**	10s. reddish brown and ultramarine	45·00	45·00
158	**37**	£1 scarlet and orange-yellow	55·00	55·00
145/58 Set of 14			£180	£120

Nos. 145/6, 148 and 150 exist in coils, constructed from normal sheets.

1954 (10 May). Royal Visit. As No. 150 but inscr "ROYAL VISIT 1954" at top.

159		3d. greenish blue	1·00	20

38 Gibraltar Candytuft

39 Moorish Castle

40 St. George's Hall

41 The Keys

42 The Rock by moonlight

43 Catalan Bay

44 Map of Gibraltar **45** Air terminal

46 American War Memorial

47 Barbary Ape

48 Barbary Partridge

49 Blue Rock Thrush

50 Rock Lily (*Narcissus niveus*)

51 Rock and Badge of Gibraltar Regiment

1d. Retouch right of flag appears as an extra flag (Pl. 1B, R. 5/5)

1d. Jagged brown flaw in wall to right of gate appears as a crack (Pl. 1B, R. 2/5)

6d. Large white spot on map S.W. of "CEUTA" (Pl. 1B, R. 4/5)

(Des J. Celecia (½d. 2d., 2½d., 2s., 10s.), N. A. Langdon frames of ½d. to 10s. and 1d. 3d., 6d. 7d. 9d., 1s.), M. Bonilla (4d.), L. V. Gomez (5s.), Sgt. T. A. Griffiths (£1). Recess (£1) or photo (others) D.L.R.)
1960 (29 Oct)–**62**. Designs as T **38/51**. W w **12** (upright). P 14 (£1) or 13 (others).

160	**38**	½d. bright purple and emerald-green	15	50
161	**39**	1d. black and yellow-green	20	10
		a. Crack in wall	13·00	
		b. "Phantom flag"	13·00	
162	**40**	2d. indigo and orange-brown	1·00	20
163	**41**	2½d. black and blue	1·75	80
		a. Black and grey-blue (16.10.62)	1·75	30
164	**42**	3d. deep blue and red-orange	1·75	10
165	**43**	4d. deep red-brown and turquoise	2·75	70
166	**44**	6d. sepia and emerald	1·00	70
		a. White spot on map	26·00	
167	**45**	7d. indigo and carmine-red	2·50	1·75
168	**46**	9d. grey-blue and greenish blue	1·00	1·00
169	**47**	1s. sepia and bluish green	1·50	70
170	**48**	2s. chocolate and ultramarine	20·00	3·25
171	**49**	5s. turquoise-blue and olive-brown	8·00	9·50
172	**50**	10s. yellow and blue	27·00	25·00
173	**51**	£1 black and brown-orange	22·00	25·00
160/73 Set of 14			80·00	60·00

New plates were made for all values other than the £1, incorporating a finer screen (250 dots per inch, rather than the original 200), giving clearer, deeper, better-defined impressions. No. 163a comes from the later plate of the 2½d.
Nos. 160/2, 164 and 166 exist in coils, constructed from normal sheets.
See also No.199.
The 1d. imperforate comes from stolen printer's waste.

1963 (4 June). Freedom from Hunger. As No. 146 of Antigua.

174		9d. sepia	2·50	2·25

1963 (2 Sept). Red Cross Centenary. As Nos. 147/8 of Antigua.

175		1d. red and black	1·00	2·00
176		9d. red and blue	2·00	5·50

1964 (23 Apr). 400th Birth Anniv of William Shakespeare. As No. 164 of Antigua.

177		7d. bistre-brown	60	20

NEW CONSTITUTION 1964.
(52)

1964 (16 Oct). New Constitution. Nos. 164 and 166 optd with T **52**.

178		3d. deep blue and red-orange	20	10
179		6d. sepia and emerald	20	60
		a. No stop after "1964" (R. 2/5)	19·00	50·00
		b. White spot on map	19·00	50·00

1965 (17 May). ITU Centenary. As Nos. 166/7 of Antigua.

180		4d. light emerald and yellow	2·00	50
		w. Wmk inverted	38·00	
181		2s. apple-green and deep blue	5·50	4·75

1965 (25 Oct). International Co-operation Year. As Nos. 168/9 of Antigua.

182		½d. deep bluish green and lavender	20	2·75
183		4d. reddish purple and turquoise-green	80	50

The value of the ½d. stamp is shown as "1/2".

1966 (24 Jan). Churchill Commemoration. As Nos. 170/3 of Antigua. Printed in black, cerise and gold and with background in colours stated.

184		½d. new blue	20	2·25
		w. Wmk inverted	75·00	
185		1d. deep green	30	10
186		4d. brown	1·50	10
187		9d. bluish violet	1·25	2·50
184/7 Set of 4			3·00	4·50

1966 (1 July). World Cup Football Championship. As Nos. 176/7 of Antigua.

188		2½d. violet, yellow-green, lake and yellow and brown	75	2·25
189		6d. chocolate, blue-green, lake and yellow and brown	1·00	75

PRINTERS. All stamps from here to No. 239 were printed in photogravure by Harrison and Sons Ltd, London.

53 Red Seabream **4d.** Break at top right corner of "d" of value (R. 9/3).

(Des A. Ryman)
1966 (27 Aug). European Sea Angling Championships, Gibraltar. T **53** and similar designs. W w **12** (sideways on 1s.). P 13½×14(1s.) or 14×13½ (others).

190		4d. rosine, bright blue and black	30	10
		a. Broken "d"	6·00	
191		7d. rosine, deep olive-green and black	60	1·50
		a. Black (value and inscr) omitted	£1800	
		w. Wmk inverted	3·00	
192		1s. lake-brown, emerald and black	50	30
190/2 Set of 3			1·25	1·75

Designs: Horiz—7d. Red Scorpionfish. Vert—1s. Stone Bass.

1966 (20 Sept). Inauguration of WHO Headquarters, Geneva. As Nos. 178/9 of Antigua.

193		6d. black, yellow-green and light blue	3·00	1·50
194		9d. black, light purple and yellow-brown	3·50	4·50

56 "Our Lady of Europa"

(Des A. Ryman)
1966 (15 Nov). Centenary of Re-enthronement of "Our Lady of Europa". W w **12**. P 14×14½.

195	**56**	2s. bright blue and black	30	80

1966 (1 Dec). 20th Anniv of UNESCO. As Nos. 196/8 of Antigua.

196		2d. slate-violet, red, yellow and orange	60	10
197		7d. orange-yellow, violet and deep olive	2·25	10
198		5s. black, bright purple and orange	4·50	3·00
196/8 Set of 3			6·50	3·00

1966 (23 Dec). As No. 165 but wmk w **12** sideways.

199		4d. deep red-brown and turquoise	30	2·75

57 HMS *Victory*

½d. Gash in shape of boomerang in topsail (Pl. 1A, R. 8/4).

½d. Grey mark in topsail resembling a stain (Pl. 1A, R. 8/6).

7d. Bold shading on sail appearing as patch (Pl. 1A, R. 10/5).

(Des A. Ryman)

1967 (3 Apr)–**69**. Horiz designs as T **57**. Multicoloured. W w **12**. P 14×14½.

200	½d. Type **57**	10	20
	a. Grey (sails, etc) omitted	£800	
	b. Gash in sail	1·50	
	c. Stained sail	1·50	
201	1d. *Arab* (early steamer)	10	10
	w. Wmk inverted	3·25	4·50
202	2d. HMS *Carmania* (merchant cruiser)	15	10
	a. Grey-blue (hull) omitted	£8500	
203	2½d. *Mons Calpe* (ferry)	40	30
204	3d. *Canberra* (liner)	20	10
	w. Wmk inverted	42·00	9·00
205	4d. HMS *Hood* (battle cruiser)	1·25	10
	w. Wmk inverted		
205b	5d. *Mirror* (cable ship) (7.7.69)	2·00	55
	bw. Wmk inverted	†	£1500
206	6d. *Xebec* (sailing vessel)	30	50
207	7d. *Amerigo Vespucci* (Italian cadet ship)	30	1·50
	a. Patched sail	14·00	
	w. Wmk inverted	19·00	
208	9d. *Raffaello* (liner)	30	1·75
209	1s. *Royal Katherine* (galleon)	30	35
210	2s. HMS *Ark Royal* (aircraft carrier), 1937	4·50	3·50
211	5s. HMS *Dreadnought* (nuclear submarine)	3·50	7·00
212	10s. *Neuralia* (liner)	12·00	22·00
213	£1 *Mary Celeste* (sailing vessel)	12·00	22·00
200/13 *Set of 15*		32·00	50·00

No. 202a results from the misaligning of the grey-blue cylinder. The bottom horizontal row of the sheet involved has this colour completely omitted except for the example above the cylinder numbers which shows the grey-blue "1A" towards the top of the stamp.

The ½d., 1d., 2d. 3d. 6d. 2s. 5s. and £1 exist with PVA gum as well as gum arabic, but the 5d. exists with PVA gum only.

Nos. 201/2, 204/5 and 206 exist in coils constructed from normal sheets.

58 Aerial Ropeway

(Des A. Ryman)

1967 (15 June). International Tourist Year. T **58** and similar designs but horiz. Multicoloured. W w **12** (sideways on 7d.). P 14½×14 (7d.) or 14×14½ (others).

214	7d. Type **58**	15	10
215	9d. Shark fishing	15	10
216	1s. Skin-diving	20	15
214/16 *Set of 3*		45	30

59 Mary, Joseph and Child Jesus

60 Church Window

1967 (1 Nov). Christmas. W w **12** (sideways* on 6d.). P 14.

217	**59**	2d. multicoloured	15	10
		w. Wmk inverted	1·00	
218	**60**	6d. multicoloured	15	10
		w. Wmk Crown to right of CA	£475	

*The normal sideways watermark shows Crown to left of CA, *as seen from the back of the stamp*.

61 Gen. Eliott and Route Map

62 Eliott directing Rescue Operations

(Des A. Ryman)

1967 (11 Dec). 250th Birth Anniv of General Eliott. Multicoloured designs as T **61** (4d. to 1s.) or T **62**. W w **12** (sideways on horiz designs). P 14×15 (1s.) or 15×14 (others).

219	4d. Type **61**	15	10
220	9d. Heathfield Tower and Monument, Sussex (38×22 *mm*)	15	10
221	1s. General Eliott (22×38 *mm*)	15	10
222	2s. Type **62**	25	50
219/22 *Set of 4*		65	70

65 Lord Baden-Powell

(Des A. Ryman)

1968 (27 Mar). 60th Anniv of Gibraltar Scout Association. T **65** and similar horiz designs. W w **12**. P 14×14½.

223	4d. buff and bluish violet	15	10
224	7d. ochre and blue-green	20	20
225	9d. bright blue, yellow-orange and black	20	30
226	1s. greenish yellow and emerald	20	30
223/6 *Set of 4*		65	75

Designs:—7d. Scout Flag over the Rock; 9d. Tent, scouts and salute; 1s. Scout badges.

66 Nurse and WHO Emblem

68 King John signing *Magna Carta*

(Des A. Ryman)

1968 (1 July). 20th Anniv of World Health Organization. T **66** and similar horiz design. W w **12**. P 14×14½.

227	2d. ultramarine, black and yellow	10	15
228	4d. slate, black and pink	10	10

Design:—4d. Doctor and WHO emblem.

(Des A. Ryman)

1968 (26 Aug). Human Rights Year. T **68** and similar vert design. W w **12** (sideways). P 13½×14.

229	1s. yellow-orange, brown and gold	15	10
230	2s. myrtle and gold	15	90

Design:—2s. "Freedom" and Rock of Gibraltar.

70 Shepherd, Lamb and Star

72 Parliament Houses

(Des A. Ryman)

1968 (1 Nov). Christmas. T **70** and similar vert design. Multicoloured. W w **12**. P 14½×13½.

231	4d. Type **70**	10	10
	a. Gold (star) omitted	£850	£850
232	9d. Mary holding Holy Child	15	20

1969 (26 May). Commonwealth Parliamentary Association Conference. T **72** and similar designs. W w **12** (sideways on 2s.). P 14×14½ (2s.) or 14½×14 (others).

233	4d. green and gold	10	10
234	9d. bluish violet and gold	10	10
235	2s. multicoloured	15	20
233/5 *Set of 3*		30	30

Designs: Horiz—9d. Parliamentary emblem and outline of "The Rock". Vert—2s. Clock Tower, Westminster (Big Ben) and Arms of Gibraltar.

75 Silhouette of Rock, and Queen Elizabeth II

77 Soldier and Cap Badge, Royal Anglian Regiment, 1969

(Des A. Ryman)

1969 (30 July). New Constitution. W w **12**. P 14×13½ (in addition, the outline of the Rock is perforated).

236	**75**	½d. gold and orange	10	10
237		5d. silver and bright green	20	10
		a. Portrait and inscr in gold and silver*		
238		7d. silver and bright purple	20	10
239		5s. gold and ultramarine	65	1·10
236/9 *Set of 4*			1·00	1·25

*No. 237a was first printed with the head and inscription in gold and then in silver but displaced slightly to lower left.

(Des A. Ryman. Photo D.L.R.)

1969 (6 Nov). Military Uniforms (1st series). T **77** and similar vert designs. Multicoloured. W w **12**. P 14.

240	1d. Royal Artillery officer, 1758 and modern cap badge	15	10
241	6d. Type **77**	20	15
242	9d. Royal Engineers' Artificer, 1786 and modern cap badge	30	15
243	2s. Private, Fox's Marines, 1704 and modern Royal Marines cap badge	75	90
240/3 *Set of 4*		1·25	1·25

Nos. 240/3 have a short history of the Regiment printed on the reverse side over the gum, therefore, once the gum is moistened the history disappears.

See also Nos. 248/51.

 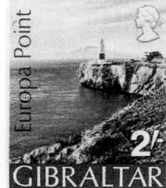

80 *Madonna of the Chair* (detail, Raphael)

83 Europa Point

(Des A. Ryman. Photo Enschedé)

1969 (1 Dec). Christmas. T **80** and similar vert designs. Multicoloured. W w **12** (sideways). P 14×Roulette 9.

244	5d. Type **80**	10	35
	a. Strip of 3. Nos. 244/6	45	1·00
245	7d. *Virgin and Child* (detail, Morales)	20	35
246	1s. *The Virgin of the Rocks* (detail, Leonardo da Vinci)	20	40
244/6 *Set of 3*		45	1·00

Nos. 244/6 were issued together in *se-tenant* strips of three throughout the sheet.

(Des A. Ryman. Photo Enschedé)

1970 (8 June). Europa Point. W w **12**. P 13½.

247	**83**	2s. multicoloured	45	1·25
		w. Wmk inverted	2·00	3·00

(Des A. Ryman. Photo D.L.R.)

1970 (28 Aug). Military Uniforms (2nd series). Vert designs as T **77**. Multicoloured. W w **12**. P 14.

248	2d. Royal Scots officer, 1839 and cap badge	25	10
249	5d. South Wales Borderers private, 1763 and cap badge	35	10
250	7d. Queens Royal Regiment private, 1742 and cap badge	35	10
251	2s. Royal Irish Rangers piper, 1969 and cap badge	1·00	90
248/51 *Set of 4*		1·75	1·00

Nos. 248/51 have a short history of the Regiment printed on the reverse side under the gum.

88 No. 191a and Rock of Gibraltar

(Des A. Ryman. Litho D.L.R.)

1970 (18 Sept). Philympia 1970 Stamp Exhibition, London. T **88** and similar horiz design. W w **12** (sideways). P 13.
252	1s. vermilion and bronze-green..............	15	10
253	2s. bright blue and magenta....................	25	65

Design:—2s. Victorian stamp (No. 23b) and Moorish Castle.
The stamps shown in the designs are well-known varieties with values omitted.

90 *The Virgin Mary* (stained-glass window by Gabriel Loire)

(Photo Enschedé)

1970 (1 Dec). Christmas. W w **12**. P 13×14.
254	**90**	2s. multicoloured	30	1·00

STAMP BOOKLETS

1906 (Oct). Black on red cover. Stapled.
SB1 2s.0½d. booklet containing 24×½d. and 12×1d.
(Nos. 56a, 67) in blocks of 6 ....

1912 (17 July). Black on red cover. Stapled.
SB2 2s.0½d. booklet containing 24×½d. and 12×1d.
(Nos. 76/7) in blocks of 6.. £7500

POSTAGE DUE STAMPS

D 1

Normal   Large "d."
(R. 9/6, 10/6)

4d. Ball of "d" broken and serif at top damaged (R. 9/5). Other stamps in 5th vertical row show slight breaks to ball of "d".

(Typo D.L.R.)

1956 (1 Dec). Chalk-surfaced paper. Wmk Mult Script CA. P 14.
D1	D **1**	1d. green..	1·50	4·25
D2		2d. sepia.......................................	2·00	2·75
		a. Large "d" (R. 9/6, 10/6)	28·00	40·00
D3		4d. blue...	1·75	5·00
		a. Broken "d"	40·00	
D1/3	*Set of 3*		4·75	11·00

Gilbert and Ellice Islands

No organised postal service existed in the Gilbert and Ellice Islands before the introduction of stamp issues in January 1911. A New Zealand Postal Agency was, however, provided on Fanning Island, one of the Line Islands, primarily for the use of the staff of the Pacific Cable Board cable station which was established in 1902. The agency opened on 29 November 1902 and although Fanning Island became part of the Gilbert and Ellice Islands colony on 27 January 1916, continued to operate until replaced by a Protectorate post office on 14 February 1939. The cable station closed on 16 January 1964. Fanning Island is now known as Tabuaeran.

Z 1

The following NEW ZEALAND stamps are known postmarked on Fanning Island with Type Z **1** (in use from November 1902 until November 1936. The earliest known cover is postmarked 20 December 1902).

1882–1900 Q.V. (P 10) ½d. (*No.* 217) (P 11) ½d., 1d., 2d. (*Nos.* 236/8)
1898 Pictorials (*no wmk*) 1d., 2d., 2½d. (*Nos.* 247/8, 260)
1900 Pictorials (*W* **38**) ½d. 1½d., 2d. (*Nos.* 273, 275b, 276)
1901 1d. "Universal" (*W* **38**) (*Nos.* 278, 280)
1902 ½d. Mt. Cook, 1d. "Universal" (*no wmk*) (*Nos.* 294/5)
1902 ½d. Pictorial, 1d. "Universal" (*W* **43**) (*Nos.* 302b, 303)
1902–09 Pictorials (*W* **43**) 2d., 2½d., 3d., 5d., 6d., 8d., 9d., 1s., 2s., 5s. (*Nos.* 309, 312/7, 319/20, 322, 326, 328/9)
1907–08 Pictorials (*W* **43**) 4d. (*No.* 379)
1908 1d. "Universal" (*De La Rue paper*) 1d. (*No.* 386)
1909–12 King Edward VII (*typo*) ½d. (*No.* 387)
1909–16 King Edward VII (*recess*) 2d., 3d., 4d., 5d., 6d., 8d., 1s. (*Nos.* 388/91, 393/6, 397/8)
1909–26 1d. "Universal" (*W* **43**) 1d. (*Nos.* 405, 410)
1915–30 King George V (*recess*) 1½d., 2d. bright violet, 2½d., 3d., 4d. bright violet, 4½d., 5d., 6d., 7½d., 9d., 1s. (*Nos.* 416/17, 419/20, 422/6, 429/30)
1915–34 King George V (*typo*) ½d., 1½d. (all 3), 2d., 3d. (*Nos.* 435/40, 446, 448/b, 449/b)
1915 "WAR STAMP" opt ½d. (*No.* 452)
1920 Victory 1d., 1½d. (*Nos.* 454/5)
1922 2d. on ½d. (*No.* 459)
1923–25 Penny Postage 1d. (*No.* 460)
1926–34 Admiral design 1d. (*No.* 468)
1935–36 Pictorials ½d., 1d., 1½d., 2d., 4d., 8d., 1s. (*Nos.* 556, 557/b, 558, 559, 562, 565, 567)
1935 Silver Jubilee ½d., 1d., 6d. (*Nos.* 573/5)
1936 Anzac ½d. + ½d., 1d. + 1d. (*Nos.* 591/2)
1899 1d. Postage due (D10)

Z 2

The following NEW ZEALAND stamps are known postmarked on Fanning Island with Type Z **2** (in use from 7 December 1936 to 13 February 1939):

1935–36 Pictorials (*W* **43**) 1d (*No.* 557)
1936–39 Pictorials (*W* **98**) ½d., 1d., 1½d. (*Nos.* 577/9)
1936 Chambers of Commerce Congress ½d. (*No.* 593)
1936 Health 1d.+1d. (*No.* 598)
1937 Coronation 1d., 2½d., 6d. (*Nos.* 599/601)
1938–39 King George VI ½d., 1d., 1½d. (*Nos.* 603, 605, 607)

The schooner which carried the mail from Fanning Island also called at Washington Island, another of the Line group. Problems arose, however, as the authorities insisted that mail from Washington must first pass through the Fanning Island Postal Agency before being forwarded which resulted in considerable delays. Matters were resolved by the opening of a New Zealand Postal Agency on Washington Island which operated from 1 February 1921 until the copra plantations were closed in early 1923. The postal agency was re-established on 15 May 1924, but finally closed on 30 March 1934. Covers from this second period occur with incorrectly dated postmarks. Manuscript markings on New Zealand Nos. 578, 599/600 and 692 are unofficial and were applied during the resettlement of the island between 1937 and 1948. Washington Island is now known as Teraina.

Z 3

The following NEW ZEALAND stamps are known postmarked on Washington Island with Type Z **3**:

1909–16 King Edward VII 5d., 8d. (*Nos.* 402, 404b)
1915–30 King George V (*recess*) 6d., 7½d., 8d., 9d., 1s. (*Nos.* 425/7, 429/30)
1915–34 King George V (*typo*) ½d., 1½d., 2d., 3d. (*Nos.* 435, 438/9, 449)
1915 "WAR STAMP" opt ½d. (*No.* 452)
1920 Victory 1d., 1½d., 6d. (*Nos.* 454/5, 457)
1922 2d. on ½d. (*No.* 459)
1926–34 Admiral design 1d. (*No.* 468/a)

The above information is based on a special survey undertaken by members of the Kiribati & Tuvalu Philatelic Society and the Pacific Islands Study Circle, co-ordinated by Mr. Michael Shaw.

PRICES FOR STAMPS ON COVER TO 1945		
Nos. 1/7	*from* × 5	
Nos. 8/11	*from* × 10	
Nos. 12/23	*from* × 6	
No. 24	—	
No. 26	*from* × 15	
Nos. 27/30	*from* × 6	
No. 35	—	
Nos. 36/9	*from* × 4	
Nos. 40/2	*from* × 12	
Nos. 43/54	*from* × 4	
Nos. D1/8	*from* × 5	

BRITISH PROTECTORATE

GILBERT & ELLICE

PROTECTORATE

(1)

2 Pandanus Pine

1911 (1 Jan). Stamps of Fiji optd with T **1**. Wmk Mult Crown CA. Chalk-surfaced paper (5d. to 1s.).
1	**23**	½d. green............................	5·50	50·00
2		1d. red...............................	50·00	28·00
3	**24**	2d. grey..............................	22·00	15·00
4	**23**	2½d. ultramarine	18·00	50·00
5		5d. purple and olive-green	65·00	95·00
6	**24**	6d. dull and bright purple	25·00	50·00
7	**23**	1s. black/*green* (R.)...........	26·00	75·00
1/7	*Set of 7*		£180	£325
1s/7s	Optd "SPECIMEN" *Set of 7*			£300

The 2d. to 6d. are on special printings which were not issued without overprint.
Examples of Nos. 1/7 are known showing a forged Ocean Island postmark dated "JY 15 11".

(Recess D.L.R.)

1911 (Mar). Wmk Mult Crown CA. P 14.
8	**2**	½d. green............................	4·75	25·00
9		1d. carmine.......................	2·00	12·00
		w. Wmk inverted	£650	
10		2d. grey..............................	1·50	7·00
11		2½d. blue	12·00	16·00
8/11	*Set of 4*..		18·00	55·00
8s/11s	Optd "SPECIMEN" *Set of 4*..................			£180

3

WAR TAX

(5)

(Typo D.L.R.)

1912 (May)–**24**. Die I (½d. to 5s.) or Die II (£1). Wmk Mult Crown CA. Chalk-surfaced paper (3d. to £1). P 14.
12	**3**	½d. green (7.12)	50	5·00
		a. *Yellow-green* (1914)	5·00	14·00
13		1d. carmine (12.12)	2·25	16·00
		a. *Scarlet* (1915)...............	3·75	14·00
14		2d. greyish slate (1.16)	15·00	26·00
15		2½d. bright blue (1.16)..........	3·00	11·00
16		3d. purple/*yellow* (1918) ...	2·50	14·00
17		4d. black and red/*yellow* (10.12)	75	4·50
18		5d. dull purple and sage-green	1·75	5·50
19		6d. dull and bright purple....	1·25	6·50
20		1s. black/*green*	1·25	4·00
21		2s. purple and blue/*blue* (10.12)	15·00	35·00
22		2s.6d. black and red/*blue* (10.12)	22·00	25·00
23		5s. green and red/*yellow* (10.12)	32·00	65·00
24		£1 purple and black/*red* (Die II) (3.24)	£550	£1600
12/24	*Set of 13*		£600	£1600
12s/24s	Optd "SPECIMEN" *Set of 13*			£600

THE FUNAFUTI PROVISIONALS. In July 1916, during a shortage of stamps at the post office in Funafuti, a number of parcels were presented for despatch. The District Officer, who also acted as Postmaster, surcharged 1d. and 2½d. stamps by handstamping to meet the need for higher values, without first seeking authorisation from the Resident Commissioner on Ocean Island (a process which would have taken several weeks). Opinion as to the legitimacy of the provisionals has varied, but it seems that they were produced to meet a short-term need and there is no evidence that they were created for financial gain. The stamps concerned are the 1d. (No. 13), surcharged "2/-" (twice) in black and the 2½d. blue (No. 11) surcharged "2/-" in red and "3/-", also in red.

CROWN COLONY

1918 (June). Optd with T **5**.
26	**3**	1d. red...............................	50	6·50
		s. Optd "SPECIMEN"........................	70·00	

1922–27. Die II. Wmk Mult Script CA. Chalk-surfaced paper (10s.). P 14.

27	3	½d. green (1923)	4·00	3·25
28		1d. violet (1927)	4·75	9·00
29		1½d. scarlet (1924)	8·50	3·50
30		2d. slate-grey	7·50	45·00
35		10s. green and red/emerald (3.24)	£160	£375
27s/35s Optd "SPECIMEN" Set of 5				£275

Examples of most values between Nos. 12 and 35 are known showing part strikes of the forged postmark mentioned below Nos. 1/7. Collectors should exercise particular caution when buying used examples of Nos. 24 and 35.

1935 (6 May). Silver Jubilee. As Nos. 91/4 of Antigua, but ptd by B.W. P 11×12.

36		1d. ultramarine and grey-black	2·25	17·00
	c.	Lightning conductor	£2000	
	d.	Flagstaff on right-hand turret	£250	£450
	e.	Double flagstaff	£475	£500
37		1½d. deep blue and scarlet	1·75	4·00
	d.	Flagstaff on right-hand turret	£250	
	e.	Double flagstaff	£475	
38		3d. brown and deep blue	6·50	26·00
	d.	Flagstaff on right-hand turret	£375	£600
	e.	Double flagstaff	£450	£650
39		1s. slate and purple	26·00	20·00
	d.	Flagstaff on right-hand turret	£600	£600
	e.	Double flagstaff	£600	£650
36/9 Set of 4			32·00	60·00
36s/9s Perf "SPECIMEN" Set of 4			£200	

For illustrations of plate varieties see Omnibus section following Zanzibar.

1937 (12 May). Coronation. As Nos. 95/7 of Antigua, but ptd by D.L.R. P 14.

40		1d. violet	35	65
41		1½d. scarlet	35	65
42		3d. bright blue	40	70
40/2 Set of 3			1·00	1·75
40s/2s Perf "SPECIMEN" Set of 3			£170	

6 Great Frigate Bird

7 Pandanus Pine

8 Canoe crossing Reef

9 Canoe and boat-house

10 Native house

11 Seascape

12 Ellice Islands canoe

13 Coconut palms

14 Cantilever jetty, Ocean Island

15 HMCS *Nimanoa*

16 Gilbert Islands canoe

17 Coat of arms

(Recess B.W. (½d., 2d., 2s.6d.), Waterlow (1d., 5d., 6d., 2s., 5s.), D.L.R. (1½d., 2½d., 3d., 1s.))

1939 (14 Jan)**–55.** T **6/17.** Wmk Mult Script CA (sideways on ½d., 2d. and 2s.6d.). P 11½×11 (½d., 2d., 2s.6d.), 12½ (1d., 5d., 6d., 2s., 5s.) or 13½ (1½d., 2½d., 3d., 1s.).

43	6	½d. indigo and deep bluish green	60	1·00
	a.	"A" of "CA" missing from wmk	£2000	
44	7	1d. emerald and plum	30	1·50
45	8	1½d. brownish black and bright carmine	30	1·25
46	9	2d. red-brown and grey-black	1·25	1·00
47	10	2½d. brownish black and deep olive	1·00	1·00
	a.	Brownish black and olive-green (12.5.43)	9·00	7·50
48	11	3d. brownish black and ultramarine	60	1·00
	a.	Perf 12. Black and bright blue (24.8.55)	1·50	4·00
49	12	5d. deep ultramarine and sepia	7·00	2·75
	a.	Ultramarine and sepia (12.5.43)	18·00	24·00
	b.	Ultramarine and blackish brown (20.10.44)	12·00	9·00
50	13	6d. olive-green and deep violet	70	60

51	14	1s. brownish black and turquoise-green	38·00	3·75
	a.	Brownish black and greenish-blue (12.5.43)	20·00	5·50
	ab.	Perf 12 (8.5.51)	4·50	20·00
52	15	2s. deep ultramarine and orange-red	10·00	11·00
53	16	2s.6d. deep blue and emerald	10·00	11·00
54	17	5s. deep rose-red and royal blue	13·00	16·00
43/54 Set of 12			42·00	45·00
43s/54s Perf "SPECIMEN" Set of 12			£600	

1946 (16 Dec). Victory. As Nos. 110/11 of Antigua.

55		1d. purple	15	65
56		3d. blue	15	65
55s/6s Perf "SPECIMEN" Set of 2			£140	

1949 (29 Aug). Royal Silver Wedding. As Nos. 112/13 of Antigua.

57		1d. violet	50	1·50
58		£1 scarlet	16·00	25·00

1949 (10 Oct). 75th Anniv of UPU As Nos. 114/17 of Antigua.

59		1d. purple	50	2·75
60		2d. grey-black	2·50	4·50
61		3d. deep blue	1·00	4·50
62		1s. blue	75	2·75
59/62 Set of 4			4·25	13·00

1953 (2 June). Coronation. As No. 120 of Antigua.

63		2d. black and grey-black	1·50	2·25

18 Great Frigate Bird

½d. Short line along top of "Y" in "PENNY" (Pl. 1, R. 10/1)

(Recess B.W. (½d., 2d., 2s.6d.), Waterlow (1d., 5d., 6d., 2s., 5s.), D.L.R. (2½d., 3d., 1s., 10s. and after 1962, 1d., 5d.))

1956 (1 Aug)**–62.** Designs previously used for King George VI issue; but with portrait of Queen Elizabeth II as in T **18.** Wmk Mult Script CA. P 11½×11 (½d., 2d., 2s.6d.), 12½ (1d., 5d., 6d., 2s., 5s.) or 12 (2½d., 3d., 1s., 10s.).

64	18	½d. black and deep bright blue	65	1·25
	a.	"Y" flaw	23·00	
65	7	1d. brown-olive and deep violet	60	1·25
66	9	2d. bluish green and deep purple	3·25	2·50
	a.	Bluish green and purple (30.7.62)	38·00	38·00
67	10	2½d. black and myrtle-green	50	60
68	11	3d. black and carmine-red	50	60
69	12	5d. ultramarine and red-orange	9·50	4·00
	a.	Ultramarine and brown-orange (D.L.R.) (30.7.62)	25·00	45·00
70	13	6d. chestnut and black-brown	70	2·75
71	14	1s. black and bronze-green	5·00	1·50
72	15	2s. deep bright blue and sepia	8·50	4·00
73	16	2s.6d. scarlet and deep blue	7·00	4·25
74	17	5s. greenish blue and bluish green	7·00	5·00
75	8	10s. black and turquoise	38·00	8·50
64/75 Set of 12			70·00	32·00

See also Nos. 85/6.

19 Loading Phosphate from Cantilever

(Des R. Turrell (2d.), M. Thoma (2½d), M. A. W. Hook and A. Larkins (1s.). Photo D.L.R.)

1960 (1 May). Diamond Jubilee of Phosphate Discovery at Ocean Island. T **19** and similar horiz designs. W w **12**. P 12.

76		2d. green and carmine-rose	1·00	85
77		2½d. black and olive-green	1·00	85
78		1s. black and deep turquoise	1·00	85
76/8 Set of 3			2·75	2·40

Designs:—2½d. Phosphate rock; 1s. Phosphate mining.

1963 (1 Aug). Freedom from Hunger. As No. 146 of Antigua.

79		10d. ultramarine	75	30

1963 (5 Oct). Red Cross Centenary. As Nos. 147/8 of Antigua.

80		2d. red and black	50	1·00
81		10d. red and blue	75	2·50

22 de Havilland DH.114 Heron 2 and Route Map

24 de Havilland DH.114 Heron 2 over Tarawa Lagoon

23 Eastern Reef Heron in Flight

(Des Margaret Barwick. Litho Enschedé)

1964 (20 July). First Air Service. W w **12** (sideways* on 3d., 3s.7d.). P 11×11½ (1s.) or 11½×11 (others).

82	22	3d. blue, black and light blue	70	30
		w. Wmk Crown to right of CA	70	30
83	23	1s. light blue, black and deep blue	1·25	30
84	24	3s.7d. deep green, black and light emerald	1·75	1·50
82/4 Set of 3			3·25	1·90

*The normal sideways watermark shows Crown to left of CA, *as seen from the back of the stamp.*

(Recess B.W. (2d.), D.L.R. (6d.))

1964 (30 Oct)**–65.** As Nos. 66a and 70 but wmk w **12.**

85	9	2d. bluish green and purple	1·00	1·25
86	13	6d. chestnut and black-brown (26.4.65)*	1·25	1·25

*Earliest known postmark date.

1965 (4 June). ITU Centenary. As Nos. 166/7 of Antigua.

87		3d. red-orange and deep bluish green	15	10
88		2s.6d. turquoise-blue and light purple	45	20

25 Maneaba and Gilbertese Man blowing Bu Shell

26 Gilbertese Women's Dance

(Des V. Whiteley from drawings by Margaret Barwick. Litho B.W.)

1965 (16 Aug). Vert designs as T **25** (½d. to 2s.) or horiz designs as T **26** (3s.7d. to £1). Centres multicoloured. W w **12**. P 12×11 (½d. to 2s.) or 11×12 (3s.7d. to £1).

89		½d. turquoise-green	10	10
90		1d. deep violet-blue	10	10
91		2d. bistre	10	10
92		3d. rose-red	10	10
93		4d. purple	15	10
94		5d. cerise	20	10
95		6d. turquoise-blue	20	10
96		7d. bistre-brown	25	10
97		1s. bluish violet	1·00	10
98		1s.6d. lemon	1·00	1·00
99		2s. yellow-olive	1·00	1·40
100		3s.7d. new blue	1·75	65
101		5s. light yellow-olive	1·75	80
102		10s. dull green	2·75	1·00
103		£1 light turquoise-blue	3·50	1·75
89/103 Set of 15			12·00	6·00

Designs:—1d. Ellice Islanders reef fishing by flare; 2d. Gilbertese girl weaving head garland; 3d. Gilbertese woman performing Ruoia; 4d. Gilbertese man performing Kamei; 5d. Gilbertese girl drawing water; 6d. Ellice islander performing a Fatele; 7d. Ellice youths performing spear dance; 1s. Gilbertese girl tending Ikaroa Babai plant; 1s.6d. Ellice islanders dancing a Fatele; 2s. Ellice islanders pounding Pulaka; 5s. Gilbertese boys playing stick game; 10s. Ellice youths beating the box for the Fatele; £1 Coat of Arms.

1965 (25 Oct). International Co-operation Year. As Nos. 168/9 of Antigua.

104		½d. reddish purple and turquoise-green	10	10
105		3s.7d. deep bluish green and lavender	50	20

1966 (24 Jan). Churchill Commemoration. As Nos. 170/3 of Antigua.

106		½d. new blue	10	10
107		3d. deep green	20	10
108		3s. brown	40	35
109		3s.7d. bluish violet	45	35
106/9 Set of 4			1·00	75

(New Currency, 100 cents = 1 Australian dollar)

 2^c

(40)

1966 (14 Feb). Decimal currency. Nos. 89/103 surch as T **40**.

110		1c. on 1d. deep violet-blue	10	10
111		2c. on 2d. bistre	10	10
112		3c. on 3d. rose-red	10	10
113		4c. on ½d. turquoise-green	10	10
114		5c. on 6d. turquoise-blue	15	10
115		6c. on 4d. purple	15	10
116		8c. on 5d. cerise	15	10
117		10c. on 1s. bluish violet	15	10
118		15c. on 7d. bistre-brown	60	1·00
119		20c. on 1s.6d. lemon	30	25
120		25c. on 2s. yellow-olive	30	20
121		35c. on 3s.7d. new blue	1·00	20
122		50c. on 5s. light yellow-olive	55	35
123		$1 on 10s. dull green	55	40
124		$2 on £1 light turquoise-blue	2·50	3·25
110/24 Set of 15			6·00	5·50

1966 (1 July). World Cup Football Championship. As Nos. 176/7 of Antigua.

125		3c. violet, yellow-green, lake and yellow-brown	20	10
126		35c. chocolate, blue-green, lake and yellow-brown	80	20

1966 (20 Sept). Inauguration of WHO Headquarters, Geneva. As Nos. 178/9 of Antigua.

127		3c. black, yellow-green and light blue	20	10
128		12c. black, light purple and yellow-brown	45	40

1966 (1 Dec). 20th Anniv of UNESCO. As Nos. 196/8 of Antigua.

129		5c. slate-violet, red, yellow and orange	25	90

130		10c. orange-yellow, violet and deep olive	35	20
131		20c. black, bright purple and orange	60	1·40
129/31 *Set of 3*			1·10	2·25

41 HMS *Royalist*

(Des V. Whiteley. Photo Harrison)

1967 (1 Sept). 75th Anniv of the Protectorate. T **41** and similar horiz designs. W w **12**. P 14½.

132		3c. red, blue and myrtle-green	30	50
133		10c. multicoloured	15	15
134		35c. sepia, orange-yellow and deep bluish green	30	50
132/4 *Set of 3*			65	1·00

Designs:—10c. Trading Post; 35c. Island family.

44 Gilbertese Women's Dance

1968 (1 Jan). Decimal Currency. Designs as Nos. 89/103 but with values inscr in decimal currency as T **44**. W w **12** (sideways on horiz designs). P 12×11 (vert) or 11×12 (horiz).

135		1c. deep violet-blue (as 1d.)	10	15
136		2c. bistre (as 2d.)	15	10
137		3c. rose-red (as 3d.)	15	10
138		4c. turquoise-green (as ½d.)	15	10
139		5c. turquoise-blue (as 6d.)	15	10
140		6c. purple (as 4d.)	20	10
141		8c. cerise (as 5d.)	20	10
142		10c. bluish violet (as 1s.)	20	10
143		15c. bistre-brown (as 7d.)	50	20
144		20c. lemon (as 1s.6d.)	65	15
		w. Wmk inverted	9·00	15·00
145		25c. yellow-olive (as 2s.)	1·25	20
146		35c. new blue	1·50	20
147		50c. light yellow-olive (as 5s.)	1·50	2·50
148		$1 dull green (as 10s.)	1·50	3·75
149		$2 light turquoise-blue (as £1)	5·50	6·00
135/49 *Set of 15*			12·00	12·00

45 Map of Tarawa Atoll

(Des V. Whiteley. Photo D.L.R.)

1968 (21 Nov). 25th Anniv of the Battle of Tarawa. T **45** and similar designs. Multicoloured. W w **12** (sideways). P 14.

150		3c. Type **45**	20	30
151		10c. Marines landing	20	20
152		15c. Beach-head assault	20	35
153		35c. Raising US and British flags	25	50
150/3 *Set of 4*			75	1·25

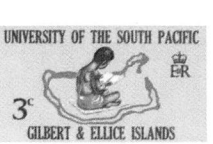

46 Young Pupil against outline of Abemama Island

47 *Virgin and Child* in Pacific Setting

(Des J.W. (from original designs by Mrs V. J. Anderson and Miss A. Loveridge) Litho D.L.R.)

1969 (2 June). End of Inaugural Year of South Pacific University. T **46** and similar horiz designs. W w **12** (sideways). P 12½.

154		3c. multicoloured	10	25
155		10c. multicoloured	10	10
156		35c. black, brown and grey-green	15	30
154/6 *Set of 3*			30	55

Designs:—10c. Boy and girl students and Tarawa atoll; 35c. University graduate and South Pacific islands.

(Des Jennifer Toombs. Litho B.W.)

1969 (20 Oct). Christmas. W w **12** (sideways). P 11½.

157		2c. olive-green and multicoloured *(shades)*	15	20
158	**47**	10c. olive-green and multicoloured *(shades)*	15	10

Design:—2c. As T **47** but foreground has grass instead of sand.

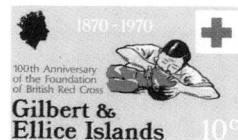

48 "The Kiss of Life"

(Des Manate Tenang Manate. Litho J.W.)

1970 (9 Mar*). Centenary of British Red Cross. W w **12** (sideways). P 14.

159	**48**	10c. multicoloured	20	10
160	–	15c. multicoloured	30	45
161	–	35c. multicoloured	60	90
159/61 *Set of 3*			1·00	1·25

Nos. 160/1 are as T **48**, but arranged differently.
*The above were released by the Crown Agents on 2 March, but not sold locally until the 9 March.

49 Foetus and Patients

(Des Jennifer Toombs. Litho Enschedé)

1970 (26 June). 25th Anniv of United Nations. T **49** and similar horiz designs. W w **12** (sideways). P 12½×13.

162		5c. multicoloured	15	30
163		10c. black, grey and red	15	15
164		15c. multicoloured	20	30
165		35c. new blue, black and turquoise-green	30	45
162/5 *Set of 4*			70	1·10

Designs:—10c. Nurse and surgical instruments; 15c. X-ray plate and technician; 35c. UN emblem and map.

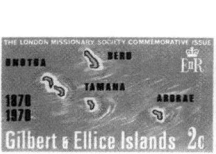

53 Map of Gilbert Islands

57 *Child with Halo* (T. Collis)

(Des G. Vasarhelyi. Litho Harrison)

1970 (1 Sept). Centenary of Landing in Gilbert Islands by London Missionary Society. T **53** and similar designs. W w **12** (sideways on vert designs). P 14½×14 (2c., 35c.) or 14×14½ (others).

166		2c. multicoloured	40	1·10
		w. Wmk inverted		
167		10c. black and pale green	50	15
168		25c. chestnut and cobalt	25	25
169		35c. turquoise-blue, black and red	60	70
166/9 *Set of 4*			1·60	2·00

Designs: Vert—10c. Sailing-ship *John Williams III*; 25c. Rev. S. J. Whitmee. Horiz—35c. M V *John Williams VII*.

(Des L. Curtis. Litho Format)

1970 (3 Oct). Christmas. Sketches. T **57** and similar vert designs. Multicoloured. W w **12**. P 14½.

170		2c. Type **57**	10	60
171		10c. Sanctuary, Tarawa Cathedral (Mrs. A. Burroughs)	10	10
172		35c. *Three ships inside star* (Mrs. C. Barnett)	20	20
170/2 *Set of 3*			35	80

POSTAGE DUE STAMPS

D 1

(Typo B.W.)

1940 (Aug). Wmk Mult Script CA. P 12.

D1	**D 1**	1d. emerald-green	13·00	25·00
D2		2d. scarlet	14·00	25·00
D3		3d. brown	18·00	26·00
D4		4d. blue	20·00	35·00
D5		5d. grey-green	25·00	35·00
D6		6d. purple	25·00	35·00
D7		1s. violet	27·00	48·00
D8		1s.6d. turquoise-green	55·00	90·00
D1/8 *Set of 8*			£180	£275
D1s/8s Perf "SPECIMEN" *Set of 8*			£250	

Examples of all values are known showing a forged Post Office Ocean Island postmark dated "16 DE 46".

Gold Coast

Gold Coast originally consisted of coastal forts, owned by the Royal African Company, trading with the interior. In 1821, due to raids by the Ashanti king, the British Government took over the forts, together with some of the hinterland, and the Gold Coast was placed under the Governor of Sierra Leone.

The administration was handed back to a mercantile company in 1828, but the forts returned to British Government rule in 1843. The colony was reconstituted by Royal Charter on 24 July 1874, and at that time also included the settlement at Lagos which became a separate colony in January 1886.

Following the end of the final Ashanti War the whole of the territory was annexed in September 1901.

A postal service was established at Cape Coast Castle in 1853. There is no record of British stamps being officially issued in the Colony before 1875, apart from those used on board the ships of the West African Squadron, but examples do, however, exist cancelled by Gold Coast postmarks.

CROWN COLONY

PRICES FOR STAMPS ON COVER TO 1945	
Nos. 1/3	*from* × 125
Nos. 4/8	*from* × 40
Nos. 9/10	*from* × 15
Nos. 11/20	*from* × 30
Nos. 22/5	—
Nos. 26/34	*from* × 10
Nos. 35/6	*from* × 20
Nos. 38/69	*from* × 6
Nos. 70/98	*from* × 3
Nos. 100/2	—
Nos. 103/12	*from* × 5
Nos. 113/16	*from* × 3
Nos. 117/19	*from* × 4
Nos. 120/32	*from* × 3
No. D1	*from* × 6
No. D2	*from* × 20
Nos. D3/4	*from* × 12

1   **(2)**

(Typo D.L.R.)

1875 (1 July)–76. Wmk Crown CC. P 12½.

1	**1**	1d. blue	£550	95·00
		a. Bisected (½d.) (on cover) (1876)	†	—
2		4d. magenta	£475	£150
3		6d. orange	£750	80·00

1876–84. Wmk Crown CC. P 14.

4	**1**	½d. olive-yellow (1879)	95·00	42·00
		w. Wmk inverted	£475	
5		1d. blue	42·00	6·50
		a. Bisected (½d.) (on cover) (1877-78 and 1882-84)	†	£4500
		w. Wmk inverted	£700	£250
6		2d. green (1879)	£140	9·00
		a. Bisected (1d.) (on cover) (1882-84)	†	£4250
		b. Quartered (½d.) (on cover) (1884)	†	£7500
7		4d. magenta	£275	6·00
		a. Bisected (2d.) (on cover) (1884).	†	£8000
		b. Quartered (1d.) (on cover) (1884)..	†	£10000
		c. Tri-quadrisected (3d.) (on cover) (1884)	†	—
		w. Wmk inverted	£1200	£375
8		6d. orange	£325	28·00
		a. Bisected (3d.) (on cover) (1884).	†	£10000
		b. Sixth (1d.) (on cover) (1884)	†	£13000

In the period 1882-84 some values were in short supply and the use of bisects and other divided stamps is known as follows:

No. 5a. Used as part of 2½d. rate from Accra, Addah and Quittah
No. 6a. Used as 1d. rate from Addah, Cape Coast Castle, Elmina, Quittah, Salt Pond, Secondee and Winnebah
No. 6b. Used as part of 2½d. rate from Cape Coast Castle
No. 7a. Used as 2d. or as part of 2½d. rate from Quittah
No. 7b. Used as 1d. rate from Appam, Axim, Cape Coast Castle, Elmina and Winnebah
No. 7c. Used as 3d. rate from Winnebah
No. 8a. Used as 3d. rate from Secondee and Winnebah
No. 8b. Used as 1d. rate from Cape Coast Castle and Winnebah.

Examples of bisects used *on piece* are worth about 10% of the price quoted for those *on cover*.

The 4d., No. 7, is known surcharged "1 d". This was previously listed as No. 8c, but there are now serious doubts as to its authenticity. The three examples reported of this stamp all show *different* surcharges!

1883. Wmk Crown CA. P 14.

9	**1**	½d. olive-yellow (1.83)	£275	85·00
10		1d. blue (5.83)	£900	85·00

PENNY

Short "P" and distorted "E" (Pl 1 R. 5/6) ("P" repaired for Pl 2)

Large "R" in "THREE" (R. 10/4)

1884 (Aug)–**91**. Wmk Crown CA. P 14.

11	1	½d. green	4·75	1·50
		a. Dull green	4·75	1·50
		w. Wmk inverted	£300	£300
		x. Wmk reversed		
12		1d. rose-carmine	6·50	50
		a. Carmine	6·50	50
		b. Bisected (½d.) (on cover)	†	£5000
		c. Short "P" and distorted "E"	£300	70·00
		w. Wmk inverted	†	£600
13		2d. grey	48·00	7·00
		aw. Wmk inverted	£400	£400
		b. Slate	18·00	50
		c. Bisected (1d.) (on cover)	†	£5000
		d. Quartered (½d.) (on cover)	†	—
14		2½d. ultramarine and orange (13.3.91)	14·00	70
		w. Wmk inverted	†	£375
15		3d. olive-yellow (9.89)	27·00	15·00
		a. Olive	27·00	13·00
		b. Large "R" in "THREE"	—	£500
16		4d. deep mauve (3.85)	28·00	4·25
		a. Rosy mauve	35·00	8·00
17		6d. orange (1.89)	27·00	6·50
		a. Orange-brown	27·00	6·50
		b. Bisected (on cover)	†	£10000
18		1s. violet (1888)	48·00	15·00
		a. Bright mauve	16·00	3·25
19		2s. yellow-brown (1888)	£110	45·00
		a. Deep brown	60·00	16·00

11/19a Set of 9 ... £180 42·00
14s/15s, 18s/19s Optd "SPECIMEN" Set of 4 ... £180

During 1884 to 1886 and in 1889 some values were in short supply and the use of bisects and other divided stamps is known as follows:

No. 12b. Used as part of 2½d. rate from Cape Coast Castle
No. 13c. Used as 1d. or as part of 2d. rate from Cape Coast Castle, Chamah, Dixcove and Elmina
No. 13d. Used as part of 2½d. rate from Cape Coast Castle
No. 17b. Used as 3d. from Appam

1889 (Mar). No. 17 surch with T **2**.

20	1	1d. on 6d. orange	£150	55·00
		a. Surch double	†	£4750

In some sheets examples may be found with the bar and "PENNY" spaced 8 mm, the normal spacing being 7 mm.

USED HIGH VALUES. Until the introduction of airmail in 1929 there was no postal use for values over 10s. Post Offices did, however, apply postal cancellations to high value stamps required for telegram fees.

3   4

1889 (Sept)–**94**. Wmk Crown CA. P 14.

22	3	5s. dull mauve and blue	80·00	29·00
23		10s. dull mauve and red	£140	18·00
		a. Dull mauve and carmine	£1100	£325
24		20s. green and black	£3500	
25		20s. dull mauve and black/red (4.94)	£170	35·00
		w. Wmk inverted	£650	£120

22s/5s Optd "SPECIMEN" Set of 4 ... £450

No. 24 was withdrawn from sale in April 1893 when a large part of the stock was stolen. No 20s. stamps were available until the arrival of the replacement printing a year later.

1898 (May)–**1902**. Wmk Crown CA. P 14.

26	3	½d. dull mauve and green	7·00	1·75
27		1d. dull mauve and rose	7·50	50
		aw. Wmk inverted	—	£225
27b	4	2d. dull mauve and orange-red (1902)	50·00	£160
28		2½d. dull mauve and ultramarine	10·00	12·00
29	4	3d. dull mauve and orange	10·00	4·75
30		6d. dull mauve and violet	15·00	3·75
31	3	1s. green and black (1899)	20·00	42·00
32		2s. green and carmine	35·00	42·00
33		5s. green and mauve (1900)	£100	60·00
34		10s. green and brown (1900)	£225	70·00

26/34 Set of 10 ... £400 £350
26s/34s Optd "SPECIMEN" Set of 10 ... £300

1901 (6 Oct). Nos. 28 and 30 surch with T **2**.

35		1d. on 2½d. dull mauve and ultramarine	12·00	8·00
		a. "ONE" omitted	£1000	
36		1d. on 6d. dull mauve and violet	12·00	5·50
		a. "ONE" omitted	£275	£550

6   7   8

1902. Wmk Crown CA. P 14.

38	6	½d. dull purple and green (8.02)	1·50	40
39		1d. dull purple and carmine (5.02)	1·50	15
		w. Wmk inverted	£275	£160
40	7	2d. dull purple and orange-red (4.02)	48·00	7·00
		w. Wmk inverted		
41	6	2½d. dull purple and ultramarine (8.02)	5·50	9·00
42	7	3d. dull purple and orange (8.02)	7·50	3·00
43		6d. dull purple and violet (8.02)	8·00	3·00
		w. Wmk inverted	—	£250
44	6	1s. green and black (8.02)	25·00	4·25
45		2s. green and carmine (8.02)	35·00	40·00
46		5s. green and mauve (8.02)	65·00	£120
47		10s. green and brown (8.02)	85·00	£160
48		20s. purple and black/red (8.02)	£190	£225

38/48 Set of 11 ... £400 £500
38s/48s Optd "SPECIMEN" Set of 11 ... £275

Examples of Nos. 45/8 are known showing a forged Accra postmark dated "25 MAR 1902".

1904–06. Wmk Mult Crown CA. Ordinary paper (½d. to 6d.) or chalk-surfaced paper (2s.6d.).

49	6	½d. dull purple and green (3.06)	2·50	7·00
50		1d. dull purple and carmine (10.04)	25·00	1·50
		a. Chalk-surfaced paper (5.06)	16·00	2·75
		w. Wmk inverted		
51	7	2d. dull purple and orange-red (11.04)	15·00	2·25
		a. Chalk-surfaced paper (8.06)	38·00	4·00
52	6	2½d. dull purple and ultramarine (6.06)	65·00	80·00
53	7	3d. dull purple and orange (8.05)	90·00	9·00
		a. Chalk-surfaced paper (4.06)	28·00	1·50
54		6d. dull purple and violet (3.06)	90·00	7·50
57		2s.6d. green and yellow (9.06)	50·00	3·50
		2s.6d. green and yellow (3.06)	35·00	£140
		s. Optd SPECIMEN	45·00	

49/57 Set of 7 ... £190 £200

1907–13. Wmk Mult Crown CA. Ordinary paper (½d. to 2½d. and 2s.) or chalk-surfaced paper (3d. to 1s., 2s.6d., 5s.). P 14.

59	6	½d. dull purple (5.07)	12·00	30
		a. Blue-green (1909)	20·00	2·75
60		1d. red (2.07)	20·00	40
61	7	2d. greyish slate (4.09)	3·00	1·00
62	6	2½d. blue (4.07)	22·00	5·00
		w. Wmk inverted	£500	£400
63	7	3d. purple/yellow (16.4.09)	8·50	1·25
64		6d. dull and deep purple (12.08)	42·00	2·25
		a. Dull and bright purple (1911)	8·50	8·00
65	6	1s. black/green (10.09)	28·00	1·50
66		2s. purple and blue/blue (1910)	8·50	16·00
		a. Chalk-surfaced paper (1912)	18·00	16·00
67	7	2s.6d. black and red/blue (1911)	42·00	£100
68	6	5s. green and red/yellow (1913)	65·00	£250

59/68 Set of 10 ... £190 £325
59s/68s Optd "SPECIMEN" Set of 10 ... £425

Prepared for use but not issued.

69s	6	10s. green and red/green (optd "SPECIMEN")	£350

Although never actually issued, No. 69s was distributed by the Universal Postal Union to all member countries. One example exists without "SPECIMEN" opt. A 20s. purple and black on red, type 6, was also prepared, and exists with "SPECIMEN" opt, but was not distributed by the UPU.

(Typo D.L.R.)
1908 (Nov). Wmk Mult Crown CA. P 14.

70	8	1d. red	9·50	10
		a. Wmk sideways	†	£3000
		s. Optd "SPECIMEN"	60·00	

9   10   11

(Typo D.L.R.)
1913–21. Die I. Wmk Mult Crown CA. Chalk-surfaced paper (3d. to 20s.). P 14.

71	9	½d. green	2·50	2·25
		a. Yellow-green (1916)	3·75	2·50
72	10	1d. red	2·25	10
		a. Scarlet (1917)	4·00	50
		ab. "A" of "CA" missing from wmk	†	£700
74	11	2d. grey	12·00	2·50
		a. Slate-grey (1920)	19·00	19·00
		w. Wmk inverted	†	£375
		x. Wmk reversed	†	£425
		y. Wmk inverted and reversed	†	£425
76	9	2½d. bright blue	15·00	2·75
		a. "A" of "CA" missing from wmk	£850	
		x. Wmk reversed	†	£400
77	11	3d. purple/yellow (8.15)	4·50	80
		as. Optd "SPECIMEN"	40·00	
		aw. Wmk inverted	—	£225
		b. White back (9.13)	1·75	40
		c. On orange-buff (1919)	15·00	9·00
		cw. Wmk inverted	—	£225
		d. On buff (1920)		
		e. Die II. On pale yellow (1921)	65·00	6·50
		ew. Wmk inverted	†	£450
78		6d. dull and bright purple	13·00	2·50
79	9	1s. black/green	6·50	2·50
		bw. Wmk inverted		
		c. On blue-green, olive back (1916)	18·00	75
		ca. Wmk sideways	†	£2000
		cs. Optd "SPECIMEN"	£100	
		cw. Wmk inverted	—	£300
		d. On emerald back (1920)	4·00	2·00
		ds. Optd "SPECIMEN"	65·00	
		e. Die II. On emerald back (1921)	3·25	50
		es. Optd "SPECIMEN"	55·00	
		ew. Wmk inverted	†	£375
80		2s. purple and blue/blue	14·00	5·00
		aw. Wmk inverted	—	£450
		b. Die II (1921)	£180	65·00
81	11	2s.6d. black and red/blue	14·00	13·00
		a. Die II (1921)	42·00	42·00
82	9	5s. green and red/yellow (1916)	29·00	70·00
		as. Optd "SPECIMEN"	65·00	
		b. White back (10.13)	29·00	70·00
		c. On orange-buff (1919)	85·00	£100
		d. On buff (1920)		
		e. On pale yellow (1921)	£110	£180
		f. Die II. On pale yellow (1921)	50·00	£180
		fw. Wmk inverted	£475	
83		10s. green and red/green	70·00	£120
		a. On blue-green, olive back (1916)	45·00	£100
		aw. Wmk inverted	£1200	
		b. On emerald back (1921)	50·00	£200
84		20s. purple and black/red	£170	£120

71/84 Set of 12 ... £275 £275

71s/6s, 77bs, 78s/81s, 82bs/4s Optd "SPECIMEN"
Set of 12 ... £325

The 10s. and 20s. were withdrawn locally from September 1920 and, in common with other Gold Coast stamps, were not available to stamp dealers from the Crown Agents in London.

WAR TAX

ONE PENNY

(**12**)

13 King George V and Christiansborg Castle

1918 (17 June). Surch with T **12**.

85	10	1d. on 1d. red	4·00	1·00
		s. Optd "SPECIMEN"	65·00	

1921–24. Die I (15s., £2) or Die II (others). Wmk Mult Script CA. Chalk-surfaced paper (6d. to £2). P 14.

86	9	½d. green	1·50	75
87	10	1d. chocolate-brown (1922)	1·00	10
88	11	1½d. red (1922)	2·75	10
89		2d. grey	2·50	30
		x. Wmk reversed	†	£500
90	9	2½d. yellow-orange (1922)	3·25	15·00
91	11	3d. bright blue (1922)	1·75	1·50
94		6d. dull and bright purple	5·00	3·50
95	9	1s. black/emerald (1924)	11·00	4·25
96		2s. purple and blue/blue (1923)	4·25	4·00
97	11	2s.6d. black and red/blue (1924)	14·00	48·00
98	9	5s. green and red/pale yellow (1924)	28·00	85·00
100	11	15s. dull purple and green (Die I)	£200	£700
		a. Die II (1924)	£140	£700
		as. Optd "SPECIMEN"	£110	
102		£2 green and orange (Die I)	£550	£2000

86/100a Set of 12 ... £180 £750
86s/102s Optd "SPECIMEN" Set of 13 ... £475

The Duty plate for the 1½d., 15s. and £2 has the words "GOLD COAST" in distinctly larger letters.

Examples of Nos. 100/a and 102 are known showing parts of forged Accra postmarks. These are dated "3 MAY 44" and "8 MAY 44", but are invariably positioned so that the year date is not shown.

(Des W. Palmer. Photo Harrison)
1928 (1 Aug). Wmk Mult Script CA. P 13½×14½.

103	13	½d. blue-green	1·50	40
104		1d. red-brown	1·00	10
105		1½d. scarlet	4·25	1·50
		w. Wmk inverted	†	£550
106		2d. slate	4·25	20
107		2½d. orange-yellow	4·50	3·50
108		3d. bright blue	4·25	40
109		6d. black and purple	5·00	40
110		1s. black and red-orange	4·00	1·75
111		2s. black and bright violet	35·00	7·00
112		5s. carmine and sage-green	65·00	55·00

103/12 Set of 10 ... £110 60·00
103s/12s Optd "SPECIMEN." Set of 10 ... £300

1935 (6 May). Silver Jubilee. As Nos. 91/4 of Antigua, but printed by B.W. P 11×12.

113		1d. ultramarine and grey-black	60	50
		a. Extra flagstaff	£140	£130
		b. Short extra flagstaff	£275	£275
		c. Lightning conductor	£190	£200
		d. Flagstaff on right-hand turret	£550	£600
		e. Double flagstaff	£550	
114		3d. brown and deep blue	3·00	7·50
		a. Extra flagstaff	£170	£250
		b. Short extra flagstaff	£500	
		c. Lightning conductor	£275	
115		6d. green and indigo	18·00	30·00
		a. Extra flagstaff	£250	£350
		b. Short extra flagstaff	£550	£650
		c. Lightning conductor	£350	£450
		d. Flagstaff on right-hand turret	£850	
116		1s. slate and purple	5·50	40·00
		a. Extra flagstaff	£200	£450
		b. Short extra flagstaff	£375	£650
		c. Lightning conductor	£350	£600

113/16 Set of 4 ... 24·00 70·00
113s/16s Perf "SPECIMEN" Set of 4 ... £120

For illustrations of plate varieties see Omnibus section following Zanzibar.

1937 (12 May). Coronation. As Nos. 95/7 of Antigua. P 11×11½.

117		1d. buff	1·75	2·50
118		2d. slate	2·25	7·00
119		3d. blue	3·75	3·00

117/19 Set of 3 ... 7·00 11·00
117s/19s Perf "SPECIMEN" Set of 3 ... £120

14   15 King George VI and Christiansborg Castle, Accra

(Recess B.W.)
1938 (1 Apr)–**43**. Wmk Mult Script CA. P 11½×12 (comb) (1s.3d., 10s.) or 12 (line) (others).

120	14	½d. green	15·00	3·75
		a. Perf 12×11½ (1939)	40	50
121		1d. red-brown	19·00	30
		a. Perf 12×11½ (1939)	40	10
122		1½d. scarlet	19·00	8·00
		a. Perf 12×11½ (1940)	40	50
123		2d. slate	16·00	2·00
		a. Perf 12×11½ (1940)	40	10

124		3d. blue	11·00	1·50
		a. Perf 12×11½ (1940)	40	35
125		4d. magenta	10·00	4·50
		a. Perf 12×11½ (1942)	80	1·25
126		6d. purple	26·00	2·00
		a. Perf 12×11½ (1939)	80	20
127		9d. orange	9·50	3·25
		a. Perf 12×11½ (1943)	1·50	55
128	15	1s. black and olive-green	28·00	2·25
		a. Perf 11½×12 (1940)	1·50	65
129		1s.3d. brown and turquoise-blue (12.4.41)	2·00	50
130		2s. blue and violet	65·00	29·00
		a. Perf 11½×12 (1940)	6·00	21·00
131		5s. olive-green and carmine	£110	35·00
		a. Perf 11½×12 (1940)	12·00	24·00
132		10s. black and violet (7.40)	13·00	32·00
120a/32 Set of 13			35·00	70·00
120s/32s Perf "SPECIMEN" Set of 13			£450	

The exact measurement of the comb perforated stamps is 12×11.8 (vertical designs) or 11.8×12 (horizontal designs).

The ½d. and 1d. values exist in coils constructed from normal sheets.

1946 (14 Oct). Victory. As Nos. 110/11 of Antigua. P 13½×14.

133		2d. slate-violet	27·00	2·75
		a. Perf 13½	10	10
		aw. Wmk inverted	£1400	
134		4d. claret	5·50	3·75
		a. Perf 13½	1·50	3·25
133s/4as Perf "SPECIMEN" Set of 2			£110	

16 Northern Territories Mounted Constabulary

17 Christiansborg Castle

18 Emblem of Joint Provincial Council

19 Talking drums

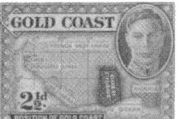

20 Map showing position of Gold Coast

21 Nsuta manganese mine

22 Lake Bosumtwi

23 Cocoa farmer

24 Breaking cocoa pods

25 Gold Coast Regt. Trooping the Colour

26 Surfboats

27 Forest

(Des B. A. Johnston (1½d.), M. Ziorkley and B. A. Abban (2d.), P.O. draughtsman (2½d.), C. Gomez (1s.), M. Ziorkley (10s.); others from photographs. Recess B.W.)

1948 (1 July). T **16/27**. Wmk Mult Script CA. P 12×11½ (vert) or 11½×12 (horiz).

135	16	½d. emerald-green	20	60
136	17	1d. blue	15	15
137	18	1½d. scarlet	1·50	1·50
138	19	2d. purple-brown	55	10
139	20	2½d. yellow-brown and scarlet	2·00	5·50
140	21	3d. light blue	4·00	1·75
141	22	4d. magenta	4·75	6·00

142	23	6d. black and orange	1·00	30
143	24	1s. black and vermilion	3·25	30
		w. Wmk inverted	†	£4500
144	25	2s. sage-green and magenta	11·00	4·75
145	26	5s. purple and black	45·00	14·00
146	27	10s. black and sage-green	22·00	17·00
135/46 Set of 12			85·00	45·00
135s/46s Perf "SPECIMEN" Set of 12			£450	

Nos. 135/6 exist in coils constructed from normal sheets.

1948 (20 Dec). Royal Silver Wedding. As Nos. 112/13 of Antigua.

147		1½d. scarlet	30	70
148		10s. grey-olive	35·00	50·00

1949 (10 Oct). 75th Anniv of UPU As Nos. 114/17 of Antigua.

149		2d. red-brown	25	20
150		2½d. orange	1·50	8·25
151		3d. deep blue	35	1·75
152		1s. blue-green	35	30
		a. "A" of "CA" missing from wmk	—	£800
149/52 Set of 4			2·25	9·50

No. 149 is known with the "A" of "CA" almost completely missing from the watermark.

28 Northern Territories Mounted Constabulary

(Recess B.W.)

1952 (19 Dec)–**54**. Designs previously used for King George VI issue, but with portrait of Queen Elizabeth II, as in T **28**. Portrait faces left on ½d., 4d., 6d., 1s. and 5s. Wmk Mult Script CA. P 12×11½ (vert) or 11½×12 (horiz).

153	20	½d. yellow-brown and scarlet (1.4.53)	20	20
		a. Bistre-brown and scarlet (7.4.54)	1·00	30
154	17	1d. deep blue (1.3.54)	40	10
155	18	1½d. emerald-green (1.4.53)	30	1·50
156	19	2d. chocolate (1.3.54)	40	10
157	28	2½d. scarlet	45	1·50
158	21	3d. magenta (1.4.53)	1·25	10
159	22	4d. blue (1.4.53)	50	30
160	23	6d. black and orange (1.3.54)	1·00	15
161	24	1s. black and orange-red (1.3.54)	2·25	15
162	25	2s. brown-olive and carmine (1.3.54)	17·00	1·00
163	26	5s. purple and black (1.3.54)	30·00	8·00
164	27	10s. black and olive-green (1.3.54)	27·00	13·00
153/64 Set of 12			70·00	23·00

Nos. 153a/4 exist in coils constructed from normal sheets.

1953 (2 June). Coronation. As No. 120 of Antigua, but ptd by B. W.

165		2d. black and sepia	1·50	10

STAMP BOOKLETS

1916 (Dec).

SB1	2s. booklet containing 12×½d. and 18×1d. (Nos. 70a, 72) in blocks of 6.	

POSTAGE DUE STAMPS

D 1

(Typo D.L.R.)

1923 (6 Mar). Yellowish toned paper. Wmk Mult Script CA. P 14.

D1	D 1	½d. black	20·00	£120
D2		1d. black	75	1·25
D3		2d. black	13·00	2·00
D4		3d. black	22·00	1·50
D1/4 Set of 4			50·00	£120
D1s/4s Optd "SPECIMEN" Set of 4			90·00	

A bottom marginal strip of six of No. D2 is known showing the "A" of "CA" omitted from the watermark in the margin below the third vertical column.

3d.	**3**d.	**1**/-	**1**/-
Normal	Lower serif at left of "3" missing (R. 9/1)	Column 4 (No. D8)	Column 5 (No. D8c)

The degree of inclination of the stroke on the 1s. value varies for each column of the sheet: Column 1, 2 and 6 104°, Column 3 108°, Column 4 107° and Column 5 (No. D8c) 100°.

1951–52. Wmk Mult Script CA. Chalk-surfaced paper. P 14.

D5	D 1	2d. black (13.12.51)	4·00	32·00
		a. Error. Crown missing, W **9a**	£1600	
		b. Error. St. Edward's Crown, W **9b**.	£750	
		c. Large "d" (R. 9/6, 10/6)	32·00	
		d. Serif on "d" (R. 1/6)	60·00	

D6		3d. black (13.12.51)	4·50	30·00
		a. Error. Crown missing, W **9a**	£1500	
		b. Error. St. Edward's Crown, W **9b**.	£700	
		c. Missing serif	70·00	
D7		6d. black (1.10.52)	1·75	18·00
		a. Error. Crown missing, W **9a**	£2250	
		b. Error. St. Edward's Crown, W **9b**.	£1300	
D8		1s. black (1.10.52)	1·75	70·00
		b. Error. St. Edward's Crown, W **9b**.	£1700	
		c. Upright stroke	12·00	
D5/8 Set of 4			11·00	£130

For illustration of Nos. D5c/d see Nos. D4/6 of Bechuanaland.

ARMY TELEGRAPHS

Nos. AT3/4, AT6 and AT8/12 listed under British Army Field Offices during the South African War were used in small quantities during the 1895 Ashanti Expedition.

Gold Coast became the Dominion of Ghana on 6 March 1957.

Grenada

The earliest recorded postmark of the British administration of Grenada dates from 1784, and, although details of the early period are unknown sparse, it would appear that the island's postal service was operated at a branch of the British GPO. In addition to a Packet Agency at St. George's, the capital, there was a further agency at Carriacou, in the Grenadines, which operated for a few years from 15 September 1847.

Stamps of Great Britain were supplied to the St. George's office from April 1858 until the colony assumed responsibility for the postal service on 1 May 1860. Following the take-over the crowned-circle handstamp, No. CC2, was again used until the Grenada adhesives were issued in 1861.

There was no internal postal service before 1861.

For illustrations of the handstamp and postmark types see BRITISH POST OFFICES ABROAD notes, following GREAT BRITAIN.

CARRIACOU

CROWNED-CIRCLE HANDSTAMPS

A crowned-circle handstamp for Carriacou is recorded in the GPO proof book but no example has been reported used from Grenada.

ST. GEORGE'S

CROWNED-CIRCLE HANDSTAMPS

CC2   CC **1** GRENADA (R.) (24.10.1850)....... *Price on cover*   £2000

Stamps of GREAT BRITAIN cancelled "A 15" as Type **2**.
1858–60.
Z1	1d. rose-red (1857), perf 14		£425
Z2	2d. blue (1858) (Plate No. 7)		£1200
Z3	4d. rose (1857)		£300
Z4	6d. lilac (1856)		£120
Z5	1s. green (1856)		£1800

PRICES FOR STAMPS ON COVER TO 1945	
Nos. 1/3	*from* × 15
Nos. 4/23	*from* × 20
Nos. 24/6	*from* × 10
No. 27	*from* × 15
No. 28	—
No. 29	*from* × 10
Nos. 30/6	*from* × 20
Nos. 37/9	*from* × 15
No. 40	*from* × 40
Nos. 41/7	*from* × 20
Nos. 48/101	*from* × 4
Nos. 109/11	*from* × 8
Nos. 112/48	*from* × 4
Nos. 149/51	*from* × 10
Nos. 152/63	*from* × 4
Nos. D1/3	*from* × 25
Nos. D4/7	*from* × 12
Nos. D8/14	*from* × 20

CROWN COLONY

PRINTERS. Types **1** and **5** recess-printed by Perkins Bacon and Co.

PERKINS BACON "CANCELLED". For notes on these handstamps, showing "CANCELLED" between horizontal bars forming an oval, see Catalogue Introduction.

2 Small Star

(Eng C. Jeens)

1861 (3 June)–**62**. No wmk. Wove paper.
(a) Rough perf 14 to 16
1	**1**	1d. bluish green (H/S "CANCELLED" in oval £10000)	£4500	£300
2		1d. green (5.62)	50·00	50·00
		a. Imperf between (horiz pair)		
3		6d. rose (*shades*) (H/S "CANCELLED" in oval £10000)	£900	90·00

(b) Perf 11 to 12½
3*a*	**1**	6d. lake-red (6.62)	£750	†

No. 3*a* is only known unused, and may be the result of perforating machine trials undertaken by Perkins Bacon. It has also been seen on horizontally laid paper (*Price* £1200).

SIDEWAYS WATERMARK. W **2/3** when sideways show two points of star downwards.

1863–71. W **2** (Small Star). Rough perf 14 to 16.
4	**1**	1d. green (3.64)	£110	17·00
		a. Wmk sideways	—	30·00
5		1d. yellowish green	£130	27·00
6		6d. rose (*shades*) (5.63)	£600	13·00
		a. Wmk sideways	—	80·00
7		6d. orange-red (*shades*) (5.66)	£650	12·00
8		6d. dull rose-red (*wmk sideways*)	£3500	£225
9		6d. vermilion (5.71)	£750	12·00
		a. Double impression	—	£2000

1873 (Jan). W **2** (Small Star, sideways). Clean-cut perf 15.
10	**1**	1d. deep green	£130	50·00
		a. Bisected diag (*on cover*)	†	£9000
		b. Imperf between (pair)		£14000

No. 10a, and later bisected 1d. values, were authorised until 1881 to pay the island newspaper rate (½d.) or the newspaper rate to Great Britain (1½d.). Examples also exist on covers to France.

3 Large Star   **4** Broad-pointed Star

1873 (Sept)–**74**. W **3** (Large Star). Intermediate perf 15.
11	**1**	1d. blue-green (*wmk sideways*) (2.74)	£110	27·00
		a. Double impression		
		b. Bisected diag (*on cover*)	†	£9000
12		6d. orange-vermilion	£700	26·00

POSTAGE

ONE SHILLING

5   **(6)**

NOTE. The early ½d., 2½d., 4d. and 1s. postage stamps were made by surcharging the undenominated Type **5** design.

The surcharges were from two founts of type—one about 1½ mm high, the other 2 mm high—so there are short and tall letters on the same stamp; also the spacing varies considerably, so that the length of the words varies.

Examples of Type **5** with surcharges, but without the "POSTAGE" inscription, are revenue stamps.

1875 (July). Surch with T **6**. W **3**. P 14.
13	**5**	1s. deep mauve (B.)	£700	12·00
		a. "SHLLIING"	£6500	£700
		b. "NE SHILLING"	†	£3000
		c. Inverted "S" in "POSTAGE"	£4000	£500
		d. "OSTAGE"	£7000	£2750

1875 (Dec). W **3** (Large Star, upright).
14	**1**	1d. green to yellow-green (P 14)	85·00	8·00
		a. Bisected diag (*on cover*)	†	£9000
15		1d. green (P 15)	£9000	£2250

No. 14 was comb perforated at Somerset House. 40 sheets of No. 15 were line perforated by Perkins Bacon to replace spoilages and to complete the order.

1878 (Aug). W **2** (Small Star, sideways). Intermediate perf 15.
16	**1**	1d. green	£250	50·00
		a. Bisected diag (*on cover*)	†	£9000
17		6d. deep vermilion	£850	38·00
		a. Double impression	—	£2000

1879 (Dec). W **2** (Small Star, upright). Rough perf 15.
18	**1**	1d. pale green (*thin paper*)	£300	29·00
		a. Double impression		
		b. Bisected diag (*on cover*)	†	—

1881 (Apr). W **2** (Small Star, sideways). Rough perf 14½.
19	**1**	1d. green	£160	9·50
		a. Bisected diag (*on cover*)	†	£9000

POSTAGE   **POSTAGE**   **POSTAGE**

HALF-PENNY   **TWO PENCE HALF-PENNY.**   **FOUR PENCE**

(7)   **(8)**   **(9)**

1881 (Apr). Surch with T **7/9**. P 14½.
*(a) W **3** (Large Star, sideways on ½d.)*
20	**5**	½d. pale mauve	40·00	11·00
21		½d. deep mauve	17·00	7·00
		a. Imperf (pair)	£300	
		ab. Ditto. "OSTAGE" (R. 9/4)	£7000	
		b. Surch double	£325	
		c. "OSTAGE" (R. 9/4)	£190	£130
		d. No hyphen	£190	£130
		e. "ALF-PENNY"	£3750	
		f. Wmk upright	£300	£140
		g. Ditto. "OSTAGE" (R. 9/4)	£2000	£800
22		2½d. rose-lake	75·00	9·00
		a. Imperf (pair)	£650	
		b. Imperf between (horiz pair)	£6500	
		c. No stop	£250	75·00
		d. "PENCF" (R. 8/12)	£475	£180
23		4d. blue	£140	8·00
		a. Wmk sideways	£1200	£500
		b. Inverted "S" in "POSTAGE"		

*(b) W **4** (Broad-pointed Star)*
24	**5**	2½d. rose-lake	£160	50·00
		a. No stop	£550	£200
		b. "PENCF" (R. 8/12)	£800	£275
25		2½d. claret	£425	£120
		a. No stop	£1100	£500
		b. "PENCF" (R. 8/12)	£1600	£700
25*c*		2½d. deep claret	£650	£225
		d. No stop	£2250	£900
		e. "PENCF" (R. 8/12)	£2750	£1100
26		4d. blue	£350	£190

Examples of the "F" for "E" error on the 2½d. value should not be confused with a somewhat similar broken "E" variety. The latter is always without the stop and shows other damage to the "E". The authentic error always occurs with the full stop shown. The "no stop" variety occurs on R. 3/4, R. 6/2, R. 8/3 and R. 9/7.

ONE PENNY   **POSTAGE.**   (POSTAGE overprints)

(10)   **(11)**   **(12)**

1883 (Jan). Revenue stamps (T **5** with green surcharge as in T **10**) optd for postage. W **2** (Small Star). P 14½.
*(a) Optd horizontally with T **11***
27	**5**	1d. orange	£400	60·00
		a. "POSTAGE" inverted	£3500	£2250
		b. "POSTAGE" double	£1400	£1100
		c. Inverted "S" in "POSTAGE"	£1000	£600
		d. Bisected diag (*on cover*)	†	£3000

*(b) Optd diagonally with T **11** twice on each stamp, the stamp being cut and each half used as ½d.*
28	**5**	Half of 1d. orange	£700	£225
		a. Unsevered pair	£3500	£1000
		b. "POSTAGE" inverted	—	£1200

*(c) Optd with T **12**, the stamps divided diagonally and each half used as ½d*
29	**5**	Half of 1d. orange	£275	£110
		a. Unsevered pair	£1500	£450

Nos. 27/9 exist with wmk either upright or sideways.
1d. Revenue stamps with "POSTAGE" added in black manuscript were used at Gouyave during February and March 1883 (*Price* £6500, *used*). Similar manuscript overprints, in red were also used at Grenville in June 1883 and in black or red at Sauteurs in September 1886 (*Price from* £10000, *used*).

13   Damaged value (R. 2/3)

d.
1
POSTAGE.   **ONE PENNY**

(14)   **15**

(Typo D.L.R.)

1883. Wmk Crown CA. P 14.
30	**13**	½d. dull green (2.83)	2·75	1·00
		a. Tête-bêche (vert pair)	5·50	21·00
31		1d. carmine (2.83)	90·00	3·25
		a. Tête-bêche (vert pair)	£325	£375
32		2½d. ultramarine (5.83)	13·00	1·00
		a. Tête-bêche (vert pair)	32·00	60·00
33		4d. greyish slate (5.83)	14·00	2·00
		a. Tête-bêche (vert pair)	35·00	65·00
34		6d. mauve (5.83)	4·50	4·25
		a. Tête-bêche (vert pair)	18·00	65·00
35		8d. grey-brown (2.83)	10·00	13·00
		a. Tête-bêche (vert pair)	40·00	90·00
		b. Damaged value	£150	£180
36		1s. pale violet (4.83)	£160	55·00
		a. Tête-bêche (vert pair)	£2000	£2250
30/36		Set of 7	£250	70·00

Types **13** and **15** were printed in rows tête-bêche in the sheets, so that 50% of the stamps have inverted watermarks.
No. 35b occurs on an inverted watermark stamp.

1886 (1 Oct–Dec). Revenue stamps (T **5** with green surch as T **10**), surch with T **14**. P 14.
*(a) Wmk Large Star, T **3***
37	**5**	1d. on 1½d. orange	60·00	50·00
		a. Surch inverted	£450	£300
		b. Surch double	£750	£300
		c. "THRFE"	£300	£225
		d. "PFNCE"	£300	£225
		e. "HALH"	£300	£225
		f. Bisected diag (*on cover*)	†	£2250
38		1d. on 1s. orange (12.86)	50·00	45·00
		a. "POSTAGE" (no stop)	£550	
		b. "SHILLNG"	£550	£375
		c. Wide space (1¾ mm) between "ONE" and "SHILLING"	£375	£250
		d. Bisected diag (*on cover*)	†	£2250

*(b) Wmk Small Star, T **2***
39	**5**	1d. on 4d. orange (11.86)	£170	90·00

1887 (Jan). Wmk Crown CA. P 14.
40	**15**	1d. carmine	4·75	1·40
		a. Tête-bêche (vert pair)	11·00	30·00
		s. Optd "SPECIMEN"	65·00	

Due to the sheet formation 50% of the stamps have inverted watermarks.
No. 40s can be found with the vertical "SPECIMEN" opt reading either upwards or downwards.

4d.   **HALF PENNY**

POSTAGE   **POSTAGE**

(16)   **(17)**

1888 (31 Mar)–**91**. Revenue stamps (T **5** with green surch as T **10**) further surcharged. W **2** (sideways on 2s.). P 14½, and No. 35.
*I. Surch with T **16***
(a) 4 mm between value and "POSTAGE"
41	**5**	4d. on 2s. orange	50·00	21·00
		a. Upright "d" (R. 5/6)	£800	£475
		b. Wide space (2¼ mm) between "TWO" and "SHILLINGS"	£300	£160

		c. First "S" in "SHILLINGS" inverted	£500	£325
		d. Imperf between (horiz pair)	£10000	

(b) 5 mm between value and "POSTAGE"

42	5	4d. on 2s. orange	70·00	38·00
		a. Wide space	£375	£225
		b. "S" inverted	£750	£550

II. Surch as T 17 (December 1889)

43	5	½d. on 2s. orange	17·00	32·00
		a. Surch double	£325	£350
		b. Wide space	£130	£150
		c. "S" inverted	£300	£325

POSTAGE **d.** AND **1** REVENUE (**18**)	POSTAGE AND REVENUE **1d.** (**19**)	**2½d.** (**20**)

III. Surch with T 18 (December 1890)

44	5	1d. on 2s. orange	85·00	85·00
		a. Surch inverted	£750	
		b. Wide space	£375	£375
		c. "S" inverted	£750	£700

IV. Surch with T 19 (January 1891)

45	5	1d. on 2s. orange	75·00	70·00
		a. No stop after "1d" (R. 3/8)	£500	£500
		b. Wide space	£300	£300
		c. "S" inverted	£550	£325
46	13	1d. on 8d. grey-brown	12·00	20·00
		a. Tête-bêche (vert pair)	40·00	70·00
		b. Surch inverted	£325	£275
		c. No stop after "1d" (R. 6/5)	£250	£250
		d. Damaged value	£150	

V. Surch with T 20 (December 1891)

47	13	2½d. on 8d. grey-brown	22·00	11·00
		a. Tête-bêche (vert pair)	55·00	65·00
		b. Surch inverted		
		c. Surch double	£850	£800
		d. Surch double, one inverted	£550	£600
		e. Surch treble	—	£900
		f. Surch treble, two inverted	—	£1000
		g. Damaged value	£225	£150
		s. Optd "SPECIMEN"	65·00	

The surcharges, Types **16/19**, were applied to half sheets as a setting of 60 (12×5).

The wide space between "TWO" and "SHILLINGS" occurs on R. 1/4 and 10/3 of the original 2s. Revenue stamp which was printed in sheets of 120 (12×10).

Type **18** was a two-step surcharge comprising "1d./Revenue", followed by "POSTAGE/AND". An example of No. 44 is known with the "POSTAGE" omitted due to faulty registration and the word applied by hand in a slightly different type style.

There are two varieties of fraction in Type **20**, which each occur 30 times in the setting; in one the "1" has horizontal serif and the "2" commences on a ball; in the other the "1" has sloping serif and the "2" is without ball.

See also D4/7.

21	**22**	**23** Flagship of Columbus. (Columbus named Grenada "La Concepcion")

(Typo D.L.R.)

1895 (6 Sept)–**99**. Wmk Crown CA. P 14.

48	22	½d. mauve and green (9.99)	4·50	1·75
49	21	1d. mauve and carmine (5.96)	6·50	75
50		2d. mauve and brown (9.99)	40·00	26·00
51		2½d. mauve and ultramarine	12·00	1·50
52	22	3d. mauve and orange	6·50	16·00
53	21	6d. mauve and green	22·00	65·00
54	22	8d. mauve and black	12·00	50·00
55		1s. green and orange	22·00	65·00
48/55 *Set of 8*			£110	£200
48s/55s Optd "SPECIMEN" *Set of 8*			£180	

(Recess D.L.R.)

1898 (15 Aug). 400th Anniv of Discovery of Grenada by Columbus. Wmk Crown CC. P 14.

56	23	2½d. ultramarine	22·00	6·00
		a. Bluish paper	40·00	40·00
		s. Optd "SPECIMEN"	85·00	

24	**25**

(Typo D.L.R.)

1902. Wmk Crown CA. P 14.

57	24	½d. dull purple and green	5·50	1·25
58	25	1d. dull purple and carmine	9·50	30
59		2d. dull purple and brown	6·00	10·00
60		2½d. dull purple and ultramarine	7·50	2·75
61	24	3d. dull purple and orange	7·50	9·00
62	25	6d. dull purple and green	6·00	17·00
63	24	1s. green and orange	12·00	42·00

64		2s. green and ultramarine	38·00	65·00
65	25	5s. green and carmine	45·00	85·00
66	24	10s. green and purple	£160	£300
57/66 *Set of 10*			£250	£475
57s/66s Optd "SPECIMEN" *Set of 10*			£200	

1904–06. Wmk Mult Crown CA. Ordinary paper. P 14.

67	24	½d. purple and green (1905)	22·00	48·00
68	25	1d. purple and carmine	23·00	2·50
69		2d. purple and brown (1905)	60·00	60·00
70		2½d. purple and ultramarine (1905)	60·00	65·00
71	24	3d. purple and orange (1905)	6·00	14·00
		a. Chalk-surfaced paper	7·00	9·00
72	25	6d. purple and green (1906)	16·00	35·00
		a. Chalk-surfaced paper	17·00	42·00
73	24	1s. green and orange (1905)	6·00	40·00
74		2s. green and ultramarine (1906)	60·00	85·00
		a. Chalk-surfaced paper	50·00	80·00
75	25	5s. green and carmine (1906)	80·00	£120
76	24	10s. green and purple (1906)	£190	£300
67/76 *Set of 10*			£450	£750

Examples of most values between Nos. 57 and 76 are known showing a forged GPO Grenada BWI postmark dated "OC 6 09".

26 Badge of the Colony	**27** Badge of the Colony

(Recess D.L.R.)

1906 (Jan). Wmk Mult Crown CA. P 14.

77	26	½d. green	4·50	30
		x. Wmk reversed	†	£400
78		1d. carmine	9·50	10
		y. Wmk inverted and reversed	—	£500
79		2d. orange	5·00	3·00
		w. Wmk inverted	£550	£400
		x. Wmk reversed	£600	
		y. Wmk inverted and reversed	£550	£550
80		2½d. blue	6·00	1·50
		a. Ultramarine	11·00	3·50

(Typo D.L.R.)

1908. Wmk Crown CA. Chalk-surfaced paper. P 14.

| 82 | 27 | 1s. black/green | 50·00 | 80·00 |
| 83 | | 10s. green and red/green | £160 | £300 |

1908–11. Wmk Mult Crown CA. Chalk-surfaced paper. P 14.

84	27	3d. dull purple/yellow	8·00	1·75
85		6d. dull purple and purple	20·00	8·00
86		1s. black/green (1911)	7·00	4·00
87		2s. blue and purple/blue	38·00	14·00
88		5s. green and red/yellow	80·00	95·00
77/88 *Set of 11*			£350	£450
77s/80s, 82s/5s, 87s/8s Optd "SPECIMEN" *Set of 10*			£250	

Examples of Nos. 82/8 are known showing a forged GPO Grenada BWI postmark dated "OC 6 09".

28	**WAR TAX** (**29**) **WAR TAX** (**30**)

(Typo D.L.R.)

1913 (3 Jan)–**22**. Wmk Mult Crown CA. Chalk-surfaced paper (3d. to 10s.). P 14.

89	28	½d. yellow-green	1·75	1·60
90		½d. green	1·25	1·00
91		1d. red	2·25	30
92		1d. scarlet (1916)	14·00	2·00
		w. Wmk inverted		
93		2d. orange	1·75	30
94		2½d. bright blue	1·75	1·25
95		2½d. dull blue (1920)	5·50	6·00
96		3d. purple/yellow	65	85
		a. White back (3.14)	65	1·50
		b. On lemon (1917)	4·00	9·00
		c. On pale yellow (1921)	7·00	30·00
97		6d. dull and bright purple	1·50	9·00
98		1s. black/green	1·00	10·00
		a. White back (3.14)	1·25	7·50
		as. Optd "SPECIMEN"	35·00	
		b. On blue-green, olive back (1917)	32·00	85·00
		c. On emerald surface	1·50	23·00
		d. On emerald back (6.22)	1·00	15·00
		ds. Optd "SPECIMEN"	35·00	
		dw. Wmk inverted	£120	
99		2s. purple and blue/blue	6·50	12·00
100		5s. green and red/yellow	17·00	60·00
		a. On pale yellow (1921)	32·00	75·00
		as. Optd "SPECIMEN"	50·00	
101		10s. green and red/green	70·00	£130
		a. On emerald back (6.22)	70·00	£190
		as. Optd "SPECIMEN"	65·00	
89/101 *Set of 10*			95·00	£200
89s/101s Optd "SPECIMEN" (1s. optd in red) *Set of 10*			£200	
98sa Optd in red *Set of*			48·00	

1916 (1 June). Optd with T **29** by Govt Press, St. George's.

109	28	1d. red (shades)	2·25	1·75
		a. Opt inverted	£275	
		b. Triangle for "A" in "TAX"	55·00	70·00
		s. Handstamped "SPECIMEN"	50·00	

A small "A" in "WAR", 2 mm high, is found on Nos. 29, 38 and 48 of the setting of 60 and a very small "A" in "TAX", 1½ mm high, on No. 11. Value about twice normal. The normal "A" is 2¼ mm high.

No. 109b is on No. 56 of the setting.

1916 (1 Sept)–**18**. Optd with T **30** in London.

111	28	1d. scarlet	30	20
		a. Carmine-red/bluish (5.18)	4·00	1·50
		s. Optd "SPECIMEN"	45·00	
		w. Wmk inverted	£130	

1921–31. Wmk Mult Script CA. Chalk-surfaced paper (3d. (No. 122) to 10s.). P 14.

112	28	½d. green	1·25	30
113		1d. carmine-red	80	75
114		1d. brown (1923)	1·50	30
115		1½d. rose-red (6.22)	2·00	1·00
116		2d. orange	1·25	30
117		2d. grey (1926)	2·50	2·75
117a		2½d. dull blue	8·00	8·00
118		2½d. grey (6.22)	1·00	9·00
119		2½d. bright blue (1926)	11·00	3·75
120		2½d. ultramarine (1931)	11·00	8·50
120a		2½d. chalky blue and blue (1928)	50·00	50·00
121		3d. bright blue (6.22)	1·25	11·00
122		3d. purple/yellow (1926)	3·00	3·00
123		4d. black and red/yellow (1926)	1·00	3·75
124		5d. dull purple and sage-green (27.12.22)	1·50	4·25
125		6d. dull and bright purple	1·25	29·00
126		6d. black and carmine (1926)	2·25	2·50
127		9d. dull purple and black (27.12.22)	2·25	9·50
128		1s. black/emerald (1923)	2·50	60·00
		y. Wmk inverted and reversed	£225	
129		1s. chestnut (1926)	3·00	6·00
130		2s. purple and blue/blue (1922)	6·00	17·00
131		2s.6d. black and carmine/blue (1929)	14·00	24·00
132		3s. green and violet (27.12.22)	12·00	27·00
133		5s. green and red/pale yellow (1923)	12·00	35·00
134		10s. green and red/emerald (1923)	55·00	£130
112/19, 121/34 *Set of 22*			£110	£350
112s/34s Optd or Perf (2s.6d.) "SPECIMEN" *Set of 23*			£400	

Some values of Nos. 89/101 and 112/34 have been seen with part strikes of the forged postmark mentioned after Nos. 67/76 and 77/88.

31 Grand Anse Beach	**32** Badge of the Colony

33 Grand Etang	**34** St. George's

(Recess Waterlow)

1934 (23 Oct)–**36**. Wmk Mult Script CA (sideways on T **32**). P 12½.

135	31	½d. green	15	1·25
		a. Perf 12½×13½ (1936)	11·00	70·00
136	32	1d. black and sepia	2·00	3·75
		a. Perf 13½×12½ (1936)	60	35
137	33	1½d. black and scarlet	9·50	7·00
		a. Perf 12½×13½ (1936)	1·25	40
138	32	2d. black and orange	1·00	75
139	34	2½d. blue	50	50
140	32	3d. black and olive-green	1·00	2·75
141		6d. black and purple	3·50	1·75
142		1s. black and brown	4·00	4·00
143		2s.6d. black and ultramarine	8·00	28·00
144		5s. black and violet	48·00	50·00
135/44 *Set of 10*			60·00	80·00
135s/44s Perf "SPECIMEN" *Set of 10*			£190	

1935 (6 May). Silver Jubilee. As Nos. 91/4 of Antigua but ptd by Waterlow. P 11×12.

145		½d. black and green	1·00	1·25
		k. Kite and vertical log	85·00	£110
		l. Kite and horizontal log	£110	£180
146		1d. ultramarine and grey	1·25	1·75
		l. Kite and horizontal log	£150	£180
147		1½d. deep blue and scarlet	1·25	3·75
		l. Kite and horizontal log	£160	£250
148		2½d. slate and purple	17·00	40·00
		l. Kite and horizontal log	£325	£475
145/8 *Set of 4*			18·00	42·00
145s/8s Perf "SPECIMEN" *Set of 4*			£100	

For illustrations of plate varieties see Omnibus section following Zanzibar.

1937 (12 May). Coronation. As Nos. 95/7 of Antigua. P 11×11½.

149		1d. violet	40	1·75
150		1d. carmine	40	50
151		2½d. blue	80	1·25
149/51 *Set of 3*			1·40	3·25
149s/51s Perf "SPECIMEN" *Set of 3*			£100	

35 King George VI

(Photo Harrison)

1937 (12 July)–**50**. Wmk Mult Script CA. Chalk-surfaced paper.
P 15×14.

152	**35**	¼d. brown	3·75	20
		a. Ordinary paper (11.42)	65	3·00
		b. Ordinary paper. *Chocolate* (1.45)	1·00	3·00
		c. Chalk-surfaced paper. *Chocolate* (8.50)	3·50	8·50

The ordinary paper is thick, smooth and opaque.

36 Grand Anse Beach

40 Badge of the Colony

Line on sail (Centre Pl 3 R. 1/1. Later partially retouched)

Colon flaw (R. 5/6. Corrected on ptg of Nov 1950)

Extra window and broken handrail (Centre Pl 2 R. 1/6)

(Recess D.L.R. (10s.), Waterlow (others))

1938 (16 Mar)–**50**. As T **31**/**4** (but portrait of King George VI as in T **36**) and T **40**. Wmk Mult Script CA (sideways on T **32**). P 12½×13 or 12×13 (10s.).

153	**36**	½d. yellow-green	17·00	2·50
		a. *Blue-green* (10.9.43)	60	1·25
		b. Perf 12½×13½ (1938)	11·00	80
		ba. *Blue-green*	6·50	5·00
154	**32**	1d. black and sepia	1·00	20
		aa. Line on sail	£190	
		ab. Extra window and broken handrail	£150	75·00
		b. Perf 13½×12½ (1938)	2·25	50
		ba. Line on sail	£150	
		bb. Extra window and broken handrail	—	90·00
155	**33**	1½d. black and scarlet	50	2·00
		a. Perf 13½×12½ (1938)	3·75	30
156	**32**	2d. black and orange	40	50
		aa. Line on sail	£250	
		ab. Extra window and broken handrail	£180	£100
		b. Perf 13½×12½ (1938)	2·75	85
		ba. Line on sail	£250	
		bb. Extra window and broken handrail	£250	£200
157	**34**	2½d. bright blue	30	30
		a. Perf 12½×13½ (?3.50)	£11000	£190
158	**32**	3d. black and olive-green	21·00	1·40
		a. Perf 13½×12½ (16.3.38)	14·00	1·00
		ab. *Black and brown-olive* (1942)	40	80
		ac. Line on sail	£180	
		ad. Extra window and broken handrail	£275	£275
		b. Perf 12½. *Black and brown-olive* (16.8.50)	1·00	2·50
		ba. Colon flaw	£170	
		bb. Extra window and broken handrail	£170	£250
159		6d. black and purple	4·50	40
		a. Perf 13½×12½ (1942)	2·25	50
		ab. Extra window and broken handrail	—	£250
		b. Line on sail	£375	
160		1s. black and brown	5·50	40
		a. Perf 13½×12½ (1941)	5·00	2·75
		ab. Extra window and broken handrail		
161		2s. black and ultramarine	45·00	3·00
		aa. Line on sail	£1000	
		a. Perf 13½×12½ (1941)	42·00	1·50
		ab. Extra window and broken handrail	£1000	£250
162		5s. black and violet	10·00	7·50
		a. Perf 13½×12½ (1947)	6·50	9·50
163	**40**	10s. steel blue and carmine (narrow) (P 12×13)	60·00	18·00
		a. Perf 14. *Steel blue and bright carmine (narrow)*	£225	60·00
		b. Perf 14. *Slate-blue and bright carmine (narrow)* (1943)	£300	£160
		c. Perf 12. *Slate-blue and bright carmine (narrow)* (1943)	£750	£1900
		d. Perf 14. *Slate-blue and carmine lake (wide)* (1944)	£140	18·00
		e. Perf 14. *Blue-black and carmine (narrow)* (1943)	50·00	18·00

		ea. Frame printed double, one albino		£4500
		f. Perf 14. *Blue-black and bright carmine (wide)* (1947)	35·00	48·00
152/63e		Set of 12	80·00	27·00
152s/63s		Perf "SPECIMEN" Set of 12	£300	

In the earlier printings of the 10s. the paper was dampened before printing and the subsequent shrinkage produced narrow frames 23½ to 23¾ mm wide. Later printings were made on dry paper producing wide frames 24¼ mm wide.

No. 163a is one of the earlier printings, line perf 13.8×14.1. Later printings of the 10s. are line perf 14.1.

Nos. 163b/c show a blurred centre caused by the use of a worn plate.

Nos. 163a and 163b may be found with gum more or less yellow due to local climatic conditions.

The ½d. and 1d. in both perforations exist from coils made up from normal sheets.

Examples of No. 163c are known showing forged St. George's postmarks dated "21 AU 42", "21 AU 43" or "2 OC 43".

1946 (25 Sept). Victory. As Nos. 110/11 of Antigua.

164		1½d. carmine	10	50
165		3½d. blue	10	1·00
164s/5s		Perf "SPECIMEN" Set of 2	90·00	

1948 (27 Oct). Royal Silver Wedding. As Nos. 112/13 of Antigua.

| 166 | | 1½d. scarlet | 15 | 10 |
| 167 | | 10s. slate-green | 24·00 | 20·00 |

(New Currency. 100 cents = 1 West Indian, later Eastern Caribbean, dollar)

1949 (10 Oct). 75th Anniv of Universal Postal Union. As Nos. 114/17 of Antigua.

168		5c. ultramarine	15	20
169		6c. olive	1·50	3·00
170		12c. magenta	15	1·00
171		24c. red-brown	15	1·00
168/71		Set of 4	1·75	4·75

41 King George VI

42 Badge of the Colony

43 Badge of the Colony

(Recess B.W. (T **41**), D.L.R. (others))

1951 (8 Jan). Wmk Mult Script CA. P 11½ (T **41**), 11½×12½ (T **42**), and 11½×13 (T **43**).

172	**41**	½c. black and red-brown	15	1·60
173		1c. black and emerald-green	15	25
174		2c. black and brown	15	50
175		3c. black and rose-carmine	15	10
176		4c. black and orange	35	40
177		5c. black and violet	20	10
178		6c. black and olive	30	60
179		7c. black and light blue	1·75	10
180		12c. black and purple	2·25	30
181	**42**	25c. black and sepia	2·50	80
182		50c. black and blue	7·00	40
183		$1.50 black and yellow-orange	9·00	8·50
184	**43**	$2.50 slate-blue and carmine	17·00	5·50
172/184		Set of 13	35·00	17·00

1951 (16 Feb). Inauguration of B.W.I. University College. As Nos. 118/19 of Antigua.

| 185 | | 3c. black and carmine | 45 | 1·25 |
| 186 | | 6c. black and olive | 45 | 50 |

NEW CONSTITUTION

1951
(44)

1951 (21 Sept). New Constitution. Nos. 175/7 and 180 optd with T **44** by B.W.

187	**41**	3c. black and rose-carmine	55	70
188		4c. black and orange	60	70
189		5c. black and violet (R.)	60	90
190		12c. black and purple	75	1·25
187/90		Set of 4	2·25	3·25

1953 (3 June). Coronation. As No. 120 of Antigua.

| 191 | | 3c. black and carmine-red | 30 | 10 |

45 Queen Elizabeth II

46 Badge of the Colony

47 Badge of the Colony

(Recess B.W. (T **45**), D.L.R. (T **46**/**7**))

1953 (15 June)–**59**. Wmk Mult Script CA. P 11½ (T **45**), 11½×12½ (T **46**), or 11½×13 (T **47**).

192	**45**	½c. black and brown (28.12.53)	10	1·00
193		1c. black and deep emerald	10	10
194		2c. black and sepia (15.9.53)	60	10

195		3c. black and carmine-red (22.2.54)	20	10
196		4c. black and brown-orange (22.2.54)	20	10
197		5c. black and deep violet (22.2.54)	20	10
198		6c. black and olive-green (28.12.53)	2·25	1·25
199		7c. black and blue (6.6.55)	2·75	10
200		12c. black and reddish purple	60	10
201	**46**	25c. black and sepia (10.1.55)	1·50	20
202		50c. black and deep blue (2.12.55)	5·50	1·00
203		$1.50 black and brown-orange (2.12.55)	17·00	14·00
204	**47**	$2.50 slate-blue and carmine (16.11.59)	40·00	26·00
192/204		Set of 13	60·00	26·00

On 23 December 1965, No. 203 was issued surcharged "2" but this was intended for fiscal and revenue purposes and it was not authorised to be used postally, although some are known to have passed through the mail (*Price* £10, *unused*).

For stamps in Types **45**/**6** watermarked w **12** see Nos. 214/20.

1958 (22 Apr). Inauguration of British Caribbean Federation. As Nos. 135/7 of Antigua.

205		3c. deep green	50	10
206		6c. blue	65	90
207		12c. scarlet	80	10
205/7		Set of 3	1·75	1·00

48 Queen Victoria, Queen Elizabeth II, Mail Van and Post Office, St George's

(Photo Harrison)

1961 (1 June). Grenada Stamp Centenary. T **48** and similar horiz designs. W w **12**. P 14½×14.

208		3c. crimson and black	25	10
209		8c. bright blue and orange	55	25
210		25c. lake and blue	55	25
208/10		Set of 3	1·25	55

Designs:—8c. Queen Victoria, Queen Elizabeth II and flagship of Columbus; 25c. Queen Victoria, Queen Elizabeth II, *Solent I* (paddle-steamer) and Douglas DC-3 aircraft.

1963 (4 June). Freedom from Hunger. As No. 146 of Antigua.

| 211 | | 8c. bluish green | 30 | 15 |

1963 (2 Sept). Red Cross Centenary. As Nos. 147/8 of Antigua.

| 212 | | 3c. red and black | 20 | 15 |
| 213 | | 25c. red and blue | 40 | 15 |

1964 (12 May)–**66**. As Nos. 194/8, 201/1, but wmk w **12**.

214	**45**	2c. black and sepia	1·25	20
215		3c. black and carmine-red	1·50	10
216		4c. black and brown-orange	50	1·25
217		5c. black and deep violet	50	10
218		6c. black and olive-green (4.1.66)	£200	85·00
219		12c. black and reddish purple	1·75	70
220	**46**	25c. black and sepia	5·00	3·00
214/20		Set of 7	£200	85·00

1965 (17 May). ITU Centenary. As Nos. 166/7 of Antigua.

| 221 | | 2c. red-orange and yellow-olive | 10 | 10 |
| 222 | | 50c. lemon and light red | 25 | 20 |

1965 (25 Oct). International Co-operation Year. As Nos. 168/9 of Antigua.

| 223 | | 1c. reddish purple and turquoise-green | 10 | 15 |
| 224 | | 25c. deep bluish green and lavender | 45 | 15 |

1966 (24 Jan). Churchill Commemoration. As Nos. 170/3 of Antigua.

225		1c. new blue	10	30
226		3c. deep green	30	20
227		25c. brown	65	10
228		35c. bluish violet	70	15
225/8		Set of 4	1·50	65

1966 (4 Feb). Royal Visit. As Nos. 174/5 of Antigua.

| 229 | | 3c. black and ultramarine | 40 | 15 |
| 230 | | 35c. black and magenta | 1·40 | 15 |

52 Hillsborough, Carriacou

53 Bougainvillea

54 Flamboyant plant

55 Levera beach

56 Carenage, St George's

57 Annandale Falls

58 Cocoa pods

59 Inner Harbour

60 Nutmeg

61 St George's

62 Grand Anse beach

63 Bananas

64 Badge of the colony

65 Queen Elizabeth II

66 Map of Grenada

(Des V. Whiteley. Photo Harrison)

1966 (1 Apr). Designs as T **52/66**. Multicoloured. W w **12**. P 14½ ($1, $2, $3) or 14½×13½ (others).

231	52	1c. Multicoloured	20	1·25
232	53	2c. carmine and myrtle green	20	10
233	54	3c. Multicoloured	1·00	1·00
234	55	5c. Multicoloured	1·25	10
235	56	6c. Multicoloured	1·00	10
236	57	8c. Multicoloured	1·00	10
		w. Wmk inverted		
237	58	10c. Multicoloured	1·25	10
		w. Wmk inverted	—	£160
238	59	12c. Multicoloured	30	1·25
239	60	15c. Multicoloured	30	1·25
240	61	25c. Multicoloured	30	10
241	62	35c. Multicoloured	30	10
242	63	50c. emerald and lavender	1·25	2·00
243	64	$1 Multicoloured	7·50	3·75
244	65	$2 Multicoloured	6·00	15·00
245	66	$3 Multicoloured	7·00	21·00
231/45 *Set of 15*			26·00	42·00

1966 (1 July). World Cup Football Championship. As Nos. 176/7 of Antigua.

246		5c. violet, yellow-green, lake and yellow-brown	10	10
247		50c. chocolate, blue-green, lake and yellow-brown	40	90

1966 (20 Sept). Inauguration of WHO Headquarters, Geneva. As Nos. 178/9 of Antigua.

248		8c. black, yellow-green and light blue	20	10
249		25c. black, light purple and yellow-brown	45	20

1966 (1 Dec). 20th Anniv of UNESCO. As Nos. 196/8 of Antigua.

250		2c. slate-violet, red, yellow and orange	10	10
251		15c. orange-yellow, violet and deep olive	15	10
252		50c. black, bright purple and orange	50	90
250/2 *Set of 3*			65	1·00

ASSOCIATED STATEHOOD

(67) **(68)**

1967 (3 Mar). Statehood. Nos. 232/3, 236 and 240 optd with T **67**, in silver.

253	53	2c. Bougainvillea	10	20
254	54	3c. Flamboyant plant	10	15
255	57	8c. Annandale Falls	15	10
256	61	25c. St George's	15	15
253/6 *Set of 4*			30	50

1967 (1 June). World Fair, Montreal. Nos. 232, 237, 239 and 243/4 surch as T **68** or optd with "Expo" emblem only.

257	60	1c. on 15c. Nutmeg	10	20
		a. Surch and opt albino	16·00	
258	53	2c. Bougainvillea	10	20
259	58	3c. on 10c. Cocoa pods	10	20
		w. Wmk inverted	12·00	
260	64	$1 Badge of the Colony	30	25
261	65	$2 Queen Elizabeth II	45	30
257/61 *Set of 5*			70	1·00

ASSOCIATED STATEHOOD
(69)

70 Kennedy and Local Flower

1967 (1 Oct). Statehood. Nos. 231/45 optd with T **69**.

262	52	1c. Hillsborough, Carriacou	10	10
263	53	2c. Bougainvillea	10	10
264	54	3c. Flamboyant plant	10	10
265	55	5c. Levera beach	10	10
266	56	6c. Carenaga St George's	10	10
267	57	8c. Annandale Falls	10	10
268	58	10c. Cocoa pods	10	10
269	59	12c. Inner harbour	10	10
270	60	15c. Nutmeg	15	10
271	61	25c. St George's	20	10
272	62	35c. Grand Anse beach	55	10
273	63	50c. Bananas	1·00	20
274	64	$1 Badge of the Colony	1·50	60
275	65	$2 Queen Elizabeth II	1·25	3·75
276	66	$3 Map of Grenada	4·50	6·00
262/76 *Set of 15*			8·50	10·50

See also No. 295.

(Des M. Shamir. Photo Harrison)

1968 (13 Jan). 50th Birth Anniv of President Kennedy. T **70** and similar horiz designs. Multicoloured. P 14½×14.

277		1c. Type **70**	10	25
278		15c. Type **70**	15	10
279		25c. Kennedy and strelitzia	20	10
280		35c. Kennedy and roses	20	10
281		50c. As 25c.	25	20
282		$1 As 35c.	30	60
277/82 *Set of 6*			1·00	1·00

73 Scout Bugler **76** Near Antibes

(Des K. Plowitz. Photo Govt Printer, Israel)

1968 (17 Feb). World Scout Jamboree, Idaho. T **73** and similar vert designs. Multicoloured. P 13×13½.

283		1c. Type **73**	10	10
284		2c. Scouts camping	10	10
285		3c. Lord Baden-Powell	10	10
286		35c. Type **73**	25	10
287		50c. As 2c.	35	20
288		$1 As 3c.	50	55
283/8 *Set of 6*			1·10	80

(Des G. Vasarhelyi. Photo Harrison)

1968 (23 Mar). Paintings by Sir Winston Churchill. T **76** and similar horiz designs. Multicoloured. P 14×14½.

289		10c. Type **76**	10	10
290		12c. *The Mediterranean*	15	10
291		15c. *St Jean Cap Ferratt*	15	10
292		25c. Type **76**	20	10
293		35c. As 15c.	25	10
294		50c. Sir Winston painting	35	25
289/94 *Set of 6*			1·10	45

(80) **(81)** **(82)**

1968 (18 May). No. 275 surch with T **80**.

295	65	$5 on $2 multicoloured	1·25	2·25

1968 (22 July–19 Aug). "Children Need Milk".

(a) Nos. 244/5 surch locally as T **81** (22 July)

296	65	2c. +3c. on $2 multicoloured	10	10
297	66	3c. +3c. on $3 multicoloured	10	10
		a. Surch inverted	55·00	21·00
		b. Surch double	28·00	
		c. Surch double, one albino		

(b) Nos. 243/4 surch locally as T **82** (19 Aug)

298	64	1c. +3c. on $1 multicoloured	10	40
		a. Surch on No. 274	75·00	75·00
		b. Surch double	38·00	
299	65	2c. +3c. on $2 multicoloured	23·00	60·00
		a. Surch on No. 275	85·00	
296/9 *Set of 4*			23·00	60·00

83 Edith McGuire (USA)

86 Hibiscus

(Des M. Shamir. Photo Harrison)

1968 (24 Sept). Olympic Games, Mexico. T **83** and similar square designs. P 12½.

300		1c. brown, black and blue	70	1·00
301		2c. orange, brown, blue and lilac	70	1·00
		a. Orange (badge, etc.) omitted		
302		3c. scarlet, brown and dull green	70	1·00
		a. Scarlet (rings, "MEXICO" etc.) omitted	£1200	£1000
303		10c. brown, black, blue and vermilion	80	1·10
304		50c. orange, brown, blue and turquoise	80	1·10
305		60c. scarlet, brown and red-orange	80	1·10
300/5 *Set of 6*			4·00	5·50

Designs:—2, 50c. Arthur Wint (Jamaica); 3, 60c. Ferreira da Silva (Brazil); 10c. Type **83**.

Nos. 300/2 and 303/5 were issued in separate composite sheets containing three strips of three with three *se-tenant* labels showing Greek athlete (Nos. 300/2) or Discobolos (Nos. 303/5). (*Price for two sheets* £8 *mint,* £12 *used*).

(Des G. Vasarhelyi (No. 314a), V. Whiteley (75c.), M. Shamir (others). Litho Format (Nos. 314a and 317a). Photo Harrison (others))

1968 (1 Oct)–**71**. Multicoloured designs as T **86**. P 13½ (Nos. 314a. and 317a), 13½×14½ (vert except No. 314a) or 14½×13½ (horiz except No. 317a).

306		1c. Type **86**	10	10
307		2c. Strelitzia	10	10
308		3c. Bougainvillea (1.7.69)	10	10
309		5c. Rock Hind (*horiz*) (4.2.69)	10	10
310		6c. Sailfish	10	10
311		8c. Red Snapper (*horiz*) (1.7.69)	10	60
312		10c. Marine Toad (*horiz*) (4.2.69)	10	10
313		12c. Turtle	15	10
314		15c. Tree Boa (*horiz*)	1·00	60
314a		15c. Thunbergia (1970)	1·50	2·50
315		25c. Greater Trinidadian Murine Opossum (4.2.69)	30	10
316		35c. Nine-banded Armadillo (*horiz*) (1.7.69)	35	10
317		50c. Mona Monkey	45	25
317a		75c. Yacht in St. George's Harbour (*horiz*) (9.10.71)	18·00	9·50
318		$1 Bananaquit	2·50	2·50
319		$2 Brown Pelican (4.2.69)	8·00	17·00
320		$3 Magnificent Frigate Bird	3·75	10·00
321		$5 Bare-eyed Thrush (1.7.69)	13·00	27·00
306/21 *Set of 18*			45·00	60·00

Nos. 314a, 317a and the dollar values are larger—29×45½, 44×28½ and 25½×48 mm respectively.

No. 317a exists imperforate from stock dispersed by the liquidator of Format International Security Printers Ltd.

102 Kidney Transplant

106 "The Adoration of the Kings" (Veronese)

(Des M. Shamir. Litho B.W.)

1968 (25 Nov). 20th Anniv of World Health Organization. T **102** and similar vert designs. Multicoloured. P 13×13½.

322		5c. Type **102**	20	10
323		25c. Heart transplant	30	10
324		35c. Lung transplant	30	10
325		50c. Eye transplant	40	50
322/5 *Set of 4*			1·10	60

(Photo Harrison)

1968 (3 Dec). Christmas. T **106** and similar square designs. P 12½.

326		5c. multicoloured	10	10
327		15c. multicoloured	10	10
328		35c. multicoloured	10	10
329		$1 multicoloured	30	40
326/9 *Set of 4*			40	45

Designs:—15c. *Madonna and Child with Sts John and Catherine* (Titian); 35c. *Adoration of the Kings* (Botticelli); $1 *A Warrior Adoring* (Catena).

VISIT CARIFTA EXPO '69
April 5-30

5c

(110)

1969 (1 Feb). Caribbean Free Trade Area Exhibition. Nos. 300/5 surch in red as T **110**.

330		5c. on 1c. brown, black and blue	20	30
		a. Surch double		
331		8c. on 2c. orange, brown, blue and lilac	20	30
		a. Surch double		

332	25c. on 3c. scarlet, brown and dull green	20	30
	a. Surch double		
333	35c. on 10c. brown, black, blue and vermilion	20	30
334	$1 on 50c. orange, brown, blue and turquoise	25	40
335	$2 on 60c. scarlet, brown and red-orange	35	60
	a. Scarlet (rings, "MEXICO" etc) omitted	†	—
330/5	Set of 6	1·25	2·00

The centre of the composite sheets is also overprinted with a commemorative inscription publicising CARIFTA EXPO 1969 (*Price for two sheets £4 mint, £7 used*).

111 Dame Hylda Bynoe (Governor) and Island Scene

(Des and litho D.L.R.)

1969 (1 May). Carifta Expo 1969. T **111** and similar horiz designs. Multicoloured. P 13×13½.

336	5c. Type **111**	10	10
337	15c. Premier E. M. Gairy and Island scene	10	10
338	50c. Type **111**	10	30
339	60c. Emblems of 1958 and 1967 World's Fairs	10	65
336/9	Set of 4	30	70

114 Dame Hylda Bynoe

115 *Balshazzar's Feast* (Rembrandt)

(Photo Enschedé)

1969 (8 June). Human Rights Year. T **114/15** and similar multicoloured design. P 12½×13 ($1) or 13×12½ (others).

340	5c. Type **114**	10	10
341	25c. Dr Martin Luther King (*vert*)	15	10
342	35c. Type **114**	15	10
343	$1 Type **115**	30	45
340/3	Set of 4	55	55

117 Batsman and Wicket-keeper

(Des M. Shamir and L. W. Denyer. Photo Harrison)

1969 (1 Aug). Cricket. T **117** and similar horiz designs. P 14×14½.

344	3c. yellow, brown and ultramarine	75	1·25
	a. Yellow (caps and wicket) omitted	£1100	
345	10c. multicoloured	75	40
346	25c. brown, ochre and myrtle-green	85	85
347	35c. multicoloured	1·00	90
344/7	Set of 4	3·00	3·00

Designs:—10c. Batsman playing defensive stroke; 25c. Batsman sweeping ball; 35c. Batsman playing on-drive.

Nos. 344/7 were each issued in small sheets of nine (3×3) with decorative borders.

129 Astronaut handling Moon Rock

(Des G. Vasarhelyi. Photo)

1969 (24 Sept). First Man on the Moon. T **129** and similar multicoloured designs. P 13½ (½c.) or 12½ (others).

348	½c. As Type **129** but larger (56×35 *mm*)	10	50
349	1c. Moon rocket and moon	10	50
350	2c. Module landing	10	50
351	3c. Declaration left on moon	10	50
352	8c. Module leaving rocket	20	10
353	25c. Rocket lifting-off (*vert*)	45	10
354	35c. Spacecraft in orbit (*vert*)	45	10
355	50c. Capsule with parachutes (*vert*)	60	30
356	$1 Type **129**	90	1·50
348/56	Set of 9	2·50	3·50
MS357	115×90 mm. Nos. 351 and 356. Imperf	1·25	3·00

130 Gandhi

(Des A. Robledo. Litho B.W.)

1969 (8 Oct). Birth Centenary of Mahatma Gandhi. T **130** and similar designs. P 11½.

358	**130** 6c. multicoloured	45	30
359	– 15c. multicoloured	60	10
360	– 25c. multicoloured	70	10
361	– $1 multicoloured	1·00	65
358/61	Set of 4	2·50	1·00
MS362	155×122 mm. Nos. 358/61. Imperf	2·75	3·75

Designs: Vert—15c. Gandhi standing; 25c. Gandhi walking. Horiz—$1 Head of Gandhi.

(134) **135** "Blackbeard" (Edward Teach)

1969 (23 Dec). Christmas. Nos. 326/9 surch with T **134** in black (2c.) or optd with new date only in silver (others).

363	2c. on 15c. multicoloured	10	2·25
	a. Surch inverted	50·00	
364	5c. multicoloured	10	15
	a. Opt double	50·00	
365	35c. multicoloured	20	10
	a. Opt inverted	50·00	
	b. Horiz pair, one with opt omitted	£225	
	c. Opt double, one vertical	55·00	
366	$1 multicoloured	80	2·25
	a. Opt inverted	50·00	
363/6	Set of 4	1·00	4·25

(Des K. Plowitz. Recess B.W.)

1970 (2 Feb). Pirates. T **135** and similar vert designs. P 13½.

367	15c. black	75	10
368	25c. dull green	1·00	10
369	50c. lilac	1·50	60
370	$1 carmine	2·25	2·75
367/70	Set of 4	5·00	3·25

Designs:—25c. Anne Bonney; 50c. Jean Lafitte; $1 Mary Read.

 (139) (140)

1970 (18 Mar). No. 348 surch with T **139**.

371	5c. on ½c. multicoloured	10	10
	a. Surch double	27·00	
	b. Surch with T **140**	70	70
	ba. Surch double, one inverted	48·00	

141/2 *The Last Supper* (detail, Del Sarto)

(Des and litho B.W.)

1970 (13 Apr). Easter. Paintings. T **141/2** and similar vert design. Mulicoloured. P 11½.

372	5c. Type **141**	20	50
	a. Horiz pair. Nos. 372/3	40	1·00
373	5c. Type **142**	20	50
374	15c. *Christ crowned with Thorns* (detail, Van Dyck)	20	50
	a. Horiz pair. Nos. 374/5	40	1·00
375	15c. As No. 374	20	50
376	25c. *The Passion of Christ* (detail, Memling)	20	50
	a. Horiz pair. Nos. 376/7	40	1·00
377	25c. As No. 376	20	50
378	60c. *Christ in the Tomb* (detail, Rubens)	25	60
	a. Horiz pair. Nos. 378/9	50	1·10
379	60c. As No. 378	25	60
372/9	Set of 8	1·50	3·75
MS380	120×140 mm. Nos. 376/9	1·00	1·75

Nos. 372/9 were issued with each design spread over two *se-tenant* stamps of the same denomination.

149 Girl with Kittens in Pram

(Des A. Robledo. Litho Questa)

1970 (27 May). Birth Bicentenary of William Wordsworth (poet). "Children and Pets". T **149** and similar horiz designs. Multicoloured. P 11.

381	5c. Type **149**	15	15
382	15c. Girl with puppy and kitten	25	15
383	30c. Boy with fishing rod and cat	30	40
384	60c. Boys and girls with cats and dogs	40	2·00
381/4	Set of 4	1·00	2·40
MS385	Two sheets each 114×126 mm. Nos. 381, 383 and Nos. 382, 384. Imperf	1·00	2·00

153 Parliament of India

(Des G. Vasarhelyi. Litho Questa)

1970 (15 June). Seventh Regional Conference of Commonwealth Parliamentary Association. T **153** and similar horiz designs. Multicoloured. P 14.

386	5c. Type **153**	10	10
387	25c. Parliament of Great Britain, Westminster	10	10
388	50c. Parliament of Canada	20	15
389	60c. Parliament of Grenada	20	15
386/9	Set of 4	50	35
MS390	126×90 mm. Nos. 386/9	50	1·00

157 Tower of the Sun

(Litho Kyodo Printing Co, Tokyo)

1970 (8 Aug). World Fair, Osaka. T **157** and similar multicoloured designs. P 13.

391	1c. Type **157**	10	65
392	2c. Livelihood and Industry Pavilion (*horiz*)	10	65
393	3c. Flower painting, 1634	10	65
394	10c. *Adam and Eve* (Tintoretto) (*horiz*)	15	10
395	25c. OECD (Organisation for Economic Co-operation and Development) Pavilion (*horiz*)	35	10
396	50c. San Francisco Pavilion	40	1·60
391/6	Set of 6	1·00	3·25
MS397	121×91 mm. $1 Japanese Pavilion (56×34 *mm*)	55	1·50

164 Roosevelt and "Raising US Flag on Iwo Jima"

(Litho Questa)

1970 (3 Sept). 25th Anniv of Ending of World War II. T **164** and similar horiz designs. Multicoloured. P 11.

398	½c. Type **164**	10	2·50
399	5c. Zhukov and "Fall of Berlin"	1·00	65
400	15c. Churchill and "Evacuation at Dunkirk"	3·25	1·50
401	25c. De Gaulle and "Liberation of Paris"	1·50	60
402	50c. Eisenhower and "D-Day Landing"	1·75	2·50
403	60c. Montgomery and "Battle of Alamein"	3·50	5·50
398/403	Set of 6	10·00	12·00
MS404	163×113 mm. Nos. 398, 400, 402/3	4·50	10·00
	a. Brown (panel) on 60c. value omitted	£1000	

PHILYMPIA LONDON 1970
(169)

170 UPU Emblem, Building and Transport

1970 (18 Sept). Philympia 1970 Stamp Exhibition, London. Nos. 353/6 optd with T **169**.
405	25c. Rocket lifting-off	10	10
	a. Albino opt	5·00	
	b. Opt inverted	17·00	
406	35c. Spacecraft in orbit	10	10
	a. Opt inverted	55·00	
	b. Opt double, one albino, one inverted	75·00	
407	50c. Capsule with parachutes	15	15
	a. Albino opt	3·50	
408	$1 Type **129** (Sil.) (optd vert upwards)	20	30
	a. Albino opt	6·50	
	b. Opt inverted (vert downwards)		
405/8 *Set of 4*		40	50

The miniature sheet was also overprinted but we understand that only 300 of these were put on sale in Grenada.

(Litho Questa)

1970 (17 Oct). New UPU Headquarters Building. T **170** and similar multicoloured designs. P 14.
409	15c. Type **170**	1·50	40
410	25c. As Type **170**, but modern transport	1·50	40
411	50c. Sir Rowland Hill and UPU Building	35	60
412	$1 Abraham Lincoln and UPU Building	45	3·25
409/12 *Set of 4*		3·50	4·25
MS413 79×85 mm. Nos. 411/12		1·00	3·75

The 50c. and $1 are both vertical designs.

171 *The Madonna of the Goldfinch* (Tiepolo)

172 19th-Century Nursing

(Des G. Vasarhelyi. Litho Questa)

1970 (5 Dec). Christmas. T **171** and similar vert designs. Multicoloured. P 13½.
414	½c. Type **171**	10	45
415	½c. *The Virgin and Child with St Peter and St. Paul* (Bouts)	10	45
416	½c. *The Virgin and Child* (Bellini)	10	45
417	2c. *The Madonna of the Basket* (Correggio)	10	45
418	3c. Type **171**	10	45
419	35c. As No. 415	50	10
420	50c. As No. 417	60	40
421	$1 As No. 416	70	1·60
414/21 *Set of 8*		1·75	3·75
MS422 102×87 mm. Nos. 420/1		1·00	3·25

(Des G. Vasarhelyi. Litho Questa)

1970 (12 Dec). Centenary of British Red Cross. T **172** and similar horiz designs. Multicoloured. P 14½×14.
423	5c. Type **172**	40	20
424	15c. Military Ambulance, 1918	1·00	20
425	25c. First-Aid Post, 1941	1·00	20
426	60c. Red Cross Transport, 1970	1·75	2·50
423/6 *Set of 4*		3·75	2·75
MS427 113×82 mm. Nos. 423/6		3·75	2·75
	a. Error. Imperf	30·00	

POSTAGE DUE STAMPS

1d.

SURCHARGE POSTAGE

D **1** (D **2**)

(Typo D.L.R.)

1892 (18 Apr–Oct).
*(a) Type D **1**. Wmk Crown CA. P 14*
D1	D **1**	1d. blue-black	40·00	1·50
D2		2d. blue-black	£250	1·50
D3		3d. blue-black	£250	2·50
D1/3 *Set of 3*			£475	5·00

*(b) Nos. 34 and 35 surch locally as Type D **2***
D4	**13**	1d. on 6d. mauve (10.92)	£130	1·25
		a. *Tête-bêche* (vert pair)	£3500	£1500
		b. Surch double	†	£275
D5		1d. on 8d. grey-brown (8.92)	£3000	3·25
		a. *Tête-bêche* (vert pair)	£12000	£2750
		b. Damaged value	—	75·00
D6		2d. on 6d. mauve (10.92)	£200	2·50
		a. *Tête-bêche* (vert pair)	£4000	£1900

D7		2d. on 8d. grey-brown (8.92)	£5000	13·00
		a. *Tête-bêche* (vert pair)	—	£5500
		b. Damaged value	—	£150

Nos. D4/7 were in use from August to November 1892. As supplies of Nos. D1/3 were available from April or May of that year it would not appear that they were intended for postage due purposes. There was a shortage of 1d. postage stamps in July and August, but this was alleviated by Nos. 44/5 which were still available. The provisionals may have been intended for postal purposes, but the vast majority appear to have been used philatelically.

1906 (1 July)–**11**. Wmk Mult Crown CA. P 14.
D8	D **1**	1d. blue-black (1911)	5·00	7·50
D9		2d. blue-black	12·00	1·50
D10		3d. blue-black (9.06)	19·00	5·00
D8/10 *Set of 3*		32·00	12·50

1921 (1 Dec)–**22**. As Type D **1**, but inscr "POSTAGE DUE". Wmk Mult Script CA. P 14.
D11		1d. black	3·00	1·00
D12		1½d. black (15.12.22)	13·00	32·00
D13		2d. black	3·25	1·75
D14		3d. black	2·25	4·00
D11/14 *Set of 4*		19·00	35·00
D11s/14s Optd "SPECIMEN" *Set of 4*		80·00	

1952 (1 Mar). As Type D **1**, but inscr "POSTAGE DUE". Value in cents. Chalk-surfaced paper. Wmk Mult Script CA. P 14.
D15		2c. black	30	12·00
		a. Error. Crown missing. W **9a**	£180	
		b. Error. St. Edward Crown. W **9b**	55·00	
D16		4c. black	30	20·00
		a. Error. Crown missing. W **9a**	£180	
		b. Error. St Edward Crown. W **9b**	60·00	
D17		6c. black	45	12·00
		a. Error. Crown missing. W **9a**	£275	
		b. Error. St. Edward Crown. W **9b**	£100	
D18		8c. black	75	17·00
		a. Error. Crown missing. W **9a**	£475	
		b. Error. St. Edward Crown. W **9b**	£225	
D15/18 *Set of 4*		1·60	55·00

Griqualand West *see* South Africa

Guyana

GUYANA INDEPENDENCE 1966
(73)

1966 (26 May)–**67**. Various stamps of British Guiana as Nos. 331/45 optd with T **73** by De La Rue.
(a) Wmk Mult Script CA
378		2c. myrtle-green	80	40
379		3c. brown-olive and red-brown	2·50	6·00
		a. "Weed" flaw	50·00	
		b. "Clubbed foot"	50·00	
380		4c. violet	3·25	75
381		6c. yellow-green	60	10
382		8c. ultramarine	3·25	2·00
		w. Wmk inverted	†	£450
383		12c. black and reddish brown	4·50	1·25
384		$5 ultramarine and black	27·00	60·00
378/84 *Set of 7*		38·00	65·00

*(b) Wmk w **12** (upright)*
385		1c. black (28.2.67)	10	30
386		3c. brown-olive and red-brown	1·25	10
387		4c. violet (28.2.67)	20	2·75
388		5c. scarlet and black	40	10
389		6c. green (28.2.67)	10	20
390		8c. ultramarine (14.3.67)	3·25	2·00
391		12c. black and yellowish brown	10	10
392		24c. black and bright orange	8·00	1·25
393		30c. carmine and black	30	30
394		48c. bright ultramarine and Venetian red	5·50	13·00
395		72c. carmine and emerald	1·00	1·50
396		$1 pink, yellow, green and black	10·00	35
397		$2 reddish mauve	1·50	1·75
398		$5 ultramarine and black	1·00	7·00
385/98 *Set of 14*		29·00	27·00

*(c) Wmk w **12** (sideways)*
399		1c. black	10	10
400		4c. violet	10	10
401		8c. ultramarine	10	10
402		12c. black and yellowish brown (28.2.67)	10	10
403		24c. black and bright orange	2·00	60
404		36c. rose-carmine and black (28.2.67)	30	2·50
405		48c. bright ultramarine and Venetian red	30	30
406		72c. carmine and emerald (28.2.67)	3·25	7·50
407		$1 pink, yellow, green and black (14.3.67)	11·00	7·00
407a		$2 reddish mauve (28.2.67)	3·00	5·50
407b		$5 ultramarine and black (28.2.67)	1·50	5·50
399/407b *Set of 11*		19·00	26·00

See also Nos. 420/40.

74 Flag and Map | **75** Arms of Guyana

(Des V. Whiteley. Photo Harrison)

1966 (26 May). Independence. P 14½.
408	**74**	5c. multicoloured	30	10
409		15c. multicoloured	40	10
410	**75**	25c. multicoloured	40	10
411		$1 multicoloured	1·10	1·25
408/11 *Set of 4*		2·00	1·25

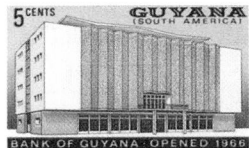

76 Bank Building

(Des B. Granger Barrett. Photo Enschedé)

1966 (11 Oct). Opening of Bank of Guyana. P 13½×14.
412	**76**	5c. multicoloured	10	10
413		25c. multicoloured	10	10

CANCELLED REMAINDERS.* In 1969 remainders of some issues were put on the market cancelled-to-order in such a way as to be indistinguishable from genuine postally used copies for all practical purposes. Our used quotations which are indicated by an asterisk are the same for cancelled-to-order or postally used copies.

77 British Guiana One Cent Stamp of 1856

(Des V. Whiteley. Litho D.L.R.)

1967 (23 Feb). World's Rarest Stamp Commemoration. P 12½.

414	**77**	5c. black, magenta, silver and light ochre	10	10*
415		25c. black, magenta, gold and light green	10	10*

78 Chateau Margot

GUYANA
INDEPENDENCE
1966
(82)

(Des R. Granger Barrett. Photo Harrison)

1967 (26 May). First Anniv of Independence. T **78** and similar multicoloured designs. P 14 (6c.), 14½×14 (15c.) or 14×14½ (others).

416	6c. Type **78**	10	10*
417	15c. Independence Arch	10	10*
418	25c. Fort Island (horiz)	10	10*
419	$1 National Assembly (horiz)	20	15
416/19 Set of 4		30	20

1967 (3 Oct)–**68**. Stamps of British Guiana as Nos. 331/45 optd with T **82** locally.

(i) Wmk Mult Script CA

420	1c. black (3.10.67)	10	10
	a. Opt inverted	60·00	
	b. Date misplaced 5 mm	13·00	13·00
	c. Date misplaced 2 mm	13·00	13·00
421	2c. myrtle-green (3.10.67)	10	10
	a. "1966" for "GUYANA"	18·00	20·00
	b. Date misplaced 5 mm	13·00	13·00
	c. Date misplaced 2 mm	13·00	13·00
422	3c. brown-olive and red-brown (3.10.67)	30	10
	a. "1966" for "GUYANA"	15·00	15·00
	b. Vert pair, one without opt	£600	
	c. Date misplaced 2 mm	13·00	13·00
423	4c. violet (10.67)	10	10
	a. Deep violet	1·50	1·25
	b. Opt inverted	80·00	85·00
424	6c. yellow-green (11.67)	25	10
	a. "1966" for "GUYANA"	28·00	42·00
	b. Opt inverted	65·00	70·00
	c. Opt double	85·00	90·00
425	8c. ultramarine (12.67)	10	10
426	12c. black and brown (12.67)	10	10
426a	24c. black and orange (date?)	£500	£170
427	$2 reddish mauve (12.67)	1·50	4·50
428	$5 ultramarine and black (12.67)	2·00	4·00

*(ii) Wmk w **12** (upright)*

429	1c. black (2.68)	10	2·50
	a. Opt omitted	£350	
430	2c. myrtle-green (2.68)	1·00	5·50
431	3c. brown-olive and red-brown (3.10.67)	30	10
	a. "1966" for "GUYANA"	85·00	85·00
	b. Opt inverted	35·00	
432	4c. violet (2.68)	20	3·75
433	5c. scarlet and black (3.10.67)	2·00	4·25
	a. Deep scarlet and black	2·00	4·50
	aw. Wmk inverted	95·00	
	c. Date misplaced 2 mm	12·00	
434	6c. yellow-green (2.68)	30	3·00
	a. Opt double, one diagonal	95·00	
435	24c. black and bright orange (11.12.67)	11·00	10
	a. Opt double, one diagonal (horiz pair)	£200	
436	36c. rose-carmine and black (12.67)	3·25	10
437	48c. bright ultramarine and Venetian red (12.67)	2·75	2·50
	a. Opt inverted	£110	£130
438	72c. carmine and emerald (12.67)	4·50	1·25
439	$1 pink, yellow, green and black (12.67)	5·00	65
440	$2 reddish mauve (12.67)	5·50	4·00
420/40 (excl. 426a) Set of 21		35·00	32·00

The "1966" errors occurred on R. 7/10 and were later corrected. Nos. 425/8 and 436/40 were issued in mid-December, but some were cancelled-to-order with a November date in error.

On Nos. 420b and 421b the "1" of "1966" is below the second "D" of "INDEPENDENCE" (R. 6/3). On Nos. 420c, 421c, 422c and 433 it is below the second "E" (R. 6/1). Lesser misplacements exist in other positions.

No. 433a is from a printing made specially for this overprint.

83 "Millie" (Blue and Yellow Macaw)

84 Wicket-keeping

(Des V. Whiteley. Photo Harrison)

1967 (6 Nov)–**68**. Christmas. P 14½×14.

(a) First issue (6 Nov 1967)

441	**83**	5c. yellow, new blue, black and bronze-green	10	10*
442		25c. yellow, new blue, black and violet	15	10*

(b) Second issue. Colours changed (22 Jan 1968)

443	**83**	5c. yellow, new blue, black and red	10	10*
444		25c. yellow, new blue, black and apple-green	15	10*

(Des V. Whiteley. Photo Harrison)

1968 (8 Jan). MCC's West Indies Tour. T **84** and similar vert designs. P 14.

445	5c. Type **84**	10	10*
	a. Strip of 3. Nos. 445/7	45	20*
446	6c. Batting	10	10*
447	25c. Bowling	30	10*
445/7 Set of 3		45	20*

Nos. 445/7 were issued in small sheets of nine containing three se-tenant strips.

87 Pike Cichlid

102 Christ of St John of the Cross (Salvador Dali)

(Des R. Granger Barrett. Photo Harrison)

1968 (4 Mar). Multicoloured designs as T **87**, showing fish (1 to 6c.), birds (10 to 40c.) or animals (others). No wmk. P 14×14½.

448	1c. Type **87**	10	10
449	2c. Red Piranha ("Pirai")	10	10
450	3c. Peacock Cichlid ("Lukunani ")	10	10
451	5c. Armoured Catfish ("Hassar")	10	10
452	6c. Black Acara ("Patua")	55	10
453	10c. Spix's Guan (vert)	75	10
454	15c. Harpy Eagle (vert)	1·60	10
455	20c. Hoatzin (vert)	1·00	10
456	25c. Guianan Cock of the Rock (vert)	70	10
457	40c. Great Kiskadee (vert)	3·00	75
458	50c. Brazilian Agouti ("Accouri")	1·50	50
459	60c. White-lipped Peccary	1·50	10
460	$1 Paca ("Labba")	1·00	10
461	$2 Nine-banded Armadillo	2·00	2·00
462	$5 Ocelot	1·00	3·00
448/62 Set of 15		13·00	6·00

For Nos. 448/62 with W **106** see Nos. 485/99.

(Des and photo Harrison)

1968 (25 Mar). Easter. P 14.

463	**102** 5c. multicoloured	10	10*
464	25c. multicoloured	20	10*

103 "Efficiency Year"

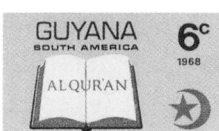

104 "Savings Bonds"

(Des W. Starzmann. Litho B.W.)

1968 (22 July). "Savings Bonds and Efficiency". P 14.

465	**103** 6c. multicoloured	10	10*
466	25c. multicoloured	10	10*
467	**104** 30c. multicoloured	10	10*
468	40c. multicoloured	10	10*
465/8 Set of 4		30	15*

105 Open Book, Star and Crescent

(Des R. Gates. Photo D.L.R.)

1968 (9 Oct). 1400th Anniv of the Holy Quran. P 14.

469	**105** 6c. black, gold and flesh	10	10*
470	25c. black, gold and lilac	10	10*
471	30c. black, gold and light apple-green	10	10*
472	40c. black, gold and cobalt	10	10*
469/72 Set of 4		30	15*

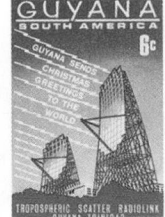

106 Lotus Blossoms

107 Broadcasting Greetings

(Des L. Pritchard; adapted G. Vasarhelyi. Litho D.L.R.)

1968 (11 Nov). Christmas. T **107** and similar vert design. W **106**. P 14.

473	6c. brown, blue and green	10	10*
474	25c. brown, reddish violet and green	10	10*
475	30c. blue-green and turquoise-green	10	10*
476	40c. red and turquoise-green	10	10*
473/6 Set of 4		30	15*

Designs:—25c. Type **107**; 30, 40c. Map showing radio link, Guyana-Trinidad.

109 Festival Ceremony

(Des J. Cooter. Litho P.B.)

1969 (26 Feb). Hindu Festival of Phagwah. T **109** and similar horiz design. Multicoloured. W **106** (sideways). P 13½.

477	6c. Type **109**	10	10
478	25c. Ladies spraying scent	10	10
479	30c. Type **109**	10	10
480	40c. As 25c.	10	10
477/80 Set of 4		30	20

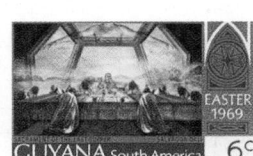

111 Sacrament of the Last Supper (Dali)

112 Map showing "CARIFTA" Countries

(Photo D.L.R.)

1969 (10 Mar). Easter. W **106** (sideways). P 13½×13.

481	**111** 6c. multicoloured	10	10
482	25c. multicoloured	10	10
483	30c. multicoloured	10	10
484	40c. multicoloured	10	10
481/4 Set of 4		30	15

1969–71. As Nos. 448/62, but Wmk **106** (sideways* on 1 to 6c. and 50c. to $5). Chalk-surfaced paper.

485	1c. Type **87**	10	10
486	2c. Red Piranha ("Pirai")	10	30
487	3c. Peacock Cichlid ("Lukunani")	10	75
488	5c. Armoured Catfish ("Hassar")	10	10
489	6c. Black Acara ("Patua")	10	1·00
490	10c. Spix's Guan	45	75
	a. Glazed paper (wmk inverted) (21.12.71)	1·00	7·00
491	15c. Harpy Eagle	60	10
	aw. Wmk inverted		
	b. Glazed paper (wmk inverted) (21.12.71)	1·25	6·00
492	20c. Hoatzin	50	80
493	25c. Guianan Cock of the Rock	45	10
	a. Glazed paper (wmk inverted) (21.12.71)	1·50	6·00
494	40c. Great Kiskadee	80	1·00
495	50c. Brazilian Agouti ("Accouri")	35	15
496	60c. White-lipped Peccary	35	1·00
497	$1 Paca ("Labba")	70	1·50
	a. Glazed paper (wmk top of blossom to right) (21.12.71)	1·75	14·00
498	$2 Nine-banded Armadillo	1·00	3·25
499	$5 Ocelot	1·00	5·00
485/99 Set of 15		5·75	14·00

*The normal sideways watermark shows the top of the blossom to the left, as seen from the back of the stamp.

These were put on sale by the Crown Agents on 25 March 1969 but although supplies were sent to Guyana in time they were not released there until needed as ample supplies remained of the stamps without watermark. It is understood that the 3c. and 5c. were put on sale in early May 1969 followed by the 25c. but there are no records of when the remainder were released.

(Des J. Cooter. Litho P.B.)

1969 (30 Apr). First Anniv of CARIFTA (Caribbean Free Trade Area). T **112** and similar design. W **106** (sideways on 25c.). P 13½.

500	6c. rose-red, ultramarine and turquoise-blue	15	15
501	25c. lemon, brown and rose-red	15	15

Design: Horiz—25c. "Strength in Unity".

114 Building Independence (first aluminium ship)

116 Scouts raising Flag

(Des R. Gates. Litho B.W.)

1969 (30 Apr). 50th Anniv of International Labour Organization. T **114** and similar design. W **106** (sideways on 40c.). P 12×11 (30c.) or 11×12 (40c.).

502	30c. turquoise-blue, black and silver	40	25
503	40c. multicoloured	60	25

Design: Horiz—40c. Bauxite processing plant.

(Des Jennifer Toombs. Litho B.W.)

1969 (13 Aug). Third Caribbean Scout Jamboree and Diamond Jubilee of Scouting in Guyana. T **116** and similar horiz design. Multicoloured. W **106** (sideways). P 13.

504	6c. Type **116**	10	10
505	8c. Camp-fire cooking	10	10
506	25c. Type **116**	10	10
507	30c. As 8c.	10	10
508	50c. Type **116**	15	15
504/8	Set of 5	30	30

118 Gandhi and Spinning-wheel

119 "Mother Sally Dance Troupe"

(Des G. Drummond. Litho Format)

1969 (1 Oct). Birth Centenary of Mahatma Gandhi. W **106** (sideways). P 14½.

509	**118** 6c. black, brown and yellowish olive	1·00	65
510	15c. black, brown and lilac	1·00	65

(Des V. Whiteley (5, 25c.), J.W. (others). Litho B.W. (5, 25c.), D.L.R. (others))

1969 (17 Nov). Christmas. T **119** and similar vert designs. Multicoloured. No wmk (5, 25c.) or W **106** (others). P 13½ (5, 25c.) or 13×13½ (others).

511	5c. Type **119**	10	10
	a. Opt omitted	32·00	
	b. Opt double	28·00	
512	6c. City Hall, Georgetown	10	10
	a. Opt omitted	32·00	
	b. Opt inverted	35·00	
513	25c. Type **119**	10	10
	a. Opt omitted	35·00	
514	60c. As 6c.	20	25
511/14	Set of 4	30	30

Nos. 511/14 are previously unissued stamps optd as in T **119** by Guyana Lithographic Co, Ltd.

REPUBLIC

121 Forbes Burnham and Map

125 The Descent from the Cross

(Des L. Curtis. Litho D.L.R.)

1970 (23 Feb). Republic Day. T **121** and similar designs. W **106** (sideways on 15 and 25c.). P 14.

515	5c. sepia, ochre and pale blue	10	10
516	6c. multicoloured	10	10
517	15c. multicoloured	15	10
518	25c. multicoloured	20	15
515/18	Set of 4	40	30

Designs: Vert—6c. "Rural Self-help". Horiz—15c. University of Guyana; 25c. Guyana House.

(Des J. Cooter. Litho Questa)

1970 (24 Mar). Easter. Paintings by Rubens. T **125** and similar vert design. Multicoloured. W **106** (inverted). P 14×14½.

519	5c. Type **125**	10	10
520	6c. Christ on the Cross	10	10
521	15c. Type **125**	20	15
522	25c. As 6c.	20	15
519/22	Set of 4	45	40

127 Peace and UN Emblem

128 Mother and Child (Philip Moore)

(Des and litho Harrison)

1970 (26 Oct). 25th Anniv of United Nations. T **127** and similar horiz design. Multicoloured. W **106** (inverted). P 14.

523	5c. Type **127**	10	10
524	6c. UN Emblem, Gold-panning and Drilling	10	10
525	15c. Type **127**	10	10
526	25c. As 6c.	15	15
523/6	Set of 4	30	30

(Des Harrison. Litho J.W.)

1970 (8 Dec). Christmas. W **106**. P 13½.

527	**128** 5c. multicoloured	10	10
528	6c. multicoloured	10	10
529	15c. multicoloured	15	15
530	25c. multicoloured	15	15
527/30	Set of 4	30	30

POSTAGE DUE STAMPS

D2

(Typo D.L.R.)

1967–68. Chalk-surfaced paper. W w **12**. P 14.

D5	D **2**	2c. black (11.12.68)	1·75	18·00
D6		4c. deep ultramarine	30	6·00
D7		12c. reddish scarlet	30	6·00
D5/7	Set of 3		2·10	27·00

Heligoland

Stamps of HAMBURG (see Part 7 (Germany) of this catalogue) were used in Heligoland until 16 April 1867. The Free City of Hamburg ran the Heligoland postal service between 1796 and 1 June 1866. Its stamps continued in use on the island until replaced by Heligoland issues.

PRICES FOR STAMPS ON COVER	
Nos. 1/19	from × 3

PRINTERS. All the stamps of Heligoland were typographed at the Imperial Printing Works, Berlin.

REPRINTS. Many of the stamps of Heligoland were subsequently reprinted at Berlin (between 1875 and 1885), Leipzig (1888) and Hamburg (1892 and 1895). Of these only the Berlin productions are difficult to distinguish from the originals so separate notes are provided for the individual values. Leipzig reprints can be identified by their highly surfaced paper and those from Hamburg by their 14 perforation. All of these reprints are worth much less than the original stamps priced below.

There was, in addition, a small reprinting of Nos. 13/19, made by the German government in 1890 for exchange purposes, but examples of this printing are far scarcer than the original stamps.

Forgeries, printed by lithography instead of typography, also exist for Nos. 1/4, 6 and 8 perforated 12½ or 13. Forged cancellations can also be found on originals and, on occasion, genuine postmarks on reprints.

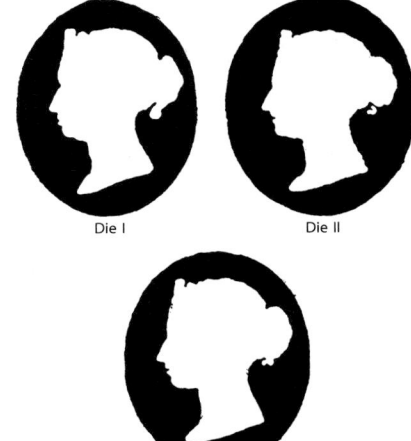

1

(Currency. 16 schillings = 1 mark)

Three Dies of Embossed Head for Types **1** and **2**:

Die I   Die II

Die III

Die I.   Blob instead of curl beneath the chignon. Outline of two jewels at top of diadem.
Die II.   Curl under chignon. One jewel at top of diadem.
Die III.   Shorter curl under chignon. Two jewels at top of diadem.

(Des Wedding. Die eng E. Schilling)

1867 (21 Mar)**–68**. Head Die I embossed in colourless relief. Roul.

1	**1**	½sch. blue-green and rose	£350	£850
		a. Head Die II (7.68)	£800	£1200
2		1sch. rose and blue-green	£180	£200
3		2sch. rose and grass-green	20·00	65·00
4		6sch. green and rose	21·00	£275

For Nos. 1/4 the second colour given is that of the spandrels on the ½ and 1sch., and of the spandrels and central background for the 2 and 6sch.

All four values exist from the Berlin, Leipzig and Hamburg reprintings. The following points are helpful in identifying originals from Berlin reprints; for Leipzig and Hamburg reprints see general note above:

½sch. – Reprints are all in yellowish green and show Head Die II
1sch. – All reprints are Head Die III
2sch. – Berlin reprints are in dull rose with a deeper blue-green
6sch. – Originals show white specks in green. Berlin reprints have a more solid bluish green

1869 (Apr)**–73**. Head embossed in colourless relief. P 13½×14½.

5	**1**	¼sch. rose and green (background) (I) (quadrillé paper) (8.73)	35·00	£1600
		a. Error. Green and rose (background) (9.73)	£190	£3250
		b. Deep rose and pale green (background) (11.73)	95·00	£1600
6		½sch. blue-green and rose (II)	£225	£250
		a. Yellow green and rose (7.71)	£160	£225
		b. Quadrillé paper (6.73)	£110	£170
7		¾sch. green and rose (I) (quadrillé paper) (12.73)	50·00	£1200
8		1sch. rose and yellow-green (III) (11.71)	£160	£200

Left column (Heligoland continued)

		a. Quadrillé paper. *Rose and pale blue-green* (6.73)	£140	£200
9		1½sch. green and rose (I) (*quadrillé paper*) (9.73)	95·00	£275

For Nos. 5/9 the second colour given is that of the spandrels on the ½ and 1sch., of the central background on the ¼ and 1½sch., and of the central background, side labels and side marginal lines of the ¾sch.

No. 5a was a printing of the ¼sch. made in the colour combination of the 1½sch. by mistake.

A further printing of the ½sch. (Head die I) in deep rose-red and yellowish green (background), on non-*quadrillé* paper, was made in December 1874, but not issued (*Price £15, unused*).

All five values exist from the Berlin, Leipzig and Hamburg reprintings. The following points are helpful in identifying originals from Berlin reprints; for Leipzig and Hamburg reprints see general note above:

¼sch. – All Berlin and some Hamburg reprints are Head Die II.
½sch. – Berlin reprints on thinner paper with solid colour in the spandrels
¾sch. – Berlin reprints on thinner, non-quadrillé paper
1sch. – Berlin reprints are on thinner paper or show many breaks in the rose line beneath "SCHILLING" at the top of the design or in the line above it at the foot
1½sch. – All Berlin and some Hamburg reprints are Head Die II
Berlin, Leipzig and Hamburg reprints also exist of the 2 and 6sch., but these values do not come as perforated originals.

(New Currency. 100 pfennig = 1 mark)

2 3 4

5

(Des H. Gätke. Die eng E. Schilling (T **2**), A. Schiffner (others))

1875 (Feb)–**90**. Head Die II on T **2** embossed in colourless relief. P 13½×14½.

10	2	1pf. (¼d.) deep green and rose	20·00	£550
11		2pf. (½d.) deep rose and deep green	20·00	£650
12	3	3pf. (5/6d.) pale green, red and yellow (6.76)	£250	£1200
		a. *Green, red and orange* (6.77)	£170	£900
13	2	5pf. (¾d.) deep yellow-green and rose	20·00	20·00
		a. *Deep green and rose* (6.90)	27·00	55·00
14		10pf. (1½d.) deep rose and deep green	42·00	23·00
		a. *Scarlet and pale blue-green* (5.87)	17·00	24·00
15	3	20pf. (2½d.) rose, green and yellow (6.76)	£275	£120
		a. *Rose-carmine, deep green and orange* (4.80)	£180	55·00
		b. *Dull red, pale green and lemon* (7.88)	26·00	30·00
		c. *Aniline vermilion, bright green and lemon* (6.90)	16·00	55·00
16	2	25pf. (3d.) deep green and rose	24·00	29·00
17		50pf. (6d.) rose and green	26·00	42·00
18	4	1m. (1s.) deep green, scarlet and black (8.79)	£170	£200
		a. *Perf 11½*	£1400	
		b. *Deep green, aniline rose and black* (5.89)	£170	£200
19	5	5m. (5s.) deep green, aniline rose, black and yellow (8.79)	£225	£950
		a. *Perf 11½*	£1400	
		ab. *Imperf between (horiz pair)*	£6000	

For stamps as Type **2** the first colour is that of the central background and the second that of the frame. On the 3pf. the first colour is of the frame and the top band of the shield, the second is the centre band and the third the shield border. The 20pf. is similar, but has the centre band in the same colour as the frame and the upper band on the shield in the second colour.

The 1, 2 and 3pf. exist from the Berlin, Leipzig and Hamburg reprintings. There were no such reprints for the other values. The following points are helpful in identifying originals from Berlin reprints; for Leipzig and Hamburg reprints see general note above:

1pf. – Berlin printings show a peculiar shade of pink
2pf. – All reprints are much lighter in shade than the deep rose and deep green of the originals
3pf. – Berlin reprints either show the band around the shield in brownish orange, or have this feature in deep yellow with the other two colours lighter

Heligoland was ceded to Germany on 9 August 1890.

Hong Kong

CROWN COLONY

Hong Kong island was formally ceded to Great Britain on 26 January 1841. The Hong Kong Post Office was established in October 1841, when much of the business previously transacted through the Macao postal agency was transferred to the island. The first cancellation is known from April 1842, but local control of the posts was short-lived as the Hong Kong Office became a branch of the British GPO on 15 April 1843.

The colonial authorities resumed control of the postal service on 1 May 1860 although the previously established postal agencies in the Chinese Treaty Ports remained part of the British GPO system until 1 May 1868.

For illustrations of the handstamp types see BRITISH POST OFFICES ABROAD notes following GREAT BRITAIN.

CROWNED-CIRCLE HANDSTAMPS

CC 1   CC 1b

CC 3

CC1	CC **1b** HONG KONG (R.) (17.10.1843) .. *Price on cover*	£800
CC2	CC **1** HONG KONG (R.) (21.8.1844)..... *Price on cover*	£1000
CC3	CC **3** HONG KONG (R.) (16.6.1852)..... *Price on cover*	£475

We no longer list the Great Britain stamps with obliteration "B 62" within oval. The Government notification dated 29 November 1862 stated that only the Hong Kong stamps to be issued on 8 December would be available for postage and the stamps formerly listed were all issued in Great Britain later than the date of the notice.

(Currency. 100 cents = 1 Hong Kong dollar)

PRICES FOR STAMPS ON COVER TO 1945

Nos. 1/7	from × 6
Nos. 8/12	from × 15
No. 13	from × 6
Nos. 14/17	from × 15
No. 18	from × 50
No. 19	from × 15
Nos. 20/27	from × 10
Nos. 28/36	from × 8
Nos. 37/9	from × 10
Nos. 40/4	from × 8
Nos. 45/50	from × 10
No. 51	from × 20
No. 52	from × 10
Nos. 53/4	—
No. 55	from × 10
Nos. 56/61	from × 10
Nos. 62/99	from × 4
Nos. 100/32	from × 3
Nos. 133/6	from × 2
Nos. 137/9	from × 4
Nos. 140/68	from × 2
Nos. D1/12	from × 10
Nos. P1/3	from × 2
Nos. F1/11	from × 20
No. F12	from × 4

PRINTERS. All definitive issues up to 1962 were typographed by De La Rue and Co., *except for some printings between 1941 and 1945.*

1   2   3

1862 (8 Dec)–**63**. No wmk. P 14.

1	1	2c. brown	£550	£120
		a. *Deep brown* (1863)	£750	£170

2		8c. yellow-buff	£750	85·00
3		12c. pale greenish blue	£650	60·00
4	3	18c. lilac	£650	55·00
5		24c. green	£1200	£120
6		48c. rose	£2750	£350
7		96c. brownish grey	£3750	£450

"GKON" of "HONGKONG" damaged at foot (Pl 1 lower right pane R. 9/5)

1863 (Aug)–**71**. Wmk Crown CC. P 14.

8	1	2c. deep brown (11.64)	£350	35·00
		a. *Brown*	£130	8·00
		b. *Pale yellowish brown*	£160	13·00
		w. Wmk inverted	£750	£150
		x. Wmk reversed	—	£325
		y. Wmk inverted and reversed	†	£900
9	2	4c. grey	£160	22·00
		ay. *Wmk inverted and reversed*	†	£950
		b. *Slate*	£120	9·00
		bw. *Wmk inverted*	£600	£140
		c. *Deep slate*	£160	16·00
		d. *Greenish grey*	£350	50·00
		dw. *Wmk inverted*	†	£450
		e. *Bluish slate*	£475	26·00
		ew. *Wmk inverted*	£1400	£225
		f. *Perf 12½. Slate* (8.70)	£12000	£900
		fw. *Wmk inverted*	—	£900
10		6c. lilac	£450	19·00
		a. *Mauve*	£650	20·00
		w. Wmk inverted	£1500	£150
		x. Wmk reversed	£1800	£225
11	1	8c. pale dull orange (10.64)	£600	13·00
		a. *Brownish orange*	£500	16·00
		b. *Bright orange*	£475	16·00
		w. Wmk inverted	£1500	£180
		x. Wmk reversed	£1600	£325
12		12c. pale greenish blue (4.65)	£1100	40·00
		a. *Pale blue*	32·00	9·00
		b. *Deep blue*	£300	14·00
		w. Wmk inverted	—	£140
		x. Wmk reversed	—	£180
13	3	18c. lilac (1866)	£7000	£150
		w. Wmk inverted	£11000	£1100
		x. Wmk reversed	£18000	£1700
		y. Wmk inverted and reversed	†	£2750
14		24c. green (10.64)	£650	12·00
		a. *Pale green*	£800	18·00
		b. *Deep green*	£1300	35·00
		w. Wmk inverted	£2750	£180
		x. Wmk reversed	£2500	£275
15	2	30c. vermilion	£1000	15·00
		a. *Orange-vermilion*	£900	16·00
		b. *"GKON" of "HONGKONG" damaged at foot*	—	£1900
		w. Wmk inverted	£3000	£190
		x. Wmk reversed	—	£300
16		30c. mauve (14.8.71)	£275	5·50
		a. *"GKON" of "HONGKONG" damaged at foot*	—	£600
		w. Wmk inverted	£1400	£160
		x. Wmk reversed	—	£300
17		48c. pale rose (1.65)	£1500	70·00
		a. *Rose-carmine*	£950	32·00
		w. Wmk inverted	£2500	£200
		x. Wmk reversed	—	£350
18		96c. olive-bistre (1.65)	£80000	£750
		w. Wmk inverted	†	£5500
19		96c. brownish grey (1865)	£1500	65·00
		a. *Brownish black*	£2000	60·00
		w. Wmk inverted	£2000	£200
		y. Wmk inverted and reversed	†	£1900

There is a wide range of shades in this issue, of which we can only indicate the main groups.

No. 12 is the same shade as No. 3 without wmk, the impression having a waxy appearance.

A single used example of the 48c. in a bright claret shade is known. No other stamps in this shade, either mint or used, have been discovered.

See also Nos. 22 and 28/31.

No. 20b

1876 (Aug)–**77**. Nos. 13 and 16 surch with T **4** or **5** by Noronha and Sons, Hong Kong.

20	3	16c. on 18c. lilac (1.4.77)	£2250	£150
		a. *Space between "n" and "t"*	£8000	£900
		b. *Space between "s" and stop*	£8000	£900
		w. Wmk inverted	£6000	£1000
21	2	28c. on 30c. mauve	£1600	50·00
		a. *"GKON" of "HONGKONG" damaged at foot*	—	£1100

1877 (Aug). New value. Wmk Crown CC. P 14.

22	3	16c. yellow	£2000	65·00
		w. Wmk inverted	£4250	£500

1880 (1 Mar–Sept). Surch with T **6** or **7** by Noronha and Sons.

23	1	5c. on 8c. bright orange (No. 11b) (9.80)	£1100	£110
		a. *Surch inverted*	†	£21000
		b. *Surch double*	†	£21000
24	3	5c. on 18c. lilac (No. 13)	£950	65·00
		x. Wmk reversed	£2500	£1100
		y. Wmk inverted and reversed	†	£3500

25	1	10c. on 12c. pale blue (No. 12a)	£1000	55·00
		a. Blue	£1700	£110
		b. Surch double................................	†	£50000
26	3	10c. on 16c. yellow (No. 22) (5.80)	£4250	£150
		a. Surch inverted	—	£95000
		b. Surch double................................	†	£75000
		w. Wmk inverted	†	£2000
27		10c. on 24c. green (No. 14) (6.80)	£1500	£100
		w. Wmk inverted	†	£700

Three examples of No. 26b are known, all used in Shanghai.

1880 (Mar–Dec). Colours changed and new values. Wmk Crown CC. P 14.

28	1	2c. dull rose	£275	40·00
		a. Rose...	£300	40·00
		w. Wmk inverted	†	£500
29	2	5c. blue (12.80).................................	£800	55·00
		w. Wmk inverted	—	£500
30		10c. mauve (11.80)............................	£900	19·00
		w. Wmk inverted	—	£500
31	3	48c. brown	£1500	£110

1882 (May)**–96.** Wmk Crown CA. P 14.

32	1	2c. rose-lake (7.82)..........................	£300	32·00
		a. Rose-pink......................................	£225	32·00
		ab. Perf 12	£75000	£75000
		w. Wmk inverted	—	£275
		x. Wmk reversed...............................	†	£700
33		2c. carmine (1884)............................	55·00	3·00
		a. Aniline carmine.............................	55·00	3·00
		w. Wmk inverted	—	£180
34	2	4c. slate-grey (1.4.96)......................	35·00	3·00
		w. Wmk inverted	—	£275
35		5c. pale blue	48·00	1·25
		a. Blue...	50·00	1·25
		aw. Wmk inverted	£500	£120
		x. Wmk reversed...............................	—	£475
36		10c. dull mauve (8.82).......................	£1000	23·00
		w. Wmk inverted	—	£475
37		10c. deep blue-green (1884).............	£1800	38·00
		a. Green (2.84)	£180	2·25
		aw. Wmk inverted	†	£750
38		10c. purple/red (1.1.91).....................	45·00	1·75
		w. Wmk inverted	£750	£120
		x. Wmk reversed...............................	£1300	£225
		y. Wmk inverted and reversed.......		
39		30c. yellowish green (1.1.91)............	£140	45·00
		a. Grey-green	£110	27·00
38s, 39as Optd "SPECIMEN" Set of 2				£400

Examples of No. 39 should not be confused with washed or faded stamps from the grey-green shade which tend to turn to a very yellow-green when dampened.

For other stamps with this watermark, but in colours changed to the UPU scheme, see Nos. 56/61.

20 CENTS (8)   50 CENTS (9)   1 DOLLAR (10)

1885 (Sept). As Nos. 15, 19 and 31, but wmk Crown CA, surch with T **8** to **10** by De La Rue.

40	2	20c. on 30c. orange-red	£200	7·50
		a. Surch double................................		
		w. Wmk inverted	£1600	£550
41	3	50c. on 48c. yellowish brown..........	£400	48·00
		w. Wmk inverted	£1600	£550
42		$1 on 96c. grey-olive	£750	85·00
40s/2s Optd "SPECIMEN" Set of 3				£1300

For the $1 on 96c. black and grey-black see Nos. 53/a.

7 cents. (11)   14 cents. (12)

弍 (13) (20c.)   五十 (14) (50c.)   壹員 (15) ($1)

1891 (1 Jan–Mar).

(a) Nos. 16 and 37 surch with T 11 or 12 by Noronha and Sons, Hong Kong

43	2	7c. on 10c. green.............................	95·00	10·00
		a. Antique "t" in "cents" (R. 1/1)	£700	£160
		b. Surch double................................	£7000	£1300
44		14c. on 30c. mauve (2.91).................	£200	80·00
		a. Antique "t" in "cents" (R. 1/1)	£2750	£950
		b. "GKON" of "HONGKONG" damaged at foot.........................	£6000	£2000

(b) As Nos. 40/2 (surch with T 8 to 10 by De La Rue), but colours changed

45	2	20c. on 30c. yellowish green (No. 39)	£170	£160
		a. Grey-green (No. 39a).....................	£110	£150
46	3	50c. on 48c. dull purple...................	£300	£325
47		$1 on 96c. purple/red.......................	£800	£350
45as/7s Optd "SPECIMEN" Set of 3				£850

(c) Nos. 45/7 with further surch, T 13/15, in Chinese characters, handstamped locally (Mar)

48	2	20c. on 30c. yellowish green	55·00	14·00
		a. Grey-green	42·00	13·00
		b. Surch double................................	£25000	£25000
49	3	50c. on 48c. dull purple....................	80·00	5·50
50		$1 on 96c. purple/red.......................	£450	22·00
		w. Wmk inverted	£2000	

The true antique "t" variety (Nos. 43a and 44a) should not be confused with a small "t" showing a short foot. In the antique "t" the crossbar is accurately bisected by the vertical stroke, which is thicker at the top. The lower curve bends towards the right and does not turn upwards to the same extent as on the normal.

The handstamped surcharges on Nos. 48/50 were applied over the original Chinese face values. The single character for "2" was intended to convert "30c." to "20c.". There were six slightly different versions of the "2" handstamp and three for the "50c.".

The errors of the Chinese surcharges previously listed on the above issue and also on Nos. 52 and 55 are now omitted as being outside the scope of the catalogue. While some without doubt possess philatelic merit, it is impossible to distinguish between the genuine errors and the clandestine copies made to order with the original chops. No. 55c is retained as this represents a distinctly different chop which was used for the last part of the printing.

1841 Hong Kong JUBILEE 1891 (16)   10 CENTS (17)   拾 (18)   拾 (19)

1891 (22 Jan). 50th Anniversary of Colony. Optd with T **16** by Noronha and Sons, Hong Kong.

51	1	2c. carmine (No. 33)	£475	£130
		a. Short "J" in "JUBILEE" (R. 1/6)	£800	£200
		b. Short "U" in "JUBILEE" (R. 1/1)	£800	£200
		c. Broken "1" in "1891" (R. 2/1)	£950	£300
		d. Tall narrow "K" in "Kong" (R. 1/3)	£1300	£475
		e. Opt double	£18000	£14000
		f. Space between "O" and "N" of "Hong" (R. 1/5)	£1700	£750

Most of the supply of No. 51, which was only on sale for three days, was overprinted from a setting of 12 (6×2) applied five times to complete each pane. There were six printings from this setting, but a second setting, possibly of 30 or 60, was used for the seventh. Positions quoted are from the setting of 12. Most varieties only occur in some printings and many less marked overprint flaws also exist.

The prices quoted for No. 51e are for examples on which the two impressions are distinctly separated. Examples on which the two impressions are almost coincidental are worth considerably less.

1898 (1 Apr). Wmk Crown CA. P 14.

(a) Surch with T 10 by D.L.R. and handstamped Chinese characters as T 15

52	3	$1 on 96c. black...............................	£250	27·00
		a. Grey-black.....................................	£200	27·00

(b) Surch with T 10 only

53	3	$1 on 96c. black...............................	£3250	£4000
		a. Grey-black.....................................	£2750	£3750
		as. Optd "SPECIMEN"........................		£600

Nos. 52/a and 53/a show considerable variation in shades, with some paler shades verging on grey. Nos. 53/a should not be confused with the 1885 $1 on 96c. grey-olive (No. 42).

1898 (1 Apr).

(a) Surch with T 17 by Noronha and Sons, Hong Kong

54	2	10c. on 30c. grey-green (No. 39a)	£600	£1200
		a. Figures "10" widely spaced (1½ mm)...	£7500	£10000
		b. Surch double................................		

(b) As No. 54, but with handstamped Chinese characters, T 18, in addition

55	2	10c. on 30c. grey-green (No. 39a)	75·00	90·00
		a. Yellowish green	85·00	£110
		b. Figures "10" widely spaced (1½ mm)...	£700	£900
		c. Chinese character large (Type 19)	£900	£1000
		d. Surch Type 17 double..................	£12000	
		s. Handstamped "SPECIMEN".........		£140

Type 17 was applied in a horizontal setting of 12, Nos. 54a and 55b appearing on position 12 for the early printings only. The true 1½ mm wide spacing is not known on No. 55c. Examples showing spacing of 1.2-1.3 mm are worth a premium over the normal prices.

1900 (Aug)**–01.** Wmk Crown CA. P 14.

56	1	2c. dull green	28·00	85
		w. Wmk inverted	£325	£140
57	2	4c. carmine (1901)............................	21·00	85
		w. Wmk inverted		†
58		5c. yellow	30·00	9·50
		w. Wmk inverted	—	£700
59		10c. ultramarine	50·00	2·50
		w. Wmk inverted	—	£130
60	1	12c. blue (1901).................................	48·00	70·00
61	2	30c. brown (1901)..............................	60·00	27·00
56/61 Set of 6			£200	£100
56s/9s, 61s Optd "SPECIMEN" Set of 5				£600

20 TWO CENTS

21 FIVE CENTS

22 SIX CENTS

23 12 CENTS

1903 (Jan–July). Wmk Crown CA. P 14.

62	20	1c. dull purple and brown	2·75	50
63		2c. dull purple (7.03)........................	23·00	2·75
		w. Wmk inverted	†	£1300
		y. Wmk inverted and reversed.......	†	£1500
64	21	4c. purple/red (7.03).........................	28·00	40
65		5c. dull green and brown-orange (7.03)...	25·00	10·00
66		8c. slate and violet (12.2.03)...........	18·00	2·00
67	20	10c. purple and blue/blue (7.03).......	70·00	1·50
68	23	12c. green and purple/yellow (12.2.03)	15·00	6·50
69		20c. slate and chestnut (6.03)..........	65·00	5·50
70	22	30c. dull green and black (21.5.03)...	65·00	26·00
71	23	50c. dull green and magenta (6.03) .	65·00	70·00

72	20	$1 purple and sage-green (6.03)....	£130	29·00
73	23	$2 slate and scarlet (7.03).............	£375	£375
74	22	$3 slate and dull blue (7.03)..........	£450	£425
75	23	$5 purple and blue-green (6.03)....	£650	£600
76	22	$10 slate and orange/blue (7.03)....	£1400	£475
		w. Wmk inverted		†
62/76 Set of 15			£3000	£1800
62s/76s Optd "SPECIMEN" Set of 15				£2000

No. 63w is known used at Shanghai.

1904 (4 Oct)**–06.** Wmk Mult Crown CA. Chalk-surfaced paper (8, 12c., $3, $5) or ordinary paper (others). P 14.

77	20	2c. dull green	28·00	2·75
		a. Chalk-surfaced paper (1906)	29·00	5·50
		aw. Wmk inverted	†	£1100
78	21	4c. purple/red	40·00	40
		a. Chalk-surfaced paper (1906)	27·00	2·00
79		5c. dull green and brown-orange...	75·00	21·00
		a. Chalk-surfaced paper (1906)	25·00	7·00
		aw. Wmk inverted		†
80		8c. slate and violet (1906)..............	21·00	2·00
81	20	10c. purple and blue/blue (3.05)......	40·00	1·25
82	23	12c. green and purple/yellow (1906)	25·00	9·00
83		20c. slate and chestnut	70·00	4·25
		a. Chalk-surfaced paper (1906)	65·00	3·75
		aw. Wmk inverted	†	£1100
84	22	30c. dull green and black	70·00	40·00
		a. Chalk-surfaced paper (1906)	70·00	24·00
85	23	50c. green and magenta...................	£110	18·00
		a. Chalk-surfaced paper (1906)	95·00	22·00
86	20	$1 purple and sage-green	£200	50·00
		a. Chalk-surfaced paper (1906)	£180	48·00
87	23	$2 slate and scarlet	£450	£170
		a. Chalk-surfaced paper (1905)	£350	£140
88	22	$3 slate and dull blue (1905)	£375	£350
89	23	$5 purple and blue-green (1905)...	£550	£475
90	22	$10 slate and orange/blue (5.05)	£1900	£1500
		aw. Wmk inverted	†	†
		b. Chalk-surfaced paper (1906)	£2000	£1200
77/90 Set of 14			£3250	£2200

No. 77aw is known used at Shanghai in October 1908 and 83aw at Hoihow in March 1908.

1907–11. Colours changed and new value. Wmk Mult Crown CA. Chalk-surfaced paper (6c. and 20c. to $2). P 14.

91	20	1c. brown (9.10)...............................	10·00	1·00
		x. Wmk reversed...............................	†	£2000
92		2c. deep green	45·00	1·75
		a. Green..	45·00	1·50
		w. Wmk inverted	£1500	£900
93	21	4c. carmine-red................................	20·00	40
		x. Wmk reversed...............................	†	£2000
94	22	6c. orange-vermilion and purple (10.07)...	42·00	8·50
95	20	10c. bright ultramarine	65·00	40
96	23	20c. purple and sage-green (3.11) ...	50·00	50·00
97	22	30c. purple and orange-yellow (3.11)	65·00	48·00
98	23	50c. black/green (3.11)......................	50·00	20·00
99		$2 carmine-red and black (1910) ...	£400	£425
91/9 Set of 9			£650	£475
91s, 93s/9s Optd "SPECIMEN" Set of 8				£1200

No. 91x is known used at Canton in December 1912 and January 1913, No. 92w at Shanghai in 1908 and 93x at Swatow in February 1911.

24 ONE CENT 壹先 1c

25 FOUR CENTS 肆先 4c

26 SIX CENTS 陸先 6c

27 20 CENTS 貳拾先 香港

28 25 CENTS 貳拾伍先 25

(A) 貳

(B) 貳

In Type A of the 25c. the upper Chinese character in the left-hand label has a short vertical stroke crossing it at the foot. In Type B this stroke is absent.

Crown broken at right (R. 9/2)

Broken flower at top right (Upper left pane R. 1/3)

1912 (9 Nov)**–21.** Wmk Mult Crown CA. Chalk-surfaced paper (12c. to $10). P 14.

100	24	1c. brown	7·00	55
		a. Black-brown.................................	9·00	3·00
		b. Crown broken at right.................	£250	£180
101		2c. deep green	18·00	30
		a. Green..	22·00	30
		w. Wmk inverted		†
		y. Wmk inverted and reversed.......	†	£1500
102	25	4c. carmine-rose..............................	12·00	30
		a. Scarlet (1914)	55·00	3·00
		aw. Wmk inverted	†	£2000
		ay. Wmk inverted and reversed.......	†	
103	26	6c. yellow-orange.............................	7·50	2·75
		a. Brown-orange...............................	8·00	3·75
		w. Wmk inverted	£1200	£1100
104	25	8c. grey..	35·00	10·00
		a. Slate (1914)..................................	50·00	7·50
105	24	10c. ultramarine	55·00	30

		a. Deep bright ultramarine	30·00	30
106	27	12c. purple/*yellow*	14·00	15·00
		a. White back (1914)	16·00	20·00
		as. Optd "SPECIMEN"	£160	
107		20c. purple and sage-green	18·00	1·75
108	28	25c. purple and magenta (Type A) (1.14)	48·00	42·00
109		25c. purple and magenta (Type B) (8.19)	£300	90·00
		a. Broken flower	£5000	
110	26	30c. purple and orange-yellow	65·00	14·00
		a. Purple and orange	42·00	9·00
111	27	50c. black/*blue-green*	29·00	3·50
		a. White back (5.14)	38·00	4·25
		as. Optd "SPECIMEN"	£180	
		b. On blue-green, olive back (1917)	1300	30·00
		c. On emerald surface (9.19)	45·00	8·00
		d. On emerald back (7.12.21)	38·00	10·00
		ds. Optd "SPECIMEN"	£200	
		w. Wmk inverted	£4000	
		y. Wmk inverted and reversed	†	£3750
112	24	$1 purple and blue/*blue*	75·00	6·00
		w. Wmk inverted	£325	£200
113	27	$2 carmine-red and grey-black	£200	75·00
114	26	$3 green and purple	£300	£130
115	27	$5 green and red/*green*	£700	£425
		a. White back (5.14)	£600	£400
		as. Optd "SPECIMEN"	£450	
		b. On blue-green, olive back (1917)	£1200	£400
		bs. Optd "SPECIMEN"	£650	
		bw. Wmk inverted	£5500	
116	26	$10 purple and black/*red*	£600	£110
100/16		*Set of* 17	£2000	£800
100s/16s		Optd "SPECIMEN" *Set of* 17	£2250	

No. 100b occurred in 1916 on R. 9/2 of the lower right pane before being retouched.

Top of lower Chinese characters at right broken (R. 9/4, lower left pane).

1921 (Jan)–**37**. Wmk Mult Script CA. Chalk-surfaced paper (12c. to $5). P 14.

117	24	1c. brown	3·00	40
118		2c. blue-green	7·00	1·00
		a. Yellow-green (1932)	32·00	3·00
		bw. Wmk inverted	£110	
118c		2c. grey (14.4.37)	25·00	12·00
119	25	3c. grey (8.10.31)	15·00	2·00
120		4c. carmine-rose	8·00	70
		a. Carmine (1932)	15·00	30
		b. Top of lower Chinese characters at right broken off	£100	80·00
121		5c. violet (16.10.31)	24·00	30
122		8c. grey	26·00	38·00
123		8c. orange (7.12.21)	8·00	2·50
		w. Wmk inverted	£1400	£1000
124	24	10c. bright ultramarine	13·00	30
		aw. Wmk inverted	£475	
		b. "A" of "CA" missing from wmk	†	—
124c	27	12c. purple/*yellow* (3.4.33)	26·00	4·50
125		20c. purple and sage-green (7.12.21)	13·00	30
126	28	25c. purple and magenta (B) (7.12.21)	9·50	2·75
		a. Broken flower	50·00	70·00
		w. Wmk inverted	†	£900
127	26	30c. purple and chrome-yellow (7.12.21)	14·00	2·50
		a. Purple and orange-yellow	45·00	8·50
		w. Wmk inverted	£475	
128	27	50c. black/*emerald* (1924)	32·00	30
129	24	$1 purple and blue/*blue* (7.12.21)	50·00	50
130	27	$2 carmine-red and grey-black (7.12.21)	£140	10·00
131	26	$3 green and dull purple (1926)	£200	70·00
132	27	$5 green and red/*emerald* (1925)	£500	80·00
117/32		*Set of* 18	£1000	£200
117s/32s		Optd or Perf (2c. grey, 3c., 5c., 12c.) "SPECIMEN" *Set of* 18	£2000	

No. 120b occurs on R. 9/4 of the lower left pane.

1935 (6 May). Silver Jubilee. As Nos. 91/4 of Antigua, but ptd by B.W. P 11×12.

133		3c. ultramarine and grey-black	4·00	4·50
		c. Lightning conductor	£375	£275
		e. Double flagstaff	£1100	
134		5c. green and indigo	8·50	3·50
		a. Extra flagstaff	£325	£275
		b. Short extra flagstaff	£425	£425
		c. Lightning conductor	£400	£275
		d. Flagstaff on right-hand turret	£650	£400
		e. Double flagstaff	£750	£500
135		10c. brown and deep blue	23·00	1·75
136		20c. slate and purple	40·00	11·00
		b. Short extra flagstaff	£900	£400
		d. Flagstaff on right-hand turret	£950	£475
		e. Double flagstaff	£1100	£500
133/6		*Set of* 4	65·00	18·00
133s/6s		Perf "SPECIMEN" *Set of* 4	£500	

For illustrations of plate varieties see Omnibus section following Zanzibar.

1937 (12 May). Coronation. As Nos. 95/7 of Antigua. P 11×11½.

137		4c. green	4·50	7·50
138		15c. carmine	8·00	3·25
139		25c. blue	10·00	6·00
137/9		*Set of* 3	20·00	15·00
137s/9s		Perf "SPECIMEN" *Set of* 3	£350	

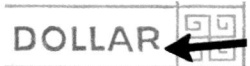

29 King George VI

Short right leg to "R" (Right pane R. 7/3, left pane R. 3/1)

Normal | Broken character (left pane R. 6/6, later repaired)

Stop after "CENTS" (Left pane R. 4/2)

1938–52. Wmk Mult Script CA. Chalk-surfaced paper (80c., $1 (No. 155), $2 (No. 157), $5 (No. 159), $10 (No. 161)). P 14.

140	29	1c. brown (24.5.38)	2·50	6·00
		aa. Doubly printed	£10000	
		a. Pale brown (4.2.52)	4·25	12·00
141		2c. grey (5.4.38)	2·00	30
		a. Perf 14½×14 (28.9.45)	1·75	7·00
142		4c. orange (5.4.38)	11·00	6·50
		a. Perf 14½×14 (28.9.45)	5·00	3·25
143		5c. green (24.5.38)	1·25	20
		a. Perf 14½×14 (28.9.45)	3·75	5·00
144		8c. red-brown (1.11.41)	1·75	3·50
		a. Imperf (pair)	£50000	
		b. Stop after "CENTS"	£350	£225
145		10c. bright violet (13.4.38)	50·00	1·50
		a. Perf 14½×14. Dull violet (28.9.45)	9·50	20
		b. Dull reddish violet (8.4.46)	9·00	1·75
		c. Reddish lilac (9.4.47)	24·00	20
146		15c. scarlet (13.4.38)	2·00	30
		a. Broken character	£130	50·00
147		20c. black (1.2.46)	1·25	30
148		20c. scarlet-vermilion (1.4.48)	14·00	40
		a. Rose-red (25.4.51)	28·00	5·50
149		25c. bright blue (5.4.38)	29·00	4·75
150		25c. pale yellow-olive (24.9.46)	8·50	4·75
151		30c. yellow-olive (13.4.38)	£150	3·75
		a. Perf 14½×14. Yellowish olive (28.9.45)	28·00	12·00
152		30c. blue (27.12.46)	7·00	20
153		50c. purple (13.4.38)	55·00	70
		a. Perf 14½×14. Deep magenta (28.9.45)	30·00	1·25
		ab. Printed both sides, inverted on reverse	£1000	
		b. Reddish purple (9.4.46)	17·00	3·50
		c. Chalk-surfaced paper. Bright purple (9.4.47)	12·00	20
154		80c. carmine (2.2.48)	6·50	1·00
155		$1 dull lilac and blue (*chalk-surfaced paper*) (27.4.38)	9·00	4·25
		a. Short right leg to "R"	£180	£190
		b. Ordinary paper. Pale reddish lilac and blue (28.9.45)	22·00	28·00
		ba. Short right leg to "R"	£350	£400
156		$1 red-orange and green (8.4.46)	27·00	30
		a. Short right leg to "R"	£275	65·00
		b. Chalk-surfaced paper (21.6.48)	55·00	1·25
		ba. Short right leg to "R"	£450	90·00
		c. Chalk-surfaced paper. Yellow-orange and green (6.11.52)	90·00	15·00
		ca. Short right leg to "R"	£750	£275
157		$2 red-orange and green (24.5.38)	80·00	40·00
158		$2 reddish violet and scarlet (8.4.46)	50·00	11·00
		a. Chalk-surfaced paper (9.4.47)	55·00	1·00
159		$5 dull lilac and scarlet (2.6.38)	70·00	50·00
160		$5 green and violet (8.4.46)	80·00	24·00
		a. Yellowish green and violet (8.4.46)	£600	40·00
		ab. Chalk-surfaced paper (9.4.47)	£120	5·00
161		$10 green and violet (2.6.38)	£700	£140
162		$10 pale bright lilac and blue (8.4.46)	£140	60·00
		a. Deep bright lilac and blue (8.4.46)	£300	75·00
		b. Chalk-surfaced paper. Reddish violet and blue (9.4.47)	£200	18·00
140/62		*Set of* 23	£1100	£250
140s/62s		Perf "SPECIMEN" *Set of* 23	£2750	

Following bomb damage to the De La Rue works on the night of 29 December 1940 various emergency arrangements were made to complete current requisitions for Hong Kong stamps:

Nos. 141a, 143a, 145a, 151a and 153a (all printings perforated 14½×14 except the 4c.) were printed and perforated by Bradbury Wilkinson & Co. Ltd. using De La Rue plates. These stamps are on rough-surfaced paper.

No. 142a was probably printed by Harrison & Sons, the major part of the printing being in undivided sheets of 120 (12×10) instead of the normal two panes of 60 (6×10).

Printings of the 1c. and dollar values and probably the 8c. were made by Williams, Lea & Co. using De La Rue plates.

With the exception of the 8c. it is believed that none of these printings were issued in Hong Kong before its occupation by the Japanese on 25 December 1941, although examples could be obtained in London from late 1941. The issue dates quoted are those on which the stamps were eventually released in Hong Kong following liberation in 1945.

Nos. 160/a and 162/a were separate printings released in Hong Kong on the same day.

No. 144a. One imperforate sheet was found and most of the stamps were sold singly to the public at a branch P.O. and used for postage.

30 Street Scene

31 *Empress of Japan* (liner) and Junk

32 The University

33 The Harbour

34 The Hong Kong Bank

35 *Falcon* (clipper) and Short S.23 Empire "C" class flying boat

(Des E. A. von Kobza Nagy and W. E. Jones. Recess B.W.)

1941 (26 Feb). Centenary of British Occupation. T **30/35**. Wmk Mult Script CA (sideways on horiz designs). P 13½×13 (2c. and 25c.) or 13×13½ (others).

163		2c. orange and chocolate	8·00	2·50
164		4c. bright purple and carmine	9·50	5·00
165		5c. black and green	3·50	50
166		15c. black and scarlet	9·50	3·00
167		25c. chocolate and blue	19·00	9·00
168		$1 blue and orange	50·00	13·00
163/8		*Set of* 6	90·00	30·00
163s/8s		Perf "SPECIMEN" *Set of* 6	£550	

Hong Kong was under Japanese occupation from 25 December 1941 until 30 August 1945. The Japanese post offices in the colony were closed from 31 August and mail was carried free, marked with cachets reading "HONG KONG/1945/POSTAGE PAID". Military administration lasted until 1 May 1946. Hong Kong stamps were re-introduced on 28 September 1945.

36 King George VI and Phoenix

Extra stroke (R. 1/2)

(Des E. I. Wynne-Jones and W. E. Jones. Recess D.L.R.)

1946 (29 Aug). Victory. Wmk Mult Script CA. P 13.

169	36	30c. blue and red (*shades*)	3·75	2·25
		a. Extra stroke	£120	90·00
170		$1 brown and red	4·00	75
		a. Extra stroke	£130	70·00
169s/70s		Perf "SPECIMEN" *Set of* 2	£275	

Spur on "N" of "KONG" (R. 2/9)

1948 (22 Dec). Royal Silver Wedding. As Nos. 112/13 of Antigua.

171		10c. violet	3·75	1·50
		a. Spur on "N"	£100	90·00
172		$10 carmine	£325	£130

Crack in rock (R. 12/5)

1949 (10 Oct). 75th Anniv of Universal Postal Union. As Nos. 114/17 of Antigua.

173	10c. violet	4·00	1·00
174	20c. carmine-red	15·00	6·00
175	30c. deep blue	13·00	6·00
176	80c. bright reddish purple	30·00	5·00
	a. Crack in rock	£400	£180
173/6	Set of 4	55·00	16·00

1953 (2 June). Coronation. As No. 120 of Antigua.

177	10c. black and slate-lilac	3·00	30

37a Queen Elizabeth II   **$2** Normal   **$2** Short character

$2 The top stroke in the right-hand upper character is shortened (Pl. 1-1, R. 6/4)

1954 (5 Jan)–**62**. Ordinary paper (5c. to 15c.) or chalk-surfaced paper (others). Wmk Mult Script CA. P 14.

178	**37a**	5c. orange	1·75	20
		a. Imperf (pair)	£2250	
179		10c. lilac	2·50	10
		aw. Wmk inverted	£400	
		b. Reddish violet (25.1.61)	12·00	10
180		15c. green	4·50	3·25
		a. Pale green (6.12.55)	4·50	2·50
181		20c. brown	6·00	30
182		25c. scarlet	5·50	5·00
		a. Rose-red (26.6.58)	4·50	4·50
183		30c. grey	5·00	20
		a. Pale grey (26.2.58)	8·00	75
184		40c. bright blue	6·50	50
		a. Dull blue (10.1.61)	15·00	2·25
185		50c. reddish purple	6·50	20
186		65c. grey (20.6.60)	22·00	19·00
187		$1 orange and green	8·00	20
		a. Short right leg to "R"	£150	23·00
188		$1.30 blue and red (20.6.60)	25·00	3·00
		a. Bright blue and red (23.1.62)	55·00	6·00
189		$2 reddish violet and scarlet	12·00	1·00
		a. Short character	£170	50·00
		b. Light reddish violet and scarlet (26.2.58)	17·00	1·00
		ba. Short character	£225	50·00
190		$5 green and purple	80·00	4·25
		a. Yellowish green and purple (7.3.61)	£120	9·50
191		$10 reddish violet and bright blue	65·00	13·00
		a. Light reddish violet and bright blue (26.2.58)	85·00	14·00
178/91		Set of 14	£200	42·00

No. 178a exists from two sheets, each of which had 90 stamps imperforate and ten perforated on three sides only.

The 10c. exists in coils constructed from normal sheets.

The duty plates for the King George VI issue were reformatted to reduce the sheet size from 120 (two panes of 60) to 100. In doing so, one of the 'short R' clichés was discarded. The other occurs on R. 10/9 of No. 187.

38 University Arms   **39** Statue of Queen Victoria

(Des and photo Harrison)

1961 (11 Sept). Golden Jubilee of Hong Kong University. W w **12**. P 11½×12.

192	**38**	$1 multicoloured	3·25	2·00
		a. Gold ptg omitted	£3250	£3250

Normal   **10c** White spot over character in lower right corner (Pl. 1A-1A, R. 1/3)

(Des Cheung Yat-man. Photo Harrison)

1962 (4 May). Stamp Centenary. W w **12**. P 14½.

193	**39**	10c. black and magenta	45	10
		a. Spot on character	9·50	
194		20c. black and light blue	1·75	2·25
195		50c. black and bistre	2·75	40
193/5		Set of 3	4·50	2·50

40 Queen Elizabeth II (after Annigoni)   **41** Queen Elizabeth II (after Annigoni)

Normal   Broken "5" 5c.

The horizontal bar of the "5" is missing (Pl. 1A, R. 3/1 and Pl. 1B, R. 2/2)

(Photo Harrison)

1962 (4 Oct)–**73**. Chalk-surfaced paper. W w **12** (upright). P 15×14 (5c. to $1) or 14×14½ (others).

196	**40**	5c. red-orange	75	60
		a. Broken "5"	21·00	
197		10c. bright reddish violet	1·50	10
		a. Reddish violet (19.11.71)	9·50	2·50
		ab. Glazed paper (14.4.72)	9·00	3·50
198		15c. emerald	3·25	4·25
199		20c. red-brown	2·50	2·00
		a. Brown (13.12.71)	7·00	6·50
		ab. Glazed paper (27.9.72)	14·00	17·00
200		25c. cerise	3·50	5·00
201		30c. deep grey-blue	2·50	10
		a. Chalky blue (19.11.71)	7·00	5·50
		ab. Glazed paper (27.9.72)	16·00	8·50
202		40c. deep bluish green	5·00	70
203		50c. scarlet	1·75	30
		a. Vermilion (13.12.71)	23·00	3·25
		ab. Glazed paper (27.9.72)	10·00	4·00
204		65c. ultramarine	18·00	2·50
205		$1 sepia	24·00	40
206	**41**	$1.30 multicoloured	2·75	20
		a. Pale yellow omitted	65·00	
		b. Pale yellow inverted (horiz pair)	£6500	
		c. Ochre (sash) omitted	60·00	
		d. Glazed paper (3.2.71)	22·00	3·00
		da. Ochre (sash) omitted	55·00	
		dw. Wmk inverted	40·00	
		dwa. Pale yellow omitted	£140	
207		$2 multicoloured	5·00	1·00
		a. Pale yellow omitted†	70·00	
		b. Ochre (sash) omitted	50·00	
		c. Pale yellow† and ochre (sash) omitted	£275	
		dw. Wmk inverted	11·00	
		e. Glazed paper (1973)*	£400	11·00
208		$5 multicoloured	14·00	1·75
		a. Ochre (sash) omitted	60·00	
		ab. Pale yellow and ochre omitted	£120	
		bw. Wmk inverted	42·00	
		c. Glazed paper (3.2.71)	35·00	13·00
		cw. Wmk inverted	70·00	50·00
209		$10 multicoloured	25·00	3·00
		a. Ochre (sash) omitted	£180	
		b. Pale yellow† and ochre (sash) omitted	£275	
		ba. Pale yellow† omitted	£200	
		cw. Wmk inverted	£150	
		d. Glazed paper (1973)*	£2250	£250
210		$20 multicoloured	80·00	26·00
		a. Ochre omitted	£325	
		w. Wmk inverted	£800	
196/210		Set of 15	£160	42·00

*These are from printings which were sent to Hong Kong in March 1973 but not released in London.

†This results in the Queen's face appearing pinkish.

No. 197 exists from coils.

It is believed that No. 206b comes from the last two vertical rows of a sheet, the remainder of which had the pale yellow omitted.

The $1.30 to $20 exist with PVA gum as well as gum arabic. The glazed paper printings are with PVA gum only.

See also Nos. 222, etc.

1963 (4 June). Freedom from Hunger. As No. 146 of Antigua, but additionally inscr in Chinese characters.

211		$1.30 bluish green	28·00	5·00

1963 (2 Sept). Red Cross Centenary. As Nos. 147/8 of Antigua, but additionally inscr in Chinese characters at right.

212		10c. red and black	2·00	30
213		$1.30 red and blue	11·00	8·00

1965 (17 May). ITU Centenary. As Nos. 166/7 of Antigua.

214		10c. light purple and orange-yellow	1·50	25
		w. Wmk inverted	70·00	
215		$1.30 olive-yellow and deep bluish green	7·50	5·50

1965 (25 Oct). International Co-operation Year. As Nos. 168/9 of Antigua.

216		10c. reddish purple and turquoise-green	1·50	25
		w. Wmk inverted	1·50	2·50
217		$1.30 deep bluish green and lavender (shades)	8·00	4·75

1966 (24 Jan). Churchill Commemoration. As Nos. 170/3 of Antigua, but additionally inscr in Chinese characters.

218		10c. new blue	2·50	15
		w. Wmk inverted	26·00	
219		50c. deep green	3·25	30
		w. Wmk inverted	1·75	4·00
220		$1.30 brown	12·00	3·00
221		$2 bluish violet	22·00	10·00
		w. Wmk inverted	£225	
218/21		Set of 4	35·00	12·00

10c. Large white dot to right of upper white Chinese character (Pl. 2B, R. 3/4).

1966 (1 Aug)–**72**. As Nos. 196/208 and 210 but wmk W w **12** (sideways*). Chalk-surfaced paper (5c. to $1) or glazed, ordinary paper ($1.30 to $20).

222	**40**	5c. red-orange (6.12.66)	65	1·25
223		10c. reddish violet (31.3.67)†	70	70
		a. Imperf (horiz pair)	£1100	
		b. Dot beside character	10·00	
		w. Wmk Crown to right of CA	£200	£170
224		15c. emerald (31.3.67)†	2·00	4·25
225		20c. red-brown	2·00	2·50
		a. Glazed, ordinary paper (14.4.72)	8·50	15·00
226		25c. cerise (31.3.67)†	3·00	6·00
		aw. Wmk Crown to right of CA	40·00	
		b. Glazed, ordinary paper (14.4.72)	15·00	23·00
227		30c. deep grey-blue (31.3.70)	10·00	5·50
		a. Glazed, ordinary paper (14.4.72)	14·00	17·00
228		40c. deep bluish green (1967)	3·75	3·25
		a. Glazed, ordinary paper (14.4.72)	14·00	20·00
229		50c. scarlet (31.3.67)†	2·75	1·00
		w. Wmk Crown to right of CA (13.5.69)	4·00	3·00
230		65c. ultramarine (29.3.67)	6·50	12·00
		a. Bright blue (16.7.68)	11·00	16·00
231		$1 sepia (29.3.67)†	15·00	1·75
		w. Wmk Crown to right of CA	75·00	
232	**41**	$1.30 multicoloured (14.4.72)	14·00	3·25
		a. Pale yellow omitted	70·00	
		w. Wmk Crown to right of CA (17.11.72)	12·00	4·75
		wa. Ochre omitted	70·00	
233		$2 multicoloured (13.12.71)	25·00	3·25
		b. Pale yellow omitted	75·00	
		w. Wmk Crown to right of CA (17.11.72)	12·00	8·00
		wa. Ochre (sash) omitted	70·00	
234		$5 multicoloured (13.12.71)	75·00	32·00
		a. Pale yellow omitted	£170	
236		$20 multicoloured (14.4.72)	£160	85·00
222/36		Set of 14	£275	£140

*The normal sideways watermark shows Crown to left of CA, as seen from the back of the stamp.

†Earliest known postmark dates.

The 5c. to 25c., 40c. and 50c. exist with PVA gum as well as gum arabic, but the 30c., and all stamps on glazed paper exist with PVA gum only. 223a also exists with both gums.

1966 (20 Sept). Inauguration of WHO Headquarters, Geneva. As Nos. 178/9 of Antigua.

237		10c. black, yellow-green and light blue	1·50	30
238		50c. black, light purple and yellow-brown	4·50	2·25

1966 (1 Dec). 20th Anniv of UNESCO. As Nos. 196/8 of Antigua.

239		10c. slate-violet, red, yellow and orange	2·50	20
240		50c. orange-yellow, violet and deep olive	5·50	90
241		$2 black, light purple and orange	32·00	20·00
239/41		Set of 3	35·00	20·00

49 Rams' Heads on Chinese Lanterns

10c. White dot after "1967" (R. 2/2)

(Des V. Whiteley. Photo Harrison)

1967 (17 Jan). Chinese New Year ("Year of the Ram"). T **49** and similar horiz design. W w **12** (sideways). P 14½.

242		10c. rosine, olive-green and light yellow-olive	2·00	50
		a. Dot after "1967"	14·00	
243		$1.30 emerald, rosine and light yellow-olive	13·00	8·00

Design:—$1.30, Three rams.

50 Cable Route Map

(Des V. Whiteley. Photo Harrison)

1967 (30 Mar). Completion of Malaysia–Hong Kong Link of SEACOM Telephone Cable. W w **12**. P 12½.

244	**50**	$1.30 new blue and red	6·00	2·00

51 Rhesus Macaques in Tree ("Year of the Monkey")

(Des R. Granger Barrett. Photo Harrison)

1968 (23 Jan). Chinese New Year ("Year of the Monkey"). T **51** and similar horiz design. W w **12** (sideways). P 14½.
245		10c. gold, black and scarlet	2·00	50
246		$1.30 gold, black and scarlet	13·00	8·00

Design:—$1.30, Family of Rhesus Macaques.

52 *Iberia* (liner) at Ocean Terminal

(Des and litho D.L.R.)

1968 (24 Apr). Sea Craft. T **52** and similar horiz design. P 13.
247		10c. multicoloured	1·75	15
	a.	Dull orange and new blue omitted .	£2750	
248		20c. cobalt-blue, black and brown	2·50	1·75
249		40c. orange, black and mauve	8·50	14·00
250		50c. orange-red, black and green	5·50	75
	a.	Green omitted	£1300	
251		$1 greenish yellow, black and red	9·00	8·00
252		$1.30 Prussian blue, black and pink	27·00	4·25
247/52		*Set of 6*	48·00	26·00

Designs:—20c. Pleasure launch; 40c. Car ferry, 50c. Passenger ferry; $1, Sampan; $1.30, Junk.

53 *Bauhinia blakeana*   **54** Arms of Hong Kong

(Des V. Whiteley. Photo Harrison)

1968 (25 Sept)–**73**. W w **12**. P 14×14½.
		(a) Upright wmk. Chalk-surfaced paper		
253	**53**	65c. multicoloured	8·00	50
	aw.	Wmk inverted	32·00	
	b.	Glazed, ordinary paper (3.73)	£120	25·00
254	**54**	$1 multicoloured	8·00	40
	a.	Glazed ordinary paper	£160	40·00
		(b) Sideways wmk. Glazed, ordinary paper		
254b	**53**	65c. multicoloured (27.9.72)	50·00	40·00
254c	**54**	$1 multicoloured (13.12.71)	8·00	2·50

Nos. 253/4 exist with PVA gum as well as gum arabic; Nos. 254b/c with PVA gum only.

55 "Aladdin's Lamp" and Human Rights Emblem

(Des R. Granger Barrett. Litho B.W.)

1968 (20 Nov). Human Rights Year. W w **12** (sideways). P 13½.
255	**55**	10c. orange, black and myrtle-green	1·00	75
256		50c. yellow, black and deep reddish purple	2·00	2·50

56 Cockerel

(Des R. Granger Barrett. Photo Enschedé)

1969 (11 Feb). Chinese New Year ("Year of the Cock"). T **56** and similar multicoloured design. P 13½.
257		10c. Type **56**	2·50	1·00
	a.	Red omitted	£400	
258		$1.30 Cockerel (*vert*)	30·00	9·00

58 Arms of Chinese University   **59** Earth Station and Satellite

---

(Des V. Whiteley. Photo Govt Ptg Bureau, Tokyo)

1969 (26 Aug). Establishment of Chinese University of Hong Kong. P 13½.
259	**58**	40c. violet, gold and pale turquoise-blue	1·75	2·25

(Des V. Whiteley. Photo Harrison)

1969 (24 Sept). Opening of Communications Satellite Tracking Station. W w **12**. P 14½.
260	**59**	$1 multicoloured	4·00	2·00

60 Chow's Head   **62** "Expo '70" Emblem

(Des R. Granger Barrett. Photo D.L.R.)

1970 (28 Jan). Chinese New Year ("Year of the Dog"). T **60** and similar design. W w **12** (sideways on $1.30). P 14½×14 (10c.) or 14×14½ ($1.30).
261		10c. lemon-yellow, orange-brown and black	3·00	1·00
262		$1.30 multicoloured	35·00	10·00

Design: Horiz—$1.30, Chow standing.

(Des and litho B.W.)

1970 (14 Mar). World Fair Osaka. T **62** and similar multicoloured design. W w **12** (sideways on 25c.). P 13½×13 (15c.) or 13×13½ (25c.).
263		15c. Type **62**	65	85
264		25c. "Expo '70" emblem and junks (*horiz*)	1·40	1·50

64 Plaque in Tung Wah Hospital   **65** Symbol

(Des M. F. Griffith. Photo Harrison)

1970 (9 Apr). Centenary of Tung Wah Hospital. W w **12** (sideways*). P 14½.
265	**64**	10c. multicoloured	50	25
266		50c. multicoloured	1·25	1·50
	w.	Wmk Crown to right of CA	8·50	

*The normal sideways watermark shows Crown to left of CA, as seen from the back of the stamp.

(Des J. Cooter. Litho B.W.)

1970 (5 Aug). Asian Productivity Year. W w **12**. P 14×13½.
267	**65**	10c. multicoloured	1·00	60

STAMP BOOKLETS

BOOKLET CONTENTS. In Nos. SB1/4 and SB6/7 the 1c. and 2c. were each in blocks of 12 and the 4c. in blocks of 12 and 4 or two blocks of 8, all having been taken from normal sheets. No. SB5 had both the 2c. and 4c. in blocks of 12 and 4 or as two blocks of 8. Other content formats exist.

The "Metal fastener" used for SB2/b, SB3 and SB7ca was a Hotchkiss "Herringbone" stapler.

1904 (1 Jan). Black on cream cover showing contents and postage rates with "K & W LD" imprint on front. Stapled.
SB1	$1 booklet containing12×1c. (No. 62), 12×2c. (No. 56) and 16×4c. (No. 57)	
	a. 4c. No. 64 (King Edward VII) instead of No. 57 (Q.V.)	£9000

1905 (May)–**07**. Black on cream cover showing contents and postage rates with "Hongkong Printing Press" imprint on front. Metal fastener.
SB2	$1 booklet containing 12×1c., 12×2c. and 16×4c. (Nos. 62/4)	£7000
	a. 2c. and 4c. (Nos. 77/8) (MCA ordinary paper) instead of Nos. 63/4 (CA) (3.06)	£9000
	b. 2c. and 4c. (Nos. 77a/8a) (MCA chalk-surfaced paper) instead of Nos. 77/8 (MCA ordinary paper) (1.07)	£10000

Some examples of No. SB2 show the reference to Australia on the front cover officially deleted in manuscript. No. SB2a has the rate information reset to omit "EXCEPT AUSTRALIA".

1907 (Nov)–**10**. Black on cream cover showing contents and postage rates for both Hong Kong and Agencies in China with "Hongkong Printing Press" imprint. Metal fastener.
SB3	$1 booklet containing 12×1c. (No. 62), 12×2c. (No. 92) and 16×4c. (No. 93)	£5500
	a. Stapled (6.10)	

1911 (Jan)–**12**. Black on cream cover showing contents, but no postage rates, with "Hongkong Printing Press" imprint on front. Stapled.
SB4	$1 booklet containing 12×1c. (No. 62), 12×2c. (No. 92) and 16×4c (No. 93)	
	a. 1c. No. 91 (MCA) instead of No. 62 (CA) (7.12) (off-white cover)	£5500

1912 (July). Black on cream cover showing contents, but no postage rates, with "Hongkong Printing Press" imprint on front. Stapled.
SB5	$1 booklet containing 4×1c., 16×2c. and 16×4c. (Nos. 91/3)	£700

1913 (Mar). Black on cream cover showing contents, but no postage rates, with "Hongkong Printing Press" imprint on front. Stapled.
SB6	$1 booklet containing 12×1c., 12×2c. and 16×4c. (Nos. 100/2) (MCA wmk)	£4500

1922 (June). Black on cream cover showing contents, but no postage rates, with "Hongkong Printing Press" imprint on front. Inscribed "Price $1" Stapled.
SB7	$1 booklet containing 12×1c., 12×2c. and 16×4c. (Nos. 117/18, 120) (Script wmk)	£5000

1923 (Jan)–**25**. Black on grey cover showing contents but no postage rates, with "Ye Olde Printerie" imprint on front. Inscribed "Price $1". Stapled.
SB7a	$1 With "Ye Olde Printerie" imprint (1.23)	£6000
	b. Imprint revised to "Ye Older Printerie Ltd" (5.23)	
	c. Inscribed "Price $" (9.24)	£6000
	ca. Bound with Metal fastener (2.25)	

1965 (10 May). Orange-brown (No. SB8) or yellow-green (No. SB9) covers. Stitched.
SB8	$2 booklet containing 8x 5c. and 16x 10c. (Nos. 196/7) in blocks of 4	35·00
SB9	$5 booklet containing 12×5c., 8×10c., 8×20c. and 4×50c. (Nos. 196/7, 199, 203) in blocks of 4	£120

POSTAGE DUE STAMPS

PRINTERS. Nos. D1/19 were typographed by De La Rue & Co.

D **1** Post-office Scales

1923 (1 Dec)–**56**. Wmk Mult Script CA. Ordinary paper. P 14.
D1	D **1**	1c. brown	2·50	65
	a.	Wmk sideways (1931)	1·50	1·00
	ab.	Chalk-surfaced paper (21.3.56)	30	1·00
D2		2c. green	42·00	11·00
	a.	Wmk sideways (1928)	11·00	5·00
D3		4c. scarlet	50·00	7·00
	a.	Wmk sideways (1928)	32·00	5·00
D4		6c. yellow	32·00	13·00
	a.	Wmk sideways (1931)	90·00	38·00
D5		10c. bright ultramarine	27·00	9·00
	a.	Wmk sideways (1934)	£130	5·00
D1/5		*Set of 5*	£130	35·00
D1a/5a		*Set of 5*	£225	50·00
D1s/5s		Optd "SPECIMEN" *Set of 5*	£425	

1938 (Feb)–**63**. Wmk Mult Script CA (sideways). Ordinary paper. P 14.
D6	D **1**	2c. grey	10·00	10·00
	a.	Chalk-surfaced paper (21.3.56)	1·10	10·00
D7		4c. orange	14·00	4·00
	a.	Chalk-surfaced paper. Orange-yellow (23.5.61)	2·50	11·00
D8		6c. scarlet	4·00	5·50
D9		8c. chestnut (26.2.46)	3·75	32·00
D10		10c. violet	25·00	50
	a.	Chalk-surfaced paper (17.9.63)	14·00	25·00
D11		20c. black (26.2.46)	4·00	2·25
D12		50c. blue (7.47)	75·00	13·00
D6a/12		*Set of 7*	95·00	60·00
D6s/12s		Perf "SPECIMEN" *Set of 7*	£475	

1965 (15 Apr)–**72**. Chalk-surfaced paper. P 14.
		*(a) Wmk w **12** (sideways)*		
D13	D **1**	4c. yellow-orange	3·00	32·00
D14		5c. red (13.5.69)	2·75	5·00
	a.	Glazed paper (17.11.72)	16·00	60·00
D15		10c. violet (27.6.67)	3·00	8·50
D16		20c. black (1965)	6·00	1·50
D17		50c. deep blue (1965)	30·00	8·00
	a.	Blue (13.5.69)	20·00	2·00
D13/17a		*Set of 5*	32·00	45·00
		*(b) Wmk w **12** (upright)*		
D18	D **1**	5c. red (20.7.67)	2·00	4·75
D19		50c. deep blue (26.8.70)	38·00	10·00

The 5c. is smaller, 21×18 mm.

POSTCARD STAMPS

Stamps specially surcharged for use on Postcards.

PRICES. Those in the left-hand column are for unused examples on complete postcards; those on the right for used examples off card. Examples used on postcards are worth much more.

3

CENTS. (P **1**)   **THREE** (P **2**)

1879 (1 Apr). Nos. 22 and 13 surch as Type P **1** by Noronha & Sons.
P1	**3**	3c. on 16c. yellow (No. 22)	£350	£450
P2		5c. on 18c. lilac (No. 13)	£375	£500

1879 (Nov). No. P2 handstamped with Type P **2**.
P3	**3**	3c. on 5c. on 18c. lilac	£9000	£9000

HAVE YOU HEARD?

Untold Stories of the thousand tribes, unfolding within the perforation of our postage stamps.

Unknown to most, and regardless of been studded with over a thousand tribes, we've only began to tell our story to the outside world through Postage Stamps. Despite our best efforts, the ongoing discoveries of flora and fauna species continue to write new chapters. Like seasoned explorers, join our existing collectors in this journey of a life-time experience. Collect Papua New Guinea Postage Stamps.

www.postpng.com.pg

PAPUA NEW GUINEA STAMPS

FREE SHIPPING

Papua New Guinea
K6.20 Traditional headdress

Papua New G

K10 Traditional headdress

Arawe mother and child K1.35

www.postpng.com.pg
customer.care@postpng.com.pg

Post PNG

POSTAL FISCAL STAMPS
I. Stamps inscribed "STAMP DUTY"

NOTE. The dated circular "HONG KONG" cancellation with "PAID ALL" in lower segment was used for fiscal purposes, in black, from 1877. Previously it appears in red on mail to the USA, but is usually not used as a cancellation.

F 1   F 2

F 3

1874–1902. Wmk Crown CC.

(a) P 15½×15

F1	F 1	$2 olive-green	£425	70·00
F2	F 2	$3 dull violet	£400	55·00
		b. Bluish paper		
F3	F 3	$10 rose-carmine	£8500	£800

(b) P 14

F4	F 1	$2 dull bluish green (10.97)	£450	£275
F5	F 2	$3 dull mauve (3.02)	£700	£550
		a. Bluish paper	£2000	
F6	F 3	$10 grey-green	£12000	£11000
F4s/5s Optd "SPECIMEN" *Set of 2*			£450	

Nos. F1/3 and F7 exist on various papers, ranging from thin to thick.

All three of the values perforated 15½×15 were authorised for postal use in 1874. The $10 rose-carmine was withdrawn from such use in 1880, the $2 in September 1897 and the $3 in 1902.

The $2 and $3 were available for postal purposes until July 1903. The $10 in grey-green was issued for fiscal purposes in 1884 and is known with postal cancellations.

12
CENTS.
(F 4)   (F 5)

1880. No. F3 surch with type F 4 by Noronha and Sons, Hong Kong.

F7	F 3	12c. on $10 rose-carmine	£950	£350

1890 (24 Dec). Wmk Crown CA. P. 14.

F8	F 5	2c. dull purple	£200	48·00
		w. Wmk inverted	£2000	

No. F8 was authorised for postal use between 24 and 31 December 1890.

5
DOLLARS
(F 6)

ONE
DOLLAR
(F 7)

FIVE CENTS
(F 8)

1891 (1 Jan). Surch with Type F 6 by D.L.R. Wmk Crown CA. P. 14.

F9	F 3	$5 on $10 purple/*red*	£400	£120
		s. Optd "SPECIMEN"	£250	

No. F9 was in use for postal purposes until June 1903.

1897 (Sept). Surch with Type F 7 by Noronha and Sons, Hong Kong, and with the value in Chinese characters subsequently applied twice by handstamp as T 15.

F10	F 1	$1 on $2 olive-green (No. F1)	£225	£130
		a. Both Chinese handstamps omitted	£4250	£3000
		b. Diagonal Chinese handstamp omitted	£22000	
F11		$1 on $2 dull bluish green (No. F4)	£250	£150
		a. Both Chinese handstamps omitted	£2000	£1700
		b. Diagonal Chinese handstamp omitted	£30000	
		c. Vertical Chinese handstamp omitted		
		s. Handstamped "SPECIMEN"	£150	

1938 (11 Jan). Wmk Mult Script CA. P. 14.

F12	F 8	5c. green	£100	17·00

No. F12 was authorised for postal use between 11 and 20 January 1938 due to a shortage of 5c., No. 121.

Forged cancellations are known on this stamp inscribed "VICTORIA 9.AM 11 JA 38 HONG KONG" without side bars between the rings.

II. Stamps overprinted "S.O." (Stamp Office) or "S.D." (Stamp Duty)

邱 厘 邱 厘
(S **1**)   (S **2**)

1891 (1 Jan). Optd with Types S **1** or S **2**.

S1	S **1**	2c. carmine (No. 33)	£950	£375
S2	S **2**	2c. carmine (No. 33)	£425	£200
		a. Opt inverted	†	£9000
S3	S **1**	10c. purple/*red* (No. 38)	£1700	£450

Examples of No. S1 exist with the "O" amended to "D" in manuscript.

Other fiscal stamps are found apparently postally used, but there is no evidence that this use was authorised.

JAPANESE OCCUPATION OF HONG KONG

Hong Kong surrendered to the Japanese on 25 December 1941. The postal service was not resumed until 22 January 1942 when the GPO and Kowloon Central Office re-opened.

Japanese postmarks used in Hong Kong can be identified by the unique combination of horizontal lines in the central circle and three stars in the lower segment of the outer circle. Dates shown on such postmarks are in the sequence Year/Month/Day with the first shown as a Japanese regnal year number so that Showa 17 = 1942 and so on.

Initially six current Japanese definitives, 1, 2, 3, 4, 10 and 30s. (Nos. 297, 315/17, 322 and 327) were on sale, but the range gradually expanded to cover all values between ½s. and 10y. with Nos. 313/14, 318, 325, 328/31, 391, 395/6, 398/9 and 405 of Japan also available from Hong Kong post offices during the occupation. Philatelic covers exist showing other Japanese stamps, but these were not available from the local post offices. Supply of these Japanese stamps was often interrupted and, during the period between 28 July 1942 and 21 April 1943, circular "Postage Paid" handstamps were sometimes used. A substantial increase in postage rates on 16 April 1945 led to the issue of the local surcharges, Nos. J1/3.

PRICES FOR STAMPS ON COVER
Nos. J1/3   from × 7

壹圓伍拾錢 暫定 叁圓 暫定

乔港總督部 香港總督部
(1)   (2)

1945 (16 Apr). Stamps of Japan surch with T **1** (No. J1) or as T **2**.

J1	1.50 yen on 1s. brown	38·00	32·00
J2	3 yen on 2s. scarlet	12·00	27·00
J3	5 yen on 5s. claret	£900	£150

Designs (18½×22 *mm*):—1s. Girl Worker; 2s. Gen. Nogi; 5s. Admiral Togo.

No. J3 has four characters of value similarly arranged but differing from T **2**.

BRITISH POST OFFICES IN CHINA

Under the terms of the 1842 Treaty of Nanking, China granted Great Britain and its citizens commercial privileges in five Treaty Ports, Amoy, Canton, Foochow, Ningpo and Shanghai. British Consuls were appointed to each Port and their offices, as was usual during this period, collected and distributed mail for the British community. This system was formally recognised by a Hong Kong Government notice published on 16 April 1844. Mail from the consular offices was postmarked when it passed through Hong Kong.

The number of Chinese Treaty Ports was increased to 16 by the ratification of the Treaty of Peking in 1860 with British postal facilities being eventually extended to the Ports of Chefoo, Hankow, Kiungchow (Hoihow), Swatow, Tainan (Anping) and Tientsin.

As postal business expanded the consular agencies were converted into packet agencies or post offices which came under the direct control of the Hong Kong postal authorities on 1 May 1868.

In May 1898 the British Government leased the territory of Wei Hai Wei from China for use as a naval station to counter the Russian presence at Port Arthur.

The opening of the Trans-Siberia Railway and the extension of Imperial Penny Postage to the Treaty Port agencies resulted in them becoming a financial burden on the colonial post office. Control of the agencies reverted to the GPO, London, on 1 January 1911.

The pre-adhesive postal markings of the various agencies are a fascinating study, most complex, but simple. Full details can be found in *Hong Kong & the Treaty Ports of China & Japan* by F. W. Webb (reprinted edition J. Bendon, Limassol, 1992) and in various publications of the Hong Kong Study Circle.

From 15 October 1864 the use of Hong Kong stamps on mail from the Treaty Ports became compulsory, although such stamps were, initially, not cancelled (with the exception of Amoy) until they reached Hong Kong where the "B62" killer was applied. Cancellation of mail at the actual Ports commenced during 1866 at Shanghai and Ningpo, spreading to the agencies during the next ten years. Shanghai had previously used a c.d.s. on adhesives during 1863 and again in 1865–66.

The main types of cancellation used between 1866 and 1930 are illustrated below. The illustrations show the style of each postmark and no attempt has been made to cover differences in type letters or figures, arrangement, diameter or colour.

Until 1885 the vertical and horizontal killers were used to obliterate the actual stamps with an impression of one of the circular date stamps shown elsewhere on the cover. Many of the early postmarks were also used as backstamps or transit marks and, in the notes which follow, references to use are for the first appearance of the mark, not necessarily its first use as an obliterator.

Illustrations in this section are taken from *Hong Kong & the Treaty Ports of China & Japan* by F. W. Webb and are reproduced with the permission of the Royal Philatelic Society, London.

Details of the stamps known used from each post office are taken, with permission, from *British Post Offices in the Far East* by Edward B. Proud, published by Proud-Bailey Co. Ltd.

Postmark Types

Type **A** Vertical killer   Type **B** Horizontal killer

Type **C** Name horizontal   Type **D** Name curved

Type **E** Double circle Name at top   Type **F** Double circle Name at foot

Type **G** Single circle Name at top

PRICES. The prices quoted in this section are for fine used stamps which show a clear impression of a substantial part of the cancellation.

AMOY

One of the five original Treaty Ports, opened to British trade by the Treaty of Nanking in 1842. A consular postal agency was established in 1844 which expanded in 1876 into two separate offices, one on the off-shore island of Ku Lang Seu and the other in Amoy itself.

Amoy "PAID" (*supplied* 1858) *used* 1859–67
Type **A** ("A1") (*supplied* 1866) *used at* Ku Lang Seu 1869–82
Type **D** (*supplied* 1866) *used* 1867–1922
Type **B** ("D27") (*supplied* 1876) *used at* Amoy 1876–84
Type **C** *used* 1876–94
Type **F** (*supplied* 1913) *used* 1916–22

Stamps of HONG KONG cancelled at Amoy between 1864 and 1916 with postmarks detailed above.

1862. No wmk (Nos. 1/7).

Z1	2c. brown	£300
Z2	8c. yellow-buff	£250
Z3	12c. pale greenish blue	£225
Z4	18c. lilac	£160
Z5	24c. green	£275
Z6	48c. rose	£1400
Z7	96c. brownish grey	£1100

1863–71. Wmk Crown CC (Nos. 8/19).

Z8	2c. brown	40·00
Z9	4c. grey	45·00
	a. Perf 12½	
Z10	6c. lilac	75·00
Z11	8c. orange	55·00
Z12	12c. blue	25·00
Z13	18c. lilac	£1100
Z14	24c. green	70·00
Z15	30c. vermilion	£160
Z16	30c. mauve	21·00
Z17	48c. rose	85·00
Z18	96c. olive-bistre	£3500
Z19	96c. brownish grey	£350

1876–77. (Nos. 20/1).
Z20	16c. on 18c. lilac	£350
Z21	28c. on 30c. mauve	£150

1877. Wmk Crown CC (No. 22).
Z22	16c. yellow	£140

1880. (Nos. 23/7).
Z23	5c. on 8c. orange	£140
Z24	5c. on 18c. lilac	£100
Z25	10c. on 12c. blue	£100
Z26	10c. on 16c. yellow	£225
Z27	10c. on 24c. green	£150

1880. Wmk Crown CC (Nos. 28/31).
Z28	2c. rose	60·00
Z29	5c. blue	95·00
Z30	10c. mauve	75·00
Z31	48c. brown	£325

1882–96. Wmk Crown CA (Nos. 32/9).
Z31a	2c. rose-lake	65·00
Z32	2c. carmine	5·00
Z33	4c. slate-grey	14·00
Z34	5c. blue	4·75
Z35	10c. dull mauve	50·00
Z36	10c. green	6·00
Z37	10c. purple/red	5·50
Z38	30c. green	50·00

1885. (Nos. 40/2).
Z39	20c. on 30c. orange-red	19·00
Z40	50c. on 48c. yellowish brown	90·00
Z41	$1 on 96c. grey-olive	£150

1891. (Nos. 43/50).
Z42	7c. on 10c. green	27·00
Z43	14c. on 30c. mauve	£140
Z44	20c. on 30c. green (No. 48)	19·00
Z45	50c. on 48c. dull purple (No. 49)	20·00
Z46	$1 on 96c. purple/red (No. 50)	60·00

1891. 50th Anniv of Colony (No. 51).
Z47	2c. carmine	£1100

1898. (No. 52).
Z48	$1 on 96c. black	75·00

1898. (No. 55).
Z49	10c. on 30c. green	£275

1900–01. Wmk Crown CA (Nos. 56/61).
Z50	2c. dull green	5·00
Z51	4c. carmine	3·75
Z52	5c. yellow	24·00
Z53	10c. ultramarine	6·00
Z54	12c. blue	£225
Z55	30c. brown	90·00

1903. Wmk Crown CA (Nos. 62/76).
Z56	1c. dull purple and brown	5·50
Z57	2c. dull green	5·00
Z58	4c. purple/red	3·25
Z59	5c. dull green and brown-orange	25·00
Z60	8c. slate and violet	8·50
Z61	10c. purple and blue/blue	4·50
Z62	12c. green and purple/yellow	19·00
Z63	20c. slate and chestnut	14·00
Z64	30c. dull green and black	70·00
Z65	50c. dull green and magenta	£120
Z67	$2 slate and scarlet	£550
Z68	$3 slate and dull blue	£800

1904–06. Wmk Mult Crown CA (Nos. 77/90).
Z71	2c. dull green	5·00
Z72	4c. purple/red	3·25
Z73	5c. dull green and brown-orange	20·00
Z74	8c. slate and violet	12·00
Z75	10c. purple and blue/blue	4·75
Z76	12c. green and purple/yellow	23·00
Z77	20c. slate and chestnut	13·00
Z78	30c. dull green and black	45·00
Z79	50c. green and magenta	42·00
Z80	$1 purple and sage-green	£110
Z81	$2 slate and scarlet	£400
Z83	$5 purple and blue-green	£700

1907–11. Wmk Mult Crown CA (Nos. 91/9).
Z85	1c. brown	5·50
Z86	2c. green	4·75
Z87	4c. carmine-red	3·25
Z88	6c. orange-vermilion and purple	20·00
Z89	10c. bright ultramarine	4·25
Z90	20c. purple and sage-green	80·00
Z91	30c. purple and orange-yellow	85·00
Z92	50c. black/green	80·00

1912–15. Wmk Crown CA (Nos. 100/16).
Z93	1c. brown	6·50
Z94	2c. green	6·00
Z95	4c. red	3·25
Z96	6c. orange	7·50
Z97	8c. grey	25·00
Z98	10c. ultramarine	4·50
Z99	12c. purple/yellow	35·00
Z100	20c. purple and sage-green	8·00
Z101	25c. purple and magenta (Type A)	95·00
Z102	30c. purple and orange-yellow	30·00
Z103	50c. black/green	17·00
Z104	$1 purple and blue/blue	30·00
Z105	$3 green and purple	£250

POSTCARD STAMPS

1879. (Nos. P1/2).
ZP106	3c. on 16c. yellow	£1000
ZP107	5c. on 18c. lilac	£1200

POSTAL FISCAL STAMPS

1874–1902. Wmk Crown CC. P 15½×15 (Nos. F1/3)
ZF109	$2 olive-green	£200
ZF110	$3 dull violet	£200

1891. (No. F9).
ZF116	$5 on $10 purple/red	£350

1897. (Nos. F10/11).
ZF118	$1 on $2 olive-green	£200
ZF119	$1 on $2 dull bluish green	£425

ANPING

Anping is the port for Tainan, on the island of Formosa, opened to British trade in 1860. A British Vice-consulate operated in the port and mail is known postmarked there between 1889 and 1895. Formosa passed under Japanese control in 1895 and British Treaty Port rights then lapsed.

Type **D** used 1889–95

Stamps of HONG KONG cancelled at Anping between 1889 and 1895 with postmark detailed above.

1882–91. Wmk Crown CA (Nos. 32/9).
Z120	2c. carmine	£1100
Z121	5c. blue	£950
Z123	10c. green	£1000
Z124	10c. purple/red	£1100

1885. (Nos. 40/2).
Z126	20c. on 30c. orange-red	£1100
Z127	50c. on 48c. yellowish brown	£3000

CANTON

A British postal service was organised in Canton from 1834, but was closed when the foreign communities were evacuated in August 1839. The city was one of the original Treaty Ports and a consular agency was opened there in 1844. The consulate closed during the riots of December 1856, being replaced by a temporary postal agency at Whampoa, further down the river. When British forces reached Canton a further temporary agency was set up on 23 March 1859, but both closed in July 1863 when the consulate was re-established.

Type **A** ("C1") (supplied 1866) used 1875–84
Type **C** (supplied 1866) used 1870–1901
Type **D** used 1890–1922

Stamps of HONG KONG cancelled at Canton between 1870 and 1916 with postmarks detailed above.

1862. No wmk (Nos. 1/7).
Z135	18c. lilac	£180

1863–71. Wmk Crown CC (Nos. 8/19).
Z136	2c. brown	42·00
Z137	4c. grey	45·00
Z138	6c. lilac	75·00
Z139	8c. orange	55·00
Z140	12c. blue	25·00
Z142	24c. green	80·00
Z143	30c. vermilion	
Z144	30c. mauve	25·00
Z145	48c. rose	£140
Z147	96c. brownish grey	£325

1876–77. (Nos. 20/1).
Z148	16c. on 18c. lilac	£300
Z149	28c. on 30c. mauve	£120

1877. Wmk Crown CC (No. 22).
Z150	16c. yellow	£170

1880. (Nos. 23/7).
Z151	5c. on 8c. orange	£170
Z152	5c. on 18c. lilac	£130
Z153	10c. on 12c. blue	£120
Z154	10c. on 16c. yellow	£275
Z155	10c. on 24c. green	£170

1880. Wmk Crown CC (Nos. 28/31).
Z156	2c. rose	60·00
Z157	5c. blue	90·00
Z158	10c. mauve	65·00

1882–96. Wmk Crown CA (Nos. 32/9).
Z159	2c. rose-lake	45·00
Z160	2c. carmine	3·75
Z161	4c. slate-grey	15·00
Z162	5c. blue	5·50
Z163	10c. dull mauve	45·00
Z164	10c. green	10·00
Z165	10c. purple/red	5·00
Z166	30c. green	50·00

1885. (Nos. 40/2).
Z167	20c. on 30c. orange-red	18·00
Z168	50c. on 48c. yellowish brown	90·00
Z169	$1 on 96c. grey-olive	£160

1891. (Nos. 43/50).
Z170	7c. on 10c. green	27·00
Z171	14c. on 30c. mauve	£150
Z171a	20c. on 30c. green (No. 45)	£300
Z172	20c. on 30c. green (No. 48)	22·00
Z173	50c. on 48c. dull purple (No. 49)	24·00
Z174	$1 on 96c. purple/red (No. 50)	75·00

1891. 50th Anniv of Colony (No. 51).
Z175	2c. carmine	£1100

1898. (No. 52).
Z176	$1 on 96c. black	£160

1898. (No. 55).
Z177	10c. on 30c. grey-green	£190

1900–01. Wmk Crown CA (Nos. 56/61)
Z178	2c. dull green	4·50
Z179	4c. carmine	4·25
Z180	5c. yellow	40·00
Z181	10c. ultramarine	4·50
Z182	12c. blue	£160
Z183	30c. brown	80·00

1903. Wmk Crown CA (Nos. 62/76).
Z184	1c. dull purple and brown	4·75
Z185	2c. dull green	5·00
Z186	4c. purple/red	3·50
Z187	5c. dull green and brown-orange	26·00
Z188	8c. slate and violet	10·00
Z189	10c. purple and blue/blue	4·75
Z190	12c. green and purple/yellow	21·00
Z191	20c. slate and chestnut	12·00
Z192	30c. dull green and black	65·00
Z193	50c. dull green and magenta	£100
Z194	$1 purple and sage-green	£120

1904–06. Wmk Mult Crown CA (Nos. 77/90).
Z199	2c. dull green	4·75
Z200	4c. purple/red	3·50
Z201	5c. dull green and brown-orange	23·00
Z202	8c. slate and violet	15·00
Z203	10c. purple and blue/blue	4·50
Z204	12c. green and purple/yellow	27·00
Z205	20c. slate and chestnut	14·00
Z206	30c. dull green and black	45·00
Z207	50c. green and magenta	50·00
Z208	$1 purple and sage-green	90·00
Z209	$2 slate and scarlet	£500
Z210	$3 slate and dull blue	£650
Z212	$10 slate and orange/blue	£1800

1907–11. Wmk Mult Crown CA (Nos. 91/9).
Z213	1c. brown	4·75
Z215	2c. green	4·75
Z216	4c. carmine-red	3·50
Z216	6c. orange-vermilion and purple	24·00
Z217	10c. bright ultramarine	4·25
Z218	20c. purple and sage-green	85·00
Z219	30c. purple and orange-yellow	75·00
Z220	50c. black/green	55·00
Z221	$2 carmine-red and black	£600

1912–15. Wmk Mult Crown CA (Nos. 100/16).
Z222	1c. brown	4·75
Z223	2c. green	4·00
Z224	4c. red	3·00
Z225	6c. orange	7·50
Z226	8c. grey	23·00
Z227	10c. ultramarine	4·50
Z228	12c. purple/yellow	24·00
Z229	20c. purple and sage-green	7·00
Z230	25c. purple and magenta (Type A)	£110
Z231	30c. purple and orange-yellow	25·00
Z232	50c. black/green	9·00
Z233	$1 purple and blue/blue	42·00
Z234	$2 carmine red and grey-black	£150
Z235	$3 green and purple	£250
Z235b	$10 purple and black/red	£400

POSTCARD STAMPS

1879. (Nos. P1/2).
ZP236	3c. on 16c. yellow	£850
ZP237	5c. on 18c. lilac	£1000

POSTAL FISCAL STAMPS

1874–1902. Wmk Crown CC. Nos. F 1/5.
		(a) P 15½×15	
ZF238	$2 olive-green		£200
		(b) P 14	
ZF242	$3 dull mauve		£900

1891. (No. F9).
ZF246	$5 on $10 purple/red	£450

1897. (No. F10).
ZF247	$1 on $2 olive-green	

CHEFOO

Chefoo was opened to British trade in 1860. Although a consulate was established in 1863 no organised postal agency was provided until 1 January 1903 when one was opened at the premises of Curtis Brothers, a commercial firm.

Type **E** (supplied 1902) used 1903–20
Type **D** (supplied 1907) used 1907–13
Type **F** used 1916–22

Stamps of HONG KONG cancelled at Chefoo between 1903 and 1916 with postmarks detailed above.

1882–96. Wmk Crown CA (Nos. 32/9).
Z249	5c. blue	42·00

1891. (Nos. 43/50).
Z250	20c. on 30c. grey-green (No. 48a)	65·00

1898. (No. 52).
Z251	$1 on 96c. black	£150

1900–01. Wmk Crown CA (Nos. 56/61).
Z252	2c. dull green	30·00
Z253	4c. carmine	29·00
Z254	5c. yellow	85·00
Z255	10c. ultramarine	30·00
Z257	30c. brown	£180

1903. Wmk Crown CA (Nos. 62/76).
Z258	1c. dull purple and brown	13·00
Z259	2c. dull green	11·00
Z260	4c. purple/red	10·00
Z261	5c. dull green and brown-orange	32·00
Z262	8c. slate and violet	22·00
Z263	10c. purple and blue/blue	14·00
Z264	12c. green and purple/yellow	42·00
Z265	20c. slate and chestnut	42·00

Z267	50c. dull green and magenta	£150
Z268	$1 purple and sage-green	£150

1904–06. Wmk Mult Crown CA (Nos. 77/90).

Z273	2c. dull green	11·00
Z274	4c. purple/red	9·00
Z275	5c. dull green and brown-orange	23·00
Z276	8c. slate and violet	20·00
Z277	10c. purple and blue/blue	11·00
Z278	12c. green and purple/yellow	38·00
Z279	20c. slate and chestnut	24·00
Z280	30c. dull green and black	75·00
Z281	50c. green and magenta	75·00
Z282	$1 purple and sage-green	£130
Z283	$2 slate and scarlet	£350
Z284	$3 slate and dull blue	£650
Z285	$5 purple and blue-green	£900

1907–11. Wmk Mult Crown CA (Nos. 91/9).

Z287	1c. brown	13·00
Z288	2c. green	12·00
Z289	4c. carmine-red	10·00
Z290	6c. orange-vermilion and purple	40·00
Z291	10c. bright ultramarine	11·00
Z292	20c. purple and sage-green	£120
Z293	30c. purple and orange-yellow	90·00
Z294	50c. black/green	75·00
Z295	$2 carmine-red and black	£700

1912–15. Wmk Mult Crown CA (Nos. 100/16).

Z296	1c. brown	10·00
Z297	2c. green	9·50
Z298	4c. red	7·50
Z299	6c. orange	20·00
Z300	8c. grey	42·00
Z301	10c. ultramarine	9·00
Z302	12c. purple/yellow	45·00
Z303	20c. purple and sage-green	15·00
Z305	30c. purple and orange-yellow	28·00
Z306	50c. black/green	15·00
Z307	$1 purple and blue/blue	23·00
Z308	$2 carmine-red and grey-black	£120
Z309	$3 green and purple	£200
Z310	$5 green and red/green	£600
Z311	$10 purple and black/red	£375

FOOCHOW

Foochow, originally known as Foochowfoo, was one of the original Treaty Ports opened to British trade in 1842. A British consulate and postal agency was established in June 1844.

Type **A** ("F1") (supplied 1866) used 1873–84
Type **D** (inscr "FOOCHOWFOO") (supplied 1866) used 1867–1905
Type **D** (inscr "FOOCHOW") (supplied 1894) used 1894–1917
Type **E** (inscr "B.P.O.") used 1906–10
Type **F** used 1915–22

Stamps of HONG KONG cancelled at Foochow between 1867 and 1916 with postmarks detailed above.

1862. No wmk (Nos. 1/7).

Z312	18c. lilac	£200

1863–71. Wmk Crown CC (Nos. 8/19).

Z313	2c. brown	38·00
Z314	4c. grey	38·00
Z315	6c. lilac	60·00
Z316	8c. orange	55·00
Z317	12c. blue	22·00
Z318	18c. lilac	£1000
Z319	24c. green	80·00
Z320	30c. vermilion	£250
Z321	30c. mauve	20·00
Z322	48c. rose	£140
Z324	96c. brownish grey	£425

1876–77. (Nos. 20/1).

Z325	16c. on 18c. lilac	£325
Z326	28c. on 30c. mauve	£150

1877. Wmk Crown CC (No. 22).

Z327	16c. yellow	£150

1880. (Nos. 23/7).

Z328	5c. on 8c. orange	£350
Z329	5c. on 18c. lilac	£130
Z330	10c. on 12c. blue	£130
Z331	10c. on 16c. yellow	
Z332	10c. on 24c. green	£180

1880. Wmk Crown CC (Nos. 28/31).

Z333	2c. rose	48·00
Z334	5c. blue	95·00
Z335	10c. mauve	55·00
Z336	48c. brown	£300

1882–96. Wmk Crown CA (Nos. 32/9).

Z336a	2c. rose-lake	42·00
Z337	2c. carmine	3·25
Z338	4c. slate-grey	9·00
Z339	5c. blue	3·75
Z340	10c. dull mauve	50·00
Z341	10c. green	11·00
Z342	10c. purple/red	4·50
Z343	30c. green	55·00

1885. (Nos. 40/2).

Z344	20c. on 30c. orange-red	20·00
Z345	50c. on 48c. yellowish brown	90·00
Z346	$1 on 96c. grey-olive	£150

1891. (Nos. 43/50).

Z347	7c. on 10c. green	70·00
Z348	14c. on 30c. mauve	£130
Z348a	20c. on 30c. green (No. 45)	£275
Z349	20c. on 30c. green (No. 48)	23·00
Z350	50c. on 48c. dull purple	30·00
Z351	$1 on 96c. purple/red	75·00

1898. (No. 52).

Z353	$1 on 96c. black	£110

1898. (No. 55).

Z354	10c. on 30c. green	£250

1900–01. Wmk Crown CA (Nos. 56/61).

Z355	2c. dull green	4·50
Z356	4c. carmine	5·00
Z357	5c. yellow	26·00
Z358	10c. ultramarine	4·50
Z360	30c. brown	£100

1903. Wmk Crown CA (Nos. 62/76).

Z361	1c. dull purple and brown	5·50
Z362	2c. dull green	4·75
Z363	4c. purple/red	3·25
Z364	5c. dull green and brown-orange	25·00
Z365	8c. slate and violet	14·00
Z366	10c. purple and blue/blue	4·75
Z367	12c. green and purple/yellow	25·00
Z368	20c. slate and chestnut	15·00
Z369	30c. dull green and black	60·00
Z370	50c. dull green and magenta	95·00
Z371	$1 purple and sage-green	85·00

1904–06. Wmk Mult Crown CA (Nos. 77/90).

Z376	2c. dull green	4·75
Z377	4c. purple/red	3·25
Z378	5c. dull green and brown-orange	19·00
Z379	8c. slate and violet	12·00
Z380	10c. purple and blue/blue	4·75
Z381	12c. green and purple/yellow	27·00
Z382	20c. slate and chestnut	13·00
Z383	30c. dull green and black	55·00
Z384	50c. green and magenta	45·00
Z385	$1 purple and sage-green	90·00

1907–11. Wmk Mult Crown CA (Nos. 91/9).

Z390	1c. brown	4·25
Z391	2c. green	4·25
Z392	4c. carmine-red	3·25
Z393	6c. orange-vermilion and purple	23·00
Z394	10c. bright ultramarine	4·00
Z395	20c. purple and sage-green	85·00
Z396	30c. purple and orange-yellow	75·00
Z397	50c. black/green	55·00

1912–15. Wmk Mult Crown CA (Nos. 100/16).

Z399	1c. brown	6·00
Z400	2c. green	4·50
Z401	4c. red	3·25
Z402	6c. orange	15·00
Z403	8c. grey	27·00
Z404	10c. ultramarine	4·50
Z405	12c. purple/yellow	38·00
Z406	20c. purple and sage-green	8·00
Z407	25c. purple and magenta (Type A)	£110
Z408	30c. purple and orange-yellow	27·00
Z409	50c. black/green	24·00

POSTCARD STAMPS

1874–1902. (Nos. P1/2).

ZP413	3c. on 16c. yellow	£1100

POSTAL FISCAL STAMPS

1874–1902. Wmk Crown CC. P 15½×15 (Nos. F1/3)

ZF415	$2 olive-green	£180
ZF416	$3 dull violet	£160

HANKOW

Hankow, on the Yangtse River 600 miles from the sea, became a Treaty Port in 1860. A British consulate opened the following year, but no organised British postal agency was established until 1872.

Type **D** (supplied 1874) used 1874–1916
Type **B** ("D29") (supplied 1876) used 1878–83
Type **F** used 1916–22

Stamps of HONG KONG cancelled at Hankow between 1874 and 1916 with postmarks detailed above.

1862. No wmk (Nos. 1/7).

Z426	18c. lilac	£400

1863–71. Wmk Crown CC (Nos. 8/19).

Z427	2c. brown	£140
Z428	4c. grey	£140
Z429	6c. lilac	£180
Z430	8c. orange	£170
Z431	12c. blue	55·00
Z432	18c. lilac	£1400
Z433	24c. green	£275
Z435	30c. mauve	£140
Z436	48c. rose	£375
Z438	96c. brownish grey	

1876–77. (Nos. 20/1).

Z439	16c. on 18c. lilac	£550
Z440	28c. on 30c. mauve	£325

1877. Wmk Crown CC (No. 22).

Z441	16c. yellow	£800

1880. (Nos. 23/7).

Z442	5c. on 8c. orange	£350
Z443	5c. on 18c. lilac	£250
Z444	10c. on 12c. blue	£275
Z445	10c. on 16c. yellow	£500
Z446	10c. on 24c. green	£325

1880. Wmk Crown CC (Nos. 28/31).

Z447	2c. rose	£110
Z448	5c. blue	£130
Z449	10c. mauve	£140
Z450	48c. brown	£450

1882–96. Wmk Crown CA (Nos. 32/9).

Z450a	2c. rose-lake	£100
Z451	2c. carmine	10·00
Z452	4c. slate-grey	22·00
Z453	5c. blue	11·00
Z454	10c. dull mauve	£120
Z455	10c. green	14·00
Z456	10c. purple/red	12·00
Z457	30c. green	80·00

1885. (Nos. 40/2).

Z458	20c. on 30c. orange-red	42·00
Z459	50c. on 48c. yellowish brown	£110
Z460	$1 on 96c. grey-olive	£200

1891. (Nos. 43/50).

Z461	7c. on 10c. green	42·00
Z462	14c. on 30c. mauve	£170
Z463	20c. on 30c. green	30·00
Z464	50c. on 48c. dull purple	32·00
Z465	$1 on 96c. purple/red	90·00

1898. (No. 52).

Z467	$1 on 96c. black	£120

1898. (No. 55).

Z468	10c. on 30c. green	£325

1900–01. Wmk Crown CA (Nos. 56/61).

Z469	2c. dull green	7·00
Z470	4c. carmine	7·50
Z471	5c. yellow	40·00
Z472	10c. ultramarine	9·00
Z473	12c. blue	£190
Z474	30c. brown	£110

1903. Wmk Crown CA (Nos. 62/76).

Z475	1c. dull purple and brown	7·50
Z476	2c. dull green	7·00
Z477	4c. purple/red	6·00
Z478	5c. dull green and brown-orange	28·00
Z479	8c. slate and violet	22·00
Z480	10c. purple and blue/blue	6·50
Z481	12c. green and purple/yellow	28·00
Z482	20c. slate and chestnut	19·00
Z483	30c. dull green and black	65·00
Z484	50c. dull green and magenta	£110
Z485	$1 purple and sage-green	90·00

1904–06. Wmk Mult Crown CA (Nos. 77/90).

Z490	2c. dull green	6·50
Z491	4c. purple/red	5·50
Z492	5c. dull green and brown-orange	26·00
Z493	8c. slate and violet	13·00
Z494	10c. purple and blue/blue	6·50
Z495	12c. green and purple/yellow	30·00
Z496	20c. slate and chestnut	20·00
Z497	30c. dull green and black	55·00
Z498	50c. green and magenta	42·00
Z499	$1 purple and sage-green	90·00
Z500	$2 slate and scarlet	£450
Z502	$5 purple and blue-green	£850
Z503	$10 slate and orange/blue	£2000

1907–11. Wmk Mult Crown CA (Nos. 91/9).

Z504	1c. brown	7·00
Z505	2c. green	6·00
Z506	4c. carmine-red	4·50
Z507	6c. orange-vermilion and purple	29·00
Z508	10c. bright ultramarine	6·50
Z509	20c. purple and sage-green	£110
Z510	30c. purple and orange-yellow	95·00

1912–15. Wmk Mult Crown CA (Nos. 100/16).

Z513	1c. brown	8·00
Z514	2c. green	7·00
Z515	4c. red	5·50
Z516	6c. orange	16·00
Z517	8c. grey	35·00
Z518	10c. ultramarine	6·50
Z520	20c. purple and sage-green	16·00
Z522	30c. purple and orange-yellow	35·00
Z523	50c. black/green	20·00
Z524	$1 purple and blue/blue	80·00
Z526	$3 green and purple	£275
Z527	$5 green and red/green	£750

POSTCARD STAMPS

1879. (Nos. P1/2).

ZP528	3c. on 16c. yellow	£1600

POSTAL FISCAL STAMPS

1874–1902. Wmk Crown CC.

	(a) P 15½×15 (Nos. F1/3)	
ZF529	$2 olive-green	£300
	(b) P 14 (Nos. F4/6)	
ZF532	$2 dull bluish green	£500

1897. (No. F11).

ZF533	$1 on $2 dull bluish green	£750

KIUNGCHOW (HOIHOW)

Kiungchow, a city on the island of Hainan, and its port of Hoihow was added to the Treaty Port system in 1860. A consular postal agency was opened at Kiungchow in 1876, being transferred to Hoihow in 1878. A second agency was opened at Kiungchow in 1879.

Type **B** ("D28") (supplied 1876) used 1879–83
Type **D** (inscr "KIUNG-CHOW") (supplied 1878) used 1879–81

"REGISTERED KIUNG-CHOW" with "REGISTERED" removed (*originally supplied 1876*) *used 1883–85*
Type **D** (inscr "HOIHOW") *used 1885–1922*

Stamps of HONG KONG cancelled at Kiungchow (Hoihow) between 1879 and 1916 with postmarks detailed above.

1863–71. Wmk Crown CC (Nos. 8/19).
Z540	2c. brown	£1000
Z541	4c. grey	£800
Z542	6c. lilac	£1700
Z543	8c. orange	£1700
Z544	12c. blue	£550
Z546	24c. green	£1700
Z547	30c. vermilion	
Z548	30c. mauve	£300
Z549	48c. rose	£2750
Z551	96c. brownish grey	£2750

1876–77. (Nos. 20/1).
Z552	16c. on 18c. lilac	£1800
Z553	28c. on 30c. mauve	£1400

1877. (No. 22).
Z554	16c. yellow	£2750

1880. (Nos. 23/7).
Z555	5c. on 8c. orange	£1200
Z556	5c. on 18c. lilac	£1000
Z557	10c. on 12c. blue	£1000
Z558	10c. on 16c. yellow	£2000
Z559	10c. on 24c. green	

1880. Wmk Crown CC (Nos. 28/31).
Z561	5c. blue	£800
Z562	10c. mauve	£950

1882–96. Wmk Crown CA (Nos. 32/9).
Z564	2c. carmine	60·00
Z565	4c. slate-grey	90·00
Z566	5c. blue	60·00
Z567	10c. dull mauve	£800
Z568	10c. green	85·00
Z569	10c. purple/*red*	60·00
Z570	30c. green	£150

1885. (Nos. 40/2).
Z571	20c. on 30c. orange-red	£160
Z572	50c. on 48c. yellowish brown	£180
Z573	$1 on 96c. grey-olive	£350

1891. (Nos. 43/50).
Z574	7c. on 10c. green	£200
Z576	20c. on 30c. green	65·00
Z577	50c. on 48c. dull purple	95·00
Z578	$1 on 96c. purple/*red*	£190

1891. 50th Anniv of Colony (No. 51).
Z579	2c. carmine	£3000

1898. (No. 52).
Z580	$1 on 96c. black	£375

1898. (No. 55).
Z581	10c. on 30c. green	£550

1900–01. Wmk Crown CA (Nos. 56/61).
Z582	2c. dull green	80·00
Z583	4c. carmine	40·00
Z584	5c. yellow	£120
Z585	10c. ultramarine	45·00
Z587	30c. brown	£225

1903. Wmk Crown CA (Nos. 62/76).
Z588	1c. dull purple and brown	30·00
Z589	2c. dull green	30·00
Z590	4c. purple/*red*	21·00
Z591	5c. dull green and brown-orange	70·00
Z592	8c. slate and violet	55·00
Z593	10c. purple and blue/*blue*	26·00
Z594	12c. green and purple/*yellow*	75·00
Z595	20c. slate and chestnut	80·00
Z596	30c. dull green and black	£150
Z597	50c. dull green and magenta	£225
Z598	$1 purple and sage-green	£300
Z599	$2 slate and scarlet	£900

1904. Wmk Mult Crown CA (Nos. 77/90).
Z603	2c. dull green	27·00
Z604	4c. purple/*red*	21·00
Z605	5c. dull green and brown-orange	70·00
Z606	8c. slate and violet	38·00
Z607	10c. purple and blue/*blue*	24·00
Z608	12c. green and purple/*yellow*	75·00
Z609	20c. slate and chestnut	80·00
Z610	30c. dull green and black	£100
Z612	$1 purple and sage-green	£450

1907–11. Wmk Mult Crown CA (Nos. 91/9).
Z617	1c. brown	27·00
Z618	2c. green	26·00
Z619	4c. carmine-red	21·00
Z620	6c. orange-vermilion and purple	70·00
Z621	10c. bright ultramarine	24·00
Z622	20c. purple and sage-green	£120
Z623	30c. purple and orange-yellow	£100

1912–15. Wmk Mult Crown CA (Nos. 100/16).
Z625	1c. brown	25·00

Z626	2c. green	24·00
Z627	4c. red	21·00
Z628	6c. orange	40·00
Z629	8c. grey	95·00
Z630	10c. ultramarine	21·00
Z631	12c. purple/*yellow*	75·00
Z632	20c. purple and sage-green	48·00
Z633	25c. purple and magenta (Type A)	£150
Z634	30c. purple and orange-yellow	£100
Z635	50c. black/*green*	85·00
Z636	$1 purple and blue/*blue*	90·00

POSTAL FISCAL STAMPS

1874–1902. Wmk CC.

(a) P 15½×15 (Nos. F1/3)
ZF641	$2 olive-green	£475

(b) P 14 (Nos. F4/6)
ZF644	$2 dull bluish green	£750

1897. (Nos. F10/11).
ZF650	$1 on $2 olive-green	£600

NINGPO

Ningpo was one of the 1842 Treaty Ports and a consular postal agency was established there in 1844.

Type **A** ("N1") (*supplied 1866*) *used 1870–82*
Type **C** (*supplied 1866*) *used 1870–99*
Type **D** *used 1899–1922*

Stamps of HONG KONG cancelled at Ningpo between 1866 and 1916 with postmarks detailed above.

1862. No wmk (Nos. 1/7).
Z652	18c. lilac	£1200

1863–71. Wmk Crown CC (Nos. 8/19).
Z653	2c. brown	£450
Z654	4c. grey	£450
	a. Perf 12½	£2750
Z655	6c. lilac	£500
Z656	8c. orange	£450
Z657	12c. blue	£170
Z658	18c. lilac	
Z659	24c. green	£475
Z660	30c. vermilion	£600
Z661	30c. mauve	£150
Z662	48c. rose	£850
Z663	96c. olive-bistre	
Z664	96c. brownish grey	£1000

1876–77. (Nos. 20/1).
Z665	16c. on 18c. lilac	£700
Z666	28c. on 30c. mauve	£400

1877. Wmk Crown CC (No. 22).
Z667	16c. yellow	£550

1880. (Nos. 23/7).
Z668	5c. on 8c. orange	£500
Z669	5c. on 18c. lilac	£425
Z670	10c. on 12c. blue	£450
Z672	10c. on 24c. green	£500

1880. Wmk Crown CC (Nos. 28/31).
Z673	2c. dull rose	£275
Z674	5c. blue	£250
Z675	10c. mauve	£250
Z676	10c. brown	£950

1882–96. Wmk Crown CA (Nos. 32/9).
Z677	2c. carmine	50·00
Z678	4c. slate-grey	85·00
Z679	5c. blue	50·00
Z680	10c. dull mauve	£250
Z681	10c. green	70·00
Z682	10c. purple/*red*	55·00
Z683	30c. green	£160

1885. (Nos. 40/2).
Z685	50c. on 48c. yellowish brown	£200

1891. (Nos. 43/50).
Z686	7c. on 10c. green	80·00
Z687	14c. on 30c. mauve	£325
Z688	20c. on 30c. green	60·00
Z689	50c. on 48c. dull purple	95·00
Z690	$1 on 96c. purple/*red*	£180

1898. (No. 52).
Z692	$1 on 96c. black	£200

1898. (No. 55).
Z693	10c. on 30c. green	£375

1900–01. Wmk Crown CA (Nos. 56/61).
Z694	2c. dull green	35·00
Z695	4c. carmine	30·00
Z697	10c. ultramarine	35·00

1903. Wmk Crown CA (Nos. 62/76).
Z700	1c. dull purple and brown	30·00
Z701	2c. dull green	30·00
Z702	4c. purple/*red*	23·00
Z703	5c. dull green and brown-orange	75·00
Z704	8c. slate and violet	40·00
Z705	10c. purple and blue/*blue*	25·00
Z706	12c. green and purple/*yellow*	85·00
Z709	50c. dull green and magenta	£150

1904–06. Wmk Mult Crown CA (Nos. 77/90).
Z715	2c. dull green	28·00
Z716	4c. purple/*red*	25·00
Z718	8c. slate and violet	60·00
Z720	12c. green and purple/*yellow*	85·00
Z721	20c. slate and chestnut	75·00
Z722	30c. dull green and black	£110

Z723	50c. green and magenta	95·00
Z724	$1 purple and sage-green	£150

1907–11. Wmk Mult Crown CA (Nos. 91/9).
Z729	1c. brown	25·00
Z730	2c. green	25·00
Z731	4c. carmine-red	22·00
Z733	10c. bright ultramarine	25·00
Z734	20c. purple and sage-green	£140
Z735	30c. purple and orange-yellow	£130

1912–15. Wmk Mult Crown CA (Nos. 100/16).
Z738	1c. brown	26·00
Z739	2c. green	25·00
Z740	4c. red	23·00
Z742	8c. grey	85·00
Z743	10c. ultramarine	25·00
Z745	20c. purple and sage-green	65·00
Z747	30c. purple and orange-yellow	£100
Z749	$1 purple and blue/*blue*	90·00

POSTCARD STAMPS

1879. (Nos. P1/2).
ZP751	3c. on 16c. yellow	£1800

POSTAL FISCAL STAMPS

1874–1902. Wmk Crown CC. P 15½×15 (Nos. F1/3).
ZF754	$2 olive-green	£450

1880. (No. F7).
ZF760	12c. on $10 rose-carmine	

1897. (No. F10).
ZF763	$1 on $2 olive-green	

SHANGHAI

Shanghai was one of the original Treaty Ports of 1842 and a packet agency was opened at the British consulate in April 1844. It moved to a separate premise in 1861 and was upgraded to a Post Office in September 1867.
British military post offices operated in Shanghai from 1927 until 1940.

Type **D** (inscr "SHANGHAE") (*supplied 1861*) *used 1861–99*

Sunburst *used 1864–65*
Type **A** ("S1") (*supplied 1866*) *used 1866–85*
Type **D** (inscr "SHANGHAI") (*supplied 1885*) *used 1886-1906*
Type **G** (inscr "B.P.O." at foot) (*supplied 1904*) *used 1904–21*
Type **G** (inscr "Br.P.O." at foot) (*supplied 1907*) *used 1907–22*
Type **E** (figures "I" to "VIII" at foot) *used 1912–22*

Stamps of HONG KONG cancelled at Shanghai between 1863 and 1916 with postmarks detailed above.

1862. No wmk (Nos. 1/7).
Z765	2c. brown	£180
Z766	8c. yellow-buff	£200
Z767	12c. pale greenish blue	£160
Z768	18c. lilac	£130
Z769	24c. green	£250
Z770	48c. rose	£600
Z771	96c. brownish grey	£750

1863–71. Wmk Crown CC (Nos. 8/19).
Z772	2c. brown	12·00
Z773	4c. grey	11·00
	a. Perf 12½	£275
Z774	6c. lilac	24·00
Z775	8c. orange	19·00
Z776	12c. blue	11·00
Z777	18c. lilac	£375
Z778	24c. green	18·00
Z779	30c. vermilion	27·00
Z780	30c. mauve	8·50
Z781	48c. rose	42·00
Z782	96c. olive-bistre	£1400
Z783	96c. brownish grey	65·00

1876–77. (Nos. 20/1).
Z784	16c. on 18c. lilac	£170
Z785	28c. on 30c. mauve	55·00

1877. Wmk Crown CC (No. 22).
Z786	16c. yellow	75·00

1880. (Nos. 23/7).
Z787	5c. on 8c. orange	£110
Z788	5c. on 18c. lilac	70·00
Z789	10c. on 12c. blue	60·00
Z790	10c. on 16c. yellow	£190
Z791	10c. on 24c. green	£120

1880. Wmk Crown CC (Nos. 28/31).
Z792	2c. rose	45·00
Z793	5c. blue	70·00
Z794	10c. mauve	22·00
Z795	48c. brown	£150

1882–96. Wmk Crown CA (Nos. 32/9).
Z795a	2c. rose-lake	38·00
Z796	2c. carmine	3·25
Z797	4c. slate-grey	3·50
Z798	5c. blue	1·50
Z799	10c. dull mauve	28·00
Z800	10c. green	2·50
Z801	10c. purple/*red*	1·90
Z802	30c. green	40·00

1885. (Nos. 40/2).
Z803	20c. on 30c. orange-red	9·50
Z804	50c. on 48c. yellowish brown	60·00
Z805	$1 on 96c. grey-olive	£110

1891. (Nos. 43/50).
Z806	7c. on 10c. green	17·00
Z807	14c. on 30c. mauve	£100
Z807a	20c. on 30c. green (No. 45)	
Z807b	50c. on 48c. dull purple (No. 46)	£350
Z807c	$1 on 96c. purple/red (No. 47)	£400
Z808	20c. on 30c. green (No. 48)	10·00
Z809	50c. on 48c. dull purple (No. 49)	8·00
Z810	$1 on 96c. purple/red (No. 50)	30·00

1898. (No. 52).
Z812	$1 on 96c. black	45·00

1898. (No. 55).
Z813	10c. on 30c. green	£130

1900–01. Wmk Crown CA (Nos. 56/61).
Z814	2c. dull green	1·25
Z815	4c. carmine	1·25
Z816	5c. yellow	12·00
Z817	10c. ultramarine	2·75
Z818	12c. blue	£110
Z819	30c. brown	42·00

1903. Wmk Crown CA (Nos. 62/76).
Z820	1c. dull purple and brown	1·00
Z821	2c. dull green	3·00
Z822	4c. purple/red	85
Z823	5c. dull green and brown-orange	16·00
Z824	8c. slate and violet	3·25
Z825	10c. purple and blue/blue	2·00
Z826	12c. green and purple/yellow	10·00
Z827	20c. slate and chestnut	6·50
Z828	30c. dull green and black	40·00
Z829	50c. dull green and magenta	85·00
Z830	$1 purple and sage-green	42·00
Z831	$2 slate and scarlet	£425
Z832	$3 slate and dull blue	£600
Z833	$5 purple and blue-green	£700
Z834	$10 slate and orange/blue	£700

1904–06. Wmk Mult Crown CA (Nos. 77/90).
Z835	2c. dull green	3·00
Z836	4c. purple/red	85
Z837	5c. dull green and brown-orange	11·00
Z838	8c. slate and violet	3·50
Z839	10c. purple and blue/blue	1·75
Z840	12c. green and purple/yellow	13·00
Z841	20c. slate and chestnut	4·75
Z842	30c. dull green and black	32·00
Z843	50c. green and magenta	23·00
Z844	$1 purple and sage-green	50·00
Z845	$2 slate and scarlet	£180
Z846	$3 slate and dull blue	£450
Z847	$5 purple and blue-green	£600
Z848	$10 slate and orange/blue	£1600

1907–11. Wmk Mult Crown CA (Nos. 91/9).
Z849	1c. brown	1·75
Z850	2c. green	2·00
Z851	4c. carmine-red	85
Z852	6c. orange-vermilion and purple	11·00
Z853	10c. bright ultramarine	85
Z854	20c. purple and sage-green	65·00
Z855	30c. purple and orange-yellow	50·00
Z856	50c. black/green	28·00
Z857	$2 carmine-red and black	£550

1912–15. Wmk Mult Crown CA (Nos. 100/16).
Z858	1c. brown	1·25
Z859	2c. green	85
Z860	4c. red	70
Z861	6c. orange	3·75
Z862	8c. grey	12·00
Z863	10c. ultramarine	75
Z864	12c. purple/yellow	19·00
Z865	20c. purple and sage-green	2·25
Z867	30c. purple and orange-yellow	16·00
Z868	50c. black/green	6·50
Z869	$1 purple and blue/blue	10·00

POSTCARD STAMPS

1879. (Nos. P1/2).
ZP871	3c. on 16c. yellow	£550
ZP872	5c. on 18c. lilac	£650

POSTAL FISCAL STAMPS

1874–1902. Wmk Crown CC.

(a) P 15½×15 (Nos. F1/5)
ZF874	$2 olive-green	80·00
ZF875	$3 dull violet	60·00
ZF876	$10 rose-carmine	£750

(b) P 14
ZF877	$2 dull bluish green	£300
ZF878	$3 dull mauve	£600

1880. (No. F7).
ZF880	12c. on $10 rose-carmine	£350

1891. (No. F9).
ZF882	$5 on $10 purple/red	£170

1897. (No. F10/11).
ZF883	$1 on $2 olive-green	£200
ZF884	$1 on $2 dull bluish green	£275

SWATOW

Swatow became a Treaty Port in 1860 and a consular packet agency was opened in the area made available for foreign firms during the following year. In 1867 the original agency was transferred to the Chinese city on the other side of the Han River, but a second agency was subsequently opened in the foreign concession during 1883.

Type **A** ("S2") (supplied 1866) used 1875–85	
Type **C** (supplied 1866) used 1866–90	
Type **D** (supplied 1883) used 1884–1922	
Type **F** used 1916–22	

Stamps of HONG KONG cancelled at Swatow between 1866 and 1916 with postmarks detailed above.

1862. No wmk (Nos. 1/7).
Z885	18c. lilac	£450

1863–71. Wmk Crown CC (Nos. 8/19).
Z886	2c. brown	£170
Z887	4c. grey	£160
	a. Perf 12½	
Z888	6c. lilac	£600
Z889	8c. orange	£160
Z890	12c. blue	60·00
Z891	18c. lilac	£1300
Z892	24c. green	£200
Z893	30c. vermilion	
Z894	30c. mauve	60·00
Z895	48c. rose	£325
Z897	96c. brownish grey	£1000

1876–77. (Nos. 20/1).
Z898	16c. on 18c. lilac	£500
Z899	28c. on 30c. mauve	£275

1877. Wmk Crown CC (No. 22).
Z900	16c. yellow	£500

1880. (Nos. 23/7).
Z901	5c. on 8c. orange	£325
Z902	5c. on 18c. lilac	£275
Z903	10c. on 12c. blue	£300
Z904	10c. on 16c. yellow	£550
Z905	10c. on 24c. green	£375

1880. Wmk Crown CC (Nos. 28/31).
Z906	5c. rose	£150
Z907	5c. blue	£170
Z908	5c. mauve	£180

1882–96. Wmk Crown CA (Nos. 32/9).
Z910	2c. carmine	8·00
Z911	4c. slate-grey	26·00
Z912	5c. blue	8·50
Z913	10c. dull mauve	£140
Z914	10c. green	12·00
Z915	10c. purple/red	8·00
Z916	30c. green	75·00

1885. (Nos. 40/2).
Z917	20c. on 30c. orange-red	24·00
Z917a	50c. on 48c. yellowish brown	£180
Z918	$1 on 96c. grey-olive	£200

1891. (Nos. 43/50).
Z919	7c. on 10c. green	40·00
Z920	14c. on 30c. mauve	£160
Z920a	50c. on 48c. dull purple (No. 46)	£425
Z921	$1 on 96c. purple/red (No. 47)	£600
Z922	20c. on 30c. green	30·00
Z923	50c. on 48c. dull purple (No. 49)	32·00
Z924	$1 on 96c. purple/red (No. 50)	75·00

1891. 50th Anniv of Colony (No. 51).
Z925	2c. carmine	£1300

1898. (No. 52).
Z926	$1 on 96c. black	£110

1898. (No. 55).
Z927	10c. on 30c. green	£300

1900–01. Wmk Crown CA (Nos. 56/61).
Z928	2c. dull green	8·50
Z929	4c. carmine	7·00
Z930	5c. yellow	32·00
Z931	10c. ultramarine	7·50
Z932	12c. blue	£225
Z933	30c. brown	80·00

1903. Wmk Crown CA (Nos. 62/76).
Z934	1c. dull purple and brown	8·00
Z935	2c. dull green	7·50
Z936	4c. purple/red	6·00
Z937	5c. dull green and brown-orange	25·00
Z938	8c. slate and violet	16·00
Z939	10c. purple and blue/blue	7·50
Z940	12c. green and purple/yellow	24·00
Z941	20c. slate and chestnut	12·00
Z942	30c. dull green and black	65·00
Z943	50c. dull green and magenta	£120
Z944	$1 purple and sage-green	£100

1904–06. Wmk Mult Crown CA (Nos. 77/90).
Z949	2c. dull green	8·00
Z950	4c. purple/red	6·00
Z951	5c. dull green and brown-orange	24·00
Z952	8c. slate and violet	15·00
Z953	10c. purple and blue/blue	7·00
Z954	12c. green and purple/yellow	25·00
Z955	20c. slate and chestnut	15·00
Z956	30c. dull green and black	60·00
Z957	50c. green and magenta	40·00
Z958	$1 purple and sage-green	95·00
Z959	$2 slate and scarlet	£350
Z962	$10 slate and orange/blue	£2000

1907–11. Wmk Mult Crown CA (Nos. 91/9).
Z963	1c. brown	9·00
Z964	2c. green	8·50
Z965	4c. carmine-red	6·00
Z966	6c. orange-vermilion and purple	21·00
Z967	10c. bright ultramarine	6·50
Z968	20c. purple and sage-green	£110
Z969	30c. purple and orange-yellow	85·00
Z970	50c. black/green	55·00

1912–15. Wmk Mult Crown CA (Nos. 100/16).
Z972	1c. brown	7·00
Z973	2c. green	6·00
Z974	4c. red	5·00
Z975	6c. orange	11·00
Z976	8c. grey	29·00
Z977	10c. ultramarine	5·00
Z978	12c. purple/yellow	25·00
Z979	20c. purple and sage-green	7·50
Z980	25c. purple and magenta (Type A)	75·00
Z981	30c. purple and orange-yellow	32·00
Z982	50c. black/green	18·00
Z983	$1 purple and blue/blue	29·00

POSTCARD STAMP

1879. (Nos. P1/2).
ZP986	3c. on 16c. yellow	£1400

POSTAL FISCAL STAMPS

1874–1902. Wmk Crown CC.

(a) P 15½×15 (Nos. F1/3)
ZF988	$2 olive-green	£180
ZF989	$3 dull violet	£160

(b) P 14
ZF991	$2 dull bluish green	£500

TIENTSIN

Tientsin became a Treaty Port in 1860. A British consulate was established in 1861, but no formal postal agency was organised there until 1882. It was not, however, very successful and was closed during 1890. The British Post Office reopened on 1 October 1906 under the management of the Chinese Engineering and Mining Company.

British military post offices operated in Tientsin from 1927 until 1940.

Type **E** used 1906–13	
Type **G** (supplied 1907) used 1907–22	

Stamps of HONG KONG cancelled at Tientsin between 1906 and 1916 with postmarks detailed above.

1903. Wmk Crown CA (Nos. 62/76).
Z998	1c. dull purple and brown	17·00
Z998b	4c. purple/red	22·00
Z999	5c. dull green and brown-orange	42·00
Z1000	8c. slate and violet	18·00
Z1000a	12c. green and purple/yellow	60·00

1904–06. Wmk Mult Crown CA (Nos. 77/90).
Z1001	2c. dull green	7·50
Z1002	4c. purple/red	5·00
Z1003	5c. dull green and brown-orange	22·00
Z1004	8c. slate and violet	17·00
Z1005	10c. purple and blue/blue	6·50
Z1006	12c. green and purple/yellow	28·00
Z1007	20c. slate and chestnut	16·00
Z1008	30c. dull green and black	55·00
Z1009	50c. green and magenta	42·00
Z1010	$1 purple and sage-green	80·00
Z1011	$2 slate and scarlet	£325
Z1012	$3 slate and dull blue	£800
Z1013	$5 purple and blue-green	£950
Z1014	$10 slate and orange/blue	£2000

1907–11. Wmk Mult Crown CA (Nos. 91/9).
Z1015	1c. brown	8·00
Z1016	2c. green	6·00
Z1017	4c. carmine-red	4·50
Z1018	6c. orange-vermilion and purple	25·00
Z1019	10c. bright ultramarine	5·50
Z1020	20c. purple and sage-green	£110
Z1021	30c. purple and orange-yellow	95·00
Z1022	50c. black/green	70·00
Z1023	$2 carmine-red and black	£750

1912–15. Wmk Mult Crown CA (Nos. 100/16).
Z1024	1c. brown	7·00
Z1025	2c. green	6·00
Z1026	4c. red	4·25
Z1027	6c. orange	10·00
Z1028	8c. grey	40·00
Z1029	10c. ultramarine	6·50
Z1030	12c. purple/yellow	45·00
Z1031	20c. purple and sage-green	10·00
Z1033	30c. purple and orange-yellow	25·00
Z1034	50c. black/green	14·00
Z1035	$1 purple and blue/blue	20·00
Z1037	$3 green and purple	£250
Z1038	$5 green and red/green	£700

WEI HAI WEI

The territory of Wei Hai Wei was leased from the Chinese by the British Government from 24 May 1898 having been previously occupied by the Japanese. At that time there were no organised postal services from the area, although a private local post did operate between the port and Chefoo from 8 December 1898 until 15 March 1899. A Chinese Imperial post office opened in March 1899 to be followed by a British postal agency on the offshore island of Liu Kung Tau on 1 September 1899. A second British agency opened at Port Edward on 1 April 1904.

Liu Kung Tau oval used 1899–1901
Type **D** (inscr "LIU KUNG TAU") (supplied 1899) used 1901–30

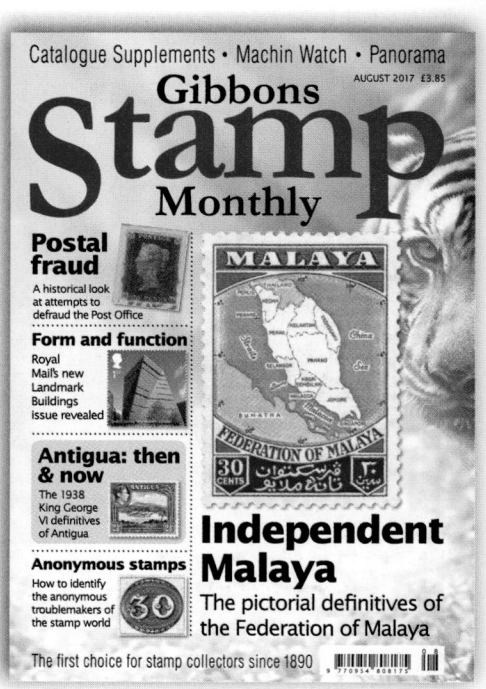

Stamps of HONG KONG cancelled at Liu Kung Tau between 1899 and
1916 with postmarks detailed above.

1863–71. Wmk Crown CC (Nos. 8/19).
Z1039   12c. pale blue .... —

1882–96. Wmk Crown CA (Nos. 32/9).
Z1040   2c. carmine .... 85·00
Z1041   4c. slate-grey £100
Z1042   5c. blue .... 85·00
Z1043   10c. purple/*red* .... 55·00
Z1044   30c. green .... 95·00

1891. (Nos. 48/50).
Z1045   20c. on 30c. green .... 70·00
Z1046   50c. on 48c. dull purple .... 75·00

1898. (No. 52).
Z1047 $1 on 96c. black £140

1900–01. Wmk Crown CA (Nos. 56/61).
Z1049   2c. dull green .... 13·00
Z1050   4c. carmine .... 13·00
Z1051   5c. yellow .... 40·00
Z1052   10c. ultramarine .... 13·00
Z1053   12c. blue £180
Z1054   30c. brown £110

1903. Wmk Crown CA (Nos. 62/76).
Z1055   1c. dull purple and brown .... 9·50
Z1056   2c. dull green .... 9·00
Z1057   4c. purple/*red* .... 8·00
Z1058   5c. dull green and brown-orange ...... 28·00
Z1059   8c. slate and violet .... 20·00
Z1060   10c. purple and blue/*blue* .... 13·00
Z1061   12c. green and purple/*yellow* .... 45·00
Z1062   20c. slate and chestnut .... 21·00
Z1063   30c. dull green and black .... 75·00
Z1064   50c. dull green and magenta £130
Z1065 $1 purple and sage-green £100

1904–06. Wmk Mult Crown CA (Nos. 77/90).
Z1070   2c. dull green .... 9·50
Z1071   4c. purple/*red* .... 9·00
Z1073   8c. slate and violet .... 18·00
Z1076   20c. slate and chestnut .... 38·00
Z1077   30c. dull green and black £110
Z1078   50c. green and magenta .... 85·00
Z1079 $1 purple and sage-green £150

1907–11. Wmk Mult Crown CA (Nos. 91/9).
Z1084   1c. brown .... 10·00
Z1085   2c. green .... 10·00
Z1086   4c. carmine-red .... 7·50
Z1088   10c. bright ultramarine .... 9·00
Z1089   20c. purple and sage-green £130
Z1090   30c. purple and orange-yellow £100
Z1091   50c. black/*green* .... 85·00

1912–15. Wmk Mult Crown CA (Nos. 100/16).
Z1093   1c. brown .... 12·00
Z1094   2c. green .... 9·00
Z1095   4c. red .... 7·00
Z1096   6c. orange .... 18·00
Z1097   8c. grey .... 42·00
Z1098   10c. ultramarine .... 8·00
Z1104 $1 purple and blue/*blue* .... 42·00

POSTAL FISCAL STAMP

1874–1902. Wmk Crown CC. P 14 (Nos. F4/6).
Z1106 $2 dull bluish green £1100

```
┌───────────────────────┐
│  PORT EDWARD          │
│  13 JUL 1904          │
│  WEI-HAI-WEI          │
└───────────────────────┘
```

Port Edward rectangle used 1904–08
Type **D** (inscr "WEI-HAI-WEI" at top and "PORT EDWARD" at foot)
(*supplied* 1907) *used* 1907–30

Stamps of HONG KONG cancelled at Port Edward between 1904 and
1916 with postmarks detailed above.

1900–01. Wmk Crown CA (Nos. 56/61).
Z1109   2c. dull green .... 95·00
Z1110   10c. ultramarine £120

1903. Wmk Crown CA (Nos. 62/76).
Z1111   1c. dull purple and brown .... 38·00
Z1112   2c. dull green .... 38·00
Z1113   4c. purple/*red* .... 32·00
Z1114   5c. dull green and brown-orange ...... 55·00
Z1115   8c. slate and violet .... 50·00
Z1116   10c. purple and blue/*blue* .... 40·00
Z1117   12c. green and purple/*yellow* .... 75·00
Z1118   20c. slate and chestnut £100
Z1119   30c. dull green and black £100
Z1120   50c. dull green and magenta £140
Z1121 $1 purple and sage-green £110

1904–06. Wmk Mult Crown CA (Nos. 77/90).
Z1126   2c. dull green .... 21·00
Z1127   4c. purple/*red* .... 19·00
Z1128   5c. dull green and brown-orange ...... 35·00
Z1129   8c. slate and violet .... 25·00
Z1132   20c. slate and chestnut .... 95·00
Z1133   30c. dull green and black .... 90·00
Z1134   50c. green and magenta .... 95·00
Z1135 $1 purple and sage-green £120

1907–11. Wmk Mult Crown CA (Nos. 91/9).
Z1140   1c. brown .... 20·00
Z1141   2c. green .... 20·00
Z1142   4c. carmine-red .... 14·00
Z1143   6c. orange-vermilion and purple .... 45·00

Z1144   10c. bright ultramarine .... 16·00
Z1145   20c. purple and sage-green £120
Z1146   30c. purple and orange-yellow £120
Z1148   50c. black/*green* .... 70·00

1912–15. Wmk Mult Crown CA (Nos. 100/16).
Z1151   1c. brown .... 18·00
Z1152   2c. green .... 13·00
Z1153   4c. red .... 8·00
Z1155   8c. grey .... 38·00
Z1156   10c. ultramarine .... 9·00
Z1157   12c. purple/*yellow* .... 48·00
Z1158   20c. purple and sage-green .... 24·00
Z1160   30c. purple and orange-yellow .... 42·00
Z1161   50c. black/*green* .... 32·00
Z1162 $1 purple and blue/*blue* .... 35·00

PRICES FOR STAMPS ON COVER	
Nos. 1/14	*from* × 50
Nos. 15/17	
Nos. 18/28	*from* × 30

The overprinted stamps Nos. 1/17 were introduced on 1 January
1917 to prevent currency speculation in the Treaty Ports. They were
used in the then-existing agencies of Amoy, Canton, Chefoo, Foochow,
Hankow, Hoihow, Ningpo, Shanghai, Swatow, Tientsin and were also
supplied to the British naval base of Wei Hai Wei.

CHINA
(1)

1917 (1 Jan)–**21.** Stamps of Hong Kong, 1912–21 (wmk Mult
Crown CA), optd with T **1**, at Somerset House.
1	1c. brown	16·00	1·50
	a. Black-brown	9·00	2·50
	b. Crown broken at right	£400	£400
	c. Wmk sideways	†	£3000
	w. Wmk inverted	†	£1800
2	2c. green	19·00	30
	w. Wmk inverted	†	£2000
	x. Wmk reversed	†	£2250
3	4c. carmine-red	12·00	30
	a. Substituted crown in wmk	†	£1800
	w. Wmk inverted	†	£2500
4	6c. orange	9·50	1·75
	w. Wmk inverted	†	£1700
5	8c. slate	15·00	1·25
6	10c. ultramarine	21·00	30
	w. Wmk inverted	†	£2000
	y. Wmk inverted and reversed	†	£1200
7	12c. purple/*yellow*	18·00	11·00
8	20c. purple and sage-green	26·00	1·50
9	25c. purple and magenta (A)	14·00	15·00
11	30c. purple and orange-yellow	50·00	11·00
12	50c. black/*blue-green* (olive back)	75·00	1·50
	a. Emerald surface (1917?)	70·00	11·00
	b. On emerald back (1919)	55·00	5·50
	c. On white back (1920)	£1300	£180
13	$1 reddish purple and bright blue/*blue*	85·00	2·50
	a. Grey-purple and blue/*blue* (1921)	90·00	8·00
14	$2 carmine-red and grey-black	£225	80·00
15	$3 green and purple	£700	£275
16	$5 green and red/*blue-green* (olive back)	£350	£350
17	$10 purple and black/*red*	£700	£700
1/17 Set of 16		£2000	£1300
12s/17s H/S "SPECIMEN" (50c.) or *SPECIMEN* Set of 6		£2250	

1922 (Mar)–**27.** As last, but wmk Mult Script CA.
18	1c. brown	3·50	7·50
19	2c. green	9·00	2·25
	w. Wmk inverted	£475	
20	4c. carmine-rose	22·00	3·50
	a. Lower Chinese character at right broken at top	£325	£350
21	6c. orange-yellow	7·50	7·00
22	8c. grey	15·00	16·00
23	10c. bright ultramarine.	24·00	4·50
	w. Wmk inverted	£300	
24	20c. purple and sage-green	22·00	5·00
25	25c. purple and magenta (B)	27·00	75·00
	a. Broken flower	£850	
26	50c. black/*emerald* (1927)	60·00	£350
	s. Handstamped *"SPECIMEN"*	£275	
27	$1 purple and blue/*blue*	80·00	80·00
28	$2 carmine-red and grey-black	£200	£250
18/28 Set of 11		£425	£750

STAMP BOOKLETS

1917. Black on red cover inscribed "BRITISH POST OFFICE
AGENCIES IN CHINA". Stapled.
SB1 $1 booklet containing 8×2c., 6×4c. and 6×10c.
    (Nos. 2/3, 6) £6500
Three settings of the front cover of No. SB1 are recognised.

1922. Cover as No. SB1. Stapled.
SB2 $1 booklet containing 8×2c., 6×4c., and 6×10c.
    (Nos. 19/20, 23) £6000

The British PO's in the Treaty Ports closed by agreement with the
Chinese on 30 November 1922, but the above over-printed issues
continued in use at the Wei Hai Wei offices until they in turn closed
on 30 September 1930. Under the terms of the Convention signed
with China the Royal Navy continued to use the base at Wei Hai Wei
until the mid-1930s.

BRITISH POST OFFICES IN JAPAN

Under the terms of the Anglo-Japanese Treaty of Yedo, signed on
26 August 1858, four Japanese ports were opened to British trade.
British consulates were established at Decima (Nagasaki), Kanagawa
(Yokohama), Hiogo (Kobe) and Hakodadi (Hakodate).The postage
stamps of Hong Kong became available at the Yokohama and
Nagasaki consulates during October 1864 and at Hiogo in 1869,
although cancellation of mail did not commence until 1866 at
Yokohama and Nagasaki and 1876 at Hiogo. Japan became a member
of the UPU on 1 June 1877 and all of the British Postal Agencies were
closed by the end of 1879.

For illustrations of postmark types see BRITISH POST OFFICES IN
CHINA.

HAKODATE

A British consular office existed at Hakodate, but it was never issued
with a c.d.s. obliterator or Hong Kong stamps. No British covers are
recorded from this consulate prior to opening of the Japanese Post
Office.

HIOGO

The Port of Hiogo (Kobe) was first opened to foreigners on 1 January
1868. The British consular mail service at Hiogo commenced during
1869 to serve the foreigners at Hiogo, Kobe and Osaka. The cities of
Hiogo and Kobe later merged to become the single city of Kobe. The
consular office at Hiogo closed on 30 November 1879.

Type **B** ("D30") (*supplied* 1876) *used* 1876–79
Type **D** (*supplied* 1876) *used* 1876–79

Stamps of HONG KONG cancelled at Hiogo between 1876 and 1879
with postmarks detailed above.

1863–71. Wmk Crown CC (Nos. 8/19).
Z1   2c. brown £6000
Z2   4c. grey £4250
Z3   6c. lilac £5500
Z4   8c. orange £5000
Z5   12c. blue £6000
Z6   18c. lilac .... —
Z7   24c. green £4500
Z8   30c. vermilion .... —
Z9   30c. mauve £6000
Z10   48c. rose £9000
Z12   96c. brownish grey £9000

1877. (Nos. 20/1).
Z13   16c. on 18c. lilac .... —

1877. Wmk Crown CC (No. 22).
Z15   16c. yellow £7000

NAGASAKI

The British Consulate opened in Nagasaki on 14 June 1859, but,
with few British residents at the port, the consular staff found it
inconvenient to carry out postal duties so that few Nagasaki c.d.s.
or "N2" cancellations exist. The postal service was terminated on
30 September 1879.

Type **A** ("N2") (*supplied* 1866) *used* 1876–79
Type **D** (*supplied* 1866) *used* 1876–79

Stamps of HONG KONG cancelled at Nagasaki between 1876 and
1879 with postmarks detailed above.

1862. No wmk (Nos. 1/8).
Z15a   18c. lilac £3750

1863–71. Wmk Crown CC (Nos. 8/19).
Z16   2c. brown £2250
Z17   4c. grey £2000
Z18   6c. lilac £2000
Z19   8c. orange £2000
Z20   12c. blue £2000
Z21   18c. lilac £7500
Z22   24c. green £3500
Z24   30c. mauve £3000
Z25   48c. rose £4000
Z27   96c. brownish grey .... —

1876–77. (Nos. 20/1).
Z28   16c. on 18c. lilac £3000
Z29   16c. on 30c. mauve £2250

1877. Wmk Crown CC (No. 22).
Z30   16c. yellow £3250

YOKOHAMA

The British Consulate opened in Kanagawa on 21 July 1859, but
was relocated to Yokohama where it provided postal services from
1 July 1860 until a separate Post Office was established in July 1867.
The British Post Office in Yokohama closed on 31 December 1879.

Type **A** ("YI") (*supplied* 1866) *used* 1867–79
Type **D** (*supplied* 1866) *used* 1866–79

Stamps of HONG KONG cancelled at Yokohama between 1866 and
1879 with postmarks detailed above.

1862. No wmk (Nos. 1/8).
Z30a   8c. yellow-buff £425
Z31   18c. lilac £140

1863–71. Wmk Crown CC (Nos. 8/19).
Z32   2c. brown .... 22·00
Z33   4c. grey .... 23·00
    a. Perf 12½ £550
Z34   6c. lilac .... 30·00
Z35   8c. orange .... 28·00
Z36   12c. blue .... 22·00
Z37   18c. lilac £750
Z38   24c. green .... 26·00
Z39   30c. vermilion .... 75·00
Z40   30c. mauve .... 22·00
Z41   48c. rose .... 65·00
Z42   96c. olive-bistre £5000
Z43   96c. brownish grey .... 85·00

1876–77. (Nos. 20/1).
Z44   16c. on 18c. lilac £325
Z45   28c. on 30c. mauve .... 90·00

1877. Wmk Crown CC (No. 22).
Z46   16c. yellow £140

POSTAL FISCAL STAMPS

1874. Wmk Crown CC. P 15½×15 (Nos. F1/3).
ZF47 $2 olive-green £160
ZF48 $3 dull violet £150
ZF49 $10 rose-carmine £1900

Selling Your Stamps?

Summary Tip #21:
5 Different Ways to Sell your Stamps: Selling via Auction

by Andrew McGavin

ANDREW PROMOTING PHILATELY ON THE ALAN TITCHMARSH SHOW ITV

Dear Colleague,

In Part 3 (page 210) of 'Selling your Stamps' we discussed the importance of selecting the right dealers/organisations to approach and ensuring the choice of those with transparent modus operandi.

Here in Part 4 of 'Selling your Stamps' we'll discuss the potential advantages and disadvantages of selling through auction on your own account.

Remember we previously discussed the importance of knowing the strength of your collection. This is never more important than when making the decision to consign your stamps to auction. We have touched upon this in previous 'Stamp Tips of the Trade'. The most important thing to remember – is 'who buys complete stamp collections at auction?'

Collectors want to buy stamps that are missing from their collections: Dealers want to buy complete collections to break out individual stamps/sets to supply to collectors. By breaking collections into individual parts dealers add value/profi t. When you consign your collection as one lot to auction – 9 times out of 10 .... it is a dealer that will be buying it. Unless you are a collector that purchases collections, extract the stamps you need, and sell on the rest – you will be looking to buy specific stamps, sets or small 'runs'.

So what is wrong with consigning stamps to auction? Nothing, if it is the right kind of stamps. For example – you need to 'quiz' the auctioneer selected as to what he/she is actually going to do with your stamps. Let's give you an example. A few weeks ago we purchased a 'Birds' thematic collection from public auction. We paid the auctioneer exactly £1011.50= ... but the actual price the stamps were 'knocked down' to us was exactly £800=. The buyer's premium was 26.4375% - and that was before the increase in VAT. If we purchased the same collection today – the buyer's premium would be 27% !

And did the collector realise £800=? NO. Even if the collector was charged just 12% + VAT selling commission – at today's rate the collector would receive £685=. Imagine, this collection has been sold to a dealer for £1011- by an auction who has put no money on the table and yet made a gross profit of £326= on the transaction. The dealer that paid £1,011.50 expects to make a profit. It follows that if you can approach the right dealers in the right way – then you can expect to eliminate much of the money that you pay for that auction to offer your stamps to dealers. Please refer to 'Selling your Stamps?' Tip 19 (page 98) for suggestions as to how this may be achieved for more valuable collections.

Unless your collection includes valuable stamps/sets that the auctioneer agrees to extract and offer individually ... you are paying an enormous percentage of the value of your stamps for that auction to sell to dealers.

The 'funniest' thing of all was that the auction does not even pack your purchases .... we had to pay another £35 for a company to collect the stamps, package them and deliver them to us by parcel delivery!

The point is that unless your collection includes valuable stamps/sets that the auctioneer agrees to extract and offer individually ... you are paying an enormous percentage of the value of your stamps for that auction to sell to dealers.

BUT, if your collection is one basically comprised of rarities – then an argument can be made for offering your collection individually lotted. In this way you are going to reach collectors + if yours is a 'named' collection often there is a 'kudos' value/premium that stamps with provenance achieve.

However – so large are the major auctions selling and buyer's premiums today – that even with collections of rarities – leading dealers can often offer to pay in excess of a fair auction estimate immediately – without risk, uncertainty of unsold lots, and immediately. The simple answer is get the auction to underwrite the minimum NET amount that they will guarantee you receive ... and then see by how much the 'trade' will improve upon this. Then you make a fully informed decision.

In Part 5 of 'Selling your Stamps?' we'll discuss the merits and obstacles of selling your stamps on-line via eBay and other on-line auctions.

Happy collecting from us all,

PS. If you find this 'tip' interesting please forward it to a philatelic friend.

Andrew McGavin
Managing Director: Universal Philatelic Auctions, Omniphil & Avon Approvals, Avon Mixtures, Universal Philatelic (Ebay)

To read the rest of this series 'SELLING YOUR STAMPS?' see the relevant pages listed below:

Summary Tip 18 – page 42 (Australia)
Summary Tip 19 – page 98 (Bechuanaland)
Summary Tip 20 – page 210 (Egypt)
Summary Tip 21 – page 272 (India)

To read the final instalment, Summary Tip 22 – 'Selling via Online Auction' simply e-mail and request to: *info@upastampauctions.co.uk*

Also, at the back of this catalogue to see how UPA can pay you upto 36% more for your collection

India

(Currency. 12 pies = 1 anna; 16 annas = 1 rupee)

ISSUE FOR SIND PROVINCE

1

1852 (1 July). "Scinde Dawk." Embossed.

S1	**1**	½a. white	£20000	£2500
S2		½a. blue	£45000	£10000
S3		½a. scarlet	—	£28000

These stamps were issued under the authority of Sir Bartle Frere, Commissioner in Sind.

No. S3 is on sealing wax (usually cracked). Perfect copies are very rare.

It is believed that examples in red were issued first followed, in turn, by those in white and blue. The latter, which shows an extra ring round the circumference, may have been produced by De La Rue. The Scinde Dawks were withdrawn in October 1854.

EAST INDIA COMPANY ADMINISTRATION

2 (*Much reduced*)

3

The ½a., 1a. and 4a. were lithographed in Calcutta at the office of the Surveyor-General. The die was engraved by Mr. Maniruddin (spelling uncertain). *Ungummed* paper watermarked as T **2** (the "No. 4" paper) with the Arms of the East India Co in the sheet. The watermark is sideways on the ½a. and 1a., and upright on the 4a. where the paper was trimmed so that only the central portion showing the oval and the Arms was used. Imperforate.

1854 (1 Apr.).

1	**3**	½a. vermilion	£3000	†
		a. Deep vermilion	£4250	†

This stamp, with 9½ arches in the side border, was prepared for use and a supply was sent to Bombay, but was not officially issued.

The vermilion shade is normally found on toned paper and the deep vermilion on white.

ILLUSTRATIONS. Types **4/8** are shown twice actual size.

4

1854 (1 Oct)–**55**. Die I.

2	**4**	½a. blue	£200	40·00
		a. Printed on both sides	†	£40000
		b. Printed double	†	£32000
3		½a. pale blue	£300	60·00
4		½a. deep blue	£225	45·00
5		½a. indigo	£700	£140

We give the official date of validity. Stamps were on sale to the public from mid September. Actual usage at Toungoo, Burma, is known from mid August.

These stamps were printed between 5 May and 29 July 1854 (Printing 30 millions).

4a

Die II.

6	**4a**	½a. blue	£170	£130
7		½a. indigo	£180	£140

The bulk were printed between 1 and 12 August 1854, with some extra sheets on or before 2 November (Printing about 2 millions).

5

Die III (1855).

8	**5**	½a. pale blue	£3000	95·00
8a		½a. blue	£2750	85·00
9		½a. greenish blue	£4250	£250
10		½a. deep blue	£3500	£150

These stamps were printed between 3 July and 25 August 1855 (Printing about 4¾ millions).

THE THREE DIES OF THE ½ ANNA

DIE I. *Chignon shading* mostly solid blobs of colour. *Corner ornaments,* solid blue stars with long points, always conspicuous. *Band below diadem* always heavily shaded. *Diadem and jewels.* The middle and right-hand jewels usually show a clearly defined cross. *Outer frame lines.* Stamps with white or faintly shaded chignons and weak frame lines are usually Die I (worn state).

DIE II. *Chignon* normally shows much less shading. A strong line of colour separates hair and chignon. *Corner ornaments.* The right blue star is characteristic (see illustration) but tends to disappear. It never obliterates the white cross. *Band below diadem.* As Die I but heavier, sometimes solid. *Diadem and jewels.* As Die I but usually fainter. *Outer frame lines.* Always strong and conspicuous.

DIE III. *Chignon shading* shows numerous fine lines, often blurred. *Corner ornaments* have a small hollow blue star with short points, which tends to disappear as in Die II. *Band below diadem,* shows light shading or hardly any shading. *Diadem and jewels.* Jewels usually marked with a solid squat star. The ornaments between the stars appear in the shape of a characteristic white "w". *Frame lines* variable.

The above notes give the general characteristics of the three Dies, but there are a few exceptions due to retouching, etc.

6 (*See note below No.* 14)

Die I.

11	**6**	1a. deep red	£1600	£110
12		1a. red	£1100	80·00

Printing of these stamps commenced on 26 July 1854, and continued into August (Printing, see note below No. 14).

7

Die II: With more lines in the chignon than in Die I, and with white curved line where chignon joins head*.

13	**7**	1a. deep red	£400	£120
14		1a. dull red	£180	85·00

*Very worn printings of Die II may be found with chignon nearly as white as in Die I.

In stamps of Die I, however, the small blob of red projecting from the hair into the chignon is always visible.

These stamps were printed in August and September 1854 (Total printing, Dies I and II together, about 7¾ millions).

8

Die III. With pointed bust (1855).

15	**8**	1a. red	£3750	£200
16		1a. dull red	£4500	£250

These stamps were printed between 7 July and 25 August 1855 (Printing, about 1½ millions).

9

NOTE. Our catalogue prices for Four Annas stamps are for cut-square specimens, with clear margins and in good condition. Cut-to-shape copies are worth from 3% to 20% of these prices according to condition.

Four Dies of the Head:—

I   II

DIE I. Band of diadem and chignon strongly shaded.

DIE II. Lines in band of diadem worn. Few lines in the upper part of the chignon, which, however, shows a strong drawn comma-like mark.

IIIA   III

DIE IIIA. Upper part of chignon partly redrawn, showing two short, curved vertical lines in the NE corner. "Comma" has disappeared.

DIE III. Upper part of chignon completely redrawn, but band of diadem shows only a few short lines.

Two Dies of the Frame:—

Die I. Outer frame lines weak. Very small dots of colour, or none at all, in the "R" and "A's". The white lines to the right of "INDIA" are separated, by a line of colour, from the inner white circle.

Die II. Outer frame lines strengthened. Dots in the "R" and "A's" strong. White lines to right of "INDIA" break into inner white circle.

(Des Capt. H. Thuillier.)

1854 (15 Oct)–**55**. W **2** upright, central portion only. Imperf.

1st Printing, Head Die I. Frame Die I. Stamps widely spaced and separated by blue wavy line

			Un	Used	Us pr
17	**9**	4a. indigo and red	£20000	£1100	£5500
18		4a. blue and pale red	£20000	£1000	£5000
		a. Head inverted	†	£140000/ £450000	

This printing was made between 13 and 28 Oct 1854 (Printing, 206,040).

27 confirmed examples of No. 18a are now known, only three of which are cut-square. The range of prices quoted reflects the difference in value between a sound and attractive cut-to-shape stamp and the finest example known. Several of the known examples are in poor condition, and these are worth much less.

2nd Printing. Head Die II. Frame Die I. Stamps widely spaced and separated by blue wavy line.

19	**9**	4a. blue and red	£18000	£700	£3750
		a. Blue (head) printed double	†	£40000	
20		4a. indigo and deep red	£18000	£750	£4000

This printing was made between 1 and 13 Dec 1854 (Printing, 393,960).

No. 19a is only known used cut-to-shape.

3rd Printing. Head Dies II, IIIA and III. Frame Dies I and II. Stamps, often in bright shades, widely spaced and separated by wavy line (1855)

21	**9**	4a. blue and red shades (Head III, Frame I)	£40000	£2250	£11000
		a. Head III, Frame I	—	£2750	£14000
		b. Head IIIA, Frame I	—	£3250	£16000
		c. Head III, Frame II	—	—	£40000

This printing was made between 10 March and 2 April 1855 (Printing, 138,960).

Correct attribution of stamps to the scarce third printing requires careful study. Examples of Nos. 21/c should only be purchased with a reliable guarantee.

4th Printing. Head Die III. Frame Die II. Stamps closely spaced 2 to 2½ mm without separating line (1855)

22	**9**	4a. deep blue and red	£12000	£650	£2250
23		4a. blue and red	£11000	£550	£2100
		a. Blue (head) printed double	†	£30000	†
24		4a. pale blue and pale red	£12000	£650	£2500

This printing was made between 3 April and 9 May 1855 (Printing, 540,960).

No. 23a is only known used cut-to-shape.

5th Printing. Head Die III. Frame Die II. Stamps spaced 4 to 6 mm without separating line (1855)

25	**9**	4a. blue and rose-red	£18000	£950	£4750
26		4a. deep blue and red	£18000	£1000	£4750

This printing was made between 4 Oct and 3 Nov 1855 (Printing, 380,064).

Serrated perf about 18, or pin-perf

27		½a. blue (Die I)	†	£18000
28		1a. red (Die I)	†	£11000
29		1a. red (Die II)	†	£10000
30		4a. blue and red (Die II)	†	£50000

This is believed to be an unofficial perforation. Most of the known specimens bear Madras circle postmarks (C122 to C126), but some are known with Bombay postmarks. Beware of fakes.

BISECTS. The bisected stamps for issues between 1854 and 1860 were used exclusively in the Straits Settlements during shortages of certain values. Prices quoted are for those with Singapore "B 172" cancellations. Penang marks are considerably rarer.

10	**11**

10a (*Much reduced*)

(Plate made at Mint, Calcutta. Typo Stamp Office)

1854 (4 Oct). Sheet wmk sideways, similar to W **2** but with "No. 3" at top left and more undulations in the frame. Imperf.

31	**10**	2a. green (*shades*)	£350	50·00
		a. Bisected (1a.) (1857) (*on cover*)	†	£250000
34		2a. emerald-green	£2750	

The 2a. was also printed on paper with watermark W **10a** sideways (*Price* £1200 *unused,* £800 *used for examples with clearly identifiable portion of watermark*).

Apart from the rare emerald-green shade, there is a range of shades of No. 31 varying from bluish to yellowish green.

Many stamps show traces of lines external to the design shown in our illustration. Stamps with this frame on all four sides are scarce.

Many reprints of the ½, 1, 2, and 4a. exist.

PRINTERS. All Indian stamps from No. 35 to 200 were typographed by De La Rue & Co.

> **PRICES.** It must be emphasised that the unused prices quoted for the early perforated stamps, especially Nos. 35/68, are for fine examples with fresh colour and original gum. Well-centred examples may command a premium.

1855 (1 Oct). Blue glazed paper. No wmk. P 14.

35	**11**	4a. black	£1400	22·00
		a. Imperf (pair)	£18000	£18000
		b. Bisected (2a.) (1859) (*on cover*)	†	£21000
36		8a. carmine (Die I)	£1100	21·00
		a. Imperf (pair)	£8500	
		b. Bisected (4a.) (1859) (*on cover*)	†	£130000

The first supply of the 4a. was on white paper, but it is difficult to distinguish it from No. 45.

In the 8a. the paper varies from deep blue to almost white.

For difference between Die I and Die II in the 8a., see illustrations above No. 73.

1856–64. Paper yellowish to white. No wmk. P 14.

37	**11**	½a. blue (Die I)	£160	6·00
38		½a. pale blue (Die I)	£110	3·75
39		1a. brown	80·00	5·50
		a. Imperf between (vert pair)		
		b. Imperf (pair)	£1400	£4750
		c. Bisected (½a.) (1859) (*on cover*)	†	£130000
40		1a. deep brown	£160	7·00
41		2a. dull pink (1860)	£1300	50·00
		a. Imperf (pair)	£7000	
42		2a. yellow-buff (1859)	£850	45·00
		a. Imperf (pair)	£3500	£7500
43		2a. yellow (1863)	£1200	55·00
44		2a. orange (1858)	£1500	60·00
		a. Imperf (pair)	£7000	
45		4a. black	£900	10·00
		a. Bisected diagonally (2a.) (1859) (*on cover*)	†	£65000
		b. Imperf (pair)	£7500	£7500
46		4a. grey-black	£800	5·50
47		4a. green (1864)	£4750	65·00
48		8a. carmine (Die I)	£1200	42·00
49		8a. pale carmine (Die I)	£1300	42·00
		a. Bisected (4a.) (1859) (*on cover*)	†	£130000

Prepared for use, but not officially issued.

50	**11**	2a. yellow-green	£3750	£4000
		a. Imperf (pair)	£8000	†

This stamp is known with trial obliterations, and a few are known postally used. It also exists *imperf,* but is not known used thus.

For difference between Die I and Die II in the ½a., see illustrations above No. 73.

CROWN COLONY

On 1 November 1858, Her Majesty Queen Victoria assumed the government of the territories in India "heretofore administered in trust by the Honourable East India Company".

12	**13**

1860 (9 May). No wmk. P 14.

51	**12**	8p. purple/*bluish*	£600	£140
52		8p. purple/*white*	90·00	7·50
		a. Bisected diagonally (4p.) (1862) (*on cover*)	†	£130000
		b. Imperf (pair)	£8500	£10000
53		8p. mauve	£170	15·00

1865. Paper yellowish to white. W **13**. P 14.

54	**11**	½a. blue (Die I)	32·00	2·50
		a. Imperf	†	£2000
		w. Wmk inverted	£600	55·00
55		½a. pale blue (Die I)	32·00	4·00
56	**12**	8p. purple	13·00	15·00
		w. Wmk inverted	55·00	
57		8p. mauve	26·00	20·00
58	**11**	1a. pale brown	18·00	2·00
59		1a. deep brown	16·00	2·00
		w. Wmk inverted	£170	80·00
60		1a. chocolate	20·00	2·25
61		2a. yellow	£450	8·50
62		2a. orange	£140	2·75
		a. Imperf (pair)	†	£7500
63		2a. brown-orange	45·00	2·75
		w. Wmk inverted	£150	85·00
64		4a. green	£1300	40·00
		w. Wmk inverted	†	£400
65		8a. carmine (Die I)	£4750	95·00
		w. Wmk inverted	£7000	£650

The 8p. mauve, No. 57, is found variously surcharged "NINE" or "NINE PIE" by local postmasters, to indicate that it was being sold for 9 pies, as was the case during 1874. Such surcharges were made without Government sanction. (*Price, from* £850 *unused*).

The stamps of India, wmk Elephant's Head, surcharged with a crown and value in "CENTS", were used in the Straits Settlements.

POSTAGE   POSTAGE

14	(**15**)	(**16**)

1866 (28 June). Fiscal stamps as T **14** optd. Wmk Crown over "INDIA". P 14 (at sides only).

(a) As T 15

66		6a. purple (G.)	£2750	£150
		a. Overprint inverted	†	£30000

There are 20 different types of this overprint.

(b) With T 16

68		6a. purple (G.)	£4750	£250

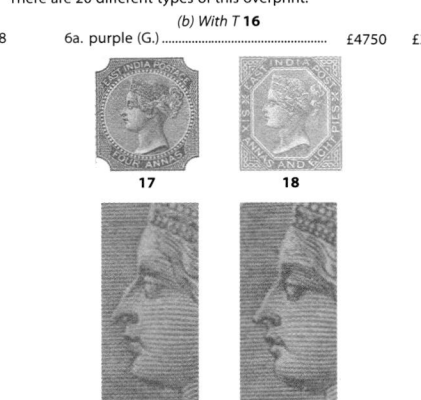

17	**18**

Die I	Die II

Two Dies of 4a.:—

Die I.—Mouth closed, line from corner of mouth downwards only. Pointed chin.

Die II.—Mouth slightly open; lips, chin, and throat defined by line of colour. Rounded chin.

1866 (1 Aug)–**78**. W **13**. P 14.

69	**17**	4a. green (Die I)	£150	5·00
70		4a. deep green (Die I)	£150	6·00
71		4a. blue-green (Die II) (1878)	48·00	3·75
		w. Wmk inverted	†	£450
72	**18**	6a.8p. slate (4.67)	95·00	32·00
		a. Imperf (pair)	£9000	

Die I (8a.)	Die I (½a.)
Die II (8a.)	Die II (½a.)

1868 (1 Jan). Die II. Profile redrawn and different diadem. W **13**. P 14.

73	**11**	8a. rose (Die II)	70·00	9·00
		w. Wmk inverted	£140	
74		8a. pale rose (Die II)	70·00	8·50

HAVE YOU HEARD?

Untold Stories of the thousand tribes, unfolding within the perforation of our postage stamps.

Unknown to most, and regardless of been studded with over a thousand tribes, we've only began to tell our story to the outside world through Postage Stamps. Despite our best efforts, the ongoing discoveries of flora and fauna species continue to write new chapters. Like seasoned explorers, join our existing collectors in this journey of a life-time experience. Collect Papua New Guinea Postage Stamps.

www.postpng.com.pg

PAPUA NEW GUINEA STAMPS

Papua New Guinea

Papua New G

K6.20 Traditional headdress

K10 Traditional headdress

Arawe mother and child K1.35

www.postpng.com.pg
customer.care@postpng.com.pg

Post PNG

1873. Die II. Features, especially the mouth, more firmly drawn. W **13**. P 14.

75	**11**	½a. deep blue (Die II)	14·00	1·60
76		½a. blue (Die II)	14·00	1·40
		w. Wmk inverted	£150	£100
		y. Wmk inverted and reversed	†	£375

	19			
	20			

1874 (18 July–1 Sept). W **13**. P 14.

77	**19**	9p. bright mauve (18.7.74)	25·00	25·00
		w. Wmk inverted	—	£500
78		9p. pale mauve	25·00	25·00
79	**20**	1r. slate (1.9.74)	£100	38·00

21	**22**

1876 (19 Aug). W **13**. P 14.

80	**21**	6a. olive-bistre	9·00	2·50
		w. Wmk inverted	£180	£150
81		6a. pale brown	10·00	2·00
82	**22**	12a. Venetian red	20·00	42·00

EMPIRE

Queen Victoria assumed the title of Empress of India in 1877, and the inscription on the stamps was altered from "EAST INDIA" to "INDIA".

23	**24**	**25**
26	**27**	**28**
29	**30**	**31**
32	**33**	**34**

1882 (1 Jan)–**90**. W **34**. P 14.

84	**23**	½a. deep blue-green (1883)	10·00	10
		w. Wmk inverted	—	£150
85		½a. blue-green	10·00	10
		a. Double impression	£1700	£3750
		w. Wmk inverted	—	£150
86	**24**	9p. rose (1883)	2·50	4·25
87		9p. aniline carmine	2·75	4·25
		w. Wmk inverted	£650	£425
88	**25**	1a. brown-purple (1883)	12·00	30
89		1a. plum	12·00	30
		w. Wmk inverted	—	£350
90	**26**	1a.6p. sepia	2·75	3·00
		w. Wmk inverted	—	£450
91	**27**	2a. pale blue (1883)	11·00	60
92		2a. blue	11·00	60
		a. Double impression	£3500	£4000
93	**28**	3a. orange	35·00	10·00
94		3a. brown-orange (1890)	17·00	2·75
		w. Wmk inverted	—	£425
95	**29**	4a. olive-green (6.85)	27·00	2·50
96		4a. slate-green	25·00	2·50
		w. Wmk inverted	£600	£350
97	**30**	4a.6p. yellow-green (1.5.86)	50·00	9·50
98	**31**	8a. dull mauve (1883)	48·00	2·75
99		8a. magenta	48·00	2·00
100	**32**	12a. purple/red (1.4.88)	18·00	5·50
		w. Wmk inverted	—	£500
101	**33**	1r. slate (1883)	45·00	8·00
		w. Wmk inverted	—	£375

84/101 Set of 11 .... £225 / 35·00

97s, 100s Handstamped "SPECIMEN." Set of 2 .... £110

No. 92a is from a sheet of 2a. stamps with a very marked double impression issued in Karachi in early 1898.

The discovery of postal forgeries of the 1r. slate (No. 101) at Bombay in 1890 led to its replacement by the type **37** bicoloured 1r. in a new design (Nos. 105/6.).

2½ As.

(**35**)	**36** **37**

1891 (1 Jan). No. 97 surch with T **35** by Govt Press, Calcutta.

102	**30**	2½a. on 4½a. yellow-green	11·00	1·25
		a. Surch double, one albino	—	£375

There are several varieties in this surcharge due to variations in the relative positions of the letters and figures.

1892 (Jan)–**97**. W **34**. P 14.

103	**36**	2a.6p. yellow-green	8·00	40
104		2a.6p. pale blue-green (1897)	9·50	80
105	**37**	1r. green and rose	55·00	14·00
106		1r. green and aniline carmine	28·00	2·25

38	(**39**)	**40**

Slanting serif (Lower pane R. 1/1)

USED HIGH VALUES. It is necessary to emphasise that used prices quoted for the following and all later high value stamps are for postally used copies.

(Head of Queen from portrait by von Angeli)

1895 (1 Sept). W **34**. P 14.

107	**38**	2r. carmine and yellow-brown	90·00	21·00
107a		2r. carmine and brown	£140	30·00
108		3r. brown and green	75·00	14·00
109		5r. ultramarine and violet	95·00	50·00

107/9 Set of 3 .... £225 / 75·00

1898 (1 Oct). No. 85 surch with T **39** by Govt Press, Calcutta.

110	**23**	¼a. on ½a. blue-green	20	1·00
		a. Surch double	£750	
		b. Double impression of stamp	£750	
		c. Slanting serif on "1"	£110	

1899. W **34**. P 14.

111	**40**	3p. aniline carmine	40	20
		w. Wmk inverted	£300	

1900 (1 Oct)–**02**. W **34**. P 14.

112	**40**	3p. grey	1·25	2·50
113	**23**	½a. pale yellow-green	3·25	70
114		½a. yellow-green	6·00	1·00
		w. Wmk inverted	†	£475
115	**25**	1a. carmine	6·50	30
116	**27**	2a. pale violet	11·00	4·25
117		2a. mauve (1902)	17·00	6·00
118	**36**	2a.6p. ultramarine	10·00	5·50

112/18 Set of 5 .... 28·00 / 12·00

41	**42**	**43**
44	**45**	**46**
47	**48**	**49**

50	**51**	**52**

1902 (9 Aug)–**11**. W **34**. P 14.

119	**41**	3p. grey	1·00	10
120		3p. slate-grey (1904)	1·00	10
121	**42**	½a. yellow-green	5·00	10
122		½a. green	5·00	20
123	**43**	1a. carmine	3·25	10
124	**44**	2a. violet (13.5.03)	11·00	50
125		2a. mauve	10·00	10
126	**45**	2a.6p. ultramarine (1902)	9·50	60
		w. Wmk inverted	†	£600
127	**46**	3a. orange-brown (1902)	9·50	60
128	**47**	4a. olive (20.4.03)	4·25	80

129		4a. pale olive	9·00	80
130		4a. olive-brown	16·00	4·00
131	**48**	6a. olive-bistre (6.8.03)	25·00	4·75
132		6a. maize	21·00	4·50
133	**49**	8a. purple (shades) (8.5.03)	8·50	1·00
134		8a. claret (1910)	25·00	1·00
135	**50**	12a. purple/red (1903)	17·00	2·00
136	**51**	1r. green and carmine (1903)	10·00	70
137		1r. green and scarlet (1911)	75·00	7·00
138	**52**	2r. rose-red and yellow-brown (1903)	£110	8·50
139		2r. carmine and yellow-brown (1903)	£110	8·50
		w. Wmk inverted	£1600	£750
140		3r. brown and green	80·00	42·00
141		3r. red-brown and green (1911)	£100	45·00
142		5r. ultramarine and violet (1904)	£180	50·00
143		5r. ultramarine and deep lilac (1911)	£300	70·00
144		10r. green and carmine (1909)	£375	50·00
146		15r. blue and olive-brown (1909)	£425	55·00
147		25r. brownish orange and blue (1909)	£2750	£1700

119/47 Set of 17 .... £3500 / £1800

No. 147 can often be found with telegraph cancellation; these can be supplied at one third of the price given above.

1905 (2 Feb). No. 122 surch with T **39**.

148	**42**	¼a. on ½a. green	55	10
		a. Surch inverted	—	£2250

It is doubtful if No. 148a exists unused with genuine surcharge.

53	**54**

1906 (6 Dec)–**07**. W **34**. P 14.

149	**53**	½a. green	3·25	10
150	**54**	1a. carmine (7.1.07)	4·00	10

55	**56**	**57**

58 *	**59**	**60**

61	**62**	**63**
64	**65**	**66**

67	"Rs" flaw in right value tablet (R. 1/4)

*T **58**. Two types of the 1½a.; (A) As illustrated. (B) Inscribed "1½ As". "ONE AND A HALF ANNAS".

1911 (1 Dec)–**22**. W **34**. P 14.

151	**55**	3p. grey (1912)	1·40	25
		w. Wmk inverted	75·00	
152		3p. pale grey	3·50	25
153		3p. bluish grey (1922)	4·00	50
		w. Wmk inverted	28·00	
154		3p. slate	3·50	25
		a. "Rs" flaw	38·00	48·00
154b		3p. violet-grey	5·50	75
155	**56**	½a. light green (1912)	6·00	25
		w. Wmk inverted	95·00	
156		½a. emerald	7·50	25
		w. Wmk inverted	†	£120
157		½a. bright green	7·50	15
159	**57**	1a. rose-carmine	6·00	20
160		1a. carmine	5·00	20
161		1a. aniline carmine	4·75	15
162		1a. pale rose-carmine (chalk-surfaced paper) (1918)	8·00	1·25
163	**58**	1½a. chocolate (Type A) (1919)	7·50	1·00
164		1½a. grey-brown (Type A)	15·00	5·00
165		1½a. chocolate (Type B) (1921)	9·00	9·50
		w. Wmk inverted	27·00	
166	**59**	2a. purple	9·00	70

Stanley Gibbons - the home of stamp collecting since 1856 and today's market leader for all your philatelic needs.

For the best quality in stamps, catalogues, albums and all other accessories log on to our website today and explore our unrivalled range of products all available at the touch of a button.

www.stanleygibbons.com

167		2a. reddish purple	12·00	70
168		2a. deep mauve	13·00	70
		w. Wmk inverted	50·00	
169		2a. bright reddish violet	16·00	1·00
		a. Stop under "s" in right value tablet (R. 4/16)	£550	
170	60	2a.6p. ultramarine (1912)	4·50	3·50
171	61	2a.6p. ultramarine (1913)	4·50	20
172	62	3a. orange	4·50	20
173		3a. dull orange	12·00	45
174	63	4a. deep olive (1912)	7·00	1·00
175		4a. olive-green	7·00	1·00
		w. Wmk inverted	60·00	
177	64	6a. yellow-bistre (1912)	4·50	2·50
178		6a. brown-ochre	7·50	1·00
179	65	8a. deep magenta (1912)	6·50	2·75
180		8a. deep mauve	25·00	1·10
		w. Wmk inverted	£180	
181		8a. bright mauve	£100	13·00
182		8a. purple	38·00	3·25
183	66	12a. carmine-lake (1912)	6·50	2·50
		w. Wmk inverted	£425	£325
184		12a. claret	27·00	3·50
185	67	1r. red-brown and deep blue-green (1913)	32·00	3·25
		w. Wmk inverted	£150	
186		1r. brown and green (*shades*)	48·00	3·00
186*a*		1r. orange-brown and deep turquoise-green	80·00	8·50
187		2r. carmine and brown (1913)	35·00	2·50
		w. Wmk inverted	£170	
188		5r. ultramarine and violet (1913)	95·00	8·50
189		10r. green and scarlet (1913)	£180	16·00
190		15r. blue and olive (1913)	£300	42·00
		w. Wmk inverted	†	£700
191		25r. orange and blue (1913)	£600	65·00
151/91 *Set of* 19			£1200	£140

Examples of the ½a. printed double are now believed to be forgeries.

FORGERIES.—Collectors are warned against forgeries of all the later surcharges of India, and particularly the errors.

NINE

PIES

(**68**)

1921 (10 June). T **57** surch with T **68**.

192		9p. on 1a. rose-carmine	1·50	30
		a. Error. "NINE NINE"	£130	£300
		b. Error. "PIES PIES"	£130	£300
		c. Surch double	£300	£425
		w. Wmk inverted	†	£400
193		9p. on 1a. carmine-pink	4·00	60
194		9p. on 1a. aniline carmine	40·00	12·00

In the initial setting of the surcharge No. 192a occurred on R. 2/13-16 of the fourth pane and No. 192b on R. 4/13-16 of the third. For the second setting No. 192a was corrected. Examples of No. 192b still occur but on R. 2/13-16 of the third pane. Later printings showed this corrected also.

1922. T 56 surch with T **39**.

195		¼a. on ½a. bright green	1·25	35
		a. Surch inverted	12·00	
		b. Surch omitted (in horiz pair with normal)	£475	
		c. Slanting serif on "1"	80·00	
		w. Wmk inverted		
196		¼a. on ½a. emerald	11·00	3·00
		w. Wmk inverted		

1922–26. W **34**. P 14.

197	57	1a. chocolate	4·50	10
		w. Wmk inverted	45·00	
198	58	1½a. rose-carmine (Type B) (1926)	4·00	30
199	61	2a.6p. orange (1926)	5·00	2·50
200	62	3a. ultramarine (1923)	21·00	60
197/200 *Set of* 4			30·00	3·25

69

70

71

Stop under "s" in right value tablet (R. 4/16)

PRINTERS. The following issues of postage and contemporary official stamps were all printed by the Security Printing Press, Nasik, *unless otherwise stated.*

1926–33. Typo. W **69**. P 14.

201	55	3p. slate	1·75	10
		w. Wmk inverted	4·25	30
202	56	½a. green	4·50	10
		w. Wmk inverted	7·00	30
203	57	1a. chocolate	1·75	10
		a. *Tête-bêche* (vert pair) (1932)	4·25	12·00
		w. Wmk inverted	1·75	10
204	58	1½a. rose-carmine (Type B) (1929)	8·50	10
		a. Wmk sideways	†	£2250
		w. Wmk inverted	10·00	30
205	59	2a. bright purple	27·00	18·00
		a. Stop under "s"	£300	
		w. Wmk inverted	†	£150
206	70	2a. purple	5·50	10
		a. *Tête-bêche* (vert pair) (1933)	14·00	42·00
		w. Wmk inverted	6·00	30
207	61	2a.6p. orange (1929)	6·00	10
		w. Wmk inverted	6·50	40
208	62	3a. ultramarine	17·00	1·00
209		3a. blue (1928)	16·00	10
		w. Wmk inverted	16·00	75
210	63	4a. sage-green (*shades*)	2·50	10
		w. Wmk inverted	—	25·00
211	71	4a. sage-green (*shades*)	6·00	10
		w. Wmk inverted	17·00	50
212	65	8a. reddish purple	9·50	10
		w. Wmk inverted	10·00	40
213	66	12a. claret	9·00	30
		w. Wmk inverted	10·00	80
214	67	1r. chocolate and green	16·00	45
		a. Chocolate (head) omitted	£26000	
		w. Wmk inverted	20·00	1·00
215		2r. carmine and orange	30·00	80
		w. Wmk inverted	35·00	2·50
216		5r. ultramarine and purple	75·00	1·25
		w. Wmk inverted	£110	4·25
217		10r. green and scarlet (1927)	£140	9·00
		w. Wmk inverted	£300	13·00
218		15r. blue and olive (1928)	£100	40·00
		w. Wmk inverted	48·00	32·00
219		25r. orange and blue (1928)	£325	60·00
		w. Wmk inverted	£375	75·00
201/19 *Set of* 18			£650	£110

Examples of the ½a. printed double are believed to be forgeries.

Nos 203a and 206a come from surplus booklet sheets issued as normal stock.

72 de Havilland DH.66 Hercules

8a. Missing tree-top (R. 11/6)

8a. Reversed serif on second "I" of "INDIA"

(Des R. Grant. Litho)

1929 (22 Oct). Air. W **69** (sideways*). P 14.

220	72	2a. deep blue-green	7·50	1·50
		w. Wmk stars pointing left	6·50	75
221		3a. blue	4·75	3·25
		a. "Q" for "O" in "Postage" (R.11/4)	£550	£375
		w. Wmk stars pointing left	4·75	3·00
222		4a. olive-green	6·50	1·25
		w. Wmk stars pointing left	7·50	1·25
223		6a. bistre	4·50	1·00
		w. Wmk stars pointing left	4·50	1·00
224		8a. purple	12·00	1·00
		a. Missing tree-top	£375	£250
		b. Reversed serif	£900	£450
		w. Wmk stars pointing left	12·00	1·00
225		12a. rose-red	25·00	9·00
		w. Wmk stars pointing left	25·00	9·00
220/5 *Set of* 6			50·00	14·50

*The normal sideways watermark shows the stars pointing right, *as seen from the back of the stamp.*

73 Purana Qila

74 War Memorial Arch

75 Council House

76 The Viceroy's House

77 Government of India Secretariat

78 Dominion Columns and the Secretariat

¼a. "F" for "P" in "PURANA" (R. 5/2)

(Des H. W. Barr. Litho)

1931 (9 Feb). Inauguration of New Delhi. T **73/78**. W **69** (sideways*). P 13½×14.

226	73	¼a. olive-green and orange-brown	4·00	6·50
		a. "F" for "P" in "PURANA"	£300	£325
		w. Wmk stars pointing left	3·00	6·50
227	74	½a. violet and green	2·75	40
		w. Wmk stars pointing left	2·00	40
228	75	1a. mauve and chocolate	1·50	20
		w. Wmk stars pointing left	3·00	45
229	76	2a. green and blue	3·75	4·50
		w. Wmk stars pointing left	2·00	1·25
230	77	3a. chocolate and carmine	8·00	3·25
		w. Wmk stars pointing left	5·00	2·75
231	78	1r. violet and green	26·00	48·00
		w. Wmk stars pointing left	24·00	48·00
226/31 *Set of* 6			32·00	50·00

*The normal sideways watermark shows the stars pointing to the right, *as seen from the back of the stamp.*

79

80

81

82

83

9p. litho. Heavier and longer lines on face. King's nose often shows six horizontal lines and always has lowest line long and thin

9p. typo. Lines lighter and shorter. Always five lines on King's nose with the lowest short and thick

(T **82/3** des T. I. Archer. 9p. litho or typo; 1a.3p, 3a.6p. litho; others typo)

1932–36. W **69**. P 14.

232	79	½a. green (1934)	13·00	10
		w. Wmk inverted	—	3·75
233	80	9p. deep green (*litho*) (22.4.32)	7·50	10
		aw. Wmk inverted	8·00	3·75
233*b*		9p. deep green (*typo*) (27.8.34)	12·00	10
234	81	1a. chocolate (1934)	8·00	10
		w. Wmk inverted	24·00	3·75
235	82	1a.3p. mauve (22.4.32)	2·25	10
		w. Wmk inverted	3·50	30
236	70	2a. vermilion	23·00	7·50
		aw. Wmk inverted	55·00	16·00
236*b*	59	2a. vermilion (1934)	3·75	50
		bw. Wmk inverted	—	48·00
236*c*		2a. vermilion (*small die*) (1936)	11·00	30
		cw. Wmk inverted	£190	18·00
237	62	3a. carmine	20·00	10
		w. Wmk inverted	£100	4·00
238	83	3a.6p. ultramarine (22.4.32)	8·50	20
		w. Wmk inverted	8·50	30
239	64	6a. bistre (1935)	18·00	1·50
		w. Wmk inverted	—	35·00
232/9 *Set of* 9			90·00	8·50

No. 236*b* measures 19×22.6 mm and No. 236*c* 18.4×21.8 mm.

"DOUBLE PRINTS". Examples of Nasik litho-printed stamps showing doubling of all or part of the design or subsequent overprint are not uncommon. These are not true 'double prints', in that they were not the result of two impressions of the inked printing plate, but were caused by incorrect tension in the rubber 'blanket' which transferred ink from the cylinder to the paper. Such varieties are outside the scope of this catalogue.

84 Gateway of India, Bombay

85 Victoria Memorial, Calcutta

86 Rameswaram Temple, Madras

87 Jain Temple, Calcutta

88 Taj Mahal, Agra

89 Golden Temple, Amritsar

90 Pagoda in Mandalay   3½a. "Bird" flaw (R. 9/3)

1935 (6 May). Silver Jubilee. T **84/90**. W **69** (sideways*). P 13½×14.

240	84	½a. black and yellow-green	2·75	20
		w. Wmk stars pointing left	1·50	15
241	85	9p. black and grey-green	3·00	20
		w. Wmk stars pointing left	2·75	1·50
242	86	1a. black and brown	6·00	20
		w. Wmk stars pointing left	5·50	10
243	87	1¼a. black and bright violet	1·25	10
		w. Wmk stars pointing left	2·25	15
244	88	2½a. black and orange	11·00	1·60
		w. Wmk stars pointing left	10·00	1·00
245	89	3½a. black and dull ultramarine	8·00	12·00
		a. "Bird" flaw	£375	£325
		w. Wmk stars pointing left	6·50	12·00
246	90	8a. black and purple	6·50	3·75
		w. Wmk stars pointing left	10·00	5·00
240/6 *Set of 7*			30·00	15·00

*The normal sideways watermark shows the stars pointing to the right, *as seen from the back of the stamp*.

91 King George VI   **92** Dak Runner

93 Dak bullock cart   **94** Dak tonga

95 Dak camel   **96** Mail train

97 *Strathnaver* (liner)   **98** Post truck

99 Armstrong Whitworth AW27 Ensign I mail plane (small head)   **100** King George VI

1937 (23 Aug)–40. T **91/100**. Typo. W **69**. P 13½×14 or 14×13½ (T **100**).

247	91	3p. slate (15.12.37)	2·00	10
		w. Wmk inverted	—	£110
248		½a. red-brown (15.12.37)	10·00	10
		w. Wmk inverted	—	£250
249		9p. green	8·50	75
		w. Wmk inverted	—	£120
250		1a. carmine	1·25	10
		a. *Tête-bêche* (vert pair) (1940)	3·25	3·00
		w. Wmk inverted (from booklets)	2·00	1·75
251	92	2a. vermilion (15.12.37)	13·00	30
		w. Wmk inverted	—	
252	93	2a.6p. bright violet (15.12.37)	1·50	20
		w. Wmk inverted	£350	90·00
253	94	3a. yellow-green (15.12.37)	13·00	30
		w. Wmk inverted	£350	90·00
254	95	3a.6p. bright blue (15.12.37)	11·00	60
		w. Wmk inverted	—	£225
255	96	4a. brown (15.12.37)	15·00	20
		w. Wmk inverted	—	90·00
256	97	6a. turquoise-green (15.12.37)	17·00	1·25
		w. Wmk inverted	—	£300
257	98	8a. slate-violet (15.12.37)	7·50	60
		w. Wmk inverted	—	£300
258	99	12a. lake (15.12.37)	18·00	1·40

259	100	1r. grey and red-brown (15.12.37)	3·00	15
		w. Wmk inverted	£120	80·00
260		2r. purple and brown (15.12.37)	14·00	30
		w. Wmk inverted	£120	
261		5r. green and blue (15.12.37)	48·00	50
		w. Wmk inverted	£180	£100
262		10r. purple and claret (15.12.37)	35·00	80
		w. Wmk inverted	£500	£180
263		15r. brown and green (15.12.37)	£180	£110
		w. Wmk inverted	£375	£275
264		25r. slate-violet and purple (15.12.37)	£275	45·00
		w. Wmk inverted	—	£275
247/64 *Set of 18*			£600	£140

No. 250a comes from surplus booklet sheets issued as normal stock following the rise in postal rates.

100a King George VI   **101** King George VI   **102** King George VI

103 Armstrong Whitworth A.W.27 Ensign I Mail Plane (large head)

1½a. and **3a.** Litho Lines thin and clean, particularly in the King's profile and the frames of the stamps. No Jubilee lines

1½a. and **3a.** Typo Lines thicker and more ragged. Value tablets and "INDIA POSTAGE" panel unevenly inked. With Jubilee lines

(T **100a/102** des T. I. Archer. Typo (1½a. and 3a. litho also))

1940 (15 Oct)–**43**. W **69**. P 13½×14.

265	100a	3p. slate (1.12.41)	30	10
		w. Wmk inverted	7·00	7·50
266		½a. purple (1.10.41)	1·25	10
		w. Wmk inverted	80·00	38·00
267		9p. green (16.8.41)	1·00	10
		w. Wmk inverted	—	45·00
268		1a. carmine (1.4.43)	1·75	10
		w. Wmk inverted	—	45·00
269	101	1a.3p. yellow-brown (1.12.41)	1·00	10
		aw. Wmk inverted	—	70·00
269b		1½a. dull violet (litho) (20.5.42)	4·00	30
		bw. Wmk inverted	—	40·00
269c		1½a. dull violet (typo) (1943)	2·25	10
		cw. Wmk inverted	—	40·00
270		2a. vermilion (15.5.41)	1·50	10
		w. Wmk inverted	65·00	40·00
271		3a. bright violet (litho) (5.1.41)	6·50	30
		aw. Wmk inverted	£150	50·00
271b		3a. bright violet (typo) (1943)	3·75	40
		bw. Wmk inverted	—	35·00
272		3½a. bright blue (1943)	1·25	1·00
		w. Wmk inverted	—	£100
273	102	4a. brown (15.5.41)	1·25	10
		w. Wmk inverted	—	85·00
274		6a. turquoise-green (15.5.41)	4·00	10
		w. Wmk inverted	†	95·00
275		8a. slate-violet (15.5.41)	1·50	30
		w. Wmk inverted	—	95·00
276		12a. lake (15.5.41)	13·00	1·00
		w. Wmk inverted	—	£160
277	103	14a. purple (15.10.40)	18·00	2·00
		w. Wmk inverted	—	£160
265/77 *Set of 14*			45·00	4·00

105 "Victory" and King George VI

3 Pies (106)

1946 (2 Jan–8 Feb). Victory. Litho. W **69**. P 13.

278	105	9p. yellow-green (8.2.46)	1·00	1·50
		w. Wmk inverted	—	£150
279		1½a. dull violet	75	30
		w. Wmk inverted	—	90·00
280		3½a. bright blue	2·00	2·50
		w. Wmk inverted	—	£150
281		12a. claret (8.2.46)	2·25	1·75
		w. Wmk inverted	—	£275
278/81 *Set of 4*			5·50	5·50

1946 (8 Aug). Surch with T **106**.

282	101	3p. on 1a.3p. yellow-brown	20	15
		w. Wmk inverted	—	90·00

DOMINION

301 Asokan Capital (Inscr reads "Long Live India")   **302** Indian National Flag

303 Douglas DC-4

"Teardrop" (R. 6/6)

(Des T. I. Archer. Litho)

1947 (21 Nov–15 Dec). Independence. W **69**. P 14×13½ (1½a.) or 13½×14 (others).

301	301	1½a. grey-green (15.12)	1·00	10
302	302	3½a. orange-red, blue and green	4·00	2·25
		a. Teardrop	55·00	65·00
		w. Wmk inverted	22·00	32·00
303	303	12a. ultramarine (15.12)	5·00	2·75
301/3 *Set of 3*			9·00	4·50

(Des T. I. Archer. Litho)

1948 (29 May). Air. Inauguration of India—UK Air Service. W **69**. P 13½×14.

304	304	12a. black and ultramarine	5·50	5·00

305 Mahatma Gandhi   **306** Mahatma Gandhi

(Photo Courvoisier)

1948 (15 Aug). First Anniv of Independence. P 11½.

305	305	1½a. brown	9·00	1·25
306		3½a. violet	15·00	5·00
307		12a. grey-green	27·00	9·50
308	306	10r. purple-brown and lake	£400	£140
305/8 *Set of 4*			£425	£140

307 Ajanta Panel   308 Konarak Horse   309 Trimurti

310 Bodhisattva   311 Nataraja   312 Sanchi Stupa, East Gate

313 Bodh Gaya Temple   314 Bhuvanesvara   315 Gol Gumbad, Bijapur

316 Kandarya Mahadeva Temple   317 Golden Temple, Amritsar

318 Victory Tower, Chittorgarh   319 Red Fort, Delhi

320 Taj Mahal, Agra   321 Qutb Minar, Delhi

322 Satrunjaya Temple, Palitana

(Des T. I. Archer and I. M. Das. Typo (low values), litho (rupee values))

1949 (15 Aug)–**52**. T **307/22** W **69** (sideways* on 6p., 1r. and 10r.). P 14 (3p. to 2a.), 13½ (3a. to 12a.), 14×13½ (1r. and 10r.), 13½×14 (2r. and 5r.), 13 (15r.).

309	**307**	3p. slate-violet	15	10
		w. Wmk inverted	†	£100
310	**308**	6p. purple-brown	25	10
		w. Wmk stars pointing right	1·50	1·50
311	**309**	9p. yellow-green	40	10
		w. Wmk inverted	†	£150
312	**310**	1a. turquoise	60	10
		w. Wmk inverted	†	£100
313	**311**	2a. carmine	1·00	10
		w. Wmk inverted	95·00	27·00
314	**312**	3a. brown-orange	2·25	10
		w. Wmk inverted	†	£200
315	**313**	3½a. bright blue	1·75	6·00
316	**314**	4a. lake	5·50	45
		w. Wmk inverted	£120	25·00
317	**315**	6a. violet	2·50	30
		w. Wmk inverted	14·00	16·00
318	**316**	8a. turquoise-green	2·25	10
		w. Wmk inverted	—	£225
319	**317**	12a. dull blue	11·00	30
		w. Wmk inverted	£100	24·00
320	**318**	1r. dull violet and green	45·00	10
		w. Wmk stars pointing left	40·00	1·25
321	**319**	2r. claret and violet	30·00	40
		w. Wmk inverted	£300	50·00
322	**320**	5r. blue-green and red-brown	70·00	2·75
		w. Wmk inverted	£325	55·00

323	**321**	10r. purple-brown and deep blue	£160	32·00
		aw. Wmk stars pointing left	£500	£150
		b. Purple-brown and blue (1952)	£275	18·00
		bw. Wmk stars pointing left	£350	£130
324	**322**	15r. brown and claret	26·00	28·00
		w. Wmk inverted	£325	
309/24 Set of 16			£325	50·00

*The normal sideways watermark has the stars pointing to the left on the 6p. value and to the right on the 1r. and 10r. (323b) *when seen from the back of the stamp.*

For T **310** with statue reversed see No. 333.

323 Globe and Asokan Capital

1949 (10 Oct). 75th Anniv of UPU Litho. W **69**. P 13.

325	**323**	9p. green	6·00	3·25
326		2a. rose	6·00	3·00
327		3½a. bright blue	7·00	3·00
328		12a. brown-purple	10·00	3·00
325/8 Set of 4			26·00	11·00

REPUBLIC

324 Rejoicing Crowds   325 Quill, ink-well and verse

326 Ear of corn and plough   327 Spinning-wheel and cloth

(Des D. J. Keymer & Co. Litho)

1950 (26 Jan). Inauguration of Republic. T **324/7**. W **69** (sideways on 3½a.). P 13.

329		2a. scarlet	6·50	50
		w. Wmk inverted	£110	22·00
330		3½a. ultramarine	10·00	12·00
		w. Wmk stars pointing right	†	£110
331		4a. violet	10·00	1·50
332		12a. maroon	16·00	8·00
		w. Wmk inverted	£130	40·00
329/32 Set of 4			38·00	15·00

The normal sideways watermark shows the top of the stars to the left, *as seen from the back of the stamp.*

328 As T **310**, but statue reversed   329 Stegodon ganesa

1950 (15 July)–**51**. Typo. W **69**. P 14 (1a.), 13½ (others).

333	**328**	1a. turquoise	13·00	10
		aw. Wmk inverted	—	42·00
333b	**313**	2½a. lake (30.4.51)	3·50	3·25
333c	**314**	4a. bright blue (30.4.51)	6·00	10
		cw. Wmk inverted		£160
333/c Set of 3			20·00	3·25

1951 (13 Jan). Centenary of Geological Survey of India. Litho. W **69**. P 13.

334	**329**	2a. black and claret	4·00	1·25

330 Torch   331 Kabir

1951 (4 Mar). First Asian Games, New Delhi. Litho. W **69** (sideways). P 14.

335	**330**	2a. reddish purple and brn-orge	3·00	1·00
		w. Wmk stars pointing right	†	£200
336		12a. chocolate and light blue	17·00	2·25

The normal sideways watermark shows the top of the stars to the left, *as seen from the back of the stamp.*

PROCESS. All the following issues were printed in photogravure, *except where otherwise stated.*

1952 (1 Oct). Indian Saints and Poets. T **331** and similar vert designs. W **69**. P 14.

337		9p. bright emerald-green	3·00	65
338		1a. carmine	3·00	20
339		2a. orange-red	3·50	50
340		4a. bright blue	18·00	60
341		4½a. bright mauve	2·00	1·25
342		12a. brown	20·00	1·25
337/42 Set of 6			45·00	4·00

Designs:—1a. Tulsidas; 2a. Meera; 4a. Surdas; 4½a. Ghalib; 12a. Tagore.

332 Locomotives of 1853 and 1953   333 Mount Everest

1953 (16 Apr). Railway Centenary. W **69**. P 14½×14.

343	**332**	2a. black	2·50	10

1953 (2 Oct). Conquest of Mount Everest. W **69**. P 14½×14.

344	**333**	2a. bright violet	2·50	10
345		14a. brown	14·00	25

334 Telegraph Poles of 1851 and 1951   335 Postal Transport, 1854

1953 (1 Nov). Centenary of Indian Telegraphs. W **69**. P 14½×14.

346	**334**	2a. blue-green	3·50	10
347		12a. blue	12·00	40

1954 (1 Oct). Stamp Centenary. T **335** and similar horiz designs. W **69**. P 14½×14.

348		1a. reddish purple	3·00	20
349		2a. cerise	2·50	10
350		4a. orange-brown	10·00	1·50
351		14a. blue	4·50	40
348/51 Set of 4			17·00	2·00

Designs:—2, 14a. "Airmail"; 4a. Postal transport, 1954.

338 UN Emblem and Lotus   339 Forest Research Institute

1954 (24 Oct). United Nations Day. W **69** (sideways). P 13.

352	**338**	2a. turquoise-green		1·25	10

1954 (11 Dec). Fourth World Forestry Congress, Dehra Dun. W **69**. P 14½×14.

353	**339**	2a. ultramarine	1·25	10

340 Tractor   341 Power loom   342 Bullock-driven Well

343 Damodar Valley Dam   344 Woman Spinning   345 Naga woman weaving with hand loom

346 Bullocks   347 "Malaria Control" (Mosquito and Staff of Aesculapius)

348 Chittaranjan Locomotive Works   349 Marine Drive, Bombay

350 Hindustan Aircraft Factory, Bangalore　**351** Kashmir Landscape

352 Telephone engineer　**353** Cape Comorin

 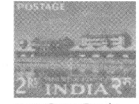

354 Mt Kangchenjunga　**355** Rare Earth Factory, Alwaye

356 Sindri Fertilizer Factory　**357** Steel Plant

1955 (26 Jan). Five Year Plan. T **340/57**. W **69** (sideways on small horiz designs). P 14×14½ (small horiz) or 14½×14 (others).

354	**340**	3p. bright purple	30	10
355	**341**	6p. violet	30	10
356	**342**	9p. orange-brown	40	10
357	**343**	1a. blue-green	45	10
358	**344**	2a. light blue	30	10
359	**345**	3a. pale blue-green	1·00	20
360	**346**	4a. rose-carmine	60	10
361	**347**	6a. yellow-brown	2·75	10
362	**348**	8a. blue	13·00	10
363	**349**	10a. turquoise-green	5·50	3·00
364	**350**	12a. bright blue	6·00	10
365	**351**	14a. bright green	5·00	60
366	**352**	1r. deep dull green	7·00	10
367	**353**	1r.2a. grey	3·00	8·00
368	**354**	1r.8a. reddish purple	18·00	8·00
369	**355**	2r. cerise	4·50	10
370	**356**	5r. brown	28·00	2·25
371	**357**	10r. orange	21·00	4·75
354/71	*Set of 18*		£100	24·00

For stamps as Nos. 366, 369/71 but W **374** see Nos. 413/16.

358 Bodhi Tree　**359** Round Parasol and Bodhi Tree

(Des C. Pakrashi (2a.), R. D'Silva (14a.))

1956 (24 May). Buddha Jayanti. W **69** (sideways on 14a.). P 13×13½ (2a.) or 13½×13 (14a.).

372	**358**	2a. sepia	2·50	10
373	**359**	14a. vermilion	10·00	3·75

360 Lokmanya Bal Gangadhar Tilak　**361** Map of India

1956 (23 July). Birth Centenary of Tilak (journalist). W **69**. P 13×13½.

374	**360**	2a. chestnut	1·00	10

(New Currency. 100 naye paise = 1 rupee)

1957 (1 Apr)–**58**. W **69** (sideways). P 14×14½.

375	**361**	1n.p. blue-green	10	10
376		2n.p. light brown	10	10
377		3n.p. deep brown	10	10
378		5n.p. bright green	5·00	10
379		6n.p. grey	10	10
379*a*		8n.p. light blue-green (7.5.58)	3·50	1·00
380		10n.p. deep dull green	6·00	10
381		13n.p. bright carmine-red	1·25	10
381*a*		15n.p. violet (16.1.58)	4·25	10
382		20n.p. blue	1·00	10
383		25n.p. ultramarine	1·00	10
384		50n.p. orange	8·00	10

385		75n.p. reddish purple	2·75	10
385*a*		90n.p. bright purple (16.1.58)	4·00	1·00
375/85*a*	*Set of 14*		32·00	2·00

The 8, 15 and 90n.p. have their value expressed as "nP".
For similar stamps but W **374** see Nos. 399/412.

362 The Rani of Jhansi　**363** Shrine

1957 (15 Aug). Indian Mutiny Centenary. W **69**. P 14½×14 (15n.p.) or 13×13½ (90n.p.).

386	**362**	15n.p. brown	1·50	10
387	**363**	90n.p. reddish purple	8·00	1·00

364 Henri Dunant and Conference Emblem　**365** "Nutrition"

1957 (28 Oct). 19th International Red Cross Conference, New Delhi. W **69** (sideways). P 13½×13.

388	**364**	15n.p. deep grey and carmine	50	10

1957 (14 Nov). Children's Day. T **365** and similar designs. W **69** (sideways on 90n.p.). P 14×13½ (90n.p.) or 13½×14 (others).

389		8n.p. reddish purple	45	25
390		15n.p. turquoise-green	1·25	10
391		90n.p. orange-brown	1·25	15
389/91	*Set of 3*		2·75	45

Designs: Horiz—15n.p. "Education". Vert—90n.p. "Recreation".

368 Bombay University　**369** Calcutta University

1957 (31 Dec). Centenary of Indian Universities. T **368/9** and similar design. W **69** (sideways on T **368**). P 14×14½ (No. 392) or 13½×14 (others).

392		10n.p. violet	1·75	60
393		10n.p. grey	1·25	60
394		10n.p. light brown	2·00	60
392/4	*Set of 3*		4·50	1·60

Design: Horiz as T **369**—No. 394, Madras University.

371 J. N. Tata (founder) and Steel Plant　**372** Dr. D. K. Karve

1958 (1 Mar). 50th Anniv of Steel Industry. W **69**. P 14½×14.

395	**371**	15n.p. orange-red	10	10

1958 (18 Apr). Birth Centenary of Karve (educationalist). W **69** (sideways). P 14.

396	**372**	15n.p. orange-brown	10	10

373 Westland Wapiti Biplane and Hawker Hunter　**374** Asokan Capital

1958 (30 Apr). Silver Jubilee of Indian Air Force. W **69**. P 14½×14.

397	**373**	15n.p. blue	1·25	25
398		90n.p. ultramarine	3·25	75

1958–63. As Nos. 366, 369/71 and 375/85*a* but W **374**.

399	**361**	1n.p. blue-green (1960)	1·00	1·00
		a. Imperf (pair)	£700	
400		2n.p. light brown (27.10.58)	10	10
401		3n.p. deep brown (1958)	10	10
402		5n.p. bright green (27.10.58)	10	10
403		6n.p. grey (1963)	55	3·25
404		8n.p. light blue-green (1958)	1·00	10
405		10n.p. deep dull green (27.10.58)	15	10
		a. Imperf (pair)	†	£1100

406		13n.p. bright carmine-red (1963)	2·50	3·50
407		15n.p. violet (10.60)	75	10
408		20n.p. blue (27.10.58)	30	10
409		25n.p. ultramarine (27.10.58)	30	10
410		50n.p. orange (1959)	30	10
411		75n.p. reddish purple (1959)	40	10
412		90n.p. bright purple (1960)	5·50	10
413	**352**	1r. deep dull green (1959)	3·75	10
414	**355**	2r. cerise (1959)	9·00	10
415	**356**	5r. brown (1959)	9·00	50
416	**357**	10r. orange (1959)	50·00	14·00
399/416	*Set of 18*		75·00	20·00

The 5, 10, 15, 20, 25 and 50n.p. with serial numbers on the back are from coils of 810 stamps prepared from sheets for experimenting with vending machines. In the event the machines were not purchased and the stamps were sold over the counter.

375 Bipin Chandra Pal　**376** Nurse with Child Patient

1958 (7 Nov). Birth Centenary of Pal (patriot). W **374**. P 14×13½.

418	**375**	15n.p. deep dull green	10	10

1958 (14 Nov). Children's Day. W **374**. P 14×13½.

419	**376**	15n.p. violet	10	10

377 Jagadish Chandra Bose　**378** Exhibition Gate

1958 (30 Nov). Birth Centenary of Bose (botanist). W **374**. P 14×13½.

420	**377**	15n.p. deep turquoise-green	20	10

1958 (30 Dec). India 1958 Exhibition, New Delhi. W **374** (sideways). P 14½×14.

421	**378**	15n.p. reddish purple	10	10

379 Sir Jamsetjee Jejeebhoy　**380** "The Triumph of Labour" (after Chowdhury)

1959 (15 Apr). Death Centenary of Jejeebhoy (philanthropist). W **374**. P 14×13½.

422	**379**	15n.p. brown	10	10

1959 (15 June). 40th Anniv of International Labour Organization. W **374** (sideways). P 14½×14.

423	**380**	15n.p. dull green	10	10

381 Boys awaiting admission to Children's Home　**382** "Agriculture"

1959 (14 Nov). Children's Day. W **374**. P 14×14½.

424	**381**	15n.p. deep dull green	10	10
		a. Imperf (pair)	£2500	

1959 (30 Dec). First World Agricultural Fair, New Delhi. W **374**. P 13½×13.

425	**382**	15n.p. grey	30	10

383 Thiruvalluvar (philosopher)

1960 (15 Feb). Thiruvalluvar Commemoration. W **374**. P 14×13½.

426	**383**	15n.p. reddish purple	10	10

384 Yaksha pleading with the Cloud (from the *Meghaduta*)

385 Shakuntala writing a letter to Dushyanta (from the *Shakuntala*)

1960 (22 June). Kalidasa (poet) Commemoration. W **374**. P 13.
427   **384**   15n.p. grey............................ 75   10
428   **385**   1r.3n.p. pale yellow and brown .... 4·00   1·50

386 S. Bharati (poet)   **387** Dr. M. Visvesvaraya

1960 (11 Sept). Subramania Bharati Commemoration. W **374**. P 14×13½.
429   **386**   15n.p. blue............................ 10   10

1960 (15 Sept). Birth Centenary of Dr. M. Visvesvaraya (engineer). W **374**. P 13×13½.
430   **387**   15n.p. brown and bright carmine 10   10

388 "Children's Health"

1960 (14 Nov). Children's Day. W **374**. P 13½×13.
431   **388**   15n.p. deep dull green 10   10

389 Children greeting UN Emblem   **390** Tyagaraja

1960 (11 Dec). UNICEF Day. W **374**. P 13½×13.
432   **389**   15n.p. orange-brown and olive-brn 10   10

1961 (6 Jan). 114th Death Anniv of Tyagaraja (musician). W **374**. P 14×13½.
433   **390**   15n.p. greenish blue........................... 10   10

391 "First Aerial Post" cancellation

392 Air India Boeing 707 Airliner and Humber Sommer Biplane

1961 (18 Feb). 50th Anniv of First Official Airmail Flight, Allahabad-Naini. T **391/2** and similar design. W **374**. P 14 (5n.p) or 13×13½ (others).
434   5n.p. olive-drab............................ 3·00   30
435   15n.p. deep green and grey .... 1·10   30
436   1r. purple and grey .... 4·25   1·75
434/6 *Set of 3* .... 7·50   2·10
   Design: Horiz as T **392**—1r. H. Pecquet flying Humber Sommer plane and "Aerial Post" cancellation.

---

394 Shivaji on horseback   **395** Motilal Nehru (politician)

1961 (17 Apr). Chatrapati Shivaji (Maratha ruler) Commemoration. W **374**. P 13×13½.
437   **394**   15n.p. brown and green........................... 80   40

1961 (6 May). Birth Centenary of Pandit Motilal Nehru. W **374**. P 14.
438   **395**   15n.p. olive-brown and brown-orge.... 30   10

396 Tagore (poet)   **397** All India Radio Emblem and Transmitting Aerials

1961 (7 May). Birth Centenary of Rabindranath Tagore. W **374**. P 13×13½.
439   **396**   15n.p. yellow-orange and blue-grn...... 1·50   40

1961 (8 June). Silver Jubilee of All India Radio. W **374**. P 13½×13.
440   **397**   15n.p. ultramarine................................. 10   10

398 Prafulla Chandra Ray   **399** V. N. Bhatkande

1961 (2 Aug). Birth Centenary of Ray (social reformer). W **374**. P 14×13½.
441   **398**   15n.p. grey........................ 10   20

1961 (1 Sept). Birth Centenary of Bhatkande (composer) (1960). W **374**. P 13×13½.
442   **399**   15n.p. olive-brown.......................... 10   10

400 Child at Lathe   **401** Fair Emblem and Main Gate

1961 (14 Nov). Children's Day. W **374**. P 14×13½.
443   **400**   15n.p. brown 10   20

1961 (14 Nov). Indian Industries Fair, New Delhi. W **374**. P 14×14½.
444   **401**   15n.p. blue and carmine......................... 10   10

402 Indian Forest

1961 (21 Nov). Centenary of Scientific Forestry. W **374**. P 13×13½.
445   **402**   15n.p. green and brown.......................... 40   30

403 Pitalkhora: Yaksha   **404** Kalibangan Seal

1961 (14 Dec). Centenary of Indian Archaeological Survey. W **374**. P 14×13½ (15 n.p.) or 13½×14 (90n.p.).
446   **403**   15n.p. orange-brown .... 1·00   10
447   **404**   90n.p. yellow-olive and light brown..... 4·75   30

405 M. M. Malaviya   **406** Gauhati Refinery

1961 (24 Dec). Birth Centenary of Malaviya (educationist). W **374**. P 14×13½.
448   **405**   15n.p. deep slate............................ 10   20

1962 (1 Jan). Inauguration of Gauhati Oil Refinery. W **374**. P 13×13½.
449   **406**   15n.p. blue........................ 1·00   20

407 Bhikaiji Cama   **408** Village Panchayati and Parliament Building

1962 (26 Jan). Birth Centenary of Bhikaiji Cama (patriot). W **374**. P 14.
450   **407**   15n.p. reddish purple......................... 10   10

1962 (26 Jan). Inauguration of Panchayati System of Local Government. W **374**. P 13×13½.
451   **408**   15n.p. bright purple........................... 10   10

409 D. Saraswati (religious reformer)   **410** G. S. Vidhyarthi (journalist)

1962 (4 Mar). Dayanard Saraswati Commemoration. W **374**. P 14.
452   **409**   15n.p. orange-brown 10   10

1962 (25 Mar). Ganesh Shankar Vidhyarthi Commemoration. W **374**. P 14×13½.
453   **410**   15n.p. red-brown 10   10

411 Malaria Eradication Emblem   **412** Dr. R. Prasad

1962 (7 Apr). Malaria Eradication. W **374**. P 13×13½.
454   **411**   15n.p. yellow and claret.......................... 10   10

1962 (13 May). Retirement of President Dr. Rajendra Prasad. W **374**. P 13.
455   **412**   15n.p. bright purple (*shades*) 30   20

413 Calcutta High Court   **416** Ramabai Ranade

1962. Centenary of Indian High Courts. T **413** and similar horiz designs. W **374**. P 14.
456   15n.p. dull green (1.7)............................ 50   20
457   15n.p. red-brown (6.8)............................ 50   20
458   15n.p. slate (14.8)............................ 50   20
456/8 *Set of 3* .... 1·40   55
   Designs:—No. 457, Madras High Court; No. 458, Bombay High Court.

1962 (15 Aug). Birth Centenary of Ramabai Ranade (social reformer). W **374**. P 14×13½
459   **416**   15n.p. orange-brown 10   30

417 Indian Rhinoceros

418 "Passing the Flag to Youth"

1962 (1 Oct). Wild Life Week. W **374**. P 13½×14.
460   **417** 15n.p. red-brown and dp turquoise   55   15

INSCRIPTIONS. From No. 461 onwards all designs except No. 463 are inscribed "BHARAT" in Devanagari in addition to "INDIA" in English.

1962 (14 Nov). Children's Day. W **374**. P 13½×13.
461   **418** 15n.p. orange-red and turquoise-grn..   15   20

419 Human Eye within Lotus Blossom

420 S. Ramanujan

1962 (3 Dec). 19th International Ophthalmology Congress, New Delhi. W **374**. P 13½×13.
462   **419** 15n.p. deep olive-brown   45   10

1962 (22 Dec). 75th Birth Anniv of Srinivasa Ramanujan (mathematician). W **374**. P 13½×14.
463   **420** 15n.p. deep olive-brown   70   40

421 S. Vivekananda   **(422)**

1963 (17 Jan). Birth Centenary of Vivekananda (philosopher). W **374**. P 14×14½.
464   **421** 15n.p. orange-brown and yell-olive .....   1·25   20

1963 (2 Feb). No. 428 surch with T **422**.
465   **385** 1r. on 1r.3n.p. pale yellow and brn   8·50   10

423 Hands reaching for FAO Emblem

424 Henri Dunant (founder) and Centenary Emblem

1963 (21 Mar). Freedom from Hunger. W **374**. P 13.
466   **423** 15n.p. grey-blue ....   3·00   30

1963 (8 May). Red Cross Centenary. W **374**. P 13.
467   **424** 15n.p. red and grey ....   3·00   40
    a. Red (cross) omitted £25000

425 Artillery and Helicopter

1963 (15 Aug). Defence Campaign. T **425** and similar horiz design. W **374**. P 14.
468   15n.p. grey-green ....   1·50   10
469   1r. red-brown ....   5·50   65
    Design:—1r. Sentry and parachutists.

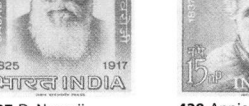

427 D. Naoroji (parliamentarian)

428 Annie Besant (patriot and theosophist)

1963 (4 Sept). Dadabhai Naoroji Commemoration. W **374**. P 13.
470   **427** 15n.p. grey   10   10

1963 (1 Oct). Annie Besant Commemoration. W **374**. P 13½×14.
471   **428** 15n.p. turquoise-green   15   10
    No. 471 is incorrectly dated "1837". Mrs. Besant was born in 1847.

429 Gaur

430 Lesser Panda

1963 (7 Oct). Wild Life Preservation. T **429/30** and similar designs. W **374**. P 13½×14 (10n.p.) or 13 (others).
472   10n.p. black and yellow-orange ....   2·25   1·50
473   15n.p. orange-brown and green ....   2·00   60
474   30n.p. slate and yellow-ochre ....   3·00   1·50
475   50n.p. orange and deep grey-green ....   3·75   80
476   1r. light brown and blue ....   4·50   50
472/6 *Set of 5* ....   14·00   4·50
    Designs: Vert—30n.p. Indian Elephant. Horiz (as T **430**) 50n.p. Tiger; 1r. Lion.

434 "School Meals"

435 Eleanor Roosevelt at Spinning-wheel

1963 (14 Nov). Children's Day. W **374**. P 14×13½.
477   **434** 15n.p. bistre-brown   10   10

1963 (10 Dec). 15th Anniv of Declaration of Human Rights. W **374**. P 13½×13.
478   **435** 15n.p. reddish purple   10   15

436 Dipalakshmi (bronze)

437 Gopabandhu Das (social reformer)

1964 (4 Jan). 26th International Orientalists Congress, New Delhi. W **374**. P 13×13½.
479   **436** 15n.p. deep ultramarine   20   15

1964 (4 Jan). Gopabandhu Das Commemoration. W **374**. P 13×13½.
480   **437** 15n.p. deep dull purple   10   10

438 Purandaradasa

1964 (14 Jan). 400th Death Anniv of Purandaradasa (composer). W **374**. P 13×13½.
481   **438** 15n.p. light brown   15   10

439 S. C. Bose and I N A Badge

440 Bose and Indian National Army

1964 (23 Jan). 67th Birth Anniv of Subhas Chandra Bose (nationalist). W **374**. P 13.
482   **439** 15n.p. yellow-bistre   50   20
483   **440** 55n.p. black, orange and orge-red ....   1·75   45

441 Sarojini Naidu

442 Kasturba Gandhi

1964 (13 Feb). 85th Birth Anniv of Sarojini Naidu (poetess). W **374**. P 14.
484   **441** 15n.p. deep grey-green and purple   10   10

1964 (22 Feb). 20th Death Anniv of Kasturba Gandhi. W **374**. P 14×13½.
485   **442** 15n.p. orange-brown   10   10

443 Dr. W. M. Haffkine (immunologist)

444 Jawaharlal Nehru (statesman)

1964 (16 Mar). Haffkine Commemoration. W **374**. P 13.
486   **443** 15n.p. deep purple-brown/*buff* ....   1·25   10

(Value expressed as paisa instead of naye paise.)

1964 (12 June). Nehru Mourning Issue. No wmk. P 13½×13.
487   **444** 15p. deep slate   40   10

445 Sir Asutosh Mookerjee

446 Sri Aurobindo

1964 (29 June). Birth Centenary of Sir Asutosh Mookerjee (education reformer). W **374**. P 13½×13.
488   **445** 15p. bistre-brown and yellow-olive   10   10

1964 (15 Aug). 92nd Birth Anniv of Sri Aurobindo (religious teacher). W **374**. P 13×13½.
489   **446** 15p. dull purple   20   10

447 Raja R. Roy (social reformer)

448 ISO Emblem and Globe

1964 (27 Sept). Raja Rammohun Roy Commemoration. W **374**. P 13×13½.
490   **447** 15n.p. brown   10   10

1964 (9 Nov). Sixth International Organization for Standardization General Assembly, Bombay. No wmk. P 13×13½.
491   **448** 15p. carmine   15   20

449 Jawaharlal Nehru (from 1r. commemorative coin)

450 St. Thomas (after statue, Ortona Cathedral, Italy)

1964 (14 Nov). Children's Day. No wmk. P 14×13½.
492   **449** 15p. slate   10   10

1964 (2 Dec). St. Thomas Commemoration. No wmk. P 14×13½.
493   **450** 15p. reddish purple   10   30
    No. 493 was issued on the occasion of Pope Paul's visit to India.

451 Globe

452 J. Tata (industrialist)

1964 (14 Dec). 22nd International Geological Congress. W **374**. P 14×13½.
494   **451** 15p. blue-green   40   30

1965 (7 Jan). Jamsetji Tata Commemoration. No wmk. P 13½×13.
495   **452** 15p. dull purple and orange   30   20

453 Lala Lajpat Rai

454 Globe and Congress Emblem

1965 (28 Jan). Birth Centenary of Lala Lajpat Rai (social reformer). No wmk. P 13×13½.
496   **453**   15p. light brown................................ 20   10

1965 (8 Feb). 20th International Chamber of Commerce Congress, New Delhi. No wmk. P 13½×13.
497   **454**   15p. grey-green and carmine............ 15   15

455 Freighter *Jalausha* and Visakhapatnam

456 Abraham Lincoln

1965 (5 Apr). National Maritime Day. W **374** (sideways). P 14½×14.
498   **455**   15p. blue.. 50   30

1965 (15 Apr). Death Centenary of Abraham Lincoln. W **374**. P 13.
499   **456**   15p. brown and yellow-ochre............ 15   10

457 ITU Emblem and Symbols

458 "Everlasting Flame"

1965 (17 May). ITU Centenary. W **374** (sideways). P 14½×14.
500   **457**   15p. reddish purple......................... 1·00   30

1965 (27 May). First Anniv of Nehru's Death. W **374**. P 13.
501   **458**   15p. carmine and blue..................... 15   10

459 ICY Emblem

460 Climbers on Summit

1965 (26 June). International Co-operation Year. P 13½×13.
502   **459**   15p. deep olive and yellow-brown.... 1·25   1·25

1965 (15 Aug). Indian Mount Everest Expedition. P 13.
503   **460**   15p. deep reddish purple 45   20

461 Bidri Vase   **462** Brass Lamp   **463** Coffee berries

464 "Family Planning"   **465** Konarak Elephant   **465a** Spotted Deer ("Chital")

466 Electric Locomotive   **467** Plucking Tea   **468** Hindustan Aircraft Industries Ajeet jet fighter

469 Indian dolls

470 Calcutta GPO

471 Mangoes

474 Woman writing a Letter (medieval sculpture)

472 Somnath Temple   **473** Hampi Chariot (sculpture)

475 Dal Lake, Kashmir

476 Bhakra Dam, Punjab

477 Atomic reactor, Trombay

1965–75. T **461/77.**
(a) W **374** (sideways on 2, 3, 5, 6, 8, 30, 50, 60p., 2, 5, 10r.).
P 14×14½ (4, 10, 15, 20, 40, 70p., 1r.) or 14½×14 (others)

504	**461**	2p. red-brown (16.10.67)	10	1·00
505	**462**	3p. brown-olive (16.10.67)	1·00	4·00
505a	**463**	4p. lake-brown (15.5.68)	10	3·75
506	**464**	5p. cerise (16.10.67)	10	10
		a. Imperf (pair)	£180	
507	**465**	6p. grey-black (1.7.66)................	30	4·25
508	**465a**	8p. red-brown (15.3.67)...............	40	4·25
509	**466**	10p. new blue (1.7.66)..................	60	10
510	**467**	15p. bronze-green (15.8.65).........	8·00	10
511	**468**	20p. purple (16.10.67)	6·00	
512	**469**	30p. sepia (15.3.67).....................	20	10
513	**470**	40p. maroon (2.10.68)	20	10
514	**471**	50p. blue-green (15.3.67).............	20	10
515	**472**	60p. deep grey (16.10.67)............	45	20
516	**473**	70p. chalky blue (15.3.67)...........	60	10
517	**474**	1r. red-brown and plum (1.7.66)	60	10
518	**475**	2r. new blue and deep slate-violet (15.3.67).......................	2·00	10
		w. Wmk capitals to right*...........	—	75·00
519	**476**	5r. deep slate-violet and brown (15.3.67)................................	3·00	90
520	**477**	10r. black and bronze-green (14.11.65).............................	32·00	80
504/20 Set of 18			50·00	17·00

(b) No wmk. P 14½×14

520a	**464**	5p. cerise (12.5.74).......................	2·25	10

(c) Wmk Large Star and "INDIA GOVT"† in sheet. P 14½×14

521	**461**	2p. red-brown (1.3.75)	2·00	2·25
		aw. Wmk reversed..........................	4·25	
521b	**464**	5p. cerise (1.3.75)..........................	2·25	10

*The normal sideways watermark shows the heads of the capital to the left, *as seen from the back of the stamp.*

†The arrangement of this watermark in the sheet results in the words and the star appearing upright, inverted or sideways.

Two different postal forgeries exist of No. 511, both printed in lithography and without watermark. The cruder version is roughly perforated 15, but the more sophisticated is perforated 14×14½.

479 G. B. Pant (statesman)   **480** V. Patel

1965 (10 Sept). Govind Ballabh Pant Commemoration. P 13.
522   **479**   15p. brown and deep green................ 10   20

1965 (31 Oct). 90th Birth Anniv of Vallabhbhai Patel (statesman). P 14×13½.
523   **480**   15p. blackish brown.......................... 10   30

481 C. Das   **482** Vidyapati (poet)

1965 (5 Nov). 95th Birth Anniv of Chittaranjan Das (lawyer and patriot). P 13.
524   **481**   15p. yellow-brown........................... 10   10

1965 (17 Nov). Vidyapati Commemoration. P 14×14½.
525   **482**   15p. yellow-brown........................... 10   10

483 Sikandra, Agra   **484** Soldier, Hindustan Aircraft Industries Ajeet jet fighters and Cruiser *Mysore*

1966 (24 Jan). Pacific Area Travel Association Conference, New Delhi. P 13½×14.
526   **483**   15p. slate 10   10

1966 (26 Jan). Indian Armed Forces. P 14
527   **484**   15p. violet .... 1·75   75

485 Lal Bahadur Shastri (statesman)   **486** Kambar (poet)

1966 (26 Jan). Shastri Mourning Issue. P 13×13½.
528   **485**   15p. black 80   10

1966 (5 Apr). Kambar Commemoration. P 14×14½.
529   **486**   15p. grey-green 10   10

487 B. R. Ambedkar   **488** Kunwar Singh (patriot)

1966 (14 Apr). 75th Birth Anniv of Dr. Bhim Rao Ambedkar (lawyer). P 14×13½.
530   **487**   15p. purple-brown............................. 10   10

1966 (23 Apr). Kunwar Singh Commemoration. P 14×13½.
531   **488**   15p. chestnut................................... 10   10

489 G. K. Gokhale   **490** Acharya Dvivedi (poet)

1966 (9 May). Birth Centenary of Gopal Krishna Gokhale (patriot). P 13½×13.
532   **489**   15p. brown-purple and pale yellow .. 10   10

1966 (15 May). Dvivedi Commemoration. P 13½×14.
533   **490**   15p. drab... 10   10

491 Maharaja Ranjit Singh (warrior)   **492** Homi Bhabha (scientist) and Nuclear Reactor

1966 (28 June). Maharaja Ranjit Singh Commemoration. P 14×13½.
534   **491**   15p. purple...................................... 60   10

1966 (4 Aug). Dr. Homi Bhabha Commemoration. P 14½×14.
535   **492**   15p. dull purple 15   30

493 A. K. Azad (scholar)   **494** Swami Tirtha

1966 (11 Nov). Abul Kalam Azad Commemoration. P 13½×14.
536   **493**   15p. chalky blue   15   15

1966 (11 Nov). 60th Death Anniv of Swami Rama Tirtha (social reformer). P 13×13½.
537   **494**   15p. turquoise-blue..........................   30   30

495 Infant and Dove Emblem   **496** Allahabad High Court

(Des C. Pakrashi)

1966 (14 Nov). Children's Day. P 13×13½.
538   **495**   15p. bright purple   60   20

1966 (25 Nov). Centenary of Allahabad High Court. P 14½×14.
539   **496**   15p. dull purple   70   30

497 Indian Family   **498** Hockey Game

1966 (12 Dec). Family Planning. P 13.
540   **497**   15p. brown   15   15

1966 (31 Dec). India's Hockey Victory in Fifth Asian Games. P 13.
541   **498**   15p. new blue..........................   1·25   60

499 "Jai Kisan"   **500** Voter and Polling Booth

1967 (11 Jan). First Anniv of Shastri's Death. P 13½×14.
542   **499**   15p. yellow-green   30   30

1967 (13 Jan). Indian General Election. P 13½×14.
543   **500**   15p. red-brown   15   15

501 Gurudwara Shrine, Patna   **502** Taj Mahal, Agra

1967 (17 Jan). 300th Birth Anniv (1966) of Guru Gobind Singh (Sikh religious leader). P 14×13½.
544   **501**   15p. bluish violet.....................   1·25   15

1967 (19 Mar). International Tourist Year. P 14½×14.
545   **502**   15p. bistre-brown and orange............   30   15

503 Nandalal Bose and "Garuda"   **504** Survey Emblem and Activities

1967 (16 Apr). First Death Anniv of Nandalal Bose (painter). P 14×13½.
546   **503**   15p. bistre-brown   15   15

1967 (1 May). Survey of India Bicentenary. P 13½×13.
547   **504**   15p. reddish lilac ....   1·00   40

505 Basaveswara   **506** Narsinha Mehta (poet)

1967 (11 May). 800th Death Anniv of Basaveswara (reformer and statesman). P 13½×14.
548   **505**   15p. orange-red........................   15   15

1967 (30 May). Narsinha Mehta Commemoration. P 14×13½.
549   **506**   15p. blackish brown................   15   15

507 Maharana Pratap   **508** Narayana Guru

1967 (11 June). Maharana Pratap (Rajput leader) Commemoration. P 14×14½.
550   **507**   15p. red-brown   20   15

1967 (21 Aug). Narayana Guru (philosopher) Commemoration. P 14.
551   **508**   15p. brown   30   20

509 President Radhakrishnan   **510** Martyrs' Memorial, Patna

1967 (5 Sept). 75th Birth Anniv of Sarvepalli Radhakrishnan (former President). P 13.
552   **509**   15p. claret   50   15

1967 (1 Oct). 25th Anniv of "Quit India" Movement. P 14½×14.
553   **510**   15p. lake   15   15

511 Route Map   **512** Wrestling

1967 (9 Nov). Centenary of Indo-European Telegraph Service. P 13½×14.
554   **511**   15p. black and light blue   70   20

1967 (12 Nov). World Wrestling Championships, New Delhi. P 13½×14.
555   **512**   15p. purple and lt orange-brown......   50   20

513 Nehru leading Naga Tribesmen   **514** Rashbehari Basu (nationalist)

1967 (1 Dec). Fourth Anniv of Nagaland as a State of India. P 13½×13½.
556   **513**   15p. ultramarine.....................   15   15

1967 (26 Dec). Rashbehari Basu Commemoration. P 14.
557   **514**   15p. maroon   15   20

515 Bugle, Badge and Scout Salute

1967 (27 Dec). 60th Anniv of Scout Movement in India. P 14½×14.
558   **515**   15p. chestnut........................   1·00   1·00

516 Men embracing Universe   **517** Globe and Book of Tamil

1968 (1 Jan). Human Rights Year. P 13.
559   **516**   15p. bronze-green   50   30

1968 (3 Jan). International Conference-Seminar of Tamil Studies, Madras. P 13.
560   **517**   15p. reddish lilac   60   15

 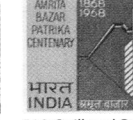

518 UN Emblem and Transport   **519** Quill and Bow Symbol

1968 (1 Feb). United Nations Conference on Trade and Development, New Delhi. P 14½×14.
561   **518**   15p. turquoise-blue..................   60   15

1968 (20 Feb). Centenary of *Amrita Bazar Patrika* (newspaper). P 13½×14.
562   **519**   15p. sepia and orange-yellow............   15   15

520 Maxim Gorky   **521** Emblem and Medal

1968 (28 Mar). Birth Centenary of Maxim Gorky. P 13½.
563   **520**   15p. plum..............................   15   50

1968 (31 Mar). First Triennale Art Exhibition, New Delhi. P 13.
564   **521**   15p. orange, royal blue and light blue..............   30   20
                  a. Orange omitted £10000

522 Letter-box and "100,000"   **523** Stalks of Wheat, Agricultural Institute and Production Graph

(Des C. Pakrashi)

1968 (1 July). Opening of 100,000th Indian Post Office. P 13.
565   **522**   20p. red, blue and black.........   40   15

1968 (17 July). Wheat Revolution. P 13.
566   **523**   20p. bluish green and orange-brn....   30   15

524 *Self-portrait*   **525** Lakshminath Bezbaruah

(Des from self-portrait)

1968 (17 Sept). 30th Death Anniv of Gaganendranath Tagore (painter). P 13.
567   **524**   20p. brown-purple and ochre............   50   15

1968 (5 Oct). Birth Centenary of Lakshminath Bezbaruah (writer). P 13½×14.
568   **525**   20p. blackish brown................   30   15

526 Athlete's Legs and Olympic Rings

1968 (12 Oct). Olympic Games, Mexico. P 14½×14.
569	**526**	20p. brown and grey	15	15
570		1r. sepia and brown-olive	85	15

527 Bhagat Singh and Followers

528 Azad Hind Flag, Swords and Chandra Bose (founder)

1968 (19 Oct). 61st Birth Anniv of Bhagat Singh (patriot). P 13.
571	**527**	20p. yellow-brown	1·00	1·00

1968 (21 Oct). 25th Anniv of Azad Hind Government. P 14×14½.
572	**528**	20p. deep blue	1·25	15

529 Sister Nivedita

530 Marie Curie and Radium Treatment

1968 (27 Oct). Birth Centenary of Sister Nivedita (social reformer). P 14×14½.
573	**529**	20p. deep bluish green	30	30

1968 (6 Nov). Birth Centenary of Marie Curie. P 14½×14.
574	**530**	20p. slate-lilac	1·40	1·25

531 Map of the World

532 Cochin Synagogue

1968 (1 Dec). 21st International Geographical Congress, New Delhi. P 13.
575	**531**	20p. new blue	15	15

1968 (15 Dec). 400th Anniv of Cochin Synagogue. P 13.
576	**532**	20p. blue and carmine	1·00	40

533 INS *Nilgiri* (frigate)

534 Red-billed Blue Magpie

1968 (15 Dec). Navy Day. P 13.
577	**533**	20p. grey-blue	1·75	40

1968 (31 Dec). Birds. T **534** and similar designs. P 14×14½ (1r.) or 14½×14 (others).
578	20p. multicoloured	1·50	50
579	50p. scarlet, black and turquoise-green	1·50	1·50
580	1r. dp blue, yellow-brown and pale bl	2·75	1·00
581	2r. multicoloured	2·25	2·50
578/81	*Set of 4*	7·25	5·00

Designs: Horiz—50p. Brown-fronted Pied Woodpecker; 2r. Yellow-backed Sunbird. Vert—1r. Slaty-headed Scimitar Babbler.

538 Bankim Chandra Chatterjee

539 Dr. Bhagavan Das

540 Dr. Martin Luther King

541 Mirza Ghalib and Letter Seal

1969 (1 Jan). 130th Birth Anniv of Bankim Chandra Chatterjee (writer). P 13½.
582	**538**	20p. ultramarine	15	20

1969 (12 Jan). Birth Centenary of Dr. Bhagavan Das (philosopher). P 13½.
583	**539**	20p. pale chocolate	15	50

1969 (25 Jan). Martin Luther King Commemoration. P 13½.
584	**540**	20p. deep olive-brown	60	20

1969 (17 Feb). Death Centenary of Mirza Ghalib (poet). P 14½×14.
585	**541**	20p. sepia, brown-red and flesh	15	15

542 Osmania University

1969 (15 Mar). 50th Anniv of Osmania University. P 14½×14.
586	**542**	20p. olive-green	15	20

543 Rafi Ahmed Kidwai and Lockheed Constellation Mail Plane

1969 (1 Apr). 20th Anniv of "ALL-UP" Air Mail Scheme. P 13.
587	**543**	20p. deep blue	1·50	30

544 ILO Badge and Emblem

545 Memorial, and Hands dropping Flowers

1969 (11 Apr). 50th Anniv of International Labour Organisation. P 14½×14.
588	**544**	20p. chestnut	15	20

1969 (13 Apr). 50th Anniv of Jallianwala Bagh Massacre, Amritsar. P 14×13½.
589	**545**	20p. rose-carmine	15	20

546 K. Nageswara Rao Pantulu (journalist)

547 Ardaseer Cursetjee Wadia, and Ships

1969 (1 May). Kasinadhuni Nageswara Rao Pantulu Commemoration. P 13½×14.
590	**546**	20p. brown	15	20

1969 (27 May). Ardaseer Cursetjee Wadia (ship-builder) Commemoration. P 14½×14.
591	**547**	20p. turquoise-green	1·00	75

548 Serampore College

549 Dr. Zakir Husain

1969 (7 June). 150th Anniv of Serampore College. P 13½.
592	**548**	20p. plum	15	20

1969 (11 June). President Dr. Zakir Husain Commemoration. P 13.
593	**549**	20p. sepia	15	20

550 Laxmanrao Kirloskar

1969 (20 June). Birth Centenary of Laxmanrao Kirloskar (agriculturalist). P 13.
594	**550**	20p. grey-black	15	15

551 Gandhi and his Wife

552 Gandhi's Head and Shoulders

553 Gandhi walking (woodcut)

554 Gandhi with Charkha

(Des Suraj Sadan (20p.), P. Chitnis (75p.), Indian Security Press (1r.) and C. Pakrashi (5r.))

1969 (2 Oct). Birth Centenary of Mahatma Gandhi. P 13½×14 (20p), 14×14½ (1r.) or 13 (others).
595	**551**	20p. blackish brown	80	40
596	**552**	75p. cinnamon and drab	2·00	3·00
597	**553**	1r. blue	2·00	65
598	**554**	5r. greyish brown and red-orge	5·00	6·50
595/8	*Set of 4*		8·75	9·50

555 *Ajanta* (bulk carrier) and IMCO Emblem

1969 (14 Oct). Tenth Anniv of Inter-Governmental Maritime Consultative Organization. P 13.
599	**555**	20p. violet-blue	1·75	40

556 Outline of Parliament Building and Globe

557 Astronaut walking beside Space Module on Moon

1969 (30 Oct). 57th Inter-Parliamentary Conference, New Delhi. P 14½×14.
600	**556**	20p. new blue	15	20

1969 (19 Nov). First Man on the Moon. P 14×14½.
601	**557**	20p. olive-brown	60	30

558 Gurudwara Nankana Sahib (birthplace)

559 Tiger's Head and Hands holding Globe

1969 (23 Nov). 500th Birth Anniv of Guru Nanak Dev (Sikh religious leader). P 13½.
602	**559**	20p. slate-violet	30	20

1969 (24 Nov). International Union for the Conservation of Nature and Natural Resources Conference, New Delhi. P 14½×14.
603	**559**	20p. orange-brown and bronze-green	1·00	45

560 Sadhu Vaswani **561** Thakkar Bapa

1969 (25 Nov). 90th Birth Anniv of Sadhu Vaswani (educationist). P 14×14½.
604 **560** 20p. grey 15 15

1969 (29 Nov). Birth Centenary of Thakkar Bapa (humanitarian). P 13½.
605 **561** 20p. chocolate 15 20

562 Satellite, Television, Telephone and Globe **563** C. N. Annadurai

1970 (21 Jan). 12th Plenary Assembly of International Radio Consultative Committee. P 13.
606 **562** 20p. Prussian blue 40 20

1970 (3 Feb). First Death Anniv of Conjeevaram Natrajan Annadurai (statesman). P 13.
607 **563** 20p. reddish purple and royal blue... 30 15

564 M. N. Kishore **565** Nalanda College

1970 (19 Feb). 75th Death Anniv of Munshi Newal Kishore (publisher). P 13.
608 **564** 20p. lake 15 20

1970 (27 Mar). Centenary of Nalanda College. P 14½×14.
609 **565** 20p. brown 60 50

566 Swami Shraddhanand (social reformer) **567** Lenin

1970 (30 Mar). Swami Shraddhanand Commemoration. P 14×13½.
610 **566** 20p. yellow-brown 75 60

1970 (22 Apr). Birth Centenary of Lenin. P 13.
611 **567** 20p. orange-brown and sepia 40 20

568 New UPU HQ Building **569** Sher Shah Suri (15th-century ruler)

1970 (20 May). New UPU Headquarters Building, Berne. P 13.
612 **568** 20p. emerald, grey and black 15 20

1970 (22 May). Sher Shah Suri Commemoration. P 13.
613 **569** 20p. deep bluish green 30 70

570 V. D. Savarkar and Cellular Jail, Andaman Islands **571** "UN" and Globe

1970 (28 May). Vinayak Damodar Savarkar (patriot) Commemoration. P 13.
614 **570** 20p. orange-brown 65 30

1970 (26 June). 25th Anniv of United Nations. P 13.
615 **571** 20p. light new blue 40 20

572 Symbol and Workers

1970 (18 Aug). Asian Productivity Year. P 14½×14.
616 **572** 20p. violet 20 20

573 Dr. Montessori and IEY Emblem

1970 (31 Aug). Birth Centenary of Dr. Maria Montessori (educationist). P 13.
617 **573** 20p. dull purple 30 30

574 J. N. Mukherjee (revolutionary) and Horse **575** V. S. Srinivasa Sastri

1970 (9 Sept). Jatindra Nath Mukherjee Commemoration. P 14½×14.
618 **574** 20p. chocolate .... 1·50 30

1970 (22 Sept). Srinivasa Sastri (educationalist) Commemoration. P 13×13½.
619 **575** 20p. yellow and brown-purple 30 30

576 I. C. Vidyasagar **577** Maharishi Valmiki

1970 (26 Sept). 150th Birth Anniv of Iswar Chandra Vidyasagar (educationalist). P 13.
620 **576** 20p. brown and purple 40 30

1970 (14 Oct). Maharishi Valmiki (ancient author) Commemoration. P 13.
621 **577** 20p. purple 70 30

578 Calcutta Port **579** University Building

1970 (17 Oct). Centenary of Calcutta Port Trust. P 13½×13.
622 **578** 20p. greenish blue .... 1·50 70

1970 (29 Oct). 50th Anniv of Jamia Millia Islamia University. P 14½×14.
623 **579** 20p. yellow-green 70 50

580 Jamnalal Bajaj **581** Nurse and Patient

1970 (4 Nov). Jamnalal Bajaj (industrialist) Commemoration. W **374**. P 13½×13.
624 **580** 20p. olive-grey 15 30

1970 (5 Nov). 50th Anniv of Indian Red Cross. W **374** (sideways). P 13×13½.
625 **581** 20p. red and greenish blue .... 1·00 40

582 Sant Namdeo **583** Beethoven

1970 (9 Nov). 700th Birth Anniv of Sant Namdeo (mystic). W **374**. P 13.
626 **582** 20p. orange 15 30

1970 (16 Dec). Birth Bicentenary of Beethoven. P 13.
627 **583** 20p. orange and greyish black .... 2·50 70

584 Children examining Stamps **585** Girl Guide

1970 (23 Dec). Indian National Philatelic Exhibition, New Delhi. T **584** and similar horiz design. P 13.
628 20p. orange and myrtle-green 50 10
629 1r. orange-brown and pale yell-brn .... 5·50 1·00
Design:—1r. Gandhi commemorative through magnifier.

1970 (27 Dec). Diamond Jubilee of Girl Guide Movement in India. P 13.
630 **585** 20p. maroon 60 30

STAMP BOOKLETS

1904. Black on green (No. SB1) or black on pink (No. SB2) covers. Stapled.
SB1 12¼a. booklet containing 24×½a. (No. 121) in blocks of 6 .... £2000
SB2 12¼a. booklet containing 12×1a. (No. 123) in blocks of 6 .... £2000

1906–11. Black on green (No. SB3), black on pink (No. SB4) or black on green and pink (No. SB5) match book type covers inscr "Post Office of India" and royal cypher of King Edward VII. Stapled.
SB3 1r. booklet containing 32×½a. (No. 149) in blocks of 4 .... £1200
a. Without "Post Office of India" inscr £1100
b. Ditto and showing royal cypher of King George V (1911) £1000
SB4 1r. booklet containing 16×1a. (No. 150) in blocks of 4 (1907) £1100
a. Without "Post Office of India" inscr £1000
b. Ditto and showing royal cypher of King George V (1911) £1100
SB5 1r. booklet containing 16×½a. and 8×1a. (Nos. 149/50) in blocks of 4 (1907) £2250
a. Without "Post Office of India" inscr £1900
b. Ditto and showing royal cypher of King George V (1911) £2000

1912–22. Black on green (Nos. SB6/7, SB12), black on pink (No. SB8), black on green and pink (No. SB9), black on purple (No. SB10) or black on blue (No. SB11) match book type covers with foreign postage rates on back. Stapled.
SB6 1r. booklet containing 64×3p. (No. 152) in blocks of 4 (blank back cover) £1600
SB7 1r. booklet containing 32×½a. (No. 155) in blocks of 4 .... £500
a. Blank back cover £500
b. Advertisement contractor's notice on back cover £700
c. Advertisement on back (1922) £700
SB8 1r. booklet containing 16×1a. (No. 159) in blocks of 4 .... £400
a. Blank back cover £400
b. Advertisements on front flap and back cover (1922) £500
SB9 1r. booklet containing 16×½a. and 8×1a. (Nos. 155, 159) in blocks of 4 (blank back cover) £350
a. Advertisement on back £400
b. Foreign postage rates on back £375

SB10	1r.8a. booklet containing 16×1½a. (No. 163) in blocks of 4 (1919)	£800
	a. Blank back cover (1921)	£600
SB11	2r. booklet containing 16×2a. (No. 169) in blocks of 4 (blank back cover) (1921)	£1400
	a. Black on purple cover with postage rates on back (1922)	£1400
SB12	2r. booklet containing 16×2a. (No. 166) in blocks of 4 (1922)	£1400
	a. Black on purple cover	£1400

1921. Black on buff match book type cover. Stapled.

| SB13 | 1r.2a. booklet containing 24×9p. on 1a. (No. 192) in blocks of 4 | £200 |

1922. Black on brown (No. SB14) or black on green and pink (No. SB15) match book type covers with foreign postage rates on back. Stapled.

SB14	1r. booklet containing 16×1a. (No. 197) in blocks of 4	£475
	a. Advertisement on back	£500
	b. Advertisements on front flap and back cover	£700
	c. Black on lilac cover with blank back	£500
	ca. Advertisements on front flap and back cover	£700
	d. Black on pink cover with blank back	£650
SB15	1r. booklet containing 16×½a. and 8×1a. (Nos. 155, 197) in blocks of 4 (blank back cover)	£1300

1926–28. Black on brown (No. SB16) or black on purple (No. SB17) match book type covers with foreign postage rates on back. Stapled.

SB16	1r. booklet containing 16×1a. (No. 203) in blocks of 4	£275
SB17	2r. booklet containing 16×2a. (No. 205) in blocks of 4	£600
	a. Containing No. 206 (1928)	£850

1929. Black on brown (No. SB18) or black on purple (No. SB19) separate leaf covers. Stitched.

SB18	1r. booklet containing 16×1a. (No. 203) in blocks of 4 (blank back cover)	£275
	a. Advertisement contractor's notice on back cover	£275
	b. Advertisements on front flap and back cover	£300
	c. Advertisement on back cover	£300
SB19	2r. booklet containing 16×2a. (No. 205) in blocks of 4 (foreign postage rates on back cover)	£800
	a. Advertisement contractor's notice on back cover	£800
	b. Containing No. 206 (foreign postage rates on back cover)	£1000
	ba. Advertisement contractor's notice on back cover	£1000

1932. Black on brown cover. Stitched.

| SB20 | 1r.4a. booklet containing 16×1¼a. (No. 235) in blocks of 4 | £850 |

1934. Black on buff cover. Stitched.

| SB21 | 1r. booklet containing 16×1a. (No. 234) in blocks of 4 | £450 |

1937. Black on red cover. Stamps with wmk upright or inverted. Stitched.

| SB22 | 1r. booklet containing 16×1a. (No. 250) in blocks of 4 | £500 |

OFFICIAL STAMPS

Stamps overprinted "POSTAL SERVICE" or "I.P.N." were not used as postage stamps, and are therefore omitted.

Service.
(O 1)

(Optd by the Military Orphanage Press, Calcutta)

1866 (1 Aug)–**72.** Optd with Type O 1. P 14.

(a) No wmk
O1	11	½a. blue	—	£650
O2		½a. pale blue	£3750	£300
		a. Opt inverted	£3750	
O3		1a. brown	—	£425
O4		1a. deep brown	—	£325
O5		8a. carmine	55·00	£100

(b) Wmk Elephant's Head, T 13
O6	11	½a. blue	£800	30·00
		w. Wmk inverted	†	£500
O7		½a. pale blue	£600	13·00
		a. Opt inverted		
		b. No dot on "i" (No. 50 on pane)..	—	£800
		c. No stop on "s" (No. 77 on pane)		£750
O8	12	8p. purple (1.72)	50·00	75·00
		a. No dot on "i"		£750
		b. No stop		£750
O9	11	1a. brown	£600	26·00
O10		1a. deep brown	£700	55·00
		a. No dot on "i"	—	£1200
		b. No stop		£1100
O11		2a. orange	£400	£170
O12		2a. yellow	£400	£180
		a. Opt inverted		
		b. Imperf		
		c. Raised stop between "c" and "e"	†	£4500
		w. Wmk inverted	£475	
		y. Wmk inverted and reversed	†	£1000
O13		4a. green	£550	£160
		a. Opt inverted		
O14	17	4a. green (Die I)	£2750	£325

A variety with wide and more open capital "S" occurs six times in sheets of all values except No. O8. Price four times the normal.

Reprints exist of Nos. O6, O9 and O14; the latter is Die II instead of Die I.

Reprints of the overprint have also been made, in a different setting, on the 8 pies, purple, no watermark.

O 2

O 6

O 3

O 4

(No. O15 surch at Calcutta, others optd at Madras)

1866 (Oct). Fiscal stamps, Nos. O15/18 with top and bottom inscrs removed, surch or optd. Wmk Crown over "INDIA".

(a) Surch as in Type O 2. Thick blue glazed paper. Imperf×perf 14
| O15 | O 2 | 2a. purple | £700 | £600 |

(b) Optd "SERVICE POSTAGE" in two lines as in Types O 3/4 and similar type. Imperf×perf 14
O16	O 3	2a. purple (G.)	£3250	£1200
		a. Optd on complete stamp (inscr "FOREIGN BILL")	†	£27000
O17	O 4	4a. purple (G.)	£10000	£3250
O18	–	8a. purple (G.)	£9000	£11000
		a. Optd on complete stamp (inscr "FOREIGN BILL")	†	£28000

(c) Optd "SERVICE POSTAGE" in semi-circle. Wmk Large Crown. P 15½×15
| O19 | O 6 | ½a. mauve/lilac (G.) | £900 | £160 |
| | | a. Opt double | | £8500 |

So-called reprints of Nos. O15 to O18 are known, but in these the surcharge differs entirely in the spacing, etc., of the words; they are more properly described as Government imitations. The imitations of No. O15 have surcharge in black or in green. No. O19 exists with reprinted overprint which has a full stop after "POSTAGE".

PRINTERS. The following stamps up to No. O96 were overprinted by De La Rue.

On
Service.
(O 7)

On
H. S.
M.
(O 8)

On
H. S.
M.
(O 9)

1867–73. Optd with Type O 7. Wmk Elephant's Head, T 13. P 14.
O20	11	½a. blue (Die I)	80·00	50
		w. Wmk inverted	†	£325
O21		½a. pale blue (Die I)	£100	3·50
O22		½a. blue (Die II) (1873)	£190	£110
O23		1a. brown	85·00	50
		w. Wmk inverted	†	£375
O24		1a. deep brown	90·00	3·25
O25		1a. chocolate	95·00	3·25
O26		2a. yellow	50·00	2·50
O27		2a. orange	17·00	2·25
		w. Wmk inverted	—	£400
O28	17	4a. pale green (Die I)	35·00	2·50
O29		4a. green (Die I)	5·50	1·50
O30	11	8a. rose (Die II) (1868)	7·00	1·50
O30a		8a. pale rose (Die II)	7·50	1·50
		aw. Wmk inverted	£150	75·00

Prepared for use, but not issued
| O30b | 18 | 6a.8p. slate | | £700 |

1874–82. Optd with Type O 8.

(a) In black
O31	11	½a. blue (Die II)	28·00	20
O32		1a. brown	28·00	20
O33		2a. yellow	£100	50·00
O33a		2a. orange	85·00	45·00
		aw. Wmk inverted	†	£350
O34	17	4a. green (Die I)	45·00	3·00
O35	11	8a. rose (Die I)	9·00	13·00

(b) Optd in blue-black
O36	11	½a. blue (Die II) (1877)	£1200	£100
		w. Wmk inverted	†	£1500
O37		1a. brown (1882)	£3500	£400

1883–99. Wmk Star, T 34. Optd with Type O 9. P 14.
O37a	40	3p. aniline carmine (1899)	20	10
O38	23	½a. deep blue-green	4·75	10
		a. Opt double	†	£4750
		b. Opt inverted	†	£1900
		w. Wmk inverted	†	£350
O39		½a. blue-green	2·75	10
O40	25	1a. brown-purple	7·50	50
		a. Opt inverted	£800	£900
		aw. Opt inverted. Wmk inverted	†	£1400
		b. Opt double	†	£5000
		c. Opt omitted (in horiz pair with normal)	£6500	
		w. Wmk inverted	†	£375
O41		1a. plum	1·75	10
O42	27	2a. pale blue	18·00	60
O43		2a. blue	19·00	60
O44	29	4a. olive-green	50·00	50

O44a		4a. slate-green	50·00	50
O45	31	8a. dull mauve	45·00	2·50
O46		8a. magenta	22·00	50
O47	37	1r. green and rose (1892)	80·00	9·50
O48		1r. green and carmine (1892)	45·00	40
O37a/48 Set of 7			£120	2·00

1900. Colours changed. Optd with Type O 9.
O49	23	½a. pale yellow-green	7·50	90
O49a		½a. yellow-green	9·50	50
		ab. Opt double	£2750	
O50	25	1a. carmine	4·75	10
		a. Opt inverted	†	£4250
		b. Opt double	†	£4500
O51	27	2a. pale violet	55·00	1·50
O52		2a. mauve	55·00	50
O49/52 Set of 3			60·00	1·00

1902–09. Stamps of King Edward VII optd with Type O 9.
O54	41	3p. grey (1903)	2·50	1·50
O55		3p. slate-grey (1905)	4·00	2·00
		a. No stop after "M" (R. 6/10)	£750	£400
O56	42	½a. green	1·50	30
O57	43	1a. carmine	1·25	10
O58	44	2a. violet	4·50	50
O59		2a. mauve	4·00	10
		v. Wmk inverted	†	£425
O60	47	4a. olive	32·00	30
O61		4a. pale olive	32·00	30
O62	48	6a. olive-bistre (1909)	2·00	15
O63	49	8a. purple (shades)	16·00	1·00
O64		8a. claret	17·00	85
O65	51	1r. green and carmine (1905)	4·25	80
O54/65 Set of 8			60·00	3·50

1906. New types. Optd with Type O 9.
O66	53	½a. green	1·25	10
		a. No stop after "M" (R. 6/10)	£350	£150
O67	54	1a. carmine	2·00	10
		a. No stop after "M" (R. 6/10)	£550	£250
		b. Opt albino (in pair with normal)	£3000	

On

H. S.

M.
(O 9a)

1909. Optd with Type O 9a.
O68	52	2r. carmine and yellow-brown	25·00	1·50
O68a		2r. rose-red and yellow-brown	25·00	1·50
O69		5r. ultramarine and violet	16·00	1·50
O70		10r. green and carmine	55·00	42·00
O70a		10r. green and scarlet	£200	17·00
O71		15r. blue and olive-brown	£150	65·00
O72		25r. brownish orange and blue	£325	£110
O68/72 Set of 5			£500	£170

NINE

| SERVICE (O 10) (14 mm) | SERVICE (O 11) (21½ mm) | PIES (O 12) |

1912–13. Stamps of King George V (wmk Single Star, T 34) optd with Type O 10 or O 11 (rupee values).
O73	55	3p. grey	40	10
O73a		3p. pale grey	75	10
O74		3p. bluish grey	4·00	10
		a. Opt omitted (in pair with normal)		
O75		3p. slate	4·00	30
		a. "Rs" Flaw		
O75b		3p. violet-grey	7·00	2·00
O76	56	½a. light green	50	10
O77		½a. emerald	1·75	15
O78		½a. bright-green	3·00	55
		a. Opt double	£130	
O80	57	1a. rose-carmine	2·25	10
O81		1a. carmine	2·50	10
O82		1a. aniline carmine	1·75	10
		a. Opt double	†	£2000
O83	59	2a. purple	3·50	30
O83a		2a. reddish purple	2·00	25
		aw. Wmk inverted	†	£350
O84		2a. deep mauve	1·25	30
O84a		2a. bright reddish violet	9·00	2·25
		ab. Stop under "s" in right value tablet (R. 4/16)	£475	
O85	63	4a. deep olive	1·25	10
O86		4a. olive-green	1·50	10
O87	64	6a. yellow-bistre	1·50	3·75
O88		6a. brown-ochre	9·00	6·00
O89	65	8a. deep magenta	4·00	1·50
O89a		8a. deep mauve	7·50	1·25
O90		8a. bright mauve	48·00	6·00
O91	67	1r. red-brown and deep blue-green (1913)	11·00	2·75
O91a		1r. brown and green	9·00	1·40
O92		2r. rose-carmine and brown (1913)	15·00	15·00
O93		5r. ultramarine and violet (1913)	38·00	50·00
O94		10r. green and scarlet (1913)	£130	£110
O95		15r. blue and olive (1913)	£225	£250
O96		25r. orange and blue (1913)	£375	£350
O73/96 Set of 13			£700	£700

Used examples of Nos. O94/6 should be purchased with caution, as the "SERVICE" opt has been extensively forged.

1921. No. O80 surch at Calcutta with Type O **12**.

O97	57	9p. on 1a. rose-carmine	2·25	2·00

1922. No. 197 optd by De La Rue with Type O **10**.

O98	57	1a. chocolate	6·00	10

PRINTERS. The 1925-26 provisional surcharges (Nos. O99/108) were applied at Calcutta.

ONE RUPEE

(O **13**)	(O **14**)

1925. Official stamps surcharged.

*(a) Issue of 1909, as Type O **13***

O99	52	1r. on 15r. blue and olive	4·75	4·25
O100		1r. on 25r. chestnut and blue	40·00	£100
O101		2r. on 10r. green and scarlet	3·75	4·25
O101a		2r. on 10r. green and carmine	£475	90·00

*(b) Issue of 1912–13 with O **14***

O102	67	1r. on 15r. blue and olive	20·00	90·00
O103		1r. on 25r. orange and blue	11·00	12·00
		a. Surch inverted	£5000	

*(c) Issue of 1912–13, as Type O **13***

O104	67	2r. on 10r. green and scarlet	£5000	

Examples of the above showing other surcharge errors are believed to be of clandestine origin.

SERVICE	
(O **15**)	(O **16**) ONE ANNA

1926. No. O62 surch with Type O **15**.

O105	48	1a. on 6a. olive-bistre	45	30

1926. Postage stamps of 1911–22 (wmk Single Star), surch as Type O **16**.

O106	58	1a. on 1½a. chocolate (A)	20	10
O107		1a. on 1½a. chocolate (B)	8·00	4·50
		a. Error. On 1a. chocolate (197)	£250	
O108	61	1a. on 2a.6p. ultramarine	60	80

The surcharge on No. O108 has no bars at top.
Examples of Nos. O106/7 with inverted or double surcharges are believed to be of clandestine origin.

PRINTERS. Official stamps from No. O109 were overprinted or printed by the Security Printing Press at Nasik, with the probable exception of No. O125.

SERVICE	SERVICE	SERVICE
(O **17a**)	(O **17b**)	(O **18**) (19½ mm)
(13½ mm)	(13½ mm)	

Two types of the 13½ mm "SERVICE" opt.
Type O **17a**: Small loop and long tail to "R"
Type O **17b**: Large loop and shorter tail to "R"

1926–31. Stamps of King George V (wmk Multiple Star, T **69**) optd with Types O **17a** or O **18** (rupee values).

O109	55	3p. slate (1.10.29)	55	10
		aw. Wmk inverted	6·50	2·75
		b. Opt Type O **17b**	—	40
O110	56	½a. green (1931)	20·00	60
		aw. Wmk inverted	75·00	3·50
		b. Opt Type O **17b**	—	2·50
O111	57	1a. chocolate	20	10
		aw. Wmk inverted	5·50	60
		b. Opt Type O **17b**	1·50	20
		bw. Wmk inverted		
O112	70	2a. purple	30	10
		w. Wmk inverted	6·50	1·75
O113	71	4a. sage-green	2·75	20
		w. Wmk inverted	7·50	2·50
O115	65	8a. reddish purple	8·50	10
		w. Wmk inverted	80	30
O116	66	12a. claret (1927)	70	2·50
		w. Wmk inverted	—	8·00
O117	67	1r. chocolate and green (1930)	16·00	1·00
		w. Wmk inverted	17·00	5·50
O118		2r. carmine and orange (1930)	25·00	16·00
		w. Wmk inverted	—	25·00
O120		10r. green and scarlet (1931)	£170	65·00
O109/20 Set of 10			£200	80·00

1930. As No. O111, but optd as Type O **10** (14 mm).

O125	57	1a. chocolate	—	14·00
		w. Wmk inverted	£180	11·00

1932–36. Stamps of King George V (wmk Mult Star, T **69**) optd with Type O **17a**.

O126	79	½a. green (1935)	4·50	10
		w. Wmk inverted	—	17·00
O127	80	9p. deep green (*litho*)	30	15
		aw. Wmk inverted	—	13·00
O127b		9p. deep green (*typo*)	7·50	15
O127c	81	1a. chocolate (1936)	2·50	10
		cw. Wmk inverted	15·00	2·50
O128	82	1a.3p. mauve	30	10
		w. Wmk inverted	1·00	40

O129	70	2a. vermilion	7·00	2·00
		w. Wmk inverted	—	16·00
O130	59	2a. vermilion (1935)	10·00	1·25
		aw. Wmk inverted	—	19·00
O130b		2a. vermilion (*small die*) (1936)	1·25	10
		bw. Wmk inverted	—	10
O131	61	2a.6p. orange (22.4.32)	60	10
			7·00	2·25
O132	63	4a. sage-green (1935)	5·50	10
		w. Wmk inverted	—	26·00
O133	64	6a. bistre (1936)	38·00	10·00
O126/33 Set of 9			50·00	11·00

1937–39. Stamps of King George VI optd as Types O **17a** or O **18** (rupee values).

O135	91	½a. red-brown (1938)	17·00	1·25
		w. Wmk inverted	—	55·00
O136		9p. green (1937)	19·00	1·50
O137		1a. carmine (1937)	3·50	10
O138	100	1r. grey and red-brown (5.38)	75	50
		w. Wmk inverted	85·00	50·00
O139		2r. purple and brown (5.38)	1·75	2·50
		w. Wmk inverted	—	75·00
O140		5r. green and blue (10.38)	15·00	7·50
		w. Wmk inverted	£130	£110
O141		10r. purple and claret (1939)	29·00	21·00
		w. Wmk inverted	£150	95·00
O135/41 Set of 7			75·00	30·00

SERVICE 1ᴬ	
(O **19**)	O **20**

1939 (May). Stamp of King George V, surch with Type O **19**.

O142	82	1a. on 1¼a. mauve	16·00	20
		w. Wmk inverted	—	9·50

(Des T. I. Archer)

1939 (1 June)–**42**. Typo. W **69**. P 14.

O143	O **20**	3p. slate	60	10
		w. Wmk inverted	—	55·00
O144		½a. red-brown	13·00	10
		aw. Wmk inverted	—	85·00
O144b		½a. purple (1.10.42)	30	10
		bw. Wmk inverted	—	26·00
O145		9p. green	30	10
		w. Wmk inverted	—	70·00
O146		1a. carmine	30	10
		w. Wmk inverted	—	26·00
O146a		1a.3p. yellow-brown (2.6.41)	8·50	70
		aw. Wmk inverted	—	85·00
O146b		1½a. dull violet (1.9.42)	65	10
		bw. Wmk inverted	—	28·00
O147		2a. vermilion	60	10
		w. Wmk inverted	—	85·00
O148		2½a. bright violet	3·00	1·25
O149		4a. brown	60	10
		aw. Wmk inverted	—	85·00
O149b		8a. slate-violet	90	30
		bw. Wmk inverted	—	85·00
O143/49b Set of 11			26·00	2·00

1948 (15 Aug). First Anniv of Independence. Nos. 305/8 optd as Type O **17a**.

O150a	305	1½a. brown	£100	90·00
O150b		3½a. violet	£7000	£2750
O150c		12a. grey-green	£25000	£8500
O150d	306	10r. purple-brown and lake	£160000	†

Nos. O150a/d were only issued to the Governor-General's Secretariat. They have been extensively forged, and examples should only be acquired with a reliable guarantee.

O **21** Asokan Capital	O **22**

(Des T.I. Archer)

1950 (2 Jan)–**51**. Typo (O **21**) or litho (O **22**). W **69**. P 14.

O151	O **21**	3p. slate-violet (1.7.50)	15	10
		w. Wmk inverted	£100	
O152		6p. purple-brown (1.7.50)	30	10
		w. Wmk inverted	—	£100
O153		9p. green (1.7.50)	1·25	10
O154		1a. turquoise (1.7.50)	1·25	10
O155		2a. carmine (1.7.50)	3·50	10
		w. Wmk inverted	—	£100
O156		3a. red-orange (1.7.50)	8·00	2·50
O157		4a. lake (1.7.50)	14·00	20
O158		4a. ultramarine (1.10.51)	75	10
O159		6a. bright violet (1.7.50)	5·00	2·00
O160		8a. red-brown (1.7.50)	2·50	10
		w. Wmk inverted	50·00	17·00
O161	O **22**	1r. violet	3·00	10
		w. Wmk inverted		
O162		2r. rose-carmine	1·00	1·00
O163		5r. bluish green	3·25	2·00
O164		10r. reddish brown	11·00	42·00
O151/64 Set of 14			50·00	45·00

Litho	Typo

Litho and typo printings: Apart from the shades, which in most cases are distinctive, unused typo stamps may be identified by the indentation of the design into the paper, *as seen from the back of the stamp*, whereas litho-printed versions are smooth on front and back. Marginal examples may also be allocated due to the fact that only the typo plates were surrounded by "Jubilee" lines. On used stamps the fine lines are generally clearer and more even in the litho printings and the white border surrounding the value tablets appears wider than on typo versions.

1957 (1 Apr)–**58**. Values in naye paise. Typo (*t*) or litho (*l*). W **69**. P 14.

O165	O **21**	1n.p. slate (*l*)	1·50	10
		a. Slate-black (*l*)	2·25	10
		b. Greenish slate (*t*)	10	10
		w. Wmk inverted	5·00	1·25
O166		2n.p. blackish violet (*t*)	10	10
		w. Wmk inverted		
O167		3n.p. chocolate (*t*)	20	10
O168		5n.p. green (*t*)	1·25	10
		a. Deep emerald (*t*)	1·50	10
		w. Wmk inverted	—	50·00
O169		6n.p. turquoise-blue (*t*)	40	10
O170		13n.p. scarlet (*t*)	40	10
O171		15n.p. reddish violet (*l*) (6.58)	9·00	2·50
		a. Reddish violet (*t*)	8·00	2·75
O172		20n.p. red (*l*)	1·25	1·25
		a. Vermilion (*t*)	3·25	1·25
		aw. Wmk inverted		
O173		25n.p. violet-blue (*l*)	1·00	20
		a. Ultramarine (*t*)	2·75	30
O174		50n.p. red-brown (*l*)	1·75	10
		a. Reddish brown (*t*)	3·00	1·25
O165/74 Set of 10			13·00	3·75

1958–71. As Nos. O165/74a and O161/4 but W **374** (upright). Litho (*l*) or typo (*t*). P 14.

O175	O **21**	1n.p. slate-black (*t*) (1.59)	10	10
O176		2n.p. blackish violet (*t*) (1.59)	10	10
O177		3n.p. chocolate (*t*) (11.58)	10	10
		w. Wmk inverted	4·00	
O178		5n.p. deep emerald (*t*) (11.58)	10	10
O179		6n.p. turquoise-blue (*t*) (5.59)	10	10
O180		10n.p. deep grey-green (*l*) (1963)	50	50
		a. Deep grey-green (*l*) (1966?)	2·50	3·25
O181		13n.p. scarlet (*t*) (1963)	1·00	3·75
O182		15n.p. deep violet (*t*) (11.58)	10	10
		a. Light reddish violet (*t*) (1961)	3·50	10
O183		20n.p. vermilion (*t*) (5.59)	70	10
		a. Red (*t*) (1966?)	12·00	1·00
O184		25n.p. ultramarine (*t*) (7.59)	10	10
O185		50n.p. reddish brown (*t*) (6.59)	70	10
		a. Chestnut (*t*) (1966?)	13·00	1·50
O186	O **22**	1r. reddish violet (*l*) (2.59)	15	10
O187		2r. rose-carmine (*l*) (1960)	25	10
		a. Wmk sideways*. *Pale rose-carmine* (*l*) (1969?)	2·50	3·50
		aw. Wmk capitals to right		
O188		5r. slate-green (*l*) (7.59)	40	1·50
		a. Wmk sideways*. *Deep grey-green* (*l*) (1969?)	90	2·00
O189		10r. brown-lake (*l*) (7.59)	1·00	2·50
		a. Wmk sideways* (*l*) (1971)	3·25	6·00
		ab. Printed on the gummed side	38·00	
		aw. Wmk capitals to right	3·75	
O175/89 Set of 15			4·50	7·25

*The normal sideways watermark shows the head of the capitals pointing left, *as seen from the back of the stamp.*

O **23**

1967 (20 Mar)–**73**. Photo. W **374** (sideways). P 15×14.

O190	O **23**	2p. violet (1973?)	3·50	3·00
O191		5p. green (1973?)	3·25	1·00
O192		10p. myrtle-green (2.7.73)	3·25	25
O193		15p. plum (2.7.73)	3·50	55
O194		20p. red (2.7.73)	11·00	8·00
O195		30p. ultramarine (1973)	15·00	2·25
O196		50p. chestnut (2.7.73)	6·00	3·00
O197		1r. dull purple (20.3.67)	85	10
		a. Deep slate-purple (1969)	4·00	45
O190/7 Set of 8			42·00	16·00

1967 (15 Nov)–**74**. Wmk Large Star and "INDIA GOVT" in sheet*. Photo. P 15×14. No gum.

O200	O **23**	2p. violet	10	1·00
O201		3p. chocolate	40	1·25
O202		5p. green	10	10
		a. Yellowish green (1969)	10	10
		w. Wmk reversed	4·00	
O203		6p. turquoise-blue	1·25	1·50
O204		10p. myrtle-green	10	30
		a. Bronze-green (1969)	2·00	2·00
		w. Wmk reversed	4·00	
O205		15p. plum	10	30
		w. Wmk reversed	4·00	
O206		20p. red	10	30
		w. Wmk reversed	4·00	
O207		25p. carmine-red (1974?)	28·00	3·75
		w. Wmk reversed	28·00	

O208	30p. ultramarine		10	60
O209	50p. chestnut		10	60
	w. Wmk reversed		4·50	
O200/9 Set of 10			28·00	8·75

*The arrangement of this watermark in the sheet results in the words and the star appearing upright, inverted or sideways.

TELEGRAPH STAMPS

PRINTERS. All Indian Telegraph stamps, including fiscal stamps optd or surch for provisional use, were typographed by De La Rue.

"SPECIMEN" and "CANCELLED" overprints. Most Indian Telegraph stamps (with the exception of Nos. T1/3, 21/31, 53 and OT1/5) are known with "SPECIMEN" or "CANCELLED" overprints, for record purposes. In the case of the earlier issues up to 1890, and particularly the higher rupee values, these are usually worth considerably less than the prices quoted for unused examples.

T 1

1860 (Jan). Inscr "ELECTRIC TELEGRAPH". Blue glazed paper. No wmk. Perf 14.

			Un	Used whole	Used half
T1	T **1**	4a. reddish purple	£3250	£2000	†
T2		1r. reddish purple	£7500	£5000	†
T3		4r. reddish purple	£30000	†	£8000

Imperforate examples are of proof status.
Used examples of this issue include whole stamps with punched holes and other forms of cancellation, but some left halves are known, indicating usage after 1869. Remainders were later optd "COURT FEES" for fiscal use.

T **2**	T **3**	T **4**

T **5**	T **6**	T **7**

T **6** (Die I): Solid lines in spandrels.
T **7** (Die II): Hollow lines in spandrels.

T **8**	T **9**	T **10**

T **8** (Die I): Dark background in portrait ovals.
T **9** (Die II): Light background in portrait ovals.

T **11**	T **12**	T **13**

T **11** (Die I): Dark background in portrait ovals. Thin lettering in inscriptions.
T **12** (Die II): Light background in portrait ovals. Thicker lettering in inscriptions.

T **14**	T **15**	T **16**

T **14** (Die I): Diagonal "25 RUPEES" without ornaments. Dark background in portrait ovals. Tall lettering (round "O").
T **15** (Die II): Diagonal "25 RUPEES" within ornaments. Light background in portrait ovals. Shorter lettering (oval "O").

T **17**	T **18**	T **19**

T **17** (Die I): Solid lines in spandrels.
T **18** (Die II): Hollow lines in spandrels.

Watermarks:
T **19** Overall height 49mm. "INDIA" 20 mm long, with wide "D" and "A". Four horizontal lines in base of crown (max width of crown 18 mm).
T **25** Overall height 46mm. "INDIA" 17 mm long, with narrow "D" and "A". Three horizontal lines in base of crown (max width of crown 17 mm).

1869 (1 Feb)–**78**. T T **2/18**. Wmk T **19**. Perf 14.

			Un	Used half	Used whole
T4	T **2**	1a. yellow-green (1878)	50·00	6·00	—
		w. Wmk inverted	£300		
T5	T **3**	2a. maroon (1869)	38·00	1·00	£200
T6	T **4**	4a. light blue	42·00	1·00	
		w. Wmk inverted	£300	£100	†
T7	T **5**	8a. brown	50·00	1·00	£200
		a. Imperf	—	£1000	†
		w. Wmk inverted	†	£100	†
T8	T **6**	1r. grey (Die I)	£800	10·00	£400
		a. Imperf	—	£1300	†
T9	T **7**	1r. grey (Die II) (1869)	85·00	1·00	£140
		a. Double impression	†	—	†
T10	T **8**	2r.8a. orange-yellow (Die I)	£550	2·00	£200
T11	T **9**	2r.8a. orange (Die II) (1878)	£110	2·00	£160
		w. Wmk inverted	†	£1400	†
T12	T **10**	5r. orange-brown (1878)	£120	3·00	
		w. Wmk inverted	†	£160	†
T13	T **11**	10r. dull blue-green (Die I)	£850	3·00	
T14	T **12**	10r. dull blue-green (Die II) (1878)	£950	2·50	£200
T15	T **13**	14r.4a. bright lilac (Jan 1870)	£325	8·00	—
T16	T **14**	25r. reddish lilac (Die I)	£1200	7·00	
T17	T **15**	25r. reddish lilac (Die II) (1878)	£500	3·50	£275
		w. Wmk inverted	†	£160	†
T18	T **16**	28r.8a. bright yellow-green (1.70)	£450	6·00	—
T19	T **17**	50r. rose (Die I)	£1500	18·00	—
T20	T **18**	50r. rose (Die II) (1874)	£850	8·00	—

The listed imperforate errors Nos. T7a and T8a were used respectively at Colombo (Ceylon) in Oct 1878 and at Bombay in May 1869. Other values also exist imperforate but are of proof status.
Several values, particularly the 2a., 4a. and 8a., exist on paper showing varying degrees of blueing.

Used prices for Nos. T4/20 are quoted for both upper halves and whole stamps. The latter are usually found with additional punched holes. Lower halves, in this and subsequent issues, result from stamps being placed inverted on the telegraph form, against regulations, and are rare.
For later printings as Nos. T4/7, T9, T11/12, T14, T17 and T20, but wmk. T **25**, see Nos. T32/41.

(T **20**)

(T **21**)

(T **22**)

(T **23**)

(T **24**)

1881 (Aug)–**82**. Fiscal stamps optd "TELEGRAPH" as T T **20/24**. Wmk T **19** (sideways). Perf 14.

*(i) Opt T T **20** (28×3 mm with stop) at Calcutta*

			Un	Used left half	Used right half
T21	T **20**	1a. dull lilac/*blued* (2.82)	£650	42·00	32·00
T22		2a. bright lilac (8.81)	£600	55·00	38·00
		a. Opt double, one albino	£1100	†	†
T23		4a. green (4.82)	£1300	42·00	32·00

*(ii) Opt T T **21** (24×2½ mm with stop) at Calcutta*

T24	T **21**	1a. dull lilac/*blued* (2.82)	£650	48·00	32·00
T25		1a. pale lilac (2.82)	£275	42·00	32·00

The Calcutta opts T T **20/1** were intended to be applied at the top of the stamp, across the Queen's diadem.

*(iii) Opt T T **22** (26×3 mm without stop) at Bombay*

T27	T **22**	2a. bright lilac (13.8.81)	†	£1100	£400

This first Bombay opt T T **22** is of rough appearance, from worn type, and like T T **23**, was applied to the centre of the stamp, across the portrait.

*(iv) Opt T T **23** (24×2½ mm with stop) at Bombay*

T28	T **23**	2a. bright lilac (15.8.81)	£1200	38·00	22·00

This second Bombay opt T T **23** is of the same size as T T **21** of Calcutta, but the "G" is narrower, and there are other minor differences.

*(v) Opt T T **24** (26×2¾ mm without stop) at Madras*

T29	T **24**	1a. pale lilac (20.3.82)	£850	£150	£150
T30		2a. bright lilac (20.3.82)	†	£1200	†
T31		4a. green (17.4.82)	—	22·00	22·00

The Madras opt T T **24** is from a bold fount, readily distinguishable from those used at Calcutta and Bombay for T T **20/3**. It was applied to the centre of the stamps, across the portrait.
Nos. T21/31, being of horizontal format, were placed *vertically* on the telegraph forms and bisected in the usual way. Used prices are quoted for both left ("TELE(G)") and right ("(G)RAPH") halves, the former being scarcer in the case of Nos. T21/8.

T **25**

1882. Designs as 1869–78 issue, but wmk T **25**. Perf 14.

			Un	Used half	Used whole
T32	T **2**	1a. green	26·00	2·00	90·00
T33	T **3**	2a. maroon	22·00	1·25	95·00

T34	T **4**	4a. light blue......................	28·00	1·00	£110
T35	T **5**	8a. brown...........................	28·00	1·00	£120
T36	T **7**	1r. grey (Die II).................	35·00	1·00	£110
T37	T **9**	2r.8a. orange (Die II)........	85·00	1·75	£170
T38	T **10**	5r. orange-brown.............	70·00	2·00	£120
		w. Wmk inverted..............	†	£140	†
T39	T **12**	10r. blue-green (Die II).....	£225	3·00	£110
T40	T **15**	25r. reddish lilac (Die II)...	£200	2·50	£150
T41	T **18**	50r. carmine (Die II).........	£400	1·75	£190

Used prices for whole stamps (often with additional punched holes), for this and subsequent issues, are quoted in the third price column.

T 26	T 27	T 28

T 29	T 30	T 31

T 32	T 33

T 34	T 35

1890 (Aug)–**91**. New designs T T **26/35**. Wmk T **25**. Perf 14.

			Un	Used half	Used whole
T42	T **26**	1a. yellowish green..............	18·00	1·50	40·00
T43	T **27**	2a. maroon (1.91)	20·00	1·25	40·00
T44	T **28**	4a. blue................................	24·00	1·00	55·00
T45	T **29**	8a. brown	24·00	1·00	45·00
T46	T **30**	1r. grey	27·00	1·00	45·00
T47	T **31**	2r.8a. orange (1.91)............	50·00	3·50	75·00
T48	T **32**	5r. brownish orange (1.91).............................	£110	2·50	75·00
T49	T **33**	10r. blue-green (1.91).........	£200	3·50	£130
T50	T **34**	25r. bright lilac (1.91)..........	£180	5·00	£100
T51	T **35**	50r. carmine (1.91).............	£225	6·50	£100

Used upper halves of this issue (with the exception of No. T47) can be difficult to distinguish from the same values of the 1904 King Edward VII issue, unless they have pre-1904 cancels or show sufficient of the lower part of the design to confirm the absence of the King's crown.

(T 36)	(T 37)

1899 (4 Sep). No. T47 surch at Calcutta, as T T **36**.

T52	T **36**	2r. on 2r.8a. orange............	£275	10·00	—
		wa. "RUPLES" for "RUPEES" in upper half..................	£500	50·00	—

1900 (24 Feb). Fiscal stamp of 1861 inscr "FOREIGN BILL" optd as T T **37** at Calcutta. Bluish glazed paper. Wmk T **2**. Perf 14.

T53	T **37**	2r. purple	£500	£170	—

(T 38)	T 39

1900 (30 Apr). No. T47 surch by De La Rue, as T T **38**.

T54	T **38**	2r. on 2r.8a. orange............	£275	10·00	£225

1900 (14 Nov). New design T T **39**. Wmk T **25**. Perf 14.

T55	T **39**	2r. yellow	£250	16·00	£250
		a. Red bar optd at foot ...	£275	†	£225
		b. Red line ruled by hand at foot..................	£500	†	—

The colour chosen for No. T55 was found to be unsuitable, as it proved difficult to discern the design under artificial light. Stocks held at Calcutta were provided with a printed red bar at foot (No. T55a), while those at the Madras and Bombay offices were ruled with a red line by hand (No. T55b) before issue, to mark the bottom half of the stamp, and ensure that stamps were affixed to telegraph forms in the correct position.

T 40	T 41	T 42

T 43	T 44	T 45

T 46	T 47

T 48	T 49

1904. New designs with portrait of King Edward VII, T T **40/9**. Wmk T **25**. Perf 14.

			Unused	Used half	Used whole
T56	T **40**	1a. yellow-green	20·00	10·00	50·00
T57	T **41**	2a. maroon...........................	22·00	9·00	45·00
T58	T **42**	4a. light blue........................	22·00	8·00	35·00
T59	T **43**	8a. brown.............................	26·00	8·00	40·00
T60	T **44**	1r. grey................................	26·00	8·00	60·00
T61	T **45**	2r. brown-orange.................	65·00	2·50	50·00
T62	T **46**	5r. orange-brown.................	80·00	11·00	55·00
T63	T **47**	10r. bluish green	£170	12·00	60·00
T64	T **48**	25r. bright lilac	£250	15·00	90·00
T65	T **49**	50r. carmine	£325	17·00	90·00

With the exception of No. T61, used upper halves are only identifiable if they show sufficient of the lower part of the design to confirm the presence of the King's crown and our prices for such examples. The designs are otherwise identical to Nos. T42/6 and T48/51.

Used whole stamps of this issue, usually without additional punched holes, result from changes in administrative practice, and often show special telegraphic circular datestamps, dated after 1 April 1908.

(T 50)	(T 51)	(T 52)

1904 (July). Nos. T46, T59 and 1861 fiscal stamp inscr "FOREIGN BILL" (blue glazed paper, Wmk T **19**, perf 14) surch with new values at Calcutta, as T T **50/2**.

			Un	Used half
T66	T **50**	1a. on 4r. purple....................	16·00	3·50
		a. Numeral "1" of "1 ANNA" omitted from upper half (R. 6/3)	£400	£150
		b. "h" for "H" in "TELEGRAPH" in upper half (R. 1/3)	£150	
		c. Small "R" in "TELEGRAPH" in upper half (R. 8/6)	£150	50·00
		d. "C" for "G" in "TELEGRAPH" in lower half (R. 6/9)	£150	†
		w. Wmk inverted..................	50·00	20·00
T67	T **51**	2a. on 8a. brown...................	26·00	3·50
T68	T **52**	4a. on 1r. grey......................	21·00	3·50

No. T66a occurred once in the setting but was soon corrected.

OFFICIAL TELEGRAPH STAMPS

(OT **1**)

1908 (?). Nos. T61/5 optd "O H M S" as T OT **1**. Perf 14.

OT1	2r. brown-orange	95·00	—
OT2	5r. orange-brown	£110	—
OT3	10r. bluish green	£140	—
OT4	25r. bright lilac	£250	—
OT5	50r. carmine	£350	—

No used examples of Nos. OT1/5 are known, but the upper halves remain identical to Nos. T61/5, and it is possible that all lower halves were destroyed.

Separate Telegraph stamps were abolished on 1 April 1908, and replaced by postage stamps. Current issues remained valid for pre-payment of telegraph charges until stocks were exhausted.

INDIA USED ABROAD

In the years following 1858 the influence of the Indian Empire, political, military and economic, extended beyond its borders into neighbouring states, the Arabian Gulf, East Africa and the Far East. Such influence often led to the establishment of Indian civil and military post offices in the countries concerned where unoverprinted stamps of India were used.

Such offices operated in the following countries. An * indicates that details will be found under that heading elsewhere in the catalogue.

ABYSSINIA

Following the imprisonment of the British Consul by King Theodore of Abyssinia, an expedition under the command of Sir Robert Napier was dispatched from India to secure his release. The expedition landed on 28 November 1867 and, having achieved its objective, withdrew the following June. A detachment of the Indian Army Postal Corps accompanied the expedition and was in operation from January to June 1868.

Contemporary Indian stamps were cancelled with Type AZ **1**.

AZ **1**

Stamps of India cancelled with Type AZ **1**

1865. (Nos. 54/65).

AZ1	½a. pale blue	95·00
AZ2	8p. purple	95·00
AZ3	1a. brown	£110
AZ4	2a. yellow	£140
AZ5	8a. carmine	£200

1866-67. (Nos. 69/72).

AZ6	4a. green	£150
AZ7	6a.8p. slate	£140

ADEN*

Unoverprinted stamps of India used from 1854 until 1937.

BAHRAIN*

Unoverprinted stamps of India used from 1884 until 1933.

BRITISH EAST AFRICA (KENYA, UGANDA AND TANGANYIKA)*

Unoverprinted stamps of India used during August and September 1890.

FRENCH INDIAN SETTLEMENTS

The first Indian post office, at Chandernagore, was open in 1784 to be followed by offices in the other four Settlements. By an agreement with the French, dating from 1814, these offices handled mail destined for British India, Great Britain, the British Empire and most other foreign destinations except France and the French colonies. In later years the system was expanded by a number of sub-offices and it continued to operate until the French territories were absorbed into India on 2 May 1950 (Chandernagore) or 1 November 1954.

Chandernagore. Opened 1784. Used numeral cancellations "B86" or "86".
  Sub-offices:
    Gondalpara (opened 1906)
    Lakhiganj (opened 1909)
    Temata (opened 1891)
Karikal. Opened 1794. Used numeral cancellations in "C147", "147" or "6/M-21".
  Sub-offices:
    Ambagarattur (opened 1904)
    Kottuchari (opened 1901)

Nedungaon (opened 1903)
Puraiyar Road (opened 1901)
Settur (opened 1905)
Tirumalrayapatnam (opened 1875) – used numeral cancellation "6/M-21/1"
Tiramilur (opened 1898)
Mahe. Opened 1795. Used numeral cancellations "C192" or "9/M-14".
Pondicherry. Opened 1787. Used numeral cancellations "C111", "111" (also used elsewhere), "6/M-19" (also used elsewhere) or "6/M-20".
  Sub-offices:
    Ariyankuppam (opened 1904)
    Bahoor (opened 1885)
    Mudaliarpet (opened 1897)
    Muthialpet (opened 1885)
    Pondicherry Bazaar (opened 1902)
    Pondicherry Railway Station (opened 1895)
    Olugarai (opened 1907)
    Vallinur (opened 1875) – used numeral cancellation "M-19/1"
    Yanam. Opened 1876. Used numeral cancellation "5/M-4".

IRAN

The British East India Company was active in the Arabian Gulf from the early years of the 17th century with their first factory (trading centre) being established at Jask in 1619. After 1853 this commercial presence was converted into a political arm of the Indian Government culminating in the appointment of a Political Resident to Bushire in 1862.

The first Indian post office in Iran (Persia) opened at Bushire on 1 May 1864 with monthly mail services operating to the Resident there and to the British Legation at Tehran. Further offices in the other Gulf ports followed, but, unless otherwise stated below, all were closed on 1 April 1923.

Details of the stamps known used from each post office are taken with permission, from the listing published by the Iran Philatelic Study Circle.

Persian Expeditionary Force

Following the occupation of Herat, on the Afghan border, by Persia, Britain declared war on 1 Nov 1856 and the Indian Expeditionary Force took Bushire (occupied 12 Dec 1856 to 2 Oct 1857) and Mohammera (occupied 26 Mar 1857 to 16 May 1858) Kharg Island was used as a supply base (Dec 1856 to Feb 1858).

The expedition was accompanied by Field Post Offices using contemporary Indian stamps cancelled "131" in a diamond of lines. It should be noted that forgeries of this cancellation are known and the number was subsequently assigned to Billimoria in India.

Z **1**

Stamps of India cancelled with Type Z **1**.

1854–55. (Nos. 2/26).

Z1	½a. blue (Die I)		£600
Z2	1a. red (Die I)		£550
	a. Die II		£650
Z3	4a. blue and red (Head die III, frame die II)		£2500

1854. (No. 31).

Z4	2a. green	£700

1856–64. (No. 37).

Z5	½a. blue (Die I)	£275

Abadan

An island at the mouth of the Shatt-el-Arab, the Anglo-Persian Oil Co. established an oil pipeline terminus there in 1909. An Indian post office was opened in 1917 and closed in 1923.

Z **2**

Z **3**

Postmark type		Approx period of use
Z **2**		1917–23
Z **3**		1918–22

1911–22. (Nos. 151/91).

Z6	3p. grey	22·00
Z7	½a. green	14·00
Z8	1a. carmine	16·00
Z9	1½a. chocolate (Type A)	35·00
Z10	2a. purple	18·00
Z11	2a.6p. ultramarine (1913)	14·00
Z12	3a. orange	16·00
Z13	4a. olive-green	21·00
Z14	6a. brown-ochre	22·00
Z15	8a. mauve	17·00
Z16	12a. carmine-lake	28·00
Z17	1r. brown and green	21·00
Z18	2r. carmine and brown	28·00
Z19	5r. ultramarine and violet	35·00
Z20	10r. green and scarlet	50·00

Prices quoted for Nos. Z6/20 are for stamps cancelled as type Z **2** or **3**. Stamps with telegraphic cancels of Abadan (showing concentric semi-circles above and below the date) are worth less.

Ahwaz

A city in south-west Iran, on the Karun River. An Indian post office was opened in 1915 and closed in 1923.

Z **4** 25 mm large date

Z **5**

Postmark type		Approx period of use
Z **4**	inscribed 'EXPERIMENTAL P.O./B504'	1915
Z **2**	inscribed "AHWAZ"	1915–22
Z **5**		1916–23

Stamps of India cancelled at Ahwaz

1911–22. (Nos. 151/91).

Z21	3p. grey	35·00
Z22	½a. green	12·00
Z23	1a. carmine	12·00
Z24	2a. purple	20·00
Z26	2a.6p. ultramarine (1913)	14·00
Z27	3a. orange	18·00
Z28	4a. olive-green	32·00
Z30	8a. mauve	45·00
Z32	1r. brown and green	65·00

1922–26. (Nos. 197/200).

Z34	1a. chocolate	35·00

OFFICIAL STAMPS

1903–09. (Nos. O54/65).

Z36	4a. olive	75·00

1906. (Nos. O66/7).

Z38	½a. green	45·00

1912–13. (Nos. O73/96).

Z43	2a. purple	

Bandar Abbas

Situated on the Strait of Hormuz, the British East India Company established a factory there in 1622. When a postal service between Bombay and Basra was established in 1862, Bandar Abbas was one of the regular ports of call but the Indian post office was not opened until 1 April 1867. It closed in 1923.

Z **6**

Z **7**

Z **8**

Z **9** Nine lines in obliterator

Z **10** Eight lines in obliterator

Z **11**

Z **12** Four thin lines in corners   Z **13**

Postmark type	Approx period of use
Z **6**	1870
Z **7**	1871–1873
Z **8**	1874–1888
Z **9**	
Z **10** (inscr "BANDARABAS")	
Z **10** (inscr "BANDAR-ABAS")	
Z **11**	1884
Z **12** (inscr "BANDARABAS")	1886–1892
Z **12** (inscr "BANDAR-ABAS")	1892–1893
Z **4** (inscr "BANDAR-ABAS")	1905–1920
Z **4** (inscr "BANDARABAS/PAR")	
Z **13**	1907–1922

Stamps of India cancelled at Bandar Abbas

1865. (Nos. 54/65).
Z46 ½a. blue .... 20·00
Z48 1a. brown .... 22·00
Z49 2a. orange .... 42·00

1866–78. (Nos. 69/72).
Z49a 4a. green (Die I) .... 55·00
Z50 4a. blue-green (Die II) .... 60·00

1868–73. (Nos. 73/6).
Z51 8a. rose (Die II) .... 70·00
Z52 ½a. blue (Die II) .... 9·50

1882–90. (Nos. 84/101).
Z53 ½a. blue-green .... 6·00
Z55 1a. plum .... 9·50
Z57 2a. blue .... 15·00
Z58 3a. orange .... 28·00
Z59 4a. olive-green .... 22·00
Z60 4a.6p. yellow-green .... 32·00
Z63 1r. slate .... 55·00

1892–97. (Nos. 103/6).
Z64 2a.6p. yellow-green .... 14·00

1899. (No. 111).
Z66 3p. aniline-carmine .... 20·00

1900. (Nos. 112/8).
Z68 ½a. yellow-green .... 9·50
Z69 1a. carmine .... 9·50
Z70 2a. pale violet .... 22·00
Z71 2a.6p. ultramarine .... 14·00

1902–11. (Nos. 119/47).
Z72 3p. grey .... 8·00
Z73 ½a. green .... 6·00
Z74 1a. carmine .... 8·00
Z75 2a. mauve .... 7·00
Z76 2a.6p. ultramarine .... 6·00
Z78 4a. olive .... 21·00
Z82 1r. green and carmine .... 35·00
Z83 2r. carmine and yellow-brown .... 65·00

1906. (Nos. 149/50).
Z84 ½a. green .... 7·00
Z85 1a. carmine .... 8·00

1911–22. (Nos. 151/91).
Z86 3p. grey .... 12·00
Z87 ½a. green .... 6·00
Z88 1a. carmine .... 6·00
Z89 1½a. chocolate (Type A) .... 26·00
Z91 2a. purple .... 8·00
Z92 2a.6p. ultramarine (1912) .... 26·00
Z93 2a.6p. ultramarine (1913) .... 6·00
Z94 3a. orange .... 15·00
Z95 4a. olive-green .... 13·00
Z96 6a. brown-ochre .... 25·00

OFFICIAL STAMPS

1883–99. (Nos. O37a/48).
Z102 4a. olive-green .... 45·00

1900. (Nos. O49/52).
Z105 2a. mauve .... 45·00

1902–09. (Nos. O54/65).
Z108 1a. carmine .... 20·00
Z109 2a. mauve .... 20·00

1906. (Nos. O66/7).
Z112 1a. carmine .... 20·00

1912–13. (Nos. O73/96).
Z113 3p. grey .... 30·00
Z114 ½a. green .... 19·00
Z115 1a. carmine .... 15·00

1921. (No. O97).
Z118 9p. on 1a. rose-carmine .... 55·00

Bushire

An Iranian Gulf port, the British East India Company's factory was transferred there from Bandar Abbas in 1762 and a political agency established. An Indian postal agency was established in 1857 and it was on the regular steamer service operated between Bombay and Basra in 1862. The Indian post office was opened on 1 May 1864 and closed in 1923.

Z **14** Three thick lines in corners   Z **15** (19 mm)

Z **16**

Postmark type	Approx period of use
Z **1** ("308" in diamond of bars)	1865–70
Z **7** ("26")	1870–74
Z **8** (inscr "BUSHIR"/K-5)	1874–78
Z **8** (inscr "BASHIR"/K-5)	1878–80
Z **10** (inscr "BUSHIRE")	1880–82
Z **11** (inscr "BUSHIRE")	1882–85
Z **11** (c.d.s. only, inscr PAR/BUSHIRE)	?
Z **11** (c.d.s. only, inscr DEP/BUSHIRE)	?
Z **12** (inscr "BUSHIRE")	1884–99
Z **13** (inscr "BUSHIRE")	1885–1904
Z **15**	1887–1892
Z **14** (inscr "BUSHIRE")	1889–1902
Z **16** (inscr "BUSHIRE")	1892–97
Z **16** (inscr "BUSHIRF")	1897–1923
Z **15** (inscr BUSHIRE/REG)	1892–1915
Z **4** (inscr BUSHIRE)	1907–1915
Z **4** (inscr BUSHIRE/REG)	1902–1921

Stamps of India cancelled at Bushire

1854. (No. 14).
Z119 1a. dull red £800

1865. (Nos. 54/65).
Z120 ½a. blue .... 15·00
Z121 1a. brown .... 13·00
Z122 2a. orange .... 15·00
Z123 4a. green £120

1866–78. (Nos. 69/72).
Z125 4a. green (Die I) .... 38·00
Z126 4a. green (Die II) .... 16·00
Z127 6a.8p. slate £100

1868–73. (Nos. 73/6).
Z128 8a. rose (Die II) .... 40·00
Z129 ½a. blue (Die II) .... 5·50

1874–76. (Nos. 77/82).
Z130 1r. slate £130
Z131 6a. brown .... 23·00
Z132 12a. Venetian red .... 75·00

1882–90. (Nos. 84/101).
Z133 ½a. blue-green .... 3·25
Z135 1a. brown-purple .... 3·25
Z136 1½a. sepia .... 14·00
Z137 2a. blue .... 5·50
Z138 3a. orange .... 15·00
Z138a 3a. brown-orange .... 7·00
Z139 4a. olive-green .... 6·00
Z140 4a.6p. yellow-green .... 12·00
Z141 8a. magenta .... 9·00
Z142 12a. purple/red .... 35·00
Z143 1r. slate .... 25·00

1891. (No. 102).
Z144 2½a. on 4a.6p. yellow-green .... 9·00

1892–95. (Nos. 103/9).
Z145 2a.6p. yellow-green .... 4·25
Z146 1r. green and carmine .... 21·00
Z147 2r. carmine and yellow-brown .... 75·00
Z147a 3r. brown and green £100
Z147b 5r. ultramarine and violet £110

1898. (No. 110).
Z148 ¼ on ½a. blue-green .... 22·00

1899. (No. 111).
Z149 3p. aniline carmine .... 9·00

1900. (Nos. 112/18).
Z151 ½a. yellow-green .... 5·50
Z152 1a. carmine .... 8·00
Z153 2a. pale violet .... 10·00
Z154 2a.6p. ultramarine .... 7·50

1902–11. (Nos. 119/47).
Z155 3p. grey .... 10·00
Z156 ½a. green .... 6·50
Z157 1a. carmine .... 6·50
Z158 2a. mauve .... 7·00
Z159 2a.6p. ultramarine .... 3·25
Z160 3a. orange-brown .... 14·00
Z161 4a. olive .... 10·00
Z162 6a. maize .... 20·00
Z163 8a. purple .... 11·00
Z165 1r. green and carmine .... 30·00
Z170 15r. blue and olive-brown £150

1905. (No. 148).
Z171 ¼ on ½a green .... 18·00

1906. (Nos. 149/50).
Z172 ½a. green .... 4·25
Z173 1a. carmine .... 4·25

1911–22. (Nos. 151/91).
Z174 3p. grey .... 10·00
Z175 ½a. green .... 3·25
Z176 1a. carmine .... 3·25
Z177 1½a. chocolate (Type A) .... 19·00
Z178 1½a. chocolate (Type B) .... 45·00
Z179 2a. purple .... 6·50
Z180 2a.6p. ultramarine (1912) .... 20·00
Z181 2a.6p. ultramarine (1913) .... 4·25
Z182 3a. orange .... 5·50
Z183 4a. olive-green .... 12·00
Z184 6a. brown-ochre .... 16·00
Z185 8a. mauve .... 20·00
Z186 12a. carmine-lake .... 33·00
Z187 1r. brown and green .... 26·00
Z191 15r. blue and olive £140

1921. (No. 192).
Z192 9p. on 1a. rose-carmine .... 24·00

OFFICIAL STAMPS

1867–73. (Nos. O20/30a).
Z193 ½a. blue (Die I) .... 25·00
Z194 1a. brown .... 25·00
Z195 8a. rose .... 22·00

1874–82. (Nos. O31/35).
Z196 ½a. blue .... 24·00
Z198 2a. orange .... 20·00
Z199 2a. blue .... 20·00

1883–99. (Nos. O37a/48).
Z202 ½a. blue-green .... 15·00
Z203 1a. plum .... 15·00
Z204 2a. blue .... 19·00
Z205 4a. olive-green .... 20·00
Z207 1r. green and carmine .... 50·00

1900. (Nos. O49/52).
Z208 ½a. yellow-green .... 26·00
Z209 1a. carmine .... 19·00
Z210 2a. mauve .... 25·00

1902–09. (Nos. O54/65).
Z212 ½a. green .... 14·00
Z213 1a. carmine .... 9·00
Z214 2a. mauve .... 12·00
Z215 4a. olive .... 18·00

1906. (Nos. O66/67).
Z218 ½a. green .... 14·00
Z219 1a. carmine .... 12·00

1912–13. (Nos. O73/96).
Z221 ½a. green .... 12·00
Z222 1a. carmine .... 7·00
Z224 2a. purple .... 12·00

Bushire Camp

A sub-post office was opened in 1921 for troops of the South West Cordon Force. It closed in 1923.

Postmark type		Approx period of use
Z **3**	(inscr "BUSHIRE CAMP")	1921–22

Stamps of India cancelled at Bushire Camp

1911–22. (Nos. 151/91).

Z229	1a. carmine	
Z232	2a.6p. ultramarine (1913)	55·00
Z233	3a. orange	60·00
Z235	6a. brown-ochre	

OFFICIAL STAMPS

1902. (Nos. O54/65).

Z237	3p. grey	

1912–13. (Nos. O73/96).

Z239	3p. grey	
Z240	½a. green	55·00
Z242	2a. mauve	

Chahbar

A port on the Gulf of Oman, the Indian post office was opened on 20 August 1913 and closed on 31 March 1923.

Postmark type		Approx period of use
Z **3**	(inscr "CHAHBAR/B.O./PERSIAN GULF")	1914–1923

Stamps of India cancelled at Chahbar

1902–11. (Nos. 119/47).

Z244	3p. grey	90·00

1906. (Nos. 149/50).

Z247	1a. carmine	£100

1911–22. (Nos. 151/91).

Z249	½a. green	90·00
Z250	1a. carmine	90·00
Z252	2a. mauve	£120

Duzdab

A small town near the frontier with India, an Indian exchange post office was opened in 1921 and closed in 1925.

Henjam

An island in the Straits of Hormuz, it was for a time a British Naval Station and telegraph relay station. The Indian post office opened on 21 June 1913 and closed in 1923.

Postmark type		Approx period of use
Z **3**	(Inscr "HENJAM/B.O./PERSIAN GULF")	1914–1922

Stamps of India cancelled at Henjam

1906. (Nos. 149/50).

Z254	½a. green	90·00

1911–22. (Nos. 151/91).

Z256	3p. grey	£100
Z257	½a. green	55·00
Z258	1a. carmine	85·00
Z260	2a. purple	£100
Z261	2a.6p. ultramarine (1913)	£110

OFFICIAL STAMPS

1912–13. (Nos. O73/96).

Z268	4a. olive-green	£200

Jask

A port on the Gulf of Oman and site of the British East India Company's first factory in 1619, the Indian post office opened on 1 September 1880 and closed on 20 March 1923.

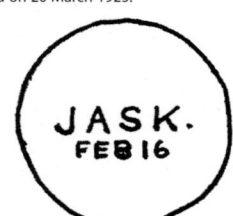

Z **17** As Z **9**/Z **10** but without obliterator

Postmark type		Approx period of use
Z **17**		1884–1888
Z **14**	(inscr JASK)	1889–1912
Z **3**	(inscr JASK/B.O.PERSIAN GULF)	1914–1920

Stamps of India cancelled at Jask

1865. (Nos. 54/65).

Z270	½a. blue	50·00

1866–78. (Nos. 69/72).

Z273	4a. green	£100

1882–90. (Nos. 84/101).

Z276	½a. blue-green	24·00
Z278	1a. brown-purple	28·00
Z281	3a. orange	45·00
Z285	12a. purple/*red*	80·00

1891. (No. 102).

Z286	2½a. on 4a.6p. yellow-green	50·00

1892–97. (Nos. 103/09).

Z287	2a.6p. yellow-green	24·00

1898. (No. 110).

Z289	¼ on ½a. blue-green	65·00

1899. (No. 111).

Z290	3p. aniline-carmine	40·00

1900. (Nos. 112/18).

Z294	2a.6p. ultramarine	30·00

1902–11. (Nos. 119/47).

Z296	½a. green	27·00
Z297	1a. carmine	27·00
Z298	2a. mauve	30·00
Z299	2a.6p. ultramarine	21·00

1906–07. (Nos. 149/50).

Z303	½a. green	21·00
Z304	1a. carmine	21·00

1911–22. (Nos. 151/91).

Z306	½a. green	42·00
Z307	1a. carmine	28·00
Z310	2a. purple	32·00
Z311	2a.6p. ultramarine (1913)	42·00
Z315	8a. mauve	90·00
Z316	12a. carmine-lake	90·00

OFFICIAL STAMPS

1902–09. (Nos. O54/69).

Z320	3p. grey	55·00

1906. (Nos. O66/7).

Z322	½a. green	32·00
Z323	1a. carmine	40·00

Kuh-Malik-Siah-Ziarat

A few miles north of Duzdab, where the frontiers of Iran, India and Afghanistan meet, an Indian exchange post office was open by January 1906. It closed in mid–1924.

Linga

A Persian Gulf port to the west of Bandar Abbas, the Indian post office there was opened on 1 April 1867. Linga was added to the regular ports of call of the Bombay–Basra steamer service in 1870. The post office closed in 1923.

Z **18** 25 mm small date

Postmark type		Approx period of use
Z **7**	(numeral "21")	1872–1875
Z **8**	(2/K-5)	1876–1880
Z **10**	(inscr "LINGA")	1880–82
Z **11**	(inscr LINGA)	1885
Z **14**	(inscr LINGA)	1882–1905
Z **12**	(inscr LINGA)	1900–1902
Z **13**	(inscr LINGA)	1905–1922
Z **18**		1912
Z **2**	(inscr LINGA)	1920–1923
Z **3**	(inscr LINGA)	1920

Stamps of India cancelled at Linga.

1865. (Nos. 54/65).

Z327	½a. blue	22·00
Z328	1a. brown	21·00
Z329	2a. orange	40·00

1866–78. (Nos. 69/72).

Z330	4a. green (Die I)	60·00
Z331	4a. green (Die II)	50·00

1868–76. (Nos. 73/82).

Z332	8a. rose	75·00
Z333	½a. blue (Die II)	11·00
Z334	6a. pale brown	42·00
Z335	12a. Venetian red	90·00

1882–90. (Nos. 84/101).

Z336	½a. blue-green	5·50
Z338	1a. plum	7·50
Z340	2a. blue	8·00
Z341	3a. orange	25·00
Z341*a*	3a. brown-orange	12·00
Z342	4a. olive-green	17·00
Z343	4a.6p. yellow-green	25·00
Z344	8a. mauve	30·00
Z345	12a. purple/*red*	42·00
Z346	1r. slate	42·00

1891. (No. 102).

Z347	2½a. on 4a.6p. yellow-green	25·00

1892–97. (Nos. 103/9).

Z348	2a.6p. yellow-green	8·50
Z349	1r. green and carmine	65·00
Z351	3r. brown and green	£130

1899. (No. 111).

Z352	3p. aniline carmine	11·00

1900–02. (Nos. 112/18).

Z353	3p. grey	55·00
Z354	½a. yellow-green	8·00
Z355	1a. green	13·00
Z356	2a. mauve	22·00
Z357	2a.6p. ultramarine	15·00

1902–11. (Nos. 119/47).

Z358	3p. grey	16·00
Z359	½a. green	6·00
Z360	1a. carmine	7·00
Z361		7·50
Z362	2a.6p. ultramarine	6·00
Z363	3a. orange-brown	16·00
Z364	4a. olive	16·00
Z368	1r. green and carmine	28·00
Z369	2r. carmine and yellow-brown	70·00

1906. (Nos. 149/50).

Z372	½a. green	7·00
Z373	1a. carmine	9·00

1911–22. (Nos. 151/91).

Z374	3p. grey	18·00
Z375	½a. green	5·00
Z376	1a. carmine	6·00
Z377	1½a. chocolate (Type A)	24·00
Z378	2a. purple	9·50
Z379	2a.6p. ultramarine (1912)	24·00
Z380	2a.6p. ultramarine (1913)	7·00
Z381	3a. orange	11·00
Z382	4a. olive-green	16·00
Z383	6a. brown-ochre	20·00

OFFICIAL STAMPS

1883–99. (Nos. O37*a*/48).

Z390	1a. plum	38·00

1906. (Nos. O66/7).

Z399	1a. carmine	38·00

1912–13. (Nos. O73/96).

Z401	½a. green	22·00
Z402	1a. carmine	24·00
Z403	2a. purple	38·00

Maidan-i-Naphtun

The site of the original oil find in Iran in the early part of the 20th-century, an Indian post office was opened during World War 1. It was closed in 1923.

Z **19**

Postmark type		Approx period of use
Z **19**		1917–1920
Z **3**	(inscr "MAIADN-I-NAPHTUN/REG")*	1922–1923

Stamps of India cancelled at Maidan-i-Naphtun

1911–22. (Nos. 151/91).

Z406	½a. green	£100
Z407	1a. carmine	£110
Z409	2a. purple	£130
Z410	2½a. ultramarine (1913)	£120
Z411	3a. orange	£150

*The "REG" c.d.s. (as Type Z **3**) shows the "MAIADN" spelling error.

Mirjawa

On the border with India (now Pakistan), an Indian post office was opened in 1921 to service the needs of a railway construction project. It was closed by 1931.

Postmark type		Approx period of use
Z **3**	(inscr "MIRJAWA")	1926

Stamps of India cancelled at Mirjawa

1911–22. (Nos. 151/91).

Z415	1½a. chocolate (Type A)	£120
Z418	2½a. ultramarine	
Z422	8a. mauve	

OFFICIAL STAMPS

1912–13. (Nos. O73/96).

Z426	3p. grey	£120
Z428	1a. carmine	
Z429	2a. purple	£130

1922. (No. O98).

Z433	1a. chocolate	

Mohammera

Now known as Khorramshahr, Mohammerah was the chief port of Iran, on the Shatt-el-Arab. The first Indian post office was opened in 1892 and closed in 1923.

Postmark type		Approx period of use
Z **16**	(inscr "MAHOMMERAH")	1894–1911
Z **16**	(inscr "MOHAMMERAH")	1896–1904
Z **4**	(inscr "MOHAMMERA")	1904–1918
Z **4**	(inscr "MOHAMMERA")	1910–1918
Z **13**	(inscr "MOHAMMERA")	1905–1923
Z **3**	(inscr "MOHOMMERAH")	1919–1923

Stamps of India cancelled at Mohammera

1882–90. (Nos. 84/101).
Z434	½a. blue-green		8·50
Z435	1a. brown-purple		13·00
Z437	2a. blue		17·00
Z438	3a. brown-orange		26·00
Z439	4a. olive-green		30·00

1892–97. (Nos. 103/09).
Z440	2a.6p. yellow-green		8·50
Z441	1r. green and carmine		50·00
Z443	3r. brown and green		£140

1899. (No. 111).
Z444	3p. aniline carmine		18·00

1900. (Nos. 112/18).
Z445	½a. yellow-green		9·00
Z446	1a. carmine		13·00
Z447	2a. pale violet		18·00
Z448	2a.6p. ultramarine		15·00

1902–11. (Nos. 119/47).
Z449	3p. grey		14·00
Z450	½a. green		6·50
Z451	1a. carmine		7·50
Z452	2a. mauve		8·00
Z453	2a.6p. ultramarine		4·50
Z454	3a. orange-brown		18·00
Z455	4a. olive		14·00
Z456	6a. olive-bistre		35·00
Z457	8a. purple		35·00
Z458	1r. green and carmine		45·00

1905. (No. 148).
Z459	¼ on ½a. green		20·00

1906. (Nos. 149/50).
Z460	½a. green		6·50
Z461	1a. carmine		6·50

1911–22. (Nos. 151/91).
Z462	3p. grey		15·00
Z463	½a. green		3·25
Z464	1a. carmine		3·25
Z465	1½a. chocolate (Type A)		19·00
Z466	2a. purple		5·50
Z467	2a.6p. ultramarine (1912)		20·00
Z468	2a.6p. ultramarine (1913)		4·50
Z469	3a. orange		7·00
Z470	4a. olive-green		9·00
Z471	6a. yellow-bistre		32·00
Z472	8a. mauve		20·00
Z474	1r. brown and green		21·00
Z475	2r. carmine and brown		45·00

1922–26. (Nos. 197/200).
Z481	1a. chocolate		16·00

OFFICIAL STAMPS

1883–99. (Nos. O37a/48).
Z482	1a. brown-purple		28·00

1902–09. (Nos. O54/65).
Z485	1a. carmine		26·00
Z486	2a. mauve		
Z488	6a. olive-bistre		

1906. (Nos. O66/67).
Z490	½a. green		16·00

1912–13. (Nos. O73/96).
Z493	½a. green		15·00
Z494	1a. carmine		13·00
Z495	2a. purple		28·00

IRAQ*

Unoverprinted stamps of India used from 1868 until 1918.

KUWAIT*

Unoverprinted stamps of India used from 1904 until 1923.

MALAYA (STRAITS SETTLEMENTS)*

Unoverprinted stamps of India used from 1854 until 1867.

MUSCAT*

Unoverprinted stamps of India used from 1864 until 1947.

NEPAL

A post office was opened in the British Residency at Kathmandu in 1816 following the end of the Gurkha War. Stamps of India were used from 1854, initially with "B137", "137" or "C-37" numeral cancellations. The Residency Post Office continued to provide the overseas mail service after Nepal introduced its own issues in 1881.

In 1920 the Residency Post Office became the British Legation Post Office. On the independence of India in 1947 the service was transferred to the Indian Embassy and continued to function until 1965.

PORTUGUESE INDIA

A British post office was open in Damaun by 1823 and Indian stamps were used there until November 1883, some with "13" and "3/B-19" numeral cancellations.

No other British post offices were opened in the Portuguese territories, but from 1854 Indian stamps were sold by the local post offices. Between 1871 and 1877 mail intended for, or passing through, British India required combined franking of India and Portuguese India issues. After 1877 the two postal administrations accepted the validity of each other's stamps.

SOMALILAND PROTECTORATE*

Unoverprinted stamps of India used from 1887 until 1903.

TIBET

The first Indian post office in Tibet accompanied the Tibetan Frontier Commission in 1903. The Younghusband Military Expedition to Lhasa in the following year operated a number of Field Post Offices which were replaced by civil post offices at Gartok (opened 23 September 1906), Gyantse (opened March 1905), Pharijong (opened 1905) and Yatung (opened 1905). All Indian post offices in Tibet closed on 1 April 1955 except Gartok which, it is believed, did not operate after 1943. A temporary post office, C-622, operated at Gyantse between July 1954 and August 1955 following a flood disaster.

TRUCIAL STATES*

Unoverprinted stamps of India used at Dubai from 19 August 1909 until 1947.

ZANZIBAR*

Unoverprinted stamps of India used from 1875 until 1895.

CHINA EXPEDITIONARY FORCE

Following the outbreak of the Boxer Rising in North China the Peking Legations were besieged by the rebels in June 1900. An international force, including an Indian Army division, was assembled for their relief. The Legations were relieved on 14 August 1900, but operations against the Boxers continued in North China with Allied garrisons at key cities and along the Peking–Tientsin–Shanhaikwan railway. The last Indian Army battalion, and accompanying Field Post Offices, did not leave North China until 1 November 1923.

Field Post Offices accompanied the Indian troops and commenced operations on 23 July 1900 using unoverprinted Indian postage and official stamps. The unoverprinted postage issues were replaced in mid-August by stamps overprinted "C.E.F." to prevent currency speculation. The use of unoverprinted official stamps continued as they were not valid for public postage.

PRICES FOR STAMPS ON COVER	
Nos. C1/10	from × 15
No. C10c	†
Nos. C11/22	from × 8
Nos. C23	from × 10
Nos. C24/5	from × 20
Nos. C26/8	from × 4
Nos. C29/34	from × 3

C. E. F.
(C 1)

Stamps of India overprinted with Type C 1, in black

1900 (16 Aug). Stamps of Queen Victoria.
C1	**40**	3p. carmine	40	1·25
		a. No stop after "F"	£275	
		b. Opt double, one albino	£180	
		c. No stop after "C" (R. 1/2)		
C2	**23**	½a. blue-green	1·00	30
		a. No stop after "F"	£300	
		b. Opt double		
C3	**25**	1a. plum	4·50	1·50
		a. No stop after "F"	£450	
C4	**27**	2a. pale blue	3·50	9·00
		a. No stop after "F"	£475	
C5	**36**	2a.6p. green	3·25	17·00
		a. No stop after "F"	£650	
C6	**28**	3a. brown-orange	3·25	18·00
		a. No stop after "F"	£650	
		b. Opt double, one albino	£140	
C7	**29**	4a. slate-green	3·25	9·50
		a. No stop after "F"	£650	
		b. Opt double, one albino	£160	
C8	**31**	8a. magenta	3·25	27·00
		a. No stop after "F"	£750	
		b. Opt double, one albino	£160	
C9	**32**	12a. purple/*red*	19·00	16·00
		a. No stop after "F"	£900	
		b. Opt double, one albino	£180	
C10	**37**	1r. green and carmine	45·00	48·00
		a. No stop after "F"	£1000	£1000
		b. Opt double, one albino	£250	
C1/10 *Set of 10*			75·00	£130

Prepared, but not issued
C10c	**26**	1a.6p. sepia	£450	†

The missing stop after "F" variety occurs in the ninth row of the upper pane on one printing only.

1904 (27 Feb).
C11	**25**	1a. carmine	50·00	8·00

1905 (16 Sept)–**11.** Stamps of King Edward VII.
C12	**41**	3p. grey (4.11)	12·00	9·50
		a. Opt double, one albino	£130	
		b. Opt triple, one albino	£450	
		c. *Slate-grey*	12·00	9·50
C13	**43**	1a. carmine	13·00	70
		a. Opt double, one albino	£100	
C14	**44**	2a. mauve (11.3.11)	15·00	6·00
		a. Opt double, one albino	£140	
C15	**45**	2a.6p. ultramarine (11.3.11)	4·00	5·00
C16	**46**	3a. orange-brown (11.3.11)	4·25	4·25
C17	**47**	4a. olive-green (11.3.11)	9·00	21·00
C18	**49**	8a. claret (11.3.11)	9·00	8·50
		a. *Purple*	85·00	65·00
C19	**50**	12a. purple/*red* (1909)	11·00	19·00
		a. No stop after "E"	£850	
C20	**51**	1r. green and carmine (11.3.11)	17·00	48·00
C12/20 *Set of 9*			85·00	£110

1908 (Dec)–**09.** "POSTAGE & REVENUE".
C21	**53**	½a. green (No. 149) (29.9.09)	1·75	1·50
		a. Opt double, one albino	£120	
C22	**54**	1a. carmine (No. 150)	7·50	30
		a. Opt double, one albino	£160	

1914 (5 May)–**22.** Stamps of King George V. Wmk Star.
C23	**55**	3p. grey (7.10.14)	10·00	48·00
		a. Opt double, one albino	£400	
C24	**56**	½a. light green	4·00	8·50
		a. *Emerald*	—	80·00
C25	**57**	1a. aniline carmine	5·00	4·00
C26	**58**	1½a. chocolate (Type A) (9.3.21)	40·00	£130
		a. Opt double, one albino	£250	
C27	**59**	2a. purple (11.19)	35·00	85·00
		a. *Deep mauve*	55·00	95·00
		ab. Opt triple	£700	
C28	**61**	2a.6p. bright blue (2.19)	24·00	29·00
C29	**62**	3a. orange (5.22)	48·00	£300
C30	**63**	4a. olive-green (5.22)	42·00	£250
		a. Opt double, one albino	£450	
C32	**65**	8a. deep mauve (12.21)	42·00	£475
C33	**66**	12a. carmine-lake (8.20)	42·00	£160
C34	**67**	1r. brown and green (10.21)	£120	£475
C23/34 *Set of 11*			£350	£1800

Most dates quoted for Nos. C23/34 are those of the earliest recorded postmarks.

On No. C27*a* two of the overprints are only lightly inked.

BRITISH RAILWAY ADMINISTRATION

As a vital communications link the North China Railway (Peking–Tientsin–Shanhaikwan) was captured by Russian forces during operations against the Boxers. Control of the line was subsequently, in February 1901, assigned to the China Expeditionary Force and a British Railway Administration was set up to run it. By international agreement the line was to provide postal services for the other national contingents and also, to a lesser extent, for the civilian population. Travelling post offices were introduced and, on 20 April 1901, a late letter service for which an additional fee of 5c. was charged.

B.R.A.
5
Five Cents
Type **32** of China
(BR **35**)

1901 (20 Apr). No. 108 of China surch with Type BR **35**.
BR133	**32**	5c. on ½c. brown (Bk.)	£450	£110
		a. Surch inverted	£10000	£2750
		b. Surch in green	£400	£150
		ba. Imperf between (horiz pair)	†	£20000

No. BR133 was used for the collection of the 5c. late letter fee and was affixed to correspondence by a postal official at the railway station. It was cancelled with a violet circular postmark showing "RAILWAY POST OFFICE" at top and the name of the station (PEKING, TIENTSIN, TONGKU, TONGSHAN or SHANHAIKWAN) at foot. With the exception of official mail it could only be used in combination with Indian stamps overprinted "C.E.F.", stamps from the other allied contingents or of the Chinese Imperial Post (*Price used on cover*: No. BR133 *from* £350. No. BR133*b from* £400).

It is suggested that stamps overprinted in black were used at Tientsin and Tongku with those in green being available at Peking, Tongshan and Shanhaikwan.

The late fee charge was abolished on 20 May 1901 and No. BR133 was then withdrawn. The British Railway Administration continued to run the line, and its travelling post offices, until it was returned to its private owners in September 1902.

INDIAN EXPEDITIONARY FORCES
1914–21

Nos. E1/13 were for use of Indian forces sent overseas during the First World War and its aftermath. Examples were first used in France during September 1914. Other areas where the stamps were used included East Africa, Mesopotamia and Turkey. "I.E.F." overprints ceased to be valid for postage on 15 October 1921.

PRICES FOR STAMPS ON COVER	
Nos. E1/13	from × 10

I. E. F.
(E 1)

1914 (Sept). Stamps of India (King George V) optd with Type E **1.**
E1	**55**	3p. grey	15	30
		a. No stop after "F"	27·00	45·00
		b. No stop after "E"	£180	£180
		c. Opt double	50·00	50·00
		d. Opt double, one albino	£120	
E2	**56**	½a. light green	50	30
		a. No stop after "F"	£120	£120
		b. Opt double	£140	£275
E3	**57**	1a. aniline carmine	1·25	30
		a. No stop after "F"	32·00	42·00
E4		1a. carmine	6·50	6·50
E5	**59**	2a. purple	1·25	30
		a. No stop after "F"	80·00	95·00
		b. No stop after "E"	£425	£450
E6	**61**	2a.6p. ultramarine	1·50	3·50
		a. No stop after "F"	£300	£325
E7	**62**	3a. orange	1·00	1·50
		a. No stop after "F"	£275	

E8	63	4a. olive-green	1·00	1·50
		a. No stop after "F"	£425	£450
E9	65	8a. deep magenta	1·25	2·50
		a. No stop after "F"	£425	£450
E10		8a. deep mauve	11·00	19·00
E11	66	12a. carmine-lake	2·25	6·00
		a. No stop after "F"	£500	£500
		b. Opt double, one albino	60·00	
E12		12a. claret		
E13	67	1r. red-brown and deep blue-green	4·00	4·25
		a. Opt double, one albino	£100	
		b. Brown and green	3·50	5·00
E1/13	*Set of 10*		12·00	18·00

The "no stop after F" variety occurred on R. 4/12 of the upper pane, in one printing.

No. E11b comes from a sheet issued at Basra in February 1916.

INDIAN CUSTODIAN FORCES IN KOREA

भारतीय
संरक्षा कटक
कोरिया
(K **1**)

1953 (17 Oct). Stamps of India optd with Type K **1**.

K1	307	3p. slate-violet	3·00	11·00
K2	308	6p. purple-brown	1·50	9·00
K3	309	9p. yellow-green	3·00	8·50
K4	328	1a. turquoise	1·50	4·75
K5	311	2a. carmine	1·50	4·75
K6	313	2½a. lake	1·50	5·50
K7	312	3a. brown-orange	1·50	8·50
K8	314	4a. bright blue	2·25	4·75
K9	315	6a. violet	12·00	9·00
K10	316	8a. turquoise-green	2·25	17·00
K11	317	12a. dull blue	2·25	17·00
K12	318	1r. dull violet and green	9·00	17·00
K1/12	*Set of 12*		38·00	£100

INDIAN U.N. FORCE IN CONGO

U.N. FORCE
(INDIA)
CONGO
(U **1**)

1962 (15 Jan). Stamps of India optd with Type U **1**. W **69** (sideways) (13n.p.) or W **374** (others).

U1	361	1n.p. blue-green	1·00	6·50
U2		2n.p. light brown	1·00	4·00
U3		5n.p. bright green	1·00	1·00
U4		8n.p. light blue-green	1·00	40
U5		13n.p. bright carmine-red	1·00	40
U6		50n.p. orange	1·00	70
U1/6	*Set of 6*		5·50	11·50

INDIAN U.N. FORCE IN GAZA (PALESTINE) UNEF

UNEF
(G **1**)

1965 (15 Jan). No. 492 of India optd with Type G **1**.

G1	449	15p. slate (C.)	3·50	10·00

INTERNATIONAL COMMISSION IN INDO-CHINA

The International Control Commissions for Indo-China were established in August 1954 as part of the Geneva Declaration which partitioned Vietnam and sought to achieve stable settlements in Cambodia and Laos. The three supervisory commissions were chaired by India with Canada and Poland as the other members. Joint inspection teams of servicemen from the three countries were also provided.

The Indian contingent included a postal unit which handled mail for the three commissions and the inspection teams. The unit arrived in Indo-China on 3 September 1954 and opened field post offices at Saigon (F.P.O. 742), Hanoi (F.P.O. 743), Vientiane (F.P.O. 744) and Phnom Penh (F.P.O. 745).

अन्तर्राष्ट्रीय आयोग कम्बोज (N **1**)	अन्तर्राष्ट्रीय आयोग लाओस (N **2**)	अन्तर्राष्ट्रीय आयोग वियत नाम (N **3**)	

1954 (1 Dec). Stamps of India. W **69**.

*(a) Optd as Type N **1**, for use in Cambodia*

N1	307	3p. slate-violet	2·75	15·00
N2	328	1a. turquoise	1·25	1·00
N3	311	2a. carmine	1·25	1·00
N4	316	8a. turquoise-green	1·75	4·00
N5	317	12a. dull blue	2·00	4·00

*(b) Optd as Type N **2**, for use in Laos*

N6	307	3p. slate-violet	2·75	15·00
N7	328	1a. turquoise	1·25	1·00
N8	311	2a. carmine	1·25	1·00
N9	316	8a. turquoise-green	1·75	3·00
N10	317	12a. dull blue	2·00	3·00

*(c) Optd as Type N **3**, for use in Vietnam*

N11	307	3p. slate-violet	2·75	9·00
N12	328	1a. turquoise	1·25	1·00
N13	311	2a. carmine	1·25	1·00
N14	316	8a. turquoise-green	1·75	3·00
N15	317	12a. dull blue	2·00	3·00
N1/15	*Set of 15*		24·00	55·00

1957 (1 Apr). Stamps of India. W **69** (sideways).

*(a) Optd as Type N **1**, for use in Cambodia*

N16	361	2n.p. light brown	75	30
N17		6n.p. grey	50	30
N18		13n.p. bright carmine-red	70	40
N19		50n.p. orange	2·25	1·25
N20		75n.p. reddish purple	2·25	1·25

*(b) Optd as Type N **2**, for use in Laos*

N21	361	2n.p. light brown	75	30
N22		6n.p. grey	50	30
N23		13n.p. bright carmine-red	70	40
N24		50n.p. orange	2·25	1·25
N25		75n.p. reddish purple	2·25	1·25

*(c) Optd as Type N **3**, for use in Vietnam*

N26	361	2n.p. light brown	75	30
N27		6n.p. grey	50	30
N28		13n.p. bright carmine-red	70	40
N29		50n.p. orange	2·25	1·25
N30		75n.p. reddish purple	2·25	1·25
N16/30	*Set of 15*		17·00	9·50

F.P.O. 744 (Vientiane) was closed on 25 July 1958 and F.P.O. 745 (Phnom Penh) on 26 June 1958.

1960 (Sept)–**65**. Stamps of India. W **374**.

*(a) Optd as Type N **2** for use in Laos*

N38	361	2n.p. light brown (15.1.62)	15	3·25
N39		3n.p. deep brown (1.8.63)	10	60
N40		5n.p. bright green (1.8.63)	10	20
N41		50n.p. orange (1965)	7·00	6·00
N42		75n.p. reddish purple (1965)	7·00	6·00

*(b) Optd as Type N **3**, for use in Vietnam*

N43	361	1n.p. blue-green	10	25
N44		2n.p. light brown (15.1.62)	15	3·25
N45		3n.p. deep brown (1.8.63)	10	60
N46		5n.p. bright green (1.8.63)	10	20
N47		50n.p. orange (1965)	7·00	6·00
N48		75n.p. reddish purple (1965)	7·00	6·00
N38/48	*Set of 11*		25·00	29·00

F.P.O. 744 (Vientiane) re-opened on 22 May 1961.

Examples of the 2n.p. value overprinted as Type N **1** for use in Cambodia exist, but were never placed on sale there as the Phnom Penh F.P.O. 745 was closed on 26 June 1958. Used examples appear to originate from unauthorised use of the F.P.O. 745 postmark which was in store at Saigon (*Price* 15p, *unused*).

अंग्रेज

ICC   ICC
(N **4**)   (N **5**)

1965 (15 Jan). No. 492 of India optd with Type N **4**, for use in Laos and Vietnam.

N49	449	15p. slate (C.)	1·00	6·00

F.P.O. 743 (Hanoi) was closed on 13 July 1966.

1968 (2 Oct). Nos. 504/5, 506, 509/10, 515 and 517/18 etc of India optd as Type N **5**, in red, for use in Laos and Vietnam.

N50		2p. red-brown	10	4·25
N51		3p. brown-olive	10	4·25
N52		5p. cerise	10	2·50
N53		10p. new blue	3·25	3·50
N54		15p. bronze-green	60	3·50
N55		60p. deep grey	35	2·50
N56		1r. red-brown and plum	50	3·50
N57		2r. new blue and deep slate-violet	1·50	13·00
N50/7	*Set of 8*		5·75	32·00

INDIAN NATIONAL ARMY

The following were prepared for use in the Japanese occupied areas of India during the drive on Imphal.

Genuine examples are inscribed "PROVISIONAL GOVERNMENT OF FREE INDIA". Forgeries also exist inscribed "PROVISIONAL GOVT. OF FREE INDIA".

Typo in Rangoon. No gum. Perf 11½ or imperf. 1p. violet, 1p. maroon, 1a. green. *Price from £70 each unused.*

Ten stamps, sharing six different designs, inscribed "AZAD HIND", were produced in Germany during the Second World War, but did no postal duty.

JAPANESE OCCUPATION OF THE ANDAMAN AND NICOBAR ISLANDS

The Andaman Islands in the Bay of Bengal were occupied on the 23 March 1942 and the Nicobar Islands in July 1942. Civil administration was resumed in October 1945.

The following Indian stamps were surcharged with large figures preceded by a decimal point:—

Postage stamps—.3 on ½a. (No. 248), .5 on 1a. (No. 250), .10 on 2a. (No. 236b), .30 on 6a. (No. 274).

Official stamps—.10 on 1a.3p. (No. O146a), .20 on 3p. (No. O143), .20 in red on 3p. (No. O143).

Prices from £450 each unused.

INDIAN CONVENTION STATES

The following issues resulted from a series of postal conventions agreed between the Imperial Government and the state administrations of Patiala (1 October 1884), Gwalior, Jind and Nabha (1 July 1885), and Chamba and Faridkot (1 January 1887).

Under the terms of these conventions the British Indian Post Office supplied overprinted British India issues to the state administrations which, in turn, had to conform to a number of conditions covering the issue of stamps, rates of postage and the exchange of mail.

Such overprinted issues were valid for postage within the state of issue, to other "Convention States" and to destinations in British India. Stamps of Chamba, Gwalior, Jind, Nabha and Patiala ceased to be valid for postage on 1 January 1951, when they were replaced by those of the Republic of India, valid from 1 April 1950.

RULERS OF INDIAN CONVENTION AND FEUDATORY STATES. Details of the rulers of the various states during the period when stamps were issued are now provided in a somewhat simplified form which omits reference to minor titles. Dates quoted are of the various reigns, extended to 1971 when the titles of the surviving rulers of the former princely states were abolished by the Indian Government.

During the absorption of the Convention and Feudatory States there was often an interim period during which the administration was handed over. In some instances it is only possible to quote the end of this interim period as the point of transfer.

STAMPS OF INDIA OVERPRINTED

In the Queen Victoria issues we omit varieties due to broken type, including the numerous small "A" varieties which may have come about through damaged type. We do, however, list the small "G", small "R" and tall "R" in "GWALIOR" as these were definitely the result of the use of type of the wrong size.

Variations in the length of the words due to unequal spacing when setting are also omitted.

PRICES. Prices quoted for unused stamps are for examples with original fresh colour and gum, in the case of King George VI issues from 1937). Stamps which have become toned by climate are worth much less. Prices for used stamps are for stamps with clearly identifiable authentic postmarks, and collectors should exercise caution when acquiring any stamps where the used prices are significantly higher than those quoted for unused, as many forgeries are in circulation.

FORGERIES. The Convention States overprints have been extensively forged on both unused and previously used Indian stamps, and rarities, particularly the errors of the Queen Victoria period, should not be purchased without a reliable guarantee. Also, genuine unused stamps have often been provided with forged postmarks; this applies especially to the King George VI period, and such stamps should only be acquired from reputable sources.

CHAMBA

PRICES FOR STAMPS ON COVER	
Nos. 1/27	from × 20
Nos. 28/120	from × 12
Nos. O1/86	from × 25

Raja Sham Singh, 1873–1904

CHAMBA STATE (1)   CHAMBA (2)

1887 (1 Jan)–**95**. Queen Victoria. Optd with T **1**.

1	23	½a. blue-green	2·25	2·00
		a. "CHMABA"	£800	£1200
		b. "8TATE"	£1000	
		c. Opt double	£650	
2	25	1a. brown-purple	4·25	4·50
		a. "CHMABA"	£800	£1000
		b. "8TATE"	£2250	
3		1a. plum	4·75	4·50
4	26	1a.6p. sepia (1895)	5·50	20·00
5	27	2a. dull blue	4·25	4·75
		b. "CHMABA"	£3250	£4250
		c. "8TATE"	£3000	
6		2a. ultramarine	3·50	3·75
7	36	2a.6p. green (1895)	50·00	£160
8	28	3a. orange (1887)	28·00	35·00
9		3a. brown-orange (1891)	4·25	8·00
		a. "CHMABA"	£7500	£10000
		b. Opt inverted		
10	29	4a. olive-green	9·00	16·00
		a. "CHMABA"	£2750	£4250
		b. "8TATE"	£7000	
11		4a. slate-green	8·50	20·00
		a. Opt double, one albino	£130	
12	21	6a. olive-bistre (1890)	10·00	28·00
		a. Opt treble, two albino	£160	
		b. Opt double, one albino	£120	
13		6a. bistre-brown	25·00	28·00
14	31	8a. dull mauve (1887)	14·00	19·00
		a. "CHMABA"	£5500	£5500
15		8a. magenta (1895)	13·00	26·00
16	32	12a. purple/red (1890)	8·50	21·00
		a. "CHMABA"	£16000	
		b. First "T" in "STATE" inverted	£16000	
		c. Opt double, one albino	80·00	
17	33	1r. slate (1887)	80·00	£200
		a. "CHMABA"	£21000	
18	37	1r. green and carmine (1895)	16·00	24·00
		a. Opt double one albino	£110	
19	38	2r. carmine and yellow-brown (1895)	£190	£550
20		3r. brown and green (1895)	£190	£475
21		5r. ultramarine and violet (1895)	£225	£950
		a. Opt double, one albino	£375	
1/21	*Set of 15*		£750	£2250

The "8TATE" error occurred once per sheet in the October 1886 printing. The "CHMABA" error occurred once per sheet in the July 1891 printing.

1900–04. Colours changed.

22	40	3p. carmine	1·25	1·75
		a. Opt double, one albino	70·00	
23		3p. grey (1904)	1·00	3·50
		a. Opt inverted	£100	
24	23	½a. pale yellow-green (1902)	4·00	6·50
25		½a. yellow-green (1903)	1·25	2·75
26	25	1a. carmine (1902)	2·50	60
27	27	2a. pale violet (1903)	19·00	50·00
22/7	*Set of 5*		22·00	50·00

Raja Bhuri Singh, 1904–1919

1903–05. King Edward VII. Optd with T 1.

28	**41**	3p. pale grey	25	2·00
29		3p. slate-grey (1905)	75	2·00
30	**42**	½a. green	2·75	1·75
31	**43**	1a. carmine	2·75	2·25
32	**44**	2a. pale violet (1904)	3·50	5·50
33		2a. mauve	3·00	5·50
34	**46**	3a. orange-brown (1905)	8·00	9·50
		a. Opt double, one albino	75·00	
35	**47**	4a. olive (1904)	13·00	40·00
36	**48**	6a. olive-bistre (1905)	7·50	40·00
		a. Opt double, one albino	70·00	
37	**49**	8a. purple (*shades*) (1904)	11·00	38·00
38		8a. claret	26·00	48·00
39	**50**	12a. purple/*red* (1905)	13·00	55·00
		a. Opt double, one albino	75·00	
40	**51**	1r. green and carmine (1904)	12·00	38·00
		a. Opt double, one albino	95·00	
28/40 *Set of 10*			65·00	£200

1907. Nos. 149/50 of India optd with T 1.

41	**53**	½a. green	3·00	4·00
		a. Opt double, one albino	65·00	
42	**54**	1a. carmine	3·75	5·00

1913. King George V optd with T 1.

43	**55**	3p. grey	40	1·50
		a. *Pale grey*	3·00	
		b. *Bluish grey*	3·75	
44	**56**	½a. light green	3·50	3·75
		a. *Emerald*	4·75	5·50
		b. *Bright green*	4·00	
		w. Wmk inverted		
45	**57**	1a. rose-carmine	20·00	22·00
		a. *Aniline carmine*	3·75	7·00
		ab. Opt double, one albino	80·00	
47	**59**	2a. purple	7·00	21·00
		a. *Reddish purple*	12·00	22·00
		b. *Deep mauve*	14·00	
		c. *Bright reddish violet*	16·00	
48	**62**	3a. orange	9·00	16·00
		a. *Dull orange*	—	15·00
49	**63**	4a. olive	4·50	8·50
50	**64**	6a. yellow-bistre	7·00	14·00
		a. *Brown-ochre*	9·00	11·00
51	**65**	8a. deep magenta	10·00	28·00
		a. *Deep mauve*	14·00	23·00
		b. *Bright mauve*	20·00	
		c. *Purple*	24·00	
52	**66**	12a. carmine-lake	6·50	22·00
		a. *Claret*	22·00	20·00
53	**67**	1r. red-brown and deep blue-green	30·00	65·00
		a. Opt double, one albino	65·00	
		b. *Brown and green*	35·00	50·00
		c. *Orange-brown and deep turquoise-green*	42·00	
43/53 *Set of 10*			75·00	£150

Raja Ram Singh, 1919–1935

1921. No. 192 of India optd with T 2.

54	**57**	9p. on 1a. rose-carmine	1·00	20·00

1923–27. Optd with T 1. New values, etc.

55	**57**	1a. chocolate	4·25	8·50
56	**58**	1½a. chocolate (Type A)	38·00	£190
57		1½a. chocolate (Type B) (1924)	5·00	9·50
58		1½a. rose-carmine (Type B) (1927)	1·75	28·00
59	**61**	2a.6p. ultramarine	1·00	7·00
60		2a.6p. orange (1927)	5·50	40·00
61	**62**	3a. ultramarine (1924)	6·00	35·00
		a. Opt double, one albino	£110	
55/61 *Set of 7*			55·00	£275

Nos. 58 and 60 with inverted overprint are of clandestine origin.

CHAMBA STATE (3)   CHAMBA STATE (4)

1927–37. King George V (Nasik printing, wmk Mult Star). Optd at Nasik with T 3 or 4 (1r.).

62	**55**	3p. slate (1928)	20	3·00
		w. Wmk inverted	8·00	
63	**56**	½a. green (1928)	30	3·75
		w. Wmk inverted	12·00	
64	**80**	9p. deep green (*litho*) (1932)	4·50	40·00
64*a*		9p. deep green (*typo*)	10·00	38·00
65	**57**	1a. chocolate	2·50	3·25
		w. Wmk inverted	9·00	3·75
66	**82**	1a.3p. mauve (1932)	3·75	9·50
		w. Wmk inverted	7·50	9·50
67	**58**	1½a. rose-carmine (B) (1932)	14·00	14·00
		w. Wmk inverted	8·00	8·00
68	**70**	2a. purple (1928)	2·50	6·50
69	**61**	2a.6p. orange (1932)	8·00	27·00
		w. Wmk inverted	5·50	30·00
70	**62**	3a. bright blue (1928)	2·00	28·00
71	**71**	4a. sage-green (1928)	1·25	12·00
72	**64**	6a. bistre (*wmk inverted*) (1937)	30·00	£225
73	**65**	8a. reddish purple (1928)	3·00	17·00
			1·50	15·00
74	**66**	12a. claret (1928)	1·75	17·00
75	**67**	1r. chocolate and green (1928)	21·00	48·00
		w. Wmk inverted	19·00	50·00
62/75 *Set of 14*			75·00	£400

Raja Lakshman Singh, 1935–1971

1935–36. New types and colours. Optd with T 3.

76	**79**	½a. green	1·10	16·00
77	**81**	1a. chocolate	4·00	2·50
78	**59**	2a. vermilion (No. 236b)	1·40	35·00
79		2a. vermilion (*small die*, No. 236c)	£140	£170
80	**62**	3a. carmine	4·00	24·00
81	**63**	4a. sage-green (1936)	9·50	30·00
76/81 *Set of 6*			£150	£250

CHAMBA STATE (5)   CHAMBA (6)   CHAMBA (7)

1938. King George VI. Nos. 247/64 optd with T 3 (3p. to 1a.), T 5 (2a. to 12a.) or T 4 (rupee values).

82	**91**	3p. slate	12·00	38·00
83		½a. red-brown	5·00	26·00
84		9p. green	18·00	55·00
85		1a. carmine	11·00	8·00
86	**92**	2a. vermilion	15·00	38·00
87	**93**	2a.6p. bright violet	15·00	55·00
88	**94**	3a. yellow-green	18·00	48·00
89	**95**	3a.6p. bright blue	17·00	55·00
90	**96**	4a. brown	38·00	50·00
91	**97**	6a. turquoise-green	50·00	£140
92	**98**	8a. slate-violet	48·00	95·00
93	**99**	12a. lake	35·00	£100
94	**100**	1r. grey and red-brown	55·00	£130
95		2r. purple and brown	90·00	£450
96		5r. green and blue	£160	£850
97		10r. purple and claret	£200	£1400
98		15r. brown and green	£180	£1900
		a. Opt double, one inverted	£1800	£3000
99		25r. slate-violet and purple	£350	£1900
		a. Optd front and back	£1800	
82/99 *Set of 18*			£1200	£6500

1942–47. Optd with T 6 (to 12a.), "CHAMBA" only, as in T 5 (14a.) or T 7 (rupee values).

(a) Stamps of 1937. W 69 (inverted on 15r.)

100	**91**	½a. red-brown	85·00	80·00
101		1a. carmine	£160	85·00
102	**100**	1r. grey and red-brown	24·00	80·00
103		2r. purple and brown	24·00	£400
104		5r. green and blue	45·00	£450
105		10r. purple and claret	85·00	£750
106		15r. brown and green	£190	£1600
		w. Wmk upright	£850	£2750
107		25r. slate-violet and purple	£160	£1600
100/7 *Set of 8*			£700	£4500

(b) Stamps of 1940–43

108	**100a**	3p. slate	1·00	8·00
109		½a. purple (1943)	1·00	8·00
110		9p. green	1·50	26·00
111		1a. carmine (1943)	2·75	6·50
112	**101**	1½a. dull violet (*typo*) (1943)	4·00	17·00
113		2a. vermilion (1943)	5·50	21·00
114		3a. bright violet (*litho*)	22·00	65·00
114*a*		3a. bright violet (*typo*)	15·00	60·00
115		3½a. bright blue	5·00	55·00
116	**102**	4a. brown	5·50	18·00
117		6a. turquoise-green	21·00	48·00
118		8a. slate-violet	24·00	65·00
119		12a. lake	27·00	80·00
120	**103**	14a. purple (1947)	18·00	4·75
108/120 *Set of 13*			£120	£375

OFFICIAL STAMPS
SERVICE

CHAMBA STATE (O 1)

1887 (1 Jan)–98. Queen Victoria. Optd with Type O 1.

O1	**23**	½a. blue-green	1·25	20
		a. "CHMABA"	£475	£475
		b. "SERV CE"		
		c. "8TATE"	£1700	
		d. Thin seriffed "I" in "SERVICE"	£400	
O2	**25**	1a. brown-purple	4·75	2·25
		a. "CHMABA"	£750	£800
		b. "SERV CE"	£5500	
		c. "8TATE"	£2500	
		d. "SERVICE" double	£3750	£1400
		e. "SERVICE" double, one albino	£110	
O3		1a. plum	4·00	30
		a. Thin seriffed "I" in "SERVICE"	£450	
O4	**27**	2a. dull blue	4·00	3·25
		a. "CHMABA"	£1700	£3750
O5		2a. ultramarine (1887)	4·00	3·75
		a. Thin seriffed "I" in "SERVICE"	£550	
O7		3a. brown-orange (1890)	3·00	19·00
		a. "CHMABA"	£5500	£5500
		b. Thin seriffed "I" in "SERVICE"		
		c. Opt double, one albino		
O8	**29**	4a. olive-green	6·50	12·00
		a. "CHMABA"	£1700	£3750
		b. "SERV CE"	£6000	
		c. "8TATE"	£4000	
O9		4a. slate-green	5·50	18·00
		a. Thin seriffed "I" in "SERVICE"	£850	
O10	**21**	6a. olive-bistre (1890)	8·50	23·00
		a. "SERVICE" double, one albino	£100	
O12	**31**	8a. dull mauve (1887)	8·50	15·00
		a. "CHMABA"	£14000	£14000
O13		8a. magenta (1895)	8·00	8·50
		a. Thin seriffed "I" in "SERVICE"	£1100	
O14	**32**	12a. purple/*red* (1890)	15·00	65·00
		a. "CHMABA"	£13000	
		b. First "T" in "STATE" inverted	£15000	
		c. Thin seriffed "I" in "SERVICE"		
		d. "SERVICE" double, one albino	£100	
		e. "CHAMBA STATE" double, one albino	90·00	
O15	**33**	1r. slate (1890)	27·00	£300
		a. "CHMABA"	£7000	
O16	**37**	1r. green and carmine (1898)	8·50	60·00
		a. Thin seriffed "I" in "SERVICE"		
O1/16 *Set of 10*			75·00	£425

Printings up to and including that of December 1895 had the "SERVICE" overprint applied to sheets of stamps already overprinted with Type 1. From the printing of September 1898 onwards both "SERVICE" and "CHAMBA STATE" were overprinted at the same time. Nos. O6, O8 and O12 only exist using the first method, and No. O16 was only printed using the second.

The thin seriffed "I" in "SERVICE" variety occurred on R. 19/12 of the September 1898 printing only.

1902–04. Colours changed. Optd as Type O 1.

O17	**40**	3p. grey (1904)	60	1·75
O18	**23**	½a. pale yellow-green	2·75	5·50
O19		½a. yellow-green	6·50	6·50
O21	**25**	1a. carmine	2·50	1·50
O21	**27**	2a. pale violet (1903)	16·00	48·00
O17/21 *Set of 4*			20·00	50·00

1903–05. King Edward VII. Stamps of India optd as Type O 1.

O22	**41**	3p. pale grey	35	15
		a. Opt double, one albino	50·00	
O23		3p. slate-grey (1905)	50	65
O24	**42**	½a. yellow-green	35	10
O25	**43**	1a. carmine	1·50	30
O26	**44**	2a. pale violet (1904)	4·25	2·75
O27		2a. mauve	2·50	2·75
O28	**47**	4a. olive (1905)	3·75	25·00
O29	**49**	8a. purple (1905)	13·00	26·00
O30		8a. claret	19·00	32·00
		a. Opt double, one albino	70·00	
O31	**51**	1r. green and carmine (1905)	3·75	21·00
O22/31 *Set of 7*			22·00	65·00

The 2a. mauve King Edward VII, overprinted "On H.M.S.", was discovered in Calcutta, but was not sent to Chamba, and is an unissued variety (*Price un.* £45).

1907. Nos. 149/50 of India, optd with Type O 1.

O32	**53**	½a. green	50	75
		a. Opt inverted	£8000	£9000
		b. Opt double, one albino	55·00	
O33	**54**	1a. carmine	2·75	3·50

The inverted overprint, No. O32a, was due to an inverted cliché on R. 20/1 which was corrected after a few sheets had been printed.

1913–23. King George V Official stamps (wmk Single Star) optd with T 1.

O34	**55**	3p. grey	20	50
		a. *Pale grey*	1·25	2·75
		b. *Bluish grey*	2·75	4·25
		c. *Slate*	1·50	3·00
O36	**56**	½a. light green	20	60
		a. *Emerald*	4·25	1·50
		b. *Bright green*	2·50	30
O38	**57**	1a. aniline carmine	20	10
		a. *Rose-carmine*	5·50	50
O40	**59**	2a. purple (1914)	1·10	23·00
		a. *Reddish purple*	20·00	
		b. *Bright reddish violet* (1923)	20·00	27·00
O41	**63**	4a. olive	1·75	28·00
O42	**65**	8a. deep magenta	3·75	38·00
		a. *Deep mauve*	15·00	38·00
O43	**67**	1r. red-brown and deep blue-green (1914)	12·00	60·00
		a. Opt double, one albino	75·00	
		b. *Brown and green*	15·00	60·00
O34/43 *Set of 7*			17·00	£140

No. O36 with inverted overprint and No. O38a with double or inverted overprint (on gummed side) are of clandestine origin.

1914. King George V. Optd with Type O 1.

O44	**59**	2a. purple	15·00	
O45	**63**	4a. olive	13·00	

1921. No. O97 of India optd with T 2 at top.

O46	**57**	9p. on 1a. rose-carmine	20	10·00

1925. As 1913–23. New colour.

O47	**57**	1a. chocolate	8·00	2·25

CHAMBA STATE SERVICE (O 2)   CHAMBA STATE SERVICE (O 3)

1927–39. King George V (Nasik printing, wmk Mult Star), optd at Nasik with Type O 2 or O 3 (rupee values).

O48	**55**	3p. slate (1928)	50	40
		w. Wmk inverted	—	6·50
O49	**56**	½a. green (1928)	75	15
O50	**80**	9p. deep green (1932)	4·50	15·00
O51	**57**	1a. chocolate	30	10
		w. Wmk inverted	4·50	30
O52	**82**	1a.3p. mauve (1932)	9·00	1·00
		w. Wmk inverted		
O53	**70**	2a. purple (1928)	5·00	1·75
O54	**71**	4a. sage-green (1928)	3·50	4·00
O55	**65**	8a. reddish purple (1930)	22·00	19·00
		w. Wmk inverted	17·00	
O56	**66**	12a. claret (1928)	7·00	38·00
		w. Wmk inverted	24·00	
O57	**67**	1r. chocolate and green (1930)	16·00	65·00
O58		2r. carmine and orange (1939)	28·00	£375
O59		5r. ultramarine and purple (1939)	48·00	£475
O60		10r. green and scarlet (1939)	75·00	£425
O48/60 *Set of 13*			£200	£1300

1935–39. New types and colours. Optd with Type O 2.

O61	**79**	½a. green	9·50	75
O62	**81**	1a. chocolate	6·50	45
O63	**59**	2a. vermilion	8·50	1·50
O64		2a. vermilion (*small die*) (1939)	18·00	29·00
O65	**63**	4a. sage-green (1936)	15·00	12·00
O61/5 *Set of 5*			50·00	40·00

1938–40. King George VI. Optd with Type O 2 or O 3 (rupee values).

O66	**91**	9p. green	50·00	90·00
O67		1a. carmine	65·00	12·00
O68	**100**	1r. grey and red-brown (1940?)	£120	£850
O69		2r. purple and brown (1939)	42·00	£800
O70		5r. green and blue (1939)	60·00	£850
O71		10r. purple and claret (1939)	90·00	£1400
O66/71 *Set of 6*			£400	£3750

CHAMBA SERVICE (O 4)

1940–43.

(a) Official stamps optd with T 6

O72	O **20**	3p. slate	70	1·40
O73		½a. red-brown	£100	£120

O74		½a. purple (1943)	70	5·00
O75		9p. green	3·00	16·00
		w. Wmk inverted	40·00	32·00
O76		1a. carmine (1941)	2·25	3·50
O77		1a.3p. yellow-brown (1941)	£160	24·00
O78		1½a. dull violet (1943)	11·00	12·00
O79		2a. vermilion	4·25	11·00
O80		2½a. bright violet (1941)	4·25	30·00
O81		4a. brown	4·25	24·00
O82		8a. slate-violet	10·00	90·00
		w. Wmk inverted	12·00	£120

(b) Postage stamps optd with Type O **4**

O83	**100**	1r. grey and red-brown (1942)	20·00	£300
O84		2r. purple and brown (1942)	35·00	£475
O85		5r. green and blue (1942)	70·00	£800
O86		10r. purple and claret (1942)	80·00	£1400
O72/86		Set of 15	£450	£2750

Chamba became part of Himachal Pradesh on 15 April 1948.

FARIDKOT

For earlier issues, see under INDIAN FEUDATORY STATES

<table>
<tr><td colspan="2">PRICES FOR STAMPS ON COVER</td></tr>
<tr><td>Nos. 1/17</td><td>from × 30</td></tr>
<tr><td>Nos. O1/15</td><td>from × 40</td></tr>
</table>

Raja Bikram Singh, 1874–1898

FARIDKOT STATE
(1)

1887 (1 Jan)–**1900**. Queen Victoria. Optd with T **1**.

1	**23**	½a. deep green	2·75	2·75
		a. "ARIDKOT"		
		b. "FAR DKOT"	—	£4000
		c. Opt double, one albino	90·00	
2	**25**	1a. brown-purple	2·50	5·00
3		1a. plum	2·75	4·50
4	**27**	2a. blue	3·25	12·00
5		2a. deep blue	6·00	14·00
6	**28**	3a. orange	12·00	21·00
7		3a. brown-orange (1893)	5·50	11·00
8	**29**	4a. olive-green	14·00	22·00
		a. "ARIDKOT"	£2500	
9		4a. slate-green	11·00	45·00
10	**21**	6a. olive-bistre	55·00	£100
		a. "ARIDKOT"	£3250	
		b. Opt double, one albino	95·00	
11		6a. bistre-brown	3·50	27·00
12	**31**	8a. dull mauve	30·00	65·00
		a. "ARIDKOT"	£4500	
13		8a. magenta	32·00	£300
		a. Opt double, one albino	65·00	
14	**32**	12a. purple/red (1900)	60·00	£600
15	**33**	1r. slate	60·00	£450
		a. "ARIDKOT"	£6000	
16	**37**	1r. green and carmine (1893)	60·00	£140
		a. Opt double, one albino	£100	
1/16		Set of 10	£200	£1200

The ½a., 1a., 2a., 3a., 4a., 8a., 12a. and 1r. (No. 16) are known with broken "O" (looking like a "C") in "FARIDKOT". This variety occurred once per sheet (in the eleventh vertical column) in the February 1894 printing, and again at R. 4/2 in 1898-1900 printings.

Raja Balbir Singh, 1898–1906

1900. Optd with T **1**.

17	**40**	3p. carmine	3·00	75·00

OFFICIAL STAMPS

SERVICE

FARIDKOT STATE
(O 1)

1887 (1 Jan)–**98**. Queen Victoria. Optd with Type O **1**.

O1	**23**	½a. deep green	75	1·50
		a. "SERV CE"	£4250	
		b. "FAR DKOT"	£4750	
		c. Thin seriffed "I" in "SERVICE"	£450	
		d. "FARIDKOT STATE" double, one albino	80·00	
		e. "ESRVICE"	£5000	
O2	**25**	1a. brown-purple	1·00	4·00
		a. Thin seriffed "I" in "SERVICE"	£475	
		b. Opt double, one albino	90·00	
O3		1a. plum	3·25	3·50
		a. "SERV CE"	£6000	
O4	**27**	2a. dull blue	3·25	18·00
		a. "SERV CE"	£6000	
O5		2a. deep blue	6·00	25·00
O6	**28**	3a. orange	9·00	19·00
		a. "SERVICE" double, one albino		
O7		3a. brown-orange (12.98)	8·00	65·00
		a. Thin seriffed "I" in "SERVICE"	£1100	
O8	**29**	4a. olive-green	7·00	50·00
		a. "SERV CE"	£5000	
		b. "ARIDKOT"		
		c. "SERVICE" treble, two albino	£170	
O9		4a. slate-green	28·00	85·00
		a. "SERVICE" double, one albino	55·00	
O10	**21**	6a. olive-bistre	65·00	£180
		a. "ARIDKOT"	£2000	
		b. "SERVIC"	£4500	
		c. "SERVICE" double, one albino	£100	
		d. "FARIDKOT STATE" double, one albino	£100	
O11		6a. bistre-brown	42·00	45·00
O12	**31**	8a. dull mauve	18·00	45·00

		a. "SERV CE"	£4500	
O13		8a. magenta	27·00	£300
O14	**33**	1r. slate	75·00	£425
		a. "SERVICE" double, one albino	£150	
O15	**37**	1r. green and carmine (12.98)	£120	£1200
		a. Thin seriffed "I" in "SERVICE"		
O1/15		Set of 9	£250	£1600

The ½a., 1a., 2a., 3a., 4a., 8a. and 1r. (No. O15) are known with the broken "O".

Printings up to and including that of November 1895 had the "SERVICE" overprint applied to sheets already overprinted with Type **1**. From December 1898 onwards "SERVICE" and "FARIDKOT STATE" were overprinted at one operation to provide fresh supplies of Nos. O1/3, O7 and O15.

This State ceased to use overprinted stamps after 31 March 1901.

The thin seriffed "I" variety occurs on the December 1898 overprinting only.

GWALIOR

<table>
<tr><td colspan="2">PRICES FOR STAMPS ON COVER</td></tr>
<tr><td>Nos. 1/3</td><td>from × 10</td></tr>
<tr><td>Nos. 4/11</td><td>from × —</td></tr>
<tr><td>Nos. 12/66</td><td>from × 5</td></tr>
<tr><td>Nos. 67/128</td><td>from × 4</td></tr>
<tr><td>Nos. 129/37</td><td>from × 5</td></tr>
<tr><td>Nos. O1/94</td><td>from × 12</td></tr>
</table>

OVERPRINTS. From 1885 to 1926 these were applied by the Government of India Central Printing Press, Calcutta, and from 1927 at the Security Press, Nasik, *unless otherwise stated.*

Maharaja Jayaji Rao Sindhia, 1843–1886

गवालियर

GWALIOR	GWALIOR
(1)	गवालियर
	(2)
GWALIOR	GWALIOR
Small "G"	Small "R"
GWALIOR	GWALIOR
Tall "R" (original state)	Tall "R" (damaged state)

OVERPRINT VARIETIES OF TYPE 2.

Small "G" — Occurs on R. 7/11 from June 1900 printing of ½, 1, 2, 3, 4a. and 3p. (No. 38), and on R. 3/1 of a left pane from May 1901 printing of 2, 3 and 5r.

Small "R" — Occurs on R. 9/3 from June 1900 printing of 3p. to 4a. and on R. 2/3 from May 1901 printing of 2, 3 and 5r.

Tall "R" — Occurs on R. 20/2 from printings between June 1900 and May 1907. The top of the letter is damaged on printings from February 1903 onwards.

1885 (1 July)–**97**. Queen Victoria.

I. Optd with T **1**.

(a) Space between two lines of overprint 13 mm.
Hindi inscription 13 to 14 mm long (May 1885)

1	**23**	½a. blue-green	£225	45·00
2	**25**	1a. brown-purple	£140	45·00
3	**27**	2a. dull blue	£120	24·00
1/3		Set of 3	£450	£100

A variety exists of the ½a. in which the space between the two lines of overprint is only 9½ mm but this is probably from a proof sheet.

(b) Space between two lines of overprint 15 mm on 4a. and 6a. and 16 to 17 mm on other values (June 1885). Hindi inscription 13 to 14 mm long

4	**23**	½a. blue-green	£100	
		a. Opt double, one albino	£110	
		b. Hindi inscr 15 to 15½ mm long	£200	
		ba. Opt double, one albino	£250	
		c. Pair. Nos. 4/4b	£1400	
5	**25**	1a. brown-purple	£100	
		a. Opt double, one albino	£120	
		b. Hindi inscr 15 to 15½ mm long	£200	
		ba. Opt double, one albino	£250	
		c. Pair. Nos. 5/5b	£1400	
6	**26**	1a.6p. sepia	£160	
		b. Hindi inscr 15 to 15½ mm long	£375	
		c. Pair. Nos. 6/6b	£1600	
7	**27**	2a. dull blue	£110	
		b. Hindi inscr 15 to 15½ mm long	£180	
		c. Pair. Nos. 7/7b	£500	
8	**17**	4a. green	£180	
		b. Hindi inscr 15 to 15½ mm long	£375	
		c. Pair. Nos. 8/8b	£1700	
9	**21**	6a. olive-bistre	£180	
		a. Opt double, one albino	£190	
		b. Hindi inscr 15 to 15½ mm long	£400	
		ba. Opt double, one albino	£400	
		c. Pair. Nos. 9/9b	£1700	
10	**31**	8a. dull mauve	£140	
		b. Hindi inscr 15 to 15½ mm long	£275	
		c. Pair. Nos. 10/10b	£1700	
11	**33**	1r. slate	£140	
		b. Hindi inscr 15 to 15½ mm long	£275	
		c. Pair. Nos. 11/11b	£1700	
4/11		Set of 8	£1000	
4b/11b		Set of 8	£2500	

The two types of overprint on these stamps occur in the same settings, with about a quarter of the stamps in each sheet showing the long inscription. Nos. 4/7 and 10/11 were overprinted in sheets of 240 and Nos. 8/9 in half-sheets of 160.

II. Optd with T **2**. *Hindi inscription 13 to 14 mm long*

(a) In red (Sept 1885)

12	**23**	½a. blue-green	2·50	20
		b. Hindi inscr 15 to 15½ mm long	2·75	2·00
		c. Pair. Nos. 12/12b	28·00	30·00

13	**27**	2a. dull blue	42·00	18·00
		b. Hindi inscr 15 to 15½ mm long	75·00	65·00
		c. Pair. Nos. 13/13b	£500	£600
14	**17**	4a. green	60·00	30·00
		aw. Wmk inverted	£250	
		b. Hindi inscr 15 to 15½ mm long	£375	£160
		c. Pair. Nos. 14/14b	£1600	
15	**33**	1r. slate	15·00	42·00
		aw. Wmk inverted	25·00	55·00
		b. Hindi inscr 15 to 15½ mm long	50·00	£110
		bw. Wmk inverted	75·00	£170
		c. Nos. 15/15b	£120	£200
		cw. Wmk inverted	£140	
12/15		Set of 4	£110	80·00
12b/15b		Set of 4	£450	£300

No. 14 was overprinted in half-sheets of 160, about 40 stamps having the Hindi inscription 15 to 15½ mm long. The remaining three values were from a setting of 240 containing 166 13 to 14 mm long and 74 15 to 15½ mm long.

Reprints have been made of Nos. 12 to 15, but the majority of the examples have the word "REPRINT" overprinted upon them.

(b) In black (1885–97)

16	**23**	½a. blue-green (1889)	6·00	3·00
		b. Opt double, one albino	38·00	
		c. Hindi inscr 15 to 15½ mm long	1·25	10
		ca. Opt double	†	£1700
		cb. Opt double, one albino	£140	
		cc. "GWALICR"	£110	£150
		cd. Small "G"	80·00	50·00
		ce. Small "R"	£100	
		cf. Tall "R"	£120	£120
		d. Pair. Nos. 16/16c	£100	£110
17	**24**	9p. carmine (1891)	42·00	80·00
		a. Opt double, one albino	70·00	
		c. Hindi inscr 15 to 15½ mm long	75·00	£110
		ca. Opt double, one albino	£100	
		d. Pair. Nos. 17/17c	£350	£550
18	**25**	1a. brown-purple	3·50	20
		c. Hindi inscr 15 to 15½ mm long	4·50	35
		d. Pair. Nos. 18/18c	26·00	30·00
19		1a. plum (*Hindi inscr 15 to 15½ mm long*)	4·50	10
		a. Small "G"	£110	60·00
		b. Small "R"	£120	
		c. Tall "R"	£180	
20	**26**	1a.6p. sepia	3·00	3·50
		c. Hindi inscr 15 to 15½ mm long	2·25	2·50
		d. Pair. Nos. 20/20c	25·00	35·00
		w. Wmk inverted	£250	
21	**27**	2a. dull blue	16·00	1·25
		c. Hindi inscr 15 to 15½ mm long	6·50	10
		ca. "R" omitted	£700	£650
		d. Pair. Nos. 21/21c	£250	£275
22		2a. deep blue	23·00	4·50
		c. Hindi inscr 15 to 15½ mm long	8·00	1·25
		ca. Small "G"	£225	£250
		cb. Small "R"	£275	
		cc. Tall "R"	£375	£425
		d. Pair. Nos. 22/22c	£325	
23	**36**	2a.6p. yellow-green (*Hindi inscr 15 to 15½ mm long*) (1896)	15·00	27·00
		a. "GWALICR"	£1000	
24	**28**	3a. orange	26·00	30·00
		a. Opt double, one albino	£110	
		c. Hindi inscr 15 to 15½ mm long	£120	85·00
		ca. Opt double, one albino		
		d. Pair. Nos. 24/24c	£500	
25		3a. brown-orange	60·00	11·00
		c. Hindi inscr 15 to 15½ mm long	8·50	15
		ca. Opt double, one albino	60·00	
		cb. Small "G"	£350	£425
		cc. Small "R"	£1500	
		cd. Tall "R"	£300	£300
		d. Pair. Nos. 25/25c	£375	
26	**29**	4a. olive-green (1889)	18·00	3·75
		c. Hindi inscr 15 to 15½ mm long	18·00	4·75
		d. Pair. Nos. 26/26c	£170	
27		4a. slate-green	18·00	4·00
		c. Hindi inscr 15 to 15½ mm long	9·50	1·75
		ca. Opt double, one albino	95·00	
		cb. Small "G"	£750	£600
		cc. Small "R"	£650	
		cd. Tall "R"	£500	£550
		d. Pair. Nos. 27/27c	60·00	
28	**21**	6a. olive-bistre	18·00	42·00
		c. Hindi inscr 15 to 15½ mm long	11·00	32·00
		ca. Opt double, one albino	60·00	
		d. Pair. Nos. 28/28c	£140	
29		6a. bistre-brown	8·00	14·00
		c. Hindi inscr 15 to 15½ mm long	9·00	19·00
		d. Pair. Nos. 29/29c	42·00	
30	**31**	8a. dull mauve	25·00	70·00
		c. Hindi inscr 15 to 15½ mm long	10·00	2·25
		d. Pair. Nos. 30/30c	£550	
31		8a. magenta (*Hindi inscr 15 to 15½ mm long*) (1897)	15·00	17·00
32	**32**	12a. purple/red (1891)	10·00	9·00
		c. Hindi inscr 15 to 15½ mm long	4·25	1·25
		ca. Pair, one without opt	£6000	
		cb. Tall "R"	£2000	£1100
		d. Pair. Nos. 32/32c	£110	
33	**33**	1r. slate (1889)	£190	£750
		c. Hindi inscr 15 to 15½ mm long	8·00	6·00
		d. Pair. Nos. 33/33c	£1000	
34	**37**	1r. green and carmine (*Hindi inscr 15 to 15½ mm long*) (1896)	15·00	9·00
		a. Opt double, one albino	£170	
		b. "GWALICR"	£1600	£3250
35	**38**	2r. carmine and yellow-brown (*Hindi inscr 15 to 15½ mm long*) (1896)	6·50	3·25
		a. Small "G"	£600	£275
		b. Small "R"	£650	£300
		c. Opt double, one albino	£140	
		d. Opt triple, two albino	£170	
36		3r. brown and green (*Hindi inscr 15 to 15½ mm long*) (1896)	9·00	3·75
		a. Small "G"	£700	£300
		b. Small "R"	£750	£325

37		5r. ultramarine and violet (*Hindi inscr 15 to 15½ mm long*) (1896)	16·00	7·00
		a. Small "G"	£650	£375
		b. Small "R"	£800	£425
16c/37	*Set of 16*		£140	£140

Printings to 1891 continued to use the setting showing both types, but subsequently a new setting containing the larger overprint only was used.

The ½a., 1a., 2a. and 3a. exist with space between "I" and "O" of "GWALIOR".

The "GWALICR" error occurs on R. 1/5 in the May 1896 printing only.

Maharaja Madhav Rao Sindhia, 1886–1925

1899–1911.

(a) Optd with T 2 (Hindi inscr 15 to 15½ mm long)

38	**40**	3p. carmine	50	20
		a. Opt inverted	£2500	£900
		b. Small "G"	70·00	70·00
		d. Small "R"	80·00	
		e. Tall "R"	75·00	95·00
		f. Opt double, one albino	60·00	
39		3p. grey (1904)	8·00	60·00
		e. Tall "R"	£300	
		f. Opt double, one albino	70·00	
40	**23**	½a. pale yellow-green (1901)	3·25	2·50
		e. Tall "R"	£110	
		f. Opt double, one albino	38·00	
40g		½a. yellow-green (1903)	5·00	2·25
		ge. Tall "R"	£170	
41	**25**	1a. carmine (1901)	1·25	35
		e. Tall "R"	£100	
		f. Opt double, one albino	75·00	
42	**27**	2a. pale violet (1903)	6·00	8·00
		e. Tall "R"	£225	
43	**36**	2a.6p. ultramarine (1903)	4·25	11·00
		e. Tall "R"	£325	
38/43	*Set of 6*		21·00	75·00

(b) Optd as T 2, but "GWALIOR" 13 mm long. Opt spaced 2¾ mm

44	**38**	3r. brown and green (1911)	£325	£325
45		5r. ultramarine and violet (1910)	95·00	70·00
		a. Opt double, one albino	£170	

1903–11. King Edward VII. Optd as T **2**.

A. "GWALIOR" 14 mm long. Overprint spaced 1¾ mm (1903–06)

46A	**41**	3p. pale grey	1·50	20
		e. Tall "R"	50·00	80·00
		f. Slate-grey (1905)	1·50	30
		fe. Tall "R"	60·00	85·00
48A	**42**	½a. green	30	10
		e. Tall "R"	50·00	75·00
49A	**43**	1a. carmine	20	10
		e. Tall "R"	60·00	80·00
		f. Opt double, one albino	75·00	
50A	**44**	2a. pale violet (1904)	3·50	1·25
		e. Tall "R"	£150	
		f. Mauve	4·75	20
		fe. Tall "R"	£250	£180
52A	**45**	2a.6p. ultramarine (1904)	32·00	85·00
		e. Tall "R"	£1700	
53A	**46**	3a. orange-brown (1904)	3·50	35
		e. Tall "R"	£160	£190
54A	**47**	4a. olive	6·00	40
		e. Tall "R"	£375	£300
		f. Pale olive	21·00	7·00
		e. Tall "R"	£750	
56A	**48**	6a. olive-bistre (1904)	3·50	4·50
		e. Tall "R"	£1500	
57A	**49**	8a. purple (*shades*) (1905)	9·50	2·50
		e. Tall "R"	£600	£500
59A	**50**	12a. purple/*red* (1905)	8·00	27·00
		e. Tall "R"	£1600	
60A	**51**	1r. green and carmine (1905)	9·50	2·00
		e. Tall "R"	£1100	£1100
61A	**52**	2r. carmine and yellow-brown (1906)	45·00	55·00
		a. Opt double, one albino	90·00	
46A/61A	*Set of 12*		£110	£160

B. "GWALIOR" 13 mm long. Overprint spaced 2¾ mm (1908–11)

46B	**41**	3p. pale grey	4·75	10
		f. Slate-grey	5·50	50
49B	**43**	1a. carmine	11·00	3·75
50fB		2a. mauve	6·50	15
52B	**45**	2a.6p. ultramarine	3·00	14·00
53B	**46**	3a. orange-brown	7·50	20
54fB		4a. pale olive	6·00	60
56B	**48**	6a. olive-bistre	14·00	2·00
57B	**49**	8a. purple (*shades*)	16·00	1·60
		f. Claret	50·00	5·00
		fa. Opt double, one albino	£100	
59B	**50**	12a. purple/*red*	7·50	3·25
		e. Tall "R"	£140	
60B	**51**	1r. green and carmine	15·00	1·25
61B	**52**	2r. carmine and yellow-brown	9·00	11·00
		a. Opt double, one albino	£110	
62B		3r. brown and green (1910)	42·00	70·00
		a. Red-brown and green	80·00	85·00
63B		5r. ultramarine and violet (1911)	22·00	29·00
46B/63B	*Set of 13*		£150	£120

1907–08. Nos. 149 and 150 of India optd as T **2**.

(a) "GWALIOR" 14 mm long. Overprint spaced 1¾ mm

64	**53**	½a. green	20	70
		e. Tall "R"	70·00	£100

(b) "GWALIOR" 13 mm long. Overprint spaced 2¾ mm (1908)

65	**53**	½a. green	2·75	20
66	**54**	1a. carmine	1·50	20

1912–14. King George V. Optd as T **2**.

67	**55**	3p. grey	10	10
		b. Opt double	†	£1700
		c. Pale grey	2·25	10
		c. Bluish grey	—	1·50
		d. Slate	2·50	30
		da. "Rs" flaw	70·00	80·00
68	**56**	½a. light green	90	10
		a. Emerald	4·00	35
		b. Bright green	2·50	10
		ba. Opt inverted	†	£500

69	**57**	1a. aniline carmine	40	10
		a. Opt double	25·00	
70	**59**	2a. purple	2·75	30
		a. Reddish purple	3·00	10
		aw. Wmk inverted	†	£250
		b. Deep mauve	7·50	2·25
		c. Bright reddish violet	9·00	2·75
71	**62**	3a. orange	1·75	15
		a. Dull orange	2·50	25
72	**63**	4a. olive (1913)	75	60
73	**64**	6a. yellow-bistre (1913)	3·25	1·75
		a. Brown-ochre	3·50	1·50
74	**65**	8a. deep magenta (1913)	5·00	1·50
		a. Deep mauve	7·00	30
		b. Bright mauve	24·00	5·00
75	**66**	12a. carmine-lake (1914)	2·50	4·00
		a. Claret	—	7·50
76	**67**	1r. red-brown and deep blue-green (1913)	18·00	1·75
		a. Opt double, one albino	24·00	
		b. Brown and green	22·00	40
		ba. Opt double	£750	
		c. Orange-brown and deep turquoise-green	35·00	8·00
77		2r. carmine-rose and brown (1913)	14·00	4·50
		a. Opt double, one albino	55·00	
78		5r. ultramarine and violet (1913)	38·00	6·50
		a. Opt double, one albino	80·00	
67/78	*Set of 12*		80·00	17·00

GWALIOR
(3)

1921. No. 192 of India optd with T **3**.

79	**57**	9p. on 1a. rose-carmine	10	50

No. 79 with inverted overprint is of clandestine origin.

1923–27. Optd as T **2**. New colours and values.

80	**57**	1a. chocolate	1·10	10
		a. Opt double, one albino	85·00	
81	**58**	1½a. chocolate (B) (1925)	4·75	1·00
82		1½a. rose-carmine (B) (1927)	20	20
83	**61**	2a.6p. ultramarine (1925)	4·25	1·75
84		2a.6p. orange (1927)	35	50
85	**62**	3a. ultramarine (1924)	5·50	75
80/5	*Set of 6*		14·50	3·75

No. 82 with inverted overprint is of clandestine origin.

Maharaja George Jivaji Rao Sindhia, 1925–1961

GWALIOR   GWALIOR
गवालियर   गवालियर
(4)   (5)

1928–36. King George V (Nasik printing, wmk Mult Star), optd at Nasik with T **4** or **5** (rupee values).

86	**55**	3p. slate (1932)	1·00	15
		w. Wmk inverted	3·25	1·25
87	**56**	½a. green (1930)	1·50	10
		w. Wmk inverted		
88	**80**	9p. deep green (*litho*) (1932)	5·50	30
		aw. Wmk inverted	5·50	80
88b		9p. deep green (*typo*)	3·50	50
89	**57**	1a. chocolate	85	10
		w. Wmk inverted	—	3·50
90	**82**	1a.3p. mauve (1936)	1·50	15
91	**70**	2a. purple	75	30
		w. Wmk inverted	75	30
92	**62**	3a. bright blue	1·75	40
93	**71**	4a. sage-green	3·00	1·10
		w. Wmk inverted	4·00	4·00
94	**65**	8a. reddish purple (*wmk inverted*)	4·25	1·10
95	**66**	12a. claret	5·50	4·00
96	**67**	1r. chocolate and green	7·50	6·50
		w. Wmk inverted	15·00	5·50
97		2r. carmine and orange	22·00	15·00
		w. Wmk inverted	8·00	4·50
98		5r. ultramarine and purple (*wmk inverted*) (1929)	35·00	32·00
99		10r. green and scarlet (1930)	£100	55·00
100		15r. blue and olive (*wmk inverted*) (1930)	£190	90·00
101		25r. orange and blue (1930)	£450	£275
86/101	*Set of 16*		£750	£425

1935–36. New types and colours. Optd with T **4**.

102	**79**	½a. green (1936)	75	20
		w. Wmk inverted	11·00	6·50
103	**81**	1a. chocolate	20	10
104	**59**	2a. vermilion (1936)	5·00	3·50
102/4	*Set of 3*		5·50	3·50

1938–48. King George VI. Nos. 247/50, 253, 255/6 and 259/64 optd with T **4** or **5** (rupee values).

105	**91**	3p. slate	15·00	10
106		3p. red-brown	15·00	10
107		9p. green (1939)	75·00	4·75
108		1a. carmine	15·00	15
109	**94**	3a. yellow-green (1939)	55·00	6·00
110	**96**	4a. brown	75·00	4·50
111	**97**	6a. turquoise-green (1939)	16·00	16·00
112	**100**	1r. grey and red-brown (1942)	13·00	1·75
113		2r. purple and brown (1948)	25·00	12·00
114		5r. green and blue (1948)	32·00	45·00
115		10r. purple and claret (1948)	32·00	48·00
116		15r. brown and purple (1948)	90·00	£225
117		25r. slate-violet and purple (1948)	80·00	£180
105/117	*Set of 13*		£475	£475

1942–45. King George VI. Optd with T **4**.

118	**100a**	3p. slate	45	10
		w. Wmk inverted	—	42·00
119		½a. purple (1943)	1·00	10
120		9p. green	1·50	10
121		1a. carmine (1943)	1·00	10
		a. Opt double	—	£350
122	**101**	1½a. dull violet (*litho*)	10·00	1·25

122a		1½a. dull violet (1943) (*typo*)	7·00	30
123		2a. vermilion	1·75	20
		a. Opt double	†	£400
124		3a. bright violet (litho)	8·50	2·75
124a		3a. bright violet (1943) (*typo*)	6·00	2·25
		ab. Opt double	—	£375
125	**102**	4a. brown	5·00	20
126		6a. turquoise-green (1945)	14·00	27·00
127		8a. slate-violet (1944)	2·25	2·00
128		12a. lake (1943)	8·00	24·00
118/28	*Set of 11*		42·00	50·00

GWALIOR
गवालियर
(6)

1949 (Apr). King George VI. Optd with T **6** at the Alizah Printing Press, Gwalior.

129	**100a**	3p. slate	5·00	60
130		½a. purple	5·00	50
131		1a. carmine	4·50	60
132	**101**	2a. vermilion	42·00	2·50
133		3a. bright violet (*typo*)	£100	35·00
134	**102**	4a. brown	17·00	3·50
135		6a. turquoise-green	75·00	85·00
136		8a. slate-violet	£150	75·00
137		12a. lake	£750	£300
129/37	*Set of 9*		£1000	£450

OFFICIAL STAMPS

गवालियर
गवालियर

गवालियर   सरविस
सरविस
(O 1)   (O 2)

1895–96. Queen Victoria. Optd with Type O **1**.

O1	**23**	½a. blue-green	1·75	10
		a. Hindi characters transposed	40·00	32·00
		b. 4th Hindi character omitted	£600	50·00
		c. Opt double	†	£1400
O2	**25**	1a. brown-purple	19·00	1·50
O3		1a. plum	6·00	10
		a. Hindi characters transposed	65·00	48·00
		b. 4th Hindi character omitted	£700	80·00
O4	**27**	2a. dull blue	6·50	50
O5		2a. deep blue	5·00	50
		a. Hindi characters transposed	£100	£140
		b. 4th Hindi character omitted	£120	£160
O6	**29**	4a. olive-green	7·50	2·50
		a. Hindi characters transposed	£700	£750
		b. 4th Hindi character omitted	£4000	£2500
O7		4a. slate-green	5·50	2·50
		a. Hindi characters transposed	£375	£550
O8	**31**	8a. dull mauve	8·50	5·00
		a. Opt double, one albino	75·00	
O9		8a. magenta	8·50	2·75
		a. Hindi characters transposed	£1600	£1900
		b. 4th Hindi character omitted		
O10	**37**	1r. green and carmine (1896)	13·00	3·50
		a. Hindi characters transposed	£3500	
O1/10	*Set of 6*		38·00	8·50

In the errors listed above it is the last two Hindi characters that are transposed, so that the word reads "Sersiv". The error occurs on R. 19/1 in the sheet from the early printings up to May 1896.

1901–04. Colours changed.

O23	**40**	3p. carmine (1902)	2·75	50
O24		3p. grey (1904)	2·50	4·00
O25	**23**	½a. pale yellow-green (1903)	8·00	15
O26		½a. yellow-green	1·75	10
O27	**25**	1a. carmine	9·50	10
O28	**27**	2a. pale violet (1903)	3·75	3·00
O23/8	*Set of 5*		18·00	7·00

1903–08. King Edward VII. Optd as O **1**.

(a) Overprint spaced 10 mm (1903–5)

O29	**41**	3p. pale grey	70	10
		a. Slate-grey (1905)	70	10
O31	**42**	½a. green	2·00	10
O32	**43**	1a. carmine	1·10	10
O33	**44**	2a. pale violet (1905)	6·50	1·00
		a. Mauve	4·75	30
O35	**47**	4a. olive (1905)	22·00	2·25
		a. Opt double, one albino	95·00	
O36	**49**	8a. purple (1905)	17·00	70
		a. Claret	35·00	8·00
		ab. Opt double, one albino	85·00	
O38	**51**	1r. green and carmine (1905)	6·50	3·25
		a. Opt double, one albino	£130	
O29/38	*Set of 7*		48·00	6·00

(b) Overprint spaced 8 mm (1907–8)

O39	**41**	3p. pale grey	10·00	15
		a. Slate-grey (1905)	20·00	2·25
O41	**42**	½a. green	8·00	15
O42	**43**	1a. carmine	4·75	10
O43	**44**	2a. mauve	19·00	75
O44	**47**	4a. olive	4·25	1·00
O45	**49**	8a. purple	9·50	3·75
O46	**51**	1r. green and carmine (1908)	65·00	13·00
O39/46	*Set of 7*		£110	17·00

1907–08. Nos. 149 and 150 of India optd as Type O **1**.

(a) Overprint spaced 10 mm (1908)

O47	**53**	½a. green	14·00	10
O48	**54**	1a. carmine	13·00	15
		a. Opt double, one albino	65·00	

(b) Overprint spaced 8 mm (1907)

O49	**53**	½a. green	1·75	15
O50	**54**	1a. carmine	80·00	2·00

1913–23. King George V. Optd with Type O 1.

O51	55	3p. grey	1·40	20
		a. Pair, one without opt	£2750	
		b. Pale grey	75	10
		c. Bluish grey	—	1·00
		d. Slate	1·25	30
		da. "Rs" flaw	£160	
O52	56	½a. light green	20	10
		b. Emerald	—	20
		ba. Opt double	£130	£190
		c. Bright green	50	20
O53	57	1a. rose-carmine	18·00	50
		a. Aniline carmine	50	10
		ab. Opt double	75·00	
O54		1a. chocolate (1923)	7·00	30
O55	59	2a. purple	3·25	1·50
		a. Reddish purple	1·75	20
		b. Deep mauve	7·00	
		c. Bright reddish violet	2·00	75
O56	63	4a. olive	75	1·50
O57	65	8a. deep magenta	2·75	3·25
		a. Deep mauve	4·25	1·60
		b. Bright mauve	10·00	
O58	67	1r. red-brown and deep blue-green	60·00	45·00
		a. Opt double, one albino	£120	
		b. Brown and green	50·00	29·00
		c. Orange-brown and deep turquoise-green	60·00	42·00
O51/8		Set of 8	55·00	30·00

1921. No. O97 of India optd with T 3.

O59	57	9p. on 1a. rose-carmine	10	30

1927–35. King George V (Nasik printing, wmk Mult Star), optd at Nasik as Type O 1 (but top line measures 13 mm instead of 14 mm) or with Type O 2 (rupee values).

O61	55	3p. slate	30	10
		w. Wmk inverted	10	60
O62	56	½a. green	10	15
		w. Wmk inverted	5·50	
O63	80	9p. deep green (1932)	20	15
O64	57	1a. chocolate	10	10
		w. Wmk inverted	2·00	50
O65	82	1a.3p. mauve (1933)	50	15
			8·00	
O66	70	2a. purple	20	15
		w. Wmk inverted	9·00	
O67	71	4a. sage-green	2·00	30
		w. Wmk inverted	—	4·00
O68	65	8a. reddish purple (1928)	75	1·75
		w. Wmk inverted	3·00	4·00
O69	67	1r. chocolate and green	1·25	2·00
		w. Wmk inverted	1·90	3·25
O70		2r. carmine and orange (1935)	30·00	35·00
O71		5r. ultramarine and purple (1932)	45·00	£300
		w. Wmk inverted	40·00	
O72		10r. green and scarlet (1932)	£225	£650
O61/72		Set of 12	£275	£900

1936–37. New types. Optd as Type O 1 (13 mm).

O73	79	½a. green	15	15
		w. Wmk inverted	—	11·00
O74	81	1a. chocolate	15	15
O75	59	2a. vermilion	20	40
O76		2a. vermilion (small die)	6·50	1·25
O77	63	4a. sage-green (1937)	60	75
O73/7		Set of 5	7·00	2·40

1938. King George VI. Optd as Type O 1 (13 mm).

O78	91	½a. red-brown	7·50	30
O79		1a. carmine	3·75	20

गवालियर (O 3)   1A—1A (O 4)

1940–42. Official stamps optd with Type O 3.

O80	O 20	3p. slate	50	10
		w. Wmk inverted		65·00
O81		½a. red-brown	15·00	25
O82		½a. purple (1942)	1·50	10
O83		9p. green (1942)	1·25	70
O84		1a. carmine	2·25	10
O85		1a.3p. yellow-brown (1942)	70·00	1·75
		w. Wmk inverted	—	60·00
O86		1½a. dull violet (1942)	1·00	30
O87		2a. vermilion	1·00	30
O88		4a. brown (1942)	1·25	30
O89		8a. slate-violet (1942)	7·00	11·00
O80/9		Set of 10	90·00	16·00

1941. Stamp of 1932 (King George V) optd with Type O 1 and surch with Type O 4.

O90	82	1a. on 1a.3p. mauve	26·00	3·50
		w. Wmk inverted	50·00	18·00

1942–47. King George VI. Optd with Type O 2.

O91	100	1r. grey and red-brown	15·00	28·00
O92		2r. purple and brown	18·00	£140
O93		5r. green and blue (1943)	30·00	£800
O94		10r. purple and claret (1947)	80·00	£1900
O91/4		Set of 4	£130	£2500

Gwalior became part of Madhya Bharat by 1 July 1948.

JIND

For earlier issues, see under INDIAN FEUDATORY STATES

PRICES FOR STAMPS ON COVER	
Nos. 1/4	from × 20
Nos. 5/16	
Nos. 17/40	from × 15
Nos. 41/149	from × 8
Nos. O1/86	from × 15

Raja Raghubir Singh, 1864–1887

JIND STATE (1)   JEEND STATE (2)   JHIND STATE (3)

1885 (1 July). Queen Victoria. Optd with T 1.

1	23	½a. blue-green	12·00	10·00
		a. Opt inverted	£160	£180
2	25	1a. brown-purple	80·00	£110
		a. Opt inverted	£1700	£1900
3	27	2a. dull blue	40·00	30·00
		a. Opt inverted	£1200	£1300
4	17	4a. green	£110	£130
5	31	8a. dull mauve	£650	
		a. Opt inverted	£18000	
6	33	1r. slate	£650	
		a. Opt inverted	£21000	
1/6		Set of 6		£1400

The overprint inverted errors occurred on R. 10/8 in the setting of 120, although it is believed that one pane of the ½a. had the overprint inverted on the entire pane. Examples of inverted overprints on the ½a., 1a. and 2a. with the lines much less curved are thought to come from a trial printing.

All six values exist with reprinted overprint. This has the words "JHIND" and "STATE" 8 and 9 mm in length respectively, whereas in the originals the words are 9 and 9½ mm.

1885. Optd with T 2.

7	23	½a. blue-green (R.)	£200	
8	25	1a. brown-purple	£200	
9	27	2a. dull blue (R.)	£225	
10	17	4a. green (R.)	£300	
		a. Opt double, one albino	£425	
11	31	8a. dull mauve	£300	
12	33	1r. slate (R.)	£300	
7/12		Set of 6	£1400	

1886. Optd with T 3, in red.

13	23	½a. blue-green	65·00	
		a. "JEIND" for "JHIND"	£2000	
14	27	2a. dull blue	65·00	
		a. "JEIND" for "JHIND"	£2000	
		b. Opt double, one albino	£140	
15	17	4a. green	90·00	
		a. Opt double, one albino	90·00	
		b. Opt treble, two albino	£150	
16	33	1r. slate	£100	
		a. "JEIND" for "JHIND"	£3000	
13/16		Set of 4	£275	

Examples of No. 14a usually show an additional albino "SERVICE" overprint as Type O 16.

1886–99. Optd with T 3.

17	23	½a. blue-green	1·25	10
		a. Opt inverted	£275	
18	25	1a. brown-purple	6·00	30
		a. "JEIND" for "JHIND"	£750	
		b. Opt double, one albino	80·00	
19		1a. plum (1899)	11·00	1·00
20	26	1a.6p. sepia (1896)	5·50	6·00
		a. Opt double, one albino	90·00	
21	27	2a. dull blue	5·50	50
22		2a. ultramarine	5·50	1·00
		a. Opt double, one albino	90·00	
23	28	3a. brown-orange (1891)	7·50	1·75
24	29	4a. olive-green	8·50	4·75
25		4a. slate-green	14·00	8·50
26	21	6a. olive-bistre (1891)	16·00	42·00
		a. Opt double, one albino	65·00	
27		6a. bistre-brown	10·00	32·00
28	31	8a. dull mauve	20·00	40·00
		a. "JEIND" for "JHIND"	£2500	
29		8a. magenta (1897)	26·00	50·00
		a. Opt double, one albino	85·00	
30	32	12a. purple/red (1896)	14·00	42·00
		a. Opt double, one albino	85·00	
31	33	1r. slate	20·00	80·00
32	37	1r. green and carmine (1897)	21·00	80·00
33	38	2r. carmine and yellow-brown (1896)	£550	£1900
34		3r. brown and green (1896)	£850	£1600
35		5r. ultramarine and violet (1896)	£900	£1300
17/35		Set of 14	£4500	

Varieties exist in which the word "JHIND" measures 10½ mm and 9¾ mm instead of 10 mm. Such varieties are to be found on Nos. 17, 18, 21, 24, 28 and 31.

Raja (Maharaja from 1911) Ranbir Singh, 1887–1959

1900–04. Colours changed.

36	40	3p. carmine	1·10	3·25
37		3p. grey (1904)	40	4·75
38	23	½a. pale yellow-green (1902)	8·00	10·00
39		½a. yellow-green (1903)	12·00	20·00
40	25	1a. carmine (1902)	3·25	13·00
		a. Opt double, one albino	60·00	
36/40		Set of 4	11·50	28·00

1903–09. King Edward VII. Optd with T 3.

41	41	3p. pale grey	60	20
		a. Opt double, one albino	28·00	
42		3p. slate-grey (1905)	80	80
43	42	½a. green	4·25	3·25
44	43	1a. carmine	3·25	2·50
45	44	2a. pale violet	7·50	3·25
46		2a. mauve (1906)	5·50	1·50
		a. Opt double, one albino	70·00	
47	45	2a.6p. ultramarine (1909)	3·00	10·00
		a. Opt double, one albino	45·00	
48	46	3a. orange-brown (1909)	7·00	1·25
		a. Opt double	£160	£325
49	47	4a. olive	17·00	16·00
		a. Opt double, one albino	70·00	
50		4a. pale olive	17·00	19·00
51	48	6a. bistre (1905)	14·00	42·00
		a. Opt double, one albino	75·00	
52	49	8a. purple (shades)	10·00	30·00
53		8a. claret	32·00	60·00

54	50	12a. purple/red (1905)	7·50	23·00
55	51	1r. green and carmine (1905)	10·00	40·00
		a. Opt double, one albino	£100	
41/55		Set of 11	75·00	£150

1907–09. Nos. 149/50 of India optd with T 3.

56	53	½a. green	1·75	30
57	54	1a. carmine (1909)	3·50	70

1913. King George V. Optd with T 3.

58	55	3p. grey	10	2·50
59	56	½a. light green	10	75
60	57	1a. aniline carmine	10	60
61	59	2a. purple	15	4·75
62	62	3a. orange	1·50	17·00
63	64	6a. yellow-bistre	14·00	50·00
58/63		Set of 6	15·00	70·00

JIND STATE (4)   JIND STATE (5)   JIND STATE (6)

1914–27. King George V. Optd with T 4.

64	55	3p. grey	2·50	1·25
		a. Pale grey	2·75	20
		b. Bluish grey	5·00	1·25
		c. Slate	5·00	
65	56	½a. light green	4·25	15
		a. Emerald	—	3·50
		b. Bright green	2·75	30
66	57	1a. aniline carmine	3·00	15
67	58	1½a. chocolate (Type A) (1922)	7·00	9·50
68		1½a. chocolate (Type B) (1924)	1·60	2·25
69	59	2a. purple	4·50	2·00
		a. Reddish purple	13·00	1·00
		b. Bright reddish violet (1922)	6·00	1·50
70	61	2a.6p. ultramarine (1922)	75	6·50
71	62	3a. orange	75	7·00
72	63	4a. olive	3·25	12·00
73	64	6a. yellow-bistre	8·50	29·00
		a. Brown-ochre	12·00	24·00
74	65	8a. deep magenta	8·00	30·00
		a. Deep mauve (1925)	22·00	35·00
		b. Bright mauve (1918)	—	45·00
75	66	12a. carmine-lake	6·00	38·00
76	67	1r. red-brown and deep blue-green	16·00	45·00
		a. Opt double, one albino	65·00	
		b. Brown and green	35·00	
77		2r. carmine and yellow-brown (1927)	18·00	£170
78		5r. ultramarine and violet (1927)	75·00	£550
64/78		Set of 15	£140	£800

No. 71 with inverted overprint is of clandestine origin.

1922. No. 192 of India optd "JIND" in block capitals.

79		9p. on 1a. rose-carmine	1·25	17·00

1924–27. Optd with T 4. New colours.

80	57	1a. chocolate	6·50	3·75
81	58	1½a. rose-carmine (Type B) (1927)	30	2·50
82	61	2a.6p. orange (1927)	2·00	11·00
83	62	3a. bright blue (1925)	3·75	8·50
80/3		Set of 4	11·00	23·00

Nos. 81/2 with inverted overprint are of clandestine origin.

1927–37. King George V (Nasik printing, wmk Mult Star), optd at Nasik with T 5 or 6 (rupee values).

84	55	3p. slate	10	10
		w. Wmk inverted	8·00	
85	56	½a. green (1929)	35	35
86	80	9p. deep green (1932)	2·25	40
87	57	1a. chocolate (1928)	15	10
		w. Wmk inverted	—	5·00
88	82	1a.3p. mauve (1932)	25	30
89	58	1½a. rose-carmine (Type B) (1930)	1·00	5·00
		w. Wmk inverted	2·00	4·25
90	70	2a. purple (1928)	6·50	1·00
		w. Wmk inverted	7·00	40
91	61	2a.6p. orange (1930)	4·50	19·00
		w. Wmk inverted	1·25	17·00
92	62	3a. bright blue (1930)	9·50	27·00
		w. Wmk inverted	11·00	
93	83	3a.6p. ultramarine (1937)	5·50	38·00
		w. Wmk inverted	75	26·00
94	71	4a. sage-green (1928)	9·50	5·00
		w. Wmk inverted	2·50	4·50
95	64	6a. bistre (1937)	75	27·00
		w. Wmk inverted	14·00	
96	65	8a. reddish purple (1930)	12·00	3·50
		w. Wmk inverted	13·00	
97	66	12a. claret (1930)	20·00	42·00
		w. Wmk inverted	13·00	32·00
98	67	1r. chocolate and green (1930)	13·00	15·00
		w. Wmk inverted	—	75·00
99		2r. carmine and orange (1930)	75·00	£200
		w. Wmk inverted	35·00	
100		5r. ultramarine and purple (1928)	19·00	55·00
		w. Wmk inverted	60·00	
101		10r. green and carmine (1928)	23·00	18·00
102		15r. blue and olive (wmk inverted) (1929)	£180	£1300
103		25r. orange and blue (1929)	£325	£1800
84/103		Set of 20	£600	£3250

1934. New types and colours. Optd with T 5.

104	79	½a. green	30	25
105	81	1a. chocolate	2·00	30
		w. Wmk inverted	—	12·00
106	59	2a. vermilion	7·00	70
107	62	3a. orange	3·25	40
108	63	4a. sage-green	3·25	1·75
104/8		Set of 5	14·00	3·00

1937–38. King George VI. Nos. 247/64 optd with T 5 or T 6 (rupee values).

109	91	3p. slate	10·00	3·50
110		½a. red-brown	1·00	7·00
111		9p. green (1937)	1·00	4·00
112		1a. carmine (1937)	75	75
113	92	2a. vermilion	3·25	28·00

114	**93**	2a.6p. bright violet	1·50	38·00
115	**94**	3a. yellow-green	7·00	35·00
116	**95**	3a.6p. bright blue	8·00	38·00
117	**96**	4a. brown	16·00	32·00
118	**97**	6a. turquoise-green	9·50	55·00
119	**98**	8a. slate-violet	13·00	42·00
120	**99**	12a. lake	4·25	50·00
121	**100**	1r. grey and red-brown	13·00	65·00
122		2r. purple and brown	15·00	£225
123		5r. green and blue	32·00	£130
124		10r. purple and claret	60·00	£110
125		15r. brown and green	£110	£1300
126		25r. slate-violet and purple	£1100	£1900
109/26 *Set of 18*			£1300	£3750

JIND
(7)

1941–43. King George VI. Optd with T **7**.

(a) Stamps of 1937. W 69 (inverted on 15r.)

127	**91**	3p. slate	20·00	27·00
128		½a. red-brown	1·25	3·75
129		9p. green	17·00	32·00
130		1a. carmine	1·00	8·00
131	**100**	1r. grey and red-brown	11·00	38·00
132		2r. purple and brown	20·00	48·00
133		5r. green and blue	45·00	£160
134		10r. purple and claret	60·00	£120
135		15r. brown and green	£200	£275
136		25r. slate-violet and purple	60·00	£450
127/36 *Set of 10*			£375	£1000

(b) Stamps of 1940–43

137	**100a**	3p. slate (1942)	50	2·00
138		½a. purple (1943)	50	2·50
139		9p. green (1942)	75	4·50
140		1a. carmine (1942)	1·00	1·50
141	**101**	1a.3p. yellow-brown	1·00	6·50
142		1½a. dull violet (litho) (1942)	10·00	6·50
142a		1½a. dull violet (typo) (1943)	3·00	8·00
143		2a. vermilion	1·00	7·00
144		3a. bright violet (litho) (1942)	10·00	8·50
144a		3a. bright violet (typo) (1943)	6·00	11·00
145		3½a. bright blue	9·00	17·00
146	**102**	4a. brown	2·75	8·50
147		6a. turquoise-green	9·00	22·00
148		8a. slate-violet	7·00	20·00
149		12a. lake	14·00	25·00
137/149 *Set of 13*			50·00	£120

STAMP BOOKLET

1929 (?). Black on brown covers (No. SB18a of India) with red opt 'JIND STATE' on front. Stitched.

SB1		1r. booklet containing 16×1a. (No. 87) in blocks of 4	£2750

OFFICIAL STAMPS

SERVICE

SERVICE	SERVICE	JHIND STATE
(O **14**)	(O **15**)	(O **16**)

1885 (1 July). Queen Victoria. Nos. 1/3 of Jind optd with Type O **14**.

O1	**23**	½a. blue green	4·25	60
		a. Opt Type **1** inverted	£150	70·00
O2	**25**	1a. brown-purple	1·00	10
		a. Opt Type **1** inverted	20·00	7·50
		w. Wmk inverted	†	£500
O3	**27**	2a. dull blue	50·00	50·00
		a. Opt Type **1** inverted	£1500	£2000

The three values have had the overprint reprinted in the same way as the ordinary stamps of 1885. See note after No. 6.

1885. Nos. 7/9 of Jind optd with Type O **15**.

O7	**23**	½a. blue-green (R.)	£170
		a. "JEEND STATE" double, one albino	£325
O8	**25**	1a. brown-purple	£160
O9	**27**	2a. dull blue (R.)	£150
O7/9 *Set of 3*			£450

1886. Optd with Type O **16**, in red.

O10	**23**	½a. blue-green	50·00
		a. "ERVICE"	£6000
		b. "JEIND"	£900
		c. "JHIND STATE" double, one albino	£120
O11	**27**	2a. dull blue	60·00
		a. "ERVICE"	£3750
		b. "JEIND"	£2000
		c. "SERVICE" double, one albino	£110
		d. "JHIND STATE" double, one albino	£110

1886–1902. Optd with Type O **16**.

O12	**23**	½a. blue-green	5·50	10
		a. "JHIND STATE" double, one albino	80·00	
O13	**25**	1a. brown-purple	55·00	
		a. "ERVICE"		
		b. "JEIND"	£750	
		c. "SERVICE" double, one albino		
O14		1a. plum (1902)	24·00	1·75
O15	**27**	2a. dull blue	7·50	1·75
		a. "SERVICE" double, one albino	65·00	
		b. "SERVICE" treble, two albino	80·00	
O16		2a. ultramarine	5·50	30
		a. "JHIND STATE" double, one albino	85·00	
O17	**29**	4a. olive-green (1892)	8·00	4·50
		a. "JHIND STATE" double, one albino	75·00	

O18		4a. slate-green	9·50	6·00
O19	**31**	8a. dull mauve (1892)	12·00	8·50
O20		8a. magenta (1897)	12·00	13·00
		a. "JHIND STATE" double, one albino	75·00	
O21	**37**	1r. green and carmine (1896)	12·00	75·00
		a. "SERVICE" double, one albino	£110	
		b. "JHIND STATE" treble, two albino	£100	
O12/21 *Set of 6*			60·00	80·00

Varieties mentioned in note after No. 35 exist on Nos. O12, O15, O17 and O20.

Printings up to and including that of October 1897 had the "SERVICE" overprint. Type O **15**, applied to sheets already overprinted with Type **3**. From the printing of December 1899 onwards "SERVICE" and "JHIND STATE" were overprinted at one operation, as Type O **16**, to provide fresh supplies of Nos. O12, O14 and O21.

1902. Colour changed. Optd with Type O **16**.

O22	**23**	½a. yellow-green	5·00	40
		a. "V" of "SERVICE" omitted	£300	£130

No. O22a normally shows a tiny trace of the "V" remaining. Examples showing the letter completely missing are worth much more.

1903–06. King Edward VII stamps of India optd with Type O **16**.

O23	**41**	3p. pale green	1·75	10
O24		3p. slate-grey (1906)	1·50	10
O25	**42**	½a. green	6·00	10
		a. "HIND"	£4250	£450
		b. Opt double, one albino	55·00	
		c. "SERV CE"	†	£600
O26	**43**	1a. carmine	6·50	10
		a. "HIND"	£6000	£450
		b. Opt double, one albino	50·00	
O27	**44**	2a. pale violet	5·50	1·50
O28		2a. mauve	3·75	10
O29	**47**	4a. olive	4·50	45
		a. Opt double, one albino	85·00	
O30	**49**	8a. purple (*shades*)	18·00	5·00
O31		8a. claret	12·00	1·50
O32	**51**	1r. green and carmine (1906)	3·25	2·25
O23/32 *Set of 7*			35·00	4·00

The "HIND" error Nos. O25a and O26a occurred on one position in the bottom row of the sheet.

1907. Nos. 149/50 of India optd with Type O **16**.

O33	**53**	½a. green	2·25	10
O34	**54**	1a. carmine	3·50	10

1914–27. King George V. Official stamps of India optd with T **4**.

O35	**55**	3p. grey	10	10
		a. "JIND STATE" double, one albino	80·00	
		b. Pale grey	30	10
		c. Bluish grey	—	1·00
O36	**56**	½a. light green	10	10
		a. Emerald	4·75	40
		b. Bright green	1·75	30
O37	**57**	1a. aniline carmine	75	10
		a. Pale rose-carmine	4·75	20
O39	**59**	2a. purple	40	20
		a. Reddish purple	—	20
		b. Deep mauve	4·50	1·50
O40	**63**	4a. olive	2·00	20
O41	**64**	6a. brown-ochre (1926)	3·50	2·25
O42	**65**	8a. deep magenta	1·25	1·50
		a. Deep mauve	6·50	2·25
O43	**67**	1r. red-brown and deep blue-green	7·50	2·25
		a. "JIND STATE" double, one albino	65·00	
		b. Brown and green	27·00	
O44		2r. carmine and yellow-brown (1927)	21·00	75·00
O45		5r. ultramarine and violet (1927)	42·00	£475
O35/45 *Set of 10*			70·00	£500

No. O40 with double overprint is of clandestine origin.

1924. As 1914–27. New colour.

O46	**57**	1a. chocolate	60	10

JIND STATE SERVICE	JIND STATE SERVICE	JIND SERVICE
(O **17**)	(O **18**)	(O **19**)

1927–37. King George V (Nasik printing, wmk Mult Star), optd with Types O **17** or O **18** (rupee values).

O47	**55**	3p. slate (1928)	10	20
O48	**56**	½a. green (1929)	10	1·00
O49	**80**	9p. deep green (litho) (1932)	1·00	15
O49a		9p. deep green (typo)	—	1·50
O50	**57**	1a. chocolate	10	10
		w. Wmk inverted	1·00	
O51	**82**	1a.3p. mauve (1932)	40	15
		w. Wmk inverted	1·60	80
O52	**70**	2a. purple (1929)	25	15
O53	**61**	2a.6p. orange (1937)	1·75	22·00
O54	**71**	4a. sage-green (1929)	35	25
		w. Wmk inverted	4·75	2·25
O55	**64**	6a. bistre (1937)	6·50	28·00
		w. Wmk inverted	7·50	27·00
O56	**65**	8a. reddish purple (1929)	—	3·25
		w. Wmk inverted	75	1·75
O57	**66**	12a. claret (1928)	2·75	26·00
O58	**67**	1r. chocolate and green (1928)	9·00	10·00
O59		2r. carmine and orange (1930)	85·00	60·00
		w. Wmk inverted	55·00	
O60		5r. ultramarine and purple (1929)	14·00	£400
O61		10r. green and carmine (1928)	55·00	£180
		w. Wmk inverted	90·00	
O47/61 *Set of 15*			£130	£650

1934. Optd with Type O **17**.

O62	**79**	½a. green	20	15
O63	**81**	1a. chocolate	20	15
O64	**59**	2a. vermilion	30	15
		w. Wmk inverted	3·25	5·50
O65	**63**	4a. sage-green (1937)	9·00	30
O62/5 *Set of 4*			9·00	65

1937–40. King George VI. Optd with Types O **17** or O **18** (rupee values).

O66	**91**	½a. red-brown (1938)	85·00	30
O67		9p. green	6·50	28·00
O68		1a. carmine	6·00	30
O69	**100**	1r. grey and red-brown (1940)	75·00	80·00
O70		2r. purple and brown (1940)	85·00	£450
O71		5r. green and blue (1940)	£150	£650
O72		10r. purple and claret (1940)	£700	£1800
O66/72 *Set of 7*			£1000	£2750

1939–43.

(a) Official stamps optd with T 7

O73	O **20**	3p. slate	60	2·00
O74		½a. red-brown	4·50	1·25
O75		½a. purple (1943)	60	30
O76		9p. green	3·00	16·00
O77		1a. carmine	3·75	15
O78		1½a. dull violet (1942)	9·00	3·00
O79		2a. vermilion	8·50	30
		w. Wmk inverted	10·00	8·00
O80		2½a. bright violet (1943)	5·00	13·00
O81		4a. brown	8·50	8·50
O82		8a. slate-violet	12·00	14·00

(b) Postage stamps optd with T 19

O83	**100**	1r. grey and red-brown (1942)	18·00	75·00
O84		2r. purple and brown (1942)	42·00	£275
O85		5r. green and blue (1942)	70·00	£700
O86		10r. purple and claret (1942)	£225	£1100
O73/86 *Set of 14*			£350	£2000

Jind was absorbed into the Patiala and East Punjab States Union by 20 August 1948

NABHA

PRICES FOR STAMPS ON COVER	
Nos. 1/3	from × 15
Nos. 4/6	
Nos. 10/36	from × 12
Nos. 37/117	from × 7
Nos. O1/68	from × 15

Raja Hira Singh, 1871–1911.

NABHA STATE (circular)	NABHA STATE
(1)	(2)

1885 (1 July). Queen Victoria. Optd with T **1**.

1	**23**	½a. blue-green	8·00	12·00
2	**25**	1a. brown-purple	90·00	£350
3	**27**	2a. dull blue	42·00	95·00
4	**17**	4a. green	£130	£375
5	**31**	8a. dull mauve	£550	
6	**33**	1r. slate	£550	
1/6 *Set of 6*			£1200	

All six values have had the overprint reprinted. On the reprints the words "NABHA" and "STATE" both measure 9¼ mm in length, whereas on the originals these words measure 11 and 10 mm respectively. The varieties with overprint double come from the reprints.

1885 (Nov)–**1900.** Optd with T **2**.

(a) In red

10	**23**	½a. blue-green	4·50	2·75
11	**27**	2a. dull blue	5·50	4·50
		a. Opt double, one albino	£110	
12	**17**	4a. green	75·00	£400
13	**33**	1r. slate	£190	£550
		a. Opt double, one albino	£275	
10/13 *Set of 4*			£250	£850

(b) In black (Nov 1885–97)

14	**23**	½a. blue-green (1888)	1·50	10
15	**24**	9p. carmine (1892)	3·50	7·00
16	**25**	1a. brown-purple	5·50	1·00
17		1a. plum	6·50	2·00
18	**26**	1a.6p. sepia (1891)	4·25	8·00
		a. "ABHA" for "NABHA"	£475	
19	**27**	2a. dull blue (1888)	6·50	3·00
20		2a. ultramarine	6·00	3·25
21	**28**	3a. orange (1889)	28·00	45·00
		a. Opt double, one albino	70·00	
22		3a. brown-orange	10·00	3·50
23	**29**	4a. olive-green (1888)	10·00	6·00
24		4a. slate-green	10·00	5·00
25	**30**	6a. olive-bistre (1889)	22·00	25·00
26		6a. bistre-brown	4·50	7·00
27	**31**	8a. dull mauve	6·50	6·50
		a. Opt double, one albino	85·00	
28	**32**	12a. purple/red (1889)	6·00	10·00
		a. Opt double, one albino	70·00	
29	**33**	1r. slate (1888)	24·00	90·00
30	**37**	1r. green and carmine (1893)	27·00	20·00
		a. "N BHA" for "NABHA"		
		b. Opt double, one albino	90·00	
31	**38**	2r. carmine and yellow-brown (1897)	£225	£400
		a. Opt double, one albino	£450	
32		3r. brown and green (1897)	£250	£650
33		5r. ultramarine and violet (1897)	£250	£950
14/33 *Set of 15*			£750	£1900

(c) New value. In black (Nov 1900)

36	**40**	3p. carmine	30	20

1903–09. King Edward VII. Optd with T **2**.

37	**41**	3p. pale grey	75	15
		a. "NAB STA" for "NABHA STATE"	£1300	
		b. Opt double, one albino	42·00	
37c		3p. slate-grey (1906)	75	15
38	**42**	½a. green	1·10	70
		a. "NABH" for "NABHA"	£1500	
39	**43**	1a. carmine	2·75	2·00
40	**44**	2a. pale violet	7·50	5·00
40a		2a. mauve	6·50	35
40b	**45**	2a.6p. ultramarine (1909)	19·00	£120
		ba. Opt double, one albino	32·00	

41	46	3a. orange-brown	2·50	40
		a. Opt double, one albino	75·00	
42	47	4a. olive	9·50	3·00
43	48	6a. olive-bistre	11·00	40·00
		a. Opt double, one albino	55·00	
44	49	8a. purple	12·00	48·00
44a		8a. claret	29·00	48·00
45	50	12a. purple/red	10·00	48·00
46	51	1r. green and carmine	12·00	30·00
37/46 *Set of 11*			80·00	£250

1907. Nos. 149/50 of India optd with T **2**.

47	53	½a. green	1·50	1·75
48	54	1a. carmine	2·25	70

Maharaja Ripudaman (Gurcharan) Singh, 1911–1928.

1913. King George V. Optd with T **2**.

49	55	3p. grey	1·75	1·60
		a. Pale grey	1·50	40
		b. Bluish grey	3·50	2·75
		c. Slate	3·75	
50	56	½a. light green	2·25	1·75
		a. Emerald	5·00	1·25
		b. Bright green	2·50	1·75
51	57	1a. aniline carmine	1·10	10
52	59	2a. purple	2·50	3·00
		a. Reddish purple	5·50	2·75
		b. Deep mauve	5·00	3·75
53	62	3a. orange	2·50	75
		a. Dull orange	4·50	2·75
		w. Wmk inverted	£180	
54	63	4a. olive	2·50	4·25
55	64	6a. yellow-bistre	5·00	8·00
		a. Brown-ochre	5·50	12·00
56	65	8a. deep magenta	21·00	16·00
		a. Deep mauve	18·00	9·50
		b. Bright mauve	24·00	
57	66	12a. carmine-lake	11·00	42·00
58	67	1r. red-brown and deep blue-green	22·00	23·00
		a. Opt double, one albino	80·00	
		b. Brown and green	45·00	26·00
		c. Orange-brown and deep turquoise-green	48·00	
49/58 *Set of 10*			60·00	80·00

1924. As 1913. New colour.

59	57	1a. chocolate	15·00	8·00

No. 59 with inverted or double overprint is of clandestine origin.

NABHA STATE	NABHA STATE
(3)	(4)

1927–36. King George V (Nasik printing, wmk Mult Star), optd as T **3** or **4** (rupee values).

60	55	3p. slate (1932)	1·75	15
		w. Wmk inverted	8·50	4·75
61	56	½a. green (1928)	2·50	30
61a	80	9p. deep green (litho) (1934)	11·00	12·00
61b		9p. deep green (typo)	5·50	1·25
62	57	1a. chocolate	2·25	15
		w. Wmk inverted	—	6·00
63	82	1a.3p. mauve (1936)	5·00	7·50
		w. Wmk inverted	1·25	
64	70	2a. purple (1932)	2·50	35
65	61	2a.6p. orange (1932)	3·75	16·00
66	62	3a. bright blue (1930)	6·50	3·00
67	71	4a. sage-green (1932)	9·00	4·75
71	67	2r. carmine and orange (1932)	55·00	£275
72		5r. ultramarine and purple (wmk inverted) (1932)	£110	£750
60/72 *Set of 11*			£180	£950

Maharaja Partab Singh, 1928–1971

1936–37. New types and colours. Optd as T **3**.

73	79	½a. green	1·25	50
74	81	1a. chocolate	1·00	50
75	62	3a. carmine (1937)	4·25	23·00
76	63	4a. sage-green (1937)	12·00	6·00
73/6 *Set of 4*			17·00	27·00

NABHA STATE	NABHA
(5)	(6)

1938. King George VI. Nos. 247/64 optd as T **3** (3p. to 1a.), T **5** (2a. to 12a.) or T **4** (rupee values). W **69** (inverted on 15r.).

77	91	3p. slate	13·00	2·75
78		½a. red-brown	7·50	2·00
79		9p. green	18·00	5·50
80		1a. carmine	5·50	2·25
81	92	2a. vermilion	2·50	15·00
82	93	2a.6p. bright violet	3·25	22·00
83	94	3a. yellow-green	2·50	10·00
84	95	3a.6p. bright blue	7·00	45·00
85	96	4a. brown	12·00	7·50
86	97	6a. turquoise-green	6·00	48·00
87	98	8a. slate-violet	3·75	45·00
88	99	12a. lake	2·75	35·00
89	100	1r. grey and red-brown	16·00	50·00
90		2r. purple and brown	35·00	£170
91		5r. green and blue	48·00	£375
92		10r. purple and claret	65·00	£800
93		15r. brown and green	£375	£1600
94		25r. slate-violet and purple	£200	£1600
		w. Wmk inverted	£450	£1900
77/94 *Set of 18*			£750	£4250

1941–45. King George VI. Optd with T **6**.

(a) Stamps of 1937

95	91	3p. slate (1942)	50·00	9·50
96		½a. red-brown (1942)	90·00	10·00
97		9p. green (1942)	12·00	17·00
98		1a. carmine (1942)	15·00	6·50
95/8 *Set of 4*			£150	38·00

(b) Stamps of 1940–43

105	100a	3p. slate (1942)	1·25	1·25
106		½a. purple (1943)	1·00	2·50

107		9p. green (1942)	1·00	2·75
108		1a. carmine (1945)	1·00	5·00
109	101	1a.3p. yellow-brown	1·00	4·50
110		1½a. dull violet (litho) (1942)	2·50	3·25
110a		1½a. dull violet (typo) (1943)	4·00	5·00
111		2a. vermilion (1943)	2·00	4·50
112		3a. bright violet (typo) (1943)	2·00	7·50
113		3½a. bright blue (1944)	10·00	£100
114	102	4a. brown	1·00	1·00
115		6a. turquoise-green (1943)	18·00	70·00
116		8a. slate-violet (1943)	17·00	60·00
117		12a. lake (1943)	16·00	90·00
105/17 *Set of 13*			65·00	£325

OFFICIAL STAMPS

SERVICE

SERVICE	NABHA STATE
(O **8**)	(O **9**)

1885 (1 July). Nos. 1/3 of Nabha optd with Type O **8**.

O1	23	½a. blue-green	12·00	3·00
O2	25	1a. brown-purple	70	20
		a. Opt Type O **8** double	†	£3500
O3	27	2a. dull blue	£130	£250
O1/3 *Set of 3*			£130	£250

The three values have had the overprint reprinted in the same way as the ordinary stamps of 1885.

1885 (Nov)–97. Optd with Type O **9**.

(a) In red

O4	23	½a. blue-green	14·00	7·50
O5	27	2a. deep blue	2·75	55

(b) In black (Nov 1885–97)

O6	23	½a. blue-green (1888)	40	10
		a. "SERVICE." with stop	£190	3·00
		b. "S ATE" for "STATE"	£190	
		c. "SERVICE" double, one albino	80·00	
O7	25	1a. brown-purple	4·00	60
O8		1a. plum	5·00	25
		a. "SERVICE." with stop	15·00	75
		ab. "SERVICE." with stop, and "NABHA STATE" double	£3250	£325
O9	27	2a. dull blue (1888)	7·00	3·25
O10		2a. ultramarine	8·00	3·75
O11	28	3a. orange (1889)	32·00	£150
O12		3a. brown-orange	45·00	£190
		a. "NABHA STATE" double, one albino	£110	
O13	29	4a. olive-green (1888)	7·50	2·50
O14		4a. slate-green	6·50	1·50
O15	21	6a. olive-bistre (1889)	32·00	55·00
		a. "SERVICE" double, one albino	80·00	
O16		6a. bistre-brown	£850	
O17	31	8a. dull mauve (1889)	7·00	3·00
O18	32	12a. purple/red (1889)	8·50	29·00
		a. SERVICE double, one albino	85·00	
		b. "NABHA STATE" double, one albino	70·00	
O19	33	1r. slate (1889)	70·00	£550
O20	37	1r. green and carmine (1.97)	42·00	£120
O6/20 *Set of 14*			£190	£800

Printings up to and including that of August 1895 had the "SERVICE" overprint applied to sheets of stamps already overprinted with Type **2**. From the printing of January 1897 onwards the two parts of the overprint were applied at one operation. This method was only used for printings of the ½a., 1a. and 1r. (O20).

1903–06. King Edward VII stamps of India optd with Type O **9**.

O24	41	3p. pale grey (1906)	12·00	42·00
O25		3p. slate-grey (1906)	6·50	28·00
		a. Opt double, one albino	50·00	
O26	42	½a. green	1·00	50
O27	43	1a. carmine	80	10
O28	44	2a. pale violet	5·50	2·25
O29		2a. mauve	6·00	40
		a. Opt double, one albino	75·00	
O30	47	4a. olive	3·25	50
O32	49	8a. purple (shades)	3·75	1·50
		a. Opt double, one albino	55·00	
O33		8a. claret	32·00	11·00
O34	51	1r. green and carmine	3·75	3·75
O24/34 *Set of 7*			22·00	32·00

1907. Nos. 149/50 of India optd with Type O **9**.

O35	53	½a. green	2·75	50
		a. Opt double, one albino	29·00	
O36	54	1a. carmine	1·50	30
		a. Opt double, one albino	45·00	

1913. King George V. Optd with Type O **9**.

O37	63	4a. olive	10·00	80·00
O38	67	1r. red-brown and deep blue-green	80·00	£600
		a. Opt double, one albino	£140	

1913. Official stamps of India optd with T **2**.

O39	55	3p. grey	2·75	14·00
		a. Pale grey	2·25	11·00
		b. Bluish grey	1·75	14·00
		c. Slate	1·50	14·00
O40	56	½a. light green	1·00	50
		a. Emerald	3·25	20
		b. Bright green	3·25	15
O41	57	1a. aniline carmine	1·50	20
O42	59	2a. purple	2·25	1·75
		a. Reddish purple	6·50	1·50
		b. Deep mauve	6·00	50
		c. Bright reddish violet		
O43	63	4a. olive	2·00	1·00
O44	65	8a. deep magenta	4·25	2·25
		a. Deep mauve	9·50	
		b. Bright mauve	16·00	
O46	67	1r. red-brown and deep blue-green	10·00	8·00
		a. Brown and green	14·00	8·50
O39/46 *Set of 7*			20·00	20·00

NABHA STATE SERVICE	NABHA SERVICE
(O **10**)	(O **11**)

1932–42?. King George V (Nasik printing, wmk Mult Star), optd at Nasik with Type O **10**.

O47	55	3p. slate	10	15
O48	81	1a. chocolate (1935)	35	15
O49	63	4a. sage-green (1942?)	29·00	2·50
O50	65	8a. reddish purple (1937)	1·00	3·25
O47/50 *Set of 4*			29·00	5·50

1938. King George VI. Optd as Type O **10**.

O53	91	9p. green	12·00	4·00
O54		1a. carmine	18·00	1·10

1940–43.

*(a) Official stamps optd with T **6***

O55	O **20**	3p. slate (1942)	1·25	3·00
O56		½a. red-brown (1942)	1·10	30
O57		½a. purple (1943)	7·00	2·50
O58		9p. green	1·25	50
O59		1a. carmine (1942)	1·75	20
O61		1½a. dull violet (1942)	70	40
O62		2a. vermilion (1942)	2·25	1·50
		w. Wmk inverted	12·00	6·00
O64		4a. brown (1942)	3·00	4·25
O65		8a. slate-violet (1942)	5·00	27·00

*(b) Postage stamps optd with Type O **11***

O66	100	1r. grey and red-brown (1942)	12·00	55·00
O67		2r. purple and brown (1942)	50·00	£400
O68		5r. green and blue (1942)	£275	£950
O55/68 *Set of 12*			£325	£1300

Nabha was absorbed into the Patiala and East Punjab States Union by 20 August 1948.

PATIALA

PRICES FOR STAMPS ON COVER	
Nos. 1/6	from × 10
Nos. 7/34	from × 6
Nos. 35/45	from × 8
Nos. 46/115	from × 4
Nos. O1/84	from × 15

Maharaja Rajindra Singh, 1876–1900

PUTTIALLA STATE	PUTTIALLA STATE	PATIALA STATE
(1)	(2)	(3)

1884 (1 Oct). Queen Victoria. Optd with T **1**, in red.

1	23	½a. blue-green	7·50	4·75
		a. Opt double, one sideways	£5000	£1200
		b. Opt double, one albino	£150	
2	25	1a. brown-purple	90·00	£130
		a. Opt double		
		b. Optd in red and in black		
3	27	2a. dull blue	21·00	16·00
4	17	4a. green	£150	£180
5	31	8a. dull mauve	£600	£1900
		a. Opt inverted	£20000	
		b. Optd in red and in black	£225	£900
		ba. Ditto. Opts inverted	£16000	
		c. Opt double, one albino	£650	
6	33	1r. slate	£225	£1000
1/6 *Set of 6 (incl No.5)*			£1000	£3000

Nos. 5a and 5ba each occur once in the setting of 120. The 8a. value also exists with a trial overprint (showing the words more curved) reading downwards (*Price £800 unused*), which should not be confused with No. 5a.

1885. Optd with T **2**.

(a) In red

7	23	½a. blue-green	4·50	30
		a. "AUTTIALLA"	26·00	70·00
		b. "STATE" only		
		c. Wide spacing between lines	13·00	16·00
8	27	2a. dull blue	22·00	1·75
		a. "AUTTIALLA"	90·00	
		b. Wide spacing between lines	60·00	80·00
		ba. Ditto "AUTTIALLA"	£1900	
9	17	4a. green	9·50	4·25
		a. Optd in red and in black	£425	
		b. Wide spacing between lines	£700	
		c. Opt double, one albino	85·00	
10	33	1r. slate	60·00	£150
		a. "AUTTIALLA"	£750	
		b. Wide spacing between lines	£650	

(b) In black

11	25	1a. brown-purple	1·25	50
		a. Optd in red and in black	30·00	£160
		b. "AUTTIALLA"	£120	
		ba. Ditto. Optd in red and in black.	£2750	
		c. Opt double	£325	£375
		d. Wide spacing between lines	£500	
12	31	8a. dull mauve	60·00	£130
		a. "AUTTIALLA"	£650	
		b. Wide spacing between lines	£130	
		c. Wide spacing between lines	£700	
7/12 *Set of 6*			£140	£250

The ½, 2 and 4a. (T **29**), and 1r. (all overprinted in black), are proofs. All six values exist with reprinted overprints, and the error "AUTTIALLA STATE" has been reprinted in complete sheets on all values and in addition in black on the ½, 2a. and 1r. Nearly all these however, are found with the word "REPRINT" overprinted upon them. On the genuine "AUTTIALLA" errors, which occur on R. 9/12 in the setting of 120, the word "STATE" is 8½ mm long; on the reprints only 7¾ mm.

Nos. 7c, 8b, 9b, 10b, 11d and 12c show 1¼ mm spacing between the two lines of overprint. The normal spacing is ¾ mm.

Nos. 7/8 and 10/12 exist with error "PUTTILLA", but their status is uncertain (*Price, from £1100, unused*).

1891–96. Optd with T **3**.

13	23	½a. blue-green (1892)	2·00	10
14	24	9p. carmine	1·75	3·00
15	25	1a. brown-purple	2·25	30
16		1a. plum	4·00	2·00
		a. "PATIALA" omitted	£375	£600
		b. "PA" omitted		
		c. "PATIA" omitted		
		d. "PATIAL" omitted		
17	26	1a.6p. sepia	3·00	3·00
18	27	2a. dull blue (1896)	3·75	40
19		2a. ultramarine	4·75	1·50
20	28	3a. brown-orange	3·75	1·25
21	29	4a. olive-green (1896)	7·00	1·50
		a. "PATIALA" omitted	£800	£375
22		4a. slate-green	7·00	1·50
23	21	6a. bistre-brown	4·75	15·00
24		6a. olive-bistre	13·00	35·00
		a. Opt double, one albino	£100	
25	31	8a. dull mauve	7·50	18·00
26		8a. magenta (1896)	6·00	19·00
27	32	12a. purple/*red*	9·00	65·00
28	37	1r. green and carmine (1896)		
29	38	2r. carmine and yellow-brown (1895)	£275	£1700
30		3r. brown and green (1895)	£325	£1800
		a. Opt double, one albino	£400	
		b. Opt treble, two albino	£325	
31		5r. ultramarine and violet (1895)	£375	£1900
13/31 *Set of 14*			£950	£5000

The errors on the 1a. plum and 4a. olive-green occur on R. 19/1 in the December 1898 printing. Nos. 16b/d are early stages of the error before the entire word was omitted.

1899–1902. Colours changed and new value. Optd with T **3**.

32	40	3p. carmine (1899)	30	15
		a. Pair, one without opt	£6500	
		b. Opt double, one albino	80·00	
33	23	½a. pale yellow-green	1·10	1·75
34	25	1a. carmine	2·50	3·00
32/4 *Set of 3*			3·50	4·25

Maharaja Bhupindra Singh, 1900–1938

1903–06. King Edward VII. Optd with T **3**.

35	41	3p. pale grey	40	10
		a. Additional albino opt of Jind Type **3**	£325	
		b. "S" in "STATE" sideways (R. 20/1)	£1100	£1300
36		3p. slate-grey (1906)	75	10
37	42	2a. green	1·50	15
38	43	1a. carmine	3·75	10
		a. Horiz pair, one without opt	£1600	
39	44	2a. pale violet	3·75	65
		a. Mauve	17·00	1·00
40	46	3a. orange-brown	3·00	50
41	47	4a. olive (1905)	6·50	1·75
42	48	6a. olive-bistre (1905)	6·50	19·00
43	49	8a. purple (1906)	7·50	6·50
44	50	12a. purple/*red* (1906)	14·00	45·00
45	51	1r. green and carmine (1905)	8·00	12·00
35/45 *Set of 10*			50·00	75·00

1912. Nos. 149/50 of India optd with T **3**.

46	53	½a. green	40	25
47	54	1a. carmine	1·75	1·50

1912–26. King George V. Optd with T **3**.

48	55	3p. grey	1·50	10
		a. Pale grey	2·50	25
		b. Bluish grey	2·25	
		c. Slate	6·00	2·00
		ca. "Rs" flaw	65·00	
49	56	½a. light green	2·25	60
		a. Emerald	5·50	1·25
		b. Bright green	5·00	2·00
50	57	1a. aniline carmine	2·50	20
51	58	1½a. chocolate (Type A) (1922)	50	55
52	59	2a. purple	3·50	1·75
		a. Reddish purple	8·00	
		b. Deep mauve	8·00	
		c. Bright reddish violet	10·00	
53	62	3a. orange	5·00	2·50
54	63	4a. olive	6·00	3·75
55	64	6a. yellow-bistre	4·75	5·50
		a. Brown-ochre (1921)	7·50	9·00
56	65	8a. deep magenta	7·00	4·75
		a. Purple (1921)	10·00	6·00
57	66	12a. carmine-lake	8·00	12·00
58	67	1r. red-brown and deep blue-green	18·00	22·00
		a. Opt double, one albino	70·00	
		b. Brown and green (1924)	32·00	
59		2r. carmine and yell-brn (1926)	24·00	£160
60		5r. ultramarine and violet (1926)	60·00	£425

1923–26. As 1912–26. New colours.

61	57	1a. chocolate	3·75	50
62	62	3a. ultramarine (1926)	6·50	17·00
48/62 *Set of 15*			£140	£600

1928–34. King George V (Nasik printing, wmk Mult Star) optd at Nasik with T **4** or **5** (rupee values).

63	55	3p. slate (1932)	2·00	10
		w. Wmk inverted	7·00	3·50
64	56	½a. green	50	10
		w. Wmk inverted	5·00	3·50
65	80	9p. deep green (*litho*) (1934)	2·25	1·00
		aw. Wmk inverted	—	11·00
65b		9p. deep green (*typo*)	4·00	50
66	57	1a. chocolate	1·75	25
		w. Wmk inverted	7·00	3·25
67	82	1a.3p. mauve (1932)	4·25	15
		w. Wmk inverted	7·00	3·75
68	70	2a. purple	2·00	40
		w. Wmk inverted	6·50	
69	61	2a.6p. orange (1934)	9·00	4·25
		w. Wmk inverted	7·00	

70	62	3a. bright blue (1929)	5·50	3·75
71	71	4a. sage-green	10·00	2·25
		w. Wmk inverted	17·00	
72	65	8a. reddish purple (1933)	12·00	6·00
73	67	1r. chocolate and green (1929)	13·00	18·00
		w. Wmk inverted	30·00	30·00
74		2r. carmine and orange	50·00	£140
		w. Wmk inverted	18·00	85·00
63/74w *Set of 12*			70·00	£110

1935–37. Optd with T **4**.

75	79	½a. blue-green (1937)	2·25	30
76	81	1a. chocolate (1936)	1·10	20
77	59	2a. vermilion (No. 236b) (1936)	40	1·50
78	62	3a. carmine	15·00	13·00
		w. Wmk inverted	7·50	17·00
79	63	4a. sage-green	3·00	4·50
75/9 *Set of 5*			12·50	18·00

1937–38. King George VI. Nos. 247/64 optd with T **4** (3p. to 1a.), T **6** (2a. to 12a.), or T **5** (rupee values).

80	91	3p. slate	15·00	35
81		½a. red-brown	8·00	50
82		9p. green (1937)	5·00	1·00
83		1a. carmine (1937)	3·00	20
84	92	2a. vermilion	3·00	17·00
85	93	2a.6p. bright violet	13·00	48·00
86	94	3a. yellow-green	16·00	18·00
87	95	3a.6p. bright blue	14·00	48·00
88	96	4a. brown	35·00	30·00
89	97	6a. turquoise-green	45·00	95·00
90	98	8a. slate-violet	50·00	85·00
91	99	12a. lake	32·00	£110
92	100	1r. grey and red-brown	38·00	60·00
93		2r. purple and brown	35·00	£170
94		5r. green and blue	45·00	£475
95		10r. purple and claret	70·00	£800
96		15r. brown and green	£150	£1600
97		25r. slate-violet and purple	£225	£1600
80/97 *Set of 18*			£750	£4750

Maharaja Yadavindra Singh, 1938–1971

1941–46. King George VI. Optd with T **7** or **8** (rupee value).

(a) Stamps of 1937

98	91	3p. slate	21·00	4·00
99		½a. red-brown	6·50	3·25
100		9p. green	£550	16·00
		w. Wmk inverted		
101		1a. carmine	40·00	3·50
102	100	1r. grey and red-brown (1946)	12·00	85·00
98/102 *Set of 5*			£600	£100

(b) Stamps of 1940–43

103	100a	3p. slate (1942)	1·00	15
104		½a. purple (1943)	1·00	15
		a. Pair, one without opt	£14000	
105		9p. green (1942)	1·75	15
		a. Vert pair, one without opt	£6000	
106		1a. carmine (1944)	2·00	10
107	101	1a.3p. yellow-brown	1·75	4·00
108		1½a. dull violet (*litho*) (1942)	4·00	4·25
108a		1½a. dull violet (*typo*) (1943)	6·00	6·00
109		2a. vermilion (1944)	2·00	50
110		3a. bright violet (*typo*) (1944)	2·00	3·75
111		3½a. bright blue (1944)	19·00	48·00
112	102	4a. brown (1944)	3·00	4·75
113		6a. turquoise-green (1944)	2·00	40·00
114		8a. slate-violet (1944)	2·00	15·00
115		12a. lake (1945)	25·00	£120
103/15 *Set of 13*			60·00	£200

Only one example of No. 104a is known, resulting from a paper fold. No. 105a occurred on one sheet, the bottom row being without opt.

OFFICIAL STAMPS

1884 (1 Oct). Nos. 1/3 of Patiala optd with Type O **2**, in black.

O1	23	½a. blue-green	30·00	50
O2	25	1a. brown-purple	1·00	10
		a. Opt Type **1** inverted	£4000	£425
		b. Opt Type **1** double	†	£170
		c. "SERVICE" double	£3000	£900
		d. "SERVICE" inverted	†	£2500
		w. Wmk inverted	†	£600
O3	27	2a. dull blue	£10000	£140

Essays of No. O3 exist on which "STATE" measures 10 mm long (normal 9 mm) and the words of the Type **1** overprint are more curved. These are rare (*Price £1200 unused*).

1885–90.

*(a) No. 7 of Patiala optd with Type O **2**, in black.*

O4	23	½a. blue-green	4·25	25
		a. "SERVICE" double	†	£900
		b. "AUTTIALLA"	90·00	22·00
		ba. "AUTTIALLA", and "SERVICE" double	†	£8000

*(b) No. 11 of Patiala optd with Type O **2**, in black*

O5	25	1a. brown-purple	2·50	10
		a. "SERVICE" double	£4000	
		b. "SERVICE" double, one inverted	†	£750
		c. "AUTTIALLA"	£1200	65·00
		d. "PUTTIALLA STATE" double	†	£2500

*(c) As No. 7 of Patiala, but optd in black, and No. 8, optd with Type O **3***

O6	23	½a. blue-green (Bk.) (1890)	3·00	10
O7	27	2a. dull brown (R.)	1·00	40
		a. "SERVICE" double, one inverted	30·00	£200

Stamps as Nos. O4/5, but with Type O **3** (in red on the ½a.), were prepared for use but not issued, although some were erroneously overprinted "REPRINT". No. O7 with overprint in black is a proof. The ½a "AUTTIALLA" has been reprinted in complete sheets, and can be found with "AUTTIALLA" double.

No. O7 exists with error "PUTTILLA", but its status is uncertain. (*Price £1500 unused*).

SERVICE

1891 (Nov)–**1900.** Optd with Type O **4**, in black.

O8	23	½a. blue-green (9.95)	1·50	10
		a. "SERVICE" inverted	65·00	
		b. "SERV CE"	£2000	
		c. "STA E"	£900	£800
		d. "S ATE"		
O9	25	1a. plum (10.1900)	9·00	10
		a. "SERVICE" inverted	65·00	
O10	27	2a. dull blue (12.98)	7·00	4·50
		a. Deep blue	5·50	4·00
		b. "SERVICE" inverted	65·00	£325
		ba. "SERV CE" inverted	£4000	
		c. Thin seriffed "I" in "SERVICE" (R. 5/4)	£425	
O12	28	3a. brown-orange	4·75	4·50
		a. "SERV CE"	£5000	
O13	29	4a. olive-green	5·00	70
		a. Slate-green (9.95)	5·00	30
		b. "SERV CE"		
O15	21	6a. bistre-brown	3·75	45
		a. Olive-bistre	£1500	
O16	31	8a. dull mauve	6·00	1·75
		a. Magenta (12.98)	6·00	3·50
		b. "SERV CE"	£6000	
		c. Thin seriffed "I" in "SERVICE" (R. 5/4)	£750	
O18	32	12a. purple/*red*	3·75	65
		a. "SERV CE"	£8000	
O19	33	1r. slate	4·25	70
		a. "SERV CE"		
O8/19 *Set of 9*			38·00	11·00

Stamps from the first printing of November 1891 (Nos. O12/13, O15/16, O18/19) had the "SERVICE" overprint, as Type O **3**, applied to sheets already overprinted with Type **3**. Subsequent printings of Nos. O8/10a, O13a and O16a had both overprints applied at one operation as shown on Type O **4**.

The errors with "SERVICE" inverted occur from a trial printing, in two operations, during 1894, which was probably not issued. Some of the "SERV CE" varieties may also come from the same trial printing.

1902 (Jan)–**03.** Optd with Type O **4**.

O20	25	1a. carmine	2·25	10
O21	37	1r. green and carmine (5.03)	7·50	10·00

1903–10. King Edward VII stamps of India optd with Type O **4**.

O22	41	3p. pale grey	50	10
		a. Slate-grey (1909)	50	15
O24	42	½a. green	1·50	10
O25	43	1a. carmine	60	10
O26	44	2a. pale violet (1905)	80	25
		a. Mauve	2·25	40
O28	46	3a. orange-brown	7·00	4·25
O29	47	4a. olive (1905)	4·25	20
		a. Opt double, one albino	85·00	
O30	49	8a. purple (*shades*)	3·25	75
		a. Claret (1910)	10·00	2·75
O32	51	1r. green and carmine (1906)	3·00	80
O22/32 *Set of 8*			18·00	5·50

1907. Nos. 149/50 of India optd with Type O **4**.

O33	53	½a. green	50	20
O34	54	1a. carmine	1·25	10

1913–26. King George V. Official stamps of India optd with T **3**.

O35	55	3p. slate	10	20
		a. Pale grey	1·25	60
		b. Slate (1926)	1·50	30
O36	56	½a. light green	10	20
		a. Emerald	5·50	85
		b. Bright green	3·50	60
O37	57	1a. aniline carmine	10	10
O38		1a. chocolate (1925)	10·00	1·25
O39	59	2a. purple	1·50	10
		a. Reddish purple	—	2·75
		b. Deep mauve	4·75	2·50
O40	63	4a. olive	50	35
O41	64	6a. brown-ochre (1926)	3·00	2·50
O42	65	8a. deep magenta	75	70
O43	67	1r. red-brown and deep blue-green	2·75	1·40
O44		2r. carmine and yellow-brown (1926)	23·00	55·00
		a. Opt double, one albino	£110	
O45		5r. ultramarine and violet (1926)	22·00	38·00
O35/45 *Set of 11*			55·00	90·00

1927–36. King George V (Nasik printing, wmk Mult Star), optd at Nasik with Type O **5** or Type O **6** (rupee values).

O47	55	3p. slate	10	10
		a. Blue opt	3·50	2·50
		w. Wmk inverted	5·00	3·25
O48	56	½a. green (1932)	1·00	55
		w. Wmk inverted	—	5·50
O49	57	1a. chocolate	15	10
		w. Wmk inverted	4·00	50
O50	82	1a.3p. mauve (1932)	40	10
		w. Wmk inverted	5·00	20
O51	70	2a. purple	30	30
		w. Wmk inverted		
O52		2a. vermilion (1933)	75	35
O53	61	2a.6p. orange (1933)	5·00	35
		w. Wmk inverted	2·25	80
O54	71	4a. sage-green (1935)	5·00	30
		w. Wmk inverted	4·75	3·75
O55	65	8a. reddish purple (1929)	3·50	65
		w. Wmk inverted	1·60	80
O56	67	1r. chocolate and green (1929)	9·00	6·00
		w. Wmk inverted	3·00	4·00
O57		2r. carmine and orange (1936)	18·00	65·00
O47/57 *Set of 11*			25·00	65·00

1935–39. New types. Optd with Type O **5**.

O58	79	½a. green (1936)	75	10
O59	81	1a. chocolate (1936)	35	30

O60	59	2a. vermilion		15	30
O61		2a. vermilion (*small die*) (1939)		25·00	6·50
O62	63	4a. sage-green (1936)		5·50	1·75
O58/62		*Set of 5*		29·00	8·00

1937–39. King George VI. Optd with Type O **5** or O **6** (rupee values).

O63	91	½a. red-brown (1938)		1·00	20
O64		9p. green (1938)		14·00	85·00
O65		1a. carmine		1·00	40
O66	100	1r. grey and red-brown (1939)		1·00	9·50
O67		2r. purple and brown (1939)		9·00	5·00
O68		5r. green and blue (1939)		19·00	85·00
O63/8		*Set of 6*		42·00	£170

1ᴬ———1ᴬ (O **7**) **1ᴬ SERVICE 1ᴬ** (O **8**) **PATIALA SERVICE** (O **9**)

1939–40. Stamp of 1932 (King George V).

*(a) Optd with Types O **5** and O **7***

O69	82	1a. on 1a.3p. mauve		22·00	5·50
		w. Wmk inverted		11·00	3·50

*(b) Optd with T **4** and O **8***

O70	82	1a. on 1a.3p. mauve (1940)		18·00	5·50
		w. Wmk inverted		24·00	14·00

"SERVICE" measures 9¼ mm on No. O69 but only 8¾ mm on O70.

1939–44.

*(a) Official stamps optd with T **7***

O71	O **20**	3p. slate (1940)		1·00	10
O72		½a. red-brown		1·50	10
		w. Wmk inverted		—	55·00
O73		½a. purple (1942)		1·25	10
O74		9p. green		1·60	50
		w. Wmk inverted			
O75		1a. carmine		1·50	10
O76		1a.3p. yellow-brown (1941)		1·40	25
O77		1½a. dull violet (1944)		5·00	1·50
O78		2a. vermilion (1940)		5·00	35
		w. Wmk inverted		20·00	8·00
O79		2½a. bright violet (1940)		4·00	1·00
O80		4a. brown (1943)		2·00	2·50
O81		8a. slate-violet (1944)		5·50	6·50

*(b) Postage stamps optd with Type O **9***

O82	100	1r. grey and red-brown (1943)		5·00	11·00
O83		2r. purple and brown (1944)		17·00	90·00
O84		5r. green and blue (1944)		29·00	£110
O71/84		*Set of 14*		70·00	£200

TELEPHONE STAMPS

From about 1930 Patiala operated a Telephone message system, available through Post Offices, for the use of both the general public and Government departments. As with a telegraph service, charges were calculated according to the length and destination of the message, but transmission was by voice over the telephone. Charges were prepaid with specially overprinted 'Telephone' or 'Telephone Service' stamps, which were affixed to message forms.

DATES OF ISSUE. Precise dates of issue have not been established, but it is clear that remaining stocks of QV and KEVII postage stamps were provided with Telephone overprints in the 1930s or even later. It seems certain that the large fount type T1 and OT1 overprints are the earliest, with type OT2 ("Service/Telephone") preceding type OT3 ("Telephone/Service"). In the case of the later King George V and King George VI issues, the underlying postage stamps give a more reliable guide.

PRICES. Although stamps were often cancelled by circular or hooded datestamps inscribed 'TELEPHONES', manuscript cancels are also frequently met with, while a considerable proportion show no obliteration at all. In these circumstances no attempt has been made to provide separate prices for 'unused' or 'used' examples.

Telephone (T**1**)   **Telephone** (T**2**)

(1) Overprinted 'Telephone' as type T1 (14½mm).
On King George V postage stamp of 1912-26. (No. 55a).

T1	6a. brown-ochre		7·50

(2) Overprinted 'Telephone' as type T2 (12½mm).
On Queen Victoria postage stamps of 1891-96. (Nos. 22/8).

T2	4a. slate-green		5·00
T3	6a. bistre-brown		5·00
T4	8a. magenta		7·50
T5	12a. purple/red		10·00
T6	1r. green and carmine		15·00

On King Edward VII postage stamps of 1903-06. (Nos. 39/45).

T7	2a. pale violet		5·00
T8	3a. orange-brown		3·00
T9	12a. purple/red		15·00
T10	1r. green and carmine		20·00

On King George V postage stamp of 1912-26. (No.51).

T11	1½a. chocolate		10·00

On King George V postage stamps of 1928-34. (Nos. 64/71).

T12	½a. green		3·00
T13	2a. purple		5·00
	w. Wmk inverted		5·00
T14	2a. 6p. orange (*wmk inverted*)		15·00
T15	4a. sage green		10·00

On King George V postage stamps of 1935-37. (Nos. 75/9).

T16	½a. blue-green		3·00
T17	2a. vermilion		3·00
T18	4a. sage-green		5·00

On King George VI postage stamps of 1937-38. (Nos. 81/3).

T19	½a. red-brown		10·00
T20	1a. carmine		10·00

On King George VI postage stamps of 1941-46. (Nos. 99/101).

T21	½a. red-brown		7·00
T22	1a. carmine		5·00

On King George VI postage stamps of 1941-46. (Nos. 104/113).

T23	½a. purple		4·00
T24	1a. carmine		4·00
T25	2a. vermilion		4·00
T26	3a. bright violet		5·00
T27	4a. brown		5·00
T28	6a. turquoise-green		5·00

OFFICIAL TELEPHONE STAMPS

Service Telephone (OT**1**)   **Service Telephone** (OT**2**)

Telephone Service (OT**3**)

(1) Overprinted 'Service/Telephone' as type OT1.
On King George V postage stamps of 1912-26. (Nos. 52/5a).

OT1	2a. purple		5·00
OT2	6a. brown-ochre		7·50

On King George V postage stamps of 1928-34. (No. 68).

OT3	2a. purple		10·00

(2) Overprinted 'Service/Telephone' as type OT2.
On King George V postage stamps of 1928-34. (Nos. 64/71).

OT4	½a. green		6·00
OT5	2a. purple		15·00
OT6	4a. sage-green		20·00

(3) Overprinted 'Telephone/Service' as type OT3.
On Queen Victoria postage stamps of 1891-96. (Nos. 22/3).

OT7	4a. slate-green		5·00
OT8	6a. bistre-brown		5·00

On King Edward VII postage stamps of 1903-06. (Nos. 39/45).

OT9	2a. pale violet		3·00
OT10	3a. orange-brown		5·00
OT11	6a. olive-bistre		7·00
OT12	8a. purple		15·00
OT13	12a. purple/red		12·00
OT14	1r. green and carmine		25·00

On King George V postage stamps of 1912-26. (Nos. 51/5a).

OT15	1½a. chocolate		10·00
OT16	6a. brown-ochre		12·00

On King George V postage stamps of 1928-34. (Nos. 64/71).

OT17	½a. green		2·00
OT18	2a. purple		2·00
	w. Wmk inverted		3·00
OT19	2a. 6p. orange		10·00
	w. Wmk inverted		7·00
OT20	4a. sage green		5·00

On King George V postage stamps of 1935-37. (Nos. 75/9).

OT21	½a. blue-green		3·00
OT22	2a. vermilion		3·00
OT23	4a. sage-green		3·00

On King George VI postage stamps of 1937-38. (Nos. 81/3).

OT24	½a. red-brown		5·00
OT25	1a. carmine		7·00

On King George VI postage stamps of 1941-46. (Nos. 104/13).

OT26	½a. purple		15·00
OT27	1a. carmine		15·00
OT28	2a. vermilion		15·00
OT29	6a. turquoise-green		15·00

(4) Overprinted 'Telephone' as type T2 on *official* stamps.
On Queen Victoria official stamp of 1891-1900. (No. O13a).

OT30	4a. slate-green		30·00

On King Edward VII official stamp of 1903-10. (No. O32).

OT31	1r. green and carmine		25·00

On King George V official stamp of 1913-26. (No. O41).

OT32	6a. brown-ochre		25·00

On King George V official stamp of 1935-39. (No. O60).

OT33	2a. vermilion		10·00

On King George VI official stamps of 1939-44. (Nos. O72/80).

OT34	½a. red-brown		10·00
OT35	1a. carmine		10·00
OT36	2a. vermilion		10·00
OT37	4a. brown		20·00

Patiala became part of the Patiala and East Punjab States Union by 20 August 1948.

INDIAN FEUDATORY STATES

These stamps were only valid for use within their respective states, *unless otherwise indicated.*

Postage stamps of the Indian States, current at that date, were replaced by those of the Republic of India on 1 April 1950.

Unless otherwise stated, all became obsolete on 1 May 1950 (with the exception of the "Anchal" stamps of Travancore-Cochin which remained current until 1 July 1951 or Sept 1951 for the Official issues).

ALWAR

PRICES FOR STAMPS ON COVER	
Nos. 1/2	*from × 30*
No. 3	*from × 100*
No. 4	—
No. 5	*from × 100*

Maharao Raja (Maharaja from 1889) Mangal Singh, 1874–1892.

1 (¼a.)

1877. Litho. Rouletted.

1	**1**	¼a. steel blue		27·00	9·50
		a. Bright greenish blue		14·00	9·50
		b. Ultramarine		6·00	1·10
		c. Grey-blue (shades)		5·00	1·10
2		1a. pale yellowish brown		22·00	9·00
		a. Brown (shades)		4·75	1·25
		b. Chocolate		10·00	8·00
		c. Pale reddish brown		3·25	1·50

Maharaja Jai Singh, 1892–1937

1899–1901. Redrawn. P 12.

(a) Wide margins between stamps

3	**1**	¼a. slate-blue		11·00	3·25
		a. Imperf between (horiz pair)		£650	£850
		b. Imperf between (vert pair)		£1600	£1700
4		¼a. emerald-green		£1100	£4000

(b) Narrower margins (1901)

5	**1**	¼a. emerald-green		8·50	2·50
		a. Imperf between (horiz pair)		£425	£550
		b. Imperf between (vert pair)		£475	£550
		c. Imperf horiz (vert pair)		£500	
		d. Imperf (pair)		£600	
		e. Pale yellow-green		10·00	2·75
		ea. Imperf (pair)		£1000	
		eb. Imperf between (horiz pair)		†	£1000

In the redrawn type only the bottom outer frameline is thick, whereas in the original 1877 issue the left-hand frameline is also thick, as shown in Type **1**.

The stamps of Alwar became obsolete on 1 July 1902.

BAHAWALPUR
See after PAKISTAN

BAMRA

PRICES FOR STAMPS ON COVER	
Nos. 1/6	—
Nos. 8/40	*from × 40*

Raja Sudhal Deo, 1869–1903

GUM. The stamps of Bamra were issued without gum.

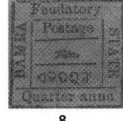

BAMRA postage ୧୨୪୦ (symbol)	BAMRA postage ୧୨୪୦ (symbol)	BAMRA postage ୧୨୪୦ (symbol)		
1 (¼a.)	**1a**	**2** (½a.)		
BAMRA postage ୧୨୪୦ (symbol)	BAMRA postage ୧୨୪୦ (symbol)	BAMRA postage ୧୨୪୦ (symbol)		
3 (1a.)	**4** (2a.)	**5** (4a.)		

BAMRA postage ୧୨୪୦ (symbol)
6 (8a.)

(illustrations actual size)

(Typo Jagannata Ballabh Press, Deogarh)

1888. Imperf.

1	**1**	¼a. black/*yellow*		£800	
		a. "g" inverted (R. 5/1)		£8500	
		b. Last native character inverted		£8500	
		c. Last native character as Type **1a**		£8500	
2	**2**	½a. black/*rose*		£130	
		a. "g" inverted (R. 5/1)		£2750	
3	**3**	1a. black/*blue*		£100	
		a. "g" inverted (R. 5/1)		£2750	
		b. Scroll inverted (R. 8/4)		£2250	
4	**4**	2a. black/*green*		£150	£600
		a. "a" omitted (R. 8/3)		£2750	
		b. Scroll inverted (R. 8/4)		£2500	
5	**5**	4a. black/*yellow*		£130	£600
		a. "a" omitted (R. 8/4)		£2500	
		b. Scroll inverted (R. 8/4)		£2500	
6	**6**	8a. black/*rose*		75·00	
		a. "a" omitted (R. 8/3)		£1900	
		b. Horiz pair, one printed on back		£1300	
		c. Scroll inverted (R. 8/4)		£1700	

These stamps were all printed from the same plate of 96 stamps, 12×8, but for some values only part of the plate was used. There are 96 varieties of the ½, 4 and 8a., 72 of the 1a., 80 of the 2a. and not less than 88 of the ¼a.

The scroll ornament can be found pointing to either the right or the left.

There are two forms of the third native character. In the first five horizontal rows it is as in T **1** and in the last three rows as in T **4**.

These stamps have been reprinted: the ¼a. and ½a. in blocks of eight varieties (all showing scroll pointing to right), and all values in blocks of 20 varieties (all showing scroll pointing to left). On the reprints the fourth character is of a quite different shape.

[Feudatory Postage / Quarter anna illustration]

8

1890 (July)–**93.** Black on coloured paper. Nos. 24/5 and 39/40 show face value as "One Rupee".

(a) "Postage" with capital "P"

8	**8**	¼a. on *rose-lilac*		8·00	15·00
		a. "Eeudatory" (R. 2/4)		30·00	80·00
		b. "Quatter" (R. 1/3)		30·00	80·00
		c. Inverted "e" in "Postage" (R. 2/3)		30·00	80·00
9		¼a. on *bright rose*		3·25	3·25
10		¼a. on *reddish purple*		2·75	3·00
		a. First "a" in "anna" inverted (R. 3/3)		75·00	90·00
		b. "AMRA" inverted (R. 4/4)		£100	£110
		c. "M" and second "A" in "BAMRA" inverted (R. 4/2)		£170	£170
11		½a. on *dull green*		7·00	6·50
		a. "Eeudatory" (R. 2/4)		£100	£150
12		½a. on *blue-green*		8·00	6·00

13		1a. on *bistre-yellow*		6·50	4·00
		a. "Eeudatory" (R. 2/4)		£225	£300
14		1a. on *orange-yellow*		75·00	75·00
		a. "annas" for "anna" (R. 3/3)		£350	£375
15		2a. on *rose-lilac*		24·00	60·00
		a. "Eeudatory" (R. 2/4)		£300	£600
16		2a. on *bright rose*		7·00	7·50
17		2a. on *dull rose*		21·00	11·00
18		4a. on *rose-lilac*		£1100	£1700
		a. "Eeudatory" (R. 2/4)		£7500	
19		4a. on *dull rose*		26·00	16·00
		a. "Eeudatory" (R. 2/4)		£2000	£2250
		b. "BAMBA" (R. 2/1)		£2000	£2250
20		4a. on *bright rose*		9·50	5·00
20a		4a. on *deep pink*		21·00	15·00
		ab. Doubly printed		†	£2000
21		8a. on *rose-lilac*		45·00	£130
		a. "Foudatory" and "Postagc" (R. 1/2)		£450	£800
		b. "BAMBA" (R. 2/1)		£450	£800
22		8a. on *bright rose*		16·00	24·00
23		8a. on *dull rose*		48·00	21·00
24		1r. on *rose-lilac*		£110	£225
		a. "Eeudatory" (R. 2/4)		£1000	£1700
		b. "BAMBA" (R. 2/1)		£850	£1400
		c. "Postagc" (R. 1/2)		£850	£1400
25		1r. on *bright rose*		25·00	25·00
		a. Small "r" in "rupee"		£425	£425

(*b*) "postage" with small "p" (1891–93)

26	8	¼a. on *bright rose*		2·50	3·75
27		¼a. on *reddish purple*		2·50	3·00
28		½a. on *dull green*		7·50	6·50
		a. First "a" in "anna" inverted (R. 3/3)		60·00	65·00
29		½a. on *blue-green*		6·00	6·00
		a. First "a" in "anna" inverted (R. 3/3)		65·00	65·00
30		1a. on *bistre-yellow*		6·50	3·75
31		1a. on *orange-yellow*		75·00	75·00
32		2a. on *bright rose*		9·00	7·00
33		2a. on *dull rose*		21·00	11·00
34		4a. on *dull rose*		28·00	17·00
35		4a. on *bright rose*		9·00	12·00
35a		4a. on *deep pink*		21·00	15·00
36		8a. on *rose-lilac*		£110	£225
37		8a. on *bright rose*		20·00	28·00
38		8a. on *dull rose*		48·00	23·00
39		1r. on *rose-lilac*		£170	£300
40		1r. on *bright rose*		25·00	25·00
		a. Small "r" in "rupee"		£450	£450
		b. Small "r" in "rupee" and native characters in the order 2, 3, 1, 4, 5 (R. 4/4)		£2750	£2750

There are ten settings of Type **8**. The first setting (of 20 (4×5)) has capital "P" throughout. The remaining settings (of 16 (4×4)) have capital "P" and small "p" mixed.

For the first setting the 8a. and 1r. values were printed within the same block, the ten left-hand stamps being 8a. values and the ten right-hand stamps 1r. The various stamps were distributed between the settings as follows:

Setting I — Nos. 8/c, 11/a, 13/a, 15/a, 18/19a, 21, 24/a
Setting II — Nos. 19, 19b, 21/b, 24, 24b/c, 34, 36, 39
Setting III — Nos. 9, 11, 13, 16, 26, 28, 30, 32
Setting IV — Nos. 20, 22, 25, 35, 37, 40
Setting V — Nos. 10, 10b/c, 20a, 27, 35a
Setting VI — Nos. 11, 12, 28, 28a, 29/a
Setting VII — Nos. 10/a, 12, 17, 19, 23, 25a, 27, 29, 33/4, 38, 40a/b
Setting VIII — Nos. 17, 33
Setting IX — Nos. 10/a, 12, 14/a, 17, 19, 23, 27, 29, 31, 33/4, 38
Setting X — Nos. 19, 34

There are four sizes of the central ornament, which represents an elephant's trunk holding a stick:—(*a*) 4 mm long; (*b*) 5 mm; (*c*) 6½ mm; (*d*) 11 mm. These ornaments are found pointing to right or left, either upright or inverted.

Ornaments (*a*) are found in all settings; (*b*) in all settings from Settings III to X; (*c*) in Settings I and II; and (*d*) only in Setting I.

The stamps of Bamra have been obsolete since 1 January 1895.

BARWANI

PRICES FOR STAMPS ON COVER	
Nos. 1/2ab	*from* × 1.5
Nos. 3/43	*from* × 3

PROCESS. All Barwani stamps are typographed from clichés, and are in sheets of four, *unless otherwise indicated.*

Nos. 1/31 were printed by the Barwani State Printing Press. The 1932-47 issues (Nos. 32A/43) were printed by the *Times of India* Press, Bombay.

GUM. Nos. 1/31 were issued without gum.

BOOKLET PANES. Those stamps which were printed in sheets of four were issued in stamp booklets, binding holes appearing in the side margin.

Rana Ranjit Singh, 1894–1930

1   **2**   **3**

1917 (May)–**21.** Blurred (Nos. 1 and 2) or clear impression. Medium wove paper. P 7 on two sides (No. 1) or all round (others).

1	1	¼a. light blue		†	£3000
		a. Imperf (pair)		†	£6000
		b. *Blue-green* (dull *to* deep) (1921)		£275	£750
2		½a. deep ultramarine		†	£5000
		a. *Dull blue*		£550	£1100
		ab. Imperf (pair)		†	£3000

The "QUARTER ANNA" inscription on No. 1 is normally doubled. No. 1b also exists perforated on two sides.

1921 (June). Blurred impression. Soft wove paper. P 7 on two or three sides.

3	1	¼a. green (*shades*)		42·00	£300
4		½a. ultramarine (dull *to* pale)		26·00	£375

NOTE. As the small sheets of Barwani stamps were often not perforated all round, many of the earlier stamps are perforated on two or three sides only. Owing to the elementary method of printing, the colours vary greatly in depth, even within a single sheet.

1921. Clear impression. Vertically laid bâtonné paper. Imperf.

5	1	¼a. green (*shades*)		27·00	£170
6		½a. green (*shades*)		7·00	
		a. Perf 11 at top or bottom only		7·00	

It is suggested that No. 5 may be an error due to printing from the wrong plate.

1922. Clear impression. Thickish glazed wove paper. P 7 on two or three sides.

7	1	¼a. dull blue			£200

1922. Smooth, soft medium wove paper. P 7 on two or three sides.

(*a*) Clear impression

8	1	¼a. deep grey-blue		£120	£275

(*b*) Poor impression

9	1	¼a. steel blue		23·00	

Examples of No. 9 exist with perforations on all four sides.

1922. P 11 on two or three sides.

(*a*) Thick, glazed white wove paper

10	2	1a. vermilion (*shades*)		4·50	35·00
		a. Imperf between (vert pair)		£750	
		b. Doubly printed		£2500	
11		2a. purple (*to* violet)		3·25	45·00
		a. Doubly printed		£500	
		b. Imperf between (horiz pair)		£475	£750
		c. Imperf between (vert pair)		£200	

(*b*) Thick, toned wove paper

12	2	2a. purple		22·00	90·00

1922. Poor impression. Thin, poor wove paper. Pin-perf 8½ on two or three sides.

13	1	¼a. grey (*to* grey-blue)		2·25	75·00
		a. Imperf (pair)		£700	
		b. Imperf between (vert pair)		£275	

1923. Thin, smooth, unglazed wove paper. P 11 on two or three sides.

14	1	½a. green (pale *to* deep)		2·00	30·00
		a. Imperf between (vert pair)		£1000	
15	2	1a. brown-red		£4000	£5000

1923. Poor impression. Thick, soft wove paper. P 7.

16	1	½a. green (pale *to* deep)		45·00	

No. 16 also exists perforated on two or three sides.

1923 (Mar?). Poor quality wove paper. P 7 on two or three sides.

17	1	¼a. black		90·00	£600
		a. Imperf between (horiz pair)		£4250	

1923 (May?). Horizontally laid bâtonné paper. P 12.

18	1	¼a. rose (*shades*)		4·25	22·00
		a. Imperf between (vert pair)		£850	
		ab. Imperf between (horiz pair)		£1800	
		b. Pin perf 6		£275	£120
		c. Perf compound of 12 and 6		75·00	£100
		d. Perf 7		£1600	£1800
		da. On wove paper		£5000	

No. 18 was issued in sheets of 12 (3 panes of 4) and was printed on paper showing a sheet watermark of Britannia and a double-lined inscription. No. 18d was only issued in booklet panes of four.

1925. Vertically laid bâtonné paper. P 11.

19	1	¼a. blue (pale *to* deep)		2·50	12·00
		a. Tête-bêche (horiz pair)		£4500	

No. 19 was issued in sheets of eight and was printed on paper with a sheet watermark of a shell and an inscription "SHELL" in double-lined capitals.

1927. Very poor impression. Thin, brittle wove paper. P 7.

20	1	¼a. milky blue (*shades*)		9·00	60·00
21		½a. yellow-green (*shades*)		10·00	£130
		a. Imperf between (horiz pair)		£2250	
22	3	4a. orange-brown		£160	£750
		a. Imperf between (horiz pair)		£3250	
20/2 *Set of 3*				£170	£850

1927. Thick wove paper. Sewing machine perf 6-10.

23	3	4a. yellow-brown		£180	
		a. Imperf between (horiz pair)		£6000	
		b. Perf 7		20·00	£450
		c. *Orange-brown*		£200	£800

1928–32? Thick glazed paper.

(*a*) P 7

24	1	¼a. deep bright blue		12·00	
25		½a. bright green		38·00	

(*b*) P 10½ (rough) (Nov 1928)

26	1	¼a. ultramarine		10·00	
		a. Tête-bêche (pair)		20·00	
		b. Horiz pair, one stamp printed on reverse		£4000	
27		½a. apple-green		6·50	
		a. Tête-bêche (vert pair)		12·00	

(*c*) P 11 (clean-cut) (1929–32?)

28	1	¼a. bright blue		3·25	22·00
		a. *Indigo*		2·75	20·00
		ab. Imperf between (horiz pair)		£170	
		ac. Imperf between (horiz strip of 4).		£750	
		b. *Deep dull blue*		2·50	19·00
		ba. Imperf between (vert pair)		£600	
		c. *Ultramarine*		2·75	21·00
		ca. Imperf between (vert pair)		£550	
29		½a. myrtle-green		3·50	25·00
		a. Imperf between (horiz pair)		£550	
		b. *Turquoise-green*		4·25	22·00
		ba. Imperf between (vert pair)		£1000	£1200
30	2	1a. rose-carmine (1931)		19·00	70·00
		a. Imperf between (vert pair)		†	£4500
31	3	4a. salmon (*to* orange) (1931)		£110	£400
		a. Imperf between (horiz pair)		£4500	
28/31 *Set of 4*				£120	£450

No. 26 was printed in sheets of eight (4×2) with the two centre pairs tête-bêche while No. 27, in similar sheets, had the two horizontal rows tête-bêche. Both sheets are always found with one long side imperforate.

Nos. 28/31 were printed in sheets of eight, the two lower values existing either 4×2 or 2×4 and the two higher values 4×2 only. No tête-bêche pairs were included in these printings. It is believed that a small printing of No. 31 was produced in sheets of four, but details are uncertain.

Rana Devi Singh, 1930–1971

4 Rana Devi Singh   **5** Rana Devi Singh

1932 (Oct)–**47.** Medium to thick wove paper.

A. Close setting (2½–4½ mm). P 11, 12 or compound (1932–41)

32A	4	¼a. slate		4·50	30·00
33A		½a. blue-green		6·00	32·00
34A		1a. brown		6·50	28·00
		a. Imperf between (horiz pair)		£2500	
35A		2a. purple (*shades*)		5·50	70·00
36A		4a. olive-green		6·00	50·00
32A/6A *Set of 5*				26·00	£190

B. Wide setting (6–7 mm). P 11 (1945–47)

32B	4	¼a. slate		7·50	45·00
33B		½a. blue-green		8·00	35·00
34B		1a. brown		24·00	32·00
		b. *Chocolate.* Perf 8½ (1947)		20·00	85·00
35aB		2a. rose-carmine		£750	£1300
36B		4a. olive-green		32·00	70·00

The measurements given in the heading indicate the vertical spacing between impressions. There are eight settings of this interesting issue: four "Close" where the overall stamp dimensions from centre to centre of perfs vary in width from 21½ to 23 mm and in height from 25 to 27½ mm; three "Wide", width 23–23½ mm and height 29–30 mm and one "Medium" (26½×31 *mm*) (No. 34B*b* only).

1933–47. P 11.

*A. Close setting (3–4½ mm). Thick, cream-surfaced wove paper (1933 and 1941 (No. 38A*a*))*

37A	1	¼a. black		9·00	£120
38A		½a. blue-green		14·00	48·00
		a. *Yellowish green* (1941)		17·00	42·00
39A	2	1a. brown (*shades*)		27·00	42·00
42A	3	4a. sage-green		70·00	£180

B. Wide setting (7–10 mm). Medium to thick wove paper (1939–47)

37B	1	¼a. black (1945)		7·00	55·00
38aB		½a. yellowish green (1945)		7·00	60·00
39B	2	1a. brown (*shades*)		17·00	42·00
		a. Perf 8½ (5 *mm*) (1947)		12·00	80·00
40B		2a. bright purple		£150	£500
41B		2a. rose-carmine (1945)		45·00	£190
42B	3	4a. sage-green (1941)		55·00	£110
		a. *Pale sage-green* (1939)		20·00	70·00

There were two "Close" settings (overall stamp size 25×29 mm) and five "Wide" settings with overall sizes 26½–31½ × 31–36½ mm. There was also one "Medium" setting (26½×31 *mm*) but this was confined to the 1a. perf 8½, No. 39Ba.

1938. P 11.

43	5	1a. brown		55·00	90·00

Stamps printed in red with designs similar to Types **3** and **5** were intended for fiscal use.

STAMP BOOKLETS

Nos. 1/17, 18d/da and 20/5 are believed to have been issued in sewn or stapled booklets, usually containing 32 examples of one value in blocks of four. These early booklets had plain covers, often in shades of brown. Few complete booklets have survived from this period.

Nos. 32/47, produced by the *Times of India* Press in a series of nine printings between 1932 and 1947, were only issued in booklet form. Booklets from the 1932, 1933, 1937 and 1939 printings had plain card or paper covers in various colours, usually containing eight blocks of four, except for the 1933 printing, which contained 20 blocks of four. Booklets from the 1945 printing had plain white tissue covers from the same stock as the interleaving. All these booklets were stapled at left.

The following booklets, from a printing in 1941, and a series of three printings in 1947, had printed covers, produced by a handstamp in the case of Nos. SB14/15.

1941. Buff (No. SB3), green (No. SB3) or blue (No. SB7) card covers inscribed "BARWANI STATE POSTAGE STAMPS", booklet value in brackets and number and value of stamps thus "(Rs 4) 32 2 Annas". Panes of 4 with margin at left only. Stapled.

(*a*) Booklets 59×55 mm

SB1	8a. booklet containing 32×¼a. (No. 32A)		£1800
SB2	1r. booklet containing 32×½a. (No. 33A)		£2500
SB3	2r. booklet containing 32×1a. (No. 34A)		£2000
SB4	4r. booklet containing 32×2a. (No. 35A)		£900
SB5	8r. booklet containing 32×4a. (No. 36A)		£1600

(*b*) Booklets 63×60 mm (No. SB6) or 73×72 mm (No. SB7)

SB6	1r. booklet containing 32×½a. (No. 38A*b*)		£2000
SB7	8r. booklet containing 32×4a. (No. 42B)		£2750

1947. Grey tissue covers inscribed "32 STAMPS VALUE ....". Panes of 4 with margins all round. Stapled at left.

(*a*) Booklets 70×95 mm

SB8	1r. booklet containing 32×½a. (No. 33B)		£1000
SB9	2r. booklet containing 32×1a. (No. 34B)		£2250
SB10	8r. booklet containing 32×4a. (No. 36B)		£1600

(*b*) Booklets 76×95 mm

SB11	8a. booklet containing 32×¼a. (No. 37B)		£1400
SB12	4r. booklet containing 32×2a. (No. 41B)		£1600
SB13	8r. booklet containing 32×4a. (No. 42B*a*)		£750

1947. Buff paper covers with violet handstamp inscribed "32 STAMPS VALUE Rs 2/-". Panes of 4 with margins all round. Sewn with twine at left.

SB14	2r. booklets (71×69 *mm*) containing 32×1a. (No. 34B*b*)		£850
SB15	2r. booklet (71×73 *mm*) containing 32×1a. (No. 39Ba)		£500

1947. Grey tissue covers inscribed "32 STAMPS VALUE As 8". Panes of 4 with margins all round. Stapled at left.

SB16	8a. booklet (70×75 *mm*) containing 32×¼a. (No. 32B)		£325
SB17	8a. booklet (85×75 *mm*) containing 32×¼a. (No. 37B)		£425

Barwani became part of Madhya Bharat by 1 July 1948.

BHOPAL

PRICES FOR STAMPS ON COVER	
Nos. 1/100	*from* × 10
Nos. O301/57	*from* × 15

The correct English inscription on these stamps is "H.H. NAWAB SHAH JAHAN BEGAM". In the case of Nos. 22 and 23 the normal stamps are spelt "BEGAN" and examples with "BEGAM" are "errors".

As the stamps were printed from lithographic stones on which each unit was drawn separately by hand, numerous errors of spelling occurred. These are constant on all sheets and are listed. Some of our illustrations inadvertently include errors of spelling.

ILLUSTRATIONS. Types **1**/**3a** and **6**/**12a** are shown actual size.

EMBOSSING. Nos. 1/99 were only valid for postage when embossed with the device, in Urdu, of the ruling Begam. On T **1**/**3** and **6** to **12a**. this was intended to fill the central part of the design. Almost all varieties can be found with the embossing inverted or sideways, as well as upright.

Shah Jahan   Sultan Jahan

(actual size)

The various basic types were often in concurrent use but for greater convenience the following list is arranged according to types instead of being in strict chronological order.

GUM. Nos. 1/99 were issued without gum.

Nawab Shah Jahan Begam, 16 November 1868–15 June 1901

1 (¼a.)

1872. Litho.

(a) Double frame. Sheets of 20 (5×4)

1	**1**	¼a. black	£1500	£900
		a. "BFGAM" (R. 3/1)	£4000	£2750
		b. "BEGAN" (R. 2/2, R. 4/4)	£2500	£1500
		c. "EGAM" (R. 4/5)	£4000	£2750
2		½a. red	21·00	75·00
		a. "BFGAM" (R. 3/1)	95·00	£300
		b. "BEGAN" (R. 2/2, R. 4/4)	60·00	£180
		c. "EGAM" (R. 4/5)	95·00	£300

2 (½a.)

(b) Single frame. Sheets of 20 (4×5)

3	**2**	¼a. black	†	£10000
4		½a. red	65·00	£140
		a. "NWAB" (R. 2/2)	£325	£600

3 (¼a.)   **3a (¼a.)**

1878 (1 Jan.). All lettered "EEGAM" for "BEGAM". Sheets of 20 (4×5).

(a) Plate 1. Frame lines extend horiz and vert between stamps throughout sheet

5	**3**	¼a. black	8·00	25·00

(b) Plate 2. Frame lines normal

5a	**3a**	¼a. black	18·00	28·00

Apart from the frame line difference between Types **3** and **3a** the stamps can also be distinguished by the differences in the value tablets, notably the thin vertical line in the centre in Type **3a** compared with the slightly diagonal and heavier line in Type **3**.

4 (¼a.)   **5 (½a.)**

1878 (June?)–**79**. Value in parenthesis (Nos. 6/7). Sheets of 32 (4×8). Imperf.

6	**4**	¼a. green (1879)	17·00	45·00
7		¼a. green (*perf*) (1879)	13·00	30·00
8	**5**	¼a. red	7·00	27·00
		a. "JAHN" (R. 5/2)	65·00	
		b. "NWAB" (R. 3/2, R. 4/2)	40·00	
		c. "EEGAM" (R. 1/3)	65·00	
9		½a. brown	48·00	80·00
		a. "JAHN" (R. 5/2)	£275	£375
		b. "NWAB" (R. 3/2, R. 4/2)	£160	£250
		c. "EEGAM" (R. 1/3)	£275	£375

The ¼a. shows the "N" of "NAWAB" reversed on R. 6/4 and the "N" of "JAHAN" reversed on R. 1/2–4 and R. 2/2–4.

1880. T **5** redrawn; value in parenthesis. Sheets of 32 (4×8).

(a) Imperf

10		¼a. blue-green	15·00	32·00
		a. "NAWA" (R. 2/2–4)	48·00	£100
		b. "CHAH" (R. 8/3)	£140	
11		½a. brown-red	18·00	28·00

(b) Perf

12		¼a. blue-green	17·00	
		a. "NAWA" (R. 2/2–4)	70·00	
		b. "CHAH" (R. 8/3)	£170	
13		½a. brown-red	21·00	

The ¼a. shows the "N" of "NAWAB" reversed on R. 8/4.
Nos. 12/13 sometimes come with gum.

1884. T **5** again redrawn. Sheets of 32 (4×8), some with value in parenthesis, others not. Perf.

14		¼a. greenish blue	9·50	26·00
		a. "ANAWAB" (R. 8/1–4)	21·00	

In this plate there is a slanting dash under and to left of the letters "JA" of "JAHAN," instead of a character like a large comma, as on all previous varieties of this design. With the exception of R. 1/1 all stamps in the sheet show "N" of "JAHAN" reversed.

1895. T **5** again redrawn. Sheets of eight (2×4). Laid paper.

15		¼a. red (*imperf*)	7·00	5·50
16		¼a. red (*perf*)	—	£1200

In these cases where the same design has been redrawn several times, and each time in a number of varieties of type, it is not easy to distinguish the various issues. Nos. 6 and 7 may be distinguished from Nos. 10 and 12 by the presence or absence of the parenthesis marks (); 8, 9 and 11 differ principally in colour; 8 and 15 are very much alike, but differ in the value as well as in paper.

6 (2a.)

1881. Sheets of 24 (4×6). Imperf.

17	**6**	¼a. black	6·00	38·00
		a. "NWAB" (R. 6/2–4)	16·00	85·00
18		½a. red	6·00	29·00
		a. "NWAB" (R. 6/2–4)	16·00	
19		1a. brown	4·50	29·00
		a. "NWAB" (R. 6/2–4)	13·00	
20		2a. blue	4·25	29·00
		a. "NWAB" (R. 6/2–4)	11·00	
21		4a. buff	35·00	£130
		a. "NWAB" (R. 6/2–4)	90·00	
17/21 Set of 5			50·00	£225

In this issue all values were produced from the same drawing, and therefore show exactly the same varieties of type. The value at foot in this and all the following issues is given in only one form.

7 (½a.)

1886. Similar to T **6** but normally lettered (incorrectly) "BEGAN"; larger lettering. Sheets of 32 (4×8).

(a) Imperf

22	**7**	½a. pale red	3·50	16·00
		a. "BEGAM" (R. 2/1)	17·00	55·00
		b. "NWAB" (R. 3/4)	17·00	

(b) Perf

23	**7**	½a. pale red	£950	
		a. "BEGAM" (R. 2/1)	£1900	
		b. "NWAB" (R. 3/4)	£1900	

8 (4a.)

1886. T **8**. T **6** redrawn. Sheets of 24 (4×6). The "M" of "BEGAM" is an inverted "W". The width of the stamps is rather greater than the height.

(a) Wove paper. Imperf

24	**8**	4a. yellow	£1300	
		a. "EEGAM" (R. 2/3–4, R. 3/3–4, R. 4/2, R. 4/4, R. 6/1)	£1700	

(b) Laid paper

25	**8**	4a. yellow	22·00	70·00
		a. "EEGAM" (R. 2/3–4, R. 3/3–4, R. 4/2, R. 4/4, R. 6/1)	27·00	
26		4a. yellow (*imperf*)	6·50	35·00
		a. "EEGAM" (R. 2/3–4, R. 3/3–4, R. 4/2, R. 4/4, R. 6/1)	10·00	48·00

1889. T **6** again redrawn. Sheets of 32 (4×8) lettered "BEGAN".

27		¼a. black (*perf*)	3·25	9·50
		a. "EEGAN" (R. 7/3)	25·00	55·00
		b. Imperf between (horiz pair)	£425	
28		¼a. black (*imperf*)	4·50	9·50
		a. "EEGAN" (R. 7/3)	30·00	55·00

9 (¼a.)

1889–90. T **9**. T **6** again redrawn. Sheets of 24 (4×6), all with "M" like an inverted "W". Wove paper.

(a) Imperf

29	**9**	¼a. black	2·25	3·75
30		1a. brown	3·50	6·50
		a. "EEGAM" (R. 2/3)	24·00	42·00
		b. "BBGAM" (R. 3/1)	24·00	42·00
31		2a. blue	2·75	4·50
		a. "BBEGAM" (R. 1/2)	16·00	23·00
		b. "NAWAH" (R. 4/2)	16·00	23·00
32		4a. orange-yellow	3·00	4·00
29/32 Set of 4			10·50	17·00

(b) Perf

33	**9**	¼a. black	4·50	8·00
		a. Imperf between (horiz pair)	£475	
34		1a. brown	5·50	13·00
		a. "EEGAM" (R. 2/3)	40·00	75·00
		b. "BBGAM" (R. 3/1)	40·00	75·00
35		2a. blue	2·75	6·00
		a. "BBEGAM" (R. 1/2)	18·00	28·00
		b. "NAWAH" (R. 4/2)	18·00	28·00
36		4a. orange-yellow	3·25	11·00
33/36 Set of 4			14·50	35·00

Nos. 32 and 36 are nearly square, in many cases rather larger in height than in width.

1891. As last, but sheets of 32 (4×8).

37	**9**	½a. red (*imperf*)	2·00	4·25
38		½a. red (*perf*)	2·25	6·50

1894–98. T **6** again redrawn.

*(a) Sheets of 24 (4×6), almost all showing a character inside the octagon below, as in T **9**. Wove paper*

39		1a. deep brown (*imperf*)	7·50	5·50
		a. Red-brown	60·00	
		b. Printed both sides	—	£1200
41		1a. deep brown (*perf*)	12·00	8·00

10 (1a.)

(b) As Nos. 39/41, but printed from a new stone showing the lines blurred and shaky. Wove paper. Imperf (1898)

42	**10**	1a. purple-brown	4·50	4·50
		a. "NAWAH" (R. 4/1)	27·00	40·00
43		1a. purple-brown/buff	4·50	5·00
		a. "NAWAH" (R. 4/1)	27·00	40·00
		b. Printed on both sides		

The above are known without embossing.

11 (¼a.)

1895. Sheets of eight (2×4), lettered "EEGAM". White laid paper.

44	**11**	¼a. black (*imperf*)	4·50	3·25
		a. "A" inserted (R. 4/2)	11·00	8·50
45		¼a. black (*perf*)	£150	50·00
		a. "NAW B" (R. 4/2)	£475	£170

On the perf stamp the second "A" in "NAWAB" was missing on R. 4/2 in the setting. This letter was later inserted for the imperf printing varying progressively from small to large.

12 (½a.)

1895. Narrow label at bottom. Sheets of eight (2×4), lettered "W W" for "H H". Laid paper.
46	**12**	½a. black (*imperf*)	2·75	2·00

12a

1896. Sheets of eight (2×4). Laid paper.
47	**12a**	½a. red (*imperf*)	3·25	2·25

No. 47 is a combination of Types **1** and **6**, having the double outer frame to the octagon and the value in one form only.

13 (¼a.)   **14** (¼a.)

1884. Sheets of 32 (4×8). Perf.
48	**13**	¼a. blue-green (*imperf*)	£200	£250
		a. "JAN" (R. 2/1–2, R. 3/1, R. 3/3–4, R. 4/1–3, R. 5/1–3)	£200	£250
		b. "BEGM" (R. 2/3–4)	£550	£650
		c. "NWAB" and "JAN" (R. 3/2)	£950	
		ca. "NWAB" and "JN" (R. 5/4)	£950	
		d. "SHAHAN" (R. 4/4)	£950	
		e. "JAHA" (R. 6/2–4)	£450	

1896. T **14**, double-lined frame round each stamp. Sheets of six (2×3), lettered "JAN". Laid paper.
49	**14**	¼a. bright green (*imperf*)	6·00	28·00

15 (½a.)   **16** (¼a.)

1884. Sheets of 32 (4×8). Laid paper.
50	**15**	¼a. blue-green (*imperf*)	£300	£325
		a. "NWAB" (R. 1/1)	£800	
		b. "SAH" (R. 1/4)	£800	
		c. "NAWA" and "JANAN" (R. 3/2)	£800	
51		¼a. blue-green (*perf*)	1·00	7·00
		a. "NWAB" (R. 1/1)	5·00	
		b. "SAH" (R. 1/4)	5·00	
		c. "NAWA" and "JANAN" (R. 3/2)	5·00	
		d. Imperf between (vert pair)	£500	
52		½a. black (*imperf*)	2·50	2·50
		a. "NWAB" (R. 1/1)	16·00	18·00
		b. "SAH" (R. 1/4)	16·00	18·00
		c. "NAWA" and "JANAN" (R. 3/2)	16·00	18·00
53		½a. black (*perf*)	1·00	3·50
		a. "NWAB" (R. 1/1)	4·75	16·00
		b. "SAH" (R. 1/4)	4·75	16·00
		c. "NAWA" and "JANAN" (R. 3/2)	4·75	16·00

The ¼a. of this issue is in *blue-green*, or *greenish blue*. Both values were printed from the same stone, the value alone being altered. There are therefore the same varieties of each. These are the only stamps of this design on laid paper.

Both values show the "N" of "NAWAB" reversed on R. 1/1–4, R. 2/1–4, R. 3/1–4 and the "N" of "JAHAN" reversed on R. 1/1–4, R. 2/1–7, R. 3/4.

1886. T **15** redrawn. Sheets of 32 (4×8). Wove paper.
54		¼a. green (*imperf*)	75	5·00
		a. "NAWA" (R. 6/3–4)	3·00	13·00
		b. "NWAB" (R. 1/1)	4·00	18·00
		c. "NWABA" (R. 7/4)	4·00	18·00
		d. "NAWAA" (R. 6/2)	4·00	18·00
		e. "BEGAAM" and "NWABA" (R. 7/3)	4·00	18·00
55		¼a. green (*perf*)	3·00	6·50
		a. "NAWA" (R. 6/3–4)	14·00	
		b. "NWAB" (R. 1/1)	21·00	
		c. "NWABA" (R. 7/4)	21·00	
		d. "NAWAA" (R. 6/2)	21·00	
		e. "BEGAAM" and "NWABA" (R. 7/3)	21·00	
		f. Imperf between (horiz pair)	£275	
56		½a. red (*imperf*)	1·00	1·75
		a. "SAH" (R. 1/4)	6·00	11·00
		b. "NAWA" (R. 6/3–4)	4·00	8·50

The ¼a. varies from *yellow-green* to *deep green*.

All examples of the ¼a. value show the "N" of "NAWAB" reversed. On the same value the "N" of "JAHAN" is reversed on all positions except R. 3/2, R. 4/1, R. 4/3. On the ½a. both "N"s are always reversed.

1888. T **15** again redrawn. Sheets of 32 (4×8), letters in upper angles smaller. "N" of "NAWAB" correct. Wove paper.
57		¼a. deep green (*imperf*)	1·00	2·00
		a. "SAH" (R. 6/2)	6·50	11·00
		b. "NAWA" (R. 4/4)	6·50	11·00
58		¼a. deep green (*perf*)	2·00	3·50
		a. "SAH" (R. 6/2)	13·00	16·00
		b. "NAWA" (R. 4/4)	13·00	16·00
		c. Imperf between (vert pair)	£375	

Nos. 50 to 58 have the dash under the letter "JA" as in No. 14.

1891. T **15** again redrawn. Sheets of 32 (4×8), lettered "NWAB." Wove paper.

(a) Imperf
59		½a. red	2·00	1·50
		a. "SAH" (R. 2/4)	8·50	

(b) P 3 to 4½, or about 7
60		½a. red	80	2·00
		a. "SAH" (R. 2/4)	7·00	

Nos. 59 and 60 have the comma under "JA". The "N" of "JAHAN" is reversed on R. 1/1–3, R. 2/1–2.

1894. T **15** again redrawn; letters in corners larger than in 1888, value in very small characters. Sheets of 32 (4×8), all with "G" in left-hand lower corner. Wove paper.
61		¼a. green (*imperf*)	2·00	3·50
		a. "NAWAH" (R. 4/4)	13·00	16·00
		b. Value in brackets (R. 1/1)	13·00	16·00
62		¼a. green (*perf*)	3·00	3·75
		a. "NAWAH" (R. 4/4)	20·00	21·00
		b. Value in brackets (R. 1/1)	20·00	21·00

Nos. 61 and 62 have neither the dash nor the comma under "JA".

1898. T **16**; oval narrower, stops after "H.H." space after "SHAH." The line down the centre is under the first "H" of "SHAH" or between "HA" instead of being under the second "H" or between "AH". Sheets of 32 (4×8). Wove paper. Imperf.
63	**16**	¼a. bright green	75	80
		a. "SHAN" (R. 1/1)	5·00	5·00
64		¼a. pale green	80	70
		a. "SHAN" (R. 1/1)	5·00	5·00
65		¼a. black	75	50
		a. "SHAN" (R. 1/1)	5·00	5·00

1899. T **15** redrawn. Sheets of 32 (4×8), the first "A" of "NAWAB" always absent. Numerous defective and malformed letters. Wove paper. Imperf.
66		½a. black	7·00	13·00
		a. "NWASBAHJANNI" (R. 2/4)	40·00	60·00
		b. "SBAH" (R. 3/3, R. 4/3–4, R.5/1–2, R. 6/4)	16·00	28·00
		c. "SBAN" (R. 8/2)	40·00	60·00
		d. "NWIB" (R. 3/2)	40·00	60·00
		e. "BEIAM" (R. 4/4)	40·00	60·00
		f. "SHH" (R. 3/4)	40·00	60·00
		g. "SBAH" and "BBGAM" (R. 3/4)	40·00	60·00
		h. "BBGAM" (R. 1/3)	40·00	60·00

17 (8a.)   **18** (¼a.)

1890. T **17**. Sheets of ten (2×5). Single-line frame to each stamp.

(a) Wove paper
67	**17**	8a. slate-green (*imperf*)	95·00	£190
		a. "HAH" (R. 3/1, R. 4/1, R. 5/1)	£120	£250
		b. "JABAN" (R. 2/2)	£140	
68		8a. slate-green (*perf*)	95·00	£190
		a. "HAH" (R. 3/1, R. 4/1, R. 5/1)	£120	
		b. "JABAN" (R. 2/2)	£140	

(b) Thin laid paper
69	**17**	8a. green-black (*imperf*)	£110	£275
		a. "HAH" (R. 3/1, R. 4/1, R. 5/1)	£140	
		b. "JABAN" (R. 2/2)	£150	
70		8a. green-black (*perf*)	£110	£275
		a. "HAH" (R. 3/1, R. 4/1, R. 5/1)	£150	£325
		b. "JABAN" (R. 2/2)	£160	

The "N" of "NAWAB" is reversed on R. 5/2 and the "N" of "JAHAN" on R. 1/1–2, R. 2/2, R. 3/2, R. 4/2 and R. 5/2.

1893. T **17** redrawn. No frame to each stamp, but a frame to the sheet. Sheets of ten (2×5).

(a) Wove paper
71		8a. green-black (*imperf*)	23·00	25·00
72		8a. green-black (*perf*)	42·00	55·00

(b) Thin laid paper. Imperf
73		8a. green-black	£325	£475

1898. Printed from a new stone. Lettering irregular. Sheets of ten (2×5). Wove paper. Imperf.
74		8a. green-black	70·00	85·00
		a. Reversed "E" in "BEGAM" (R. 1/2, R. 3/2)	£140	£160
75		8a. black	65·00	85·00
		a. Reversed "E" in "BEGAM" (R. 1/2, R. 3/2)	£140	£160

1896–1901. Sheets of 32 (4×8).

(a) Wove paper. Imperf
76	**18**	¼a. black	2·75	1·50

(b) Printed from a new stone, lines shaky (1899)
77	**18**	¼a. black	4·50	5·00

(c) The same, on thick wove paper (1901)
78	**18**	¼a. black	£550	£650

Nawab Sultan Jahan Begam, 16 June 1901–17 May 1926

19 (¼a.)   **20**

1902. T **19**. With the octagonal embossed device of the previous issues. Sheets of 16 (4×4) ¼a. or eight (2×4) others. Thin, yellowish wove paper. Imperf.
79	**19**	¼a. rose	6·50	12·00
80		¼a. rose-red	4·50	8·50
81		½a. black	6·00	9·00
		a. Printed both sides	£1400	£1400
82		1a. brown	14·00	21·00
83		1a. red-brown	10·00	17·00
84		2a. blue	15·00	25·00
85		4a. orange	£100	£150
86		4a. yellow	38·00	85·00
87		8a. lilac	£130	£325
88		1r. rose	£400	£650
79/88	Set of 7		£550	£1000

1903. With a circular embossed device. Sheets of 16 (4×4) ¼a. (two plates) or eight (2×4) (others). Wove paper.
89	**19**	¼a. rose-red	1·50	7·50
		a. Laid paper	1·00	10·00
90		¼a. rose-red	1·50	7·50
		a. Laid paper	30	7·50
91		½a. black	1·75	5·50
		a. Laid paper	1·00	11·00
92		1a. brown	7·50	15·00
		a. Laid paper	£130	
93		1a. red-brown	12·00	
		a. Laid paper		
94		2a. blue	15·00	38·00
		a. Laid paper	£250	£350
95		4a. orange (*laid paper*)	£600	£600
96		4a. yellow	20·00	65·00
		a. Laid paper	£225	£160
97		8a. lilac	75·00	£160
		a. Laid paper	£2000	
98		1r. rose	£120	£325
		a. Laid paper	£1900	
89/98	Set of 7		£200	£550

1903. No. 71 optd with initial of the new Begam, either six or 11 mm long, in red.
99		8a. green-black	£275	£300
		a. Opt inverted	£600	£650

Some of the previous stamps remained on sale (and probably in use) after the issue of the series of 1902, and some of these were afterwards put on sale with the new form of embossing; fresh plates were made of some of the old designs, in imitation of the earlier issues, and impressions from these were also sold with the new embossed device. We no longer list these doubtful items.

(Recess Perkins Bacon & Co)

1908. P 13½.
100	**20**	1a. green	3·75	7·00
		a. Printed both sides	£180	
		b. Imperf (pair)		

The ordinary postage stamps of Bhopal became obsolete on 1 July 1908.

OFFICIAL STAMPS

SERVICE   SERVICE
(O 1)   (O 2)

(Recess and optd Perkins Bacon)

1908–11. As T **20**, but inscribed "H.H. BEGUM'S SERVICE" at left. No wmk. P 13 to 14. Overprinted.

(a) With Type O 1 (typo)
O301		½a. yellow-green	3·00	10
		a. Imperf (pair)	£250	
		b. Pair, one without overprint	£1100	
		c. Opt double, one inverted	£140	
		ca. Ditto. Imperf (pair)	£180	
		d. Opt inverted	£275	£190
		e. Imperf between (horiz pair)	£1400	
		f. Imperf 3 sides (vert pair)*	£1000	
O302		1a. carmine-red	5·00	40
		a. Opt inverted	£190	£130
		b. Imperf (pair)	£200	
		c. Red	9·00	10
O303		2a. ultramarine	30·00	10
		a. Imperf (pair)	80·00	
O304		4a. brown (1911)	16·00	75
O301/4	Set of 4		50·00	95

(b) With Type O 2 (litho)
O305		½a. yellow-green	13·00	2·25
O306		1a. carmine-red	15·00	90
O307		2a. ultramarine	5·50	1·00
		a. Opt inverted	25·00	
O308		4a. brown (1911)	£100	1·50
		a. Opt inverted	20·00	70·00
		b. Opt double	£225	
		c. Imperf (pair)	90·00	
		d. Imperf (pair) and opt inverted	90·00	
O305/8	Set of 4		£120	5·00

The two overprints differ in the shape of the letters, noticeably in the "R".

*No. O301f occurs in a block of four with the other vertical pair imperf at left.

Nawab Mohammad Hamidullah. Khan
17 May 1928 to transfer of administration to India, 1 June 1949

(O 4)

(Des T. I. Archer. Litho Indian Govt Ptg Wks, Nasik)

1930 (1 July)**–31**. Type O **4** (25½×30½ *mm*). P 14.
O309	O **4**	½a. sage-green (1931)	20·00	1·75
O310		1a. carmine-red	21·00	15
O311		2a. ultramarine	15·00	45

O312	4a. chocolate	21·00	90
O309/12 *Set of 4*		70·00	3·00

The 1a. is inscribed "POSTAGE AND REVENUE" at left.

(Litho Perkins Bacon)

1932–34. As Type O **4** (21×25 *mm*), but inscr "POSTAGE" at left. Optd with Type O **1**.

(a) "BHOPAL STATE" at right. P 13

O313	¼a. orange	2·50	1·25
	a. Perf 11½ (1933)	12·00	20
	b. Perf 14 (1934)	14·00	30
	c. Perf 13½ (1934)	8·00	30
	ca. Vert pair, one without opt	£150	

(b) "BHOPAL GOVT" at right. P 13½

O314	½a. yellow-green	10·00	10
O315	1a. carmine-red	13·00	15
	a. Vert pair, one without opt	£275	
O316	2a. ultramarine	20·00	45
O317	4a. chocolate	16·00	1·00
	a. Perf 14 (1934)	23·00	40
O313/17 *Set of 5*		55·00	1·20

No. O317 is comb-perforated and No. O317a line-perforated.

¼A (O **5**)   **THREE PIES** (O **6**)   **ONE ANNA** (O **7**)

1935–36. Nos. O314, O316 and O317 surch as Types O **5** to O **7**.

O318	O **5**	¼a. on ½a. yellow-green (R.)	55·00	20·00
		a. Surch inverted	£425	£140
		b. Vert pair. Nos. O318/19	80·00	32·00
		ba. Ditto. Surch inverted	£800	£300
O319	O **6**	3p. on ½a. yellow-green (R.)	5·50	4·75
		a. Surch inverted	£150	45·00
		b. "THEEE PIES" (R. 7/10)	£140	80·00
		ba. Ditto. Surch inverted	£1700	
		c. "THRFE" for "THREE" (R. 10/6)	£140	80·00
		ca. Ditto. Surch inverted	£1700	
O320	O **5**	¼a. on 2a. ultramarine (R.)	50·00	30·00
		a. Surch inverted	£425	£120
		b. Vert pair. Nos. O320/1	75·00	55·00
		ba. Ditto. Surch inverted	£800	£300
O321	O **6**	3p. on 2a. ultramarine (R.)	4·50	6·00
		a. Surch inverted	£150	45·00
		b. "THEEE PIES" (R. 7/10)	£140	80·00
		c. "THRFE" for "THREE" (R. 10/6)	£140	80·00
		ca. Ditto. Surch inverted	£1600	£1000
O322	O **5**	¼a. on 4a. chocolate (R.)	£2000	£600
		a. Vert pair. Nos. O322 and O324.	£3500	£1000
O323		¼a. on 4a. chocolate (No. O317a) (Blk.) (25.5.36)	£150	40·00
		a. Vert pair. Nos. O323 and O325.	£200	75·00
O324	O **6**	3p. on 4a. chocolate (R.)	£350	£130
		a. "THEEE PIES" (R. 7/10)	£1600	£1000
		c. "THRFE" for "THREE" (R. 10/6)	£1600	£1000
O325		3p. on 4a. chocolate (No. O317a) (Blk.) (25.5.36)	2·50	3·75
		a. "THRER" for "THREE" (R. 8/2)	£750	£425
		b. "FHREE" for "THREE" (R. 3/10, R. 10/1)	£850	£650
		c. "PISE" for "PIES" (R. 10/10)	£1400	£1000
		d. "PIFS" for "PIES" (R. 7/9)	£750	£425
O326	O **7**	1a. on ½a. yellow-green (V.)	5·00	1·50
		a. Surch inverted	£130	55·00
		b. First "N" in "ANNA" inverted (R. 4/5)	£160	75·00
		ba. Ditto. Surch inverted	£1500	£900
O327		1a. on 2a. ultramarine (R.)	2·25	3·00
		a. Surch inverted	£160	40·00
		b. First "N" in "ANNA" inverted (R. 4/5)	£110	75·00
		ba. Ditto. Surch inverted	£1600	£900
O327d		1a. on 2a. ultramarine (V.)	75·00	£120
		da. Surch inverted	£140	£170
		db. First "N" in "ANNA" inverted (R. 4/5)	£1300	£1600
		dc. Ditto. Surch inverted	£2000	£2250
O328		1a. on 2a. ultram (Blk.) (25.5.36)	70	2·50
		a. "ANNO"	£3500	
O329		1a. on 4a. chocolate (B.)	7·50	7·00
		a. First "N" in "ANNA" inverted (R. 4/5)	£180	£150
		b. Perf 14	28·00	10·00
		ba. Ditto. First "N" in "ANNA" inverted (R. 4/5)	£450	£170

Nos. O318 to O325 are arranged in composite sheets of 100 (10×10). The two upper horizontal rows of each value are surcharged as Type O **5** and the next five rows as Type O **6**. The remaining three rows are also surcharged as Type O **6** but in a slightly narrower setting.

The surcharge on No. O323 differs from Type O **5** in the shape of the figures and letter.

O **8**

(Des T. I. Archer. Litho Indian Govt Ptg Wks, Nasik (No. O330). Typo Bhopal Govt Ptg Wks (others))

1935–39. As Type O **8**.

(a) Litho. Inscr "BHOPAL GOVT POSTAGE". Optd "SERVICE" (13½ mm). P 13½

O330	1a.3p. blue and claret	3·50	2·25

(b) Typo. Inscr "BHOPAL STATE POSTAGE". Optd "SERVICE" (11 mm). P 12

O331	1a.6p. blue and claret (1937)	2·50	1·75
	a. Imperf between (pair)	£325	£350
	b. Opt omitted	£275	£200
	c. Opt double, one inverted	£950	£1000
	d. Imperf (pair)	†	£275
	e. Blue printing double	†	£200

O332	1a.6p. claret (1939)	6·00	3·00
	a. Imperf between (pair)	£400	£425
	b. Opt omitted	—	£800
	c. Opt double, one inverted	—	£800
	d. Opt double	—	£800
	e. Bright rose-red	—	20·00

PRINTERS. From No. O333 all issues were printed by the Bhopal Govt Ptg Wks in typography.

O **9**   O **10** The Moti Mahal

O **11** The Moti Masjid   O **12** Taj Mahal and Be-Nazir Palaces

O **13** Ahmadabad Palace

O **14** Rait Ghat

1936 (July)–**38.** Optd "SERVICE". P 12.

O333	O **9**	¼a. orange (Br.)	90	60
		a. Imperf between (vert pair)	£275	
		ab. Imperf between (horiz pair)	†	£800
		b. Opt inverted	£800	£650
		c. Black opt	8·50	75
		ca. Opt inverted	†	£500
		cb. Opt double	†	£425
O334		¼a. yellow (Br.) (1938)	13·00	2·50
O335		1a. scarlet	1·50	10
		a. Imperf between (horiz pair)	£275	£250
		b. Imperf between (vert pair)	†	£550
		c. Imperf between (block of 4)	£800	£750
		d. Imperf vert (horiz pair)	†	£300

1936–49. T O **10/14**. P 12.

(a) Optd "SERVICE" (13½ mm)

O336	O **10**	½a. purple-brown and yellow-green	70	80
		a. Imperf between (vert pair)	†	£425
		ab. Imperf between (horiz pair)	†	£450
		b. Opt double	£350	£190
		c. Frame double	£120	15·00
		d. Purple-brown and green (1938)	70	50

(b) Optd "SERVICE" (11 mm)

O337	O **11**	2a. brown and blue (1937)	2·00	1·25
		a. Imperf between (vert pair)	†	£600
		ab. Imperf between (horiz pair)	†	£425
		b. Opt inverted	£300	£400
		c. Opt omitted	£500	
		d. Pair, one without opt	£1000	
		e. As d. but opt inverted	£1800	
O338		2a. green and violet (1938)	19·00	40
		a. Imperf between (vert pair)	†	£500
		b. Imperf between (vert strip of 3)	£275	£375
		c. Frame double	†	£550
		d. Centre double	†	£650
O339	O **12**	4a. blue and brown (1937)	3·75	50
		a. Imperf between (horiz pair)	†	£1400
		b. Opt omitted	†	£550
		c. Opt double	†	£250
		d. Centre double	†	£750
		e. Blue and reddish brown (1938)	4·25	65
		ea. Frame double	†	£550
O340	O **13**	8a. bright purple and blue (1938)	6·00	2·50
		a. Imperf between (vert pair)	†	£800
		b. Opt omitted	†	£325
		c. Opt double	†	£275
		d. Imperf vert (horiz pair) and opt omitted	†	£550
		e. Imperf (pair) and opt omitted	†	£550
		f. Frame double	†	£500
O341	O **14**	1r. blue and reddish purple (Br.) (1938)	30·00	11·00
		a. Imperf horiz (vert pair)	†	£3500
		b. Opt in black (1942)	24·00	4·50
		ba. Light blue and bright purple	60·00	45·00
		bb. Laid paper	£1700	£1800
O336/41b *Set of 6*			50·00	8·50

(c) Optd "SERVICE" (11½ mm) with serifs

O342	O **14**	1r. dull blue and bright purple (Blk.) (1949)	75·00	£160

	a. "SREVICE" for "SERVICE" (R. 6/6)	£200	£475
	b. "SERVICE" omitted	£1700	

(d) Optd "SERVICE" (13½ mm) with serifs

O343	O **13**	8a. bright purple and blue (1949)	£140	£200
		a. "SERAICE" for "SERVICE" (R. 6/5)	£800	£1200
		b. Fig "1" for "I" in "SERVICE" (R. 7/1)	£850	£1300

The ½a. is inscr "BHOPAL GOVT" below the arms, other values have "BHOPAL STATE".

O **15** Tiger   O **16** Spotted Deer

1940. T O **15/16**. P 12.

O344	O **15**	¼a. bright blue	7·00	1·75
O345	O **16**	1a. bright purple	55·00	4·75

1941. As Type O **8** but coloured centre inscr "SERVICE"; bottom frame inscr "BHOPAL STATE POSTAGE". P 12.

O346	1a.3p. emerald-green	3·50	3·25
	a. Imperf between (pair)	£700	£700

O **17** The Moti Mahal

O **18** The Moti Masjid   O **19** Be-Nazir Palaces

1944–47. T O **17/19**. P 12.

O347	O **17**	½a. green	1·00	1·00
		a. Imperf (pair)	†	£130
		b. Imperf between (vert pair)	†	£375
		c. Doubly printed	†	£250
O348	O **18**	2a. violet	25·00	4·25
		a. Imperf (pair)	†	£140
		c. Bright purple (1945)	8·00	3·75
		d. Mauve (1947)	14·00	15·00
		e. Error. Chocolate (imperf)	£375	£375
O349	O **19**	4a. chocolate	13·00	2·25
		a. Imperf (pair)	†	£160
		b. Imperf vert (horiz pair)	†	£450
		c. Doubly printed	†	£300
O347/9 *Set of 3*			20·00	6·25

O **20** Arms of Bhopal   **2 As.** (O **21**)   **2 As.** (O **22**)

1944–49. P 12.

O350	O **20**	3p. bright blue	1·00	1·00
		a. Imperf between (vert pair)	£200	£225
		b. Imperf between (horiz pair)	†	£450
		c. Stamp doubly printed	95·00	
O351		9p. chestnut (*shades*) (1945)	11·00	4·25
		a. Imperf (pair)	†	£225
		b. Orange-brown	3·00	5·00
O352		1a. purple (1945)	11·00	1·75
		a. Imperf horiz (vert pair)	†	£750
		b. Violet (1946)	19·00	3·25
O353		1½a. claret (1945)	5·00	1·25
		a. Imperf between (horiz pair)	†	£600
		b. Imperf horiz (vert pair)	†	£650
O354		3a. yellow	26·00	26·00
		a. Imperf (pair)	†	£275
		b. Imperf horiz (vert pair)	†	£425
		c. Imperf vert (horiz pair)		
		d. Orange-brown (1949)	£160	£160
O355		6a. carmine (1945)	35·00	75·00
		a. Imperf (pair)	†	£425
		b. Imperf horiz (vert pair)	†	£550
		c. Imperf vert (horiz pair)	†	£550
O350/5 *Set of 6*			75·00	£100

1949 (July). Surch with Type O **21**. P 12.

O356	O **20**	2a. on 1½a. claret	3·50	10·00
		a. Stop omitted	21·00	55·00
		b. Imperf (pair)	£425	£475
		ba. Ditto. Stop omitted	£1500	£1600
		c. "2" omitted (in pair with normal)	£2000	

The "stop omitted" variety occurs on positions 60 and 69 in the sheet of 81.

1949. Surch with Type O **22**. Imperf.

O357	O **20**	2a. on 1½a. claret	£2250	£2250
		a. Perf 12	£2500	£2500

Three different types of "2" occur in the setting of Type O **22**. This surcharge has been extensively forged, and should not be purchased without a reliable guarantee.

BHOR

PRICES FOR STAMPS ON COVER	
Nos. 1/2	*from* × 50
No. 3	*from* × 7

GUM. The stamps of Bhor were issued without gum.

Pandit Shankar Rao, 1871–1922

1   **2**

1879. Handstamped. Very thick to thin native paper. Imperf.

1	**1**	½a. carmine (*shades*)	5·50	8·00
		a. *Tête-bêche* (pair)	£1300	
2	**2**	1a. carmine (*shades*)	8·00	11·00

3

1901. Typo. Wove paper. Imperf.

3	**3**	½a. red	22·00	48·00

BIJAWAR

PRICES FOR STAMPS ON COVER
The stamps of Bijawar are very rare used on cover.

Maharaja Sarwant Singh, 1899–1941

1   **2**

(Typo Lakshmi Art Ptg Works, Bombay)

1935 (1 July)**–36.**

(a) P 11

1	**1**	3p. brown	12·00	8·00
		a. Imperf (pair)	14·00	
		b. Imperf between (vert pair)	£110	
		c. Imperf horiz (vert pair)	70·00	
2		6p. carmine	10·00	8·00
		a. Imperf (pair)	£110	
		b. Imperf between (vert pair)	£100	
		c. Imperf between (horiz pair)	£110	£180
		d. Imperf horiz (vert pair)	£120	
3		9p. violet	14·00	8·50
		a. Imperf (pair)	£180	
		b. Imperf between (vert pair)	£130	
		c. Imperf between (horiz pair)	£110	
		d. Imperf horiz (vert pair)	£120	
4		1a. blue	18·00	8·00
		a. Imperf (pair)	£110	
		b. Imperf between (vert pair)	£120	
		c. Imperf between (horiz pair)	£190	
		d. Imperf horiz (vert pair)	£140	
		e. Imperf vert (horiz strip of 3)	£225	
5		2a. deep green	14·00	8·50
		a. Imperf (pair)	£140	
		b. Imperf horiz (vert pair)	18·00	
		c. Imperf between (vert pair)	45·00	
		d. Imperf between (horiz pair)	75·00	£120
1/5 *Set of 5*			60·00	35·00

(b) Roul 7 (1936)

6	**1**	3p. brown	9·00	13·00
		a. Printed on gummed side	£700	
7		6p. carmine	9·00	35·00
8		9p. violet	9·00	£200
9		1a. blue	10·00	£225
10		2a. deep green	20·00	£250
6/10 *Set of 5*			50·00	£650

1937 (May). Typo. P 9.

11	**2**	4a. orange	25·00	£170
		a. Imperf between (vert pair)	£170	
		b. Imperf (pair)	£225	
12		6a. lemon	25·00	£170
		a. Imperf between (vert pair)	£180	
		b. Imperf (pair)	£225	
13		8a. emerald-green	28·00	£225
		a. Imperf (pair)	£250	
14		12a. greenish blue	30·00	£250
		a. Imperf (pair)	£250	
15		1r. bright violet	55·00	£325
		a. "1 Rs" for "1 R" (R. 1/2)	75·00	£550
		b. Imperf (pair)	£300	
		ba. "1 Rs" for "1 R" (R. 1/2)	£850	
11/15 *Set of 5*			£150	£1000

The stamps of Bijawar were withdrawn in 1941.

BUNDI

PRICES FOR STAMPS ON COVER	
No. 1	*from* × 2
No. 2	*from* × 4
Nos. 3/53	*from* × 10
Nos. 54/63	*from* × 5
Nos. 64/78	*from* × 2
Nos. 79/92	*from* × 10
Nos. O1/52	*from* × 15
Nos. O53/7	*from* × 20
Nos. O58/9	—

GUM. Nos. 1/17 were issued without gum.

ILLUSTRATIONS. Types **1/10** and the tablet inscriptions for Type **11** are shown actual size.

In Nos. 1 to 17 characters denoting the value are below the dagger, except in Nos. 2a, 11 and 17.

All Bundi stamps until 1914 are lithographed and imperforate.

Maharao Raja Raghubir Singh, 1889–1927

1

1894 (May). Each stamp with a distinct frame and the stamps not connected by the framing lines. Three vertical lines on dagger. Laid paper.

1	**1**	½a. slate-grey	£21000	£4000
		a. Last two letters of value below the rest	†	£12000

2 (Block of four stamps)

1894 (Dec). Stamps joined together, with no space between them. Two vertical lines on dagger. Thin wove paper.

2	**2**	½a. slate-grey	70·00	75·00
		a. Value at top, name below	£450	£700
		b. Right upper ornament omitted	£4250	£5500
		c. Last two letters of value below the rest	£2500	£2500
		d. Left lower ornament omitted	£4250	£5500

No. 2 was printed in sheets of 294, comprising two panes (10×14 and 11×14) side by side, in *tête-bêche* format. In the 10×14 pane No. 2a occurs on R1/1-10, No. 2b on R11/7 and No. 2d on R2/9. In the 11×14 pane No. 2c occurs on R2/11, 8/3 and 10/1.

3

1896 (Nov). Dagger shorter, lines thicker. Stamps separate. Laid paper.

3	**3**	½a. slate-grey	8·00	12·00
		a. Last two letters of value below the rest	£475	£700

No. 3 was printed in sheets of 168, comprising two panes (7×12) side by side.

4 (1 anna)   **5** (4 annas)

6 (2 annas)

1897–98. No shading in centre of blade of dagger. The stamps have spaces between them, but are connected by the framing lines, both vertically and horizontally. Laid paper.

I. Blade of dagger comparatively narrow, and either triangular, as in T 4 and 6, or with the left-hand corner not touching the bar behind it, as in T 5 (1897–98)

4	**4**	1a. Indian red	21·00	45·00
5	**5**	1a. red	26·00	40·00
6		2a. green	25·00	42·00
7	**6**	2a. yellow-green	25·00	48·00
8	**5**	4a. green	£120	£180
9		8a. Indian red	£200	£650
10		1r. yellow/*blue*	£700	£1100
4/10 *Set of 5*			£950	£1800

7

II. Blade varying in shape, but as a rule not touching the bar; value above and name below the dagger, instead of the reverse (Jan 1898)

11	**7**	4a. emerald-green	90·00	
		a. Yellow-green	50·00	£120

8 (½ anna)   **9** (1 anna)

III. Blade wider and (except on the ½a.) almost diamond shaped; it nearly always touches the bar (1898–1900)

12	**8**	½a. slate-grey (5.2.98)	8·00	8·00
13	**9**	1a. Indian red (7.98)	7·50	8·00
14		2a. pale green (9.11.98)	24·00	28·00
		a. First two characters of value (= two) omitted	£2750	£2750
15		8a. Indian red (7.98)	38·00	38·00
16		1r. yellow/*blue* (7.98)	48·00	95·00
		a. On wove paper	35·00	50·00
12/16a *Set of 5*			£100	£120

10

IV. Inscriptions as on No. 11; point of dagger to left (9.11.98)

17	**10**	4a. green	90·00	£100
		a. Yellow-green	40·00	48·00

All the above stamps are lithographed in large sheets, containing as many varieties of type as there are stamps in the sheets.

11 Raja protecting Sacred Cows

Type **11** was produced from separate clichés printed as a block of four. The same clichés were used for all values, but not necessarily in the same order within the block. The Devanagari inscriptions, "RAJ BUNDI" at top and the face value at bottom, were inserted into the basic clichés as required so that various differences exist within the 58 settings which have been identified.

The denominations may be identified from the following illustrations. The ½a., 3a. and rupee values can be easily distinguished by their colours.

Bottom tablets:—

पाव आना — ¼a.	एक आना — 1a.
दो आना — 2a.	ढाई आना — 2½a.
चार आना — 4a.	छे आना — 6a.
आठ आना — 8a.	दस आना — 10a.
बारह आना — 12a.	एक रुपया — 1r.

The nine versions of the inscriptions are as follows:

Top tablet

Type A. Top tablet has inscription in two separate words with a curved line over the first character in the second. The second word has three characters. Bottom tablet has short line above the first character in the second word.

Type B. Top tablet as Type A, but without the curved line over the first character in the second word. Bottom tablet as Type A.

Type C. Top tablet as Type B, but with large loop beneath the first character in the second word. This loop is usually joined to the main character, but is sometimes detached as in the illustration. Bottom tablet as Type A.

Top tablet   Bottom tablet

Type D. Top tablet in thinner lettering with the inscription shown as one word of six characters. The fourth character has a curved line above it, as in Type A, and a loop beneath, as in Type C. Bottom tablet as Type A, but thinner letters.

Type E. Top tablet as Type C. Bottom tablet shows a redrawn first character to the second word. This has the line at top extending over the entire character.

Bottom tablet

Type F. Top tablet as Type B. Bottom tablet as Type E, but first character in second word differs.

G   H

Type G. Top tablet as Type C, but without dot over first character in second word. There are now four characters in the second word. Bottom tablet as Type E.

Type H. Top tablet as Type G, but with characters larger and bolder. Bottom tablet as Type E, but with characters larger and bolder.

I

Type I. Top tablet as Type H. Bottom tablet as Type E.

Some settings contained more than one inscription type within the block of four so that *se-tenant* examples are known of Type B with Type C (¼, 1, 2, 4, 8, 10 and 12a.), Type C with Type E (¼, ½ and 4a.) and Type E with Type F (½ and 4a.). Type F only exists from this mixed setting.

1914 (Oct)–**41**. T **11**. Typo. Ungummed paper except for Nos. 73/8.

I. Rouletted in colour

(a) Inscriptions as Type A. Thin wove paper (1916–23)

18	½a. black....................................		3·50	12·00
19	1a. vermilion..............................		12·00	35·00
20	2a. emerald................................		6·00	60·00
	a. Deep green (coarse ptg on wove paper) (1923)		6·50	9·00
21	2½a. chrome-yellow (*shades*) (1917)		22·00	70·00
	a. Printed both sides...............		£2000	
22	3a. chestnut (1917)....................		40·00	70·00
23	4a. yellow-green........................		21·00	
24	6a. cobalt (1917)........................		32·00	£150
25	1r. reddish violet (1917)............		40·00	£150

A special printing of the 1a. took place in late 1917 in connection with the "OUR DAY" Red Cross Society Fund. This had the "RAJ BUNDI" inscription in the bottom tablet with the face value below it. The top tablet carried four Devanagri characters for "OUR DAY". No evidence has been found to suggest that this 1a. stamp was used for postal purposes (*Price*, £250 *unused*).

(b) Inscriptions as Type B. Thin wove or pelure paper (1914–23)

25a	¼a. cobalt (1916).......................		5·00	32·00
	ab. Stamp doubly printed..........		£1000	

26	¼a. ultramarine (*shades*) (1917).......		2·25	5·50
	a. Indigo (1923)........................		4·25	11·00
27	½a. black....................................		3·00	8·00
28	1a. vermilion (1915)...................		5·50	19·00
	a. Carmine (1923).....................		17·00	21·00
	b. Red (shades) (1923)..............		6·50	19·00
29	2a. emerald (*shades*) (1915)......		17·00	45·00
30	2½a. olive-yellow (1917)..............		20·00	40·00
31	3a. chestnut (1917)....................		16·00	75·00
32	4a. apple-green (1915)...............		4·50	55·00
32a	4a. olive-yellow (1917)...............		£200	£350
33	6a. pale ultramarine (*shades*) (1917)		21·00	£160
	a. Deep ultramarine (1917).......		7·00	£140
34	8a. orange (1915)......................		7·50	£170
35	10a. olive-sepia (1917).................		£250	£650
	a. Yellow-brown........................		£300	
36	12a. sage-green (1917)................		£650	£850
36a	1r. lilac (*shades*) (1915)...........		25·00	

(c) Inscriptions as Type C. Thin to medium wove paper (1917–41)

37	¼a. ultramarine (*shades*) (1923).......		15·00	17·00
	a. Indigo (1923)........................		15·00	18·00
	c. Cobalt (medium wove paper) (1937)		40·00	32·00
38	½a. black....................................		5·50	7·00
39	1a. orange-red...........................		40·00	48·00
	a. Carmine (1923).....................		40·00	48·00
	b. Deep red (medium wove paper) (1936)		30·00	38·00
40	2a. emerald................................		22·00	42·00
	a. Sage-green...........................		27·00	45·00
41	4a. yellow-green (*shades*)........		£110	£225
	a. Olive-yellow.........................		£160	£300
	b. Bright apple-green (medium wove paper) (1936)		£1100	£400
42	8a. reddish orange....................		9·50	85·00
43	10a. brown-olive..........................		19·00	£160
	a. Olive-sepia..........................		48·00	£200
	b. Yellow-brown........................		90·00	
44	12a. sage-green...........................		23·00	£150
45	1r. lilac...................................		38·00	£300
46	2r. red-brown and black............		£120	£300
	a. Chocolate and black (medium wove paper) (1936)		70·00	£400
47	3r. blue and red-brown..............		£190	£400
	a. Grey-blue and chocolate (medium wove paper) (1941)		£120	
	ab. Chocolate (inscriptions) inverted		£30000	
48	4r. emerald and scarlet.............		£450	£550
49	5r. scarlet and emerald.............		£450	£550

Type II (2½a.)

(d) Inscriptions as Type D. Thin wove paper (1918?)

50	2½a. buff (*shades*).....................		25·00	85·00
	a. Type II value........................			
51	3a. red-brown...........................		42·00	48·00
	a. Semi-circle and dot omitted from 4th character....................		55·00	65·00
52	10a. bistre...................................		45·00	£190
	a. 4th character turned to left instead of downwards.....................		65·00	£300
53	12a. grey-olive.............................		70·00	£200
	a. 4th character turned to left instead of downwards.....................		£100	
	b. Blackish green......................		70·00	
	ba. 4th character turned to left instead of downwards.....................		£100	

(e) Inscriptions as Type E

(i) Medium wove paper (1930–37)

54	¼a. deep slate...........................		23·00	35·00
54a	¼a. indigo (*thin wove paper*) (1935)		48·00	48·00
	b. Cobalt (1937)........................		42·00	32·00
55	½a. black....................................		22·00	25·00
56	1a. carmine-red........................		28·00	48·00
57	3a. chocolate (*shades*) (1936)..		11·00	55·00
58	4a. yellow-olive (1935)..............		£1300	£375
	a. Bright apple-green (1936).....		£1300	£350
	ab. No tail to 4th character.........		£2000	£600

(ii) Very thick wove paper (1930–32)

59	¼a. indigo (1932).......................		42·00	48·00
60	½a. black....................................		£150	£160
61	1a. bright scarlet (1931)............		25·00	40·00
	a. Carmine-red..........................		£110	£120

(iii) Thin horizontally laid paper (1935)

62	¼a. indigo...................................		5·50	28·00
63	1a. scarlet-vermilion.................		17·00	50·00

Nos. 62 and 63 exist in *tête-bêche* blocks of four on the same or opposite sides of the paper.

(f) Inscriptions as Type F. Medium wove paper (1935)

63a	½a. black....................................		£190	£275
63b	4a. yellow-olive.........................		£2500	£1100

(g) Inscriptions as Type G

(i) Horizontally laid paper (1935)

64	½a. black....................................		£100	£100
	a. Vert laid paper.....................		£100	£100
65	1a. scarlet.................................		80·00	50·00
66	4a. bright green.........................		20·00	50·00

(ii) Medium wove paper (1936)

66a	½a. black....................................		6·00	38·00
66b	4a. bright green.........................		£2000	£750

(h) Inscriptions as Type H. Medium wove paper (1935–41)

67	¼a. ultramarine..........................		2·50	7·00
68	½a. black (1938).........................		80·00	80·00
69	1a. deep red..............................		8·50	45·00
	a. Rosine (1938)........................		28·00	50·00
70	4a. emerald (1938).....................		26·00	40·00
71	4r. yellow-green and vermilion (1941)		£190	
72	5r. vermilion and yellow-green (1941)..		£250	

No. 70 shows the currency spelt as "ANE" with the last letter missing and an accent over the Devanagri "N".

II. P 11

(a) Inscriptions as Type H. Medium wove paper with gum (1939–41)

73	¼a. ultramarine..........................		25·00	38·00
	a. Greenish blue (1941)............		1·75	50·00
74	½a. black....................................		42·00	45·00
75	1a. scarlet-vermilion (1940).......		£200	65·00
	a. Rose (1940)...........................		12·00	60·00
76	2a. yellow-green (1941).............		16·00	90·00

(b) Inscriptions as Type I. Medium wove paper with gum (1940)

77	½a. black....................................		£300	£180
78	2a. bright apple-green...............		75·00	80·00

FISCAL USE. Collectors are warned that the low values of the later settings of Type **11** were extensively used for fiscal purposes. Stamps which have been fraudulently cleaned of pen-cancels, regummed or provided with forged postmarks are frequently met with. Particular care should be exercised with examples of Nos. 58/a, 64/5, 68/70, 74/5a and 77.

Maharao Raja Ishwari Singh, 1927–1945

20

1941–**44**. Typo. P 11.

79	**20**	3p. bright blue..........................	3·50	7·00
80		6p. deep blue............................	7·00	11·00
81		1a. orange-red.........................	9·00	13·00
82		2a. chestnut..............................	10·00	25·00
		a. Deep brown (no gum) (1944)..	15·00	20·00
83		4a. bright green........................	16·00	80·00
84		8a. dull green...........................	22·00	£400
85		1r. deep blue...........................	48·00	£500
79/85	Set of 7		£100	£900

The first printing only of Nos. 79/85 is usually with gum; all further printings, including No. 82a, are without gum.

Maharao Raja Bahadur Singh, 1945–1971

21 Maharao Raja Bahadur Singh   **22** Maharoa Raja Badahur Singh

23 Bundi

(Typo *Times of India* Press, Bombay)

1947. P 11.

86	**21**	¼a. blue-green..........................	2·25	48·00
87		½a. violet..................................	2·25	38·00
88		1a. yellow-green.......................	2·00	40·00
89	**22**	2a. vermilion............................	2·00	85·00
90		4a. orange................................	3·25	£100
91	**23**	8a. ultramarine.........................	3·25	
92		1r. chocolate...........................	20·00	
86/92	Set of 7		30·00	

OFFICIAL STAMPS

PRICES. Prices for Nos. O1/52 are for unused examples. Used stamps are generally worth a small premium over the prices quoted.

  BUNDI

(O **1**)   (O **2**)

BUNDI

SERVICE

(O **3**)

1915–**41**. T **11** handstamped as Types O 1/3. Ungummed paper except Nos. O47/52.

*A. Optd with Type O **1**. B. Optd with Type O **2**. C. Optd with Type O **3**.*

I. Rouletted in colour

(a) Inscriptions as Type A. Thin wove paper

			A	B	C
O1		½a. black....................	£450	†	†
		a. Red opt.................	£400	†	†
O1b		2a. emerald................	8·50	£375	†
		ba. Deep green (coarse ptg on medium wove paper)	6·50	15·00	£450
		bb. Red opt.................	32·00	24·00	†

No.	Type	Description			
O2		2½a. chrome-yellow (shades)	10·00	25·00	£500
		a. Red opt.	£425	£475	†
O3		3a. chestnut	10·00	23·00	†
		a. Green opt.	£375	†	†
		b. Red opt.	£650	£700	†
O4		6a. cobalt	50·00	48·00	£550
		a. Red opt.	£600	£650	£700
O5		1r. reddish violet	95·00	£100	†
		a. Red opt.	£700	£800	†

(b) Inscriptions as Type B. Thin wove or pelure paper

No.	Description			
O6	¼a. ultramarine (shades)	1·75	5·00	7·50
	a. Red opt.	1·25	4·00	£400
	b. Green opt.	£200	†	†
O7	½a. black	16·00	7·50	50·00
	a. Red opt.	5·00	15·00	£400
	b. Green opt.	£180	†	†
O8	1a. vermilion	8·00	†	†
	a. Red opt.	—	†	†
	b. Carmine	60·00	23·00	£170
	c. Red (shades)	8·00	7·00	£275
O9	2a. emerald (shades)	50·00	75·00	†
	a. Red opt.		£300	†
O9b	3a. chestnut (R.)	—	†	†
O10	4a. apple-green	12·00	£130	£475
	a. Red opt.	£600	†	†
O10b	4a. olive-yellow	£350	£500	†
	ba. Red opt.	£850	£850	†
O11	6a. pale ultramarine (shades)	18·00	£375	†
	a. Red opt.	£750	£750	†
	b. Deep ultramarine	80·00	90·00	†
	ba. Red opt.	£250	£225	†
O12	8a. orange	90·00	£140	£750
	a. Red opt.	£700	†	†
O13	10a. olive-sepia	£325	£350	£1000
	a. Red opt.	£1300	£1500	£1600
O14	12a. sage-green	£200	£700	£1300
	a. Red opt.	†	†	£1600
O14b	1r. lilac	†	†	†

(c) Inscriptions as Type C. Thin to medium wove paper

No.	Description			
O15	¼a. ultramarine (shades)	9·50	4·75	23·00
	a. Red opt.	1·50	5·50	£425
	b. Green opt.	10·00	90·00	†
	c. Cobalt (medium wove paper)	80·00	80·00	£600
	ca. Red opt.	55·00	40·00	£180
O16	½a. black	15·00	3·50	21·00
	a. Red opt.	3·00	8·00	£400
	b. Green opt.	5·00	†	†
O17	1a. orange-red	1·25	—	†
	a. Carmine	45·00	15·00	55·00
	b. Deep red (medium wove paper)	55·00	75·00	£170
	ba. Red opt.	†	£350	†
O18	2a. emerald	14·00	28·00	£190
	a. Red opt.	†	£250	†
	b. Sage-green	20·00	16·00	£140
O19	4a. yellow-green (shades)	20·00	†	£130
	b. Red opt.	—	£550	†
	c. Olive-yellow	£180	£180	†
	ca. Red opt.	£500	£650	†
	d. Bright apple-green (medium wove paper)	£2000	†	†
O20	8a. reddish orange	21·00	65·00	£425
	a. Red opt.	£600	£600	†
O21	10a. brown-olive	£110	£170	£800
	a. Red opt.	£850	£850	£1100
O22	12a. sage-green	90·00	£190	£900
	a. Red opt.	£800	†	£1000
O23	1r. lilac	£200	†	†
	a. Red opt.	£650	†	†
O24	2r. red-brown and black	£550	£225	†
	a. Red opt.	†	£2000	†
	b. Green opt.	£2000	†	†
	c. Chocolate and black (medium wove paper)	£1300	£1300	†
O25	3r. blue and red-brown	£450	£250	†
	a. Red opt.	£1900	†	†
	b. Grey-blue and chocolate (medium wove paper)	£2250	£2250	†
	ba. Red opt.	£2500	†	†
O26	4r. emerald and scarlet	£400	£375	†
O27	5r. scarlet and emerald	£400	£375	†

(d) Inscriptions as Type D. Thin wove paper

No.	Description			
O28	2½a. buff (shades)	15·00	25·00	†
	a. Type II value	†	£850	†
	b. Red opt.	£500	£650	†
O29	3a. red-brown	60·00	45·00	†
	a. Variety as No. 51a	80·00	75·00	†
	b. Red opt.	†	£850	†
O30	10a. bistre	80·00	£120	£850
	a. Variety as No. 52a	£120	£190	£1300
	b. Red opt.	£800	£750	†
	ba. Variety as No. 52a	£1100	†	†
O31	12a. grey-olive	£100	£160	£900
	a. Variety as No. 53a	£150	£250	£1400
	b. Red opt.	£700	£1000	†
	ba. Variety as No. 53a	£950	†	†

(e) Inscriptions as Type E

(i) Medium wove paper

No.	Description			
O32	¼a. deep slate	50·00	20·00	†
	a. Red opt.	38·00	70·00	†
O32b	¼a. indigo (thin wove paper)	80·00	55·00	†
	ba. Red opt.	75·00	75·00	†
	bb. Green opt.	£200	£275	†
	c. Cobalt	80·00	80·00	£600
	ca. Red opt.	50·00	40·00	£170
O33	½a. black	65·00	13·00	†
	a. Red opt.	35·00	13·00	†
	b. Green opt.	£300	£375	†
O34	1a. carmine-red	70·00	75·00	£450
O35	3a. chocolate (shades)	£190	£140	£325
	b. Red opt.	£1000	£1000	†
O35b	4a. yellow-olive	†	£2500	†
	ba. Bright apple-green	£2750	£2750	†

(ii) Very thick wove paper

No.	Description			
O36	¼a. indigo	13·00	19·00	†
	a. Red opt.	40·00	90·00	†
	b. Green opt.	£120	†	†
O37	½a. black	£300	£225	†
O38	1a. bright scarlet	22·00	21·00	£550
	a. Carmine-red	£170	£190	†

(iii) Thin horizontally laid paper

No.	Description			
O39	¼a. indigo	£120	£120	†
	a. Red opt.	5·50	13·00	£350
O40	1a. scarlet-vermilion	90·00	50·00	†
	a. Red opt.	£700	£750	†

Nos. O39/40a exist in *tête-bêche* blocks of four on the same or opposite sides of the paper.

(f) Inscriptions as Type F. Medium wove paper

No.	Description			
O40b	½a. black	£600	£650	†
	ba. Red opt.	£500	£550	†
	bb. Green opt.	£800	†	†
O40c	4a. yellow-olive	†	£2750	†

(g) Inscriptions as Type G

(i) Horizontally laid paper

No.	Description			
O41	½a. black	£500	£650	†
	a. Red opt.	£180	£275	†
	b. Vert laid paper	£275	£225	†
		£350	90·00	£750
O42	4a. bright green	£325	£325	†
	a. Red opt.	£375	£450	†

(ii) Medium wove paper

No.	Description			
O42b	½a. black	£500	£600	†
	ba. Red opt.	£425	£425	†

(h) Inscriptions as Type H. Medium wove paper

No.	Description			
O43	¼a. ultramarine	25·00	90·00	†
	a. Red opt.	£225	£500	†
O44	½a. black	80·00	£130	†
	a. Red opt.	70·00	†	£900
O45	1a. rosine	£275	£250	£900
	a. Deep red	£450	£450	†
O46	4a. emerald	£375	£400	£750
	a. Red opt.	£1000	†	£1000

II. P 11

(a) Inscriptions as Type H. Medium wove paper with gum

No.	Description			
O47	¼a. ultramarine	50·00	65·00	£170
	a. Red opt.	90·00	£120	†
	b. Greenish blue	75·00	75·00	£200
	ba. Red opt.	£200	†	†
O48	½a. black	55·00	95·00	£475
	a. Red opt.	£130	£650	£375
O49	1a. scarlet-vermilion	£425	£450	£950
	a. Stamp doubly printed	†	†	£2500
	b. Rose	£225	£180	£500
O50	2a. yellow-green	£850	£400	£500

(b) Inscriptions as Type I. Medium wove paper with gum

No.	Description			
O51	½a. black	£275	£450	£750
	a. Red opt.	£1100	£1100	—
O52	2a. bright apple-green	£900	£800	£2750

Until 1941 it was the general practice to carry official mail free but some of the above undoubtedly exist postally used.

1941. Nos. 79 to 85 optd "SERVICE".

O53	20	3p. bright blue (R.)	11·00	22·00
O54		6p. deep blue (R.)	26·00	21·00
O55		1a. orange-red	19·00	22·00
O56		2a. brown	30·00	18·00
O57		4a. bright green	95·00	£250
O58		8a. dull green	£375	£1100
O59		1r. deep blue (R.)	£425	£1200
O53/9		Set of 7	£900	£2250

Two different types of "R" occur in the "SERVICE" overprint. On five positions in the sheet of 12 the "R" shows a larger loop and a pointed diagonal leg.

Bundi became part of the Rajasthan Union by 15 April 1948.

BUSSAHIR (BASHAHR)

PRICES FOR STAMPS ON COVER	
Nos. 1/21	from × 8
Nos. 22/23	from × 2
Nos. 24/43	from × 8

Raja Shamsher Singh, 1850–1914

The initials are those of the Tika Raghunath Singh, son of the then Raja, who was the organiser and former director of the State Post Office.

(Litho at the Bussahir Press by Maulvi Karam Bakhsh, Rampur)

1895 (20 June). Laid paper. Optd with T **9** in pale greenish blue (B.), rose (R.), mauve (M.) or lake (L.). With or without gum.

(a) Imperf

No.	Type	Description		
1	1	¼a. pink (M.) (1.9.95)	£4000	
		a. Monogram in rose	£7000	
2	2	½a. grey (R.)	£900	£1200
		a. Monogram in mauve		
3	3	1a. vermilion (M.)	£400	
4	4	2a. orange-yellow (M.)	£130	£350
		a. Monogram in rose	£250	£375
		b. Monogram in lake	£180	
		c. Monogram in blue	£500	
5	5	4a. slate-violet (M.)	£275	
		a. Monogram in rose	£300	
		b. Monogram in lake	£325	
		c. Without monogram	£500	
		d. Thick paper	£275	
6	6	8a. red-brown (M.)	£275	£400
		a. Monogram in blue	£325	
		b. Monogram in lake	£375	
		c. Without monogram	£400	
		d. Without monogram	£275	
		e. Thick paper	£275	
7	7	12a. green (L.)	£375	
		a. Monogram in mauve	£225	
8	8	1r. ultramarine (R.)	£350	
		a. Monogram in lake	£300	
		b. Monogram in mauve	£650	£850

(b) Perf with a sewing machine; gauge and size of holes varying between 7 and 11½

No.	Type	Description		
9	1	¼a. pink (B.)	£120	£160
		a. Monogram in mauve	—	£300
		b. Without monogram	£800	£300
10	2	½a. grey (R.)	32·00	£190
		a. Without monogram	£1500	
11	3	1a. vermilion (M.)	32·00	£130
12	4	2a. orange-yellow (B.)	42·00	£130
		a. Monogram in rose		
		b. Monogram in mauve	£275	
		c. Without monogram		£300
13	5	4a. slate-violet (B.)	40·00	£130
		a. Monogram in rose	55·00	£170
		b. Monogram in mauve	85·00	
		c. Without monogram	55·00	
14	6	8a. red-brown (M.)	28·00	£130
		a. Monogram in blue	£100	£275
		b. Monogram in rose	£190	
		c. Without monogram	£170	£425
15	7	12a. green (R.)	£100	£170
		a. Monogram in mauve	£250	
		b. Monogram in lake	£170	
		c. Without monogram	£350	
16	8	1r. ultramarine (R.)	65·00	£150
		a. Monogram in mauve	£200	
		b. Without monogram	£500	£700
9/16		Set of 8	£400	£1100

1899. As 1895, but pin-perf or rouletted.

No.	Type	Description		
17	3	1a. vermilion (M.)	£275	£300
18	4	2a. orange-yellow (M.)	£110	£225
		a. Monogram in lake	£120	£250
		b. Monogram in rose	£150	
		c. Monogram in blue	£325	
		d. Without monogram	£650	
19	5	4a. slate-violet (L.)	£400	
		a. Monogram in blue	£650	
		b. Monogram in rose	£600	
		c. Monogram in mauve	£475	
20	7	12a. green (R.)	£500	£700
21	8	1r. ultramarine (R.)	£650	£750

Nos. 1 to 21 were in sheets of 24. They seem to have been overprinted and perforated as required. Those first issued for use were perforated, but they were subsequently supplied imperf, both to collectors and for use. Nos. 17 to 21 were some of the last supplies. No rule seems to have been observed as to the colour of the overprinted monogram; pale blue, rose and mauve were used from the first. The pale blue varies to greenish blue or blue-green, and appears quite green on the yellow stamps. The lake is possibly a mixture of the mauve and the rose—it is a quite distinct colour and apparently later than the others. Examples without overprint are either remainders left in the Treasury or copies that have escaped accidentally; they have been found sticking to the backs of others that bore the overprint.

Varieties may also be found doubly overprinted, in two different colours.

T **11**. Lines of shading above and at bottom left and right of shield.
T **12**. White dots above shield and ornaments in bottom corners.

(Printed at the Bussahir Press by Maulvi Karam Bakhsh)

1896–97. Wove paper. Optd with monogram "R.S.", T **9**, in rose. Recess singly from line-engraved dies. With or without gum. Various perfs.

22	10	¼a. deep violet (1897)	—	£2250
23	11	½a. grey-blue	£1400	£500
23a		½a. deep blue (1897)	—	£750

No. 23 exists sewing-machine perf about 10 and also perf 14½–16. Nos. 22 and 23a are pin-perf.

1896–1900. As Nos. 22/3, but lithographed in sheets of various sizes. No gum.

(a) Imperf

24	10	¼a. slate-violet (R.)	16·00	
		a. Monogram in mauve	15·00	
		b. Monogram in blue	18·00	
		c. Monogram in lake	38·00	
25	11	½a. blue (*shades*) (R.)	19·00	28·00
		a. Monogram in mauve	14·00	28·00
		b. Monogram in lake	19·00	
		c. Without monogram	£375	
		d. Laid paper (B.)	£375	
		da. Laid paper in lake		
26	13	1a. olive (*shades*) (R.)	26·00	70·00
		a. Monogram in mauve	80·00	
		b. Monogram in lake	80·00	

(b) Pin-perf or rouletted

27	10	¼a. slate-violet (R.)	30·00	30·00
		a. Monogram in mauve	28·00	30·00
		b. Monogram in mauve	—	48·00
28	11	½a. blue (*shades*) (R.)	24·00	48·00
		a. Monogram in mauve	21·00	48·00
		b. Monogram in lake	60·00	70·00
		c. Monogram in mauve	£250	
		d. Laid paper (M.)	£250	
29	13	1a. olive (*shades*) (R.)	38·00	
		a. Monogram in mauve	£110	£110
		b. Monogram in lake	85·00	85·00
30	14	2a. orange-yellow (B.)*	£2500	£2500

Originally printings of the ¼a. and ½a. were in sheets of eight (stone I), but this was subsequently increased to 24 (4×6). The 1a. and 2a. were always in sheets of four.

Nos. 25d/da were printed from stone I and care is needed to distinguish this laid paper printing from some of the reprints on similar paper. Stamps from stone I are without marginal lines and are very clear impressions; reprints from stone IV have thick marginal lines and, in those shades similar to No. 25, show indistinct impressions.

*The prices quoted for No. 30 are for examples with a clear impression of the T **9** "TRS" monogram. The type **14** 2a. is often found as a remainder with the T **17** "RNS" monogram, both imperf and pin-perf. (*Prices from £50, unused or c.t.o.*)

1900–01. ¼a., 1a, colours changed; ½a. redrawn type; 2a. with dash before "STATE" and characters in lower left label; 4a. new value. No gum.

(a) Imperf

31	10	¼a. vermilion (M.)	6·50	13·00
		a. Monogram in blue	8·00	19·00
		b. Without monogram		
31c	12	½a. blue (M.)	11·00	38·00
		ca. Monogram in rose	45·00	
		cb. Without monogram	90·00	
32	13	1a. vermilion (M.)	7·00	22·00
		a. Monogram in blue	11·00	19·00
		b. Monogram in lake		
		c. Without monogram	90·00	
33	15	2a. ochre (M.) (9.00)	75·00	£140
		a. Without monogram	£140	
34		2a. yellow (M.) (11.00)	90·00	
		a. Monogram in mauve	90·00	£160
		b. Without monogram	£130	
35		2a. orange (B.) (1.01)	90·00	£160
		a. Monogram in mauve	90·00	£140
		b. Without monogram	90·00	
36	16	4a. claret (R.)	90·00	£180
		a. Monogram in mauve	£100	£200
		b. Monogram in blue	£140	£225
		c. Without monogram	55·00	

(b) Pin-perf or rouletted

37	10	¼a. vermilion (M.)	7·50	19·00
		a. Monogram in blue	7·50	
		b. Without monogram		
37c	12	½a. blue (M.)	£150	£200
38	13	1a. vermilion (M.)	15·00	25·00
		a. Monogram in blue	18·00	20·00
39		1a. brown-red (M.) (3.01)	—	£275
40	15	2a. ochre (M.) (9.00)	£110	
		a. Without monogram		
41		2a. yellow (M.) (11.00)	90·00	£120
		a. Monogram in rose	£100	£160
		b. Monogram in blue	£140	£180
42		2a. orange (M.) (1.01)	£100	£110
		a. Monogram in blue	£140	£130
		b. Without monogram	—	£500
43	16	4a. claret (R.)	£160	
		a. Monogram in blue	£160	£275
		b. Monogram in mauve	£170	

The ¼a., ½a. and 1a. are in sheets of 24; the 2a. in sheets of 50 differing throughout in the dash and the characters added at lower left; the 4a. in sheets of 28.

(**17**)

The stamps formerly catalogued with large overprint "R.N.S." (T **17**) are now believed never to have been issued for use.

Remainders are also found with overprint "P.S.", the initials of Padam Singh who succeeded Raghunath Singh in the direction of the Post Office, and with the original monogram "R.S." in a damaged state, giving it the appearance of a double-lined "R".

The stamps of Bussahir have been obsolete since 1 April 1901. Numerous remainders were sold after this date, and all values were later reprinted in the colours of the originals, or in fancy colours, from the original stones, or from new ones. Printings were also made from new types, similar to those of the second issue of the 8a., 12a. and 1r. values, in sheets of eight.

Reprints are frequently found on laid paper.

Collectors are warned against obliterated copies bearing the Rampur postmark with date "19 MA 1900." Many thousand remainders and reprints were thus obliterated for export after the closing of the State Post Office.

CHARKHARI

PRICES FOR STAMPS ON COVER	
Nos. 1/2	*from* × 2
Nos. 3/4	—
Nos. 5/26	*from* × 20
Nos. 27/44	*from* × 3
Nos. 45/53	*from* × 100
Nos. 54/5	*from* × 5
No. 56	*from* × 2

Maharaja Malkhan Singh, 1880–1908

1

$$\frac{1}{4} \quad \frac{1}{2} \quad 1 \quad 2 \quad 4$$
$$\frac{1}{4} \quad \frac{1}{2} \quad 1 \quad 2 \quad 4$$

The top row shows the figures of value used in the stamps of 1894–97, and the bottom row those for the 1904 issue. In the 4a. the figure slopes slightly to the right in the first issue, and to the left in the second.

1894. Typo from a single die. No gum. Imperf.

1	**1**	¼ anna, rose	£2250	£750
2		1 annas, dull green	£3250	£4000
3		2 annas, dull green	£4250	
4		4 annas, dull green	£2750	

Nos. 1/2 are known pin-perforated.

1897. Inscr "ANNA". No gum. Imperf.

5	**1**	¼a. magenta	£140	£150
		a. Purple	4·25	4·50
		b. Violet	4·25	4·25
6		½a. purple	4·25	5·00
		a. Violet	2·50	3·50
7		1a. blue-green	6·50	11·00
		a. Turquoise-blue	4·75	8·50
		b. Indigo	24·00	38·00
		c. Figure of value inverted	£2750	
8		2a. blue-green	10·00	17·00
		a. Turquoise-blue	7·00	13·00
		b. Indigo	25·00	38·00
9		4a. blue-green	13·00	22·00
		a. Turquoise-blue	8·50	19·00
		b. Indigo	50·00	80·00
		ba. Figure of value sideways	£2750	
5/9	*Set of 5*		24·00	42·00

Minor varieties may be found with the first "A" in "ANNA" not printed.

All values are known on various coloured papers, but these are proofs or trial impressions.

1902–04. Numerals changed as illustrated. No gum.

10	**1**	¼a. violet	2·00	2·50
11		½a. violet	5·50	5·50
12		1a. green	5·00	24·00
13		2a. green	35·00	45·00
14		4a. green	38·00	48·00
10/14	*Set of 5*		75·00	£110

Stamps of this issue can be found showing part of the papermaker's watermark. "Mercantile Script Extra Strong John Haddon & Co.".

Maharaja Jujhar Singh, 1908–1914

2 (Right-hand sword over left)

POSTAGE STAMP

Type I

POSTAGE STAMP

Type II

Type I. "P" of "POSTAGE" in same size as other letters. "E" small with long upper and lower arms. White dot often appears on one or both of the sword hilts.

Type II. "P" larger than the other letters. "E" large with short upper and lower arms. No dots occur on the hilts.

1909–19. Litho in Calcutta. Wove paper. P 11.

(a) Type I

15	**2**	1p. chestnut	75·00	75·00
		a. Pale chestnut	6·50	38·00
		b. Orange-brown	6·50	38·00
		c. "CHARKHAPI" (R. 5/5)	85·00	
16		1p. turquoise-blue	1·75	75
		a. Imperf between (horiz pair)	£250	
		b. Greenish blue (1911)	1·75	1·00
		c. Pale turquoise-green	2·00	1·00
17		½a. vermilion	3·50	1·50
		a. Imperf (pair)	£2000	
		b. Deep rose-red	2·00	1·50
18		1a. sage-green	6·00	3·50
		a. Yellow-olive	4·50	3·00
19		2a. grey-blue	3·75	3·50
		a. Dull violet-blue	3·00	5·50
20		4a. deep green	4·25	5·50
21		8a. brown-red	8·00	25·00
22		1r. pale chestnut	13·00	70·00
15a/22	*Set of 8*		38·00	£130

(b) Type II

24	**2**	1p. turquoise-blue	6·50	4·50
25		½a. vermilion	4·50	2·00
		b. Deep rose-red	12·00	9·00
26		1a. yellow-olive (1919)	5·00	3·00
		a. Sage-green	5·00	3·00
24/6	*Set of 3*		14·50	8·50

No. 15, from the original printing, shows an upstroke to the "1", not present on other brown printings of this value.
See also Nos. 31/44.

3 ".II" below Swords. Right sword overlaps left. Double framelines.

4 "JI" below Swords. Left sword overlaps right. Single frameline.

1912–17. Handstamped. Wove paper. No gum. Imperf.

27	**3**	1p. violet	£1400	£130
		a. Dull purple	—	£160
28	**4**	1p. violet (1917)	8·50	5·00
		a. Dull purple	38·00	5·50
		b. Tête-bêche (pair)	£100	£100
		c. Laid paper	—	£1200
		d. Pair, one stamp sideways		£190

Maharaja Ganga Singh, 1914–1920
Maharaja Arimardan Singh, 1920–1942

5 (*actual size 63×25 mm*)

6 (Left-hand sword over right)

1921. Handstamped. No gum.

(a) Wove paper. Imperf

29	**5**	1a. violet	£120	£130
		a. Dull violet	£130	£150

(b) Laid paper. P 11

30	**5**	1a. violet	£120	£190
		a. Imperf	£250	£275

(Typo State Ptg Press, Charkhari)

1930–45. Wove paper. No gum. Imperf.

31	**6**	1p. deep blue	1·75	18·00
		a. Vert pair, top ptd inverted on back, bottom normal upright	15·00	
		b. Tête-bêche (vert pair)	£1800	
		c. Perf 11×imperf (horiz pair) (1939)	£190	£160
		d. Bluish slate (1944)	32·00	55·00
		e. Laid paper	—	£600
		ea. Tête-bêche (vert pair)	£2750	
32		1p. dull to light green (*pelure*) (1943)	85·00	£425
33		1p. violet (1943)	26·00	£275
		a. Tête-bêche (vert pair)	75·00	
34		½a. deep olive	3·25	18·00
35		½a. red-brown (1940)	6·50	32·00
		a. Tête-bêche (vert pair)	£1600	
36		½a. black (*pelure*) (1943)	85·00	£375
37		½a. red (*shades*) (1940)	28·00	60·00
		a. Tête-bêche (vert pair)	60·00	
		b. Laid paper (1944)	—	£600
38		½a. grey-brown (*shades*)	£140	£140
39		1a. green	3·75	24·00
		a. Emerald (1938)	£140	£150
		b. Yellow-green	£110	£150
40		1a. chocolate (*shades*) (1940)	17·00	35·00
		a. Tête-bêche (vert pair)	90·00	
		b. Lake-brown	—	£110
41		1a. red (*shades*) (1940)	£275	£120
		a. Carmine	—	£120
		b. Laid paper (1944)	—	£600
42		2a. light blue	2·00	23·00
		a. Tête-bêche (vert pair)	14·00	
43		2a. greenish grey (1941?)	90·00	£130
		a. Tête-bêche (vert pair)	£180	
		b. Laid paper (1944)	—	£600
		c. Greyish green	£160	£350
43d		2a. yellow-green (1945)	£3000	£1900
44		4a. carmine	3·00	25·00
		a. Tête-bêche (vert pair)	14·00	

There are two different versions of No. 37a, one with the stamps *tête-bêche* base to base and the other showing them top to top.

The 1p. value is also known unused in deep olive (as No. 34), light blue (as No. 42) and carmine (as No. 44). These may be colour trials. (*Price, from £500 each*).

7 The Lake   **8** Imlia Palace

9 Industrial School   **10** Bird's-eye view of City

11 The Fort   **12** Guest House

13 Palace Gate   **14** Temples at Rainpur

15 Goverdhan Temple

½ As.
(16)

(Typo Batliboi Litho Works, Bombay)

1931 (25 June). T **7/15**. Thick, surfaced wove paper. P 11, 11½, 12 or compound.

45	**7**	½a. blue-green (a) (b) (c)	2·50	10
		a. Imperf between (horiz pair) (b)	60·00	12·00
		b. Imperf between (vert pair) (b) ..	70·00	40·00
		c. Imperf horiz (vert pair) (a) (b)..	55·00	
46	**8**	1a. blackish brown (a) (b) (c)	1·60	10
		a. Imperf between (horiz pair) (a) (b)	11·00	8·50
		b. Imperf between (vert pair) (a) (b)	27·00	13·00
		c. Imperf horiz (vert pair) (b)	18·00	
		d. Imperf (pair)	30·00	
47	**9**	2a. violet (a) (b) (c)	2·00	10
		a. Imperf vert (horiz pair) (b)	38·00	40·00
		b. Imperf between (vert pair) (b) ..	42·00	28·00
		c. Imperf horiz (vert pair) (b)	24·00	24·00
		d. Doubly printed (a)	10·00	
		e. Imperf (pair)	30·00	
48	**10**	4a. olive-green (a) (b)	2·50	20
		a. Imperf between (vert pair) (b) ..	90·00	90·00
49	**11**	8a. magenta (a) (b) (c)	4·00	10
		a. Imperf between (horiz pair) (b) (c)	85·00	35·00
		b. Imperf between (vert pair) (b) ..	70·00	55·00
		c. Imperf horiz (vert pair) (b)	85·00	25·00
50	**12**	1r. green and rose (a) (b)	5·50	25
		a. Imperf between (vert pair) (a) (b)	£140	£120
		b. Green (centre) omitted (b)	—	£325
		c. Imperf horiz (vert pair) (a)	£150	
		d. Imperf (pair)	80·00	
51	**13**	2r. red and brown (a) (b) (c)	10·00	40
		a. Imperf horiz (vert pair) (b)	£275	30·00
52	**14**	3r. chocolate and blue-green (a) (b)	24·00	60
		a. Imperf between (horiz pair) (b)	—	£325
		b. Tête-bêche (pair) (a) (b)	£600	20·00
		c. Chocolate (centre) omitted (b) .	22·00	
53	**15**	5r. turquoise and purple (a) (b)	10·00	50
		a. Imperf between (horiz pair) (a)	£350	
		b. Centre inverted (b)	£150	42·00
		c. Centre doubly printed (b)	—	£275
45/53		*Set of 9*	55·00	2·00

Three different perforating heads were used for this issue: (a) perf 11; (b) perf 12; (c) perf 11½. Values on which each perforation occur are shown above. Nos. 46 and 53 are known perf compound of 11 and 12.

This issue was the subject of speculative manipulation, large stocks being thrown on the market cancelled-to-order at very low prices and unused at less than face value. The issue was an authorized one but was eventually withdrawn by the State authorities.

1939 (1 Dec)–**40**. Nos. 21/2 surch as T **16**.

54	**2**	½a. on 8a. brown-red (1940)	55·00	£190
		a. No space between "½" and "As"	55·00	£190
		b. Surch inverted	£450	£650
		c. "1" of "½" inverted	£425	
55		1a. on 1r. chestnut (1940)	£200	£700
		a. Surch inverted	£500	
56		"1 ANNA" on 1r. chestnut	£2250	£1400

Maharaja Jaiendra Singh, 1942–1971

Charkhari became part of Vindhya Pradesh by 1 May 1948.

COCHIN

(6 puttans = 5 annas. 12 pies = 1 anna; 16 annas = 1 rupee)

Stamps of Cochin were also valid on mail posted to Travancore.

PRICES FOR STAMPS ON COVER	
Nos. 1/3	*from* × 30
Nos. 4/5	*from* × 10
Nos. 6/6b	*from* × 3
Nos. 7/9	*from* × 20
Nos. 11/22	*from* × 15
Nos. 26/128	*from* × 8
Nos. O1/105	*from* × 15

Raja Kerala Varma I, 1888–1895

1   **2**

(Dies eng P. Orr & Sons, Madras; typo Cochin Govt, Ernakulam)

1892 (13 Apr). No wmk, or wmk large Umbrella in the sheet. P 12.

1		1 ½ put. buff	3·50	3·00
		a. Orange-buff	4·50	3·00
		b. Yellow	3·75	3·50
		c. Imperf (pair)		
2		1 put. purple	3·75	3·00
		a. Imperf between (vert pair)	†	£4750
3	**2**	2 put. deep violet	3·00	2·25
1/3		*Set of 3*	9·25	7·50

1893. Laid paper. P 12.

4		1 ½ put. orange-buff	£750	£170
		a. Orange	£1000	£200
		b. Yellow	£1000	£225

WATERMARKS. Prior to the 1911–23 issue, printed by Perkins Bacon & Co, little attention was paid to the position of the watermark. Inverted and sideways watermarks are frequently found in the 1898 and 1902–03 issues.

1894. Wmk small Umbrella on each stamp. P 12.

5		1 ½ put. buff	15·00	5·00
		a. Orange	6·50	1·50
		ab. Imperf (pair)		
		b. Yellow	9·00	1·00
6		1 put. purple	15·00	8·50
7	**2**	2 put. deep violet	11·00	4·50
		a. Imperf (pair)		
		b. Doubly printed	†	£2750
		c. Printed both sides	£2750	
		d. Tête-bêche (pair)	£7500	
5/7		*Set of 3*	30·00	12·50

The paper watermarked with a small umbrella is more transparent than that of the previous issue. The wmk is not easy to distinguish. The 1 put. in deep violet was a special printing for fiscal use only.

Raja Rama Varma I, 1895–1914

1896 (End). Similar to T **1**, but 28×33 mm. P 12.

(a) Wmk Arms and inscription in sheet

8		1 put. violet	£140	£150

(b) Wmk Conch Shell to each stamp

9		1 put. deep violet	19·00	32·00

Nos. 8/9 were intended for fiscal use, but are also known used for postal purposes.

3   **4**

5   **6**

1898–1905. Thin yellowish paper. Wmk small Umbrella on each stamp. With or without gum. P 12.

11	**3**	3 pies. blue	1·40	1·10
		a. Imperf between (horiz pair)	£950	
		b. Imperf between (vert pair)	£950	
		c. Doubly printed	£1100	
12		4 ½ put. green	1·75	1·50
		a. Imperf between (horiz pair)	£2000	£2000
		b. Stamp sideways (in pair)	†	£4500
13		5 1 put. pink	6·00	1·75
		a. Tête-bêche (pair)	£7500	£3750
		b. Laid paper (1905)	†	£2000
		ba. Laid paper. Tête-bêche (pair)	†	£13000
		c. Red	7·50	1·75
		d. Carmine-red	8·50	2·50
14		6 2 put. deep violet	4·00	2·25
		a. Imperf between (vert pair)	£950	
		b. Imperf between (vert strip of 3)...	£1300	
11/14		*Set of 4*	12·00	5·50

1902–03. Thick white paper. Wmk small Umbrella on each stamp. With or without gum. P 12.

16	**3**	3 pies. blue	1·50	10
		a. Doubly printed	—	£450
		b. Imperf between (horiz pair)	†	£2000
17		4 ½ put. green	1·25	40
		a. Stamp sideways (in pair)	£1800	£1800
		b. Doubly printed	—	£475
		c. Imperf between (horiz pair)	†	£2000
18		5 1 put. pink (1903)	3·25	20
		a. Tête-bêche (pair)	†	£6000
19		6 2 put. deep violet	3·75	40
		a. Doubly printed	£2500	£500
16/19		*Set of 4*	9·00	1·00

2   **2**   **2**
(7)   (7a)   (7b)

1909. T **3** (Paper and perf of 1903), surch with T **7**. Wmk is always sideways. No gum.

22	**3**	2 on 3 pies. rosy mauve	15	50
		a. Surch Type **7** inverted	£170	£170
		b. Surch Type **7a**	£1600	£800
		c. Surch Type **7b**	£190	
		d. Stamps tête-bêche	£325	£375
		e. Stamps and surchs tête-bêche...	£375	£450

Varieties a, d and e were caused by the inversion of one stamp (No. 7) in the plate and the consequent inversion of the corresponding surcharge to correct the error.

Types **7a** and **7b** were applied by handstamp to correct the omission of the surcharge on R. 3/2 in different settings. Other sheets show a handstamped version of Type **7**.

8 Raja Rama Varma I   **8a**

(Recess Perkins, Bacon & Co)

1911–13. Currency in pies and annas. W **8a**. P 14.

26	**8**	2p. brown	50	10
		a. Imperf (pair)	†	£300
		w. Wmk inverted	—	£300
27		3p. blue	3·25	10
		a. Perf 14×12½	30·00	1·00
		w. Wmk inverted	—	£250
28		4p. green	4·00	10
		aw. Wmk inverted	—	£300
28b		4p. apple-green	4·25	40
		bw. Wmk inverted	—	£300
29		9p. carmine	3·75	10
		a. Wmk sideways		
30		1a. brown-orange	3·75	10
31		1½a. purple	12·00	45
32		2a. grey (1913)	8·00	40
33		3a. vermilion (1913)	70·00	48·00
26/33		*Set of 8*	95·00	48·00

No. 27a is line perforated. Nos. 27 and 33 exist perforated 14 either from comb or line machines. The other values only come from the comb machine.

Raja (Maharaja from 1921) Rama Varma II, 1914–1932

9 Raja Rama Varma II   **10** Raja Rama Varma II

I   II
(2p.)

I   II
(1a.)

(Recess Perkins, Bacon & Co)

1916–30. W **8a**. P 13½ to 14.

35	**10**	2p. brown (Die I) (a) (b) (c)	8·00	10
		a. Imperf (pair)	£850	
		b. Die II (b) (1930)	1·60	10
36		4p. green (a) (b)	1·00	10
37		6p. red-brown (a) (b) (c) (d) (1922)..	2·50	10
		w. Wmk inverted	—	£275
38		8p. sepia (1923)	3·00	10
39		9p. carmine (a)	32·00	60
40		10p. blue (1923)	10·00	10
41	**9**	1a. orange (Die I) (a) (b) (c)	32·00	4·75
		a. Die II (b) (1922)	18·00	35
42	**10**	1½a. purple (b) (1923)	7·50	20
43		2a. grey (a) (b) (d)	4·50	10
44		2¼a. yellow-green (a) (d) (1922)	14·00	3·25
45		3a. vermilion (a) (b)	12·00	35
35/45		*Set of 11*	95·00	4·75

Four different perforating heads were used for this issue: (a) comb 13.9; (b) comb 13.6; (c) line 13.8; (d) line 14.2. Values on which each perforation occur are shown above. Stamps with perforation (a) are on hand-made paper, while the other perforations are on softer machine-made paper with a horizontal mesh.

An unused example of the 9p. value (as No. 39, but perf (c)) has been seen with W **7** of Hyderabad. The status of this variety is uncertain.

2   **2**   **2**

Two pies   **Two pies**   **Two pies**
(11)   (12)   (13)

2   **2**

Two Pies   **Two Pies**
(14)   (15)

1922–29. T **8** (P 14), surch with T **11/15**.

46	**11**	2p. on 3p. blue	1·00	30
		a. Surch double	£450	£450
47	**12**	2p. on 3p. blue	5·50	1·10
		a. Surch double	£1300	
		b. "Pies" for "pies" (R. 4/8)	75·00	22·00
		ba. Surch double		
		c. Perf 12½ at foot		
48	**13**	2p. on 3p. blue (6.24)	13·00	35
		a. "Pies" for "pies" (R. 4/8)	£110	16·00
		b. Perf 14×12½	15·00	18·00
		ba. Ditto. "Pies" for "pies" (R. 4/8)	£475	£600
49	**14**	2p. on 3p. blue (1929)	20·00	15·00
		a. Surch double	£600	
		b. Surch with Type **15**	£140	£225
		ba. Ditto. Surch double	£4250	

There are four settings of these surcharges. The first (July 1922) consisted of 39 stamps with Type **11**, and nine with Type **12**, and in Type **11** the centre of the "2" is above the "o" of "Two". In the second setting (March 1923) there were 36 of Type **11** and 12 of Type **12**, and the centre of the figure is above the space between "Two" and "Pies". The third setting (June 1924) consists of stamps with Type **13** only.

The fourth setting (1929) was also in sheets of 48. No. 49b being the first stamp in the fourth row.

No. 47c is from the bottom row of a sheet and was re-perforated 12½ line at foot as the bottom line of 14 perforations were too far from the design.

Three Pies

ONE ANNA
ഒരു അണ

ANCHAL & REVENUE
(16)

ന

3

മൂന്ന പൈ
(17)

1928. Surch with T **16**.

50	**10**	1a. on 2¼a. yellow-green (a)	6·50	12·00
		a. "REVENUF" for "REVENUE"	90·00	£150
		b. Surch double		

1932–33. Surch as T **17**. W **8a**. P 13½.

51	**10**	3p. on 4p. green (b)	2·75	2·50
		a. "r" in "Three" inverted	†	£600
52		3p. on 8p. sepia (b)	3·00	3·25
53		9p. on 10p. blue (b)	2·75	3·25
51/3	Set of 3		7·75	8·00

Maharaja Rama Varma III, 1932–1941

18 Maharaja Rama Varma III	**18a**

(Recess Perkins Bacon & Co)

1933–38. T **18** (but frame and inscription of 1a. as T **9**). W **8a**. P 13×13½.

54	**18**	2p. brown (1936)	1·75	50
55		4p. green	60	10
56		6p. red-brown	70	10
57	**18a**	1a. brown-orange	2·75	30
		w. Wmk inverted	†	£350
58	**18**	1a.8p. carmine	3·00	8·00
59		2a. grey (1938)	11·00	2·25
60		2¼a. yellow-green	2·25	40
61		3a. vermilion (1938)	11·00	1·60
62		3a.4p. violet	1·75	2·00
63		6a.8p. sepia	1·75	20·00
64		10a. blue	3·00	20·00
54/64	Set of 11		35·00	50·00

For stamps in this design, but lithographed, see Nos. 67/71.

1934. Surcharged as T **14**. W **8a**. P 13½.

65	**10**	6p. on 8p. sepia (R.) (b)	1·00	60
66		6p. on 10p. blue (R.) (b)	1·75	2·00

"DOUBLE PRINTS". The errors previously listed under this description are now identified as blanket offsets, a type of variety outside the scope of this catalogue. Examples occur on issues from 1938 onwards.

SPACING OF OVERPRINTS AND SURCHARGES. The typeset overprints and surcharges issued from 1939 onwards show considerable differences in spacing. Except for specialists, however, these differences have little significance as they occur within the same settings and do not represent separate printings.

(Litho The Associated Printers, Madras)

1938. W **8a**. P 11.

67	**18**	2p. brown	1·00	40
		aw. Wmk inverted	£350	£160
		b. Perf 13×13½	12·00	70
68		4p. green	1·00	35
		aw. Wmk inverted	†	£300
		b. Perf 13×13½	11·00	18·00
69		6p. red-brown	2·25	10
		aw. Wmk inverted	†	£250
		b. Perf 13×13½	†	£6000
70	**18a**	1a. brown-orange	£100	£130
		aw. Wmk inverted		
		b. Perf 13×13½	£160	£225
71	**18**	2¼a. sage-green	6·00	25
		a. Perf 13×13½	22·00	7·00
67/71	Set of 5		£100	£130

Most examples of Nos. 70/b were used fiscally. Collectors are warned against examples which have been cleaned and regummed or provided with forged postmarks.

ANCHAL   ANCHAL   **THREE PIES**
(19)   (19a)   (20)

SURCHARGED   **ANCHAL**

ONE ANNA THREE PIES   **NINE PIES**
(21)   (22)

ANCHAL   **ANCHAL**

NINE PIES   **SURCHARGED NINE PIES**
(23)   (24)

1939 (Jan). Nos. 57 and 70 optd with T **19** or **19a**.

72	**18a**	1a. brown-orange (recess) (T **19**)	10·00	2·00
		w. Wmk inverted	†	£300
73		1a. brown-orange (litho) (T **19**)	£700	2·25
		aw. Wmk inverted	†	
		b. Perf 13×13½	—	£500
74		1a. brown-orange (litho) (T **19a**)	1·50	1·60
		a. Perf 13×13½	18·00	75

In 1939 it was decided that there would be separate 1a. stamps for revenue and postal purposes. The "ANCHAL" overprints were applied to stamps intended for postal purposes.

1942–44. T **18** and **18a** variously optd or surch.

I. Recess-printed stamp. No. 58

75		3p. on 1a.8p. carmine (T **20**)	£500	£200
76		3p. on 1a.8p. carmine (T **21**)	13·00	17·00
77		6p. on 1a.8p. carmine (T **20**)	6·00	27·00
78		1a.3p. on 1a.8p. carmine (T **21**)	1·00	60

II. Lithographed stamps. Nos. 68, 70 and 70b

79		3p. on 4p. (T **21**)	7·50	4·25
		a. Perf 13×13½	24·00	4·00
80		6p. on 1a. (T **22**)	£1100	£375
		a. "SIX PIES" double	†	£2250
81		6p. on 1a. (T **23**)	£550	£300
		a. Perf 13×13½	£275	£100
82		9p. on 1a. (T **22**)	£250	£170
83		9p. on 1a. (T **23**) (P 13×13½)	£650	42·00
84		9p. on 1a. (T **24**) (P 13×13½)	50·00	13·00

Maharaja Kerala Varma II, 1941–1943

26 Maharaja Kerala Varma II

27 (The actual measurement of this wmk is 6¼×3⁵⁄₈ in.)

(Litho The Associated Printers, Madras)

1943. Frame of 1a. inscr "ANCHAL & REVENUE". P 13×13½.

*(a) W **8a***

85	**26**	2p. grey-brown	9·00	10·00
		a. Perf 11	†	£3750
85b		4p. green	£2750	£850
85c		1a. brown-orange	£160	£200
85/c	Set of 3		£2750	£950

*(b) W **27***

86	**26**	2p. grey-brown	55·00	6·50
		a. Perf 11	†	£5500
87		4p. green	7·50	22·00
		a. Perf 11	4·75	6·00
88		6p. red-brown	9·00	10
		a. Perf 11	8·50	1·60
89		9p. ultramarine (P 11)	90·00	1·50
		a. Imperf between (horiz pair)	£4250	
90		1a. brown-orange	£225	£275
		a. Perf 11	26·00	75·00
91		2¼a. yellow-green	38·00	5·00
		a. Perf 11	38·00	9·00

Part of W **27** appears on many stamps in each sheet, while others are entirely without wmk. The watermark can appear upright, inverted or sideways.

Although inscribed "ANCHAL (= Postage) & REVENUE" most examples of Nos. 85c and 90/a were used fiscally. Collectors are warned against examples which have been cleaned and regummed or provided with forged postmarks.

Maharaja Ravi Varma, 1943–1946

1943. T **26** variously optd or surch. P 13×13½.

*(a) W **8a***

92		3p. on 4p. (T **21**)	£180	45·00
92a		9p. on 1a. (T **23**)	14·00	6·50
		aw. Wmk inverted	†	£425
92b		9p. on 1a. (T **24**)	14·00	4·50
92c		1a.3p. on 1a. (T **21**)	†	£8500

*(b) W **27***

93		2p. on 6p. (T **20**)	75	5·00
		a. Perf 11	2·25	2·75
94		3p. on 4p. (T **20**) (P 11)	13·00	10
95		3p. on 4p. (T **21**)	9·00	10
96		3p. on 6p. (T **20**)	3·50	20
		a. Perf 11	1·25	85
97		4p. on 6p. (T **20**)	8·50	17·00

No. 92c is believed to be an error; one or more sheets of No. 85c, having been included in a stock of No. O70 intended to become No. O80.

28 Maharaja Ravi Varma	**29** Maharaja Ravi Varma

I   II

(Litho The Associated Printers, Madras)

1944–48. W **27**. No gum.

(a) Type I. P 11

98	**28**	9p. ultramarine (1944)	30·00	8·50

(b) Type II. P 13

98a	**28**	9p. ultramarine (1946)	38·00	8·00
		ab. Perf 13×13½	65·00	8·00
99		1a.3p. magenta (1948)	12·00	10·00
		a. Perf 13×13½	£550	£130
100		1a.9p. ultramarine (shades) (1948)	11·00	7·00
98a/100	Set of 3		55·00	32·00

Nos. 98a/100 are line-perforated, Nos. 98ab and 99a comb-perforated.

Maharaja Kerala Varma III, 1946–48

(Litho The Associated Printers, Madras)

1946–48. Frame of 1a. inscr "ANCHAL & REVENUE". W **27**. No gum (except for stamps perf 11). P 13.

101	**29**	2p. chocolate	4·00	20
		a. Imperf horiz (vert pair)	£5000	£5000
		c. Perf 11	11·00	60
		d. Perf 11×13	£500	£180
102		3p. carmine	1·00	40
103		4p. grey-green	£4000	85·00
104		6p. red-brown (1947)	28·00	11·00
		a. Perf 11	£300	9·00
105		9p. ultramarine	3·75	10
		a. Imperf between (horiz pair)	†	£4750
106		1a. orange (1948)	10·00	45·00
		a. Perf 11	£800	
107		2a. black	£180	12·00
		a. Perf 11	£225	10·00
108		3a. vermilion	£120	4·00
101/8	Set of 8		£4000	£140

Although inscribed "ANCHAL (=Postage) & REVENUE" most examples of No. 106 were used fiscally.

The 1a.3p. magenta, 1a.9p. ultramarine and 2¼a. yellow-green in Type **29** subsequently appeared surcharged or overprinted for official use. Examples of the 1a.3p. magenta exist without overprint, but may not have been issued in this state (*Price £150 unused*).

30 Maharaja Kerala Varma III

Die I   Die II

Two dies of 2p.:

Die I. Back of headdress almost touches value tablet. Narrow strip of tunic visible below collar.

Die II. Back of headdress further away from tablet. Wider strip of tunic visible below collar.

| Die I. | Die II. |

Two dies of 3a.4p.

Die I. Frame around head broken by value tablets. Two white lines below value inscription.
Die II. Continuous frame around head. Single white line below value inscription. (R. 6/1-2 on sheet 8×6).

Tail to turban flaw (R. 1/7)

(Litho The Associated Printers, Madras)

1948–50. W **27** (upright or inverted). P 11.

109	30	2p. grey-brown (I)	1·75	15
		a. Imperf vert (horiz pair)	†	£4750
		b. Imperf horiz (vert pair)	†	£4750
		c. Die II	£100	4·50
110		3p. carmine	3·75	15
		a. Imperf between (vert pair)	—	£3250
111		4p. green	17·00	6·50
		a. Imperf vert (horiz pair)	£350	£475
112		6p. chestnut	26·00	25
		a. Imperf vert (horiz pair)	£950	
113		9p. ultramarine	2·50	1·25
114		2a. black	£100	3·25
115		3a. orange-red	£120	1·00
		a. Imperf vert (horiz pair)	£4500	
116		3a.4p. violet (1950)	70·00	£475
		a. Tail to turban flaw	£400	£1400
		b. Die II	£350	
109/16 Set of 8			£300	£475

Maharaja Rama Varma IV, 1948–1964

31 Chinese Nets   **32** Dutch Palace

(Litho The Associated Printers, Madras)

1949. W **27**. P 11.

117	31	2a. black	9·00	15·00
		a. Imperf vert (horiz pair)	£800	
118	32	2¼a. green	3·50	15·00
		a. Imperf vert (horiz pair)	£800	

A used example of a 2¼a. value in a slightly different design exists showing a larger portrait of the ruler, the conch shell at upper right pointing to the right and with shading below "DUTCH PALACE". This may have come from a proof sheet subsequently used for postal purposes.

SIX PIES

ആറു പൈ
(33)

Normal   Error (first character more open with longer tail)

Due to similarities between two Malayalam characters some values of the 1948 provisional issue exist with an error in the second word of the Malayalam surcharge. On Nos. 119, 122 and O103 this occurs twice in the setting of 48. No. 125 shows four examples and No. O104b one. Most instances are as illustrated above, but in two instances on the setting for No. 125 the error occurs on the second character.

1949. Surch as T **33**.

(i) On 1944–48 issue. P 13

119	28	6p. on 1a.3p. magenta	11·00	7·50
		a. Incorrect character	70·00	50·00
120		1a. on 1a.9p. ultramarine (R.)	2·75	1·75

(ii) On 1946–48 issue

121	29	3p. on 9p. ultramarine	12·00	26·00
122		6p. on 1a.3p. magenta	21·00	19·00
		a. Surch double	†	£900
		b. Incorrect character	£150	£130
123		1a. on 1a.9p. ultramarine (R.)	7·50	3·00
		a. Surch in black	†	£4750
		b. Black surch with smaller native characters 7½ mm instead of 10 mm long	†	£7000

(iii) On 1948–50 issue

124	30	3p. on 9p. ultramarine	5·50	3·25
		a. Larger native characters 20 mm instead of 16½ mm long	2·75	50
		ab. Imperf between (vert pair)	†	£3750
		b. Surch double	£800	£900
		c. Surch both sides	£650	
125		3p. on 9p. ultramarine (R.)	10·00	3·50
		a. Incorrect character	55·00	40·00
126		6p. on 9p. ultramarine (R.)	2·50	1·00
119/26 Set of 8			65·00	55·00

The 9p. ultramarine (T **29**) with 6p. surcharge (T **33**) in red was prepared for use but not issued (*Price* £150 *unused*).

1949. Surch as T **20**. W **27**. P 13.

127	29	4p. on 1a. orange	£110	£250
128		9p. on 1a. orange	£180	£275

OFFICIAL STAMPS

On   ON   ON

C   G C   G C   G

S   S   S

(O **1**)   (O **2** Small "ON")   (O **3** "G" without serif)

1913. Optd locally by typography with Type O **1** (3p.) or lithographically by Perkins Bacon with Type O **2** (others).

O1	8	3p. blue (R.)	£170	10
		a. Black opt	†	£1900
		b. Inverted "S"	—	60·00
		c. Opt double	†	£800
O2		4p. green (*wmk sideways*)	18·00	10
		a. Opt inverted	—	£350
O3		9p. carmine	£170	10
		a. Wmk sideways	24·00	10
		w. Wmk inverted	†	£300
O4		1½a. purple	75·00	10
		a. Opt double	—	£1100
O5		2a. grey	16·00	10
O6		3a. vermilion	80·00	45
O7		6a. violet	95·00	2·25
O8		12a. ultramarine	50·00	7·50
O9		1½r. deep green	35·00	80·00
O1/9 Set of 9			£500	85·00

8

1919–33. Optd by Perkins Bacon as Type O **3** (typo).

O10	10	4p. green (*a*) (*b*)	9·00	10
		a. Opt double	—	£750
		w. Wmk inverted	†	£275
O11		6p. red-brown (*a*) (*b*) (1922)	23·00	10
		a. Opt double	—	£750
		w. Wmk inverted	†	£550
O12		8p. sepia (*b*) (1923)	12·00	10
		w. Wmk inverted	†	£550
O13		9p. carmine (*a*) (*b*)	95·00	10
O14		10p. blue (*b*) (1923)	25·00	10
		a. Opt double	†	£1000
O15		1½a. purple (*a*) (*b*) (1921)	5·50	10
		a. Opt double	†	£1000
O16		2a. grey (*b*) (1923)	55·00	30
O17		2¼a. yellow-green (*a*) (*b*) (1922)	23·00	10
		a. Opt double	†	£700
O18		3a. vermilion (*a*) (*b*) (*c*)	18·00	25
		a. Opt inverted	†	£650
O19		6a. violet (*a*) (*b*) (1924)	50·00	50
O19*a*		12a. ultramarine (*a*) (*b*) (1929)	24·00	7·50
O19*b*		1½r. deep green (*a*) (*b*) (1933)	30·00	£170
O10/19*b* Set of 12			£325	£170

All values exist showing a straight-backed "C" variety on R. 3/1.

8

ON   ON

C   G C   G

Eight pies S   S

(O **4** 27½ *mm* high)   (O **5** Straight back to "C")   (O **6** Circular "O"; "N" without serifs)

1923 (Jan)–**24.** T **8** and **10** surch locally with Type O **4**.

O20		8p. on 9p. carmine (No. O3)	£450	2·00
		a. "Pies" for "pies" (R. 4/8)	£1800	60·00
		b. Wmk sideways	£130	20
		ba. "Pies" for "pies" (R. 4/8)	£550	18·00
		c. Surch double	†	£450
O21		8p. on 9p. carm (*a*) (*b*) (No. O13) (7.24)	70·00	10
		a. "Pies" for "pies" (R. 4/8)	£225	12·00
		b. Surch double	†	£325
		c. Opt Type O **3** double	†	£475

Varieties with smaller "i" or "t" in "Eight" and small "i" in "Pies" are also known from a number of positions in the setting.

1925 (Apr). T **10** surch locally as Type O **4**.

O22		10p. on 9p. carmine (*b*) (No. O13)	90·00	1·00
		b. Surch double	†	£450
		c. Surch 25 mm high (*a*)	£400	2·00
		ca. Surch double	†	£500

1929. T **8** surch locally as Type O **4**.

O23		10p. on 9p. carmine (No. O3a)	£2750	20·00
		a. Surch double	†	£850
		b. Wmk upright	—	90·00

1929–31. Optd by Perkins Bacon with Type O **5** (typo).

O24	10	4p. green (*b*) (1931)	28·00	3·25
		a. Inverted "S"	£375	28·00
O25		6p. red-brown (*b*) (*c*) (*d*) (1930)	22·00	10
		a. Inverted "S"	£200	4·75
O26		8p. sepia (*b*) (1930)	8·50	10
		a. Inverted "S"	90·00	5·00
O27		10p. blue (*b*)	6·50	10
		a. Inverted "S"	95·00	5·50
O28		2a. grey (*b*) (1930)	55·00	25
		a. Inverted "S"	£450	14·00
O29		3a. vermilion (*b*) (1930)	12·00	20
		a. Inverted "S"	£170	12·00
O30		6a. violet (*b*) (*d*) (1930)	£130	3·25
		a. Inverted "S"	£800	£110
O24/30 Set of 7			£225	6·50

1933. Nos. O26/7 surch locally as T **14**, in red.

O32	10	6p. on 8p. sepia (*b*)	3·75	10
		a. Inverted "S"	40·00	6·00
O33		6p. on 10p. blue (*b*)	4·00	10
		a. Inverted "S"	50·00	4·00

The inverted "S" varieties occur on R. 2/1 of one setting of this overprint only.

1933–38. Recess-printed stamps of 1933–38 optd.

*(a) With Type O **5***

O34	18	4p. green	10·00	10
O35		6p. red-brown (1934)	9·00	10
O36	18a	1a. brown-orange	32·00	10
O37	18	1a.8p. carmine	1·50	30
O38		2a. grey	42·00	10
O39		2¼a. yellow-green	14·00	10
O40		3a. vermilion	70·00	10
O41		3a.4p. violet	15·00	15
O42		6a.8p. sepia	1·50	20
O43		10a. blue	1·75	75
O34/43 Set of 10			£170	2·75

*(b) With Type O **6** (typo)*

O44	18a	1a. brown-orange (1937)	48·00	75
O45	18	2a. grey-black (1938)	35·00	3·00
O46		3a. vermilion (1938)	11·00	2·50
O44/6 Set of 3			85·00	5·50

ON   ON

C   G C   G

S   S

(O **7** Curved back to "c")   (O **8**)

ON   ON   ON

C   G C   G C   G

S   S   S

(O **9** Circular "O";   (O **10** Oval "O")   (O **11**)
"N" with serifs)

1938–44. Lithographed stamps of 1938. W **8a**, optd.

*(a) With Type O **7** or O **8** (1a.) P 11*

O47	18	4p. green	45·00	3·00
		a. Inverted "S"	55·00	2·75
		b. Perf 13×13½	26·00	3·25
O48		6p. red-brown	42·00	40
		a. Inverted "S"	50·00	50
O49	18a	1a. brown-orange	£475	2·50
O50	18	2a. grey-black	20·00	1·10
		a. Inverted "S"	23·00	1·25

*(b) With Type O **9** (litho) or O **10** (6p.)*

O51	18	6p. red-brown (P 13×13½)	20·00	7·00
O52	18a	1a. brown-orange	1·00	10
O53	18	3a. vermilion	4·25	3·25

*(c) With Type O **11***

O53*a*	18	6p. red-brown	£1500	£650

The inverted "S" varieties, Nos. O47a, O48a and O50a, occur 21 times in the setting of 48.

1942–43. Unissued stamps optd with Type O **10**. Litho. W **27**. P 11.

O54	18	4p. green	£140	16·00
		a. Perf 13×13½	2·50	80
O55		6p. red-brown	£300	12·00
		a. Perf 13×13½	20·00	1·00
		ab. Optd both sides	†	£250
O56	18a	1a. brown-orange	16·00	5·00
		a. Perf 13×13½	5·00	4·25
		ab. Optd both sides	†	£250
		ac. Stamp printed both sides	†	£900
O56*b*	18	2a. grey-black (1943)	£130	1·25
		ba. Opt omitted	†	£2500
O56*c*		2¼a. sage-green (1943)	£3750	12·00
O56*d*		3a. vermilion (1943)	30·00	11·00

1943. Official stamps variously surch with T **20** or **21**.

(i) On 1½a. purple of 1919–33

O57	10	9p. on 1½a. (*b*) (T **20**)	£1300	40·00

*(ii) On recess printed 1a.8p. carmine of 1933–44 (Type O **5** opt)*

O58		3p. on 1a.8p. (T **21**)	12·00	4·25
O59		9p. on 1a.8p. (T **20**)	£200	42·00
O60		1a.9p. on 1a.8p. (T **20**)	5·50	4·00
O61		1a.9p. on 1a.8p. (T **21**)	5·00	75

(iii) On lithographed stamps of 1938–44. P 11

*(a) W **8a***

O62	18	3p. on 4p. (Types O **7** and **20**) (P 13×13½)	70·00	19·00
		a. Surch double	£650	£275

COCHIN (continued)

O63		3p. on 4p. (Types O **7** and **21**) (P 13×13½)	£350	90·00
O64	**18a**	3p. on 1a. (Types O **9** and **20**)	7·00	5·00
O65		9p. on 1a. (Types O **9** and **20**)	£450	75·00
O66		1a.3p. on 1a. (Types O **9** and **21**)	£500	£140
		(b) W **27**		
O67	**18**	3p. on 4p. (Types O **10** and **20**) (P 13×13½)	£160	75·00
O67a		3p. on 4p. (Types O **10** and **21**) (P 13×13½)	£3500	
O67b	**18a**	3p. on 1a. (Types O **10** and **20**)	£250	£110
		ba. Perf 13×13½	£170	£100

1943-44. Optd with Type O **10**. W **27**. P 13×13½.

O68	**26**	4p. green	95·00	11·00
		a. Perf 11	£275	7·50
		b. Perf 13	£700	70·00
O69		6p. red-brown	6·50	10
		a. Opt double	—	£100
		b. Perf 11	2·75	10
		ba. Opt double	—	£100
		c. Perf 13	8·00	3·75
O70		1a. brown-orange	£12000	75·00
O71		2a. black	7·00	1·25
O72		2¼a. yellow-green	6·50	1·10
		a. Optd both sides	†	£225
O73		3a. vermilion	14·00	3·75
		a. Perf 11	17·00	40

Stamps perforated 13×13½ are from a comb machine; those perforated 13 from a line perforator.

1944. Optd with Type O **10** and variously surch as Types **20** and **21**. W **27**.

O74	**26**	3p. on 4p. (T **20**)	6·50	10
		a. Perf 11	15·00	60
		ab. Optd Type O **10** on both sides	†	£200
O75		3p. on 4p. (T **21**)	9·00	75
		a. Perf 11	£500	£200
O76		3p. on 1a. (T **20**)	45·00	13·00
O77		9p. on 6p. (T **20**)	18·00	6·00
		a. Stamp printed both sides	†	£800
O78		9p. on 6p. (T **21**)	8·50	1·25
O79		1a.3p. on 1a. (T **20**)	24·00	5·00
O80		1a.3p. on 1a. (T **21**)	5·00	10
O74/80	*Set of 7*		£100	24·00

1946-47. Stamps of 1944-48 (Head Type II) optd with Type O **10**. P 13.

O81	**28**	9p. ultramarine	4·25	10
		a. Stamp printed both sides	†	£900
		b. Perf 13×13½	6·00	10
O82		1a.3p. magenta (1947)	1·60	20
		a. Opt double	25·00	12·00
		b. Optd on both sides	£225	
		ba. Optd both sides, opt double and inverted on reverse	£120	£120
O83		1a.9p. ultramarine (1947)	40	1·25
		a. Opt double	†	£225
		b. Pair, one without opt	†	£3250
O81/3	*Set of 3*		5·50	1·40

1946-48. Stamps of 1946-48 and unissued values optd with Type O **2**. P 13.

O84	**29**	3p. carmine	2·75	10
		a. Stamp printed both sides	†	£900
O85		4p. grey-green	38·00	8·00
O86		6p. red-brown	28·00	4·50
		a. Stamp printed both sides	†	£900
O87		9p. ultramarine	1·25	10
		a. Stamp printed both sides (one inverted)	†	£900
O88		1a.3p. magenta	7·50	2·00
O89		1a.9p. ultramarine	9·00	40
O90		2a. black	16·00	3·00
O91		2¼a. yellow-green	35·00	11·00
O84/91	*Set of 8*		£120	26·00

1948-49. Stamps of 1948-50 and unissued values optd with Type O **7**.

O92	**30**	3p. carmine	1·25	15
		a. "C" for "G" in opt	25·00	3·25
O93		4p. green	3·25	40
		a. Imperf between (horiz pair)	†	£2250
		b. Imperf between (vert pair)	†	£2500
		c. Optd on both sides	£150	£150
		d. "C" for "G" in opt	32·00	7·00
O94		6p. chestnut	4·50	30
		a. Imperf between (vert pair)	†	£3750
		b. "C" for "G" in opt	45·00	4·00
O95		9p. ultramarine	5·00	10
		a. "C" for "G" in opt	50·00	3·75
O96		2a. black	3·75	25
		a. "C" for "G" in opt	45·00	4·25
O97		2¼a. yellow-green	5·50	9·00
		a. "C" for "G" in opt	50·00	90·00
O98		3a. orange-red	1·10	1·50
		a. "C" for "G" in opt	30·00	14·00
O99		3a.4p. violet (I)	80·00	70·00
		a. "C" for "G" in opt	£475	£500
		b. Tail to turban flaw	£475	£500
		c. Die II	£300	£300
O92/9	*Set of 8*		95·00	75·00

The "C" for "G" variety occurs on R. 1/4. Nos. O92/9, O103/4 and O104b also exist with a flat back to "G" which occurs twice in each sheet on R. 1/5 and R. 2/8.

No. O93 exists with watermark sideways, but can usually only be identified when in multiples.

1949. Official stamps surch as T **33**.

		(i) On 1946 issue		
O100	**28**	1a. on 1a.9p. ultramarine (R.)	60	70
		(ii) On 1948 issue		
O101	**29**	1a. on 1a.9p. ultramarine (R.)	40·00	17·00
		(iii) On 1949 issue		
O103	**30**	6p. on 3p. carmine	1·25	75
		a. Imperf between (vert pair)	†	£2500
		b. Surch double	†	£450
		c. "C" for "G" in opt	25·00	13·00
		d. Incorrect character	21·00	11·00
O104		9p. on 4p. green (18 *mm long*)	75	3·25
		a. Imperf between (horiz pair)	£1000	£1100

		b. Larger native characters, 22 mm long	1·10	1·40
		ba. Ditto. Imperf between (horiz pair)	£950	£950
		bb. Incorrect character	28·00	30·00
		c. "C" for "G" in opt	28·00	32·00
		ca. Ditto. Larger native characters, 22 mm long	30·00	32·00
O100/4	*Set of 4*		38·00	18·00

No. O104 exists with watermark sideways, but can usually only be identified when in multiples.

1949. No. 124a, but with lines of surch 17½ mm apart, optd "SERVICE".

O105	**30**	3p. on 9p. ultramarine	60	80
		a. Imperf between (horiz pair)	†	£3750

From 1 July 1949 Cochin formed part of the new state of Travancore-Cochin. Existing stocks of Cochin issues continued to be used in conjunction with stamps of Travancore surcharged in Indian currency.

DHAR

PRICES FOR STAMPS ON COVER

Nos. 1/4	from × 50
No. 5	from × 30
No. 6	—
Nos. 7/9	from × 50
No. 10	—

Raja (Maharaja from 1877) Anand Rao Puar III, 1857–1898

1 (¼a.)   **2**

अर्धो बलड. अधॉ लबड. आर्धॊ डवल.
No. 1c   No. 1d   No. 2

1897–1900. Type-set. Colour-fugitive paper. With oval hand-stamp in black. No gum. Imperf.

1	**1**	½p. black/*red* (three characters at bottom left)	4·25	4·50
		a. Handstamp omitted	£700	
		b. Line below upper inscription (R. 2/2)	95·00	95·00
		c. Character transposed (R. 2/3)	42·00	48·00
		d. Character transposed (R. 2/5)	£110	
2		½p. black/*red* (four characters at bottom left)	4·25	6·50
		a. Handstamp omitted	£450	
3		¼a. black/*orange*	4·50	8·00
		a. Handstamp omitted	£500	
4		½a. black/*magenta*	5·50	8·50
		a. Handstamp omitted	£700	£500
		b. Line below upper inscription (R. 2/2)	£150	£180
5		1a. black/*green*	10·00	23·00
		a. Handstamp omitted	£1000	
		b. Printed both sides	£1500	
		c. Line below upper inscription (R. 2/2)	£475	£700
6		2a. black/*yellow*	48·00	90·00
		e. Top right corner ornament transposed with one from top of frame (R. 2/5)	£190	£300
1/6	*Set of 6*		70·00	£130

Nos. 1/6 were each issued in sheets of ten (5×2), but may, on the evidence of a single sheet of the ½ pice value, have been printed in sheets of 20 containing *two* of the issued sheets *tête-bêche*.

Research has identified individual characteristics for stamps printed from each position in the sheet.

The same research suggests that the type remained assembled during the entire period of production, being amended as necessary to provide the different values. Seven main settings have been identified with changes sometimes occurring during their use which form sub-settings.

The distribution of stamps between the main settings was as follows:

Setting I — ½p.
Setting II — ½a., 1a.
Setting III — 1a.
Setting IV — ½p., ½a., 1a.
Setting V — ½p.
Setting VI — ½p. (No. 2). ¼a.
Setting VII — 2a.

The listed constant errors all occurred during Setting IV.

In No. 1c the three characters forming the second word in the lower inscription are transposed to the order (2) (3) (1) and in No. 1d to the order (3) (2) (1).

On Nos. 1b, 4b and 5c the line which normally appears above the upper inscription is transposed so that it appears below the upper inscription.

All values show many other constant varieties including mistakes in the corner and border ornaments, and also both constant and non-constant missing lines, dots and characters.

Examples of complete forgeries and faked varieties on genuine stamps exist.

Raja (Maharaja from 1918) Udaji Rao Puar II, 1898–1926

(Typo at Bombay)

1898–1900. P 11 to 12.

7	**2**	½a. carmine	9·00	9·50
		a. Imperf (pair)	60·00	
		b. Deep rose	7·00	7·00
8		1a. claret	8·00	9·00
9		1a. reddish violet	7·50	21·00
		a. Imperf between (horiz pair)	£950	
		b. Imperf (pair)	£200	
10		2a. deep green	14·00	38·00
7/10	*Set of 4*		32·00	70·00

The stamps of Dhar have been obsolete since 31 March 1901

DUNGARPUR

PRICES FOR STAMPS ON COVER

Nos. 1/15	from × 2

Maharawal Lakshman Singh, 1918–1971

1 State Arms

(Litho Shri Lakshman Bijaya Printing Press, Dungarpur)

1933–43. P 11.

1	**1**	¼a. bistre-yellow	—	£375
2		¼a. rose (1935)	£8000	£1400
		a. Salmon	—	£1300
3		¼a. red-brown (1937)	—	£750
4		1a. pale turquoise-blue	—	£300
5		1a. rose (1938)	—	£5000
6		1a.3p. deep reddish violet (1935)	—	£500
7		2a. deep dull green (1943)	£4500	£500
8		4a. rose (1934)	—	£1500

Nos. 2 and 5 are known in a *se-tenant* strip of three, the centre stamp being the 1a. value.

2   **3**   **4**

Maharawal Lakshman Singh

Three dies of ½a. (*shown actual size*):

Die I. Size 21×25½ mm. Large portrait (head 5 *mm* and turban 7½ *mm* wide), correctly aligned (sheets of 12 and left-hand stamps in subsequent blocks of four *se-tenant* horizontally with Die II)

Die II. Size 20×24½ mm. Large portrait (head 4¾ *mm* and turban 7 *mm* wide), but with less detail at foot and with distinct tilt to left (right-hand stamps in sheets of four horizontally *se-tenant* with Die I)

Die III. Size 21×25½ mm. Small portrait (head 4½ *mm* and turban 6½ *mm* wide) (sheets of four)

(Typo L. V. Indap & Co, Bombay)

1939–46. T **2** (various frames) and 3/4. Various perfs.

9	**2**	¼a. orange-yellow (P 12)	—	£180
		a. No fraction bar at right	†	£750
		b. Perf 11. Yellow-orange (1940)	—	£200
		c. Perf 10½. Yellow-orange or orange (1941)	—	£160
		d. Perf 10. Yellow-orange or orange (1945)	£2000	£170
10		½a. vermilion (Die I) (P 12)	—	£180
		a. Perf 11. Carmine-vermilion (1943)	—	£180
		b. Perf 10½ (1944)	£750	£200
		c. Die II (P 10½)	£750	£200
		ca. Horiz pair Die I and Die II	£1700	£500
		d. Die III (P 10) (1945)	£1000	£120
		da. Imperf between (vert pair)	†	£6000
11		1a. deep blue (P 12)	—	£180
		a. Perf 11 (1941)	—	£180
		b. Perf 10½ (1940)	£900	£130
		c. Perf 10 (1946)	£700	£130

12	**3**	1a.3p. bright mauve (P 10½) (1944)	—	£500
		a. Perf 10 (1945)	£2500	£550
13	**4**	1½a. deep violet (P 10) (1946)	£2750	£450
14	**2**	2a. bright green (P 12) (1943)	£4000	£1100
15		4a. brown (P 12) (1940)	—	£500
		a. Perf 10½ (1943)	—	£500
		b. Perf 10 (1945)	£2750	£500

Stamps perforated 12 and 11 were printed in sheets of 12 (4×3) which were imperforate along the top, bottom and, sometimes, at right so that examples exist with one or two adjacent sides imperforate. The ¼a., 1a., 1a.3p. and 4a. perf 10½ were printed in similar sheets of 12, but the ½a. perf 10½ (Nos. 10b, c, ca) was always in sheets of four, imperforate at top, bottom and right, comprising dies I (left vertical pair) and II (right vertical pair) se-tenant. Stamps perforated 10 were printed in sheets of four either imperforate at top, bottom and right-hand side or fully perforated.

Dungarpur became part of Rajasthan by 15 April 1948.

DUTTIA (DATIA)

PRICES FOR STAMPS ON COVER

Nos. 1/7	—
Nos. 8/11	*from × 5*
Nos. 12/15	—
Nos. 16/40	*from × 20*

All the stamps of Duttia were impressed with a circular handstamp (usually in *blue*) before issue.

This handstamp shows the figure of Ganesh in the centre, surrounded by an inscription in Devanagari reading "DATIYA STET POSTAJ 1893". Stamps were not intended to be used for postage without this control mark.

PROCESS. Nos. 1/15 were type-set and printed singly. Nos. 16/40 were typo from plates comprising eight or more clichés.

GUM. The stamps of Duttia (*except* No. 25c) were issued without gum.

Maharaja Bhawani Singh, 1857–1907

Rectangular labels each showing a double hand-drawn frame (in black for the 1a. and in red for the others), face value in black and the Ganesh handstamp as known on thin cream (½a.), rose (1a.), orange (2a.) or pale yellow (4a.) paper. These are considered by some specialists to be the first stamps of Duttia, possibly issued during 1893, but the evidence for this is inconclusive (*Price for set of 4, £25,000, unused*).

1 (2a.)   **2 (1a.) Ganesh**   **3 (¼a.)**

1894? Rosettes in lower corners. Control handstamp in blue. Imperf.

1	**1**	½a. black/*green*	£26000	
2		2a. grey-blue/*yellow*	£7000	
		a. Handstamp in black	£8500	
		b. Handstamp in red	†	£40000

Only three examples of No. 1 have been reported. In each instance the Devanagari inscription was originally 8a., but was amended in manuscript to ½a.

1896. Control handstamp in blue. Imperf.

3	**2**	1a. red	£5500	£12000
		a. Handstamp in black	£7500	£12000
		b. Handstamp in brown	£12000	
3c		2a. deep blue (handstamp in black)	£30000	
		d. Handstamp in brown	£25000	

1896. Control handstamp in blue. Imperf.

4	**3**	¼a. black/*orange*	£7500	
		a. Without handstamp	£4750	
5		½a. black/*blue-green*	£22000	
		a. Without handstamp	£5000	£11000
6		2a. black/*yellow*	£4250	
		a. Without handstamp	£17000	
7		4a. black/*rose*	£1800	
		a. Without handstamp	£24000	

Two types of centre:

I   II

Type I. Small Ganesh. Height 13 mm. Width of statue 11 mm. Width of pedestal 8 mm.

Type II. Large Ganesh. Height 13½ mm. Width of statue 11½ mm. Width of pedestal 11½ mm. "Flag" in god's right hand; "angle" above left. All stamps also show dot at top right corner.

1897–98. Imperf.

8	**2**	½a. black/*green* (I) (value in one group)	£120	£650
		a. *Tête-bêche* (horiz pair)	£2000	
		b. Value in two groups	22·00	£425
		ba. *Tête-bêche* (vert pair)	£1900	
		bb. Doubly printed	£6000	
		bc. Type II (1898)	45·00	

9		1a. black/*white* (I)	£170	£500
		a. *Tête-bêche* (horiz pair)	£2000	
		b. Laid paper	32·00	
		ba. *Tête-bêche* (vert pair)	£1400	
		c. Type II (1898)	£200	
		ca. Laid paper	45·00	
		cb. Doubly printed	£6000	
10		2a. black/*yellow* (I)	50·00	£450
		a. On lemon	75·00	£475
		b. Type II (1898)	80·00	£500
11		4a. black/*rose* (I)	40·00	£250
		a. *Tête-bêche* (horiz pair)	£375	
		b. *Tête-bêche* (vert pair)	£200	£750
		d. Type II (1898)	65·00	
		da. Doubly printed	£6000	

A used example of the 4a. is known showing black roulettes at foot.

4 (2a.)   **5 (2a.)**

1897. Name spelt "DATIA". Imperf.

12	**4**	½a. black/*green*	£180	£850
13		1a. black/*white*	£325	
14		2a. black/*yellow*	£200	£850
		a. *Tête-bêche* (vert pair)	£8000	
15		4a. black/*rose*	£200	£850
		a. *Tête-bêche* (vert pair)	£8000	
12/15		Set of 4	£800	

1899–1906.

(a) Rouletted in colour or in black, horizontally and at end of rows

16	**5**	¼a. vermilion	4·50	
		a. Rose-red	3·25	
		b. Pale rose	3·75	
		c. Lake	3·75	30·00
		d. Carmine	4·50	32·00
		e. Brownish red	11·00	
		ea. *Tête-bêche* (pair)	£4500	
17		½a. black/*blue-green*	3·00	30·00
		a. On deep green	6·50	
		b. On yellow-green (pelure)	5·50	32·00
		c. On dull green (1906)	4·25	
18		1a. black/*white*	4·25	30·00
19		2a. black/*lemon-yellow*	15·00	
		a. On orange-yellow	25·00	
		b. On buff-yellow	7·00	35·00
		ba. Handstamp in black	32·00	
		bb. Without handstamp	£800	
		c. On pale yellow (1906)	5·50	35·00
20		4a. black/*deep rose*	6·00	32·00
		a. *Tête-bêche* (pair)	—	
		b. Handstamp in black	42·00	
		c. Without handstamp	£650	

(b) Rouletted in colour between horizontal rows, but imperf at top and bottom and at ends of rows

20d	**5**	¼a. brownish red	65·00	£160
21		1a. black/*white*	20·00	85·00
		a. Without handstamp	£1000	
		b. Handstamp in black	£175	

One setting of 16 (8×2) of the ¼a. value (No. 16e) showed an inverted cliché at R. 1/2.

1904–05. Without rouletting.

22	**5**	¼a. red	7·00	50·00
		a. Without handstamp	£700	
23		½a. black/*green*	27·00	
24		1a. black (1905)	21·00	65·00

Maharaja Govind Singh, 1907–1955

1911. P 13½. Stamps very wide apart.

25	**5**	¼a. carmine	7·00	90·00
		a. Imperf horiz (vert pair)	£500	
		b. Imperf between (horiz pair)	£650	
		c. Stamps closer together (with gum)	13·00	75·00
		d. As c. Imperf vert (horiz pair)	£225	
		e. As c. imperf between (horiz strip of 5)	£750	
25f		1a. black	£1800	£1900

No. 25f was mainly used for fiscal purposes (*Price on piece, £140*).

1912? Printed close together.

(a) Coloured roulette×imperf

26	**5**	½a. black/*green*	10·00	45·00

(b) Printed wide apart. P 13½×coloured roulette (¼a.) or 13½×imperf (½a.)

27	**5**	¼a. carmine	5·50	65·00
		a. Without handstamp	£550	
28		½a. black/*dull green*	13·00	75·00

1916. Colours changed. Control handstamp in blue (Nos. 29/33) or black (No. 34). Imperf.

29	**5**	¼a. deep blue	5·50	40·00
30		½a. green	8·00	42·00
		a. Without handstamp	†	£1800
31		1a. purple	14·00	48·00
		a. *Tête-bêche* (vert pair)	27·00	
		ab. Without handstamp	£2250	
32		2a. brown	15·00	90·00
33		2a. lilac	9·50	29·00
		a. Handstamp in black	55·00	
		b. Without handstamp	£550	
34		4a. Venetian red (date?)	95·00	
		a. Without handstamp	£1000	

1918. Colours changed.

(a) Imperf

35	**5**	½a. blue	5·00	25·00
36		1a. pink	5·00	23·00
		a. Handstamp in black	22·00	
		b. Without handstamp	£500	

(b) P 11½

37	**5**	¼a. black	7·00	40·00

1920. Rouletted.

38	**5**	¼a. blue	2·75	19·00
		a. Roul×perf 7	50·00	50·00
		b. Imperf between (vert pair)	£850	
		c. Without handstamp	£275	
		d. Handstamp in black	18·00	
39		½a. pink	4·50	19·00
		a. Roul×perf 7	£325	
		b. Without handstamp	£425	
		c. Handstamp in black	55·00	

1920. Rough perf about 7.

40	**5**	½a. dull red	24·00	65·00
		a. Handstamp in black	80·00	£170
		b. Without handstamp	£550	

The stamps of Duttia have been obsolete since 1 April 1921.

FARIDKOT

PRICES FOR STAMPS ON COVER

Nos. N1/4	*from × 10*
Nos. N5/6	*from × 50*
Nos. N7/8	—

GUM. The stamps of Faridkot (Nos. N1/8) were issued without gum.

Raja Bikram Singh, 1874–1898

N **1** (1 folus = ¼a.)   N **2** (1 paisa = ¼a.)   N **3**

1879–86. Rough, handstamped impression. Imperf.

(a) Native thick laid paper

N1	N **1**	1f. ultramarine	70·00	75·00
N2	N **2**	1p. ultramarine	£275	£275

(b) Ordinary laid paper

N3	N **1**	1f. ultramarine	19·00	22·00
N4	N **2**	1p. ultramarine	£140	£170

(c) Wove paper, thick to thinnish

N5	N **1**	1f. ultramarine	3·25	4·75
		a. *Tête-bêche* (pair)	£275	
		b. Pair, one stamp sideways	£2500	
N6	N **2**	1p. ultramarine	6·50	17·00
		a. Pair, one stamp sideways	£3000	

(d) Thin wove whitey brown paper

N7	N **2**		40·00	42·00

Faridkot signed a postal convention with the Imperial Government which led to the provision of India issues overprinted "FARIDKOT STATE" from 1 January 1887. These are listed in the Convention States section.

Although the previous issues were no longer valid for postal purposes the state authorities continued to sell them to collectors for many years after 1887. Initially remaining stocks of Nos. N1/7 were on offer, but these were soon supplemented by Type N **1** handstamped in other colours, examples of a ½a., handstamped in various colours, which had originally been prepared in 1877 and by a replacement 1p, as Type N **3**, (*Price £2.00 unused, tête-bêche pair, £225, unused*) which had not done postal duty before the convention came into force. The sale of such items was clearly an important source of revenue as the 1f. as Type N **1**, yet another version of the 1p. and the ½a. subsequently appeared printed in sheets by lithography for sale to stamp collectors.

HYDERABAD

PRICES FOR STAMPS ON COVER

Nos. 1/3	*from × 20*
Nos. 4/12	—
Nos. 13/60	*from × 5*
Nos. O1/53	*from × 10*

The official title of the State in English was The Dominions of the Nizam and in Urdu "Sarkar-i-Asafia" (State of the successors of Asaf). This Urdu inscription appears in many of the designs.

Nawab Mir Mahbub Ali Khan Asaf Jah VI, 1869–1911

1   **2**

(Eng Mr. Rapkin. Plates by Nissen & Parker, London. Recess Mint, Hyderabad)

1869 (8 Sept). P 11½.

1	**1**	1a. olive-green	25·00	9·00
		a. Imperf between (horiz pair)	£325	
		b. Imperf horiz (vert pair)	£1000	£190
		c. Imperf (pair)	£700	£700
		d. Imperf vert (horiz pair)	†	£700

Reprints in the colour of the issue, and also in fancy colours, were made in 1880 on white wove paper, perforated 12½. Fakes of No. 1c are known created by the removal of the outer perforations from examples of Nos. 1a/b.

1870 (16 May). Locally engraved; 240 varieties of each value; wove paper. Recess. P 11½.

2	**2**	½a. brown	4·00	4·25
3		2a. sage-green	85·00	60·00

Stamps exist showing traces of lines in the paper, but they do not appear to be printed on true laid paper.

Reprints of both values were made in 1880 on white wove paper, perforated 12½: the ½a. in grey-brown, yellow-brown, sea-green, dull blue and carmine and the 2a. in bright green and in blue-green.

3

A Normal   **2a.**   B Variety

In A the coloured lines surrounding each of the four labels join a coloured circle round their inner edge, in B this circle is missing.

C Normal   **2a.**   D Character ∧ omitted

½a. Left side of central inscription omitted (Pl 4 R. 2/11)

½a., 1a., 2a. Dot at top of central inscription omitted

1a. Second dot in bottom label omitted

2a. Centre dot in bottom label omitted

8a. Character at left of bottom label omitted

(Plates by Bradbury Wilkinson & Co. Recess Mint, Hyderabad)
1871–1909.

(a) No wmk
(i) Rough perf 11½

4	3	½a. red-brown	21·00	24·00
		a. Dot at top of central inscription omitted	£225	
5		1a. purple-brown	£170	£180
		a. Imperf horiz (vert pair)	†	£3250
		b. Dot at top of central inscription omitted	£1300	£1300
6		2a. green (A)	£2750	
7		3a. ochre-brown	70·00	£100
8		4a. slate	£225	£225
9		8a. deep brown		
10		12a. dull blue	£475	

(ii) Pin perf 8-9

11	3	½a. red-brown	£1500	£650
12		1a. drab	£450	£200

(iii) P 12½

13	3	½a. orange-brown	4·00	10
		a. Imperf vert (horiz pair)	†	£130
		ab. Imperf horiz (vert pair)	†	£1300
		b. *Orange*	4·00	10
		c. *Red-brown*	4·00	10
		d. *Brick-red*	4·00	10
		da. Imperf vert (horiz pair)	†	£130
		db. Doubly printed	£500	£180
		e. *Rose-red*	3·25	20
		ea. Doubly printed	†	£275
		f. Error. Magenta	65·00	8·00
		g. Left side of central inscription omitted	£500	£110
		h. Dot at top of central inscription omitted	£100	4·00
14		1a. purple-brown	16·00	9·50
		a. Doubly printed	£500	
		b. *Drab*	2·50	15
		ba. Imperf (pair)		£550
		bb. Doubly printed	£250	
		c. *Grey-black*	3·50	10
		ca. Imperf (pair)	†	£1400
		cb. Imperf between (vert pair)	†	£1500
		d. *Black* (1909)	3·50	10
		da. Doubly printed	£650	£300
		db. Imperf vert (horiz pair)	†	£1500
		dc. Imperf horiz (vert pair)	†	£1500
		e. Dot at top of central inscription omitted	—	£225
		f. Second dot in bottom label omitted	£200	55·00
15		2a. green (A)	4·50	15
		a. *Deep green* (A)	6·00	40
		b. *Blue-green* (A)	6·50	40
		ba. *Blue-green* (B)	£425	70·00
		c. *Pale green* (A)	4·50	15
		ca. *Pale green* (B)	£425	80·00
		d. *Sage-green* (A) (1909)	6·00	35
		da. *Sage-green* (B) (1909)	£300	55·00
		e. Dot at top of central inscription omitted	£600	£150
		f. Centre dot in bottom panel omitted	£300	60·00
		g. *Perf 11½, 12 (Blue-green)*	—	£800
16		3a. ochre-brown (C)	4·50	1·50
		a. Character omitted (D)	£375	85·00
		b. *Chestnut* (C)	3·75	1·50
		ba. Character omitted (D)	£325	70·00
17		4a. slate	13·00	3·50
		a. Imperf horiz (vert pair)	£1400	£1400
		b. *Greenish grey*	5·50	3·25
		ba. Imperf vert (horiz pair)	£2500	
		c. *Olive-green*	6·00	2·50
18		8a. deep brown	3·75	4·25
		a. Imperf vert (horiz pair)	£1200	
		b. Character omitted	£500	
19		12a. pale ultramarine	5·50	12·00
		a. *Grey-green*	8·00	9·00
13/19a		*Set of 7*	26·00	16·00

(b) W 7. P 12½

19b	3	1a. black (1909)	£200	26·00
19c		2a. sage-green (A) (1909)	£650	£160
19d		12a. bluish grey (1909)	£1600	

پاو آنه

(4)   **5**

1898. Surch with T **4**. P 12½.

20	3	¼a. on ½a. orange-brown	50	85
		a. Surch inverted	50·00	28·00
		b. Pair, one without surcharge	£850	
		c. Left side of central inscription omitted	£275	

(Des Khusrat Ullah. Recess Mint, Hyderabad)
1900 (20 Sept). P 12½.

21	5	¼a. deep blue	7·00	4·50
		a. *Pale blue*	5·50	4·00

6   **7**

(Plates by Allan G. Wyon, London. Recess Mint, Hyderabad)
1905 (7 Aug). W **7**. P 12½.

22	6	¼a. dull blue	6·00	60
		a. Imperf (pair)	40·00	£200
		b. *Dull ultramarine*	5·00	80
		ba. Perf 11×12½	65·00	40·00
		c. *Pale blue-green*	28·00	3·00
23		½a. orange	9·00	35
		a. Perf 11	—	£250
		b. *Vermilion*	5·50	25
		ba. Imperf (pair)	38·00	£200
		c. *Yellow*	£130	17·00

1908–11. W **7**. P 12½.

24	6	¼a. grey	2·50	10
		a. Imperf between (horiz pair)	£750	£600
		b. Imperf between (vert pair)	†	£600
		c. Perf 11½, 12.	2·75	35
		d. Perf 11	£130	30·00
25		½a. green	11·00	10
		a. Imperf between (vert pair)	£650	
		b. Perf 11½, 12.	13·00	10
		c. Perf 13½	£250	60·00
		d. *Pale green*	12·00	20
		da. Perf 11½, 12.	14·00	30
		e. *Blue-green*	14·00	1·00
26		1a. carmine	9·00	10
		a. Perf 11½, 12.	16·00	1·00
		b. Perf 11	70·00	14·00
		c. Double impression (P 12½×11)		
27		2a. lilac	7·00	40
		a. Perf 11½, 12.	9·00	1·10
		b. Perf 11	3·00	55
		c. Perf 13½	3·75	15
		ca. Imperf between (horiz pair)	†	£950
		cb. *Rose-lilac*	3·00	10
28		3a. brown-orange (1909)	8·50	1·00
		a. Perf 11½, 12.	12·00	2·50
		b. Perf 11	5·00	1·50
		c. Perf 13½	5·50	30
29		4a. olive-green (1909)	8·50	2·50
		a. Perf 11½, 12.	13·00	7·00
		b. Perf 11	70·00	19·00
		ba. Imperf between (pair)	£1500	£1500
		c. Perf 13½	2·75	40
30		8a. purple (1911)	12·00	11·00
		a. Perf 11½, 12.		
		b. Perf 11	3·25	7·00
		c. Perf 13½	2·50	2·25
31		12a. blue-green (1911)	£250	£150
		a. Perf 11½, 12.	35·00	55·00
		b. Perf 11		
		c. Perf 13½	13·00	7·00
24/31c		*Set of 8*	45·00	9·25

The above perforations also exist compound.

Nawab Mir Osman Ali Khan Asaf Jah VII, 1911–1967

1912. New plates engraved by Bradbury Wilkinson & Co. W **7**. P 12½.

32	6	¼a. grey-black	4·00	10
		a. Imperf horiz (vert pair)	†	£550
		b. Perf 11½, 12.	3·00	35
		c. Perf 11	2·75	15
		ca. Imperf between (horiz pair)	†	£600
		cb. Imperf between (vert pair)	†	£600
		d. Perf 13½	2·50	10
33		¼a. brown-purple (*shades*) (P 13½).	3·75	10
		a. Imperf horiz (vert pair)	†	£600
34		½a. deep green	4·50	10
		a. Imperf between (pair)	†	£650
		b. Imperf (pair). Laid paper	£225	£160
		c. Perf 11½, 12.	16·00	55
		d. Perf 11	11·00	10
		e. Perf 13½		

The above perforations also exist compound.

In Wyon's ¼a. stamp the fraction of value is closer to the end of the label than in the B.W. issue. In the Wyon ¼a. and ½a. the value in English and the label below are further apart than in the B.W.

Wyon's ¼a. measures 19½×20 mm and the ½a. 19½×20½ mm; both stamps from the Bradbury plates measure 19¾×21½ mm.

8 Symbols   **9**

1915. Inscr "Post & Receipt". W **7**. P 13½.

35	8	½a. green	2·75	10
		a. Imperf between (pair)	£150	£160
		b. *Emerald-green*	4·25	20
		c. Perf 12½	12·00	35
		ca. Imperf between (pair)		
		d. Perf 11	75	10
		da. Imperf between (pair)	†	£500
		db. Imperf vert (pair)	†	£500
		e. Imperf (pair)	£350	£200
36		1a. carmine	4·50	10
		a. Imperf between (pair)	£600	
		b. *Scarlet*	5·00	10
		ba. Imperf between (horiz pair)	†	£500
		bb. Imperf between (vert pair)	†	£500
		bc. Imperf (pair)	†	£500
		c. Perf 12½	25·00	85
		ca. Imperf between (pair)		
		cc. *Scarlet*		
		d. Perf 11	1·25	20
		da. *Scarlet*	—	42·00
		e. Imperf (pair)	£400	£400

The above perforations also exist compound.
For ½a. claret, see No. 58.

1927 (1 Feb). As W **7**, but larger and sideways. P 13½.

37	9	1r. yellow	13·00	12·00

10 (4 pies) **11** (8 pies)

1930 (6 May). Surch as T **10** and **11**. W **7**. P 13½.

38	**6**	4p. on ¼a. grey-black (R.)	£130	32·00
		a. Perf 11	†	£200
		b. Perf 12½	†	85·00
		c. Perf 11½, 12	†	£450
39		4p. on ¼a. brown-purple (R.)	2·50	10
		a. Imperf between (pair)	£800	£800
		b. Surch double	†	£300
		c. Perf 11	†	£550
		d. Black surch	£650	£500
40	**8**	8p. on ½a. green (R.)	1·75	10
		a. Imperf between (horiz pair)	†	£400
		b. Perf 11	£325	£140
		c. Perf 12½	†	£275

12 Symbols

13 The Char Minar

14 High Court of Justice

15 Osman Sagar Reservoir

16 Entrance to Ajanta Caves

17 Bidar College

18 Victory Tower, Daulatabad

(Plates by De La Rue. Recess Stamps Office, Hyderabad)

1931 (12 Nov)–**47**. T **12/18**. W **7**. Wove paper. P 13½.

41	**12**	4p. black	30	10
		a. Laid paper (1947)	2·50	7·50
		b. Imperf (pair)	50·00	£180
		c. Imperf between (vert pair)	†	£1000
42		8p. green	1·50	10
		a. Imperf between (vert pair)	£1100	£950
		b. Imperf (pair)	60·00	£180
		c. Laid paper (1947)	3·00	4·50
43	**13**	1a. brown (*shades*)	1·25	10
		a. Imperf between (horiz pair)	—	£1000
		b. Perf 11	†	£1000
44	**14**	2a. violet (*shades*)	3·75	10
		a. Imperf (pair)	£140	£425
45	**15**	4a. ultramarine	3·25	70
		a. Imperf (pair)	£140	£475
46	**16**	8a. orange (*shades*)	12·00	4·50
		a. Yellow-orange (1944)	£100	35·00
47	**17**	12a. scarlet	14·00	12·00
48	**18**	1r. yellow	8·00	5·00
41/8 Set of 8			38·00	20·00

Nos. 41a and 42c have a large sheet watermark "THE NIZAM's GOVERNMENT HYDERABAD DECCAN" and arms within a circle, but this does not appear on all stamps.

19 Unani General Hospital

20 Osmania General Hospital

21 Osmania University

22 Osmania Jubilee Hall

(Litho Indian Security Printing Press, Nasik)

1937 (13 Feb). T **19/22**, inscr "H.E.H. THE NIZAM'S SILVER JUBILEE". P 14.

49	**19**	4p. slate and violet	1·25	3·00
50	**20**	8p. slate and brown	1·25	3·00

51	**21**	1a. slate and orange-yellow	1·75	2·00
52	**22**	2a. slate and green	2·50	5·50
49/52 Set of 4			6·00	12·00

23 Family Reunion

24 Town Hall

(Des T. I. Archer. Typo)

1945 (6 Dec). Victory. W **7** (very faint). Wove paper. P 13½.

53	**23**	1a. blue	10	10
		a. Imperf between (vert pair)	£1000	
		b. Laid paper	1·50	1·75

No. 53b shows the sheet watermark described beneath Nos. 41/8.

(Des. T. I. Archer. Litho Government Press)

1947 (17 Feb). Reformed Legislature. P 13½.

54	**24**	1a. black	2·25	1·90
		a. Imperf between (pair)	—	£1500

25 Power House, Hyderabad

26 Kaktyai Arch, Warangal Fort

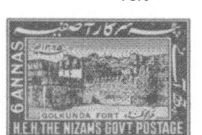

27 Golkunda Fort

(Des T. I. Archer. Typo)

1947–49. As T **25/27** (inscr "H. E. H. THE NIZAM'S GOVT. POSTAGE"). W **7**. P 13½.

55	**25**	1a.4p. green	1·40	2·75
56	**26**	3a. greenish blue	3·00	7·00
		a. Bluish green	8·00	8·50
57	**27**	6a. sepia	4·50	24·00
		a. Red-brown (1949)	20·00	42·00
		ab. Imperf (pair)	£250	
55/7 Set of 3			8·00	30·00

1947. As 1915 issue but colour changed. P 13½.

58	**8**	½a. claret	3·00	75
		a. Imperf between (horizontal pair)	—	£475
		b. Imperf between (vert pair)	—	£900
		c. Doubly printed	†	£450

An Independence commemorative set of four, 4p., 8p., 1a. and 2a., was prepared in 1948, but not issued.

1948. As T **12** ("POSTAGE" at foot). Recess. W **7**. P 13½.

59		6p. claret	12·00	10·00

Following intervention by the forces of the Dominion of India during September 1948 the Hyderabad postal system was taken over by the Dominion authorities, operating as an agency of the India Post Office.

1949. T **12** ("POSTAGE" at top). Litho. W **7**. P 13½.

60	**12**	2p. bistre-brown	3·00	3·25
		a. Imperf between (horizontal pair)	†	£1200
		b. Imperf (pair)	£150	£500

No. 60 was produced from a transfer taken from a plate of the 4p., No. 41, with each impression amended individually.

OFFICIAL STAMPS

Official stamps became valid for postage to destinations within India from 1910.

(O **1**) (O **1a**) (O **2**)

1873.

*I. Handstamped as Type O **1** in red*

O1	**1**	1a. olive-green	£180	50·00
		a. Black opt	—	£600
O2	**2**	½a. brown	—	£1300
		a. Black opt	—	£1000
O3		2a. sage-green	—	£950
		a. Black opt	—	£325

At least ten different handstamps as Type O **1** were used to produce Nos. O1/17. These differ in the size, shape and spacing of the characters. The prices quoted are for the cheapest versions where more than one is known to exist on a particular stamp.

Imitations of these overprints on genuine stamps and on reprints are found horizontally or vertically in various shades of red, in magenta and in black.

*II. T **3** handstamped as Type O **1** in red*

(a) Rough perf 11½

O4		½a. red-brown		
		a. Black opt	—	£1400
O5		1a. purple-brown	—	£2500
		a. Black opt	£190	£225
O6		2a. green (A)		
		a. Black opt	—	£2250

O7		4a. slate	—	£2750
		a. Black opt		
O8		8a. deep brown		
		a. Black opt	£1900	£1000
O8b		12a. dull blue	—	£2750
		(b) Pin perf 8–9		
O8c		1a. drab (*black opt*)	16·00	£120
		ca. Second dot in bottom label omitted	£300	
		(c) P 12½		
O9		½a. red-brown	48·00	13·00
		a. Black opt	20·00	5·50
		ab. Left side of central inscription omitted	—	£400
		ac. Dot at top of central inscription omitted	—	£110
O11		1a. purple-brown	£400	£160
		a. Black opt	—	85·00
O12		1a. drab	60·00	48·00
		aa. Dot at top of central inscription omitted	—	£275
		a. Black opt	7·50	4·50
		ab. Second dot in bottom label omitted	£200	£150
O13		2a. green (*to deep*) (A)	£160	75·00
		a. Black opt	18·00	12·00
		ab. Inner circle missing (B)	£650	
		ac. Centre dot in bottom label omitted	£350	£250
O14		3a. ochre-brown	£425	£325
		a. Black opt	£110	75·00
O15		4a. slate	£200	£110
		a. Black opt	60·00	48·00
O16		8a. deep brown	£200	£275
		a. Imperf vert (horiz pair)	£900	
		b. Black opt	£100	75·00
O17		12a. blue	£350	£375
		a. Black opt	£130	£170

Imitations and forgeries of these overprints are frequently met with. The prices quoted for Nos. O9/17a are for genuine examples.

The use of Official Stamps (Sarkari) was discontinued in 1878, but was resumed in 1909, when the current stamps were overprinted from a new die.

1909–11. Optd with Type O **1a**.

*(a) On Type **3**. P 12½*

O18		½a. orange-brown	£200	10·00
		a. Opt inverted	†	£800
O19		1a. black	£130	50
		a. Second dot in bottom label omitted		11·00
O20		2a. sage-green (A)	£150	2·00
		a. Optd on No. 15da (B)	—	22·00
		b. Stamp doubly printed	†	£225
		c. Centre dot in bottom label omitted	—	22·00
		d. Opt double	—	£300
O20e		3a. ochre-brown	17·00	7·50
		ea. Character omitted (D)	—	£750
O20f		4a. olive-green	£600	13·00
		fa. Perf 11½, 12	—	£500
O20g		8a. deep brown	—	65·00
O20h		12a. grey-green	—	£120
		*(b) On Type **6** (Wyon ptgs). P 12½*		
O21		½a. orange	—	4·50
		a. Vermilion	£250	40
		ab. Opt inverted	†	£650
		ac. Imperf horiz (vert pair)	†	£750
O22		½a. green	48·00	10
		a. Pale green	48·00	10
		b. Opt inverted	†	£130
		c. Imperf between (vert pair)	†	£600
		d. Imperf between (horiz pair)	†	£550
		e. Stamp doubly printed	†	£180
		f. Perf 11½, 12	40·00	30
		fa. Pale green	40·00	30
		fb. Opt inverted	†	£130
		g. Perf 11	—	£140
		ga. Pale green		
		h. Perf 13½	—	£140
O23		1a. carmine	£110	15
		a. Opt double	£450	
		b. Perf 11½, 12	£170	30
		ba. Stamp doubly printed	—	£200
		c. Perf 11		7·00
O24		2a. lilac	£110	60
		a. Perf 11½, 12	£190	5·50
		b. Perf 11	£550	
O25		3a. brown-orange	£375	32·00
		a. Perf 11½, 12	£500	42·00
		ba. Opt inverted	†	£325
		c. Perf 11	£600	85·00
		d. Perf 13½	—	£180
O26		4a. olive-green (1911)	65·00	3·00
		a. Perf 11½, 12	£180	4·50
		b. Perf 11	—	35·00
O27		8a. purple (1911)	24·00	3·50
		a. Perf 11½, 12	£225	20·00
		b. Perf 11	£600	£180
O28		12a. blue-green (1911)	28·00	5·00
		a. Imperf between (horiz pair)	†	£2250
		b. Perf 11½, 12	65·00	7·00
		c. Perf 11	†	£400
		*(c) On Type **6** (Bradbury Wilkinson ptgs). P 11*		
O28d	**6**	¼a. grey-black	£1000	
O28e		½a. deep green	£1000	

1911–12. Optd with Type O **2**.

*(a) Type **6** (Wyon printings). P 13½ (8a, 12a.) or 12½ (others)*

O29		¼a. grey	£100	1·00
		a. Perf 11½, 12	50·00	75
		ab. Imperf between (vert pair)	†	£650
		b. Perf 11	£225	75·00
		c. Perf 13½		
O30		½a. pale green	90·00	2·00
		a. Perf 11½, 12	—	30
		ab. Imperf between (vert pair)	†	£700
		b. Perf 13½		
O31		1a. carmine	3·75	15
		a. Opt inverted	—	65·00
		b. Imperf horiz (vert pair)	†	£700
		c. Perf 11½, 12	5·50	15
		d. Perf 11	3·00	15
		e. Perf 13½		

O32		2a. lilac	21·00	1·75
	a.	Perf 11½, 12	40·00	5·00
	b.	Perf 11	5·50	1·25
	c.	Perf 13½	15·00	10
	ca.	Imperf between (horiz pair)	†	£800
	cb.	*Rose-lilac*	4·00	10
O33		3a. brown-orange	55·00	8·50
	a.	Perf 11½, 12	70·00	8·50
	b.	Perf 11	†	£140
	ba.	Opt inverted	†	£150
	c.	Perf 11	65·00	7·00
	ca.	Opt inverted	†	£140
	d.	Perf 13½	42·00	1·25
	da.	Opt inverted	†	£120
O34		4a. olive-green	35·00	3·75
	a.	Opt inverted	—	£140
	b.	Perf 11½, 12	11·00	4·25
	ba.	Opt inverted	—	£150
	c.	Perf 11	11·00	1·75
	d.	Perf 13½	8·50	15
	da.	Opt inverted	†	£140
O35		8a. purple	15·00	30
	a.	Perf 11½, 12	—	£650
	b.	Perf 11	£650	£100
	c.	Perf 13½	—	£425
O36		12a. blue-green	70·00	5·50
	a.	Perf 11½, 12		
	b.	Perf 11		
	c.	Perf 12½		

(b) Type 6 (Bradbury Wilkinson printings). P 12½

O37		¼a. grey-black	7·50	75
	a.	Opt inverted	†	85·00
	b.	Pair, one without opt		
	c.	Imperf between (vert pair)	†	£550
	d.	Perf 11½, 12	18·00	1·75
	da.	Opt inverted	†	85·00
	db.	Pair, one without opt		
	e.	Perf 11	5·50	40
	ea.	Opt sideways	†	£110
	eb.	Blue opt	†	£110
	f.	Perf 13½	8·00	10
	fa.	Opt inverted	†	90·00
	fb.	Pair, one without opt	†	£180
	fc.	Imperf between (horiz pair)	†	£500
O38		¼a. brown-purple (*shades*) (P 13½)	4·75	10
	a.	Imperf between (horiz pair)	†	£500
	ab.	Imperf between (vert pair)	†	£550
	b.	Imperf between (vert pair)	†	£550
	c.	Perf 11		
O39		½a. deep green	11·00	25
	a.	Opt inverted	—	40·00
	b.	Perf 11½, 12	19·00	2·00
	ba.	Pair, one without opt	†	£180
	c.	Perf 11	12·00	10
	ca.	Opt inverted	—	42·00
	cb.	Imperf horiz (vert pair)	†	£550
	d.	Perf 13½	7·00	10
	da.	Imperf between (horiz pair)	†	£450
	db.	Imperf between (vert pair)	†	£550
	dc.	*Yellow-green*	—	70

1917–20. T **8** optd with Type O **2**. P 13½.

O40		½a. green	3·50	10
	a.	Opt inverted	†	40·00
	b.	Pair, one without opt	†	£140
	c.	Imperf between (horiz pair)	†	£325
	ca.	Imperf vert (horiz pair)	†	£350
	d.	Imperf between (vert pair)	†	£475
	e.	Emerald-green	8·50	40
	f.	Perf 12½	—	4·25
	g.	Perf 11	17·00	30
	ga.	Opt inverted	†	42·00
	gb.	Pair, one without opt		
O41		1a. carmine	15·00	10
	a.	Opt inverted	†	45·00
	b.	Opt double	†	£140
	c.	Imperf horiz (vert pair)	†	£500
	ca.	Imperf between (horiz pair)	†	£600
	d.	Stamp printed double		
	e.	*Scarlet* (1920)	7·50	10
	ea.	Stamp printed double	†	£275
	eb.	Imperf between (horiz pair)	†	£550
	ec.	Imperf between (vert pair)	†	£425
	ed.	Imperf horiz (vert pair)	†	£475
	ee.	Opt inverted	†	£140
	f.	Perf 12½	—	3·50
	g.	Perf 11	26·00	15
	ga.	Opt inverted	†	32·00
	gb.	*Scarlet* (1920)	—	35·00

1930–34. T **6** and **8** optd as Type O **2** and surch at top of stamp, in red, as T **10** or **11**.

O42		4p. on ¼a. grey-black (O37f) (1934)	£800	26·00
O43		4p. on ¼a. brown-purple (O38)	4·50	10
	b.	Imperf between (horiz pair)	†	£400
	c.	Imperf between (vert pair)	†	£400
	d.	Imperf horiz (vert pair)	†	£375
	e.	Red surch double	†	£140
	f.	Black opt double	†	£275
	g.	Perf 11	†	£500
	h.	Stamp doubly printed	†	£225
O44		8p. on ½a. green (O40)	4·50	10
	c.	Imperf between (horiz pair)	†	£375
	ca.	Imperf between (vert pair)	†	£425
	d.	Red surch double	†	£140
	e.	Stamp doubly printed	†	£225
	f.	Black opt double	†	£275
O45		8p. on ½a. yellow-green (O39dc)	50·00	80·00

For Nos. O42/5 the red surcharge was intended to appear on the upper part of the stamp, above the official overprint, Type O **2**, but surcharge and overprint are not infrequently found superimposed on one another.

1934–44. Nos. 41/8 optd with Type O **2**.

O46		4p. black	6·50	10
	a.	Imperf (pair)	£120	
	b.	Imperf between (vert pair)	£900	£700
	c.	Imperf between (horiz pair)	†	£700
	d.	Opt double	†	£300
O47		8p. green	2·75	10
	a.	Opt inverted	†	£190
	b.	Imperf between (horiz pair)	—	£750

	c.	Opt double	†	£150
	d.	Imperf (pair)	£275	£350
O48		1a. brown	6·50	10
	a.	Imperf between (vert pair)	£800	£700
	b.	Imperf between (horiz pair)	—	£600
	c.	Imperf (pair)	£140	£250
	d.	Opt double	—	£250
O49		2a. violet	15·00	10
	a.	Imperf vert (horiz pair)	†	£2250
	b.	Opt double	†	£500
O50		4a. ultramarine	14·00	25
	a.	Opt inverted	†	£700
	b.	Imperf between (vert pair)	†	£2750
O51		8a. orange (1935)	30·00	70
	a.	*Yellow-orange* (1944)	—	45·00
O52		12a. scarlet (1935)	38·00	1·75
O53		1r. yellow (1935)	40·00	3·50
O46/53		*Set of 8*	£140	6·00

1947. No. 58 optd with Type O **2**.

O54	**8**	½a. claret	6·00	8·00

1949. No. 60 optd with Type O **2**.

O55	**12**	2p. bistre-brown	7·00	12·00

1950. No. 59 optd with Type O **2**.

O56		6p. claret	11·00	28·00

IDAR

PRICES FOR STAMPS ON COVER	
Nos. 1/2b	*from* × 2
Nos. 3/6	*from* × 3
Nos. F1/5	*from* × 3

Maharaja Himmat Singh, 1931–1960

1 Maharaja Himmat Singh   **2** Maharaja Himmat Singh

(Typo M. N. Kothari & Sons, Bombay)

1932–43. P 11*.

(a) White panels

1	**1**	½a. light green	£650	£100
	a.	*Pale yellow-green (thick paper)* (1939)	38·00	38·00
	ab.	Imperf between (horiz pair)	£3000	
	b.	*Emerald* (1941)	35·00	38·00
	ba.	Imperf between (pair)	£4500	
	c.	*Yellow-green* (*shades*) (1943)	22·00	30·00

(b) Coloured panels

2	**1**	½a. pale yellow-green (*thick paper*) (1939)	55·00	40·00
	a.	*Emerald* (1941)	32·00	35·00
	b.	*Yellow-green* (*shades*) (1943)	15·00	30·00

In No. 2 the whole design is composed of half-tone dots. In No. 1 the dots are confined to the oval portrait.

*Two different perforating heads were used for Nos 1/2b. Nos. 1, 1b and 2a are P 11.3, whereas Nos. 1a, 1c, 2 and 2b are P 10.8. Apart from the difference in shade, No. 1 can be distinguished from No. 1b by the height of the stamp. No. 1 was printed in panes with wide outer imperforate margins, giving stamps 35-37 mm high. The average height of Nos. 1a/c and 2/b is only 28-30 mm.

(Typo P. G. Mehta & Co, Hitmatnagar)

1944 (21 Oct). P 12.

3	**2**	½a. blue-green	4·00	85·00
	a.	Imperf between (vert pair)	£450	
	b.	*Yellow-green*	4·50	85·00
	ba.	Imperf between (vert pair)	15·00	
4		1a. violet	4·00	70·00
	a.	Imperf (pair)	£225	
	b.	Imperf vert (horiz pair)	£300	
5		2a. blue	3·50	£120
	a.	Imperf between (vert pair)	£130	
	b.	Imperf between (horiz pair)	£300	
6		4a. vermilion	4·50	£120
	a.	Doubly printed	£2000	
3/6		*Set of 4*	14·50	£350

Nos. 1 to 6 are from booklet panes of four stamps, producing single stamps with one or two adjacent sides imperf.

The 4a. violet is believed to be a colour trial (*Price £650, unused*).

POSTAL FISCAL STAMPS

F 1   **F 2**

1936 (?). Typo. P 11½ on two or three sides.

F1	**F 1**	1a. reddish lilac and bright green	—	£1000

1940 (?)–**45.** Typo. P 12 on two or three sides.

F2	–	1a. violet (*shades*)	£325	£200
		a. Perf 11*	£200	£200
F3	**F 2**	1a. violet (1943)	£170	£200
F4		1¼a. on 1a. violet	£425	£550

F5		1¼a. yellow-green (1945)	26·00	
	a.	Imperf between (vert pair)	55·00	
	b.	*Blue-green* (1945)	£110	£180

No. F2 shows the portrait as Type **1**. Used prices are for examples with postal cancellations. No. F4 shows a handstamped surcharge in Gujerati.

*No. F2a exists both P 10.8 and P 11.3. Fiscally used examples have been seen with a "1¼a" Gujerati handstamped surcharge, similar to No. F4.

Idar became part of Bombay Province on 10 June 1948.

INDORE
(HOLKAR STATE)

PRICES FOR STAMPS ON COVER	
Nos. 1/2a	*from* × 20
No. 3	*from* × 3
Nos. 4/14	*from* × 20
No. 15	*from* × 10
Nos. 16/43	*from* × 6
Nos. S1/7	*from* × 40

Maharaja Tukoji Rao Holkar II, 1843–1886

1 Maharaja Tukoji Rao Holkar II

(Litho Waterlow & Sons)

1886 (6 Jan). P 14½–15.

(a) Thick white paper

1	**1**	½a. bright mauve	38·00	30·00

(b) Thin white or yellowish paper

2	**1**	½a. pale mauve	8·00	3·50
	a.	*Dull mauve*	7·50	4·25

Nos. 2 and 2a can be found with papermaker's watermark reading "WATERLOW & SONS LIMITED LONDON".

Maharaja Shivaji Rao Holkar, 1886–1903

2 Type I   **2a** Type II

TYPES 2 AND 2a. In addition to the difference in the topline character (marked by arrow), the two Types can be distinguished by the difference in the angles of the 6-pointed stars and the appearance of the lettering. In Type I the top characters are smaller and more cramped than the bottom; in Type II both are in the same style and similarly spaced.

1889 (Sept). Handstamped. No gum. Imperf.

3	**2**	½a. black/*pink*	50·00	38·00
4	**2a**	½a. black/*pink*	5·50	4·00
	a.	*Tête-bêche* (pair)	£375	

3 Maharaja Shivaji Rao Holkar   **4** Maharaja Tukoji Holkar III   **5** Maharaja Tukoji Holkar III

(Recess Waterlow)

1889–92. Medium wove paper. P 14 to 15.

5	**3**	¼a. orange (9.2.92)	3·75	1·50
	a.	Imperf between (horiz pair)	†	£950
	b.	Very thick wove paper	4·50	4·50
	c.	*Yellow*	5·00	4·25
6		½a. dull violet	6·50	1·75
	a.	*Brown-purple*	5·00	25
	b.	Imperf between (vert pair)	£1000	
7		1a. green (7.2.92)	7·50	2·50
	a.	Imperf between (vert pair)	£1600	
	b.	Very thick wove paper	75·00	
8		2a. vermilion (7.2.92)	13·00	3·00
	a.	Very thick wove paper	14·00	3·75
5/8		*Set of 4*	26·00	6·50

Maharaja Tukoji Rao Holkar III, 1903–1926

(Recess Perkins Bacon & Co)

1904–20. P 13½, 14.

9	**4**	¼a. orange	2·00	10
10	**5**	½a. lake (1909)	16·00	10
	a.	*Brown-lake* (*shades*)	22·00	15
	b.	Imperf (pair)	48·00	£850
11		1a. green	4·50	10
	a.	Imperf (pair)	£160	
	b.	Perf 12½ (1920)	£1400	£225
12		2a. brown	17·00	1·00
	a.	Imperf (pair)	£130	

13		3a. violet	45·00	7·00
14		4a. ultramarine	32·00	6·50
		a. Dull blue	14·00	1·40
9/14*a* Set of 6			90·00	8·75

पाव स्रना.
(6)

7 Maharaja Yeshwant Rao Holkar II

1905 (June). No. 6a surch "QUARTER ANNA" in Devanagari, as T **6**.

15	**3**	¼a. on ½a. brown-purple	13·00	30·00

On 1 March 1908 the Indore State postal service was amalgamated with the Indian Imperial system. Under the terms of the agreement stamps showing the Maharaja would still be used for official mail sent to addresses within the state. Initially Nos. 9/14 were used for this purpose, the "SERVICE" overprints, Nos. S1/7, being withdrawn.

Maharaja Yeshwant Rao Holkar II, 1926–1961

(Recess Perkins Bacon & Co)

1927–37. P 13 to 14.

16	**7**	¼a. orange (*a*) (*d*) (*e*)	2·25	20
17		½a. claret (*a*) (*d*) (*e*)	4·50	20
18		1a. green (*a*) (*d*) (*e*)	5·50	10
19		1¼a. green (*c*) (*d*) (1933)	7·50	2·25
20		2a. sepia (*a*)	14·00	3·75
21		2a. bluish green (*d*) (1936)	15·00	2·25
		a. Imperf (pair)	27·00	£325
22		3a. deep violet (*d*)	7·00	11·00
23		3a. Prussian blue (*d*) (1935?)	26·00	
		a. Imperf (pair)	55·00	£850
24		3½a. violet (*d*) (1934)	7·00	15·00
		a. Imperf (pair)	£100	£850
25		4a. ultramarine (*a*)	16·00	5·50
26		4a. yellow-brown (*d*) (1937)	45·00	2·50
		a. Imperf (pair)	30·00	£550
27		8a. slate-grey (*a*)	13·00	4·50
28		8a. red-orange (*d*) (1937)	38·00	28·00
29		12a. carmine (*d*) (1934)	5·00	10·00
30	–	1r. black and light blue (*b*)	17·00	19·00
31	–	2r. black and carmine (*b*)	95·00	£110
32	–	5r. black and brown-orange (*b*)	£170	£180

Nos. 30/32 are as Type **7**, but larger, size 23×28 mm.

Five different perforating heads were used for this issue: (*a*) comb 13.6; (*b*) comb 13.9; (*c*) line 13.2; (*d*) line 13.8; (*e*) line 14.2. Values on which each perforation occur are indicated above.

Nos. 21a, 23a, 24a and 26a were specifically ordered by the state government in 1933 and are known used for postage *circa* 1938–42. A plate proof of the 1r. in green and carmine is also known postally used (*Price of pair* £45 *unused,* £500 *used*).

Nos. 16/19 and 28/32 also exist as imperforate plate proofs, but these were never sent to India.

QUARTER ANNA
(8)

9

1940 (1 Aug). Surch in words as T **8** by *The Times of India* Press, Bombay.

33	**7**	¼a. on 5r. black and brown-orange (*b*)	28·00	1·75
		a. Surch double (Blk.+G.)	†	£550
34		½a. on 2r. black and carmine (*b*)	35·00	3·25
35		1a. on 1¼a. green (*c*) (*e*)	45·00	1·00
		b. Surch inverted (*d*)	£120	
		c. Surch double (*c*)	£650	
33/5 Set of 3			95·00	5·50

(Typo *Times of India* Press, Bombay)

1940–46. P 11.

36	**9**	¼a. red-orange	2·25	20
37		½a. claret (1941)	7·00	10
38		1a. green (1941)	11·00	20
39		1¼a. yellow-green (1941)	22·00	3·25
		a. Imperf (pair)	£450	
40		2a. turquoise-blue (1941)	16·00	1·00
41		4a. yellow-brown (1946)	21·00	15·00
		Larger size (23×28 mm)		
42		2r. black and carmine (1943)	22·00	£275
43		5r. black and yellow-orange (1943)	22·00	£400
36/43 Set of 8			£110	£650

OFFICIAL STAMPS

SERVICE SERVICE
(S **1**) (S **2**)

1904–06.

(a) Optd with Type S **1** (*typo*)

S1	**4**	¼a. orange (1906)	2·00	2·00
S2	**5**	½a. lake	75	10
		a. Opt inverted	50·00	90·00
		b. Opt double	60·00	
		c. Imperf (pair)	£150	
		d. Brown-lake	1·00	20
		da. Opt inverted	50·00	
		e. Pair, one without opt	£900	
S3		1a. green	25	25
S4		2a. brown (1905)	35	35
		a. Vert pair, one without opt	£1400	
S5		3a. violet (1906)	3·25	5·50
		a. Imperf (pair)	£450	
S6		4a. ultramarine (1905)	9·00	2·50

(b) Optd with Type S **2** (*litho*)

S7	**5**	½a. lake	20	1·50
		a. Opt double	£700	
S1/7 Set of 7			14·50	10·50

Types S **1** and S **2** differ chiefly in the shape of the letter "R".

Indore became part of Madhya Bharat by 1 July 1948.

JAIPUR

PRICES FOR STAMPS ON COVER	
No. 1	*from* × 3
No. 2	*from* × 2
Nos. 3/5	*from* × 10
Nos. 6/70	*from* × 4
Nos. 71/80	*from* × 6
Nos. O1/34	*from* × 8

Maharaja Sawai Madho Singh II, 1880–1922

1 (redrawn state) 1a 2

Chariot of the Sun God, Surya

Type **1** – Value at sides in small letters and characters. "HALF ANNA", shown as one word except for R. 1/1 and 1/3, measuring between 13½ and 15 mm. Sheets of 12 (4×3) with stamps 2 to 2½ mm apart.

Type **1a** – Value in large letters and characters. "HALF ANNA", always with a gap between the two words, measuring between 14½ and 15½ mm. Sheets of 24 (4×6) with stamps 3 to 4 mm apart.

Type **2** – Value in large letters and characters. "HALF ANNA" measuring 16 to 17 mm. Both side inscriptions start below the inner frame line. Sheets of 24 (4×6) with stamps 1½ to 2 mm apart.

(Litho Durbar Press, Jaipur)

1904 (14 July). Roughly perf 14.

1	**1**	½a. pale blue	£250	£325
		a. Ultramarine	£375	£425
		b. Imperf, *ultramarine*	£550	
		c. Pale slate-blue*	£2000	
		d. Imperf, *pale slate-blue*	£1500	£1500
2	**1a**	½a. grey-blue	£4500	£300
		a. Imperf	£475	£900
		b. Ultramarine	—	£550
3	**2**	½a. pale blue	5·50	10·00
		a. Deep blue	6·00	9·50
		b. Ultramarine	6·50	10·00
		c. Imperf	£425	£425
4	**1**	1a. dull red	8·00	18·00
		a. Scarlet	8·00	18·00
5		2a. pale green	11·00	18·00
		a. Emerald-green	11·00	

Nos. 1b, 1d, 2a and 3c are on gummed paper. Imperforate plate proofs also exist for Nos. 1/5, but these are ungummed (*Prices, from* £550 *per pair*).

*Nos. 1c/d, in pale slate-blue, were printed from the *original* state of the first stone of 12 (4×3), which was then extensively re-drawn. Nos. 1/a/b, in pale blue or ultramarine, were printed from the second, redrawn state. In the original state the inner white lines are thin, and on all sheet positions there is a noticeable gap between the top of the umbrella and the inner frameline (below the "U" of "JAIPUR"). In the redrawn state the inner white lines are much thicker, and on all positions except R. 1/1 the top of the umbrella has been raised so that it touches or nearly touches the inner frameline. These differences can clearly be seen in the enlarged illustrations of R. 3/2 on the sheet in its original and redrawn states.

Type I (original state) Type I (redrawn state)

3 Chariot of the Sun God, Surya

(Recess Perkins Bacon & Co)

1904. P 12.

6	**3**	½a. blue	12·00	15·00
		a. Perf 12½	48·00	30·00
		b. Perf comp of 12 and 12½	23·00	30·00
7		1a. brown-red	75·00	75·00
		a. Perf 12½	£225	£225
		b. Perf comp of 12 and 12½	£150	£150
		c. Carmine	4·75	8·00
		ca. Imperf between (vert pair)	£750	£1000
		cb. Perf comp of 12 and 12½	15·00	22·00
8		2a. deep green	15·00	21·00
		a. Perf 12½	£375	£190
		b. Perf comp of 12 and 12½	29·00	50·00

Nos. 6b, 7b, 7cb and 8b occur on the bottom two rows of sheets otherwise perforated 12.

1905–09. Wmk "JAs WRIGLEY & SON Ld. 219" "SPECIAL POSTAGE PAPER LONDON" or "PERKINS BACON & Co Ld LONDON" in sheet. P 13½

9	**3**	¼a. olive-yellow (1906)	2·75	2·50
10		½a. blue (1906)	10·00	3·75
		a. Indigo	4·25	1·75
11		1a. brown-red (1906)	16·00	7·00
		a. Bright red (1908)	8·00	1·75
12		2a. deep green (1906)	11·00	3·25
13		4a. chestnut	14·00	3·75
14		8a. bright violet	12·00	2·75
15		1r. orange-yellow	70·00	50·00
		a. Yellow (1909)	42·00	16·00
		b. Yellow-ochre	50·00	40·00
9/15*a* Set of 7			85·00	28·00

4 Chariot of the Sun God, Surya
(5)

(Typo Jaipur State Press)

1911. Thin wove paper. No gum. Imperf.

16	**4**	¼a. green	5·00	6·00
		a. Printed double	15·00	
		ab. Ditto, one inverted		
		b. "¼" inverted in right upper corner (R. 1/2)	8·50	
		c. No stop after "STATE" (R. 3/1)	8·50	
17		¼a. greenish yellow	40	2·50
		a. Printed double	2·75	
		b. Printed double, one sideways		
		c. "¼" inverted in right upper corner (R. 1/2)	1·50	
		d. No stop after "STATE" (R. 3/1)	1·50	
18		½a. ultramarine	50	2·50
		a. Printed double	2·25	
		b. No stop after "STATE" (R. 3/1)	1·00	
		c. Large "J" in "JAIPUR" (R. 1/2)	1·00	
		d. "1/3" for "½" at lower left (R. 3/1)	1·50	
		e. "1½a." at lower right (R. 3/2)	1·50	
19		½a. grey-blue	6·00	6·00
		a. No stop after "STATE" (R. 3/1)	10·00	
		b. Large "J" in "JAIPUR" (R. 1/2)	10·00	
		c. "1/3" for "½" at lower left (R. 3/1)	12·00	
		d. "1½a." at lower right (R. 3/2)	13·00	
20		1a. rose-red	50	2·50
		a. Printed double	£300	
21		2a. greyish green	2·75	6·00
		a. Deep green	2·00	8·00
		b. Imperf between (vert pair)	£850	

Issued in sheets of six (2×3). There are three recognised settings. Nos. 18d/e and 19c/d come from Setting B, and Nos. 16b/c, 17b/c, 18b/c and 19a/b from Setting C.

One sheet of the ¼a. is known in blue.

(Typo Jaipur State Press)

1912–22. Paper-maker's wmk "DORLING & CO. LONDON" in sheet. P 11.

22	**3**	¼a. pale olive-yellow	2·00	3·25
		a. Imperf horiz (vert pair)	£325	£325
		b. Imperf vert (horiz pair)	—	£225
23		¼a. olive	2·00	3·50
		a. Imperf between (horiz pair)	£300	£350
		b. Imperf vert (horiz pair)	£325	£350
		c. Imperf horiz (vert pair)	£325	
		d. Tête-bêche (pair)	£2500	
24		¼a. bistre	2·00	3·50
		a. Imperf between (horiz pair)	£400	
		b. Imperf between (vert pair)	†	£800
		c. Imperf horiz (vert pair)	†	£800
		d. Doubly printed	†	£1500
25		½a. pale ultramarine	4·00	3·00
		a. Imperf vert (horiz pair)	†	£1200
		ab. Imperf between (vert pair)	†	£1400
		b. Blue	2·50	2·75
		ba. Imperf between (horiz pair)	£750	
26		1a. carmine (1918)	6·00	12·00
		a. Imperf between (vert pair)	†	£1800
		b. Imperf horiz (vert pair)	†	£1800
		c. Imperf between (horiz pair)	£1800	£1800
27		1a. rose-red	13·00	18·00
		a. Imperf between (vert pair)	£1800	
28		1a. scarlet (1922)	8·50	7·00
		a. Imperf between (vert pair)	£1900	£1900
29		2a. green (1918)	10·00	12·00
30		4a. chocolate	14·00	20·00
31		4a. pale brown	14·00	20·00
		a. Imperf vert (horiz pair)	£1000	
22/31 Set of 5			32·00	40·00

Maharaja Sawai Man Singh II 1922–1970

1926. Surch with T **5**.

32	**3**	3a. on 8a. bright violet (R.)	5·00	6·00
		a. Surch inverted	£325	£200
33		3a. on 1r. yellow (R.)	6·00	10·00
		a. Surch inverted	£850	£300
		c. Yellow-ochre	28·00	32·00

1928. As 1912–22 issue. Wmk "DORLING & CO. LONDON" (½a., 1a., 2a.) or "OVERLAND BANK" (all values) in sheet. No gum. P 12.

34	**3**	½a. ultramarine	4·25	4·00
		a. Perf comp of 12 and 11	21·00	12·00
35		1a. rose-red	42·00	22·00
		a. Imperf between (vert pair)	£1000	
36		1a. scarlet	65·00	15·00
		a. Perf comp of 12 and 11	£110	35·00
37		2a. green	£130	40·00
		a. Perf comp of 12 and 11	£375	85·00
39		1r. orange-vermilion	£950	£1300

The "OVERLAND BANK" paper has a coarser texture. The ½a. and 2a. values also exist on this paper perforated 11, but such stamps are difficult to distinguish from examples of Nos. 25 and 29.

6 Chariot of the Sun God, Surya

7 Maharaja Sawai Man Singh II

8 Elephant and State Banner

9 Sowar in Armour

10 Common Peafowl

11 Bullock carriage

12 Elephant carriage

13 Albert Museum

14 Sireh Deorhi Gate

15 Chandra Mahal

16 Amber Palace

17 Maharajas Jai Singh and Man Singh

(Des T. I. Archer. Litho Indian Security Printing Press, Nasik)

1931 (14 Mar). Investiture of Maharaja. T **6/17**. No wmk. P 14.

40	**6**	¼a. black and deep lake	7·00	4·75
41	**7**	½a. black and violet	75	20
42	**8**	1a. black and blue	20·00	18·00
43	**9**	2a. black and buff	18·00	16·00
44	**10**	2½a. black and carmine	50·00	70·00
45	**11**	3a. black and myrtle	35·00	60·00
46	**12**	4a. black and olive-green	48·00	90·00
47	**13**	6a. black and deep blue	14·00	80·00
48	**14**	8a. black and chocolate	32·00	£140
49	**15**	1r. black and pale olive	£120	£700
50	**16**	2r. black and yellow-green	£140	£850
51	**17**	5r. black and purple	£160	£950
40/51		*Set of 12*	£600	£2750

18 of these sets were issued for presentation purposes with a special overprint "INVESTITURE-MARCH 14,1931" in red (*Price for set of 12 £9000 unused, £10000 used*).

"DOUBLE PRINTS". Examples of Nasik litho-printed stamps showing doubling of all or part of the design or subsequent overprint are not uncommon. These are not true "double prints", in that they were not the result of two impressions of the inked printing plate, but were caused by incorrect tension in the rubber "blanket" which transferred ink from the cylinder to the paper. Such varieties are outside the scope of this catalogue.

18 Maharaja Sawai Man Singh II

One Rupee

(19)

(Des T. I. Archer. Litho Indian Security Printing Press, Nasik)
1932–46. P 14.

(a) Inscr "POSTAGE & REVENUE"

52	**18**	1a. black and blue	6·00	3·50
53		2a. black and buff	10·00	3·75
54		4a. black and grey-green	5·00	22·00
55		8a. black and chocolate	6·00	35·00
56		1r. black and yellow-bistre	48·00	£350
57		2r. black and yellow-green	£170	£950
52/7		*Set of 6*	£225	£1200

(b) Inscr "POSTAGE"

58	**7**	¼a. black and brown-lake	1·00	50
59		¾a. black and brown-red (1943?)	14·00	6·50
60		1a. black and blue (1943?)	18·00	9·00
61		2a. black and buff (1943?)	21·00	8·00
62		2½a. black and carmine	8·50	3·50
63		3a. black and green	5·00	1·00
64		4a. black and grey-green (1943?)	75·00	£275
65		6a. black and deep blue	13·00	60·00
		a. Black and pale blue (1946)	18·00	£130
66		8a. black and chocolate (1946)	55·00	£250
67		1r. black and yellow-bistre (1946)	20·00	£250
58/67		*Set of 10*	£200	£800

1936. Nos. 57 and 51 surch with T **19**.

68	**18**	1r. on 2r. black and yellow-green (R.)	17·00	£225
69	**17**	1r. on 5r. black and purple	20·00	£150

3 PIES

पाव आना ▬ ▬
(20)   **(21)**

1938 (Dec). No. 41 surch "QUARTER ANNA" in Devanagari, T **20**.

70	**7**	¼a. on ½a. black and violet (R.)	23·00	24·00

1947 (1 Dec). No. 41 surch with T **21**.

71	**7**	3p. on ½a. black and violet (R.)	22·00	38·00
		a. "PIE" for "PIES"	70·00	£200
		b. Bars at left vertical	£110	£250
		c. Surch inverted	70·00	65·00
		d. Surch inverted and "PIE" for "PIES"	£425	£375
		e. Surch double, one inverted	£110	80·00
		f. As variety e, but inverted surch showing "PIE" for "PIES"	£650	£550

There were three settings of Type **21**, each applied to quarter sheets of 30 (6×5). No. 71a occurs in two of these settings on R. 5/5 and one of these settings also shows No. 71b on R. 6/1.

22 Palace Gate

23 Maharaja and Amber Palace

24 Map of Jaipur

25 Observatory

26 Wind Palace

27 Coat of Arms

28 Amber Fort Gate

29 Chariot of the Sun

30 Maharaja's portrait between State Flags

(Recess D.L.R.)

1948 (1 Mar–22 Nov). Silver Jubilee of Maharaja's Accession to Throne. T **22/30**. P 13½×14.

72	**22**	¼a. red-brown and green (22.11)	3·50	7·50
73	**23**	½a. green and violet	50	4·50
74	**24**	¾a. black and lake (22.11)	4·00	11·00
75	**25**	1a. red-brown and ultramarine	1·50	4·75
76	**26**	2a. violet and scarlet	1·50	7·00
77	**27**	3a. green and black (22.11)	5·00	13·00
78	**28**	4a. ultramarine and brown	1·50	7·50
79	**29**	8a. vermilion and brown	1·50	7·50
80	**30**	1r. purple and green (22.11)	6·00	80·00
72/80		*Set of 9*	22·00	£130

OFFICIAL STAMPS

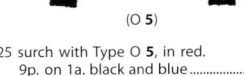

SERVICE   SERVICE
(O **1**)   (O **2**)

1928 (13 Nov)–**31**. T **3** typographed. No gum (except for Nos. O6/a). P 11, 12, or compound. Wmk "DORLING & CO. LONDON" (4a.) or "OVERLAND BANK" (others).

*(a) Optd with Type O **1***

O1		¼a. olive	6·50	6·50
		a. Bistre	6·50	5·50
O2		½a. pale ultramarine (Blk.)	3·00	40
		a. Imperf between (horiz pair)	£750	£750
		b. Imperf between (vert pair)	†	£1500
		c. Opt inverted	†	£900
		d. Opt double (R. and Blk.)	†	£1200
O3		½a. pale ultramarine (R.) (13.10.30)	8·50	75
		a. Imperf horiz (vert pair)	£1600	
		b. Stamp doubly printed	†	£1200
O3c		1a. rose-red	6·00	1·50
		d. Imperf between (horiz pair)	†	£1700
O4		1a. scarlet	5·50	1·25
		a. Opt inverted	£2000	£2000
		b. Imperf between (horiz pair)	†	£1700
O5		2a. green	5·50	1·00
		a. Imperf between (vert pair)	†	£2500
		b. Imperf between (horiz pair)	£2500	£2500
O6		4a. pale brown (with gum)	12·00	1·75
		a. Chocolate (with gum)	6·50	1·75
O7		8a. bright violet (13.10.30)	18·00	80·00
O8		1r. orange-vermilion	55·00	£650

*(b) Optd with Type O **2***

O9		½a. ultramarine (Blk.) (11.2.31)	£250	75
		a. Imperf vert (horiz pair)	†	£2000
O10		½a. ultramarine (R.) (15.10.30)	£275	1·00
		a. Imperf between (vert pair)	†	£2000
O11		8a. bright violet (11.2.31)	£1100	£350
O12		1r. orange-vermilion (11.2.31)	£1300	£650

SERVICE   आध आना
(O **3**)   (O **4**)

1931–37. Nos. 41/3 and 46 optd at Nasik with Type O **3**, in red.

O13	**7**	½a. black and violet	40	10
O14	**8**	1a. black and blue	£750	8·50
O15	**9**	2a. black and buff (1936)	9·50	10·00
O16	**12**	4a. black and olive-green (1937)	90·00	75·00
O13/16		*Set of 4*	£800	85·00

1932. No. O5 surch with Type O **4**.

O17	**3**	½a. on 2a. green	£300	6·00

1932–37. Nos. 52/6 optd at Nasik with Type O **3**, in red.

O18	**18**	1a. black and blue	9·50	15
O19		2a. black and buff	14·00	15
O20		4a. black and grey-green (1937)	£450	18·00
O21		8a. black and chocolate	20·00	1·75
O22		1r. black and yellow-bistre	70·00	50·00
O18/22		*Set of 5*	£500	65·00

1936–46. Stamps of 1932–46, inscr "POSTAGE".

*(a) Optd at Nasik with Type O **3**, in red*

O23	**7**	¼a. black and brown-lake (1936)	50	10
O24		¾a. black and brown-red (1944)	2·50	50
O25		1a. black and blue (1941?)	8·50	30
O26		2a. black and buff (date?)	6·50	3·25
O27		2½a. black and carmine (1946)	14·00	£110
O28		4a. black and grey-green (1942)	9·00	7·50
O29		8a. black and chocolate (1943)	5·00	10·00
O30		1r. black and yellow-bistre (date?)	35·00	
O23/9		*Set of 7*	40·00	£120

*(b) Optd locally as Type O **2** (16 mm long), in black*

O31	**7**	¼a. black and red-brown (1936)	£170	£120

9 PIES

▬ ▬
(O **5**)

1947. No. O25 surch with Type O **5**, in red.

O32	**7**	9p. on 1a. black and blue	3·75	3·75

1947 (Dec). No. O13 surch as T **21**, but "3 PIES" placed higher.

O33	**7**	3p. on ½a. black and violet (R.)	12·00	19·00
		a. Surch double, one inverted	75·00	75·00
		ab. "PIE" for "PIES" in inverted surcharge	£500	£500
		c. Surch inverted	—	£2500

1948 (Dec). No. O13 surch "THREE-QUARTER ANNA" in Devanagari, as T **20**, but with two bars on each side.

O34	**7**	¾a. on ½a. black and violet (R.)	35·00	25·00
		a. Surch double	£2500	£1900

There are three different types of surcharge in the setting of 30, which vary in one or other of the Devanagari characters.

Jaipur became part of Rajasthan by 7 April 1949.

JAMMU AND KASHMIR

PRICES FOR STAMPS ON COVER

Nos. 1/73	from × 3
Nos. 74/84	from × 2
No. 85	—
Nos. 86/9	from × 2
Nos. 90/101	from × 10
Nos. 101*b*/23	from × 5
Nos. 124/36	from × 10
Nos. 138/9	from × 100
Nos. 140/61*a*	from × 15
Nos. 162/8	from × 5
No. O1	from × 2
Nos. O2/4	from × 4
No. O5	—
Nos. O6/14	from × 30
Nos. O15/18	—

ILLUSTRATIONS. Designs of Jammu and Kashmir are illustrated actual size.

Maharaja Ranbir Singh, 1857–1885

1 (½a.)   **2** (1a.)

3 (4a.)

Characters denoting the value (on the circular stamps only) are approximately as shown in the central circles of the stamps illustrated above.

These characters were taken from Punjabi merchants' notation and were not familiar to most of the inhabitants of the state. Type **1** was certainly the ½ anna value, but there has long been controversy over the correct face values of Types **2** and **3**.

The study of surviving material suggests that, to some extent, this confusion involved contemporary post office officials. Although covers posted at Jammu, where the stamps were in use for 12 years, show Type **2** used as the 1a. value and Type **3** as the 4a., those originating from Srinagar (Kashmir) during 1866–68 show both Types **2** and **3** used as 1a. stamps.

In the following listing we have followed contemporary usage at Jammu and this reflects the prevailing opinion amongst modern authorities.

GUM. The stamps of Jammu and Kashmir were issued without gum.

PRICES. Prices for the circular stamps, Nos. 1/49, are for cut-square examples. In practice, stamps were often cut to shape before use, especially in the early period (1866-67), and such examples are worth from 20% to 50% of the prices quoted, according to condition.

A. Handstamped in watercolours

1866 (23 Mar). Native paper, thick to thin, usually having the appearance of laid paper and tinted grey or brown. For Jammu and Kashmir.

1	**1**	½a. grey-black	£500	£200
2		½a. ultramarine	£8500	£8500
3	**2**	1a. royal blue	—	£1000
3*a*		1a. ultramarine	£1300	£300
4		1a. grey-black	£4000	£2750
5	**3**	4a. royal blue		
5*a*		4a. ultramarine	£2250	£850

No. 4 may be an error of colour. It is only known used in Kashmir.

1867–76. Reissued for use in Jammu only.

6	**3**	4a. grey-black	£4750	
7		4a. indigo	£5000	£3250
8		4a. red (1869)	£180	£250
9		4a. orange-red (1872)	£475	£600
10		4a. orange (1872)		
11		4a. carmine-red (1876)	£2500	

1874–76. Special Printings.

12	**1**	½a. red	£200	£475
12*a*		½a. orange-red	£1200	£1200
13	**2**	1a. red	£475	£500
13*a*		1a. orange-red	£1000	£1100
13*b*		1a. orange	£2500	
14	**1**	½a. deep black	60·00	£250
		a. *Tête-bêche* (pair)	£1800	
15	**2**	1a. deep black	£600	
16	**3**	4a. deep black	£550	
17	**1**	½a. bright blue (1876)	£750	£850
18	**2**	1a. bright blue (1876)	£250	£550
		a. *Tête-bêche* (pair)	£3750	
19	**3**	4a. bright blue (1876)	£475	
20	**1**	½a. emerald-green	£300	£450
21	**2**	1a. emerald-green	£325	£550
22	**3**	4a. emerald-green	£550	£900
23	**1**	½a. yellow	£1000	£1700
24	**2**	1a. yellow	£1800	
25	**3**	4a. yellow	£1000	
25*a*		4a. deep blue-black (1876)	£3500	£1800

These special printings were available for use, but little used.

B. Handstamped in oil colours. Heavy blurred prints

1877 (June)–78.

(a) Native paper

26	**1**	½a. red	75·00	£120
27	**2**	1a. red	95·00	£350
28	**3**	4a. red	£550	£750
29	**1**	½a. black	70·00	£130
		a. *Tête-bêche* (pair)	£4500	
32		½a. slate-blue	£325	£425
34	**2**	1a. slate-blue	75·00	£450
35	**1**	½a. sage-green	£200	
36	**2**	1a. sage-green	£250	
37	**3**	4a. sage-green	£250	

(b) European laid paper, medium to thick

38	**1**	½a. red	—	£2250
39	**3**	4a. red	£650	£850
41	**1**	½a. black	65·00	£130
		a. Printed both sides	£2000	
		b. *Tête-bêche* (pair)	£1500	
44		½a. slate-blue	£140	£475
45	**2**	1a. slate-blue	£150	£550
46	**3**	4a. slate-blue	£1400	£1400
47		4a. sage-green	£3000	£3500
48	**1**	½a. yellow	£250	

(c) Thick yellowish wove paper

49	**1**	½a. red (1878)	—	£1800

Forgeries exist of the ½a. and 1a. in types which were at one time supposed to be authentic.

Reprints and imitations (of which some of each were found in the official remainder stock) exist in a great variety of fancy colours, both on native paper, usually thinner and smoother than that of the originals, and on various thin European *wove* papers, on which the originals were never printed.

The imitations, which do not agree in type with the above illustrations, are also to be found on *laid* paper.

All the reprints, etc. are in oil colours or printer's ink. The originals in oil colour are usually blurred, particularly when on native paper. The reprints, etc. are usually clear.

FOR USE IN JAMMU

½a.   ½a.

1a.   ½a.

4

T **4** to **11** have a star at the top of the oval band; the characters denoting the value are in the upper part of the inner oval. All are dated 1923, corresponding with A.D. 1866.

T **4**. Printed in blocks of four, three varieties of ½ anna and one of 1 anna.

1867 (Sept). In watercolour on native paper.

52		½a. grey-black	£2500	£750
53		1a. grey-black	£6000	£3750
54		½a. indigo	£900	£550
55		1a. indigo	£1800	£850
56		½a. deep ultramarine	£700	£350
57		1a. deep ultramarine	£1700	£800
58		½a. deep violet-blue	£475	£180
59		1a. deep violet-blue	£1800	£750

1868 (May)–72. In watercolour on native paper.

60		½a. red (*shades*)	20·00	11·00
61		1a. red (*shades*)	45·00	24·00
62		½a. orange-red	£425	£110
63		1a. orange-red	£1700	£700
64		½a. orange (1872)	£250	£300
65		1a. orange (1872)	£5500	£3500

1874–76. Special printings; in watercolour on native paper.

66		½a. bright blue (1876)	£3250	£700
67		1a. bright blue (1876)	£950	£950
68		½a. emerald-green	£4000	£2000
69		1a. emerald-green	£6500	£3250
69*a*		½a. jet-black	£325	£400
69*b*		1a. jet-black	£5000	£3750

1877 (June)–78. In oil colour.

(a) Native paper

70		½a. red	25·00	20·00
71		1a. red	75·00	50·00
72		½a. brown-red (1878)	—	85·00
73		1a. brown-red (1878)	—	£275
74		½a. black	†	£2250
75		1a. black	†	£4750
76		½a. deep blue-black	†	£3750
77		1a. deep blue-black	†	£7500

(b) Laid paper (medium or thick)

78		½a. red	—	£2250

(c) Thick wove paper

79		½a. red	†	£1000
80		1a. red		

(d) Thin laid, bâtonné paper

84		½a. red	†	£3500
85		1a. red	£7500	

The circular and rectangular stamps listed under the heading "Special Printings' did not supersede those in *red*, which was the normal colour for Jammu down to 1878. It is not known for what reason other colours were used during that period, but these stamps were printed in 1874 or 1875 and were certainly put into use. The rectangular stamps were again printed in *black* (jet-black, as against the greyish black of the 1867 printings) at that time, and impressions of the two periods can also be distinguished by the obliterations, which until 1868 were in *magenta* and after that in *black*.

There are reprints of these, in oil colour, *brown-red* and *bright blue*, on native paper; they are very clearly printed, which is not the case with the originals in *oil colour*.

4a

1877 (Sept). Provisional. Seal obliterator of Jammu handstamped in red watercolour on pieces of native paper, and used as a ½ anna stamp.

86	**4a**	(½a.) rose-red	—	£3000

FOR USE IN KASHMIR

5

1866 (Sept(?)). Printed from a single die. Native laid paper.

87	**5**	½a. black	£6500	£750

Forgeries of this stamp are commonly found, copied from an illustration in *Le Timbre-Poste*.

6 (½a.)   **7** (1a.)

1867 (Apr). Native laid paper.

88	**6**	½a. black	£3500	£375
89	**7**	1a. black	£4750	£850

Printed in sheets of 25 (5×5), the four top rows being ½a. and the bottom row 1a.

8 (¼a.)   **9** (2a.)

10 (4a.)   **11** (8a.)

1867–77. Native laid paper.

90	**8**	¼a. black	9·50	10·00
		a. *Tête-bêche* (vert pair)	£10000	
91	**6**	½a. ultramarine (6.67)	12·00	5·50
		a. Bisected (¼a.) (on cover) (1877)	†	£14000
92		½a. violet-blue (1870)	30·00	13·00
93	**7**	1a. ultramarine (6.67)	£7500	£3500
94		1a. orange (7.67)	35·00	24·00
95		1a. brown-orange (1868)	35·00	24·00
96		1a. orange-vermilion (1876)	42·00	30·00
97	**9**	2a. yellow	45·00	50·00
98		2a. buff	70·00	60·00
99	**10**	4a. emerald-green	£110	90·00
		a. *Tête-bêche* (pair)	£2500	
		b. Stamp sideways (in pair)	£8000	
100		4a. sage-green	£650	£325
100*a*		4a. myrtle-green	£1800	£1500

101	**11**	8a. red (1868)	£120	95·00
		a. *Tête-bêche* (pair)	£10000	£10000

Of the above, the ½a. and 1a. were printed from the same plate of 25 as Nos. 88/9, the ¼a. and 2a. from a new plate of ten (5×2), the top row being ¼a. and the lower 2a., and the 4a. and 8a. from single dies. Varieties at one time catalogued upon European papers were apparently never put into circulation, though some of them were printed while these stamps were still in use.

No. 86 to 101 are in watercolour.

No. 91a was used at Srinagar, in conjunction with an India ½a., and was cancelled "KASHMIR 5/L-6".

FOR USE IN JAMMU AND KASHMIR

In the following issues there are 15 varieties on the sheets of the ⅛a., ¼a. and ½a.; 20 varieties of the 1a. and 2a. and eight varieties of the 4a. and 8a. The value is in the lower part of the central oval.

12 (¼a.)   **13** (½a.)

14 (1a.)   **15** (2a.)

16 (4a.)   **17** (8a.)

1878 (May)–**79**. Provisional printings.

I. Ordinary white laid paper, of varying thickness

(a) Rough perf 10 to 12 (i) or 13 to 16 (ii)

101b	**12**	¼a. red (i)		
102	**13**	½a. red (i)	21·00	25·00
103	**14**	1a. red (i)	£2000	
104	**13**	½a. slate-violet (i)	£130	£130
104a	**14**	1a. violet (ii)		
104b	**15**	2a. violet (i)	£3000	

(b) Imperf

105	**13**	½a. slate-violet (*shades*)	29·00	25·00
106	**14**	1a. slate-purple	45·00	48·00
107		1a. mauve	90·00	80·00
108	**15**	2a. violet	55·00	60·00
109		2a. bright mauve	70·00	65·00
110		2a. slate-blue	£130	£130
111		2a. dull blue	£200	£200
112	**12**	¼a. red	42·00	42·00
113	**13**	½a. red	19·00	21·00
114	**14**	1a. red	19·00	22·00
115	**15**	2a. red	£150	£150
116	**16**	4a. red	£425	£350

II. Medium wove paper

(a) Rough perf 10 to 12

117	**13**	½a. red	—	£750

(b) Imperf

117b	**12**	¼a. red		
118	**13**	½a. red	27·00	25·00
119	**14**	1a. red	32·00	25·00
120	**15**	2a. red	£130	

III. Thick wove paper. Imperf

121	**13**	½a. red	65·00	90·00
122	**14**	1a. red	90·00	55·00
123	**15**	2a. red	45·00	55·00

Of the above stamps those in red were intended for use in Jammu and those in shades of violet and blue for use in Kashmir.

1879. Definitive issue. Thin wove paper, fine to coarse.

(a) Rough perf 10 to 12

124	**13**	½a. red	£900	£750

(b) Imperf

125	**12**	¼a. red	8·00	9·00
126	**13**	½a. red	2·75	2·75
		a. Bisected (¼a.) (*on cover or postcard*)	†	£9500
127	**14**	1a. red	5·50	7·50
		a. Bisected (½a.) (*on cover*)	†	£8500
128	**15**	2a. red	7·50	9·50
129	**16**	4a. red	28·00	22·00
130	**17**	8a. red	32·00	26·00

The plates were transferred from Jammu to Srinagar in early 1881 when further printings in red and all orange stamps were produced.

1880 (Mar). Provisional printing in watercolour on thin bâtonné paper. Imperf.

130a	**12**	¼a. ultramarine	£1600	£1000

1881–83. As Nos. 124 to 130. Colour changed.

(a) Rough perf 10 to 12

130b	**13**	½a. orange		

(b) Imperf

131	**12**	¼a. orange	30·00	35·00

132	**13**	½a. orange	32·00	28·00
		a. Bisected (¼a.) (*on cover*)		
133	**14**	1a. orange	50·00	32·00
		a. Bisected (½a.) (*on cover*)	†	£14000
134	**15**	2a. orange	42·00	32·00
135	**16**	4a. orange	85·00	90·00
136	**17**	8a. orange	£130	£130

Nos. 126a and 133a were used at Leh between April and July 1883. Nos. 125/30 and 132/6 were re-issued between 1890 and 1894 and used concurrently with the stamps which follow. Such re-issues can be identified by the "three circle" cancellations, introduced in December 1890.

18 (⅛a.)

1883–94. New colours. Thin wove papers, toned, coarse to fine, or fine white (1889). Imperf.

138	**18**	⅛a. yellow-brown	3·00	3·75
139		⅛a. yellow	3·00	3·75
140	**12**	¼a. sepia	2·75	1·25
141		¼a. brown	2·75	1·25
		a. Double impression	£1500	
142		¼a. pale brown	2·75	1·25
		a. Error. Green	£140	
143	**13**	½a. dull blue	20·00	
144		½a. bright blue	£100	
145		½a. vermilion	2·75	1·75
146		½a. rose	3·00	1·75
147		½a. orange-red	1·50	1·75
148	**14**	1a. greenish grey	2·50	2·75
149		1a. bright green	2·50	3·00
		a. Double impression		
150		1a. dull green	2·75	3·00
151		1a. blue-green	3·50	
152	**15**	2a. red/*yellow*	7·00	3·50
153		2a. red/*yellow-green*	8·50	11·00
154		2a. red/*deep green*	38·00	45·00
155	**16**	4a. deep green	6·50	7·50
156		4a. green	6·50	7·00
157		4a. pale green	6·50	4·50
158		4a. sage-green	8·00	
159	**17**	8a. pale blue	18·00	18·00
159a		8a. deep blue	25·00	29·00
160		8a. bright blue	18·00	21·00
161		8a. indigo-blue	24·00	27·00
161a		8a. slate-lilac	20·00	35·00

Well-executed forgeries of the ¼a. to 8a. have come from India, mostly postmarked; they may be detected by the type, which does not agree with any variety on the genuine sheets, and also, in the low values, by the margins being filled in with colour, all but a thin white frame round the stamp. The forgeries of the 8a. are in sheets of eight like the originals.

Other forgeries of nearly all values also exist, showing all varieties of type. All values are on thin, coarse wove paper.

In February 1890, a forgery, in watercolour, of the ½a. orange on thin wove or on thin laid paper appeared, and many have been found genuinely used during 1890 and 1891 (*Price* £7).

Nos. 143 and 144 were never issued.

Examples of the ¼a. brown, ½a. orange-red and 1a. green on wove paper exist with clean-cut perf 12.

There is a reference in the Jammu and Kashmir State Administration Report covering 1890–91 to the re-introduction of perforating and the machine-gumming of paper at the Jammu printing works.

The few known examples, the ¼a. being only recorded used, the others unused or used, would appear to date from this period, but there is, as yet, no direct confirmation as to their status.

Maharaja Partap Singh, 1885–1925

1887–94. Thin creamy laid paper. Imperf.

162	**18**	⅛a. yellow	£120	£130
163	**12**	¼a. brown	13·00	9·50
164	**13**	½a. brown-red (3.87)	—	£140
165		½a. orange-red	19·00	13·00
166	**14**	1a. grey-green	£110	£110
168	**17**	8a. blue (*Printed in watercolour*)	£180	£180
		a. On wove paper	£120	£120

19

T **19** represents a ¼a. stamp, which exists in sheets of 12 varieties, in *red* and *black* on thin wove and laid papers, also in *red* on native paper, but which does not appear ever to have been issued for use. It was first seen in 1886.

The ¼a. *brown* and the 4a. *green* both exist on ordinary white laid paper and the ½a. *red* on native paper. None of these are known to have been in use.

OFFICIAL STAMPS

1878.

I. White laid paper

(a) Rough perf 10 to 12

O1	**13**	½a. black	—	£4000

(b) Imperf

O2	**13**	½a. black	£170	£160
O3	**14**	1a. black	£120	£120

O4	**15**	2a. black	90·00	95·00

II. Medium wove paper. Imperf

O5	**14**	1a. black	£700	

1880–94. Thin wove papers, toned, coarse to fine, or fine white (1889). Imperf.

O6	**12**	¼a. black	3·25	3·75
		a. Double print	£250	
O7	**13**	½a. black	50	1·75
		a. Printed both sides	£650	
O8	**14**	1a. black	1·50	2·25
O9	**15**	2a. black	75	85
O10	**16**	4a. black	3·00	3·50
O11	**17**	8a. black	4·75	3·00

1887–94. Thin creamy laid paper. Imperf.

O12	**12**	¼a. black	21·00	17·00
O13	**13**	½a. black	14·00	11·00
O14	**14**	1a. black	7·50	7·50
O15	**15**	2a. black	28·00	
O16	**16**	4a. black	90·00	£100
O17	**17**	8a. black	60·00	85·00

1889. Stout white wove paper. Imperf.

O18	**12**	¼a. black	£425	£275

The stamps of Jammu and Kashmir have been obsolete since 1 November 1894.

TELEGRAPH STAMPS

Telegraph lines from Srinagar to Jammu and to Gilgit were constructed according to a treaty of 1878 between the State Government and the Government of India. The lines were later extended along the State railway lines according to a further treaty of 1890.

PRICES. Unused prices quoted are always for whole stamps. The status of prices for used stamps is explained by the following note.

USED STAMPS. From 1884 until 1910 (Nos T1/40 and OT1/15) stamps were intended to be affixed vertically to Telegraph forms, and were then bisected, with the upper halves on the receipt portion given to the sender, while the lower halves remained on the message portion retained by the authorities. Since Nos T1/14 and OT1/15 are in horizontal format, used left and right halves survive in roughly equal quantities, and used whole stamps can be found. But Nos T15/40, in "double" vertical format, like the Telegraph stamps of India, were designed to be affixed to forms in such a way that only the upper halves remained on the receipt portion, and used lower halves are very rare.

After 1910, bisection in use ceased, and Nos T51/82 were always used as whole stamps, although few examples survive.

T 1

T 2

T 3

T 4

T 5

T 6

T 7

1884. Design of State Arms, inscribed "Jammu Kashmir Tibet Telegraphs" in Dogra script. Handstamped from single brass dies, with differing face values in Persian script at left and right, as Types T **1/7**. Thin white or toned wove paper. No gum. Imperf.

			Unused	Used half
T1	T **1**	1a. green	2·00	35·00
		a. yellow-green	2·50	35·00
		b. blue-green	2·50	—
		c. olive-green	3·00	35·00
T2	T **2**	2a. sepia	2·50	30·00
		a. dark brown	3·00	30·00
		b. yellow-brown	5·00	—
T3	T **3**	4a. ultramarine	3·00	30·00
T4	T **4**	8a. orange	6·00	50·00
		a. yellow	4·00	50·00
T5	T **5**	1r. scarlet	5·00	35·00
		a. brown-red	6·00	35·00
		b. vermilion	8·00	—
T6	T **6**	2r. blackish green	10·00	—
T7	T **7**	15r.	15·00	—
T8	–	10r. vermilion	£5000	—
T9	–	25r. violet	£5000	—

A contemporary forgery of the 1r. value was produced, apparently to defraud the authorities. It differs especially in the shield shape, which is much more narrow, and the supporters.

Cancellations on used stamps of the 1884 and 1887 issues take several forms, including manuscript, oval intaglio seals (in black or violet), and straight-line or circular datestamps. The straight-line datestamps are in Dogra script, but the circular datestamps include "triple-ring" types with office name in English. Used examples are best collected on piece.

1887 (?). Handstamped from single brass dies. As 1884 issue, but thin toned laid paper. No gum. Imperf.

T10	T **1**	1a. yellow-green	6·00	—
T11	T **2**	2a. brown	5·00	50·00
T12	T **3**	4a. ultramarine	12·00	—
T13	T **4**	8a. brownish yellow	12·00	—
T14	T **5**	1r. scarlet	10·00	75·00

T 8   **T 11**

T 9   **T 10**

(Typo De la Rue)

1897. Double stamps as Type T **8**. Duty tablets in second colour, with face value in Persian script at centre on upper half and in English on lower half. Unwatermarked paper. Perf 14.

T15	T **8**	1a. bright blue and carmine	55·00	27·00
T16		2a. reddish violet and olive-brown	£110	38·00
T17		4a. rose-carmine and olive-brown	£120	55·00
T18		8a. yellow and bright blue	£110	55·00
T19		1r. brown-orange and reddish violet	£160	80·00
T20		2r. brown and light blue	£160	£110
T21		5r. blue-green and carmine	£160	

Prices quoted for used examples of Nos T15/21 and the subsequent 1899-1909 and 1906-09 issues (Nos T22/40) are for upper halves, usually with shield-shaped datestamps, although manuscript cancels and circular datestamps are also known. Dates follow the Samvat era, 57 years ahead of dates A.D., so that "1963" is equivalent to 1906 A.D. Nos T22/29 were also later used whole after a change in regulations in 1910, when bisection in use ceased, prior to their replacement by the 1911-21 Type T **12** "single" design.

(Typo De la Rue)

1899-1909. Double stamps. As 1897 issue, but wmk Multiple Rosettes (horiz. or vert.). Perf 14.

T22	T **8**	½a. blackish olive and blue-green (1909)	55·00	65·00
T23		1a. bright blue and carmine	55·00	27·00
T24		2a. reddish violet and olive-brown	£110	27·00
T25		4a. rose-carmine and olive-brown	£110	25·00
T26		6a. violet and sage-green (1909)	£275	—
T27		8a. yellow and bright blue	£110	55·00
T28		1r. brown-orange and reddish violet	£160	55·00
T29		2r. brown and light blue	£225	£110

The 5r. value was also printed on watermarked paper, but was apparently only issued with local surcharges.

1906-09. Type T **8** surcharged locally with new values in English as Types T **9/11**, in complete sheets.

a) On 1897 unwatermarked issue.

T31	1a. on 2r. brown and light blue	
T32	2a. on 2r. brown and light blue	
T33	4a. on 2r. brown and light blue	
T34	4a. on 5r. blue-green and carmine	— £750

b) On 1899 watermarked issue, and similar 5r. value.

T35	½a. on 1a. bright blue and carmine	£2500	
T36	1a. on 2r. brown and light blue	£2500	£250
T37	2a. on 2r. brown and light blue	£2500	£250
T38	4a. on 1r. brown-orange and reddish violet	—	£750
T39	4a. on 2r. brown and light blue	—	£750
T40	8a. on 5r. blue-green and carmine	£160	£200

Different types of surcharges are known on most values, expressed as numeral + word (in one line) or as two words (usually in two lines, but in one line on No. T35) with whole unused examples often showing different styles on the upper and lower halves, and it seems likely that composite settings were used. At least eight varieties of the 8a. on 5r. have been recorded. A more detailed listing will be provided when fuller information is available.

T 12   **T 13**

T 14

(Typo De la Rue)

1911-21. Single stamps with trilingual face value, as Type T **12**. Duty tablets in second colour. Wmk Multiple Rosettes (horiz. or vert.). Perf 14.

			Unused	Used
T51	T **12**	½a. blackish olive and blue-green (1913)	£120	£120
T52		1a. bright blue and carmine	£170	£120
T53		2a. reddish violet and olive-brown (1913)	£170	£140
T54		4a. rose-carmine and olive-brown (1912)	£225	£140
T55		6a. violet and sage-green (1913)	£275	£170
T56		8a. yellow and bright blue (1912)	£275	£170
T57		1r. brown-orange and reddish violet (1916)	—	£275
T58		2r. brown and light blue (1921)		
T59		5r. blue-green and carmine (1921)		

Used examples of Nos T51/9 and subsequent issues were cancelled by circular datestamps.

[?]. Local surcharges in English on 1911-21 issue.

T60	–	1a. on 2a. reddish violet and olive-brown	£1500
T61	T **13**	12a. on 6a violet and sage-green	† £800

The only example seen of No. T60 shows the surcharge as "ONE / ANNA." (in two lines).

1930. Surcharged by De la Rue.

T65	T **14**	12a. on 1r. brown-orange and reddish violet	£500

T 15   **T 16**

(Recess De la Rue)

1933-34. New design Type T **15** with portrait of Maharajah Sir Hari Singh, and differing face values in side tablets, in Devanagari at left and Persian script at right. Wmk mult rosettes (horiz.). Perf 14.

T66	T **15**	1a. deep blue	£100
T67		2a. chocolate (1934)	£150
T68		4a. bluish green	£150
T69		8a. reddish orange	£200
T70		12a. yellow-orange	£200
T71		1r. violet	£375
T72		2r. rose-carmine	£800
T73		5r. black	£1300

A similar 1a. stamp without 'TELEGRAPH' at foot was issued for fiscal purposes.

[?]. Local surcharges in English on 1933-34 issue.

T74	8a. on 12a. yellow-orange	

The only example seen shows shows "EIGHT ANNAS" at foot, with bars through the original face values at left and right.

1941 [?]. New design Type T**16** with bilingual face values as 1933-34 issue. Litho, Security Press Nasik. No wmk. Perf 14.

T75	T **16**	1a. deep blue	75·00
T76		2a. chocolate	£100
T77		4a. deep green	£150
T78		8a. red orange	£150
T79		12a. yellow-orange	£200
T80		1r. violet	£250
T81		2r. rose-carmine	£1100
T82		5r. black	

A similar 1a. stamp without 'TELEGRAPH' at foot was issued for fiscal purposes.

OFFICIAL TELEGRAPH STAMPS

1884. Handstamped from single brass dies. Thin white or toned wove paper. No gum. Imperf.

			Unused	Used half
OT1	T **1**	1a. black	6·00	50·00
OT2	T **2**	2a. black	6·00	50·00
OT3	T **3**	4a. black	6·00	50·00
OT4	T **4**	8a. black	20·00	
OT5	T **5**	1r. black	15·00	
OT6	T **6**	2r. black	30·00	
OT7	T **7**	5r. black	75·00	
OT8	–	10r. black	—	
OT9	–	25r. black		

1887 (?). Handstamped from single brass dies. As 1884 issue, but thin toned laid paper.

OT10	T **1**	1a. black	12·00	
OT11	T **2**	2a. black	20·00	
OT12	T **3**	4a. black	30·00	
OT14	T **5**	1r. black	75·00	
OT15	T **7**	5r. black		

JASDAN

PRICES FOR STAMPS ON COVER
Nos. 1/2	from × 2
No. 3	from × 3
Nos. 4/6	from × 4

Darbar Ala Khachar, 1919–1971

1 Sun

(Typo L. V. Indap & Co, Bombay)

1942 (15 Mar)**–47**. Stamps from booklet panes. Various perfs.

1	**1**	1a. deep myrtle-green (P 10½)	£3000	£1500
2		1a. light green (P 12)	£1500	£1400
3		1a. green (*shades*) (P 10½)	£275	£325
4		1a. pale yellow-green (P 8½–9) (1946)	25·00	£325
5		1a. dull yellow-green (P 10) (1945)	50·00	£350
6		1a. bluish green (P 8½–9) (1947)	45·00	£325

Nos. 1/4 were issued in panes of four with the stamps imperforate on one or two sides; Nos. 5/6 were in panes of eight perforated all round.

No.3 exists in a variety of shades, from light to deep green, and comes from several printings. The evidence of dated covers suggests that some examples may pre-date the stamps currently listed as Nos. 1/2.

A 1a. rose with the arms of Jasdan in the centre is a fiscal stamp.

Jasdan was merged with the United State of Kathiawar (later Saurashtra) by 15 April 1948.

JHALAWAR

PRICES FOR STAMPS ON COVER	
Nos. 1/2	*from* × 30

Maharaj Rana Zalim Singh, 1875–1896

1 (1 paisa)   **2 (¼ anna)**

(Figure of an Apsara, "RHEMBA", a dancing nymph of the Hindu Paradise)

1886–90. Typo in horizontal strips of 12. Laid paper. Imperf. No gum.

1	1	1p. yellow-green	6·50	24·00
		a. Blue-green	£275	£100
2	2	¼a. green (shades) (1890)	2·25	3·25

The stamps formerly listed as on wove paper are from sheets on laid paper, with the laid paper lines almost invisible. The laid lines are normally vertical, with stamps printed on horizontally laid paper scarce.

The Maharaj Rana was deposed in 1896 and much of the state's territory transferred to Kotah on 1 January 1899.

Raj (Maharaj from 1918) Rana Rhawani Singh, 1899–1929

The stamps of Jhalawar have been obsolete since 1 November 1900.

JIND

PRICES FOR STAMPS ON COVER	
The stamps of Jind are very rare used on cover.	

ILLUSTRATIONS. Designs of Jind are illustrated actual size.

Raja Raghubir Singh, 1864–1887

J 1 (½a.)   **J 2 (1a.)**   **J 3 (2a.)**

J 4 (4a.)   **J 5 (8a.)**

(Litho Jind State Rajah's Press, Sungroor)

1874. Thin yellowish paper. Imperf.

J1	J 1	½a. blue	16·00	8·50
		a. No frame to value. (Retouched all over) (R. 4/7)	£800	£475
J2	J 2	1a. rosy mauve	11·00	9·00
J3	J 3	2a. yellow	2·75	8·50
J4		2a. brown-buff	£550	£275
J5	J 4	4a. green	40·00	6·00
J6	J 5	8a. dull purple	£1200	£375
J6a		8a. bluish violet	£450	£180
J7		8a. slate-blue	£400	£170

Nos. J1/7 were produced from two sets of stones. Those from the first set had rather blurred impressions, but those from the second are clearer with a conspicuous white frame around the value. Nos. J4 and J6a/13 were only printed from the second set.

1876. Bluish laid card-paper. No gum. Imperf.

J8	J 1	½a. blue	1·75	7·50
J9	J 2	1a. purple	4·75	20·00
J10	J 3	2a. brown	7·50	25·00
J11	J 4	4a. green	4·25	25·00
J11a	J 5	8a. bluish violet	14·00	30·00
J12		8a. slate-blue	11·00	13·00
J13		8a. steel-blue	13·00	20·00

Stocks of the ½a. (No. J8) and 2a. (No. J4) were perforated 12 in 1885 for use as fiscal stamps.

J 6 (¼a.)   **J 7 (½a.)**

J 8 (1a.)   **J 9 (2a.)**

J 10 (4a.)   **J 11 (8a.)**

(Litho Jind State Rajah's Press, Sungroor)

1882–85. Types J **6** to J **11**. No gum.

A. Imperf (1882–4)

(a) Thin yellowish wove paper

J15	¼a. buff (shades)	40	1·50
J16	¼a. red-brown	50	1·50
	a. Doubly printed	£100	
J17	½a. lemon	3·75	3·25
J18	½a. buff	3·25	2·75
J19	½a. brown-buff	2·00	75
J20	1a. brown (shades)	2·00	3·25
J21	2a. blue	3·25	12·00
J22	2a. deep blue	4·50	3·00
J23	4a. sage-green	4·00	2·75
J24	4a. blue-green	4·25	5·50
J25	8a. red	9·00	5·00

(b) Various thick laid papers

J26	¼a. brown-buff	2·25	
J27	½a. lemon	1·25	
J28	½a. brown-buff		
J29	1a. brown	1·25	2·50
J30	2a. blue	23·00	21·00
J31	8a. red	2·50	13·00

(c) Thick white wove paper

J32	¼a. brown-buff	38·00	
J33	½a. brown-buff	60·00	
J34	1a. brown	9·00	
J35	8a. red	8·00	13·00

B. Perf 12 (1885)

(a) Thin yellowish wove paper

J36	¼a. buff (shades)	1·50	3·75
	a. Doubly printed	£180	
J37	¼a. red-brown	5·50	
J38	½a. lemon	£250	£250
J39	½a. buff	1·25	5·00
J40	½a. brown-buff	4·50	9·50
J41	1a. brown (shades)	2·50	9·50
J42	2a. blue	7·00	17·00
J43	2a. deep blue	5·00	7·50
J44	4a. sage-green	8·50	18·00
J45	4a. blue-green	4·75	
	a. Imperf vert (horiz pair)	£900	
J46	8a. red	21·00	

(b) Various thick laid papers

J47	¼a. brown-buff	11·00	
J48	½a. lemon	£200	35·00
J49	1a. brown	3·25	
J50	2a. blue	38·00	38·00
J51	8a. red	2·75	15·00

(c) Thick white wove paper

J52	1a. brown		
J53	8a. red	15·00	

The perforated stamps ceased to be used for postal purposes in July 1885, but were used as fiscals to at least the mid-1920s. Other varieties exist, but they must either be fiscals or reprints, and it is not quite certain that all those listed above were issued as early as 1885.

Jind became a Convention State and from 1 July 1885 used overprinted Indian stamps.

KISHANGARH

PRICES FOR STAMPS ON COVER	
Nos. 1/3	—
Nos. 4/91	*from* × 8
Nos. O1/32	*from* × 30

GUM. The stamps of Kishangarh were issued without gum, *except for* Nos. 42/50 and O17/24.

Maharaja Sardul Singh, 1879–1900

1

1899–1900. Medium wove paper. Typo from a plate of eight (4×2).

1	1	1a. green (imperf)	24·00	85·00
2		1a. green (pin-perf) (1900)	95·00	

1900. Thin white wove paper. Printed from a single die. Imperf.

3	1	1a. blue	£800	

ILLUSTRATIONS. Types **2** to **10a** are shown actual size.

2 (¼a.)   **3 (½a.)**

4 (1a.)   **5 (2a.)** Maharaja Sardul Singh

6 (4a.)   **7 (1r.)**

8 (2r.)   **9 (5r.)**

1899 (Sept)**–1900**. Thin white wove paper.

(a) Imperf

4	2	¼a. yellow-green (1900)	£700	£1000
5		¼a. carmine	14·00	
		a. Rose-pink	2·50	4·50
6		¼a. magenta	5·00	6·00
		a. Doubly printed	£275	
7	3	½a. lilac (1900)	£300	£550
8		½a. red (1899)	£4750	£2000
9		½a. green (1899)	38·00	42·00
10		½a. pale yellow-olive	65·00	65·00
11		½a. slate-blue (1900)	65·00	65·00
		b. Deep blue	9·00	10·00
		c. Light blue	2·25	1·75
		ca. Pair, one stamp sideways	£2500	
12	4	1a. slate	12·00	5·00
		a. Laid paper	80·00	
12b		1a. pink	£140	£425
13		1a. mauve	10·00	7·50
		a. Laid paper	60·00	
14		1a. brown-lilac	1·10	1·00
		a. Laid paper	40·00	
15	5	2a. dull orange	8·50	4·50
		a. Laid paper	£900	£750
16	6	4a. chocolate	7·50	
		a. Lake-brown	7·50	15·00
		b. Chestnut	7·00	15·00
		c. Laid paper (shades)	£170	£160
17	7	1r. dull green	32·00	48·00
18		1r. brown-lilac	21·00	28·00
19	8	2r. brown-red	£110	£180
		a. Laid paper	90·00	
20	9	5r. mauve	£110	£160
		a. Laid paper	£110	

(b) Pin-perf 12½ or 14 (from Nov 1899)

21	2	¼a. yellow-green	£500	£800
		a. Imperf between (pair)	£2250	
22		¼a. carmine	10·00	10·00
		a. Rose-pink	25	50
		ab. Tête-bêche (horiz pair)	£2500	
		ac. Doubly printed	£190	£200
		ad. Trebly printed	£500	
		ae. Imperf between (horiz pair)	£225	
		b. Rose		
23		¼a. magenta	5·00	7·00
		a. Bright purple		
		ab. Doubly printed		
24	3	½a. green	21·00	27·00
		a. Imperf between (pair)	£450	
25		½a. pale yellow-olive	13·00	16·00
		a. Imperf vert (horiz pair)	£375	
		b. Imperf between (horiz pair)	†	£850
26		½a. deep blue	5·50	3·25
		a. Light blue	1·75	50
		ab. Doubly printed	£275	£275
		ac. Imperf between (pair)	£475	
27	4	1a. slate	8·00	6·00
		a. Laid paper	80·00	35·00
27b		1a. pink	£170	£450
28		1a. mauve	2·25	3·00
		a. Laid paper	55·00	18·00
29		1a. brown-lilac	1·25	1·00
		a. Laid paper	45·00	14·00
		b. Pair, one stamp sideways	£3250	
30	5	2a. dull orange	4·50	5·00
		a. Laid paper	£850	£850
31	6	4a. chocolate	3·25	8·50
		a. Lake-brown	3·25	8·50
		b. Chestnut	3·50	8·50
		c. Laid paper (shades)	£100	85·00
32	7	1r. dull green	11·00	15·00
		a. Laid paper	£120	
		b. Imperf between (vert pair)	£1600	
33		1r. pale olive-yellow	£1500	
34	8	2r. brown-red	35·00	55·00
		a. Laid paper	50·00	
35	9	5r. mauve	35·00	70·00
		a. Laid paper	95·00	

All the above, both imperf and pin-perf, were printed singly, sometimes on paper with spaces marked in pencil. They exist in vertical *tête-bêche* pairs imperf between from the centre of the sheet. *Prices from* 3×*normal, unused.* No. 22ab is an error.

FISCAL STAMPS. Many of the following issues were produced in different colours for fiscal purposes. Such usage is indicated by the initials "M.C.", punched hole or violet Stamp Office handstamp.

Maharaja Madan Singh, 1900–1926

10 (¼a.)	10a (1r.)

1901. Toned wove paper. Pin-perf.

36	**10**	¼a. dull pink	8·00	6·00
37	**4**	1a. violet	60·00	30·00
38	**10a**	1r. dull green	14·00	16·00
36/8 *Set of 3*				48·00

Nos. 36/8 were printed in sheets of 24. Sheets of the 1r. were always torn to remove R. 5/4 where the cliché is believed to have been defective.

The 1a. (No. 37) differs from T **4** in having an inscription in native characters below the words "ONE ANNA".

11 (½a.)	12 Maharaja Sardul Singh

1903. Litho. Thick white wove glazed paper. Imperf.

39	**11**	½a. pink	18·00	3·00
		a. Printed both sides	†	£3000
40	**12**	2a. dull yellow	3·00	7·50

12a (8a.)

1904. Printed singly. Thin paper. Pin-perf.

41	**12a**	8a. grey	5·00	9·00
		a. *Tête-bêche* (vert pair)	42·00	
		b. Doubly printed	£275	

13 Maharaja Madan Singh	14 Maharaja Madan Singh

(Recess Perkins Bacon & Co)

1904–10. With gum. P 12½.

42	**13**	¼a. carmine	60	1·00
		a. Perf 13½ (1910)	1·75	1·00
		b. Perf 12×12½	£300	
43		½a. chestnut	4·25	1·75
		a. Perf 13½ (1906)	1·25	30
44		1a. blue	7·50	4·00
		a. Perf 13½ (1906)	4·00	2·75
45		2a. orange-yellow	15·00	8·00
		a. Perf 13½ (1907)	27·00	20·00
46		4a. brown	27·00	30·00
		a. Perf 13½ (1907)	15·00	22·00
		b. Perf 12	£190	£120
		c. Perf comp of 12 and 12½	£325	
47		8a. violet (1905)	32·00	60·00
48		1r. green	30·00	95·00
49		2r. olive-yellow	50·00	£325
50		5r. purple-brown	28·00	£250
42/50 *Set of 9*			£160	£700

Stamps in other colours, all perforated 13½, were produced by Perkins Bacon as business samples.

1912. Printed from half-tone blocks. No ornaments to left and right of value in English; large ornaments on either side of value in Hindi. Small stop after "STATE".

(a) Thin wove paper. Rouletted

51	**14**	2a. deep violet ("TWO ANNA")	7·50	18·00
		a. *Tête-bêche* (vert pair)	15·00	80·00
		b. Imperf (pair)	£850	

No. 51 is printed in four rows, each inverted in respect to that above and below it.

(b) Thick white chalk-surfaced paper. Imperf

52	**14**	2a. lilac ("TWO ANNA")	£3500	£1200

(c) Thick white chalk-surfaced paper. Rouletted in colour (Medallion only in half-tone)

53	**14**	¼a. ultramarine	25·00	16·00

1913. No ornaments on either side of value in English. Small ornaments in bottom label. With stop after "STATE". Thick white chalk-surfaced paper. Rouletted.

54	**14**	2a. purple ("TWO ANNAS")	2·50	5·00

15

पाव ग्रना

पाव अना

No. 59e. This occurs on R. 3/3 on one setting only

2 **TWO ANNAS** 2	2 **TWO ANNAS** 2
No. 60. Small figures	No. 60b. Large figures

(Typo Diamond Soap Works, Kishangarh)

1913 (Aug). Thick surfaced paper. Half-tone centre. Type-set inscriptions. Rouletted. Inscr "KISHANGARH".

59	**15**	¼a. pale blue	30	90
		a. Imperf (pair)	9·00	
		b. Roul×imperf (horiz pair)	48·00	
		ba. Imperf between (horiz pair)	80·00	
		c. "OUARTER" (R. 4/4)	5·00	7·00
		ca. As last, imperf (pair)	42·00	
		cb. As last, roul×imperf (horiz pair)	£100	
		d. "KISHANGAHR" (R. 2/3)	5·00	7·00
		da. As last, imperf (pair)	42·00	
		db. As last, roul×imperf (horiz pair)	£100	
		dc. As last, imperf between (horiz pair)	£160	
		e. Character omitted	7·00	7·00
		ea. As last, imperf (pair)	48·00	
60		2a. purple	15·00	32·00
		a. "KISHANGAHR" (R. 2/3)	60·00	£170
		b. Large figures "2"	35·00	90·00

1913–16. Stamps printed far apart, horizontally and vertically, otherwise as No. 54, except as noted below.

63	**14**	¼a. blue	30	45
64		½a. green (1915)	30	1·75
		a. Printed both sides	£400	
		b. Imperf (pair)	£275	£300
		c. *Emerald-green* (1916)	1·75	4·00
65		1a. red	2·25	3·25
		a. Without stop*	1·75	8·00
		ab. Imperf (pair)	£275	
66		2a. purple ("TWO ANNAS") (1915)	6·50	8·00
67		4a. bright blue	6·00	8·00
68		8a. brown	7·00	65·00
69		1r. mauve	25·00	£250
		a. Imperf (pair)	£450	
70		2r. deep green	£150	£600
71		5r. brown	40·00	£500
63/71 *Set of 9*			£200	£1300

*For this issue, ornaments were added on either side of the English value (except in the ¼a.) and the inscription in the right label was without stop, except in the case of No. 65.

In Nos. 70 and 71 the value is expressed as "RUPIES" instead of "RUPEES".

Initial printings of the ¼a., 1a. and 4a. values were in sheets of 20 containing two panes of ten separated by a central gutter margin. Stamps from these sheets measure 20×25½ mm and have heavier screening dots on the margins than on the designs. Subsequent printings of these stamps, and of other values in the set, were from single pane sheets of 20 on which the designs measured 19½×23¾ mm and with the screening dots uniform across the sheet.

Maharaja Yagyanarayan Singh, 1926–1939

16 Maharaja Yagyanarayan Singh	17 Maharaja Yagyanarayan Singh

1928–36. Thick surfaced paper. Typo. Pin-perf.

72	**16**	¼a. light blue	1·75	2·00
73		½a. yellow-green	4·00	2·50
		a. *Deep green*	6·50	3·00
		ab. Imperf (pair)	£300	£300
		ac. Imperf between (vert or horiz pair)	£375	£375
74	**17**	1a. carmine	1·75	2·00
		a. Imperf (pair)	£425	£275
75		2a. purple	3·00	8·50
75a		2a. magenta (1936)	8·50	13·00
		ab. Imperf (pair)	£650	£650
76	**16**	4a. chestnut	2·50	2·00
		a. Imperf (pair)	£300	
77		8a. violet	6·50	40·00
78		1r. light green	21·00	95·00
79		2r. lemon-yellow (1929)	35·00	£450
80		5r. claret (1929)	70·00	£475
		a. Imperf (pair)	£325	
72/80 *Set of 9*			£130	£950

The 4a. to 5r. are slightly larger than, but otherwise similar to, the ¼a. and ½a. The 8a. has a dotted background covering the whole design.

Maharaja Samar Singh, 1939–1971

1943–47. As last, but thick, soft, unsurfaced paper. Poor impression. Typo. Pin-perf.

81	**16**	¼a. pale dull blue (1945)	7·50	22·00
		a. Imperf (pair)	60·00	
82		¼a. greenish blue (1947)	4·25	24·00
		a. Imperf (pair)	55·00	

83		½a. deep green (1944)	4·25	3·75
		a. Imperf (pair)	45·00	38·00
84		½a. yellow-green (1946)	11·00	18·00
		a. Imperf (pair)	60·00	55·00
85	**17**	1a. carmine-red (1944)	11·00	6·50
		a. Double print	£475	
		b. Imperf (pair)	60·00	60·00
		d. *Red-orange* (1947)	£130	70·00
		da. Imperf (pair)	£250	£180
86		2a. bright magenta	17·00	13·00
		a. Imperf (pair)	£160	£170
87		2a. maroon (1947)	£200	40·00
		a. Imperf (pair)	90·00	£100
88	**16**	4a. brown (1944)	35·00	22·00
		a. Imperf (pair)	£160	
89		8a. violet (1945)	48·00	£250
90		1r. green (1945)	90·00	£225
		a. Imperf (pair)	£425	£600
90b		2r. yellow (date?)		
		ba. Imperf (pair)	£1300	
91		5r. claret (1945)	£1600	£1700
		a. Imperf (pair)	£750	

Imperforate between pairs of the ½a., 1a. and 2a. values of this issue, formerly listed as Nos. 83b, 84b, 85c and 87b, are now considered to be faked.

OFFICIAL STAMPS

ON K S D

(O **1**)

1917–18. Handstamped with Type O **1**.

(a) Stamps of 1899–1901

(i) Imperf

O1	**2**	¼a. yellow-green	—	£350
O2		¼a. rose-pink	—	14·00
		a. Pair, one without opt	—	£250
		b. Stamp doubly printed	†	£200
O3	**4**	1a. mauve	—	£120
O3a		1a. brown-lilac	£100	5·50
		ab. Pair, one without opt	£450	£225
O4	**6**	4a. chocolate	—	£250

(ii) Pin-perf

O5	**2**	¼a. yellow-green	—	£225
O6		¼a. rose-pink	2·50	60
		a. Pair, one without opt	£250	£120
		b. Stamp doubly printed	£300	£160
O7	**3**	½a. light blue	£750	75·00
O8	**4**	1a. mauve	£100	1·50
		a. Pair, one without opt	†	£250
O9		1a. brown-lilac	85·00	3·75
		a. Pair, one without opt	†	£275
O10	**5**	2a. dull orange	—	£200
O11	**6**	4a. chocolate	£120	16·00
		a. Pair, one without opt	—	£250
O12	**7**	1r. dull green	£275	£190
O13	**8**	2r. brown-red	—	£1400
O14	**9**	5r. mauve	—	£4000

(b) Stamp of 1901

O14a	**10a**	1r. dull green	—	£1200

(c) Stamps of 1903 and 1904

O15	**12**	2a. dull yellow	£160	5·00
		a. Stamp printed both sides	†	£1400
		b. Red opt	£750	£500
O16	**12a**	8a. grey	£150	28·00
		a. Red opt	—	£550

(d) Stamps of 1904–10. P 13½ (¼a. to 4a.) or 12½ (others)

O17	**13**	¼a. carmine	—	£475
O18		½a. chestnut	3·25	1·50
		a. Pair, one without opt	£190	£130
O19		1a. blue	17·00	4·00
		a. Red opt	30·00	10·00
		b. Pair, one without opt	—	£180
O20		2a. orange-yellow	—	£1400
O21		4a. brown	85·00	70·00
		a. Red opt	£225	
		b. Pair, one without opt	—	£325
O22		8a. violet	£500	£375
		a. Red opt	—	£325
		b. Pair, one without opt	†	£1300
O23		1r. green	£1600	£1400
		a. Red opt	—	£1000
O24		5r. purple-brown	—	£1400

(e) Stamps of 1913

O25	**15**	¼a. pale blue	14·00	
		a. Imperf (pair)	£190	
		b. Roul×imperf (horiz pair)	£400	
		c. "OUARTER"	55·00	
		ca. As last, imperf (pair)	£325	
		d. "KISHANGAHR"	55·00	
		da. As last, imperf (pair)	£325	
		e. Character omitted	55·00	
		ea. As last, imperf (pair)	£325	
O26	**14**	2a. purple (No. 54)		£150
		a. Red opt	£325	20·00
O27	**15**	2a. purple	£900	£950
		a. "KISHANGAHR"	£2500	
		b. Large figures "2"	£1500	£1600

(f) Stamps of 1913–16

O28	**14**	¼a. blue	3·25	1·50
		a. Red opt	3·75	2·00
		b. Imperf (pair)	£550	
O29		½a. green	2·50	75
		a. Pair, one without opt	—	£160
		b. Red opt	7·00	1·60
		ba. Pair, one without opt	—	£300
O30		1a. red	40·00	18·00
		a. Without stop (No. 65a)	1·50	1·00
		ab. Pair, one without opt	£250	£250
		ac. Red opt	£200	£110

O31		2a. purple	22·00	11·00
		a. Red opt	£200	£100
		b. Pair, one without opt	—	£200
O32		4a. bright blue	50·00	23·00
		a. Red opt	£200	£200
O33		8a. brown	£200	80·00
		a. Red opt	—	£130
O34		1r. mauve	£550	£450
O35		2r. deep green		
O36		5r. brown	£2500	

This overprint is found inverted as often as it is upright; and many other "errors" exist.

Kishangarh became part of Rajasthan by 15 April 1948.

LAS BELA

PRICES FOR STAMPS ON COVER	
Nos. 1/12	*from × 8*

Mir Kamal Khan, 1896–1926

1   **2**

(Litho Thacker & Co, Bombay)

1897–98. Thick paper. P 11½.

1	**1**	½a. black on *white*	60·00	28·00

1898–1900. P 11½.

2	**1**	½a. black on *greyish blue* (1898)	40·00	16·00
3		½a. black on *greenish grey* (1899)	35·00	16·00
		a. "BFLA" for "BELA"	£425	
4		½a. black on *thin white surfaced paper* (1899)	60·00	£100
5		½a. black on *slate* (1900)	55·00	60·00
		a. Imperf between (horiz pair)	£2000	

1901–02. P 11½.

6	**1**	½a. black on *pale grey*	30·00	16·00
		a. "BFLA" for "BELA"	£375	£450
7		½a. black on *pale green* (1902)	45·00	45·00
8	**2**	1a. black on *orange*	60·00	65·00

There are at least 14 settings of the above ½a. stamps, the sheets varying from 16 to 30 stamps.

No. 6a occurred on R. 3/2 of the July 1901 printing in sheets of 16 (4×4).

1904 (Feb–Nov). Stamps printed wider apart. P 11½.

11	**1**	½a. black on *pale blue*	28·00	14·00
		a. Imperf between (pair)	£1600	
		b. Imperf between (horiz strip of 3)	£2250	
		c. Perf 12½ (11.04)	50·00	23·00
12		½a. black on *pale green*	30·00	14·00
		c. Perf 12½ (11.04)	50·00	23·00

There are five plates of the above two stamps, each consisting of 18 (3×6) varieties.

All the coloured papers of the ½a. show coloured fibres, similar to those in granite paper.

The stamps of Las Bela have been obsolete since 1 April 1907.

MORVI

PRICES FOR STAMPS ON COVER	
Nos. 1/17	*from × 6*
Nos. 18/19	*from × 3*

Thakur (Maharaja from 1926) Lakhdirji, 1922–48

1 Maharaja Lakhdirji   **2** Maharaja Lakhdirji   **3** Maharaja Lakhdirji

1931 (1 Apr). Typo. P 12.

(a) Printed in blocks of four. Stamps 10 mm apart (Nos. 1/2) or 6½ mm apart (No. 3). Perf on two or three sides

1	**1**	3p. deep red	4·50	15·00
2		½a. blue	35·00	70·00
3		2a. yellow-brown	£190	
1/3 *Set of 3*			£200	

(b) Printed in two blocks of four. Stamps 5½ mm apart. Perf on four sides

4	**1**	3p. bright scarlet	8·50	32·00
		a. Error. Dull blue	5·00	32·00
		b. Ditto. Double print	£950	
		c. Ditto. Printed on gummed side	£1100	
5		½a. dull blue	9·50	32·00
		a. Chalk-surfaced paper	9·50	25·00
6		1a. brown-red	3·25	42·00
7		2a. yellow-brown	4·50	55·00
4/7 *Set of 4*			23·00	£140

Nos. 1/3 were supplied to post offices in panes of four sewn into bundles with interleaving.

1932–33. Horizontal background lines wider apart and portrait smaller than in T **1**. Typo. P 11.

8	**2**	3p. carmine-rose (*shades*)	5·00	21·00
9		6p. green	11·00	29·00

---

		a. Imperf between (horiz pair)	£4500	
		b. *Emerald-green*	8·50	23·00
10		1a. ultramarine (*to deep*)	10·00	23·00
		a. Imperf between (vert pair)	£3750	
11		2a. bright violet (1933)	19·00	70·00
		a. Imperf between (vert pair)	£4000	
8/11 *Set of 4*			38·00	£120

1934. Typo. London ptg. P 14.

12	**3**	3p. carmine	6·00	9·00
13		6p. emerald-green	4·50	12·00
14		1a. purple-brown	5·00	23·00
		a. Imperf between (horiz pair)	†	£3250
15		2a. bright violet	5·50	45·00
12/15 *Set of 4*			19·00	80·00

1935–48. Typo. Morvi Press ptg. Rough perf 11.

16	**3**	3p. scarlet (*shades*)	2·50	7·50
		a. Imperf between (horiz pair)	£3250	
17		6p. grey-green	6·50	8·00
		a. *Emerald-green*	14·00	40·00
		b. *Yellow-green*	20·00	
18		1a. brown	12·00	22·00
		a. *Pale yellow-brown*	16·00	35·00
		b. *Chocolate*	26·00	42·00
19		2a. dull violet (*to deep*)	3·00	25·00
16/19 *Set of 4*			21·00	55·00

Nos. 17a, 18a and 18b were issued between 1944 and 1948.

Maharaja Mahendra Singh, 1948–1957

Morvi was merged with the United State of Kathiawar (later Saurashtra) by 15 April 1948.

NANDGAON

PRICES FOR STAMPS ON COVER
The stamps of Nandgaon are very rare used on cover.

GUM. The stamps of Nandgaon were issued without gum.

Raja Mahant Balram Das, 1883–1897

1   **2** (½a.)

(Litho at Poona)

1891. Imperf.

1	**1**	½a. blue	11·00	£250
		a. *Dull blue*	11·00	
2		2a. green	38·00	£750

The few covers in existence franked with Nos. 1/2 have undated manuscript cancellations, but other forms are known on loose examples.

The state was under Imperial administration from January 1888 to November 1891 and it is possible that Nos. 1/2 may have appeared in late 1887.

Last character in top line omitted

(Typo Balram Press, Raj-Nandgaon)

1893 (1 Jan)–**94**. Printed in sheets of 16 (4×4). Imperf.

(a) Stamps printed wide apart (8 to 10 mm) without wavy lines between them. Thin, toned wove paper

3	**2**	½a. dull to deep green	16·00	£140
4		2a. red	20·00	£140
		b. *Dull rose*	19·00	£140

(b) Stamps printed closer together (4 to 7 mm) with wavy lines between them. Thin, white wove paper (1894)

5	**2**	½a. green	42·00	£100
		a. Last character in top line omitted (R. 4/3)	£180	
6		1a. rose	95·00	£170
		ba. Laid paper	£325	

There were three settings of Type **2** with a number of separate printings made from the third: Setting I - Nos. 3, 4, 4b, O2

Setting II - Nos. 5, 6

Setting III - Nos. 5, 6ba, O3, O4, O4a, O5 and subsequent reprints. The same clichés were used for all values with the face value inscriptions changed. These exist in two different sizes with both occurring on the ½a., the small on the 1a. and the large on the 2a. except for No. O5 which has the small type.

The ordinary postage stamps of Nandgaon became obsolete on 1 July 1894.

OFFICIAL STAMPS

(O **1**) ("M.B.D." = Mahant Balram Das)

1893. Handstamped with ruler's initials in oval. Type O **1**, in purple.

O1	**1**	½a. blue	£500	
O2		2a. rose	£1400	

1894. Handstamped with Type O **1** in purple.

(a) Stamps printed wide apart (8 to 10 mm) without wavy lines between them. Thin, toned wove paper

O2a	**2**	½a. dull green	£800	
O3		2a. red	48·00	£225

(b) Stamps printed closer together (4 to 7 mm) with wavy lines between them. Thin, white wove paper

O4	**2**	½a. yellow-green	10·00	20·00
		a. *Sage-green*	11·00	
O5		1a. rose (*shades*)	20·00	60·00
		a. Thin laid paper	18·00	£140
O6		2a. rose (*shades*)	16·00	45·00

Further printings took place in 1895 after the Official stamps were withdrawn from postal use on 31 December 1894. These were all on thin, white wove paper with the ½a. and 2a. in slightly different shades and the 1a. in brown or ultramarine.

There is a forgery of the handstamp, Type O **1**, which shows 8 mm between the two ornaments below the initials instead of the normal 4 mm.

NAWANAGAR

PRICES FOR STAMPS ON COVER	
No. 1	*from × 20*
No. 2	*from × 8*
Nos. 3/4	*from × 2*
No. 5	—
Nos. 6/12	—
Nos. 13/15	*from × 100*
Nos. 16/18	—

GUM. The stamps of Nawanagar were issued without gum.

Jam Vibhaji 1882–1895

1 (1 docra)   **2** (2 docra)   **3** (3 docra)

1877. Typo in sheets of 32 (4×8 or 8×4). Laid paper.

(a) Imperf

1	**1**	1doc. blue (*shades*)	1·50	35·00
		a. *Tête-bêche* (pair)	£2250	
		b. Doubly printed	£150	

(b) Perf 12½ (line)

2	**1**	1doc. slate-blue	£140	£275
		a. Perf 11 (harrow)	£160	
		ab. *Tête-bêche* (pair)	£3500	

The inverted clichés which cause the *tête-bêche* pairs come from different settings and occur on R. 3/2 (No. 1a) or R. 4/4 (No. 2ab) of sheets of 32 (4×8).

1877. T **2** and **3**. Type-set in black. Wove paper. Thick horizontal and vertical frame lines. Stamp 19 mm wide.

3		1doc. deep mauve	£6000	£450
		a. Stamp 14½-15 mm wide	†	£850
		b. Stamp 16 mm wide	†	£650
4		2doc. green	£6000	£3000
5		3doc. yellow	£5000	£2750

1880. As last, but thin frame lines, as illustrated. Stamp 15 to 18 mm wide.

6		1doc. deep mauve	5·00	20·00
		a. *On rose*	6·00	
		ab. Stamp 14 mm wide	6·00	20·00
		b. Error. Green		
7		1doc. magenta (*stamp 14 mm wide*)	6·00	
8		2doc. yellow-green	12·00	24·00
		a. *On blue-green*	22·00	
		b. Error. Yellow	£650	
		c. Stamp 14 mm wide	6·00	20·00
		ca. *On blue-green*	18·00	
9		3doc. orange-yellow	24·00	
		a. *On yellow*	10·00	32·00
		ab. On laid paper	£180	
		b. Stamp 14 mm wide. *On yellow*	7·00	17·00
		ba. On laid paper	75·00	

There are several different settings of each value of this series.
No. 8b occurs in the sheet of the 3 doc. value from one setting only.

4 (1 docra)

1893. Typo in sheets of 36. P 12.

(a) Thick paper

10	**4**	1doc. black	11·00	
		a. Imperf (pair)	£1100	
11		3doc. orange	12·00	

(b) Thick laid paper

12	**4**	1doc. black	£1100	

(c) Thin wove paper

13	**4**	1doc. black *to* grey	2·75	11·00
		a. Imperf between (pair)	£850	
		b. Imperf (pair)	£750	
		c. Imperf horiz (vert pair)	£900	
		d. Imperf between (horiz strip of 6)	£2250	
14		2doc. green	4·50	18·00
		a. Imperf (pair)	£1000	
		b. Imperf between (vert pair)	£1000	
		c. Imperf horiz (vert pair)	£1000	
15		3doc. orange-yellow	5·00	24·00
		a. Imperf between (pair)	£1300	
		b. *Orange*	4·50	21·00
		ba. Imperf (pair)	£950	
		bb. Imperf vert (horiz pair)	£950	
		bc. Imperf between (horiz pair)	£950	

(d) Thin, soft wove paper

16	**4**	1doc. black		
17		2doc. deep green	8·00	
18		3doc. brown-orange	10·00	

Cancellations for postal purposes were intaglio seals, applied in black. Other forms of cancellation were only used on remainders.

The stamps of Nawanagar became obsolete on 1 January 1895.

NEPAL

Nepal being an independent state, its stamps will be found listed in Part 21 (*South-East Asia*) of this catalogue.

ORCHHA

PRICES FOR STAMPS ON COVER	
Nos. 1/2	—
Nos. 3/7	*from* × 8
Nos. 8/30	*from* × 50
Nos. 31/45	*from* × 4

A set of four stamps, ½a. red, 1a. violet, 2a. yellow and 4a. deep blue-green, in a design similar to T **2**, was prepared in 1897 with State authority but not put into use. These exist both imperforate and pin-perforated. (*Price for set of 4, £30 unused or c.t.o.*)

Maharaja Partab Singh, 1874–1930

1   **2**

(T **1/2** litho Shri Pratap Prabhakar)

1913. Background to Arms unshaded, Very blurred impression. Wove paper. No gum. Imperf.

1	**1**	½a. green	50·00	£160
2		1a. red	24·00	£275

1914–35. Background shaded with short horizontal lines. Clearer impression. Wove paper. No gum. Imperf.

3	**2**	¼a. bright ultramarine	2·50	8·00
		a. *Grey-blue*	40	5·50
		b. *Deep blue*	1·60	4·00
		ba. Laid paper	£900	
4		½a. green (*shades*)	55	7·50
		a. *Dull green*	2·50	9·50
		b. *Apple-green*	3·75	5·00
5		1a. scarlet	2·50	9·00
		a. Laid paper	—	£1000
		b. *Indian red*	1·75	15·00
		c. *Carmine*	3·50	8·50
		ca. Laid paper (1935)	£400	£450
6		2a. red-brown (1916)	4·50	24·00
		a. *Light brown*	18·00	45·00
		b. *Chestnut*	21·00	45·00
7		4a. ochre (1917)	11·00	65·00
		a. *Yellow-orange*	12·00	65·00
		b. *Yellow*	14·00	65·00
3/7	*Set of 5*		16·00	95·00

There are two sizes of T **2** in the setting of eight (4×2). In each value stamps from the upper row are slightly taller than those from the lower.

Maharaja Vir Singh II, 1930–1956

3 Maharaja Vir Singh II   **4** Maharaja Vir Singh II

(Typo Lakshmi Art Ptg Wks, Bombay)

1935 (1 Apr). Thick, chalk-surfaced wove paper. Various perfs*.

8	**3**	¼a. purple and slate (P 11½)	2·75	8·50
		a. Imperf between (vert pair)		
		b. Ordinary paper (P 11, 11½ or 12)	75	7·00

5 Maharaja Vir Singh II   **6** Maharaja Vir Singh II

9		ba. Imperf between (vert pair)		18·00	
		bb. Imperf vert (horiz pair)		70·00	
		bc. Imperf horiz (vert pair)		65·00	
		½a. olive-grey and emerald (P 11½ or 12)		1·75	4·50
		a. Imperf (pair)		85·00	
10		¾a. magenta and deep myrtle-green (P 11½, 12 or compound with 11)		50	4·25
		a. Imperf (pair)		80·00	
11		1a. myrtle-green and purple-brown (P 12)		50	5·00
		a. Imperf (pair)		90·00	£160
		b. Imperf horiz (vert pair)			
		c. Imperf vert (horiz pair)			
12		1¼a. slate and mauve (P 11½, 12 or compound)		50	5·00
		a. Imperf between (horiz pair)		80·00	£500
		b. Imperf between (horiz pair)		80·00	
		c. Frame doubly printed		75·00	
13		1½a. brown and scarlet (P 12 or compound with 11½)		75	4·50
		a. Imperf between (vert pair)		85·00	
		b. Imperf between (horiz pair)		80·00	
14		2a. blue and red-orange (P 12 or compound with 11)		50	5·00
		a. Imperf (pair)		22·00	
		b. Imperf between (horiz pair)		80·00	
15		2½a. olive-brown and dull orange (P 11½ or 12)		65	5·00
		a. Imperf (pair)		22·00	
		b. Imperf between (horiz pair)		80·00	
16		3a. bright blue and magenta (P 11½ or 12)		75	4·50
		a. Imperf between (horiz pair)		80·00	£160
		b. Imperf (pair)		75·00	
17		4a. deep reddish purple and sage-green (P 11½ or 12)		65	8·00
		a. Imperf (pair)		13·00	
		b. Imperf between (horiz pair)		85·00	
		c. Imperf vert (horiz pair)		85·00	
		d. Perf 9½–10		1·50	
18		6a. black and pale ochre (P 11 or 12)		2·50	9·50
		a. Imperf (pair)		13·00	
		d. Perf 9½–10		3·75	
19		8a. brown and purple (P 11 or 12)		2·50	14·00
		a. Imperf (pair)		13·00	
		b. Imperf between (vert pair)		95·00	
		d. Perf 9½–10		3·75	
20		12a. bright emerald and bright purple (P 12)		1·00	14·00
		a. Imperf (pair)		13·00	
		b. Imperf between (vert pair)		95·00	
		d. Perf 9½–10		3·75	
21		12a. pale greenish blue and bright purple (P 12)		55·00	£225
		d. Perf 9½–10		90·00	
22		1r. chocolate and myrtle-green (P 11½ or 12)		1·50	13·00
		a. Imperf (pair)		14·00	
		b. Imperf between (horiz pair)		95·00	
		d. Perf 9½–10		3·50	
23	**4**	1r. chocolate and myrtle-green (P 12)		20·00	70·00
		a. Imperf (pair)		£120	
		b. Imperf between (horiz pair)		£160	
24	**3**	2r. purple-brown and bistre-yellow (P 11½ or 12)		3·25	45·00
		a. Imperf (pair)		14·00	
		d. Perf 9½–10		3·75	
25		3r. black and greenish blue (P 11½, 12 or compound)		3·75	50·00
		a. Imperf (pair)		16·00	
		d. Perf 9½–10		3·50	
26		4r. black and brown (P 11½ or 12)		7·00	55·00
		a. Imperf (pair)		14·00	
		d. Perf 9½–10		4·25	
27		5r. bright blue and plum (P 12)		4·75	65·00
		a. Imperf (pair)		16·00	
		d. Perf 9½–10		4·75	
28		10r. bronze-green and cerise (P 12)		7·00	70·00
		a. Imperf (pair)		20·00	
		b. Imperf between (horiz pair)		£170	
		d. Perf 9½–10		7·50	
29		15r. black and bronze-green (P 11½ or 12)		12·00	£170
		a. Imperf (pair)		18·00	
		d. Perf 9½–10		16·00	
30		25r. red-orange and blue (P 12)		22·00	£190
		a. Imperf (pair)		28·00	
		d. Perf 9½–10		16·00	
8/20, 22/30	*Set of 22*			75·00	£750

*Three 'regular' line perforations were used, measuring P 11, 11½ or 12, as noted above for the individual values. There was also an irregular P 9½–10 with large holes, listed separately as Nos. 17d/30d. Stamps P 9½–10 are invariably without gum, whereas stamps with the other perforations are gummed.

Values to 5r. except the 1a., are inscribed "POSTAGE", and the remaining values "POSTAGE & REVENUE".

The central portrait of Type **3** is taken from a half-tone block and consists of large square dots. The portrait of Type **4** has a background of lines.

Owing to a lack of proper State control considerable quantities of these stamps circulated at below face value and the issue was subsequently withdrawn, supplies being exchanged for the 1939–42 issue. We are, however, now satisfied that the lower values at least did genuine postal duty until 1939.

Used prices are for stamps cancelled-to-order, postally used examples being worth considerably more.

(Litho Indian Security Printing Press, Nasik)

1939–42?. P 13½×14 (T **5**) or 14×13½ (T **6**).

31	**5**	¼a. chocolate	8·00	£140
32		½a. yellow-green	7·50	90·00
33		¾a. bright blue	8·50	£170
34		1a. scarlet	7·50	32·00
35		1¼a. blue	10·00	£170
36		1½a. mauve	8·00	£190
37		2a. vermilion	7·50	£110
38		2½a. turquoise-green	9·50	£425
39		3a. slate-violet	9·00	£180
40		4a. slate	11·00	42·00
41		8a. magenta	14·00	£400
42	**6**	1r. grey-green	40·00	£1000
43		2r. bright violet	£110	£1400
44		5r. yellow-orange	£350	£5500
45		10r. turquoise-green (1942)	£1300	£8500
46		15r. slate-lilac (date ?)	£28000	
47		25r. claret (date ?)	£21000	

The used prices quoted for Nos. 31/45 are for stamps with identifiable authentic postal cancellations. This issue was extensively used for fiscal purposes, and forged postmarks are frequently met with.

Orchha became part of Vindhya Pradesh by 1 May 1948.

POONCH

PRICES FOR STAMPS ON COVER	
No. 1	*from* × 3
Nos. 1a/2	*from* × 2
Nos. 3/63	*from* × 10
Nos. O1/10	*from* × 30

Poonch was ruled by a junior branch of the Jammu and Kashmir princely family and by treaty, was subject to the "advice and consent" of the Maharaja of that state.

The Poonch postal service operated an office at Kahuta in the Punjab which acted as the office of exchange between the state post and that of British India.

GUM. The stamps of Poonch were issued without gum, except for some examples of Nos. 7/10.

The stamps of Poonch are all imperforate, and handstamped in watercolours.

DATES OF ISSUE. Precise dates of issue are difficult to establish, with some papers of the 1885-94 series reappearing after long intervals. It is, however, known that the 1 pice value (T **7**) was not issued until 1887.

ILLUSTRATIONS. Designs of Poonch are illustrated actual size.

Raja Moti Singh, 1852–1892

1   **2**

1876? T **1** (22×21 *mm*). Central face value in circle and five rosettes in outer frame. Yellowish white, wove paper.

1		6p. red	£20000	£225
		aa. Pair, one stamp sideways	†	£27000

Earliest recorded use of No. 1: July 20 1878.

1877? As T **1** (19×17 *mm*). Central face value in oval and two rosettes in outer frame. Same paper.

1a		½a. red	£27000	£13000

Earliest recorded use of No. 1a: May 1879.

1879? T **2** (21×19 *mm*). Central face value in oval and one rosette in outer frame. Same paper.

2		½a. red	—	£6500

Earliest recorded use of No. 2: April 16 1880.

3 (½a.)   **4** (1a.)

5 (2a.)   **6** (4a.)

1883. Yellowish white, wove paper.

3	**3**	½a. red	75·00	28·00
4	**4**	1a. red	£275	£130
5	**5**	2a. red	£650	£350
6	**6**	4a. red	£750	£450

1885. Toned wove bâtonné paper.

7	**3**	½a. red	12·00	8·00
8	**4**	1a. red	50·00	
9	**5**	2a. red	55·00	45·00
10	**6**	4a. red	£120	£120
		a. Pair, one stamp sideways	£5000	

These are sometimes found gummed.

7 (1 pice)

1885–94. Various papers.

(a) White laid bâtonné or ribbed bâtonné

11	7	1p. red (1887)	70·00	70·00
		a. Pair, one stamp sideways	£700	
		b. *Tête-bêche* (pair)	£750	
12	3	½a. red	6·00	6·00
		a. *Tête-bêche* (pair)	£5000	
13	4	1a. red	35·00	
		a. Pair, one stamp sideways	£3000	
14	5	2a. red	40·00	40·00
15	6	4a. red	50·00	
		a. Pair, one stamp sideways	£5000	

(b) Thick white laid paper (1885-87)

22	7	1p. red	£450	
23	3	½a. red	£150	
24	4	1a. red	£160	
25	5	2a. red	£160	
26	6	4a. red	£200	

(c) Yellow wove bâtonné

27	7	1p. red	5·50	5·50
		a. Pair, one stamp sideways	75·00	
28	3	½a. red	20·00	20·00
29	4	1a. red	£140	
30	5	2a. red	22·00	23·00
		a. Pair, one stamp sideways	£3000	
31	6	4a. red	17·00	15·00

(d) Orange-buff wove bâtonné

32	7	1p. red	8·00	8·50
		a. Pair, one stamp sideways	50·00	70·00
		b. *Tête-bêche* (pair)	80·00	
33	3	½a. red	55·00	
34	5	2a. red	£180	
35	6	4a. red	50·00	

(e) Yellow laid paper

36	7	1p. red	4·75	5·00
		a. Pair, one stamp sideways	35·00	
		b. *Tête-bêche* (pair)	55·00	
37	3	½a. red	11·00	
38	4	1a. red	£130	
39	5	2a. red	£130	£140
40	6	4a. red	£120	

(f) Yellow laid bâtonné

41	7	1p. red	22·00	20·00

(g) Buff laid or ribbed bâtonné paper thicker than (d)

42	4	1a. red	£150	
43	6	4a. red	£140	

(h) Blue-green laid paper (1887)

44	3	½a. red	85·00	
45	4	1a. red	11·00	11·00
46	5	2a. red	95·00	
47	6	4a. red	£160	

(i) Yellow-green laid paper

48	3	½a. red	£100	90·00

(j) Blue-green wove bâtonné

49	7	1p. red	£100	90·00
49a	3	½a. red	£2250	
50	4	1a. red	8·00	7·00

(k) Lavender wove bâtonné

51	4	1a. red	£150	£170
52	5	2a. red	8·50	8·50
		a. Pair, one stamp sideways	£4750	

(l) Blue wove bâtonné (1887)

53	7	1p. red	5·00	5·00
		a. Pair, one stamp sideways	50·00	70·00
		b. *Tête-bêche* (pair)	85·00	
53c		½a. red	£2250	
54	4	1a. red	£500	£550
54a		2a. red	£2250	

(m) Various coloured papers

55	7	1p. red/grey-blue laid (1894)	24·00	17·00
		a. *Tête-bêche* (pair)	£550	
56		1p. red/lilac laid (1894)	95·00	£100
		a. Pair, one stamp sideways	£650	£650
		b. *Tête-bêche* (pair)	£600	

1887–94. Printed in aniline rose on various papers.

57	7	1p. on *blue wove bâtonné*	13·00	
		a. *Tête-bêche* (pair)	£130	
58		1p. on *buff laid*	28·00	
		a. *Tête-bêche* (pair)	£200	
		b. Pair, one stamp sideways	£200	
59	3	½a. on *white laid*	50·00	
60	4	1a. on *green laid*	30·00	38·00
61		1a. on *green wove laid*	20·00	24·00
62	5	2a. on *lavender wove bâtonné*	20·00	20·00
63	6	4a. on *yellow laid*	32·00	38·00
		a. Pair, one stamp sideways	£2000	
		b. *Tête-bêche* (pair)	£2000	

Raja Baldeo Singh, 1892–1918

OFFICIAL STAMPS

1887.

(a) White laid bâtonné paper

O1	7	1p. black	6·00	6·00
		a. Pair, one stamp sideways	28·00	35·00
		b. *Tête-bêche* (pair)	35·00	
O2	3	½a. black	7·00	7·50
O3	4	1a. black	7·00	7·00
O4	5	2a. black	13·00	13·00
O5	6	4a. black	18·00	22·00

(b) White or toned wove bâtonné paper

O6	7	1p. black	4·50	
		a. Pair, one stamp sideways	35·00	42·00
		b. *Tête-bêche* (pair)	55·00	

O7	3	½a. black	6·00	7·00
		a. Pair, one stamp sideways	£4000	
O8	4	1a. black	20·00	20·00
O9	5	2a. black	12·00	13·00
O10	6	4a. black	17·00	

The stamps of Poonch became obsolete for postal purposes on 1 Jan 1895, but the 1a and 4a values continued in fiscal use until 1898.

RAJASTHAN

Rajasthan was formed in 1948–49 from a number of States in Rajputana; these included Bundi, Jaipur and Kishangarh, whose posts continued to function more or less separately until ordered by the Indian Government to close on 1 April 1950.

PRICES FOR STAMPS ON COVER	
Nos. 1/12	*from × 4*
Nos. 13/14	—
Nos. 15/25	*from × 4*
Nos. 26/42	*from × 3*
No. 43	*from × 5*
Nos. 44/60	*from × 3*
No. 61	*from × 5*
Nos. 62/5	—

FORGERIES. Collectors are warned that the Rajasthan type **1** opt on stamps of Bundi and especially Kishangarh has been extensively forged. The more expensive stamps should not be purchased without a reliable guarantee.

BUNDI

(1)

1948 (15 Oct)–**49.** Nos. 86/92 of Bundi.

*(a) Handstamped with T **1** in black*

1A		¼a. blue-green	10·00	£140
		a. Pair, one without opt	£650	
2A		½a. violet	9·00	90·00
		a. Pair, one without opt	£700	
3A		1a. yellow-green	9·00	65·00
4A		2a. vermilion	27·00	£180
5A		4a. orange	90·00	£300
6A		8a. ultramarine	17·00	

*(b) Handstamped with T **1** in violet*

1B		¼a. blue-green	9·00	£180
2B		½a. violet	9·50	70·00
		a. Pair, one without opt	£650	
3B		1a. yellow-green	28·00	80·00
		a. Pair, one without opt	£650	
4B		2a. vermilion	55·00	£170
5B		4a. orange	55·00	£180
6B		8a. ultramarine	17·00	
7B		1r. chocolate	£550	

*(c) Handstamped with T **1** in blue*

1C		¼a. blue-green	65·00	
2C		½a. violet	90·00	
3C		1a. yellow-green	90·00	90·00
4C		2a. vermilion	—	£800
5C		4a. orange	£275	
6C		8a. ultramarine	£150	
7C		1r. chocolate	£170	

Many of these handstamps are known sideways, inverted or double. It is believed that the blue handstamps (Nos. 1C/7C) were issued first, followed by violet and then black.

*(d) Machine-printed as T **1** in black (1949)*

11		2a. vermilion	21·00	£110
		a. Opt inverted	£500	
12		4a. orange	8·50	£110
		a. Opt double	£425	
13		8a. ultramarine	18·00	
		a. Opt inverted	£1100	
		b. Opt double	£550	
14		1r. chocolate	9·00	

JAIPUR

राजस्थान

RAJASTHAN

(2)

1950 (26 Jan). T **7** of Jaipur optd with T **2**.

15		¼a. black and brown-lake (No. 58) (B.)	13·00	32·00
16		½a. black and violet (No. 41) (R.)	13·00	32·00
17		¾a. black and brown-red (No. 59) (Blue-blk.)	13·00	42·00
		a. Opt in pale blue	22·00	60·00
18		1a. black and blue (No. 60) (R.)	13·00	85·00
19		2a. black and buff (No. 61) (R.)	13·00	£120
20		2½a. black and carmine (No. 62) (B.)	13·00	50·00
21		3a. black and green (No. 63) (R.)	14·00	£130
22		4a. black and grey-green (No. 64) (R.)	14·00	£160
23		6a. black and pale blue (No. 65a) (R.)	14·00	£200
24		8a. black and chocolate (No. 66) (R.)	18·00	£275
25		1r. black and yellow-bistre (No. 67) (R.)	28·00	£425
15/25 *Set of 11*			£150	£1400

Collectors are warned that the used prices quoted for Nos. 15/25 are for stamps with identifiable authentic cancellation. Forged postmarks on this issue are frequently seen.

KISHANGARH

1948 (Oct)–**49.** Various stamps of Kishangarh handstamped with T **1** in red.

(a) On stamps of 1899–1901

26		¼a. rose-pink (No. 5a) (B.)		£600
26a		¼a. rose-pink (No. 22a)	—	£550
27		½a. deep blue (No. 26)	£1500	
28		1a. mauve (No. 28)	£150	
29		1a. brown-lilac (No. 29)	22·00	70·00
		a. *Tête-bêche* (horiz pair)	£2500	
		b. Imperf (pair)	65·00	£180
		c. Violet handstamp	£750	£750
		d. Black handstamp	—	£850
30		4a. chocolate (No. 31)	£140	£180
		a. Violet handstamp	—	£1000
31		1r. dull green (No. 32)	£650	£650
31a		2r. brown-red (No. 34)	£700	£700
32		5r. mauve (No. 35)	£700	£700

(b) On stamps of 1904–10

33	13	½a. chestnut	—	£400
33a		1a. blue		£450
34		4a. brown	13·00	
		a. Blue handstamp	£275	
35	12a	8a. grey	£200	£350
36	13	8a. violet	11·00	
37		1r. green	12·00	
38		2r. olive-yellow	19·00	
39		5r. purple-brown	45·00	
		a. Blue handstamp	£750	

(c) On stamps of 1912–16

40	14	½a. green (No. 64)	£650	£400
41		1a. red	—	£500
42		2a. deep violet (No. 51)	£1500	
43		2a. purple (No. 66)	7·50	17·00
		a. Pair, one without handstamp	£850	
44		4a. bright blue	—	£1300
45		8a. brown	5·00	
		a. Pair, one without handstamp	£850	
46		1r. mauve	10·00	
47		2r. deep green	10·00	
		a. Pair, one without handstamp	£1200	
48		5r. brown	£650	

(d) On stamps of 1928–36

49	16	½a. yellow-green	£450	
49a		2a. magenta	—	£1000
50		4a. chestnut	£600	
51		8a. violet	6·50	90·00
		a. Pair, one without handstamp	£750	
52		1r. light green	29·00	
53		2r. lemon-yellow	17·00	
54		5r. claret	16·00	

(e) On stamps of 1943–47

55	16	¼a. pale dull blue	£225	£225
56		¼a. greenish blue	85·00	85·00
		a. Imperf (pair)	£550	
57		½a. deep green	48·00	50·00
		a. Violet handstamp	—	£550
57b		½a. yellow-green	45·00	45·00
		ba. Imperf (pair)	£550	
		bb. Blue handstamp	—	£550
58	17	1a. carmine-red	£225	£200
		a. Violet handstamp	—	£550
58b		1a. orange-red (*imperf*)	£350	
		ba. Blue handstamp	£375	
59		2a. bright magenta	£450	£450
60		2a. maroon (*imperf*)	£600	
61	16	4a. brown	7·50	18·00
		a. Pair, one without handstamp	£650	
62		8a. violet	21·00	£130
63		1r. green	6·50	
64		2r. yellow	£170	
65		5r. claret	60·00	£300

A 1a. value in deep violet-blue was issued for revenue purposes, but is known postally used (*Price £150 used*).

RAJPIPLA

PRICES FOR STAMPS ON COVER	
No. 1	*from × 50*
Nos. 2/3	—

Maharana Ganbhir Singh, 1860–1897

The Rajpipla state post was opened to the public sometime in the late 1870s. Adhesive stamps were preceded by postal stationery lettersheets which were first reported in 1879.

1 (1 pice)	**2** (2a.)	**3** (4a.)

1880. Litho. With or without gum (1p.) or no gum (others). P 11 (1p.) or 12½.

1	**1**	1p. blue (1.6)	7·00	55·00
2	**2**	2a. green	38·00	£170
		a. Imperf between (horiz pair)	£1000	£1200
3	**3**	4a. red	20·00	£110
1/3 *Set of 3*			60·00	£300

No. 1 was produced in sheets of 64 (8×8) and the higher values in sheets of 20 (5×4).

These stamps became obsolete in 1886 when the Imperial postal service absorbed the Rajpipla state post.

SHAHPURA

PRICES FOR STAMPS ON COVER	
Nos. 1/4	from × 2
No. F1	from × 2

DATES. Those quoted are of first known use.

Rajadhiraj Nahar Singh, 1870–1932

RAJ SHAHPURA	**RAJ SHAHPURA**	
Postage 1 pice	**1 pice**	
1	2	

1914–17. Typo.
1	**1**	1p. carmine/*bluish grey* (P 11)...........	—	£800
2		1p. carmine/*drab* (*imperf*) (1917).....	—	£1100

Some examples of No. 1 are imperforate on one side or on two adjacent sides.

1920–28. Typo. Imperf.
3	**2**	1p. carmine/*drab* (1928).....................	—	£1300
4		1a. black/*pink*..............................	—	£1500

Nos. 3/4 were also used for fiscal purposes. Manuscript cancellations must be assumed to be fiscal, unless on cover showing other evidence of postal use.

POSTAL FISCAL

Rajadhiraj Umaid Singh, 1932–1947
Rajadhiraj Sudarshan Deo, 1947–1971

F 1

1932–47. Typo. P 11, 11½ or 12.
F1	**F 1**	1a. red (*shades*)............................	75·00	£250
		a. Pin-perf 7 (1947).....................	—	£350
		ab. *Tête-bêche* (horiz pair)............	—	£1000

Nos. F1/a were used for both fiscal and postal purposes. Manuscript cancellations must be assumed to be fiscal, unless on cover showing other evidence of postal use. The design was first issued for fiscal purposes in 1898.

Shahpura became part of Rajasthan by 15 April 1948.

SIRMOOR

PRICES FOR STAMPS ON COVER
The stamps of Sirmoor are very rare used on cover.

Raja Shamsher Parkash, 1886–1898

1 (1 pice)	**2**	**3** Raja Shamsher Parkash

1878 (June)–**80.** Litho. P 11½.
1	**1**	1p. pale green..................................	35·00	£450
2		1p. blue (on *laid* paper) (1880)........	9·00	£225
		a. Imperf between (pair)...............		£600
		b. Imperf (pair)...........................		£600

(Litho at Calcutta)

1892. Thick wove paper. P 11½.
3	**2**	1p. yellow-green..............................	1·75	1·75
		a. Imperf between (vert pair).........	85·00	
		b. Imperf between (horiz pair).......	£250	
		c. *Deep green*............................	1·25	1·25
		ca. Imperf between (vert pair)........	85·00	95·00
4		1p. blue..	3·00	1·50
		a. Imperf between (vert pair).........	75·00	85·00
		b. Imperf between (horiz pair).......	75·00	85·00
		c. Imperf vert (horiz pair).............	75·00	
		d. Imperf (pair)...........................	85·00	

These were originally made as reprints, about 1891, to supply collectors, but there being very little demand for them they were put into use. The design was copied (including the perforations) from an illustration in a dealer's catalogue. Typographed forgeries, particularly of the perforation varieties, are frequently found.

A	B

C	D

There were seven printings of stamps as Type **3**, all in sheets of 70 (10×7) and made up from groups of transfers which can be traced through minor varieties.

Printings I to V and VII of the 3p. and 6p. are as Types A and C (both with large white dots evenly spaced between the ends of the upper and lower inscriptions).

Printing VI is as Type B (small white dots and less space) and Type D (large white dots unevenly positioned between the inscriptions).

(Litho Waterlow)

1885–96. P 14 to 15.
5	**3**	3p. chocolate (A)............................	2·25	1·25
		a. *Brown* (B) (1896).....................	40	50
6		3p. orange (A) (1888).....................	3·50	1·25
		a. Type B (1896)..........................	1·00	40
		ab. Imperf (pair)...........................	£850	
7		6p. blue-green (C)..........................	7·00	5·00
		a. *Green* (C) (1888).....................	3·50	2·25
		b. *Bright green* (C) (1891)............	90·00	90·00
		c. *Deep green* (C) (1894)..............	75	60
		d. *Yellowish green* (D) (1896).......	40	1·50
8		1a. bright blue...............................	5·50	6·00
		a. *Dull blue* (1891).....................	15·00	8·50
		b. *Steel-blue* (1891)....................	£130	£130
		c. *Grey-blue* (1894)....................	2·50	1·25
		d. *Slate-blue* (1896)...................	50	3·00
9		2a. pink...	10·00	18·00
		a. *Carmine* (1894)......................	3·50	3·00
		b. *Rose-red* (1896).....................	3·25	4·00

Composition of the various printings was as follows:

Printing I	—	Nos. 5, 7, 8 and 9
Printing II	—	Nos. 6 and 7a
Printing III	—	Nos. 6, 7b and 8a
Printing IV	—	Nos. 5, 6, 7a, and 8b
Printing V	—	Nos. 6, 7c, 8c and 9a
Printing VI	—	Nos. 5a, 6a, 7d, 8d and 9b
Printing VII	—	Only exists overprinted "On S. S. S." (Nos. 78/81).

4 Indian Elephant	**5** Raja Shamsher Parkash

(Recess Waterlow & Sons)

1894–99. P 12 to 15 and compounds.
22	**4**	3p. orange-brown	7·50	40
23		6p. green......................................	3·75	1·00
		a. Imperf between (vert pair).........	£4250	
24		1a. blue...	12·00	3·25
25		2a. rose...	11·00	3·50
26		3a. yellow-green.............................	42·00	70·00
27		4a. deep green...............................	32·00	42·00
28		8a. deep blue.................................	38·00	48·00
29		1r. vermilion.................................	60·00	£120
22/9 *Set of 8*			£180	£250

Raja Surindra Bikram Parkash, 1898–1911

(Recess Waterlow & Sons)

1899. P 13 to 15.
30	**5**	3a. yellow-green.............................	10·00	22·00
31		4a. deep green...............................	12·00	30·00
32		8a. deep blue.................................	14·00	38·00
33		1r. vermilion.................................	21·00	75·00
30/3 *Set of 4*			50·00	£150

OFFICIAL STAMPS

NOTE. The varieties occurring in the machine-printed "On S.S.S." overprints may, of course, also be found in the inverted and double overprints, and many of them are known thus.

Roman figures denote printings of the basic stamps (Nos. 6/9b). Where more than one printing was overprinted the prices quoted are for the commonest.

I. MACHINE-PRINTED

On
S.   S.
S.
(11)

1890. Optd with T **11**.
50	**3**	6p. green (C).................................	£2250	£2250
		a. Stop before first "S".................		
51		2a. pink...	£120	£375
		a. Stop before first "S".................	£275	

(b) In red
52	**3**	6p. green (C).................................	38·00	4·25
		a. Stop before first "S".................	80·00	25·00
53		1a. bright blue...............................	£110	38·00
		a. Stop before first "S".................	£250	90·00
		b. Opt inverted............................	£2250	£1200

(c) Doubly optd in red and in black
53c	**3**	6p. green (C).................................	£1800	£1800
		ca. Stop before first "S".................	£4000	£4000

Nos. 50, 52 and 53c are from Printing II and the remainder from Printing I.

On   On
S.   S.   S.   S.
S.   S.
(12)   **(13)**

1891. Optd with T **12**.

(a) In black
54	**3**	3p. orange (A)...............................	8·00	50·00
		a. Opt inverted............................	£900	
55		6p. green (C).................................	1·75	1·75
		a. Opt double..............................	£300	
		b. No stop after lower "S"..............	28·00	35·00
		c. Raised stop before lower "S".......	£300	£250
56		1a. bright blue...............................	£650	£750
57		2a. pink...	35·00	95·00

(b) In red
58	**3**	6p. green (C).................................	45·00	3·00
		a. Opt inverted............................	£425	£325
		b. Opt double..............................	£425	£350
59		1a. bright blue...............................	40·00	50·00
		a. Opt inverted............................	†	£900
		b. Opt double..............................	†	£850
		c. No stop after lower "S"..............	£325	£375

(c) In black and red
59d	**3**	6p. green (C).................................		£1800

Nos. 54/5, 58 and 59d are from Printing II and the others from Printing I.

1892–97. Optd with T **13**.

(a) In black
60	**3**	3p. orange (A)...............................	1·00	50
		a. Type B....................................	5·00	60
		b. Opt inverted............................	£425	
		c. First "S" inverted and stop raised.	7·50	6·50
		d. No stop after lower "S"..............	5·00	5·00
		e. Raised stop after second "S"......	65·00	22·00
		f. Vertical pair, Types **12** and **13**.	£375	
61		6p. green (C).................................	14·00	2·50
		a. *Deep green* (C)........................	4·25	50
		b. First "S" inverted and stop raised.	70·00	22·00
		c. Raised stop after second "S"......	70·00	20·00
		d. No stop after lower "S"..............	80·00	27·00
		e. Opt double..............................	£900	
62		1a. steel-blue.................................		
		a. *Grey-blue*..............................	23·00	1·00
		b. Opt double..............................	£650	
		c. First "S" inverted and stop raised.	80·00	10·00
		d. No stop after lower "S"..............	£375	£140
		e. Raised stop after second "S"......	£140	12·00
63		2a. pink...	23·00	28·00
		a. *Carmine*................................	10·00	7·00
		b. Opt inverted............................	£1500	£1500
		c. First "S" inverted and stop raised.	55·00	40·00
		d. No stop after lower "S"..............	55·00	40·00
		e. Raised stop after second "S"......	£300	£180

(b) In red
64	**3**	6p. green (C).................................	12·00	50
		a. *Bright green* (C)......................	17·00	2·25
		b. Opt inverted............................	£250	£160
		c. First "S" inverted and stop raised.	40·00	5·00
		d. Vertical pair, Types **12** and **13**.	£375	£375
65		1a. bright blue...............................	26·00	6·50
		a. *Steel-blue*..............................	26·00	1·00
		b. Opt inverted............................	£550	£375
		c. Opt double..............................	£475	
		d. First "S" inverted and stop raised.	70·00	8·00
		e. No stop after lower "S"..............	70·00	8·50

(c) Doubly overprinted in black and red
65f	**3**	6p. bright green (C)........................	—	£1800
		fa. *Green* (C). Red opt inverted........	†	£2750

The printings used for this issue were as follows:

Printing I	—	Nos. 63 and 65
Printing II	—	Nos. 60, 64 and 65fa
Printing III	—	Nos. 60, 64a and 65f
Printing IV	—	Nos. 61, 62, 64 and 65a
Printing V	—	Nos. 60, 61a, 62a and 63a
Printing VI	—	No. 60a

There are seven settings of this overprint, the first of which was a composite setting of 20 (10×2), with examples of Type **12** in the upper row. The inverted "S" and the missing stop occur in the third and sixth settings with the latter also including the raised stop after second "S".

On   On
S.   S.   S.   S.
S.   S.
(14)   **(15)**

1896–97. Optd as T **14**.
66	**3**	3p. orange (B) (1897).....................	19·00	1·25
		a. Comma after first "S"................	70·00	35·00
		b. Opt inverted............................		
		c. Opt double..............................	†	£1000
67		6p. deep green (C).........................	7·50	60
		a. *Yellowish green* (D).................	—	11·00
		b. Comma after first "S"................	60·00	20·00
		c. Comma after lower "S"..............	£400	24·00
		d. "S" at right inverted..................	£400	80·00

68		1a. grey-blue	15·00	1·25
		a. Comma after first "S"	75·00	22·00
		b. Comma after lower "S"	£425	26·00
		c. "S" at right inverted	—	90·00
69		2a. carmine (1897)	17·00	15·00
		a. Comma after first "S"	£130	£130

Nos. 66 and 67a are from Printing VI and the remainder from Printing V.

There are four settings of this overprint, (1) 23 mm high, includes the comma after lower "S"; (2) and (3) 25 mm high, with variety, comma after first "S" (4) 25 mm high, with variety, "S" at right inverted.

1898 (Nov). Optd with T **15**.

70	**3**	6p. deep green (C)	£450	24·00
		a. Yellowish green (D)	£425	13·00
		b. Small "S" at right	£700	28·00
		c. Comma after lower "S"	—	80·00
		d. Lower "S" inverted and stop raised		85·00
71		1a. grey-blue	£475	28·00
		a. Small "S" at right	£750	65·00
		b. Small "S" without stop	—	£300

No. 70a is from Printing VI and the others Printing V.

There are two settings of this overprint. Nos. 70b and 71a/b occur in the first setting, and Nos. 70c/d in the second setting.

(16) (17)

1899 (July). Optd with T **16**.

72	**3**	3p. orange (B)	£600	16·00
73		6p. deep green (C)	—	35·00

No. 72 is from Printing VI and No. 73 from Printing V.

1899 (Dec)–**1900**. Optd as T **17**.

74	**3**	3p. orange (B)	—	19·00
		a. Raised stop after lower "S"	†	£110
		b. Comma after first "S"	†	£475
		c. No stop after first "S"	†	£300
75		6p. deep green (C)	—	19·00
		a. Yellowish green (D)		15·00
		b. Raised stop after lower "S"	†	£110
		c. Comma after first "S"	†	£425
		d. No stop after first "S"	†	£400
76		1a. bright blue	†	£400
		a. Grey-blue	†	30·00
		b. Slate-blue	—	35·00
		c. Raised stop after lower "S"	†	£180
		d. Comma after first "S"	†	£500
		e. No stop after first "S"	†	£350
77		2a. carmine	—	£225
		a. Raised stop after lower "S"	†	£750

There are two settings of this overprint: (1) 22 mm high, with raised stop variety; (2) 23 mm high, with "comma" and "no stop" varieties.

The printings used for this issue were as follows:
Printing I — No. 76
Printing V — Nos. 75, 76a and 77
Printing VI — Nos. 74, 75a and 76b

(18) (19)

(Optd by Waterlow & Sons)

1900. Optd with T **18**.

78	**3**	3p. orange	3·75	12·00
79		6p. green	2·00	60
80		1a. blue	35	70
81		2a. carmine	6·50	70·00

Nos. 78/81 were from Printing VII which was not issued without the overprint.

II. HANDSTAMPED

The words "On" and each letter "S" struck separately (except for Type **22** which was applied in one operation).

1894. Handstamped with T **19**.

(a) In black

82	**3**	3p. orange (A)	3·25	3·75
		a. "On" only		£100
83		6p. green (C)	8·50	8·50
		a. Deep green (C)	21·00	23·00
		b. "On" only	85·00	85·00
84		1a. bright blue	£130	85·00
		a. Dull blue	40·00	40·00
		b. Steel-blue		
		c. Grey-blue	50·00	42·00
		d. "On" only	—	£130
85		2a. carmine	32·00	24·00
		a. "On" only		£150

(b) In red

86	**3**	6p. green (C)	£200	£225
86a		1a. grey-blue	£600	£600

The printings used for this issue were as follows:
Printing I — No. 84
Printing III — No. 84a
Printing IV — Nos. 83, 84b and 86
Printing V — Nos. 82, 83a, 84c, 85 and 86a

1896. Handstamped with letters similar to those of T **13**, with stops, but irregular.

87	**3**	3p. orange (A)	£140	£100
		a. Type B		
88		6p. green (C)		
		a. Deep green (C)	£110	85·00
		b. "On" omitted	£225	
88c		1a. grey-blue	£170	£170
89		2a. carmine	£350	

Printings used for this issue were as follows:
Printing II — No. 88
Printing III — No. 87
Printing IV — No. 88
Printing V — Nos. 87, 88a, 88c and 89
Printing VI — No. 87a

1897. Handstamped with letters similar to those of T **14**, with stops, but irregular.

90	**3**	3p. orange (B)	22·00	28·00
91		6p. deep green (C)	£110	£120
		a. "On" only	—	£140
92		1a. grey-blue	£550	£550
		a. "On" only	—	£140
93		2a. carmine	£275	£275

No. 90 was from Printing VI and the remainder from Printing V.

1897. Handstamped with letters similar to those of T **16**, with stops, but irregular.

93a	**3**	6p. deep green (C)	£400	£325

No. 93a is from Printing V.

(20) (21)

1896.

*(a) Handstamped with T **20***

94	**3**	3p. orange (A)	£140	£150
95		2a. carmine	£150	£160

*(b) Handstamped with T **21***

96	**3**	3p. orange (A)	£325	£350
97		6p. bright green (C)		
98		1a. bright blue	£550	
		a. Dull blue		
98b		2a. carmine	£550	

No. 98 comes from Printing 1, No. 98a from Printing III, No. 97 possibly from Printing IV and the remainder from Printing V.

(22) (23)

*(c) Handstamped with T **22***

99	**3**	3p. orange (B)		£200
100		6p. deep green		£325
101		1a. grey-blue		£375
101a		2a. carmine		£550

No. 99 is from Printing VI and the others from Printing V.

1899. Handstamped with T **23**.

102	**3**	3p. orange (A)	—	£375
		a. Type B	30·00	7·00
103		6p. green (C)		
		a. Deep green (C)	45·00	28·00
		b. Yellowish green (D)	20·00	18·00
104		1a. bright blue	—	£300
		a. Grey-blue	75·00	65·00
105		2a. pink		
		a. Carmine	£100	48·00
		b. Rose-red	£130	80·00
		c. "On" only	—	£190

Printings used for this issue were as follows:
Printing I — Nos. 104 and 105
Printing IV — Nos. 102 and 103
Printing V — Nos. 102, 103a, 104a and 105a
Printing VI — Nos. 102a, 103b and 105b

(24)

1901 (?). Handstamped with T **24**.

105d	**3**	6p. yellowish green (D)	—	£800

From Printing VI.

III. MIXED MACHINE-PRINTED AND HANDSTAMPED

1896.

*(i) Handstamped "On" as in T **19**, and machine-printed opt T **13** complete*

106	**3**	6p. green (C)	—	£800

*(ii) Handstamped opt as T **14**, and machine-printed opt T **13** complete*

107	**3**	6p. deep green (C)		

No. 106 is from Printing IV and No. 107 from Printing V.

Various other types of these handstamps are known to exist, but in the absence of evidence of their authenticity we do not list them. Stamps of T **4** (Nos. 22/5) exist with overprints similar to T **13** and T **22**. These are believed to have been produced for sale to collectors. The 6p. value is known in vertical pair, imperforate between (as No. 23a), with the former overprint. (*Price*, £2000, *unused*).

The stamps of Sirmoor have been obsolete since 1 April 1902.

SORUTH

PRICES FOR STAMPS ON COVER	
Nos. 1/2	*from* × 5
Nos. 4/4a	—
Nos. 5/7	*from* × 1
No. 8	*from* × 3
No. 9	*from* × 1
Nos. 10/11	*from* × 5
No. 11e	*from* × 1
No. 12	*from* × 4
No. 13	*from* × 5
Nos. 14/15	*from* × 3
Nos. 16/24	*from* × 20
Nos. 33/6	*from* × 50
Nos. 37/8	*from* × 10
Nos. 40/1	*from* × 50
Nos. 42/57	*from* × 10
Nos. O1/13	*from* × 20
No. 58	*from* × 15
No. 59	*from* × 6
No. 60	*from* × 10
No. 61	*from* × 6

The name "Saurashtra", corrupted to "Sorath" or "Soruth", was originally used for all the territory later known as Kathiawar. Strictly speaking the name should have been applied only to a portion of Kathiawar including the state of Junagadh. As collectors have known these issues under the heading of "Soruth" for so long, we retain the name.

GUM. Nos. 1/47 of Soruth were issued without gum.

JUNAGADH
Nawab Mahabat Khan II, 1851–1882
(Currency 40 dokras or 16 annas = 1 koree)

1 (="Saurashtra Post 1864–65")

1864 (Nov). Handstamped in water-colour. Imperf.

1	**1**	(1a.) black/*azure to grey* (laid)	£800	£140
		a. Tête-bêche (horiz pair)	†	£16000
2		(1a.) black/*azure to grey* (wove)	—	£300
3		(1a.) black/*cream* (laid)	†	£3500
4		(1a.) black/*cream* (wove)	—	£1600

ILLUSTRATIONS. Types **2** to **11** are shown actual size.

2 (1a.) (Devanagari numeral) **3 (1a.)** (Gujarati numeral)

4 (4a.) (Devanagari numeral) **5 (4a.)** (Gujarati numeral)

Differences in first character of bottom line on Nos. 8/a:

Type A "ka" (correct) Type B "u" (error)

(Typeset Nitiprakash Ptg Press, Junagadh)

1868 (June)–**75**. Designs as T **2** to **5**. Imperf.

A. Inscriptions in Gujarati characters. Wove paper

5		1a. black/*yellowish*	†	£35000

B. Inscriptions in Devanagari characters (as in the illustrations)
I. Accents over first letters in top and bottom lines. Wove paper

6		1a. red/*green*	†	£10000
7		1a. red/*blue*	†	£13000
7a		1a. red/*yellow*	†	£20000
8		1a. black/*pink* (first character in bottom line as Type A)	£3000	£275
		a. First character in bottom line as Type B (R. 1/3)	†	£6500
		b. Bottom line with accent over second letter	£6000	£1100
9		2a. black/*yellow* (1869)	†	£20000

II. Accents over second letters in top and bottom lines

(a) Wove paper

10	**2**	1a. black/*pink* (1869)	£950	£140
		a. Printed both sides	†	£3500
		b. First two characters in last word of bottom line omitted (R. 4/1).	—	£1400
		c. *Se-tenant* pair. Nos. 8/10.	†	£2750

(b) Laid paper

11	**2**	1a. black/*azure* (1870)	£180	15·00
		a. Final character in both top and bottom lines omitted (R. 1/1).	—	£325
		b. First two characters in last word of bottom line omitted (R. 4/1)...	—	£250
		c. Doubly printed	†	£1300
		d. *Se-tenant* pair. Nos. 11/12	£950	£325
11e		1a. black/*white*	†	£14000
12	**3**	1a. black/*azure* (1870)	£500	38·00
		a. Printed both sides	†	£1600
		b. Final character in bottom line omitted (R. 1/1)	£1300	£250
		c. Accent omitted from last word in bottom line (R. 5/2, 5/4)	—	£180
		d. Large numeral (R. 4/1)	£1500	£325
		e. First character in middle line omitted (R. 2/4)	—	£650
		f. Central two characters in middle line omitted (R. 2/4)	—	£1100
13		1a. red/*white* (1875)	42·00	48·00
		a. First two characters in bottom line omitted (R. 5/1)	£190	£250
14	**5**	4a. black/*white*	£500	£750
		a. First two characters in last word of bottom line omitted (R. 4/1)		£2500
		b. Final character in bottom line omitted (R. 5/2)		£6500
15	**4**	4a. black/*white*	£325	£450
		a. Final character in bottom line omitted (R. 1/1)		£1100

The settings of Nos. 5/7a are unknown.

Nos. 10/15, and probably Nos. 8/9, were printed in sheets of 20 (4×5). The same type was used throughout, but changes occurred as the loose type was amended.

Specialists now recognise four main settings for the 1a., one of which was amended for the 2a. and another for the 4a. There are sub-settings within some of these groups:

1a. Setting I (pink wove paper) (No. 8 with No. 8a at R. 1/3)
Setting II (pink wove paper) (No. 8)
Setting III (pink wove paper) (No. 10)
Setting IV (Devanagri numerals only) (pink wove paper) (Nos. 10/b)
Setting IVA (Devanagri numerals only) (azure vertical laid paper) (Nos. 11, 11b)
Setting IVB (Devanagri and Gujarati numerals mixed) (azure horizontal laid paper) (Nos. 11/a, 11d, 12)
Setting IVC (Devanagri and Gujarati numerals mixed) (azure or white vertical laid paper) (Nos. 11, 11c/d, 11e, 12/b, 12e/f)
Setting IVD (Devanagri and Gujarati numerals mixed) (azure vertical laid paper) (Nos. 11, 11d, 12, 12d)
Setting IVE (Gujarati numerals only) (white vertical laid paper) (Nos. 13/a)

2a. Setting I (probably derived from 1a. Setting II) (yellow wove paper) (No. 9)

4a. Setting IA (Gujarati numerals only) (white vertical laid paper) (Nos. 14/a)
Setting IB (Devanagri numerals only) (white horizontal laid paper) (No. 15)
Setting IC (Devanagri numerals only) (white vertical laid paper) (Nos. 15/a)
Setting ID (only Gujarati numerals so far identified) (white vertical laid paper) (Nos. 14, 14b)

Settings IVA/D of the 1a. were subsequently adapted to form settings IA/D of the 4a.

Official imitations, consisting of 1a. carmine-red on white wove and white laid, 1a. black on blue wove, 4a. black on white wove, 4a. black on blue wove, 4a. red on white laid—all imperforate; 1a. carmine-red on white laid, 1a. black on blue wove, 4a. black on white laid and blue wove—all perforated 12, were made in 1890. Entire sheets of originals have 20 stamps (4×5), the imitations only 4 or 16.

6 **7**

(Typo Nitiprakash Ptg Press, Junagadh)
1878 (16 Jan)**-86**. Laid paper with the lines wide apart. Imperf

16	**6**	1a. green	1·00	1·25
		a. Printed both sides	£750	£800
		b. Laid lines close together (1886)	1·00	50
17	**7**	4a. vermilion	2·75	1·75
		a. Printed both sides	£1000	
		b. Scarlet/bluish	7·00	7·00
18		4a. brown	32·00	

Nawab Bahadur Khan III, 1882–1892

1886. P 12.

(a) On toned laid paper with the lines close together

19	**6**	1a. green	50	25
		a. Imperf vert (horiz pair)	£250	
		b. Imperf between (horiz pair)	†	£600
		c. Imperf horiz (vert pair)	†	£600
		d. Doubly printed	†	£800
		e. Error. Blue	£650	£650
		f. On bluish white laid paper	3·75	4·75
		fa. Imperf between (horiz pair)	£425	£475
		fb. Imperf vert (horiz pair)	£375	
		g. Emerald-green	4·25	2·50
20	**7**	4a. red	3·25	2·50
		a. On bluish white laid paper	18·00	26·00
		ab. Printed both sides	£750	
		b. Carmine	9·00	8·00

21		4a. brown	45·00	

(b) Wove paper

22	**6**	1a. green	4·25	2·50
		a. Imperf (pair)	£150	£275
		b. Error. Blue	—	£650
		c. Imperf horiz (vert pair)	£325	
23	**7**	4a. red	14·00	20·00
		a. Imperf (pair)	£450	£600
		b. Imperf between (horiz pair)	£700	
		c. Imperf vert (horiz pair)	£700	
24		4a. brown	45·00	

There is a very wide range of colours in both values. The laid paper, on which imperforate printings continued to appear until 1912, is found both vertical and horizontal.

The 1a. was originally issued in sheets of 15 (5×3), but later appeared in sheets of 20 (5×4) with marginal inscriptions. Stamps were sometimes printed in double sheets showing two impressions of the plate printed *tête-bêche* on the same or opposite sides of the paper.

The 4a. was in horizontal strips of five. No. 20 exists as a sheet of ten (5×2), with two impressions of the plate printed *tête-bêche*, and No. 23 in a similar sized sheet but with both impressions upright.

Nawab Rasul Khan 1892–1911
Nawab Mahabat Khan III, 1911–1959
(Indian currency)

(8) **(9)**

1913 (1 Jan). Surch in Indian currency with T **8** or **9**. P 12.

(a) On toned wove paper

33	**6**	3p. on 1a. emerald-green	25	40
		a. Imperf (pair)	£475	
		b. Imperf between (horiz pair)	£475	
		c. Imperf vert (horiz pair)	£475	
		d. Doubly printed	£400	
		e. Imperf between (vert pair)	£500	
34	**7**	1a. on 4a. red	4·50	16·00
		a. Imperf (pair)	£1100	
		b. Capital "A" in "Anna"	10·00	
		c. Surch inverted	£1100	
		d. Imperf between (horiz pair)		

(b) On white wove paper

35	**6**	3p. on 1a. emerald-green	25	30
		a. Imperf between (vert pair)	£600	
		b. Surch inverted	45·00	20·00
		c. Surch double	†	£850
36	**7**	1a. on 4a. carmine	4·50	15·00
		a. Imperf (pair)		
		b. Surch both sides	£1100	
		c. Capital "A" in "Anna"	22·00	

(c) On white laid paper

37	**6**	3p. on 1a. emerald-green	85·00	35·00
		a. Imperf (pair)	—	£900
		b. Larger English surch (21 mm long with capital "P" in "Pies" inverted	£4500	£4500
38	**7**	1a. on 4a. red	11·00	70·00
		a. Capital "A" in "Anna"	£650	
		b. Surch inverted	£1000	
		c. Surch double	£1000	
		d. Surch double, one inverted	£1000	

The 1a. surcharge with capital "A" in "Anna" comes from a separate setting.

10 **11**

(Dies eng Thacker & Co, Bombay. Typo Junagadh State Press)
1914 (1 Sept). New plates. T **6/7** redrawn as T **10/11**. Wove paper. P 12.

40	**10**	3p. green	3·25	35
		a. Imperf (pair)	16·00	55·00
		b. Imperf vert (horiz pair)	£180	
		c. Laid paper	6·50	2·50
		ca. Imperf (pair)	40·00	80·00
		d. Error. Red (imperf)	†	£4250
41	**11**	1a. red	2·50	3·50
		a. Imperf (pair)	38·00	£200
		b. Imperf horiz (vert pair)	£650	
		ba. Imperf vert (horiz pair)	£650	
		c. Laid paper	£250	£110

12 Nawab Mahabat Khan III **13** Nawab Mahabat Khan III

(Dies eng Popatlal Bhimji Pandya. Typo Junagadh State Press)
1923 (1 Sept). Blurred impression. Laid paper. Pin-perf 12.

42	**12**	1a. red	3·75	16·00

Sheets of 16 stamps (8×2).
This setting was later printed on wove paper, but single examples cannot be readily distinguished from No. 46b.

ત્રણ પાઇ ત્રણ પાઇ

(14) **(14a)**

1923 (1 Sept). Surch with T **14**.

43	**12**	3p. on 1a. red	8·00	11·00
		a. Surch with T **14a**	9·50	14·00

Four stamps in the setting have surch. T **14a**, i.e. with top of last character curved to right.

1923 (Oct). Blurred impression. Wove paper. Pin-perf 12, small holes.

44	**13**	3p. mauve	45	45

Sheets of 16 (4×4).

1924. Clear impression. Wove paper. P 12, large holes.

45	**13**	3p. mauve (1.24)	4·50	35
		a. Imperf (pair)	£300	
46	**12**	1a. red (4.24)	11·00	11·00
		a. Imperf (pair)	£100	
		b. Pin perf	4·50	5·00

The first plate of the 3p., which printed No. 44, produced unsatisfactory impressions, so it was replaced by a second plate, producing two panes of 16 (4×4), from which No. 45 comes. Sheets printed from the first plate had very large margins.

The 1a. is also from a new plate, giving a clearer impression. Sheets of 16 stamps (4×4).

1929. Clear impressions. Laid paper. P 12, large holes.

47	**13**	3p. mauve	5·50	7·50
		a. Imperf (pair)	7·00	50·00
		b. Perf 11	21·00	26·00
		ba. Imperf between (horiz pair)	3·50	26·00

Sheets of two panes of 16 (4×4).
The laid paper shows several sheet watermarks.
No. 47ba was intentional to create a 6p. franking required by a rate change in October 1929.

15 Junagadh City

16 Gir Lion

17 Nawab Mahabat Khan III **18** Kathi Horse

(Des Amir Sheikh Mahamadbhai. Litho Indian Security Printing Press, Nasik)

1929 (1 Oct). Inscr "POSTAGE". P 14.

49	**15**	3p. black and blackish green	1·75	10
50	**16**	½a. black and deep blue	8·50	10
51	**17**	1a. black and carmine	10·00	2·00
52	**18**	2a. black and dull orange	15·00	2·25
		a. Grey and dull yellow	30·00	2·00
53	**15**	3a. black and carmine	7·00	22·00
54	**16**	4a. black and purple	14·00	45·00
55	**18**	8a. black and yellow-green	30·00	35·00
56	**17**	1r. black and pale blue	30·00	65·00
49/56		Set of 8	£100	£150

1935 (1 Jan). As T **17**, but inscr "POSTAGE AND REVENUE". P 14.

57	**17**	1a. black and carmine	10·00	1·00

OFFICIAL STAMPS

SARKARI

(O **1**)

1929 (1 Oct). Optd with Type O **1**, in vermilion, at Nasik.

O1	**15**	3p. black and blackish green	2·50	15
		a. Red opt	4·00	10
O2	**16**	½a. black and deep blue	6·00	10
		a. Red opt	7·00	40
O3	**17**	1a. black and carmine (No. 51)	4·50	45
		a. Red opt	8·00	15
O4	**18**	2a. black and dull orange	3·00	1·25
		a. Grey and dull yellow	30·00	75
		b. Red opt	28·00	2·75
O5	**15**	3a. black and carmine	1·00	30
		a. Red opt	18·00	2·25
O6	**16**	4a. black and purple	6·50	45
		a. Red opt	30·00	4·00
O7	**18**	8a. black and yellow-green	7·00	3·25
O8	**17**	1r. black and pale blue	9·00	48·00
O1/8		Set of 8	35·00	48·00

SARKARI **SARKARI**

(O **2**) (O **3**)

1932 (Jan)**-35**. Optd with Type O **2**, in red, at Junagadh State Press.

O9	**15**	3a. black and carmine	24·00	18·00
		a. Optd with Type O **3** (1.35)	£150	4·00
O10	**16**	4a. black and purple	30·00	17·00
O11	**18**	8a. black and yellow-green	55·00	18·00
O12	**17**	1r. black and pale blue	65·00	£170
		a. Optd with Type O **3** (1.35)	£300	£225
O9/12		Set of 4	£160	£190

1938. No. 57 optd with Type O **1**, in vermilion.

O13	**17**	1a. black and carmine	32·00	2·25
		a. Brown-red opt	21·00	1·50

The state was occupied by Indian troops on 9 November 1947 following the flight of the Nawab to Pakistan.

UNITED STATE OF SAURASHTRA

The administration of Junagadh state was assumed by the Government of India on 9 November 1947. An Executive Council took office on 1 June 1948.

Under the new Constitution of India the United State of Saurashtra was formed on 15 February 1948, comprising 221 former states and estates of Kathiawar, including Jasdan, Morvi, Nawanagar and Wadhwan, but excluding Junagadh. A referendum was held by the Executive Council of Junagadh which then joined the United State on 20 January 1949. It is believed that the following issues were only used in Junagadh.

The following issues were surcharged at the Junagadh State Press.

POSTAGE & REVENUE

ONE ANNA
(**19**)

Postage & Revenue

ONE ANNA
(**20**)

1949. Stamps of 1929 surch.

(a) With T 19 in red

58	**16**	1a. on ½a. black and deep blue (5.49)	9·50	6·50
		a. Surch double	†	£750
		b. "AFNA" for "ANNA" and inverted "N" in "REVENUE"	£5000	£5000
		c. Larger first "A" in "ANNA" (R. 2/5)	90·00	60·00

(b) With T 20 in green

59	**18**	1a. on 2a. grey and dull yellow (2.49)	21·00	32·00
		a. "evenue" omitted	—	£1200

No. 58b may have occurred on R. 2/5 with No. 58c being caused by its correction.

A number of other varieties occur on No. 58, including: small "V" in "REVENUE" (R. 2/3); small "N" in "REVENUE" (R. 2/4, 3/4); small "E" in "POSTAGE" (R. 3/2); thick "A" in "POSTAGE" (R. 4/4); inverted "N" in "REVENUE" and small second "A" in "ANNA" (R. 4/5); small "O" in "ONE" (R. 5/1); small "V" and "U" in "REVENUE" (R. 6/3); small "N" in "ONE" (R. 7/2).

In No. 59 no stop after "ANNA" is known on R. 1/4, 4/2, 7/4 and 8/3 and small "N" in "ONE" on R. 2/4.

(Typo Waterlow)

1949 (Sept). Court Fee stamps of Bhavnagar state optd "SAURASHTRA" and further optd "U.S.S. REVENUE & POSTAGE" as in T **21**, in black. P 11.

60	**21**	1a. purple	11·00	10·00
		a. "POSTAGE" omitted (R. 1/2)	£650	£425
		b. Opt double	£550	£650

The Court Fee stamps were in sheets of 80 (8×10) and were overprinted in a setting of 40 applied twice to each sheet.

Minor varieties include small "S" in "POSTAGE" (R. 2/1 of the setting); small "N" in "REVENUE" (R. 2/7); small "U" in "REVENUE" (R. 3/2); small "V" in "REVENUE" (R. 3/8, 5/5); and small O" in "POSTAGE" (R. 4/7).

Various missing stop varieties also occur.

POSTAGE & REVENUE
ONE ANNA
(**22**)

1950 (2 Mar). Stamp of 1929 surch with T **22**.

61	**15**	1a. on 3p. black and blackish green	40·00	75·00
		a. "P" of "POSTAGE" omitted (R. 8/1)	£500	£800
		b. "O" of "ONE" omitted (R. 6/1)	£750	

Other minor varieties include small second "A" in "ANNA" (R. 1/2); small "S" in "POSTAGE" with small "V" in "REVENUE" (R. 3/4, 6/1) and small "V" in "REVENUE" (R. 2/3, 3/1).

OFFICIAL STAMPS

1948 (July–Dec). Nos. O4/O7 surch "ONE ANNA" (2¼ mm high) by Junagadh State Press.

O14	**18**	1a. on 2a. grey and dull yellow (B.)	£30000	26·00
O15	**15**	1a. on 3a. black and carmine (8.48)	£11000	£100
		a. Surch double	†	£7500
O16	**16**	1a. on 4a. black and purple (12.48)	£650	£100
		a. "ANNE" for "ANNA" (R. 5/4)	£6000	£700
		b. "ANNN" for "ANNA" (R. 7/5)	£6000	£700
O17	**18**	1a. on 8a. black and yellow-green (12.48)	£550	80·00
		a. "ANNE" for "ANNA" (R. 5/4)	£5500	£550
		b. "ANNN" for "ANNA" (R. 7/5)	£5500	£550

Numerous minor varieties of fount occur in this surcharge.

1948 (Nov). Handstamped "ONE ANNA" (4 mm high).

O18	**17**	1a. on 1r. (No. O8)	£5500	85·00
O19		1a. on 1r. (No. O12)	£1600	85·00
		a. Optd as O12a	—	£130

A used copy of No. O12 is known surcharged in black as on Nos. O14/17. This may have come from a proof sheet.

1949 (Jan). Postage stamps optd with Type O **2**, in red.

O20	**15**	3p. black and blackish green	£325	27·00
O21	**16**	½a. black and deep blue	£800	19·00
O22	**18**	1a. on 2a. grey and dull yellow (No. 59)	£140	24·00

Various wrong fount letters occur in the above surcharges.

MANUSCRIPT OVERPRINTS. Nos. 49, 50, 57, 58, 59 and 60 are known with manuscript overprints reading "Service" or "SARKARI" (in English or Gujerati script), usually in red. Such provisionals were used at Gadhda and Una between June and December 1949 (*Price from £200 each, used on piece*).

The United State of Saurashtra postal service was incorporated into that of India on 30 March 1950.

TRAVANCORE

(16 cash = 1 chuckram; 28 chuckrams = 1 rupee)

"Anchel" or "Anchal" = Post Office Department.

The stamps of Travancore were valid on mail posted to Cochin.

PRINTERS. All stamps of Travancore were printed by the Stamp Manufactory, Trivandrum, *unless otherwise stated*.

PRINTING METHODS. The dies were engraved on brass from which electrotypes were made and locked together in a forme for printing the stamps. As individual electrotypes became worn they were replaced by new ones and their positions in the forme were sometimes changed. This makes it difficult to plate the early issues. From 1901 plates were made which are characterised by a frame (or "Jubilee" line) round the margins of the sheets.

Up to the 6 cash of 1910 the dies were engraved by Dharmalingham Asari.

SHADES. We list only the main groups of shades but there are many others in view of the large number of printings and the use of fugitive inks. Sometimes shade variation is noticeable within the same sheet.

Maharaja Rama Varma X, 1885–1924

1 Conch or Chank
Shell

1888 (16 Oct). As T **1**, but each value differs slightly. Laid paper. P 12.

1	**1**	1ch. ultramarine (*shades*)	5·00	6·00
2		2ch. red	8·00	12·00
3		4ch. green	25·00	18·00
1/3	*Set of 3*		35·00	32·00

The paper bears a large sheet watermark showing a large conch shell surmounted by "GOVERNMENT" in large outline letters, in an arch with "OF TRAVANCORE" at foot in a straight line. Many stamps in the sheet are without watermark.

These stamps on laid paper in abnormal colours are proofs.

The paper is normally horizontally laid, but the 1ch. is also known on vertically laid paper.

2

Three forms of watermark Type **2**. (*as seen from the back of the stamp*)

WATERMARKS AND PAPERS.
Type A appeared upright on early printings of the 1, 2 and 4ch. values on odd-sized sheets which did not fit the number of shells. Later it was always sideways with 15 mm between the shells on standard-sized sheets of 84 (14×6) containing 60 shells (10×6). It therefore never appears centred on the stamps and it occurs on hand-made papers only.

Type B is similar in shape but can easily be distinguished as it is invariably upright, with 11 mm between the shells, and is well centred on the stamps. It also occurs on hand-made papers. It was introduced in 1904 and from 1914, when Type A was brought back into use, it was employed concurrently until 1924.

Type C is quite different in shape and occurs on machine-made papers. There are two versions. The first, in use from 1924 to 1939, has 84 shells 11 mm apart and is always upright and well centred. The second, introduced in 1929 and believed to have been used after 1930, has 60 shells (12×5) 15 mm apart and is invariably badly centred so that some stamps in the sheet are without watermark.

This second version is normally found upright, but a few sideways watermark varieties are known and listed as Nos. 35g, 37c, O31j and O32i. We do not distinguish between the two versions of Type C in the lists, but stamps known to exist in the second version are indicated in footnotes. The machine-made paper is generally smoother and of more even texture.

WATERMARK VARIETIES. Little attention seems to have been paid to the orientation of the watermark by the printers, with the result that inverted, reversed and inverted and reversed watermarks are frequently encountered. We do not list such varieties.

STAMPS WITHOUT WATERMARK. Some of these were formerly listed but we have now decided to omit them as they do not occur in full sheets. They arise in the following circumstances: (*a*) on sheets with wmk A; (*b*) on sheets with the wide-spaced form of wmk C; and (*c*) on late printings of the pictorial issues of 1939–46. They are best collected in pairs, with and without watermark.

DATES OF ISSUE. In the absence of more definite information the dates noted usually refer to the first reported date of new printings on different watermarks but many were not noted at the time and the dates of these are indicated by a query. Dated postmarks on single stamps are difficult to find.

3   **4**   **5**

6   **7**   **8**

1889–1904. Wove paper. Wmk A (upright or sideways). P 12 (sometimes rough).

4	**1**	½ch. slate-lilac (1894)	3·25	50
		a. Doubly printed	†	£475
		b. Reddish lilac	75	25
		ba. Imperf between (vert pair)	£500	£500
		bb. Doubly printed	†	£475
		c. Purple (1899)	1·50	25
		ca. Doubly printed	†	£475
		d. Dull purple (1904)	1·50	25
5	**5**	¾ch. black (14.3.01)	2·00	1·40
6	**1**	1ch. ultramarine	1·50	15
		a. Tête-bêche (pair)	£4000	£3000
		b. Doubly printed	†	£650
		c. Imperf vert (horiz pair)	†	£700
		d. Imperf between (vert pair)	†	£650
		e. Pale ultramarine (1892)	3·00	20
		f. Violet-blue (1901)	3·75	40
7		2ch. salmon (1890)	4·00	1·00
		a. Rose (1891)	3·50	30
		ab. Imperf (pair)	†	£800
		b. Pale pink (1899)	3·00	35
		ba. Imperf between (vert pair)	£200	
		bb. Doubly printed	£300	
		c. Red (1904)	3·00	15
		ca. Imperf between (horiz pair)	£550	£550
8		4ch. green	3·25	70
		a. Yellow-green (1901)	2·50	55
		b. Dull green (1904)	7·00	1·00
		ba. Doubly printed	†	£700

Nos. 6, 6d, 7, 7c, 8 and 8a occur with the watermark upright and sideways. No. 7a is known only with the watermark upright. The remainder exist only with the watermark sideways.

The sheet sizes were as follows:
½ch. 56 (14×4) except for No. 4d which was 84 (14×6), initially without border, later with border.
¾ch. 84 (14×6) with border.
1ch. No. 6, 80 (10×8) and later 84 (14×6) without border and then with border; No. 6d, 96 (16×6); No. 6e, 84 (14×6) with border.
2ch. No. 7, 80 (10×8); No. 7a, 70 (10×7); Nos. 7b, 7c, 60 (10×6).
4ch. No. 8, 60 (10×6); Nos. 8a/b, 84 (14×6) with border.
After 1904 all stamps in Types **3** to **8** were in standard-sized sheets of 84 (14×6) with border.

For later printings watermarked Type A, see Nos. 23/30.

1904–20. Wmk B, upright (centred). P 12, sometimes rough.

9	**3**	4ca. pink (11.08)	30	10
		a. Imperf between (vert pair)	£475	£475
10	**1**	6ca. chestnut (2.10)	30	10
		a. Imperf between (horiz pair)	†	£400
11		½ch. reddish lilac	2·25	10
		a. Reddish violet (6.10)	2·25	10
		ab. Doubly printed	†	£425
		b. Lilac	2·00	30
		c. "CHUCRRAM" (R. 5/6)	13·00	6·00
		d. Imperf horiz (vert pair)	†	£375
		e. Printed both sides	†	£425
12	**4**	10ca. pink (1920)	42·00	5·50
13	**5**	¾ch. black	2·50	25
14	**1**	1ch. bright blue		
		a. Blue	5·50	1·00
		b. Deep blue	5·00	75
		c. Indigo (8.10)	1·00	10
		d. Chalky blue (1912)	6·00	1·00
15		1¼ch. claret (*shades*) (10.14)	55	55
		a. Imperf between (horiz pair)	£550	£550
16		2ch. salmon	23·00	7·00
		a. Red (8.10)	75	10
17	**6**	3ch. violet (11.3.11)	2·75	20
		a. Imperf between (vert pair)	£475	£375
		b. Imperf between (vert strip of 3)		£425
18	**1**	4ch. dull green	26·00	10·00
		a. Slate-green	4·50	45
19	**7**	7ch. claret (1916)	2·75	1·75
		a. Error. Carmine-red	—	50·00
20	**8**	14ch. orange-yellow (1916)	2·75	3·25
		a. Imperf vert (horiz strip of 3)	£750	

(9)   (10)

1906. Surch as T **9**. Wmk B.

21	**1**	¼ on ½ch. reddish lilac	1·25	30
		a. Reddish violet	1·25	20
		b. Lilac	2·25	50
		c. "CHUCRRAM" (R. 5/6)	9·00	5·50
		d. Surch inverted	£130	75·00
22		³⁄₈ on ½ch. reddish lilac	1·25	35
		a. Reddish violet	1·00	35
		b. Lilac	1·75	50
		c. "CHUCRRAM" (R. 5/6)	9·50	7·00
		d. Surch inverted		£110
		e. Surch double		
		f. "8" omitted	—	65·00

1914–22. Reversion to wmk A (sideways). P 12 (sometimes rough).

23	**3**	4ca. pink (1915)	8·00	60
24	**4**	5ca. olive-bistre (30.10.21)	80	40
		a. Imperf between (horiz pair)	75·00	85·00
		b. Imperf between (horiz strip of 3)	£190	£200
		c. "TRAVANCOPE" (R. 6/13)	30·00	18·00
25	**1**	6ca. orange-brown (2.15)	10·00	40
26		½ch. reddish violet (12.14)	4·50	75
		a. "CHUCRRAM" (R. 5/6)	23·00	6·50
		b. Imperf between (horiz pair)	£375	
27	**4**	10ca. pink (26.10.21)	40	10
28	**1**	1ch. grey-blue (5.22)	24·00	4·50
		a. Deep blue	22·00	4·50
29		1¼ch. claret (12.19)	24·00	1·25
		a. Imperf between (horiz pair)	†	£550
30	**6**	3ch. reddish lilac (8.22)	30·00	1·50

1921 (Mar). Surch as T **10**. Wmk A (sideways).

31	**3**	1c. on 4ca. pink	15	20
		a. Surch inverted	45·00	22·00
		b. On wmk B (upright)		
32	**1**	5c. on 1ch. grey-blue (R.)	1·00	10
		a. Deep blue	1·00	10
		b. Stamp printed both sides		
		c. Imperf between (vert pair)	†	£425
		d. Surch inverted	13·00	8·50
		e. Surch double	£120	90·00
		f. On wmk B (upright). Deep blue.	38·00	27·00
		fa. Surch inverted		£200

ALBINO OVERPRINT VARIETIES. Stamps with overprint double, one albino are frequently found in the provisional and official issues of Travancore, and are only worth a small premium over the normal prices.

Maharaja Bala Rama Varma XI, 1924–1971

1924–39. Wmk C. Machine-made paper. P 12.

33	**4**	5ca. olive-bistre (18.6.25)	11·00	3·00
		a. Imperf between (horiz pair)	£250	
		b. "TRAVANCOPE" (R. 6/13)	—	30·00
34		5ca. chocolate (1930)	3·75	60
		a. Imperf between (horiz pair)	50·00	
		b. Imperf between (vert pair)	†	£375
35	**1**	6ca. brown-red (3.24)	4·25	10
		a. Imperf between (horiz pair)	32·00	48·00
		b. Imperf between (vert pair)	£250	£250
		c. Printed both sides	50·00	
		d. Perf 12½	5·00	50
		e. Perf comp of 12 and 12½	6·50	4·00
		f. Perf 12½×11	—	£250
		g. Wmk sideways	—	35·00
36		½ch. reddish violet (date?)	5·00	5·50
		a. "CHUCRRAM" (R. 5/6)	38·00	
37	**4**	10ca. pink (8.24)	2·50	10
		a. Imperf between (horiz pair)	£160	£170
		b. Imperf between (vert pair)	35·00	48·00
		c. Wmk sideways (16.9.28)	—	10·00
38	**5**	¾ch. black (4.10.32)	11·00	1·00
39		¾ch. mauve (16.11.32)	75	10
		a. Imperf between (horiz pair)	†	£350
		ab. Imperf between (vert pair)	†	£375
		b. Perf 12½ (8.37)	18·00	70
		ba. Imperf between (horiz pair)	£225	
		c. Perf comp of 12 and 12½	23·00	9·50
		ca. Imperf between (horiz pair)	£325	
40		¾ch. reddish violet (1939)	7·00	1·25
		a. Perf 12½	7·00	50
		b. Perf comp of 12 and 12½	11·00	2·50
		c. Perf 11	£375	£170
		d. Perf comp of 12 and 11	—	£170
		e. Perf 12½×11	—	£190
41	**1**	1ch. slate-blue (8.26)	3·00	30
		a. Indigo	5·50	20
		b. Imperf between (horiz pair)	†	£425
		c. Imperf between (vert pair)	†	£425
		d. Perf 12½	11·00	2·75
42		1½ch. rose (1932)	2·75	10
		a. Imperf between (horiz strip of 3)	£375	
		b. Perf 12½	23·00	2·75
		c. Perf comp of 12 and 12½	—	75·00
43		2ch. carmine-red (4.6.29)	3·00	30
44	**6**	3ch. violet (4.25)	7·00	15
		a. Imperf between (vert pair)	£100	£120
		b. Wmk sideways	—	75·00
		c. Perf 12½	—	12·00
		d. Perf comp of 12 and 12½	—	70·00
45	**1**	4ch. grey-green (5.4.34)	5·00	45
46	**7**	7ch. claret (1925)	15·00	2·00
		a. Doubly printed	†	£800
		b. Carmine-red (date?)	65·00	55·00
		c. Brown-purple (1932)	22·00	7·00
		ca. Perf 12½	9·00	22·00
		cb. Perf comb of 12 and 12½	9·00	22·00
46d	**8**	14ch. orange-yellow (date?)	48·00	
		da. Perf 12½	£275	

It is believed that the 12½ perforation and the perf 12 and 12½ compound were introduced in 1937 and that the 11 perforation came later, probably in 1939.

The 5ca. chocolate, 6ca., 10ca. and 3ch. also exist on the wide-spaced watermark (60 shells to the sheet of 84).

11 Sri Padmanabha Shrine

12 State Chariot   **13** Maharaja Bala Rama Varma XI

(Des M. R. Madhawan Unnithan. Plates by Calcutta Chromotype Co. Typo Stamp Manufactory, Trivandrum)

1931 (6 Nov). Coronation. Cream or white paper. Wmk C. P 11½, 12.

47	**11**	6ca. black and green	1·60	1·75
		a. Imperf between (horiz pair)	£180	£250
48	**12**	10ca. black and ultramarine	1·25	70
		a. Imperf between (vert pair)	†	£900
49	**13**	3ch. black and purple	2·75	3·50
47/9 Set of 3			5·00	5·50

(14)   (15)

1932 (14 Jan).

*(i) Surch as T **14***

(a) Wmk A (sideways)

50	**1**	1c. on 1¼ch. claret	15	50
		a. Imperf between (horiz pair)	£250	
		b. Surch inverted	4·25	9·00
		c. Surch double	48·00	60·00
		d. Pair, one without surch	£190	£225
		e. "c" omitted	60·00	70·00
		f. "1" omitted	60·00	
51		2c. on 1¼ch. claret	15	30
		a. Surch inverted	4·25	7·00
		b. Surch double	42·00	
		c. Surch double, one inverted	95·00	
		d. Surch treble	90·00	
		e. Surch treble, one inverted	75·00	85·00
		f. Pair, one without surch	£170	£180
		g. "2" omitted	55·00	60·00
		h. "c" omitted	55·00	60·00
		i. Imperf between (horiz pair)	£275	
		j. Imperf between (vert pair)	£275	

(b) Wmk B (upright)

52	**1**	1c. on 1¼ch. claret	2·75	1·75
		a. Surch inverted	28·00	21·00
		b. Surch double	50·00	
		c. "c" omitted	85·00	
53		2c. on 1¼ch. claret	6·50	7·50
		a. Imperf between (horiz pair)	£275	

(c) Wmk C

54	**1**	1c. on 1¼ch. claret	18·00	26·00
		a. Surch inverted	£100	£130
		b. "1" omitted	£140	
		c. "c" omitted	£140	
55		2c. on 1¼ch. claret	60·00	55·00

*(ii) Surch as T **10**. Wmk B*

56	**1**	2c. on 1¼ch. claret	5·50	18·00

1932 (5 Mar). Surch as T **15**. Wmk C.

57	**4**	1c. on 5ca. chocolate	15	15
		a. Imperf between (horiz pair)	£250	
		b. Surch inverted	7·50	10·00
		c. Surch inverted on back only	£150	
		d. Pair, one without surch	£250	
		e. "1" omitted	55·00	
		f. "c" omitted	—	55·00
		g. "TRAVANCOPE" (R. 6/13)	13·00	
58		1c. on 5ca. slate-purple	2·50	75
		a. Surch inverted	†	£425
		b. "1" inverted	£140	£140
59		2c. on 10ca. pink	15	15
		a. Imperf between (horiz pair)	£250	
		b. Surch inverted	5·00	9·00
		c. Surch double	32·00	35·00
		d. Surch double, one inverted	£150	£150
		e. Surch double, both inverted	65·00	

No. 58 was not issued without the surcharge.

16 Maharaja Bala Rama Varma XI and Subramania Shrine   **17** Sri Padmanabha

18 Mahadeva   **19** Kanyakumari

(Plates by Indian Security Printing Press, Nasik. Typo Stamp Manufactory, Trivandrum)

1937 (29 Mar). Temple Entry Proclamation. T **16/19**. Wmk C. P 12.

60	**16**	6ca. carmine	4·25	1·75
		a. Imperf between (horiz strip of 3).	£700	
		b. Perf 12½	3·25	2·75
		c. Compound perf	85·00	90·00
61	**17**	12ca. bright blue	6·00	1·25
		a. Perf 12½	7·00	1·25
		ab. Imperf between (vert pair)	£650	
		b. Compound perf	£120	
62	**18**	1½ch. yellow-green	1·75	3·50
		a. Imperf between (vert pair)	£500	
		b. Perf 12½	42·00	13·00
		c. Compound perf		£190
63	**19**	3ch. violet	7·50	3·00
		a. Perf 12½	8·00	5·00
60/3 Set of 4			16·00	8·50

COMPOUND PERFS. This term covers stamps perf compound of 12½ and 11, 12 and 11 or 12 and 12½, and where two or more combinations exist the prices are for the commonest. Such compounds can occur on values which do not exist perf 12 all round.

20 Lake Ashtamudi   **21** Maharaja Bala Rama Varma XI

22   **23**

24 Sri Padmanabha Shrine

25 Cape Comorin

26 Pachipari Reservoir

(Des Nilakantha Pellai. Plates by Indian Security Printing Press, Nasik. Typo Stamp Manufactory, Trivandrum)

1939 (9 Nov). Maharaja's 27th Birthday. T **20/26**. Wmk C. P 12½.

64	**20**	1ch. yellow-green	13·00	10
		a. Imperf between (horiz pair)	45·00	
		b. Perf 11	18·00	10
		ba. Imperf between (horiz pair)	75·00	£110
		bb. Imperf between (vert strip of 3).	40·00	80·00
		c. Perf 12	42·00	3·50
		ca. Imperf between (horiz pair)	35·00	
		cb. Imperf between (vert pair)	80·00	£140
		d. Compound perf	50·00	6·00
		da. Imperf between (vert pair)	£300	
65	**21**	1½ch. scarlet	7·00	7·00
		a. Doubly printed	£700	
		b. Imperf between (horiz pair)	55·00	
		c. Imperf between (vert pair)	48·00	
		d. Perf 11	8·00	42·00
		da. Imperf horiz (vert pair)	11·00	
		e. Perf 12	80·00	9·00
		f. Perf 13½	30·00	£110
		g. Compound perf	£100	20·00
		h. Imperf (pair)	38·00	
66	**22**	2ch. orange	12·00	4·50
		a. Perf 11	28·00	2·00
		b. Perf 12	£200	9·00
		c. Compound perf	£225	8·00
67	**23**	3ch. brown	13·00	10
		a. Doubly printed	—	£375
		b. Imperf between (horiz pair)	70·00	£110
		c. Perf 11	30·00	30
		ca. Doubly printed	65·00	£100
		d. Perf 12	75·00	7·00
		da. Imperf between (vert pair)	£200	£300
		e. Compound perf	90·00	1·50
68	**24**	4ch. red	19·00	40
		a. Perf 11	65·00	50
		b. Perf 12	70·00	15·00
		c. Compound perf	£350	£275
69	**25**	7ch. pale blue	17·00	25·00
		a. Perf 11	£170	70·00
		ab. Blue	£170	65·00
		b. Perf 12	£250	80·00
70	**26**	14ch. turquoise-green	8·00	85·00
		a. Perf 11	16·00	£170
64/70 Set of 7			80·00	£110

27 Maharaja and Aruvikara Falls

2 CASH (29)

28 Marthanda Varma Bridge, Alwaye

(Des Nilakantha Pellai. Plates by Indian Security Printing Press, Nasik. Typo Stamp Manufactory, Trivandrum)

1941 (20 Oct). Maharaja's 29th Birthday. T **27/28**. Wmk C. P 12½.

71	27	6ca. blackish violet	7·50	10
		a. Perf 11	6·50	10
		ab. Imperf between (vert pair)	35·00	
		ac. Imperf horiz (vert pair)	80·00	£110
		b. Perf 12	35·00	3·00
		ba. Imperf between (horiz pair)	38·00	
		bb. Imperf between (vert pair)	95·00	
		bc. Imperf between (vert strip of 3)	40·00	
		c. Compound perf	14·00	3·50
72	28	¾ch. brown	9·50	30
		a. Imperf between (vert pair)	†	£800
		b. Perf 11	10·00	20
		ba. Imperf between (horiz pair)	£375	
		bb. Imperf between (vert pair)	32·00	75·00
		bc. Imperf between (vert strip of 3)	42·00	
		bd. Block of four imperf between (horiz and vert)	£425	
		c. Perf 12	75·00	15·00
		d. Compound perf	20·00	1·10

1943 (17 Sept). Nos. 65, 71 (colour changed) and 72 surch as T **29**. P 12½.

73		2ca. on 1½ch. scarlet	1·75	1·75
		a. Imperf between (vert pair)	85·00	
		b. "2" omitted	£500	£500
		c. "CA" omitted	£900	
		d. "ASH" omitted	£900	
		e. Perf 11	40	60
		ea. "CA" omitted	£900	
		eb. Imperf between (horiz pair)	†	£475
		f. Compound perf	1·25	2·50
		fa. Imperf between (vert pair)	£300	
		fb. "2" omitted	£500	
74		4ca. on ¾ch. brown	7·00	2·25
		a. Perf 11	8·00	60
		b. Perf 12	—	£250
		c. Compound perf	10·00	1·50
75		8ca. on 6ca. scarlet	5·00	30
		a. Perf 11	5·00	10
		ab. Imperf between (horiz pair)	55·00	
		b. Perf 12	—	£150
		c. Compound perf	25·00	13·00
73/5		*Set of 3*	11·00	1·00

30 Maharaja Bala Rama Varma XI

SPECIAL (31)

(Des Nilakantha Pellai. Plates by Indian Security Printing Press, Nasik. Typo Stamp Manufactory, Trivandrum)

1946 (24 Oct). Maharaja's 34th Birthday. Wmk C. P 12½.

76	30	8ca. carmine	65·00	6·00
		a. Perf 11	4·00	2·25
		b. Perf 12	65·00	2·50
		ba. Imperf between (horiz pair)	70·00	£110
		bb. Imperf between (horiz strip of 3).	£110	
		c. Compound perf		

1946. No. O103 revalidated for ordinary postage with opt T **31**, in orange. P 12½.

77	19	6ca. blackish violet	8·50	5·00
		a. Perf 11	65·00	10·00
		b. Compound perf	8·50	9·50

OFFICIAL STAMPS

GUM. Soon after 1911 the Official stamps were issued without gum. Thus only the initial printings of the 1, 2, 3 and 4ch. values were gummed. As Nos. O38/9, O41/2 and O95 were overprinted on stamps intended for normal postage these, also, have gum.

PRINTINGS. Sometimes special printings of postage stamps were made specifically for overprinting for Official use, thus accounting for Official stamps appearing with watermarks or in shades not listed in the postage issues.

SETTINGS. These are based on the study of complete sheets of 84, and the measurements given are those of the majority of stamps on the sheet. Examples are known showing different measurements as each overprint was set individually in loose type, but these are not included in the listings.

On   **On**

S.   **S**   **S**   **S**

(O **1**)   (O **2**)

Rounded "O"

1911 (16 Aug)–**30**. Contemporary stamps optd with Type O **1** (13 *mm* wide). P 12, sometimes rough.

(a) Wmk B (upright) (16.8.11-21)

O1	3	4ca. pink (1916)	20	10
		a. Opt inverted	†	£110
		b. Opt double	£160	£120
		c. "S S" inverted	55·00	27·00
		d. Imperf (pair)	£500	£500
		e. Stamp doubly printed	†	£500
		f. Left "S" inverted	—	26·00
		g. "O" inverted	—	40·00
O2	1	6ca. chestnut (date ?)	65·00	65·00
O3		½ch. reddish lilac (R.) (1919)	4·00	35
		a. "CHUCRRAM" (R. 5/6)	25·00	8·50
O4	4	10ca. pink (1921)	50·00	8·00
		a. "O" inverted	£180	28·00
		b. Left "S" inverted	£180	28·00
		c. Right "S" inverted	£180	28·00
		d. Opt inverted	†	£225
O5	1	1ch. chalky blue (R.)	3·00	10
		a. Imperf between (vert pair)	†	£300
		b. Opt inverted	7·00	4·25
		c. Opt double	90·00	50·00
		d. "nO" for "On" (R. 5/7)	£140	£110
		e. "O" inverted	18·00	3·25
		f. Left "S" inverted	18·00	3·00
		g. Right "S" inverted	18·00	3·25
		h. "S S" inverted	—	85·00
O6		2ch. red	35	10
		a. Opt inverted	9·00	9·00
		b. "O" inverted	16·00	1·25
		c. Left "S" inverted	16·00	1·25
		d. Right "S" inverted	16·00	2·50
		e. Opt double	†	£120
O7		2ch. red (B.) (date ?)	—	£180
O8	6	3ch. violet	35	10
		a. Imperf between (vert pair)	£325	£375
		b. Imperf vert (horiz pair)	£190	
		c. Opt inverted	10·00	10·00
		d. Opt double	£110	70·00
		e. Right "S" inverted	7·50	1·00
		f. Right "S" omitted	£275	£170
		g. Left "S" omitted	£275	£160
O9		3ch. violet (B.) (date ?)	£275	£120
O10	1	4ch. slate-green	55	10
		a. Imperf between (horiz pair)	—	£475
		b. Opt inverted	75·00	15·00
		c. Opt double	£150	90·00
		d. "O" inverted	20·00	3·50
		e. Left "S" inverted	21·00	6·00
		f. Right "S" inverted	23·00	7·00
		g. Left "S" omitted	£275	£180
O11		4ch. slate-green (B.) (1921)	—	£100
		a. "O" inverted	—	£325
		b. Left "S" inverted	—	£325
		c. Right "S" inverted	—	£325

(b) Wmk A (sideways) (1919–25)

O12	3	4ca. pink	6·50	15
		a. Imperf (pair)	£600	£600
		b. Opt inverted	£120	17·00
		c. "O" inverted	70·00	8·50
		d. Left "S" inverted	80·00	13·00
		e. Right "S" inverted	80·00	18·00
		f. Stamp doubly printed	†	£500
		g. Imperf between (horiz pair)	†	£550
O13		4ca. pink (B.) (1921)	65·00	75
		a. "O" inverted	—	32·00
O14	4	5ca. olive-bistre (1921)	2·75	10
		a. Opt inverted	24·00	9·50
		b. "O" inverted	14·00	4·00
		c. Left "S" inverted	16·00	4·00
		d. Right "S" inverted	16·00	4·00
O15	1	6ca. orange-brown (1921)	50	10
		a. Imperf between (vert pair)	†	£425
		b. Opt inverted	23·00	16·00
		c. Opt double	£120	£100
		d. "O" inverted	6·00	3·25
		e. Left "S" inverted	14·00	3·75
		f. Right "S" inverted	15·00	3·75
O16		6ca. orange-brown (B.) (1921)	27·00	3·25
		a. Opt inverted	£250	£180
		b. "O" inverted	£110	22·00
		c. Left "S" inverted	£110	22·00
		d. Right "S" inverted	£110	22·00
O17		½ch. reddish violet (R.) (date ?)	4·00	70
		a. *Reddish lilac (date ?)*	3·50	70
		b. Imperf between (horiz pair)	£325	£225
		c. Imperf between (vert pair)	95·00	£100
		d. Stamp doubly printed	75·00	
		e. Opt inverted	21·00	9·00
		f. Opt double, both inverted	£250	
		g. "CHUCRRAM" (R. 5/6)	24·00	9·00
		h. "On" omitted	—	£275
		i. Right "S" inverted	—	48·00
		j. Right "S" omitted	—	£275
O18	4	10ca. pink (3.21)	3·25	10
		a. *Scarlet (1925?)*	—	22·00
		b.	—	19·00
		c. Opt double	£120	85·00
		d. "O" inverted	20·00	4·75
		e. Left "S" inverted	19·00	3·75
		f. Right "S" inverted	20·00	4·75
		g. Imperf between (horiz pair)	—	£325
O19		10ca. pink (B.) (date ?)	£150	42·00
		a. Opt inverted	—	£140
		b. "O" inverted	—	£120
O20	1	1ch. grey-blue (R.) (date ?)	11·00	60
		a. *Deep blue*	12·00	80
		b. "O" inverted	75·00	80·00
		c. Left "S" inverted	85·00	18·00
		d. "On" omitted	†	
		e. Opt inverted	†	£100
O21		1¼ch. claret (12.19)	75	10
		a. Stamp doubly printed	—	£500
		b. Opt inverted	16·00	8·00
		c. Opt double	50·00	
		d. "O" inverted	22·00	2·00
		e. Left "S" inverted	27·00	5·00
		f. Right "S" inverted	27·00	5·50
		g. Error. Carmine	50·00	
O22		1¼ch. claret (B.) (1921)	—	£140
		a. "O" inverted	—	£375

	b. Left "S" inverted	—	£375
	c. Right "S" inverted	—	£375

(c) Wmk C (1925–30)

O23	4	5ca. olive-bistre (1926)	40	40
		a. Imperf between (horiz pair)	£425	£425
		b. Opt inverted	48·00	38·00
		c. "O" inverted (R. 1/7)	11·00	5·50
		d. Left "S" inverted (R. 6/1, 6/8)	8·50	4·50
		e. Right "S" inverted (R. 6/7)	11·00	5·50
O24		10ca. pink (1926)	7·50	15
		a. Imperf between (vert pair)	—	£325
		b. Opt inverted	75·00	75·00
		c. "O" inverted (R. 1/7)	45·00	5·00
		d. Left "S" inverted (R. 6/1, 6/8)	38·00	4·50
		e. Right "S" inverted (R. 6/7)	45·00	5·00
		f. Stamp doubly printed	†	
		g. Opt double	—	£170
O25	1	1¼ch. claret (1926)	26·00	1·00
		a. "O" inverted (R. 1/7)	£120	10·00
		b. Left "S" inverted (R. 6/1, 6/8)	£100	9·00
		c. Right "S" inverted (R. 6/7)	£120	10·00
		d. Opt double	†	£150
O26	7	7ch. claret	2·75	30
		a. "O" inverted (R. 1/7)	30·00	5·00
		b. Left "S" inverted (R. 6/1, 6/8)	24·00	3·50
		c. Right "S" inverted (R. 6/7)	30·00	5·00
		d. *Carmine-red*	60·00	
O27	8	14ch. orange-yellow	2·25	40
		a. "O" inverted (R. 1/7)	25·00	5·00
		b. Left "S" inverted (R. 6/1, 6/8)	14·00	3·00
		c. Right "S" inverted (R. 6/7)	25·00	5·00

1926–30. Contemporary stamps optd with Type O **2** (16½ *mm* wide). Wmk C. P 12.

O28	4	5ca. olive-bistre	7·50	30
		a. Right "S" inverted (R. 4/9)	40·00	8·50
		b. Left "S" inverted	42·00	10·00
O29		5ca. chocolate (1930)	25	75
		a. Imperf between (vert pair)	†	£475
		b. Opt inverted	24·00	
		c. "O" inverted	7·50	10·00
		d. Left "S" inverted	7·50	10·00
O30	1	6ca. brown-red (date ?)	4·75	1·00
		a. "O" inverted	38·00	10·00
		b. Left "S" inverted	45·00	13·00
		c. Opt double	†	£200
O31	4	10ca. pink	40	10
		a. Imperf between (horiz pair)	£100	£110
		b. Imperf between (vert pair)	£110	£110
		c. Imperf vert (horiz strip of 3)	†	£225
		d. Opt inverted	9·00	11·00
		e. "Ou" for "On"	65·00	50·00
		f. "O" inverted	9·00	3·25
		g. Left "S" inverted	8·50	3·00
		h. Right "S" inverted	8·00	1·75
		i. Left "S" omitted	65·00	55·00
		j. Wmk sideways	30·00	16·00
O32	1	1¼ch. claret (*shades*)	3·50	30
		a. Imperf between (horiz pair)	£140	£150
		b. Imperf between (vert pair)	£190	£190
		c. Opt inverted	30·00	35·00
		d. "O" inverted	30·00	7·00
		e. Left "S" inverted	30·00	7·00
		f. Right "S" inverted (R. 4/9)	30·00	7·00
		g. Left "S" omitted	£225	£170
		h. Right "S" omitted	£225	£170
		i. Wmk sideways	—	16·00
		ia. Imperf between (vert pair)	£250	
O33	6	3ch. violet	21·00	80
		a. Opt inverted	†	£170
		b. "O" inverted	80·00	22·00
		c. "O" omitted	£150	95·00
		d. "Ou" for "On"	£250	£180
		e. Left "S" inverted	—	42·00
O34	7	7ch. claret (date?)	£160	7·50
O35	8	14ch. orange-yellow	65·00	85
		a. Imperf between (vert pair)	£800	
		b. Opt inverted	£170	12·00

The 5ca. olive-bistre, 3ch. and 7ch. exist only with the normal watermark spaced 11 mm; the 5ca. chocolate and 14ch. exist only with the wide 15 mm spacing; the 6ca., 10ca. and 1¼ch. exist in both forms.

On   **On**   **On**

S   **S**   **S**   **S**   **S**   **S**

(O **3**)   (O **4**)   (O **5**)

Italic "S S".

1930. Wmk C. P 12.

*(a) Optd with Type O **3***

O36	4	10ca. pink	£200	£150
O37	1	1¼ch. carmine-rose	10·00	3·25

*(b) Optd with Type O **4***

O38	5	¾ch. black (R.)	50	30
		a. Left "S" omitted	£150	£150
		b. Right "S" omitted	£150	
		c. Large Roman "S" at left	—	£160

*(c) Optd with Type O **5***

O39	5	¾ch. black (R.)	35	15
		a. Opt inverted	†	£325
		b. "n" omitted	£170	£170
O40	1	4ch. slate-green (R.)	40·00	16·00

On   **On**   **On**

S   **S**   **S**   **S**   **S**

(O **6**)   (O **7**)   (O **8**)

Oval "O"

1930–39? Contemporary stamps overprinted. P 12.

(a) With Type O 6 (16 mm high)
(i) Wmk A (sideways)

Cat		Description	Un	Used
O41	3	4ca. pink	45·00	£120
		a. Large right "S" as Type O 2 (R. 6/14)	£325	

(ii) Wmk B

Cat		Description	Un	Used
O42	3	4ca. pink	28·00	£120
		a. Large right "S" as Type O 2 (R. 6/14)	£250	

(iii) Wmk C

Cat		Description	Un	Used
O43	1	6ca. brown-red (1932)	35	10
		a. Opt inverted	26·00	
		b. Opt double	50·00	50·00
		c. "O" inverted (R. 5/11-12)	15·00	9·50
		d. Imperf between (vert pair)	†	£200
O44	4	10ca. pink	3·25	1·25
O45	5	¾ch. mauve (1933)	6·50	10
		a. Imperf between (horiz pair)	£140	95·00
		b. Imperf between (horiz strip of 3)	†	£225
		c. Imperf between (vert pair)	†	£225
		d. Stamp doubly printed	†	£325
		e. Perf 12½	7·50	50
		f. Perf comp of 12 and 12½	28·00	4·50
		g. Right "S" inverted	—	50·00
O46	1	1¼ch. carmine-rose	19·00	1·75
		a. Opt double	£160	£120
		b. Large right "S" as Type O 2 (R. 6/14)	£190	70·00
O47		4ch. grey-green	1·75	7·00
O48		4ch. grey-green (R.) (27.10.30)	70	20
		a. Imperf between (horiz pair)	£250	£200
		b. Opt double	29·00	29·00
		c. "O" inverted (R. 5/11-12)	55·00	27·00
		d. Large right "S" as Type O 2 (R. 6/14)	75·00	40·00
		e. Imperf between (vert pair)	£325	
O49	8	14ch. orange-yellow (1931)	17·00	2·25
		a. Imperf between (vert pair)	†	£250

For the 1½ch. and 3ch., and for Nos. O43 and O48/9 but perf 12½, see Nos. O66/70 (new setting combining Types O 6 and O 8).

(b) With Type O 7 (14 mm high). Wmk C

Cat		Description	Un	Used
O50	3	4ca. pink	12·00	70·00
		a. "O" inverted	75·00	£275
O51	4	5ca. chocolate (1932)	48·00	15·00
		a. Opt inverted	£110	£130
O52	1	6ca. brown-red	20	10
		a. Imperf between (vert pair)	£110	£110
		b. Opt inverted	29·00	
		c. Opt double	†	90·00
		d. "nO" for "On"	£275	£275
		e. Right "S" inverted	50·00	35·00
		f. Left "S" omitted	—	£150
		g. Large "n" as Type O 5 (R. 1/1, 1/14)	26·00	16·00
		h. Large italic left "S" as Type O 5	38·00	27·00
		i. Perf 12½	—	30·00
		j. Perf compound of 12 and 12½	—	45·00
O53		½ch. reddish violet (1932)	1·25	15
		a. "CHUCRRAM" (R. 5/6)	17·00	10·00
		b. "Ou" for "On"	£120	£110
		c. Left "S" omitted	—	£250
		d. "O" of "On" omitted	£375	
O54		½ch. reddish violet (R.) (1935)	20	10
		a. Imperf between (vert pair)	£170	£180
		b. "CHUCRRAM" (R. 5/6)	4·50	4·00
		c. Left "S" inverted	50·00	45·00
O55	4	10ca. pink (date ?)	7·50	5·00
		a. Imperf between (horiz pair)	20·00	38·00
		b. Imperf between (vert pair)	11·00	28·00
		c. "O" inverted	85·00	50·00
		d. Right "S" inverted	85·00	50·00
		e. Right "S" omitted	†	£250
O56	5	¾ch. mauve (1933?)	75	15
		a. Imperf between (vert pair)	†	£250
		b. "Ou" for "On"	£120	95·00
		c. "O" inverted	48·00	32·00
		d. Right "S" inverted	—	42·00
		e. Opt double	†	£200
		f. Perf comp of 12 and 12½	55·00	38·00
O57	1	1ch. deep blue (R.) (1935)	2·25	75
		a. Slate-blue	1·50	50
		b. Imperf between (horiz pair)	£275	£275
		c. Imperf between (vert pair)	30·00	60·00
		d. Perf 12½	19·00	11·00
		e. Perf comp of 12 and 12½	42·00	20·00
		ea. Imperf between (vert pair)	†	£325
		f. Left "S" inverted	—	65·00
O58		1¼ch. claret	2·50	2·00
O59		1½ch. rose (1933)	40	10
		a. Imperf between (vert pair)	†	£225
		b. Opt double	75·00	75·00
		c. "O" inverted	8·50	4·25
		e. Large "n" as Type O 5 (R. 1/1, 1/14)	55·00	25·00
		f. Large italic left "S" as Type O 5	75·00	38·00
		g. Left "S" inverted	—	48·00
		h. Perf 12½	60·00	20·00
		i. Perf comp of 12 and 12½	—	55·00
		ia. Stamp doubly printed	—	£400
O60	6	3ch. reddish violet (1933)	1·50	60
		a. "O" inverted	45·00	18·00
		b. Opt double	†	£150
O61		3ch. violet (R.) (1934)	1·50	10
		a. Imperf between (horiz pair)	£170	80·00
		b. Imperf between (vert pair)	£110	65·00
		c. Opt inverted	—	6·00
		d. "O" inverted	42·00	20·00
		e. Perf 12½	—	6·00
		ea. Imperf between (vert pair)	†	£325
		f. Perf comp of 12 and 12½	—	21·00
		fa. Imperf between (vert pair)	†	£325
		g. "Ou" for "On"	—	£120
O63		4ch. grey-green (R.) (1935?)	4·75	20
		a. "Ou" for "On" (R. 1/1)	£100	55·00
O64	7	7ch. claret (*shades*)	2·25	30
		a. Imperf between (vert pair)	50·00	65·00
		b. "O" inverted	70·00	20·00
		c. Left "S" inverted	90·00	45·00
		d. Perf 12½	—	26·00
		e. Perf comp of 12 and 12½	60·00	16·00
		ea. Imperf between (vert pair)	†	£190
		eb. Imperf between (vert strip of 3)	£225	£225
O65	8	14ch. orange (1933)	2·50	40
		a. Imperf between (horiz pair)	60·00	85·00
		b. Imperf between (vert pair)	£325	
		c. Opt inverted	£500	£500

(c) New setting combining Type O 8 (18 mm high) in top row with Type O 6 (16 mm high) for remainder. Wmk C (dates?)

A. Type O 8

Cat		Description	Un	Used
O66A	1	6ca. brown-red	15·00	8·00
		a. Perf 12½	15·00	8·00
		b. Perf comp of 12 and 12½	—	85·00
O67A		1½ch. rose	£100	9·00
		a. Perf 12½	£150	17·00
		ab. Imperf between (horiz pair)	†	£450
		b. Perf comp of 12 and 12½	—	£120
O68A	6	3ch. violet (R.)	£140	14·00
		a. Perf 12½	£250	50·00
		b. Perf comp of 12 and 12½	£250	40·00
O69A	1	4ch. grey-green (R.)	55·00	45·00
		a. Perf 12½	£150	45·00
O70A	8	14ch. orange-yellow	£140	40·00
		a. Perf 12½	£140	40·00

B. Type O 6

Cat		Description	Un	Used
O66Ba	1	6ca. brown-red (P 12½)	6·00	1·50
		ab. Imperf between (vert pair)	£275	£275
		ac. "O" inverted	30·00	17·00
		b. Perf comp of 12 and 12½	85·00	32·00
O67B		1½ch. rose	26·00	1·00
		aa. "O" inverted	—	45·00
		a. Perf 12½	40·00	1·25
		ab. "O" inverted	£150	35·00
		c. Perf comp of 12 and 12½	—	48·00
O68B	6	3ch. violet (R.)	26·00	1·50
		a. Perf 12½	42·00	2·00
		b. Perf comp of 12 and 12½	65·00	14·00
O69Ba	1	4ch. grey-green (R.) (P 12½)	18·00	7·00
		ab. Imperf between (horiz pair)	†	£375
		ac. "O" inverted	£150	65·00
O70Ba	8	14ch. orange-yellow (P 12½)	25·00	1·50

Nos. O66/70A/B in vertical *se-tenant* pairs are very scarce. As with the postage issues it is believed that the 12½ and compound perforations were issued between 1937 and 1939.

1 ch

8 c   1 ch
(O 9)   Wrong fount "1 c" (R. 6/7)

1932. Official stamps surch as T 14 or with Type O 9. P 12.

(a) With opt Type O 1
(i) Wmk A (sideways)

Cat		Description	Un	Used
O71	4	6c. on 5ca. olive-bistre	85·00	48·00
		a. "O" inverted	£375	£190
		b. Left "S" inverted	£300	£160
		c. Right "S" inverted	£375	£190
O71d		12c. on 10ca. pink	†	£550

(ii) Wmk C

Cat		Description	Un	Used
O72	4	6c. on 5ca. olive-bistre	48·00	21·00
		a. "O" inverted	£160	60·00
		b. Left "S" inverted	£130	48·00
		c. Right "S" inverted	£160	60·00
O73		12c. on 10ca. pink	£275	

(b) With opt Type O 2. Wmk C

Cat		Description	Un	Used
O74	4	6c. on 5ca. olive-bistre	2·00	2·00
		a. Opt and surch inverted	95·00	
		b. Surch inverted	£110	
		c. Left "S" inverted	22·00	20·00
		d. Right "S" inverted	22·00	20·00
		e. "6" omitted	—	£160
O75		6c. on 5ca. chocolate	1·00	1·00
		a. Surch inverted	11·00	12·00
		b. Surch double	£140	
		c. Surch double, one inverted	£120	
		d. "O" inverted	7·50	8·00
		e. Left "S" inverted	9·00	9·00
		f. Pair, one without surch	£500	
		g. Right "S" inverted	11·00	
O76		12c. on 10ca. pink	3·75	1·50
		a. Opt inverted	30·00	38·00
		b. Surch inverted	7·00	10·00
		c. Opt and surch inverted	75·00	85·00
		d. Pair, one without surch	£275	
		e. "O" inverted	20·00	9·50
		f. Left "S" inverted	19·00	8·50
		g. "Ou" for "On"	£160	£160
		h. Right "S" inverted	19·00	9·50
		i. "c" omitted (R. 6/1)	£130	£140
O77	1	1ch.8c. on 1¼ch. claret	4·50	1·50
		a. Surch inverted	†	£170
		b. "O" inverted	23·00	9·00
		c. Left "S" inverted	23·00	9·00
		d. Right "S" inverted	23·00	9·00
		e. Wrong fount "1 c"	55·00	28·00

(c) With opt Type O 3. Wmk C

Cat		Description	Un	Used
O78	4	12c. on 10ca. pink	†	£750
O79	1	1ch.8c. on 1¼ch. carmine-rose	65·00	48·00
		a. "n" omitted	£450	
		b. Wrong fount "1 c"	£400	£275

(d) With opt Type O 6. Wmk C

Cat		Description	Un	Used
O80	4	12c. on 10ca. pink	£100	48·00
O81	1	1ch.8c. on 1¼ch. carmine-rose	£200	32·00
		a. Wrong fount "1 c"	£650	£180
		b. "h" omitted	—	
		c. Large right "S" as Type O 2 (R. 6/14)	†	£225
		d. *Brown-red*	—	42·00

(e) With opt Type O 7. Wmk C

Cat		Description	Un	Used
O82	4	6c. on 5ca. chocolate	20	30
		a. Opt inverted	90·00	90·00
		b. Surch inverted	11·00	15·00
		c. Right "S" inverted	£180	£180
		d. Two quads for right "S"	£750	
		e. Right "S" inverted	60·00	
		f. Surch double	£120	
O83		12c. on 10ca. pink	20	15
		a. Opt inverted	11·00	13·00
		b. Surch inverted	6·00	10·00
		c. Opt and surch inverted	50·00	55·00
		d. Opt double	†	£110
		e. "O" inverted	28·00	28·00
		f. Right "S" inverted	32·00	32·00
		g. "On" omitted	—	£225
		h. "n" omitted	—	£225
		i. "c" omitted (R. 6/1)	65·00	70·00
		j. Surch double	£300	
		k. Surch on back and front	£300	
O84	1	1ch.8c. on 1¼ch. claret	35	25
		a. Imperf between (vert pair)	†	£425
		c. Surch inverted	14·00	15·00
		d. Surch double	65·00	
		e. "O" inverted	5·00	4·50
		f. Wrong fount "1 c"	28·00	24·00
		g. "1ch" omitted	£150	
		h. Large left "S" as Type O 2	—	50·00

SERVICE	SERVICE	SERVICE 8 CASH
(O 10) 13 mm ("R" with curved tail)	(O 11) 13½ mm ("R" with straight tail)	(O 12)

1939–41. Nos. 35 and 40 with type-set opt, Type O 10. P 12½.

Cat		Description	Un	Used
O85	1	6ca. brown-red (1941)	1·00	40
		a. Perf 11	1·75	1·00
		b. Perf 12	70	30
		c. Compound perf	70	1·10
O86	5	¾ch. reddish violet	£350	£180
		a. Perf 12	42·00	2·50
		b. Compound perf	£325	£170

1939 (9 Nov). Maharaja's 27th Birthday. Nos. 64/70 with type-set opt, Type O 10. P 12½.

Cat		Description	Un	Used
O87		1ch. yellow-green	13·00	1·00
O88		1½ch. scarlet	25·00	2·75
		a. "SESVICE"	£200	45·00
		b. Perf 12	£130	32·00
		ba. "SESVICE"	—	£300
		bb. Imperf between (horiz pair)	†	£550
		c. Compound perf	42·00	6·50
O89		2ch. orange	8·00	14·00
		a. "SESVICE"	£170	£225
		b. Compound perf	£275	£275
O90		3ch. brown	8·50	20
		a. "SESVICE"	£140	22·00
		b. Perf 12	55·00	1·25
		ba. "SESVICE"	£425	65·00
		c. Compound perf	24·00	9·00
O91		4ch. red	27·00	9·00
O92		7ch. pale blue	30·00	7·00
O93		14ch. turquoise-green	48·00	13·00
O87/93		*Set of 7*	£140	42·00

The "SESVICE" error occurs on the left pane, R. 6/5.

1940 (?)**–44.** Nos. 40a and 42b optd with Type O 11 from stereos. P 12½.

Cat		Description	Un	Used
O94	5	¾ch. reddish violet	25·00	20
		a. Imperf between (horiz pair)	£225	£250
		b. Perf 11	90·00	1·10
		c. Perf 12	32·00	20
		d. Compound perf	48·00	75
O95	1	1½ch. rose (1944)	18·00	8·50
		a. Perf 12	8·50	1·00
		b. Compound perf	27·00	15·00

1941 (?)**–42.** Nos. 64/70 optd with Type O 11 from stereos. P 12½.

Cat		Description	Un	Used
O96		1ch. yellow-green	1·50	10
		a. Imperf between (vert pair)	85·00	90·00
		b. Opt inverted	†	65·00
		c. Opt double	29·00	
		d. Perf 11	1·50	10
		da. Imperf between (vert pair)	65·00	
		db. Opt double	£225	£225
		e. Perf 12	4·75	1·00
		ea. Imperf between (vert pair)	£130	£140
		eb. Stamp doubly printed	£180	
		ec. Opt inverted	†	£200
		ed. Opt double	27·00	45·00
		f. Compound perf	9·00	3·25
		fa. Imperf between (vert pair)	†	£325
		fb. Opt double	£150	
O97		1½ch. scarlet	7·00	10
		a. Imperf between (horiz pair)	£100	
		b. Perf 11	4·75	15
		ba. Imperf between (vert pair)	£300	£300
		bb. Imperf between (vert strip of 3)	£225	
		bc. Imperf between (horiz pair)	†	£300
		c. Perf 12	12·00	1·75
		ca. Imperf between (vert strip of 3)	£350	
		d. Compound perf	6·50	75
		da. Imperf between (vert strip of 3)	£190	
		e. Imperf (pair)	32·00	
O98		2ch. orange	7·00	30
		a. Perf 11	25·00	5·00
		ab. Imperf between (vert pair)	†	£1100
		b. Perf 12	£275	£275
		ba. Imperf between (vert pair)	£1300	£1300
		c. Compound perf	£275	£275
O99		3ch. brown	8·50	10
		a. Imperf between (vert pair)	†	£900
		b. Perf 11	6·00	10
		c. Perf 12	11·00	4·00
		ca. Imperf between (vert pair)	£1200	£1200
		d. Compound perf	35·00	75
O100		4ch. red	7·50	1·00
		a. Perf 11	7·00	50

		b. Perf 12	32·00	11·00
		c. Compound perf	80·00	40·00
O101		7ch. pale blue	11·00	35
		a. Perf 11	11·00	6·00
		b. Perf 12	38·00	18·00
		c. Compound perf	30·00	5·00
		d. Blue (P 11)	30·00	15·00
		da. Perf 12	12·00	12·00
		db. Compound perf	60·00	48·00
O102		14ch. turquoise-green	17·00	70
		a. Perf 11	28·00	1·50
		b. Perf 12	17·00	2·50
		c. Compound perf	£150	27·00
O96/102 *Set of 7*			48·00	1·90

1942. Maharaja's 29th Birthday. Nos 71/2 optd with Type O **11**.
P 12½.

O103		6ca. blackish violet	60	50
		a. Perf 11	70	10
		b. Perf 12	£110	20·00
		c. Compound perf	1·50	1·75
O104		¾ch. brown	6·50	10
		a. Imperf between (vert pair)	†	£700
		b. Perf 11	8·50	10
		c. Perf 12	£140	6·50
		d. Compound perf	11·00	85

1943. Surch with Type O **12**. P 12½.

O105	**27**	8ca. on 6ca. scarlet	3·50	30
		a. Perf 11	2·00	10
		ab. Surch inverted	†	£1800
		b. Compound perf	9·00	1·25
		c. "SERVIC"	†	—

1943–45. Nos 73/4 optd with Type O **11**. P 12½.

O106		2ca. on 1½ch. scarlet	60	1·00
		a. Perf 11	50	15
		ab. Pair, one without surch	£550	
		b. Compound perf	70	1·50
		ba. "2" omitted	£650	£650
		c. Perf 12		
O107		4ca. on ¾ch. brown (1945)	9·00	1·00
		a. Perf 11	3·00	20
		b. Compound perf	4·50	1·75

1946. Maharaja's 34th Birthday. Optd with Type O **11**. P 11.

O108	**30**	8ca. carmine	5·50	2·00
		a. Imperf between (horiz pair)	65·00	
		ab. Imperf between (vert pair)	†	£425
		b. Opt double	†	£375
		c. Perf 12½	5·00	1·10
		ca. Stamp doubly printed	60·00	
		d. Perf 12	4·00	1·40
		da. Stamp doubly printed	75·00	

From 1 July 1949 Travancore formed part of the new State of Travancore-Cochin and stamps of Travancore surcharged in Indian currency were used.

TRAVANCORE-COCHIN

On 1 July 1949 the United State of Travancore and Cochin was formed ("U.S.T.C.") and the name was changed to State of Travancore-Cochin ("T.C.") by the new constitution of India on 26 January 1950.

PRICES FOR STAMPS ON COVER	
Nos. 1/13	*from* × 8
Nos. O1/17	*from* × 15

NO WATERMARK VARIETIES. These were formerly listed but we have now decided to omit them as they do not occur in full sheets. They are best collected in pairs, with and without watermarks.

COMPOUND PERFS. The notes above Type **20** of Travancore also apply here.

VALIDITY OF STAMPS. From 6 June 1950 the stamps of Travancore-Cochin were valid on mail from both Indian and state post offices to destinations in India and abroad.

ONE ANNA
ഒരണ
(1)

രണ്ട് പൈസ	രണ്ട് രപൈസ
Normal	2p. on 6ca. 1st character of 2nd group as 1st character of 1st group (Rt pane R. 14/2)

1949 (1 July). Stamps of Travancore surch in "PIES" or "ANNAS" as T **1**. P 12½.

1	**27**	2p. on 6ca. blackish violet (R.)	3·50	1·75
		a. Surch inverted	65·00	
		b. Character error	£275	£160
		c. "O" inverted (Rt pane R. 13/1)	60·00	22·00
		d. Perf 11	2·25	40
		da. Imperf between (vert pair)	£400	£400
		db. Pair, one without surch	£170	
		dc. Character error	£250	£160
		dd. "O" inverted (Rt pane R. 13/1)	75·00	30·00
		e. Perf 12	1·00	20
		ea. Imperf between (horiz pair)	£120	
		eb. Imperf between (vert pair)	8·00	22·00
		ec. Surch inverted	£180	
		ed. Character error	£250	£160
		ee. Imperf between (vert strip of 3)	45·00	
		ef. Block of four imperf between (horiz and vert)	85·00	
		eg. "O" inverted (Rt pane R. 13/1)	60·00	28·00
		eh. Imperf between (horiz strip of 3)	£110	

		f. Perf 14	†	£850
		g. Imperf (pair)	11·00	
		ga. Character error	£350	
		h. Compound perf	—	70·00
2	**30**	4p. on 8ca. carmine	1·75	40
		a. Surch inverted	85·00	
		b. "S" inverted (Rt pane R. 3/7)	£120	50·00
		c. Perf 11	2·75	30
		ca. Imperf between (vert pair)	£275	£300
		cb. Surch inverted	£180	
		cc. Pair, one without surch	£300	
		cd. "FOUP" for "FOUR"	£275	£160
		ce. "S" inverted (Rt pane R. 3/7)	£120	55·00
		d. Perf 12	1·50	30
		da. Imperf between (vert pair)	28·00	
		db. Pair, one without surch	£325	
		dc. "FOUP" for "FOUR"	£225	£140
		dd. "S" inverted (Rt pane R. 2/4 and R. 3/7)	£120	60·00
		de. Surch inverted	£250	
		e. Imperf (pair)	£100	
		f. Compound perf	£200	65·00
		g. Perf 13½	†	£900
3	**20**	½a. on 1ch. yellow-green	4·75	30
		a. "NANA" for "ANNA" (Lt pane R. 3/3)	£275	£110
		b. Inverted "H" in "HALF"	—	£140
		c. Imperf between (vert pair)	†	£300
		d. Perf 11	3·75	30
		da. Imperf between (vert pair)	48·00	
		db. Surch inverted	†	£325
		dc. "NANA" for "ANNA" (Lt pane R. 3/3)	£400	£170
		dd. Inverted "H" in "HALF"	—	£140
		e. Perf 12	1·00	40
		ea. Imperf between (horiz pair)	£120	£120
		eb. Imperf between (vert pair)	6·50	18·00
		ec. Surch inverted	5·00	
		ed. "NANA" for "ANNA" (Lt pane R. 3/3)	£375	£180
		ee. Block of four imperf between (horiz and vert)	65·00	
		f. Perf 14	†	£700
		g. Imperf (pair)	11·00	24·00
		h. Compound perf	—	65·00
4	**22**	1a. on 2ch. orange	4·75	30
		a. Perf 11	1·50	30
		ab. Surch double	60·00	
		b. Perf 12	5·00	50
		ba. Imperf between (horiz pair)	15·00	
		bb. Imperf between (vert pair)	5·00	18·00
		bc. Block of four imperf between (horiz and vert)	70·00	
		c. Perf 13½	£225	2·00
		d. Imperf (pair)	13·00	
		e. Compound perf	70·00	28·00
5	**24**	2a. on 4ch. red (68)	5·00	60
		a. Surch inverted	†	£400
		b. "O" inverted	70·00	23·00
		c. Perf 11	4·50	60
		ca. "O" inverted	—	25·00
		d. Perf 12	6·00	55
		da. "O" inverted	80·00	25·00
		e. Compound perf	80·00	50·00
6	**25**	3a. on 7ch. pale blue (69)	13·00	8·00
		a. Perf 11	6·50	5·50
		ab. Blue	90·00	5·50
		ac. "3" omitted	†	£1500
		b. Perf 12	13·00	4·50
		c. Compound perf	—	£130
		ca. Blue	—	£170
7	**26**	6a. on 14ch. turquoise-green (70)	28·00	60·00
		a. Accent omitted from native surch (Rt pane R. 13/4)	£650	£700
		b. Perf 11	28·00	48·00
		ba. Accent omitted from native surch (Rt pane R. 13/4)	£650	£700
		c. Perf 12	30·00	50·00
		ca. Accent omitted from native surch (Rt pane R. 13/4)	£650	£700
		d. Compound perf	90·00	£100
		da. Accent omitted from native surch (Rt pane R. 13/4)	£950	
		e. Imperf (pair)		
1/7 *Set of 7*			40·00	50·00

There are two settings of the ½a. surcharge. In one the first native character is under the second downstroke of the "H" and in the other it is under the first downstroke of the "A" of "HALF". They occur on stamps perf 12½, 11 and 12 equally commonly and also on the Official stamps.

U. S. T. C.   T.-C.   SIX PIES
(2)   (3)   (4)

1949. No. 106 of Cochin optd with T **2**.

8	**29**	1a. orange	10·00	£110
		a. No stop after "S" (R. 1/6)	95·00	
		b. Raised stop after "T" (R. 4/1)	95·00	

1950 (1 Apr). No. 106 of Cochin optd with T **3**.

9	**29**	1a. orange	7·50	90·00
		a. No stop after "T"	65·00	£375
		b. Opt inverted	£300	
		ba. No stop after "T"	£2000	

The no stop variety occurs on No. 5 in the sheet and again on No. 8 in conjunction with a short hyphen.

1950 (1 Apr). No. 9 surch as T **4**.

10	**29**	6p. on 1a. orange	4·75	75·00
		a. No stop after "T" (R. 1/5)	24·00	
		b. Error. Surch on No. 8	15·00	
		ba. No stop after "S"	£225	
		bb. Raised stop after "T"	£225	
11		9p. on 1a. orange	4·50	75·00
		a. No stop after "T" (R. 1/5)	23·00	
		b. Error. Surch on No. 8	£225	
		ba. No stop after "S"	£950	
		bb. Raised stop after "T"	£950	

5 Conch or Chank Shell   **6** Palm Trees

(Litho Indian Security Printing Press, Nasik)

1950 (24 Oct). W **69** of India. P 14.

12	**5**	2p. rose-carmine	3·00	4·75
13	**6**	4p. ultramarine	5·00	18·00

The ordinary issues of Travancore-Cochin became obsolete on 1 July 1951.

OFFICIAL STAMPS

VALIDITY. Travancore-Cochin official stamps were valid for use throughout India from 30 September 1950.

SERVICE   SERVICE
(O 1)   (O 2)

1949 (1 July)–**51**. Stamps of Travancore surch with value as T **1** and optd "SERVICE". No gum. P 12½.

(a) With Type O **1**

(i) Wmk C of Travancore

O1	**27**	2p. on 6ca. blackish violet (R.)	2·00	80
		a. Imperf between (vert pair)	£350	£350
		b. Character error (Rt pane R. 14/2)	48·00	32·00
		c. "O" inverted (Rt pane R. 13/1)	35·00	22·00
		d. Pair, one without surch	£325	
		e. Perf 11	1·25	20
		ea. Imperf between (vert pair)	£450	£450
		eb. Character error (Rt pane R. 14/2)	50·00	35·00
		ec. "O" inverted (Rt pane R. 13/1)	35·00	22·00
		f. Perf 12	2·00	75
		fa. Imperf between (horiz pair)	14·00	32·00
		fb. Imperf between (vert pair)	6·50	
		fc. Character error (Rt pane R. 14/2)	48·00	35·00
		fd. "O" inverted (Rt pane R. 13/1)	38·00	
		fe. Block of four imperf between (horiz and vert)	28·00	
		g. Imperf (pair)	10·00	30·00
		ga. Character error (Rt pane R. 14/2)	£350	
		h. Compound perf	£100	
O2	**30**	4p. on 8ca. carmine	8·00	1·50
		a. "FOUB" for "FOUR" (Lt pane R. 2/3)	£350	£120
		b. Perf 11	5·00	30
		ba. "FOUB" for "FOUR" (Lt pane R. 2/3)	£130	32·00
		c. Perf 12	6·50	1·25
		ca. "FOUB" for "FOUR" (Lt pane R. 2/3)	£170	60·00
		cb. "FOUR PIES" omitted (in pair with normal)	£1200	
		d. Compound perf	35·00	30·00
O3	**20**	½a. on 1ch. yellow-green	2·25	25
		a. Pair, one without surch	£140	
		b. Surch inverted	42·00	
		c. "NANA" for "ANNA" (Lt pane R. 3/3)	£400	£110
		d. Perf 11	3·25	25
		da. Pair, one without surch	£275	
		db. Surch inverted	£100	£120
		dc. "NANA" for "ANNA" (Lt pane R. 3/3)	£400	£130
		e. Perf 12	23·00	3·25
		ea. "NANA" for "ANNA" (Lt pane R. 3/3)	£750	£275
		eb. Pair, one without surch	£180	
		ec. Surch inverted on back only	£500	
		f. Compound perf	—	50·00
O4	**22**	1a. on 2ch. orange	18·00	8·00
		a. Surch inverted	£110	
		b. Pair, one without surch	£900	
		c. Perf 11	16·00	7·50
		ca. Pair, one without surch	£1000	
O5	**24**	2a. on 4ch. red (68)	4·50	1·00
		a. "O" inverted	—	£110
		b. Perf 11	9·00	60
		ba. Surch inverted	£1700	†
		bb. "O" inverted	—	75·00
		c. Perf 12	12·00	6·00
		ca. "O" inverted	—	£150
		cb. Pair, one without surch	£475	
		d. Compound perf	—	70·00
		e. Imperf (pair)	15·00	
O6	**25**	3a. on 7ch. pale blue (69)	7·00	3·25
		a. Imperf between (vert pair)	25·00	
		b. Blue	90·00	14·00
		c. Perf 11	7·50	1·00
		ca. Blue	£110	24·00
		d. Perf 12	5·00	8·50
		da. Imperf between (horiz pair)	25·00	
		db. Imperf between (vert pair)	9·00	
		dc. Block of four imperf between (horiz and vert)	50·00	
		dd. Blue	90·00	7·50
		dda. Imperf between (horiz pair)	†	£900
		e. Imperf (pair)	13·00	
O7	**26**	6a. on 14ch. turquoise-green (70)	20·00	15·00

		a. Imperf between (vert pair)	40·00	
		b. Perf 11	16·00	12·00
		c. Perf 12	70·00	11·00
		ca. Imperf between (horiz pair)	35·00	
		cb. Imperf between (vert pair)	40·00	
		cc. Block of four imperf between (horiz and vert)	70·00	
		d. Imperf (pair)	16·00	
O1/7	Set of 7		42·00	19·00

*(ii) W **27** of Cochin*

O8	**27**	2p. on 6ca. blackish violet (R.)	40	2·25
		a. Type O 1 double	18·00	
		b. Perf 11	50	2·25
		c. Perf 12	1·25	1·75
O9	**24**	2a. on 4ch. red (68)	3·25	2·75
		a. Perf 11	1·75	1·10
		ab. Imperf between (vert pair)	£500	£500
		b. Perf 12	£120	£100
		c. Compound perf	80·00	50·00

*(b) With Type O **2***
(i) Wmk C of Travancore

O10	**30**	4p. on 8ca. carmine	1·25	20
		a. "FOUB" for "FOUR" (Lt pane R. 2/3)	£130	42·00
		b. 2nd "E" of "SERVICE" in wrong fount	£150	60·00
		c. "S" in "PIES" inverted	—	90·00
		d. Imperf between (vert pair)	†	£300
		e. Perf 11	50	20
		ea. Imperf between (horiz pair)	5·00	
		eb. Imperf between (vert pair)	60·00	
		ec. "FOUB" for "FOUR" (Lt pane R. 2/3)	£110	38·00
		ed. 2nd "E" of "SERVICE" in wrong fount	£140	70·00
		ee. "S" in "PIES" inverted	—	£100
		ef. Block of four imperf between (horiz and vert)	45·00	
		f. Perf 12	30	20
		fa. Imperf between (horiz pair)	7·00	
		fb. Imperf between (vert pair)	2·25	
		fc. Block of four imperf between (horiz and vert)	16·00	42·00
		fd. "FOUB" for "FOUR" (Lt pane R. 2/3)	£130	45·00
		ff. 2nd "E" of "SERVICE" in wrong fount	£140	60·00
		fg. "FOUK" for "FOUR"	†	£1000
		fh. Imperf between (vert strip of 3)	50·00	
		fi. Imperf between (horiz strip of 3)	60·00	
		fj. "S" in "PIES" inverted	£130	
		g. Perf 13½	3·00	1·25
		h. Compound perf	14·00	14·00
		i. Imperf (pair)	6·00	
		ia. 2nd "E" of "SERVICE" in wrong fount	£250	
O11	**20**	½a. on 1ch. yellow-green	2·50	20
		a. "AANA" for "ANNA" (Rt pane R. 13/1)	£350	85·00
		b. Perf 11	75	20
		ba. Imperf between (horiz pair)	£130	£130
		bb. Imperf between (vert pair)	11·00	
		bc. Block of four imperf between (horiz and vert)	85·00	
		bd. "AANA" for "ANNA" (Rt pane R. 13/1)	£110	42·00
		c. Perf 12	1·25	15
		ca. Imperf between (horiz pair)	3·50	
		cb. Imperf between (vert pair)	3·50	17·00
		cc. "AANA" for "ANNA" (Rt pane R. 13/1)	£140	65·00
		cd. Block of four imperf between (horiz and vert)	35·00	
		d. Compound perf	60·00	30·00
		da. "AANA" for "ANNA" (Rt pane R. 13/1)	—	£375
		e. Imperf (pair)	9·00	25·00
O12	**22**	1a. on 2ch. orange	50	30
		a. Imperf between (vert pair)	†	£350
		ab. Imperf between (horiz pair)	†	£350
		b. Perf 11	3·75	50
		ba. Imperf between (horiz pair)	13·00	27·00
		bb. Imperf between (vert pair)	£180	£180
		c. Perf 12	60	20
		ca. Imperf between (horiz pair)	13·00	
		cb. Imperf between (vert pair)	4·50	20·00
		cc. Block of four imperf between (horiz and vert)	28·00	
		d. Compound perf	35·00	28·00
		e. Imperf (pair)	16·00	
O13	**24**	2a. on 4ch. red (68)	4·50	80
		a. "O" inverted (Lt pane R. 14/3)	£120	42·00
		b. Perf 11	1·50	1·10
		ba. "O" inverted (Lt pane R. 14/3)	85·00	42·00
		c. Perf 12	17·00	1·10
		ca. Imperf between (horiz pair)	£130	£140
		cb. "O" inverted (Lt pane R. 14/3)	£250	60·00
		cc. Pair, one without surch	†	£1600
		d. Compound perf	35·00	24·00
O14	**25**	3a. on 7ch. pale blue (69)	8·50	1·10
		a. "S" inverted in "SERVICE" (Lt pane R. 6/3)	75·00	32·00
		b. First "E" inverted (Lt pane R. 7/4)	£200	£140
		c. "C" inverted (Rt pane R.4/1 and 5/1)	£110	80·00
		d. Second "E" inverted (Lt pane R. 3/2)	£190	£130
		e. Perf 11	1·50	1·10
		ea. "S" inverted in "SERVICE" (Lt pane R. 6/3)	50·00	32·00
		f. Perf 12	5·50	2·25
		fa. "S" inverted in "SERVICE" (Lt pane R. 6/3)	£130	80·00
		g. Compound perf	—	90·00
		h. Imperf (pair)	55·00	
O15	**26**	6a. on 14ch. turquoise-green (70)	1·50	4·50

		a. Accent omitted from native surch	16·00	14·00
		b. "S" inverted in "SERVICE" (Lt pane R. 11/4)	85·00	45·00
		c. Perf 11	14·00	7·00
		ca. Accent omitted from native surch	60·00	26·00
		cb. "S" inverted in "SERVICE" (Lt pane R. 11/4)	£160	55·00
		d. Perf 12	50·00	7·50
		da. Accent omitted from native surch	£150	30·00
		db. "S" inverted in "SERVICE" (Lt pane R. 11/4)	£375	65·00
		e. Compound perf	£160	£150
O10/15	Set of 6		5·50	6·25

*(ii) W **27** of Cochin*

O16	**20**	½a. on 1ch. yellow-green	5·50	75
		a. Perf 11	40	40
		b. Perf 12	25·00	18·00
		c. Compound perf	24·00	3·00
O17	**22**	1a. on 2ch. orange	1·00	1·00
		a. Perf 11	50	40
		b. Perf 12	13·00	4·00
		c. Perf 13½	1·50	1·00
		d. Compound perf	8·00	3·00

Nos. O2, O10, O12 and O17 have the value at top in English and at bottom in native characters with "SERVICE" in between. All others have "SERVICE" below the surcharge.

Type O **2** was overprinted at one operation with the surcharges. Nos. O10b, O10ed, O10ff and O10ia, show the second "E" of "SERVICE" with serifs matching those on the surcharge. The variety occurred on Right pane R. 10/6 and R. 11/6, but was soon corrected.

The "accent omitted" varieties on No. O15 occur on Left pane R. 5/1 and Right pane R. 1/4, 12/4, 14/1 and 13/4.

The Official stamps became obsolete in September 1951.

WADHWAN

PRICES FOR STAMPS ON COVER	
No. 1	*from* × 30
No. 2	—
Nos. 3/6	*from* × 30

Thakur Bal Singh, 1885–1910

1

(Litho Thacker & Co, Bombay)

1888–94.

(a) Thin toned wove paper

1	1 ½ pice, black (I, III) (P 12½ *large holes*)	38·00	£120
	a. Imperf between (vert pair) (I)		
	b. Pin-perf 6½ irregular (I)	£160	
	c. Compound of 12½ and pin-perf 6½ (I)	£300	
2	½ pice, black (II) (P 12½ *irregular small holes*)	65·00	

(b) Medium toned wove paper

3	1 ½ pice, black (III) (P 12½)	19·00	80·00
4	½ pice, black (V) (P 12)	16·00	20·00

(c) Thick off-white or toned wove paper

5	1 ½ pice, black (IV, VI) (P 12) (7.92)	13·00	14·00
	a. Perf compound of 12 and 11 (IV)	29·00	70·00
6	½ pice, black (VII) (*fine impression*) (P 12) (1894)	13·00	29·00

Sheets from the Stone IV printing had at least one horizontal line of perforations gauging 11, normally between the bottom two rows of the sheet.

These stamps were lithographed from seven different stones taken from a single die. Brief details of the individual stones are as follows:

Stone I – No. 1. Sheet size not known, but possibly 28 (4×7). Sheet margins imperforate

Stone II – No. 2. Sheets of 42 (7×6) with imperforate margins

Stone III – Nos. 1 (thin paper) and 3 (medium paper). Sheets of 40 (4×10) with imperforate margins

Stone IV – Nos. 5/a. Sheets of 32 (4×8) with imperforate margins at top and right

Stone V – No. 4. Sheets of 20 (4×5) with imperforate margins at top, right and bottom

Stone VI – No. 5. Sheets of 30 (5×6) with all margins perforated

Stone VII – No. 6. Sheets of 32 (4×8) with all margins perforated. Much finer impression than the other stones

Stamps from stones I and II come with or without the dot before "STATE". Those from the later stones always show the dot. The shading on the pennant above the shield can also be used in stone identification. Stamps from stones I to III show heavy shading on the pennant, but this is less evident on stone IV and reduced further to a short line or dot on stones V to VII. There is a ")" hairline after "HALF" on the majority of stamps from Stone III.

The stamps of Wadhwan became obsolete on 1 January 1895.

Ionian Islands

The British occupation of the Ionian Islands was completed in 1814 and the archipelago was placed under the protection of Great Britain by the Treaty of Paris of 9 November 1815. The United States of the Ionian Islands were given local self-government, which included responsibility for the postal services. Crowned-circle handstamps were, however, supplied in 1844, although it is believed these were intended for use on prepaid mail to foreign destinations.

Examples of the Great Britain 1855 1d. red-brown stamp are known used at Corfu, cancelled as No. CC2, but it is believed that these originate from mail sent by the British garrison.

For illustrations of the handstamp types see BRITISH POST OFFICES ABROAD notes, following GREAT BRITAIN.

CEPHALONIA
CROWNED-CIRCLE HANDSTAMPS

CC1	CC **1**	CEPHALONIA (19.4.1844)........Price on cover	£1800

CORFU
CROWNED-CIRCLE HANDSTAMPS

CC2	CC **1**	CORFU (19.4.1844) ....Price on cover	£650
CC3	CC **1**	CORFU (G. or B.) (1844) ....Price on cover	—

ZANTE
CROWNED-CIRCLE HANDSTAMPS

CC4	CC **1**	ZANTE (G. or B.) (19.4.1844) ....Price on cover	£1400

Nos. CC1/2 were later, circa 1860/1, struck in green (Cephalonia) or red (Corfu).

It is believed that examples of No. CC4 in black are from an unauthorised use of this handstamp which is now on display in the local museum. A similar handstamp, but without "PAID AT" was introduced in 1861.

PRICES FOR STAMPS ON COVER	
Nos. 1/3	from × 10

PERKINS BACON "CANCELLED". For notes on these handstamps, showing "CANCELLED" between horizontal bars forming an oval, see Catalogue Introduction.

1

(Eng C. Jeens. Recess Perkins Bacon & Co)

1859 (15 June). Imperf.

1	**1**	(½d.) orange (no wmk) (H/S "CANCELLED" in oval £12000) ...	£140	£750
2		(1d.) blue (wmk "2") (H/S "CANCELLED" in oval £12000) ...	35·00	£300
3		(2d.) carmine (wmk "1") (H/S "CANCELLED" in oval £12000) ...	28·00	£300

On 30 May 1864, the islands were ceded to Greece, and these stamps became obsolete.

Great care should be exercised in buying used stamps, on or off cover, as forged postmarks are plentiful.

Iraq

(Currency. 16 annas = 1 rupee)

I. INDIAN POST OFFICES

Indian post offices were opened at Baghdad and Basra, then part of the Turkish Empire, on 1 January 1868. Unoverprinted stamps of India were used, cancels as detailed below.

Baghdad

Z **1**

Z **2**

Z **3**

Z **4**   Z **5**

Z **6**

Z **7**

Postmark Type	Approx period of use
Z **1**	1868–69
Z **2**	1870–75
Z **3**	1877–80
Z **4**	1884–85
Z **5**	1885–86
Z **6**	1894–1914
Z **7**	1901–1914

Between 1881 and 1887 stamps were often cancelled with a "B" in a square or circle of bars. Off cover, such stamps are indistinguishable from those used in other offices in the Bombay postal circle.

Type Z **1** may be found with the numeral obliterator and datestamp applied separately.

Type Z **4** exists with an acute accent over the first "A" of "BAGHDAD".

Stamps of India cancelled at Baghdad between 1868 and 1914 with postmarks detailed above.

1856–64. (Nos. 37/49).
Z1	2a. yellow-buff.......................................	£110
Z2	4a. black...	90·00

1865. (Nos. 54/65).
Z3	½a. blue (Die I)	12·00
Z4	1a. pale brown	15·00
Z5	2a. orange..	26·00
Z7	8a. carmine (Die I)............................	£250

1866–78. (Nos. 69/72).
Z8	4a. green (Die I).................................	40·00
Z9	4a. blue-green (Die II)......................	42·00

1868. (Nos. 73/4).
Z10	8a. rose (Die II)...................................	45·00

1873. (Nos. 75/6).
Z11	½a. blue (Die II)	9·00

1874. (Nos. 77/9).
Z12	9p. mauve..	75·00

1876. (Nos. 80/2).
Z14	6a. olive-bistre	26·00
	a. Pale brown.....................................	26·00
Z15	12a. Venetian red	75·00

1882–90. (Nos. 84/101).
Z16	½a. blue-green	5·50
Z18	1a. brown-purple..............................	5·50
Z19	1a.6p. sepia..	14·00
Z20	2a. blue..	7·00
Z21	3a. orange..	16·00
	a. Brown-orange................................	8·50
Z22	4a. olive-green...................................	9·00
Z23	4a.6p. yellow-green	30·00
Z24	8a. dull mauve....................................	20·00
Z25	12a. purple/red......................................	30·00
Z26	1r. slate..	26·00

1891. (No. 102).
Z27	2½a. on 4a.6p. yellow-green...............	23·00

1892. (Nos. 103/6).
Z28	2a.6p. yellow-green	11·00
Z29	1r. green and aniline carmine.......	60·00

1895. (Nos. 107/9).
Z30	2r. carmine and yellow-brown.....	80·00
Z31	3r. brown and green.......................	60·00
Z32	5r. ultramarine and violet............	£100

1899. (No. 111).
Z34	3p. aniline carmine	21·00

1900. (Nos. 112/8).
Z36	½a. yellow-green	8·50
Z37	1a. carmine	10·00
Z38	2a. pale violet	13·00
Z39	2a.6p. ultramarine................................	13·00

1902–11. (Nos. 119/47).
Z40	3p. grey..	16·00
Z41	½a. yellow-green	8·00
Z42	1a. carmine	8·00
Z43	2a. violet	11·00
Z44	2a. mauve..	7·50
Z45	2a.6p. ultramarine................................	5·50
Z46	3a. orange-brown	26·00
Z47	4a. olive..	10·00
Z49	8a. purple..	17·00
Z51	1r. green and carmine....................	35·00
Z52	2r. rose-red and yellow-brown....	65·00
Z54	5r. ultramarine and violet............	£120

1905. (No. 148).
Z55	¼ on ½a. green	24·00

1906–07. (Nos. 149/50).
Z56	½a. green	5·50
Z57	1a. carmine	5·50

1911–22. (Nos. 151/91).
Z58	3p. grey..	16·00
Z59	½a. light green	7·50
Z60	1a. carmine	7·50
Z61	2a. purple..	9·50
Z62	2a.6p. ultramarine (No. 170)..............	13·00
Z63	2a.6p. ultramarine (No. 171)..............	11·00
Z64	3a. orange..	20·00
Z67	8a. deep magenta	32·00
Z68	12a. carmine-lake	40·00

OFFICIAL STAMPS

1867–73. (Nos. O20/30a).
Z76	4a. green (Die I).................................	50·00
Z77	8a. rose (Die II)...................................	75·00

1874–82. (Nos. O31/5).
Z80	2a. orange..	45·00

1883–99. (Nos. O37a/48).
Z84	½a. blue-green	20·00
Z85	1a. brown-purple..............................	22·00
Z86	2a. blue..	25·00

1900. (Nos. O49/51).
Z90	½a. yellow-green	28·00
Z92	2a. pale violet	38·00

1902–09. (Nos. O54/65).
Z95	1a. carmine	19·00
Z96	2a. mauve..	15·00
Z97	4a. olive..	15·00
Z98	6a. olive-bistre	30·00
Z99	8a. purple..	45·00

1906. (Nos. O66/7).
Z101	½a. green	15·00
Z102	1a. carmine	20·00

1912–13. (Nos. O73/96).
Z108	½a. light green	14·00
Z109	1a. carmine	16·00
Z112	6a. yellow-bistre	32·00

The post office at Baghdad closed on 30 September 1914.

Basra

Z 8

Z 9   **Z 10**

Postmark Type	Approx period of use
Z 1 (inscr "BUSSORAH/357")	1868–73
Z 2 (inscr "BUSREH/19")	1870–73
Z 3 (inscr "BUSREH/1/K-6")	1877–79
Z 8	1884
Z 4 (inscr "BUSRAH")	1889–92
Z 7	1905–18
Z 9	1894–1916
Z 10	1899–1903
Z 12 (inscr "BUSRA")	1915–1918

Between 1881 and 1887 stamps were often cancelled with a "B" in a square or circle of bars. As at Baghdad, such stamps are indistinguishable from those used at other offices in the Bombay postal circle.

Stamps of India cancelled at Basra between 1868 and 1918 with postmarks detailed above.

1865. (Nos. 54/65).
Z121	½a. blue (Die I)	15·00
Z123	1a. pale brown	14·00
Z124	2a. orange	25·00
Z126	8a. carmine (Die I)	£250

1866–78. (Nos. 69/72).
Z127	4a. green (Die I)	35·00
Z128	4a. blue-green (Die II)	42·00

1868. (Nos. 73/4).
Z129	8a. rose (Die II)	75·00

1873. (Nos. 75/6).
Z130	½a. blue (Die II)	9·00

1876. (Nos. 80/2).
Z133	6a. pale brown	35·00
Z134	12a. Venetian red	90·00

1882–90. (Nos. 84/101).
Z135	½a. blue-green	5·50
Z136	9p. rose	50·00
Z137	1a. brown-purple	5·50
Z138	1a.6p. sepia	12·00
Z139	2a. blue	7·00
Z140	3a. orange	16·00
	a. Brown-orange	8·50
Z141	4a. olive-green	10·00
Z142	4a.6p. yellow-green	17·00
Z143	8a. dull mauve	16·00
Z145	1r. slate	38·00

1891. (No. 102).
Z146	2½a. on 4½a. yellow-green	13·00

1892–97. (Nos. 103/6).
Z147	2a.6p. yellow-green	6·50
Z148	1r. green and aniline carmine	80·00

1898. (No. 110).
Z152	¼ on ½a. blue-green	30·00

1899. (No. 111).
Z153	3p. aniline carmine	11·00

1900. (Nos. 112/8).
Z155	½a. yellow-green	8·50
Z156	1a. carmine	8·50
Z157	2a. pale violet	12·00
Z158	2a.6p. ultramarine	12·00

1902–11. (Nos. 119/47).
Z159	3p. grey	18·00
Z160	½a. yellow-green	7·50
Z161	1a. carmine	9·50
Z162	2a. violet	10·00
	a. Mauve	9·50
Z163	2a.6p. ultramarine	5·50
Z165	4a. olive	14·00
Z167	8a. purple	20·00
Z169	1r. green and carmine	50·00

1905. (No. 148).
Z172	¼ on ½a. green	20·00

1906–07. (Nos. 149/50).
Z173	½a. green	7·50
Z174	1a. carmine	9·50

1911–22. (Nos. 151/91).
Z175	3p. grey	19·00
Z176	½a. light green	5·50
Z177	1a. carmine	5·50
Z178	2a. purple	7·50
Z179	2a.6p. ultramarine (No. 170)	14·00

Z180	2a.6p. ultramarine (No. 171)	8·00
Z181	3a. orange	23·00
Z182	4a. deep olive	14·00
Z186	1r. brown and green	40·00

OFFICIAL STAMPS

1867–73 (Nos. O20/30a).
Z196	4a. green (Die II)	80·00
Z197	8a. rose (Die II)	85·00

1874–82. (Nos. O30/5).
Z200	2a. orange	50·00

1883–99. (Nos. O37a/48).
Z204	½a. blue-green	20·00
Z205	1a. brown-purple	20·00
Z206	2a. blue	27·00
Z207	4a. olive-green	32·00
Z208	8a. dull mauve	50·00

The post office at Basra closed on 30 September 1914. In November Basra was captured by the invading Indian Expeditionary Force and the post office was reopened the following month.

Basra City

Z 11   **Z 12**

The office at Basra City opened in March 1915

Postmark Type	Approx period of use
Z 11	1915
Z 12	1915–18

1911–22. (Nos. 151/91).
Z222	½a. light green	20·00
Z223	1a. carmine	25·00
Z229	8a. deep mauve	50·00
Z230	12a. carmine-lake	60·00
Z231	1r. brown and green	50·00

The sale of Indian stamps by these offices was forbidden from 1 September 1918, being replaced by issues for Iraq, Nos. 1–14 (ex.4). The Indian post offices closed on 30 April 1919.

Other offices opened in Iraq after 1914 are believed to have been operated by the Indian Army, using stamps overprinted "I.E.F.". Unoverprinted Indian stamps are also known cancelled at these offices (Amara, Ezra's Tomb, Fao, Magil and Naseriyeh) but their status is unclear.

II. ISSUES FOR BAGHDAD

PRICES FOR STAMPS ON COVER	
Nos. 1/7	from × 8
No. 8	from × 4
Nos. 9/15	from × 8
No. 16	from × 3
Nos. 17/24	from × 8
No. 25	from × 5

BRITISH OCCUPATION

British and Indian troops took Baghdad from the Turks on 11 March 1917.

IN BRITISH BAGHDAD OCCUPATION

2 Ans

(1)

1917 (1 Sept). Stamps of Turkey, surch as T **1** in three operations.

(a) Pictorial designs of 1914. T **32**, *etc., and* **31**
1	32	¼a. on 2pa. claret (Obelisk)	£450	£500
		a. "IN BRITISH" omitted	£16000	
2	34	¼a. on 5pa. dull purple (Leander's Tower)	£350	£375
		b. "IN BRITISH" double	£2500	
3	36	½a. on 10pa. green (Lighthouse garden)	£1800	£2000
4	31	½a. on 10pa. green (Mosque of Selim)	£4000	£4250
		a. "½ An" double	£8000	
5	37	1a. on 20pa. red (Castle)	£1200	£1300
		a. "BAGHDAD" double	£3000	
6	38	2a. on 1pi. bright blue (Mosque)	£500	£550

(b) As (a), but overprinted with small five-pointed Star
7	37	1a. on 20pa. red (B.)	£800	£850
		b. "BAGHDAD" double	£3000	
8	38	2a. on 1pi. bright blue (R.)	£9000	£9500

(c) Postal Jubilee stamps (Old GPO). P 12½
9	60	1a. on 10pa. carmine	£1400	£1500
		a. Perf 13½	£5000	
10		1a. on 20pa. blue	£16000	
		a. Perf 13½	£3250	£3750
		ab. Value omitted	£20000	
11		2a. on 1pi. black and violet	£750	£800
		a. Value omitted	£18000	
		b. Perf 13½	£375	£400
		ba. "IN BRITISH" twice	†	£17000

(d) T **30** *(GPO, Constantinople) with opt T* **26**
12	30	2a. on 1pi. ultramarine	£1400	£1600
		a. "IN BRITISH" omitted	£18000	

No. 11ba shows "BAGHDAD" superimposed on a second impression of "IN BRITISH" at the top of the stamp. The only known example is on cover.

The ¼a. on 5pa. value omitted, 1a. on 20pa. "OCCUPATION" omitted and 2a. on 1pi. "BAGHDAD" omitted, formerly listed as Nos. 2a, 7a and 11a, are all in the Royal Philatelic Collection.

(e) Stamps optd with six-pointed Star and Arabic date "1331" within Crescent. T **53** *(except No. 16, which has five-pointed Star and Arabic "1332", T* **57**)
13	30	½a. on 10pa. green (R.)	£350	£375
14		1a. on 20pa. rose	£1200	£1300
		a. Value omitted	£12000	£8000
		b. Optd with T **26** (Arabic letter "B") also	£12000	£12000
15	23	1a. on 20pa. rose (No. 554a)	£1300	£1400
		a. Value omitted	£20000	
16	21	1a. on 20pa. carmine (No. 732)	£11000	£14000
17	30	2a. on 1pi. ultramarine (R.)	£375	£400
		a. "BAGHDAD" omitted		† £18000
18	21	2a. on 1pi. dull blue (No. 543) (R.).	£500	£550
		a. "OCCUPATION" omitted	£17000	

(f) Stamps with similar opt, but date between Star and Crescent (Nos. 19 and 22, T **54**; *others T* **55** *five-pointed Star)*
19	23	½a. on 10pa. grey-green (No. 609a) (R.)	£375	£425
		a. "OCCUPATION" omitted	£16000	
		b. "IN BRITISH" omitted	£18000	
20	60	½a. on 10pa. carmine (P 12½) (B.).	£500	£550
		a. Perf 13½	£1000	£1200
		ab. "BAGHDAD" double	£6000	
		ac. Value double	£6000	
21	30	1a. on 20pa. rose	£375	£425
22	28	1a. on 20pa. rose (Plate II) (No. 617)	£1300	£1400
23	15	1a. on 10pa. on 20pa. claret (No. 630)	£600	£650
		a. "OCCUPATION" omitted		† £17000
24	30	2a. on 1pi. ultramarine (R.)	£500	£600
		a. "OCCUPATION" omitted	£17000	
		b. "BAGHDAD" omitted	£15000	
25	28	2a. on 1pi. ultramarine (Pl. II) (No. 645)	£4250	£4500

Each element of the overprint was applied separately using a small hand press, resulting in variable spacing between the lines.

The last group (*f*) have the Crescent obliterated by hand in violet-black ink, as this included the inscription, "Tax for the relief of children of martyrs".

No. 23a does exist unused, but the only example is in the Royal Philatelic Collection.

Other Ottoman stamps were also overprinted, but not issued due to the small quantities available; these include a ½a. on 10pa. green with five-pointed star and a 2a. on 40pa. blue.

III. ISSUES FOR MOSUL

PRICES FOR STAMPS ON COVER	
Nos. 1/8	from × 50

BRITISH OCCUPATION

A British and Indian force occupied Mosul on 1 November 1918.

As the status of the vilayet was disputed stocks of "IRAQ IN BRITISH OCCUPATION" surcharges were withdrawn in early 1919 and replaced by Nos. 1/8.

1   **2**

3   **4**

5   **6**

4   **4**
I   II

Two types of tougra in central design:
    (a) Large "tougra" or sign-manual of El Ghazi 7 mm high.
    (b) Smaller "tougra" of Sultan Rechad 5½ mm high.

Two types of 4a. surcharge:
    I. Normal "4". Apostrophes on D 3½ mm apart.
    II. Small "4". Apostrophes on D 4½ mm apart.

1919 (1 Feb). Turkish Fiscal stamps surch as T **1/6** by Govt Press, Baghdad. P 11½ (½a.), 12 (1a.), or 12½ (others).

1	**1**	½a. on 1pi. green and red	2·25	1·90
2	**2**	1a. on 20pa. black/*red* (*a*)	1·40	1·75
		a. Imperf between (horiz pair)	£1000	
		b. Surch double	£650	
		c. "A" of "Anna" omitted	£275	
3		1a. on 20pa. black/*red* (*b*)	4·00	3·00
		b. Surch double	£750	
4	**3**	2½a. on 1pi. mauve and yellow (*b*)	1·50	1·50
		a. No bar to fraction (R. 2/4)	85·00	£110
		b. Surch double	£1400	
5	**4**	3a. on 20pa. green (*a*)	1·60	4·00
		a. Surch double, one albino	£550	
6		3a. on 20pa. green and orange (*b*)	£100	£140
7	**5**	4a. on 1pi. deep violet (*a*) (I)	3·00	3·50
		a. "4" omitted	£1900	
		c. Surch double	£1200	
7d		4a. on 1pi. deep violet (*a*) (II)	20·00	27·00
		da. Surch double, one with "4" omitted	£3250	
8	**6**	8a. on 10pa. lake (*a*)	4·00	5·00
		a. Surch inverted	£900	£1000
		b. Surch double	£750	£850
		c. No apostrophe after "D" (R. 1/5)	65·00	85·00
		d. Surch inverted. No apostrophe after "D"		
		e. "na" omitted	£325	
		f. Error. 8a. on 1pi. deep violet	£3500	

The ½a. and 1a. are on paper with a sheet watermark of Turkish characters and the 2½a. and 3a. (No. 6) are on paper with a sheet watermark of Turkish characters and the 3a. (No. 5), 4a. and 8a. are on paper watermarked with a series of parallel zig-zag lines.

No. 4a occurs on some sheets only. No. 8c comes from the first setting only.

Nos. 1/8 were replaced by "IRAQ IN BRITISH OCCUPATION" surcharges during 1921 and invalidated on 1 September 1922.

In December 1925 the League of Nations awarded the vilayet of Mosul to Iraq.

IV. ISSUES FOR IRAQ

PRICES FOR STAMPS ON COVER	
Nos. 1/18	from × 6
Nos. 41/154	from × 2
Nos. O19/171	from × 4

BRITISH OCCUPATION

1 Leander's Tower

1a Lighthouse Garden, Stamboul

1b Castle of Europe

1c Mosque of Sultan Ahmed

1d Martyrs of Liberty Monument

1e Fountains of Suleiman

1f Cruiser *Hamidiye*

1g Candilli, Bosphorus

1h Former Ministry of War

1i Sweet Waters of Europe

1j Suleiman Mosque

1k Bosphorus at Rumeli Hisar

1l Sultan Ahmed's Fountain

A

B

(Litho (¼a. and 1½a.) or recess (others), surch in litho. Bradbury Wilkinson)

1918 (1 Sept)–**21**. Turkish pictorial issue of 1914. P 12.

(a) No wmk. Tougra as A (1 Sept 1918–20)

1	**1**	¼a. on 5pa. dull purple	1·00	1·00
2	**1a**	½a. on 10pa. green	1·00	20
3	**1b**	1a. on 20pa. red	65	10
4	**1**	1½a. on 5pa. dull purple (1920)	20·00	50
5	**1c**	2½a. on 1pi. bright blue	1·75	1·40
		a. Surch double	£11000	
6	**1d**	3a. on 1½pi. grey and rose	1·75	25
		a. Surch double (Bk. + R.)	£4500	£5500
7	**1e**	4a. on 1¾pi. red-brown and grey	1·75	25
		a. Centre inverted	† £32000	
8	**1f**	6a. on 2pi. black and green (32 *mm* surch)	3·00	1·75
		a. Centre omitted	£22000	
		b. Surch 27 mm wide	£140	1·75
9	**1g**	8a. on 2½pi. green and orange (30 *mm* surch)	4·50	2·00
		a. Surch inverted	† £20000	
		b. Surch 27 mm wide	20·00	70
10	**1h**	12a. on 5pi. deep lilac	2·50	6·00
11	**1i**	1r. on 10pi. red-brown	2·75	1·40
12	**1j**	2r. on 25pi. yellow-green	13·00	3·25
13	**1k**	5r. on 50pi. rose (32 *mm* surch)	32·00	30·00
		a. Surch 27 mm wide	75·00	42·00
14	**1l**	10r. on 100pi. indigo	£110	17·00
		1/14 *Set of 14*	£180	55·00
		1s/14s (ex 1½a. on 5pa.) Perf "SPECIMEN" *Set of 13*	£850	

(b) No wmk. Tougra as B (one device instead of two) (1921)

15	**1i**	1r. on 10pi. red-brown	£350	27·00

(c) Wmk Mult Script CA (sideways on ½a., 1½a.) (1921)

16	**1a**	½a. on 10pa. green	7·50	2·75
17	**1**	1½a. on 5pa. dull purple	5·00	1·50
18	**1j**	2r. on 25pi. yellow-green	38·00	15·00
		16/18 *Set of 3*	45·00	17·00
		16s/18s Optd "SPECIMEN" *Set of 3*	£180	

The original settings of Nos. 1/18 showed the surcharge 27 mm wide, except for the 2½a. (24 mm), 4a. (26½ mm), 6a. (32 mm), 8a. (30½ mm), 12a. (33 mm), 1r. (31½ mm), 2r. (30 mm) and 5r. (32 mm). The 6a., 8a. and 5r. came from a subsequent setting with the surcharge 27 mm wide. Minor variations in the width of the surcharge on other values exist, but are not significant. On all surcharged values apart from the 2½a. and 12a. there is a stop after the "An". On these two values there is no stop.

Nos. 2, 3, 5, 6 and 7/9 are known bisected and used on philatelic covers. All such covers have Makinah or F.P.O. 339 cancellations.

During January 1923 an outbreak of cholera in Baghdad led to the temporary use for postal purposes of the above issue overprinted "REVENUE".

LEAGUE OF NATIONS MANDATE

On 25 April 1920 the Supreme Council of the Allies assigned to the United Kingdom a mandate under the League of Nations to administer Iraq.

The Emir Faisal, King of Syria in 1920, was proclaimed King of Iraq on 23 August 1921.

King Faisal I
23 August 1921–8 September 1933

2 Sunni Mosque, Muadhdham

3 Gufas on the Tigris

4 Winged Cherub

5 Bull from Babylonian wall-sculpture

6 Arch of Ctesiphon

7 Tribal Standard, Dulaim Camel Corps

8 Shiah Mosque, Kadhimain

9 Allegory of Date Palm

(Des Miss Edith Cheesman (½a., 1a., 4a., 6a., 8a., 2r., 5r., 10r.), Mrs. C. Garbett (Miss M. Maynard) (others). Typo (1r.) or recess (others) Bradbury, Wilkinson)

1923 (1 June)–**25**. T **2/4** and similar designs. Wmk Mult Script CA (sideways on 2a., 3a., 4a., 8a., 5r.). P 12.

41	**2**	½a. olive-green	3·50	10
42	**3**	1a. brown	7·50	10
43	**4**	1½a. lake	2·50	10
44	**5**	2a. orange-buff	3·00	15
45	**6**	3a. grey-blue (1923)	6·00	15
46	**7**	4a. violet	7·00	30
		w. Wmk Crown to left of CA	£550	£250
47	**8**	6a. greenish blue	2·50	30
48	**7**	8a. olive-bistre	6·50	30
49	**9**	1r. brown and blue-green	35·00	1·50
50	**2**	2r. black	26·00	8·50
51		2r. olive-bistre (1925)	90·00	3·25
52	**7**	5r. orange	60·00	13·00
53	**8**	10r. lake	70·00	22·00
		41/53 *Set of 13*	£300	45·00
		41s/53s Optd "SPECIMEN." *Set of 13*	£800	

The normal sideways watermark on Nos. 44, 45, 46, 48 and 52 shows the crown to right of CA, *as seen from the back of the stamp.*

With the exception of Nos. 49 and 50, later printings of these stamps and of No. 78 are on a thinner paper.

10

11 King Faisal I

12

(Recess Bradbury Wilkinson)

1927 (1 Apr). Wmk Mult Script CA. P 12.

78	**10**	1r. red-brown	18·00	1·00
		s. Optd "SPECIMEN."	£110	

See note below No. 53.

(Recess Bradbury Wilkinson)

1931 (17 Feb). Wmk Mult Script CA (sideways on 1r. to 25r.). P 12.

80	**11**	½a. green	3·50	30
81		1a. red-brown	3·50	30
82		1½a. scarlet	3·50	50
83		2a. orange	3·00	10
84		3a. blue	3·00	20
85		4a. slate-purple	3·25	4·25
86		6a. greenish blue	3·25	80
87		8a. deep green	3·25	4·50
88	**12**	1r. chocolate	10·00	4·50
89		2r. yellow-brown	19·00	10·00
90		5r. orange	55·00	70·00
91		10r. scarlet	£170	£190
92	**10**	25r. violet	£1800	£2250
		80/91 *Set of 12*	£250	£250
		80s/92s Perf "SPECIMEN" *Set of 13*	£1500	

(New Currency. 1000 fils = 1 dinar)

10 Fils	½ Dinar
(13)	(14)

Normal "SIN"

3f. Error "SAD" (R. 8/16 of second setting)

(Surcharged at Govt Ptg Wks, Baghdad)

1932 (1–21 Apr). Nos. 80/92 and 46 surch in "Fils" or "Dinar" as T **13** or **14**.

106	**11**	2f. on ½a. green (21.4.32) (R.)	50	10
		a. Wide space between "2" and "Fils"	55·00	32·00
107		3f. on ½a. green	1·25	10
		a. Surch double	£350	
		b. Surch inverted	£300	
		c. Arabic letter "SAD" instead of "SIN"	70·00	38·00
		d. Wide space between "3" and "Fils"	55·00	32·00
		e. Horiz pair, one without surcharge	£1500	
108		4f. on 1a. red-brown (21.4.32) (G.)	3·25	25
		a. Wide space between "4" and "Fils"	£120	50·00
109		5f. on 1a. red-brown	75	10
		a. Inverted Arabic "5" (R. 8/11)	85·00	60·00
		b. Surch inverted	£475	
110		8f. on 1½a. scarlet	1·00	50
		a. Surch inverted	£275	
111		10f. on 2a. orange	50	10
		a. Inverted Arabic "1" (R. 8/13)	65·00	38·00
		b. No space between "10" and "Fils"	50	10
112		15f. on 3a. blue	1·50	1·00
113		20f. on 4a. slate-purple	3·50	3·50
		a. Surch inverted	£500	

114	–	25f. on 4a. violet (No. 46)	6·00	10·00
		a. "Flis" for "Fils" (R. 2/1, 10/8, 10/15)	£850	£1100
		b. Inverted Arabic "5" (R. 10/7, 10/14)	£1000	£1500
		c. Vars a and b in se-tenant pair	£2500	
		d. Error 20f. on 4a. violet (R. 10/1, 10/9)	£6500	
115	11	30f. on 6a. greenish blue	7·50	2·00
		a. Error 80f. on 6a. greenish blue..	£6500	
116		40f. on 8a. deep green	4·50	8·50
117	12	75f. on 1r. chocolate	6·00	8·50
		a. Inverted Arabic "5"	£140	£160
118		100f. on 2r. yellow-brown	11·00	4·00
119		200f. on 5r. orange	60·00	55·00
120		½d. on 10r. scarlet	£140	£190
		a. No bar in English "½"	£1800	£2000
		b. Scarlet-vermilion	£160	£250
121	10	1d. on 25r. violet	£325	£450
106/21 Set of 16			£500	£650

Nos. 106/13 and 115/16 were in sheets of 160 (16×10) No. 114 sheets of 150 (15×10) and Nos. 117/21 sheets of 100 (10×10). There were three settings of the surcharge for the 3f. and two settings for the 5, 10, 25, 40, 100 and 200f. Nos. 107c, 111b and 114a/b come from the second.

The "wide space" varieties, Nos. 106a, 107a and 108a, show a 2 mm space between the numeral and "Fils" instead of 1 mm. On No. 106a it occurs R. 8/5 and R. 8/13, on 107d on R. 10/5 and R. 10/10 of the first setting and Nos. 107c, 111b and 114a/b come from the second.

No. 109a occurs in the first setting and can be easily identified as it shows the point of the Arabic numeral at the foot of the surcharge.

All 10f. stamps from the second setting are as No. 111b except for R. 4/7–8 and 15–16 where the spacing is the same as for the first setting (Type 13).

No. 114d shows "20" instead of "25". Many examples of this error were removed from the sheets before issue. The Arabic value "25" was unaltered.

No. 115a shows the error in the English face value only.

No. 117a occurs on R. 1/2, 1/7 and a third position in the first vertical row not yet identified.

No. 120a occurs on R. 1/2, R. 2/3 and R. 10/1.

No. 120b was a special printing of No. 91 which does not exist unsurcharged.

15

1932 (9 May–June). T **10** to **12**, but with values altered to "FILS" or "DINAR" as in T **15**. Wmk Mult Script CA (sideways on 50f. to 1d.) P 12.

138	11	2f. ultramarine (6.32)	75	20
139		3f. green	50	10
140		4f. brown-purple (6.32)	2·00	10
141		5f. grey-green	1·25	10
142		8f. scarlet	3·00	10
143		10f. yellow	2·25	10
144		15f. blue	2·25	10
145		20f. orange	4·75	50
146		25f. mauve	5·00	50
147		30f. bronze-green	5·00	15
148		40f. violet	4·00	1·00
149	12	50f. brown	6·00	50
150		75f. dull ultramarine	14·00	5·50
151		100f. deep green	18·00	2·00
152		200f. scarlet	30·00	4·50
153	10	½d. deep blue	95·00	75·00
154		1d. claret	£225	£180
138/54 Set of 17			£375	£225
138s/54s Perf "SPECIMEN" Set of 17			£800	

OFFICIAL STAMPS

ON STATE SERVICE
(O **2**)

1920 (16 May)–**23**. As Nos. 1/18, but surch includes additional wording "ON STATE SERVICE" as Type O **2** in black.

(a) No wmk. Tougra as A

O19	1a	½a. on 10pa. blue-green	29·00	2·00
O20	1b	1a. on 20pa. red	9·00	1·00
O21	1	1½a. on 5pa. purple-brown	70·00	3·00
O22	1c	2½a. on 1pi. purple	9·00	9·50
O23	1d	3a. on 1½pi. black and rose	28·00	1·25
O24	1e	4a. on 1¾pi. red-brown and grey-blue	60·00	5·50
O25	1f	6a. on 2pi. black and green	48·00	12·00
O26	1g	8a. on 2½pi. yellow-green and orange-brown	60·00	7·00
O27	1h	12a. on 10pi. purple	38·00	15·00
O28	1i	1r. on 10pi. red-brown	55·00	15·00
O29	1j	2r. on 25pi. olive-green	50·00	24·00
O30	1k	5r. on 50pi. rose-carmine	95·00	75·00
O31	1l	10r. on 100pi. slate-blue	£150	£180
O19/31 Set of 13			£650	£325

(b) No wmk. Tougra as B (No. 15) (1922)

O32	1i	1r. on 10pi. red-brown	50·00	7·00

(c) Wmk Mult Script CA (sideways on ½a. to 8a.) (1921–23)

O33	1a	½a. on 10pa. green	1·50	1·00
O34	1b	1a. on 20pa. red	13·00	1·00
O35	1	1½a. on 5pa. purple-brown	2·75	1·50
O36	1e	4a. on 1¾pi. red-brown and grey-blue	2·00	3·25
O37	1f	6a. on 2pi. black and green (10.3.23)	45·00	£190
O38	1g	8a. on 2½pi. yellow-green and orange-brown	3·50	2·25
O39	1h	12a. on 5pi. purple (10.3.23)	45·00	£110
O40	1i	2r. on 25pi. olive-green (10.3.23)	£130	£180
O33/40 Set of 8			£200	£450
O33s/40s Optd "SPECIMEN". Set of 8			£500	

Nos. O25/6, O30 and O37/8 only exist from the setting with the surcharge 27½ mm wide.

On Nos. O19/40 there is a stop after the "An" on every value apart from the 2½a. (No. O22).

The "SPECIMEN" opt on No. O34 is of a different type, without the full stop present on Nos. O33 and O35/40.

ON STATE SERVICE
(O **6**)

ON STATE SERVICE
(O **7**)

1923. Optd with Types O **6** (horiz designs) or O **7** (vert designs).

O54	2	½a. olive-green	1·50	1·75
O55	3	1a. brown	1·75	30
O56	4	1½a. lake	1·75	3·25
O57	5	2a. orange-buff	2·00	55
O58	6	3a. grey-blue	2·50	1·50
O59	7	4a. violet	4·25	3·25
O60	8	6a. greenish blue	4·00	1·25
O61	7	8a. olive-bistre	4·00	5·00
O62	9	1r. brown and blue-green	20·00	4·50
O63	2	2r. black (R.)	38·00	17·00
O64	7	5r. orange	90·00	65·00
O65	8	10r. lake	£200	85·00
O54/65 Set of 12			£325	£160
O54s/65s Optd "SPECIMEN." Set of 12			£800	

ON STATE SERVICE

(O **8**)

ON STATE SERVICE

(O **9**)

1924–25. Optd with Types O **8** (horiz designs) or O **9** (vert designs).

O66	2	½a. olive-green	1·50	10
O67	3	1a. brown	1·25	10
O68	4	1½a. lake	1·25	30
O69	5	2a. orange-buff	1·50	10
O70	6	3a. grey-blue	2·00	10
O71	7	4a. violet	4·00	30
O72	8	6a. greenish blue	1·75	20
O73	7	8a. olive-bistre	3·75	35
O74	9	1r. brown and blue-green	22·00	4·25
O75	2	2r. olive-bistre (1925)	45·00	3·75
O76	7	5r. orange	95·00	50·00
O77	8	10r. lake	£180	42·00
O66/77 Set of 12			£325	£100
O66s/77s Optd "SPECIMEN." Set of 12			£800	

1927 (1 Apr). Optd with Type O **9**.

O79	10	1r. red-brown	16·00	3·00
		s. Optd "SPECIMEN."	£110	

ON STATE SERVICE

ON STATE SERVICE

(O **12**)

(O **13**)

1931. Optd.

*(a) As Type O **12***

O93	11	½a. green	65	2·75
O94		1a. red-brown	3·50	10
O95		1½a. scarlet	4·50	29·00
O96		2a. orange	80	10
O97		3a. blue	85	1·25
O98		4a. slate-purple	1·00	1·50
O99		6a. greenish blue	6·50	32·00
O100		8a. deep green	6·50	32·00

*(b) As Type O **13**, horizontally*

O101	12	1r. chocolate	24·00	29·00
O102		2r. yellow-brown	40·00	90·00
O103		5r. orange	60·00	£180
O104		10r. scarlet	£225	£325

*(c) As Type O **13**, vertically upwards*

O105	10	25r. violet	£1800	£2500
O93/104 Set of 12			£325	£650
O93s/105s Perf "SPECIMEN" Set of 13			£1500	

1932 (1 Apr). Official issues of 1924–25 and 1931 surch in "FILS" or "DINAR", as T **13** or **14**.

O122	11	3f. on ½a. green	8·50	4·50
		a. Pair, one without surch	£1100	
O123		4f. on 1a. red-brown (G.)	2·50	10
O124		5f. on 1a. red-brown	2·50	10
		a. Inverted Arabic "5" (R. 8/11)	£120	50·00
O125	4	8f. on 1½a. lake (No. O68)	16·00	50
O126	11	10f. on 2a. orange	6·00	10
		a. Inverted Arabic "1" (R. 8/13)	£130	45·00
		b. "10" omitted	†	£3250
		c. No space between "10" and "Fils"	6·00	10
O127		15f. on 3a. blue	4·25	8·50
O128		20f. on 4a. slate-purple	6·00	5·50
O129		25f. on 4a. slate-purple	4·75	2·00
O130	8	30f. on 6a. greenish blue (No. O72)	16·00	1·75
O131	11	40f. on 8a. deep green	4·75	3·50
		a. "Flis" for "Fils" (R. 7/5, 7/13)	£850	£950
O132	12	50f. on 1r. chocolate	22·00	5·00
		a. Inverted Arabic "5" (R. 1/2)	£325	£225
O133		75f. on 1r. chocolate	8·50	13·00
		a. Inverted Arabic "5"	£160	£180

O134	2	100f. on 2r. olive-bistre (surch at top)	48·00	3·50
		a. Surch at foot	48·00	15·00
O135	7	200f. on 5r. orange (No. O76)	28·00	26·00
O136	8	½d. on 10r. lake (No. O77)	£160	£180
		a. No bar in English "½" (R. 2/10)	£2000	£2500
O137	10	1d. on 25r. violet	£350	£500
O122/37 Set of 16			£625	£700

Nos. O122/4, O126/9 and O131 were in sheets of 160 (16×10), Nos. O130, O134 and O136 150 (15×10), No. O135 150 (15×10) and Nos. O125, O132/3 and O137 in sheets of 100 (10×10). There was a second setting of the surcharge for the 3f. (equivalent to the third postage setting), 10f. to 25f., 40f. to 100f. and 1d. Nos. O126c, O131a and O134a come from the second setting.

All 100f. stamps from the second setting are as No. O134a.

For notes on other varieties see below No. 121.

1932 (9 May). Optd.

*(a) As Type O **12***

O155	11	2f. ultramarine	1·75	10
O156		3f. green	1·50	10
O157		4f. brown-purple	1·50	10
O158		5f. grey-green	1·50	10
O159		8f. scarlet	1·50	10
O160		10f. yellow	2·25	10
O161		15f. blue	2·50	10
O162		20f. orange	2·50	15
O163		25f. mauve	2·50	15
O164		30f. bronze-green	3·50	20
O165		40f. violet	4·50	30

*(b) As Type O **13**, horizontally*

O166	12	50f. brown	3·25	20
O167		75f. dull ultramarine	3·00	1·00
O168		100f. deep green	11·00	4·00
O169		200f. scarlet	35·00	6·50

*(c) As Type O **13**, vertically upwards*

O170	10	½d. deep blue	27·00	48·00
O171		1d. claret	£150	£170
O155/71 Set of 17			£225	£200
O155s/71s Perf "SPECIMEN" Set of 17			£750	

The British Mandate was given up on 3 October 1932 and Iraq became an independent kingdom. Later issues will be found listed in the Stanley Gibbons *Middle East Catalogue*.

Ireland

All the issues of Ireland to 1970 are listed together here, in this section of the Gibbons Catalogue, purely as a matter of convenience to collectors.

PROVISIONAL GOVERNMENT

16 January—6 December 1922

Stamps of Great Britain overprinted.
T 104/8, W 100; T 109, W 110

RIALTAR
SEALADAĊ
NA
hÉIREANN
1922
(1)

RIALTAR
SEALADAĊ
NA
hÉIREANN
1922.
(2)

RIALTAR
SEALADAĊ
NA hÉIREAnn
1922
(3)

("Provisional Government of Ireland, 1922")

1922 (17 Feb–July). T **104** to **108** (W **100**) and **109** of Great Britain overprinted in black.

*(a) With T **1**, by Dollard Printing House Ltd. Optd in black**

1	**105**	½d. green	2·25	40
		a. Opt inverted	£475	£600
		w. Wmk inverted	—	£600
2	**104**	1d. scarlet	4·25	70
		a. Opt inverted	£275	£350
		b. Opt double, both inverted, one albino	£350	
		c. Opt double	†	£1600
		w. Wmk inverted	—	£450
3		1d. carmine-red	13·00	2·25
4		2½d. bright blue	2·50	10·00
		a. Opt double, one albino	£475	
		b. Red opt (1.4)	3·50	4·50
		ba. Opt double, one albino	£475	
5	**106**	3d. bluish violet	7·00	7·50
6		4d. grey-green	6·00	26·00
		a. Opt double, one albino	£475	
		b. Red opt (1.8)	11·00	16·00
		c. Carmine opt (7.22)	48·00	70·00
7	**107**	5d. yellow-brown	7·00	8·50
		x. Wmk reversed	—	£500
8	**108**	9d. agate	17·00	45·00
		a. Opt double, one albino	£375	
		b. Red opt (1.4)	19·00	19·00
		c. Carmine opt (7.22)	90·00	95·00
9		10d. turquoise-blue	11·00	65·00
1/9 *Set of 8*			50·00	£110

*All values except 2½d. and 4d. are known with greyish black overprint, but these are difficult to distinguish.

The carmine overprints on the 4d. and 9d. were produced by Alex Thom & Co. Ltd. There was a further overprinting of the 2½d. at the same time, but this is difficult to distinguish.

The ½d. with red overprint is a trial or proof printing (*Price* £160).

Bogus inverted T **1** overprints exist on the 2d., 4d., 9d and 1s. values.

*(b) With T **2**, by Alex Thom & Co Ltd*

10	**105**	1½d. red-brown (*shades*)	3·50	2·50
		a. Error. ""PENCF"	£375	£325
		w. Wmk inverted	—	£375
		x. Wmk reversed	—	£400
12	**106**	2d. orange (Die I)	9·50	50
		a. Opt inverted	£200	£300
		w. Wmk inverted	—	£400
		x. Wmk reversed	£600	£375
13		2d. orange (Die II)	6·50	50
		a. Opt inverted	£400	£500
		b. Opt double, one albino	£425	£375
		y. Wmk inverted and reversed	£400	
14	**107**	6d. reddish purple (*chalk-surfaced paper*)	23·00	30·00
		a. Deep reddish purple	28·00	35·00
		y. Wmk inverted and reversed	£500	
15	**108**	1s. bistre-brown	13·00	18·00
10/15 *Set of 5*			50·00	45·00

Varieties occur throughout the T **2** overprint in the relative positions of the lines of the overprint, the "R" of "Rialtas" being over either the "Se" or "S" of "Sealadac" or intermediately.

*(c) With T **3** by Dollard Printing House Ltd*

17	**109**	2s.6d. sepia-brown	60·00	85·00
		a. Opt double, one albino	£1600	

18		2s.6d. reddish brown	75·00	95·00
		a. Opt double, one albino	£750	
19		5s. rose-carmine	90·00	£170
21		10s. dull grey-blue	£180	£375
17/21 *Set of 3*			£300	£550

1922 (19 June–Aug). Optd as T **2**, in black, by Harrison & Sons, for use in horiz and vert coils.

26	**105**	½d. green	3·00	23·00
27	**104**	1d. scarlet	3·75	10·00
28	**105**	1½d. red-brown (21.6)	4·00	55·00
29	**106**	2d. bright orange (Die I)	22·00	55·00
29a		2d. bright orange (Die II) (8.22)	22·00	45·00
		ay. Wmk inverted and reversed	—	£400
26/9a *Set of 5*			50·00	£170

The Harrison overprint measures 15×17 mm (maximum) against the 14½×16 mm of T **2** (Thom printing) and is a much bolder black than the latter, while the individual letters are taller, the "i" of "Rialtas" being specially outstanding as it extends below the foot of the "R".

The "R" of "Rialtas" is always over the "Se" of "Sealadac".

1922. Optd by Thom.

*(a) As T **2** but bolder, in dull to shiny blue-black or red (June–Nov)*

30	**105**	½d. green	3·75	80
31	**104**	1d. scarlet	3·25	50
		a. "Q" for "O" (No. 357ab)	£1400	£1200
		b. Reversed "Q" for "O" (No. 357ac)	£375	£250
		w. Wmk inverted	†	£550
32	**105**	1½d. red-brown	4·00	4·75
		a. Chestnut	4·00	4·50
		y. Wmk inverted and reversed	†	£600
33	**106**	2d. orange (Die I)	18·00	1·50
34		2d. orange (Die II)	6·00	50
		y. Wmk inverted and reversed	£180	£150
35	**104**	2½d. blue (R.)	8·50	30·00
36	**106**	3d. violet	11·00	2·25
		a. Dull reddish violet	5·00	2·00
		y. Wmk inverted and reversed	£150	£150
37		4d. grey-green (R.)	4·50	13·00
38	**107**	5d. yellow-brown	6·00	14·00
39		6d. reddish purple (*chalk-surfaced paper*)	17·00	7·50
		a. Deep reddish purple	13·00	5·50
		w. Wmk inverted	£275	£140
		y. Wmk inverted and reversed	†	£375
40	**108**	9d. agate (R.)	14·00	29·00
41		9d. olive-green (R.)	6·50	50·00
42		10d. turquoise-blue	29·00	75·00
43		1s. bistre-brown	17·00	17·00
30/43 *Set of 14*			£110	£200

Both 2d. stamps exist with the overprint inverted but there remains some doubt as to whether they were issued.

These Thom printings are distinguishable from the Harrison printings by the size of the overprint, and from the previous Thom printings by the intensity and colour of the overprint, the latter being best seen when the stamp is looked through with a strong light behind it.

*(b) As with T **3**, but bolder, in shiny blue-black (17 Oct–Nov)*

44	**109**	2s.6d. sepia-brown	£250	£350
45		5s. rose-carmine (11.22)	£275	£375
46		10s. dull grey-blue	£1000	£1400
44/6 *Set of 3*			£1400	£1900

The above differ from Nos. 17/21 not only in the bolder impression and colour of the ink but also in the "h" and "e" of "heireann" which are closer together and horizontally aligned.

RIALTAR
SEALADAĊ
NA
hÉIREAnn
1922.
(4)

SAORSTÁT
ÉIREAnn
1922
(5 Wide date) ("Irish Free State 1922")

1922 (21 Nov–Dec). Optd by Thom with T **4** (wider setting) in shiny blue-blue.

47	**105**	½d. green	1·00	2·50
		a. Opt in dull black	£100	90·00
48	**104**	1d. scarlet	6·00	3·75
		w. Wmk inverted	†	£275
49	**105**	1½d. red-brown (4.12)	3·00	14·00
50	**106**	2d. orange (Die II)	10·00	7·00
51	**108**	1s. olive-bistre (4.12)	50·00	90·00
47/51 *Set of 5*			60·00	£100

The overprint T **4** measures 15¾ × 16 mm (maximum).

IRISH FREE STATE

6 December 1922—29 December 1937

1922 (Dec)–**23**.

*(a) Optd by Thom with T **5**, in dull to shiny blue-black or red*

52	**105**	½d. green	2·00	30
		a. No accent in "Saorstat"	£1400	£1000
		b. Accent inserted by hand	£110	£130
53	**104**	1d. scarlet	2·75	50
		aa. No accent in "Saorstat"	£17000	£10000
		a. No accent and final "t" missing	£15000	£8000
		b. Accent inserted by hand	£160	£180
		c. Accent and "t" inserted	£250	£300
		d. Accent and "at" inserted	£250	£300
		e. Reversed "Q" for "O" (No. 357ac)	£375	£250
		f. Opt triple, two albino	£600	
54	**105**	1½d. red-brown	3·50	8·50
55	**106**	2d. orange (Die II)	1·50	1·00
56	**104**	2½d. bright blue (R.) (6.1.23)	7·50	14·00
		a. No accent	£160	£200
57	**106**	3d. bluish violet (6.1.23)	6·50	11·00
		a. No accent	£325	£425
58		4d. grey-green (R.) (16.1.23)	6·50	15·00
		a. No accent	£180	£225
59	**107**	5d. yellow-brown	5·50	5·00

60		6d. reddish purple (*chalk-surfaced paper*) (*shades*)	3·75	2·00
		a. Accent inserted by hand	£850	£900
		y. Wmk inverted and reversed	85·00	70·00
61	**108**	9d. olive-green (R.)	11·00	5·50
		aa. Pale olive-green	15·00	12·00
		a. No accent	£275	£325
62		10d. turquoise-blue	24·00	75·00
63		1s. bistre-brown (*shades*)	8·00	11·00
		a. No accent	£12000	£12000
		b. Accent inserted by hand	£700	£800
64	**109**	2s.6d. chocolate-brown	50·00	70·00
		aa. Pale brown	50·00	70·00
		a. Major re-entry (R. 1/2)	£1200	£1400
		b. No accent	£450	£600
		c. Accent reversed	£700	£850
65		5s. rose-carmine	85·00	£160
		a. No accent	£600	£900
		b. Accent reversed	£900	£1200
66		10s. dull grey-blue	£190	£350
		a. No accent	£3000	£4000
		b. Accent reversed	£4500	£5500
52/66 *Set of 15*			£350	£650

The "no accent" and "accent inserted" varieties on the ½d. to 1s. values occur on R. 15/12. On the 2s.6d. to 10s. values the "no accent" varieties occur on R. 3/2 and R. 8/2, the "accent reversed" on R. 7/4.

The accents inserted by hand are in dull black. The reversed accents are grave (thus "à") instead of acute ("á"). A variety with "S" of "Saorstát" directly over "é" of "éireann", instead of to left, may be found in all values except the 2½d. and 4d. In the 2s.6d., 5s. and 10s. it is very slightly to the left in the "S" over "é" variety, bringing the "à" of "Saorstát" directly above the last "n" of "éireann".

*(b) Optd with T **5**, in dull or shiny blue-black, by Harrison, for use in horiz or vert coils (7.3.23)*

67		½d. green	1·75	11·00
		a. Long "1" in "1922"	20·00	55·00
		y. Wmk inverted and reversed	†	—
68		1d. scarlet	8·00	24·00
		a. Long "1" in "1922"	80·00	£140
69		1½d. red-brown	6·50	55·00
		a. Long "1" in "1922"	85·00	£225
70		2d. orange (Die II)	9·50	17·00
		a. Long "1" in "1922"	35·00	60·00
		w. Wmk inverted	—	£300
67/70 *Set of 4*			23·00	95·00

In the Harrison overprint the characters are rather bolder than those of the Thom overprint, and the foot of the "1" of "1922" is usually rounded instead of square. The long "1" in "1922" has a serif at foot. The second "e" of "éireann" appears to be slightly raised.

PRINTERS. The following and all subsequent issues to No. 148 were printed at the Government Printing Works, Dublin, *unless otherwise stated.*

6 "Sword of Light"

7 Map of Ireland

8 Arms of Ireland

9 Celtic Cross

10

(Des J. J. O'Reilly, T **6**; J. Ingram, T **7**; Miss M. Girling, T **8**; and Miss L. Williams, T **9**. Typo. Plates made by Royal Mint, London)

1922 (6 Dec)–**34**. W **10**. P 15×14.

71	**6**	½d. bright green (20.4.23)	3·00	90
		a. Imperf×perf 14, Wmk sideways (11.34)	23·00	50·00
		w. Wmk inverted	40·00	25·00
72	**7**	1d. carmine (23.2.23)	2·25	10
		aw. Wmk inverted	38·00	10·00
		b. Perf 15×imperf (single perf) (1933)	£100	£250
		bw. Ditto. Wmk inverted	£120	£250
		c. Perf 15×imperf (7.34)	12·00	42·00
		d. Booklet pane. Three stamps plus three printed labels (21.8.31)	£450	£550
		dw. Wmk inverted	£450	£550
73		1½d. claret (2.2.23)	3·75	2·00
		w. Wmk inverted	£1300	£1100
74		2d. grey-green (6.12.22)	2·25	10
		a. Imperf×perf 14, Wmk sideways (11.34)	40·00	85·00
		b. Perf 15×imperf (1934)	£13000	£1600
		w. Wmk inverted	35·00	10·00
		y. Wmk inverted and reversed	38·00	38·00
75	**8**	2½d. red-brown (7.9.23)	6·00	3·75
		w. Wmk inverted	60·00	27·00
76	**9**	3d. ultramarine (16.3.23)	3·25	2·00
		w. Wmk inverted	75·00	32·00
77	**8**	4d. slate-blue (28.9.23)	2·75	4·00
		w. Wmk inverted	£180	60·00
78	**6**	5d. deep violet (11.5.23)	10·00	6·50
79		6d. claret (21.12.23)	7·00	3·00
		w. Wmk inverted	£180	75·00
80	**8**	9d. deep violet (26.10.23)	15·00	5·50
81	**9**	10d. brown (11.5.23)	8·00	14·00
82	**6**	1s. light blue (15.6.23)	16·00	4·50
		w. Wmk inverted	†	£1100
71/82 *Set of 12*				

No. 72b is imperf vertically except for a single perf at each top corner. It was issued for use in automatic machines.

See also Nos. 111/22.

SAORSCÁC ÉIREANN 1922
(11 Narrow Date)

12 Daniel O'Connell

1925 (Aug)–**28**. T **109** of Great Britain (Bradbury Wilkinson printing) optd at the Government Printing Works, Dublin or at Somerset House, London.

*(a) With T **11** in black or grey-black (25.8.25)*

83		2s.6d. chocolate-brown	40·00	£100
	a.	Wide and narrow date (pair) (1927)	£300	£650
84		5s. rose-carmine	60·00	£150
	a.	Wide and narrow date (pair) (1927)	£450	£1100
85		10s. dull grey-blue	£150	£350
	a.	Wide and narrow date (pair) (1927)	£1200	£2750
83/5	*Set of 3*		£225	£550

The varieties with wide and narrow date *se-tenant* are from what is known as the "composite setting," in which some stamps showed the wide date, as T **5**, while in others the figures were close together, as in T **11**.

Single examples of this printing with wide date may be distinguished from Nos. 64 to 66 by the colour of the ink, which is black or grey-black in the composite setting and blue-black in the Thom printing.

The type of the "composite" overprint usually shows distinct signs of wear.

*(b) As T **5** (wide date) in black (1927–28)*

86		2s.6d. chocolate-brown (9.12.27)	50·00	60·00
	a.	Circumflex accent over "a"	£275	£375
	b.	No accent over "a"	£450	£550
	c.	Flat accent on "a"	£550	£650
87		5s. rose-carmine (2.28)	80·00	£100
	a.	Circumflex accent over "a"	£425	£600
	c.	Flat accent on "a"	£750	£900
88		10s. dull grey-blue (15.2.28)	£190	£225
	a.	Circumflex accent over "a"	£1000	£1400
	c.	Flat accent on "a"	£1700	£2000
86/8	*Set of 3*		£275	£350

This printing can be distinguished from the Thom overprints in dull black, by the clear, heavy impression (in deep black) which often shows in relief on the back of the stamp.

The variety showing a circumflex accent over the "a" occurred on R. 9/2. The overprint in this position finally deteriorated to such an extent that some examples of the 2s.6d. were without accent (No. 86b). A new cliché was then introduced with the accent virtually flat and which also showed damage to the "a" and the crossbar of the "t".

(Des L. Whelan. Typo)

1929 (22 June). Catholic Emancipation Centenary. W **10**. P 15×14.

89	**12**	2d. grey-green	1·00	45
90		3d. blue	3·75	11·00
91		9d. bright violet	3·75	5·00
89/91	*Set of 3*		7·50	15·00

13 Shannon Barrage   **14** Reaper

(Des E. L. Lawrenson. Typo)

1930 (15 Oct). Completion of Shannon Hydro-Electric Scheme. W **10**. P 15×14.

92	**13**	2d. agate	1·25	55

(T **14** and **15** des G. Atkinson. Typo)

1931 (12 June). Bicentenary of the Royal Dublin Society. W **10**. P 15×14.

93	**14**	2d. blue	1·00	30

15 The Cross of Cong   **16** Adoration of the Cross   **17** Hurler

1932 (12 May). International Eucharistic Congress. W **10**. P 15×14.

94	**15**	2d. grey-green	2·50	30
		w. Wmk inverted	†	—
95		3d. blue	3·75	6·50

(T **16** to **19** des R. J. King. Typo)

1933 (18 Sept). "Holy Year". W **10**. P 15×14.

96	**16**	2d. grey-green	2·50	15
		w. Wmk inverted	†	£600
97		3d. blue	4·25	2·50

1934 (27 July). Golden Jubilee of the Gaelic Athletic Association. W **10**. P 15×14.

98	**17**	2d. green	2·25	55
		w. Wmk inverted	†	£1000

1935 (Mar–July). T **109** of Great Britain (Waterlow re-engraved printings) optd as T **5** (wide date), at Somerset House, London.

99	**109**	2s.6d. chocolate (No. 450)	48·00	60·00
	a.	Flat accent on "a" (R. 9/2)	£300	£300
100		5s. bright rose-red (No. 451)	90·00	90·00
	a.	Flat accent on "a" (R. 9/2)	£425	£425
101		10s. indigo (No. 452)	£300	£325
	a.	Flat accent on "a" (R. 9/2)	£1100	£1100
	b.	Opt double	£8500	£6500
99/101	*Set of 3*		£400	£425

18 St. Patrick   **19** Ireland and New Constitution

1937 (8 Sept). W **10**. P 14×15.

102	**18**	2s.6d. emerald-green	£160	70·00
		w. Wmk inverted	£950	£425
103		5s. maroon	£180	£120
		w. Wmk inverted	£850	£425
104		10s. deep blue	£150	55·00
		w. Wmk inverted	£1300	£1500
102/4	*Set of 3*		£450	£200

See also Nos. 123/5.

EIRE

29 December 1937–17 April 1949

1937 (29 Dec). Constitution Day. W **10**. P 15×14.

105	**19**	2d. claret	2·00	20
		w. Wmk inverted	—	£350
106		3d. blue	5·00	3·75

For similar stamps see Nos. 176/7.

20 Father Mathew

(Des S. Keating. Typo)

1938 (1 July). Centenary of Temperance Crusade. W **10**. P 15×14.

107	**20**	2d. agate	3·00	50
		w. Wmk inverted	†	£400
108		3d. blue	10·00	5·50

21 George Washington, American Eagle and Irish Harp   **22**

(Des G. Atkinson. Typo)

1939 (1 Mar). 150th Anniv of US Constitution and Installation of First US President. W **10**. P 15×14.

109	**21**	2d. scarlet	3·00	1·00
110		3d. blue	4·25	5·50

SIZE OF WATERMARK. T **22** can be found in various sizes from about 8 to 10 mm high. This is due to the use of two different dandy rolls supplied by different firms and to the effects of paper shrinkage and other factors such as pressure and machine speed.

White line above left value tablet joining horizontal line to ornament (R. 3/7)

1940–68. Typo. W **22**. P 15×14 or 14×15 (2s.6d. to 10s.).

111	**6**	½d. bright green (24.11.40)	3·75	40
		w. Wmk inverted	60·00	17·00
112	**7**	1d. carmine (26.10.40)	50	10
		aw. Wmk inverted	2·00	30
	b.	From coils. Perf 14×imperf (9.40)	60·00	65·00
	c.	From coils. Perf 15×imperf (20.3.46)	42·00	24·00
		cw. Wmk inverted	42·00	24·00
	d.	Booklet pane. Three stamps plus three printed labels	£3250	
		dw. Wmk inverted	£3250	
113		1½d. claret (1.40)	19·00	30
		w. Wmk inverted	30·00	16·00
114		2d. grey-green (1.40)	50	10
		w Wmk inverted	2·75	2·75
115	**8**	2½d. red-brown (3.41)	16·00	15
		w. Wmk inverted	25·00	6·50
116	**9**	3d. blue (12.40)	85	10
		w. Wmk inverted	4·00	2·00
117	**8**	4d. slate-blue (12.40)	55	10
		w. Wmk inverted	23·00	6·00
118	**6**	5d. deep violet (7.40)	1·00	10
		w. Wmk inverted	45·00	32·00
119		6d. claret (3.42)	3·00	50
		aw. Wmk inverted	38·00	12·00
	b.	Chalk-surfaced paper (1967)	1·25	20
		bw. Wmk inverted	11·00	3·50

119c		8d. scarlet (12.9.49)	80	1·50
		w. Wmk inverted	50·00	60·00
120	**8**	9d. deep violet (7.40)	1·50	80
		w. Wmk inverted	13·00	6·50
121	**9**	10d. brown (7.40)	75	80
		aw. Wmk inverted	15·00	12·00
121b		11d. rose (12.9.49)	2·25	3·50
122	**6**	1s. light blue (6.40)	70·00	18·00
		w. Wmk inverted	£1100	£275
123	**18**	2s.6d. emerald-green (10.2.43)	40·00	1·00
		aw. Wmk inverted	£100	45·00
	b.	Chalk-surfaced paper (1967)	1·50	3·25
		bw. Wmk inverted	38·00	6·00
124		5s. maroon (15.12.42)	40·00	1·50
	a.	Line flaw	£275	50·00
		bw. Wmk inverted	£225	55·00
	c.	Chalk-surfaced paper (1968?)	13·00	4·25
		ca. Purple	4·00	9·50
	cb.	Line flaw	£100	65·00
		cw. Wmk inverted	38·00	10·00
125		10s. deep blue (7.45)	60·00	6·00
		aw. Wmk inverted	£325	£110
	b.	Chalk-surfaced paper (1968)	19·00	13·00
		ba. Blue (shades)	4·00	16·00
		bw. Wmk inverted		
111/25ba	*Set of 17*		£110	30·00

There is a wide range of shades and also variations in paper used in this issue.

See also Nos. 227/8.

1941 I ʒcuimne aiséiṙʒe 1916
(**23** Trans "In memory of the rising of 1916")

24 Volunteer and GPO, Dublin

1941 (12 Apr). 25th Anniv of Easter Rising (1916). Provisional issue. T **7** and **9** (2d. in new colour), optd with T **23**.

126	**7**	2d. orange (G.)	2·50	1·00
127	**9**	3d. blue (V.)	27·00	11·00

(Des V. Brown. Typo)

1941 (27 Oct). 25th Anniv of Easter Rising (1916). Definitive issue. W **22**. P 15×14.

128	**24**	2½d. blue-black	3·25	1·25

25 Dr. Douglas Hyde   **26** Sir William Rowan Hamilton   **27** Bro. Michael O'Clery

(Des S. O'Sullivan. Typo)

1943 (31 July). 50th Anniv of Founding of Gaelic League. W **22**. P 15×14.

129	**25**	½d. green	1·25	70
130		2½d. claret	2·00	10
		w. Wmk inverted	†	£425

(Des S. O'Sullivan from a bust by Hogan. Typo)

1943 (13 Nov). Centenary of Announcement of Discovery of Quaternions. W **22**. P 15×14.

131	**26**	½d. green	75	70
132		2½d. brown	2·25	20

(Des R. J. King. Typo)

1944 (30 June). Tercentenary of Death of Michael O'Clery. (Commemorating the *Annals of the Four Masters*). W **22** (sideways*). P 14×15.

133	**27**	½d. emerald-green	10	10
		w. Wmk facing right	80	35
134		1s. red-brown	1·50	10
		w. Wmk facing right	4·25	2·00

*The normal sideways watermark shows the top of the e facing left, *as seen from the back of the stamp.*

Although issued as commemoratives these two stamps were kept in use as part of the current issue, replacing Nos. 111 and 122.

28 Edmund Ignatius Rice   **29** "Youth Sowing Seeds of Freedom"

(Des S. O'Sullivan. Typo)

1944 (29 Aug). Death Centenary of Edmund Rice (founder of Irish Christian Brothers). W **22**. P 15×14.

135	**28**	2½d. slate	1·75	45
		w. Wmk inverted	†	£350

(Des R. J. King. Typo)

1945 (15 Sept). Centenary of Death of Thomas Davis (founder of Young Ireland Movement). W **22**. P 15×14.

136	**29**	2½d. green	2·50	75
		w. Wmk inverted	—	£350
137		6d. claret	7·00	9·50

30 "Country and Homestead"

(Des R. J. King. Typo)

1946 (16 Sept). Birth Centenaries of Davitt and Parnell (land reformers). W **22**. P 15×14.

| 138 | 30 | 2½d. scarlet | 2·50 | 25 |
| 139 | | 3d. blue | 3·50 | 4·25 |

31 Angel Victor over Rock of Cashel

32 Over Lough Derg

33 Over Croagh Patrick

34 Over Glendalough

(Des R. J. King. Recess Waterlow (1d. to 1s.3d. until 1961), D.L.R. (8d., 1s.3d. from 1961 and 1s.5d.))

1948 (7 Apr)–**65**. Air. T **31**/**34**. W **22**. P 15 (1s.5d.) or 15×14 (others).

140	31	1d. chocolate (4.4.49)	3·00	6·50
141	32	3d. blue	3·00	3·50
142	33	6d. magenta	1·00	2·50
142b	32	8d. lake-brown (13.12.54)	8·50	11·00
143	34	1s. green (4.4.49)	1·00	2·00
143a	31	1s.3d. red-orange (13.12.54)	8·50	1·75
		aw. Wmk inverted	£700	£425
143b		1s.5d. deep ultramarine (shades) (1.4.65)	4·00	2·50
140/3b Set of 7			26·00	26·00

35 Theobald Wolfe Tone

(Des K. Uhlemann. Typo)

1948 (19 Nov). 150th Anniv of Insurrection. W **22**. P 15×14.

144	35	2½d. reddish purple	1·50	10
		w. Wmk inverted	†	—
145		3d. violet	3·50	4·50

REPUBLIC OF IRELAND

18 April 1949

36 Leinster House and Arms of Provinces

37 J. C. Mangan

(Des Muriel Brandt. Typo)

1949 (21 Nov). International Recognition of Republic. W **22**. P 15×14.

146	36	2½d. reddish brown	2·25	10
		w. Wmk inverted	†	—
147		3d. bright blue	6·50	4·25

(Des R. J. King. Typo)

1949 (5 Dec). Death Centenary of James Clarence Mangan (poet). W **22**. P 15×14.

| 148 | 37 | 1d. green | 1·50 | 35 |
| | | w. Wmk inverted | † | — |

38 Statue of St. Peter, Rome

(Recess Waterlow & Sons)

1950 (11 Sept). Holy Year. W **22**. P 12½.

149	38	2½d. violet	1·00	40
150		3d. blue	6·00	12·00
151		9d. brown	7·50	15·00
149/51 Set of 3			13·00	25·00

PRINTERS. Nos. 152 to 200 were recess-printed by De La Rue & Co, Dublin, *unless otherwise stated.*

39 Thomas Moore

40 Ireland at Home

(Eng W. Vacek)

1952 (10 Nov). Death Centenary of Thomas Moore (poet). W **22**. P 13.

152	39	2½d. reddish purple	1·00	10
		w. Wmk inverted	†	—
153		3½d. deep olive-green	1·75	4·25

(Des F. O'Ryan. Typo Government Printing Works, Dublin)

1953 (9 Feb). "An Tóstal" (Ireland at Home) Festival. W **22** (sideways). P 14×15.

| 154 | 40 | 2½d. emerald-green | 2·00 | 35 |
| 155 | | 1s.4d. blue | 20·00 | 30·00 |

41 Robert Emmet

42 *Madonna and Child* (Della Robbia)

43 Cardinal Newman (first Rector)

(Eng L. Downey)

1953 (21 Sept). 150th Death Anniv of Emmet (patriot). W **22**. P 13.

| 156 | 41 | 3d. deep bluish green | 3·00 | 15 |
| 157 | | 1s.3d. carmine | 32·00 | 10·00 |

(Eng A. R. Lane)

1954 (24 May). Marian Year. W **22**. P 15.

| 158 | 42 | 3d. blue | 1·00 | 10 |
| 159 | | 5d. myrtle-green | 1·75 | 3·25 |

(Des L. Whelan. Typo Govt Printing Works, Dublin)

1954 (19 July). Centenary of Founding of Catholic University of Ireland. W **22**. P 15×14.

160	43	2d. bright purple	2·25	10
		w. Wmk inverted	—	£350
161		1s.3d. blue	13·00	7·00

44 Statue of Commodore Barry

45 John Redmond

46 Thomas O'Crohan

(Des and eng H. Woyty-Wimmer)

1956 (16 Sept). Barry Commemoration. W **22**. P 15.

| 162 | 44 | 3d. slate-lilac | 1·00 | 10 |
| 163 | | 1s.3d. deep blue | 5·00 | 8·00 |

1957 (11 June). Birth Centenary of John Redmond (politician). W **22**. P 14×15.

| 164 | 45 | 3d. deep blue | 1·25 | 10 |
| 165 | | 1s.3d. brown-purple | 10·00 | 16·00 |

1957 (1 July). Birth Centenary of Thomas O'Crohan (author). W **22**. P 14×15.

166	46	2d. maroon	1·00	20
		w. Wmk inverted	†	£400
167		5d. violet	1·25	4·50

47 Admiral Brown

48 *Father Wadding* (Ribera)

49 Tom Clarke

(Des S. O'Sullivan. Typo Govt Printing Works, Dublin)

1957 (23 Sept). Death Centenary of Admiral William Brown. W **22**. P 15×14.

| 168 | 47 | 3d. blue | 3·00 | 20 |
| 169 | | 1s.3d. carmine | 22·00 | 17·00 |

1957 (25 Nov). 300th Death Anniv of Father Luke Wadding (theologian). W **22**. P 15.

| 170 | 48 | 3d. deep blue | 2·00 | 10 |
| 171 | | 1s.3d. lake | 15·00 | 8·50 |

1958 (28 July). Birth Centenary of Thomas J. ("Tom") Clarke (patriot). W **22**. P 15.

| 172 | 49 | 3d. deep green | 2·00 | 10 |
| 173 | | 1s.3d. red-brown | 4·00 | 11·00 |

50 Mother Mary Aikenhead

51 Arthur Guinness

(Eng Waterlow. Recess Imprimerie Belge de Securité, Brussels subsidiary of Waterlow & Sons)

1958 (20 Oct). Death Centenary of Mother Mary Aikenhead (foundress of Irish Sisters of Charity). W **22**. P 15×14.

| 174 | 50 | 3d. Prussian blue | 2·00 | 10 |
| 175 | | 1s.3d. rose-carmine | 11·00 | 8·00 |

(Typo Govt Printing Works, Dublin)

1958 (29 Dec). 21st Anniv of the Irish Constitution. W **22**. P 15×14.

| 176 | 19 | 3d. brown | 1·00 | 10 |
| 177 | | 5d. emerald-green | 1·00 | 4·50 |

1959 (20 July). Bicentenary of Guinness Brewery. W **22**. P 15.

| 178 | 51 | 3d. brown-purple | 2·50 | 10 |
| 179 | | 1s.3d. blue | 10·00 | 8·00 |

52 "The Flight of the Holy Family"

(Des K. Uhlemann)

1960 (20 June). World Refugee Year. W **22**. P 15.

| 180 | 52 | 3d. purple | 40 | 10 |
| 181 | | 1s.3d. sepia | 60 | 3·75 |

53 Conference Emblem

(Des P. Rahikainen)

1960 (19 Sept). Europa. W **22**. P 15.

| 182 | 53 | 6d. light brown | 3·50 | 1·00 |
| 183 | | 1s.3d. violet | 17·00 | 20·00 |

The ink of No. 183 is fugitive.

54 Dublin Airport, de Havilland DH.84 Dragon Mk 2 *Iolar* and Boeing 720

55 St. Patrick

(Des J. Flanagan and D. R. Lowther)

1961 (26 June). 25th Anniv of Aer Lingus. W **22**. P 15.

184	54	6d. blue	1·75	3·75
		w. Wmk inverted		
185		1s.3d. green	2·25	5·50

(Recess B.W.)

1961 (25 Sept). 15th Death Centenary of St. Patrick. W **22**. P 14½.

186	55	3d. blue	1·00	10
187		8d. purple	2·75	5·50
188		1s.3d. green	2·75	1·60
186/8 Set of 3			6·00	6·50

56 John O'Donovan and Eugene O'Curry

(Recess B.W.)

1962 (26 Mar). Death Centenaries of O'Donovan and O'Curry (scholars). W **22**. P 15.

| 189 | 56 | 3d. carmine | 30 | 10 |
| 190 | | 1s.3d. purple | 1·25 | 2·25 |

57 Europa "Tree"

(Des L. Weyer)

1962 (17 Sept). Europa. W **22**. P 15.
191	**57**	6d. carmine-red	70	1·00
192		1s.3d. turquoise	80	1·50

58 Campaign Emblem

(Des K. Uhlemann)

1963 (21 Mar). Freedom from Hunger. W **22**. P 15.
193	**58**	4d. deep violet	50	10
194		1s.3d. scarlet	3·25	2·75

59 "Co-operation"

(Des A. Holm)

1963 (16 Sept). Europa. W **22**. P 15.
195	**59**	6d. carmine	1·00	75
196		1s.3d. blue	3·25	3·75

60 Centenary Emblem

(Des P. Wildbur. Photo Harrison & Sons)

1963 (2 Dec). Centenary of Red Cross. W **22**. P 14½×15.
197	**60**	4d. red and grey	40	10
198		1s.3d. red, grey and light emerald	1·10	2·00

61 Wolfe Tone

(Des P. Wildbur)

1964 (13 Apr). Birth Bicentenary of Wolfe Tone (revolutionary). W **22**. P 15.
199	**61**	4d. black	50	10
200		1s.3d. ultramarine	1·90	2·00

62 Irish Pavilion at Fair

(Des A. Devane. Photo Harrison & Sons)

1964 (20 July). New York World's Fair. W **22**. P 14½×14.
201	**62**	5d. blue-grey, brown, violet and yellow-olive	50	10
		a. Brown omitted*	£6000	
202		1s.5d. blue-grey, brown, turquoise blue and light yellow-green	2·00	2·00

*No 201a comes from the top row of the sheet and shows part of the brown cross which would appear in the sheet margin. As the second horizontal row was normal it would appear that the brown cylinder was incorrectly registered.

63 Europa "Flower"   **64** "Waves of Communication"

(Des G. Bétemps. Photo Harrison)

1964 (14 Sept). Europa. W **22** (sideways). P 14×14½.
203	**63**	8d. olive-green and blue	1·50	1·25
204		1s.5d. red-brown and orange	6·00	4·25

(Des P. Wildbur. Photo Harrison)

1965 (17 May). ITU Centenary. W **22**. P 14½×14.
205	**64**	3d. blue and green	30	10
206		8d. black and green	1·25	1·60

PRINTERS Nos. 207 onwards were photogravure-printed by the Stamping Branch of the Revenue Commissioners, Dublin *unless otherwise stated.*

65 W. B. Yeats (poet)   **66** ICY Emblem

(Des R. Kyne, from drawing by S. O'Sullivan)

1965 (14 June). Yeats' Birth Centenary. W **22** (sideways). P 15.
207	**65**	5d. black, orange-brown and deep green	50	10
208		1s.5d. black, grey-green and brown	2·75	2·00
		a. Brown omitted	£6000	

1965 (16 Aug). International Co-operation Year. W **22**. P 15.
209	**66**	3d. ultramarine and new blue	60	10
210		10d. deep brown and brown	1·00	3·25

67 Europa "Sprig"

(Des H. Karlsson)

1965 (27 Sept). Europa. W **22**. P 15.
211	**67**	8d. black and brown-red	1·50	1·00
212		1s.5d. purple and light turquoise-blue	7·00	3·50

68 James Connolly   **69** "Marching to Freedom"

(Des E. Delaney (No. 216), R. Kyne, after portraits by S. O'Sullivan (others))

1966 (12 Apr). 50th Anniv of Easter Rising. T **68/9** and similar horiz portraits. W **22**. P 15.
213		3d. black and greenish blue	80	10
		a. Horiz pair. Nos. 213/14	1·60	3·00
214		3d. black and bronze-green	80	10
215		5d. black and yellow-olive	80	10
		a. Horiz pair. Nos. 215/16	1·60	2·50
216		5d. black, orange and blue-green	80	10
217		7d. black and light orange-brown	1·00	2·50
		a. Horiz pair. Nos. 217/18	2·00	7·50
218		7d. black and blue-green	1·00	2·50
219		1s.5d. black and turquoise	1·00	2·75
		a. Horiz pair. Nos. 219/20	2·00	10·00
220		1s.5d. black and bright green	1·00	2·75
213/20 *Set of 8*			6·50	9·50

Designs:—No. 213, Type **68**; No. 214, Thomas J. Clarke; No. 215, P. H. Pearse; No. 216, Type **69**; No. 217, Eamonn Ceannt; No. 218, Sean MacDiarmada; No. 219, Thomas MacDonagh; No. 220, Joseph Plunkett.

Nos. 213/14, 215/16, 217/18 and 219/20 were each printed together, *se-tenant*, in horizontal pairs throughout the sheet.

76 R. Casement   **77** Europa "Ship"

(Des R. Kyne)

1966 (3 Aug). 50th Death Anniv of Roger Casement (patriot). W **22** (sideways). P 15.
221	**76**	5d. black	15	10
222		1s. red-brown	40	50

(Des R. Kyne, after G. and J. Bender)

1966 (26 Sept). Europa. W **22** (sideways). P 15.
223	**77**	7d. emerald and orange	1·00	75
224		1s.5d. emerald and light grey	2·00	2·75

---

78 Interior of Abbey (from lithograph)   **79** Cogwheels

1966 (8 Nov). 750th Anniv of Ballintubber Abbey. W **22**. P 15.
225	**78**	5d. red-brown	10	10
226		1s. black	20	25

1966–67. As Nos. 116, 118 but photo. Smaller design (17×21 mm). Chalk-surfaced paper. W **22**. P 15.
227	**9**	3d. blue (1.8.67)	40	15
228	**6**	5d. bright violet (1.12.66)	30	15
		w. Wmk inverted (from booklets)	1·75	1·50

No. 228 was only issued in booklets (Nos. SB16/17) at first but was released in sheets on 1.4.68 in a slightly brighter shade. In the sheet stamps the lines of shading are more regular.

(Des O. Bonnevalle)

1967 (2 May). Europa. W **22** (sideways). P 15.
229	**79**	7d. light emerald, gold and pale cream	60	75
230		1s.5d. carmine-red, gold and pale cream	1·90	2·75

80 Maple Leaves

(Des P. Hickey)

1967 (28 Aug). Canadian Centennial. W **22**. P 15.
231	**80**	5d. multicoloured	10	10
232		1s.5d. multicoloured	20	1·25

81 Rock of Cashel (from photo by Edwin Smith)

1967 (25 Sept). International Tourist Year. W **22** (inverted). P 15.
233	**81**	7d. sepia	15	30
234		10d. slate-blue	15	70

82 1c. Fenian Stamp Essay   **83** 24c. Fenian Stamp Essay

1967 (23 Oct). Centenary of Fenian Rising. W **22** (sideways). P 15.
235	**82**	5d. black and light green	10	10
236	**83**	1s. black and light pink	20	30

84 Jonathan Swift   **85** Gulliver and Lilliputians

(Des M. Byrne)

1967 (30 Nov). 300th Birth Anniv of Jonathan Swift. W **22** (sideways). P 15.
237	**84**	3d. black and olive-grey	10	10
238	**85**	1s.5d. blackish brown and pale blue	20	45

86 Europa "Key"

(Des H. Schwarzenbach and M. Biggs)

1968 (29 Apr). Europa. W **22**. P 15.
239	**86**	7d. brown-red, gold and brown	50	50
240		1s.5d. new blue, gold and brown	75	1·00

87 St. Mary's Cathedral, Limerick

(Des from photo by J. J. Bambury. Recess B.W.)

1968 (26 Aug). 800th Anniv of St. Mary's Cathedral, Limerick. W **22**. P 15.

| 241 | **87** | 5d. Prussian blue | 10 | 10 |
| 242 | | 10d. yellow-green | 20 | 90 |

88 Countess Markievicz   89 James Connolly

1968 (23 Sept). Birth Centenary of Countess Markievicz (patriot). W **22** (inverted on 1s.5d.). P 15.

| 243 | **88** | 3d. black | 10 | 10 |
| 244 | | 1s.5d. deep blue and blue | 70 | 1·75 |

1968 (23 Sept). Birth Centenary of James Connolly (patriot). W **22** (sideways). P 15.

| 245 | **89** | 6d. deep brown and chocolate | 20 | 80 |
| 246 | | 1s. blackish green, apple-green and myrtle-green | 20 | 20 |

90 Stylised Dog   91 Stag
(brooch)

92 Winged Ox (Symbol of St. Luke)

93 Eagle (Symbol of St. John The Evangelist)

(Des H. Gerl)

1968–70. Pence values expressed with "p". W **22** (sideways* on ½d. to 1s.9d.). P 15.

247	**90**	½d. red-orange (7.6.69)	10	30
248		1d. pale yellow-green (7.6.69)	15	30
		a. Coil stamp. Perf 14×15 (8.70?)	1·50	3·00
249		2d. light ochre (14.10.68)	50	10
		a. Coil stamp. Perf 14×15 (8.70?)	1·50	7·50
250		3d. blue (7.6.69)	35	10
		a. Coil stamp. Perf 14×15 (8.70?)	1·50	3·75
251		4d. deep brown-red (31.3.69)	30	10
252		5d. myrtle-green (31.3.69)	1·25	1·75
253		6d. bistre-brown (24.2.69)	30	10
		w. Wmk e facing right	5·50	3·25
254	**91**	7d. brown and yellow (7.6.69)	45	4·50
255		8d. chocolate and orange-brown (14.10.68)	45	3·50
256		9d. slate-blue and olive-green (24.2.69)	50	10
257		10d. chocolate and bluish violet (31.3.69)	1·50	3·50
258		1s. chocolate and red-brown (31.3.69)	40	10
259		1s.9d. black and light turquoise-blue (24.2.69)	4·00	3·50
260	**92**	2s.6d. multicoloured (14.10.68)	1·75	30
261		5s. multicoloured (24.2.69)	3·00	2·50
262	**93**	10s. multicoloured (14.10.68)	5·25	7·25
247/62 *Set of 16*			17·00	21·00

*The normal sideways watermark shows the top of the e facing left, *as seen from the back of the stamp.*

The 1d., 2d., 3d., 5d., 6d., 9d., 1s. and 2s.6d. exist with PVA gum as well as gum arabic. The coil stamps exist on PVA only, and the rest on gum arabic only.

Stamps in similar designs were issued from 1974 to 1983.

94 Human Rights   95 Dáil Éireann Assembly
Emblem

1968 (4 Nov). Human Rights Year. W **22** (sideways). P 15.

| 263 | **94** | 5d. yellow, gold and black | 15 | 10 |
| 264 | | 7d. yellow, gold and red | 15 | 40 |

(Des M. Byrne)

1969 (21 Jan). 50th Anniv of Dáil Éireann (First National Parliament). W **22** (sideways). P 15×14½.

| 265 | **95** | 6d. myrtle-green | 15 | 10 |
| 266 | | 9d. Prussian blue | 15 | 30 |

96 Colonnade   97 Quadruple ILO Emblems

(Des L. Gasbarra and G. Belli; adapted Myra Maguire)

1969 (28 Apr). Europa. W **22**. P 15.

| 267 | **96** | 9d. grey, ochre and ultramarine | 1·00 | 1·10 |
| 268 | | 1s.9d. grey, gold and scarlet | 1·25 | 2·25 |

(Des K. C. Dabczewski)

1969 (14 July). 50th Anniv of International Labour Organization. W **22** (sideways). P 15.

| 269 | **97** | 6d. black and grey | 20 | 10 |
| 270 | | 9d. black and yellow | 20 | 25 |

98 *The Last Supper and Crucifixion* (Evie Hone Window, Eton Chapel)

(Des R. Kyne)

1969 (1 Sept). Contemporary Irish Art (1st issue). W **22** (sideways). P 15×14½.

| 271 | **98** | 1s. multicoloured | 30 | 1·50 |

See also No. 280.

99 Mahatma Gandhi

1969 (2 Oct). Birth Centenary of Mahatma Gandhi. W **22**. P 15.

| 272 | **99** | 6d. black and green | 60 | 10 |
| 273 | | 1s.9d. black and yellow | 90 | 90 |

100 Symbolic Bird in Tree

(Des D. Harrington)

1970 (23 Feb). European Conservation Year. W **22**. P 15.

| 274 | **100** | 6d. bistre and black | 20 | 10 |
| 275 | | 9d. slate-violet and black | 25 | 80 |

101 "Flaming Sun"

(Des L. le Brocquy)

1970 (4 May). Europa. W **22**. P 15.

276	**101**	6d. bright violet and silver	55	10
277		9d. brown and silver	90	1·25
278		1s.9d. deep olive-grey and silver	1·75	2·00
276/8 *Set of 3*			2·75	3·00

102 *Sailing Boats*   103 *Madonna of*
(Peter Monamy)   *Eire* (Mainie Jellett)

(Des P. Wildbur and P. Scott)

1970 (13 July). 250th Anniv of Royal Cork Yacht Club. W **22**. P 15.

| 279 | **102** | 4d. multicoloured | 15 | 10 |

1970 (1 Sept). Contemporary Irish Art (2nd issue) (sideways). W **22**. P 15.

| 280 | **103** | 1s. multicoloured | 15 | 20 |

104 Thomas   106 Kevin Barry
MacCurtain

(Des P. Wildbur)

1970 (26 Oct). 50th Death Anniversaries of Irish Patriots. T **104** and similar vert design. W **22** (sideways). P 15.

281		9d. black, bluish violet and greyish black	1·25	25
		a. Pair. Nos. 281/2	2·50	2·75
282		9d. black, bluish violet and greyish black	1·25	25
283		2s.9d. black, new blue and greyish black	2·00	3·75
		a. Pair. Nos. 283/4	4·00	11·00
284		2s.9d. black, new blue and greyish black	2·00	3·75
281/4 *Set of 4*			6·00	7·25

Designs:—Nos. 281 and 283, Type **104**; others, Terence MacSwiney. Nos. 281/2 and 283/4 were each printed together, *se-tenant*, in horizontal and vertical pairs throughout the sheet.

(Des P. Wildbur)

1970 (2 Nov). 50th Death Anniv of Kevin Barry (patriot). W **22** (inverted). P 15.

| 285 | **106** | 6d. olive-green | 30 | 10 |
| 286 | | 1s.2d. royal blue | 40 | 1·10 |

STAMP BOOKLETS

B **1** Harp and Monogram

B **2** Harp and "EIRE"

1931 (21 Aug)–**40**. Black on red cover as Type B **1**.

| SB1 | 2s. booklet containing 6×½d., 6×2d. (Nos. 71, 74), in block of 6, and 9×1d. (No. 72) in block of 6 and pane of 3 stamps and 3 labels (No. 72d or 72dw) | *From* | £4000 |

Edition Nos.:—31–1, 31–2, 32–3, 33–4, 33–5, 34–6, 34–7, 35–8, 35–9, 36–10, 36–11, 37–12, 37–13, 37–14, 15–38, 16–38, 17–38

| | Cover as Type B **2** | *From* | £4750 |

Edition Nos.:–18–39, 19–39, 20–39, 21–40, 22–40

1940. Black on red cover as Type B **2**.

| SB2 | 2s. booklet containing 6×½d., 6×2d. (Nos. 71, 74), each in block of 6, and 9×1d. in block of 6 (No. 72) and pane of 3 stamps and 3 labels (No. 112d or 112dw) | | £12000 |

Edition No.:—22–40

1940. Black on red cover as Type B **2**.

| SB3 | 2s. booklet containing 6×½d., 6×2d. (Nos. 111, 114), each in block of 6, and 9×1d. in block of 6 (No. 112) and pane of 3 stamps and 3 labels (No. 112d or 112dw) | | £12000 |

Edition No.:—23–40

1941–44. Black on red cover as Type B **2**.

| SB4 | 2s. booklet containing 12×½d., 6×1d. and 6×2d. (Nos. 111/12, 114) in blocks of 6 | *From* | £2500 |

Edition Nos.:—24–41, 25–42, 26–44

B 3

1945. Black on red cover as Type B **3.**
SB5   2s. booklet containing 12×½d., 6×1d. and
       6×2d. (Nos. 111/12, 114) in blocks of 6 .... £2500
       Edition No.:—27–45

1946. Black on buff cover as Type B **2.**
SB6   2s. booklet containing 12×½d., 6×1d. and
       6×2d. (Nos. 111/12, 114) in blocks of 6 .... £1400
       Edition No.:—28–46

1946–47. Black on buff cover as Type B **2.**
SB7   2s. booklet containing 12×½d, 6×1d. and 6×2d.
       (Nos. 133, 112, 114) in
       blocks of 6.. From   £750
       Edition Nos.:—29–46, 30–47

B 4 Harp only

1948–50. Black on orange-buff cover as Type B **4.**
SB8   2s.6d. booklet containing 6×½d., 12×1d. and
       6×2½d. (Nos. 133, 112, 115) in
       blocks of 6.. From   £325
       Edition Nos.:—31–48, 32–49, 33–50

1951–53. Black on buff cover as Type B **4.**
SB9   2s.6d. booklet containing 6×½d., 12×1d. and
       6×2½d. (Nos. 133, 112, 115) in
       blocks of 6..   70·00
       Edition Nos.:—34–51, 35–52, 36–53

1954 (24 Nov). Black on buff cover as Type B **4.**
SB10   4s. booklet containing 6×½d. and
       12×3d. (Nos. 133, 113, 116) in blocks of 6.........   £120
       Edition No.:—37–54.

1956 (17 Dec). Black on buff cover as Type B **4.**
SB11   4s. booklet containing 12×1d. and 12×3d.
       (Nos. 112, 116) in blocks of 6......................   £130
       Edition No.:—38–56.

B 5

1958–61. Black on buff cover as Type B **5.**
SB12   4s. booklet containing 12×1d. and 12×3d.
       (Nos. 112, 116) in blocks of 6......................   £130
       Edition Nos.:—39–58, 40–59, 41–60, 42–61.

1962 (23 Oct)–**63.** Black on buff cover as Type B **5.**
SB13   3s. booklet containing 6×2d. and 6×4d.
       (Nos. 114, 117) in blocks of 6.......... From   £110
       Edition Nos.:—43–62, 44–63 (6.63).

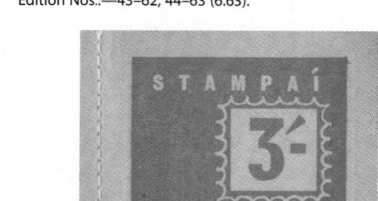

B 6

1964 (Sept). Red on yellow cover as Type B **6.**
SB14   3s. booklet containing 12×1d. and 6×4d.
       (Nos. 112, 117) in blocks of 6......................   60·00

B 7

1966 (1–9 Dec). Covers as Type B **7** in red (No. SB15), blue (No. SB16) or green (No. SB17).
SB15   2s.6d. booklet containing 6×2d. and 6×3d.
       (Nos. 114, 116) in blocks of 6 (9.12) ....   19·00
SB16   2s.6d. booklet containing 6×5d. (No. 228) in
       block of 6 (9.12)....................................   15·00
SB17   5s. booklet containing 12×5d. (No. 228) in
       blocks of 6..   30·00

B 8

1969 (12 Sept). Plain blue-green cover as Type B **8.**
SB18   6s. booklet containing 12×6d. (No. 253) in
       blocks of six..   50·00

POSTAGE DUE STAMPS

From 1922 to 1925 Great Britain postage due stamps in both script and block watermarks were used without overprint.

D 1

(Des Ruby McConnell. Typo Govt Printing Works, Dublin)
1925 (20 Feb). W **10.** P 14×15.
D1	D **1**	½d. emerald-green..........................	12·00	16·00
D2		1d. carmine................................	15·00	3·50
		a. Wmk sideways........................	£1200	£600
		y. Wmk inverted and reversed.......	£170	£170
D3		2d. deep green...........................	50·00	5·50
		a. Wmk sideways........................	55·00	17·00
		aw. Wmk sideways inverted.............	85·00	45·00
		w. Wmk inverted.........................	90·00	35·00
D4		6d. plum....................................	7·00	7·50
D1/4	Set of 4		75·00	29·00

The normal sideways watermark shows the top of "e" to the left, *as seen from the back of the stamp.*

1940–70. W **22.** P 14×15.
D5	D **1**	½d. emerald-green (1942)	35·00	25·00
		w. Wmk inverted.........................	—	£500
D6		1d. carmine (1941)	1·50	70
		w. Wmk inverted.........................	—	£475
D7		1½d. vermilion (1953)...................	4·00	12·00
		w. Wmk inverted.........................	19·00	45·00
D8		2d. deep green (1940)	2·75	70
		w. Wmk inverted.........................	£500	£100
D9		3d. blue (10.11.52)......................	5·00	5·00
		w. Wmk inverted.........................	12·00	6·50
D10		5d. blue-violet (3.3.43)	6·00	2·25
		w. Wmk inverted.........................	6·50	7·00
D11		6d. plum (21.3.60).......................	6·00	4·75
		a. Wmk sideways (1968)..............	15·00	15·00
		aw. Wmk sideways inverted.............	1·00	2·75
D12		8d. orange (30.10.62)	9·00	19·00
		w. Wmk inverted.........................	17·00	38·00
D13		10d. bright purple (27.1.65)	8·50	8·50
D14		1s. apple-green (10.2.69)	8·50	11·00
		a. Wmk sideways (1970).............	75·00	11·00
D5/14	Set of 10		70·00	75·00

The normal sideways watermark shows the top of "e" to the left, as seen from the back of the stamp.

Stamps in these designs but in different colours were issued between 1971 and 1978.

Jamaica

Records show that the first local Postmaster for Jamaica on a regular basis was appointed as early as 1671, although a reasonably organised service did not evolve until 1687–8. In the early years of the 18th-century overseas mail was carried by the British packets, but between 1704 and 1711 this service was run on a commercial basis by Edmund Dummer. Following the collapse of the Dummer scheme Jamaica was virtually without a Post Office until 1720 and it was not until 1755 that overseas mail was again carried by British packets.

Stamps of Great Britain were used in Jamaica from 8 May 1858, initially on overseas mail only, but their use was extended to mail sent to Jamaican addresses from 1 February 1859. The island assumed responsibility for the postal service on 1 August 1860 and the use of Great Britain stamps then ceased.

KINGSTON

Z 1

Stamps of GREAT BRITAIN cancelled "A 01" as Type Z **1.**
1858–60.
Z1	1d. rose-red (1857), *perf* 16..................	£850
Z2	1d. rose-red (1857), *perf* 14..................	£120
Z4	4d. rose-carmine *or* rose (1857)...........	80·00
Z5	6d. lilac (1856)...................................	85·00
Z6	1s. green (1856).................................	£425

Z 2

Stamps of GREAT BRITAIN cancelled "A 01" as Type Z **2.**
1859–60.
Z7	1d. rose-red (1857), *perf* 14..................	£400
Z9	4d. rose-carmine *or* rose (1857)...........	85·00
Z10	6d. lilac (1856)...................................	90·00
Z11	1s. green (1856).................................	£850

Z 3

Stamps of GREAT BRITAIN cancelled "A 01" as Type Z **3.**
1859–60.
Z12	1d. rose-red (1857), *perf* 14..................	£600
Z14	4d. rose-carmine *or* rose (1857)...........	£375
	a. Thick *glazed* paper......................	£700
Z15	6d. lilac (1856)...................................	£375
Z16	1s. green (1856).................................	£375

Cancellation "A 01" was later used by the London, Foreign Branch Office.

OTHER JAMAICA POST OFFICES

British stamps were issued to several District post offices between 8 May 1858 and 1 March 1859 (i.e. before the Obliterators A 27—A 78 were issued). These can only be distinguished (off the cover) when they have the Town's date-stamp on them. They are worth about three times the price of those with an obliteration number.

Stamps of GREAT BRITAIN cancelled "A 27" to "A 78"as Type Z **1.**
1859–60.

"A 27". ALEXANDRIA
Z17	1d. rose-red (1857), *perf* 14..................	£1100
Z17a	2d. blue (1855) Large Crown, *perf* 14 (Plate 6)	£2000
Z18	4d. rose (1857)...................................	£425
Z19	6d. lilac (1856)...................................	£800

"A 28". ANNOTTO BAY
Z20	1d. rose-red (1857), *perf* 14..................	£550
Z21	4d. rose (1857)...................................	£250
Z22	6d. lilac (1856)...................................	£475

"A 29". BATH
Z23	1d. rose-red (1857), *perf* 14..................	£400
Z24	4d. rose (1857)...................................	£250
Z25	6d. lilac (1856)...................................	£700

"A 30". BLACK RIVER
Z26	1d. rose-red (1857), *perf* 14..................	£400
Z27	4d. rose (1857)...................................	£180
Z28	6d. lilac (1856)...................................	£350

"A31". BROWN'S TOWN
Z29	1d. rose-red (1857), *perf* 14..................	£500
Z30	4d. rose (1857)...................................	£425
Z31	6d. lilac (1856)...................................	£425

"A 32". BUFF BAY
Z32	1d. rose-red (1857), *perf* 14..................	£450
Z33	4d. rose (1857)...................................	£350
Z34	6d. lilac (1856)...................................	£325

"A 33". CHAPELTON

Z35	1d. rose-red (1857), *perf* 14	£450
Z36	4d. rose (1857)	£300
Z37	6d. lilac (1856)	£400

"A34". CLAREMONT

Z38	1d. rose-red (1857), *perf* 14	£750
Z39	4d. rose (1857)	£375
Z40	6d. lilac (1856)	£425

"A35". CLARENDON

Z41	1d. rose-red (1857), *perf* 14	£500
Z42	4d. rose (1857)	£275
Z43	6d. lilac (1856)	£425

"A 36". DRY HARBOUR

Z44	1d. rose-red (1857), *perf* 14	£800
Z45	4d. rose (1857)	£550
Z46	6d. lilac (1856)	£475

"A 37". DUNCANS

Z47	1d. rose-red (1857), *perf* 14	£900
Z48	4d. rose (1857)	£700
Z49	6d. lilac (1856)	£550

"A 38". EWARTON

A 38 was allocated to EWARTON but this office was closed towards the end of 1858 before the postmark arrived. A 38 was re-issued to Falmouth in 1862.

"A 39". FALMOUTH

Z53	1d. rose-red (1857), *perf* 14	£300
Z54	4d. rose (1857)	£160
Z55	6d. lilac (1856)	£170
Z56	1s. green (1856)	£1600

"A40". FLINT RIVER

Z57	1d. rose-red (1857), *perf* 14	£450
Z58	4d. rose (1857)	£325
Z59	6d. lilac (1856)	£375
Z60	1s. green (1856)	£1600

"A 41". GAYLE

Z61	1d. rose-red (1857), *perf* 14	£750
Z62	4d. rose (1857)	£250
Z63	6d. lilac (1856)	£350
Z64	1s. green (1856)	£1000

"A 42". GOLDEN SPRING

Z65	1d. rose-red (1857), *perf* 14	£550
Z66	4d. rose (1857)	£450
Z67	6d. lilac (1856)	£750
Z68	1s. green (1856)	£1400

"A 43". GORDON TOWN

Z69	1d. rose-red (1857), *perf* 14	
Z70	4d. rose (1857)	
Z71	6d. lilac (1856)	£900

"A 44". GOSHEN

Z72	1d. rose-red (1857), *perf* 14	£350
Z73	4d. rose (1857)	£300
Z74	6d. lilac (1856)	£170

"A 45". GRANGE HILL

Z75	1d. rose-red (1857), *perf* 14	£375
Z76	4d. rose (1857)	£150
Z77	6d. lilac (1856)	£180
Z77a	1s. green (1856)	£1500

"A 46". GREEN ISLAND

Z78	1d. rose-red (1857), *perf* 14	£500
Z79	4d. rose (1857)	£350
Z80	6d. lilac (1856)	£475
Z81	1s. green (1856)	£1500

"A 47". HIGHGATE

Z82	1d. rose-red (1857), *perf* 14	£400
Z83	4d. rose (1857)	£275
Z84	6d. lilac (1856)	£475

"A 48". HOPE BAY

Z85	1d. rose-red (1857), *perf* 14	£750
Z86	4d. rose (1857)	£375
Z87	6d. lilac (1856)	£800

"A 49". LILLIPUT

Z88	1d. rose-red (1857), *perf* 14	£350
Z89	4d. rose (1857)	£375
Z90	6d. lilac (1856)	£225

"A 50". LITTLE RIVER

A 50 was allocated for use at LITTLE RIVER but this office was closed late in 1858, before the obliterator could be issued. Issued to Malvern in 1862.

"A 51". LUCEA

Z91	1d. rose-red (1857), *perf* 14	£500
Z92	4d. rose (1857)	£170
Z93	6d. lilac (1856)	£375

"A 52". MANCHIONEAL

Z94	1d. rose-red (1857), *perf* 14	£650
Z95	4d. rose (1857)	£375
Z96	6d. lilac (1856)	£700

"A 53". MANDEVILLE

Z97	1d. rose-red (1857), *perf* 14	£375
Z98	4d. rose (1857)	£160
Z99	6d. lilac (1856)	£350

"A 54". MAY HILL

Z100	1d. rose-red (1857), *perf* 14	£275
Z101	4d. rose (1857)	£225
Z102	6d. lilac (1856)	£160
Z102a	1s. green (1856)	£2000

"A 55". MILE GULLY

Z103	1d. rose-red (1857), *perf* 14	£475
Z104	4d. rose (1857)	£400
Z105	6d. lilac (1856)	£400

"A 56". MONEAGUE

Z106	1d. rose-red (1857), *perf* 14	£450
Z107	4d. rose (1857)	£425
Z108	6d. lilac (1856)	£800

"A 57". MONTEGO BAY

Z109	1d. rose-red (1857), *perf* 14	£375
Z110	4d. rose (1857)	£130
Z111	6d. lilac (1856)	£150
Z112	1s. green (1856)	£1400

"A 58". MONTPELIER

Z113	1d. rose-red (1857), *perf* 14	
Z114	4d. rose (1857)	
Z115	6d. lilac (1856)	£1300

"A 59". MORANT BAY

Z116	1d. rose-red (1857), *perf* 14	£600
Z117	4d. rose (1857)	£160
Z118	6d. lilac (1856)	£180

"A 60". OCHO RIOS

Z119	1d. rose-red (1857), *perf* 14	£1200
Z120	4d. rose (1857)	£200
Z121	6d. lilac (1856)	£425

"A 61". OLD HARBOUR

Z122	1d. rose-red (1857), *perf* 14	£400
Z123	4d. rose (1857)	£275
Z124	6d. lilac (1856)	£325

"A 62". PLANTAIN GARDEN RIVER

Z125	1d. rose-red (1857), *perf* 14	£325
Z126	4d. rose (1857)	£225
Z127	6d. lilac (1856)	£325

"A 63". PEAR TREE GROVE

No genuine specimen of A 63 has been found on a British stamp.

"A 64". PORT ANTONIO

Z131	1d. rose-red (1857), *perf* 14	£650
Z132	4d. rose (1857)	£425
Z133	6d. lilac (1856)	£450

"A 65". PORT MORANT

Z134	1d. rose-red (1857), *perf* 14	£450
Z135	4d. rose (1857)	£225
Z136	6d. lilac (1856)	£450

"A 66". PORT MARIA

Z137	1d. rose-red (1857), *perf* 14	£450
Z138	4d. rose (1857)	£180
Z139	6d. lilac (1856)	£450

"A 67". PORT ROYAL

Z140	1d. rose-red (1857), *perf* 14	£700
Z140a	2d. blue (1858) (plate 9)	£3000
Z141	4d. rose (1857)	£750
Z142	6d. lilac (1856)	£750

"A 68". PORUS

Z143	1d. rose-red (1857), *perf* 14	£450
Z144	4d. rose (1857)	£225
Z145	6d. lilac (1856)	£650

"A 69". RAMBLE

Z146	1d. rose-red (1857), *perf* 14	£375
Z147	4d. rose (1857)	£350
	a. Thick *glazed* paper	£650
Z149	6d. lilac (1856)	£475

"A 70". RIO BUENO

Z150	1d. rose-red (1857), *perf* 14	£450
Z151	4d. rose (1857)	£350
Z152	6d. lilac (1856)	£275

"A 71". RODNEY HALL

Z153	1d. rose-red (1857), *perf* 14	£350
Z154	4d. rose (1857)	£225
Z155	6d. lilac (1856)	£275

"A 72". ST. DAVID

Z156	1d. rose-red (1857), *perf* 14	£450
Z157	4d. rose (1857)	£600
Z158	6d. lilac (1856)	

"A 73". ST. ANN'S BAY

Z159	1d. rose-red (1857), *perf* 14	£375
Z160	4d. rose (1857)	£200
Z161	6d. lilac (1856)	£325
Z161a	1s. green (1856)	£1800

"A 74". SALT GUT

Z162	1d. rose-red (1857), *perf* 14	£450
Z163	4d. rose (1857)	£300
Z164	6d. lilac (1856)	£400

"A 75". SAVANNAH-LA-MAR

Z165	1d. rose-red (1857), *perf* 14	£225
Z166	4d. rose (1857)	£160
Z167	6d. lilac (1856)	£350
Z168	1s. green (1856)	£1400

"A 76". SPANISH TOWN

Z169	1d. rose-red (1857), *perf* 14	£250
Z170	4d. rose (1857)	£140
Z171	6d. lilac (1856)	£180
Z172	1s. green (1856)	£1100

"A 77". STEWART TOWN

Z173	1d. rose-red (1857), *perf* 14	£700
Z174	4d. rose (1857)	£500
Z175	6d. lilac (1856)	£400

"A 78". VERE

Z176	1d. rose-red (1857), *perf* 14	£550
Z177	4d. rose (1857)	£225
Z178	6d. lilac (1856)	£160
Z179	1s. green (1856)	£1600

PRICES FOR STAMPS ON COVER

Nos. 1/6	*from* × 4	
Nos. 7/15	*from* × 6	
Nos. 16/26	*from* × 8	
Nos. 27/9	*from* × 6	
No. 30	*from* × 5	
Nos. 31/2	*from* × 15	
Nos. 33/6	*from* × 5	
Nos. 37/56	*from* × 3	
No. 57	*from* × 4	
Nos. 58/67	*from* × 6	
Nos. 68/77	*from* × 6	
Nos. 78/89	*from* × 3	
Nos. 90/103	*from* × 4	
Nos. 104/7	*from* × 5	
Nos. 108/17	*from* × 3	
Nos. 118/20	*from* × 5	
Nos. 121/33a	*from* × 4	
Nos. 134/40	*from* × 8	
Nos. F1/9	*from* × 3	
Nos. O1/5	*from* × 3	

CROWN COLONY

PRINTERS. Until 1923, all the stamps of Jamaica were typographed by De La Rue & Co, Ltd, London, *unless otherwise stated.*

The official dates of issue are given, where known, but where definite information is not available the dates are those of earliest known use, etc.

1   2   3

4   5   6

7   A

1860 (23 Nov)–**70**. W **7**. P 14.

1	**1**	1d. pale blue		75·00	15·00
		a. Pale greenish blue		£110	21·00
		b. Blue		70·00	12·00
		c. Deep blue (1865)		£140	35·00
		d. Bisected (½d.) (20.11.61) (*on cover*)		†	£650
		w. Wmk inverted		£180	55·00
2	**2**	2d. rose		£225	55·00
		a. Deep rose		£170	55·00
		w. Wmk inverted		—	£100
3	**3**	3d. green (10.9.63)		£160	25·00
		w. Wmk inverted		£200	50·00
4	**4**	4d. brown-orange		£275	50·00
		a. Red-orange		£225	22·00
		w. Wmk inverted			
5	**5**	6d. dull lilac		£200	22·00
		a. Grey-purple		£275	35·00
		b. Deep purple (1870)		£850	55·00
		w. Wmk inverted		—	£110
6	**6**	1s. yellow-brown		£500	25·00
		a. Purple-brown (1862)		£550	23·00
		b. Dull brown (1868)		£200	27·00
		c. "$" for "S" in "SHILLING" (A)		£3000	£600
		w. Wmk inverted		—	85·00

The diagonal bisection of the 1d. was authorised by a PO notice dated 20 November 1861 to pay the ½d. rate for newspapers or book post. Examples are only of value when on original envelope or wrapper. The authority was withdrawn as from 1 December 1872. Fakes are frequently met with. Other bisections were unauthorised.

The so-called "dollar variety" of the 1s. occurs once in each sheet of stamps in all shades and in later colours, etc, on the second stamp in the second row of the left upper pane. The prices quoted above are for the dull brown shade, the prices for the other shades being proportionate to their normal value.

All values except the 3d. are known imperf, mint only.

There are two types of watermark in the 3d. and 1s., one being short and squat and the other elongated.

8   9   10

1870–83. Wmk Crown CC.

(a) P 14

7	**8**	½d. claret (29.10.72)		22·00	3·50
		a. Deep claret (1883)		28·00	5·50
		w. Wmk inverted		—	70·00
8	**1**	1d. blue (4.73)		£100	75
		a. Deep blue		£110	1·50
		w. Wmk inverted		£225	40·00

9	2	2d. rose (4.70)	£100	70
		a. Deep rose	£110	1·00
		w. Wmk inverted	£180	40·00
10	3	3d. green (1.3.70)	£150	10·00
		w. Wmk inverted	—	£120
11	4	4d. brown-orange (1872)	£325	12·00
		a. Red-orange (1883)	£425	6·00
		w. Wmk inverted	—	£100
12	5	6d. mauve (10.3.71)	95·00	5·50
		w. Wmk inverted	—	75·00
13	6	1s. dull brown (to deep) (23.2.73)	25·00	8·50
		a. "$" for "S" in "SHILLING" (A)	£1400	£600
		w. Wmk inverted	—	£110

(b) P 12½

14	9	2s. Venetian red (27.8.75)	45·00	35·00
		w. Wmk inverted	70·00	80·00
15	10	5s. lilac (27.8.75)	£120	£170
		w. Wmk inverted	£150	£225
7/15 Set of 9			£900	£200

The ½d., 1d., 4d., 2s. and 5s. are known imperforate.

1883–97. Wmk Crown CA. P 14.

16	8	½d. yellow-green (2.85)	11·00	1·50
		a. Green	3·50	10
		w. Wmk inverted	—	50·00
		x. Wmk reversed	—	£120
17	1	1d. blue (1884)	£325	8·00
		w. Wmk inverted	†	—
18		1d. rose (to deep) (3.3.85)	80·00	2·25
		a. Carmine (1886)	65·00	1·00
		w. Wmk inverted	—	65·00
19	2	2d. rose (to deep) (17.3.84)	£225	5·50
		w. Wmk inverted	—	85·00
20		2d. grey (1885)	£150	8·50
		a. Slate (1886)	£110	65
		w. Wmk inverted	—	42·00
21	3	3d. sage-green (11.86)	4·00	2·00
		a. Pale olive-green	2·75	2·75
22	4	4d. red-orange* (9.3.83)	£450	22·00
		aw. Wmk inverted		
		b. Red-brown (shades) (1885)	2·00	35
		bw. Wmk inverted	£100	42·00
23	5	6d. deep yellow (4.10.90)	38·00	8·00
		a. Orange-yellow	5·00	3·50
24	6	1s. brown (to deep) (3.97)	10·00	6·00
		a. "$" for "S" in "SHILLING" (A)	£800	£500
		b. Chocolate	17·00	12·00
25	9	2s. Venetian red (2.97)	32·00	35·00
26	10	5s. lilac (2.97)	65·00	95·00
16/26 Set of 11			£750	£130
16s, 18s, 20s/3s Optd "SPECIMEN" Set of 6			£800	

*No. 22 is the same colour as No. 11a.
The 1d. carmine, 2d. slate, and 2s. are known imperf. All values to the 6d. inclusive are known perf 12. These are proofs.

TWO PENCE HALF-PENNY

11   (12)

1889 (8 Mar)–91. Value tablet in second colour. Wmk Crown CA. P 14.

27	11	1d. purple and mauve	13·00	20
		w. Wmk inverted	—	50·00
28		2d. green	40·00	7·00
		a. Deep green (brown gum)	24·00	8·50
		aw. Wmk inverted	80·00	
29		2½d. dull purple and blue (25.2.91)	9·50	50
		w. Wmk inverted	£140	
27/9 Set of 3			42·00	7·00
27s/9s Optd "SPECIMEN" Set of 3			£150	

A very wide range of shades may be found in the 1d. The headplate was printed in many shades of purple, and the duty plate in various shades of mauve and purple and also in carmine, etc. There are fewer shades for the other values and they are not so pronounced.
1d. stamps with the duty plate in blue are colour changelings.

1890 (4 June)–91. No. 22b surch with T 12 by C. Vendryes, Kingston.

30	4	2½d. on 4d. red-brown	40·00	17·00
		a. Spacing between lines of surch 1½ mm (2.91)	50·00	21·00
		b. Surch double	£325	£225
		c. "PFNNY" for "PENNY"	90·00	65·00
		ca. Ditto and broken "K" for "Y"	£160	£110
		w. Wmk inverted	£150	48·00

This provisional was issued pending receipt of No. 29 which is listed above for convenience of reference.
Three settings exist. (1) Ten varieties arranged in a single vertical row and repeated six times in the pane. (2) 12 varieties, in two horizontal rows of six, repeated five times, alternate rows show 1 and 1½ mm spacing between lines of surcharge. (3) Three varieties, arranged horizontally and repeated 20 times. All these settings can be reconstructed by examination of the spacing and relative position of the words of the surcharge and of the broken letters, etc, which are numerous.
A variety reading "PFNNK", with the "K" unbroken, is a forgery.
Surcharges misplaced either horizontally or vertically are met with, the normal position being central at the foot of the stamp with "HALF-PENNY" covering the old value.

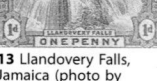

13 Llandovery Falls, Jamaica (photo by Dr. J. Johnston)
14 Arms of Jamaica

(Recess D.L.R.)

1900 (1 May)–01. Wmk Crown CC (sideways*). P 14.

31	13	1d. red	14·00	20
		w. Wmk Crown to left of CC	14·00	50
		x. Wmk reversed	—	85·00
		y. Wmk sideways inverted and reversed		
32		1d. slate-black and red (25.9.01)	13·00	20
		a. Blued paper	£110	£100
		b. Imperf between (vert pair)	£23000	
		w. Wmk Crown to left of CC	28·00	11·00
		x. Wmk reversed	—	85·00
		y. Wmk sideways inverted and reversed		
31s/2s Optd "SPECIMEN" Set of 2			£140	

*The normal sideways wmk shows Crown to right of CC, as seen from the back of the stamp.
Many shades exist of both centre and frame of the bi-coloured 1d. which was, of course, printed from two plates and the design shows minor differences from that of the 1d. red which was printed from a single plate.

1903 (16 Nov)–04. Wmk Crown CA. P 14.

33	14	½d. grey and dull green	2·50	30
		a. "SER.ET" for "SERVIET"	40·00	45·00
		w. Wmk inverted	35·00	38·00
34		1d. grey and carmine (24.2.04)	4·75	10
		a. "SER.ET" for "SERVIET"	32·00	35·00
35		2½d. grey and ultramarine	9·00	30
		a. "SER.ET" for "SERVIET"	65·00	75·00
36		5d. grey and yellow (1.3.04)	17·00	23·00
		a. "SER.ET" for "SERVIET"	£800	£1000
		w. Wmk inverted	£150	
33/6 Set of 4			30·00	23·00
33s/6s Optd "SPECIMEN" Set of 4			£100	

The "SER.ET" variety occurs on R. 4/2 of the left upper pane. It was corrected by De La Rue in July 1905, following the printing of Nos. 37 and 43.
The centres of the above and later bi-coloured stamps in the Arms type vary in colour from grey to grey-black.

15 Arms type redrawn   **16** Arms type redrawn

1905–11. Wmk Mult Crown CA. P 14.

(a) Arms types. Chalk-surfaced paper

37	14	½d. grey and dull green (20.11.05)	2·50	20
		a. "SER.ET" for "SERVIET"	26·00	40·00
		w. Wmk inverted		
		y. Wmk inverted and reversed	†	£200
38	15	½d. yellow-green (ordinary paper) (8.11.06)	12·00	50
		aw. Wmk inverted	†	£170
		b. Dull green	3·00	50
		c. Deep green	4·75	20
39	14	1d. grey and carmine (20.11.05)	18·00	1·75
		w. Wmk inverted	—	£150
40	16	1d. carmine (ordinary paper) (1.10.06)	1·50	10
		w. Wmk inverted	65·00	
41	14	2½d. grey and ultramarine (12.11.07)	7·00	9·00
42		2½d. pale ultramarine (ordinary paper) (21.9.10)	5·00	1·25
		a. Deep ultramarine	2·50	1·75
43		5d. grey and orange-yellow (24.4.07)	65·00	80·00
		a. "SER.ET" for "SERVIET"	£1400	£1600
44		6d. dull and bright purple (18.8.11)	14·00	22·00
45		5s. grey and violet (11.05)	55·00	55·00
37/45 Set of 9			£150	£150
38s, 40s, 42s, 44s/5s Optd "SPECIMEN" Set of 5			£200	

See note below No. 36 concerning grey centres.

(b) Queen Victoria types. Ordinary paper

46	3	3d. olive-green (3.8.05)	12·00	4·50
		a. Sage-green (1907)	7·50	3·00
47		3d. purple/yellow (10.3.10)	11·00	3·50
		a. Chalk-surfaced paper. Pale purple/yellow (11.7.10)	2·00	1·50
		aw. Wmk inverted	55·00	65·00
48	4	4d. red-brown (6.6.08)	75·00	80·00
49		4d. black/yellow (chalk-surfaced paper) (21.9.10)	17·00	55·00
50		4d. red/yellow (3.10.11)	1·50	3·25
51	5	6d. dull orange (27.6.06)	16·00	25·00
		a. Golden yellow (9.09)	42·00	65·00
52		6d. lilac (19.11.09)	32·00	60·00
		a. Chalk-surfaced paper. Purple (7.10)	10·00	35·00
53	6	1s. brown (11.06)	26·00	50·00
		a. Deep brown	40·00	65·00
		b. "S" for "S" in "SHILLING" (A)	£1400	£1500
54		1s. black/green (chalk-surfaced paper) (21.9.10)	13·00	8·50
		a. "S" for "S" in "SHILLING" (A)	£950	£1200
55	9	2s. Venetian red (11.08)	£120	£170
56		2s. purple/blue (chalk-surfaced paper) (21.9.10)	15·00	8·00
46/56 Set of 11			£250	£375
47s, 49s, 50s, 52s, 54s, 56s Optd "SPECIMEN" Set of 6			£325	

No. 38 exists in coils constructed from normal sheets.

17   18

(T 17/18 typo D.L.R.)

1911 (3 Feb). Wmk Mult Crown CA. P 14.

57	17	2d. grey	9·50	13·00
		s. Optd "SPECIMEN"	70·00	

1912–20. Wmk Mult Crown CA. Chalk-surfaced paper (3d. to 5s.). P 14.

58	18	1d. carmine-red (5.12.12)	1·50	10
		a. Scarlet (1916)	9·50	70
59		1½d. brown-orange (13.7.16)	2·00	60
		a. Yellow-orange	18·00	1·00
		b. Wmk sideways	†	£1700
		w. Wmk inverted	†	£200
60		2d. grey (2.8.12)	2·25	1·75
		a. Slate-grey	4·25	3·00
61		2½d. blue (13.2.13)	1·75	15
		a. Deep bright blue	80	1·00
62		3d. purple/yellow (6.3.12)	50	45
		a. White back (2.4.13)	55	40
		b. On lemon (25.9.16)	3·75	1·50
		bs. Optd "SPECIMEN"	32·00	
		w. Wmk inverted		
63		4d. black and red/yellow (4.4.13)	50	2·25
		a. White back (7.5.14)	75	2·75
		b. On lemon (1916)	23·00	19·00
		bs. Optd "SPECIMEN"	32·00	
		c. On pale yellow (1919)	22·00	15·00
64		6d. dull and bright purple (14.11.12)	4·50	10·00
		a. Dull purple and bright mauve (1915)	1·00	1·00
		b. Dull purple and bright magenta (1920)	7·00	2·25
65		1s. black/green (2.8.12)	2·25	1·50
		a. White back (4.1.15)	6·00	4·75
		b. On blue-green, olive back (1920)	4·50	12·00
66		2s. purple and bright blue/blue (10.1.19)	26·00	42·00
67		5s. green and red/yellow (5.9.19)	80·00	£100
		a. On pale yellow (1920)	£120	£130
		b. On orange-buff (1920)	£190	£225
58/67 Set of 10			£100	£130
58s/67s Optd "SPECIMEN" Set of 10			£225	

No. 58 exists in coils constructed from normal sheets.
The paper of No. 67 is a bright yellow and the gum rough and dull. No. 67a is on practically the normal creamy "pale yellow" paper, and the gum is smooth and shiny. The paper of No. 67b approaches the "coffee" colour of the true "orange-buff", and the colours of both head and frame are paler, the latter being of a carmine tone.
For the ½d. and 6d. with Script wmk see Nos. 92/3.

RED CROSS LABELS. A voluntary organization, the Jamaica War Stamp League later the Jamaica Patriotic Stamp League, was founded in November 1915 by Mr. Lewis Ashenheim, a Kingston solicitor. The aims of the League were to support the British Red Cross, collect funds for the purchase of aircraft for the Royal Flying Corps and the relief of Polish Jews.
One fund-raising method used was the sale, from 1 December 1915, of ½d. charity labels. These labels, which were available from post offices, depicted a bi-plane above a cross and were printed in red by Dennison Manufacturing Company, Framingham, USA, the stamps being perforated 12 except for those along the edges of the sheet which have one side imperforate.
From 22 December 1915 supplies of the labels were overprinted "JAMAICA" in red, the colour of this overprint being changed to black from 15 January 1916. Copies sold from 11 March 1916 carried an additional "Half-Penny" surcharge, also in black.
Such labels had no postal validity when used by the general public, but, by special order of the Governor, were accepted for the payment of postage on the League's official mail. To obtain this concession the envelopes were to be inscribed "Red Cross Business" or "Jamaica Patriotic Stamp League" and the labels used endorsed with Mr. Ashenheim's signature. Such covers are rare.

WAR STAMP.	WAR STAMP.	WAR STAMP.
(19)	(20)	(21)

(T 19/21 optd Govt Printing Office, Kingston)

1916 (1 Apr–Sept). Optd with T 19.

68	15	½d. yellow-green	30	35
		a. No stop after "STAMP" (R. 18/2)	17·00	27·00
		b. Opt double	£140	£160
		c. Opt inverted	£130	£150
		d. Space between "W" and "A" (R. 20/1)	20·00	35·00
		e. Blue-green	30	60
		ea. No stop after "STAMP" (R. 3/11 or 11/1)	17·00	32·00
		eb. Space between "W" and "A" (R. 20/1)	20·00	40·00
		w. Wmk inverted		
69	18	3d. purple/yellow (white back)	35·00	50·00
		a. On lemon (6.16)	3·00	24·00
		ab. No stop after "STAMP" (R. 8/6 or 9/6)	42·00	£100
		b. On pale yellow (9.16)	16·00	38·00

Minor varieties: ½d. (i) Small "P"; (ii) "WARISTAMP" (raised quad between words); (iii) Two stops after "STAMP". 3d. "WARISTAMP." There were several settings of the overprint used for each value. Where two positions are quoted for a variety these did not occur on the same sheet.

NOTE. The above and succeeding stamps with "WAR STAMP" overprint were issued for payment of a special war tax on letters and postcards or on parcels. Ordinary unoverprinted stamps could also be used for this purpose.

1916 (Sept–Dec). Optd with T 20.

70	15	½d. blue-green (shades) (2.10.16)	10	30
		a. No stop after "STAMP" (R. 5/7)	22·00	55·00
		b. Opt omitted (in pair with normal)	£6000	£5000
		c. "R" inserted by hand (R. 1/10)	£1800	£1500
		w. Wmk inverted	75·00	
71	18	1½d. orange (1.9.16)	10	15
		aa. Wmk sideways	†	£2000
		a. No stop after "STAMP" (R. 4/12, 8/6, 10/10, 11/1, 18/12, 19/12)	5·00	7·50
		b. "S" in "STAMP" omitted (R. 6/12) (12.16)	£200	£225
		c. "S" inserted by hand	£425	
		d. "R" in "WAR" omitted (R. 1/10)	£3500	£3000

e. "R" inserted by hand (R. 1/10) ... £1500 £1200
f. Inverted "d" for "P"........................ £200 £160
w. Wmk inverted.............................. 17·00 16·00
72 3d. purple/*lemon* (2.10.16)................ 7·00 1·00
aa. Opt inverted............................... £325
a. No stop after "STAMP" (R. 5/7)... 70·00 75·00
b. "S" in "STAMP" omitted
(R. 6/12) (12.16)...................... £900 £900
c. "S" inserted by hand.................. £200 £200
e. On yellow (12.16)....................... 16·00 10·00
ea. "S" in "STAMP" omitted
(R. 6/12)................................... £1200 £1200
eb. "S" inserted by hand.................. £425 £375

Nos. 70c, 71c, 71e, 72c and 72eb show the missing "R" or "S" inserted by handstamp. The 3d. is known with this "S" handstamp inverted or double.

Minor varieties, such as raised quads, small stop, double stop, spaced letters and letters of different sizes, also exist in this overprint. The setting was altered several times.

1917 (Mar). Optd with T **21**.
73 **15** ½d. blue-green (*shades*) (25.3.17)... 2·25 30
a. No stop after "STAMP" (R. 2/5,
8/11, 8/12)................................ 18·00 29·00
b. Stop inserted and "P"
impressed a second time
(R. 7/6)..................................... £250
c. Optd on back only...................... £250
d. Opt inverted.............................. 26·00 55·00
74 **18** 1½d. orange (3.3.17)......................... 20 10
aa. Wmk sideways............................ † £1700
a. No stop after "STAMP" (R. 2/5,
8/11, 8/12)................................ 3·00 18·00
b. Stop inserted and "P"
impressed a second time
(R. 7/6)..................................... £250
c. Opt double............................... 80·00 85·00
d. Opt inverted.............................. 80·00 75·00
e. "WAP STAMP" (R. 6/2)................. 16·00 21·00
w. Wmk inverted............................. 2·50 1·40
75 3d. purple/*yellow* (3.3.17)............... 2·50 1·40
a. No stop after "STAMP" (R. 2/5,
8/11, 8/12)................................ 26·00 50·00
b. Stop inserted and "P"
impressed a second time
(R. 7/6)..................................... £225
c. Opt inverted.............................. £140 £180
d. Opt sideways (reading up)......... £425
da. Opt omitted (in horiz pair with
No. 75d).................................... £4000

Examples of No. 75d. exist showing parts of two or more overprints. No. 75da shows the left-hand stamp as No. 75d and the right-hand stamp entirely without overprint.

There are numerous minor varieties in this overprint with the setting being altered several times.

WAR STAMP
(**22**)

1919 (4 Oct)–**20**. Optd with T **22** in red by D.L.R.
76 **15** ½d. green.................................... 20 15
77 **18** 3d. purple/*yellow*...................... 15·00 3·75
a. Short opt (right pane R. 10/1)....
b. Pale purple/buff (3.1.20).......... 6·00 1·50
c. Deep purple/buff (1920)............ 16·00 8·50
76s/7s Optd "SPECIMEN" *Set of 2*.................... 90·00

We list the most distinct variations in the 3d. The buff tone of the paper varies considerably in depth.

No. 77a shows the overprint 2 mm high instead of 2½ mm. The variety was corrected after the first overprinting. It is not found on the ½d.

23 Jamaica Exhibition, 1891

24 Arawak Woman preparing Cassava

25 War Contingent embarking, 1915

26 King's House, Spanish Town

Re-entry. Nos. 80a, 96a (R. 8/4)

The greater part of the design is re-entered, the hull showing in very solid colour and the people appear very blurred. There are also minor re-entries on stamps above (R. 7/4 and 6/4).

27 Return of War Contingent, 1919

A B

28 Landing of Columbus, 1494

29 Cathedral, Spanish Town

30 Statue of Queen Victoria, Kingston

31 Admiral Rodney Memorial, Spanish Town

32 Sir Charles Metcalfe Statue, Kingston

33 Jamaican scenery

34

(Typo (½d., 1d.), recess (others) D.L.R.)

1919–21. T **23/34**. Wmk Mult Crown CA (sideways* on 1d., 1½d. and 10s.). Chalk-surfaced paper (½d., 1d.). P 14.
78 **23** ½d. green and olive-green
(12.11.20)............................... 1·00 1·00
w. Wmk inverted............................
x. Wmk reversed.............................
y. Wmk inverted and reversed.......
79 **24** 1d. carmine and orange (3.10.21)... 1·75 1·75
w. Wmk Crown to left of CA...........
80 **25** 1½d. green (*shades*) (4.7.19)............. 40 1·00
a. Major re-entry (R. 8/4)............... £180
b. "C" of "CA" missing from wmk..... † £350
c. "A" of "CA" missing from wmk..... £450 £350
w. Wmk Crown to left of CA........... 35·00 38·00
x. Wmk reversed............................. — £120
y. Wmk sideways inverted and
reversed................................... £100 80·00
81 **26** 2d. indigo and green (18.2.21)........ 1·00 4·00
w. Wmk inverted............................. 65·00
y. Wmk inverted and reversed....... 65·00
82 **27** 2½d. deep blue and blue (A)
(18.2.21).................................. 14·00 3·00
a. Blue-black and deep blue........... 2·00 1·75
b. "C" of "CA" missing from wmk..... £350 £300
c. "A" of "CA" missing from wmk..... £350
w. Wmk inverted............................. 35·00
x. Wmk reversed............................. 60·00
y. Wmk inverted and reversed....... 60·00
83 **28** 3d. myrtle-green and blue (8.4.21). 6·50 2·50
w. Wmk inverted............................. 50·00 55·00
x. Wmk reversed............................. † £250
84 **29** 4d. brown and deep green (21.1.21) 2·50 9·00
w. Wmk inverted.............................
x. Wmk reversed.............................
85 **30** 1s. orange-yellow and red-orange
(10.12.20)............................... 3·75 5·50
a. Frame inverted........................... £40000 £25000
b. "C" of "CA" missing from wmk..... £1100
c. "A" of "CA" missing from wmk..... £1200 £150
w. Wmk inverted............................. † £150
x. Wmk reversed............................. † £400
86 **31** 2s. light blue and brown (10.12.20) 9·00 35·00
b. "C" of "CA" missing from wmk..... £800
c. "A" of "CA" missing from wmk.....
w. Wmk inverted............................. 45·00 70·00

87 **32** 3s. violet-blue and orange
(10.12.20)............................... 28·00 £130
a. "C" of "CA" missing from Wmk ... £1100
88 **33** 5s. blue and yellow-orange
(15.4.21)................................. 60·00 90·00
a. Blue and pale dull orange.......... 50·00 80·00
w. Wmk inverted.............................
x. Wmk reversed.............................
89 **34** 10s. myrtle-green (6.5.20)................ 80·00 £150
78/89 *Set of 12*.. £160 £350
78s/89s Optd "SPECIMEN" *Set of 12*................ £300

*The normal sideways wmk on Nos. 79/80 shows Crown to right of CA, *as seen from the back of the stamp.*

The 2½d. of the above series showed the Union Jack at left, incorrectly, as indicated in illustration A. In the issue on paper with Script wmk the design was corrected (Illustration B).

An example of No. 80 has been reported with the "A" inverted to the left of and above its normal position.

The "C" omitted variety has been reported on an example of No. 88 overprinted "SPECIMEN".

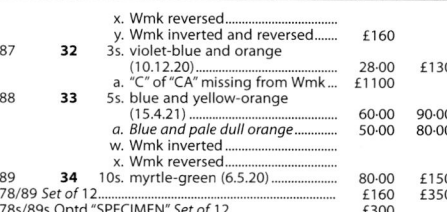

34a "Abolition of Slavery" 1st August 1838

Prepared for use but not issued

1921. Recess. P 14.
(a) Wmk Mult Crown CA
90 **34a** 6d. red and dull blue-green............. £60000
s. Optd "SPECIMEN"........................ £850
xs. Ditto, wmk reversed..................... £1300
(b) Wmk Mult Script CA (Sideways)
91 6d. red and dull blue-green............. £38000
s. Optd "SPECIMEN"........................ £800

The 6d. stamps were prepared and sent out to Jamaica, but for political reasons were not issued, and the stocks destroyed. "SPECIMEN" examples of both watermarks were distributed by the UPU in the normal way, but only one example of No. 90 and four examples of No. 91 exist in private hands without opt.

"Bow" flaw (R. 18/12)

1921 (21 Oct)–**27**. Wmk Mult Script CA. Chalk-surfaced paper (6d.). P 14.
92 **18** ½d. green (3.11.27)......................... 4·00 10
a. Bow flaw................................... £120 35·00
93 6d. dull purple and bright magenta 18·00 4·00
92s/3s Optd "SPECIMEN" *Set of 2*................... £100

35 "POSTAGE & REVENUE" added

36 *Port Royal in 1853* (A. Duperly)

(Printing as before; the 6d. recess-printed)

1921–29. As Nos. 78/89. Wmk Mult Script CA (sideways* on 1d. and 1½d.). Chalk-surfaced paper (½d., 1d.). P 14.
94 **23** ½d. green and olive-green (5.2.22).. 50 50
a. Green and deep olive-green......... 50 50
w. Wmk inverted............................. 55·00 55·00
95 **35** 1d. carmine and orange (5.12.22) ... 1·50 10
w. Wmk Crown to right of CA......... 3·00 10
x. Wmk reversed............................. — £120
96 **25** 1½d. green (*shades*) (2.2.21)............. 3·50 45
a. Major re-entry (R. 8/4)............... £200
w. Wmk Crown to left of CA........... — 35·00
x. Wmk reversed............................. 48·00 48·00
y. Wmk sideways inverted and
reversed................................... — 85·00
97 **26** 2d. indigo and green (4.11.21)........ 8·50 80
a. Indigo and grey-green (1925)...... 16·00 1·00
w. Wmk inverted............................. †
98 **27** 2½d. deep blue and blue (B)
(4.11.21).................................. 6·00 1·75
a. Dull blue and blue (B)................. 6·50 60
w. Wmk inverted............................. 40·00 40·00
x. Wmk reversed............................. — £100
y. Wmk inverted and reversed.......
99 **28** 3d. myrtle-green and blue (6.3.22). 6·00 70
a. Green and pale blue................... 3·50 20
w. Wmk inverted.............................
x. Wmk reversed............................. — £250
100 **29** 4d. brown and deep green
(5.12.21).................................. 1·25 30
a. Chocolate and dull green........... 1·75 30
w. Wmk inverted............................. 55·00
x. Wmk reversed............................. 90·00
101 **36** 6d. black and blue (5.12.22)........... 17·00 1·50
a. Grey and dull blue..................... 15·00 1·00
w. Wmk inverted............................. † £550
x. Wmk reversed............................. † £425

102	30	1s. orange and red-orange (4.11.21)	2·00	80
		a. Orange-yellow and brown-orange	2·00	65
		w. Wmk inverted	—	£250
		x. Wmk reversed	—	£250
103	31	2s. light blue and brown (5.2.22)	3·50	65
		w. Wmk inverted	40·00	40·00
104	32	3s. violet-blue and orange (23.8.21)	19·00	9·00
105	33	5s. blue and yellow-brown (8.11.23)	30·00	25·00
		a. Blue and pale dull orange	80·00	80·00
		b. Blue and yellow-orange (1927)	42·00	23·00
		c. Blue and pale bistre-brown (1929)	48·00	22·00
		w. Wmk inverted	—	£400
		x. Wmk reversed	—	£400
106	34	10s. myrtle-green (3.22)	55·00	70·00
94/106 Set of 13			£130	95·00
94s/106s Optd "SPECIMEN" Set of 13			£300	

*The normal sideways wmk shows Crown to left of CA on No. 95 or Crown to right of CA on No. 96, both as seen from the back of the stamp.
The frame of No. 105a is the same colour as that of No. 88a.
The designs of all values of the pictorial series, with the exception of the 5s. and 10s. (which originated with the Governor, Sir Leslie Probyn), were selected by Mr. F. C. Cundall, F.S.A. The 1d. and 5s. were drawn by Miss Cundall, the 3d. by Mrs. Cundall, and the 10s. by De La Rue & Co. The 6d. is from a lithograph. The other designs are from photographs, the frames of all being the work of Miss Cundall and Miss Wood.

37

38

39

(Centres from photos by Miss V. F. Taylor. Frames des F. C. Cundall, F.S.A., and drawn by Miss Cundall. Recess B.W.)

1923 (1 Nov). Child Welfare. Wmk Mult Script CA. P 12.

107	37	½d. +½d. black and green	1·25	5·50
107b	38	1d. +½d. black and scarlet	4·00	12·00
107c	39	2½d. +½d. black and blue	23·00	19·00
107/7c Set of 3			25·00	32·00
107as/7cs Optd "SPECIMEN." Set of 3			£140	

Sold at a premium of ½d. for the Child Welfare League, these stamps were on sale annually from 1 November to 31 January, until 31 January 1927, when their sale ceased, the remainders being destroyed on 21 February 1927.

40

41

42

Die I

Die II

(Recess D.L.R.)

1929–32. Wmk Mult Script CA. P 14.

108	40	1d. scarlet (Die I) (15.3.29)	16·00	20
		a. Die II (1932)	16·00	10
109	41	1½d. chocolate (18.1.29)	9·50	15
110	42	9d. maroon (5.3.29)	9·50	1·00
108/10 Set of 3			32·00	1·10
108s/10s Perf "SPECIMEN" Set of 3			£110	

In Die I the shading below JAMAICA is formed of thickened parallel lines, and in Die II of diagonal cross-hatching.

43 Coco Palms at Don Christopher's Cove

44 Wag Water River, St. Andrew

45 Priestman's River, Portland

(Dies eng and recess Waterlow)

1932. Wmk Mult Script CA (sideways on 2d. and 2½d.). P 12½.

111	43	2d. black and green (4.11.32)	38·00	4·25
		a. Imperf between (vert pair)	£14000	
112	44	2½d. turquoise-blue and ultramarine (5.3.32)	6·50	1·50
		a. Imperf between (vert pair)	£24000	£24000
113	45	6d. grey-black and purple (4.2.32)	35·00	6·00
111/13 Set of 3			70·00	10·50
111s/13s Perf "SPECIMEN" Set of 3			£120	

1935 (6 May). Silver Jubilee. As Nos. 91/4 of Antigua, but ptd by B.W. P 11×12.

114		1d. deep blue and scarlet	50	15
		b. Short extra flagstaff	£1700	
		d. Flagstaff on right-hand turret	£140	£160
		e. Double flagstaff	£140	£160
115		1½d. ultramarine and grey-black	60	1·50
		a. Extra flagstaff	90·00	£130
		b. Short extra flagstaff	£130	£160
		c. Lightning conductor	£110	£140
116		6d. green and indigo	14·00	20·00
		a. Extra flagstaff	£200	£275
		b. Short extra flagstaff	£375	
		c. Lightning conductor	£250	£325
117		1s. slate and purple	8·50	24·00
		a. Extra flagstaff	£250	£325
		b. Short extra flagstaff	£425	
		c. Lightning conductor	£300	£375
114/17 Set of 4			21·00	40·00
114s/17s Perf "SPECIMEN" Set of 4			£110	

For illustrations of plate varieties see Omnibus section following Zanzibar.

1937 (12 May). Coronation. As Nos. 95/7 of Antigua, but printed by D.L.R. P 14.

118		1d. scarlet	30	15
119		1½d. grey-black	65	30
120		2½d. bright blue	1·00	70
118/20 Set of 3			1·75	1·00
118s/20s Perf "SPECIMEN" Set of 3			£100	

46 King George VI

47 Coco Palms at Don Christopher's Cove

47a Wag Water River, St. Andrew

48 Bananas

49 Citrus Grove

49a Priestman's River, Portland

50 Kingston Harbour

51 Sugar Industry

52 Bamboo Walk

52a Jamaican scenery

53 King George VI

53a Tobacco Growing and Cigar Making

2d. Extra branch (Centre plate (1) with frame Pl (1) to 7, R. 6/1)

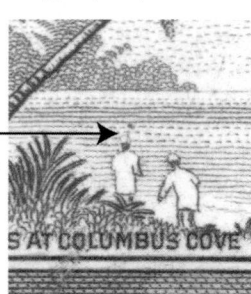
2d. Fishing rod (Centre plate (1) with frame Pl (1) to 7, R. 6/10)

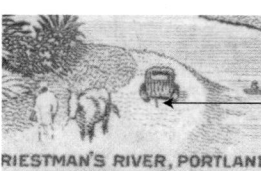
6d. "Exhaust pipe" variety (Centre plate (1), R. 6/1)

1s. Repaired chimney (Centre plate 1, R. 11/1)

(Recess D.L.R. (T **48**, 5s. and 10s.), Waterlow (others))

1938 (10 Oct)–**52**. T **46/53a** and as Nos. 88, 112/13, but with inset portrait of King George VI, as in T **49**. Wmk Mult Script CA. P 13½×14 (½d., 1d., 1½d.), 14 (5s., 10s.) or 12½ (others).

121	46	½d. blue-green	2·00	10
		a. Wmk sideways	†	£10000
121b		½d. orange (25.10.51)	3·25	30
122		1d. scarlet	1·25	10
122a		1d. blue-green (25.10.51)	4·75	10
123		1½d. brown	1·25	10
124	47	2d. grey and green (10.12.38)	1·25	1·00
		a. Extra branch	60·00	30·00
		b. Fishing rod	60·00	30·00
		c. Perf 13×13½ (1939)	2·75	50
		cb. "C" of "CA" missing from wmk	£1500	
		d. Perf 12½×13 (1951)	1·25	10
125	47a	2½d. greenish blue and ultramarine (10.12.38)	9·50	2·75
126	48	3d. ultramarine and green (10.12.38)	1·00	1·50
		a. "A" of "CA" missing from wmk	£1500	
126b		3d. greenish blue and ultramarine (15.8.49)	4·50	1·25
126c		3d. green and scarlet (1.7.52)	6·00	30
127	49	4d. brown and green (10.12.38)	1·00	10
128	49a	6d. grey and purple (10.12.38)	9·50	30
		aa. "Exhaust pipe"	£350	50·00
		a. Perf 13½×13 (10.10.50)	3·25	10
129	50	9d. lake (10.12.38)	1·00	50
		a. "A" of "CA" missing from wmk	£1600	
130	51	1s. green and purple-brown (10.12.38)	16·00	20
		a. Repaired chimney	£650	£110
		b. "A" of "CA" missing from wmk	†	£1400
131	52	2s. blue and chocolate (10.12.38)	35·00	1·00
		a. "A" of "CA" missing from wmk	†	£1500
132	52a	5s. slate-blue and yellow-orange (10.12.38)	20·00	3·75
		a. Perf 14, line (1941)	£7000	£250
		b. Perf 13 (24.10.49)	12·00	3·00
		ba. Blue and orange (10.10.50)	12·00	3·00
133	53	10s. myrtle-green (10.12.38)	11·00	11·00
		aa. Perf 13 (10.10.50)	18·00	7·00
133a	53a	£1 chocolate and violet (15.8.49)	60·00	38·00
121/33a Set of 18			£150	£350
121s/33s Perf "SPECIMEN" Set of 13			£350	

No. 130a occurred in conjunction with Frame plate 2 on printings between 1942 and 1951.
No. 132a shows the emergency use of a line perforation machine, giving an irregular gauge of 14–14.15, after the De La Rue works were damaged in December 1940. The normal comb measures 13.8×13.7.
Nos. 121 and 122 exist in coils constructed from normal sheets.

SELF-GOVERNMENT

54 Courthouse, Falmouth

55 King Charles II and King George VI

56 Institute of Jamaica

57 House of Assembly

58 "Labour and Learning"

59 Scroll, flag and King George VI

(Recess Waterlow)

1945 (20 Aug)–**46**. New Constitution. T **54/9**. Wmk Mult Script CA. P 12½.

134	**54**	1½d. sepia	30	30
		a. Perf 12½×13 (1946)	16·00	2·75
135	**55**	2d. green	17·00	2·00
		a. Perf 12½×13 (1945)	30	50
136	**56**	3d. ultramarine	30	50
		a. Perf 13 (1946)	3·25	2·75
137	**57**	4½d. slate	1·50	30
		a. Perf 13 (1946)	6·50	6·00
138	**58**	2s. red-brown	2·00	50
139	**59**	5s. indigo	4·25	1·75
140	**56**	10s. green	3·50	2·25
134/40 *Set of 7*			11·00	5·50
134s/40s Perf "SPECIMEN" *Set of 7*			£200	

1946 (14 Oct). Victory. As Nos. 110/11 of Antigua.

141		1½d. purple-brown	3·00	10
		a. Perf 13½	1·00	4·50
142		3d. blue	8·50	3·00
		a. Perf 13½	1·00	9·00
141s/2s Perf "SPECIMEN" *Set of 2*			90·00	

1948 (1 Dec). Royal Silver Wedding. As Nos. 112/13 of Antigua.

143		1½d. red-brown	30	10
144		£1 scarlet	28·00	75·00

1949 (10 Oct). 75th Anniv of Universal Postal Union. As Nos. 114/17 of Antigua.

145		1½d. red-brown	20	15
		a. "A" of "CA" missing from wmk	£700	
146		2d. deep blue-green	1·25	7·50
147		3d. deep blue	50	1·75
148		6d. purple	50	2·50
145/8 *Set of 4*			2·25	10·50

(Recess Waterlow)

1951 (16 Feb). Inauguration of B.W.I. University College. As Nos. 118/19 of Antigua.

149		2d. black and red-brown	30	50
150		6d. grey-black and purple	70	30

60 Scout Badge and Map of Caribbean

61 Scout Badge and Map of Jamaica

(Des. C. D'Souza. Litho B.W.)

1952 (5 Mar). First Caribbean Scout Jamboree. Wmk Mult Script CA. P 13½×13 (2d.) or 13×13½ (6d.).

151	**60**	2d. blue, apple-green and black	30	10
152	**61**	6d. yellow-green, carmine-red and black	70	60

1953 (2 June). Coronation. As No. 120 of Antigua.

153		2d. black and deep yellow-green	1·75	10

62 Coco Palms at Don Christopher's Cove

(Recess Waterlow)

1953 (25 Nov). Royal Visit. Wmk Mult Script CA. P 12½×13.

154	**62**	2d. grey-black and green	55	10

63 HMS *Britannia* (ship of the line) at Port Royal

64 Old Montego Bay

65 Old Kingston

66 Proclamation of Abolition of Slavery, 1838

(Recess D.L.R.)

1955 (10 May). Tercentenary Issue. T **63/6**. Wmk Mult Script CA. P 12½.

155	**63**	2d. black and olive-green	85	10
156	**64**	2½d. black and deep bright blue	15	45
157	**65**	3d. black and claret	15	35
158	**66**	6d. black and carmine-red	30	25
155/8 *Set of 4*			1·25	1·00

67 Coconut Palms

68 Sugar Cane

69 Pineapples

70 Bananas

71 Mahoe

72 Breadfruit

73 Ackee

74 Streamertail

75 Blue Mountain Peak

76 Royal Botanic Gardens, Hope

77 Rafting on the Rio Grande

78 Fort Charles

79 Arms of Jamaica

80 Arms of Jamaica

(Recess B.W. (T **79/80**), D.L.R. (others))

1956 (1 May)–**58**. T **67/80**. Wmk Mult Script CA. P 13 (½d. to 6d.), 13½ (8d. to 2s.) or 11½ (3s. to £1).

159	**67**	½d. black and deep orange-red	10	10
160	**68**	1d. black and emerald	10	10
161	**69**	2d. black and carmine-red (2.8.56)	15	10
162	**70**	2½d. black and deep bright blue (2.8.56)	1·50	50
163	**71**	3d. emerald and red-brown (17.12.56)	30	10
164	**72**	4d. bronze-green and blue (17.12.56)	1·00	10
		w. Wmk inverted	£250	£160
165	**73**	5d. scarlet and bronze-green (17.12.56)	1·50	2·75
166	**74**	6d. black and deep rose-red (3.9.56)	4·75	10
167	**75**	8d. ultramarine and red-orange (15.11.56)	2·50	10
168	**76**	1s. yellow-green and blue (15.11.56)	2·50	10
169	**77**	1s.6d. ultramarine and reddish purple (15.11.56)	1·25	10
170	**78**	2s. blue and bronze-green (15.11.56)	17·00	3·25
		a. *Grey-blue and bronze-green* (24.4.58)	35·00	4·25
171	**79**	3s. black and blue (2.8.56)	3·75	4·00
172		5s. black and carmine-red (15.8.56)	4·75	8·50
173	**80**	10s. black and blue-green (15.8.56)	35·00	23·00
174		£1 black and purple (15.8.56)	35·00	23·00
159/74 *Set of 16*			95·00	55·00

An earlier £1 value, in the design of No. 133*a* but showing the portrait of Queen Elizabeth II, was prepared, but not issued.

1958 (22 Apr). Inauguration of British Caribbean Federation. As Nos. 135/7 of Antigua.

175		2d. deep green	1·00	10
176		5d. blue	1·25	3·75
177		6d. scarlet	1·25	40
175/7 *Set of 3*			3·25	3·75

81 Bristol 175 Britannia 312 flying over *City of Berlin*, 1860

83 1s. Stamps of 1860 and 1956

82 Postal mule-cart and motor van

(Recess Waterlow)

1960 (4 Jan). Stamp Centenary. T **81/83** and similar design. W w **12**. P 13×13½ (1s.) or 13½×14 (others).

178	**81**	2d. blue and reddish purple	85	10
179	**82**	6d. carmine and olive-green	85	70
180	**83**	1s. red-brown, yellow-green and blue	85	75
178/80 *Set of 3*			2·25	1·40

INDEPENDENT

INDEPENDENCE (84)

INDEPENDENCE 1962 (85)

86 Military Bugler and Map

(Des V. Whiteley. Photo D.L.R. (2, 4d., 1s.6d., 5s.))

1962 (8 Aug)–**63**. Independence.

*(a) Nos. 159/60, 162, 171, 173/4 optd as T **84** and Nos. 163, 165/8, 170 optd with T **85***

181	**67**	½d. black and deep orange-red	10	1·00
182	**68**	1d. black and emerald	10	10
183	**70**	2½d. black and deep bright blue	15	1·00
184	**71**	3d. emerald and red-brown	15	10
185	**73**	5d. scarlet and bronze-green	25	80
186	**74**	6d. black and deep rose-red	4·25	10
187	**75**	8d. ultramarine and red-orange (opt at upper left)	30	10
		a. Opt at lower left (17.9.63?)	1·25	30
188	**76**	1s. yellow-green and blue	30	10

189	78	2s. blue and bronze-green..............	2·00	1·50
		a. Deep blue and deep bronze-green (20.8.63)............	17·00	7·00
190	79	3s. black and blue............	1·50	1·50
191	80	10s. black and blue-green............	5·50	4·50
192		£1 black and purple............	5·50	5·50

(b) Horiz designs as T **86**. W w **12**. P 13

193		2d. multicoloured............	2·25	10
194		4d. multicoloured............	1·50	10
195		1s.6d. black and red............	5·50	85
196		5s. multicoloured............	13·00	9·50
181/96		*Set of 16*............	38·00	24·00

Designs:—2, 4d. Type **86**; 1s.6d. Gordon House and banner; 5s. Map, factories and fruit.

For these overprints on stamps watermarked w **12** see Nos. 205/13.

89 Kingston Seal, Weightlifting, Boxing, Football and Cycling

90 Kingston Seal, diving, sailing, swimming and water polo

91 Kingston Seal, pole-vaulting, javelin throwing, discus throwing, relay racing and hurdling

92 Kingston Coat of Arms and athlete

(Photo Harrison)

1962 (11 Aug). Ninth Central American and Caribbean Games, Kingston. T **89/92**. W w **12**. P 14½×14.

197	89	1d. sepia and carmine-red................	40	10
198	90	6d. sepia and greenish blue............	20	10
199	91	8d. sepia and bistre............	20	10
200	92	2s. multicoloured............	30	90
197/200		*Set of 4*............	1·00	1·00

An imperf miniature sheet exists, but this was never available at face value or at any post office.

93 Farmer and Crops

(Des M. Goaman. Litho D.L.R.)

1963 (4 June). Freedom from Hunger. P 12½.

201	93	1d. multicoloured............	40	10
202		8d. multicoloured............	1·60	60

1963 (4 Sept). Red Cross Centenary. As Nos. 147/8 of Antigua.

203		2d. red and black............	15	10
204		1s.6d. red and blue............	50	1·50

1963–64. As Nos. 181/90, but wmk w **12**.

205	67	½d. black and deep orange-red (3.12.63*)............	10	15
206	68	1d. black and emerald (3.4.64)............	10	2·25
207	70	2½d. black and deep bright blue (3.4.64)............	25	2·75
208	71	3d. emerald and red-brown (17.12.63*)............	15	15
209	73	5d. scarlet and bronze-green (3.4.64)............	40	2·75
210	75	8d. ultramarine and red-orange (3.4.64)............	20	1·25
211	76	1s. yellow-green and blue (21.12.63*)............	35	1·00
212	78	2s. deep blue and deep bronze-green (3.4.64)............	60	8·00
213	79	3s. black and blue (5.2.64)............	3·00	5·00
205/13		*Set of 9*............	4·50	21·00

The overprint on the 8d., 1s. and 2s. is at lower left, the others are as before.

*These are the earliest known dates recorded in Jamaica.

95 Carole Joan Crawford ("Miss World 1963")

(Des and photo D.L.R.)

1964 (14 Feb–25 May). "Miss World 1963" Commemoration. P 13.

214	95	3d. multicoloured............	10	10
215		1s. multicoloured............	15	10
216		1s.6d. multicoloured............	20	50
214/16		*Set of 3*............	40	60
MS216a		153×101 mm. Nos. 214/16. Imperf (25.5.64)............	1·40	2·75

96 *Lignum Vitae*

97 Ackee

98 Blue Mahoe

99 Land shells

100 National Flag over Jamaica

101 Antillean Murex (*Murex formosus*) (shell)

102 *Papilio homerus* (butterfly)

103 Streamertail

104 Gypsum Industry

105 National Stadium

106 Palisadoes International Airport

107 Bauxite mining

108 Blue Marlin (sport fishing)

109 Exploration of sunken city

110 Arms of Jamaica

110a Queen Elizabeth II and National Flag

111 Multiple "J" and Pineapple

(Des V. Whiteley. Photo Harrison)

1964 (4 May)–68. T **96/110a**. W **111**. P 14½ (1d., 2d., 2½d., 6d., 8d.), 14×14½ (1½d., 3d., 4d., 10s.), 14½×14 (9d., 1s., 3s., 5s., £1) or 13½×14½ (1s.6d., 2s.).

217	1d. violet-blue, deep green and light brown (shades)............	10	10
218	1½d. multicoloured............	15	10
219	2d. red, yellow and grey-green............	15	10
	w. Wmk inverted............	13·00	
220	2½d. multicoloured............	1·00	60
221	3d. yellow, black and emerald............	25	10
222	4d. ochre and violet............	50	10
223	6d. multicoloured............	2·25	10
	a. Blue omitted............	£100	
	b. Value omitted............	£2250	
	w. Wmk inverted............	18·00	
224	8d. mult (yellowish green background)............	2·50	1·50
	a. Red (beak) omitted............	£225	
	b. Greyish green background (16.7.68)............	11·00	10·00
225	9d. blue and yellow-bistre............	1·50	10
226	1s. black and light brown............	20	10
	a. Light brown omitted............	£3250	£3250
	ab. Value only omitted............	£1600	
	b. Black omitted............	£2250	
	ba. "NATIONAL STADIUM" etc omitted............	£1100	£1100
227	1s.6d. black, light blue and buff............	4·00	15
228	2s. red-brown, black and light blue............	2·75	15
229	3s. blue and dull green............	1·00	80
	aw. Wmk inverted............	13·00	
	b. Perf 13½×14½............	35	65
230	5s. black, ochre and blue............	1·25	1·25
	w. Wmk inverted............	£100	
231	10s. multicoloured............	1·50	1·25
	a. Blue ("JAMAICA", etc) omitted............	£450	
232	£1 multicoloured............	3·00	10
217/32	*Set of 16*............	19·00	6·25

No. 223b. Two left half sheets are known with the black printing shifted downwards to such an extent that the value is omitted from the top row.

Nos. 226a/ab came from a sheet on which the two bottom rows had the colour omitted with the next row showing it missing from the lower third of the stamps.

No. 226b comes from the bottom row of one sheet and rows seven and eight of a second sheet; the latter also being the source of No. 226ba.

112 Scout Belt

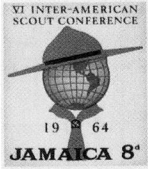
113 Globe, Scout Hat and Scarf

114 Scout Badge and Alligator

(Photo Harrison)

1964 (27 Aug). Sixth Inter-American Scout Conference, Kingston. W **111**. P 14 (1s.) or 14½×14 (others).

233	112	3d. red, black and pink............	10	10
234	113	8d. bright blue, olive and black............	15	25
		w. Wmk inverted............	45·00	
235	114	1s. gold, deep blue and light blue............	20	45
		w. Wmk inverted............	20	45
233/5		*Set of 3*............	40	70

115 Gordon House, Kingston

116 Headquarters House, Kingston

117 House of Assembly, Spanish Town

118 Eleanor Roosevelt

(Des V. Whiteley. Photo Harrison)

1964 (16 Nov). Tenth Commonwealth Parliamentary Conference, Kingston. T **115/7**. W **111**. P 14½×14.

236	115	3d. black and yellow-green............	10	10
237	116	6d. black and carmine-red............	30	10
238	117	1s.6d. black and bright blue............	50	30
236/8		*Set of 3*............	80	40

(Des V. Whiteley. Photo Harrison)

1964 (10 Dec). 16th Anniv of Declaration of Human Rights. W **111**. P 14½×14.

239	118	1s. black, red and light green............	10	10

119 Guides' Emblem on Map

120 Guide Emblems

(Photo Harrison)

1965 (17 May). Golden Jubilee of Jamaica Girl Guides Association. W **111** (sideways on 3d.). P 14×14½ (3d.) or 14 (1s.).
240	**119**	3d. yellow, green and light blue	10	10
241	**120**	1s. yellow, black and apple-green..	20	40
		w. Wmk inverted	20	40

121 Uniform Cap

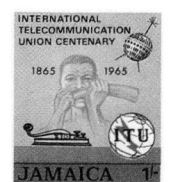
122 Flag-bearer and Drummer

(Photo Harrison)

1965 (23 Aug). Salvation Army Centenary. W **111**. P 14×14½ (3d.) or 14½×14 (1s.6d.).
242	**121**	3d. multicoloured	30	10
		w. Wmk inverted	22·00	
243	**122**	1s.6d. multicoloured	1·00	50
		w. Wmk inverted	48·00	

123 Paul Bogle, William Gordon and Morant Bay Court House

124 Abeng-blower, *Telstar*, Morse Key and ITU Emblem

(Photo Enschedé)

1965 (29 Dec). Centenary of Morant Bay Rebellion. No wmk. P 14×13.
244	**123**	3d. light brown, ultramarine and black	10	10
245		1s.6d. light brown, yellow-green and black	20	15
246		3s. light brown, rose and black	30	1·75
244/6 Set of 3			55	1·75

(Photo Harrison)

1965 (29 Dec). ITU Centenary. W **111**. P 14×14½.
247	**124**	1s. black, grey-blue and red	40	20

ROYAL VISIT MARCH 1966
(**125**)

126 Sir Winston Churchill

1966 (3 Mar). Royal Visit. Nos. 221, 223, 226/7 optd with T **125**.
248		3d. yellow, black and emerald	15	15
249		6d. multicoloured	2·25	80
250		1s. black and light brown	55	15
251		1s.6d. black, light blue and buff	2·50	4·00
248/51 Set of 4			5·00	4·50

(Des Jennifer Toombs. Photo Harrison)

1966 (18 Apr). Churchill Commemoration. W **111**. P 14.
252	**126**	6d. black and olive-green	65	30
253		1s. bistre-brown and deep violet-blue	85	80

127 Statue of Athlete and Flags

131 Bolivar's Statue and Flags of Jamaica and Venezuela

(Des V. Whiteley. Photo Harrison)

1966 (4 Aug). Eighth British Empire and Commonwealth Games. T **127** and similar horiz designs. W **111**. P 14½×14.
254		3d. multicoloured	10	10

255		6d. multicoloured	60	10
		w. Wmk inverted	40·00	
256		1s. multicoloured	10	10
257		3s. bright gold and deep blue	35	45
		w. Wmk inverted	40·00	
254/7 Set of 4			1·00	55
MS258 128×103 mm. Nos. 254/7. Imperf.			4·00	8·00

Designs:—6d. Racing cyclists; 1s. National Stadium, Kingston; 3s. Games emblem.
No. **MS**258 has been seen with the whole printing inverted except for the brown background.

(Des and photo Harrison)

1966 (5 Dec). 150th Anniv of "Jamaica Letter". W **111**. P 14×15.
259	**131**	8d. multicoloured	20	10
		w. Wmk inverted	38·00	

132 Jamaican Pavilion

133 Sir Donald Sangster (Prime Minister)

(Des V. Whiteley. Photo Harrison)

1967 (28 Apr). World Fair, Montreal. W **111**. P 14½.
260	**132**	6d. multicoloured	10	15
261		1s. multicoloured	10	15
		w. Wmk inverted	12·00	

(Des and photo Enschedé)

1967 (28 Aug). Sangster Memorial Issue. P 13½.
262	**133**	3d. multicoloured	10	10
263		1s.6d. multicoloured	20	20

134 Traffic Duty

135 Personnel of the Force

(Des V. Whiteley. Photo Enschedé)

1967 (28 Nov). Centenary of the Constabulary Force. T **134**/**5** and similar horiz design. Multicoloured. W **111**. P 13½×14.
264		3d. Type **134**	40	10
		a. Wmk sideways	1·50	3·00
265		1s. Type **135**	40	10
266		1s.6d. Badge and Constables of 1867 and 1967 (as T **134**)	50	75
264/6 Set of 3			1·10	85

136 Wicket-keeping

137 Sir Alexander and Lady Bustamante

(Des V. Whiteley. Photo Harrison)

1968 (8 Feb). MCC's West Indian Tour. T **136** and similar vert designs. Multicoloured. W **111** (sideways*). P 14.
267		6d. Type **136**	50	65
		a. Horiz strip of 3. Nos. 267/9	1·25	1·75
		w. Wmk top of J to right	50	65
268		6d. Batting	50	65
		w. Wmk top of J to right	50	65
269		6d. Bowling	50	65
		w. Wmk top of J to right	50	65
267/9 Set of 3			1·25	1·75

*The normal sideways watermark shows the top of the "J" to left, *as seen from the back of the stamp.*
Nos. 267/9 were issued in small sheets of nine comprising three se-tenant strips as No. 267a.
Nos. 267/9 exist on PVA gum as well as on gum arabic.

(Des and photo Harrison)

1968 (23 May). Labour Day. W **111**. P 14.
270	**137**	3d. rose and black	10	15
271		1s. olive and black	10	15

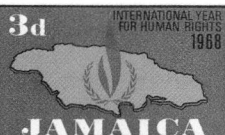
138 Human Rights Emblem over Map of Jamaica

(Photo Harrison)

1968 (3 Dec). Human Rights Year. T **138** and similar multicoloured designs. W **111**. P 14.
272		3d. Type **138**	10	10
		a. Gold (flame) omitted	£160	
		w. Wmk inverted	7·00	
273		1s. Hands cupping Human Rights emblem (*vert*)	20	10
274		3s. Jamaican holding "Human Rights"	60	1·50
		a. Gold (flame) omitted	£180	
272/4 Set of 3			75	1·50

Three designs, showing 3d. Bowls of Grain, 1s. Abacus, 3s. Hands in Prayer, were prepared but not issued (*Price for set of 3 mint £200*).

141 ILO Emblem

142 Nurse, and Children being weighed and measured

(Des V. Whiteley. Litho Format)

1969 (23 May). 50th Anniv of International Labour Organization. P 14.
275	**141**	6d. orange-yellow and blackish brown	10	10
276		3s. bright emerald and blackish brown	30	45

(Des and photo Harrison)

1969 (30 May). 20th Anniv of WHO T **142** and similar designs. W **111**. P 14.
277		6d. grey, brown and orange	10	15
278		1s. black, sepia and blue-green	10	15
279		3s. grey-black, brown and pale bright blue	20	1·25
277/9 Set of 3			30	1·40

Designs: Horiz—1s. Malaria eradication. Vert—3s. Trainee nurse.

(New Currency. 100 cents = 1 Jamaica dollar)

C-DAY
8th September
1969
1c
(145)

146 *The Adoration of the Kings* (detail, Foppa)

1969 (8 Sept). Decimal currency. Nos. 217, 219, 221/3 and 225/32 surch as T **145**. Sterling values unobliterated except 1c. to 4c. and 8c.
280		1c. on 1d. violet-blue, deep green and light brown	10	10
281		2c. on 2d. red, yellow and grey-green	10	10
		w. Wmk inverted	3·25	
282		3c. on 3d. yellow, black and emerald	10	10
283		4c. on 4d. ochre and violet	1·25	10
		a. "8t" of "8th" omitted (R. 10/1)	70·00	
284		5c. on 6d. multicoloured	1·25	10
		a. Blue omitted	£110	
285		8c. on 9d. blue and yellow-bistre	10	10
286		10c. on 1s. black and light brown	10	10
287		15c. on 1s.6d. black, light blue and buff	50	90
288		20c. on 2s. red-brown, black and light blue	1·50	1·50
		a. "8th" omitted	£1800	
289		30c. on 3s. blue and dull green	2·50	3·00
290		50c. on 5s. black, ochre and blue	1·25	3·00
291		$1 on 10s. multicoloured	1·25	6·50
		w. Wmk inverted	£130	
292		$2 on £1 multicoloured	2·25	6·50
280/92 Set of 13			10·50	19·00

No. 281 exists with PVA gum as well as gum arabic.
Unlike the positional No. 283a the similar variety on the 20c. on 2s. was caused by a paper fold.

(Des J. Cooter. Litho D.L.R.)

1969 (25 Oct). Christmas. Paintings. T **146** and similar vert designs. Multicoloured. W **111**. P 13.
293		2c. Type **146**	20	40
294		5c. *Madonna, Child and St. John* (Raphael)	25	40
295		8c. *The Adoration of the Kings* (detail, Dosso Dossi)	25	40
293/5 Set of 3			65	1·10

149 Half Penny, 1869

151 George William Gordon

(Des G. Drummond. Litho P.B.)

1969 (27 Oct). Centenary of First Jamaican Coins. T **149** and similar horiz design. w. W **111**. P 12½.

296		3c. silver, black and mauve	15	25
		b. Wmk sideways	1·25	2·50
297		15c. silver, black and light emerald	10	10

Design:—15c. One penny, 1869.

(Des G. Vasarhelyi. Litho Enschedé)

1970 (11 Mar). National Heroes. T **151** and similar vert designs. Multicoloured. P 12×12½.

298		1c. Type **151**	10	30
		a. Yellow (from flags) omitted	£400	
299		3c. Sir Alexander Bustamante	20	10
300		5c. Norman Manley	20	10
301		10c. Marcus Garvey	30	10
302		15c. Paul Bogle	35	25
298/302 *Set of 5*			1·00	60

156 *Christ appearing to St. Peter* (Carracci)

2c

(159)

(Des G. Drummond. Photo Enschedé)

1970 (23 Mar). Easter. T **156** and similar vert designs. Multicoloured. W **111**. P 12×12½.

303		3c. Type **156**	10	10
		w. Wmk inverted		
304		10c. *Christ Crucified* (Antonello da Messina)	10	10
		w. Wmk inverted		
305		20c. Easter Lily	20	60
303/5 *Set of 3*			30	70

1970 (16 July). No. 219 surch with T **159**.

306		2c. on 2d. red, yellow and grey-green	20	20

160 *Lignum Vitae*

161 Cable Ship *Dacia*

1970 (7 Sept–2 Nov). Decimal Currency. Designs as Nos. 217/32 but inscr as T **160** in new currency. W **111** (sideways on 2, 4, 15, 20c. and $1). P 14½ (1, 5c.), 14×14½ (4c., $1), 13½×14½ (15, 20c.) or 14½×14 (others).

307		1c. violet-blue, deep green and light brown	75	2·25
308		2c. red, yellow and grey-green (as 2d.)	30	10
309		3c. yellow, black and emerald (as 3d.)	1·00	1·00
310		4c. ochre and violet (as 4d.)	3·00	30
311		5c. multicoloured (as 6d.)	3·00	65
312		8c. blue and yellow-bistre (as 9d.)	2·25	10
		a. Wmk sideways	2·00	45
313		10c. black and light brown (as 1s.)	60	20
314		15c. black, light blue and buff (as 1s.6d.) (2.11)	3·00	3·50
315		20c. red-brown, black and light blue (as 2s.) (2.11)	1·25	3·00
316		30c. blue and dull green (as 3s.) (2.11)	4·25	6·50
317		50c. black, ochre and blue (as 5s.) (2.11)	1·75	4·75
318		$1 multicoloured (as 10s.) (2.11)	1·00	5·50
319		$2 multicoloured (as £1) (2.11)	1·50	4·00
307/19 *Set of 13*			21·00	28·00

(Des G. Drummond. Litho J.W.)

1970 (12 Oct). Centenary of Telegraph Service. T **161** and similar horiz designs. W **111** (sideways). P 14½×14.

320		3c. yellow, red and black	25	10
321		10c. black and turquoise	35	10
322		50c. multicoloured	80	1·00
320/2 *Set of 3*			1·25	1·10

Designs:—10c. Bright's cable gear aboard *Dacia*; 50c. Morse key and chart.

164 Bananas, Citrus, Sugar-Cane and Tobacco

165 Locomotive *Projector* (1845)

(Des G. Drummond. Litho Questa)

1970 (2 Nov). 75th Anniv of Jamaican Agricultural Society. W **111**. P 14.

323	164	2c. multicoloured	30	60
		w. Wmk inverted	8·50	
324		10c. multicoloured	70	10

(Des V. Whiteley. Litho Format)

1970 (21 Nov). 125th Anniv of Jamaican Railways. T **165** and similar horiz designs. Multicoloured. W **111** (sideways). P 13½.

325		3c. Type **165**	30	10
326		15c. Steam locomotive No. 54 (1944)	65	30
327		50c. Diesel locomotive No. 102 (1967)	1·25	1·75
325/7 *Set of 3*			2·00	2·00

STAMP BOOKLETS

1912. Black on red covers. Stapled.

SB1	2s. booklet containing 24×1d. (No. 40) in blocks of 6 (9.3)	
SB2	2s. booklet containing 12×½d. and 18×1d. (Nos. 38, 58), each in blocks of 6 (5.12)	£1800

1923 (Dec). Black on red cover. Stapled.

SB3	2s. booklet containing 12×½d. (No. 94) in blocks of 4 and 18×1d. (No. 95) in blocks of 6	£1200

1928. Black on red cover. Stapled.

SB4	2s. booklet containing 12×½d. and 18×1d. (Nos. 92, 95) in blocks of 6	£2000

1928 (5 Sept). Black on red cover. Stapled.

SB5	1s.6d. booklet containing 12×½d. and 12×1d. (Nos. 92, 95), each in blocks of 6	

1929 (July)–**32**. Black on red cover. Stapled.

SB6	2s. booklet containing 6×½d., 12×1d. and 6×1½d. (Nos. 92, 108/9) in blocks of 6	£1500
	a. With 1d. Die II (No. 108a) (1932)	

1930–**33**. Black on red cover. Stapled.

SB7	2s. booklet containing 12×½d. and 18×1d. (Nos. 92, 108), each in blocks of 6	
	a. With 1d. Die II (No. 108a) (1933)	£1300
	b. Black on blue cover (1933)	£1800

1935. Silver Jubilee. Black on pink cover. Stapled.

SB8	2s. booklet containing 24×1d. (No. 114) in blocks of 6	£1500
	a. In blocks of 4	£2250

1938–**40**. Black on green cover inscr "JAMAICA POSTAGE STAMPS" in one line. Inland Postage Rates on interleaf. Stapled.

SB9	2s. booklet containing 12×½d. and 18×1d. (Nos. 121/2), each in blocks of 6 (inland letter rate 1d. per oz)	£500
	a. Inland letter rate 1½d. for first 2 oz (1940)	£550

1942–**47**. Black on blue cover inscr "JAMAICA POSTAGE STAMPS" in three lines. Inland Postage Rates on inside front cover. Stapled.

SB10	2s. booklet containing 12×½d. and 18×1d. (Nos. 121/2), each in blocks of 6 (Inland letter rate 1½d. for first 2 oz)	£250
	a. Black on yellow cover (1947)	£110

1946. New Constitution. Black on blue cover. Stapled.

SB12	2s. booklet containing 16×1½d. (No. 134a) in blocks of 4	£225

1952. Black on yellow cover. Stapled.

SB13	2s. booklet containing 12×½d and 18×1d. (Nos. 121b, 122a), each in blocks of 6	25·00

1956. Black on green cover. Stitched.

SB14	3s. booklet containing ½d., 1d., 2d. and 2½d. (Nos. 159/62) in blocks of 6	11·00

1965 (15 Nov). Black on green cover. Stitched.

SB15	3s. booklet containing 1d., 2d. and 3d. (Nos. 217, 219, 221) in blocks of 6	5·00

POSTAL FISCALS

Revenue stamps were authorised for postal use by Post Office notice of 12 October 1887.

F 1

(Typo D.L.R.)

1865–**73**. P 14.

(a) Wmk Pineapple (T **7**)

F1	F **1**	1d. rose (1865)	£100	£110
		a. Imperf (pair)	£550	

(b) Wmk Crown CC

F2	F **1**	1d. rose (1871)	75·00	55·00

(c) Wmk CA over Crown (Type w **7** sideways, covering two stamps)

F3	F **1**	1d. rose (1873)	55·00	7·00
		a. Imperf		

F **2**

F **3**

(Typo D.L.R.)

1855–**74**. (Issued). Glazed paper. P 14.

(a) No wmk

F4	F **2**	1½d. blue/*blue* (1857)	65·00	50·00
		a. Imperf (1855)		
		b. Blue on white	80·00	60·00
F5		3d. purple/*blue* (1857)	65·00	55·00
		a. Imperf (1855)		
		b. Purple on lilac (1857)	65·00	55·00
		ba. Imperf (1855)	£700	
		c. Purple on white (1857)	85·00	55·00

(b) Wmk Crown CC

F6	F **2**	3d. purple/*lilac* (1874)	29·00	29·00

All the above stamps *imperf* are exceedingly rare postally used.

1858 (1 Jan). (Issued). No wmk. P 15½×15.

F7	F **3**	1s. rose/*bluish*	£110	90·00
F8		5s. lilac/*bluish*	£500	£500
F9		10s. green/*bluish*	£650	£650

OFFICIAL STAMPS

OFFICIAL

(O **1**)

OFFICIAL

(O **2**)

1890 (1 Apr)–**91**. No. 16a optd with Type O **1** by C. Vendryes, Kingston.

(a) "OFFICIAL" 17 to 17½ mm long

O1	**8**	½d. green	18·00	2·25
		a. "O" omitted	£800	
		b. One "I" omitted	£900	£900
		c. Both "I"s omitted	£900	£900
		d. "L" omitted	£950	£950
		e. Opt inverted	£100	£110
		f. Opt double	£100	£110
		g. Opt double, one inverted	£550	£550
		h. Opt double, one vertical	£900	
		j. Pair, overprints tête-bêche		

(b) "OFFICIAL" 15 to 16 mm long

O2	**8**	½d. green (3.91)	45·00	28·00
		a. Opt inverted	£800	

There were five settings of the locally-overprinted Officials. No. O1 occurred from settings I (2×10), II (3×6), IV and V (horizontal row of six each). No. O2 came from setting III (2×6). There are numerous minor varieties, due to broken type, etc. (*e.g.* a broken "E" used for "F"). Stamps with the 17–17½ mm opt were reissued in 1894 during a temporary shortage of No. O3.

1890 (1 Apr)–**91**. Optd with Type O **2** by D.L.R. Wmk Crown CA. P 14.

O3	**8**	½d. green (1891)	10·00	1·75
O4	**11**	1d. rose	8·00	1·25
O5		2d. grey	30·00	1·25
O3/5 *Set of 3*			42·00	3·75
O3s/5s Optd "SPECIMEN" *Set of 3*			£150	

Nos. O4/5 were not issued without overprint.

The use of Official stamps ceased from 1 January 1898.

TELEGRAPH STAMPS

T **1**

T **2**

(Typo D.L.R.)

1879 (Oct). Wmk Crown CC (sideways on 3d.). P 14.

T1	T **1**	3d. lilac (*shades*)	50·00	10·00
T2	T **2**	1s. brown-brown (*shades*)	27·00	2·50
		s. Optd "SPECIMEN"	70·00	

1889. Wmk Crown CA (sideways). P14.

T3	T **1**	3d. lilac (*shades*)	12·00	3·50
		s. Optd "SPECIMEN"	70·00	

Nos. T2s and T3s were distributed to UPU member countries in March 1892.

1904. Wmk Mult Crown CA (sideways). P 14.

T4	T **1**	3d. lilac	40·00	25·00

Kenya

INDEPENDENT

(Currency. 100 cents = 1 East Africa, later Kenya Shilling)

1 Cattle Ranching

2 Wood-carving

3 National Assembly

(Des V. Whiteley. Photo Harrison)

1963 (12 Dec). Independence. T **1/3** and similar designs. P 14×15 (small designs) or 14½ (others).

1	5c. brown, deep blue, green and bistre	10	55
2	10c. brown	10	10
3	15c. magenta	1·00	10
4	20c. black and yellow-green	15	10
5	30c. black and yellow	15	10
6	40c. brown and light blue	15	30
	a. Printed on the gummed side	£100	
7	50c. crimson, black and green	60	10
8	65c. deep turquoise-green and yellow	55	65
9	1s. multicoloured	20	10
10	1s.30 brown, black and yellow-green	5·00	30
11	2s. multicoloured	1·25	40
12	5s. brown, ultramarine and yellow-green	1·25	1·25
13	10s. brown and deep blue	9·00	3·00
14	20s. black and rose	4·00	11·00
1/14 *Set of 14*		21·00	16·00

Designs: As T **1/2**—15c. Heavy industry; 20c. Timber industry; 30c. Jomo Kenyatta and Mt Kenya; 40c. Fishing industry; 50c. Kenya flag 65c. Pyrethrum industry. As T **3**—1s.30, Tourism (Treetops Hotel); 2s. Coffee industry; 5s. Tea industry; 10s. Mombasa Port; 20s. Royal College, Nairobi.

The 10c. was produced in coils of 1000 in addition to normal sheets.

4 Cockerel

(Des M. Goaman. Photo J. Enschedé)

1964 (12 Dec). Inauguration of Republic. T **4** and similar vert designs. Multicoloured. P 13×12½.

15	15c. Type **4**	15	15
16	30c. President Kenyatta	15	10
17	50c. Lion	15	10
18	1s.30 Hartlaub's Turaco	2·00	50
19	2s.50 Nandi flame	20	4·50
15/19 *Set of 5*		2·40	4·75

5 Thomson's Gazelle

6 Sable Antelope

7 Greater Kudu

15c. Grey flaw under snout of Aardvark resembles antheap (Pl. 1A, R. 10/5)

(Des Rena Fennessy. Photo Harrison)

1966 (12 Dec)–**71**. Various designs as T **5/7**. Chalk-surfaced paper. P 14×14½ (5c. to 70c.) or 14½ (others).

20	5c. orange, black and sepia	20	20
21	10c. black and apple-green	10	10
	a. Glazed, ordinary paper (13.7.71)	1·00	5·00
22	15c. black and orange	10	10
	a. "Antheap"	9·00	
	b. Glazed, ordinary paper (13.7.71)	1·25	1·00
23	20c. ochre, black and blue	10	15
	a. Glazed, ordinary paper (22.1.71)	1·00	1·50
24	30c. Prussian blue, blue and black	20	10
25	40c. black and yellow-brown	60	30
	a. Glazed, ordinary paper (19.2.71)	1·25	3·00
26	50c. black and red-orange	60	10
	a. Glazed, ordinary paper (19.2.71)	14·00	5·00

27	65c. black and light green	1·25	2·00
28	70c. black and claret (15.9.69)	4·50	1·75
	a. Glazed, ordinary paper (19.2.71)	35·00	16·00
29	1s. olive-brown, black and slate-blue	30	10
	a. Glazed, ordinary paper (22.1.71)	1·25	85
30	1s.30 indigo, light olive-green and black	4·00	20
31	1s.50 black, orange-brown and dull sage green (15.9.69)	2·00	3·00
	a. Glazed, ordinary paper (22.1.71)	2·00	6·00
32	2s.50 yellow, black and olive-brown	3·50	1·25
	a. Glazed, ordinary paper (22.1.71)	1·50	5·50
33	5s. yellow, black and emerald	75	70
	a. Glazed, ordinary paper (22.1.71)	1·50	12·00
34	10s. yellow-ochre, black and red-brown	3·00	3·00
35	20s. yellow-ochre, yellow-orange, black and gold	8·00	13·00
20/35 *Set of 16*		26·00	23·00
21a/33a *Set of 10*		50·00	50·00

Designs: As T **5/6**—15c. Aardvark ("Ant Bear"); 20c. Lesser Bushbaby; 30c. Warthog; 40c. Common Zebra; 50c. African Buffalo; 65c. Black Rhinoceros; 70c. Ostrich. As T **7**—1s.30, African Elephant; 1s.50, Bat-eared Fox; 2s.50, Cheetah; 5s. Savanna Monkey ("Vervet Monkey"); 10s. Giant Ground Pangolin; 20s. Lion.

On chalk-surfaced paper, all values except 30c., 50c. and 2s.50 exist with PVA gum as well as gum arabic but the 70c. and 1s.50 exist with PVA gum only. The stamps on glazed, ordinary paper exist with PVA gum only.

Nos. 21 and 26 exist in coils constructed from normal sheets.

STAMP BOOKLETS

1964. Black on blue cover. Stitched.

SB1	5s. booklet containing 10c., 15c., 20c., 30c. and 50c. (Nos. 2/5, 7) in blocks of 4	20·00

1966 (12 Dec). Black on bluish grey (No. SB2) or buff (No. SB3) covers. Stitched.

SB2	3s. booklet containing 4×5c., 4×10c. and 8×30c. (Nos. 20/1, 24), each in blocks of 4	18·00
SB3	5s. booklet containing 4×5c., 4×10c., 4×50c. and 8×30c. (Nos. 20/1, 24, 26), each in blocks of 4	30·00

POSTAGE DUE STAMPS

The Postage Due stamps of Kenya, Uganda and Tanganyika were used in Kenya until 2 January 1967.

D 3

1967 (3 Jan). Chalk-surfaced paper. P 14×13½.

D13	D **3**	5c. scarlet	15	2·75
		a. Perf 14. Ordinary paper. *Dull scarlet* (16.12.69)	40	7·50
D14		10c. green	20	2·50
		a. Perf 14. Ordinary paper (16.12.69)	55	4·25
D15		20c. blue	70	2·75
		a. Perf 14. Ordinary paper. *Deep blue* (16.12.69)	55	8·50
D16		30c. brown	80	3·25
		a. Perf 14. Ordinary paper. *Light red-brown* (16.12.69)	80	25·00
D17		40c. bright purple	65	5·00
		a. Perf 14. Ordinary paper. *Pale bright purple* (16.12.69)	65	25·00
D18		1s. bright orange	1·75	7·00
		a. Perf 14. Ordinary paper. *Dull bright orange* (18.2.70)	2·00	25·00
D13/18 *Set of 6*			3·75	21·00
D13a/18a *Set of 6*			4·50	85·00

OFFICIAL STAMPS

Intended for use on official correspondence of the Kenya Government only but there is no evidence that they were so used.

OFFICIAL
(O **4**)

(15c. 30c. opt typo; others in photogravure)

1964 (1 Oct). Nos. 1/5 and 7 optd with Type O **4**.

O21	5c. brown, deep blue, green and bistre	10
O22	10c. brown	10
O23	15c. magenta	1·25
O24	20c. black and yellow-green	20
O25	30c. black and yellow	30
O26	50c. crimson, black and green	2·75
O21/26 *Set of 6*		4·00

Kenya, Uganda and Tanganyika

BRITISH EAST AFRICA

The area which became British East Africa had been part of the domain of the Zanzibari Sultans since 1794. In 1887 the administration of the province was granted to the British East Africa Association, incorporated as the Imperial British East Africa Company the following year.

Company post offices were established at Lamu and Mombasa in May 1890, British mails having been previously sent via the Indian post office on Zanzibar, opened in 1875.

A German postal agency opened at Lamu on 22 November 1888 and continued to operate until 31 March 1891, using German stamps. These can be identified by the "LAMU/OSTAFRIKA" cancellations and are listed under German East Africa in our *Germany* catalogue.

PRICES FOR STAMPS ON COVER	
Nos. 1/3	from × 10
Nos. 4/19	from × 30
Nos. 20/1	from × 3
No. 22	—
No. 23	from × 3
No. 24	—
No. 25	from × 1
No. 26	from × 3
Nos. 27/8	from × 8
Nos. 29/30	from × 20
No. 31	from × 10
No. 32	—
Nos. 33/42	from × 10
Nos. 43/7	—
No. 48	from × 15
Nos. 49/64	from × 12
Nos. 65/79	from × 15
Nos. 80/91	from × 8
Nos. 92/6	from × 12
Nos. 97/9	—

(Currency. 16 annas = 1 rupee)

BRITISH EAST AFRICA COMPANY ADMINISTRATION

BRITISH EAST AFRICA COMPANY
(1)

BRITISH EAST AFRICA COMPANY
(2)

HALF ANNA
(1)

1 ANNA
(2)

(Surch D.L.R.)

1890 (23 May). Stamps of Great Britain (Queen Victoria) surch as T **1** or T **2** (1a. and 4a.).

1	½a. on 1d. deep purple (No. 173)	£275	£200
2	1a. on 2d. grey-green and carmine (No. 200)	£500	£275
3	4a. on 5d. dull purple and blue (No. 207a)	£600	£325

The second stamp of each horizontal row of the 4a. on 5d. had the "BRITISH" shifted to the left, placing the "B" directly over the "S" of "EAST". In the normal overprint the "B" is over "ST" as shown in Type (**2**).

A copy of the ½a. with the short crossbar of "F" in "HALF" omitted exists in the Royal Collection but is the only known example.

Following the exhaustion of stocks of Nos. 1/3, stamps of India were used at Mombasa (and occasionally at Lamu) from late July 1890 until the arrival of Nos. 4/19. The following listing is for stamps clearly cancelled with the MOMBASA 21 mm circular date stamp (code "C"). Examples with LAMU circular date stamp are worth much more. Indian stamps used after October 1890, including other values, came from ship mail.

Stamps of INDIA 1882–90 (Nos. 84/101) cancelled at Mombasa between July and October 1890.

Z1	½a. blue-green	£600
Z2	1a. brown-purple	£500
Z3	1a.6p. sepia	£850
Z4	2a. blue	£950
Z5	3a. orange	£950
Z5a	4a. olive-green	£1000
Z6	4a.6p. yellow-green	£375
Z7	8a. dull mauve	£550
Z8	1r. slate	£950

3

4

5 ANNAS.
(5)

1a. "ANL" (broken "D") (R. 6/5)

(Litho B.W.)

1890 (13 Oct)–95. P 14.

4	**3**	½a. dull brown	9·50	13·00
		a. Imperf (pair)	£1500	£700
		b. *Deep brown* (21.10.93)	70	11·00
		ba. Imperf (pair)	£900	£375
		bb. Imperf between (horiz pair)	£1700	£650
		bc. Imperf between (vert pair)	£1400	£500
		c. *Pale brown* (16.1.95)	1·00	16·00
5		1a. blue-green	9·50	15·00
		aa. "ANL" (broken "D")	£1000	£1100
		a. Imperf (pair)	£5000	£1300
		ab. Ditto. "ANL" (broken "D")	£20000	
		b. *Deep blue-green* (16.1.95)	1·00	
6		2a. vermilion	6·50	7·50
		a. Imperf (pair)	£4750	£1400
7	**3**	2½a. black/*yellow-buff* (9.91)	£100	35·00
		aa. Imperf (pair)	£6000	
		a. Imperf between (horiz pair)	£8000	
		ab. Block of four imperf between (horiz and vert)	£16000	
		b. *Black/pale buff* (9.92)	£100	13·00
		c. *Black/bright yellow* (21.10.93)	6·00	9·50
		cc. Imperf between (horiz pair)	£1200	£500
		cc. Imperf between (horiz pair)	£1400	£450
		cd. Imperf between (vert pair)	£1400	£600
8		3a. black/*dull red* (30.3.91)	25·00	26·00
		a. *Black/bright red* (21.10.93)	3·75	18·00
		ab. Imperf (pair)	£1200	£450
		ac. Imperf between (horiz pair)	£900	£425
		ad. Imperf between (vert pair)	£700	£400
9		4a. yellow-brown	2·50	14·00
		a. Imperf (pair)	£5000	£1700
10		4a. grey (*imperf*)	£1200	£1400
11		4½a. dull violet (30.3.91)	38·00	21·00
		a. *Brown-purple* (21.10.93)	2·50	23·00
		ab. Imperf (pair)	£2000	£450
		ac. Imperf between (horiz pair)	£1500	£1000
		ad. Imperf between (vert pair)	£1100	£500
12		8a. blue	5·50	11·00
		a. Imperf (pair)	£10000	£1500
13		8a. grey	£275	£225
14		1r. carmine	6·00	9·00
		a. Imperf (pair)	£15000	£1700
15		1r. grey	£225	£225
16	**4**	2r. brick-red	14·00	50·00
17		3r. slate-purple	13·00	55·00
18		4r. ultramarine	12·00	55·00
19		5r. grey-green	30·00	75·00
4/9, 11/19 *Set of 15*			£550	£650

For the 5a. and 7½a. see Nos. 29/30.

The paper of Nos. 7, 7b, 7c, 8 and 8a is coloured on the surface only.

Printings of 1890/92 are on thin paper having the outer margins of the sheets imperf and bearing sheet watermark "PURE LINEN WOVE BANK" and "W. C. S. & Co." in a monogram, the trademark of the makers, Messrs. William Collins, Sons & Co.

1893/94 printings are on thicker coarser paper with outer margins perforated through the selvedge and without watermark. Single specimens cannot always be distinguished by lack of watermark alone. Exceptions are the 1893 printings of the 2½a. and 3a. which were on Wiggins Teape paper showing a sheet watermark of "1011" in figures 1 centimetre high.

Nos. 7 (coloured through) and 16/19 on thick unwatermarked paper are from a special printing made for presentation purposes.

The printings of the 4a., 8a. and 1r. values in grey were intended for fiscal purposes, but in the event, were made available for postal use.

Forgeries of the 4a., 8a., 1r. grey and 2 to 5r. exist. The latter are common and can be distinguished by the scroll above "LIGHT" where there are five vertical lines of shading in the forgeries and seven in the genuine stamps. Forged cancellations exist on the commoner stamps. Beware of "imperf" stamps made by trimming margins of stamps from marginal positions.

1891. Mombasa Provisionals.

(a) New value handstamped in dull violet, with original face value obliterated and initials added in black manuscript

20	**3**	"½ Anna" on 2a. vermilion ("A.D.") (1.91)	£11000	£1100
		a. "½ Anna" double	†	£13000
		b. Original face value not obliterated	†	£3750
21		"1 Anna" on 4a. brown ("A.B.") (2.91)	£18000	£2250

(b) Manuscript value and initials in black

22	**3**	"½ Anna" on 2a. vermilion ("A.D.") (original face value not obliterated) (1.91)	†	£4750
23		"½ Anna" on 2a. vermilion ("A.B.") (2.91)	£11000	£1100
		a. Error. "½ Annas" ("A.B.")	†	£1200
24		"½ Anna" on 3a. black/*dull red* ("A.B.") (5.91)	£18000	£2250
25		"1 Anna" on 3a. black/*dull red* ("V.H.M.") (6.91)	£16000	£1400
26		"1 Anna" on 4a. brown ("A.B.") (3.91)	£10000	£2000

A.D. = Andrew Dick, Chief Accountant.
A.B. = Archibald Brown, Cashier of the Company.
V.H.M. = Victor H. Mackenzie, Bank Manager.

Nos. 23 and 26 exist with manuscript surcharges in different hands. Examples with a heavy surcharge applied with a thick nib were mainly used at Lamu. Most of the surviving unused examples show this style, but used examples are worth a premium over the prices quoted.

(Surch B.W.)

1894 (1 Nov). Surch as T **5**.

27	**3**	5a. on 8a. blue	75·00	95·00
28		7½a. on 1r. carmine	75·00	95·00
27s/8s Handstamped "SPECIMEN" *Set of 2*			95·00	

Forgeries exist.

1895 (16 Jan). No wmk. P 14.

29	**3**	5a. black/*grey-blue*	1·25	13·00
30		7½a. black	1·25	19·00
29s/30s Handstamped "SPECIMEN" *Set of 2*			75·00	

The date quoted is that of earliest known use of stamps from this consignment.

These two stamps have "LD" after "COMPANY" in the inscription.

The paper of No. 29 is coloured on the surface only.

1895 (Feb). No. 8 surch with manuscript value and initials ("T.E.C.R."). Original face value obliterated in manuscript.

31	**3**	"½ anna" on 3a. black/*dull red* (19.2.)	£600	55·00
32		"1 anna" on 3a. black/*dull red* (22.2.)	£10000	£7000

T.E.C.R. = T.E.C. Remington, Postmaster at Mombasa.
Similar manuscript surcharges on the black/*bright red* shade (No. 8a) are believed to be forgeries.

The Company experienced considerable financial problems during 1894 with the result that the British Government agreed to assume the administration of the territory, as a protectorate, on 1 July 1895.

IMPERIAL ADMINISTRATION

BRITISH EAST AFRICA
(6)

2½
(7)

(Handstamped at Mombasa)

1895 (9 July). Handstamped with T **6**.

33	**3**	½a. deep brown	80·00	38·00
		a. *Pale brown*	£120	55·00
		b. *Dull brown*	†	£3500
		c. Double	£475	£450
		d. Inverted	£7500	
34		1a. blue-green	£200	£120
		a. Double	£750	£500
		b. "ANL" (broken "D") (R. 6/5)	£3500	£3750
		c. *Deep blue-green*	†	£4500
35		2a. vermilion	£200	£100
		a. Double	£850	£550
36		2½a. black/*bright yellow*	£200	70·00
		a. Double	£850	£500
		b. *Black/pale buff*	†	£3000
37		3a. black/*dull red*	£100	50·00
38		4a. yellow-brown	70·00	45·00
		a. Double	£600	£500
39		4½a. dull violet	£225	£100
		a. Double	£900	£650
		b. *Brown-purple*	£1200	£1000
		ba. Double	£3250	£2250
40		5a. black/*grey-blue*	£300	£150
		a. Double	£1100	£850
		b. Inverted	†	£5000
41		7½a. black	£140	90·00
		a. Double	£850	£650
42		8a. blue	£100	80·00
		a. Double	£750	£650
		b. Inverted	£8000	
43		1r. carmine	65·00	55·00
		a. Double	£700	£550
44	**4**	2r. brick-red	£500	£325
45		3r. slate-purple	£275	£160
		a. Double	£1200	£1000
		b. Inverted		
46		4r. ultramarine	£200	£180
		a. Double	£1100	£900
47		5r. grey-green	£450	£300
		a. Double	£1500	£1400
33/47 *Set of 15*			£2750	£1600

Forgeries exist.

The ½a. stamps used for this issue were mainly from the 1893–94 printings on thicker paper, but two used examples are known on the 1890 thin paper printing with sheet watermark (No. 4). The 1a. stamps were mostly from the 1890 thin paper printing (No. 5), but one example is known from the 1895 printing on thick paper (No. 5b). The 2½a. stamps were mainly from the 1893 printing (No. 7c), but three used examples have been reported from the 1892 printing on thin pale buff paper (No. 7b).

1895 (29 Sept). No. 39 surch with T **7** by *The Zanzibar Gazette*.

48	**3**	2½a. on 4½a. dull violet (R.)	£250	90·00
		a. Opt (T **6**) double	£1200	£950

British East Africa
(8)

British East Africa
(9)

SETTING OF TYPE 8. This consisted of 120 impressions in ten horizontal rows of 12 stamps. This matched the size of the pane for all the Indian issues to 1r. with the exception of the 6a. The sheets of this value contained four panes, each 8×10, which meant that the outer vertical margins also received the overprint.

The setting of Type **9** is not known.

Although only the one setting was used for the low values it is known that some of the overprint errors occurred, or were corrected, during the course of the various printings.

(Overprinted at the offices of *The Zanzibar Gazette*)

1895 (27 Oct)–96. Stamps of India (Queen Victoria) optd with T **8** or **9** (2r. to 5r.). W **13** (Elephant Head) (6a.) or W **34** (Large Star) (others) of India.

49		½a. blue-green (No. 85) (8.11.95)	7·00	5·50
		a. "Britlsh" for "British"	£10000	£8000
		b. "Br1tish" for "British" (R. 10/12)	£600	
		c. "Afr1ca" for "Africa" (R. 1/11)	£800	
		d. Opt double, one albino	£225	
		e. "Briti" for "British" (R. 1/6)	£4000	
50		1a. plum (No. 89) (8.11.95)	7·00	6·00
		a. "Britlsh" for "British"	£18000	£5500
		b. "Br1tish" for "British" (R. 10/12)	£650	£700
		c. "Afr1ca" for "Africa" (R. 1/11)	£850	
		d. "Briti" for "British" (R. 1/6)	£4250	
51		1a.6p. sepia (No. 90) (23.11.95)	4·75	4·00
		a. "Br1tish" for "British" (R. 10/12)	£700	£550
		b. "Afr1ca" for "Africa" (R. 1/11)	£900	
52		2a. blue (No. 92) (28.10.95)	9·50	3·50
		a. "Britlsh" for "British"	£10000	£8500
		b. "Br1tish" for "British" (R. 10/12)	£600	£275
		c. "Afr1ca" for "Africa" (R. 1/11)	£850	£375
		d. "h" of "British" inserted by hand	£3000	

53		2a.6p. yellow-green (No. 103)	17·00	2·50
		c. "Br1tish" for "British"	†	£5500
		d. "Eas" for "East" (R. 2/12)	£1300	£1500
		e. "Br1tish" for "British" (R. 10/12)	£800	£300
		f. "Afr1ca" for "Africa" (R. 1/11)	£1000	£400
		g. "Briti" for "British" (R. 1/6)	£4500	
		h. Opt double	£1200	
54		3a. brown-orange (No. 94) (18.12.95)	25·00	11·00
		a. "Br1tish" for "British" (R. 10/12)	£800	£550
		b. "Afr1ca" for "Africa" (R. 1/11)	£1100	
		c. Opt double, one albino	£750	
55		4a. olive-green (No. 95) (18.12.95)	50·00	48·00
		a. "Br1tish" for "British" (R. 10/12)	£1400	
		b. *Slate-green*	29·00	32·00
		ba. "Br1tish" for "British" (R. 10/12)	£1000	£650
		bb. "Afr1ca" for "Africa" (R. 1/11)	£1300	£850
56		6a. pale brown (No. 81) (18.12.95)	50·00	50·00
		a. "Br1tish" for "British" (R. 10/8)	£2000	
		b. "Afr1ca" for "Africa" (R. 1/7)	£2500	
		c. "E st" for "East"	†	—
		d. Opt double, one albino	£300	
57		8a. dull mauve (No. 98) (18.12.95)	£100	70·00
		a. "Br1tish" for "British" (R. 10/12)	£800	
		b. "Afr1ca" for "Africa" (R. 1/11)	£900	
		c. *Magenta* (1896)	35·00	55·00
		ca. "Br1tish" for "British" (R. 10/12)	£950	£900
		cb. "Afr1ca" for "Africa" (R. 1/11)	£1100	£950
		cc. Inverted "a" for "t" of "East" (R. 2/12)	†	£25000
58		12a. purple/*red* (No. 100) (18.12.95)	22·00	42·00
		a. "Br1tish" for "British" (R. 10/12)	£900	£950
		b. "Afr1ca" for "Africa" (R. 1/11)	£1300	£1400
59		1r. slate (No. 101) (18.12.95)	£100	70·00
		a. "Br1tish" for "British" (R. 10/12)	£900	
		b. "Afr1ca" for "Africa" (R. 1/11)	£950	
60		1r. green and aniline carmine (No. 106) (1896)	50·00	£130
		a. Inverted "a" for "t" of "East" (R. 2/12)	£18000	
		b. "Br1tish" for "British" (R. 10/12)	£2250	
		c. "Afr1ca" for "Africa" (R. 1/11)	£2250	
		d. Opt double, one sideways	£425	£900
		e. Opt double, one albino	£750	
61		2r. carmine and yellow-brown (No. 107) (18.12.95)	£140	£200
		a. "B" handstamped	£8500	£8500
62		3r. brown and green (No. 108) (18.12.95)	£160	£200
		a. "B" handstamped	£8500	£8500
		b. Opt double, one albino	£2000	
63		5r. ultramarine and violet (No. 109) (18.12.95)	£170	£225
		a. Opt double, one albino	£3500	
		b. "B" handstamped	£7500	£6500
		c. Opt double, one albino	£2000	
49/63 *Set of 15*			£700	£900

The relative horizontal positions of the three lines of the overprint vary considerably but the distance vertically between the lines of the overprint is constant.

In both the "Br1tish" and "Afr1ca" errors the figure one is in a smaller type size.

There are other varieties, such as inverted "s" in "British", wide and narrow "B", and inverted "V" for "A" in "Africa" (R. 1/1 and R. 6/7).

During the overprinting of Nos. 61/3 the "B" of "British" sometimes failed to print so that only traces of the letter appeared. It was replaced by a handstamped "B" which is often out of alignment with the rest of the overprint. The handstamp is known double.

The 2, 3r. and 5r., normally overprinted in larger type than the lower values, are also known with a smaller overprint, for use as specimen stamps for the UPU. These were not issued for postal purposes (*Price* £500 *un per set*). The lower values were reprinted at the same time using similar type to the original overprint.

Forgeries exist.

2½
(10)

11

1895 (19 Dec). No. 51 surch locally with T **10** in bright red.

64		2½ on 1½a. sepia	£120	50·00
		a. Inverted "1" in fraction (R. 5/7, 10/7)	£1200	£700
		b. "Br1tish" for "British" (R. 10/12)	£1800	
		c. "Afr1ca" for "Africa" (R. 1/11)	£1800	

The setting of Type **10** was in five horizontal rows of 12 stamps, repeated twice for each pane.

No. 51 also exists surcharged with T **12**, **13** and **14** in bright red-brown. These stamps were sent to the Postal Union authorities at Berne, but were never issued to the public (*Price unused*: T **12** £110, T **13** £225, T **14** £150).

(Recess D.L.R.)

1896 (26 May)–1901. Wmk Crown CA. P 14.

65	**11**	½a. yellow-green	6·50	1·00
		x. Wmk reversed	£450	£300
66		1a. carmine-rose	17·00	40
		a. *Bright rose-red*	16·00	40
		b. *Rosine* (1901)	32·00	4·50
		w. Wmk inverted	£250	£160
		x. Wmk reversed	£375	£200
		y. Wmk inverted and reversed	†	£425
67		2a. chocolate	14·00	9·00
		x. Wmk reversed	†	£200
68		2½a. deep blue	18·00	3·00
		a. *Violet-blue*	26·00	3·75
		b. Inverted "S" in "ANNAS" (R. 1/1).	£250	85·00
		w. Wmk inverted	†	£325
		x. Wmk reversed	£325	£200
69		3a. grey	11·00	16·00
		x. Wmk reversed	£180	£250
70		4a. deep green	9·00	6·00
71		4½a. orange-yellow	19·00	20·00
72		5a. yellow-bistre	8·50	8·50
73		7½a. mauve	13·00	27·00
		w. Wmk inverted	†	£600
		x. Wmk reversed	†	£500
74		8a. grey-olive	12·00	8·00
75		1r. pale dull blue	80·00	29·00
		a. *Ultramarine*	£140	70·00
76		2r. orange	70·00	35·00

77		3r. deep violet	70·00	40·00
78		4r. carmine-lake	70·00	80·00
79		5r. sepia	70·00	42·00
		a. Thin "U" in "RUPEES" (R. 3/2)	£1800	£1400
		x. Wmk reversed	†	£900
65/79 *Set of 15*			£400	£275
65s/79s Optd "SPECIMEN" *Set of 15*			£350	

Examples of some values exist apparently without watermark or with double-lined lettering from the marginal watermark due to the paper being misplaced on the press.

(Overprinted at the offices of *The Zanzibar Gazette*)

1897 (2 Jan). Nos. 156/7, 159 and 165/7 of Zanzibar optd with T **8**. Wmk Single Rosette.

80		½a. yellow-green and red	60·00	50·00
81		1a. indigo and red	£100	95·00
82		2a. red-brown and red	50·00	26·00
83		4½a. orange and red	60·00	32·00
		a. No right serif to left-hand "4" (R. 1/1)	£1400	
		b. No fraction bar at right (R. 2/1)	£1400	£850
84		5a. bistre and red	65·00	50·00
		a. "Bri" for "British"	£2000	£2000
85		7½a. mauve and red	70·00	50·00
		a. "Bri" for "British"	£2500	
		b. Optd on front and back	£350	
80/5 *Set of 6*			£375	£250

Nos. 84a and 85a appear to have occurred when the type was obscured during part of the overprinting.

The above six stamps exist with an overprint similar to T **8** but normally showing a stop after "Africa" (in red on the 1a.) were made officially to supply the UPU (*Price* £300 *un per set*). However, the stop does not always show. Pieces are known showing overprints with and without stop *se-tenant* (including the red overprint on the 1a.).

Stamps of Zanzibar, wmk "Multiple Rosettes" and overprinted with T **8** are forgeries.

$2\frac{1}{2}$ $2\frac{1}{2}$ $2\frac{1}{2}$
(12)   (13)   (14)

SETTING OF TYPES 12/14. The setting of 60 (6×10) contained 26 examples of Type **12**, 10 of Type **13** and 24 of Type **14**.

1897 (2 Jan). Nos. 157 and 162 of Zanzibar optd with T **8** and further surch locally, in red.

86	**12**	2½ on 1a. indigo and red	£130	70·00
		b. Opt Type **8** double	£7500	
87	**13**	2½ on 1a. indigo and red	£325	£120
88	**14**	2½ on 1a. indigo and red	£150	75·00
		a. Opt Type **8** double	£7500	
89	**12**	2½ on 3a. grey and red	£130	65·00
90	**13**	2½ on 3a. grey and red	£325	£120
91	**14**	2½ on 3a. grey and red	£150	70·00
86/91 *Set of 6*			£1100	£475

Both the notes after No. 85 also apply here.

A special printing for UPU requirements was made with the 2½ surcharge on the 1a. and 3a. stamps overprinted as T **8** but *with stop after "Africa"* (*Price from* £100 *per stamp*). It also included a "2" over "1" error in T **14** (*Price*, £2750, either value) and a diagonal fraction bar variety in T **12**. The surcharge on the 3a. is known double, one albino.

15

(Recess D.L.R.)

1897 (Nov)–**1903**. Wmk Crown CC. P 14.

92	**15**	1r. grey-blue	£130	55·00
		a. *Dull blue* (1901)	£110	65·00
		b. *Bright ultramarine* (1903)	£550	£400
93		2r. orange	£150	£160
94		3r. deep violet	£180	£190
95		4r. carmine	£500	£550
		x. Wmk reversed	£850	£950
		y. Wmk inverted and reversed	£1800	
96		5r. deep sepia	£450	£550
97		10r. yellow-bistre	£450	£650
		s. Optd "SPECIMEN"	85·00	
		x. Wmk reversed	£1700	
98		20r. pale green (f.c. £110)	£1200	£2750
		s. Optd "SPECIMEN"	£180	
99		50r. mauve (f.c. £300)	£2500	£9000
		s. Optd "SPECIMEN"	£400	
		x. Wmk reversed	£2750	£9000
		xs. Optd "SPECIMEN"	£425	
92s/6s Optd "SPECIMEN" *Set of 5*			£250	

On 1 April 1901 the postal administrations of British East Africa and Uganda were merged. Subsequent issues were inscribed "EAST AFRICA AND UGANDA PROTECTORATES".

EAST AFRICA AND UGANDA PROTECTORATES

For earlier issues see BRITISH EAST AFRICA and UGANDA.

For the issues of the Mandated Territory of Tanganyika and the war-time issues that preceded them, see TANGANYIKA.

PRICES FOR STAMPS ON COVER TO 1945		
Nos. 1/43	*from* × 3	
Nos. 44/75	*from* × 2	
Nos. 76/95	*from* × 3	
Nos. 96/105	—	
Nos. 110/23	*from* × 2	
Nos. 124/7	*from* × 3	
Nos. 128/30	*from* × 5	
Nos. 131/54	*from* × 3	
Nos. D1/12	*from* × 8	

PRINTERS. All the stamps issued between 1903 and 1927 were typographed by De La Rue & Co. Ltd, London.

USED HIGH VALUES. Beware of cleaned fiscally cancelled examples with faked postmarks.

1   2

1903 (24 July)–04. P 14.

(a) Wmk Crown CA

1	**1**	½a. green (16.2.04)	6·50	22·00
2		1a. grey and red	2·25	1·75
3		2a. dull and bright purple (24.7.03)	8·50	2·50
		w. Wmk inverted	£250	£225
4		2½a. blue	12·00	55·00
5		3a. brown-purple and green	28·00	70·00
6		4a. grey-green and black	11·00	22·00
7		5a. grey and orange-brown	19·00	55·00
8		8a. grey and pale blue	27·00	50·00

(b) Wmk Crown CC. Ordinary paper

9	**2**	1r. green	26·00	65·00
		a. Chalk-surfaced paper	90·00	£140
10		2r. dull and bright purple	90·00	£100
11		3r. grey-green and black	£170	£300
12		4r. grey and emerald-green	£170	£325
13		5r. grey and red	£170	£325
14		10r. grey and ultramarine	£450	£650
		a. Chalk-surfaced paper	£600	£700
		w. Wmk inverted	£1200	
15		20r. grey and stone	£800	£1900
		s. Optd "SPECIMEN"	£180	
16		50r. grey and red-brown (f.c. £225)	£2500	£4500
		s. Optd "SPECIMEN"	£450	
		w. Wmk inverted (f.c. £500)	£5500	
1/13 *Set of 13*			£650	£1200
1s/14s Optd "SPECIMEN" *Set of 14*			£475	

1904–07. Wmk Mult Crown CA. Ordinary paper (½a. to 8a.) or chalk-surfaced paper (1r. to 50r.).

17	**1**	½a. grey-green	8·50	3·00
		a. Chalk-surfaced paper	16·00	3·25
18		1a. grey and red	11·00	80
		a. Chalk-surfaced paper	17·00	1·75
19		2a. dull and bright purple	3·25	2·75
		a. Chalk-surfaced paper	3·50	2·75
20		2½a. blue	8·00	30·00
21		2½a. ultramarine and blue	7·50	17·00
22		3a. brown-purple and green	5·50	45·00
		a. Chalk-surfaced paper	6·00	48·00
23		4a. grey-green and black	7·50	18·00
		a. Chalk-surfaced paper	9·50	18·00
24		5a. grey and orange-brown	8·00	15·00
		a. Chalk-surfaced paper	6·50	32·00
25		8a. grey and pale blue	7·00	8·50
		a. Chalk-surfaced paper	7·00	23·00
26	**2**	1r. green (1907)	35·00	70·00
		w. Wmk inverted	£1300	£950
27		2r. dull and bright purple (1906)	50·00	75·00
28		3r. grey-green and black (1907)	95·00	£150
29		4r. grey and emerald-green (1907)	£130	£200
		w. Wmk inverted	£1100	
30		5r. grey and red (1907)	£170	£190
31		10r. grey and ultramarine (1907)	£375	£425
		w. Wmk inverted	£1100	£1200
32		20r. grey and stone (1907)	£850	£1500
33		50r. grey and red-brown (1907)		
		(f.c. £425)	£2750	£4500
17/30 *Set of 13*			£475	£750

(New Currency. 100 cents = 1 rupee)

1907–08. Wmk Mult Crown CA. Chalk-surfaced paper (10, 12, 25, 50, 75c.). P 14.

34	**1**	1c. brown	2·50	15
35		3c. grey-green	21·00	70
		a. *Blue-green*	26·00	4·00
36		6c. red	3·00	10
37		10c. lilac and pale olive	12·00	8·50
38		12c. dull and bright purple	10·00	2·75
39		15c. bright blue	32·00	8·50
40		25c. black and red	24·00	7·00
41		50c. grey-green and orange-brown	18·00	16·00
42		75c. grey and pale blue (1908)	4·75	45·00
34/42 *Set of 9*			£110	80·00
34s/42s Optd "SPECIMEN" *Set of 9*			£250	

    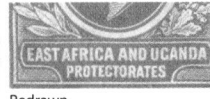
Original   Redrawn

1910. T **1** redrawn. Printed from a single plate. Wmk Mult Crown CA. P 14.

43		6c. red	26·00	30

In the redrawn type a fine white line has been cut around the value tablets and above the name tablet separating the latter from the leaves above, EAST AFRICA AND UGANDA is in shorter and thicker letters and PROTECTORATES in taller letters than in No. 36.

3   4   (5)

**4
cents**

1912–21. Wmk Mult Crown CA. Chalk-surfaced paper (25c. to 500r.). P 14.

44	**3**	1c. black	30	1·75
		a. "C" of "CA" missing from wmk	†	£1000
		y. Wmk inverted and reversed	†	£650
45		3c. green	2·00	60
		a. *Deep blue-green* (1917)	4·50	1·75
		w. Wmk inverted	†	
46		6c. red	1·25	40
		a. *Scarlet* (1917)	25·00	3·00
		w. Wmk inverted	—	£650
		y. Wmk inverted and reversed	—	£650
47		10c. yellow-orange	2·00	50
		a. *Orange* (1921)	13·00	6·00
		w. Wmk inverted	£700	
48		12c. slate-grey	2·75	50
		a. Wmk sideways		
49		15c. bright blue	2·75	80
		w. Wmk inverted	£650	£650
50		25c. black and red/*yellow*	50	1·25
		a. *White back* (5.14)	50	4·50
		as. Optd "SPECIMEN"	38·00	
		b. *On lemon* (1916)	11·00	11·00
		bs. Optd "SPECIMEN"	42·00	
		c. *On orange-buff* (1921)	48·00	18·00
		d. *On pale yellow* (1921)	14·00	7·00
51		50c. black and lilac	1·50	1·50
52		75c. black/*green*	1·50	17·00
		a. *White back* (5.14)	1·00	16·00
		as. Optd "SPECIMEN"	40·00	
		b. *On blue-green, olive back*	10·00	7·50
		bs. Optd "SPECIMEN"	48·00	
		c. *On emerald, olive back* (1919)	45·00	£150
		d. *On emerald back* (1921)	12·00	60·00
53	**4**	1r. black/*green*	2·50	4·25
		aw. Wmk inverted	£800	
		b. *On emerald back* (1919)	5·00	50·00
54		2r. red and black/*blue*	25·00	42·00
		w. Wmk inverted	£475	
		x. Wmk reversed	†	—
55		3r. violet and green	30·00	£120
56		4r. red and green/*yellow*	60·00	£110
		a. *On pale yellow*	£140	£200
57		5r. blue and dull purple	65·00	£160
58		10r. red and green/*green*	£250	£350
59		20r. black and purple/*red*	£475	£450
60		20r. purple and blue/*blue* (1918)	£550	£850
61		50r. dull rose-red and dull greyish green (f.c. £75)	£900	£950
		a. *Carmine and green*	£1500	£1500
		s. Optd "SPECIMEN"	£700	
62		100r. purple and black/*red* (f.c. £250)	£9500	£3750
		s. Optd "SPECIMEN"	£700	
63		500r. green and red/*green* (f.c. £850)	£40000	
		s. Optd "SPECIMEN"	£1500	
44/58 *Set of 15*			£400	£700
44s/60s Optd "SPECIMEN" *Set of 17*			£900	

For values in this series overprinted "G.E.A." (German East Africa) see Tanganyika Nos. 45/62.

1919 (7 Apr). No. 46a surch with T **5** by the Swift Press, Nairobi.

64	**3**	4c. on 6c. scarlet (*shades*)	1·25	15
		a. Bars omitted	50·00	70·00
		b. Surch double	£160	£250
		c. Surch inverted	£350	£450
		d. Pair, one without surch	£2000	£2250
		e. Surch on back	£475	
		s. Handstamped "SPECIMEN"	65·00	

1921. Wmk Mult Script CA. Chalk-surfaced paper (50c. to 50r.). P 14.

65	**3**	1c. black	80	1·75
		w. Wmk inverted	£425	£425
66		3c. green	6·00	16·00
		a. *Blue-green*	25·00	21·00
67		6c. carmine-red	10·00	21·00
68		10c. orange (12.21)	8·50	1·25
		w. Wmk inverted	†	£650
69		12c. slate-grey	11·00	£140
70		15c. bright blue	11·00	21·00
71		50c. black and dull purple	14·00	£120
72	**4**	2r. red and black/*blue*	75·00	£180
73		3r. violet and green	£150	£425
74		5r. blue and dull purple	£180	£350
75		50r. carmine and green (f.c. £450)	£3250	£9000
		s. Optd "SPECIMEN"	£500	
65/74 *Set of 10*			£425	£1100
65s/74s Optd "SPECIMEN" *Set of 10*			£400	

For values in this series overprinted "G.E.A." see Tanganyika Nos. 63/73.

KENYA AND UGANDA

(New Currency. 100 cents = 1 East Africa shilling)

On 23 July 1920, Kenya became a Crown Colony with the exception of the coastal strip, previously part of the Sultan of Zanzibar's territories, which remained a protectorate.

The northern province of Jubaland was ceded to Italy on 29 June 1925 and later incorporated into Italian Somaliland.

6   7

1922 (1 Nov)–27. Wmk Mult Script CA. P 14.

(a) Wmk upright. Ordinary paper

76	**6**	1c. pale brown	1·00	4·75
		a. *Deep brown* (1923)	1·50	3·50
		ax. Wmk reversed	£350	
77		5c. dull violet	7·00	75
		a. *Bright violet*	12·00	1·50
78		5c. green (1927)	2·00	30
		sa. Opt "SPECIMEN" double	£500	
79		10c. green	1·50	30
		w. Wmk inverted	£650	
80		10c. black (5.27)	4·00	20

81		12c. jet-black	15·00	38·00
	a.	Grey-black	15·00	26·00
82		15c. rose-carmine	1·25	10
83		20c. dull orange-yellow	3·25	10
	a.	Bright orange	6·50	10
84		30c. ultramarine	4·25	50
85		50c. grey	2·50	10
86		75c. olive	10·00	9·00

(b) Wmk sideways*. Chalk-surfaced paper

87	7	1s. green	7·00	2·50
88		2s. dull purple	9·00	20·00
		w. Wmk Crown to right of CA	£190	£275
89		2s.50 brown (1.10.25)	19·00	£120
90		3s. brownish grey	19·00	6·50
	a.	Jet-black	55·00	50·00
91		4s. grey (1.10.25)	40·00	£130
		w. Wmk Crown to right of CA	80·00	£250
92		5s. carmine-red	24·00	22·00
		w. Wmk Crown to right of CA	—	£550
93		7s.50 orange-yellow (1.10.25)	£130	£325
94		10s. bright blue	80·00	75·00
		w. Wmk Crown to right of CA (f.c. £75)	£550	£550
95		£1 black and orange (f.c. £20)	£225	£325
96		£2 green and purple (1.10.25) (f.c. £170)	£1100	£2000
		s. Optd "SPECIMEN"	£325	
97		£3 purple and yellow (1.10.25) (f.c. £300)	£1800	
		s. Optd "SPECIMEN"	£375	
98		£4 black and magenta (1.10.25) (f.c. £300)	£3000	
		s. Optd "SPECIMEN"	£500	
99		£5 black and blue (f.c. £120)	£3250	
		s. Optd "SPECIMEN"	£600	
		w. Wmk Crown to right of CA	£3500	
100		£10 black and green (f.c. £325)	£14000	
		s. Optd "SPECIMEN"	£850	
		w. Wmk Crown to right of CA (f.c. £375)	£22000	
101		£20 red and green (1.10.25) (f.c. £850)	£29000	
		s. Optd "SPECIMEN"	£1500	
102		£25 black and red (f.c. £500)	£38000	
		s. Optd "SPECIMEN"	£1600	
		w. Wmk Crown to right of CA	£48000	
103		£50 black and brown (f.c. £650)	£50000	
		s. Optd "SPECIMEN"	£2000	
104		£75 purple and grey (1.10.25) (f.c. £3500)	£150000	
		s. Optd "SPECIMEN"	£4000	
105		£100 red and black (1.10.25) (f.c. £2250)	£160000	
		s. Optd "SPECIMEN"	£4500	
76/95 Set of 20			£500	£900
76s/95s Optd "SPECIMEN" Set of 20			£850	

Nos. 87/94 were printed in two operations sometimes causing shade differences between the head and the frame.

*The normal sideways watermark shows Crown to left of CA, as seen from the back of the stamp.

KENYA, UGANDA AND TANGANYIKA

The postal administrations of Kenya, Tanganyika and Uganda were amalgamated on 1 January 1933. On the independence of the three territories the combined administration became the East African Posts and Telecommunications Corporation.

8 South African Crowned Cranes

9 Dhow on Lake Victoria

10 Lion

11 Kilimanjaro

12 Nile Railway Bridge, Ripon Falls

13 Mt. Kenya

14 Lake Naivasha

 I

 II

(Des 1c., 20c., 10s., R. C. Luck, 10c., £1, A. Ross, 15c., 2s., G. Gill Holmes, 30c., 5s., R. N. Ambasana, 65c., L. R. Cutts. T **10** typo, remainder recess D.L.R.)

1935 (1 May)–37. Wmk Mult Script CA. Chalk-surfaced paper (10c., £1). P 12×13 (**10**), 14 (**9** and **14**) and 13 (remainder).

110	**8**	1c. black and red-brown	1·00	1·50
111	**9**	5c. black and green (I)	3·75	20
		a. Rope joined to sail (II) (1937)	40·00	8·00
		b. Perf 13×12 (I)	£9500	£950
		ba. Rope joined to sail (II) (1937)	£850	£225
112	**10**	10c. black and yellow	7·50	60
113	**11**	15c. black and scarlet	4·25	10
		a. Frame double, one albino	†	—
114	**8**	20c. black and orange	3·50	20
115	**12**	30c. black and blue	5·00	1·00
116	**9**	50c. bright purple and black (I)	6·50	10
117	**13**	65c. black and brown	8·50	2·00
118	**14**	1s. black and green	5·50	1·50
		a. Frame double, one albino	†	£1100
		b. Perf 13×12 (1936)	£1500	£140
		ba. Frame treble, two albino	†	£1500
119	**11**	2s. lake and purple	12·00	4·50
120	**14**	3s. blue and black	19·00	15·00
		a. Perf 13×12 (1936)	£2500	
121	**12**	5s. black and carmine	25·00	27·00
122	**8**	10s. purple and blue	£100	£130
123	**10**	£1 black and red	£325	£425
110/23 Set of 14			£475	£550
110s/23s Perf "SPECIMEN" Set of 14			£500	

Line through "0" of 1910 (R. 4/2)

(Des H. Fleury. Recess D.L.R.)

1935 (6 May). Silver Jubilee. As Nos. 91/4 of Antigua. Wmk Mult Script CA. P 13½×14.

124		20c. light blue and olive-green	2·75	10
		f. Diagonal line by turret	£140	50·00
		g. Dot to left of chapel	£275	90·00
		h. Dot by flagstaff	£275	90·00
		i. Dash by turret	£350	£130
125		30c. brown and deep blue	3·50	3·00
		f. Diagonal line by turret	£225	£225
		g. Dot to left of chapel	£500	£450
		h. Dot by flagstaff	£500	£450
		i. Dash by turret	£550	
126		65c. green and indigo	2·00	3·00
		f. Diagonal line by turret	£250	£250
		g. Dot to left of chapel	£500	£550
127		1s. slate and purple	2·25	5·50
		f. Diagonal line by turret	£250	£325
		g. Dot to left of chapel	£550	£500
		h. Dot by flagstaff	£550	
		i. Dash by turret	£650	
		l. Line through "0" of 1910	£140	£180
124/7 Set of 4			9·50	10·50
124s/7s Perf "SPECIMEN" Set of 4			£170	

For illustrations of the other plate varieties see Omnibus section following Zanzibar.

Broken leaf (R. 6/1)

(Des and recess D.L.R.)

1937 (12 May). Coronation. As Nos. 95/7 of Antigua.

128		5c. green	20	10
129		20c. orange	40	30
		a. Broken leaf	75·00	
130		30c. bright blue	60	1·75
128/30 Set of 3			1·10	1·90
128s/30s Perf "SPECIMEN" Set of 3			£150	

15 Dhow on Lake Victoria

Damaged left-hand value tablet (Frame Pl 2–2, with Centre Pl 4A or 4B, R. 9/6)

Retouched value tablet (Frame Pl 2–2, with Centre Pls 4A, 4B, 5, 6 or 7, R. 9/6)

1c. 'Tadpole' flaw (Frame Pl 2–2, with centre Pl 4B R. 10/8)

1c. Break in bird's breast (Frame Pl 2–2, with Centre Pls 4A or 4B, R. 2/5)

5c. Crescent-shaped "shadow" on sail (Pl 2A, R.8/1)

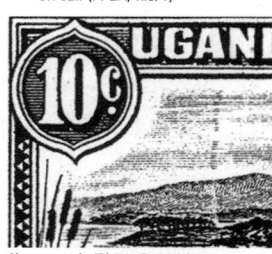

Sky retouch (Pl 7A, R. 10/6)

1s., 3s. Damage on mountain (Pl 7B, R. 6/7. August 1948 ptg. Retouched in June 1949 for 10c. and 1s.)

10c., 1s. Mountain retouch (Covering the peak and the slopes to the left) (Pl 7B, R. 6/7)

10c., 1s. Mountain retouch (Covering the peak and the hills to its right) (Pl 7B, R. 5/10)

50c. With dot

Dot removed

In the 50c. printing of 14 June 1950 using Frame-plate 3, the dot was removed by retouching on all but five stamps (R. 5/2, 6/1, 7/2, 7/4 and 9/1). In addition, other stamps show traces of the dot where the retouching was not completely effective. Examples of the 10c. (135/c and 136) and 1s. (145a) are known with the dot apparently removed, but these are due to random flaws on the plate rather than a deliberate attempt to retouch and are not listed.

PERFORATIONS. In this issue, to aid identification, the perforations are indicated to the nearest quarter.

(T **10** typo, others recess D.L.R.)

1938 (11 Apr)–54. As T **8** to **14** (but with portrait of King George VI in place of King George V, as in T **15**). Wmk Mult Script CA. Chalk-surfaced paper (£1).

131	**8**	1c. black and red-brown (P 13¼) (2.5.38)	4·75	85
		a. Perf 13¼×13¾. *Black and chocolate-brown* (1942)	30	50
		ab. "A" of "CA" missing from wmk	£225	
		ac. Damaged value tablet	£100	
		ad. Retouched value tablet	45·00	70·00
		ae. Break in bird's breast	90·00	
		af. 'Tadpole' flaw	£100	£200
		ag. *Black and deep chocolate-brown* (10.6.46)	2·25	3·50
		ah. *Ditto. Retouched value tablet*	50·00	80·00
		ai. *Black and red-brown* (26.9.51)	8·00	7·00

132	**15**	5c. black and green (II) (P 13×11¾)...	6·50	50
		a. "Shadow" on sail.....................	£300	
133		5c. reddish brown and orange (P 13×11¾) (1.6.49).....	2·50	8·00
		a. Perf 13×12½ (14.6.50).............	4·50	5·00
134	**14**	10c. red-brown and orange (P 13×11¾) (2.5.38)........	2·25	10
		a. "A" of "CA" missing from wmk...	£1500	
		aw. Wmk inverted.....................	†	£3000
		b. Perf 14 (22.4.41).................	£130	8·50
135		10c. black and green (P 13×11¾) (1.6.49)..............	30	2·00
		a. Mountain retouch (R. 6/7)........	95·00	£130
		ab. Mountain retouch (R. 5/10)......	£500	£650
		b. Sky retouch........................	£275	
		c. Perf 13×12½ (14.6.50)............	5·00	10
136		10c. brown and grey (P 13×12½) (1.4.52)..............	1·75	55
137	**11**	15c. black and rose-red (P 13¼) (2.5.38)............	32·00	55
		a. Perf 13¾×13¼ (2.43).............	8·00	4·00
		ab. "A" of "CA" missing from wmk....	£1700	
138		15c. black and green (P 13¾×13¼) (1.4.52)............	3·00	6·00
139	**8**	20c. black and orange (P 13¼) (2.5.38)	42·00	30
		a. Perf 14 (19.5.41).................	55·00	1·75
		b. Perf 13¼×13¾ (25.2.42)........	9·50	10
		ba. *Deep black and deep orange* (21.6.51)........	28·00	2·25
		bw. Wmk inverted.....................	†	£5000
140	**15**	25c. black and carmine-red (P 13×12½) (1.4.52).......	2·00	2·25
141	**12**	30c. black and dull violet-blue (P 13¼) (2.5.38).......	55·00	40
		a. Perf 14 (3.7.41).................	£160	11·00
		b. Perf 13¼×13¾ (10.5.42)........	3·25	10
142		30c. dull purple and brown (P 13¾×13¼) (1.4.52).....	1·75	40
		w. Wmk inverted.....................	†	£4500
143	**8**	40c. black and blue (P 13¼×13¾) (1.4.52)............	2·00	4·25
144	**15**	50c. purple and black (II) (P 13×11¾) (2.5.38).......	23·00	1·00
		a. Rope not joined to sail (I) (R. 2/5)	£325	£250
		b. *Dull claret and black* (29.7.47)	£110	11·00
		c. *Brown-purple and black* (4.48)...	£120	10·00
		d. *Reddish purple and black* (28.4.49)................	50·00	6·50
		e. Ditto. Perf 13×12½ (10.49).......	14·00	55
		ea. Dot removed (14.6.50)............	32·00	55
		eb. Ditto. In pair with normal.........	£500	£1500
		ew. Wmk inverted.....................	†	£5000
145	**14**	1s. black and yellowish brown (P 13×11¾) (2.5.38).....	38·00	30
		a. Black and brown (9.42)..........	22·00	30
		ab. Damage on mountain..............	—	£1500
		ac. Mountain retouch (R. 6/7).......	£1400	£500
		ad. Mountain retouch (R. 5/10)......	£4500	£700
		aw. Wmk inverted.....................	†	£4000
		b. Perf 13×12½ (10.49).............	22·00	60
		ba. *Deep black and brown (clearer impression)* (14.6.50).........	48·00	2·25
146	**11**	2s. lake-brown and brown-purple (P 13¼) (shades) (2.5.38).....	£140	3·50
		a. Perf 14 (1941)....................	80·00	20·00
		b. Perf 13¾×13¼ (24.2.44)........	50·00	30
147	**14**	3s. dull ultramarine and black (P 13×11¾) (2.5.38)......	50·00	8·50
		a. Deep violet-blue and black (29.4.47)....................	85·00	17·00
		ab. Damage on mountain..............	£7000	£2750
		ac. Perf 13×12½ (14.6.50)...........	50·00	8·50
148	**12**	5s. black and carmine (P 13¼) (2.5.38)................	£150	21·00
		a. Perf 14 (1941)....................	50·00	3·00
		b. Perf 13¼×13¾ (24.2.44)........	50·00	2·00
149	**8**	10s. purple and blue (P 13¼) (2.5.38).................	£140	35·00
		a. Perf 14. Reddish purple and blue (1941)............	50·00	25·00
		b. Perf 13¼×13¾ (24.2.44)........	55·00	8·00
150	**10**	£1 black and red (P 11¾×13) (12.10.38)..............	£500	£160
		a. Perf 14 (1941)....................	42·00	25·00
		ab. Ordinary paper (24.2.44).........	42·00	26·00
		b. Perf 12½ (21.1.54)...............	18·00	42·00
131/50b (*cheapest*) *Set of 20*			£250	50·00
131s/50s Perf "SPECIMEN" *Set of 13*........			£1000	

No. 131ab occurs once in some sheets, always in the sixth vertical row.

The two varieties described as 'Mountain retouch', Nos. 135a/ab and 145ac/ad, are found on printings from June 1949 onwards.

The first printing of the 50c. utilised the King George V centre plate on which each impression had been individually corrected to show the rope joined to sail. R. 2/5 was missed, however, and this continued to show Type I until replaced by a further printing from a new plate in September 1938.

Stamps perf 14, together with Nos. 131a, 137a, 139b, 141b, 146b, 148b and 149b, are the result of air raid damage to the De La Rue works which destroyed the normal perforators. Dates quoted for these stamps represent earliest known postmarks.

10c KENYA TANGANYIKA UGANDA (16)

70c. on 1s. A screw head in the surcharging forme appears as a crescent moon (R. 20/4)

1941 (1 July)–**42**. Pictorial Stamps of South Africa variously surch as T **16** by Government Printer, Pretoria. Inscr alternately in English and Afrikaans.

			Unused pair	Used pair	Used single
151		5c. on 1d. grey and carmine (No. 56)................	1·75	1·75	15
152		10c. on 3d. ultramarine (No. 59)	6·00	9·00	30
153		20c. on 6d. green and vermilion (No. 61c).............	4·00	3·50	20
154		70c. on 1s. brown and chalky blue (No. 62) (20.4.42)........	22·00	5·00	45
		a. Crescent moon flaw............	70·00	75·00	
151/4 *Set of 4*			30·00	17·00	1·00
151s/4s Handstamped "SPECIMEN" *Set of 4 pairs*........			£650		

1946 (11 Nov). Victory. As Nos. 110/11 of Antigua.

155		20c. red-orange...................		50	10
156		30c. blue........................		50	75
155s/6s Perf "SPECIMEN" *Set of 2*........			£130	

Examples of Nos. 155/6 were pre-released at Lindi on 15 October 1946.

1948 (1 Dec). Royal Silver Wedding. As Nos. 112/13 of Antigua.

157		20c. orange.....................		1·00	50
158		£1 scarlet......................		50·00	70·00

1949 (10 Oct). 75th Anniv of Universal Postal Union. As Nos. 114/17 of Antigua.

159		20c. red-orange.................		15	10
		a. "A" of "CA" missing from wmk...		†	£1000
160		30c. deep blue..................		1·75	2·25
		a. "A" of "CA" missing from wmk...		£1100	
161		50c. grey......................		45	1·00
		a. "A" of "CA" missing from wmk...		£1000	
162		1s. red-brown..................		50	60
159/62 *Set of 4*........			2·50	3·50

17 Lake Naivasha

(Recess D.L.R.)

1952 (1 Feb). Visit of Princess Elizabeth and Duke of Edinburgh. Wmk Mult Script CA. P 13×12½.

163	**17**	10c. black and green...........		30	1·50
164		1s. black and brown...........		1·60	2·50

1953 (2 June). Coronation. As No 120 of Antigua.

165		20c. black and red-orange......		30	10

1954 (28 Apr). Royal Visit. As No. 171 but inscr "ROYAL VISIT 1954" below portrait.

166		30c. black and deep ultramarine....		1·00	60

18 Owen Falls Dam   **19** Giraffe

20 African Elephants   **21** Lion

22 Mount Kilimanjaro   **23** Royal Lodge, Sagana

24 Queen Elizabeth II

(Des G. Gill Holmes (10, 50c.), H. Grieme (15c., 1s.30, 5s.), R. McLellan Sim (10s.), De La Rue (65c., 2s., £1), O.C. Meronti (others). Recess D.L.R.)

1954 (1 June)–**59**. Designs as T **18/24**. Wmk Mult Script CA. P 13 (£1); others, 12½×13 (vert) or 13×12½ (horiz).

167	**18**	5c. black and deep brown...........		1·75	50
		a. Vignette inverted...............		†	£60000
168	**19**	10c. carmine-red...................		2·50	10

169	**20**	15c. black and light blue (28.3.58)....		2·50	1·50
		a. Redrawn. Stop below "c" of "15 c" (29.4.59)............		1·75	1·25
170	**21**	20c. black and orange		2·00	10
		a. Imperf (pair)................		£1500	£1700
171	**18**	30c. black and deep ultramarine......		1·50	10
		a. Vignette inverted.............		†	£30000
172	**21**	40c. bistre-brown (28.3.58)........		1·50	75
		w. Wmk inverted................			
173	**19**	50c. reddish purple...............		3·50	10
		a. *Claret* (23.1.57).............		9·00	40
174	**22**	65c. bluish green and brown-purple (1.12.55).........		2·75	1·50
175	**21**	1s. black and claret.............		3·75	10
176	**20**	1s.30 deep lilac and orange (1.12.55)		18·00	10
177	**22**	2s. black and green.............		16·00	1·50
		a. Black and bronze-green (19.4.56)............		29·00	3·00
178	**20**	5s. black and orange...........		42·00	3·50
179	**23**	10s. black and deep ultramarine......		48·00	5·50
180	**24**	£1 brown-red and black.........		19·00	22·00
		a. Venetian red and black (19.4.56)		65·00	28·00
167/80 *Set of 14*........				£140	32·00

Only one example of No. 167a and three of No. 171a have been found, all being used.

The 5, 10 and 50c. exist from coils made up from normal sheets.

25 Map of E. Africa showing Lakes

(Recess Waterlow)

1958 (30 July). Centenary of Discovery of Lakes Tanganyika and Victoria by Burton and Speke. W w **12**. P 12½.

181	**25**	40c. blue and deep green		1·00	40
182		1s.30c. green and violet		1·00	1·60

26 Sisal   **27** Cotton

28 Mt Kenya and Giant Plants   **29** Queen Elizabeth II

5c. "Snake" variety (Pl 2, R. 6/2)

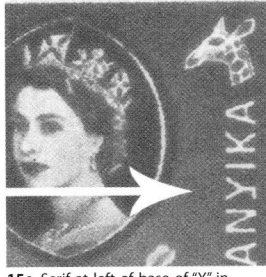

15c. Serif at left of base of "Y" in "TANGANYIKA" (Pl 1, R. 2/7). This was later retouched but traces still remain

1s. Re-entry. Whole of "TANGANYIKA" is doubled (Pl 1-1 and 1-2, R. 9/4).

(Des M. Goaman. Photo (5c. to 65c.), recess (others) D.L.R.)

1960 (1 Oct)–**62**. Designs as T **26/9**. W w **12**. P 15×14 (5c. to 65c.), 13 (20s.) or 14 (others).

183		5c. Prussian blue................		10	15
		a. "Snake" variety (Pl 2, R. 6/2)...		£250	
184		10c. yellow-green...............		10	10

185	15c. dull purple		30	10
	a. "Serif" variety		15·00	10·00
	b. "Serif" retouched		15·00	10·00
186	20c. magenta		20	10
187	25c. bronze-green		3·25	1·25
188	30c. vermilion		15	10
189	40c. greenish blue		15	20
190	50c. slate-violet		15	10
191	65c. yellow-olive		30	2·00
192	1s. deep reddish violet and reddish purple		2·25	10
	a. Blackish lilac and reddish purple (23.1.62)		18·00	1·50
	b. Re-entry		40·00	
193	1s.30 chocolate and brown-red		6·50	15
194	2s. deep grey-blue and greenish blue		9·50	40
195	2s.50 olive-green and deep bluish green		11·00	2·75
196	5s. rose-red and purple		5·00	60
197	10s. blackish green and olive-green		16·00	8·50
	a. Imperf (pair)		£1700	
198	20s. violet-blue and lake		30·00	30·00
183/98 Set of 16			70·00	40·00

Designs: Vert as T **26/7**—15c. Coffee; 20c. Blue Wildebeest; 25c. Ostrich; 30c. Thomson's Gazelle; 40c. Manta; 50c. Common Zebra; 65c. Cheetah. Horiz as T **28**—1s.30, Murchison Falls and Hippopotamus; 2s. Mt Kilimanjaro and Giraffe; 2s.50, Candelabra Tree and Black Rhinoceros; 5s. Crater Lake and Mountains of the Moon; 10s. Ngorongoro Crater and African Buffalo.

The 10c. and 50c. exist in coils with the designs slightly shorter in height, a wider horizontal gutter every 11 stamps and, in the case of the 10c. only, printed with a coarser 200 screen instead of the normal 250. (Price for 10c., 10p. unused.) Plate 2 of 30c. shows coarser 200 screen. (Price 25p. unused.).

PRINTERS. All the following stamps were printed in photogravure by Harrison, unless otherwise stated.

30 Land Tillage

(Des V. Whiteley)

1963 (21 Mar). Freedom from Hunger. T **30** and similar horiz design. P 14½.

199	**30**	15c. blue and yellow-olive	45	10
200	–	30c. red-brown and yellow	60	10
201	**30**	50c. blue and orange-brown	80	10
202	–	1s.30 red-brown and light blue	1·25	1·75
199/202 Set of 4			2·75	1·75

Design:—30c., 1s.30, African with Corncob.

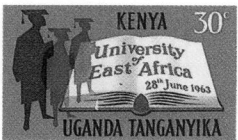

31 Scholars and Open Book

1963 (28 June). Founding of East African University. P 14½.

203	**31**	30c. lake, violet, black and greenish blue	10	10
204		1s.30 lake, blue, red and light yellow-brown	20	30

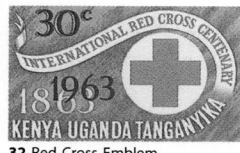

32 Red Cross Emblem

(Des V. Whiteley)

1963 (2 Sept). Centenary of Red Cross. P 14½.

205	**32**	30c. red and blue	1·75	30
206		50c. red and yellow-brown	2·25	1·25

33 Chrysanthemum Emblems   **34**

35 East African "Flags"

(Des V. Whiteley)

1964 (21 Oct). Olympic Games. Tokyo. P 14½.

207	**33**	30c. yellow and reddish violet	15	10

208	**34**	50c. deep reddish violet and yellow	20	10
209	**35**	1s.30 orange-yellow, deep green and light blue	50	10
210		2s.50 magenta, deep violet-blue and light blue	60	3·00
207/10 Set of 4			1·25	3·00

KENYA, UGANDA AND TANZANIA

The following stamps were issued by the East African Postal Administration for use in Uganda, Kenya and Tanzania, excluding Zanzibar.

36 Rally Badge   **37** Cars en route

1965 (15 Apr*). 13th East African Safari Rally. P 14.

211	**36**	30c. black, yellow and turquoise	10	10
212		50c. black, yellow and brown	10	10
		a. Imperf (pair)	£900	
213	**37**	1s.30 deep bluish green, yellow-ochre and blue	35	10
214		2s.50 deep bluish green, brown-red and light blue	60	2·75
211/14 Set of 4			1·00	2·75

*This is the local release date. The Crown Agents in London issued the stamps the previous day.

38 ITU Emblem and Symbols

1965 (17 May). ITU Centenary. P 14½.

215	**38**	30c. gold, chocolate and magenta	25	10
216		50c. gold, chocolate and grey	40	10
217		1s.30 gold, chocolate and blue	90	10
218		2s.50 gold, chocolate and turquoise-green	1·25	2·50
215/18 Set of 4			2·50	2·50

39 ICY Emblem

1965 (4 Aug). International Co-operation Year. P 14½×14.

219	**39**	30c. deep bluish green and gold	20	10
220		50c. black and gold	25	10
221		1s.30 ultramarine and gold	50	10
222		2s.50 carmine-red and gold	1·00	3·50
219/22 Set of 4			1·75	3·50

40 Game Park Lodge, Tanzania

(Des Rena Fennessy)

1966 (4 Apr). Tourism. T **40** and similar horiz designs. Multicoloured. P 14½.

223		30c. Type **40**	90	10
224		50c. Murchison Falls, Uganda	1·00	10
		a. Blue omitted	£425	
225		1s.30 Lesser Flamingoes, Lake Nakuru, Kenya	3·25	30
226		2s.50 Deep Sea Fishing, Tanzania	2·00	2·25
223/6 Set of 4			6·50	3·00

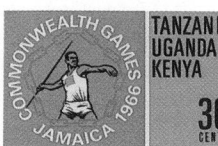

41 Games Emblem

1966 (2 Aug). Eighth British Empire and Commonwealth Games Jamaica. P 14½.

227	**41**	30c. black, gold, turquoise-green and grey	10	10
228		50c. black, gold, cobalt and cerise	15	10
229		1s.30 black, gold, rosine and deep bluish green	20	10
230		2s.50 black, gold, lake and ultramarine	35	1·50
227/30 Set of 4			70	1·50

---

42 UNESCO Emblem

(Des Harrison)

1966 (3 Oct). 20th Anniv of UNESCO. P 14½×14.

231	**42**	30c. black, emerald and red	80	10
232		50c. black, emerald and light brown	90	10
233		1s.30 black, emerald and grey	2·25	20
234		2s.50 black, emerald and yellow	2·75	6·50
231/4 Set of 4			6·00	6·50

43 de Havilland DH.89 Dragon Rapide

(Des R. Granger Barrett)

1967 (23 Jan). 21st Anniv of East African Airways. T **43** and similar horiz designs. P 14½.

235		30c. slate-violet, greenish blue and myrtle-green	30	10
236		50c. multicoloured	40	10
		a. Red omitted	£800	
237		1s.30 multicoloured	85	30
238		2s.50 multicoloured	1·25	3·00
235/8 Set of 4			2·50	3·00

Designs:—50c. Vickers Super VC-10; 1s.30, Hawker Siddeley Comet 4B; 2s.50, Fokker F.27 Friendship.

44 Pillar Tomb   **45** Rock Painting

(Des Rena Fennessy)

1967 (2 May). Archaeological Relics. T **44/5** and similar designs. P 14½.

239		30c. ochre, black and deep reddish purple	15	10
240		50c. orange-red, black and greyish brown	65	10
241		1s.30 black, greenish yellow and deep yellow-green	85	15
242		2s.50 black, ochre and brown-red	1·40	2·50
239/42 Set of 4			2·75	3·00

Designs:—1s.30, Clay head; 2s.50, Proconsul skull.

48 Unified Symbols of Kenya, Tanzania, and Uganda

(Des Rena Fennessy)

1967 (1 Dec). Foundation of East African Community. P 14½×14.

243	**48**	5s. gold, black and grey	40	1·50

49 Mountaineering

(Des Rena Fennessy)

1968 (4 Mar). Mountains of East Africa. T **49** and similar horiz designs. Multicoloured. P 14.

244		30c. Type **49**	15	10
245		50c. Mount Kenya	30	10
246		1s.30 Mount Kilimanjaro	50	10
247		2s.50 Ruwenzori Mountains	70	2·25
244/7 Set of 4			1·50	2·25

50 Family and Rural Hospital

(Des Rena Fennessy. Litho D.L.R.)

1968 (13 May). 20th Anniv of World Health Organization. T **50** and similar horiz designs. P 13½.

248		30c. deep yellow-green, lilac and chocolate	10	10

249	50c. slate-lilac, lilac and black......................	15	10
250	1s.30 yellow-brown, lilac and chocolate....	20	15
251	2s.50 grey, black and reddish lilac.............	30	1·90
248/51 Set of 4		60	2·00

Designs:—50c. Family and nurse; 1s.30, Family and microscope; 2s.50, Family and hypodermic syringe.

51 Olympic Stadium, Mexico City

(Des V. Whiteley)

1968 (14 Oct). Olympic Games, Mexico. T **51** and similar designs. P 14.

252	30c. light green and black...........................	10	10
253	50c. black and blue-green	15	10
254	1s.30 carmine-red, black and grey	25	15
255	2s.50 blackish brown and yellow-brown...	35	1·50
252/5 Set of 4		70	1·60

Designs: Horiz—50c. High-diving boards; 1s.30, Running tracks. Vert—2s.50, Boxing ring.

52 Umoja (railway ferry)

(Des A. Grosart)

1969 (20 Jan). Water Transport. T **52** and similar horiz designs. P 14.

256	30c. deep blue, light blue and slate-grey	50	10
	a. Slate-grey omitted.................................	60·00	
257	50c. multicoloured	60	10
258	1s.30 bronze-green, greenish blue and blue..	1·00	20
259	2s.50 red-orange, deepp blue and pale blue..	1·50	3·25
256/9 Set of 4		3·25	3·25

Designs:—50c. SS *Harambee*; 1s.30, MV *Victoria*; 2s.50, *St. Michael*.

53 ILO Emblem and Agriculture

54 Pope Paul VI and Ruwenzori Mountains

(Des Rena Fennessy)

1969 (14 Apr). 50th Anniv of International Labour Organization. T **53** and similar horiz designs. P 14.

260	30c. black, green and greenish yellow.....	10	10
261	50c. black, plum, cerise and rose	10	10
262	1s.30 black, orange-brown and yellow-orange	10	10
263	2s.50 black, ultramarine and turquoise-blue	20	90
260/3 Set of 4		35	1·00

Designs:—50c. ILO emblem and building work; 1s.30, ILO emblem and factory workers; 2s.50, ILO emblem and shipping.

(Des Harrison)

1969 (31 July). Visit of Pope Paul VI to Uganda. P 14.

264	**54** 30c. black, gold and royal blue	15	10
265	70c. black, gold and claret........................	20	10
266	1s.50 black, gold and deep blue..........	25	20
267	2s.50 black, gold and violet.......................	30	1·40
264/7 Set of 4		80	1·50

55 Euphorbia Tree shaped as Africa and Emblem

56 Marimba

(Des Rena Fennessy. Litho B.W.)

1969 (8 Dec). Fifth Anniv of African Development Bank. P 13½.

268	**55** 30c. deep bluish green, gold and blue-green	10	10
269	70c. deep bluish green, gold and reddish purple	15	10
270	1s.50 deep bluish green, gold and light turquoise-blue	30	10
271	2s.50 deep bluish green, gold and orange-brown	35	2·00
268/71 Set of 4		75	2·00

(Des Rena Fennessy. Litho B.W.)

1970 (16 Feb). Musical Instruments. T **56** and similar horiz designs. P 11×12.

272	30c. buff, yellow-brown and bistre-brown	15	10
273	70c. olive-green, yellow-brown and yellow	25	10
274	1s.50 chocolate and yellow...........................	40	10
275	2s.50 salmon, yellow and chocolate...........	60	2·50
272/5 Set of 4		1·25	2·50

Designs:— 70c. Amadinda; 1s.50, Nzomari; 2s.50, Adeudeu.

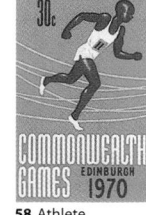

57 Satellite Earth Station

58 Athlete

(Des V. Whiteley. Litho J.W.)

1970 (18 May). Inauguration of East African Satellite Earth Station. T **57** and similar horiz designs. P 14½×14.

276	30c. multicoloured	10	10
277	70c. multicoloured	15	10
278	1s.50 black, slate-violet and pale orange ..	30	10
279	2s.50 multicoloured	60	2·50
276/9 Set of 4		1·00	2·50

Designs:— 70c. Transmitter in daytime; 1s.50, Transmitter at night; 2s.50, Earth and satellite.

(Des Rena Fennessy. Litho Walsall)

1970 (13 July). Ninth Commonwealth Games. P 14×14½.

280	**58** 30c. orange-brown and black.............	10	10
281	70c. olive-green and black........................	10	10
282	1s.50 slate-lilac and black.........................	15	10
283	2s.50 turquoise-blue and black.................	20	1·25
280/3 Set of 4		40	1·40

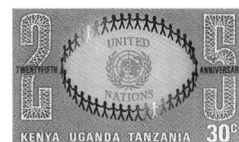

59 "25" and UN Emblem

(Des Rena Fennessy)

1970 (19 Oct). 25th Anniv of United Nations. P 14½.

284	**59** 30c. multicoloured	10	10
285	70c. multicoloured	10	10
286	1s.50 multicoloured	20	10
287	2s.50 multicoloured	45	2·00
284/7 Set of 4		70	2·00

STAMP BOOKLETS

1912–17. Black on pink cover. Letter rate given as 6 cents per oz. Stapled.

SB1	1r.80, booklet containing 12×3c. and 24×6c. (Nos. 45/6), each in blocks of 6............	£2500
	a. Letter rate 6 cents per ½oz. Contains Nos. 45a/6a...	
SB2	2r. booklet containing 6×3c. and 30×6c. (Nos. 45/6), each in blocks of 6............	£2500

1938. Black on pink cover. Stapled.

SB3	3s.40, booklet containing 12×15c. and 8×20c. (Nos. 137, 139), each in blocks of 4................	£300

1950–52. Blue on yellow cover. Stapled.

SB4	1s. booklet containing 4×5c. and 8×10c. (Nos. 133a, 135c), each in blocks of 4........	£750
	a. Contents as SB4, but 10c. changed to No. 136. Stitched (1952)	50·00

1954 (3 Sept). Blue on yellow cover. Stitched.

SB6	1s. booklet containing four 5c. and eight 10c. (Nos. 167/8), each in blocks of 4	3·00

1958 (16 Jan). Black on yellow cover. Stitched.

SB7	5s. booklet containing 4×5c., 4×20c., 4×30c., 4×50c. and 8×10c. (Nos. 167/8, 170/1, 173), each in blocks of 4.......................................	21·00

1958 (16 Dec)–**59**. Black on rose-red cover. Stitched.

SB8	5s. booklet containing 10c., 15c., 20c., 30c. and 50c. (Nos. 168/9, 170/1, 173), in blocks of 4 ..	85·00
	a. Contents as No. SB8, but 15c. changed to No. 169a (20.4.59)...................................	50·00

1961 (1 Feb). Black on rose-red cover. Stitched.

SB9	5s. booklet containing 10c., 15c., 20c., 30c. and 50c. (Nos. 184/6, 188, 190) in blocks of 4........	18·00

OFFICIAL STAMPS

For use on official correspondence of the Tanganyika Government.

OFFICIAL
(O **1**)

OFFICIAL

£1 Broken "O" in "OFFICIAL" (R. 1/6).

1959 (1 July). Nos. 167/71, 173 and 175/80 optd as Type O **1**.

O1	**18**	5c. black and deep brown	10	1·25
O2	**19**	10c. carmine-red..................................	30	1·25
O3	**20**	15c. black and light blue (No. 169a).	75	1·25
O4	**21**	20c. black and orange........................	20	20
		a. Opt double	—	£1600
O5	**18**	30c. black and deep ultramarine.......	15	80
O6	**19**	50c. reddish purple	1·75	20
O7	**21**	1s. black and claret...........................	20	75
O8	**20**	1s.30 orange and deep lilac.................	10·00	1·00
O9	**22**	2s. black and bronze-green	1·25	1·00
O10	**20**	5s. black and orange........................	13·00	4·00
O11	**23**	10s. black and deep ultramarine.......	3·25	7·50
		a. Opt at top.......................................	4·25	3·25
O12	**24**	£1 brown-red and black.....................	7·00	25·00
		a. Broken "O"	75·00	£180
O1/12 Set of 12			32·00	35·00

The 30c., 50c., 1s. and 1s.30 exist with overprint double, but with the two impressions almost coincident.

OFFICIAL	**OFFICIAL**
(O **2**)	(O **3**)

1960 (18 Oct). Nos. 183/6, 188, 190, 192 and 196 optd with Type O **2** (cents values) or O **3**.

O13	5c. Prussian blue	10	3·50
O14	10c. yellow-green..	10	3·00
O15	15c. dull purple	10	3·50
	a. "Serif" variety..	14·00	
	b. "Serif" retouched.....................................	14·00	
O16	20c. magenta	10	75
O17	30c. vermilion..	10	10
O18	50c. slate-violet	30	1·00
O19	1s. deep reddish violet and reddish purple..	30	10
	a. Re-entry	25·00	
O20	5s. rose-red and purple	22·00	65
O13/20 Set of 8		22·00	11·00

The use of these overprints ceased on 8 December 1961.

POSTAGE DUE STAMPS

D 1

D 2

(Typo Waterlow)

1928 (Sept)–**33**. Wmk Mult Script CA. P 15×14.

D1	D **1**	5c. violet..	2·50	75
D2		10c. vermilion..	2·50	15
D3		20c. yellow-green.....................................	4·00	4·25
D4		30c. brown (1931)...................................	27·00	19·00
D5		40c. dull blue	6·50	14·00
D6		1s. grey-green (1933)..........................	70·00	£140
D1/6 Set of 6			£100	£160
D1s/6s Optd or Perf (30c., 1s.) "SPECIMEN" Set of 6..			£350	

(Typo D.L.R.)

1935 (1 May)–**60**. Wmk Mult Script CA. P 14.

D7	D **2**	5c. violet..	2·75	1·75
D8		10c. scarlet...	30	50
D9		20c. green..	40	50
D10		30c. brown...	1·50	50
		a. Bistre-brown (19.7.60)......................	3·00	10·00
D11		40c. ultramarine......................................	1·50	3·00
D12		1s. grey...	19·00	19·00
D7/12 Set of 6			23·00	23·00
D7s/12s Perf "SPECIMEN" Set of 6...........			£300	

Come and Visit us at 399 Strand

1856   1896   1936   1976   2017

- Get advice from our experienced and knowledgeable staff
- See first hand our superb range of top quality stamps, albums and accessories
- Get insider tips on how to enhance and expand your collection
- Ask for guidance on techniques for care and storage of your stamps and covers
- View our specialist material
- All Stanley Gibbons stamps come with a lifetime guarantee of authenticity from our stamp specialists.

Everything for the stamp collector.

399 Strand opening hours
- Mon-Fri 9am-5.30pm   • Sat 9:30am-5.30pm
- Sun Closed

For more information visit
stanleygibbons.com

BY APPOINTMENT TO
HER MAJESTY THE QUEEN
PHILATELISTS
STANLEY GIBBONS LTD
LONDON

STANLEY GIBBONS
LONDON 1856

399 Strand, WC2R 0LX, London
Phone: **+44 1425 472 363** | Email: **support@stanleygibbons.com**
www.stanleygibbons.com

Kuwait

Kuwait, an independent Arab sheikhdom since 1756, placed itself under British protection in 1899 to counter the spread of Ottoman influence in the Arabian Gulf.

The first, somewhat limited, postal service, via Bushire, commenced with the appointment of a Political Agent to Kuwait in August 1904. Because of diplomatic problems this system continued until 21 January 1915 when a regular Indian post office was established.

Limited supplies of Indian stamps were used by the Political Agency postal service, but these became available to the general public from 21 January 1915. Stamps seen postally used from Kuwait before 1923 are usually ½a., 1a., 1r. or 5r. values, with the occasional Official issue. Much more common are values to 15r., both postage and Official, used telegraphically.

Before 1910 the name of the sheikhdom was spelt "KOWEIT" and this spelling appears on various circular postmarks used between 1915 and 1923. The more modern version of the name was first used for a postal cancellation in 1923.

1915 "KOWEIT"

1923 "KUWAIT"

On 1 August 1921 responsibility for the Kuwait postal service passed to the Iraq Post Office.

PRICES FOR STAMPS ON COVER TO 1945	
Nos. 1/15	from × 6
Nos. 16/29	from × 4
Nos. 31/51	from × 3
Nos. 52/63	from × 4
Nos. O1/27	from × 20

USED HIGH VALUES. It is necessary to emphasize that used prices quoted for high value stamps are for postally used examples. Nos. 12/15 and O10/14 with telegraphic cancels are frequently met with and are worth about one-third of the prices quoted.

(Currency. 16 annas = 1 rupee)

KUWAIT (1) **KUWAIT** (2)

1923 (1 Apr)–**24**. Stamps of India (King George V), optd with T **1** or **2** (rupee values, 15½ *mm*) by Indian Govt Ptg Wks. W **34** (Large Star) of India. P 14.

1	½a. emerald (No. 156)	4·50	16·00
	a. Opt double	£350	
	b. Vert pair, one without opt	£1800	
	c. Light green		
2	1a. chocolate (No. 197)	8·00	5·50
	a. Opt double	£500	
	b. Opt omitted (lower stamp of vert pair)	£2000	
3	1½a. chocolate (A) ("ANNA") (No. 163)	6·50	13·00
4	2a. bright reddish violet (No. 169)	5·50	9·50
	a. Reddish purple	14·00	
5	2a.6p. ultramarine (No. 171)	4·25	8·50
6	3a. dull orange (No. 173)	4·25	26·00
7	3a. ultramarine (No. 200) (1924)	10·00	4·25
8	4a. deep olive (No. 174)	10·00	26·00
	a. Olive-green	13·00	
9	6a. brown-ochre (No. 178)	8·50	13·00
10	8a. purple (No. 182)	8·00	55·00
11	12a. carmine-lake (No. 183)	14·00	60·00
	a. Claret	15·00	55·00
12	1r. brown and green (No. 186)	48·00	60·00
	a. Orange-brown and deep turquoise-green	60·00	75·00
13	2r. carmine and brown (No. 187)	65·00	£120
	a. Opt double, one albino	£700	
14	5r. ultramarine and violet (No. 188)	£140	£275
15	10r. green and scarlet (No. 189)	£275	£550
1/15 Set of 15		£550	£1100

Essays of the overprint using the obsolete spelling "KOWEIT" were prepared in 1923 and can be found on the original 14 values of the postage stamps and on the 13 stamps of the Official series. (*Price for set of 27 unused £42000*).

Nos. 1/4 and 6/7 are all known with inverted overprint (*Price, from* £35 *each, unused*) and the overprint is also known (upright or inverted) on examples of India No. 165 ("ANNAS"). It is doubtful if such errors were actually sold at the Kuwait Post Office, although some are known on registered or ordinary covers.

KUWAIT (3) **KUWAIT** (4)

1929–37. Stamps of India (King George V, Nasik printing), optd with T **3** or **4** (rupee values). W **69** (Mult Stars) of India. P 14.

16	½a. green (No. 202)	16·00	3·00
	aw. Wmk inverted	6·50	4·50
16b	½a. green (No. 232) (1934)	11·00	1·75
	bw. Wmk inverted	—	25·00
17	1a. chocolate (No. 203)	8·00	3·75
	aw. Wmk inverted	26·00	7·50
17b	1a. chocolate (No. 234) (1934)	17·00	1·25
18	2a. purple (No. 206)	9·50	2·00
19	2a. vermilion (No. 236)	20·00	95·00
	aw. Wmk inverted	20·00	£100
19b	2a. vermilion (No. 236b) (1934)	16·00	6·50
19c	2a. vermilion (small die) (No. 236c) (1937)	10·00	3·00
20	3a. blue (No. 209)	3·50	3·25
21	3a. carmine (No. 237)	5·50	4·25
22	4a. sage-green (wmk inverted) (No. 211w)	25·00	£100
	w. Wmk upright	80·00	
22a	4a. pale sage-green (No. 210) (1934)	18·00	14·00
22b	6a. bistre (No. 239) (1937)	28·00	70·00
23	8a. reddish purple (No. 212)	50·00	13·00
	w. Wmk inverted	9·00	22·00
24	12a. claret (wmk inverted) (No. 213w) (1933)	22·00	50·00
	w. Wmk upright	—	£140
25	1r. chocolate and green (No. 214)	85·00	55·00
	a. Extended "T"	£1400	
	w. Wmk inverted	25·00	50·00
	wa. Extended "T"	£800	
26	2r. carmine and orange (wmk inverted) (No. 215w)	25·00	70·00
	a. Extended "T"	£800	£1300
	w. Wmk upright	£225	£225
27	5r. ultramarine and purple (No. 216) (1937)	£140	£325
	a. Extended "T"	£1600	
28	10r. green and scarlet (No. 217) (1934)	£300	£550
	a. Extended "T"	£3250	
29	15r. blue and olive (wmk inverted) (No. 218w) (1937)	£950	£1200
	a. Extended "T"	£6000	
16/29 Set of 20		£1500	£2250

The "T" of "KUWAIT" shows a ¾ mm downward extension on R. 3/2, lower left pane.

Nos. 16, 17, 18/19 and 22 are inscribed "INDIA POSTAGE & REVENUE". The remainder are inscribed "INDIA POSTAGE".

No. 19b measures 19×22.6 mm and No. 19c 18.4×21.8 mm.

Examples of most values are known showing a forged Kuwait postmark dated "11 NOV 37".

1933 (1 Feb)–**34**. Air. Nos. 220/3 of India optd as T **2** (16½ *mm*).

31	2a. deep blue-green	25·00	27·00
	w. Wmk stars to right	25·00	27·00
32	3a. blue	5·50	3·25
	a. "Q" for "O" in "POSTAGE"	£1100	£550
	w. Wmk stars to right	5·50	3·25
33	4a. olive-green	£150	£225
34	6a. bistre (2.34)	10·00	5·00
	w. Wmk stars to right	10·00	5·00
31/4 Set of 4		£180	£225

The normal sideways watermark on Nos. 31/4 shows stars pointing to left, *as seen from the back of the stamp*.

The 3a. value exists with a most pronounced lithography double print. *Price* £1000 *un.*, £1000 *used*. Examples of this and other stamps with slight double prints are of little additional value.

1939. Nos. 248, 250/1, 253, 255/63 of India (King George VI) optd with T **3** or **4** (rupee values).

36	½a. red-brown	7·00	4·50
38	1a. carmine	7·50	3·50
39	2a. vermilion	9·50	5·50
41	3a. yellow-green	13·00	3·50
43	4a. brown	42·00	30·00
44	6a. turquoise-green	26·00	23·00
45	8a. slate-violet	29·00	38·00
46	12a. lake	20·00	90·00
47	1r. grey and red-brown	38·00	9·00
	a. Extended "T"	£1100	£700
	b. Opt triple, one inverted	£4000	
48	2r. purple and brown	10·00	29·00
	a. Extended "T"	£1100	£1200
49	5r. green and blue	19·00	32·00
	a. Extended "T"	£1400	
50	10r. purple and claret	85·00	£100
	a. Opt double	£700	
	b. Extended "T"	£2500	
51	15r. brown and green	£375	£400
	a. Extended "T"	£4500	
	w. Wmk inverted	£120	£250
	wa. Extended "T"	£3000	
36/51w Set of 13		£375	£550

On later printings the extended "T" variety was corrected in two stages.

Examples of most values are known showing a forged Kuwait postmark dated "17 NOV 39".

> Following the rebellion in Iraq, control of the Kuwait postal service was assumed by the Indian authorities on 24 May 1941. Unoverprinted stamps of INDIA were used in Kuwait between 1941 and 1945.
> The Victory stamps of India are also known used there.

1945. Nos. 265/8 and 269b/77 of India (King George VI, on white background) optd with T **3**.

52	3p. slate	4·00	12·00
53	½a. purple	4·00	6·50
54	9p. green	3·75	20·00
55	1a. carmine	4·00	2·50
56	1½a. dull violet	4·25	13·00
57	2a. vermilion	5·00	9·50
58	3a. bright violet	6·00	18·00
59	3½a. bright blue	6·50	19·00
60	4a. brown	6·50	5·00
60a	4a. turquoise-green	14·00	24·00
61	8a. slate-violet	7·00	18·00
62	12a. lake	8·50	9·50
63	14a. purple	17·00	24·00
52/63 Set of 13		75·00	£160

Following a short period of Pakistani control, from August 1947 the Kuwait postal service passed to British administration on 1 April 1948.

KUWAIT (5)

KUWAIT (6)

I ANNA (5) **5 RUPEES** (6)

NOTE. From 1948 onwards, for stamps with similar surcharges, but without name of country, see British Postal Agencies in Eastern Arabia.

1948 (1 Apr)–**49**. Nos. 470, 475, 476b/7, 478b and 485/90 of Great Britain (King George VI), surch as T **5** or **6** (rupee values).

64	½a. on ½d. pale green	3·75	4·25
65	1a. on 1d. pale scarlet	3·75	1·75
66	1½a. on 1½d. pale red-brown	4·00	1·75
67	2a. on 2d. pale orange	3·75	1·75
68	2½a. on 2½d. light ultramarine	4·00	1·00
69	3a. on 3d. pale violet	4·00	80
	a. Pair, one surch albino	£12000	
70	6a. on 6d. purple	4·00	75
71	1r. on 1s. bistre-brown	8·50	2·00
72	2r. on 2s. 6d. yellow-green	9·00	9·00
73	5r. on 5s. red	12·00	9·00
73a	10r. on 10s. ultramarine (4.7.49)	60·00	11·00
64/73a Set of 11		£100	38·00

KUWAIT 2½ ANNAS (7) **KUWAIT 15 RUPEES** (8)

1948 (1 May). Royal Silver Wedding. Nos. 493/4 of Great Britain surch with T **7** or **8**.

74	2½a. on 2½d. ultramarine	2·25	2·50
75	15r. on £1 blue	38·00	50·00
	a. Short bars (R. 3/4)	£250	£300

No. 75a has the bars cancelling the original face value 3 mm long. In other positions the bars measure between 3½ and 4 mm. R. 3/4 also exists with bars of normal length.

1948 (29 July). Olympic Games. Nos. 495/8 of Great Britain surch as T **7**, but in one line (6a.) or two lines (others).

76	2½a. on 2½d. ultramarine	1·50	5·00
77	3a. on 3d. violet	1·25	5·00
78	6a. on 6d. bright purple	1·50	4·50
79	1r. on 1s. brown	1·50	4·50
76/9 Set of 4		5·25	17·00

1949 (10 Oct). 75th Anniv of UPU. Nos. 499/502 of Great Britain surch "KUWAIT" and new values.

80	2½a. on 2½d. ultramarine	1·50	3·50
	a. Lake in India	85·00	£150
81	3a. on 3d. violet	1·25	5·50
82	6a. on 6d. bright purple	1·25	3·75
83	1r. on 1s. brown	1·25	1·75
80/3 Set of 4		4·75	13·00

KUWAIT **KUWAIT**

2 RUPEES Type I (8a) **2 RUPEES** Type II

KUWAIT

10 RUPEES Type I (8b)

KUWAIT

10 RUPEES Type II (8b)

2r. Type I. Type-set surcharge. "2" level with "RUPEES". Surcharge sharp.

Type II. Plate-printed surcharge. "2" raised. Surcharge worn.

Type III. Similar to Type II, but the space between the bars and the "K" is 2½ mm rather than 3mm and the "2 RUPEES" is set slightly further to the left, with the "S" directly below the "T".

10r. Type I. Type-set surcharge. "1" and "0" spaced. Surcharge sharp and clean.

Type II. Plate-printed surcharge. "1" and "0" closer together. Surcharge appears heavy and worn, see especially "A", "R" and "P".

KUWAIT Extra bar in centre (R. 7/2) **KUWAIT** Extra bar at top (R. 2/2)

1950 (2 Oct)–**55**. Nos. 503/11 of Great Britain (King George VI) surch as T **5** or **8a/b** (rupee values).

84	½a. on ½d. pale orange (3.5.51)	2·75	1·50
85	1a. on 1d. light ultramarine (3.5.51)	2·75	1·60

BC Stamps

for quality British Commonwealth Stamps

Buy singles and sets online from our fast changing stock.
Search and save areas of interest.
View our latest stock additions.

www.bcstamps.co.uk

BC Stamps Limited
Mail only address : 3 Coates Place, Edinburgh, EH3 7AA, UK

Email us at
info@bcstamps.co.uk

86	1½a. on 1½d. pale green (3.5.51)		3·25	2·25
87	2a. on 2d. pale red-brown (3.5.51)		3·25	1·50
88	2½a. on 2½d. pale scarlet (3.5.51)		3·25	2·75
89	4a. on 4d. light ultramarine		2·75	1·50
90	2r. on 2s.6d. yellow-green (I) (3.5.51)		25·00	9·00
	a. Extra bar in centre		£1400	£800
	b. Type II surch (1954)		£375	55·00
	c. Type III surch (1955)		—	£275
91	5r. on 5s. red (3.5.51)		32·00	11·00
	a. Extra bar at top		£1100	£700
92	10r. on 10s. ultramarine (I) (3.5.51)		55·00	18·00
	a. Type II surch (1952)		£350	70·00
84/92 Set of 9			£110	45·00

No. 92a is known with surch spaced 10 mm apart instead of 9 mm.

1952 (10 Dec)–**54**. Nos. 515/21, 523 and 530/1 of Great Britain (Queen Elizabeth II. W **153**), surch as T **5** (in two lines only on 2½ and 6a.).

93	½a. on ½d. orange-red (31.8.53)		20	3·50
94	1a. on 1d. ultramarine (31.8.53)		20	10
95	1½a. on 1½d. green (31.8.53)		15	1·75
96	2a. on 2d. red-brown (31.8.53)		35	10
97	2½a. on 2½d. carmine (31.8.53)		15	1·75
98	3a. on 3d. deep lilac (B.) (18.1.54)		40	10
99	4a. on 4d. ultramarine (2.11.53)		1·25	1·00
100	6a. on 6d. reddish purple (18.1.54)		2·00	10
101	12a. on 1s.3d. green (2.11.53)		7·00	2·50
102	1r. on 1s.6d. grey-blue (2.11.53)		5·50	10
93/102 Set of 10			15·00	9·50

The word KUWAIT is in taller letters on the 1½a, 2½a, 3a. and 6a. In early printings of the ½a. the "½" was printed in a separate operation to "KUWAIT" and "ANNA". Later printings of No. 93 and all printings of other values were printed in a single operation.

1953 (3 June). Coronation. Nos. 532/5 (Queen Elizabeth) of Great Britain surch "KUWAIT" and new values.

103	2½a. on 2½d. carmine-red		3·50	3·50
104	4a. on 4d. ultramarine		4·00	3·50
105	12a. on 1s.3d. deep yellow-green		5·00	5·50
106	1r. on 1s.6d. deep grey-blue		4·00	1·25
103/6 Set of 4			15·00	12·50

KUWAIT 2 RUPEES
I

KUWAIT 2 RUPEES
II
(9)

KUWAIT 5 RUPEES
I

KUWAIT 5 RUPEES
II
(10)

KUWAIT 10 RUPEES
I

KUWAIT 10 RUPEES
II
(11)

Type I (**9/11**). Type-set overprints by Waterlow. Bold (generally thicker) letters with sharp corners and straight edges. Bars close together and usually slightly longer than in Type II.

Type II (**9/11**). Plate-printed overprints by Harrison. Thinner letters, rounder corners and rough edges. Bars wider apart.

1955 (23 Sept)–**57**. Nos. 536/8 of Great Britain ("Castles" high values) surch with T **9/11**.

107	2r. on 2s.6d. black-brown (I)		11·00	3·50
	a. Type II (10.10.57)		75·00	8·50
108	5r. on 5s. rose-carmine (I)		11·00	9·50
	a. Type II (10.10.57)		£120	40·00
109	10r. on 10s. ultramarine (I)		11·00	6·00
	a. Type II (10.10.57)		£180	£140
107/9 Set of 3			30·00	17·00
107a/9a Set of 3			£350	£160

1956. Nos. 540/6, 548 and 555/6 of Great Britain (Queen Elizabeth II. W **165**) surch as T **5** (in two lines only on 2½ and 6a.).

110	½a. on ½d. orange-red		30	2·25
111	1a. on 1d. ultramarine (3.12.56)		50	4·50
112	1½a. on 1½d. green		40	1·00
113	2a. on 2d. red-brown		40	50
114	2½a. on 2½d. carmine-red		60	5·50
116	4a. on 4d. ultramarine (22.11.56)		4·75	3·25
117	6a. on 6d. reddish purple (3.12.56)		2·25	40
118	12a. on 1s.3d. green		11·00	8·00
119	1r. on 1s.6d. grey-blue (3.12.56)		16·00	30
110/19 Set of 9			32·00	23·00

KUWAIT   KUWAIT   KUWAIT

NP 1 NP NP 3 NP 75 NP
(12)   (13)   (14)

1957 (1 June)–**58**. Nos. 540/2, 543a/8, 551 and 555 of Great Britain (Queen Elizabeth II. W **165**) surch as T **12** (1, 15, 25, 40, 50n.p.), **14** (75n.p.) or **13** (others).

120	1n.p. on 5d. brown		10	70
121	3n.p. on ½d. orange-red		60	4·75
122	6n.p. on 1d. ultramarine		60	1·25
123	9n.p. on 1½d. green		60	4·50
124	12n.p. on 2d. light red-brown		60	5·00
125	15n.p. on 2½d. carmine-red (Type I)		60	7·00
	a. Type II (11.58)		50·00	£120
126	20n.p. on 3d. deep lilac (B.)		60	30
127	25n.p. on 4d. ultramarine		2·75	3·25
128	40n.p. on 6d. reddish purple		1·00	30
129	50n.p. on 9d. bronze-green		5·50	4·00
130	75n.p. on 1s.3d. green		6·00	8·50
120/30 Set of 11			17·00	35·00

20 Sheikh Abdullah

(Recess De La Rue)

1958 (1 Feb)–**59**. T **20** and similar designs. P 12½ (Nos. 131/6), 13½×13.

131	**20**	5n.p. bluish green	1·00	20
132		10n.p. rose-red	75	20
136		40n.p. maroon	4·75	1·50
131/6 Set of 3			6·00	1·75

Nos. 131/6 were only valid for internal use in Kuwait prior to 1 February 1959. Further values were added to this series following the closure of the British Agency Post Offices on 31 January 1959. Responsibility of the postal service then passed to the Kuwait Government and later issues are listed in the Stanley Gibbons *Arabia Catalogue*.

OFFICIAL STAMPS

KUWAIT   KUWAIT

KUWAIT

SERVICE   SERVICE
(O **1**)   (O **2**)

1923–24. Stamps of India (King George V), optd with Type O **1** or O **2** (rupee values, 15½–16 mm). W **34** (Large Star) of India. P 14.

O1	½a. light green (No. 155)		8·00	65·00
	a. Opt double, one albino		£170	
O2	1a. chocolate (No. 197)		7·00	29·00
	a. Opt double, one albino		£140	
O3	1½a. chocolate (A) (No. 163)		5·00	75·00
O4	2a. bright reddish violet (No. 169)		14·00	60·00
	a. Reddish purple		15·00	
O5	2a.6p. ultramarine (No. 171)		4·50	85·00
O6	3a. dull orange (No. 173)		6·00	85·00
O7	3a. ultramarine (No. 200) (1924)		5·00	85·00
O8	4a. olive-green (No. 175)		4·75	85·00
O9	8a. purple (No. 182)		6·00	£130
O10	1r. brown and green (No. 186)		42·00	£200
	a. Orange-brown and deep turquoise-green		50·00	£225
	b. Opt double, one albino		£200	
O11	2r. carmine and brown (No. 187)		42·00	£300
O12	5r. ultramarine and violet (No. 188)		£130	£475
	a. Opt double, one albino		£200	
O13	10r. green and scarlet (No. 189)		£275	£425
O14	15r. blue and olive (No. 190)		£425	£650
O1/14 Set of 14			£850	£2500

1929–33. Nos. 203, 206, 209 and 211/18w of India (King George V, Nasik printing) optd as Types O **1** (spaced 10 mm) or O **2** (14½ mm×19–20 mm wide). W **69** (Mult Stars) of India. P 14.

O16	1a. chocolate			
	w. Wmk inverted		8·00	55·00
O17	2a. purple		70·00	£275
O19	3a. blue		4·50	65·00
O20	4a. sage-green		4·25	£100
	w. Wmk inverted			
O21	8a. reddish purple		6·50	£150
	w. Wmk inverted		9·50	£160
O22	12a. claret		50·00	£250
	w. Wmk inverted		70·00	
O23	1r. chocolate and green		16·00	£300
O24	2r. carmine and orange (wmk inverted)		20·00	£425
O25	5r. ultramarine and purple (wmk inverted)		55·00	£500
O26	10r. green and scarlet		95·00	£850
O27	15r. blue and olive (wmk inverted)		£325	£1500
O16w/27 Set of 11			£600	£4000

Labuan *see* North Borneo

Lagos *see* Nigeria

Leeward Islands

The Federal Colony of the Leeward Islands was constituted in 1871 formalising links between Antigua, British Virgin Islands, Dominica, Montserrat and St. Kitts-Nevis which stretched back to the 1670s. Issues for the individual islands were superseded by those inscribed "LEEWARD ISLANDS", but were in concurrent use with them from 1903 (British Virgin Islands from 1899). Dominica was transferred to the Windward Islands on 31 December 1939.

PRICES FOR STAMPS ON COVER TO 1945	
Nos. 1/8	from × 10
Nos. 9/16	from × 12
Nos. 17/19	from × 8
Nos. 20/8	from × 5
Nos. 29/35	from × 4
Nos. 36/45	from × 5
Nos. 46/57	from × 4
Nos. 58/87	from × 5
Nos. 88/91	from × 6
Nos. 92/4	from × 10
Nos. 95/114	from × 5

PRINTERS. All the stamps of Leeward Islands were typographed by De La Rue & Co, Ltd, London, *except where otherwise stated*.

1   2

4d. Damaged "S" (R. ?/6, left pane)

1890 (31 Oct). Name and value in second colour. Wmk Crown CA. P 14.

1	**1**	½d. dull mauve and green	3·50	1·25
2		1d. dull mauve and rose	8·50	20
3		2½d. dull mauve and blue	9·00	30
		w. Wmk inverted	£450	£200
4		4d. dull mauve and orange	11·00	9·00
		a. Damaged "S"	£275	
5		6d. dull mauve and brown	13·00	16·00
6		7d. dull mauve and slate	11·00	21·00
7	**2**	1s. green and carmine	23·00	60·00
8		5s. green and blue	£140	£325
1/8 Set of 8			£190	£375
1s/8s Optd "SPECIMEN" Set of 8			£275	

The colours of this issue are fugitive.

(3)

One Penny
(4)

One Penny
(5)

1897 (22 July). Queen Victoria's Diamond Jubilee. Handstamped with T **3**.

9	**1**	½d. dull mauve and green	8·00	25·00
		a. Opt double	£1400	
		b. Opt triple	£6000	
10		1d. dull mauve and rose	9·00	25·00
		a. Opt double	£1000	
		b. Opt triple	£6000	
11		2½d. dull mauve and blue	9·50	25·00
		a. Opt double	£1200	
12		4d. dull mauve and orange	55·00	80·00
		a. Opt double	£1300	
13		6d. dull mauve and brown	60·00	£130
		a. Opt double	£1700	
14		7d. dull mauve and slate	60·00	£130
		a. Opt double	£1700	£2000
15	**2**	1s. green and carmine	£130	£275
		a. Opt double	£2250	
16		5s. green and blue	£450	£800
		a. Opt double	£6000	
9/16 Set of 8			£700	£1300

Beware of forgeries. The prices quoted above for overprint varieties are for certified examples showing two (or three) clear impressions of the handstamp. Stamps with slight or partial doubling are frequently encountered, and are worth little premium over the normal prices.

1902 (11 Aug). Nos. 4/6 surch locally.

17	**4**	1d. on 4d. dull mauve and orange	6·50	11·00
		a. Pair, one with tall narrow "O" in "One"	45·00	85·00
		b. Surch double	£6000	
		c. Damaged "S"	£180	
18		1d. on 6d. dull mauve and brown	8·00	18·00
		a. Pair, one with tall narrow "O" in "One"	65·00	£150
19	**5**	1d. on 7d. dull mauve and slate	6·50	15·00
17/19 Set of 3			19·00	40·00

The tall narrow "O" variety occurred on R. 1/1, 5/3, 5/5 and 7/4.

6   7   8

2½d. Wide "A" (R. 6/1 of both panes. Replaced in 1912)

1s. Dropped "R" (R. 1/1 of both panes from Pl 1 and 2)

1902 (1 Sept–Oct). Wmk Crown CA. P 14.

20	6	½d. dull purple and green	6·00	1·00
21		1d. dull purple and carmine	10·00	20
22	7	2d. dull purple and ochre (10.02)	3·00	4·25
23	6	2½d. dull purple and ultramarine	6·50	2·25
		a. Wide "A" in "LEEWARD"	£275	£160
24	7	3d. dull purple and black (10.02)	11·00	7·50
25	6	6d. dull purple and brown	2·50	8·00
26	8	1s. green and carmine	11·00	30·00
		a. Dropped "R" in "LEEWARD"	£550	£850
27	7	2s.6d. green and black (10.02)	30·00	80·00
28	8	5s. green and blue	65·00	95·00
20/8 Set of 9			£120	£200
20s/8s Optd "SPECIMEN" Set of 9			£190	

1905 (Apr)–**08**. Wmk Mult Crown CA. Ordinary paper (½d., 3d.) or chalk-surfaced paper (others).

29	6	½d. dull purple and green (2.06)	5·00	2·50
		a. Chalk-surfaced paper (25.7.08)	32·00	22·00
30		1d. dull purple and carmine (29.8.06)	11·00	80
31	7	2d. dull purple and ochre (25.7.08)	13·00	26·00
32	6	2½d. dull purple and ultramarine (23.7.06)	80·00	50·00
		a. Wide "A" in "LEEWARD"	£800	£550
33	7	3d. dull purple and black	26·00	60·00
		a. Chalk-surfaced paper (18.4.08)	60·00	£100
34	6	6d. dull purple and brown (15.7.08)	55·00	£100
35	8	1s. green and carmine (15.7.08)	50·00	£140
29/35 Set of 7			£200	£325

1907 (14 Apr)–**11**. Wmk Mult Crown CA. Chalk-surfaced paper (3d. to 5s.). P 14.

36	7	¼d. brown (7.8.09)	2·75	1·75
37	6	½d. dull green	6·00	1·75
		y. Wmk inverted and reversed	†	£800
38		1d. bright red (7.07)	16·00	80
		a. Rose-carmine (1910)	48·00	3·50
39	7	2d. grey (3.8.11)	5·50	14·00
40	6	2½d. bright blue (5.07)	9·00	4·25
		a. Wide "A" in "LEEWARD"	£300	£180
41	7	3d. purple/yellow (28.10.10)	3·50	7·50
42	6	6d. dull and bright purple (3.8.11)	9·50	11·00
43	8	1s. black/green (3.8.11)	9·00	21·00
44	7	2s.6d. black and red/blue (15.9.11)	42·00	55·00
45	8	5s. green and red/yellow (21.11.10)	48·00	65·00
36/45 Set of 10			£130	£160
36s/45s Optd "SPECIMEN" Set of 10			£300	

10   11

12   13

1912 (23 Oct)–**22**. Die I (¼d. to 3d., 6d., 1s., 2s.6d. 5s.) or Die II (4d., 2s.). Wmk Mult Crown CA. Chalk-surfaced paper (3d. to 5s.). P 14.

46	10	¼d. brown	1·75	1·00
		a. Pale brown	5·50	2·75
47	11	½d. yellow-green (12.12)	5·50	2·00
		a. Deep green (1916)	8·00	1·50
48		1d. red	5·00	1·00
		a. Bright scarlet (8.15)	15·00	1·00
49	10	2d. slate-grey (9.1.13)	4·00	5·50
50	11	2½d. bright blue	3·25	7·00
		a. Deep bright blue (1914)	8·00	4·50
51	10	3d. purple/yellow (9.1.13)	3·75	25·00
		a. White back (11.13)	95·00	£180
		as. Optd "SPECIMEN"	50·00	
		b. On lemon (11.14)	7·00	26·00
		c. On buff (1920)	35·00	50·00
		cs. Optd "SPECIMEN"	45·00	
		d. On orange-buff (1920)	8·50	28·00
		dw. Wmk inverted	£475	£500
52		4d. black and red/pale yellow (Die II) (12.5.22)	7·50	23·00
53	11	6d. dull and bright purple (9.1.13)	4·50	9·00

54	12	1s. black/green (9.1.13)	3·75	8·00
		a. White back (11.13)	90·00	38·00
		as. Optd "SPECIMEN"	50·00	
		b. On blue-green, olive back (1917)	17·00	8·00
		bs. Optd "SPECIMEN"	£110	
55	10	2s. purple and blue/blue (Die II) (12.5.22)	18·00	65·00
56		2s.6d. black and red/blue (11.13)	23·00	55·00
57	12	5s. green and red/yellow (9.14)	65·00	£120
		a. White back (11.13)	55·00	90·00
		as. Optd "SPECIMEN"	60·00	
		b. On lemon (1915)	50·00	85·00
		c. On orange-buff (1920)	£120	£200
46/57b Set of 12			£110	£250
46s/57s Optd "SPECIMEN" Set of 12			£300	

Nos. 51a, 54a and 57a were only on sale from Montserrat.

1d., 1s. "D I" shaved at foot 1d. R. 7/3 of left pane (printings from Sept 1947 until corrected during first printing in green in Oct 1948). 1s. R. 9/6 of right pane (all ptgs between 1932 and 1938). A less pronounced flaw, with the "D" chamfered also exists on the 1s.

1921 (Oct)–**32**. Wmk Mult Script CA or Mult Crown CA (£1). Chalk-surfaced paper (3d. to £1). P 14.

(a) Die II (1921–29)

58	10	¼d. brown (1.4.22)	2·25	1·00
59	11	½d. blue-green	1·25	75
60		1d. carmine-red	2·25	55
61		1d. bright violet (21.8.22)	2·25	1·00
62		1d. bright scarlet (1929)	18·00	2·25
63	10	1½d. carmine-red (10.9.26)	9·00	1·50
64		1½d. red-brown (1929)	2·25	10
65		2d. slate-grey (6.22)	3·00	1·00
		w. Wmk inverted	†	£375
		x. Wmk reversed		
66	11	2½d. orange-yellow (22.9.23)	13·00	65·00
67		2½d. bright blue (1.3.27)	3·50	1·25
68	10	3d. light ultramarine (22.9.23)	17·00	40·00
		a. Deep ultramarine (1925)	65·00	60·00
69		3d. purple/yellow (1.7.27)	8·50	6·50
70		4d. black and red/pale yellow (2.24)	4·00	21·00
71		5d. dull purple and olive-green (12.5.22)	2·50	4·25
72	11	6d. dull and bright purple (17.7.23)	20·00	50·00
73	12	1s. black/emerald (17.7.23)	11·00	8·00
		a. "DI" flaw		
74	10	2s. purple and blue/blue (12.5.22)	25·00	45·00
		a. Red-purple and blue/blue (1926)	14·00	48·00
		aw. Wmk inverted	£400	
75		2s.6d. black and red/blue (17.7.23)	13·00	27·00
76		3s. bright green and violet (12.5.22)	12·00	45·00
77		4s. black and red (12.5.22)	20·00	42·00
78	12	5s. green and red/pale yellow (17.7.23)	50·00	85·00
79	13	10s. green and green/green (1928)	80·00	£140
		a. Break in scroll	£300	£400
		b. Broken crown and scroll	£300	
		c. Nick in top right scroll	£300	
		e. Break in lines below left scroll	£300	
		f. Damaged leaf at bottom right	£300	
80		£1 purple and black/red (1928)	£225	£325
		a. Break in scroll	£550	
		b. Broken crown and scroll	£550	
		e. Break in lines below left scroll	£550	
		f. Damaged leaf at bottom right	£550	
58/80 Set of 23			£450	£800
58s/80s Optd or Perf (1d. bright scarlet, 1½d. red-brown, 10s. £1) "SPECIMEN" Set of 23			£700	

(b) Reversion to Die I (Plate 23) (1931–32)

81	10	¼d. brown	18·00	26·00
82	11	½d. blue-green	25·00	70·00
83		1d. bright scarlet	45·00	1·25
84	10	1½d. red-brown	4·25	2·75
85	11	2½d. bright blue	7·00	3·50
86		6d. dull and bright purple	32·00	£100
87	12	1s. black/emerald	60·00	85·00
		a. "D I" flaw	£600	
		x. "A" of "CA" missing from wmk	—	£2250
81/7 Set of 7			£170	£250

No. 66 was issued in Montserrat and 68a in St. Kitts-Nevis.
Nos. 59, 62 and 82/3 exist in coils, constructed from normal sheets. No. 82 was only issued in this form.
For illustrations of varieties on Nos. 79/80 see above No. 51b of Bermuda.
Nos. 81/7 result from the use, in error, of Die I which had previously been "retired" in late 1920, to produce Plate 23.

1935 (6 May). Silver Jubilee. As Nos. 91/4 of Antigua, but printed by Waterlow. P 11×12.

88		1d. deep blue and scarlet	1·90	3·50
89		1½d. ultramarine and grey	2·75	1·25
90		2½d. brown and deep blue	5·00	4·75
91		1s. slate and purple	28·00	48·00
		k. Kite and vertical log	£650	
		l. Kite and horizontal log	£650	£700
88/91 Set of 4			35·00	50·00
88s/91s Perf "SPECIMEN" Set of 4			75·00	

For illustrations of plate varieties see Omnibus section following Zanzibar.

1937 (12 May). Coronation. As Nos. 95/7 of Antigua, but printed by D.L.R.

92		1d. scarlet	80	1·00
93		1½d. buff	80	1·50
94		2½d. bright blue	90	1·50
92/4 Set of 3			2·25	3·50
92s/4s Perf "SPECIMEN" Set of 3			£120	

14   15

(Die A)   (Die B)

In Die B the figure "1" has a broader top and more projecting serif.

½d. "ISl.ANDS" flaw (R. 1/2 of right pane) (Pl 2 ptg of May 1944)

6d. Broken second "E" in "LEEWARD" (R. 4/1 of right pane) (Pl 2 and 3 ptgs from March 1942 until corrected in June 1949) (The similar variety on the 5s. shows traces of the top bar)

5s. Damaged value tablet (R. 3/5 of left pane, first printing only)

Broken top right scroll (R. 5/11) (1942 ptg of 10s. only. Corrected on £1 value from same period)

Broken lower right scroll (R. 5/12. 1942 ptgs only)

Missing pearl (R. 5/1. 1944 ptgs only)

Gash in chin (R. 2/5. 1942 ptgs only)

1938 (25 Nov)–**51**. T **14** (and similar type, but shaded value tablet, ½d., 1d., 2½d., 6d.) and **15** (10s., £1). Chalk-surfaced paper (3d. to £1). P 14.

(a) Wmk Mult Script CA

95		¼d. brown	60	1·50
		a. Chalk-surfaced paper. Deep brown (13.6.49)	30	2·25
96		½d. emerald	1·75	70
		a. "ISIANDS" flaw	£170	£225
97		½d. slate-grey (chalk-surfaced paper) (1.7.49)	2·00	1·50
98		1d. scarlet (Die A)	13·00	2·75
99		1d. scarlet (shades) (Die B) (1940)	2·25	1·75
		a. "D I" flaw (9.47)	£200	
		b. Carmine (9.42)	3·00	15·00
		c. Red (13.9.48)	6·00	8·00
		ca. "D I" flaw	£200	£275
100		1d. blue-green (chalk-surfaced paper) (1.7.49)	55	15
		a. "D I" flaw	£200	£225
101		1d. chestnut	1·00	50
102		1½d. yellow-orange and black (chalk-surfaced paper) (1.7.49)	1·75	40
103		2d. olive-green	3·50	2·25
		a. Slate-grey (11.42)	6·50	4·00
104		2d. scarlet (chalk-surfaced paper) (1.7.49)	1·40	1·25
105		2½d. bright blue	35·00	4·00
		a. Light bright blue (11.42)	80	1·25
106		2½d. black and purple (chalk-surfaced paper) (1.7.49)	1·00	15
107		3d. orange	35·00	2·75
		a. Ordinary paper. Pale orange (3.42)	50	85
108		3d. bright blue (1.7.49)	1·00	15

109	6d. deep dull purple and bright purple	32·00	7·50
	a. Ordinary paper (3.42)	12·00	3·50
	ab. Broken "E"	£550	£400
	b. Purple and deep magenta (29.9.47)	18·00	6·00
	ba. Broken "E"	£750	£450
110	1s. black/emerald	17·00	2·00
	a. "D I" flaw	£650	£400
	b. Ordinary paper (3.42)	5·50	1·00
	ba. Grey and black/emerald (8.42)	24·00	2·75
	bb. Black and grey/emerald (11.42)	£130	13·00
111	2s. reddish purple and blue/blue	32·00	3·00
	a. Ordinary paper (3.42)	16·00	2·00
	ab. Deep purple and blue/blue (29.9.47)		2·50
112	5s. green and red/yellow	50·00	24·00
	a. Broken "E" (R. 4/3 of left pane)	£1700	£1000
	ab. Damaged value tablet	£1700	£1000
	b. Ordinary paper (12.43)	35·00	15·00
	ba. Broken "E" (R. 4/3 of left pane)	£1200	
	c. Bright green and red/yellow (24.10.51)	65·00	£100
113	10s. bluish green and deep red/green	£200	£130
	a. Ordinary paper. Pale green and dull red/green (26.6.44*)	£850	£375
	ad. Broken top right scroll	£8000	
	ae. Broken lower right scroll	£8000	£4750
	af. Gash in chin	£8000	£4750
	b. Ordinary paper. Green and red/green (22.2.45*)	£150	90·00
	c. Ordinary paper. Deep green and deep vermilion/green (15.10.47*)	£120	£100
	ca. Missing pearl	£1700	
	(b) Wmk Mult Crown CA		
114	£1 brown-purple and black/red	£375	£400
	a. Purple and black/carmine (21.9.42*)	90·00	55·00
	ae. Broken lower right scroll	£2000	£1300
	af. Gash in chin	£2250	£1300
	b. Brown-purple and black/salmon (5.2.45*)	45·00	32·00
	ba. Missing pearl	£1700	£1500
	c. Perf 13. Violet and black/scarlet (4.1.52*)	35·00	42·00
	ca. Wmk sideways	£7000	
	cw. Wmk inverted	£7000	
95/114c Set of 19		£200	£140
95s/114s Perf "SPECIMEN" Set of 13		£750	

*Dates quoted for Nos. 113a/14c are earliest known postmark dates. Nos. 113a and 114a were despatched to the Leeward Islands in March 1942, Nos. 113b and 114b in December 1943, No. 113c in June 1944 and No. 114c on 13 December 1951.

Nos. 96, 98 and 99 exist in coils constructed from normal sheets.

Printings of the 10s. in March 1942 (No. 113a) and of the £1 in February and October 1942 (No. 114a) were made by Williams Lea & Co. Ltd. following bomb damage to the De La Rue works in 1940.

For illustrations of Nos. 99a, 99ca, 100a and 110a see above No. 58.

1946 (1 Nov). Victory. As Nos. 110/11 of Antigua.
115	1½d. brown	15	75
116	3d. red-orange	15	75
115s/16s Perf "SPECIMEN" Set of 2		£100	

1949 (2 Jan). Royal Silver Wedding. As Nos. 112/13 of Antigua.
| 117 | 2½d. ultramarine | 10 | 10 |
| 118 | 5s. green | 7·00 | 11·00 |

1949 (10 Oct). 75th Anniv of Universal Postal Union. As Nos. 114/17 of Antigua.
119	2½d. blue-black	15	3·00
120	3d. deep blue	2·00	3·00
121	6d. magenta	15	3·00
122	1s. blue-green	15	3·00
119/22 Set of 4		2·25	11·00

(New Currency. 100 cents = 1 B.W.I. dollar)

1951 (16 Feb). Inauguration of B.W.I. University College. As Nos. 118/19 of Antigua.
| 123 | 3c. orange and black | 30 | 2·00 |
| 124 | 12c. rose-carmine and reddish violet | 1·00 | 2·00 |

1953 (2 June). Coronation. As No. 120 of Antigua.
| 125 | 3c. black and green | 1·00 | 2·25 |

16 Queen Elizabeth II

17

"Loop" flaw (R. 2/2)

Broken scroll (R. 4/3)

1954 (22 Feb). Chalk-surfaced paper. Wmk Mult Script CA. P 14 (T **16**) or 13 (T **17**).
126	**16**	½c. brown	10	60
		a. "Loop" flaw	5·00	
127		1c. grey	1·25	1·25
		a. "Loop" flaw	15·00	
128		2c. green	1·75	10
		a. "Loop" flaw	20·00	
129		3c. yellow-orange and black	2·50	1·00
		a. "Loop" flaw	25·00	
130		4c. rose-red	1·75	10
		a. "Loop" flaw	20·00	
131		5c. black and brown-purple	2·25	1·00
		a. "Loop" flaw	25·00	

132		6c. yellow-orange	2·25	60
		a. "Loop" flaw	25·00	
133		8c. ultramarine	2·50	10
		a. "Loop" flaw	25·00	
134		12c. dull and reddish purple	2·50	10
		a. "Loop" flaw	25·00	
135		24c. black and green	2·00	20
		a. "Loop" flaw	25·00	
136		48c. dull purple and ultramarine	8·00	2·75
		a. "Loop" flaw	65·00	
137		60c. brown and green	6·00	2·25
		a. "Loop" flaw	55·00	
138		$1.20 yellow-green and rose-red	7·00	4·00
		a. "Loop" flaw	60·00	
139	**17**	$2.40 bluish green and red	14·00	8·00
		a. Broken scroll	£110	
140		$4.80 brown-purple and black	18·00	11·00
		a. Broken scroll	£140	
126/40 Set of 15			60·00	30·00

The 3c., 4c., 6c., 8c., 24c., 48c., 60c. and $1.20 have their value tablets unshaded.

The stamps of Leeward Islands were withdrawn and invalidated on 1 July 1956 when the federal colony was dissolved.

Lesotho

INDEPENDENT KINGDOM

King Moshoeshoe II, 4 October 1966–November 1990 (deposed)

33 Moshoeshoe I and Moshoeshoe II

(Des and photo Harrison)

1966 (4 Oct). Independence. P 12½×13.
106	**33**	2½c. light brown, black and red	10	10
107		5c. light brown, black and new blue	10	10
108		10c. light brown, black and emerald	15	10
109		20c. light brown, black and bright purple	20	15
106/9 Set of 4			45	30

LESOTHO
(**34**)

35 "Education Culture and Science"

1966 (1 Nov). Stamps of Basutoland optd as T **34**.

A. On Nos. 69/71 and 73/9 (Script CA wmk)
110A	½c. grey-black and sepia	10	10
111A	1c. grey-black and bluish green	10	10
112A	2c. deep bright blue and orange	60	10
114A	3½c. indigo and deep ultramarine	30	10
115A	5c. chestnut and deep grey-green	10	10
116A	10c. bronze-green and purple	10	10
117A	12½c. brown and turquoise-green	4·75	35
118A	25c. deep ultramarine and crimson	30	20
119A	50c. black and carmine-red	1·00	2·00
120A	1r. black and maroon	2·75	7·00
	a. "LSEOTHO" (R. 4/2)	85·00	
	b. Opt double	£300	
	ba. Ditto. "LSEOTHO" (R. 4/2)		
110A/20A Set of 10		9·00	9·00

*B. On Nos. 84/92 and unissued 1r. (wmk w **12**)*
111B	1c. grey-black and bluish green	10	10
113B	2½c. pale yellow-green and rose-red	50	10
115B	5c. chestnut and deep grey-green	20	10
117B	12½c. brown and turquoise-green	30	20
119B	50c. black and carmine-red	70	50
120B	1r. black and maroon	65	1·00
	a. "LSEOTHO" (R. 4/2)	50·00	70·00
111B/20B Set of 6		2·00	1·60

(Des V. Whiteley. Litho D.L.R.)

1966 (1 Dec). 20th Anniv of UNESCO. P 14½×14.
121	**35**	2½c. orange-yellow and emerald-green	10	10
122		5c. light green and olive	15	10
123		12½c. light blue and red	35	15
124		25c. red-orange and deep greenish blue	60	85
121/4 Set of 4			1·10	1·00

36 Maize

37 Moshoeshoe II

(Des and photo Harrison)

1967 (1 Apr). Designs as T **36/7**. No wmk. P 14½×13½ (2r.) or 13½×14½ (others).
125	½c. bluish green and light bluish violet	10	10
126	1c. sepia and rose-red	10	10
127	2c. orange-yellow and light green	10	1·75
128	2½c. black and ochre	10	10
129	3½c. chalky blue and yellow	10	1·00
130	5c. bistre and new blue	20	10
131	10c. yellow-brown and bluish grey	10	10
132	12½c. black and red-orange	20	10
133	25c. black and bright blue	55	20
134	50c. black, new blue and turquoise	4·50	2·00
135	1r. multicoloured	65	75
136	2r. black, gold and magenta	1·00	1·75
125/36 Set of 12		6·25	6·75

Designs: Horiz as T **36**—1c. Cattle; 2c. Agaves (wrongly inscr "Aloes"); 2½c. Basotho Hat; 3½c. Merino Sheep ("Wool"); 5c. Basotho Pony; 10c. Wheat; 12½c. Angora Goat ("Mohair"); 25c. Maletsunyane Falls; 50c. Diamonds; 1r. Arms of Lesotho.

See also Nos. 147/59.

46 Students and University

(Des V. Whiteley. Photo Harrison)

1967 (7 Apr). First Conferment of University Degrees. P 14×14½.

137	**46**	1c. sepia, ultramarine and light yellow-orange	10	10
138		2½c. sepia, ultramarine and light greenish blue	10	10
139		12½c. sepia, ultramarine and rose	10	10
140		25c. sepia, ultramarine and light violet	15	15
137/40 *Set of 4*			30	30

47 Statue of Moshoeshoe I

(Des and photo Harrison)

1967 (4 Oct). First Anniv of Independence. T **47** and similar triangular designs. P 14½×14.

141		2½c. black and light yellow-green	10	10
142		12½c. multicoloured	25	15
143		25c. black, green and light ochre	35	25
141/3 *Set of 3*			65	40

Designs:—12½c. Lesotho flag; 25c. Crocodile (National Emblem).

50 Lord Baden-Powell and Scout Saluting

(Des V. Whiteley. Photo Harrison)

1967 (1 Nov). 60th Anniv of Scout Movement. P 14×14½.

144	**50**	15c. multicoloured	20	10

51 WHO Emblem and World Map

(Des G. Vasarhelyi. Photo Harrison)

1968 (7 Apr). 20th Anniv of World Health Organization. T **51** and similar horiz design. P 14×14½.

145		2½c. blue, gold and carmine-red	5	10
		a. Gold (emblem) omitted	£850	
146		25c. multicoloured	45	60

Design:—25c. Nurse and child.

53 Basotho Hat

54 Sorghum

1968–69. As Nos. 125/36 and T **54**, but wmk **53** (sideways on 2r.).

147		½c. bluish green and light bluish violet (26.11.68)	10	10
		a. Blue-green and violet (30.9.69)	2·75	2·75
148		1c. sepia and rose-red (26.11.68)	10	10
149		2c. orange-yellow and light green (26.11.68)	10	10
		a. Orange-yellow and yellow-green (30.9.69)	1·00	1·75
150		2½c. black and ochre (21.10.68)	15	10
		a. Black and yellow-ochre (30.9.69)	1·00	1·00
151		3c. chocolate, green and yellow-brown (1.8.68)	15	15
152		3½c. chalky blue and yellow (26.11.68)	15	40
153		5c. bistre and brown (22.7.68)	60	10
154		10c. yellow-brown and pale bluish grey (26.11.68)	15	10
155		12½c. black and red-orange (30.9.69)	60	35
156		25c. black and bright blue (30.9.69)	1·50	1·00

157	50c. black, new blue and turquoise (30.9.69)	11·00	5·00
158	1r. multicoloured (26.11.68)	1·50	2·75
159	2r. black, gold and magenta (30.9.69)	7·00	14·00
147/59 *Set of 13*		21·00	21·00

55 Running Hunters

(Des Jennifer Toombs. Photo Harrison)

1968 (1 Nov). Rock Paintings. T **55** and similar designs. W **53** (sideways on 5c., 15c.). P 14×14½ (5c., 15c.) or 14½×14 (others).

160		3c. yellow-brown, light blue-green and blackish green	20	10
161		3½c. greenish yellow, yellow-olive and sepia	25	10
162		5c. Venetian red, yellow-ochre and blackish brown	25	10
163		10c. yellow, rose and deep brown	35	10
164		15c. light buff, pale olive-yellow and blackish brown	50	30
165		20c. yellow-green, greenish yellow and blackish brown	60	55
166		25c. yellow, orange-brown and black	65	75
160/6 *Set of 7*			2·50	1·75

Designs:—Horiz—3½c. Baboons; 10c. Archers; 20c. Eland; 25c. Hunting scene. Vert—5c. Spear throwing; 15c. Blue Cranes.

62 Queen Elizabeth II Hospital

(Des C. R. Househam and G. Drummond. Litho P.B.)

1969 (11 Mar). Centenary of Maseru (capital). T **62** and similar horiz designs. Multicoloured. W **53** (sideways). P 14×13½.

167		2½c. Type **62**	10	10
168		10c. Lesotho Radio Station	10	10
169		12½c. Leabua Jonathan Airport	35	10
170		25c. Royal Palace	25	15
167/70 *Set of 4*			65	30

66 Rally Car passing Mosotho Horseman

(Des P. Wheeler. Photo Harrison)

1969 (26 Sept). Roof of Africa Car Rally. T **66** and similar horiz designs. W **53**. P 14.

171		2½c. yellow, mauve and plum	15	10
172		12½c. cobalt, greenish yellow and olive-grey	20	10
173		15c. blue, black and mauve	20	10
174		20c. black, red and yellow	20	10
171/4 *Set of 4*			65	30

Designs:—12½c. Rally car on mountain road; 15c. Chequered flags and mountain scenery; 20c. Map of rally route and Rally Trophy.

71 Gryponyx and Footprints

75 Moshoeshoe I, when a Young Man

(Des Jennifer Toombs. Photo Harrison)

1970 (5 Jan). Prehistoric Footprints. T **71** and similar designs. W **53** (sideways*). P 14×14½ (3c.) or 14½×14 (others).

175		3c. pale brown, yellow-brown and sepia	90	70
176		5c. dull purple, pink and sepia	1·10	30
		w. Wmk hat pointing right	3·25	
177		10c. pale yellow, black and sepia	1·25	35
178		15c. olive-yellow, black and sepia	1·50	2·25
179		25c. cobalt and black	2·25	2·25
175/9 *Set of 5*			6·25	5·25

Designs: (60×23 *mm*)—3c. Dinosaur footprints at Moyeni. (40×24 *mm*)—10c. Plateosaurvus and footprints; 15c. Tritylodon and footprints; 25c. Massospondylus and footprints.

*The normal sideways watermark shows the hat pointing left, *when seen from the back of the stamp.*

(Des G. Vasarhelyi. Litho D.L.R.)

1970 (11 Mar). Death Centenary of King Moshoeshoe I. T **75** and similar vert design. W **53**. P 13½.

180		2½c. pale green and magenta	10	10
181		25c. pale blue and chesnut	20	20

Design:—25c. Moshoeshoe I as an old man.

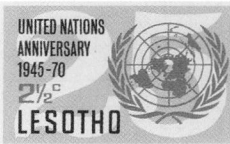

77 UN Emblem and "25"

(Des V. Whiteley. Litho Questa)

1970 (26 June). 25th Anniv of United Nations. T **77** and similar horiz designs. W **53** (sideways). P 14½×14.

182		2½c. light pink, light blue and maroon	10	10
183		10c. multicoloured	10	10
184		12½c. brown-red, cobalt and drab	10	25
185		25c. multicoloured	15	65
182/5 *Set of 4*			30	60

Designs:—10c. UN Building; 12½c. "People of the World"; 25c. Symbolic Dove.

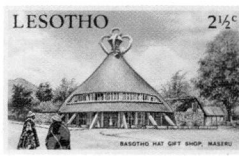

78 Basotho Hat Gift Shop, Maseru

(Des G. Drummond. Litho Questa)

1970 (27 Oct). Tourism. T **78** and similar horiz designs. Multicoloured. W **53** (sideways). P 14.

186		2½c. Type **78**	10	10
187		5c. Trout fishing	20	10
188		10c. Pony trekking	25	10
189		12½c. Skiing	50	10
190		20c. Holiday Inn, Maseru	40	50
186/90 *Set of 5*			1·25	70

POSTAGE DUE STAMPS

D 3

1966 (1 Nov). Nos. D9/10 of Basutoland optd as T **34** but smaller.

D11	**D 2**	1c. carmine	30	75
		a. "LSEOTHO" (R. 4/7)	32·00	
D12		5c. deep reddish violet	30	90
		a. "LSEOTHO" (R. 4/7)	50·00	

No. D11 exists with the overprint centred near the foot of the stamp (just above "POSTAGE DUE") (*price £50 mint*). It is believed that this comes from proof sheets which were issued in the normal way. They contain the "LSEOTHO" error, which only occurred in the first printing.

(Litho B.W.)

1967 (18 Apr). No wmk. P 13½.

D13	**D 3**	1c. blue	15	3·00
D14		2c. brown-rose	15	3·50
D15		5c. emerald	20	3·50
D13/15 *Set of 3*			45	9·00

Long Island

PRICES FOR STAMPS ON COVER
Most covers from Long Island are philatelic, but these are worth from × 2 (Nos. 1/3) or from × 6 (Nos. 4/36).

The Turkish island of Chustan (or Keustan) in the Gulf of Smyrna was occupied by the Royal Navy during April 1916 and renamed Long Island.

The following stamps were provided by the Civil Administrator, Lieut-Cmdr H. Pirie-Gordon, for the postal service inaugurated on 7 May 1916.

USED STAMPS. Stamps of Long Island were cancelled by hand-drawn circular date stamps in blue crayon for the Northend post office ("N") or in red crayon for Nikola post office ("S").

QUANTITIES ISSUED. The figures quoted do not include the remainders subsequently recorded as having been destroyed.

 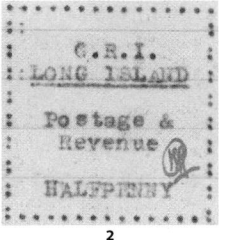

(1) 2

1916 (7 May). Turkish fiscal stamps surch by typewriter as in T **1**. No wmk. P 12.

1	½d. on 20pa. green and buff (new value in red, remainder of surch in black).	£8000	£10000
2	1d. on 10pa. carmine and buff	£9000	£10000
3	2½pi. violet and buff (R.)	£8000	£10000

Quantities issued: ½d. 25; 1d. 20; 2½d. 25.

1916 (7 May). Typewritten as T **2** in various colours of ribbon and carbon. Each stamp initialled by the Civil Administrator. No gum. Imperf.

(a) On pale green paper with horizontal grey lines. No wmk. Sheets of 12 (4×3) or 16 (4×4) with stamps initialled in red ink

4	½d. black	£3000	£2500
	a. "G.R.I." double	£5500	
	b. "7" for "&"	£8500	
5	½d. blue	£2500	
	a. "G.R.I." double	£5500	
	b. "7" for "&"	£8500	
6	½d. mauve	£1000	£1200
	a. "G.R.I." double	£2750	
	b. "7" for "&"	£7000	

Quantity issued: 140 in all.

(b) On thin horiz laid paper with sheet wmk of "Silver Linen" in double-lined letters. Sheets of 20 (4×5) or 16 (some ptgs of 1s.) with stamps initialled in red ink

7	½d. black	£1200	£1500
	a. "postage" for "Postage"	£6500	
	b. "7" for "&"	£6500	
8	½d. blue	£1700	£1800
	b. "7" for "&"	£6500	
9	½d. mauve	£600	£700
	a. "postage" for "Postage"	£3000	
	b. "7" for "&"	£4000	
10	1d. black	£450	£700
	a. "7" for "&"	£3750	
	b. "Rvevue" for "Revenue"	£3750	
	g. "Postagg" for "Postage"	£6000	
11	1d. blue	£600	£900
	a. "7" for "&"	£6000	
	c. "postage" for "Postage"	£6000	
	e. "G.R?I?" for "G.R.I."	£6000	
	f. "ONR" for "ONE"	£3000	
12	1d. mauve	£325	£550
	a. "7" for "&"	£4250	
	b. "Rvevue" for "Revenue"	£6000	
	c. "postage" for "Postage"	£6000	
	e. "G.R?I?" for "G.R.I."	†	£6000
	f. "ONR" for "ONE"	£2250	£3000
	g. "Postagg" for "Postage"	£4000	
13	1d. red	£375	£650
	a. "7" for "&"	£4000	
	c. "postage" for "Postage"	£6000	
	f. "ONR" for "ONE"	£3000	£3500
14	2½d. black	£3250	
15	2½d. blue	£3250	£3250
16	2½d. mauve	£7500	£3250
17	6d. black (inscr "SIX PENCE")	£3750	£4500
	a. "SIXPENCE" (one word)	£7000	
	b. Without red ink initials	†	£6500
19	6d. mauve (inscr "SIX PENCE")	£1600	£2500
	a. "SIXPENCE" (one word)	£5500	
20	1s. black	£325	£750
	a. "ISLANA" for "ISLAND"	£6000	
	b. "Postge" for "Postage"	£3000	£4500
	c. "Rebenue" for "Revenue"	£6000	
21	1s. blue	£3250	
22	1s. mauve	£325	£1000
	a. "ISLANA" for "ISLAND"	£4500	
	b. "Postge" for "Postage"	£6000	
	c. "Rebenue" for "Revenue"	£6000	

Quantities issued (all colours): ½d. 237; 1d. 881; 2½d. 80; 6d. 89; 1s. 383.

(c) On thin wove paper. No wmk. Sheets of 24 with stamps initialled in indelible pencil

23	½d. black	£700	£1100
25	½d. mauve	£1900	
26	1d. black	£1200	£1300
27	1d. red	£14000	£2500

30	2d. black	£550	£1100
	b. Error. 1d. and 2d. se-tenant	£14000	
	c. Initialled in red ink	£2500	£2750
31	2d. mauve	£550	£750
	a. Error. 1d. and 2d. se-tenant	£14000	
32	2½d. black	£1100	£1300
33	2½d. blue	£3250	
34	2½d. mauve	£3000	£3000
35	6d. black	£550	£1100
	a. "Rvenne &" for "Revenue"	£6000	
	b. Error. 2d. and 6d. se-tenant, also "ISLND" for "ISLAND"	£16000	£16000
	c. "PENCC"	£5000	
36	6d. blue	£2500	
	a. "Rvenne &" for "Revenue"	£7000	
	b. Error. 2d. and 6d. se-tenant, also "ISLND" for "ISLAND"	£17000	
	c. "PENCC"	£6000	

Quantities issued (all colours); ½d. 114; 1d. 120; 2d. 249; 2½d. 115; 6d. 200.

TOP SHEETS AND CARBONS. It is believed that the production sequence of the typewritten stamps was as follows:

½d. on pale green (Nos. 4/6)
Two black top sheets of 12 (4×3) and one of 16 (4×4)
Two blue carbon sheets of 12 (4×3) and one of 16 (4×4)
Five mauve carbon sheets of 12, two from one top sheet and three from the other
Varieties: "7" for "&" occurs on an unknown position from one of the sheets of 12 and "G.R.I." double occurs on R. 3/2-4 of the other

½d. on laid paper (Nos. 7/9) in sheets of 20 (4×5)
Three black top sheets
Three blue carbon sheets
Eight mauve carbon sheets, two or three from each top sheet
Varieties: "postage" occurs on R. 3/2 of one top sheet and "7" for "&" on R. 4/2 of another

1d. on laid paper (Nos. 10/13) in sheets of 20 (4×5)
11 red top sheets
15 black carbon sheets, three each from five of the top sheets
Six blue carbon sheets, one each from six of the top sheets
22 mauve carbon sheets, probably two from each top sheet
Varieties: "7" for "&" on R. 3/3, "postage" on R. 3/3, "Rvevue" on R. 1/3 and "Postagg" on R. 2/4, all from different top sheets
The position of "G.R?I?" is not known. "ONR" occurs from three different top sheets on R. 5/1, R. 5/2 and 4 or R. 4/1 and 5/2

2½d. on laid paper (Nos. 14/16) in sheets of 20 (4×5)
One black top sheet
One blue carbon sheet
Two mauve carbon sheets

6d. on laid paper (Nos. 17/19) in sheets of 20 (4×5)
One black top sheet
One blue carbon sheet*
Three mauve carbon sheets
Variety: "SIXPENCE" occurs on R. 1/2-3

1s. on laid paper (Nos. 20/2)
Five black top sheets, four of 20 (4×5) and one of 16 (4×4)
Nine black carbon sheets three each from two of the top sheets of 20 and three from the top sheet of 16
Two blue carbon sheets, one each from two of the top sheets of 20
12 mauve carbon sheets, nine from various top sheets of 20 and three from the top sheet of 16
Varieties: "ISLANA" occurs on R. 1/2 of one of the sheets of 20 and "Postge" on R. 1/3 of the sheet of 16. "Rebenue" comes from one of the other sheets of 20

½d. on wove paper (Nos. 23/5) in sheets of 24 (4×6)
One black top sheet
Three black carbon sheets
One blue carbon sheet*
One mauve carbon sheet

1d. on wove paper (Nos. 26/7) in sheets of 24 (4×6)
One red top sheet
Three black carbon sheets
One blue carbon sheet*
One mauve carbon sheet*

2d. on wove paper (Nos. 30/1) in sheets of 24 (4×6)
Two black top sheets
Six black carbon sheets, three from each top sheet. One initialled in red ink
Four mauve carbon sheets, two from each top sheet
Variety: the "1d." error occurs on R. 5/2 from one top sheet

2½d. on wove paper (Nos. 32/4) in sheets of 24 (4×6)
One black top sheet
Three black carbon sheets
One blue carbon sheet
One mauve carbon sheet

6d. on wove paper (Nos. 35/6) in sheets of 24 (4×6)
Two black top sheets
Six black carbon sheets, three from each top sheet
Two blue carbon sheets, one from each top sheet
Varieties: the "2d." error occurs on R. 5/3 from one top sheet which also showed "PENCC" on R. 3/2, and "Rvenne &" on R. 4/1 of the other

*These carbons are described in written records, but their existence has yet to be confirmed by actual examples.

Madagascar

PRICES FOR STAMPS ON COVER

Nos. 1/47	—
Nos. 50/6	from × 100
Nos. 57/62	from × 30

BRITISH CONSULAR MAIL

After May 1883 mail from the British community at Antananarivo, the capital, was sent by runner to the British Consulate at Tamatave for forwarding via the French Post Office.

In March of the following year the British Vice-Consul at Antananarivo, Mr. W. C. Pickersgill, reorganised this service and issued stamps for use on both local and overseas mail. Such stamps were only gummed at one of the top corners. This was to facilitate their removal from overseas mail where they were replaced by Mauritius stamps (at Port Louis) or by French issues (at the Vice-Consulate) for transmission via Tamatave and Réunion. Local mail usually had the stamps removed also, being marked with a "PAID" or a Vice-Consular handstamp, although a few covers have survived intact.

CONDITION. Due to the type of paper used, stamps of the British Consular Mail are usually found with slight faults, especially thins and creases. Our prices are for fine examples.

USED STAMPS. Postmarks are not usually found on these issues. Cancellations usually take the form of a manuscript line or cross in crayon, ink or pencil or as five parallel horizontal bars in black, red or violet, approximately 15 mm long. Examples of Nos. 1/3, 5/8 and 11 showing a red diagonal line may have been pre-cancelled for accounting purposes.

1

2

1884 (Mar). Typo British Mission at Antananarivo. Rouletted vertically in colour. No gum, except on one upper corner. With circular consular handstamp reading "BRITISH VICE-CONSULATE ANTANANARIVO" around Royal arms in black.

(a) Inscr "LETTER"

1	**1**	6d. (½ oz) magenta	£475	£475
		a. Violet handstamp	£2750	
2		1s. (1 oz) magenta	£500	£450
3		1s.6d. (1½ oz) magenta	£500	£500
4		2s. (2 oz) magenta	£850	£900

(b) Inscr "POSTAL PACKET"

5	**1**	1d. (1 oz) magenta	£550	£425
		a. Without handstamp	£10000	£10000
6		2d. (2 oz) magenta	£375	£300
7		3d. (3 oz) magenta	£400	£325
8		4d. (1 oz amended in ms to "4 oz") magenta	£1000	£700
		a. Without manuscript amendment	£6000	£5000
		b. Violet handstamp	£1800	
		ac. Without handstamp	£9000	£9000

Nos. 1/8 were printed in horizontal strips of four, each strip containing two impressions of the setting. Each strip usually contained two stamps with normal stops after "B.C.M." and two with a hollow stop after "B" (1d., 2d., 3d., 4d., 6d. and 2s.) or after "M" (1s. and 1s.6d.), although the 2d. and 3d. have also been seen with a hollow stop after "M" and the 6d. with hollow stops after both "B" and "C". Several values are known with the handstamp either inverted or double.

1886. Manuscript provisionals.

(a) No. 2 with "SHILLING" erased and "PENNY" written above in red ink

9	**1**	1d. on 1s. (1 oz) magenta		†	—

(b) No. 2 surch "4½d." and "W.C.P." in red ink with a line through the original value

10	1	4½d. on 1s. (1 oz) magenta	†	—

1886. As No. 1, but colour changed. Handstamped with circular "BRITISH VICE-CONSULATE ANTANANARIVO" in black.

11	1	6d. (½ oz) rose-red	£1400	£800

1886. As No. 8a, but handstamped "BRITISH CONSULAR MAIL ANTANANARIVO" in black.

12	1	4d. (1 oz) magenta	£1600	
		a. Violet handstamp	£7500	

1886. Typo British Mission at Antananarivo. "POSTAGE" and value in words printed in black. Rouletted vertically in colour. No gum, except on one upper corner.

I. "POSTAGE" 29½ mm long. Stops after "POSTAGE" and value.
(a) Handstamped "BRITISH VICE-CONSULATE ANTANANARIVO" in black

14	2	1d. rose	£140	£275
		a. Violet handstamp	£400	
15		1½d. rose	£3000	£1300
		a. Violet handstamp	£1500	£850
16		2d. rose	£200	
		a. Violet handstamp	£400	
17		3d. rose	£4000	£1400
		a. Violet handstamp	£550	£375
18		4½d. rose	£3750	£550
		a. Violet handstamp	£700	£325
19		8d. rose	£5000	£3000
		a. Violet handstamp	£2750	£1800
20		9d. rose	£4750	£2750
		a. Violet handstamp	£1300	

(b) Handstamped "BRITISH CONSULAR MAIL ANTANANARIVO" in black.

21	2	1d. rose	£130	
22		1½d. rose	£160	£275
23		2d. rose	£190	
24		3d. rose	£160	£250
		a. Handstamp in red	† £20000	
25		4½d. rose	£180	£225
		a. Handstamp in red	† £12000	
26		8d. rose	£200	
		a. Handstamp in violet	£1700	
27		9d. rose	£225	£350
		a. Without handstamp	£8500	
		b. Handstamp in violet	£450	

II. "POSTAGE" 29½ mm long. No stops after "POSTAGE" or value.
(a) Handstamped "BRITISH VICE-CONSULATE ANTANANARIVO" in violet

28	2	1d. rose	£1300
29		1½d. rose	£3000
30		3d. rose	£1300
31		4½d. rose	£2250
32		6d. rose	£1700

(b) Handstamped "BRITISH CONSULAR MAIL ANTANANARIVO" in black

33	2	1d. rose	£130	£225
		a. Without handstamp	£4750	
		b. Violet handstamp	£170	
34		1½d. rose	£140	£200
		a. Without handstamp	£5000	
		b. Violet handstamp	£275	
35		2d. rose	£150	£200
		b. Violet handstamp	£325	
36		3d. rose	£160	£225
		a. Without handstamp	£8000	
		b. Violet handstamp	£200	
37		4½d. rose	£150	£200
		a. Without handstamp	£9000	
		b. Violet handstamp	£225	
38		6d. rose	£160	£275
		a. Without handstamp	£9500	
		b. Violet handstamp	£500	

III. "POSTAGE" 24½ mm long. No stop after "POSTAGE", but stop after value
(a) Handstamped "BRITISH VICE-CONSULATE ANTANANARIVO" in violet

39	2	4d. rose	£500
40		8d. rose	£700
40a		1s. rose	£22000
41		1s.6d. rose	£12000
42		2s. rose	£6500
		a. Handstamp in black	£18000

(b) Handstamped "BRITISH CONSULAR MAIL ANTANANARIVO" in black

43	2	4d. rose	£375
		a. Without handstamp	£6000
		b. Violet handstamp	£450
44		8d. rose	£2250
		a. Without handstamp	£6000
		b. Violet handstamp	£1400
45		1s. rose	£600
		a. Without handstamp	£8500
		b. Violet handstamp	£1700
46		1s.6d. rose	£750
		a. Without handstamp	£7500
		b. Violet handstamp	£1700
47		2s. rose	£750
		a. Without handstamp	£8500
		b. Violet handstamp	£1700

Nos. 14/47 were also printed in horizontal strips of four.

The stamps of the British Consular Mail were suppressed in 1887, but the postal service continued with the charges paid in cash.

BRITISH INLAND MAIL

In January 1895 the Malagasy government agreed that a syndicate of British merchants at Antananarivo, including the Vice-Consul, should operate an inland postal service during the war with France. Mail was sent by runner to the port of Vatomandry and forwarded via Durban where Natal stamps were added.

Nos. 50/62 were cancelled with dated circular postmarks inscribed "BRITISH MAIL".

4

5 Malagasy Runners

(Typeset London Missionary Society Press, Antananarivo)

1895 (1 Jan). Rouletted in black.

(a) Thick laid paper

50	4	4d. black	65·00	22·00
		a. "FUOR" for "FOUR" (R. 3/2)	—	£1200

(b) In black on coloured wove paper

51	4	1d. blue-grey	50·00	13·00
52		6d. pale yellow	50·00	13·00
53		8d. salmon	50·00	13·00
54		1s. fawn	60·00	13·00
55		2s. bright rose	75·00	30·00
		a. Italic "2" at left (R. 1/2)	£150	65·00
56		4s. grey	75·00	13·00
50/6 Set of 7			£375	£100

There are six types of each value, printed in blocks of six (2×3) separated by gutters, four times on each sheet; the upper and lower blocks being *tête-bêche*.

Nos. 51/6 have been reported on paper showing a sheet watermark in four lines, including a date and the words "Tinted", "Tul..." and "Austria".

(Typo John Haddon & Co, London)

1895 (Mar). The inscription in the lower label varies for each value. P 12.

57	5	2d. blue	14·00	60·00
		a. Imperf between (horiz pair)	£450	
		b. Imperf between (vert pair)	£750	
58		4d. rose	14·00	60·00
		a. Imperf between (horiz pair)	£250	
		b. Imperf between (vert pair)	£300	
		c. Imperf vert (horiz pair)	£275	
59		6d. green	14·00	75·00
		a. Imperf between (horiz pair)	£950	
60		1s. slate-blue	14·00	£120
		a. Imperf between (horiz pair)	£550	
61		2s. chocolate	32·00	£160
		a. Imperf between (horiz pair)	£700	
		b. Imperf between (vert pair)	£1000	
62		4s. bright purple	55·00	£225
		a. Imperf between (horiz pair)	£2250	
57/62 Set of 6			£130	£650

This post was suppressed when the French entered Antananarivo on 30 September 1895.

Malawi

INDEPENDENT

44 Dr. H. Banda (Prime Minister) and Independence Monument

(Des M. Goaman. Photo Harrison)

1964 (6 July). Independence. T **44** and similar horiz designs. P 14½.

211		3d. yellow-olive and deep sepia	10	10
212		6d. red, gold, blue, carmine and lake	10	10
213		1s.3d. red, green, black and bluish violet	45	60
214		2s.6d. multicoloured	45	1·25
		a. Blue omitted	£2750	
211/14 Set of 4			1·00	1·40

Designs:—6d. Banda and rising sun; 1s.3d. Banda and Malawi flag; 2s.6d. Banda and Malawi Coat of Arms.

Six examples of No. 214a are known from the top horizontal row of an otherwise normal sheet.

48 Tung Tree

49 Christmas Star and Globe

(Des V. Whiteley. Photo Harrison)

1964 (6 July)–**65**. As Nos. 199/210 of Nyasaland, but inscr "MALAWI" and T **48** (9d.). No wmk. P 14½.

215		½d. reddish violet	10	60
216		1d. black and green	10	10
217		2d. light red-brown	10	10
218		3d. red-brown, yellow-green and bistre-brown	15	10
219		4d. black and orange-yellow	85	15
220		6d. bluish violet, yellow-green and light blue	75	10
221		9d. bistre-brown, green and yellow	30	15
222		1s. brown, turquoise-blue and pale yellow	25	10
223		1s.3d. bronze-green and chestnut	50	60
224		2s.6d. brown and blue	1·10	1·00
225		5s. blue, green, yellow and sepia	65	3·25
225a		5s. blue, green, yellow and sepia (1.6.65)	13·00	1·00
226		10s. green, orange-brown and black	1·50	2·50
227		£1 deep reddish purple and yellow	5·00	5·50
215/27 Set of 14			22·00	13·00

No. 225a is inscribed "LAKE MALAWI" instead of "LAKE NYASA". See also Nos. 252/62.

(Des V. Whiteley. Photo Harrison)

1964 (1 Dec). Christmas. P 14½.

228	49	3d. blue-green and gold	10	10
		a. Gold (star) omitted	£650	
229		6d. magenta and gold	10	10
230		1s.3d. reddish violet and gold	10	10
231		2s.6d. blue and gold	20	50
228/31 Set of 4			45	70
MS231a 83×126 mm. Nos. 228/31. Imperf			1·00	1·75

No. 228a comes from a sheet on which 41 examples had the gold colour omitted due to a paper fold.

50 Coins   **(51)**

(Des V. Whiteley. Photo Enschedé)

1965 (1 Mar). Malawi's First Coinage. Coins in black and silver. P 13½.

232	50	3d. green	10	10
233		9d. magenta	20	10
		a. Silver omitted	†	—
234		1s.6d. purple	25	10
235		3s. blue	35	1·10
232/5 Set of 4			80	1·25
MS235a 126×104 mm. Nos. 232/5. Imperf			1·60	1·60

1965 (14 June). Nos. 223/4 surch as T **51**.

236		1s.6d. on 1s.3d. bronze-green and chestnut	10	10
237		3s. on 2s.6d. brown and blue	20	20

On No. 237 "3/-" is placed below the bars.

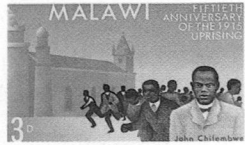

52 Chilembwe leading Rebels

(Des M. Goaman. Photo Harrison)

1965 (20 Aug). 50th Anniv of 1915 Rising. P 14×14½.
238	**52**	3d. violet and light olive-green........	10	10
239		9d. olive-brown and red-orange	10	10
240		1s.6d. red-brown and grey-blue.......	15	10
241		3s. turquoise-green and slate-blue	20	25
238/41 Set of 4			40	60
MS241*a* 127×83 mm. Nos. 238/41			5·00	6·00

53 "Learning and Scholarship"

(Des H. E. Baxter. Photo Harrison)

1965 (6 Oct). Opening of Malawi University. P 14½.
242	**53**	3d. black and emerald....................	10	10
243		9d. black and magenta....................	10	10
244		1s.6d. black and reddish violet..............	10	10
245		3s. black and blue.........................	15	40
242/5 Set of 4			30	50
MS246 127×84 mm. Nos. 242/5			2·50	2·50

54 *Papilio ophidicephalus*

(Des V. Whiteley. Photo Enschedé)

1966 (15 Feb). Malawi Butterflies. T **54** and similar horiz designs. Multicoloured. P 13½.
247		4d. Type **54**	80	10
248		9d. *Papilio desmondi (magdae)*	1·00	10
249		1s.6d. *Epamera handmani*	1·50	10
250		3s. *Amauris crawshayi*	2·25	6·00
247/50 Set of 4			5·00	6·00
MS251 130×100 mm. Nos. 247/50			17·00	10·00

55 Cockerels

56 Burley Tobacco

57 *Cyrestis camillus* (butterfly)

(New values des V. Whiteley (1s.6d.), M. Goaman (£2). Photo Harrison)

1966–67. As Nos. 215 etc. but W **55** (sideways on ½d., 2d.), and new values and designs (1s.6d., £2). P 14½.
252	–	½d. reddish violet (1.4.66)	10	10
253	–	1d. black and green (1.4.66)	15	10
254	–	2d. light red-brown (4.6.66)*	15	10
255	–	3d. red-brown, yellow-green and bistre-brown (4.3.67)*	20	35
256	–	6d. bluish violet, yellow-green and light blue (2.7.66)*	3·00	1·00
257	**48**	9d. bistre-brown, green and yellow (5.12.66)*	3·50	10
258	–	1s. brown, turquoise-blue and pale yellow (1.4.66)	25	10
259	**56**	1s.6d. chocolate and yellow-green (15.11.66)	55	10
260	–	5s. blue, green, yellow and sepia (6.10.66)*	8·50	5·00
261	–	10s. green, orange-brown and black (6.10.66)*	22·00	27·00
262	**57**	£2 black, orange-yellow, pale yellow and slate-violet (7.9.66)	27·00	24·00
252/62 Set of 11			55·00	50·00

*These are local dates of issue. The Crown Agents, in London, did not distribute these printings until some time later.
No. 260 is inscribed "LAKE MALAWI".
The 2d. exists with both PVA gum and gum arabic.

58 British Central Africa 6d. Stamp of 1891   **59** President Banda

(Des V. Whiteley. Photo Harrison)

1966 (4 May–10 June). 75th Anniv of Postal Services. W **55**. P 14½.
263	**58**	4d. grey-blue and yellow-green.......	10	10
264		9d. grey-blue and claret..............	15	10
265		1s.6d. grey-blue and reddish lilac........	20	10
266		3s. grey-blue and new blue	30	70
263/6 Set of 4			60	80
MS267 83×127 mm. Nos. 263/6 (10.6)........			4·50	3·25

REPUBLIC

(Des M. Goaman. Photo Harrison)

1966 (6 July). Republic Day. W **55**. P 14×14½.
268	**59**	4d. brown, silver and emerald.........	10	10
269		9d. brown, silver and magenta	10	10
270		1s.6d. brown, silver and violet	15	10
271		3s. brown, silver and blue..........	25	15
268/71 Set of 4			50	30
MS272 83×127 mm. Nos. 268/71			1·60	3·50

60 Bethlehem

(Des and photo Harrison)

1966 (12 Oct). Christmas. W **55**. P 14½.
273	**60**	4d. myrtle-green and gold.............	10	10
274		9d. brown-purple and gold	10	10
275		1s.6d. orange-red and gold.............	15	10
276		3s. blue and gold	40	80
273/6 Set of 4			65	1·00

61 *Ilala I*

(Des Mrs. H. Breggar. Photo Harrison)

1967 (4 Jan). Lake Malawi Steamers. T **61** and similar horiz designs. W **55**. P 14½.
277		4d. black, yellow and bright green..........	30	10
		a. Yellow omitted	†	£850
278		9d. black, yellow and magenta	35	10
279		1s.6d. black, red and violet	50	20
280		3s. black, red and bright blue	80	1·75
277/80 Set of 4			1·75	1·90

Designs:—9d. *Dove*; 1s.6d. *Chauncy Maples I* (wrongly inscr "Chauncey"); 3s. *Gwendolen*.
No. 277a occurs on first day covers from Blantyre.

62 Golden Mbuna (female)

(Des R. Granger Barrett. Photo Enschedé)

1967 (3 May). Lake Malawi Cichlids. T **62** and similar horiz designs. Multicoloured. W **55** (sideways). P 12½×12.
281		4d. Type **62**	25	10
282		9d. Scraper-mouthed Mbuna	40	10
283		1s.6d. Zebra Mbuna	50	25
		a. Imperf (pair)	£400	
284		3s. Orange Mbuna	80	2·00
		a. Imperf (pair)	£400	
281/4 Set of 4			1·75	2·25

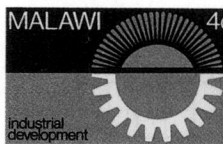

63 Rising Sun and Gearwheel

(Des Jennifer Toombs. Litho D.L.R.)

1967 (5 July). Industrial Development. P 13½×13.
285	**63**	4d. black and emerald	10	10

286		9d. black and carmine	10	10
287		1s.6d. black and reddish violet	10	10
288		3s. black and bright blue...........	15	30
285/8 Set of 4			30	50
MS289 134×108 mm. Nos. 285/8			1·25	2·50

64 Mary and Joseph beside Crib

(Des Jennifer Toombs. Photo Harrison)

1967 (21 Nov–1 Dec). Christmas. W **55**. P 14×14½.
290	**64**	4d. royal blue and turquoise-green	10	10
291		9d. royal blue and light red	10	10
292		1s.6d. royal blue and yellow	10	10
293		3s. royal blue and new blue	15	30
290/3 Set of 4			30	50
MS294 114×100 mm. Nos. 290/3. Wmk sideways. P 14×13½ (1.12)			1·00	3·00

65 *Calotropis procera*

(Des G. Drummond. Litho D.L.R.)

1968 (24 Apr). Wild Flowers. T **65** and similar horiz designs. Multicoloured. W **55** (sideways). P 13½×13.
295		4d. Type **65**	15	10
296		9d. *Borreria dibrachiata*	15	10
297		1s.6d. *Hibiscus rhodanthus*	15	10
298		3s. *Bidens pinnatipartita*	20	95
295/8 Set of 4			60	1·10
MS299 135×91 mm. Nos. 295/8			1·50	3·75

66 Bagnall Steam Locomotive No. 1, *Thistle*

(Des R. Granger Barrett. Photo Harrison)

1968 (24 July). Malawi Locomotives. T **66** and similar horiz designs. W **55**. P 14×14½.
300		4d. grey-green, slate-blue and red	20	10
301		9d. red, slate-blue and myrtle-green	25	15
302		1s.6d. multicoloured	35	30
303		3s. multicoloured	55	3·00
300/3 Set of 4			1·25	3·00
MS304 120×88 mm. Nos. 300/3. P 14½			1·50	6·00

Designs:—9d. Class G steam locomotive No. 49; 1s.6d. Class "Zambesi" diesel locomotive No. 202; 3s. Diesel railcar No. DR1.

67 The Nativity (Piero della Francesca)

(Des and photo Harrison)

1968 (6 Nov). Christmas. Paintings. T **67** and similar horiz designs. Multicoloured. W **55** (sideways on 4d.). P 14×14½.
305		4d. Type **67**	10	10
306		9d. *The Adoration of the Shepherds* (Murillo)	10	10
307		1s.6d. *The Adoration of the Shepherds* (Reni)	10	10
308		3s. *Nativity with God the Father and Holy Ghost* (Pittoni)	15	15
305/8 Set of 4			30	30
MS309 115×101 mm. Nos. 305/8. P 14×13½			35	1·60

68 Scarlet-chested Sunbird   **69** Nyasa Lovebird

70 Carmine Bee-eater

(Des V. Whiteley. Photo Harrison)

1968 (13 Nov). Birds. T **68/70** and similar designs. Multicoloured. W **55** (sideways on 1d. to 4d. and 3s. to £1). P 14½.

310	1d. Type **68**	15	65
311	2d. Violet Starling	30	40
312	3d. White-browed Robin Chat	30	10
313	4d. Red-billed Fire Finch	50	40
	a. Red omitted	†	—
314	6d. Type **69**	2·50	15
315	9d. Yellow-rumped Bishop	2·50	60
316	1s. Type **70**	1·00	15
317	1s.6d. Grey-headed Bush Shrike	3·00	8·00
318	2s. Paradise Whydah	3·00	8·00
319	3s. African Paradise Flycatcher	7·00	4·25
320	5s. Bateleur	3·50	4·25
321	10s. Saddle-bill Stork	3·50	7·50
322	£1 Purple Heron	6·00	16·00
323	£2 Knysna Turaco ("Livingstone's Loerie")	42·00	50·00
310/23 Set of 14		65·00	90·00

Sizes:—2d. to 4d. as T **68**; 9d. as T **69**; 1s.6d., 2s, £2 as T **70**; 3s. to £1 as T **70** but vertical.

No. 310 exists in coils, constructed from normal sheets.

An example of No. 313a is known used on local cover from Limbe in September 1970.

71 ILO Emblem

(Des G. Drummond. Photo, emblem die-stamped Harrison)

1969 (5 Feb). 50th Anniv of the International Labour Organization. W **55** (sideways on No. **MS**328). P 14.

324	**71**	4d. gold and myrtle-green	10	10
325		9d. gold and chocolate	10	10
326		1s.6d. gold and blackish brown	10	10
327		3s. gold and indigo	15	15
324/7 Set of 4			30	30
MS328 127×89 mm. Nos. 324/7			1·00	4·75

72 White-fringed Ground Orchid

73 African Development Bank Emblem

(Des J.W. Litho B.W.)

1969 (9 July). Orchids of Malawi. T **72** and similar horiz designs. Multicoloured. W **55**. P 13½×13.

329	4d. Type **72**	15	10
330	9d. Red Ground Orchid	20	10
331	1s.6d. Leopard Tree Orchid	30	20
332	3s. Blue Ground Orchid	60	2·00
329/32 Set of 4		1·10	2·00
MS333 118×86 mm. Nos. 329/32		1·10	4·00

(Des G. Vasarhelyi. Litho D.L.R.)

1969 (10 Sept). Fifth Anniv of African Development Bank. W **55**. P 14.

334	**73**	4d. yellow, yellow-ochre and chocolate	10	10
335		9d. yellow, yellow-ochre and myrtle-green	10	10
336		1s.6d. yellow, yellow-ochre and blackish brown	10	10
337		3s. yellow, yellow-ochre and indigo	15	15
334/7 Set of 4			30	30
MS338 102×137 mm. Nos. 334/7			50	1·25

74 Dove over Bethlehem

75 *Zonocerus elegans* (Grasshopper)

(Des Jennifer Toombs. Photo Harrison)

1969 (5 Nov). Christmas. W **55**. P 14½×14.

339	**74**	2d. black and olive-yellow	10	10
340		4d. black and deep turquoise	10	10
341		9d. black and scarlet	10	10
342		1s.6d. black and deep bluish violet	10	10
343		3s. black and ultramarine	15	15
339/43 Set of 5			30	30
MS344 130×71 mm. Nos. 339/43			1·00	2·25
	a. Ultramarine (background of 3s.) omitted		£4000	

(Des V. Whiteley. Litho Format)

1970 (4 Feb). Insects of Malawi. T **75** and similar vert designs. Multicoloured. W **55**. P 14.

345	4d. Type **75**	15	10
346	9d. *Mylabris dicincta* (Beetle)	15	10
347	1s.6d. *Henosepilachna elaterii* (Ladybird)	20	15
348	3s. *Sphodromantis speculabunda* (Mantid)	35	1·60
345/8 Set of 4		75	1·75
MS349 86×137 mm. Nos. 345/8		1·25	3·00

Rand Easter Show 1970

(**76**)

1970 (18 Mar). Rand Easter Show. No. 317 optd with T **76**.

350	1s.6d. multicoloured	50	2·25

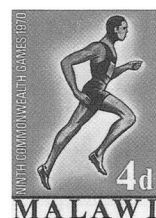

77 Runner

(Des J. Cooter. Litho B.W.)

1970 (3 June). Ninth British Commonwealth Games, Edinburgh. W **55**. P 13.

351	**77**	4d. royal blue and blue-green	10	10
352		9d. royal blue and carmine	10	10
353		1s.6d. royal blue and dull yellow	10	10
354		3s. royal blue and new blue	15	15
351/4 Set of 4			30	30
MS355 146×96 mm. Nos. 351/4			65	1·00

(New Currency, 100 tambalas = 1 kwacha)

10t
(**78**)

79 *Aegocera trimeni*

1970 (2 Sept). Decimal Currency. Nos. 316 and 318 surch as T **78**.

356	10t. on 1s. multicoloured	3·00	25
	a. Surch double	†	—
357	20t. on 2s. multicoloured	3·00	4·50

(Des R. Granger Barrett. Litho B.W.)

1970 (30 Sept). Moths. T **79** and similar horiz designs. Multicoloured. W **55**. P 11×11½.

358	4d. Type **79**	20	10
359	9d. *Faidherbia bauhiniae*	30	10
360	1s.6d. *Parasa karschi*	50	20
361	3s. *Teracotona euprepia*	1·25	3·50
358/61 Set of 4		2·00	3·50
MS362 112×92 mm. Nos. 358/61		3·75	6·50

80 Mother and Child

(Des Brother W. Meyer. Litho J.W.)

1970 (4 Nov). Christmas. W **55** (sideways). P 14.

363	**80**	2d. black and light yellow	10	10
364		4d. black and emerald	10	10
365		9d. black and orange-red	10	10
366		1s.6d. black and light purple	10	10
367		3s. black and blue	15	15
363/7 Set of 5			30	30
MS368 166×100 mm. Nos. 363/7			1·00	3·00

POSTAGE DUE STAMPS

D **2**

(Litho Bradbury Wilkinson)

1967 (1 Sept). W **55**. P 11½.

D6	D **2**	1d. carmine	15	4·50
D7		2d. sepia	20	4·50
D8		4d. reddish violet	25	4·75
D9		6d. blue	25	5·00
D10		8d. emerald	50	5·50
D11		1s. black	60	6·00
D6/11 Set of 6			1·75	27·00

Malaysia

The Federation of Malaya was formed on 1 February 1948 by the former Straits Settlements of Malacca and Penang, the four Federated Malay States and the five Unfederated States. It did not, however, issue any stamps until it became an independent member of the Commonwealth in 1957.

The philatelic history of the component parts of the federation is most complex.

The method adopted is to show the general issues for the area first, before dealing with the issues for the individual States. The section is divided as follows:

I. STRAITS SETTLEMENTS
II. FEDERATED MALAY STATES
III. MALAYAN POSTAL UNION
IV. MALAYA (BRITISH MILITARY ADMINISTRATION)
V. MALAYAN FEDERATION
VI. MALAYSIA
VII. MALAYAN STATES—Johore, Kedah, Kelantan, Malacca, Negri Sembilan (with Sungei Ujong), Pahang, Penang, Perak, Perlis, Sabah, Selangor, Trengganu
VIII. JAPANESE OCCUPATION OF MALAYA 1942–45
IX. THAI OCCUPATION OF MALAYA 1943–45

I. STRAITS SETTLEMENTS

The three original Settlements, Malacca, Penang (with Province Wellesley) and Singapore (with Christmas Island), were formed into a Crown Colony on 1 April 1867. The Cocos (Keeling) Islands were transferred to Straits Settlements on 7 February 1886. Labuan was attached to the Colony in 1896, becoming the fourth Settlement in 1906, but was transferred to North Borneo in 1946.

The first known prestamp cover with postal markings from Penang (Prince of Wales Island) is dated March 1806 and from Malacca, under British civil administration, February 1841. The civil post office at Singapore opened on 1 February 1823.

The stamps of India were used at all three post offices from late in 1854 until the Straits Settlements became a separate colony on 1 September 1867.

The Indian stamps were initially cancelled by dumb obliterators and their use in the Straits Settlements can only be identified from complete covers. In 1856 cancellations of the standard Indian octagonal type were issued, numbered "B 109" for Malacca, "B 147" for Penang and "B 172" for Singapore.

CURRENCY. Before 1867 official accounts of the East India Company administration for the Straits Settlements were kept in rupees, although the vast majority of commercial transactions used Spanish American silver dollars, supplies of which reached Malaya via the Philippines.

This confusing situation was rapidly amended when the Straits Settlements became a Crown Colony on 1 April 1867 and Spanish American dollars were declared to be the only legal currency. In 1874 American trade dollars and Japanese yen were also accepted, but in 1890 recognition of the Spanish American dollars was restricted to those from the Mexican mints. A shortage of silver coinage led to the introduction of silver British trade dollars in 1895 which also circulated in Hong Kong and Labuan.

Dollar banknotes first appeared in 1899, but Mexican dollars were not finally replaced until the issue of silver Straits Settlements dollars in 1903, the gold value of which was set at 2s.4d. in January 1906.

A   B

C

The Penang and Singapore octagonals were replaced by a duplex type, consisting of a double-ringed datestamp and a diamond-shaped obliterator containing the office number, in 1863 and 1865 respectively.

D

E

PRICES. Catalogue prices in this section are for stamps with clearly legible, if partial, examples of the postmarks.

EAST INDIA COMPANY ADMINISTRATION

MALACCA

Stamps of INDIA cancelled with Type A.

1854. (Nos. 2/34).
Z1	½a. blue (Die I)	£3000
Z2	1a. red (Die I)	£3250
Z3	1a. dull red (Die II)	£3500
Z4	2a. green	£3500
Z4a	4a. blue and pale red (Head Die I) (cut-to-shape)	£3250
Z5	4a. blue and red (Head Die II) (cut-to-shape)	£3250
Z5a	4a. blue and red (Head Die III) (cut-to-shape)	£3250

1855. (Nos. 35/6).
Z6	8a. carmine (Die I)/blue glazed	£1000

1856–64. (Nos. 37/49).
Z7	½a. pale blue (Die I)	£700
Z8	1a. brown	£550
Z8a	2a. dull pink	£750
Z9	2a. yellow-buff	£600
Z10	2a. yellow	£650
Z10a	4a. black	£1000
Z11	4a. green	£950
Z12	8a. carmine (Die I)	£700

1860. (Nos. 51/3).
Z13	8p. purple/bluish	£1700
Z14	8p. purple/white	£900

1865. (Nos. 54/65).
Z15	4a. green	£1000

PENANG

Stamps of INDIA cancelled with Type B.

1854. (Nos. 2/34).
Z20	½a. blue (Die I)	£950
Z21	1a. red (Die I)	£400
Z21a	1a. red (Die II)	£3750
Z22	2a. green	£500
Z23	4a. blue and pale red (Head Die I)	£3750
Z24	4a. blue and red (Head Die II)	£3750
Z25	4a. blue and red (Head Die III)	£2500

1855. (Nos. 35/6).
Z26	4a. black/blue glazed	£160
Z27	8a. carmine (Die I)/blue glazed	£150
	a. Bisected (4a.) (1860) (on cover)	£130000

1856–64. (Nos. 37/49).
Z28	½a. pale blue (Die I)	£160
Z29	1a. brown	90·00
Z30	2a. dull pink	£140
Z31	2a. yellow-buff	£130
Z32	2a. yellow	£130
Z33	2a. orange	£130
Z34	4a. black	90·00
Z35	8a. carmine (Die I)	£120

1860. (Nos. 51/3).
Z36	8p. purple/white	£325

Stamps of INDIA cancelled with Type D.

1854. (Nos. 2/34).
Z38	1a. red (Die I)	£5000

1856–64. (Nos. 37/49).
Z39	½a. pale blue (Die I)	£400
Z40	1a. brown	£100
Z40a	2a. yellow-buff	£140
Z41	2a. yellow	£120
Z42	4a. black	£100
Z43	4a. green	£350
Z44	8a. carmine (Die I)	£120

1860. (Nos. 51/3).
Z45	8p. purple/white	£180
Z46	8p. mauve	£200

1865. (Nos. 54/65).
Z47	8p. purple	
Z48	1a. deep brown	£100
Z49	2a. yellow	£120
Z50	4a. green	£375
Z51	8a. carmine (Die I)	

1866–67. (Nos. 69/72).
Z52	4a. green (Die 1)	£425

OFFICIAL STAMP

1866–67. (No. O2).
Z54	½a. pale blue	

SINGAPORE

Stamps of INDIA cancelled with Type C.

1854. (Nos. 2/34).
Z60	½a. blue (Die I)	£425
Z61	1a. red (Die I)	£325
Z62	1a. dull red (Die II)	£300
Z63	1a. red (Die III)	£3250
Z64	2a. green	£140
	a. Bisected (1a.) (1857) (on cover)	£250000
Z65	4a. blue and pale red (Head Die I)	£3250
Z66	4a. blue and red (Head Die II)	£3000
Z67	4a. blue and red (Head Die III)	£1700

1855. (Nos. 35/6).
Z68	4a. black/blue glazed	60·00
	a. Bisected (2a.) (1859) (on cover)	£21000
Z69	8a. carmine/blue glazed	60·00
	a. Bisected (4a.) (1859) (on cover)	£130000

1856–66. (Nos. 37/49).
Z70	½a. pale blue (Die I)	80·00
Z71	1a. brown	38·00
	a. Bisected (½a.) (1859) (on cover)	£130000
Z72	2a. dull pink	75·00
Z73	2a. yellow-buff	65·00
Z74	2a. yellow	70·00
Z75	2a. orange	75·00
Z76	4a. black	40·00
	a. Bisected (2a.) (1859) (on cover)	£65000
Z77	4a. green	£225
Z78	8a. carmine (Die I)	60·00
	a. Bisected (4a.) (1866) (on cover)	£130000

1860–61. (Nos. 51/3).
Z79	8p. purple/bluish	£950
Z80	8p. purple/white	£110
	a. Bisected diagonally (4p.) (1861) (on cover)	£130000
Z81	8p. mauve	£130

1865. (Nos. 54/65).
Z82	½a. blue (Die I)	90·00
Z83	1a. red	£250
Z84	1a. deep brown	75·00
Z85	2a. yellow	80·00
Z86	2a. orange	80·00
Z87	4a. green	£170
Z88	8a. carmine (Die I)	£325

1866–67. (Nos. 69/72).
Z89	4a. green (Die I)	£250
Z90	6a.8p. slate	£650

Stamps of INDIA cancelled with Type E.

1856–64. (Nos. 37/49).
Z100	1a. brown	£475
Z101	2a. yellow	£650
Z102	4a. black	£650
Z103	8a. carmine (Die I)	£650

1860. (Nos. 51/3).
Z104	8p. purple/white	£700

1865. (Nos. 54/65).
Z105	2a. yellow	£600
Z106	2a. orange	£600
Z107	4a. green	£750

OFFICIAL STAMPS

Stamps of INDIA cancelled with Type C.

1866–67. (Nos. O6/14).
Z91	½a. pale blue	£950
Z92	2a. yellow	£1300

PRICES FOR STAMPS ON COVER	
Nos. 1/9	from × 20
No. 10	—
Nos. 11/19	from × 12
Nos. 20/1	from × 30
Nos. 22/39	from × 15
Nos. 41/6	from × 25
No. 47	—
Nos. 48/9	from × 12
Nos. 50/3	from × 20
Nos. 54/62	from × 30
Nos. 63/71	from × 15
No. 72	—
Nos. 73/80	from × 30
Nos. 82/7	from × 20
Nos. 88/94	from × 15
Nos. 95/105	from × 8
Nos. 106/9	from × 20
Nos. 110/21	from × 6
No. 122	—
Nos. 123/6	from × 5
Nos. 127/38	from × 4
Nos. 139/40	—
Nos. 141/51	from × 15
Nos. 152/67	from × 4
Nos. 168/9	—
Nos. 193/212	from × 3
Nos. 213/15	—
Nos. 216/17	from × 10
Nos. 218/40a	from × 3
Nos. 240b/d	—
Nos. 241/55	from × 15
Nos. 256/9	from × 4
Nos. 260/98	from × 3
Nos. D1/6	from × 20
No. F1	—

PRINTERS. All Straits Settlements issues were printed in typography by De La Rue & Co, Ltd, London, *unless otherwise stated*. All surcharges were applied by the Government Printer, Singapore, *unless otherwise stated*.

USED PRICES. The prices quoted for Nos. 1/9 are for fine used examples. Those showing parts of commercial "chops" are worth less.

CROWN COLONY

(Currency. 100 cents = 1 Spanish American dollar)

THREE HALF CENTS	32 CENTS
(1)	(2)

1867 (1 Sept). Nos. 54, 59, 61, 69 and 73 of India surch as T **1** or **2** (24c., 32c.) by De La Rue. W **13** (Elephant's head) of India. P 14.

1	1½c. on ½a. blue (Die I) (R.)	£130	£200
2	2c. on 1a. deep brown (R.)	£200	95·00
3	3c. on 1a. deep brown (B.)	£190	95·00
4	4c. on 1a. deep brown (Bk.)	£325	£275
5	6c. on 2a. yellow (P.)	£900	£250
6	8c. on 2a. yellow (G.)	£350	42·00
7	12c. on 4a. green (R.)	£1500	£325
	a. Surch double	£4000	
8	24c. on 8a. rose (Die II) (B.)	£750	£100
9	32c. on 2a. yellow (Bk.)	£500	£110

The 32c. was re-issued for postal use in 1884.
No. 7a. is only known unused.

1869. (?) No. 1 with "THREE HALF" deleted and "2" written above, in black manuscript.

10	2 on 1½c. on ½a. blue	£20000	£6500

This stamp has been known from very early days and was apparently used at Penang, but nothing is known of its history.

5	6	7

8	9

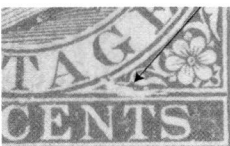

6c. "Slug" flaw (R. 2/4 of one pane)

1867 (Dec)–**72.** Ornaments in corners differ for each value. Wmk Crown CC. P 14.

11	**5**	2c. brown (6.68)	60·00	8·50
		a. Yellow-brown	65·00	8·50
		b. Deep brown	£160	19·00
		w. Wmk inverted	£650	£225
12		4c. rose (7.68)	95·00	15·00
		a. Deep rose	£130	17·00
		w. Wmk inverted	£350	
13		6c. dull lilac (1.68)	£150	22·00
		a. Bright lilac	£180	22·00
		b. "Slug" flaw	—	£325
		w. Wmk inverted	†	£350
		y. Wmk inverted and reversed	†	£450
14	**6**	8c. orange-yellow	£275	18·00
		a. Orange	£275	18·00
		w. Wmk inverted	£700	£200
15		12c. blue	£225	9·00
		a. Ultramarine	£250	11·00
		w. Wmk inverted	£700	
16	**7**	24c. blue-green	£200	8·00
		a. Yellow-green	£350	21·00
		w. Wmk inverted	†	£425
17	**8**	30c. claret (12.72)	£425	17·00
		w. Wmk inverted	†	£650
18	**9**	32c. pale red	£650	70·00
		w. Wmk inverted	†	£500
19		96c. grey	£400	55·00
		a. Perf 12½ (6.71)	£2500	£225

Five Cents.	Seven Cents.
(10)	(11)

1879 (May). Nos. 14a and 18 surch with T **10** and **11**.

20	**6**	5c. on 8c. orange	£150	£190
		a. No stop after "Cents"	£1100	£1300
		b. "F i" spaced	£1200	£1400
21	**9**	7c. on 32c. pale red	£180	£200
		a. No stop after "Cents"	£1800	£2500

The no stop variety occurred once in the setting.

10

cents.

(12)

10	**10**	**10**	**10**
(a)	(b)	(c)	(d)
10	**10**	**10**	**10**
(e)	(f)	(g)	(h)
10	**10**	**10**	**10**	**10**
(i)	(j)	(jj)	(k)	(l)

(a) "1" thin curved serif and thin foot; "0" narrow.
(b) "1" thick curved serif and thick foot: "0" broad. Both numerals heavy.
(c) "1" as (a); "0" as (b).
(d) "1" as (a) but thicker; "0" as (a).
(e) As (a) but sides of "0" thicker.
(f) "1" as (d); "0" as (a).
(g) As (a) but "0" narrower.
(h) "1" thin, curved serif and thick foot; "0" as (g).
(i) "1" as (b); "0" as (a).
(j) "1" as (d); "0" as (g) but raised.
(jj) "1" as (a) but shorter, and with shorter serif and thicker foot; "0" as (g) but level with "1".
(k) "1" as (jj); "0" as (a).
(l) "1" straight serif; "0" as (g).

1880 (Mar). No. 17 surch with T **12** (showing numerals (a) to (jj)).

22	10c. on 30c. claret (a)	£650	£100
23	10c. on 30c. claret (b)	£600	95·00
24	10c. on 30c. claret (c)	£12000	£1100
25	10c. on 30c. claret (e)	£4500	£325
26	10c. on 30c. claret (f)	£23000	£2500
27	10c. on 30c. claret (g)	£7000	£650
28	10c. on 30c. claret (g)	£23000	£2500
29	10c. on 30c. claret (h)	£23000	£2500
30	10c. on 30c. claret (i)	£23000	£2500
31	10c. on 30c. claret (j)	£23000	£2500
32	10c. on 30c. claret (jj)	£23000	£2500

Nos. 22/32 come from the same setting of 60 (6×10) containing 20 examples of No. 22 (R. 1/1-2, 1/4, 1/6, 2/1-6, 3/1, 3/3, 3/5, 4/1, 4/3-4, 10/1, 10/3-5), 22 of No. 23 (R. 4/6, 5/1-6, 6/1-6, 7/1-6, 8/2-4, 9/1-5), six of No. 25 (R. 1/5, 3/2, 3/4, 4/2, 4/5, 10/2), four of No. 28 (R. 7/2-5), two of No. 24 (R. 9/6, 10/6) and one each of Nos. 26 (R. 3/6), 27 (R. 1/3), 29 (R. 7/6), 30 (R. 8/1), 31 (R. 8/6) and 32 (R. 8/5).

No. 23 is known with large stop after "cents" and also with stop low.

1880 (Apr). No. 17 surch as T **12**, but without "cents.", showing numerals (a) to (c), (g) to (i), (k) and (l).

33	10 on 30c. claret (a)	£300	60·00
	w. Wmk inverted	†	£475
34	10 on 30c. claret (b)	£325	60·00
	w. Wmk inverted	†	£475
35	10 on 30c. claret (c)	£900	£130
	w. Wmk inverted	†	£850
36	10 on 30c. claret (g)	£2500	£375
	aw. Wmk inverted	†	£1700
36b	10 on 30c. claret (h)		† £25000
37	10 on 30c. claret (i)	£8500	£1100
38	10 on 30c. claret (k)	£8500	£1100
39	10 on 30c. claret (l)	£8500	£1100

Nos. 33/9 were surcharged from an amended setting of 60 (6×10) of which 59 positions have been identified. Of those known No. 33 occurs on 24 (R. 6/1-6, 7/1-6, 8/1-6, 9/1-2, 9/6, 10/1-3), No. 34 on 21 (R. 1/2-6, 2/1-6, 3/1-6, 4/3-5, 5/6), No. 35 on eight (R. 1/1, 4/2, 4/6, 5/1-5), No. 36 on three (R. 9/3-5) and Nos. 37 (R. 10/6), 38 (R. 10/4) and 39 (R. 10/5) on one each. R. 4/1 remains unidentified.

However, the existence of No. 36b, known as a single example from the sixth vertical column, a stamp in the Royal Collection with "1" as (b) and "0" as (g), and a block of three comprising R. 9/4 and 10/4-5 with No. 38 (rather than 39) at R. 10/5, indicates that there must have been another setting or sub-setting.

5	**5**	**5**
cents.	*cents.*	*cents.*
(13)	(14)	(15)

1880 (Aug). No. 14a surch with T **13** to **15**.

41	**13**	5c. on 8c. orange	£200	£250
42s	**14**	5c. on 8c. orange	£190	£225
43	**15**	5c. on 8c. orange	£700	£900

Surcharged in a setting of 60 (6×10) with T **13** on rows one to four, T **14** on rows five to nine and T **15** on row ten.

10	**5**
cents.	*cents.*
(16)	(17)

1880 (Dec)–**81.** Nos. 13, 15/a and 17 surch with T **16**.

44	10c. on 6c. lilac (11.81)	90·00	6·00
	a. Surch double	—	£3000
	b. "Slug" flaw	—	£200
45	10c. on 12c. ultramarine (1.81)	95·00	17·00
	a. Blue	75·00	9·00
46	10c. on 30c. claret (12.80)	£500	£100

A second printing of the 10c. on 6c. has the surcharge heavier and the "10" usually more to the left or right of "cents". This latter surcharge was applied individually to each stamp and a number of different overprinting units were employed.

1882 (Jan). No. 12 surch with T **17**.

47	5c. on 4c. rose	£375	£400

18	19

1882 (Jan). Wmk Crown CC. P 14.

48	**18**	5c. purple-brown	£120	£140
49	**19**	10c. slate	£550	80·00
		s. Optd "SPECIMEN"	£1000	

1882. Wmk Crown CA. P 14.

50	**5**	2c. brown (8.82)	£375	50·00
51		4c. rose (4.82)	£160	15·00
52	**6**	8c. orange (9.82)	7·00	1·00
		w. Wmk inverted	†	£500
53	**19**	10c. slate (10.82)	17·00	1·25
		w. Wmk inverted	£950	

For the 4c. in deep carmine see No. 98.

TWO CENTS	TWO CENTS	TWO CENTS
20a "S" wide	20b "E" and "S" wide	20c "N" wide
TWO CENTS	TWO CENTS	TWO CENTS
20d All letters narrow	20e "EN" and "S" wide	20f "E" wide

1883 (Apr). Nos. 52 and 18 surch with T **20a/f.**

54	**20a**	2c. on 8c. orange	£350	£130
55	**20b**	2c. on 8c. orange	£350	£130
56	**20c**	2c. on 8c. orange	£350	£130
		w. Wmk inverted		
57	**20d**	2c. on 8c. orange	£180	90·00
		a. Surch double	£3500	£1300
58	**20e**	2c. on 8c. orange	£3250	£1000
59	**20a**	2c. on 32c. pale red	£900	£250
		a. Surch double	£4500	£2250
60	**20f**	2c. on 32c. pale red	£1400	£350
		a. Surch double		

The 8c. was surcharged using one of two triplet settings, either 54 + 55 + 56 or 57 + 57 + 57, applied to rows 2 to 10. A single handstamp, either No. 57 or No. 58, was then used to complete row 1. The 32c. was surcharged in the same way with a triplet of 59 + 60 + 59 and a single handstamp as No. 60.

2	**4**	**8**
Cents.	*Cents*	*Cents*
(21)	(22)	(23)

1883 (June–July). Nos. 51 and 15 surch with T **21**.

61	2c. on 4c. rose	£100	£100
	a. "s" of "Cents" inverted	£1700	£1800
62	2c. on 12c. blue (7.83)	£475	£170
	a. "s" of "Cents" inverted	£8000	£3500

The inverted "S" error occurred once in the first column of the setting of 60.

Broken oval above "O" of "POSTAGE" (Lower right pane R. 10/5)

1883 (July)–**91.** Wmk Crown CA. P 14.

63	**5**	2c. pale rose	50·00	4·75
		a. Bright rose (1889)	13·00	85
		aw. Wmk inverted	—	£550
64		4c. pale brown	55·00	6·00
		a. Broken oval	£650	£150
		b. Deep brown	70·00	7·50
		ba. Broken oval	£800	£190
		w. Wmk inverted	£325	£180
65	**18**	5c. blue (8.83)	19·00	1·25
		w. Wmk inverted	†	£500
66	**5**	6c. lilac (11.84)	26·00	24·00
		a. Violet	3·00	17·00
		b. "Slug" flaw	£225	£300
		w. Wmk inverted	—	£350
67	**6**	12c. brown-purple	85·00	19·00
68	**7**	24c. yellow-green (2.84)	80·00	12·00
		a. Blue-green	12·00	6·50
		w. Wmk inverted	†	£450
69	**8**	30c. claret (9.91)	23·00	25·00
		w. Wmk inverted	£180	£100
70	**9**	32c. orange-vermilion (1.87)	17·00	5·50
		w. Wmk inverted	£100	£100

71		96c. olive-grey (7.88)	75·00	55·00
63a/71		Set of 9	£275	£120
63s/5s, 67s Optd "SPECIMEN" *Set of 4*			£2500	

Most examples of the 4c. in shades of olive-bistre are thought to be colour changelings.

For the 4c. in deep carmine and 12c. in claret see Nos. 98 and 102.

1884 (Feb–Aug). Nos. 65, 15 and 67 surch with T **22** or **23**.

72	**18**	4c. on 5c. blue (8.84)	£3500	£5500
73		4c. on 5c. blue (R.) (8.84)	£190	£140
74	**6**	8c. on 12c. blue	£1200	£160
		w. Wmk inverted	†	£900
75		8c. on 12c. brown-purple (8.84)	£750	£170
		b. "s" of "Cents" low (R. 5/1)	£6500	£1800

1884 (Aug). No. 65 surch with T **20d/f**.

76	**20d**	2c. on 5c. blue	£170	£180
		a. Surch double	†	—
77	**20e**	2c. on 5c. blue	£170	£180
		a. Pair, with and without surch		
		b. Surch double		
78	**20f**	2c. on 5c. blue	£170	£180

Surcharged as a triplet, 77 + 76 + 78. On No. 76 "TS" are dropped below the line.

8 (24)   3 CENTS (25)   THREE CENTS (26)

1884 (Sept). No. 75 additionally surch with large numeral as T **24** in red.

80	**6**	8 on 8c. on 12c. dull purple	£550	£500
		a. Surch T **24** double	£6000	
		b. Surch T **23** in blue	£11000	
		c. "s" of "Cents" low	£4500	£4750

Examples as No. 75, but with Type **23** in blue, were further surcharged in error.

A similar "4" surcharge in red on No. 73 exists from a trial printing of which seven examples are known, all used on an official's correspondence (*Price* £42000 *used*).

1885. No. 65 and T **9** in new colour, wmk Crown CA, surch with T **25** or **26**.

82	**25**	3c. on 5c. blue (9.85)	£170	£275
		a. Surch double	£3250	
83	**26**	3c. on 32c. pale magenta (12.85)	8·00	4·25
		a. *Deep magenta*	3·25	1·00
		s. Optd "SPECIMEN"	£375	

The surcharge on No. 82 was applied locally by a triplet setting. No. 83 was surcharged by De La Rue in complete panes.

3 cents (27)   2 Cents (28)

1886 (Apr). No. 48 surch with T **27**.

84	**18**	3c. on 5c. purple-brown	£325	£350

The surcharge on No. 84 was applied by a triplet setting.

1887 (July). No. 65 surch with T **28**.

85	**18**	2c. on 5c. blue	50·00	£100
		a. "C" of "Cents" omitted		£4250
		b. Surch double	£1700	£1500

The surcharge on No. 85 was applied by a triplet setting.

10 CENTS (29)   THIRTY CENTS (30)

1891 (Nov). Nos. 68 and 70 surch with T **29** and **30**.

86	**7**	10c. on 24c. yellow-green	8·50	1·25
		a. Narrow "0" in "10" (R. 4/6)	30·00	35·00
		w. Wmk inverted	£120	£130
87	**9**	30c. on 32c. orange-vermilion	17·00	3·50
		w. Wmk inverted		

The "R" of "THIRTY" and "N" of "CENTS" are found wide or narrow and in all possible combinations.

ONE CENT (31)   ONE CENT (32)

1892. Stamps of 1882–91 (wmk Crown CA) surch with T **31**.

88		1c. on 2c. bright rose (3.92)	2·00	5·00
89		1c. on 4c. brown (4.92)	10·00	7·50
		a. Surch double	£1800	
		b. Broken oval	£275	£275
		w. Wmk inverted	£325	
90		1c. on 6c. lilac (2.92)	3·00	13·00
		a. Surch double, one inverted	£2250	£2000
		b. "Slug" flaw	£130	£275
		w. Wmk inverted	£325	£375
91		1c. on 8c. orange (1.92)	1·00	4·25
92		1c. on 12c. brown-purple (3.92)	5·00	9·50
88/92		*Set of 5*	19·00	35·00

The three settings used for Nos. 88/92 contained various combinations of the following varieties: "ON" of "ONE" and "N" of "CENT" wide; "O" wide, "N" of "ONE" narrow and "N" of "CENT" wide; "O" narrow and both letters "N" wide; "ON" narrow and "N" of "CENT" wide; "O" wide and both letters "N" narrow; "ON" and "N" of "CENT" narrow; "O" narrow; "N" of "ONE" wide and "N" of "CENT" narrow. Antique "N" and "E" letters also occur.

1892–94. Colours changed. Wmk Crown CA. P 14. Surch with T **32** and **26** by De La Rue.

93	**6**	1c. on 8c. green (3.92)	1·00	1·50
94	**9**	3c. on 32c. carmine-rose (6.94)	2·25	70
		a. Surch omitted	£4500	
93s/4s Optd "SPECIMEN" *Set of 2*			£170	

No. 94a comes from a sheet found at Singapore on which all stamps in the upper left pane had the surcharge omitted. Five vertical inter-panneau pairs still exist with the surcharge omitted on the upper stamps (*Price* £45000 *unused*). The only used example of the error is on cover.

33	34	4 cents. (35)
Normal	Malformed "S"	Repaired "S"

The malformed "S" occurs on R. 7/3 of the left pane from Key Plate 2. It is believed that the repair to it took place in mid-1898. Both states may occur on other stamps in Types **33** and **34**. Stamps subsequently printed from Key Plate 3 showed the "S" normal.

1892–99. Wmk Crown CA. P 14.

95	**33**	1c. green (9.92)	9·00	70
		a. Malformed "S"	£850	£275
		b. Repaired "S"	£800	£250
		w. Wmk inverted	†	£750
96		3c. carmine-rose (2.95)	12·00	40
		a. Malformed "S"	£1100	£350
		b. Repaired "S"	—	£400
97		3c. brown (3.99)	18·00	1·25
		a. Repaired "S"	£1100	£275
		b. *Yellow-brown*	17·00	1·75
		w. Wmk inverted	£500	
98	**5**	4c. deep carmine (7.99)	16·00	1·25
		a. Broken oval	£550	£170
99	**18**	5c. brown (6.94)	18·00	1·00
100		5c. magenta (7.99)	6·00	2·00
101	**6**	8c. ultramarine (6.94)	4·50	50
		a. *Bright blue*	9·50	80
		w. Wmk inverted	†	£400
102		12c. claret (3.94)	29·00	17·00
103	**33**	25c. purple-brown and green (3.92)	48·00	8·50
		a. Malformed "S"	£2000	£950
		b. Repaired "S"	£1700	£750
		c. *Dull purple and green*	35·00	8·50
104		50c. olive-green and carmine	28·00	3·50
		a. Repaired "S"	£1800	£700
105	**34**	$5 orange and carmine (10.98)	£450	£325
		a. Repaired "S"	£6500	£6500
95/105 *Set of 11*			£550	£325
95s/101s, 103s/5s Optd "SPECIMEN" *Set of 10*			£1000	

1898 (26 Dec). T **18** and **6** surch with T **35** at Singapore.

106		4c. on 5c. brown (No. 99)	2·75	4·75
107		4c. on 5c. blue (No. 65)	14·00	32·00
		a. Surch double	†	£3500
108		4c. on 8c. ultramarine (No. 101)	4·00	4·00
		a. Surch double	£1500	£1500
		b. *Bright blue* (No. 101a)	4·00	2·25
106/8b *Set of 3*			19·00	35·00

Nos. 107 and 108b exist with stop spaced 1½ mm from the "S" (R. 10/6).

FOUR CENTS (36)   37   38

1899 (Mar). T **18** (wmk Crown CA. P 14), surch with T **36** by De La Rue.

109		4c. on 5c. carmine	1·00	30
		a. Surch omitted	£40000	
		s. Optd "SPECIMEN"	65·00	
		x. Wmk reversed	£140	

No. 109a is only known unused.

1902 (Apr)–**03**. Wmk Crown CA. P 14.

110	**37**	1c. grey-green (7.02)	2·75	5·00
		a. *Pale green*	6·50	5·50
111		3c. dull purple and orange	3·50	20
		w. Wmk inverted	£900	£425
112		4c. purple/*red* (9.02)	4·75	30
113	**38**	5c. dull purple (8.02)	5·50	2·50
114		8c. purple/*blue*	4·50	20
115		10c. purple and black/*yellow* (8.02)..	28·00	1·50
116	**37**	25c. dull purple and green (8.02)	18·00	13·00
117	**38**	30c. grey and carmine (7.02)	24·00	10·00
118	**37**	50c. deep green and carmine (9.02	23·00	22·00
		a. *Dull green and carmine*	23·00	24·00
119	**38**	$1 dull green and black (9.02)	23·00	80·00
120	**37**	$2 dull purple and black (9.02)	85·00	80·00

121	**38**	$5 dull green and brown-orange (10.02)	£225	£180
122	**37**	$100 purple and green/*yellow* (3.03) (F.C. £250)	£22000	
		s. Optd "SPECIMEN"	£750	
110/21 *Set of 12*			£400	£350
110s/21s Optd "SPECIMEN" *Set of 12*			£500	

(Currency 100 cents = 1 Straits, later Malayan, dollar)

39	40	
41	42	

(Des N. Trotter and W. Egerton)

1903 (Dec)–**04**. Wmk Crown CA. P 14.

123	**39**	1c. grey-green	4·00	9·50
124	**40**	3c. dull purple (1.04)	11·00	4·50
125	**41**	4c. purple/*red* (4.04)	16·00	30
		w. Wmk inverted	†	£475
126	**42**	8c. purple/*blue* (7.04)	50·00	1·25
123/6 *Set of 4*			70·00	14·00
123s/6s Optd "SPECIMEN" *Set of 4*			£225	

1904 (Aug)–**10**. Wmk Multiple Crown CA. Ordinary paper (1c. to $1 and $5) or chalk-surfaced paper ($2, $25, $100). P 14.

127	**39**	1c. deep green (9.04)	5·50	10
		a. Chalk-surfaced paper (12.05)	25·00	1·75
		aw. Wmk inverted	£200	£130
		b. *Blue-green* (3.10)	23·00	1·10
128	**40**	3c. dull purple	3·00	30
		a. Chalk-surfaced paper (8.06)	22·00	2·50
		aw. Wmk inverted	£225	£150
		b. *Plum* (2.08)	15·00	1·75
129	**41**	4c. purple/*red* (11.04)	28·00	1·75
		a. Chalk-surfaced paper (10.05)	27·00	1·25
		aw. Wmk inverted	£130	£100
130	**38**	5c. dull purple (12.06)	29·00	3·50
		a. Chalk-surfaced paper (12.06)	40·00	14·00
		ay. Wmk inverted and reversed	†	£700
131	**42**	8c. purple/*blue* (8.05)	55·00	1·50
		a. Chalk-surfaced paper (12.05)	55·00	2·75
132	**38**	10c. purple and black/*yellow* (8.05)	8·50	80
		a. Chalk-surfaced paper (11.05)	12·00	3·25
133	**37**	25c. dull purple and green (1.05)	60·00	50·00
		a. Chalk-surfaced paper (11.05)	65·00	48·00
134	**38**	30c. grey and carmine (3.05)	50·00	4·00
		a. Chalk-surfaced paper (3.06)	60·00	3·75
135	**37**	50c. dull green and carmine (10.05)	60·00	28·00
		a. Chalk-surfaced paper (11.06)	35·00	20·00
136	**38**	$1 dull green and black (3.05)	75·00	48·00
		a. Chalk-surfaced paper (3.06)	65·00	28·00
137	**37**	$2 dull green and black (10.05)	£120	90·00
138	**38**	$5 dull green and brown-orange (10.05)	£350	£200
		a. Chalk-surfaced paper (1.08)	£350	£180
139	**37**	$25 grey-green and black (7.06)	£3500	£3500
		s. Optd "SPECIMEN"	£475	
140		$100 purple and green/*yellow* (6.10) (F.C. £450)	£22000	
127/38a *Set of 12*			£700	£350

STRAITS SETTLEMENTS. (43)   Straits Settlements. (44)

STRAITS SETTLEMENTS.

FOUR CENTS. (45)

1906 (20 Dec)–**07**. T **18** of Labuan (Nos. 117 etc.) optd with T **43** or **44** (10c.) or additionally surch with T **45**, in black (No. 145), claret (No. 151) or brown-red (others) at Singapore.

141		1c. black and purple (P 14½–15)	70·00	£180
		a. Perf 14	£425	£600
		b. Line through "B"	£1100	
		c. Perf 13½–14 comp 12–13	—	£1500
142		2c. black and green	£425	£180
		a. Perf 14½–15	£180	£325
		b. Perf 13½–14 comp 12–13	£1400	£1400
		c. Line through "B"	£2000	
143		3c. black and sepia (1.07)	26·00	95·00
		a. Line through "B"	£750	
144		4c. on 12c. black and yellow	4·00	14·00
		a. No stop after "CENTS" (R. 1/8, 6/8)	£650	
		b. Line through "B"	£375	£600
145		4c. on 16c. green and brown	12·00	15·00
		a. "STRAITS SETTLEMENTS" in both brown-red and normal	£650	£1000
		b. Ditto. In vert pair with normal	£9000	
		c. Line through "B"	£450	£650
146		4c. on 18c. black and pale brown	2·75	14·00
		a. No stop after "CENTS" (R. 1/8, 6/8)	£425	£650
		b. "FOUR CENTS" and bar double	£17000	
		c. "FOUR CENTS" and bar 1½ mm below normal position (pair with normal)	£2750	
		d. Line through "B"	£350	£550

147		8c. black and vermilion	7·50	14·00
		a. Line through "B"	£425	£650
148		10c. brown and slate	13·00	16·00
		a. No stop after "Settlements" (R. 1/4, 6/4)	£750	£800
		b. Line through "B"	£475	£650
149		25c. green and greenish blue (1.07)	38·00	50·00
		a. Perf 14½–15	£110	£160
		b. Perf 13½–14 comp 14½–15	£600	
		c. Line through "B"	£800	
150		50c. dull purple and lilac (1.07)	25·00	70·00
		c. Line through "B"	£800	
151		$1 claret and orange (Claret) (1.07)	50·00	£120
		a. Perf 14½–15	£1000	
		b. Line through "B"	£1200	£1900
141/51		*Set of 11*	£375	£800

Nos. 141/51 were overprinted by a setting of 50 (10×5) applied twice to the sheets of 100. The "FOUR CENTS" surcharges were applied separately by a similar setting.

No. 145a shows impressions of Type **43** in both brown-red and black. It is known from one complete sheet and the top half of another. In the latter the two overprints are almost coincident, whereas in the former they are clearly separated.

No. 146b occurred on row 5 from one sheet only. No. 146c occurred on R. 4/10 and 9/10 of the first printing.

The line through "B" flaw occurs on R. 5/10 of the basic stamp. For illustration see Labuan.

46

47

1906 (Sept)–**12**. Wmk Mult Crown CA. Ordinary paper (3c. to 10c.) or chalk-surfaced paper (21c. to $500). P 14.

153	40	3c. red (6.08)	8·00	10
154	41	4c. red (7.07)	9·50	2·50
155		4c. dull purple (2.08)	6·00	10
		a. Chalk-surfaced paper (1.12)	11·00	3·00
		as. Optd "SPECIMEN"	£180	
156		4c. claret (9.11)	4·25	80
157	38	5c. orange (4.09)	2·75	2·50
158	42	8c. blue	4·25	60
159	38	10c. purple/*yellow* (7.08)	19·00	1·00
		a. Chalk-surfaced paper (5.12)	32·00	22·00
160	46	21c. dull purple and claret (11.10)	6·50	40·00
161	37	25c. dull and bright purple (7.09)	30·00	12·00
162	38	30c. purple and orange-yellow (11.09)	55·00	4·25
163	46	45c. black/*green* (11.10)	3·00	4·00
164	37	50c. black/*green* (4.10)	12·00	5·00
165	38	$1 black and red/*blue* (10.10)	15·00	8·00
166	37	$2 green and red/*yellow* (12.09)	32·00	24·00
167	38	$5 green and red/*green* (11.09)	£150	75·00
		w. Wmk inverted	£1800	£850
168	47	$25 purple and blue/*blue* (5.11) (F.C. £180)	£3500	£2250
		s. Optd "SPECIMEN"	£750	
169		$500 purple and orange (5.10) (F.C. £900)	£170000	
		s. Optd "SPECIMEN"	£4750	
153/67		*Set of 15*	£325	£160
153s/67s		Optd "SPECIMEN" *Set of 15*	£1100	

Beware of dangerous forgeries of No. 169 both "unused" and "used". These are on watermarked paper, but the paper is not chalk-surfaced.

 48   **49**   **50**

 51   **52**   **53**

54

1912–23. $25, $100 and $500 as T **47**, but with head of King George V. Die I (5, 10, 25, 30, 50c., $1, $2, $5). Wmk Mult Crown CA. Ordinary paper (Nos. 193/6, 198/201, 203) or chalk-surfaced paper (others). P 14.

193	48	1c. green (9.12)	14·00	1·50
		a. *Pale green* (1.14)	14·00	1·50
		b. *Blue-green* (1917)	14·00	2·00
		bw. Wmk inverted	†	£400
194		1c. black (2.19)	4·00	2·50
		w. Wmk inverted	†	£500
		y. Wmk inverted and reversed	£750	
195	52	2c. green (10.19)	2·25	50
		w. Wmk inverted	£750	
196	49	3c. red (2.13)	3·25	1·25
		a. *Scarlet* (2.17)	3·00	10
		y. Wmk inverted and reversed	£500	

197	50	4c. dull purple (3.13)	4·50	60
		a. Wmk sideways	†	£3000
		w. Wmk inverted	†	£550
198		4c. rose-scarlet (2.19)	4·00	15
		aw. Wmk inverted	£550	£500
		b. *Carmine*	2·00	20
199	51	5c. orange (8.12)	2·00	1·00
		a. *Yellow-orange*	5·50	1·50
		w. Wmk inverted	†	£550
200	52	6c. dull claret (3.20)	2·00	50
		a. *Deep claret*	7·50	2·75
		aw. Wmk inverted	£275	£300
201		8c. ultramarine (3.13)	3·50	80
		w. Wmk inverted	†	£550
202	51	10c. purple/*yellow* (9.12)	1·50	1·00
		aw. Wmk inverted	†	£550
		b. *White back* (1913)	2·50	1·10
		bs. Optd "SPECIMEN"	65·00	
		bx. Wmk reversed	†	£800
		c. *On lemon* (1916)	18·00	1·25
		cs. Optd "SPECIMEN"	£100	
		d. Wmk sideways	†	£4500
203		10c. deep bright blue (1918)	10·00	1·50
		a. *Bright blue* (1919)	4·00	50
204	53	21c. dull and bright purple (11.13)	16·00	16·00
205	54	25c. dull purple and mauve (7.14)	16·00	14·00
		aw. Wmk inverted and reversed	£325	£325
		ay. Wmk inverted and reversed	£425	
		b. *Dull purple and violet* (1919)	75·00	23·00
207	51	30c. dull purple and orange (12.14)	8·50	6·50
		w. Wmk inverted	†	£750
208	53	45c. black/*green* (*white back*) (12.14)	7·50	22·00
		a. *On blue-green, olive back* (7.18)	12·00	32·00
		ab. "C" of "CA" missing from wmk.	£1000	
		as. Optd "SPECIMEN"	80·00	
		b. *On emerald back* (6.22)	8·00	13·00
209	54	50c. black/*green* (7.14)	6·00	5·00
		aa. Wmk sideways	†	£5500
		a. *On blue-green, olive back* (1918)	35·00	13·00
		b. *On emerald back* (1921)	15·00	10·00
		c. Die II. *On emerald back* (1922).	3·25	4·75
		cs. Optd "SPECIMEN"	80·00	
		cw. Wmk inverted	£750	
210	51	$1 black and red/*blue* (10.14)	20·00	17·00
		w. Wmk inverted	£275	£250
211	54	$2 green and red/*yellow, white back* (1914)	16·00	55·00
		a. *Green and red/yellow* (1915)	23·00	55·00
		as. Optd "SPECIMEN"	80·00	
		b. *On orange-buff* (1921)	80·00	90·00
		c. *On pale yellow* (1921)	85·00	£100
212	51	$5 green and red/*green, white back* (11.13)	£130	55·00
		a. *Green and red/green* (1915)	£140	80·00
		as. Optd "SPECIMEN"	£130	
		b. *On blue-green, olive back* (1918)	£225	£110
		bw. Wmk inverted		
		c. *On emerald back* (1920)	£250	£130
		d. Die II. *On emerald back* (1923).	£140	85·00
		ds. Optd "SPECIMEN"	£140	
213	–	$25 purple and blue/*blue*	£2500	£650
		a. Break in scroll	£6500	
		b. Broken crown and scroll	£6500	
		e. Break in lines below scroll	£6500	
		f. Damaged leaf at bottom right	£6500	
		s. Optd "SPECIMEN"	£550	
214	–	$100 black and carmine/*blue* (8.12)	£12000	
		a. Break in scroll	£25000	
		b. Broken crown and scroll	£25000	
		e. Break in lines below scroll		
		f. Damaged leaf at bottom right.		
		s. Optd "SPECIMEN"	£1300	
215	–	$500 purple and orange-brown (8.12) (F.C. £600)	£100000	
		a. Break in scroll	£130000	
		b. Broken crown and scroll	£140000	
		f. Damaged leaf at bottom right		
		s. Optd "SPECIMEN"	£5500	
193/212		*Set of 19*	£225	£170
193s/212s		Optd "SPECIMEN" *Set of 19*		

The 6c. is similar to T **52**, but the head is in a beaded oval as in T **53**. The 2c., 6c. (and 12c. below) have figures of value on a circular ground while in the 8c. this is of oval shape.

For illustrations of the varieties on Nos. 213/15 see above No. 51*b* of Bermuda.

RED CROSS

MALAYA-
BORNEO
2c. EXHIBITION.
(55) (56)

1917 (1 May). Surch with T **55**.

216	49	3c. + 2c. scarlet	2·75	32·00
		a. No stop (R. 2/3)	£475	£950
217	50	4c. + 2c. dull purple	3·75	32·00
		a. No stop (R. 2/3)	£550	£950

Nos 216/17 were sold at face, plus 2c. on each stamp for Red Cross funds.

Nos. 216a and 217a occur in the first setting only.

Type I Type II

The duty plate for the 25c. value was replaced in 1926. In Type II the solid shading forming the back of the figure 2 extends to the top of the curve; the upturned end of the foot of the 2 is short; two background lines above figure 5; c close to 5; STRAITS SETTLEMENTS in taller letters.

1921–33. Wmk Mult Script CA. Ordinary paper (1c. to 6c., 10c. (No. 230), 12c.) or chalk-surfaced paper (others). P 14.

218	48	1c. black (3.22)	60	10
219	52	2c. green (5.21)	60	10
		w. Wmk inverted	55·00	
		x. Wmk reversed	†	£500
		y. Wmk inverted and reversed	£425	
220		2c. brown (3.25)	7·00	4·75
221	49	3c. green (9.23)	1·50	80
		w. Wmk inverted	55·00	80·00
222	50	4c. carmine-red (9.21)	2·00	6·00
		y. Wmk inverted and reversed	†	£475
223		4c. bright violet (8.24)	60	10
		w. Wmk inverted	50·00	
224		4c. orange (8.29)	1·00	10
225	51	5c. orange (Die I) (5.21)	5·50	15
		a. Wmk sideways	†	£4000
		bw. Wmk inverted	50·00	
		bx. Wmk reversed	†	—
		c. Die II (1922)	2·25	1·25
226		5c. brown (Die II) (1932)	3·00	10
		a. Die I (1933)	5·00	10
		ab. Face value omitted	£30000	
227	52	6c. dull claret (10.22)	2·25	15
228		6c. rose-pink (2.25)	45·00	55·00
229		6c. scarlet (1.27)	32·00	9·50
			2·50	10
230	51	10c. bright blue (Die I) (1921)	1·75	4·00
		w. Wmk inverted	55·00	95·00
231		10c. purple/*pale yellow* (Die I) (1923)	3·00	16·00
		a. Die II (11.26)	4·50	30
		b. *Purple/bright yellow* (Die II) (1932)	35·00	3·25
		ba. Die I (1933)	20·00	20
232	52	12c. blue (Die II) (1.22)	1·25	20
		w. Wmk inverted	70·00	
233	53	21c. dull and bright purple (2.23)	6·00	55·00
234	54	25c. dull purple and mauve (Die I, Type I) (1921)	42·00	90·00
		a. Die II, Type I (1923)	12·00	3·75
		b. Die II, Type II (1927)	5·00	1·75
235	51	30c. dull purple and orange (Die I) (1921)	32·00	55·00
		a. Die II (1922)	2·00	1·25
236	53	35c. dull purple and orange-yellow (8.22)	12·00	6·00
		a. *Dull purple and orange*	3·50	2·25
237		35c. scarlet and purple (4.31)	10·00	2·25
238	54	50c. black/*emerald* (9.25)	1·75	40
239	51	$1 black and red/*blue* (Die II) (1921)	6·00	2·00
240	54	$2 green and red/*pale yellow* (Die II) (1923)	10·00	8·00
240a	51	$5 green and red/*green* (Die II) (1926)	£120	45·00
240b	–	$25 purple and blue/*blue* (5.23)	£1400	£200
		ba. Break in scroll	£3500	
		bb. Broken crown and scroll	£3500	£1600
		be. Break through lines below left scroll		
		bf. Damaged leaf at bottom right..		
		bs. Optd "SPECIMEN"	£425	
240c	–	$100 black and carmine/*blue* (5.23) (F.C. £150)	£10000	£3000
		ca. Break in scroll	£19000	
		cb. Broken crown and scroll	£19000	
		ce. Break through lines below left scroll		
		cf. Damaged leaf at bottom right..		
		cs. Optd "SPECIMEN"	£1000	
240d	–	$500 purple and orange-brown (4.23) (F.C. £600)	£75000	
		da. Break in scroll	£90000	
		db. Broken crown and scroll	£95000	
		de. Break through lines below left scroll		
		ds. Optd "SPECIMEN"	£5000	
218/40a		*Set of 24*	£200	£120
218s/40as		(*ex* 6c. rose-pink) Optd or Perf (Nos. 224s, 226s, 237s) "SPECIMEN" *Set of 23*	£1100	

Prepared for use but not issued

240e	52	8c. carmine		
		s. Optd "SPECIMEN"	£600	

No. 240e was prepared in 1922 but never issued. "SPECIMEN" examples were distributed through the UPU, and a few unoverprinted examples are known.

Nos. 240b/d are as Type **47**, but with portrait of George V.

No. 226ab was caused by a progressive inking failure, resulting in the value being completely omitted on R.10/10 of a single sheet.

The 2c. green was reissued in 1927, and exists with "SPECIMEN" overprint 15.5×1.75 mm instead of the 14.5×2.5 mm of the original issue (*Price*, £75).

The paper of Nos. 231*b*/*ba* is the normal *pale yellow* at the back, but with a bright yellow surface.

In 1926 new Key and Duty plates were made of 100 (10×10) instead of the usual 60 (6×10).

For illustrations of the varieties on Nos. 240*b*/*d* see above No. 51*b* of Bermuda.

SETTINGS OF TYPE 56. Nos. 241/55 were produced using a typeset block of 12 (6×2) overprints from which ten stereos were taken to provide a forme for the complete sheet of 120. Two such formes were prepared of which the second was only used for a limited number of Straits Settlements sheets in addition to the Kedah and Trengganu issues.

Several constant varieties occur on the original typeset block of 12 and so appear ten times on sheets printed from both Settings I and II. These include:

Oval last "O" in "BORNEO" (R. 1/3 of typeset block of 12)
Raised stop after "EXHIBITION" (R. 2/2 of typeset block of 12)
Small second "A" in "MALAYA" (R. 2/6 of typeset block of 12).

The two formes also produced constant varieties in each setting which include:

Setting I
No hyphen (Left pane. R. 7/1 or 9/2)
No stop (Left and right panes. Either on R. 10/4 (right pane) or, for some sheets, on other stamps from even numbered horizontal rows in the 4th vertical column (both panes))
Third "I" in "EXHIBITION" omitted (R. 8/5, 10/5 (left pane)). This must have occurred very late in the use of this setting and is only found on the 5c. and 10c.

Setting II

No stop (Left pane. R. 1/5)

"EXH.BITION" (Left pane. Stamps from even numbered horizontal rows in the 3rd vertical column)

1922 (31 Mar). Malaya-Borneo Exhibition, Singapore. Optd with T **56**.

(a) Wmk Mult Crown CA (Nos. 195, 198/9, 201, 205, 208a, 210, 211b and 212b)

241	**52**	2c. green	48·00	90·00
		b. Oval last "O" in "BORNEO"	£100	£160
		c. Raised stop after "EXHIBITION"	£100	£160
		d. Small second "A" in "MALAYA"	£100	£160
		e. No hyphen	£325	
		f. No stop	£140	£250
242	**50**	4c. rose-scarlet	11·00	28·00
		b. Oval last "O" in "BORNEO"	21·00	55·00
		c. Raised stop after "EXHIBITION"	21·00	55·00
		d. Small second "A" in "MALAYA"	21·00	55·00
		e. No hyphen	£100	
		f. No stop	28·00	65·00
		h. "EXH.BITION"	£100	
243	**51**	5c. orange	12·00	19·00
		b. Oval last "O" in "BORNEO"	22·00	40·00
		c. Raised stop after "EXHIBITION"	22·00	40·00
		d. Small second "A" in "MALAYA"	22·00	40·00
		e. No hyphen	80·00	
		f. No stop	24·00	48·00
		h. "EXH.BITION"	75·00	
244	**52**	8c. ultramarine	2·50	12·00
		b. Oval last "O" in "BORNEO"	6·50	23·00
		c. Raised stop after "EXHIBITION"	6·50	23·00
		d. Small second "A" in "MALAYA"	6·50	23·00
		e. No hyphen	50·00	
		f. No stop	9·00	28·00
		h. "EXH.BITION"	50·00	
245	**54**	25c. dull purple and mauve	5·50	50·00
		b. Oval last "O" in "BORNEO"	12·00	95·00
		c. Raised stop after "EXHIBITION"	12·00	95·00
		d. Small second "A" in "MALAYA"	12·00	95·00
		e. No hyphen	70·00	
		f. No stop	15·00	£110
		h. "EXH.BITION"	65·00	
246	**53**	45c. black/blue-green (olive back)	4·00	48·00
		b. Oval last "O" in "BORNEO"	10·00	95·00
		c. Raised stop after "EXHIBITION"	10·00	95·00
		d. Small second "A" in "MALAYA"	10·00	95·00
		e. No hyphen	55·00	
		f. No stop	14·00	£100
247	**51**	$1 black and red/blue	£650	£1800
		b. Oval last "O" in "BORNEO"	£1200	
		c. Raised stop after "EXHIBITION"	£1200	
		d. Small second "A" in "MALAYA"	£1200	
		e. No hyphen	£2000	
		f. No stop	£1400	
248	**54**	$2 green and red/orange-buff	26·00	£160
		a. On pale yellow (No. 211c)	65·00	£190
		b. Oval last "O" in "BORNEO"	60·00	£325
		c. Raised stop after "EXHIBITION"	60·00	£325
		d. Small second "A" in "MALAYA"	60·00	£325
		e. No hyphen	£350	
		f. No stop	90·00	£400
		h. "EXH.BITION"	£1100	
249	**51**	$5 green and red/blue-green (olive-back)	£450	£800
		b. Oval last "O" in "BORNEO"	£800	
		c. Raised stop after "EXHIBITION"	£800	
		d. Small second "A" in "MALAYA"	£800	
		e. No hyphen	£2500	
		f. No stop	£900	

(b) Wmk Mult Script CA (Nos. 218/19, 222, 225c, 230 and 239)

250	**48**	1c. black	3·00	26·00
		b. Oval last "O" in "BORNEO"	8·00	50·00
		c. Raised stop after "EXHIBITION"	8·00	50·00
		d. Small second "A" in "MALAYA"	8·00	50·00
		e. No hyphen	55·00	
		f. No stop	11·00	55·00
		h. "EXH.BITION"	55·00	
251	**52**	2c. green	2·50	16·00
		b. Oval last "O" in "BORNEO"	6·50	30·00
		c. Raised stop after "EXHIBITION"	6·50	30·00
		d. Small second "A" in "MALAYA"	6·50	30·00
		e. No hyphen	45·00	£140
		f. No stop	8·00	35·00
		h. "EXH.BITION"	45·00	
252	**50**	4c. carmine-red	4·75	50·00
		b. Oval last "O" in "BORNEO"	11·00	95·00
		c. Raised stop after "EXHIBITION"	11·00	95·00
		d. Small second "A" in "MALAYA"	11·00	95·00
		e. No hyphen	55·00	
		f. No stop	14·00	95·00
253	**51**	5c. orange (Die II)	2·75	50·00
		b. Oval last "O" in "BORNEO"	8·00	50·00
		c. Raised stop after "EXHIBITION"	8·00	95·00
		d. Small second "A" in "MALAYA"	8·00	95·00
		e. No hyphen	55·00	
		f. No stop	10·00	£110
		g. Third "I" in "EXHIBITION" omitted	£4000	
254		10c. bright blue	2·25	26·00
		b. Oval last "O" in "BORNEO"	7·00	55·00
		c. Raised stop after "EXHIBITION"	7·00	55·00
		d. Small second "A" in "MALAYA"	7·00	55·00
		e. No hyphen	45·00	
		f. No stop	8·50	65·00
		g. Third "I" in "EXHIBITION" omitted	£850	
255		$1 black and red/blue (Die II)	22·00	£160
		b. Oval last "O" in "BORNEO"	60·00	£350
		c. Raised stop after "EXHIBITION"	60·00	£350
		d. Small second "A" in "MALAYA"	60·00	£350
		e. No hyphen	£800	
		f. No stop	75·00	£425
		h. "EXH.BITION"		
242/55 Set of 11			£475	£1200

Examples of most values are known with part strikes of a forged Singapore postmark dated "AU 1 1910".

1935 (6 May). Silver Jubilee. As Nos. 91/4 of Antigua. but ptd by Waterlow & Sons. P 11×12.

256		5c. ultramarine and grey	3·00	30
		m. "Bird" by turret	£1000	£700
257		8c. green and indigo	3·00	3·25
258		12c. brown and deep blue	3·00	8·00
		j. Damaged turret	£1000	
259		25c. slate and purple	5·50	12·00
256/9 Set of 4			13·00	21·00
256s/9s Perf "SPECIMEN" Set of 4			£225	

For illustration of plate varieties see Omnibus section following Zanzibar.

57   **58**

1936 (1 Jan)–37. Chalk-surfaced paper. Wmk Mult Script CA. P 14.

260	**57**	1c. black (1.1.37)	2·50	20
261		2c. green (1.2.36)	2·50	70
262		4c. orange (15.6.36)	2·25	70
263		5c. brown (1.8.36)	1·00	30
264		6c. scarlet (1.2.36)	1·50	1·10
265		8c. grey	3·75	70
266		10c. dull purple (1.7.36)	2·25	60
267		12c. bright ultramarine (1.9.36)	2·00	2·50
268		25c. dull purple and scarlet (1.2.36)	1·50	50
269		30c. dull purple and orange	1·50	3·25
270		40c. scarlet and dull purple	1·50	2·50
271		50c. black/emerald (1.9.36)	4·50	1·25
272		$1 black and red/blue (1.7.36)	20·00	1·75
273		$2 green and scarlet (1.4.36)	60·00	10·00
274		$5 green and red/emerald (1.1.37)	£140	10·00
260/74 Set of 15			£225	32·00
260s/74s Perf "SPECIMEN" Set of 15			£550	

1937 (12 May). Coronation. As Nos. 95/7 of Antigua, but printed by D.L.R.

275		4c. orange	1·25	10
276		8c. grey-black	1·50	10
277		12c. bright blue	3·50	1·00
275/7 Set of 3			5·75	1·10
275s/7s Perf "SPECIMEN" Set of 3			£225	

1937–41. Chalk-surfaced paper. Wmk Mult Script CA. P 14 or 15×14 (15c.).

(a) Die I (printed at two operations)

278	**58**	1c. black (1.1.38)	14·00	10
279		2c. green (6.12.37)	21·00	20
280		4c. orange (1.1.38)	32·00	1·50
281		5c. brown (19.11.37)	24·00	30
282		6c. scarlet (10.1.38)	11·00	60
283		8c. grey (26.1.38)	38·00	10
284		10c. dull purple (8.11.37)	15·00	10
285		12c. ultramarine (10.1.38)	15·00	50
286		25c. dull purple and scarlet (11.12.37)	48·00	1·10
287		30c. dull purple and orange (1.12.37)	20·00	2·00
288		40c. scarlet and dull purple (20.12.37)	19·00	2·25
289		50c. black/emerald (26.1.38)	16·00	10
290		$1 black and red/blue (26.1.38)	19·00	20
291		$2 green and scarlet (26.1.38)	48·00	16·00
292		$5 green and red/emerald (26.1.38)	29·00	9·00

(b) Die II (printed at one operation)

293	**58**	2c. green (28.12.38)	60·00	40
294		2c. orange (thin striated paper) (6.10.41)	2·00	19·00
295		3c. green (ordinary paper) (5.9.41)	13·00	4·00
296		4c. orange (29.10.38)	90·00	10
297		5c. brown (18.2.39)	45·00	10
298		15c. ultramarine (ordinary paper) (6.10.41)	12·00	10·00
278/98 Set of 18			£350	55·00
278s/92s 294s/5s, 298s Perf "SPECIMEN" Set of 18			£900	

Die I. Lines of background outside central oval touch the oval and the foliage of the palm tree is usually joined to the oval frame. The downward-pointing palm frond, opposite the King's eye, has two points.

Die II. Lines of background are separated from the oval by a white line and the foliage of the palm trees does not touch the outer frame. The palm frond has only one point.

Nos. 295 and 298 were printed by Harrison and Sons following bomb damage to the De La Rue works on 29 December 1940.

The 6c. grey, 8c. scarlet and $5 purple and orange were only issued with the BMA overprint, but the 8c. without overprint is known although in this state it was never issued (Price £15).

STAMP BOOKLETS

1914–19. Black on blue (No. SB1) or grey (No. SB1b) covers, Stapled.

SB1 $1 booklet containing 25×4c. dull purple (No. 197) in two blocks of 12 and one single.

a. Containing 4c. rose-scarlet (No. 198) (1919)...

SB1b $1 booklet containing 4×1c., 16×3c. and 12×4c. (Nos. 193, 196/7) in blocks of four

1921. Black on blue cover. Stapled.

SB2 $1 booklet containing 25×4c. (No. 222) in two blocks of 12 and one single.

a. Contents as SB2, but four blocks of 6 and one single

1922. Black on red cover. Stapled.

SB3 $1 booklet containing 5c. (No. 225) in block of 6 and 6c. (No. 227) in block of 10 ...... £2250

1925–29. Black on red cover. Stapled.

SB4 $1.20 booklet containing 30×4c. bright violet (No. 223) in blocks of 10 ...... £3500

a. Containing 4c. orange (No. 224) (1929) £3750

1927. Black on grey (No. SB5), green (No. SB6) or blue (No. SB7) covers. Stapled.

SB5 $1 booklet containing 4c. and 6c. (Nos. 223, 229) in blocks of 10 ...... £3750

SB6	$1.20 booklet containing 20×6c. (No. 229) in blocks of 10	£3000
SB7	$1.20 booklet containing 2c., 4c. and 6c. (Nos. 219, 223, 229) in blocks of 10	£3750

1933. Black on buff cover. Stapled.

SB8	$1 booklet containing 20×5c. (No. 226a) in blocks of 10	

1936. Stapled.

SB9	$1 booklet containing 20×5c. (No. 263) in blocks of 10	
SB10	$1.30 booklet containing 5c. and 8c. (Nos. 263, 265) in blocks of 10	

1938. Black on buff (No. SB11) or black on green (No. SB12) covers. Stapled.

SB11	$1 booklet containing 20×5c. (No. 281) in blocks of 10	£4500
SB12	$1.30 booklet containing 5c. and 8c. (Nos. 281, 283) in blocks of 10 and pane of airmail labels	£4750

POSTAGE DUE STAMPS

D **1**

1924 (1 Jan)–**26**. Wmk Mult Script CA. P 14.

D1	D **1**	1c. violet	13·00	5·50
D2		2c. black	3·25	1·00
D3		4c. green (5.26)	2·00	2·50
D4		8c. scarlet	4·50	55
D5		10c. orange	6·00	85
D6		12c. bright blue	7·00	65
		sa. Opt "SPECIMEN" double	£550	
D1/6 Set of 6			32·00	10·00
D1s/6s Optd "SPECIMEN" Set of 6			£350	

For later issues of Postage Due stamps, see MALAYAN POSTAL UNION.

POSTAL FISCAL STAMPS

1938. T **47** but with head of King George VI and inscribed "REVENUE" at each side. Wmk Mult Script CA. P 14.

F1		$25 purple and blue/blue	£1400	£650

No. F1 was regularly used for postal purposes in 1941, although no specific authorisation for such use has been discovered.

The Straits Settlements were occupied by the Japanese in 1942.

After the Second World War the stamps of MALAYA (BRITISH MILITARY ADMINISTRATION) were used. In 1946 Singapore became a separate Crown Colony and Labuan was transferred to North Borneo. Separate stamps were issued for Malacca and Penang, which both joined the Malayan Federation on 1 February 1948.

II. FEDERATED MALAY STATES

On 1 July 1896, the States of Negri Sembilan, Pahang, Perak and Selangor were organised on a federal basis to be known as the Federated Malay States. For the time being each State continued with individual issues, although each state's issues were valid for use in the others from 27 January 1899. Stamps for the use of the Federation replaced these in 1900.

PRICES FOR STAMPS ON COVER		
Nos. 1/13	from × 15	
No. 14	—	
Nos. 15/22	from × 10	
Nos. 23/5	from × 3	
No. 26	—	
Nos. 27/50	from × 6	
No. 51	—	
Nos. 52/81	from × 5	
No. 82	—	
Nos. D1/6	from × 10	

PRINTERS. All issues of the Federated Malay States were printed in typography by De La Rue & Co, Ltd, London, *unless otherwise stated.*

FEDERATED MALAY STATES   **FEDERATED MALAY STATES**

(1)   (2)

1900. Optd with T **1** (cent values) or **2** (dollar values).

(a) Stamps of Negri Sembilan (T 3)

1		1c. dull purple and green	3·00	13·00
2		2c. dull purple and brown	29·00	70·00
3		3c. dull purple and black	2·75	7·50
4		5c. dull purple and olive-yellow	75·00	£190
5		10c. dull purple and orange	17·00	60·00
6		20c. green and olive	90·00	£130
7		25c. green and carmine	£275	£425
8		50c. green and black	£110	£170
1/8 Set of 8			£600	£950
1s/8s Optd "SPECIMEN" Set of 8			£250	

(b) Stamps of Perak (T 44 and 45)

9		5c. green and olive-yellow	30·00	75·00
10		10c. dull purple and orange	85·00	65·00
11		$1 green and pale green	£200	£275
		w. Wmk inverted	£1000	£1100
12		$2 green and carmine	£190	£325
13		$5 green and ultramarine	£550	£800
14		$25 green and orange (F.C. £600)	£16000	
		s. Optd "SPECIMEN"	£550	
11s/13s Optd "SPECIMEN" Set of 3			£190	

The Negri Sembilan 3c. dull purple and black does not exist without overprint Type **1**.

Nos. 1/4 were never put on sale in Selangor, nor Nos. 1/3 in Perak.

The stamps of STRAITS SETTLEMENTS were used in Federated Malay States from 16 July 1900 until 31 December 1901.

3   **4**

1900–01. P 14.

(a) T 3. Wmk Crown CA, sideways (1901)

15	1c. black and green	22·00	13·00
	a. Grey and green	6·00	1·25
	b. Grey-brown and green	15·00	45
16	3c. black and brown	27·00	8·00
	a. Grey and brown	7·50	35
	b. Grey-brown and brown	14·00	20
17	4c. black and carmine	25·00	14·00
	a. Grey and carmine	13·00	10·00
	b. Grey-brown and carmine	25·00	5·50
18	5c. green and carmine/yellow	2·50	3·75
19	8c. black and ultramarine	48·00	29·00
	a. Grey and ultramarine	25·00	10·00
	b. Grey-brown and ultramarine	27·00	3·75
20	10c. black and claret	£140	65·00
	a. Grey and claret	80·00	17·00
	b. Black and purple	£170	65·00
	c. Grey and purple	85·00	21·00
	d. Grey-brown and purple	90·00	10·00
21	20c. mauve and black	18·00	17·00
22	50c. grey and orange-brown	£190	£160
	a. Grey and orange-brown	£100	65·00
	b. Grey-brown and orange-brown	£120	50·00
15/22b Set of 8		£200	75·00
15s/22s Optd "SPECIMEN" Set of 8		£275	

Later printings in 1903–4 show the two upper lines of shading in the background at the corner nearest to the "S" of "STATE" blurred and running into one another, whereas in earlier printings these lines are distinct. Two plates were used for printing the central design of T **3**. In Plate 1 the lines of background are regular throughout, but in Plate 2 they are lighter around the head and back of the tiger. The 5c. was the only value with single wmk to be printed from Plate 2. Stamps with multiple wmk were printed for a short time from Plate 1, and show the two blurred lines of background near "S" of "STATE", but the majority of these stamps were printed from Plate 2 and later plates.

(b) T 4. Wmk Crown CC (1900)

23	$1 green and pale green	£190	£190
	w. Wmk inverted	†	—
24	$2 green and carmine	£180	£200
25	$5 green and bright ultramarine	£450	£475
	a. Green and pale ultramarine	£425	£425
26	$25 green and orange (F.C. £110)	£4750	£1900
	s. Optd "SPECIMEN"	£450	
23s/5s Optd "SPECIMEN" Set of 3		£190	

Two dies for 1c. green and 4c. scarlet

Die I. "Head" and duty plates. Thick frame line below "MALAY" and in the 1c. the "c" is thin whilst in the 4c. it is thick.

Die II. Single working plate. Thin frame line below "MALAY" and in the 1c. the "c" is thicker whilst in the 4c. it is thinner.

1904 (Aug)**–22.** T **3** and T **4** (dollar values). Wmk Mult Crown CA (sideways* on T **3**). Ordinary paper (1c. to 50c.) or chalk-surfaced paper ($1 to $25).

27	1c. grey and green (8.04)	85·00	10·00
	a. Grey-brown and green	48·00	70
28	1c. green (Die I) (8.7.06)	28·00	30
29	1c. green (Die II) (1908)	16·00	20
	a. Yellow-green	27·00	3·00
	aw. Wmk Crown to right of CA	90·00	12·00
	b. Blue-green	42·00	1·75
30	1c. deep brown (21.1.19)	2·25	90
	w. Wmk Crown to right of CA	†	£300
31	2c. green (18.2.19)	2·50	30
	w. Wmk Crown to right of CA	95·00	18·00
32	3c. grey and brown (10.04)	75·00	1·75
	a. Grey-brown and brown (12.05)	55·00	1·75
	ab. Chalk-surfaced paper	48·00	2·75
33	3c. brown (11.7.06)	10·00	15
34	3c. carmine (2.2.09)	5·00	10
	aw. Wmk Crown to right of CA	35·00	50
	b. Scarlet (1.17)	32·00	50
	bw. Wmk Crown to right of CA	60·00	4·50
35	3c. grey (29.10.18)	2·50	20
	w. Wmk Crown to right of CA	90·00	18·00
36	4c. grey and scarlet (8.04)	70·00	9·50
	a. Chalk-surfaced paper. Grey and rose	48·00	5·50
	b. Grey-brown and scarlet	60·00	4·25
	c. Black and scarlet	32·00	3·50
	d. Black and rose	9·00	80
	dw. Wmk Crown to right of CA	16·00	1·00
	e. Black and deep rose (aniline) (1909)	60·00	6·00
	f. Jet black and rose (1914)	45·00	4·00
37	4c. scarlet (Die I) (11.2.19)	3·50	4·75
38	4c. scarlet (Die II) (15.4.19)	1·75	15
	aw. Wmk Crown to right of CA	70·00	6·50
	b. Wmk upright (2.22)	£900	£375
39	5c. green and carmine/yellow (5.06)	12·00	3·25
	aw. Wmk Crown to right of CA	£110	26·00
	b. Chalk-surfaced paper	50·00	8·50
	c. Deep green and carmine/yellow	15·00	4·00
	d. On orange-buff (1921)	23·00	18·00
	e. On pale yellow (4.22)	15·00	15·00

40	6c. orange (11.2.19)	2·75	3·75
41	8c. grey and ultramarine (2.05)	85·00	29·00
	aw. Wmk Crown to right of CA	†	
	b. Grey-brown and ultramarine (12.05)	21·00	5·50
	ba. Chalk-surfaced paper	95·00	22·00
	bb. Wmk upright (3.07)	9·00	6·50
42	8c. ultramarine (8.3.10)	13·00	1·00
	aw. Wmk Crown to right of CA	£140	40·00
	b. Deep blue (1918)	16·00	1·25
43	10c. grey-brown and claret (5.04)	90·00	14·00
	a. Chalk-surfaced paper (1905)	£140	22·00
	b. Black and claret	42·00	75
	bw. Wmk Crown to right of CA	65·00	1·50
	c. Grey-brown and purple (1905)	80·00	3·75
	d. Black and purple	50·00	3·50
	dy. Wmk Crown to right of CA and reversed	†	£450
	e. Jet-black and bright purple (1914)	£110	5·00
44	10c. deep blue (3.6.19)	8·00	2·00
	a. Bright blue	6·50	1·00
	ab. Wmk inverted	†	—
	ac. Substituted crown in wmk	†	£1100
	aw. Wmk Crown to right of CA	£110	25·00
45	20c. mauve and black (3.05)	23·00	1·25
	a. Chalk-surfaced paper	13·00	3·50
	w. Wmk Crown to right of CA	£150	32·00
46	35c. scarlet/pale yellow (25.8.22)	5·50	17·00
47	50c. grey and orange (3.05)	95·00	20·00
	aw. Wmk Crown to right of CA	£375	£100
	b. Wmk inverted	†	
	c. Grey-brown and orange-brown (1906)	70·00	18·00
	caw. Wmk Crown to right of CA	†	
	d. Chalk-surfaced paper. Grey-brown and orange-brown	75·00	9·00
	da. Grey and orange-brown	80·00	16·00
	db. Black and orange-brown	£130	35·00
	dc. Jet-black and orange-brown (1914)	£180	42·00
	dw. Wmk Crown to right of CA	†	£150
48	$1 grey-green and green (10.07)	£120	50·00
	a. Green and pale green	£160	50·00
	aw. Wmk inverted	£1100	
	ax. Wmk reversed	†	—
49	$2 green and carmine (4.12.07)	£130	£140
	a. Printed on the gummed side		
	w. Wmk inverted		
	y. Wmk inverted and reversed	†	£1200
50	$5 green and blue (1.08)	£325	£160
51	$25 green and orange (12.09) (F.C. £60)	£2250	£900
27/50 Set of 22		£800	£350
28s, 30s/1s, 33s/5s, 38s, 40s, 42s, 44s, 46s Optd "SPECIMEN" Set of 11		£800	

*The normal sideways watermark shows Crown to left of CA, as seen from the back of the stamp. The watermark on No. 47b is vertical, inverted.

Nos. 29/b, 30, 31, 33, 34/b and 35 were printed from single working plates and all the rest from double plates.

Most examples of No. 47b have fiscal cancellations (Price £200), but at least one is known postally used.

The 3c. scarlet (No. 34b) was surcharged '4/CENTS.' between horizontal lines in early 1918, but was never issued. The entire printing of five million stamps was sunk at sea, nevertheless a few examples do exist. (Price, £5000, unused).

1922–34. Wmk Mult Script CA (sideways* on T **3**). Ordinary paper (1c. to 10c. (No. 66), 12c., 20c. (No. 69a), 35c. (No. 72)) or chalk-surfaced paper (others).

52	**3**	1c. deep brown (1.8.22)	1·50	4·75
		w. Wmk Crown to right of CA	£100	£100
53		1c. black (12.6.23)	75	20
54		2c. brown (5.8.25)	14·00	15·00
55		2c. green (15.6.26)	3·00	10
56		3c. grey (27.12.22)	1·75	7·50
		w. Wmk Crown to right of CA	£130	£130
57		3c. green (22.1.24)	1·25	1·50
58		3c. brown (31.5.27)	5·00	50
59		4c. carmine-red (Die II) (27.11.23)	4·00	50
		w. Wmk Crown to right of CA	55·00	22·00
60		4c. orange (9.11.26)	1·50	10
		a. No watermark	£375	£275
		c. "A" of "CA" missing from wmk	†	£900
61		5c. mauve/pale yellow (17.3.22)	1·00	20
		w. Wmk Crown to right of CA	£100	55·00
62		5c. brown (1.3.32)	3·50	10
63		6c. orange (2.5.22)	1·00	45
		w. Wmk Crown to right of CA	£170	
64		6c. scarlet (9.11.26)	1·50	10
65		10c. bright blue (23.10.23)	1·25	8·50
		w. Wmk Crown to right of CA		
66		10c. black and blue (18.1.24†)	2·00	75
67		10c. purple/pale yellow (14.7.31)	3·75	40
68		12c. ultramarine (12.9.22)	1·25	10
		w. Wmk Crown to right of CA	£110	40·00
		x. Wmk sideways reversed	£400	
69		20c. dull purple and black (chalk-surfaced paper) (3.4.23)	4·00	2·75
		a. Ordinary paper (29.12.26)	70·00	5·50
		b. Wmk inverted	†	£550
70		25c. purple and bright magenta (3.9.29)	2·75	3·50
71		30c. purple and orange-yellow (3.9.29)	3·25	5·00
72		35c. scarlet/pale yellow (6.11.28)	3·25	27·00
73		35c. scarlet and purple (29.9.31)	13·00	14·00
74		50c. black and orange (24.4.24)	13·00	20·00
		aw. Wmk Crown to right of CA	£180	
		b. Black and orange-brown	42·00	7·50
75		50c. black/green (16.6.31)	4·00	2·50
76	**4**	$1 pale green and green (2.2.26)	23·00	£100
		a. Grey-green and emerald (5.10.26)	23·00	55·00
		sa. Opt "SPECIMEN" double	£475	
77	**3**	$1 black and red/blue (10.3.31)	12·00	5·00
78	**4**	$2 green and carmine (17.8.26)	45·00	95·00
79	**3**	$2 green and red/yellow (6.2.34)	65·00	50·00
80	**4**	$5 green and blue (24.2.25)	£200	£275
		w. Wmk inverted	£1600	
81	**3**	$5 green and red/green (7.34)	£350	£275
82	**4**	$25 green and orange (14.2.28) (F.C. £170)	£2250	£2500
		s. Optd "SPECIMEN"	£500	
52/81 Set of 30			£700	£750
52s/81s Optd or Perf (No. 62s, 67s, 70s/1s, 73s, 77s, 79s, 81s) "SPECIMEN" Set of 30			£1900	

*The normal sideways watermark shows Crown to left of CA, as seen from the back of the stamp.

†No. 66 was released in London by the Crown Agents some months earlier but this is the official date of issue in the States.

The 2c. green (No. 55), 3c. brown (No. 58), 4c. orange (No. 60) and 6c. scarlet (No. 64) exist with wmk upright. These were formerly listed as Nos. 55a, 58a, 60b and 64a, but are now known to be colour trials, of unissued status. (Prices, £800 each).

Nos. 52, 56 and 59 were printed from single working plates and the rest from double plates.

No. 55 exists in coils constructed from normal sheets.

The 5c. mauve on white Script paper is the result of soaking early printings of No. 61 in water.

STAMP BOOKLETS

1909. Black on pink (Nos. SB1/2) or black on buff (No. SB3) covers. Stapled.

SB1	25c. booklet containing 4×1c. (No. 29) in blocks of 6	£2500
	a. Black on green cover (1917)	£2500
	b. Black on blue cover	£2500
SB2	73c. booklet containing 24×3c. (No. 34) in blocks of 6	£2500
	a. Black on red cover (1917)	£2500
	b. Black on blue cover	£2500
SB3	97c. booklet containing 24×4c. (No. 36d) in blocks of 6	£2750

1919. Black on green (No. SB4) or black on pink (No. SB5) covers. Stapled.

SB4	49c. booklet containing 24×2c. (No. 31) in blocks of 6	£5500
SB5	97c. booklet containing 24×4c. (No. 37) in blocks of 6	£2250

1922. Black on buff cover (No. SB7). Stapled.

SB6	$1.21 booklet containing 24×5c. (No. 61) in blocks of 6	£3250
SB7	$1.45 booklet containing 24×6c. (No. 63) in blocks of 6	£2750

1926. As Nos. SB4, SB3 and SB7, but sold at face value without premium. Black on green (No. SB8), black on pink (No. SB9) or black on buff (No. SB10) covers. Stapled.

SB8	48c. booklet containing 24×2c. (No. 55) in blocks of 6	
SB9	96c. booklet containing 24×4c. (No. 60) in blocks of 6	£2750
SB10	$1.44 booklet containing 24×6c. (No. 64) in blocks of 6	£2750

1926. Black on grey cover. Stapled.

SB11	$1 booklet containing 4c. and 6c. (Nos. 60, 64) each in block of 10	£2750

1927. Black on bluish green cover. Stapled.

SB12	$1.50 booklet containing 2c., 3c., 4c. and 6c. (Nos. 55, 58, 60, 64) each in block of 10	£3250

1927–30. Black on red (No. SB13), black on green (No. SB14) or black on blue (No. SB15) covers. Stapled.

SB13	$1.20 booklet containing 30×4c. (No. 60) in blocks of 10	£3000
	a. Black on orange cover (1930)	
SB14	$1.20 booklet containing 20×6c. (No. 64) in blocks of 10 (1928)	£3500
SB15	$1.20 booklet containing 2c., 4c. and 6c. (Nos. 55, 60, 64) each in block of 10 (1928)	£2750
	a. Black on white cover (1930)	

1934. Black on buff cover. Stapled.

SB16	$1 booklet containing 20×5c. (No. 62) in blocks of 10	£3250

POSTAGE DUE STAMPS

D 1

(Typo Waterlow)

1924 (1 Dec)**–26.** Wmk Mult Script CA (sideways*). P 15×14.

D1	D **1**	1c. violet	4·75	50·00
		w. Wmk Crown to left of CA (1926)	27·00	45·00
D2		2c. black	1·75	12·00
		w. Wmk Crown to left of CA (1926)	4·00	3·25
D3		4c. green (wmk Crown to left of CA) (27.4.26)	2·25	5·00
D4		8c. red	5·50	48·00
		w. Wmk Crown to left of CA (1926)	15·00	18·00
D5		10c. orange	9·00	15·00
		w. Wmk Crown to left of CA (1926)	42·00	24·00
D6		12c. blue	9·00	27·00
		w. Wmk Crown to left of CA (1926)	15·00	7·00
D1/6 Set of 6			29·00	85·00
D1s/6s Optd "SPECIMEN" Set of 6			£250	

*The normal sideways watermark shows Crown to right of CA, as seen from the back of the stamp.

The issues of the Federated Malay States were replaced by stamps for the individual States from 1935 onwards.

III. MALAYAN POSTAL UNION

The Malayan Postal Union was organised in 1934 and, initially, covered the Straits Settlements and the Federated Malay States. Stamps of the Straits Settlements together with issues for the individual States continued to be used, but Malayan Postal Union postage due stamps were introduced in 1936.

Following the end of the Second World War the use of these postage dues spread throughout Malaya and to Singapore.

PRICES FOR STAMPS ON COVER TO 1945	
Nos. D1/6	from × 10
Nos. D7/13	from × 4

POSTAGE DUE STAMPS

D **1**　　　(D **2**)

(Typo Waterlow until 1961, then D.L.R.)

1936 (June)–**38**. Wmk Mult Script CA. P 15×14.

D1	D **1**	1c. slate-purple (4.38)	18·00	70
D2		4c. green (9.36)	40·00	1·00
D3		8c. scarlet	20·00	2·75
D4		10c. yellow-orange	26·00	30
D5		12c. pale ultramarine (9.36)	40·00	14·00
D6		50c. black (1.38)	30·00	4·50
D1/6 Set of 6			£160	21·00
D1s/6s Perf "SPECIMEN" Set of 6			£275	

For use in Negri Sembilan, Pahang, Perak, Selangor and Straits Settlements including Singapore.

1945–49. New values and colours. Wmk Mult Script CA. P 15×14.

D7	D **1**	1c. purple	5·00	2·00
D8		3c. green	10·00	2·25
D9		5c. scarlet	6·00	2·00
D10		8c. yellow-orange (1949)	13·00	14·00
		s. Perf "SPECIMEN"	90·00	
D11		9c. yellow-orange	40·00	50·00
D12		15c. pale ultramarine	£110	29·00
D13		20c. blue (1948)	10·00	5·00
		s. Perf "SPECIMEN"	90·00	
D7/13 Set of 7			£170	95·00

1951 (8 Aug)–**63**. Wmk Mult Script CA. P 14.

D14	D **1**	1c. violet (21.8.52)	70	1·60
D15		2c. deep slate-blue (16.11.53)	1·25	2·25
		a. Perf 12½ (15.11.60)	4·25	25·00
		ab. Chalk-surfaced paper (10.7.62)	1·75	16·00
		ac. Ditto. Imperf horiz (vert pair)	†	£20000
D16		3c. deep green (21.8.52)	40·00	22·00
D17		4c. sepia (16.11.53)	70	7·00
		a. Perf 12½ (15.11.60)	3·50	27·00
		ab. Chalk-surfaced paper. Bistre-brown (10.7.62)	1·00	21·00
D18		5c. vermilion	48·00	12·00
D19		8c. yellow-orange	2·50	10·00
D20		12c. bright purple (1.2.54)	1·25	6·00
		a. Perf 12½. Chalk-surfaced paper (10.7.62)	5·00	35·00
D21		20c. blue	10·00	6·50
		a. Perf 12½. Deep blue (10.12.57)	7·00	26·00
		ab. Chalk-surfaced paper (15.10.63)	12·00	50·00
D14/21 Set of 8			90·00	55·00

Nos. D7 to D21ab were for use in the Federation and Singapore.

1964 (14 Apr)–**65**. Chalk-surfaced paper. Wmk w **12** (sideways on 1c.). P 12½.

D22	D **1**	1c. maroon	30	21·00
		a. Perf 12. Wmk upright (4.5.65)	2·00	18·00
D23		2c. deep slate-blue	1·75	18·00
		a. Perf 12 (9.3.65)	1·25	24·00
D24		4c. bistre-brown	1·00	18·00
		a. Perf 12 (9.3.65)	2·50	18·00
D25		8c. yellow-orange (P 12) (4.5.65)	2·00	24·00
D27		12c. bright purple	1·50	22·00
		a. Perf 12 (4.5.65)	8·50	48·00
D28		20c. deep blue	2·50	40·00
		a. Perf 12 (4.5.65)	12·00	60·00
D22/8 Set of 6			7·50	£130

1964 (1 Dec). As No. D19 surch locally with Type D **2**.

D29	D **1**	10c. on 8c. yellow-orange	60	3·00

First supplies of this stamp differed from No. D19 in that they had been climatically affected, but later a fresh printing of No. D19 was surcharged.

1966. Unsurfaced paper. Wmk w **12**. P 15×14.

D30	D **1**	50c. black	£2250	£2000

Nos. D22/9 were for use throughout Malaysia and Singapore. They were superseded on 15 August 1966 by the postage dues inscribed "MALAYSIA", but continued in use, together with No. D30, for Singapore until 31 January 1968 when they were replaced by Singapore Postage Dues.

IV. MALAYA (BRITISH MILITARY ADMINISTRATION)

Following the Japanese surrender on 2 September 1945 British troops landed in Malaya which was placed under a British Military Administration. The Director of Posts was ashore at Singapore on 6 September and had reached Kuala Lumpur by 13 September. Postal services in Singapore and Johore resumed on 17 September and had spread to the remainder of the country by 5 October. No stamps were initially available so all mail up to 1 oz. was carried free until the first overprinted stamps appeared on 19 October.

De La Rue had overprinted available stocks of pre-war Straits Settlements stamps earlier in 1945 and initial supplies of these London overprints were placed on sale from 19 October (Nos. 1, 2a, 4, 6a, 7 and 8a) with the 15c. and 25c. (Nos. 11 and 13a) issued later. A second consignment contained dollar values including the $5 purple and orange. Duplicate plates were subsequently sent to the Government Printing Office at Kuala Lumpur, where the overprinting of surviving local stocks of the 1c., 5c., 10c., 15c. (available in black) and $5 green and red on emerald took place, and to Australia for those shipments which had been diverted there in 1941.

The stamps were used throughout all Malay States and in Singapore. From 1948 this general issue was gradually replaced by individual issues for each state. The last usage was in Kelantan where B M A overprints were not withdrawn until 10 July 1951.

B M A
MALAYA
(1)

1945 (19 Oct)–**48**. T **58** of Straits Settlements from Die I (double-plate printing) or Die II (single-plate printing) optd with T **1**. Wmk Mult Script CA. Chalk-surfaced paper. P 14 or 15×14 (No. 11).

1		1c. black (I) (R.)	7·50	70
		aa. Opt double, one albino	£1500	
		ab. Magenta opt	£7000	£1000
		b. Ordinary paper	10	30
		c. Thin striated paper (8.46)	38·00	18·00
2		2c. orange (II) (8.7.47)	9·00	60
		a. Ordinary paper (19.10.45)	20	10
		b. Thin striated paper (7.46)	19·00	8·50
		w. Wmk inverted	†	£2500
3		2c. orange (I) (ordinary paper) (9.46)	30·00	7·50
4		3c. yellow-green (II) (ordinary paper)	8·00	50
		a. Blue-green (27.1.47)	13·00	8·00
		b. Chalk-surfaced paper. Blue-green (8.7.47)	26·00	1·00
5		5c. brown (II) (24.10.45)	70	1·00
6		6c. grey (II) (22.3.48)	30·00	7·00
		a. Ordinary paper (19.10.45)	30	20
		b. Thin striated paper (6.46)	20·00	12·00
7		8c. scarlet (II) (ordinary paper)	30	10
		a. Thin striated paper (6.46)	20·00	18·00
8		10c. purple (I) (12.45)	14·00	1·25
		a. Ordinary paper (19.10.45)	50	10
		b. Slate-purple (12.45)	10·00	30
		c. Magenta (22.3.48)	14·00	70
		d. Thin striated paper (8.46)	24·00	15·00
9		10c. purple (II) (28.7.48)	19·00	8·50
10		12c. bright ultramarine (I) (11.45)	1·75	21·00
11		15c. bright ultramarine (II) (ordinary paper) (11.45)	2·50	13·00
12		15c. bright ultramarine (II) (R.) (22.3.48)	50·00	2·25
		a. Ordinary paper (12.45)	75	20
		b. Blue (27.11.47)	75·00	85
		ba. Ordinary paper (8.7.47)	£150	22·00
13		25c. dull purple and scarlet (I) (22.3.48)	40·00	4·75
		a. Ordinary paper (12.45)	1·40	30
		ab. Opt double	£7000	
		ac. "A" of "CA" missing from watermark	†	£2750
		ad. Opt double, one albino	£1300	
		b. Thin striated paper (8.46)	25·00	8·00
14		50c. black/emerald (I) (ordinary paper) (R.) (12.45)	1·00	10
15		$1 black and red (I) (ordinary paper) (12.45)	2·00	10
		a. "A" of "CA" missing from watermark	†	£2750
16		$2 green and scarlet (I) (ordinary paper) (12.45)	2·75	75
17		$5 green and red/emerald (I) (11.45)	£110	£160
18		$5 purple and orange (I) (ordinary paper) (12.45)	6·50	3·00
1/18 Set of 15			£120	£170

1as/7s, 8as, 10s, 12as/16s, 18s Perf "SPECIMEN" Set of 14 .... £850

The 8c. grey with "BMA" opt was prepared but not officially issued (*Price* £550 *unused*).

Nos. 3 and 9 do not exist without the overprint.

Initial printings on ordinary paper were produced by Harrison and Sons in 1941 following bomb damage to the De La Rue works on 29 December 1940.

For a description of the thin striated paper, see the introduction to this catalogue.

No. 8 with reddish purple medallion and dull purple frame is from a 1947 printing with the head in fugitive ink which discolours with moisture.

Postal forgeries of the 50c. value exist made by dyeing examples of the 1c. and then altering the face value to 50c.

In 1946 8c. and 15c. stamps in the Crown Colony Victory design were prepared for the Malayan Union, but not issued. Examples of the 8c. carmine from this issue exist from unofficial leakages (Price £600 unused).

V. MALAYAN FEDERATION

The Malayan Federation, formed on 1 February 1948 by Malacca, Penang, and the five Federated Malay States and the five Unfederated States, became an independent member of the British Commonwealth on 31 August 1957.

Commemoratives and a limited series of definitives were issued by the Federation and were used concurrently with the stamps from the individual States.

1 Tapping Rubber　　**2** Federation Coat of Arms

3 Tin dredger　　**4** Map of the Federation

(Centre recess, frame litho (6c., 25c.); centre litho, frame recess (12c.); recess (30c.), D.L.R.)

1957 (5 May)–**63**. T **1**, **4** and similar designs. W w **12**. P 13×11½-12½* (No. 4) or 13 (others).

1		6c. deep blue, red, yellow and grey-blue	50	10
		a. Indigo, red, yellow and grey-blue (20.6.61)	10·00	1·25

		b. Indigo, red, yellow and slate-blue (12.2.63)	8·00	1·25
		c. Yellow (star and crescent) omitted	£140	£750
		w. Wmk inverted	†	£750
2		12c. red, yellow, blue, black and scarlet	2·25	1·00
3		25c. maroon, red, yellow and dull greenish blue	4·75	20
4		30c. orange-red and lake	2·00	20
		a. Perf 13. Orange-red and deep lake	2·50	2·25
		ab. Orange-red and lake (10.7.62)	3·75	10
1/4 Set of 4			8·50	1·25

* On No. 4 the top section of the stamp is perf 11½, with the remainder perf 12½.

5 Prime Minister Tunku Abdul Rahman and Populace greeting Independence

(Des A. B. Seeman. Recess Imprimerie Belge de Sécurité SA)

1957 (31 Aug). Independence Day. Wmk Mult Script CA. P 12½.

5	**5**	10c. bistre-brown	80	10

6 United Nations Emblem　　**7** United Nations Emblem

(Recess D.L.R.)

1958 (5 Mar). UN Economic Commission for Asia and Far East Conference, Kuala Lumpur. W w **12**. P 13½ (12c.) or 13×11½-12½ (30c.).

6	**6**	12c. carmine-red	30	80
7	**7**	30c. maroon	40	80

8 Merdeka Stadium, Kuala Lumpur　　**9** The Yang di-Pertuan Agong (Tuanku Abdul Rahman)

(Photo Harrison)

1958 (31 Aug). First Anniv of Independence. W w **12**. P 13½×14½ (10c.) or 14½×13½ (30c.).

8	**8**	10c. green, yellow, red and blue	15	10
9	**9**	30c. red, yellow, violet-blue and green	40	70

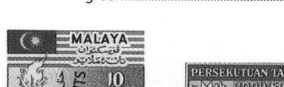

10 "Human Rights"　　**11** Malayan with Torch of Freedom

(Des J. P. Hendroff. Litho (10c.), photo (30c.) D.L.R.)

1958 (10 Dec). Tenth Anniv of Declaration of Human Rights.

(a) W w **12**. P 12½×13

10	**10**	10c. blue, black, carmine and orange	15	10

(b) Wmk Mult Script CA. P 13×12½

11	**11**	30c. deep green	45	60

12 Mace and Malayan Peoples

(Photo Enschedé)

1959 (12 Sept). Inauguration of Parliament. No wmk. P 13×14.

12	**12**	4c. rose-red	10	10
13		10c. violet	10	10
14		25c. yellow-green	75	20
12/14 Set of 3			85	30

13 **14**

(Recess D.L.R.)

1960 (7 Apr). World Refugee Year. W w **12**. P 13½ (12c.) or 12½×13 (30c.)

15	**13**	12c. purple	15	60
16	**14**	30c. deep green	15	10

15 Seedling Rubber Tree and Map

16 The Yang di-Pertuan Agong (Tuanku Syed Putra)

(Photo Japanese Govt Ptg Wks)

1960 (19 Sept). Natural Rubber Research Conference and 15th International Rubber Study Group Meeting, Kuala Lumpur. T **15** and similar vert design. No wmk. P 13.

17		6c. yellow-green, black, orange and red-brown	20	1·25
18		30c. yellow-green, black, orange and bright blue	50	75

No. 18 is inscribed "INTERNATIONAL RUBBER STUDY GROUP 15th MEETING KUALA LUMPUR" at foot.

(Photo Harrison)

1961 (4 Jan). Installation of Yang di-Pertuan Agong, Tuanku Syed Putra. W w **12**. P 14×14½.

19	**16**	10c. black and blue	10	10

17 Colombo Plan Emblem

18 Malaria Eradication Emblem

(Photo Japanese Govt Ptg Works)

1961 (30 Oct). Colombo Plan Conference, Kuala Lumpur. P 13.

20	**17**	12c. black and magenta	35	3·00
21		25c. black and apple-green	80	2·50
22		30c. black and turquoise-blue	70	1·00
20/2	*Set of 3*		1·75	6·00

(Photo Harrison)

1962 (7 Apr). Malaria. Eradication. W w **13**. P 14×14½.

23	**18**	25c. orange-brown	20	40
24		30c. deep lilac	20	15
25		50c. ultramarine	40	80
23/5	*Set of 3*		70	1·25

19 Palmyra Palm Leaf

20 "Shadows of the Future"

(Photo Harrison)

1962 (21 July). National Language Month. W w **13** (upright or inverted). P 13½.

26	**19**	10c. light brown and deep reddish violet	30	10
27		20c. light brown and deep bluish green	1·25	1·25
28		50c. light brown and magenta	2·50	1·75
26/8	*Set of 3*		3·50	2·75

Nos. 26/8 were printed *tête-bêche*.

(Photo Enschedé)

1962 (1 Oct). Introduction of Free Primary Education. W w **13**. P 13½.

29	**20**	10c. bright purple	10	10
		w. Wmk inverted	60·00	
30		25c. ochre	60	1·25
31		30c. emerald	3·00	10
29/31	*Set of 3*		3·25	1·25

21 Harvester and Fisherman

22 Dam and Pylon

(Photo Courvoisier)

1963 (21 Mar). Freedom from Hunger. P 11½.

32	**21**	25c. carmine and apple-green	3·25	3·25
33		30c. carmine and crimson	3·75	1·75
34		50c. carmine and bright blue	3·50	3·00
32/4	*Set of 3*		9·50	7·25

(Photo Harrison)

1963 (26 June). Cameron Highlands Hydro-Electric Scheme. W w **13**. P 14.

35	**22**	20c. green and reddish violet	60	10
36		30c. blue-green and ultramarine	1·00	10

The definitive general issue for Malaysia and the low value sets for the individual states superseded the stamps of the Malayan Federation by 15 November 1965.

VI. MALAYSIA

On 16 September 1963, the Malayan Federation, Sabah (North Borneo), Sarawak and Singapore formed the Federation of Malaysia. Singapore left the Federation on 9 August 1965, and became an independent republic. Stamps of Singapore continued to be valid in Malaysia, and those of Malaysia in Singapore, until 1 February 1967.

Individual issues for the component States continued, but were restricted to low value definitives and the occasional "State" commemorative. The higher value definitives and the vast majority of commemoratives were issued on a "National" basis.

NATIONAL ISSUES

General issues for use throughout the Malaysian Federation.

1 Federation Map

2 Bouquet of Orchids

(Photo Harrison)

1963 (16 Sept). Inauguration of Federation. W w **13**. P 14½.

1	**1**	10c. yellow and bluish violet	1·25	10
		a. Yellow omitted	£550	
2		12c. yellow and deep green	1·50	60
3		50c. yellow and chocolate	1·50	10
1/3	*Set of 3*		3·75	65

(Photo Enschedé)

1963 (3 Oct). Fourth World Orchid Conference, Singapore. No wmk. P 13×14.

4	**2**	6c. multicoloured	1·25	1·25
5		25c. multicoloured	1·25	25

4 Parliament House, Kuala Lumpur

(Des V. Whiteley. Photo Harrison)

1963 (4 Nov). Ninth Commonwealth Parliamentary Conference, Kuala Lumpur. W w **13** (inverted). P 13½.

7	**4**	20c. deep magenta and gold	1·25	40
8		30c. deep green and gold	1·75	15

5 "Flame of Freedom" and Emblems of Goodwill, Health and Charity

6 Microwave Tower and ITU Emblem

(Photo Harrison)

1964 (10 Oct). Eleanor Roosevelt Commemoration. W w **13**. P 14½×13½.

9	**5**	25c. black, red and greenish blue	20	10
10		30c. black, red and deep lilac	20	15
11		50c. black, red and ochre-yellow	20	10
9/11	*Set of 3*		55	30

(Photo Courvoisier)

1965 (17 May). ITU Centenary. P 11½.

12	**6**	2c. multicoloured	75	3·00
13		25c. multicoloured	2·00	60
14		50c. multicoloured	2·75	10
12/14	*Set of 3*		5·00	3·25

7 National Mosque

8 Air Terminal

(Photo Harrison)

1965 (27 Aug). Opening of National Mosque, Kuala Lumpur. W w **13**. P 14×14½.

15	**7**	6c. carmine	10	10
16		15c. red-brown	20	10
17		20c. deep bluish green	20	15
15/17	*Set of 3*		45	30

(Photo Harrison)

1965 (30 Aug). Opening of International Airport, Kuala Lumpur. W w **13**. P 14½×14.

18	**8**	15c. black, yellow-green and new blue	40	10
		a. Yellow-green omitted	38·00	
19		30c. black, yellow-green and magenta	60	20

9 Crested Wood Partridge

17 Sepak Raga (ball game) and Football

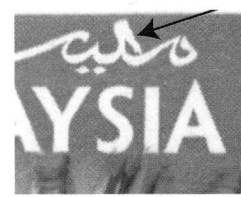

75c. Extra stroke in Malay inscription above "S" of "MALAYSIA" (Pl. 1A, R. 9/4)

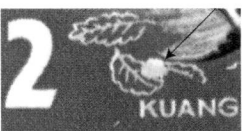

$2 Oval flaw above "KU" of "KUANG" resembles an egg (Pl. 1A, R.5/6)

(Des A. Fraser-Brunner. Photo Harrison)

1965 (9 Sept). T **9** and similar vert designs. Multicoloured. W w **13**. P 14½.

20		25c. Type **9**	50	10
		w. Wmk inverted	4·50	
21		30c. Blue-backed Fairy Bluebird	60	10
		a. Blue (plumage) omitted	£375	
		b. Yellow omitted	£550	
		w. Wmk inverted	12·00	
22		50c. Black-nailed Oriole	1·25	10
		a. Yellow omitted	£300	
		c. Scarlet (inscr and berries) omitted	£120	
		w. Wmk inverted	26·00	
23		75c. Rhinoceros Hornbill	1·00	10
		a. Inscription flaw	20·00	
24		$1 Zebra Dove	1·50	10
		w. Wmk inverted	50·00	
25		$2 Great Argus Pheasant	9·00	30
		b. "Egg" flaw	65·00	
		w. Wmk inverted	16·00	
26		$5 Asiatic Paradise Flycatcher	20·00	3·25
		w. Wmk inverted	50·00	
27		$10 Blue-tailed Pitta	48·00	13·00
20/7	*Set of 8*		70·00	15·00

All values except the 75c. and $10 exist with PVA gum as well as gum arabic, 21a and 22c exist on both papers.

Nos 20/7 exist imperforate. The 50c., $2 and $10 were formerly listed as Nos 22b, 25a and 27a, but are now considered to be of proof status. (*Price for set of 8 imperforate pairs, £1000*).

(Des E. A. F. Anthony. Litho Japanese Govt Ptg Wks)

1965 (14 Dec). Third South East Asian Peninsular Games. T **17** and similar vert designs. P 13×13½.

28		25c. black and olive-green	40	1·25
29		30c. black and bright purple	40	20
30		50c. black and light blue	1·00	30
28/30	*Set of 3*		1·60	1·60

Designs:—30c. Running; 50c. Diving.

20 National Monument

21 The Yang di-Pertuan Agong (Tuanku Ismail Nasiruddin Shah)

(Photo Harrison)

1966 (8 Feb). National Monument, Kuala Lumpur. W w **13**. P 13½.
31	**20**	10c. multicoloured	50	10
		a. Blue omitted	£225	
32		20c. multicoloured	1·00	40

Nos. 31/2 were printed *tête-bêche*.

(Photo Japanese Govt Ptg Wks)

1966 (11 Apr). Installation of Yang di-Pertuan Agong, Tuanku Ismail Nasiruddin Shah.
33	**21**	15c. black and light yellow	10	10
34		50c. black and greenish blue	20	20

22 School Building   **23** "Agriculture"

(Photo D.L.R.)

1966 (21 Oct). 150th Anniv of Penang Free School. W w **13** (sideways). P 13.
35	**22**	20c. multicoloured	70	10
36		50c. multicoloured	90	10

The 50c. is also inscr "ULANG TAHUN KE-150" at foot and bears a shield at bottom left corner.

(Des Enche Ng Peng Nam. Photo Japanese Govt Ptg Wks)

1966 (1 Dec). First Malaysia Plan. T **23** and similar horiz designs. Multicoloured. P 13½.
37		15c. Type **23**	20	10
38		15c. "Rural Health"	20	10
39		15c. "Communications"	2·75	15
40		15c. "Education"	20	10
41		15c. "Irrigation"	20	10
37/41		*Set of 5*	3·25	50

28 Cable Route Maps

(Des Enche Ng Peng Nam. Photo Japanese Govt Ptg Wks)

1967 (30 Mar). Completion of Malaysia–Hong Kong Link of SEACOM Telephone Cable. P 13½.
42	**28**	30c. multicoloured	80	50
43		75c. multicoloured	2·50	4·25

29 Hibiscus and Paramount Rulers

(Photo Harrison)

1967 (31 Aug). Tenth Anniv of Independence. W w **13**. P 14½.
44	**29**	15c. multicoloured	20	10
		w. Wmk inverted	4·00	
45		50c. multicoloured	1·25	80

30 Mace and Shield   **31** Straits Settlements 1867 8c. and Malaysia 1965 25c. Definitive

(Des Enche Ng Peng Nam. Photo Harrison)

1967 (8 Sept). Centenary of Sarawak Council. W w **13**. P 14½.
46	**30**	15c. multicoloured	10	10
47		50c. multicoloured	30	60

(Des Enche Ng Peng Nam. Photo Japanese Govt Ptg Works)

1967 (2 Dec). Stamp Centenary. T **31** and similar shaped designs. Multicoloured. P 11½.
48		25c. Type **31**	1·60	3·25
		a. *Tête-bêche* (horiz pair)	3·00	6·50
49		30c. Straits Settlements 1867 24c. and Malaysia 1965 30c. definitive	1·60	2·75
		a. *Tête-bêche* (horiz pair)	3·00	5·50
50		50c. Straits Settlements 1867 32c. and Malaysia 1965 50c. definitive	2·50	3·50
		a. *Tête-bêche* (horiz pair)	5·00	7·00
48/50		*Set of 3*	5·25	8·50

Nos. 48/50 were each printed in sheets with the stamps arranged horizontally *tête-bêche*.

34 Tapping Rubber, and Molecular Unit   **37** Mexican Sombrero and Blanket with Olympic Rings

(Litho B.W.)

1968 (29 Aug). Natural Rubber Conference, Kuala Lumpur. T **34** and similar horiz designs. Multicoloured. W w **13**. P 12.
51		25c. Type **34**	30	10
52		30c. Tapping rubber, and export consignment	40	20
53		50c. Tapping rubber, and aircraft tyres	40	10
51/3		*Set of 3*	1·00	35

(Litho B.W.)

1968 (12 Oct). Olympic Games Mexico. T **37** and similar vert design. Multicoloured. W w **13**. P 12×11½.
54		30c. Type **37**	20	10
55		75c. Olympic rings and Mexican embroidery	55	20

39 Tunku Abdul Rahman against background of Pandanus Weave   **40** Tunku Abdul Rahman against background of Pandanus Weave

(Photo Japanese Govt Ptg Wks)

1969 (8 Feb). Solidarity Week. T **39/40** and similar multicoloured design. P 13½.
56		15c. Type **39**	15	10
57		20c. Type **40**	45	1·25
58		50c. Tunku Abdul Rahman with pandanus pattern (*horiz*)	50	20
56/8		*Set of 3*	1·00	1·40

42 Peasant Girl with Sheaves of Paddy

(Des Enche Hoessein Anas. Photo Harrison)

1969 (8 Dec). National Rice Year. W w **13**. P 13½.
59	**42**	15c. multicoloured	15	10
60		75c. multicoloured	55	1·50

43 Satellite tracking Aerial

44 *Intelsat III* in Orbit

(Photo Enschedé)

1970 (6 Apr). Satellite Earth Station. W w **13**. P 14×13 (15c.) or 13½×13 (30c.).
61	**43**	15c. multicoloured	1·00	15
		a. *Tête-Bêche* (horiz pair)	2·00	2·50
62	**44**	30c. multicoloured*	1·00	2·75
63		30c. multicoloured*	1·00	2·75
61/3		*Set of 3*	2·75	5·00

No. 61 was issued horizontally and vertically *tête-bêche* in the sheets.
*Nos. 62/3 are of the same design, differing only in the lettering colours (No. 62 white; No. 63 gold).

45 *Euploea leucostictus*   **46** Emblem

(Des V. Whiteley. Litho B.W. (to 1976) or Harrison)

1970 (31 Aug–16 Nov). Butterflies. T **45** and similar vert designs. Multicoloured. P 13×13½.
64		25c. Type **45**	1·00	10
65		30c. *Zeuxidia amethystus*	1·50	10
66		50c. *Polyura athamas*	2·00	10
67		75c. *Papilio memnon*	2·00	10
68		$1 *Appias nero* (16.11)	3·00	10
69		$2 *Trogonoptera brookiana* (16.11)	3·50	10
70		$5 *Narathura centaurus* (16.11)	5·00	3·75
71		$10 *Terinos terpander* (16.11)	17·00	5·00
64/71		*Set of 8*	32·00	8·50

There are considerable variations in the shades found on Nos. 64/71, with the Harrison printings appearing less green than the Bradbury Wilkinson.

(Litho Harrison)

1970 (7 Sept). 50th Anniv of International Labour Organization. P 14½.
72	**46**	30c. grey and new blue	10	20
73		75c. pink and new blue	20	30

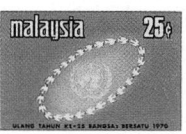

47 UN Emblem encircled by Doves

(Des Enche Ng Peng Nam. Litho D.L.R.)

1970 (24 Oct). 25th Anniv of United Nations. T **47** and similar horiz designs. P 13×12½.
74		25c. gold, black and brown	35	40
75		30c. multicoloured	35	35
76		50c. black and dull yellow-green	40	75
74/6		*Set of 3*	1·00	1·40

Designs:—30c. Line of doves and UN emblem; 50c. Doves looping UN emblem.

POSTAGE DUE STAMPS

Until 15 August 1966 the postage due stamps of MALAYAN POSTAL UNION were in use throughout MALAYSIA.

D 1

(Litho Harrison)

1966 (15 Aug)–**71**. Ordinary paper. W w **13** (upright). P 14½×14.
D1	**D 1**	1c. rose	20	7·00
D2		2c. indigo	25	2·75
D3		4c. apple-green	1·00	14·00
D4		8c. blue-green	2·00	24·00
		a. Chalk-surfaced paper. *Bright blue green* (1.6.71)	4·50	19·00
D5		10c. bright blue	1·50	1·50
		a. Chalk-surfaced paper (1.6.71)	4·50	13·00
D6		12c. reddish violet	60	4·50
D7		20c. red-brown	2·00	2·25
		a. Chalk-surfaced paper. *Brown purple* (22.4.69)	2·75	15·00
D8		50c. brownish bistre	2·00	4·50
		a. Chalk-surfaced paper. *Olive-bistre* (1.6.71)	4·50	16·00
D1/8		*Set of 8*	8·50	50·00

Later issues in this design were printed on glazed or unwatermarked paper.

VII. MALAYSIAN STATES

PRINTERS. All Malaysian States stamps were printed in typography by De La Rue and Co. Ltd, London, *unless otherwise stated*.

JOHORE

A British adviser was appointed to Johore in 1914. The state joined the Federation of Malaya on 1 February 1948.

Until 1 January 1899 mail for addresses outside Malaya had the external postage paid by stamps of the STRAITS SETTLEMENTS.

PRICES FOR STAMPS ON COVER TO 1945	
Nos. 1/2	—
Nos. 3/5	*from* × 15
No. 6	*from* × 20
Nos. 7/8	—
Nos. 9/15	*from* × 25
No. 16	—
Nos. 17/20	*from* × 15
Nos. 21/31	*from* × 10
Nos. 32/8	*from* × 15
Nos. 39/53	*from* × 8
Nos. 54/60	*from* × 6
Nos. 61/74	*from* × 8
Nos. 75/7	
Nos. 78/87	*from* × 8
No. 88	*from* × 10
Nos. 89/102	*from* × 6
Nos. 103/25	*from* × 5
Nos. 126/8	
Nos. 129/30	*from* × 6
Nos. D1/5	*from* × 5

All overprints and surcharges were applied by the Government Printer, Singapore.

(1) (sideways)

1876 (July). No. 11 of Straits Settlements handstamped with T **1** (sideways or upright).
1		2c. brown	£25000	£8500

No. 1 is known with the handstamp double.

A single used example of the 4c. rose (Straits Settlements No. 12) exists with the T **1** handstamp.

From September 1878 to August 1884 no overprinted stamps were supplied by Singapore to Johore.

JOHORE
(2)

JOHORE JOHORE JOHORE
(3) ("H" and "E" (4) ("H" wide, (5) ("H" and
wide. "J" raised.   "E" narrow. Opt   "E" wide. Opt
Opt 16 *mm* long)   16 *mm* long)   16¾ *mm* long)

JOHORE. JOHORE JOHORE
(6)   (7)   (8)

1884 (June)–86. No. 63 of Straits Settlements optd with T **2/8**.

2	**2**	2c. pale rose	£10000	
3	**3**	2c. pale rose (8.84)	£3750	£800
		a. Opt double	£6500	£2500
4	**4**	2c. pale rose (8.84)	£3750	£1100
		a. Opt double		£2500
5	**5**	2c. pale rose (8.84)	£3750	£800
		a. Opt double	—	£2500
6	**6**	2c. pale rose (3.85)	£225	£225
		a. Opt double	£1100	£1000
7	**7**	2c. pale rose (1885)	£9500	
8	**8**	2c. pale rose (4.86)	£130	£140

Nos. 3 to 6 and 8 were from triplet settings, either 3+4+5 or three examples of the same overprint. Nos. 2 and 7 are probably single unit handstamps.

JOHOR JOHOR JOHOR
(9) (All letters (10)   (11) ("H" wide)
narrow)

JOHOR JOHOR JOHOR.
(12)   (13)   (14)

JOHOR JOHOR JOHOR
(15)   (16)   Thin, narrow "J"

1884 (Aug)–91. Nos. 63/a of Straits Settlements optd with T **9/16**.

9	**9**	2c. pale rose	27·00	20·00
		a. Opt double	£800	
		w. Wmk inverted	—	£500
10	**10**	2c. pale rose (10.84)	26·00	12·00
		a. Thin, narrow "J" (R. 6/6)	£300	£180
		b. Opt double	£950	
		c. Bright rose (1890)	23·00	12·00
		ca. Thin, narrow "J" (R. 6/6)	£275	£200
		cb. Opt double	£1200	
11	**11**	2c. pale rose (2.85)	£120	£110
		a. Opt double	£1500	
12	**12**	2c. pale rose (1886)	80·00	60·00
		a. Opt double	£750	
13	**13**	2c. pale rose (1886)	70·00	60·00
14	**14**	2c. pale rose (1888)	£225	75·00
		a. Thin, narrow "J"	£1300	£450
		b. Opt double	£850	
15	**15**	2c. bright rose (9.90)	30·00	29·00
16	**16**	2c. bright rose (1891)	£9500	

Settings:
No. 9 – various triplets with the length of the overprint varying from 12 to 15 mm.
No. 10 – triplet or 60 (6×10)
No. 11 – two types, length 13¼ mm and 14¼ mm, from separate printings, both triplets of 11+9+9
No. 12 – triplet
No. 13 – triplet
No. 14 – 30 (3×10)
No. 15 – 60 (6×10)
No. 16 – not known. As no used examples are known it is possible that this stamp was not issued.

JOHOR **JOHOR**
Two *Two*
CENTS CENTS

(17)   (18)

JOHOR **JOHOR**
Two *Two*
CENTS CENTS

(19)   (20)

1891 (May). No. 68 of Straits Settlements surch as T **17/20**.

17	**17**	2c. on 24c. green	28·00	40·00
		a. "CENST" (R. 5/4)	£950	£500
		b. Thin, narrow "J" (R. 5/6)	£500	£500
		w. Wmk inverted	£250	£250
18	**18**	2c. on 24c. green	£140	£150
		a. Thin, narrow "J" (R. 6/6)	£600	£600
		w. Wmk inverted	£700	
19	**19**	2c. on 24c. green	42·00	55·00
		w. Wmk inverted	£400	£400
20	**20**	2c. on 24c. green	£130	£140
		w. Wmk inverted	£700	£700

Nos. 17/20 come from the same setting of 60. Type **17** occurs on horizontal rows 1 to 5, Type **18** on row 6, Type **19** on rows 7, 8 and 9 and Type **20** on row 10.

The setting was altered to remove the "CENST" error and in doing so the thin, narrow "J" was moved from R. 5/6 to 6/6. Otherwise the two settings were the same.

One example of the "CENST" error (No. 17a) has been recorded with inverted watermark (*Price*, £4000 *used*).

---

21 Sultan Abu Bakar

3 cents.
(22)   **KEMAHKOTAAN**
(23)

1891 (16 Nov)–94. No wmk. P 14.

21	**21**	1c. dull purple and mauve (7.94)	1·00	50
22		2c. dull purple and yellow	60	1·50
23		3c. dull purple and carmine (7.94)	60	60
24		4c. dull purple and black	2·75	21·00
25		5c. dull purple and green	7·00	21·00
26		6c. dull purple and blue	8·00	21·00
27		$1 green and carmine	85·00	£170
21/7		*Set of 7*	95·00	£200

1894 (Mar). Surch with T **22**.

28	**21**	3c. on 4c. dull purple and black	2·50	50
		a. No stop (R. 5/11)	£120	75·00
29		3c. on 5c. dull purple and green	2·00	4·75
		a. No stop (R. 5/11)	£140	£170
		b. "3 cents." spaced 3½ mm from bar	£200	£110
30		3c. on 6c. dull purple and blue	3·50	8·50
		a. No stop (R. 5/11)	£200	£225
31		3c. on $1 green and carmine	12·00	75·00
		a. No stop (R. 5/11)	£475	£900
28/31		*Set of 4*	18·00	80·00

No. 29b shows the surcharge spaced 3½ mm instead of the normal 7½ mm. It appears to come from a separate setting as a cancelled-to-order block of eight is known.

1896 (16 Mar). Coronation of Sultan Ibrahim. Optd with T **23**.

32	**21**	1c. dull purple and mauve	50	1·00
		a. "KETAHKOTAAN"	6·00	5·50
33		2c. dull purple and yellow	50	1·00
		a. "KETAHKOTAAN"	8·00	8·50
34		3c. dull purple and carmine	55	1·00
		a. "KETAHKOTAAN"	16·00	22·00
35		4c. dull purple and black	80	2·25
		a. "KETAHKOTAAN"	2·75	22·00
36		5c. dull purple and green	5·50	7·50
		a. "KETAHKOTAAN"	3·50	7·50
37		6c. dull purple and blue	3·50	6·50
		a. "KETAHKOTAAN"	9·50	22·00
38		$1 green and carmine	65·00	£130
		a. "KETAHKOTAAN"	38·00	£180
32/8		*Set of 7*	70·00	£140
32a/8a		*Set of 7*	75·00	£225

Stamps overprinted "KETAHKOTAAN" (= We mourn) come from the first overprinting. The overprint was subsequently changed to the intended "KEMAHKOTAAN" (= Coronation), but both were issued together some months after the Coronation of Sultan Ibrahim had taken place.

24 Sultan Ibrahim

25 Sultan Ibrahim

26

27

1896 (26 Aug)–99. W **27**. P 14.

39	**24**	1c. green	80	3·25
40		2c. green and blue	50	1·25
41		3c. green and purple	4·00	5·50
		a. Green and dull claret	7·00	3·50
42		4c. green and carmine	1·00	3·75
43		4c. yellow and red (1899)	1·50	2·25
44		5c. green and brown	2·00	5·00
45		6c. green and yellow	2·00	7·50
46	**25**	10c. green and black (1898)	7·00	50·00
47		25c. green and mauve (1898)	9·00	50·00
48		50c. green and carmine (1898)	16·00	50·00
49	**24**	$1 dull purple and green (1898)	32·00	75·00
50	**26**	$2 dull purple and carmine (1898)	55·00	80·00
51		$3 dull purple and blue (1898)	50·00	£120
52		$4 dull purple and brown (1898)	50·00	85·00
53		$5 dull purple and yellow (1898)	£100	£130
39/53		*Set of 15*	£300	£600

Nos. 42 and 43 were reissued in 1918 to meet a shortage of 4c. stamps.

3 cents.   ## 10 cents.
(28)   (29)

1903 (Apr). Surch with T **28** or **29**.

54	**24**	3c. on 4c. yellow and red	60	1·10
		a. Original value uncancelled	3·75	27·00
55		10c. on 4c. green and carmine	3·50	17·00
		a. Tall "1" in "10" (R. 9/12)	80·00	£140
		b. Original value uncancelled	20·00	85·00
		ba. As b, with tall "1" in "10" (R. 9/12)	£1300	£1900

The bars on these stamps were ruled by hand with pen and ink.

---

50 Cents.   One Dollar
(30)   (31)

1903 (Oct). Surch with T **30** or **31**.

56	**26**	50c. on $3 dull purple and blue	30·00	85·00
57		$1 on $2 dull purple and carmine	65·00	£120
		a. "e" of "One" inverted (R. 7/9)	£1900	

10 CENTS.
(32)

1904. Surch as T **32**.

58	**24**	10c. on 4c. yellow and red (4.04)	20·00	40·00
		a. Surcharge double	£8500	
59		10c. on 4c. green and carmine (8.04)	9·50	70·00
60	**26**	50c. on $5 dull purple and yellow (5.04)	80·00	£170
58/60		*Set of 3*	£100	£250

33

34

35 Sultan Sir Ibrahim

1904 (Sept)–10. W **27**. Ordinary paper. P 14.

61	**33**	1c. dull purple and green	2·00	40
		a. Chalk-surfaced paper (10.09)	23·00	13·00
62		2c. dull purple and orange	3·00	4·25
		a. Chalk-surfaced paper (10.10)	25·00	26·00
63		3c. dull purple and olive-black	4·75	60
		a. Chalk-surfaced paper	—	£120
64		4c. dull purple and carmine	8·00	4·75
65		5c. dull purple and sage-green	2·50	4·00
66	**35**	8c. dull purple and blue	4·25	21·00
67	**34**	10c. dull purple and black	50·00	11·00
		a. Chalk-surfaced paper (1910)	£120	80·00
68		25c. dull purple and green	8·50	40·00
69		50c. dull purple and red	45·00	17·00
70	**33**	$1 green and mauve	16·00	65·00
71	**35**	$2 green and carmine	35·00	50·00
72		$3 green and blue	48·00	85·00
73		$4 green and brown	48·00	£120
74		$5 green and orange	70·00	90·00
75	**34**	$10 green and black	£140	£200
76		$50 green and ultramarine (F.C. £50)	£475	£650
77		$100 green and scarlet (F.C. £50)	£650	£1000
61/75		*Set of 15*	£425	£650

1910–19. Wmk Mult Rosettes (vertical). Chalk-surfaced paper. P 14.

78	**33**	1c. dull purple and green (1912)	1·25	15
79		2c. dull purple and orange (1912)	6·00	1·00
80		3c. dull purple and olive-black (1912)	10·00	65
		a. Wmk horizontal (1910)	10·00	19·00
81		4c. dull purple and carmine (1912)	35·00	1·00
		a. Wmk horizontal (1910)	20·00	65·00
82		5c. dull purple and sage-green (1912)	10·00	3·00
83	**35**	8c. dull purple and blue (1912)	4·00	15·00
84	**34**	10c. dull purple and black (1912)	60·00	3·00
		a. Wmk horizontal (1911)	30·00	90·00
85		25c. dull purple and green (1912)	27·00	60·00
86		50c. dull purple and red (1919)	80·00	£150
87	**33**	$1 green and mauve (1917)	£120	£130
78/87		*Set of 10*	£275	£350

3 CENTS.
(36)

37 Sultan Sir Ibrahim and Sultana

1912 (Mar). No. 66 surch with T **36**.

88		3c. on 8c. dull purple and blue	18·00	14·00
		a. "T" of "CENTS" omitted	£1700	
		b. Bars double	†	£5000

No. 88b shows the bars printed twice with the upper pair partly erased.

1918–20. Wmk Mult Crown CA. Chalk-surfaced paper. P 14.

89	**33**	2c. dull purple and green (1919)	50	2·50
		w. Wmk inverted	†	£500
90		2c. purple and orange (1919)	1·00	8·00
91		4c. dull purple and red	1·75	70
92		5c. dull purple and sage-green (1920)	2·00	16·00
		w. Wmk inverted	£200	
		ws. Ditto, optd "SPECIMEN"	£100	
93	**34**	10c. dull purple and blue	2·00	1·40
		w. Wmk inverted	†	£500
94		21c. dull purple and orange (1919)	2·25	2·50
95		25c. dull purple and green (1920)	8·00	50·00
96		50c. dull purple and red (6.18)	24·00	65·00
97	**33**	$1 green and mauve	14·00	75·00
98	**35**	$2 green and carmine	23·00	65·00
99		$3 green and blue	75·00	£150
100		$4 green and brown	95·00	£225
101		$5 green and orange	£150	£250
102	**34**	$10 green and black	£450	£650
89/102		*Set of 14*	£750	£1400
89s/102s		Optd "SPECIMEN" *Set of 14*	£700	

1922–41. Wmk Mult Script CA. Chalk-surfaced paper. P 14.

103	**33**	1c. dull purple and black	30	20
104		2c. purple and sepia (1924)	1·25	4·25
105		2c. green (1928)	60	40
106		3c. green (1925)	2·00	7·50
107		3c. purple and sepia (1928)	1·40	1·75
108		4c. purple and carmine (1924)	2·50	20
109		5c. dull purple and sage-green	50	30
		w. Wmk inverted		
110		6c. dull purple and claret	50	50
111	**34**	10c. dull purple and blue	16·00	32·00
		w. Wmk inverted	†	£500
		ws. Ditto, opt "SPECIMEN"	£140	
112		10c. dull purple and yellow	50	25
		a. Thin striated paper (1941)	£130	£190
113	**33**	12c. dull purple and blue	1·00	1·25
114		12c. ultramarine (1940)	55·00	1·75
115	**34**	21c. dull purple and orange (1928)	2·00	3·00
116		25c. dull purple and myrtle	6·00	1·00
117	**35**	30c. dull purple and orange (1936)	11·00	17·00
118		40c. dull purple and brown (1936)	12·00	18·00
119	**34**	50c. dull purple and red	4·00	1·60
		a. Thin striated paper (1941)	£375	£400
120	**33**	$1 green and mauve	3·75	1·25
		a. Thin striated paper (1941)	£225	£250
121	**35**	$2 green and carmine (1923)	10·00	4·50
		a. Thin striated paper (1941)	16·00	19·00
122		$3 green and blue (1925)	85·00	£110
123		$4 green and brown (1926)	£120	£200
		w. Wmk inverted	£1200	
124		$5 green and orange	70·00	50·00
		a. Thin striated paper (1941)	90·00	
125	**34**	$10 green and black (1924)	£350	£450
		a. Thin striated paper (1941)	£600	
126		$50 green and ultramarine (F.C. £100)	£1500	
		s. Optd "SPECIMEN"	£275	
127		$100 green and scarlet (F.C. £150)	£2000	
		s. Optd "SPECIMEN"	£350	
128	**35**	$500 blue and red (1926) (F.C. £425)	£24000	
		s. Optd "SPECIMEN"	£1300	
103/25 *Set of 23*			£700	£800
103s/25s Optd or Perf (12c. ultramarine, 30c., 40c.)				
"SPECIMEN" *Set of 23*			£1000	

For a description of the thin striated paper, see the introduction to this catalogue.

(Recess Waterlow)

1935 (15 May). 50th Anniv of Treaty Relations with Great Britain. Wmk Mult Script CA (sideways). P 12½.

129	**37**	8c. bright violet and slate	7·00	3·25
		s. Perf "SPECIMEN"	80·00	

38 Sultan Sir Ibrahim

39 Sultan Sir Ibrahim

(Recess D.L.R.)

1940 (Feb). Wmk Mult Script CA. P 13½.

130	**38**	8c. black and pale blue	25·00	1·75
		s. Perf "SPECIMEN"	£100	

Due to a stamp shortage in August and September 1941, meter stamps inscribed "POSTAGE PAID JOHORE" but without a machine number in denominations of 80c., $1, $1.40 and $2 were printed onto strips of paper and affixed to the item being posted. They were subsequently postmarked in the normal way.

1948 (1 Dec). Royal Silver Wedding. As Nos. 112/13 of Antigua.

131		10c. violet	20	75
132		$5 green	26·00	50·00

1949 (2 May)–**55.** Wmk Mult Script CA. Chalk-surfaced paper. P 17½×18.

133	**39**	1c. black	1·00	10
134		2c. orange	50	20
		a. Orange-yellow (22.1.52)	3·50	4·00
135		3c. green	2·50	1·00
		a. Yellow-green (22.1.52)	28·00	6·00
136		4c. brown	2·00	10
136a		5c. bright purple (1.9.52)	3·00	30
137		6c. grey	2·25	20
		a. Pale grey (22.1.52)	1·50	50
		ac. Error. St. Edward's Crown W **9b**	£3250	£2250
138		8c. scarlet	6·50	1·25
138a		8c. green (1.9.52)	11·00	2·25
139		10c. magenta	1·50	10
		aa. Imperf (pair)	£5500	
139a		12c. scarlet (1.9.52)	13·00	9·00
140		15c. ultramarine	5·50	10
141		20c. black and green	4·50	1·00
141a		20c. bright blue (1.9.52)	2·00	10
142		25c. purple and orange	3·75	10
142a		30c. scarlet and purple (4.9.55)	3·25	2·75
142b		35c. scarlet and purple (1.9.52)	13·00	1·75
143		40c. red and purple	9·50	18·00
144		50c. black and blue	6·00	10
145		$1 blue and purple	14·00	2·00
146		$2 green and scarlet	32·00	13·00
147		$5 green and brown	50·00	1·75
133/47 *Set of 21*			£160	60·00

1949 (10 Oct). 75th Anniv of UPU As Nos. 114/17 of Antigua.

148		10c. purple	30	40
149		15c. deep blue	2·00	2·00
150		25c. orange	65	4·25
151		50c. blue-black	1·25	4·50
148/51 *Set of 4*			3·75	10·00

1953 (2 June). Coronation. As No. 120 of Antigua.

152		10c. black and reddish purple	1·25	10

40 Sultan Sir Ibrahim

41 Sultan Sir Ismail and Johore Coat of Arms

(Recess D.L.R.)

1955 (1 Nov). Diamond Jubilee of Sultan. Wmk Mult Script CA. P 14.

153	**40**	10c. carmine-red	10	10

(Photo Courvoisier)

1960 (10 Feb). Coronation of Sultan. No wmk. P 11½.

154	**41**	10c. multicoloured	20	20

1960. As T **9/19** of Kedah, but with portrait of Sultan Ismail. P 13½ ($1); others 12½×13 (vert) or 13×12½ (horiz).

155		1c. black (7.10.60)	10	1·00
156		2c. orange-red (7.10.60)	10	2·00
157		4c. sepia (19.8.60)	10	10
158		5c. carmine-lake (7.10.60)	10	10
159		8c. myrtle-green (9.12.60)	4·25	5·00
160		10c. deep maroon (10.6.60)	30	10
161		20c. blue (9.12.60)	2·00	1·00
162		50c. black and bright blue (19.8.60)	50	20
163		$1 ultramarine and reddish purple (9.12.60)	8·50	8·50
164		$2 bronze-green and scarlet (9.12.60)	21·00	27·00
165		$5 brown and bronze-green (7.10.60)	42·00	48·00
155/65 *Set of 11*			70·00	80·00

In No. 161 there are only two figures in the boat, the steersman being missing. In the 20c. value for all the other dates there are three figures.

The 6, 12, 25 and 30c. values used with this issue were Nos. 1/4 of Malayan Federation.

42 *Vanda hookeriana* (Inset portrait of Sultan Ismail)

(Des A. Fraser-Brunner. Photo Harrison)

1965 (15 Nov). T **42** and similar horiz designs. W w **13** (upright). P 14½.

166		1c. Type **42**	10	30
		a. Black (orchid's name and part of flower) omitted	£425	
		w. Wmk inverted	5·50	
167		2c. *Arundina graminifolia*	10	1·00
168		5c. *Paphiopedilum niveum*	10	10
		b. Yellow (flower) omitted	£110	
169		6c. *Spathoglottis plicata*	40	30
170		10c. *Arachnis flos-aeris*	40	20
		a. Green omitted	£200	
171		15c. *Rhyncostylis retusa*	1·50	10
		b. Green (face value and leaves) omitted	£750	
172		20c. *Phalaenopsis violacea*	1·75	75
		a. Bright purple (blooms omitted)	£325	
166/72 *Set of 7*			3·75	2·25

The 2c. to 15c. exist with both PVA gum and gum arabic.

The 2c. with black (name of State, Arms and head) omitted is listed under Sarawak No. 213a as there is some evidence that a sheet was issued there; if it also exists from any of the other states it would, of course, be identical.

The higher values used with this issue were Nos. 20/27 of Malaysia (National Issues).

1970. As No. 166 and 170 but W w **13** (sideways).

173		1c. multicoloured (20.11)	1·75	9·50
174		10c. multicoloured (27.5)	1·75	2·50

STAMP BOOKLETS

1928. Black on white card. Interleaved with tissue. Stapled.

SB1	$2 booklet containing 10×1c. and 10×2c. (Nos. 103, 105), 20×4c. (No. 108), each in blocks of 10 and 18×5c. (No. 109) in blocks of 6	£2750

1929. Black on pink cover. Stapled.

SB2	$1 booklet containing 2c., 3c. and 5c. (Nos. 105, 107, 109) in blocks of 10	

1930. Black on buff cover. Stapled.

SB3	$1 booklet containing 10×1c. and 10×5c. (Nos. 103, 109) and 20×2c. (Nos. 105) in blocks of 10	

POSTAGE DUE STAMPS

D 1

(Typo Waterlow)

1938 (1 Jan). Wmk Mult Script CA. P 12½.

D1	**D 1**	1c. carmine	22·00	50·00
D2		4c. green	45·00	40·00
D3		8c. orange	50·00	£160
D4		10c. brown	50·00	50·00
D5		12c. purple	55·00	£140
D1/5 *Set of 5*			£200	£400
D1s/5s Perf "SPECIMEN" *Set of 5*			£160	

KEDAH

The Thai monarchy exercised suzerainty over Kedah and the other northern states of the Malay peninsula from the 16th-century onwards. The extent of Thai involvement in its internal affairs was very variable, being dependent on the strength, or otherwise, of the Bangkok administration and the degree of co-operation of the local ruler.

The Thai postal service, which had been inaugurated in 1883, gradually extended into the north of the Malay penninsula and an office was opened at Alor Star in Kedah during 1887 with the earliest known postmark being dated 27 October. Further post offices at Kuala Muda (3 Oct 1907), Kulim (7 July 1907) and Langkawi (16 Feb 1908) followed.

Stamps of Thailand used in Kedah

Types of Thailand (Siam)

    1   2   9

    49   50

    53

The following types of postmark were used on Siamese stamps from the Malay tributary states:

Type A. Single ring with date at foot (examples from 1900 show the year in manuscript)

Type B. Single ring with date in centre

Type C. Double ring. Bilingual

Type D. Double ring. English at top and ornament at foot

PRICES are for stamps showing a large part of the postmark with the inscription clearly visible.

The Siamese post office at Alor Star was opened during 1887 with the first known postmark being dated 27 October. Further post offices at Kuala Muda (3 Oct 1907), Kulim (7 July 1907) and Langkawi (16 Feb 1908) followed.

A straight-line obliteration showing "KEDAH" between short vertical dashes is not believed to be genuine.

Alor Star

Stamps of SIAM cancelled as Type A inscribed "KEDAH".

1883. (Nos. 1/5).

Z2	**1**	1att. rose-carmine	£325
Z3		1sio. red	£550
Z4	**2**	1sik. yellow	£550

1887–91. (Nos. 11/18).

Z6	**9**	1a. green	£110
Z7		2a. green and carmine	95·00
Z8		3a. green and blue	£120
Z9		4a. green and brown	£100
Z10		8a. green and yellow	£110
Z11		12a. purple and carmine	95·00
Z12		24a. purple and blue	£120
Z13		64a. purple and brown	£200

1889–91. Surch as T **12** (Nos. Z15, Z19), T **17** (No. Z21) or T **18** (No. 20/30).

Z15	**9**	1a. on 2a. rose-carmine	£130
Z19		1a. on 3a. red	£150
Z21		2a. on 3a. yellow	£200
Z22		2a. on 3a. green and blue	£250

1892. Surch as T **24/5** (with or without stop) and Siamese handstamp (Nos. 33/6).

Z28	**9**	4a. on 24a. purple and blue (Type **24**)	£130
Z29		4a. on 24a. purple and blue (Type **25**)	£150
Z30		4a. on 24a. purple and blue (Type **24** with stop)	£150
Z31		4a. on 24a. purple and blue (Type **25** with stop)	£150

1894. Surch as T **27** with variations of English figures as T **28** and **33** (Nos. 37/44).

Z34	**9**	2a. on 64a. purple and brown (Type **28**)	£130
Z39		2a. on 64a. purple and brown (Type **33**)	£130

1894. Surch with T **34** (No. 45).

Z41		2a. on 64a. purple and brown	£150

1894–95. Surch with T **35** with variations of English figures as T **36/9** (Nos. 46/50).

Z42	**9**	1a. on 64a. purple and brown (Type **35**)	£130
Z43		1a. on 64a. purple and brown (Type **36**)	£130
Z44		2a. on 64a. purple and brown (Type **37**)	£130
Z45		2a. on 64a. purple and brown (Type **38**)	£130
Z46		10a. on 24a. purple and blue (Type **39**)	£130

1896. Surch as T **39** (Siamese) and T **40** (English) (No. 51).

Z47	**9**	4a. on 12a. purple and carmine	£120

1897. Surch as T **39** (Siamese) and T **41** (English) (No. 52).

Z48	**9**	4a. on 12a. purple and carmine	£120

1898–99. Surch as T **42** with variations of English section as T **44/6** (Nos. 53/62).

Z49	**9**	1a. on 12a. purple and carmine (Type **42**– 11½ mm long)	£170
Z52		2a. on 64a. purple and brown (Type **44**)	£150
Z53		3a. on 12a. purple and carmine (Type **45**– 13½ mm long)	£130
Z54		3a. on 12a. purple and carmine (Type **45**– 11½ to 11¾ mm long)	£130
Z55		4a. on 12a. purple and carmine (Type **46**–8 mm long)	£130
Z56		4a. on 12a. purple and carmine (Type **46**– 8½ to 9 mm long)	£130

1899. Surch in Siamese and English with T **48a** (Nos. 63/6).

Z62	**9**	2a. on 64a. purple and brown	£140

1899–1904. (Nos. 67/81).

Z63	**49**	1a. olive-green (wide Siamese characters in face value)	£130
Z64		2a. grass-green	95·00
Z65		3a. red and blue	£100
Z66		4a. carmine	95·00
Z67		8a. deep green and orange	95·00
Z69		12a. brown-purple and carmine	£150
Z70		24a. brown-purple and blue	£250
Z71		64a. brown-purple and chestnut	£190

1899. (Nos. 82/6).

Z72	**50**	1a. green	£400
Z73		2a. green and red	£600

Stamps of SIAM cancelled as Type B inscr "KEDAH" (from March 1901).

1887–91. (Nos. 11/18).

Z74	**9**	12a. purple and carmine	90·00
Z75		24a. purple and brown	95·00

1898–99. Surch with T **42** with variations of English section as T **45/6** (Nos. 53/62).

Z76	**9**	1a. on 12a. purple and carmine (Type **42**– 11½ mm long)	£130
Z81		3a. on 12a. purple and carmine (Type **45**– 11½ to 11¾ mm long)	95·00
Z83		4a. on 12a. purple and carmine (Type **46**– 8½ to 9 mm long)	95·00
Z84		4a. on 24a. purple and blue (Type **46**)	£100

1899–1904. (Nos. 67/81).

Z86	**49**	1a. olive-green (wide Siamese characters in face value)	90·00
		a. Narrow Siamese characters in face value	90·00
Z87		2a. grass-green	75·00
Z88		2a. scarlet and pale blue	80·00
Z89		3a. red and blue	85·00
Z90		3a. deep green	90·00
Z91		4a. carmine	75·00
Z92		4a. chocolate and pink	85·00
Z93		8a. deep green and orange	80·00
Z94		10a. ultramarine	75·00
Z95		12a. brown-purple and carmine	90·00
Z96		24a. brown-purple and blue	£180
Z97		64a. brown-purple and chestnut	£170

1905–09. (Nos. 92/105).

Z102	**53**	1a. green and orange	80·00
Z103		2a. grey and deep violet	75·00
Z104		3a. green	90·00
Z105		4a. pale red and sepia	75·00
Z106		5a. carmine	85·00
Z107		8a. olive-bistre and dull black	80·00
Z108		12a. blue	90·00
Z109		24a. red-brown	£225
Z110		1t. bistre and deep blue	£225

Stamps of SIAM cancelled as Type C inscr "Kedah" at foot (from July 1907).

1887–91. (Nos. 11/18).

Z111	**9**	12a. purple and carmine	£110

1899–1904. (Nos. 67/81).

Z112	**49**	1a. olive-green (wide Siamese characters in face value)	85·00
		a. Narrow Siamese characters in face value	80·00
Z113		2a. scarlet and pale blue	80·00
Z114		3a. red and blue	90·00
Z116		8a. deep green and orange	85·00
Z117		10a. ultramarine	85·00
Z118		12a. brown-purple and carmine	85·00

1905–09. (Nos. 95/105).

Z128	**53**	1a. green and orange	75·00
Z129		2a. grey and deep violet	80·00
Z130		3a. green	85·00
Z131		4a. pale red and sepia	75·00
Z132		4a. scarlet	80·00
Z133		5a. carmine	80·00
Z134		8a. olive-bistre and dull black	75·00
Z135		9a. blue	75·00
Z136		18a. red-brown	£130
Z137		24a. red-brown	£225
Z138		1t. bistre and deep blue	£225

1907. Surch with T **56** (No. 109).

Z139	**9**	1a. on 24a. purple and blue	90·00

Kuala Muda

Stamps of SIAM cancelled as Type B inscr "KUALA MUDA" (from July 1907)

1887–91. (Nos. 11/18).

Z143	**9**	12a. purple and carmine	£450

1899–1904. (Nos. 67/81).

Z144	**49**	2a. scarlet and pale blue	£450
Z145		24a. brown-purple and blue	£500

1905–09. (Nos. 92/105).

Z146	**53**	1a. green and orange	£450
Z147		2a. grey and deep violet	£450
Z148		3a. green	£475
Z150		5a. carmine	£450
Z151		8a. olive-bistre and dull black	£450

Stamps of SIAM cancelled as Type C inscr "Kwala Muda" at foot (from 1907).

1887–91. (Nos. 11/18).

Z155	**9**	12a. purple and carmine	£225

1899–1904. (Nos. 67/81).

Z156	**49**	8a. deep green and orange	£250
Z157		10a. ultramarine	£275

1905–09. (Nos. 92/105).

Z158	**53**	1a. green and orange	£275
Z159		2a. grey and deep violet	£275
Z160		3a. green	£300
Z161		4a. pale red and sepia	£250
Z162		4a. scarlet	£275
Z163		5a. carmine	£325
Z164		8a. olive-bistre and dull black	£275
Z165		9a. blue	£225
Z166		24a. red-brown	£500

1907. Surch with T **56** (No. 109).

Z167	**9**	1a. on 24a. purple and blue	£225

Kulim

Stamps of SIAM cancelled as Type D inscr "KULIM" (from July 1907).

1887–91. (Nos. 11/18).

Z173	**9**	12a. purple and carmine	£450

1899–1904. (Nos. 67/81).

Z174	**49**	8a. deep green and orange	£450

1905–09. (Nos. 92/105).

Z175	**53**	1a. green and orange	£475
Z176		2a. grey and deep violet	£475
Z177		3a. green	£500
Z178		4a. pale red and sepia	£450
Z179		4a. scarlet	£425
Z180		5a. carmine	£475
Z181		8a. olive-bistre and dull black	£450
Z182		9a. blue	£450

1907. Surch with T **56** (No. 109).

Z184	**9**	1a. on 24a. purple and blue	£450

Stamps of SIAM cancelled as Type C inscr "Kulim" at foot (from Feb 1908).

1887–91. (Nos. 11/18).

Z190	**9**	12a. purple and carmine	£190

1899–1904. (Nos. 67/81).

Z191	**49**	8a. deep green and orange	£180
Z192		10a. ultramarine	£200

1905–09. (Nos. 92/105).

Z196	**53**	4a. pale red and sepia	£190
Z197		4a. scarlet	£190
Z198		5a. carmine	£200
Z199		9a. blue	£200
Z200		24a. red-brown	£450
Z201		1t. bistre and deep blue	£450

1907. Surch with T **56** (No. 109).

Z202	**9**	1a. purple and blue	£200

Langkawi

Stamps of SIAM cancelled as Type D inscr "LANGKAWI" (from Feb 1908).

1899–1904. (Nos. 67/81).

Z208	**49**	8a. deep green and orange	£450
Z209		10a. ultramarine	£450

1905–09. (Nos. 92/105).

Z212	**53**	3a. green	£475
Z213		4a. pale red and sepia	£450
Z215		8a. olive-bistre and dull black	£450

Stamps of SIAM cancelled as Type C inscr "Langkawi" at foot (from Nov 1908).

1887–91. (Nos. 11/18).

Z219	**9**	12a. purple and carmine	£200

1899–1904. (Nos. 67/81).

Z220	**49**	1a. olive-green (Type B)	£225
Z221		8a. green and orange	£190

1905–09. (Nos. 92/105).

Z222	**53**	2a. grey and deep violet	£200
Z223		3a. green	£300
Z224		4a. pale red and sepia	£200
Z225		4a. scarlet	£225
Z226		8a. olive-bistre and dull black	£200
Z228		24a. red-brown	£500
Z229		1t. bistre and deep blue	£500

1907. Surch with T **56** (No. 109).

Z230	**9**	1a. on 24a. purple and blue	£225

Suzerainty over Kedah was transferred by Thailand to Great Britain on 15 July 1909 and the following day stamps of the FEDERATED MALAY STATES were placed on sale in post offices in the state.

A Treaty of Friendship between Great Britain and Kedah was signed on 1 November 1923 and the state joined the Federation of Malaya on 1 February 1948.

Stamps of the Federated Malay States used in Kedah
Alor Star

Cancelled as Type C inscribed "Kedah"

1909–12. (Nos. 29/49).

Z231	**3**	1c. green (Die II)	40·00
Z232		3c. carmine	45·00
Z233		4c. black and rose	48·00
Z234		5c. green and carmine/yellow	£110
Z235		8c. grey-brown and ultramarine	£110
		a. Wmk upright	70·00
Z236		10c. black and purple	85·00
Z237		20c. mauve and black (chalk-surfaced paper)	90·00
Z238		50c. grey-brown and orange-brown (chalk- surfaced paper)	£100
Z239	**4**	$1 grey-green and green	£225

Type F

Cancelled as Type F

1909–12. (No. 34).
Z241   **3**   3c. carmine .... 70·00

Type G

Cancelled as Type G

1909–12. (Nos. 34/47dc).
Z242	**3**	1c. green (Die II)..................................	60·00
Z243		3c. carmine..	60·00
Z244		4c. black and rose.............................	85·00
Z245		8c. grey-brown and ultramarine	85·00
		a. Wmk upright...............................	85·00
Z246		10c. black and purple	90·00
Z247		50c. grey-brown and orange-brown (chalk-surfaced paper)	£100

Kulim

Type H

Cancelled as Type H

1909–12. (Nos. 34/45a).
Z248	**3**	1c. green (Die II)..................................	75·00
Z249		3c. carmine..	65·00
Z250		4c. black and rose.............................	75·00
Z251		5c. green and carmine/*yellow*	£110
Z252		10c. black and purple	£110
Z253		20c. mauve and black (chalk-surfaced paper)	95·00

Type I

Cancelled as Type I

1909–12. (Nos. 34/43d).
Z254		3c. carmine..	65·00
Z255		4c. black and rose.............................	75·00
Z255a		10c. black and purple	£120

Langkawi

Cancelled as Type H inscribed "LANGKAWI"

1909–12. (Nos. 34/49).
Z256	**3**	3c. carmine..	£100
Z256a		5c. green and carmine/*yellow*	£130
Z257		8c. grey-brown and ultramarine (wmk upright)...	£110
Z258	**4**	$1 grey-green and green..................	£275
Z259		$2 green and carmine	£375

Cancelled as Type I inscribed "LANGKAWI"

1909–12. (Nos. 34/43d).
Z260	**3**	1c. green (Die II)..................................	£100
Z261		3c. carmine..	55·00
Z262		10c. black and purple	£110

Kuala Muda

Cancelled as Type B inscribed "KUALA MUDA"

1909–12. (Nos. 29/41bb).
Z263	**3**	1c. green (Die II)..................................	85·00
Z264		3c. carmine..	55·00
Z265		4c. black and rose.............................	95·00
Z266		5c. green and carmine/*yellow*	95·00
Z267		8c. grey-brown and ultramarine (wmk upright)...	90·00

Jitra

The post office in Jitra was opened in 1910.

Type J

Cancelled as Type J

1910–12. (No. 34).
Z268   **3**   3c. carmine .... 90·00

Cancelled as Type I inscribed "JITRA"

1910–12. (Nos. 29/34).
Z269	**3**	1c. green (Die II)..................................	55·00
Z270		3c. carmine..	48·00

Lunas

The post office in Lunas was opened in 1910.

Type K

Cancelled as Type K

1910–12. (No. 34).
Z271   **3**   3c. carmine £120

Cancelled as Type I inscribed "LUNAS"

1910–12. (Nos. 29/36d).
Z272	**3**	1c. green (Die II)..................................	75·00
Z273		3c. carmine..	75·00
Z274		4c. black and rose.............................	£100

Semiling

The post office in Semiling was opened in 1910.

Cancelled as Type I inscribed "SEMILING"

1910–12. (Nos. 29/41b).
Z275	**3**	1c. green (Die II)..................................	65·00
Z276		3c. carmine..	£100
Z277		4c. black and rose.............................	£100
Z278		8c. grey-brown and ultramarine (wmk upright)...	£100

Sungei Patani

The post office in Sungei Patani was opened in 1911.

Cancelled as Type I inscribed "SUNGEI PATANI"

1911–12. (Nos. 29/34).
Z279	**3**	1c. green (Die II)..................................	£120
Z280		3c. carmine..	£120

Yen

The post office in Yen was opened in 1910.

Cancelled as Type I inscribed "YEN"

1910–12. (Nos. 29/34).
Z281	**3**	1c. green (Die II)..................................	£130
Z282		3c. carmine..	£130

PRICES FOR STAMPS ON COVER TO 1945	
Nos. 1/14	from × 15
Nos. 15/23	from × 10
Nos. 24/40	from × 8
Nos. 41/8	from × 12
Nos. 49/51	—
Nos. 52/9	from × 4
Nos. 60/8	from × 3
Nos. 68a/9	from × 4

1 Sheaf of Rice   **2** Malay ploughing

3 Council Chamber, Alor Star

"Feather in hat" flaw (Pl. 1, R. 9/5)

(Recess D.L.R.)

1912 (16 June). Wmk Mult Crown CA (sideways* on 10c. to $5). P 14.
1	**1**	1c. black and green.............................	60	25
		y. Wmk inverted and reversed........	£1000	£450
2		3c. black and red................................	4·50	30
3		4c. rose and grey	10·00	25
4		5c. green and chestnut.......................	2·25	3·00
5		8c. black and ultramarine	4·00	4·75
6	**2**	10c. blue and sepia	2·25	1·00
		a. "Feather in hat"..........................	£100	60·00
		w. Wmk Crown to left of CA	†	—
		y. Wmk Crown to left of CA and reversed..	†	£450
7		20c. black and green.............................	15·00	6·00
		x. Wmk reversed...............................	£350	
8		30c. black and rose	3·50	11·00
9		40c. black and purple	3·50	25·00
		a. "Feather in hat"..........................	£130	
10		50c. brown and blue	9·00	13·00
11	**3**	$1 black and red/*yellow*	16·00	22·00
		w. Wmk Crown to left of CA	85·00	
		x. Wmk reversed...............................	£500	
		y. Wmk Crown to left of CA and reversed..		
12		$2 green and brown..........................	27·00	85·00
13		$3 black and blue/*blue*	£130	£170
		a. "A" of "CA" missing from wmk....	£2000	
14		$5 black and red...............................	£130	£170
1/14 Set of 14			£325	£450
1s/14s Optd "SPECIMEN" Set of 14			£375	

*The normal sideways watermark shows the Crown to right of CA, as seen from the back of the stamp.

The "Feather in hat" variety was present on printings from 1919.

Due to an increase in postal rates 1c. and 4c. stamps of STRAITS SETTLEMENTS were used in Kedah for some months from March 1919.

4c. Short sheaf (R. 10/1)

    (i)   (ii)

DOUBLE AND SINGLE PLATES. (i) Printed from separate plates for frame and centre, with dotted shading extending close to the central sheaf. Soft impression of centre with little clear detail.

(ii) Printed from single plate, with white space around sheaf. Centre more deeply etched with sharp image.

1919 (June)–**21**. New colours and values. Wmk Mult Crown CA (sideways* on 21c., 25c.). P 14.
15	**1**	1c. brown (i) (18.8.19)........................	75	50
		w. Wmk inverted	£160	£200
		y. Wmk inverted and reversed........	†	£550
18		2c. green (i)...	50	30
		x. Wmk reversed...............................	†	£500
19		3c. deep purple (i) (1920)...................	65	4·25
		x. Wmk reversed...............................	£400	
		y. Wmk inverted and reversed........	90·00	£150
20		4c. rose (i)...	11·00	2·25

21		4c. red (ii) (18.8.19)	6·00	1·00
		a. Short sheaf	£225	65·00
		w. Wmk inverted		
22	**2**	21c. mauve and purple (18.8.19)	5·50	70·00
		a. "A" of "CA" missing from wmk	—	£950
		c. "Feather in hat"	£100	
		w. Wmk Crown to left of CA	£225	£300
		ws. Ditto, optd "SPECIMEN"	£150	
		x. Wmk reversed	£400	
		y. Wmk Crown to left of CA and reversed	£425	
23		25c. blue and purple (1921)	1·75	38·00
		a. "A" of "CA" missing from wmk	£700	
		b. "C" of "CA" missing from wmk		
		c. "Feather in hat"	48·00	
		x. Wmk reversed	£400	
15/23	*Set of 6*		13·50	£100
15s/23s	Optd "SPECIMEN" *Set of 6*			£170

*The normal sideways watermark shows Crown to right of CA, *as seen from the back of the stamp.*

ONE

MALAYA-

DOLLAR

BORNEO

EXHIBITION.

(4)   (5)

(Surch by Ribeiro & Co, Penang)

1919 (Mar). Surch as T **4**.

24	**3**	50c. on $2 green and brown	70·00	80·00
		a. "C" of "CENTS" inserted by handstamp (R. 6/4)	£1300	£1500
25		$1 on $3 black and blue/*blue*	20·00	95·00

Nos. 24/5 were surcharged from settings of 30 (5×6).

Two types of centre plate for Type **2** wmkd Mult Script CA:

Type I (Plate 1) (produced by electrotyping)

Type II (Plate 2) (produced by transfer die)

A new common centre plate, 2, was prepared from the original die in 1926. Stamps from Plate 2, produced using a transfer die, show considerably more detail of the ground and have the oxen, ploughman's hat and his clothing much more deeply cut as illustrated in Type II above.

1921–32. Wmk Mult Script CA (sideways* on 10c. to $5). P 14.

26	**1**	1c. brown (ii)	1·50	20
		w. Wmk inverted	†	£500
		y. Wmk inverted and reversed	†	£500
27		2c. dull green (ii) (Type I)	1·50	20
28		3c. deep green (ii)	80	70
		w. Wmk inverted	£450	
29		4c. deep carmine (ii)	5·00	20
		a. Short sheaf	£225	38·00
30	**2**	10c. blue and sepia (I)	2·75	75
		a. "Feather in hat"	60·00	30·00
		bx. Wmk reversed	£425	
		by. Wmk Crown to left of CA and reversed	£170	
		c. Type II (wmk Crown to left of CA) (1927)	65·00	1·25
		cy. Wmk Crown to right of CA and reversed	£550	£375
31		20c. black and yellow-green (I)	10·00	2·00
		a. "Feather in hat"	£160	45·00
32		21c. mauve and purple (I)	2·25	13·00
		a. "Feather in hat"	50·00	
33		25c. blue and purple (I)	2·25	9·00
		a. "Feather in hat"	50·00	
		b. Type II (wmk Crown to left of CA) (1932)	£100	4·00
34		30c. black and rose (I) (1922)	3·75	11·00
		a. "Feather in hat"	70·00	
		b. Type II (wmk Crown to left of CA) (1927)	65·00	3·00
35		40c. black and purple (I)	8·50	65·00
		a. "Feather in hat"	£140	
		bw. Wmk Crown to left of CA (1924)	50·00	55·00
		c. Type II (wmk Crown to left of CA) (1932)	£130	35·00
36		50c. brown and grey-blue (I)	6·00	28·00
		a. "Feather in hat"	95·00	
		bw. Wmk Crown to left of CA (1924)	55·00	27·00
		c. Type II (wmk Crown to left of CA) (1932)	£130	9·50
37	**3**	$1 black and red/*yellow* (1924)	80·00	85·00
		w. Wmk Crown to left of CA	10·00	8·50
38		$2 myrtle and brown	13·00	£100
		w. Wmk Crown to left of CA (1924)	32·00	90·00
39		$3 black and blue/*blue*	80·00	£100
		w. Wmk Crown to left of CA (1924)	£140	90·00

40		$5 black and deep carmine	£110	£160
		w. Wmk Crown to left of CA (1926)	£170	£160
26/40	*Set of 15*		£225	£375
26s/40s	Optd "SPECIMEN" *Set of 15*			£400

*The normal sideways watermark shows Crown to right of CA, *as seen from the back of the stamp.*

Nos. 26/40 were produced by De La Rue using the "wet" method of recess-printing during which the stamps contracted when they were dried before gumming. From 1933 the firm adopted the "dry" method, using pre-gummed paper, with the result that stamps were up to 0.5 mm larger in size. Of the low values as Type **1** in this series only the 2c. was still current when the "dry" method was introduced.

Stamps as Type **1** can be found perforated either comb or line. The 1c. and 4c. come comb only, the 3c. line only and the 2c. either way.

Examples of Nos. 37/40 are known with part strikes of a forged Sungei Patang postmark dated "14 JY 1920".

For the 2c. Type II see No. 69.

OVERPRINT SETTINGS FOR NOS. 41/51. The low values in Type **1** were overprinted using Setting II as detailed under Straits Settlements. The three listed constant varieties from the original typeset block of 12 occur in the same positions for these Kedah stamps as does the No Stop variety from R. 1/5 of the left pane.

For the higher values in Type **2**, which were in sheets of 60 (5×12), a further setting was prepared using the first four vertical rows of the typeset block with each horizontal row completed by a single random impression of the overprint. This means that, in addition to their positions in the truncated typeset block, the Oval last "O" additionally occurs on R. 11/5 and the Raised stop on R. 5/5 of the sheet. In this setting, as for the low values, "BORNEO" was 14 mm long.

Further supplies were subsequently required of the 21, 25 and 50c. values and these were produced using a completely different setting of 20 (5×4), applied three times to each sheet, on which "BORNEO" was 15–15½ mm long. The small "Y" in "MALAYA" occurs on R. 4/2, 8/2 and 12/2.

1922 (Apr). Malaya-Borneo Exhibition, Singapore. Optd as T **5** at Singapore.

I. "BORNEO" 14 mm long

(a) Wmk Mult Crown CA (Nos. 10, 18 and 22/3)

41	**1**	2c. green (ii)	5·50	29·00
		b. Oval last "O" in "BORNEO"	11·00	55·00
		c. Raised stop after "EXHIBITION"	11·00	55·00
		d. Small second "A" in "MALAYA"	11·00	55·00
		f. No stop	48·00	
42	**2**	21c. mauve and purple	45·00	85·00
		b. Oval last "O" in "BORNEO"	75·00	£140
		c. Raised stop after "EXHIBITION"	75·00	£140
		d. "Feather in hat"	£350	
43		25c. blue and purple	45·00	85·00
		a. Opt inverted	£1600	
		b. Oval last "O" in "BORNEO"	75·00	£140
		c. Raised stop after "EXHIBITION"	75·00	£140
		d. "Feather in hat"	£350	
44		50c. brown and blue	45·00	£100
		b. Oval last "O" in "BORNEO"	75·00	£160
		c. Raised stop after "EXHIBITION"	75·00	£160
		d. "Feather in hat"	£350	

(b) Wmk Mult Script CA (Nos. 26 and 28/30)

45	**1**	1c. brown (ii)	7·50	35·00
		b. Oval last "O" in "BORNEO"	15·00	60·00
		c. Raised stop after "EXHIBITION"	15·00	60·00
		d. Small second "A" in "MALAYA"	15·00	60·00
		f. No stop	65·00	
46		3c. deep purple (ii)	6·00	50·00
		b. Oval last "O" in "BORNEO"	12·00	75·00
		c. Raised stop after "EXHIBITION"	12·00	75·00
		d. Small second "A" in "MALAYA"	12·00	75·00
		f. No stop	50·00	
47		4c. deep carmine (ii)	6·50	25·00
		a. Short sheaf	£250	
		b. Oval last "O" in "BORNEO"	13·00	45·00
		c. Raised stop after "EXHIBITION"	13·00	45·00
		d. Small second "A" in "MALAYA"	13·00	45·00
		f. No stop	50·00	
48	**2**	10c. blue and sepia (I)	15·00	50·00
		b. Oval last "O" in "BORNEO"	26·00	75·00
		c. Raised stop after "EXHIBITION"	26·00	75·00
		d. "Feather in hat"	£170	
41/8	*Set of 8*		£160	£400

II. "BORNEO" 15–15½ mm long. Wmk Mult Crown CA (Nos. 10 and 22/3)

49	**2**	21c. mauve and purple	32·00	£110
		a. Small "Y" in "MALAYA"	90·00	
		b. "Feather in hat"	£275	
50		25c. blue and purple	32·00	£130
		a. Small "Y" in "MALAYA"	90·00	
		b. "Feather in hat"	£275	
51		50c. brown and blue	75·00	£180
		a. Small "Y" in "MALAYA"	£170	
		b. "Feather in hat"	£425	
49/51	*Set of 3*		£120	£375

Examples of all values are known with part strikes of the forged postmark mentioned after Nos. 26/40.

1922–40. New colours, etc. Wmk Mult Script CA (sideways* on 12, 35c.). P 14.

52	**1**	1c. black (ii) (Type I)	1·00	10
53		3c. green (ii) (1924)	2·25	90
54		4c. violet (ii) (1926)	1·00	10
		a. Short sheaf	85·00	13·00
55		5c. yellow (ii)	3·25	10
		w. Wmk inverted	90·00	£110
		x. Wmk reversed	†	£425
		y. Wmk inverted and reversed	†	£425
56		6c. carmine (ii) (1926)	3·25	65
		a. Carmine-red (1940)	12·00	48·00
57		8c. grey-black (ii) (10.36)	24·00	10
58	**2**	12c. black and indigo (II) (1926)	12·00	3·50
59		35c. purple (II) (1926)	24·00	48·00
52/9	*Set of 8*		60·00	48·00
52s/9s	Optd or Perf (8c.) "SPECIMEN" *Set of 8*			£450

*The normal sideways watermark shows Crown to left of CA, *as seen from the back of the stamp.*

With the exception of the 6c. and 8c. the printing plates for the Type **1** values listed above were, as for the previous issue, produced by electrotyping with the face values added to the plates by pantograph. The plates for the 6c. and 8c. values were constructed by the more modern method of using a transfer die to enter each impression.

Printings after November 1933 were normally produced by the "dry" method as described beneath Nos. 26/40. There were late "wet" printings of the 1c. (No. 68a) and 2c. (No. 27) in August 1938. The 3c. only exists from a "wet" printing, the 6c. (No. 56a) and 8c. from dry printings and the remainder from either method.

Stamps as Type **1** can be found perforated either comb or line. The 3c. and 6c. (No. 56) come comb only, the 6c. (No. 56a) and 8c. line only and the 1, 4 and 5c. either way.

For the 1c. Type II see No. 68a.

6 Sultan Abdul Hamid Halimshah

(Recess Waterlow)

1937 (30 June). Wmk Mult Script CA. P 12½.

60	**6**	10c. ultramarine and sepia	8·00	2·25
61		12c. black and violet	70·00	3·25
		a. "A" of "CA" missing from wmk	£1700	
62		25c. ultramarine and purple	16·00	5·00
63		30c. green and scarlet	16·00	10·00
64		40c. black and purple	9·00	18·00
65		50c. brown and blue	16·00	6·00
66		$1 black and green	8·00	10·00
67		$2 brown and green	£130	75·00
68		$5 black and scarlet	42·00	£180
60/8	*Set of 9*		£275	£275
60s/8s	Perf "SPECIMEN" *Set of 9*			£325

I   II   I   II

1938 (May)–**40**. As Nos. 52 and 27, but face values redrawn as Types II.

68a	**1**	1c. black	£160	1·75
69		2c. bright green (1940)	£350	5·50

1c. Type II. Figures "1" have square-cut corners instead of rounded, and larger top serif. Larger "C". Line perf. Produced from a new electrotyped Plate 2 with different engraved face values. Printings exist from either the "wet" or "dry" methods.

2c. Type II. Figures "2" have circular instead of oval drops and the letters "c" are thin and tall instead of thick and rounded. Produced from a new plate, made from a transfer die, and printed by the "dry" method.

1948 (1 Dec). Royal Silver Wedding. As Nos. 112/13 of Antigua.

70		10c. violet	20	40
71		$5 carmine	28·00	50·00

1949 (10 Oct). 75th Anniv of UPU. As Nos. 114/17 of Antigua.

72		10c. purple	25	1·25
73		10c. deep blue	2·00	1·50
74		25c. orange	65	5·00
75		50c. blue-black	1·00	6·50
		a. "A" of "CA" missing from watermark.	£1000	
72/5	*Set of 4*		3·50	13·00

7 Sheaf of Rice   **8** Sultan Badlishah

1950 (1 June)–**55**. Wmk Mult Script CA. Chalk-surfaced paper. P 17½×18.

76	**7**	1c. black	1·00	30
77		2c. orange	50	15
78		3c. green	2·00	1·00
79		4c. brown	75	10
79a		5c. bright purple (1.9.52)	6·00	3·00
		ab. *Bright mauve* (24.9.53)	6·00	1·00
80		6c. grey	70	15
81		8c. scarlet	4·00	5·00
81a		8c. green (1.9.52)	7·50	3·75
		ab. *Deep green* (24.9.53)	27·00	26·00
82		10c. magenta	70	10
82a		12c. scarlet (1.9.52)	7·50	3·00
83		15c. ultramarine	6·00	35
84		20c. black and green	6·00	2·50
84a		20c. bright blue (1.9.52)	2·50	10
85	**8**	25c. purple and orange	1·50	30
85a		30c. scarlet and purple (4.9.55)	6·00	1·25
85b		35c. scarlet and purple (1.9.52)	8·00	1·50
86		40c. red and purple	8·50	10·00
87		50c. black and blue	6·50	35
88		$1 blue and purple	8·50	11·00
89		$2 green and scarlet	30·00	55·00
90		$5 green and brown	70·00	95·00
76/90	*Set of 21*		£160	£170

1953 (2 June). Coronation. As No. 120 of Antigua.

91		10c. black and reddish purple	2·50	60

9 Copra   **10** Pineapples

11 Ricefield   **12** Alwi Mosque, Kangar

13 East Coast Railway

14 Tiger

15 Fishing Prau

16 Aborigines with Blowpipes

17 Government Offices   **18** Bersilat

19 Weaving

(Recess D.L.R.)

1957. Inset portrait of Sultan Badlishah. W w **12**. P 13×12½ (1c. to 8c.), 12½×13 (10c., 20c.), 13×11½-12½ (50c.), 11½-12½×13 ($2, $5) or 13½ ($1).

92	**9**	1c. black (21.8)	10	60
93	**10**	2c. orange-red (25.7)	1·00	2·75
94	**11**	4c. sepia (21.8)	30	1·50
95	**12**	5c. carmine-lake (21.8)	30	1·25
96	**13**	8c. myrtle-green (21.8)	2·50	8·00
97	**14**	10c. deep brown (4.8)	80	40
98	**15**	20c. blue (26.6)	2·75	3·25
99	**16**	50c. black and blue (25.7)	3·75	4·25
100	**17**	$1 ultramarine and reddish purple (25.7)	15·00	25·00
101	**18**	$2 bronze-green and scarlet (21.8)	45·00	55·00
102	**19**	$5 brown and bronze-green (26.6)	60·00	60·00
92/102		Set of 11	£120	£140

The 6, 12, 25 and 30c. values used with this issue were Nos. 1/4 of Malayan Federation.

For a description of the compound perforations on Nos. 99, 101 and 102 see below Federation of Malaya No. 4. On horizontal stamps the perf 11½ section is at the left.

20 Sultan Abdul Halim Mu'Adzam Shah   **21** Sultan Abdul Halim Shah

(Photo Harrison)

1959 (20 Feb). Installation of the Sultan. W w **12**. P 14×14½.

103	**20**	10c. multicoloured	1·00	10

1959 (1 July)**–62**. As Nos. 92/102 but with inset portrait of Sultan Abdul Halim Shah as in T **21**.

104	**21**	1c. black	10	75
105	**9**	2c. orange-red	10	2·00
106	**11**	4c. sepia	10	75
107	**12**	5c. carmine-lake	10	10
108	**13**	8c. myrtle-green	3·50	3·50
109	**14**	10c. deep brown	1·00	10
109a		10c. deep maroon (19.12.61)	18·00	1·50
110	**15**	20c. blue	1·00	1·00
111	**16**	50c. black and blue (P 12½)	30	1·75
		a. Perf 12½×13 (14.6.60)	30	60
112	**17**	$1 ultramarine and reddish purple	6·00	2·25
113	**18**	$2 bronze-green and scarlet	13·00	24·00
114	**19**	$5 brown and bronze-green (P 12½)	16·00	20·00
		a. Perf 13×12½ (26.11.62)	45·00	27·00
104/14		Set of 12	50·00	50·00

On Nos. 113/14 the perf 11½ section of the compound perforation is at the right of the stamp.

22 *Vanda hookeriana*

1965 (15 Nov). As Nos. 166/72 of Johore but with inset portrait of Sultan Abdul Halim Shah as in T **22**. W w **13** (upright).

115		1c. multicoloured	10	2·00
		a. Black omitted (orchid's name and part of flower)	£250	
116		2c. multicoloured	10	2·50
		b. Yellow (flower) omitted	£275	
		c. Dark green omitted	£325	
117		5c. multicoloured	10	55
		a. Black (country name and head) omitted	£325	
		c. Red omitted	£130	
118		6c. multicoloured	15	60
119		10c. multicoloured	30	40
		a. Red omitted	£800	
		b. Green (leaves) omitted	£1000	
120		15c. multicoloured	1·50	10
121		20c. multicoloured	2·00	1·75
		a. Bright purple (blooms) omitted	£550	
		b. Yellow (leaves) omitted	75·00	
115/21		Set of 7	3·75	7·00

The 1c. to 15c. exist with PVA gum as well as gum arabic.

The 6c. value exists with black (country name, Arms and head) omitted and is listed under Sarawak where it was issued.

The higher values used with this issue were Nos. 20/27 of Malaysia (National Issues).

1970 (27 May). As Nos. 115 and 119 but W w **13** (sideways).

122	**22**	1c. multicoloured	2·50	9·00
123	**–**	10c. multicoloured	1·00	4·50

KELANTAN

The Thai monarchy exercised suzerainty over Kelantan and the other northern states of the Malay peninsula from the 16th century onwards.

The first Siamese post office in Kelantan opened at Kota Bharu in 1895. It appears that in the early years this office only accepted letters franked with stamps for delivery within Kelantan.

The initial cancellation, of which no complete example has been discovered, showed Thai characters only. Partial examples have been reported on the 1887–91 8a. and 1896 4a. on 12a.

The operations of the Duff Development Company in Kelantan from 1903 led to a considerable expansion of the postal service based on the company's river steamers. A further post office opened at Batu Mengkebang in 1908, but may have been preceded by manuscript endorsements of "B.M." and date known from early 1907 onwards.

Type E. Double ring. English at top and bottom

For other stamps and postmark types, See under Kedah.

Kota Bharu

Stamps of SIAM cancelled as Type B inscr "KALANTAN" (from March 1898).

1887–91. (Nos. 11/18).

Z301	**9**	2a. green and carmine	£140
Z302		3a. green and blue	£150
Z303		4a. green and brown	£150
Z304		8a. green and yellow	£150
Z305		12a. purple and carmine	£130
Z306		24a. purple and blue	£140

1894. Surch as T **27** with variation of English figures as T **33** (Nos. 37/44).

Z307	**9**	2a. on 64a. purple and brown	£200

1894–95. Surch as T **35** with variation of English figures as T **36** (Nos. 46/50).

Z308	**9**	1a. on 64a. purple and brown	£170

1896. Surch as T **39** (Siamese) and T **40** (English) (No. 51).

Z309	**9**	4a. on 12a. purple and carmine	£170

1897. Surch as T **39** (Siamese) and T **41** (English) (No. 52).

Z310	**9**	4a. on 12a. purple and carmine	£170

1898–99. Surch as T **42** with variation of English section as T **46** (Nos. 53/62).

Z311	**9**	3a. on 12a. (11½–11¾ mm long)	£180
Z312		4a. on 12a. purple and carmine (8 mm long)	£170

1899–1904. (Nos. 67/81).

Z313	**49**	1a. olive-green (wide Siamese characters in face value)	£140
Z314		2a. grass-green	£130
Z315		2a. scarlet and pale blue	£130
Z316		3a. red and blue	£150
Z317		4a. carmine	£130
Z318		4a. chocolate and pink	£150
Z319		8a. deep green and orange	£130
Z320		10a. ultramarine	£140
Z321		12a. brown-purple and carmine	£130
Z322		64a. brown-purple and chestnut	£325

1905–09. (Nos. 92/105).

Z323	**53**	2a. green and orange	£120
Z324		2a. grey and deep violet	£140
Z325		4a. pale red and sepia	£130
Z326		4a. scarlet	£140
Z327		5a. carmine	£160
Z328		8a. olive-bistre and dull black	£120
Z329		12a. blue	£160
Z330		24a. red-brown	£400
Z331		1t. bistre and deep blue	£400

1907. Surch with T **56** (No. 109).

Z332	**9**	1a. on 24a. purple and blue	£170

Stamps of SIAM cancelled as Type E inscr "Kota Bahru/Kelantan" (from July 1908).

1887–91. (Nos. 11/18).

Z333	**9**	12a. purple and carmine	£130
Z334		24a. purple and blue	£170

1899–1904. (Nos. 67/81).

Z335	**49**	8a. deep green and orange	£140
Z336		64a. brown-purple and chestnut	£200

1905–09. (Nos. 92/105).

Z337	**53**	1a. green and orange	£140
Z338		2a. grey and deep violet	£140
Z339		2a. pale yellow-green	£140
Z340		4a. pale red and sepia	£140
Z341		4a. scarlet	£140
Z342		8a. olive-bistre and dull black	£140
Z343		9a. blue	£140
Z344		18a. red-brown	£225

1907. Surch with T **56** (No. 109).

Z345	**9**	1a. on 24a. purple and blue	£140

1908. Surch as T **59** (Nos. 110/12).

Z346	**9**	2a. on 24a. purple and blue	£200
Z347	**53**	4a. on 5a. carmine	£275
Z348	**49**	9a. on 10a. ultramarine	£150

Batu Mengkebang

Stamps of SIAM cancelled as Type E inscr "Batu Menkebang/Kelantan" (from July 1908).

1887–91. (Nos. 11/18).

Z349	**9**	12a. purple and carmine	£275
Z349a		24a. purple and blue	£475

1899–1904. (Nos. 67/81).

Z350	**49**	8a. deep green and orange	£275

1905–09. (Nos. 92/105).

Z351	**53**	2a. green and orange	£250
Z352		2a. grey and deep violet	£250
Z353		2a. pale yellow-green	£275
Z354		4a. pale red and sepia	£275
Z355		4a. scarlet	£250
Z356		8a. olive-bistre and dull black	£200
Z357		9a. blue	£190
Z358		12a. blue	£325
Z359		24a. red-brown	£450
Z360		1t. bistre and deep blue	£475

1907. Surch with T **56** (No. 109).

Z361	**9**	1a. on 24a. purple and blue	£200

1908. Surch as T **59** (Nos. 110/12).

Z362	**49**	9a. on 10a. ultramarine	£325

Suzerainty over Kelantan was transferred by Thailand to Great Britain on 15 July 1909.

Siamese stamps were withdrawn from sale and replaced the following day by stamps of the Federated Malay States.

Stamps of the Federated Malay States used in Kelantan
Kota Bharu

Type M

Cancelled as Type E

1909–11. (Nos. 29/49).

Z367	**3**	1c. green (Die II)	90·00
Z368		3c. carmine	75·00
Z369		4c. black and rose	90·00
Z370		8c. grey-brown and ultramarine	80·00
		a. Wmk upright	95·00
Z373	**4**	$2 green and carmine	£350

Cancelled as Type M

1909–11. (Nos. 29/45a).

Z375	**3**	1c. green (Die II)	70·00
Z376		3c. carmine	70·00
Z377		4c. black and rose	70·00
Z378		5c. green and carmine/yellow	£110
Z379		8c. grey-brown and ultramarine	90·00
		a. Wmk upright	£100
Z380		10c. black and purple	£120
Z381		20c. mauve and black (chalk-surfaced paper)	£120

Batu Menkebang

Cancelled as Type E inscribed "Batu Menkebang"

1909–11. (Nos. 34/43d).

Z385	**3**	3c. carmine	£130
Z386		5c. green and carmine/yellow	£150
Z387		10c. black and purple	£150

Cancelled as Type M inscribed "BATU MENKEBANG" at top

1909–11. (Nos. 29/45a).

Z391	**3**	1c. green (Die II)	95·00
Z392		3c. carmine	70·00
Z393		4c. black and rose	85·00
Z394		5c. green and carmine/yellow	£140
Z395		8c. grey-brown and ultramarine (wmk upright)	£110
Z396		20c. mauve and black (chalk-surfaced paper)	£140

Federated Malay States stamps were replaced by those of Kelantan in January 1911.

A British adviser was appointed to Kelantan in 1923 and the state joined the Federation of Malaya on 1 February 1948.

PRICES FOR STAMPS ON COVER TO 1945	
Nos. 1/11	*from* × 30
No. 12	—
Nos. 14/23	*from* × 30
Nos. 30/8	*from* × 15
Nos. 39/a	*from* × 10
Nos. 40/8	*from* × 30
Nos. 49/52	*from* × 20
No. 53	*from* × 3
No. 54	—

MALAYA BORNEO EXHIBITION

1   (**2**)

1911 (Jan)–**15**. Wmk Mult Crown CA. Ordinary paper (1c. to 10c.) or chalk-surfaced paper (30c. to $25). P 14.

1	**1**	1c. yellow-green	7·00	1·00
		a. Blue-green	6·00	30
2		3c. red	4·25	15
3		4c. black and red	1·50	15
4		5c. green and red/*yellow*	10·00	2·00
		w. Wmk inverted	†	£750
5		8c. ultramarine	5·50	1·00
6		10c. black and mauve	30·00	75
7		30c. dull purple and red	11·00	2·00
		a. Purple and carmine	27·00	14·00
8		50c. black and orange	8·50	2·00
9		$1 green and emerald	50·00	35·00
9a		$1 green and brown (5.15)	75·00	2·00
10		$2 green and carmine	1·50	2·25
11		$5 green and blue	4·00	2·50
12		$25 green and orange	50·00	£120
1/12 *Set of 13*			£225	£150
1s/12s Optd "SPECIMEN" *Set of 13*			£275	

1921 (5 May)–**28**. Wmk Mult Script CA. Ordinary paper (1c. to 10c.) or chalk-surfaced paper (30c. to $1). P 14.

14	**1**	1c. dull green (7.21)	4·25	60
15		1c. black (24.2.23)	1·00	50
16		2c. brown (29.7.22)	7·50	3·75
16a		2c. green (24.7.26)	5·50	40
16b		3c. brown (5.3.27)	5·00	1·00
		ba. "C" of "CA" missing from wmk		
17		4c. black and red (15.7.22)	3·50	10
18		5c. green and red/*pale yellow* (12.22)	1·75	10
19		6c. claret (29.7.22)	3·50	1·00
19a		6c. scarlet (26.5.28)	4·00	1·25
20		10c. black and mauve (24.7.26)	3·00	10
21		30c. purple and carmine (24.7.26)	4·00	4·00
22		50c. black and orange (21.3.25)	6·50	45·00
23		$1 green and brown (9.2.24)	32·00	90·00
14/23 *Set of 13*			70·00	£130
14s/23s Optd "SPECIMEN" *Set of 13*			£400	

Examples of Nos. 22/3 are known showing part strikes of a forged Kota Bharu postmark dated "27 JUL 11".

For the 4c., 5c. and 6c. surcharged, see issues under "Japanese Occupation".

OVERPRINT SETTINGS FOR NOS. 30/8. All values were overprinted using a triplet of three slightly different types. It is not known if this was applied to the sheets three stamps at a time or if a forme to overprint a pane of 60 was constructed from it.

On the normal setting "MALAYA" is 13 mm long. The 1c. and 5c. only are also known with "MALAYA" 14 mm from a different triplet setting. It has been suggested that this was a trial overprint which was subsequently included in postal stocks.

1922 (31 Mar). Malaya-Borneo Exhibition, Singapore. Optd with T **2** ("MALAYA" 13 *mm* long) by Govt Survey Office, Kota Bharu.

(a) Wmk Mult Crown CA

30	**1**	4c. black and red	7·00	50·00
		a. Opt double	£4250	
31		5c. green and red/*pale yellow*	7·00	50·00
		a. "MALAYA" 14 mm long	£400	
32		30c. dull purple and red	7·00	80·00
33		50c. black and orange	10·00	85·00
34		$1 green and brown	32·00	£110
35		$2 green and carmine	£100	£275
36		$5 green and blue	£275	£500

(b) Wmk Mult Script CA

37	**1**	1c. green	4·50	55·00
		a. Opt double	£4250	
		b "MALAYA" 14 mm. long	£750	
38		10c. black and mauve	7·50	75·00
30/8 *Set of 9*			£400	£1100

Nos. 30a and 37a show all three lines of the overprint double.

Examples of all values are known showing part strikes of the forged postmark mentioned below Nos. 14/23.

3 Sultan Ismail

4 Sultan Ismail

(Recess Harrison (No. 39) or D.L.R. (No. 39a))

1928–35. Wmk Mult Script CA. P 12.

39	**3**	$1 blue	15·00	90·00
		a. Perf 14 (1935)	75·00	50·00
		s. Perf "SPECIMEN"	£130	

(Recess B.W.)

1937 (July)–**40**. Wmk Mult Script CA. P 12.

40	**4**	1c. grey-olive and yellow	2·75	55
41		2c. green	9·00	20
42		4c. scarlet	9·00	1·00
43		5c. red-brown	4·75	10
44		6c. lake (10.37)	26·00	15·00
45		8c. grey-olive	4·75	10
46		10c. purple (10.37)	40·00	2·75
47		12c. blue	8·50	8·00
48		25c. vermilion and violet	9·00	4·25
49		30c. violet and scarlet (10.37)	65·00	26·00
50		40c. orange and blue-green	12·00	48·00
51		50c. grey-olive and orange (10.37)	90·00	10·00
52		$1 violet and blue-green (10.37)	65·00	16·00
53		$2 red-brown and scarlet (3.40)	£425	£250
54		$5 vermilion and lake (3.40)	£950	£950
40/54 *Set of 15*			£1600	£1200
40s/54s Perf "SPECIMEN" *Set of 15*			£950	

For above issue surcharged see issues under "Japanese Occupation".

1948 (1 Dec). Royal Silver Wedding. As Nos. 112/13 of Antigua.

55		10c. violet	75	2·75
56		$5 carmine	30·00	50·00

1949 (10 Oct). 75th Anniv of UPU. As Nos. 114/17 of Antigua.

57		10c. purple	25	30
58		15c. deep blue	2·25	4·00
59		25c. orange	40	8·00
60		50c. blue-black	70	3·50
57/60 *Set of 4*			3·25	14·00

Due to the exhaustion of certain B.M.A. values PERAK 2c., 3c., 4c., 6c., 15c., 20c. black and green, 25c., 40c. and 50c. stamps were used in Kelantan from 27 November 1950 until the issue of Nos. 61/81.

5 Sultan Ibrahim

Normal

No. 62a Tiny stop (R. 1/2)

1951 (11 July)–**55**. Chalk-surfaced paper. Wmk Mult Script CA. P 17½×18.

61	**5**	1c. black	50	30
62		2c. orange	1·25	35
		a. Tiny stop	32·00	42·00
		b. Orange-yellow (11.5.55)	15·00	6·00
63		3c. green	6·50	1·25
64		4c. brown	2·00	15
65		5c. bright purple (1.9.52)	1·50	50
		a. Bright mauve (9.12.53)	3·75	1·00
66		6c. grey	75	20
67		8c. scarlet	6·00	4·75
68		8c. green (1.9.52)	7·00	1·75
69		10c. magenta	65	10
70		12c. scarlet (1.9.52)	7·00	4·25
71		15c. ultramarine	9·00	60
72		20c. black and green	7·00	15·00
73		20c. bright blue (1.9.52)	2·00	25
74		25c. purple and orange	2·00	55
75		30c. scarlet and purple (4.9.55)	1·50	6·50
76		35c. scarlet and purple (1.9.52)	2·25	4·00
77		40c. red and purple	17·00	27·00
78		50c. black and blue	8·00	40
79		$1 blue and purple	9·50	18·00
80		$2 green and scarlet	50·00	70·00
81		$5 green and brown	75·00	85·00
		a. Green and sepia (8.12.53)	£150	£150
61/81 *Set of 21*			£200	£200

1953 (2 June). Coronation. As No. 120 of Antigua.

82		10c. black and reddish purple	1·75	1·40

1957 (26 June)–**63**. As Nos. 92/102 of Kedah but with inset portrait of Sultan Ibrahim.

83	**9**	1c. black (21.8.57)	10	30
84	**10**	2c. orange-red (25.7.57)	75	1·50
		a. Red-orange (17.11.59)	18·00	9·00
85	**11**	4c. sepia (21.8.57)	40	10
86	**12**	5c. carmine-lake (21.8.57)	40	10
87	**13**	8c. myrtle-green (21.8.57)	4·00	4·50
88	**14**	10c. deep brown (4.8.57)	3·00	10
89		10c. deep maroon (19.4.61)	21·00	15·00
90	**15**	20c. blue	2·50	30
91	**16**	50c. black and blue (P 12½) (25.7.57)	50	2·25
		a. Perf 12½×13 (28.6.60)	1·00	1·50
92	**17**	$1 ultramarine and reddish purple (25.7.57)	13·00	1·50
93	**18**	$2 bronze-green and scarlet (P 12½) (21.8.57)	22·00	12·00
		a. Perf 13×12½ (9.4.63)	15·00	48·00
94	**19**	$5 brown and bronze-green (P 12½)	29·00	12·00
		a. Perf 13×12½ (13.8.63)	26·00	55·00
83/94 *Set of 12*			75·00	42·00

The 6, 12, 25 and 30c. values used with this issue were Nos. 1/4 of Malayan Federation.

6 Sultan Yahya Petra and Crest of Kelantan

(Photo Harrison)

1961 (17 July). Coronation of the Sultan. W w **12**. P 15×14.

95	**6**	10c. multicoloured	60	1·50

---

7 Sultan Yahya Petra

8 *Vanda hookeriana*

(Recess D.L.R.)

1961–63. As Nos. 92/8 of Kedah but with inset portrait of Sultan Yahya Petra as in T **7**. W w **13**. P 12½×13 (vert) or 13×12½ (horiz).

96		1c. black (1.3.62)	25	3·00
97		2c. orange-red (1.3.62)	2·25	4·00
98		4c. sepia (1.3.62)	3·00	3·25
99		5c. carmine-lake (1.3.62)	3·00	1·00
100		8c. myrtle-green (1.3.62)	20·00	17·00
		a. Deep green (15.1.63)	28·00	18·00
101		10c. deep maroon (2.12.61)	1·75	60
102		20c. blue (1.3.62)	12·00	3·25
96/102 *Set of 7*			38·00	28·00

1965 (15 Nov). As Nos. 166/72 of Johore but with inset portrait of Sultan Yahya Petra as in T **8**. W w **13** (upright).

103		1c. multicoloured	10	1·75
		b. Magenta omitted	£400	
104		2c. multicoloured	10	1·75
105		5c. multicoloured	15	30
106		6c. multicoloured	70	3·00
107		10c. multicoloured	30	25
		a. Red omitted	£225	
108		15c. multicoloured	1·50	25
109		20c. multicoloured	2·75	3·50
		a. Bright purple (blooms) omitted	£400	
		b. Yellow (leaves) omitted	£100	
103/9 *Set of 7*			5·00	9·75

The 5c. and 10c. exist with PVA as well as gum arabic.

A used example of No. 104 has been reported with yellow omitted.

The higher values used with this issue were Nos. 20/27 of Malaysia (National Issues).

1970 (20 Nov). As Nos. 103 and 107 but W w **13** (sideways).

110	**8**	1c. multicoloured	1·50	10·00
111	**–**	10c. multicoloured	3·75	7·00

STAMP BOOKLETS

1927 (June). Black on white (No. SB1) or black on grey (No. SB2) covers. Stapled.

SB1	36c. booklet containing 36×1c. (No. 15) in blocks of 6		£3750
SB2	96c. booklet containing 24×4c. (No. 17) in blocks of 6		£3750

1927 (Dec). Black on white (No. SB3) or on grey (No. SB4) covers. Stapled.

SB3	40c. booklet containing 40×1c. (No. 15) in blocks of 10		£3750
SB4	80c. booklet containing 20×4c. (No. 17) in blocks of 10		£3750

MALACCA

One of the Straits Settlements which joined the Federation of Malaya on 1 February 1948.

1948 (1 Dec). Royal Silver Wedding. As Nos. 112/13 of Antigua.

1		10c. violet	30	1·75
2		$5 brown	35·00	50·00

1949 (1 Mar)–**52**. As T **58** of Straits Settlements, but inscr "MALACCA" at foot. Wmk Mult Script CA. Chalk-surfaced paper. P 17½×18.

3		1c. black	30	70
4		2c. orange	80	45
5		3c. green	30	1·75
6		4c. brown	30	10
6a		5c. bright purple (1.9.52)	6·50	1·50
7		6c. grey	75	85
8		8c. scarlet	75	7·00
8a		8c. green (1.9.52)	9·00	7·50
9		10c. purple	30	10
9a		12c. scarlet (1.9.52)	9·00	17·00
10		15c. ultramarine	3·50	60
11		20c. black and green	1·00	8·50
11a		20c. bright blue (1.9.52)	11·00	3·00
12		25c. purple and orange	1·00	70
12a		35c. scarlet and purple (1.9.52)	12·00	3·00
13		40c. red and purple	1·50	11·00
14		50c. black and blue	1·50	1·25
15		$1 blue and purple	21·00	35·00
16		$2 green and scarlet	32·00	35·00
17		$5 green and brown	65·00	60·00
3/17 *Set of 15*			£150	£160

1949 (10 Oct). 75th Anniv of UPU. As Nos. 114/17 of Antigua.

18		10c. purple	30	50
19		15c. deep blue	2·00	3·25
20		25c. orange	40	13·00
21		50c. blue-black	60	4·75
18/21 *Set of 4*			3·00	19·00

1953. Coronation. As No. 120 of Antigua.

22		10c. black and reddish purple	1·75	1·50

1 Queen Elizabeth II

2 Copra

1954 (9 June)–**57**. Chalk-surfaced paper. Wmk Mult Script CA.
P 17½×18.

23	**1**	1c. black (27.4.55)	10	60
24		2c. yellow-orange (27.4.55)	30	1·25
25		4c. brown	2·00	10
		a. Pale brown (24.4.57)	20·00	4·75
26		5c. bright purple (12.7.54)	30	2·50
27		6c. grey	10	40
28		8c. green (5.1.55)	40	2·75
29		10c. brown-purple (5.1.55)	2·25	10
		a. Reddish purple (27.3.57)	11·00	2·25
30		12c. rose-red (5.1.55)	30	3·00
31		20c. bright blue (5.1.55)	30	1·25
32		25c. brown-purple and yellow-orange (27.4.55)	30	1·50
33		30c. rose-red and brown-purple (5.9.55)	30	30
34		35c. rose-red and brown-purple (8.9.54)	30	1·50
35		50c. black and bright blue (5.1.55)	5·00	2·50
36		$1 bright blue and brown-purple (8.9.54)	7·00	17·00
37		$2 emerald and scarlet (27.4.55)	26·00	50·00
38		$5 emerald and brown (27.4.55)	26·00	55·00
23/38		Set of 16	60·00	£120

1957. As Nos. 92/102 of Kedah but with inset portrait of Queen Elizabeth II.

39	**9**	1c. black (21.8)	10	50
40	**10**	2c. orange-red (25.7)	10	50
41	**11**	4c. sepia (21.8)	50	10
42	**12**	5c. carmine-lake (21.8)	50	10
43	**13**	8c. myrtle-green (21.8)	2·75	2·50
44	**14**	10c. deep brown (4.8)	40	10
45	**15**	20c. blue (26.6)	2·75	2·25
46	**16**	50c. black and blue (25.7)	1·50	2·00
47	**17**	$1 ultramarine and reddish purple (25.7)	10·00	9·00
48	**18**	$2 bronze-green and scarlet (21.8)	27·00	48·00
49	**19**	$5 brown and bronze-green (26.6)	29·00	50·00
39/49		Set of 11	65·00	£100

The 6, 12, 25 and 30c. values used with this issue were Nos. 1/4 of Malayan Federation.

(Recess D.L.R.)

1960 (15 Mar)–**62**. As Nos. 39/49, but with inset picture of Melaka tree and Pelandok (mouse deer) as in T **2**. W w **12**. P 13×12½ (1c. to 8c., $2, $5), 12½×13 (10c. to 50c.) or 13½ ($1).

50		1c. black	10	30
51		2c. orange-red	10	65
52		4c. sepia	10	10
53		5c. carmine-lake	10	10
54		8c. myrtle-green	5·00	3·00
55		10c. deep maroon	40	10
56		20c. blue	3·00	80
57		50c. black and blue	2·25	1·00
		a. Black and ultramarine (9.1.62)	8·00	2·00
58		$1 ultramarine and reddish purple	7·00	3·00
59		$2 bronze-green and scarlet	7·00	17·00
60		$5 brown and bronze-green	17·00	14·00
50/60		Set of 11	35·00	35·00

3 Vanda hookeriana

1965 (15 Nov)–**68**. As Nos. 166/72 of Johore but with Arms of Malacca inset and inscr "MELAKA" as in T **3**. W w **13** (upright).

61		1c. multicoloured	10	2·50
62		2c. multicoloured	10	2·50
63		5c. multicoloured	1·00	40
		b. Yellow (flower) omitted	75·00	
		c. Red omitted	£150	
64		6c. multicoloured	1·00	1·00
65		10c. multicoloured	30	10
66		15c. multicoloured	1·75	40
67		20c. multicoloured (purple-brown background)	2·25	1·00
		a. Red-brown background (2.4.68)	5·00	4·25
61/7		Set of 7	6·00	7·00

The 5c., 6c., 10c. and 20c. exist with PVA gum as well as gum arabic.
The higher values used with this issue were Nos. 20/27 of Malaysia (National Issues).

1970. As Nos. 61 and 65 but W w **13** (sideways).

68	**3**	1c. multicoloured (27.5.70)	1·75	10·00
69	–	10c. multicoloured (20.11.70)	5·50	8·50

NEGRI SEMBILAN

A federation of smaller states reconstituted in 1886. Sungei Ujong, taken under British protection in 1874, was absorbed into Negri Sembilan by Treaty of 8 August 1895. The Negri Sembilan federation joined the Federated Malay States in 1896.

A. SUNGEI UJONG

Until 1 January 1899, when the Federated Malay States joined the UPU, mail for addresses outside Malaya was franked with the stamps of the STRAITS SETTLEMENTS.

PRICES FOR STAMPS ON COVER	
Nos. 1/14	
Nos. 15/27	from × 25
Nos. 28/36	from × 8
Nos. 37/49	from × 10
Nos. 50/5	from × 25

Overprints and surcharges were applied by the Government Printer, Singapore, *unless otherwise stated*.

---

(1)

1878. No. 11 of Straits Settlements handstamped with T **1**.

1	2c. brown	£4750	£5000

This overprint on India No. 54 is bogus.

SUNGEI **(2)** (Narrow letters) **SUNGEI** **(3)** ("N" wide) **SUNGEI** **(4)** ("S" wide)

UJONG **(5)** ("N" wide) **UJONG** **(6)** (Narrow letters, "UJ" close together) **UJONG** **(7)** (Narrow letters, evenly spaced)

1881. No. 11 of Straits Settlements optd with T **2/7**.

2	**2+5**	2c. brown	£6000	£4000
3	**3+5**	2c. brown	£4250	£3000
4	**2+6**	2c. brown	£475	
		a. Opt Type **6** double	£1800	
5	**4+6**	2c. brown	£1600	
6	**2+7**	2c. brown	£425	

The two lines of this surcharge were applied as separate operations. On Nos. 2/3 "SUNGEI" was printed as a triplet, probably 2+3+3 "UJONG" being added by a single unit handstamp. Nos. 4 and 5 come from a similar triplet, 4+4+5, completed by another single unit handstamp. No. 6 comes from a single type triplet with the second line added as a triplet instead of by a single unit handstamp.
The 10c. slate overprinted Types **2** + **7** is bogus.

SUNGEI **(8)** ("N" and "E" wide) **SUNGEI** **(9)** ("SUN" and "E" wide) **SUNGEI** **(10)** ("SUN" wide)

SUNGEI **(11)** ("S" wide) **SUNGEI** **(12)** (Narrow letters)

UJONG **(13)** ("U" and "NG" wide) **UJONG** **(14)** (Narrow letters)

1881. No. 11 of Straits Settlements optd with T **8/14**.

7	**8+13**	2c. brown	£400
8	**9+13**	2c. brown	£400
9	**10+13**	2c. brown	£400
10	**11+14**	2c. brown	£400
		a. "S" inverted	£4250
11	**12+14**	2c. brown	£250

Nos. 7/11 also had the two lines of the overprint applied at separate operations. "SUNGEI" as a triplet, either 7+8+9 or 10+11+11, and "UJONG" as a single unit.

S. U.
(15)

1882. Nos. 50/1 of Straits Settlements optd as T **15**.

12	2c. brown (with stops)	£325	
	a. Opt double	£3750	
13	2c. brown (without stops)	£275	£325
14	4c. rose (with stops)	£6000	£6500

Each of the above was applied by a triplet setting.
Examples of Straits Settlements No. 11 with a similar overprint, including stops, are trials which were not issued.

SUNGEI **(16)** ("S" and "E" wide) **SUNGEI** **(17)** ("E" wide) **UJONG** **(18)** ("N" wide)

1882 (Dec)–**84**. Nos. 12, 50, 52/3 and 63 of Straits Settlements optd with T **11/12, 14** and **16/18**.

15	**12+14**	2c. brown	£1800	£800
16	**11+14**	2c. brown	£2750	£1200
17	**12+14**	2c. pale rose (1884)	£300	£300
18	**11+14**	2c. pale rose (1884)	£300	£300
		a. Opt Type **14** double		
19	**16+14**	2c. pale rose (1884)	£140	£140
		a. Opt Type **16** double	†	£1200
20	**17+14**	2c. pale rose (1884)	£150	£160
21	**12+18**	2c. pale rose (1884)	£150	£160
		a. Opt Type **18** double	£1200	
22	**12+14**	4c. rose	£1800	£1900
		a. Opt Type **12** double	†	£4750
23	**11+14**	4c. rose	£2750	£3000
24	**12+14**	8c. orange	£1900	£1500
25	**11+14**	8c. orange	£3250	£2750
26	**12+14**	10c. slate	£650	£475
27	**11+14**	10c. slate	£900	£750

Nos. 15/27 had the two lines of the overprint applied by separate triplets. Settings so far identified are. Nos. 15+16+15, 17+18+19, 19+20+21, 22+23+22, 24+25+24 and 26+27+26.
The 4c. rose overprinted Types **16** + **14** is now believed to be a trial.

UJONG. **(19)** (With stop. Narrow letters) **UJONG.** **(20)** (With stop. "N" wide) **UJONG** **(21)** (Without stop. Narrow letters)

1883–**84**. Nos. 50 and 63/4 of Straits Settlements optd with T **12, 16/17** and **19/21**.

28	**12+19**	2c. brown	65·00	£190
29	**16+19**	2c. brown	65·00	£190
30	**12+20**	2c. brown	65·00	£190
		a. Opt Type **12** double	£1200	
31	**16+21**	2c. pale rose (1884)	£140	£150
32	**17+21**	2c. pale rose (1884)	£140	£150
33	**12+21**	2c. pale rose (1884)	£140	£150
		a. Opt Type **21** double	£1200	

34	**16+21**	4c. brown (1884)	£300	£425
		a. Opt Type **16** double		
		b. Opt Type **21** double	£2750	
35	**17+21**	4c. brown (1884)	£300	£425
36	**12+21**	4c. brown (1884)	£300	£425
		a. Opt Type **21** double	£4000	

Nos. 28/36 had the two lines of the overprint applied by separate triplets. Settings were Nos. 28+29+30, 31+32+33, 33+31+32 and 34+35+36.
The 8c. orange overprinted Types **12** + **19** is now believed to be a trial (*Price £1000 unused*).

Sungei Ujong **(22)** **SUNGEI UJONG** **(23)** **SUNGEI UJONG** **(24)**

SUNGEI UJONG **(25)** **SUNGEI UJONG** **(26)** **SUNGEI UJONG** **(27)**

SUNGEI UJONG **(28)** **SUNGEI UJONG.** **(29)** **SUNGEI UJONG** **(30)**

Antique "G" in "SUNGEI" (R. 6/1)

1885–**90**. Nos. 63/a of Straits Settlements optd with T **22/30**.

37	**22**	2c. pale rose	90·00	£100
		a. Opt double	£850	£950
38	**23**	2c. pale rose	60·00	65·00
		a. Opt double	£750	
39	**24**	2c. pale rose (1886)	£110	£130
40	**25**	2c. pale rose (1886)	£140	£150
		a. Opt double	£750	
41	**26**	2c. pale rose (1886)	£110	£110
		a. Opt double		
42	**27**	2c. pale rose (1887)	26·00	50·00
43	**28**	2c. pale rose (1889)	16·00	18·00
		a. Narrow "E" (2 mm wide) (R. 3/4 and 4/3)	£160	
		c. Opt double	£1400	
		d. Bright rose (1890)	22·00	15·00
		da. Narrow "E" (2 mm wide) (R. 3/4 and 4/3)	£200	
		db. Antique "N" in "UJONG" (R. 10/6)	£350	
44	**29**	2c. pale rose (1889)	£100	70·00
		a. "UNJOG" (R. 7/3)	£5000	£3500
45	**30**	2c. bright rose (1890)	50·00	28·00
		a. Antique "G" in "SUNGEI" (R. 6/1)	£900	
		b. Antique "G" in "UJONG" (R. 8/3)	£900	
		c. Pale rose		

All the above overprints had both lines applied at the same operation. Nos. 37/42 were from different triplet settings. The first printing of Type **28** was from a triplet (No. 43) but this was followed by two further settings of 60 (6×10), the first containing No. 43a and the second Nos. 43d/db. Nos. 44/5 were both from settings of 60.
The antique letter varieties on Types **28** and **30** are similar in style to those on Types **25** and **26**.

SUNGEI UJONG Two CENTS **(31)** **SUNGEI UJONG Two CENTS** **(32)** **SUNGEI UJONG Two CENTS** **(33)**

SUNGEI UJONG Two CENTS **(34)**

1891. No. 68 of Straits Settlements surch with T **31/4**.

46	**31**	2c. on 24c. green	£1100	£1100
		w. Wmk inverted	£2750	
47	**32**	2c. on 24c. green	£475	£475
		w. Wmk inverted	£1100	£2250
48	**33**	2c. on 24c. green	£1100	£1100
		w. Wmk inverted	£2750	£2250
49	**34**	2c. on 24c. green	£275	£275
		a. Antique "G" in "SUNGEI" (R. 6/1)	£1900	
		b. Antique "G" in "UJONG" (R. 8/3)	£1900	
		w. Wmk inverted	£700	£800

Nos. 46/9 come from the same setting of 60 on which "SUNGEI UJONG" was from the same type as No. 45. No. 46 occurs in row 1. No. 47 from rows 2 to 4, No. 48 from row 5 and No. 49 from rows 6 to 10.

35

3 CENTS
(36)

37

1891 (Nov)–**94**. Wmk Crown CA. P 14.

50	**35**	2c. rose	40·00	27·00
51		2c. orange (12.94)	1·75	4·25
52		5c. blue (3.93)	11·00	6·50
50/2		Set of 3	48·00	35·00
50s/2s		Optd "SPECIMEN" Set of 3	90·00	

1894 (Dec). Surch as T **36** by De La Rue. Wmk Mult Crown CA.
P 14.

53	**35**	1c. on 5c. green	1·00	70
54		3c. on 5c. rose	2·50	9·00

1895 (Oct). Wmk Crown CA. P 14.

55	**37**	3c. dull purple and carmine	26·00	8·50
53s/5s		Optd "SPECIMEN" Set of 3	90·00	

B. NEGRI SEMBILAN

Stamps of the STRAITS SETTLEMENTS were used in Negri Sembilan during 1891, until replaced by the stamps listed below. Until the Federated Malay States joined the UPU on 1 January 1899 Straits Settlements stamps continued to be used for mail to addresses outside Malaya.

PRICES FOR STAMPS ON COVER TO 1945	
No. 1	from × 200
Nos. 2/4	from × 10
Nos. 5/14	from × 8
Nos. 15/20	from × 10
Nos. 21/49	from × 4

Negri Sembilan
(1)   2   3

1891 (Aug?). No. 63a of Straits Settlements optd with T **1**.

1		2c. bright rose	3·00	13·00

2c. Short "N" in "SEMBILAN" (Top left pane R. 8/3)

1891 (Nov)–**94**. Wmk Crown CA. P 14.

2	**2**	1c. green (6.93)	3·25	1·00
3		2c. rose	3·25	18·00
		a. Short "N"	£120	
4		5c. blue (11.94)	30·00	48·00
2/4 Set of 3			32·00	60·00
2s/4s Optd "SPECIMEN" Set of 3			95·00	

1895–**99**. Wmk Crown CA. P 14.

5	**3**	1c. dull purple and green (1899)	26·00	14·00
6		2c. dull purple and brown (1898)	35·00	£130
7		3c. dull purple and carmine	18·00	3·50
8		5c. dull purple and olive-yellow (1897)	17·00	19·00
9		8c. dull purple and ultramarine (1898)	29·00	26·00
10		10c. dull purple and orange (1897)	27·00	14·00
11		15c. green and violet (1896)	50·00	90·00
12		20c. green and olive (1897)	75·00	40·00
13		25c. green and carmine (1896)	80·00	£100
14		50c. green and black (1896)	95·00	70·00
5/14 Set of 10			£400	£450
5s/14s Optd "SPECIMEN" Set of 10			£300	

Four cents.

(4)   **Four cents.**   (5)

1898 (Dec)–**1900**.

(a) Surch as T **4**

15	**3**	1c. on 15c. green and violet (1900)	£110	£350
		a. Raised stop (R. 5/1 and R. 10/1 of each pane)	£500	£1400
		b. Surch double, one albino	£450	
16	**2**	4c. on 1c. green	3·50	26·00
17	**3**	4c. on 3c. dull purple and carmine	7·00	28·00
		a. Horiz pair, one without surch	£15000	£7500
		b. Surch double	£2500	£1000
		ba. Ditto. "Four cents" albino	£1000	
		c. Surch inverted	£2500	£1600
		d. "cents" repeated at left	£4500	£3750
		e. "Four" repeated at right	£4500	£3750
		f. Without bar	£800	£650
		g. Bar double	†	£800
18	**2**	4c. on 5c. blue	1·50	15·00

On Nos. 15 and 17 the bar is at the top of the stamp.
The surcharges were applied as a setting of 30 (6×5).

(b) Surch as T **5**

19	**3**	4c. on 8c. dull purple and ultramarine (G.) (12.98)	16·00	4·25
		a. Vert pair, one without surch	£10000	£5500
		b. Surch double	£3000	£2500
		c. Surch double (G.+R.)	£850	£950
20		4c. on 8c. dull purple and ultramarine (Blk.)	£1500	£1600

Care should be taken in distinguishing the true black surcharge, No. 20, from very deep shades of the green surcharge, No. 19.

Pending the arrival of the permanent Federated Malay States issue the stamps of SELANGOR, FEDERATED MALAY STATES provisional overprints, STRAITS SETTLEMENTS and PERAK were used at various times between October 1899 and April 1901.
The general issues for FEDERATED MALAY STATES were used in Negri Sembilan from 29 April 1901 until 1935.

6 Arms of Negri Sembilan   **7** Arms of Negri Sembilan

1935 (2 Dec)–**41**. Wmk Mult Script CA. Ordinary paper (6c. grey, 15c.) or chalk-surfaced paper (others). P 14.

21	**6**	1c. black (1.1.36)	1·00	20
22		2c. green (1.1.36)	1·00	20
23		2c. orange (Thin striated paper) (11.12.41)	4·25	75·00
24		3c. green (ordinary paper) (21.8.41)	48·00	8·00
		a. Thin striated paper (12.41)	8·00	23·00
25		4c. orange	2·00	10
26		5c. brown (5.12.35)	2·00	10
27		6c. scarlet (1.1.37)	18·00	4·00
		a. Stop omitted at right (R. 10/4)	£900	£275
28		6c. grey (18.12.41)	4·75	£130
		a. Stop omitted at right (R. 10/4)	£350	
29		8c. grey	2·00	10
30		10c. dull purple (1.1.36)	1·25	10
31		12c. bright ultramarine (1.1.36)	3·25	50
32		15c. ultramarine (1.10.41)	11·00	60·00
33		25c. dull purple and scarlet (1.4.36)	1·50	70
		a. Thin striated paper (1941)	—	£110
34		30c. dull purple and orange (1.1.36)	3·50	3·00
		a. Thin striated paper	£110	
35		40c. scarlet and dull purple	3·75	2·00
36		50c. black/emerald (1.2.36)	6·50	2·25
37		$1 black and red/blue (1.4.36)	5·00	7·50
38		$2 green and scarlet (16.5.36)	60·00	22·00
39		$5 green and red/emerald (16.5.36)	42·00	£130
21/39 Set of 19			£160	£375
21s/39s Perf "SPECIMEN" Set of 19			£475	

The stamps issued in 1941 were printed by Harrison and Sons following bomb damage to the De La Rue works on 29 December 1940. The used prices quoted for Nos. 23, 28 and 32 are for examples with clearly identifiable 1941 cancellations. These stamps, and No. 39, are commonly found with forged cancellations.

An 8c. scarlet on both ordinary and thin striated paper was printed but only issued with opt during Japanese Occupation of Malaya. Unoverprinted specimens result from leakages.

During shortages in 1941 stamps of STRAITS SETTLEMENTS (2c. green, 25c., 30c.), SELANGOR (2c. green, 2c. orange (both perfs), 8c. grey, 25c.), PERAK (2c. orange, 25c., 50c.) and PAHANG (8c. scarlet) were issued in Negri Sembilan.

1948 (1 Dec). Royal Silver Wedding. As Nos. 112/13 of Antigua.

40		10c. violet	40	50
41		$5 green	23·00	32·00

1949 (1 Apr)–**55**. Chalk-surfaced paper. Wmk Mult Script CA.
P 17½×18.

42	**7**	1c. black	1·25	10
43		2c. orange	1·25	10
44		3c. green	60	30
45		4c. brown	30	10
46		5c. bright purple (1.9.52)	4·50	1·25
		a. Bright mauve (25.8.53)	4·25	45
47		6c. grey	2·75	10
		a. Pale grey (25.8.53)	12·00	2·50
48		8c. scarlet	1·00	75
49		8c. green (1.9.52)	8·00	1·60
50		10c. purple	40	10
51		12c. scarlet (1.9.52)	8·00	3·00
52		15c. ultramarine	5·00	10
53		20c. black and green	3·75	4·00
54		20c. bright blue (1.9.52)	4·00	10
55		25c. purple and orange	1·25	10
56		30c. scarlet and purple (4.9.55)	1·25	2·50
57		35c. scarlet and purple (1.9.52)	7·00	1·00
58		40c. red and purple	7·00	4·75
59		50c. black and blue	7·00	10
60		$1 blue and purple	7·50	2·00
61		$2 green and scarlet	25·00	45·00
62		$5 green and brown	55·00	£110
42/62 Set of 21			£130	£150

1949 (10 Oct). 75th Anniv of UPU. As Nos. 114/17 of Antigua.

63		10c. purple	20	20
64		15c. deep blue	1·40	3·50
		a. "A" of "CA" missing from wmk	£900	
65		25c. orange	30	3·00
66		50c. blue-black	60	3·25
63/6 Set of 4			2·25	9·00

1953 (2 June). Coronation. As No. 120 of Antigua.

67		10c. black and reddish purple	1·50	50

1957 (26 June)–**63**. As Nos. 92/102 of Kedah but with inset Arms of Negri Sembilan.

68	**9**	1c. black (21.8.57)	10	10
69	**10**	2c. orange-red (25.7.57)	10	10
70	**11**	4c. sepia (21.8.57)	10	10
71	**12**	5c. carmine-lake (21.8.57)	10	10
72	**13**	8c. myrtle-green (21.8.57)	2·75	1·40
73	**14**	10c. deep brown (4.8.57)	2·00	10
74		10c. deep maroon (10.1.61)	14·00	10
75	**15**	20c. blue	1·00	10
76	**16**	50c. black and blue (P 12½) (25.7.57)	30	1·40
		a. Perf 12½×13 (19.7.60)	75	10
77	**17**	$1 ultramarine and reddish purple (25.7.57)	10·00	2·00
78	**18**	$2 bronze-green and scarlet (P 12½) (21.8.57)	18·00	19·00
		a. Perf 13×12½ (15.1.63)	24·00	55·00
79	**19**	$5 brown and bronze-green (P 12½)	20·00	30·00
		a. Perf 13×12½ (6.3.62)	35·00	42·00
		ab. Perf 13×12½. Brown and yellow-olive (13.11.62)	£350	£110
68/79 Set of 12			60·00	48·00

The 6, 12, 25 and 30c. values used with this issue were Nos. 1/4 of Malayan Federation.

8 Tuanku Munawir   **9** Vanda hookeriana

(Photo Enschedé)

1961 (17 Apr). Installation of Tuanku Munawir as Yang di-Pertuan Besar of Negri Sembilan. No wmk. P 14×13.

80	**8**	10c. multicoloured	30	70

A 10c. stamp similar to Type **8** but in red was intended for release on 26 November 1959 to mark Tuanku Abdul Rahman's silver jubilee, but was cancelled due to his ill health and subsequent death.

1965 (15 Nov)–**69**. As Nos. 166/72 of Johore but with Arms of Negri Sembilan inset and inscr "NEGERI SEMBILAN" as in T **9**. W w **13** (upright).

81		1c. multicoloured	10	1·60
82		2c. multicoloured	10	1·60
		w. Wmk inverted	5·50	
83		5c. multicoloured	1·75	10
		b. Yellow omitted	£100	
		c. Red (leaves, etc) omitted	£100	
84		6c. multicoloured	40	60
85		10c. multicoloured	1·00	10
86		15c. multicoloured	80	10
87		20c. jet-black and multicoloured	2·25	1·00
		a. Blackish brown and mult (19.12.69)	9·00	3·00
81/7 Set of 7			5·50	4·50

The 2c., 6c., 15c. and 20c. exist with PVA gum as well as gum arabic. The higher values used with this issue were Nos. 20/27 of Malaysia (National Issues).
See also No. 90.

10 Negri Sembilan Crest and Tuanku Ja'afar

(Des Z. Noor. Photo Japanese Govt Ptg Wks)

1968 (8 Apr). Installation of Tuanku Ja'afar as Yang di-Pertuan Besar of Negri Sembilan. P 13.

88	**10**	15c. multicoloured	20	1·25
89		50c. multicoloured	40	1·40

1970 (27 May). As No. 81 but with W w **13** (sideways).

90	**9**	1c. multicoloured	2·75	9·50

STAMP BOOKLETS

1935. Stapled.

SB1	$1 booklet containing 205c. (No. 26) in blocks of 10	£3750	
SB2	$1.30 booklet containing 5c. and 8c. (Nos. 26, 29), each in block of 10	£4250	

PAHANG

The first British Resident was appointed in 1888. Pahang joined the Federated Malay States in 1896.

Until 1 January 1899, when the Federated Malay States joined the U.P.U., mail for addresses outside Malaya was franked with stamps of the STRAITS SETTLEMENTS.

PRICES FOR STAMPS ON COVER TO 1945	
No. 1	from × 50
Nos. 2/3	
No. 4	from × 100
No. 5	
No. 6	from × 100
Nos. 7/10	from × 8
Nos. 11/13	from × 25
Nos. 14/16	from × 20
No. 17/a	
Nos. 18/d	from × 6
Nos. 19/24	from × 8
No. 25	from × 20
Nos. 26/7	—
No. 28	from × 15
Nos. 29/46	from × 6

Overprints and surcharges were applied by the Government Printer, Singapore.

PAHANG   **PAHANG**   **PAHANG**
(1)   (2)   (2a) (Antique letters)

1889 (Jan). Nos. 52/3 and 63 of Straits Settlements optd with T **1**.

1		2c. pale rose	£170	50·00
2		8c. orange	£1800	£1800
3		8c. slate	£225	£275

All three values were overprinted from a triplet setting, but the 2c. also exists from a similar setting of 30 or 60.

1889. No. 63 of Straits Settlements optd with T **2**.

4		2c. pale rose	27·00	32·00
		a. Bright rose	18·00	17·00
		ab. Opt Type **2a**. Antique letters	£225	

No. 4 was overprinted from a setting of 60. No. 4ab usually occurs on R. 10/1, but has also been found on R. 8/1 as the result of revision of the setting.

PAHANG

PAHANG (3)   PAHANG (4)

1890 (Feb–Dec). No. 63a of Straits Settlements optd.

5	**3**	2c. bright rose	£13000	£3250
6	**4**	2c. bright rose (12.90)	£140	14·00
		w. Wmk inverted	—	£550

No. 5 may have been overprinted from a triplet setting. No. 6 was from a setting of 60.

PAHANG Two CENTS (5)   PAHANG Two CENTS (6)

PAHANG Two CENTS (7)   PAHANG Two CENTS (8)

1891 (May). No. 68 of Straits Settlements surch with T **5/8**.

7	**5**	2c. on 24c. green	£275	£300
8	**6**	2c. on 24c. green	£1200	£1300
9	**7**	2c. on 24c. green	£450	£475
10	**8**	2c. on 24c. green	£1200	£1300

Nos. 7/10 come from one setting used to surcharge the panes of sixty. No. 7 occurs in rows 1 to 5, No. 8 on row 6, No. 9 on rows 7 to 9 and No. 10 on row 10.

9   10

1891 (Nov)–**95**. Wmk Crown CA. P 14.

11	**9**	1c. green (3.95)	4·25	3·25
12		2c. rose	4·50	3·75
13		5c. blue (6.93)	11·00	48·00
11/13		*Set of 3*	18·00	50·00
11s/13s		Optd "SPECIMEN" *Set of 3*	90·00	

Following an increase of postage rates on 1 March 1894 1 cent stamps of STRAITS SETTLEMENTS were used in Pahang until the spring of the following year.

1895 (Nov)–**99**. Wmk Crown CA. P 14.

14	**10**	3c. dull purple and carmine	13·00	4·25
15		4c. dull purple and carmine (8.99)	17·00	21·00
16		5c. dull purple and olive-yellow (10.97)	55·00	24·00
14/16		*Set of 3*	75·00	45·00
14s/16s		Optd "SPECIMEN" *Set of 3*	85·00	

1897 (2 Aug). No. 13 bisected, surch in red manuscript at Kuala Lipis and initialled "JFO".

(a) Bisected horizontally

17	2c. on half of 5c. blue (surch "2" and bar across "5")	—	£2750
17a	3c. on half of 5c. blue (surch "3")	£7000	£2750

(b) Bisected diagonally

18	2c. on half of 5c. blue (surch "2" and bar across "5")	£1500	£400
	a. Unsevered pair. Nos. 18 and 18d	£15000	£4250
	b. Se-tenant pair. Nos. 18 and 18d	£4500	£1100
	c. Surch in black manuscript	£11000	£3500
18d	3c. on half of 5c. blue (surch "3")	£1500	£400
	dc. Surch in black manuscript	£11000	£3500

The initials are those of John Fortescue Owen, the Superintendent at Kuala Lipis.

Nos. 17 and 18 only occur on the bottom half of the 5c. and Nos. 17a and 18d on the top half. No. 18a is a complete example of No. 13 showing the two surcharges. No. 18b is a *se-tenant* pair of bisects from adjoining stamps.

Three types of these manuscript surcharges may be distinguished. an initial group, including the black surcharges Nos. 18c and 18dc, showed the value as "2cts" or "3cts". A second group, including the horizontal bisects Nos. 17 and 17a, had figures of value only ("2" or "3"). A third group, in which the values (but not the initials) were written by Owen's clerk, Mr. Mitchell, showed the values as "2c" and "3c", with a vertical stroke through the "c". Examples of diagonal bisects from the first and third groups, with "cts" or "c" after the figure of value, are worth a premium over the prices quoted above.

Pahang. (11)   **Pahang.** (12)

1898 (18 Mar–Sept).

*(a) Nos. 72/5 of Perak optd with T **11***

19	10c. dull purple and orange	29·00	32·00
20	25c. green and carmine	85·00	£170
21	50c. dull purple and greenish black (9.98)	£475	£550
22	50c. green and black	£300	£425

*(b) Nos. 76 and 79 of Perak optd with T **12***

23	$1 green and pale green	£425	£700
24	$5 green and ultramarine	£1700	£3250

Pahang

Four cents (13)

Four cents. (14)

1899.

*(a) No. 71 of Perak surch with T **13***

25	4c. on 8c. dull purple and ultramarine (1.99)	14·00	14·00
	a. Surch inverted	£5000	£1800
	b. Surch double	£950	

*(b) T **13** on plain paper (no stamp), but issued for postage. Imperf*

26	4c. black (4.99)	—	£5000
27	5c. black	£3000	

No. 26 also exists pin-perforated.

1899 (May). No. 16 surch with T **14**.

28	**10**	4c. on 5c. dull purple and olive-yellow	26·00	75·00
		a. Surch double, one albino inverted	£500	

Pending the arrival of the permanent Federated Malay States issue the stamps of SELANGOR, FEDERATED MALAY STATES provisional overprints and PERAK were used at various times between November 1899 and July 1902.
The general issues for the FEDERATED MALAY STATES were used in Pahang from July 1902 until 1935.

15 Sultan Sir Abu Bakar   16 Sultan Sir Abu Bakar

1935 (2 Dec)–**41**. Chalk-surfaced paper. Wmk Mult Script CA. P 14.

29	**15**	1c. black (1.1.36)	30	40
30		2c. green (1.1.36)	4·25	50
31		3c. green (ordinary paper) (21.8.41)	65·00	8·00
		a. Thin striated paper	30·00	30·00
32		4c. orange	70	50
33		5c. brown (5.12.35)	70	10
34		6c. scarlet (1.1.37)	32·00	1·75
35		8c. grey	60	10
36		8c. scarlet (Thin striated paper) (11.12.41)	13·00	80·00
37		10c. dull purple (1.1.36)	3·25	10
		a. Thin striated paper (1941)	£300	£120
38		12c. bright ultramarine (1.1.36)	7·00	1·25
39		15c. ultram (ordinary paper) (1.10.41)	45·00	70·00
40		25c. dull purple and scarlet (1.4.36)	3·75	1·50
41		30c. dull purple and orange (1.1.36)	2·25	1·10
		a. Thin striated paper (1941)	25·00	
42		40c. scarlet and dull purple	1·50	2·00
43		50c. black/emerald (1.2.36)	8·00	1·50
44		$1 black and red/blue (1.4.36)	8·00	9·00
45		$2 green and scarlet (16.5.36)	48·00	50·00
46		$5 green and red/emerald (16.5.36)	17·00	90·00
29/46		*Set of 18*	£200	£275
29s/46s		Perf "SPECIMEN" *Set of 18*	£500	

The stamps issued during 1941 were printed by Harrison and Sons following bomb damage to the De La Rue works on 29 December 1940. The used prices quoted for Nos. 36 and 39 are for examples with clearly identifiable 1941 cancellations.
Examples of the 1c. on thin striated paper exist from a sheet with misplaced type **16** Japanese Occupation opt. See No. J239a in the Japanese Occupation listing.
A 2c. orange and a 6c. grey, both on thin striated paper, were prepared but not officially issued. (*Price mint £4 each*).

During shortages in 1941 stamps of STRAITS SETTLEMENTS (2c., 25c.), SELANGOR (2c. orange, 3c., 8c.), NEGRI SEMBILAN (6c.) and PERAK (2c. orange) were issued in Pahang.

1948 (1 Dec). Royal Silver Wedding. As Nos. 112/13 of Antigua.

47	10c. violet	15	60
48	$5 brown	25·00	50·00

1949 (10 Oct). 75th Anniv of UPU. As Nos. 114/17 of Antigua.

49	10c. purple	30	25
50	15c. deep blue	1·10	1·50
51	25c. orange	35	2·75
52	50c. blue-black	70	5·00
49/52	*Set of 4*	2·25	8·50

1950 (1 June)–**56**. Wmk Mult Script CA. Chalk-surfaced paper. P 17½×18.

53	**16**	1c. black	20	10
54		2c. orange	30	10
55		3c. green	55	80
56		4c. brown	2·75	10
		a. Chocolate (24.3.54)	22·00	3·75
57		5c. bright purple (1.9.52)	1·00	70
		a. Bright mauve (10.9.53)	1·00	15
58		6c. grey	1·50	30
59		8c. scarlet	65	50
60		8c. green (1.9.52)	1·50	50
61		10c. magenta	35	10
62		12c. scarlet (1.9.52)	3·50	1·25
63		15c. ultramarine	1·25	10
64		20c. black and green	2·25	3·00
65		20c. bright blue (1.9.52)	4·50	10
		a. Ultramarine (8.3.56)	13·00	3·25
66		25c. purple and orange	1·00	10
67		30c. scarlet and brown-purple (4.9.55)	5·00	35
		a. Scarlet and purple (8.3.56)	42·00	10·00
68		35c. scarlet and purple (1.9.52)	1·50	25
69		40c. red and purple	5·50	11·00
70		50c. black and blue	1·75	10
71		$1 blue and purple	6·00	3·50
72		$2 green and scarlet	18·00	30·00
73		$5 green and brown	85·00	£110
		a. Green and sepia (24.3.54)	£140	£150
53/73		*Set of 21*	£120	£140

1953 (2 June). Coronation. As No. 120 of Antigua.

74	10c. black and reddish purple	2·75	10

1957 (26 June)–**62**. As Nos. 92/102 of Kedah but with inset portrait of Sultan Sir Abu Bakar.

75	**9**	1c. black (21.8.57)	10	10
76	**10**	2c. orange-red (25.7.57)	15	10
77	**11**	4c. sepia (21.8.57)	15	10
78	**12**	5c. carmine-lake (21.8.57)	15	10
79	**13**	8c. myrtle-green (21.8.57)	5·50	2·25
80	**14**	10c. deep brown (4.8.57)	1·25	10
81		10c. deep maroon (21.2.61)	7·50	30
82	**15**	20c. blue	2·25	20
83	**16**	50c. black and blue (P 12½) (25.7.57)	45	75
		a. Perf 12½×13 (17.5.60)	1·00	20
84	**17**	$1 ultramarine and reddish purple (25.7.57)	17·00	2·25
85	**18**	$2 bronze-green and scarlet (P 12½) (21.8.57)	15·00	9·00
		a. Perf 13×12½ (13.11.62)	16·00	38·00
86	**19**	$5 brown and bronze-green (P 12½)	12·00	5·00
		a. Perf 13×12½ (17.5.60)	13·00	40·00
		b. Perf 13×12½. Brown and yellow olive (23.10.62)	60·00	70·00
75/86		*Set of 12*	55·00	26·00

The 6, 12, 25 and 30c. values used with this issue were Nos. 1/4 of Malayan Federation.

17 *Vanda hookeriana*

1965 (15 Nov). As Nos. 166/72 of Johore but with inset portrait of Sultan Sir Abu Bakar as in T **17**. W w **13** (upright).

87	**17**	1c. multicoloured	10	1·25
		c. Grey (flower name, etc) omitted	£150	
		w. Wmk inverted	12·00	
88		2c. multicoloured	10	1·25
89		5c. multicoloured	15	10
		c. Red (leaves, etc) omitted	£150	
90		6c. multicoloured	30	1·25
91		10c. multicoloured	20	10
		a. Red omitted	£150	
92		15c. multicoloured	1·00	10
93		20c. multicoloured	1·60	40
87/93		*Set of 7*	3·75	

The 2c., 5c. and 6c. exist with PVA gum as well as gum arabic.
The higher values used with this issue were Nos. 20/27 of Malaysia (National Issues).

1970 (27 May). As Nos. 87 and 91 but W w **13** (sideways).

94	**17**	1c. multicoloured	2·50	9·00
95	**–**	10c. multicoloured	1·00	3·75

STAMP BOOKLETS

1935. Black on buff covers. Stapled.

SB1	$1 booklet containing 20×5c. (No. 33) in blocks of 10	£3750
SB2	$1.30 booklet containing 5c. and 8c. (Nos. 33, 35) each in block of 10 and pane of airmail labels	£4000

PENANG

One of the Straits Settlements which joined the Federation of Malaya on 1 February 1948.

1948 (1 Dec). Royal Silver Wedding. As Nos. 112/13 of Antigua.

1	10c. violet	30	20
2	$5 brown	38·00	38·00

1949 (21 Feb)–**52**. As T 58 of Straits Settlements, but inscr "PENANG" at foot. Wmk Mult Script CA. Chalk-surfaced paper. P 17½×18.

3	1c. black	1·75	20
4	2c. orange	1·75	20
5	3c. green	60	1·00
6	4c. brown	50	10
7	5c. bright purple (1.9.52)	9·00	4·75
8	6c. grey	2·00	20
9	8c. scarlet	1·25	8·00
10	8c. green (1.9.52)	8·50	4·50
11	10c. purple	50	10
12	12c. scarlet (1.9.52)	8·50	16·00
13	15c. ultramarine	3·50	30
14	20c. black and green	3·50	1·50
15	20c. bright blue (1.9.52)	9·00	1·50
16	25c. purple and orange	3·75	1·50
17	35c. scarlet and purple (1.9.52)	9·00	1·25
18	40c. red and purple	8·00	18·00
19	50c. black and blue	8·00	20
20	$1 blue and purple	20·00	3·50
21	$2 green and scarlet	23·00	2·00
22	$5 green and brown	48·00	3·00
3/22	*Set of 20*	£140	55·00

1949 (10 Oct). 75th Anniv of UPU. As Nos. 114/17 of Antigua.

23	10c. purple	20	10
24	15c. deep blue	2·50	3·75
25	25c. orange	45	5·00
26	50c. blue-black	1·50	3·25
23/6	*Set of 4*	4·25	11·00

1953 (2 June). Coronation. As No. 120 of Antigua.

27	10c. black and reddish purple	2·75	10

1954 (9 June)–**57**. As T 1 of Malacca (Queen Elizabeth II) but inscr "PENANG" at foot. Chalk-surfaced paper. Wmk Mult Script CA. P 17½×18.

28	1c. black (5.1.55)	10	70
29	2c. yellow-orange (8.9.54)	1·00	30
30	4c. brown (1.9.54)	2·00	10
	a. Yellow-brown (17.7.57)	15·00	11·00
31	5c. bright purple (1.10.54)	2·00	5·00
	a. Bright mauve (17.7.57)	15·00	11·00
32	6c. grey	20	80
33	8c. green (5.1.55)	40	3·50
34	10c. brown-purple (1.9.54)	20	10
35	12c. rose-red (5.1.55)	40	3·50

36		20c. bright blue (1.9.54)	50	10
37		25c. brown-purple and yellow-orange (1.12.54)	40	10
38		30c. rose-red and brown-purple (5.9.55).	40	10
39		35c. rose-red and brown-purple (8.9.54).	70	60
40		50c. black and bright blue (1.12.54)	1·50	10
41		$1 bright blue and brown-purple (1.10.54)	3·00	30
42		$2 emerald and scarlet (1.10.54)	21·00	3·75
43		$2 emerald and brown (5.1.55)	48·00	3·75

28/43 Set of 16 ..... 70·00   20·00

1957. As Nos. 92/102 of Kedah, but with inset portrait of Queen Elizabeth II.

44	9	1c. black (21.8)	10	1·50
45	10	2c. orange-red (25.7)	10	1·00
46	11	4c. sepia (21.8)	10	10
47	12	5c. carmine-lake (21.8)	10	30
48	13	8c. myrtle-green (21.8)	3·00	2·25
49	14	10c. deep brown (4.8)	30	10
50	15	20c. blue (26.6)	1·25	40
51	16	50c. black and blue (25.7)	2·00	70
52	17	$1 ultramarine and reddish purple (25.7)	15·00	1·00
53	18	$2 bronze-green and scarlet (21.8)	24·00	22·00
54	19	$5 brown and bronze-green (26.6)	29·00	14·00

44/54 Set of 11 ..... 65·00   38·00

The note after No. 86 of Pahang also applies here.

1 Copra

2 *Vanda hookeriana*

(Recess D.L.R.)

1960 (15 Mar). As Nos. 44/54, but with inset Arms of Penang as in T **1**. W w **12**. P 13×12½ (1c. to 8c., $2, $5), 12½×13 (10c. to 50c.) or 13½ ($1).

55		1c. black	10	1·60
56		2c. orange-red	10	1·60
57		4c. sepia	10	10
58		5c. carmine-lake	10	10
59		8c. myrtle-green	2·75	4·50
60		10c. deep maroon	30	10
61		20c. blue	55	10
62		50c. black and blue	30	30
		a. Imperf (pair)	£650	
63		$1 ultramarine and reddish purple	7·50	1·75
64		$2 bronze-green and scarlet	13·00	9·00
65		$5 brown and bronze-green	15·00	9·00

55/65 Set of 11 ..... 35·00   25·00

No. 62a comes from four panes which had the upper five horizontal rows imperforate.

1965 (15 Nov)–**68**. As Nos. 166/72 of Johore but with Arms of Penang inset and inscr "PULAU PINANG" as in T **2**. W w **13** (upright).

66		1c. multicoloured	10	1·25
67		2c. multicoloured	10	1·50
68		5c. multicoloured	1·75	10
		b. Yellow (flower) omitted	85·00	
		c. Red omitted	£150	
		d. Blue (background and inscr) omitted	£950	
		da. Blue and yellow omitted	£900	
		w. Wmk inverted	4·00	
69		6c. multicoloured	30	1·25
		b. Yellow omitted	85·00	
70		10c. grey and multicoloured	20	10
		a. Jet-black and multicoloured (12.11.68)	2·50	75
71		15c. multicoloured	1·00	10
		b. Green (value and leaves) omitted	£700	
		c. Black (country name and Arms) omitted (horizontal pair with normal)	£1600	
72		20c. multicoloured	1·60	30
		a. Bright purple (blooms) omitted	£1000	
		b. Yellow (leaves) omitted	£1000	

66/72 Set of 7 ..... 4·50   4·00

The 2c., 5c., 6c., 10c. and 20c. exist with PVA gum as well as gum arabic.

The higher values used with this issue were Nos. 20/27 of Malaysia (National Issues).

1970. As Nos. 66 and 70 but W w **13** (sideways).

73	2	1c. multicoloured (27.5.70)	1·60	7·00
74	–	10c. multicoloured (20.11.70)	7·00	4·50

PERAK

Perak accepted a British Resident in 1874, although he was later murdered.

The state joined the Federated Malay States in 1896.

> The stamps of the STRAITS SETTLEMENTS were used in Perak during 1877/8.
> Until 1 January 1899, when the Federated Malay States joined the UPU, mail for addresses outside Malaya was franked with stamps of the STRAITS SETTLEMENTS.

PRICES FOR STAMPS ON COVER TO 1945	
No. 1	—
Nos. 2/9	from × 60
Nos. 10/13	from × 30
Nos. 14/16	from × 8
Nos. 17/22	from × 20
No. 23	—
Nos. 24/5	
Nos. 26/8	from × 15
No. 29	from × 75
No. 30	—
Nos. 31/2	from × 20
Nos. 33/40	from × 15
Nos. 43/60	from × 6
Nos. 61/5	from × 20

PRICES FOR STAMPS ON COVER TO 1945	
Nos. 66/79	from × 12
No. 80	—
Nos. 81/7	from × 8
Nos. 88/102	from × 4
Nos. 103/21	from × 3

The Official stamps of Perak are rare used on cover.

Overprints and surcharges were applied by the Government Printer, Singapore, *unless otherwise stated.*

(1)

1878. No. 11 of Straits Settlements handstamped with T **1**.

1		2c. brown	£2000	£2250

P E R A K
(**2**) (14½ mm long)

PERAK
(**3**) (11 mm long)

PERAK
(**4**) (10¼ mm long)

PERAK
(**5**) (17 mm long)

P E R A K
(**6**) ("RA" narrow)

P E R A K
(**7**) ("R" narrow)

P E R A K
(**8**) ("P" and "K" wide)

PERAK
(**9**) (12 to 13½ mm long)

1880–81. No. 11 (wmk Crown CC) of Straits Settlements optd with T **2/9**.

2	2	2c. brown	£4750	£1400
3	3	2c. brown	£4000	£850
4	4	2c. brown	£2500	£900
5	5	2c. brown (1881)	50·00	85·00
		w. Wmk inverted	†	£750
6	6	2c. brown (1881)	£350	£350
7	7	2c. brown (1881)	£200	£225
8	8	2c. brown (1881)	£1300	£1100
		a. Opt double	†	£3250
9	9	2c. brown (1881)	£200	£200

Of the above No. 2 is from a single unit overprint, No. 5 from a setting of sixty and the remainder from settings applied as horizontal strips of three. Nos. 6/8 come from mixed triplets, either 6+7+7 or 7+7+8. No. 4 is believed to come from a single unit overprint in addition to a triplet.

P E R A K
(**10**) ("A" wide)

P E R A K
(**11**) ("E" wide)

1882–83. Nos. 50 (wmk Crown CA) and 63 of Straits Settlements optd with T **9/11**.

10	9	2c. brown	27·00	85·00
		a. Opt double	£700	
11		2c. pale rose (1883)	50·00	65·00
		a. Opt double	£700	
12	10	2c. pale rose (1883)	55·00	£120
13	11	2c. pale rose (1883)	50·00	80·00
		a. Opt double	£700	

The above were all overprinted as triplet settings. Those for the 2c. rose were 11+12+13, 13+11+11 and 13+11+12.

2 CENTS PERAK
(**12**)

2 OENTS
(**13**)

1883 (July). No. 51 (wmk Crown CA) of Straits Settlements surch.

(a) Surch with T 12

14		2c. on 4c. rose		£4500
		a. On Straits Settlements No. 12 (wmk Crown CC)		£8000

(b) Optd as T 9 or 11 and surch with T 13

15	11	2c. on 4c. rose	£1200	£500
16	9	2c. on 4c. rose	£750	£325

It is believed that No. 14 occurred on the top row of the sheet with the remaining nine rows surcharged with a triplet containing 15+16+16.

Only one unused example, with defects, of No. 14a is recorded.

PERAK
(**14**) ("E" wide)

PERAK
(**15**) ("E" narrow)

PERAK
(**16**) (12½–13 mm long)

PERAK
(**17**) (12–12½ mm long)

PERAK
(**18**) (10½ mm long)

PERAK
(**19**) (10 mm long)

PERAK
(**20**) (13 mm long)

1884–91. Nos. 63/*a* of Straits Settlements optd with T **14/20**.

17	14	2c. pale rose	10·00	3·75
		a. Opt double	£650	£650
		b. Opt inverted	£450	£600
		c. Bright rose (1889)	13·00	2·75
18	15	2c. pale rose	70·00	70·00
		a. Opt double	£1100	
		b. Opt inverted	£1600	£1700
		c. Opt triple	£1500	
		d. Bright rose	£150	

19	16	2c. pale rose (1886)	£150	42·00
		a. Bright rose (1891)	2·25	7·50
		ab. Optd "FERAK" *	£425	£600
20	17	2c. pale rose (1886)	17·00	55·00
		a. Opt double	£1600	
21	18	2c. pale rose (1886)	£200	£225
		a. Bright rose		
22	19	2c. bright rose (1890)	29·00	60·00
23	20	2c. bright rose (1891)	£3750	

Settings:

Nos. 17/18 – triplets (either 17 + 17 + 17 or 18 + 17 + 17) 30 (3×10) (containing 28 as No. 17 and two as No. 18) 60 (6×10) (containing either 57 as No. 17 and three as No. 18 or all as No. 17)

No. 19 – 60 (6×10) (*No. 19ab occurs on one position of the setting, it is often found amended in manuscript)

No. 20 – triplet
No. 21 – triplet
No. 22 – 60 (6×10)
No. 23 – not known

1 CENT
(**21**)

1886. No. 17 surch with T **21**.

24	14	1c. on 2c. pale rose	£4750	£3750

ONE CENT PERAK
(**22**)

ONE CENT PERAK.
(**23**)

ONE CENT PERAK.
(**24**) ("N" wide in "ONE" and "CENT")

1886. No. 63 of Straits Settlements surch with T **22/4**.

25	22	1c. on 2c. pale rose	£850	£850
26	23	1c. on 2c. pale rose	75·00	90·00
		a. Surch double	£1200	
27	24	1c. on 2c. pale rose	£130	£140

Nos. 26/7 are from a triplet setting, Types 23-24-23, in which the two Type 23's can be differentiated by the height of the right upright of the "N" of "CENT", which is short on one. This triplet was used for the top nine rows of the sheet. Type 22 may have been used on the bottom row.

1 CENT PERAK
(**25**)

One CENT PERAK
(**26**)

ONE CENT PERAK
(**27**)

1886. No. 63 of Straits Settlements surch with T **25**.

28		1c. on 2c. pale rose	£200	£200
		a. Surch double	£1800	£1800

No. 28 comes from a triplet setting.

1886. No. 63 of Straits Settlements surch with T **26**.

29		1c. on 2c. pale rose	4·00	20·00
		a. "One" inverted	£3750	
		b. Surch double	£1200	

No. 29 comes from a triplet setting. It is believed that No. 29a occurred when the type was dropped and "One" replaced upside down.

1887. No. 63 of Straits Settlements surch with T **27** in blue.

30		1c. on 2c. pale rose	75·00	75·00
		a. Optd in black	£2000	£1500

No. 30 was printed from a setting of 60.

I CENT PERAK
(**28**)

1 CENT PERAK
(**29**)

1887. No. 63 of Straits Settlements surch with T **28**.

31		1c. on 2c. pale rose	£1700	£950

No. 31 comes from a triplet setting.

1887. No. 63 of Straits Settlements surch with T **29**.

32		1c. on 2c. pale rose	£3250	£3250

The size of setting used for No. 32 is not known.

One CENT PERAK
(**30**)

One CENT PERAK
(**31**)

One CENT PERAK
(**32**)

One CENT PERAK
(**33**)

One CENT PERAK
(**34**)

One CENT PERAK
(**35**)

One CENT PERAK
(**36**)

One CENT PERAK
(**37**)

Short "R" (different positions in different settings of No. 37, but R. 8/2 on Nos. 46 and 51)

1887–89. No. 63 of Straits Settlements surch with T **30/7.**

33	**30**	1c. on 2c. pale rose	4·50	12·00
		a. Surch double	£1300	
		b. Bright rose	2·75	4·25
34	**31**	1c. on 2c. pale rose (1889)	£130	£160
		b. Bright rose	£180	
35	**32**	1c. on 2c. pale rose (1889)	30·00	55·00
		a. "PREAK" (R. 6/1)	£900	£1100
		b. Bright rose	28·00	50·00
		ba. "PREAK" (R. 6/1)	£950	£1200
		w. Wmk inverted	£450	
36	**33**	1c. on 2c. pale rose (1889)	20·00	28·00
		b. Bright rose	8·00	28·00
37	**34**	1c. on 2c. pale rose (1889)	20·00	30·00
		b. Bright rose	5·00	27·00
		c. Short "R"	85·00	
38	**35**	1c. on 2c. bright rose (1889)	£700	£950
39	**36**	1c. on 2c. bright rose (1889)	£400	£500
40	**37**	1c. on 2c. bright rose (1889)	42·00	55·00
		b. Bright rose	18·00	50·00

Settings. No. 33 originally appeared as a triplet, then as a block of 30 (3×10) and, finally, as part of a series of composite settings of 60. Specialists recognise four such composite settings:

Setting I contained No. 33 in Rows 1 to 4, R. 5/1 to 5/5 and Row 7; No. 34 on R. 5/6, 6/1 and 6/2; No. 35 on R. 6/3–6; No. 36 on Row 8; No. 37 on Rows 9 and 10.

Setting II was similar, but had the example of No. 33 on R. 3/5 replaced by No. 38 and those on R. 7/4 and R. 7/6 by No. 39.

Setting III contained No. 33 in Rows 1 to 5; No. 35 in Row 6 with the "PREAK" error on the first position; No. 36 in Row 7; No. 37 in Rows 8 and 9; No. 40 in Row 10.

Setting IV was similar, but showed the "PREAK" error on R. 6/1 corrected.

ONE CENT. / ONE CENT
(38) / (39)

1889 (Nov)–**90.** No. 17 surch with T **38/9.**

41	**38**	1c. on 2c. bright rose	£350	£130
42	**39**	1c. on 2c. bright rose (1890)	—	£250

PERAK / PERAK
Two / One
CENTS / CENT
(40) / (41)

1891. Nos. 63a, 66 and 68 of Straits Settlements surch.

*(a) As T **30, 32/4** and **37,** but with "PERAK" at top and a bar through the original value (May 1891)*

43	**30**	1c. on 6c. lilac	60·00	35·00
44	**32**	1c. on 6c. lilac	£190	£160
45	**33**	1c. on 6c. lilac	£190	£160
46	**34**	1c. on 6c. lilac	£110	80·00
		a. Short "R"	£325	£275
47	**37**	1c. on 6c. lilac	£190	£160

*(b) With T **40** and as T **32/4** and **37** but with "PERAK" at top, all with a bar through the original value (May 1891)*

48	**40**	2c. on 24c. green	35·00	16·00
		w. Wmk inverted	£450	
49	**32**	2c. on 24c. green	£120	65·00
		w. Wmk inverted	£1000	
50	**33**	2c. on 24c. green	£120	65·00
		w. Wmk inverted	£1000	
51	**34**	2c. on 24c. green	75·00	35·00
		a. Short "R"	£250	£140
52	**37**	2c. on 24c. green	£120	65·00

*(c) With T **41** and as T **30, 34** and **37,** but with "PERAK" at top (July 1891)*

(i) Without bar over original value

53	**30**	1c. on 2c. bright rose	£200	
		a. Narrow "O" in "One" (R. 3/3)	£3000	
54	**41**	1c. on 2c. bright rose	£1000	
55	**34**	1c. on 2c. bright rose	£450	
56	**37**	1c. on 2c. bright rose	£1000	

(ii) With bar through original value

57	**30**	1c. on 2c. bright rose	2·25	16·00
		a. Narrow "O" in "One" (R. 3/3)	38·00	£110
58	**41**	1c. on 2c. bright rose	8·50	55·00
59	**34**	1c. on 2c. bright rose	2·25	23·00
60	**37**	1c. on 2c. bright rose	8·50	55·00

Settings. Nos. 43/7 were arranged as Setting IV described under Nos. 33/40.

Nos. 48/52 were similar except that Type 40 replaced Type 30 on the first five rows.

The first printing of the 1c. on 2c. was without a bar through the original face value. Both printings, Nos. 53/60, were from the same setting with Type **30** on Rows 1 to 5, **41** on Row 6, **34** on Rows 7 to 9 and **37** on Row 10.

PERAK POSTAGE 1 (image of stamp)
42
3 CENTS
(43)

1892 (1 Jan)–**95.** Wmk Crown CA. P 14.

61	**42**	1c. green	2·25	15
62		2c. rose	1·75	30
63		2c. orange (9.9.95)	1·00	11·00
64		5c. blue	3·25	7·50
61/4 Set of 4			7·50	17·00
61s/4s Optd "SPECIMEN" Set of 4			£120	

1895 (26 Apr). Surch with T **43** by De La Rue. Wmk Crown CA. P 14.

65	**42**	3c. on 5c. rose	3·75	6·50
		s. Optd "SPECIMEN"	35·00	

44 / 45

Malformed "C"
in left value tablet
(R. 9/3, both panes)

1895 (2 Sept)–**99.** P 14.

(a) Wmk Crown CA

66	**44**	1c. dull purple and green	2·75	50
		a. Malformed "C"	£140	65·00
67		2c. dull purple and brown	3·25	50
68		3c. dull purple and carmine	5·50	50
69		4c. dull purple and carmine (1899)	22·00	8·00
70		5c. dull purple and olive-yellow	13·00	75
71		8c. dull purple and ultramarine	45·00	90
72		10c. dull purple and orange	19·00	50
73		25c. green and carmine (1897)	£225	13·00
74		50c. dull purple and greenish black	48·00	50·00
75		50c. green and black (12.98)	£225	£170

(b) Wmk Crown CC

76	**45**	$1 green and pale green (1896)	£300	£225
77		$2 green and carmine (1896)	£450	£375
78		$3 green and ochre (1898)	£650	£550
79		$5 green and ultramarine (1896)	£650	£600
80		$25 green and orange (1899?)	£12000	£4500
		s. Optd "SPECIMEN"	£400	
66/76 Set of 11			£800	£425
66s/79s Optd "SPECIMEN" Set of 14			£500	

Pending the arrival of the permanent Federated Malay States issue the stamps of FEDERATED MALAY STATES provisional overprints, SELANGOR and STRAITS SETTLEMENTS were used at various times between June 1900 and 31 December 1901.

The general issues for the FEDERATED MALAY STATES were used in Perak from 1901 until 1935.

One / ONE
Cent. / CENT.
(46) / (47)

Three / THREE
Cent. / Cent.
(48) / (49)

Three Cent.
Thinner "t" in "Cent"

1900. Stamps of 1895–99 surch.

81	**46**	1c. on 2c. dull purple and brown (13.7*)	1·00	2·50
		a. Antique "e" in "One" (R. 5/2)	60·00	£130
		b. Antique "e" in "Cent" (R. 9/4)	60·00	£130
82	**47**	1c. on 4c. dull purple and carmine (25.7*)	1·00	17·00
		a. Surch double	£1300	
83	**46**	1c. on 5c. dull purple and olive-yellow (30.6*)	3·00	23·00
		a. Antique "e" in "One" (R. 5/2)	£100	£325
		b. Antique "e" in "Cent" (R. 9/4)	£100	£325
84	**48**	3c. on 8c. dull purple and ultramarine (22.9*)	15·00	20·00
		a. Antique "e" in "Cent" (R. 9/4)	£225	£325
		b. No stop after "Cent" (R. 9/5)	£225	£325
		c. Surch double	£550	£600
85		3c. on 50c. green and black (31.8*)	6·50	14·00
		a. Antique "e" in "Cent" (R. 9/4)	£150	£225
		b. No stop after "Cent" (R. 9/5)	£150	£225
86	**49**	3c. on $1 green and pale green (20.10*)	55·00	£150
		a. Thinner "t" in "Cent"	£300	£550
		b. Surch double	£1600	
		w. Wmk inverted	£400	£600
87		3c. on $2 green and carmine (23.10*)	50·00	85·00
		a. Surch double, one albino		
81/7 Set of 7			£110	£275

*Earliest known postmark date.

With exception of No. 86a, whose sheet position is not known, the remaining surcharge varieties all occur in the left-hand pane.

No. 86b is also known showing the thinner "t" in "Cent" variety. (Price £4500 unused.)

During a shortage of low values, on 22 October 1900 the Government of Perak announced that articles on which postage was less than 4 cents could be handed in at the post office and the postage paid in cash. The stamp vendor gave the sender a perforated and postmarked receipt inscribed "Postal/Receipt for/1 cent", some of which are known attached to envelopes, although this is not what the authorities intended. Collectors know these as the "Tanjong Malim provisionals", although they were also used in other offices.

The $5, No. 79, surcharged "Three cents/Revenue/only" is also known used postally during the shortage.

50 Sultan Iskandar / 51 Sultan Iskandar / Malformed "2c." (R. 10/10)

1935 (2 Dec)–**37.** Chalk-surfaced paper. Wmk Mult Script CA. P 14.

88	**50**	1c. black (1.1.36)	3·50	10
89		2c. green (1.1.36)	3·50	10
90		4c. orange	3·75	10
91		5c. brown (5.12.35)	75	10
92		6c. scarlet (1.1.37)	14·00	7·00
93		8c. grey	1·00	10
94		10c. dull purple (1.1.36)	80	15
95		12c. bright ultramarine (1.1.36)	5·50	1·00
96		25c. dull purple and scarlet (1.4.36)	3·50	1·00
97		30c. dull purple and orange (1.1.36)	5·50	1·50
98		40c. scarlet and dull purple	8·50	8·00
99		50c. black/emerald (1.2.36)	10·00	1·50
100		$1 black and red/blue (1.4.36)	3·00	1·25
101		$2 green and scarlet (16.5.36)	48·00	7·00
102		$5 green and red/emerald (16.5.36)	£170	35·00
88/102 Set of 15			£250	55·00
88s/102s Perf "SPECIMEN" Set of 15			£475	

No. 91 exists in coils constructed from normal sheets in 1936.

1938 (2 May)–**41.** Wmk Mult Script CA. Chalk-surfaced paper. P 14.

103	**51**	1c. black (4.39)	20·00	10
104		2c. green (13.1.39)	16·00	10
105		2c. orange (Thin striated paper) (30.10.41)	3·50	23·00
		a. Malformed "2c"	£110	£450
		b. Ordinary paper	9·00	11·00
		ba. Malformed "2c"	£180	£200
106		3c. green (ordinary paper) (21.8.41)	50·00	21·00
		a. Thin striated paper (10.41)	2·75	16·00
107		4c. orange (5.39)	42·00	10
108		5c. brown (1.2.39)	6·50	10
109		6c. scarlet (12.39)	27·00	10
110		8c. grey (1.12.38)	40·00	10
111		8c. scarlet (Thin striated paper) (18.12.41)	1·00	90·00
		a. Ordinary paper	2·50	
112		10c. dull purple (17.10.38)	40·00	10
113		12c. bright ultramarine (17.10.38)	30·00	1·00
114		15c. bright ultramarine (ordinary paper) (8.41)	4·25	13·00
115		25c. dull purple and scarlet (12.39)	50·00	3·50
116		30c. dull purple and orange (17.10.38)	12·00	2·25
		a. Thin striated paper (1941)	15·00	35·00
117		40c. scarlet and dull purple	50·00	3·00
118		50c. black/emerald (17.10.38)	32·00	1·00
119		$1 black and red/blue (7.40)	£150	38·00
120		$2 green and scarlet (9.40)	£250	80·00
121		$5 green and red/emerald (1.41)	£450	£500
103/21 Set of 19			£1100	£700
103s/21s perf "SPECIMEN" Set of 19			£600	

No. 108 exists in coils constructed from normal sheets.

The stamps issued during 1941 were printed by Harrison and Sons following bomb damage to the De La Rue works on 29 December 1940. The used price quoted for No. 111 is for an example with clearly identifiable 1941 cancellation.

During shortages in 1941 stamps of STRAITS SETTLEMENTS (2c. green) and SELANGOR (2c. orange (both perfs), 3c.) were issued in Perak.

1948 (1 Dec). Royal Silver Wedding. As Nos. 112/13 of Antigua.

122		10c. violet	15	10
123		$5 green	23·00	50·00

1949 (10 Oct). 75th Anniv of UPU. As Nos. 114/17 of Antigua.

124		10c. purple	15	10
125		15c. deep blue	1·50	2·00
126		25c. orange	30	6·00
127		50c. blue-black	1·25	3·00
		a. "C" of "CA" missing from Wmk	£800	
124/7 Set of 4			2·75	10·00

52 Sultan Yussuf 'Izzuddin Shah / 53 Sultan Idris Shah

1950 (17 Aug)–**56.** Chalk-surfaced paper. Wmk Mult Script CA. P 17½×18.

128	**52**	1c. black	10	10
129		2c. orange	20	10
130		3c. green	7·00	10
		a. Yellowish green (15.11.51)	23·00	9·00
131		4c. brown	80	10
		a. Yellow-brown (20.6.56)	21·00	1·00
132		5c. bright purple (1.9.52)	75	2·75
		a. Bright mauve (10.11.54)	1·50	2·75
133		6c. grey	50	10
134		8c. scarlet	4·25	4·00
135		8c. green (1.9.52)	1·50	10
136		10c. purple	30	10
		a. Brown-purple (20.6.56)	20·00	65
137		12c. scarlet (1.9.52)	1·50	9·00
138		15c. ultramarine	1·25	10
139		20c. black and green (1.9.52)	2·25	65
140		25c. bright blue (1.9.52)	1·50	10
141		25c. purple and orange	1·00	10
142		30c. scarlet and purple (4.9.55)	4·00	20
143		35c. scarlet and purple (1.9.52)	1·75	25

144		40c. red and purple	10·00	7·50
145		50c. black and blue	10·00	10
146		$1 blue and purple	10·00	1·00
147		$2 green and scarlet	24·00	7·00
148		$5 green and brown	45·00	32·00
128/48		*Set of 21*	£110	55·00

1953 (2 June). Coronation. As No. 120 of Antigua.

149		10c. black and reddish purple	2·50	10

1957 (26 June)–**61**. As Nos. 92/102 of Kedah but with inset portrait of Sultan Yussuf 'Izzuddin Shah.

150	9	1c. black (21.8.57)	10	20
151	10	2c. orange-red (25.7.57)	30	1·00
		a. Red-orange (15.12.59)	1·75	3·50
152	11	4c. sepia (21.8.57)	20	10
153	12	5c. carmine-lake (21.8.57)	20	10
154	13	8c. myrtle-green (21.8.57)	2·00	3·50
155	14	10c. deep brown (4.8.57)	2·75	10
156		10c. deep maroon (21.2.61)	11·00	10
157	15	20c. blue	2·25	10
158	16	50c. black and blue (P 12½) (25.7.57)	1·00	1·00
		a. Perf 12½×13 (24.5.60)	40	10
159	17	$1 ultramarine and reddish purple (25.7.57)	6·50	40
160	18	$2 bronze-green and scarlet (P 12½) (21.8.57)	4·00	8·50
		a. Perf 13×12½ (21.2.61)	10·00	8·00
161	19	$5 brown and bronze-green (P 12½)	19·00	10·00
		a. Perf 13×12½ (24.5.60)	18·00	9·00
150/61		*Set of 12*	42·00	20·00

The 6, 12, 25 and 30c. values used with this issue were Nos. 1/4 of Malayan Federation.

(Photo Harrison)

1963 (26 Oct). Installation of the Sultan of Perak. W w **13**. P 14½.

162	53	10c. red, black, blue and yellow	15	10

54 *Vanda hookeriana*

1965 (15 Nov)–**68**. As Nos. 166/72 of Johore but with inset portrait of Sultan Idris as in T **54**. W w **13** (upright).

163		1c. multicoloured	10	50
		w. Wmk inverted	8·00	
164		2c. multicoloured	10	70
		a. Dark green omitted	£140	
		w. Wmk inverted	18·00	
165		5c. pale blue and multicoloured	10	10
		a. Grey-black and multicoloured (2.4.68)	3·50	30
		b. Yellow (flower) omitted	90·00	
166		6c. multicoloured	15	40
167		10c. multicoloured	15	10
		a. Red omitted	£140	
168		15c. multicoloured	80	10
		a. Black (country name and head) omitted (horizontal pair with normal)	£1600	
		c. Magenta (background) omitted	£1400	
169		20c. multicoloured	1·25	10
		a. Bright purple (blooms) omitted	£190	
163/9		*Set of 7*	2·40	1·60

No. 168a comes from a horizontal strip of three, the centre stamp having the black completely omitted. The two outer stamps show the colour partly omitted.

The 2c. to 15c. exist with PVA gum as well as gum arabic.

The higher values used with this issue were Nos. 20/27 of Malaysia (National Issues).

1970. As Nos. 163 and 167, but W w **13** (sideways).

170	54	1c. multicoloured (27.5.70)	2·50	8·00
171	–	10c. multicoloured (20.11.70)	10·00	4·25

STAMP BOOKLETS

1935.

SB1	$1 booklet containing 20×5c. (No. 91) in blocks of 10		
SB2	$1.30 booklet containing 5c. and 8c. (Nos. 91, 93), each in block of 10		

1938.

SB3	$1 booklet containing 20×5c. (No. 108) in blocks of 10	£3750	
SB4	$1.30 booklet containing 5c. and 8c. (Nos. 108, 110), each in block of 10	£4000	

OFFICIAL STAMPS

P.G.S.   Service.
(O **1**)   (O **2**)

1889 (1 Nov). Stamps of Straits Settlements optd Type O **1**. Wmk Crown CC (Nos. O6 and O8) or Crown CA (others).

O1		2c. bright rose	9·00	11·00
		a. Opt double	£900	£900
		b. Wide space between "G" and "S"	90·00	£110
		c. No stop after "S"	95·00	£120
O2		4c. brown	38·00	40·00
		a. Wide space between "G" and "S"	£160	£180
		b. No stop after "S"	£200	£250
		c. Broken oval	£650	
		w. Wmk inverted	£170	
O3		6c. lilac	45·00	55·00
		a. Wide space between "G" and "S"	£200	£225
O4		8c. orange	50·00	65·00
		a. Wide space between "G" and "S"	£225	£275
O5		10c. slate	75·00	75·00
		a. Wide space between "G" and "S"	£325	£325
O6		12c. blue (CC)	£325	£400
		a. Wide space between "G" and "S"	£1200	
O7		12c. brown-purple (CA)	£250	£325
		a. Wide space between "G" and "S"	£850	

O8		24c. green (CC)	£750	£850
		a. Wide space between "G" and "S"	£2500	
O9		24c. green (CA)	£200	£225
		a. Wide space between "G" and "S"	£750	

Nos. O1/9 were overprinted from a setting of 30 (3×10). The variety "wide space between G and S" occurs on R. 10/3 and R. 10/6 of the original printing. A later printing of the 2c. and 4c. values had this variety corrected, but was without a stop after "S" on R. 10/1 and R. 10/4.

The broken oval flaw occurs on R. 10/5 (lower right pane) of the basic stamp. For illustration see Straits Settlements.

1894 (1 June). No. 64 optd with Type O **2**.

O10		5c. blue	£130	1·00
		a. Overprint inverted	£1700	£500

1897. No. 70 optd with Type O **2**.

O11		5c. dull purple and olive-yellow	3·00	50
		a. Overprint double	£700	£400

PERLIS

The Thai monarchy exercised suzerainty over Perlis and the other northern states of the Malay peninsula from the 16th-century onwards.

The Siamese post office is recorded as opening during 1894. It is believed that the initial cancellation showed Thai characters only, but no complete example has so far been discovered.

Stamps of SIAM cancelled as Type B inscr "PERLIS" (from July 1904).

1887–91. (Nos. 11/18).

Z401	9	12a. purple and carmine	£350
Z402		24a. purple and blue	£450

1897. Surch as T **39** (Siamese) and T **41** (English) (No. 52).

Z403	9	4a. on 12a. purple and carmine	£550

1899–1904. (Nos. 67/81).

Z404	49	1a. olive-green (wide Siamese characters in face value)	£350
Z405		2a. grass-green	£350
Z406		2a. scarlet and pale blue	£350
Z407		3a. red and blue	£500
Z408		4a. carmine	£325
Z409		4a. chocolate and pink	£350
Z410		8a. deep green and orange	£350
Z411		10a. ultramarine	£350
Z412		12a. brown-purple and carmine	£325
Z413		24a. brown-purple and blue	£600

1905–09. (Nos. 97/105).

Z416	53	1a. green and orange	£325
Z417		2a. grey and deep violet	£325
Z418		3a. green	£350
Z419		4a. pale red and sepia	£300
Z420		5a. carmine	£350
Z421		8a. olive-bistre and dull black	£325
Z422		12a. blue	£375
Z423		24a. red-brown	£500

Stamps of SIAM cancelled as Type C inscr "Perlis" at foot (from Sept. 1907).

1887–91. (Nos. 11/18).

Z425	9	12a. purple and carmine	£375

1899–1904. (Nos. 67/81).

Z426	49	1a. olive-green (narrow Siamese characters in face value)	£375
Z427		8a. deep green and orange	£350
Z428		10a. ultramarine	£375

1905–09. (Nos. 92/105).

Z429	53	1a. green and orange	£375
Z430		2a. grey and deep violet	£350
Z431		3a. green	£375
Z432		4a. pale red and sepia	£325
Z433		4a. scarlet	£375
Z434		5a. carmine	£375
Z435		8a. olive-bistre and dull black	£375
Z436		9a. blue	£350
Z437		24a. red-brown	£600

1907. Surch with T **56** (No. 109).

Z438	9	1a. on 24a. purple and blue	£375

Suzerainty over Perlis was transferred by Thailand to Great Britain on 15 July 1909, although the use of Siamese stamps appears to have extended into early August. Stamps of the Federated Malay States were used there until 1912.

Stamps of the Federated Malay States used in Perlis

Cancelled as Type C inscribed "Perlis" at foot.

1909–12. (Nos. 29/34).

Z441	3	1c. green (Die II)	£190
Z442		3c. carmine	£190

Cancelled as Type B inscribed "PERLIS".

1909–12. (Nos. 29/36d).

Z443	3	1c. green (Die II)	£190
Z444		3c. carmine	£110
Z445		4c. black and rose	£190

Federated Malay States stamps were withdrawn on 15 June 1912. The stamps of Kedah were in use in Perlis between 1912 and 1941, as were contemporary 1c. and 4c. stamps of Straits Settlements for a period following March 1919.

A Treaty of Friendship between Great Britain and Perlis was signed on 28 April 1930 and the state joined the Federation of Malaya on 1 February 1948.

1948 (1 Dec). Royal Silver Wedding. As Nos. 112/13 of Antigua.

1		10c. violet	30	2·75
2		$5 brown	32·00	55·00

1949 (10 Oct). 75th Anniv of UPU. As Nos. 114/17 of Antigua.

3		10c. purple	30	2·25
4		15c. deep blue	1·25	5·00
5		25c. orange	45	6·50
6		50c. blue-black	1·00	3·75
		a. "A" of "CA" missing from wmk	£1600	
3/6		*Set of 4*	2·75	16·00

Due to the exhaustion of certain B.M.A. values, KEDAH 2c., 3c., 6c., 15c. and 25c. stamps were used in Perlis from 1st June 1950 until the issue of Nos. 7/27.

1 Raja Syed Putra

1951 (26 Mar)–**55**. Chalk-surfaced paper. Wmk Mult Script CA. P 17½×18.

7	1	1c. black	20	1·00
8		2c. orange	1·00	1·75
9		3c. green	3·00	7·00
10		4c. brown	3·00	1·75
11		5c. bright purple (1.9.52)	1·00	5·50
12		6c. grey	1·50	2·75
13		8c. scarlet	7·50	13·00
14		8c. green (1.9.52)	3·00	3·50
15		10c. purple	2·50	75
		a. Error. St. Edward's Crown W **9b**	£16000	
16		12c. scarlet (1.9.52)	4·25	9·00
17		15c. ultramarine	8·50	12·00
18		20c. black and green	8·50	18·00
19		20c. bright blue (1.9.52)	2·00	2·00
20		25c. purple and orange	3·75	5·00
21		30c. scarlet and purple (4.9.55)	3·50	18·00
22		35c. scarlet and purple (1.9.52)	5·00	9·50
23		40c. red and purple	8·50	45·00
24		50c. black and blue	6·50	8·00
25		$1 blue and purple	12·00	38·00
26		$2 green and scarlet	28·00	70·00
27		$5 green and brown	80·00	£140
7/27		*Set of 21*	£160	£350

1953 (2 June). Coronation. As No. 120 of Antigua.

28		10c. black and reddish purple	2·50	3·75

1957 (26 June)–**62**. As Nos. 92/102 of Kedah but with inset portrait of Raja Syed Putra.

29	9	1c. black (21.8.57)	10	50
30	10	2c. orange-red (25.7.57)	15	50
31	11	4c. sepia (21.8.57)	15	40
32	12	5c. carmine-lake (21.8.57)	15	15
33	13	8c. myrtle-green (21.8.57)	2·00	1·75
34	14	10c. deep brown (4.8.57)	1·50	2·25
35		10c. deep maroon (14.3.61)	19·00	5·00
36	15	20c. blue	4·00	6·00
37	16	50c. black and blue (P 12½) (25.7.57)	1·50	4·50
		a. Perf 12½×13 (8.5.62)	3·50	6·00
38	17	$1 ultramarine and reddish purple (25.7.57)	17·00	23·00
39	18	$2 bronze-green and scarlet (25.7.57)	16·00	12·00
40	19	$5 brown and bronze-green (21.8.57)	17·00	17·00
29/40		*Set of 12*	70·00	65·00

The 6, 12, 25 and 30c. values used with this issue were Nos. 1/4 of Malayan Federation.

1965 (15 Nov). As Nos. 166/72 of Johore but with inset portrait of Raja Syed Putra.

41	9	1c. multicoloured	10	1·00
		w. Wmk inverted	20·00	
42		2c. multicoloured	10	1·50
43		5c. multicoloured	25	40
44		6c. multicoloured	1·00	1·50
45		10c. multicoloured	1·00	40
46		15c. multicoloured	1·00	40
47		20c. multicoloured	1·00	1·75
41/7		*Set of 7*	3·75	6·25

The 6c. exists with PVA gum as well as gum arabic.

The higher values used with this issue were Nos. 20/27 of Malaysia (National Issues).

SABAH

SABAH (136)   SABAH (137)

1964 (1 July)–**65**. Nos. 391/406 of North Borneo (D.L.R. printings), optd with T **136** (Nos. 408/19) or T **137** (Nos. 420/3).

408		1c. emerald and brown-red	10	10
409		4c. bronze-green and orange	15	50
410		5c. sepia and violet	30	10
		a. Light sepia and deep violet (17.8.65)	6·00	4·00
411		6c. black and blue-green	1·25	10
412		10c. green and red	2·25	10
413		12c. brown and grey-green	20	10
414		20c. blue-green and ultramarine	6·00	10
415		25c. grey-black and scarlet	1·25	90
416		30c. sepia and olive	30	10
417		35c. slate-blue and red-brown	30	20
418		50c. emerald and yellow-brown	30	10
419		75c. grey-blue and bright purple	5·50	1·00
420		$1. brown and yellow-green	15·00	2·25
421		$2. brown and slate	17·00	3·25
422		$5. emerald and maroon	17·00	16·00
423		$10. carmine and blue	20·00	40·00
408/23		*Set of 16*	75·00	55·00

Old stocks bearing Waterlow imprints of the 4c., 5c., 20c. and 35c. to $10 were used for overprinting, but in addition new printings of all values by De La Rue using the original plates with the De La Rue imprint replacing the Waterlow imprint were specially made for overprinting.

138 *Vanda hookeriana*

1965 (15 Nov)–**68**. As Nos. 166/72 of Johore, but with Arms of Sabah inset as in T **138**. W w **13** (upright).

424	1c. multicoloured		10	1·25
425	2c. multicoloured		10	2·00
	a. Dark green omitted		£180	
426	5c. multicoloured		10	10
427	6c. multicoloured		30	1·50
428	10c. multicoloured		30	10
429	15c. multicoloured (pale black panel)		3·25	10
	a. Brown-black panel (20.2.68)		5·50	55
430	20c. multicoloured		3·25	75
424/30	*Set of 7*		6·50	5·00

The 5c. to 15c. exist with PVA gum as well as gum arabic. The higher values used with this issue were Nos. 20/27 of Malaysia (National Issues).

1970 (20 Nov). As No. 428, but W w **13** (sideways).

431	10c. multicoloured		5·00	7·00

SARAWAK

Sarawak joined the Federation of Malaysia at its formation on 16 September 1963. For the convenience of collectors, stamps issued after this date continue to be listed with earlier issues of Sarawak.

SELANGOR

The first British Resident was appointed in 1874. Selangor joined the Federated Malay States in 1896.

> The stamps of the STRAITS SETTLEMENTS were used in Selangor from 1879 until 1881.
> Until 1 January 1899, when the Federated Malay States joined the UPU, mail for addresses outside Malaya was franked with stamps of the STRAITS SETTLEMENTS.

PRICES FOR STAMPS ON COVER TO 1945	
Nos. 1/8	
Nos. 9/19	*from* × 10
Nos. 20/30	*from* × 12
Nos. 31/3	*from* × 25
Nos. 34/6	*from* × 20
Nos. 37/8	*from* × 15
Nos. 38a/40	
Nos. 41/2	*from* × 8
Nos. 43	
Nos. 44/8	*from* × 8
Nos. 49/53	*from* × 30
Nos. 54/66	*from* × 10
Nos. 66a/7	*from* × 4
Nos. 68/85	*from* × 3
Nos. 86/7	*from* × 4

Overprints and surcharges were applied by the Government Printer, Singapore, *unless otherwise stated*.

The Straits Settlements 1867 2c. brown with Crown CC watermark (No. 11) has been known since 1881 overprinted in black with a crescent and star over a capital S, all within an oval, similar in style to the overprints listed for Perak and Sungei Ujong.

The status of this item remains unclear, but it may well represent the first issue of distinctive stamps of Selangor. A similar overprint in red on the Straits Settlements 2c. brown with Crown CA watermark also exists and may have been produced for sale to collectors (*Price £400, unused*).

This overprint should not be confused with a somewhat similar cancellation used on Selangor stamps of the same period. This cancellation differs in having a circular frame with the capital S shown above the crescent and star. It is usually struck in red.

SELANGOR **SELANGOR** **SELANCOR**
(1) ("S" inverted and narrow letters) **(2)** ("S" wide) **(3)** (narrow letters)

SELANCOR **SELANGOR** **SELANCOR**
(4) ("N" wide) **(5)** ("SE" and "AN" wide) **(6)** ("SEL" and "N" wide)

SELANGOR
(7) ("SELAN" wide)

1881 (Oct)–**82**. No. 11 (wmk Crown CC) of Straits Settlements optd with T **1**/**7**.

1	1	2c. brown	£950	£1200
2	2	2c. brown	£275	£375
3	3	2c. brown	£170	£190
4	4	2c. brown	£9000	£3500
5	5	2c. brown (1882)	£275	£400
6	6	2c. brown (1882)	£275	£400
7	7	2c. brown (1882)	£275	£400

Nos. 1/3 and 5/7 have been identified as coming from triplet settings, either Nos. 1+2+3, 2+3+1 or 5+6+7. The setting for No. 4 is unknown.

S.
(8)

1882 (June). No. 50 (wmk Crown CA) of Straits Settlements optd with T **8**.

8	8	2c. brown	—	£5000

SELANGOR **SELANGOR** **SELANGOR**
(9) ("SEL" and "NG" wide) **(10)** ("E" and "ANG" wide) **(11)** ("ELANG" wide)

SELANGOR **SELANCOR** **SELANGOR**
(12) ("S" and "L" wide) **(13)** ("S" and "A" wide) **(14)** ("E" wide)

SELANGOR **SELANCOR** **SELANGOR**
(15) ("EL" wide) **(16)** ("SE" and "N" wide) **(17)** ("S" and "N" wide)

1882 (Oct)–**83**. No. 50 (wmk Crown CA) of Straits Settlements optd with T **2**/**3** and **9**/**17**.

9	9	2c. brown	£400	£500
10	10	2c. brown	£400	£500
11	11	2c. brown	£400	£500
12	2	2c. brown (1883)	£200	£160
13	3	2c. brown (1883)	£350	£190
14	12	2c. brown (1883)	—	£3750
15	13	2c. brown (1883)	£950	£750
16	14	2c. brown (1883)	£650	£475
17	15	2c. brown (1883)	£650	£475
18	16	2c. brown (1883)	£225	£225
		a. Opt double	£1100	
19	17	2c. brown (1883)	£225	£225

The above were all printed from triplet settings. Those so far identified are Nos. 9+10+11, 12 (with defective "G") +13+13, 15+16+17 and 18+12+19. No. 14 occurs as the first position of a triplet, but the second and third units are not yet known.

SELANCOR **SELANGOR** **SELANCOR**
(18) ("E" and "A" wide) **(19)** ("A" wide) **(20)** ("L" wide)

SELANGOR **SELANGOR** **SELANGOR**
(21) ("L" narrow) **(22)** ("A" narrow) **(23)** (wide letters)

1883 (Sept)–**85**. No. 63 of Straits Settlements optd with T **2**, **4**, **12**, **14**/**15** and **18**/**23**.

20	12	2c. pale rose	£300	£190
21	14	2c. pale rose	£200	£130
		a. Opt double		
22	4	2c. pale rose (1884)	£225	£180
23	15	2c. pale rose (1884)	£170	£120
		a. Opt double	£1000	
		b. Opt triple		
24	2	2c. pale rose (1884)	£200	£150
25	18	2c. pale rose (1884)	£190	£140
26	19	2c. pale rose (1884)	£500	£190
27	20	2c. pale rose (1884)	£950	£300
28	21	2c. pale rose (1885)	£170	£100
29	22	2c. pale rose (1885)	£225	£170
30	23	2c. pale rose (1885)	£1000	£300
		a. Opt double	†	£1500

The above come from triplet settings with Nos. 20+21+21, 22+22+23, 23+26 (with defective "A") +26, 24+25+23 and 28+29+28 so far identified. The triplets for Nos. 27 and 30 are not known.

SELANGOR *Selangor* **SELANGOR**
(24) **(25)** **(26)**

SELANGOR **SELANGOR** **SELANGOR** **SELANGOR**
(27) **(28)** **(29)** **(30)**

SELANGOR **SELANGOR** **SELANGOR** **SELANGOR**
(31) **(32)** **(33)** **(34)**

1885–**91**. Nos. 63/a of Straits Settlements optd with T **24**/**34**.

31	24	2c. pale rose	23·00	42·00
		a. Opt double	£1100	£950
		w. Wmk inverted	—	£700
32	25	2c. pale rose	£3000	£3000
33	26	2c. pale rose	50·00	55·00
34	27	2c. pale rose (1886)	75·00	65·00
		a. Opt double	†	£800
35	28	2c. pale rose (horiz opt without stop) (1887)	25·00	2·75
		a. Opt double	£800	
		b. *Bright rose*	25·00	2·25
36		2c. pale rose (horiz opt with stop) (1887)	£170	90·00
		a. *Bright rose*		
37	29	2c. pale rose (1889)	£400	90·00
38	30	2c. pale rose (vert opt) (1889)	95·00	6·00
		a. *Bright rose*		
38b		2c. bright rose (horiz opt) (1889)	£4750	
39	31	2c. pale rose (diagonal opt) (1889)	£5000	
40	32	2c. pale rose (1889)	£750	50·00
41	28	2c. bright rose (vert opt without stop) (1890)	30·00	50·00
42	33	2c. bright rose (1890)	£120	3·00
		a. Opt double	†	£600
43	34	2c. bright rose (1891)	£375	£150

Settings:
Nos. 31/4 – each in triplet containing three examples of the same stamp
No. 35 – triplet or 60 (6×10)
No. 36 – 60 (6×10)
Nos. 37/8 – 60 (6×10) containing both overprints in an unknown combination, but with No. 38 predominating
Nos. 38b/9 – not known
Nos. 40/3 – each in 60 (6×10)

SELANGOR **SELANGOR** **SELANGOR**
Two CENTS *Two* CENTS *Two* CENTS
(35) **(36)** **(37)**

SELANGOR **SELANGOR**
Two CENTS *Two* CENTS
(38) **(39)**

1891 (May). No. 68 of Straits Settlements, surch with T **35**/**9**, each with bar obliterating old value.

44	35	2c. on 24c. green	55·00	75·00
45	36	2c. on 24c. green	£300	£325
46	37	2c. on 24c. green	£300	£325
47	38	2c. on 24c. green	£150	£160
		a. "SELANGCR"		
48	39	2c. on 24c. green	£300	£325

Nos. 44/8 come from the one setting used to surcharge the panes of 60. No. 44 occurs in rows 1 to 5, No. 45 on row 6, No. 46 on row 7, No. 47 on rows 8 and 9, and No. 48 on row 10.

The error, No. 47a, occurs in the first printing only and is No. 45 (R. 8/3) on the pane.

40

3 CENTS
(41)

1891 (1 Nov)–**95**. Wmk Crown CA. P 14.

49	40	1c. green (5.93)	1·50	25
50		2c. rose	3·50	2·25
51		2c. orange (27.5.95)	2·75	2·50
52		5c. blue (8.92)	24·00	8·00
49/52	*Set of 4*		29·00	11·50
49s/52s	*Optd "SPECIMEN" Set of 4*		£120	

1894 (Dec). Surch with T **41** by De La Rue. Wmk Crown CA. P 14.

53	40	3c. on 5c. rose	6·00	50
		s. Optd "SPECIMEN"	35·00	

42 **43**

50c. Dented frame above "A" of "SELANGOR" (left pane R. 4/5).

1895 (Sept)–**99**. Wmk Crown CA or Crown CC (dollar values). P 14.

54	42	3c. dull purple and carmine	6·50	30
55		5c. dull purple and olive-yellow	15·00	1·00
56		8c. dull purple and ultramarine (1898)	50·00	10·00
57		10c. dull purple and orange	14·00	4·00
58		25c. green and carmine (1896)	80·00	65·00
59		50c. dull purple and greenish black (1896)	£100	38·00
		a. Dented frame	£1000	
60		50c. green and black (1898)	£450	£130
		a. Dented frame		
61	43	$1 green and yellow-green	75·00	£170
62		$2 green and carmine (1897)	£300	£350
63		$3 green and ochre (1896)	£700	£700
64		$5 green and blue	£350	£450
65		$10 green and purple (1899)	£900	£1500
		s. Optd "SPECIMEN"	£180	
66		$25 green and orange (1897)	£5000	£5000
		s. Optd "SPECIMEN"	£400	
54/62	*Set of 9*		£1000	£700
54s/64s	*Optd "SPECIMEN" Set of 11*		£500	

> Pending the arrival of the permanent Federated Malay States issue the stamps of STRAITS SETTLEMENTS and PERAK were used at various times between July 1900 and 31 December 1901.
> The general issues for the FEDERATED MALAY STATES were used in Selangor from 1901 until 1935.

One cent.
(44)

Three cents.
(45)

nts.

Antique "t" (R. 3/4 and 8/4)

1900 (Oct). Nos. 55 and 59 surch with T **44** or **45**.

66a	42	1c. on 5c. dull purple and olive-yellow (31.10*)	70·00	£130
66b		1c. on 50c. green and black (22.10*)	6·50	42·00
		bc. "cent" repeated at left	£4250	
		bd. Dented frame	£275	
67		3c. on 50c. green and black (24.10*)	6·50	32·00
		a. Antique "t" in "cents"	£375	£650
		b. Dented frame	£400	

*Earliest known postmark date.

It is believed that these stamps were surcharged from settings of 30, repeated four times to complete the sheet of 120.

No. 66bc occurred on two separate vertical strips of five stamps where two impressions of the setting overlapped.

46 Mosque at Palace, Klang   **47** Sultan Suleiman

2c. Joined script (R. 2/1)

(Des E. J. McNaughton)

1935 (2 Dec)–**41**. Wmk Mult Script CA (sideways on T **46**). Chalk-surfaced paper. P 14 or 14×14½ (No. 70).

68	**46**	1c. black (1.1.36)	30	10
69		2c. green (1.1.36)	1·00	10
		a. Joined script	75·00	30·00
70		2c. orange (*ordinary paper*) (P 14×14½) (21.8.41)	8·00	75
		aa. Joined script	£190	55·00
		a. Perf 14. Ordinary paper (9.41)	20·00	1·00
		ab. Joined script	£425	75·00
		b. Perf 14. Thin striated paper	£160	
		ba. Joined script		
71		3c. green (*ordinary paper*) (21.8.41)	6·50	10·00
		a. Thin striated paper (10.41)	50·00	2·75
72		4c. orange	50	10
73		5c. brown (5.12.35)	70	10
74		6c. scarlet (1.1.37)	14·00	10
75		8c. grey	60	10
76		10c. dull purple (1.1.36)	60	10
77		12c. bright ultramarine (1.1.36)	2·00	10
78		15c. bright ultramarine (*ordinary paper*) (1.10.41)	12·00	32·00
79		25c. dull purple and scarlet (1.4.36)	1·00	60
		a. Thin striated paper (1941)	4·00	£100
80		30c. dull purple and orange (1.4.36)	1·00	85
		a. Thin striated paper (1941)	4·00	£100
81		40c. scarlet and dull purple	1·50	1·00
82		50c. black/*emerald* (1.2.36)	1·00	15
83	**47**	$1 black and rose/*blue* (1.4.36)	17·00	90
84		$2 green and scarlet (16.5.36)	38·00	7·00
85		$5 green and red/*emerald* (16.5.36)	£110	20·00
68/85 *Set of 18*			£180	60·00
68s/85s Perf "SPECIMEN" *Set of 18*			£500	

The stamps issued during 1941 were printed by Harrison and Sons following bomb damage to the De La Rue works on 29 December 1940. The used prices quoted for Nos. 79a and 80a are for examples with clearly indentifiable 1941 cancellations.

No. 69 exists in coils constructed from normal sheets.

Supplies of an unissued 8c. scarlet on thin striated paper were diverted to Australia in 1941. Examples circulating result from leakages of this supply (*Price* £1200).

48 Sultan Hisamud-din Alam Shah   **49** Sultan Hisamud-din Alam Shah

1941. Wmk Mult Script CA. Chalk-surfaced paper. P 14.

86	**48**	$1 black and red/*blue* (15.4.41)	24·00	7·50
87		$2 green and scarlet (7.7.41)	50·00	50·00
		s. Perf "SPECIMEN"		

A $5 green and red on emerald, T **48**, was issued overprinted during the Japanese occupation of Malaya. Unoverprinted examples are known, but were not issued (*Price* £180).

> During shortages in 1941 stamps of STRAITS SETTLEMENTS (2c. and 30c.) and PERAK (2c., 25c. and 50c.) were issued in Selangor.

1948 (1 Dec). Royal Silver Wedding. As Nos. 112/13 of Antigua.

88		10c. violet	20	30
89		$5 green	27·00	22·00

1949 (12 Sept)–**55**. Wmk Mult Script CA. Chalk-surfaced paper. P 17½×18.

90	**49**	1c. black	10	60
91		2c. orange	30	1·50
92		3c. green	4·50	1·00
93		4c. brown	60	10
94		5c. bright purple (1.9.52)	2·00	3·25
		a. Bright mauve (17.9.53)	50	2·00
95		6c. grey	30	40
96		8c. scarlet	4·00	1·00
97		8c. green (1.9.52)	1·25	1·75
98		10c. purple	20	10
99		12c. scarlet (1.9.52)	2·50	4·50
		w. Wmk inverted	£1200	
100		15c. ultramarine	10·00	10
101		20c. black and green	10·00	35
102		20c. bright blue (1.9.52)	1·00	10
103		25c. purple and orange	2·00	20
104		30c. scarlet and purple (4.9.55)	3·50	2·25
105		35c. scarlet and purple (1.9.52)	1·25	1·50
106		40c. scarlet and purple	17·00	9·50
107		50c. black and blue	3·50	10
108		$1 blue and purple	3·50	60
109		$2 green and scarlet	15·00	10
110		$5 green and brown	48·00	3·75
90/110 *Set of 21*			£110	27·00

1949 (10 Oct). 75th Anniv of UPU. As Nos. 114/17 of Antigua.

111		10c. purple	30	10
112		15c. deep blue	2·50	2·50
113		25c. orange	35	4·50
114		50c. blue-black	1·00	7·00
111/14 *Set of 4*			3·75	12·50

1953 (2 June). Coronation. As No. 120 of Antigua.

115		10c. black and reddish purple	2·00	10

1957 (26 June)–**61**. As Nos. 92/102 of Kedah but with inset portrait of Sultan Hisamud-din Alum Shah.

116	**9**	1c. black (21.8.57)	10	2·25
117	**10**	2c. orange-red (25.7.57)	30	1·00
		a. *Red-orange* (10.11.59)	13·00	7·50
118	**11**	4c. sepia (21.8.57)	10	10
119	**12**	5c. carmine-lake (21.8.57)	10	10
120	**13**	8c. myrtle-green (21.8.57)	4·25	3·00
121	**14**	10c. deep brown (4.8.57)	2·50	10
122		10c. deep maroon (9.5.61)	17·00	10
123	**15**	20c. blue	2·75	20
124	**16**	50c. black and blue (P 12½) (25.7.57)	75	10
		a. Perf 12½×13 (10.5.60)	2·00	30
125	**17**	$1 ultramarine and reddish purple (25.7.57)	10·00	10
126	**18**	$2 bronze-green and scarlet (P 12½) (21.8.57)	9·50	3·00
		a. Perf 13×12½ (6.12.60)	10·00	3·00
127	**19**	$5 brown and bronze-green (P 12½)	16·00	3·25
		a. Perf 13×12½ (10.5.60)	16·00	2·50
116/27 *Set of 12*			55·00	10·50

The 6, 12, 25 and 30c. values used with this issue were Nos. 1/4 of Malayan Federation.

50 Sultan Salahuddin Abdul Aziz Shah   **51** Sultan Salahuddin Abdul Aziz Shah

(Photo Harrison)

1961 (28 June). Coronation of the Sultan. W w **12**. P 15×14.

128	**50**	10c. multicoloured	20	10

A sheet existed showing the black printing so misplaced as to produce an effect of a "Double-headed" Sultan (*Price* £180 un.).

1961–62. As Nos. 92/8 of Kedah but with inset portrait of Sultan Salahuddin Abdul Aziz as in T **51**. W w **13**. P 12½×13 (vert) or 13×12½ (horiz).

129		1c. black (1.3.62)	1·75	3·75
130		2c. orange-red (1.3.62)	2·50	3·75
131		4c. sepia (1.3.62)	2·50	10
132		5c. carmine-lake (1.3.62)	2·50	10
133		8c. myrtle-green (1.3.62)	9·00	8·50
134		10c. deep maroon (1.11.61)	1·50	10
135		20c. blue (1.3.62)	11·00	2·25
129/35 *Set of 7*			28·00	16·00

52 *Vanda hookeriana*

1965 (15 Nov). As Nos. 166/72 of Johore but with inset portrait of Sultan Salahuddin Abdul Aziz Shah as in T **52**.

136		1c. multicoloured	10	20
		b. Magenta omitted	£180	
		w. Wmk inverted	1·00	
137		2c. multicoloured	10	1·75
		b. Yellow (flower) omitted	75·00	
138		5c. multicoloured	2·00	10
		b. Yellow (flower) omitted	80·00	
		c. Red (leaves, etc) omitted	£375	
139		6c. multicoloured	15	10
140		10c. multicoloured	15	10
		a. Red omitted	£150	
141		15c. multicoloured	1·25	10
		b. Green (value and leaves) omitted	£800	
142		20c. multicoloured	1·90	70
		a. Bright purple (blooms) omitted	£200	
		b. Yellow (leaves) omitted	85·00	
136/42 *Set of 7*			5·00	2·50

The 2c. to 20c. values exist with PVA gum as well as gum arabic. The higher values used with this issue were Nos. 20/27 of Malaysia (National Issues).

1970 (20 Nov). As Nos. 136 etc. but W w **13** (sideways).

143	**52**	1c. multicoloured	1·75	9·00
144	–	10c. multicoloured	5·00	2·00
145	–	20c. multicoloured	9·00	15·00
143/5 *Set of 3*			14·00	23·00

STAMP BOOKLETS

1935. Stapled.

SB1	$1 booklet containing 20×5c. (No. 73) in blocks of 10	£4000
SB2	$1.30 booklet containing 5c. and 8c. (Nos. 73, 75), each in block of 10	£4000

TRENGGANU

A Thai post office operated at Kuala Trengganu between 1892 and 1895. A single example of the 1887-91 8a. green and yellow has been seen with a type B circular postmark inscribed "TRINGANU".

Suzerainty over Trengganu was transferred by Thailand to Great Britain in 1909. A British adviser was appointed in 1919. The state joined the Federation of Malaya on 1 February 1948.

PRICES FOR STAMPS ON COVER TO 1945	
Nos. 1/15	*from* × 12
No. 16/18	—
Nos. 19/22	*from* × 10
Nos. 23/33	*from* × 12
Nos. 34/6	—
Nos. 37/47	*from* × 15
Nos. 48/60	*from* × 6
Nos. D1/4	—

RED CROSS

1 Sultan Zain ul ab din   **2** Sultan Zain ul ab din

2c. (**3**)

1910 (14 Dec)–**19**. Wmk Mult Crown CA. Ordinary paper (1c. to 10c.) or chalk-surfaced paper (20c. to $25). P 14.

1	**1**	1c. blue-green	1·75	1·00
		a. *Green*	2·75	1·50
2		2c. brown and purple (1915)	1·00	1·00
3		3c. carmine-red	2·25	2·25
4		4c. orange	3·50	7·50
5		4c. red-brown and green (1915)	2·00	4·75
5a		4c. carmine-red (1919)	1·25	2·75
6		5c. grey	1·25	7·50
7		5c. grey and brown (1915)	2·25	2·00
8		8c. ultramarine	1·25	17·00
9		10c. purple/*yellow*	6·50	22·00
		a. *On pale yellow*	3·50	17·00
10		10c. green and red/*yellow* (1915)	1·25	2·25
11		20c. dull and bright purple	4·00	9·50
12		25c. green and dull purple (1915)	14·00	50·00
13		30c. dull purple and black (1915)	14·00	70·00
14		50c. black/*green*	4·50	17·00
15		$1 black and carmine/*blue*	17·00	28·00
16		$3 green and red/*green* (1915)	£250	£650
17	**2**	$5 green and dull purple (1912)	£275	£900
18		$25 rose-carmine and green (1912) (F.C. £200)	£1700	£4000
		s. Optd "SPECIMEN"	£400	
1/17 *Set of 17*			£500	£1600
1s/17s Optd "SPECIMEN" *Set of 18*			£750	

The 8c. is known used bisected at Kretai in December 1918. Such use was not officially authorised.

1917 (June)–**18**. Surch with T **3**.

19	**1**	3c. + 2c. carmine-red	50	11·00
		a. Comma after "2c."	10·00	48·00
		b. "SS" in "CROSS" inverted	£425	£500
		c. "CSOSS" for "CROSS"	95·00	£225
		d. "2" in thick block type	22·00	75·00
		e. Surch inverted	£1200	£1300
		f. Pair, one without surch	£5000	£4500
		g. "RED CROSS" omitted	£450	
		h. "RED CROSS" twice	£550	
		i. "2c." omitted	£450	
		j. "2c." twice	£550	
20		4c. + 2c. orange	1·50	20·00
		a. Comma after "2c."	18·00	70·00
		b. "SS" in "CROSS" inverted	£2000	£1600
		c. "CSOSS" for "CROSS"	£180	£425
		d. Surch double	£1300	
		e. "RED CROSS" omitted	£500	
		f. "RED CROSS" twice	£750	
		g. "2c." omitted	£500	
		h. "2c." twice	£700	
21		4c. + 2c. red-brown and green (1918)	3·75	50·00
		a. Pair, one without surch	£4750	50·00
		b. "RED CROSS" omitted	£1000	
		c. "RED CROSS" twice	£1000	
		d. "SS" in "CROSS" inverted	—	£4000
22		8c. + 2c. ultramarine (1917)	1·25	38·00
		a. Comma after "2c."	9·00	85·00
		b. "SS" in "CROSS" inverted	£1000	£1100
		c. "CSOSS" for "CROSS"	£150	£425
		d. "RED CROSS" omitted	£500	
		e. "RED CROSS" twice	£650	
		f. "2c." omitted	£500	
		g. "2c." twice	£600	

Nos. 19/22 were sold at face, plus 2c. on each stamp for Red Cross funds.

The surcharges on Nos. 19/22 were arranged in settings of 18 (6×3) applied three times to cover the top nine rows of the sheet with the tenth row completed by a further impression so that "RED CROSS" from the centre row of the setting appears on the bottom sheet margin. Specialists recognise six different settings:

Setting I – Shows comma after "2" on both R. 1/3 and 1/5, "SS" inverted on R. 1/6 and "CSOSS" for "CROSS" on R. 2/1. Used for 3c., 4c. orange and 8c.

Setting Ia – Inverted "SS" on R. 1/6 corrected. Other varieties as Setting I. Used for 3c., 4c. orange and 8c.

Setting II – "CSOSS" on R. 2/1 corrected. Comma varieties as Setting I. Used for 3c., 4c. orange and 8c.

Setting III – Both comma varieties now corrected. Used for 3c., both 4c. and 8c.

Setting IIIa – "SS" inverted on R. 2/5. Used for 3c. only

Setting IV – Thick block "2" on R. 2/2. Inverted "SS" on R. 2/5 corrected. Used for 3c. only.

Nos. 19g/j, 20e/h, 21b/c and 22d/g result from the misplacement of the surcharge.

During a temporary shortage between March and August 1921 2c., 4c. and 6c. stamps of the STRAITS SETTLEMENTS were authorised for use in Trengganu.

4 Sultan Suleiman

5 Sultan Suleiman

2 CENTS
(6)

1921–41. Chalk-surfaced paper. P 14.

(a) Wmk Mult Crown CA
23	**4**	$1 purple and blue/*blue*	12·00	23·00
24		$3 green and red/*emerald*	£130	£275
25	**5**	$5 green and red/*pale yellow*	£170	£450

23/5 *Set of 3* £275 £700
23s/5s Optd "SPECIMEN" *Set of 3* £200

(b) Wmk Mult Script CA
26	**4**	1c. black (1926)	1·75	1·50
		a. Ordinary paper (1941)	—	£110
27		2c. green	2·25	2·00
		a. Ordinary paper (1941)	£425	£110
28		3c. green (1926)	2·00	1·00
29		3c. reddish brown (1938)	45·00	14·00
		a. Ordinary paper. *Chestnut* (1941)	—	32·00
30		4c. rose-red	4·50	1·25
		a. Ordinary paper. *Scarlet-vermilion* (1941)	£425	50·00
31		5c. grey and deep brown	2·00	5·00
32		5c. purple/*yellow* (1926)	1·75	1·25
		a. *Deep reddish purple/bright yellow* (1939)	£250	5·00
33		6c. orange (1924)	8·00	1·00
		a. Ordinary paper (1941)	—	£300
34		8c. grey (1938)	50·00	9·50
		a. Ordinary paper (1941)	—	50·00
35		10c. bright blue	3·75	1·25
36		12c. bright ultramarine (1926)	4·25	1·75
37		20c. dull purple and orange	4·25	1·50
38		25c. green and deep purple	5·00	2·50
39		30c. dull purple and black	4·00	3·75
40		35c. carmine/*yellow* (1926)	4·75	3·25
41		50c. green and bright carmine	12·00	2·75
42		$1 purple and blue/*blue* (1929)	9·00	3·25
43		$3 green and lake/*green* (1926)	65·00	£190
		a. Green and brown-red/*green* (1938)	£170	
44	**5**	$5 green and red/*yellow* (1938)	£500	£3750
45		$25 purple and blue (F.C. £200)	£1300	£3000
		s. Optd "SPECIMEN"	£325	
46		$50 green and yellow (F.C. £600)	£3250	£5000
		s. Optd "SPECIMEN"	£600	
47		$100 green and scarlet (F.C. £600)	£9500	£11000
		s. Optd "SPECIMEN"	£1100	

26/43 *Set of 18* £200 £225
26s/44s Optd or Perf (3c. reddish brown, 8c., $1, $5) "SPECIMEN" *Set of 19* £1000

The used price quoted for No. 44 is for an example with an identifiable cancellation from 1938–41.

Printings of the 2c. yellow-orange, 3c. blue-green, 4c. purple/*yellow*, 6c. slate-grey, 8c. rose, 15c. ultramarine and $1 black and red/*blue* on ordinary paper were despatched to Malaya in late 1941, but did not arrive before the Japanese occupation. Unused examples are known of the 2, 3, 6, 8 and 15c. (*Prices,* 3c. £1400, *others* £325 *each, unused*).

The 12c. bright ultramarine was also printed on ordinary paper, and exists overprinted during the Japanese occupation. See No. J107b.

OVERPRINT SETTINGS FOR NOS. 48/58. The low values in Types **1** and **4** were overprinted using Setting II as detailed under Straits Settlements. The three listed constant varieties from the original typeset block of 12 occur in the same positions for these Trengganu stamps as does the No stop variety from R. 1/5 of the left pane.

A separate setting, believed to be of 30 (6×5), was required for the $5 in the larger design. This was constructed by duplicating the second horizontal row of the original typeset block five times so that the raised stop after "EXHIBITION" variety occurs on all stamps in the second vertical row and the small second "A" in "MALAYA" on all stamps in the sixth.

1922 (Apr). Malaya-Borneo Exhibition, Singapore. Optd as T **56** of Straits Settlements at Singapore.
48	**4**	2c. green	8·00	45·00
		b. Oval last "O" in "BORNEO"	17·00	80·00
		c. Raised stop after "EXHIBITION"	17·00	80·00
		d. Small second "A" in "MALAYA"	17·00	80·00
		f. No stop	95·00	
49		4c. rose-red	6·50	50·00
		b. Oval last "O" in "BORNEO"	14·00	85·00
		c. Raised stop after "EXHIBITION"	14·00	85·00
		d. Small second "A" in "MALAYA"	14·00	85·00
		f. No stop	90·00	
50	**1**	5c. grey and brown	3·50	50·00
		b. Oval last "O" in "BORNEO"	8·00	85·00
		c. Raised stop after "EXHIBITION"	8·00	85·00
		d. Small second "A" in "MALAYA"	8·00	85·00
		f. No stop	90·00	
51		10c. green and red/*yellow*	5·50	50·00
		b. Oval last "O" in "BORNEO"	12·00	85·00
		c. Raised stop after "EXHIBITION"	12·00	85·00
		d. Small second "A" in "MALAYA"	12·00	85·00
		f. No stop	£100	
52		20c. dull and bright purple	9·00	50·00
		b. Oval last "O" in "BORNEO"	19·00	85·00
		c. Raised stop after "EXHIBITION"	19·00	85·00
		d. Small second "A" in "MALAYA"	19·00	85·00
		f. No stop	£130	
53		25c. green and dull purple	9·00	50·00
		b. Oval last "O" in "BORNEO"	11·00	85·00
		c. Raised stop after "EXHIBITION"	11·00	85·00
		d. Small second "A" in "MALAYA"	11·00	85·00
		f. No stop	90·00	
54		30c. dull purple and black	5·50	50·00
		b. Oval last "O" in "BORNEO"	12·00	85·00
		c. Raised stop after "EXHIBITION"	12·00	85·00
		d. Small second "A" in "MALAYA"	12·00	85·00
		f. No stop	£100	
55		50c. black/*green*	10·00	50·00
		b. Oval last "O" in "BORNEO"	21·00	95·00
		c. Raised stop after "EXHIBITION"	21·00	95·00
		d. Small second "A" in "MALAYA"	21·00	95·00
		f. No stop	£130	
56		$1 black and carmine/*blue*	14·00	75·00
		b. Oval last "O" in "BORNEO"	27·00	£160
		c. Raised stop after "EXHIBITION"	27·00	£160
		d. Small second "A" in "MALAYA"	27·00	£160
		f. No stop	£190	
57		$3 green and red/*green*	£225	£475
		b. Oval last "O" in "BORNEO"	£425	£900
		c. Raised stop after "EXHIBITION"	£425	£900
		d. Small second "A" in "MALAYA"	£425	£900
		f. No stop	£2750	
58	**2**	$5 green and dull purple	£375	£700
		c. Raised stop after "EXHIBITION"	£600	£1200
		d. Small second "A" in "MALAYA"	£600	£1200

48/58 *Set of 11* £600 £1400

1941 (1 May). Nos. 32a and 35 surch as T **6**.
59	**4**	2c. on 5c. deep reddish purple/*bright yellow*	6·50	3·50
60		8c. on 10c. bright blue	7·00	9·00

1948 (2 Dec). Royal Silver Wedding. As Nos. 112/13 of Antigua.
61		10c. violet	15	1·75
62		$5 carmine	26·00	42·00

1949 (10 Oct). 75th Anniv of UPU. As Nos. 114/17 of Antigua.
63		10c. purple	30	75
64		15c. deep blue	1·90	4·25
65		25c. orange	40	4·00
66		50c. blue-black	1·00	3·50
		a. "C" of "CA" missing from wmk	£900	

63/6 *Set of 4* .... 3·25 11·00

7 Sultan Ismail

8 *Vanda hookeriana*

1949 (27 Dec)–**55.** Wmk Mult Script CA. Chalk-surfaced paper. P 17½×18.
67	**7**	1c. black	1·00	75
68		2c. orange	1·25	75
69		3c. green	7·00	7·50
70		4c. brown	30	60
71		5c. bright purple (1.9.52)	50	1·75
72		6c. grey	2·25	60
73		8c. scarlet	1·00	4·50
74		8c. green (1.9.52)	1·25	1·75
		a. Deep green (11.8.53)	20·00	20·00
75		10c. purple	30	30
76		12c. scarlet (1.9.52)	1·25	4·00
77		15c. ultramarine	10·00	30
78		20c. black and green	10·00	3·75
79		20c. bright blue (1.9.52)	1·50	40
80		25c. purple and orange	3·00	2·00
81		30c. scarlet and purple (4.9.55)	1·25	2·25
82		35c. scarlet and purple (1.9.52)	2·50	2·25
83		40c. red and purple	15·00	29·00
84		50c. black and blue	2·25	2·25
85		$1 blue and purple	7·00	18·00
86		$2 green and scarlet	45·00	50·00
87		$5 green and brown	75·00	70·00

67/87 *Set of 21* £160 £180

1953 (2 June). Coronation. As No. 120 of Antigua.
88		10c. black and reddish purple	2·50	1·25

1957 (26 June)–**63.** As Nos. 92/102 of Kedah, but with inset portrait of Sultan Ismail.
89	**9**	1c. black (21.8.57)	10	20
90	**10**	2c. orange-red (25.7.57)	1·50	30
		a. Red-orange (21.2.61)	45·00	15·00
91	**11**	4c. sepia (21.8.57)	15	10
92	**12**	5c. carmine-lake (21.8.57)	15	10
93	**13**	8c. myrtle-green (21.8.57)	4·00	60
94	**14**	10c. deep brown (4.8.57)	2·75	10
94a		10c. deep maroon (21.2.61)	14·00	30
95	**15**	20c. blue	2·75	1·60
96	**16**	50c. black and blue (P 12½) (25.7.57)	55	2·50
		a. Perf 12½×13 (17.5.60)	55	2·75
		ab. *Black and ultramarine* (20.3.62)	2·00	1·75
97	**17**	$1 ultramarine and reddish purple (25.7.57)	16·00	10·00
98	**18**	$2 bronze-green and scarlet (21.8.57)	19·00	9·50
99	**19**	$5 brown and bronze-green	35·00	22·00
		a. Perf 13×12½ (13.8.63)	25·00	45·00

89/99 *Set of 12* .... 70·00 42·00

The 6, 12, 25 and 30c. values used with this issue were Nos. 1/4 of Malayan Federation.

1965 (15 Nov). As Nos. 166/72 of Johore but with inset portrait of Sultan Ismail Nasiruddin Shah as in T **8**.
100		1c. multicoloured	10	2·00
101		2c. multicoloured	10	2·00
102		5c. multicoloured	15	1·00
		w. Wmk inverted		
103		6c. multicoloured	15	2·00
104		10c. multicoloured	20	25
105		15c. multicoloured	1·50	10
		a. Black (country name and portrait) omitted (horizontal pair with normal)	£1700	
106		20c. multicoloured	1·50	1·50
		a. Bright purple (blooms) omitted	£250	

100/6 *Set of 7* .... 3·25 8·00

The 5c. value exists with PVA gum as well as gum arabic.
No. 101a, formerly listed here, is now listed as Sarawak No. 213a.
The higher values used with this issue were Nos. 20/27 of Malaysia (National Issues).

9 Sultan of Trengganu

(Des Enche Nik Zainal Abidin. Photo Harrison)

1970 (16 Dec). 25th Anniv of Installation of H.R.H. Tuanku Ismail Nasiruddin Shah as Sultan of Trengganu. P 14½×13½.
107	**9**	10c. multicoloured	1·00	3·25
108		15c. multicoloured	75	1·25
109		50c. multicoloured	1·25	3·25

107/9 *Set of 3* .... 2·75 7·00

POSTAGE DUE STAMPS

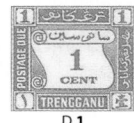
D 1

1937 (10 Aug). Wmk Mult Script CA (sideways). P 14.
D1	**D 1**	1c. scarlet	8·50	55·00
D2		4c. green	9·50	60·00
D3		8c. yellow	55·00	£350
D4		10c. brown	£120	£100

D1/4 *Set of 4* £170 £500
D1s/4s Perf "SPECIMEN" *Set of 4* £160

VIII. JAPANESE OCCUPATION OF MALAYA

PRICES FOR STAMPS ON COVER
Nos. J1/55	*from × 10*
Nos. J56/76	*from × 12*
Nos. J77/89	*from × 20*
Nos. J90/1	*from × 15*
Nos. J92/115	*from × 6*
Nos. J116/18	—
Nos. J119/32	*from × 12*
Nos. J133/45	*from × 10*
Nos. J146/223	*from × 6*
Nos. J224/58	*from × 12*
No. J259	*from × 15*
Nos. J260/96	*from × 12*
Nos. J297/310	*from × 20*
Nos. J311/17	—
Nos. JD1/10	*from × 30*
Nos. JD11/16	*from × 12*
Nos. JD17/20	*from × 30*
Nos. JD21/7	*from × 20*
Nos. JD28/33	*from × 30*
Nos. JD34/41	*from × 60*

Japanese forces invaded Malaya on 8 December 1941 with the initial landings taking place at Kota Bharu on the east coast. Penang fell, to a force which crossed the border from Thailand, on 19 December, Kuala Lumpur on 11 January 1942 and the conquest of the Malay peninsula was completed by the capture of Singapore on 15 February.

During the Japanese Occupation various small Dutch East Indies islands near Singapore were administered as part of Malaya. Stamps of the Japanese Occupation of Malaya were issued to the post offices of Dabo Singkep, Puloe Samboe, Tanjong Balei, Tanjong Batu, Tanjong Pinang and Terempa between 1942 and 1945. The overprinted issues were also used by a number of districts in Atjeh (Northern Sumatra) whose postal services were administered from Singapore until the end of March 1943.

Malayan post offices were also opened in October 1943 to serve camps of civilians working on railway construction and maintenance in Thailand. Overprinted stamps of the Japanese Occupation of Malaya were used at these offices between October 1943 and the end of the year after which mail from the camps was carried free. Their postmarks were inscribed in Japanese Katakana characters, and, uniquely, showed the Japanese postal symbol.

JOHORE

The postal service in Johore was reconstituted in mid-April 1942 using Nos. J146/60 and subsequently other general issues. Stamps of Johore overprinted "DAI NIPPON 2602" were, however, only used for fiscal purposes. Overprinted Johore postage due stamps were not issued for use elsewhere in Malaya.

POSTAGE DUE STAMPS

馬來軍政部郵政局印
大日本郵便
大日本郵便

(**1**) (Upright)　(**2**)　Second character sideways (R. 6/3)

1942 (1 Apr). Nos. D1/5 of Johore optd as T **1** in brown.
JD1	**D 1**	1c. carmine	50·00	85·00
		a. Black opt	20·00	70·00
JD2		4c. green	80·00	£100
		a. Black opt	65·00	80·00
JD3		8c. orange	£140	£160
		a. Black opt	80·00	95·00
JD4		10c. brown	50·00	70·00
		a. Black opt	16·00	50·00

JD5		12c. purple	£100	£110
	a.	Black opt	48·00	55·00

1943. Nos. D1/5 of Johore optd with T **2**.

JD6	D **1**	1c. carmine	10·00	35·00
	a.	Second character sideways	£375	£800
JD7		4c. green	8·00	40·00
	a.	Second character sideways	£400	£800
JD8		8c. orange	10·00	40·00
	a.	Second character sideways	£450	£850
JD9		10c. brown	9·50	50·00
	a.	Second character sideways	£450	£950
JD10		12c. purple	11·00	65·00
	a.	Second character sideways	£500	£1100
JD6/10 *Set of 5*			45·00	£200

KEDAH

Postal services resumed by 31 January 1942 using unoverprinted Kedah values from 1c. to 8c. which were accepted for postage until 13 May 1942.

During the Japanese occupation Perlis was administered as part of Kedah.

DAI NIPPON   DAI NIPPON

2602   2602

(3)   (4)

1942 (13 May)–**43**. Stamps of Kedah (Script wmk) optd with T **3** (1c. to 8c.) or **4** (10c. to $5), both in red.

J1	**1**	1c. black (No. 68a)	10·00	16·00
J2		2c. bright green (No. 69)	27·00	30·00
J3		4c. violet	12·00	4·00
	a.	Short sheaf	£300	£180
J4		5c. yellow	5·50	6·50
	a.	Black opt (1943)	£200	£225
J5		6c. carmine (No. 56) (Blk.)	7·50	25·00
	a.	*Carmine-red* (No. 56a)	50·00	75·00
J6		8c. grey-black	8·50	5·00
J7	**6**	10c. ultramarine and sepia	18·00	20·00
J8		12c. black and violet	42·00	60·00
J9		25c. ultramarine and purple	16·00	28·00
	a.	Black opt (1943)	£475	£350
J10		30c. green and scarlet	70·00	80·00
J11		40c. black and purple	42·00	50·00
J12		50c. brown and blue	42·00	50·00
J13		$1 black and green	£140	£150
	a.	Opt inverted	£900	£1000
J14		$2 green and brown	£170	£170
	a.	Opt double	—	£1400
J15		$5 black and scarlet	80·00	£110
	a.	Black opt (1943)	£1600	£1300
J1/15 *Set of 15*			£600	£700

Nos. J1/15 were gradually replaced by issues intended for use throughout Malaya. Kedah and Perlis were ceded to Thailand by the Japanese on 19 October 1943.

KELANTAN

Postal services resumed on 1 June 1942. Stamps used in Kelantan were overprinted with the personal seals of Sunagawa, the Japanese Governor, and of Handa, the Assistant Governor.

(5) Sunagawa (6) Handa
Seal   Seal

$1.00

40 CENTS ■ ■ ■
(7)   (8)

1 Cents

(9)

1942 (June). Stamps of Kelantan surch.

*(a) As T **7** or **8** (dollar values). Optd with T **5** in red*

J16	**4**	1c. on 50c. grey-olive and orange	£475	£250
J17		2c. on 40c. orange and blue-green	£1400	£400
J18		4c. on 30c. violet and scarlet	£3750	£2250
J19		5c. on 12c. blue (R.)	£450	£250
J20		6c. on 25c. vermilion and violet	£450	£250
J21		8c. on 5c. red-brown (R.)	£700	£170
J22		10c. on 6c. lake	95·00	£140
	a.	"CENST" for "CENTS"	£15000	
J23		12c. on 8c. grey-olive (R.)	65·00	£130
J24		25c. on 10c. purple (R.)	£2500	£2250
J25		30c. on 4c. scarlet	£3250	£3000
J26		40c. on 2c. green (R.)	75·00	£100
	a.	Surch double (B.+R.)	£7000	
J27		50c. on 1c. grey-olive and yellow	£2500	£2000
J28	**1**	$1 on 4c. black and red (R., bars Blk.)	50·00	95·00
J29		$2 on 5c. green and red/*yellow*	50·00	95·00
J30		$5 on 6c. scarlet	50·00	95·00
	a.	Surch double	£600	

*(b) As T **7**. Optd with T **6** in red*

J31	**4**	12c. on 8c. grey-olive	£275	£450
	a.	Type **6** omitted (in horiz pair with normal)	£5500	

*(c) As T **9**. Optd with T **5** in red*

J32	**4**	1c. on 50c. grey-olive and orange	£300	£130
	a.	"Cente" for "Cents" (R. 5/1)	£4000	£1700
J33		2c. on 40c. orange and blue-green	£400	£190
	a.	"Cente" for "Cents" (R. 5/1)	£4500	£2250
J34		5c. on 12c. blue (R.)	£225	£250
	a.	"Cente" for "Cents" (R. 5/1)	£3500	

J35		8c. on 5c. red-brown (R.)	£190	95·00
	a.	"Cente" for "Cents" (R. 5/1)	£2750	£1500
J36		10c. on 6c. lake	£600	£650
	a.	"Cente" for "Cents" (R. 5/1)	£5500	

*(d) As T **9**. Optd with T **6** in red*

J41	**4**	1c. on 50c. grey-olive and orange	£190	£250
	a.	"Cente" for "Cents" (R. 5/1)	£2750	
J42		2c. on 40c. orange and blue-green	£200	£250
	a.	"Cente" for "Cents" (R. 5/1)	£3000	
J43		8c. on 5c. red-brown (R.)	90·00	£170
	a.	"Cente" for "Cents" (R. 5/1)	£1900	
J44		10c. on 6c. lake	£140	£250
	a.	"Cente" for "Cents" (R. 5/1)	£2500	

As stamps of the above series became exhausted the equivalent values from the series intended for use throughout Malaya were introduced. Stamps as Nos. J28/30, J32/3 and J35/6, but without Type **5** or **6**, are from remainders sent to Singapore or Kuala Lumpur after the state had been ceded to Thailand (*Price from £16 each unused*). Nos. J19, J21, J23 and J25/6 have also been seen without Type **5** (*Price from £90 each unused*).

The 12c. on 8c., 30c. on 4c., 40c. on 2c. and 50c. on 1c. surcharged with Type **9**, formerly listed as Nos. J37/40, are now believed to exist only as remainders without the Type **5** red handstamp (*Price from £20 each, unused*).

Kelantan was ceded to Thailand by the Japanese on 19 October 1943.

MALACCA

Postal services from Malacca resumed on 21 April 1942, but there were no stamps available for two days.

PRICES. Those quoted are for single stamps. Blocks of four showing complete handstamp are worth from five times the price of a single stamp.

(10) "Military Administration Malacca State Government Seal"

1942 (23 Apr). Stamps of Straits Settlements handstamped as T **10**, in red, each impression covering four stamps.

J45	**58**	1c. black	£130	95·00
J46		2c. orange	70·00	75·00
J47		3c. green	75·00	85·00
J48		5c. brown	£180	£180
J49		8c. grey	£350	£140
J50		10c. dull purple	£150	£150
J51		12c. ultramarine	£140	£150
J52		15c. ultramarine	£100	£120
J53		40c. scarlet and dull purple	£650	£800
J54		50c. black/*emerald*	£1300	£1300
J55		$1 black and red/*blue*	£1500	£1500

The 30c., $2 and $5 also exist with this overprint, but these values were not available to the public. (*Price for set of 3 £11000 unused*).

POSTAGE DUE STAMPS

1942 (23 Apr). Postage Due stamps of Malayan Postal Union handstamped as T **10**, in red, each impression covering four stamps.

JD11	D **1**	1c. slate-purple	£300	£250
JD12		4c. green	£250	£250
JD13		8c. scarlet	£4250	£3000
JD14		10c. yellow-orange	£550	£500
JD15		12c. ultramarine	£900	£800
JD16		50c. black	£3750	£2750

Nos. J45/55 and JD11/16 were replaced during May 1942 by the overprinted issues intended for use throughout Malaya.

PENANG

Postal services on Penang Island resumed on 30 March 1942 using Straits Settlements stamps overprinted by Japanese seals of the Government Accountant, Mr. A. Okugawa, and his assistant, Mr. Itchiburi.

    DAI NIPPON

2602

PENANG

(11) Okugawa (12) Itchiburi   (13)
Seal   Seal

1942 (30 Mar). Straits Settlements stamps optd.

*(a) As T **11** (three forms of the seal)*

J56	**58**	1c. black	14·00	18·00
J57		2c. orange	24·00	29·00
	a.	Pair, one without handstamp	£1600	
J58		3c. green	20·00	29·00
J59		5c. brown	24·00	42·00
J60		8c. grey	40·00	50·00
J61		10c. dull purple	55·00	55·00
J62		12c. ultramarine	50·00	55·00
J63		15c. ultramarine	60·00	60·00
J64		40c. scarlet and dull purple	£110	£120
J65		50c. black/*emerald*	£225	£225
J66		$1 black and red/*blue*	£300	£350
J67		$2 green and scarlet	£950	£800
J68		$5 green and red/*emerald*	£3250	£1700

*(b) With T **12***

J69	**58**	1c. black	£200	£170
J70		2c. orange	£200	£140
J71		3c. green	£120	£120
J72		5c. brown	£3500	£3500
J73		8c. grey	£120	£120
J74		10c. dull purple	£200	£225
J75		12c. ultramarine	£140	£150
J76		15c. ultramarine	£160	£160

Straits Settlements 1, 2, 3, 4 and 5c. values exist with a similar but circular seal containing four characters, but these were not available to the public.

1942 (15 Apr). Straits Settlements stamps optd with T **13** by Penang Premier Press.

J77	**58**	1c. black (R.)	9·50	3·75
	a.	Opt inverted	£700	£700
	b.	Opt double	£325	£325
J78		2c. orange	12·00	5·00
	a.	"PE" for "PENANG"	£140	£100
	b.	Opt inverted	£170	
	c.	Opt double	£650	
J79		3c. green (R.)	9·50	9·00
	a.	Opt double, one inverted	£450	
J80		5c. brown (R.)	4·50	9·00
	a.	"N PPON"	£200	
	b.	Opt double, one inverted	£650	£500
J81		8c. grey (R.)	2·75	1·40
	a.	"N PPON"	70·00	65·00
	b.	Opt double, one inverted	£600	
J82		10c. dull purple (R.)	1·50	2·25
	a.	Opt inverted	£475	£475
	b.	Opt double, one inverted	£425	£425
J83		12c. ultramarine (R.)	6·00	25·00
	a.	"N PPON"	£550	
	b.	Opt double	£475	
	c.	Opt double, one inverted	£700	£700
J84		15c. ultramarine (R.)	1·75	4·75
	a.	"N PPON"	£110	£140
	b.	Opt inverted	£425	£425
	c.	Opt double, one inverted	£650	£650
J85		40c. scarlet and dull purple	8·50	25·00
J86		50c. black/*emerald* (R.)	3·75	40·00
J87		$1 black and red/*blue*	6·00	50·00
	a.	Opt inverted	£1300	
J88		$2 green and scarlet	65·00	£110
J89		$5 green and red/*emerald*	£900	£950
J77/89 *Set of 13*			£950	£1100

Nos. J77/89 were replaced by the overprinted issues intended for use throughout Malaya.

SELANGOR

Postal services resumed in the Kuala Lumpur area on 3 April 1942 and gradually extended to the remainder of the state. Stamps of the general overprinted issue were used, but the following commemorative set was only available in Selangor.

SELANGOR
EXHIBITION
DAI NIPPON
2602
MALAYA

(14)

1942 (3 Nov). Selangor Agri-horticultural Exhibition. Nos. 294 and 283 of Straits Settlements optd with T **14**.

J90	**58**	2c. orange	12·00	24·00
	a.	"C" for "G" in "SELANGOR" (R. 1/9)	£400	£450
	b.	Opt inverted	£300	£400
J91		8c. grey	13·00	24·00
	a.	"C" for "G" in "SELANGOR" (R. 1/9)	£400	£450
	b.	Opt inverted	£300	£400

SINGAPORE

The first post offices re-opened in Singapore on 16 March 1942.

(15) "Malaya Military Government Division Postal Services Bureau Seal"

(Handstamped at Singapore)

1942 (16 Mar). Stamps of Straits Settlements optd with T **15** in red.

J92	**58**	1c. black	22·00	22·00
J93		2c. orange	16·00	13·00
	a.	Pair, one without handstamp	£2500	
J94		3c. green	55·00	70·00
J95		8c. grey	28·00	19·00
J96		15c. ultramarine	21·00	15·00
J92/6 *Set of 5*			£130	£120

The overprint Type **15** has a double-lined frame, although the two lines are not always apparent, as in the illustration. Three chops were used, differing slightly in the shape of the characters, but forgeries also exist. It is distinguishable from Type **1**, used for the general issues, by its extra width, measuring approximately 14 mm against 12½ mm.

The 6, 10, 30, 40, 50c., $2 and $5 also exist with this overprint, but were not sold to the public.

Nos. J92/6 were replaced on the 3 May 1942 by the stamps overprinted with Type **1** which were intended for use throughout Malaya.

TRENGGANU

Postal services resumed in Trengganu on 5 March 1942 using unoverprinted stamps up to the 35c. value. These remained in use until September 1942.

1942 (Sept). Stamps of Trengganu (Script wmk) optd as T **1** at Kuala Lumpur.

J97	**4**	1c. black (No. 26a)	90·00	£100
		a. Chalk-surfaced paper (No. 26)	—	£325
		b. Red opt	£225	£225
		c. Brown opt (chalk-surfaced paper)	£750	£400
J98		2c. green (No. 27a)	£140	£140
		a. Chalk-surfaced paper (No. 27)	—	£450
		b. Red opt	£275	£300
		c. Brown opt	£750	£425
J99		2c. on 5c. deep reddish purple/bright yellow (No. 59)	40·00	40·00
		a. Red opt	65·00	80·00
J100		3c. chestnut (No. 29a)	£100	90·00
		a. Brown opt	£1000	£650
J101		4c. scarlet-vermilion (No. 30a)	£200	£150
J102		5c. deep reddish purple/bright yellow (No. 32a)	11·00	19·00
		a. Purple/yellow (No. 32)	£250	£250
		b. Red opt	42·00	
J103		6c. orange (No. 33a)	14·00	27·00
		a. Red opt	£475	
		b. Brown opt	£1100	£1100
J104		8c. grey (No. 34a)	9·00	13·00
		a. Chalk-surfaced paper (No. 34)	£350	
		b. Brown to red opt	70·00	75·00
J105		8c. on 10c. bright blue (No. 60)	13·00	50·00
		a. Red opt	26·00	
J106		10c. bright blue	40·00	50·00
		a. Red opt	£425	
		b. Brown opt	£1100	£1100
J107		12c. bright ultramarine (No. 36)	8·00	50·00
		a. Red opt	38·00	65·00
		b. Ordinary paper	50·00	
J108		20c. dull purple and orange	15·00	55·00
		a. Red opt	32·00	
J109		25c. green and deep purple	10·00	55·00
		a. Red opt	35·00	
		b. Brown opt	£1200	£1200
J110		30c. dull purple and black	18·00	50·00
		a. Red opt	48·00	75·00
J111		35c. carmine/yellow	40·00	65·00
		a. Red opt	42·00	
J112		50c. green and bright carmine	90·00	£100
J113		$1 purple and blue/blue	£5500	£5500
J114		$3 green and brown-red/green (No. 43a)	80·00	£130
		a. Green and lake/green (No. 43)	£475	
		b. Red opt	85·00	
J115	**5**	$5 green and red/yellow	£350	£425
J116		$25 purple and blue	£2250	
		a. Red opt	£10000	
J117		$50 green and yellow	£20000	
J118		$100 green and scarlet	£2500	

DAI NIPPON
2602
MALAYA
(16)

1942 (Sept). Stamps of Trengganu (Script wmk) optd with T **16**.

J119	**4**	1c. black (No. 26a)	17·00	12·00
J120		2c. green (No. 27a)	£325	£325
J121		2c. on 5c. deep reddish purple/bright yellow (No. 59)	6·50	8·00
J122		3c. chestnut (No. 29a)	23·00	28·00
J123		4c. scarlet-vermilion (No. 30a)	23·00	11·00
J124		5c. deep reddish purple/bright yellow (No. 32a)	5·50	13·00
J125		6c. orange (No. 33a)	9·00	13·00
J126		8c. grey (No. 34a)	95·00	29·00
J127		8c. on 10c. bright blue (No. 60)	9·00	10·00
J128		12c. bright ultramarine (No. 36)	10·00	50·00
J129		20c. dull purple and orange	21·00	20·00
J130		25c. green and deep purple	10·00	50·00
J131		30c. dull purple and black	15·00	50·00
J132		$3 green and brown-red/green (No. 43a)	£100	£190
J119/32 *Set of 14*			£600	£700

1943. Stamps of Trengganu (Script wmk) optd with T **2**.

J133	**4**	1c. black (No. 26a)	27·00	29·00
		a. Chalk-surfaced paper	85·00	
J134		2c. green (No. 27a)	19·00	50·00
J135		2c. on 5c. bright reddish purple/bright yellow (No. 59)	12·00	32·00
J136		5c. bright reddish purple/bright yellow (No. 32a)	17·00	50·00
J137		6c. orange (No. 33a)	18·00	50·00
J138		8c. grey (No. 34a)	90·00	£120
J139		8c. on 10c. bright blue (No. 60)	35·00	55·00
J140		10c. bright blue	£110	£250
J141		12c. bright ultramarine (No. 36)	21·00	50·00
J142		20c. dull purple and orange	28·00	50·00
J143		25c. green and deep purple	28·00	55·00
J144		30c. dull purple and black	40·00	55·00
J145		35c. carmine/yellow	30·00	75·00
J133/45 *Set of 13*			£400	£800

POSTAGE DUE STAMPS

1942 (Sept). Nos. D1/4 of Trengganu optd with T **1** sideways.

JD17	**D 1**	1c. scarlet	55·00	90·00
JD18		4c. green	90·00	£130
		a. Brown opt	50·00	90·00
JD19		8c. yellow	14·00	50·00
JD20		10c. brown	14·00	50·00

The Trengganu 8c. postage due also exists overprinted with Type **16**, but this was not issued (*Price* £600 *unused*).

Trengganu was ceded to Thailand by the Japanese on 19 October 1943.

GENERAL ISSUES

The following stamps were produced for use throughout Malaya, except for Trengganu.

1942 (3 Apr). Stamps optd as T **1**.

(a) On Straits Settlements

J146	**58**	1c. black (R.)	4·25	3·25
		a. Black opt	£400	£400
		b. Violet opt	£1600	£750
J147		2c. green (V.)	£4000	£3000
J148		2c. orange (R.)	4·00	2·25
		a. Black opt	£140	£150
		b. Violet opt	£250	£225
		c. Brown opt	£1200	£750
J149		3c. green (R.)	4·50	2·25
		a. Black opt	£425	£450
		b. Violet opt	£1600	£800
J150		5c. brown (R.)	27·00	30·00
		a. Black opt	£600	£600
J151		8c. grey (R.)	9·00	2·25
		a. Pair, one without handstamp	†	£3000
		b. Black opt	£275	£275
J152		10c. dull purple (R.)	75·00	50·00
		a. Brown opt	£1500	£850
J153		12c. ultramarine (R.)	£120	£160
J154		15c. ultramarine (R.)	3·75	3·75
		a. Violet opt	£1000	£750
J155		30c. dull purple and orange (R.)	£4250	£4250
J156		40c. scarlet and dull purple (R.)	£160	£550
		a. Brown opt	£1200	£550
J157		50c. black/emerald (R.)	75·00	50·00
J158		$1 black and red/blue (R.)	£100	£75·00
J159		$2 green and scarlet (R.)	£180	£225
J160		$5 green and red/emerald (R.)	£275	£300

The 2c. green is known with the overprint in red, but this was not available to the public (*Price*, £375 *unused*).

(b) On Negri Sembilan

J161	**6**	1c. black (R.)	19·00	13·00
		a. Violet opt	23·00	20·00
		b. Brown opt	13·00	21·00
		c. Black opt	70·00	40·00
		d. Pair. Nos. J161/a	£300	
		e. Pair. Nos. J161 and J161b	£350	
J162		2c. orange (R.)	40·00	26·00
		a. Violet opt	55·00	30·00
		b. Black opt	38·00	32·00
		c. Brown opt	70·00	55·00
J163		3c. green (R.)	55·00	26·00
		a. Violet opt	26·00	29·00
		c. Brown opt	£250	75·00
		d. Black opt	80·00	55·00
J164		5c. brown	50·00	24·00
		a. Pair, one without opt	£2500	
		b. Brown opt	17·00	15·00
		c. Red opt	24·00	11·00
		d. Violet opt	65·00	42·00
		e. Pair. Nos. J164c/d	£375	
J165		6c. grey	£200	£170
		a. Brown opt	£325	£350
J166		8c. scarlet (*ordinary paper*)	£325	£250
J167		10c. dull purple	£350	£275
		a. Red opt	£750	£500
		b. Brown opt	£950	£650
J168		12c. bright ultramarine (Br.)	£2500	£2500
J169		15c. ultramarine (R.)	42·00	8·00
		a. Violet opt	£160	30·00
		b. Brown opt	50·00	12·00
J170		25c. dull purple and scarlet	28·00	38·00
		a. Red opt	70·00	80·00
		b. Brown opt	£950	£700
J171		30c. dull purple and orange	£350	£300
		a. Brown opt	£2250	£1500
J172		40c. scarlet and dull purple	£3000	£1600
		a. Brown opt	£1700	£1300
J173		50c. black/emerald	£2250	£2000
J174		$1 black and red/blue	£275	£300
		a. Red opt	£180	£200
		b. Brown opt	£475	£475
J175		$5 green and red/emerald	£800	£900
		a. Red opt	£1800	£1800

Nos. J161a and J163a exist with the handstamped overprint sideways.

(c) On Pahang

J176	**15**	1c. black	55·00	50·00
		a. Red opt	80·00	75·00
		b. Violet opt	£425	£275
		c. Brown opt	£325	£250
J177		3c. green	£600	£325
		a. Red opt	£225	£275
		b. Violet opt	£650	£475
J178		5c. brown	20·00	13·00
		a. Red opt	£375	£130
		b. Brown opt	£300	£120
		c. Violet opt	£500	£275
		d. Pair. Nos. J178/b	£850	
J179		8c. grey	£1600	£1000
J180		8c. scarlet	32·00	8·00
		a. Red opt	£120	50·00
		b. Violet opt	£110	60·00
		c. Brown opt	£110	65·00
		d. Pair. Nos. J180a/c	£475	
J181		10c. dull purple	£550	£200
		a. Red opt	£375	£250
		b. Brown opt	£425	£275
J182		12c. bright ultramarine	£2750	£2750
		a. Brown to red opt	£1200	£1200
J183		15c. ultramarine	£180	£120
		a. Red opt	£550	£275
		b. Violet opt	£800	£500
		c. Brown opt	£700	£350
J184		25c. dull purple and scarlet	28·00	30·00
J185		30c. dull purple and orange	20·00	32·00
		a. Red opt	£150	£170
J186		40c. scarlet and dull purple	30·00	38·00
		a. Brown opt	£600	£350
		b. Red opt	£100	£100
J187		50c. black/emerald	£1900	£1900
		a. Red opt	£2250	£2250

J188		$1 black and red/blue (R.)	£170	£180
		a. Black opt	£325	£325
		b. Brown opt	£750	£750
J189		$5 green and red/emerald	£850	£950
		a. Red opt	£1400	£1500

(d) On Perak

J190	**51**	1c. black	75·00	50·00
		a. Violet opt	£425	£180
		b. Brown opt	£130	£110
J191		2c. orange	38·00	20·00
		a. Violet opt	90·00	70·00
		b. Red opt	85·00	40·00
		c. Brown opt	80·00	60·00
J192		3c. green	35·00	32·00
		a. Violet opt	£550	£350
		b. Brown opt	£225	£160
		c. Red opt	£400	£275
J193		5c. brown	13·00	6·00
		a. Pair, one without opt	£1500	
		b. Brown opt	55·00	38·00
		c. Violet opt	£375	£200
		d. Red opt	£225	£200
J194		8c. grey	£110	65·00
		a. Red opt	£650	£250
		b. Brown opt	£475	£250
J195		8c. scarlet	55·00	48·00
		a. Violet opt	£700	£350
J196		10c. dull purple	26·00	24·00
		a. Red opt	£550	£325
J197		12c. bright ultramarine	£300	£250
J198		15c. ultramarine	24·00	32·00
		a. Red opt	£250	£250
		b. Violet opt	£750	£375
		c. Brown opt	£450	£300
J199		25c. dull purple and scarlet	14·00	28·00
		a. Red opt	£450	
J200		30c. dull purple and orange (No. 116a)	17·00	32·00
		a. Pair, one without opt	£2000	
		b. Brown opt	£1200	£650
		c. Red opt	45·00	60·00
		ca. Pair, one without opt	£2750	
J201		40c. scarlet and dull purple	£850	£400
		a. Brown opt	£650	£450
J202		50c. black/emerald	55·00	60·00
		a. Red opt	60·00	65·00
		b. Brown opt	£700	£400
J203		$1 black and red/blue	£650	£425
		a. Brown opt	£450	£400
J204		$2 green and scarlet	£5500	£5500
J205		$5 green and red/emerald	£600	
		a. Brown opt	£3750	

(e) On Selangor

J206	**46**	1c. black, S	15·00	28·00
		a. Red opt, SU	55·00	42·00
		b. Violet opt, SU	65·00	50·00
J207		2c. green, SU	£2750	£1500
		a. Violet opt, SU	£3250	£1500
J208		2c. orange (P 14×14½), S	£100	60·00
		a. Red opt, U	£200	£170
		b. Violet opt, U	£225	£160
		c. Brown opt, S	85·00	80·00
J209		2c. orange (P 14), S	£180	£100
		a. Red opt, U	£250	£170
		b. Violet opt, U	£500	£170
		c. Brown opt, S	—	£180
J210		3c. green, SU	23·00	15·00
		a. Red opt, SU	28·00	16·00
		b. Violet opt, SU	80·00	50·00
		c. Brown opt, SU	19·00	15·00
		d. Pair. Nos. J210a/c	£350	
J211		5c. brown, SU	7·50	5·50
		a. Red opt, SU	24·00	19·00
		b. Violet opt, SU	21·00	22·00
		c. Brown opt, SU	60·00	50·00
J212		6c. scarlet, SU	£450	£450
		a. Red opt, S	£225	£275
		b. Brown opt, S	£1300	£1300
J213		8c. grey, S	35·00	17·00
		a. Red opt, SU	70·00	40·00
		b. Violet opt, U	50·00	35·00
		c. Brown opt, S	£225	80·00
J214		10c. dull purple, S	23·00	21·00
		a. Red opt, S	£120	90·00
		b. Brown opt, S	£275	£120
J215		12c. bright ultramarine, S	70·00	80·00
		a. Red opt, S	£180	£180
		b. Brown opt, S	£170	£170
J216		15c. ultramarine, S	19·00	27·00
		a. Red opt, SU	£100	£100
		b. Violet opt, U	£225	£110
		c. Brown opt, S	£170	£110
J217		25c. dull purple and scarlet, S	£130	£160
		a. Red opt, S	65·00	90·00
J218		30c. dull purple and orange, S (No. 80a)	11·00	24·00
		a. Brown opt, S	£650	£300
J219		40c. scarlet and dull purple, S	£200	£150
		a. Brown opt, S	£600	£300
		b. Red opt, S	£500	
J220		50c. black/emerald, S	£225	£225
		a. Red opt, S	£250	£300
		b. Brown opt, S	£900	£500
J221	**48**	$1 black and red/blue	40·00	55·00
		a. Red opt	£160	£180
J222		$2 green and scarlet	42·00	70·00
		a. Pair, one without opt	£2500	
		b. Red opt	£1100	£1100
J223		$5 green and red/emerald	£100	£120

On T **46** the overprint is normally sideways (with "top" to either right or left), but on T **48** it is always upright.

S	= Sideways.
U	= Upright.
SU	= Sideways or upright (our prices being for the cheaper).

Specialists recognise nine slightly different chops as Type **1**. Initial supplies with the overprint in red were produced at Singapore. Later overprintings took place at Kuala Lumpur in violet, red or brown and finally, black. No. J155 was from the Kuala Lumpur printing only. Except where noted, these overprints were used widely in Malaya and, in some instances, Sumatra.

The following stamps also exist with this overprint, but were not available to the public:
Straits Settlements (in red) 6, 25c.
Kelantan (in black) 10c.
Negri Sembilan 2c. green (Blk. or Brn.), 4c. (Blk.), 6c. scarlet (Blk.), 8c. grey (Blk.), 12c. (Blk.), $2 (Blk. or Brn.).
Pahang (in black, 2c. also in brown) 2, 4, 6c., $2.
Perak 2c. green (R.), 6c. (Blk.).
Selangor 4c. (Blk.).

1942 (May). Optd with T **16**.

(a) On Straits Settlements

J224	**58**	2c. orange	3·50	60
		a. Opt inverted	16·00	28·00
		b. Opt double, one inverted	55·00	65·00
J225		3c. green	50·00	65·00
J226		8c. grey	12·00	4·50
		a. Opt inverted	21·00	48·00
J227		15c. blue	26·00	15·00
J224/7 Set of 4			80·00	80·00

(b) On Negri Sembilan

J228	**6**	1c. black (*Thin striated paper*)	3·00	60
		a. Opt inverted	9·00	30·00
		b. Opt double, one inverted	35·00	55·00
		c. Chalk-surfaced paper	4·00	1·00
J229		2c. orange	13·00	50
J230		3c. green (No. 24a)	9·00	50
J231		5c. brown	1·75	7·00
J232		6c. grey	7·00	7·00
		a. Opt inverted	†	£1900
		b. Stop omitted at right (R. 10/4)	£250	£275
J233		8c. scarlet (*Ordinary paper*)	9·00	1·25
		a. Thin striated paper	11·00	3·25
J234		10c. dull purple	3·25	2·50
J235		15c. ultramarine	25·00	2·50
J236		25c. dull purple and scarlet (*Ordinary paper*)	7·00	24·00
J237		30c. dull purple and orange (*Thin striated paper*)	13·00	6·50
J238		$1 black and red/*blue*	85·00	£110
J228/38 Set of 11			£150	£140

(c) On Pahang

J239	**15**	1c. black (*Thin striated paper*)	3·50	5·00
		a. Opt omitted (in pair with normal)	£600	
J240		5c. brown	1·25	70
J241		8c. scarlet	40·00	3·50
		a. Opt omitted (in pair with normal)	£1700	
J242		10c. dull purple	17·00	10·00
J243		12c. bright ultramarine	4·50	24·00
J244		25c. dull purple and scarlet (*Thin striated paper*)	9·00	40·00
J245		30c. dull purple and orange (No. 41a)	3·75	18·00
J239/45 Set of 7			70·00	90·00

(d) On Perak

J246	**51**	2c. orange (No. 105)	4·50	4·00
		a. Opt inverted	75·00	75·00
J247		3c. green (No. 106a)	1·50	1·50
		a. Opt inverted	18·00	28·00
		b. Opt omitted (in pair with normal)	£800	
J248		8c. scarlet (No. 111)	1·50	50
		a. Opt inverted	4·50	7·00
		b. Opt double, one inverted	£225	£250
		c. Opt omitted (in horiz pair with normal)	£400	
J249		10c. dull purple (*Thin striated paper*)	22·00	9·50
		a. Chalk-surfaced paper	—	17·00
J250		15c. ultramarine	18·00	2·00
J251		50c. black/*emerald*	4·00	7·50
J252		$1 black and red/*blue*	£600	£650
J253		$5 green and red/*emerald*	70·00	95·00
		a. Opt inverted	£325	£425
J246/53 Set of 8			£650	£700

(e) On Selangor

J254	**46**	3c. green (No. 71a)	2·25	6·00
		a. Ordinary paper		
J255		12c. bright ultramarine	2·75	25·00
J256		15c. ultramarine	9·00	1·50
J257		40c. scarlet and dull purple	2·25	7·50
J258	**48**	$2 green and scarlet	11·00	55·00
J254/8 Set of 5			25·00	85·00

On T **46** the overprint is sideways, with "top" to left or right.
The following stamps also exist with this overprint, but were not available to the public.
Perak 1, 5, 30c. (*Price for set of 3 £400 unused*).
Selangor 1, 5, 10, 30c., $1, $5 (*Price for set of 6 £850 unused*).

DAI NIPPON		**DAI NIPPON**
2602		
MALAYA		**YUBIN**
2 Cents		**2 Cents**
(**17**)		(**18**) *"Japanese Postal Service"*

1942 (Nov). No. 108 of Perak surch with T **17**.

J259	**51**	2c. on 5c. brown	1·75	5·50
		a. Inverted "s" in "Cents" (R. 3/5)	70·00	£100

1942 (Nov). Perak stamps surch or opt only, as in T **18**.

J260	**51**	1c. black (*Thin striated paper*)	7·00	11·00
		a. Opt inverted	19·00	48·00
J261		2c. on 5c. brown	2·75	6·50
		a. "DAI NIPPON YUBIN" inverted	17·00	48·00
		b. Ditto and "2 Cents" omitted	50·00	70·00
		c. Inverted "s" in "Cents" (R. 3/5)	75·00	£140
J262		8c. scarlet (No. 111)	14·00	3·50
		a. Opt inverted	13·00	28·00
J260/2 Set of 3			21·00	19·00

A similar overprint exists on the Selangor 3c. but this was not available to the public (*Price £350 unused*).

On 8 December 1942 contemporary Japanese 3, 5, 8 and 25s. stamps were issued without overprint in Malaya and the 1, 2, 4, 6, 7, 10, 30 and 50s. and 1y. values followed on 15 February 1943.

大日本郵便	**6 cts.**	**6 cts.**		
(**19**)	(**20**)	(**21**)		
2 Cents	**6 cts.**	**$1·00**		
(**22**)	(**23**)	(**24**)		

1942 (4 Dec)–**44**. Stamps of various Malayan territories optd "Japanese Postal Service" in Kanji characters as T **2** or **19**, some additionally surch as T **20** to **24**.

*(a) Stamps of Straits Settlements optd with T **2***

J263	**58**	8c. grey (Blk.) (1943)	1·40	50
		a. Opt inverted	60·00	75·00
		b. Opt omitted (in pair with normal)	£850	
		c. Red opt	2·50	3·50
J264		12c. ultramarine (1943)	1·75	17·00
J265		40c. scarlet and dull purple (1943)	4·00	7·50
J263/5 Set of 3			6·50	22·00

*(b) Stamps of Negri Sembilan optd with T **2** or surch also*

J266	**6**	1c. black (*Thin striated paper*)	75	5·00
		a. Opt inverted	13·00	35·00
		b. Sideways second character	35·00	45·00
		ba. Opt inverted with sideways second character	£800	
		c. Chalk-surfaced paper	1·25	5·00
J267		2c. on 5c. brown (surch as T **20**)	1·00	2·75
J268		6c. on 5c. brown (surch T **21**) (1943)	40	3·50
		a. Opt Type **2** and surch as Type **21** both inverted	£275	£275
		b. Opt Type **2** and surch as Type **21** both double	£150	
J269		25c. dull purple and scarlet (*Ordinary paper*) (1943)	2·75	27·00
J266/9 Set of 4			4·50	35·00

*(c) Stamp of Pahang optd with T **2** and surch also*

J270	**15**	6c. on 5c. brown (surch T **20**) (1943)	50	75
J271		6c. on 5c. brown (surch T **21**) (1943)	1·00	2·50

*(d) Stamps of Perak optd with T **2** or surch also*

J272	**51**	1c. black (*Thin striated paper*)	1·25	1·75
		a. Sideways second character	£225	£250
J273		2c. on 5c. brown (surch as T **20**)	1·00	2·00
		a. Opt Type **2** and surch Type **20** both inverted	25·00	40·00
		b. Opt Type **2** inverted	25·00	40·00
		c. Sideways second character	65·00	70·00
J274		2c. on 5c. brown (surch T **22**)	60	50
		a. Surch Type **22** inverted	20·00	38·00
		b. Opt Type **2** and surch Type **22** both inverted	40·00	48·00
		c. Sideways second character	30·00	42·00
		ca. Surch Type **22** inverted	£1500	
		cb. Opt Type **2** with sideways second character and surch Type **22** both inverted	£1500	
J275		5c. brown	55	65
		a. Opt inverted	50·00	60·00
		b. Sideways second character	£550	£425
J276		8c. scarlet (No. 111)	1·25	3·25
		a. Opt inverted	17·00	35·00
		b. Sideways second character	50·00	70·00
		ba. Opt inverted with sideways second character	£750	
		c. Opt omitted (in pair with normal)	£1400	
J277		10c. dull purple (No. 112) (1943)	75	1·50
		a. Thin striated paper	75	1·50
J278		30c. dull purple and orange (No. 116a) (1943)	5·50	9·50
J279		50c. black/*emerald* (1943)	4·50	32·00
J280		$5 green and red/*emerald* (1943)	90·00	£150
J272/80 Set of 9			95·00	£170

*(e) Stamps of Selangor optd with T **2** (sideways on T **46**)*

J281	**46**	1c. black (No. 68) (1943)	1·50	5·00
		a. Thin striated paper	1·25	5·00
J282		3c. green (No. 71a)	40	1·50
		a. Sideways second character	17·00	28·00
J283		12c. bright ultramarine	45	2·50
		a. Sideways second character	£110	£140
J284		15c. ultramarine	4·50	3·75
		a. Sideways second character	50·00	55·00
J285	**48**	$1 black and red/*blue*	3·00	30·00
		a. Opt inverted	£250	£250
		b. Sideways second character	£375	£500
J286		$2 green and scarlet (1943)	10·00	55·00
J287		$5 green and red/*emerald* (1943)	22·00	85·00
		a. Opt inverted	£325	£375
J281/7 Set of 7			38·00	£160

*(f) Stamps of Selangor optd with T **19** or surch also*

J288	**46**	1c. black (No. 68) (R.) (1943)	50	60
		a. Thin striated paper	35	50
J289		2c. on 5c. brown (surch as T **21**) (R.) (1943)	2·00	50
J290		3c. on 5c. brown (surch as T **21**) (1943)	30	50
		a. "s" in "cts." inverted (R. 4/3)	35·00	80·00
		b. Comma after "cts" (R. 9/3)	35·00	80·00
J291		5c. brown (R.) (1944)	2·50	9·50
J292		6c. on 5c. brown (surch T **21**) (1944)	1·25	1·75
J293		6c. on 5c. brown (surch T **23**) (1944)	50	70
		a. "6" inverted (R. 7/8)	£1200	
		b. Full stop between "6" and "cts" (R. 8/6)		
		c. Surch and opt double	£650	
J294		15c. ultramarine	4·00	4·00
J295		$1 on 10c. dull purple (surch T **24**) (18.12.1944)	40	1·25
J296		$1·50 on 30c. dull purple and orange (No. 80a) (surch T **24**) (18.12.1944)	40	1·25
J288/96 Set of 9			10·50	22·00

The error showing the second character in Type **2** sideways occurred on R. 6/3 in the first of four settings only.
The 2c. orange, 3c. and 8c. grey of Perak also exist overprinted with Type **2**, but these stamps were not available to the public (*Price for set of 3 £100 unused*).
Examples of No. J275 are known postally used from the Shan States (part of pre-war Burma).
In 1943 the use of Japanese stamps was approved in occupied Malaya.

25 Tapping Rubber

26 Fruit

27 Tin dredger

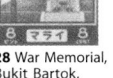
28 War Memorial, Bukit Bartok, Singapore

29 Fishing village

30 Japanese shrine, Singapore

31 Sago Palms

32 Straits of Johore

33 Malay Mosque, Kuala

(Litho Kolff & Co, Batavia)

1943 (29 Apr–1 Oct). P 12½.

J297	**25**	1c. grey-green (1.10)	1·75	55
J298	**26**	2c. pale emerald (1.6)	1·00	20
J299	**25**	3c. drab (1.10)	1·00	20
J300	**27**	4c. carmine-rose	3·00	20
J301	**28**	8c. dull blue	50	20
J302	**29**	10c. brown-purple (1.10)	1·25	20
J303	**30**	15c. violet (1.10)	1·75	5·00
J304	**31**	30c. olive-green (1.10)	1·50	35
J305	**32**	50c. blue (1.10)	5·00	5·00
J306	**33**	70c. blue (1.10)	32·00	14·00
J297/306 Set of 10			45·00	25·00

The 2c. and 4c. values exist, printed by letterpress, in paler shades either imperforate or rouletted. It is suggested that these may have been available in Singapore at the very end of the Japanese Occupation.

34 Ploughman

35 Rice-Planting

1943 (1 Sept). Savings Campaign. Litho. P 12½.

J307	**34**	8c. violet	9·50	2·75
J308		15c. scarlet	6·50	2·75

(Des Hon Chin. Litho)

1944 (15 Feb). "Re-birth" of Malaya. P 12½.

J309	**35**	8c. rose-red	17·00	3·25
J310		15c. magenta	4·00	3·25

大日本	大日本	大日本
マライ郵便	マライ郵便	マライ郵便
50 セント	1 ドル	1½ ドル
(**36**)	(**37**)	(**38**)

1944 (16 Dec). Stamps intended for use on Red Cross letters. Surch with T **36/8** in red.

(a) On Straits Settlements

J311	**58**	50c. on 50c. black/*emerald*	10·00	24·00
J312		$1 on $1 black and red/*blue*	22·00	35·00
J313		$1·50 on $2 green and scarlet	48·00	70·00

(b) On Johore

J314	**34**	50c. on 50c. dull purple and red (No. 119a)	9·00	20·00
J315	**35**	$1·50 on $2 green and carmine (No. 121a)	4·00	12·00

(c) On Selangor

J316	**48**	$1 on $1 black and red/*blue*	3·50	14·00
J317		$1·50 on $2 green and scarlet	11·00	20·00
J311/17 Set of 7			95·00	£180

Nos. J311/17 were issued in Singapore but were withdrawn after one day, probably because supplies of Nos. J295/6 were received and issued on the 18 December.
A similar 6c. surcharge exists on the Straits Settlements 5c. but this was not available to the public (*Price £700 unused*).

STAMP BOOKLETS

1942. Nos. SB3/4 of Perak and SB2 of Selangor with covers optd with T **1**.

SB1	$1 booklet containing 20×5c. (No. J193) in blocks of 10		£4000
SB2	$1.30 booklet containing 5c. and 8c. (Nos. J193/4), each in block of 10		£4000
SB3	$1.30 booklet containing 5c. and 8c. (Nos. J211 and J213), each in block of 10		£4000

POSTAGE DUE STAMPS

Postage Due stamps of the Malayan Postal Union overprinted.

1942 (3 Apr). Handstamped as T **1** in black.

JD21	D **1**	1c. slate-purple	12·00	35·00
		a. Red opt	£200	£250
		b. Brown opt	£190	£225
JD22		3c. green	90·00	£100
		a. Red opt	£475	£500
JD23		4c. green	£100	60·00
		a. Red opt	70·00	60·00
		b. Brown opt	£200	£250
JD24		8c. scarlet	£200	£150
		a. Red opt	£275	£180
		b. Brown opt	£400	£400
JD25		10c. yellow-orange	42·00	65·00
		a. Red opt	£500	£500
		b. Brown opt	£120	£150
JD26		12c. ultramarine	25·00	60·00
		a. Red opt	£500	£475
JD27		50c. black	80·00	£120
		a. Red opt	£800	£850

1942. Optd with T **16**.

JD28	D **1**	1c. slate-purple	3·50	10·00
JD29		3c. green	26·00	32·00
JD30		4c. green	24·00	11·00
JD31		8c. scarlet	38·00	27·00
JD32		10c. yellow-orange	2·00	17·00
JD33		12c. ultramarine	1·75	50·00
JD28/33 *Set of 6*			85·00	£130

The 9c. and 15c. also exist with this overprint, but these were not issued (*Price* £800 *each unused*).

1943–45. Optd with T **2**.

JD34	D **1**	1c. slate-purple	2·25	6·00
JD35		3c. green	2·25	4·50
		a. Opt omitted (in pair with normal)	£850	
JD36		4c. green	65·00	50·00
JD37		5c. scarlet	1·50	5·00
JD38		9c. yellow-orange	80	8·50
		a. Opt inverted	22·00	28·00
JD39		10c. yellow-orange	2·25	9·00
		a. Opt inverted	90·00	90·00
JD40		12c. ultramarine	2·25	25·00
JD41		15c. ultramarine	2·25	9·00
JD34/41 *Set of 8*			70·00	£100

IX. THAI OCCUPATION OF MALAYA

Stamps issued for use in the Malay States of Kedah (renamed Syburi), Kelantan, Perlis and Trengganu, ceded by Japan to Thailand on 19 October 1943. British rule was restored on 9 (Kelantan), 18 (Perlis), 22 (Kedah) and 24 September 1945 (Trengganu). Nos. TM1/6 continued to be used for postage until replaced by the overprinted B.M.A. Malaya issues on 10 October 1945.

PRICES FOR STAMPS ON COVER	
Nos. TK1/5	*from* × 30
Nos. TM1/6	*from* × 25
Nos. TT1/35	—

KELANTAN

TK **1**

(Typo Kelantan Ptg Dept, Khota Baru)

1943 (15 Nov). Handstamped with State Arms in violet. No gum. P 11.

TK1	TK **1**	1c. black	£250	£450
TK2		2c. black	£400	£300
		a. Handstamp omitted	£750	
TK3		4c. black	£400	£450
		a. Handstamp omitted	£950	
TK4		8c. black	£400	£300
		a. Handstamp omitted	£650	
TK5		10c. black	£500	£700
TK1/5 *Set of 5*			£1800	£2000

Nos. TK1/5 were printed in sheets of 84 (12×7) and have sheet watermarks in the form of "STANDARD" in block capitals with curved "CROWN" above and "AGENTS" below in double-lined capitals. This watermark occurs four times in the sheet.

Sheets were imperforate at top and left so that stamps exist imperforate at top, left or at top and left.

Genuine examples have a solid star at the top centre of the Arms, as shown in Type TK **1**. Examples with a hollow outline star in this position are forgeries.

Similar stamps, but with red handstamps, were for fiscal use.

GENERAL ISSUE

TM **1** War Memorial

(Litho Defence Ministry, Bangkok)

1944 (15 Jan–4 Mar). Thick opaque, or thin semi-transparent paper. Gummed or ungummed. P 12½.

TM1	TM **1**	1c. yellow (4.3)	30·00	32·00
TM2		2c. red-brown	12·00	20·00
		a. Imperf (pair)	£1000	
		b. Perf 12½×11	20·00	20·00
TM3		3c. green (4.3)	20·00	38·00
		a. Perf 12½×11	30·00	42·00
TM4		4c. purple (4.3)	14·00	28·00
		a. Perf 12½×11	20·00	35·00
TM5		8c. carmine (4.3)	14·00	20·00
		a. Perf 12½×11	20·00	20·00
TM6		15c. blue (4.3)	38·00	60·00
		a. Perf 12½×11	42·00	60·00
TM1/6 *Set of 6*			£110	£180

5c. and 10c. stamps in this design were prepared, but never issued.

TRENGGANU

TRENGGANU

(TT **1**)

(Overprinted at Trengganu Survey Office)

1944 (1 Oct). Various stamps optd with Type TT **1**.

(a) On Trengganu without Japanese opt

TT1	**4**	1c. black (26a)		
TT2		30c. dull purple and black (39)		

*(b) On Trengganu stamps optd as T **1** of Japanese Occupation*

TT2a	**4**	1c. black (J97)	—	£4000
TT3		8c. grey (J104)	£1300	£800

*(c) On stamps optd with T **16** of Japanese Occupation*

(i) Pahang

TT4	**15**	12c. bright ultramarine (J243)	£900	£250

(ii) Trengganu

TT5	**4**	2c. on 5c. deep reddish purple/bright yellow (J121)*	£1000	£1000
TT6		8c. on 10c. bright blue (J127) (inverted)	£900	£900
TT7		12c. bright ultramarine (J128) (inverted)	£950	£950

*This is spelt "TRENGANU" with one "G".

*(d) On stamps optd with T **2** of Japanese Occupation*

(i) Straits Settlements

TT8	**58**	12c. ultramarine (J264)	£950	£950
TT9		40c. scarlet and dull purple (J265)	£950	£950

(ii) Negri Sembilan

TT9a	**6**	25c. dull purple and scarlet (J269)	—	£4000

(iii) Pahang

TT10	**15**	6c. on 5c. brown (J271)		

(iv) Perak

TT11	**51**	1c. black (J272)		
TT12		10c. dull purple (J277)		
TT13		30c. dull purple and orange (J278)	£1800	£950
TT13a		50c. black/emerald (J279)	—	£4000

(v) Selangor

TT14	**46**	3c. green (J282)	£650	£650
TT15		12c. brt ultramarine (J283) (L. to R.)	£250	£140
TT16		12c. brt ultramarine (J283) (R. to L.)	£225	£140
		a. Sideways second character	£3750	£3750

*(e) On Selangor stamps optd with T **19** of Japanese Occupation*

TT16b	**46**	1c. black (J288)	—	£4000
TT17		2c. on 5c. brown (J289)	£900	£900
		a. Opt inverted	—	£4000
TT18		3c. on 5c. brown (J290)	£900	£900

(f) On pictorials of 1943 (Nos. J297/306)

TT19	**25**	1c. grey-green	£650	£475
TT20	**26**	2c. pale emerald	£650	£275
TT21	**25**	3c. drab	£375	£180
TT22	–	4c. carmine-rose	£600	£275
TT23	–	8c. dull blue	£900	£850
TT24	–	10c. brown-purple	£2000	£1100
TT25	**27**	15c. violet	£600	£275
TT26	–	30c. olive-green	£850	£225
TT27	–	50c. blue	£850	£425
TT28	–	70c. blue	£2250	£1400

(g) On Savings Campaign stamps (Nos. J307/8)

TT29	**28**	8c. violet	£1000	£900
TT30		15c. scarlet	£700	£275

(h) On stamps of Japan

TT31	–	3s. green (No. 319)		
TT32	–	5s. claret (No. 396)	£850	£650
TT33	–	25c. brown and chocolate (No. 326)	£600	£180
TT34	–	30c. blue-green (No. 327)	£850	£275

*(i) On Trengganu Postage Due stamp optd with T **1** of Japanese Occupation*

TT35	D **1**	1c. scarlet (JD17)	£5000	£5000

Maldive Islands

BRITISH PROTECTORATE
(Currency. 100 cents = 1 Ceylon rupee)

MALDIVES
(1)

2 Minaret, Juma Mosque, Malé

3

1906 (9 Sept). Nos. 277/9, 280a and 283/4 of Ceylon optd with T **1**. Wmk Mult Crown CA. P 14.

1	**44**	2c. red-brown	25·00	50·00
2	**45**	3c. green	40·00	55·00
3		4c. orange and ultramarine	55·00	90·00
4	**46**	5c. dull purple	4·00	6·50
5	**48**	15c. blue	£110	£180
6		25c. bistre	£120	£225
1/6 *Set of 6*			£300	£550

The T **1** opt has been extensively forged.

Supplies of Nos. 1/6 were exhausted by March 1907 and the stamps of CEYLON were used until 1909.

(Recess D.L.R.)

1909 (May). T **2** (18½×22½ *mm*). W **3**. P 14×13½ (2c., 5c.) or 13½×14 (3c., 10c.).

7	**2**	2c. orange-brown	2·25	4·50
		a. Perf 13½×14	2·50	90
8		3c. deep myrtle	75	70
9		5c. purple	75	35
10		10c. carmine	7·50	80
7/10 *Set of 4*			10·00	2·50

These stamps perforated 14×13½ (14×13.7) are from a line machine and those perforated 13½×14 (13.7×13.9) from a comb machine.

4

(Photo Harrison)

1933. T **2** redrawn (reduced to 18×21½ *mm*). W **4**. P 15×14.

A. Wmk upright

11A	**2**	2c. grey	2·75	2·00
12A		3c. red-brown	70	2·75
14A		5c. mauve	55·00	10·00
15A		6c. scarlet	1·50	5·50
16A		10c. green	85	55
17A		15c. black	9·50	30·00
18A		25c. brown	9·00	30·00
19A		50c. purple	10·00	35·00
20A		1r. deep blue	17·00	28·00
11A/20A *Set of 9*			95·00	£130

B. Wmk sideways

11B	**2**	2c. grey	11·00	5·50
12B		3c. red-brown	5·00	1·75
13B		5c. claret	40·00	32·00
15B		6c. scarlet	10·00	9·50
16B		10c. green	3·75	12·00
17B		15c. black	11·00	39·00
18B		25c. brown	11·00	24·00
19B		50c. purple	16·00	27·00
20B		1r. deep blue	16·00	5·50
11B/20B *Set of 9*			£110	£130

(New Currency. 100 larees = 1 rupee)

5 Palm Tree and Dhow

(Recess B.W.)

1950 (24 Dec)–**52**. P 13.

21	**5**	2l. olive-green	5·00	6·00
		a. *Olive-brown* (1952)	13·00	13·00
22		3l. blue	18·00	3·50
23		5l. emerald-green	18·00	3·50
24		6l. red-brown	1·25	1·75
25		10l. scarlet	1·25	1·00
26		15l. orange	1·25	1·25
27		25l. purple	1·25	4·00
28		50l. violet	1·50	6·00
29		1r. chocolate	14·00	42·00
21/9 *Set of 9*			55·00	65·00

7 Fish

8 Native Products

1952. P 13.

30	**7**	3l. blue	2·00	60
31	**8**	5l. emerald	1·00	2·00

SULTANATE
Sultan Mohamed Farid Didi
20 November 1953–10 November 1968

The Maldive Islands became a republic on 1 January 1953, but reverted to a sultanate on 29 November 1953.

9 Malé Harbour

10 Fort and Building

(Recess B.W.)

1956 (1 Feb). P 13½ (T **9**) or 11½×11 (T **10**).

32	**9**	2l. purple	10	10
33		3l. slate	10	10
34		5l. red-brown	10	10
35		6l. blackish violet	10	10
36		10l. emerald	10	10
37		15l. chocolate	10	85
38		25l. rose-red	10	10
39		50l. orange	10	10
40	**10**	1r. bluish green	15	10
41		5r. blue	2·50	30
42		10r. magenta	2·75	1·25
32/42 *Set of 11*			5·50	2·75

11 Cycling   **12** Basketball

(Des C. Bottiau. Recess and typo B.W.)

1960 (20 Aug). Olympic Games. P 11½×11 (T **11**) or 11×11½ (T **12**).

43	**11**	2l. purple and green	15	90
44		3l. greenish slate and purple	15	90
45		5l. red-brown and ultramarine	15	25
46		10l. emerald-green and brown	15	25
47		15l. sepia and blue	15	25
48	**12**	15l. rose-red and olive	15	25
49		50l. orange and violet	20	40
50		1r. emerald and purple	40	1·25
43/50 *Set of 8*			1·40	4·00

13 Tomb of Sultan

14 Custom House

15 Cowrie Shells

16 Old Royal Palace

17 Road to Junin Mosque, Malé

18 Council House

19 New Government Secretariat

20 Prime Minister's Office

21 Old Ruler's Tomb

22 Old Ruler's Tomb (distant view)

23 Maldivian Port

24 "Care of Refugees"

(Recess B.W.)

1960 (15 Oct). T **13/23**. P 11½×11.

51	**13**	2l. purple	10	10
52	**14**	3l. emerald-green	10	10
53	**15**	5l. orange-brown	3·75	4·00
54	**16**	6l. bright blue	10	10
55	**17**	10l. carmine	10	10
56	**18**	15l. sepia	10	10
57	**19**	25l. deep violet	10	10
58	**20**	50l. slate-grey	10	10
59	**21**	1r. orange	15	10
60	**22**	5r. deep ultramarine	10·00	60
61	**23**	10r. grey-green	15·00	1·25
51/61 *Set of 11*			26·00	6·00

25r, 50r and 100r values in similar designs were also issued, intended mainly for fiscal use (*Price* £150 *for set of 3, unused*).

(Recess B.W.)

1960 (15 Oct). World Refugee Year. P 11½×11.

62	**24**	2l. deep violet, orange and green	10	15
63		3l. brown, green and red	10	15
64		5l. deep green, sepia and red	10	10
65		10l. bluish green, reddish violet and red	10	10
66		15l. reddish violet, grey-green and red	10	10
67		25l. red, red-brown and bronze-green	10	10
68		50l. yellow-olive, rose-red and blue	10	10
69		1r. carmine, slate and violet	15	35
62/9 *Set of 8*			60	1·00

25 Coconuts

26 Map of Malé

(Photo Harrison)

1961 (20 Apr). P 14×14½ (Nos. 70/74) or 14½×14 (others).

70	**25**	2l. yellow-brown and deep green	10	1·00
71		3l. yellow-brown and bright blue	10	1·00
72		5l. yellow-brown and magenta	10	15
73		10l. yellow-brown and red-orange	15	15
74		15l. yellow-brown and black	20	15
75	**26**	25l. multicoloured	55	20
76		50l. multicoloured	55	40
77		1r. multicoloured	60	70
70/7 *Set of 8*			2·00	3·25

27 5c. Stamp of 1906

30 Malaria Eradication Emblem

(Des M. Shamir. Photo Harrison)

1961 (9 Sept). 55th Anniv of First Maldivian Stamp. T **27** and similar horiz designs. P 14½×14.

78		2l. brown-purple, ultramarine and light green	10	1·10
79		3l. brown-purple, ultramarine and light green	10	1·10
80		5l. brown-purple, ultramarine and light green	10	15
81		6l. brown-purple, ultramarine and light green	10	1·40
82		10l. green, claret and maroon	10	15
83		15l. green, claret and maroon	15	15
84		20l. green, claret and maroon	15	20
85		25l. claret, green and black	20	20
86		50l. claret, green and black	35	80
87		1r. claret, green and black	50	2·00
78/87 *Set of 10*			1·60	6·50
MS87*a*		114×88 mm. No. 87 (block of four). Imperf.	1·50	7·00

Designs:—2 to 6l. Type **27**; 10 to 20l. 1906 3c. and posthorn; 25l. to 1r. 1906 2c. and olive sprig.

(Recess B.W.)

1962 (7 Apr). Malaria Eradication. P 13½×13.

88	**30**	2l. chestnut	10	1·50
89		3l. emerald	10	1·50
90		5l. turquoise-blue	10	15
91		10l. red	10	15
92	–	15l. deep purple-brown	15	15
93	–	25l. deep blue	20	20
94	–	50l. deep green	25	55
95	–	1r. purple	55	80
88/95	*Set of 8*		1·40	4·50

Nos. 92/5 are as T **30**, but have English inscriptions at the side.

31 Children of Europe and America

33 Sultan Mohamed Farid Didi

(Des C. Bottiau. Photo Harrison)

1962 (9 Sept). 15th Anniv of UNICEF T **31** and similar horiz design. Multicoloured. P 14½×14.

96	2l. Type **31**	10	1·50
97	6l. Type **31**	10	1·50
98	10l. Type **31**	10	15
99	15l. Type **31**	10	15
100	25l. Children of Middle East and Far East...	15	15
101	50l. As 25l.	20	15
102	1r. As 25l.	25	20
103	5r. As 25l.	1·25	5·00
96/103 *Set of 8*		2·00	8·00

(Photo Harrison)

1962 (29 Nov). Ninth Anniv of Enthronement of Sultan. P 14×14½.

104	**33**	3l. orange-brown and bluish green	10	1·50
105		5l. orange-brown and indigo	15	20
106		10l. orange-brown and blue	20	20
107		20l. orange-brown and olive-green ...	30	25
108		50l. orange-brown and deep magenta...	35	45
109		1r. orange-brown and slate-lilac ...	45	65
104/9	*Set of 6*		1·40	3·00

34 Royal Angelfish

(Des R. Hegeman. Photo Enschedé)

1963 (2 Feb). Tropical Fish. T **34** and similar triangular designs. Multicoloured. P 13½.

110	2l. Type **34**	15	1·50
111	3l. Type **34**	15	1·50
112	5l. Type **34**	20	55
113	10l. Moorish Idol	35	55
114	25l. As 10l.	1·00	55
115	50l. Diadem Soldierfish	1·50	70
116	1r. Powder-blue Surgeonfish	1·75	75
117	5r. Racoon Butterflyfish	6·25	12·00
110/17 *Set of 8*		10·00	16·00

39 Fish in Net

40 Handful of Grain

(Photo State Ptg Wks, Vienna)

1963 (21 Mar). Freedom from Hunger. P 12.

118	**39**	2l. brown and deep bluish green ..	40	3·50
119	**40**	5l. brown and orange-red...	75	2·00
120	**39**	7l. brown and turquoise...	95	2·00
121	**40**	10l. brown and blue	1·25	2·00
122	**39**	25l. brown and brown-red...	3·25	4·00
123	**40**	50l. brown and violet...	4·75	8·00
124	**39**	1r. brown and deep magenta...	7·00	12·00
118/24	*Set of 7*		16·00	30·00

 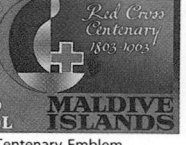

41 Centenary Emblem

42 Maldivian Scout Badge

(Photo Harrison)

1963 (1 Oct). Centenary of Red Cross. P 14×14½.

125	**41**	2l. red and deep purple...	30	2·00
126		15l. red and deep bluish green	1·00	1·00
127		50l. red and deep brown	1·75	1·75
128		1r. red and indigo	2·50	2·00
129		4r. red and deep brown-olive	5·00	21·00
125/9	*Set of 5*		9·50	25·00

(Photo Enschedé)

1964. World Scout Jamboree, Marathon (1963). P 13½.

130	**42**	2l. green and violet	10	65
131		3l. green and bistre-brown...	10	65
132		25l. green and blue	15	15
133		1r. green and crimson	55	1·50
130/3	*Set of 4*		80	2·50

43 Mosque, Malé

44 Putting the Shot

(Recess B.W.)

1964 (10 Aug). "Maldives Embrace Islam". W w **12**. P 11½.

134	**43**	2l. purple	10	60
135		3l. emerald-green	10	60
136		10l. carmine	10	10
137		40l. deep dull purple	30	25
138		60l. blue	50	40
139		85l. orange-brown	60	60
134/9	*Set of 6*		1·50	2·25

(Litho Enschedé)

1964 (1 Oct). Olympic Games, Tokyo. T **44** and similar horiz design. W w **12**. P 14×13½.

140	2l. deep maroon and turquoise-blue....	10	2·00
141	3l. crimson and chestnut	10	2·00
142	5l. bronze-green and deep green	15	35
143	10l. slate-violet and reddish purple	20	35
144	15l. sepia and yellow-brown	30	35
145	25l. indigo and deep blue	50	35
146	50l. deep olive-green and yellow-olive..	75	40
147	1r. deep maroon and olive-grey	1·25	75
140/7 *Set of 8*		3·00	6·00

MS147a 126×140 mm. Nos. 145/7. Imperf ... 2·25 4·50

Designs:—2 to 10l. Type **44**; 15l. to 1r. Running.

46 Telecommunications Satellite

(Des M. Shamir. Photo Harrison)

1965 (1 July). International Quiet Sun Years. P 14½.

148	**46**	5l. blue	20	75
149		10l. brown	25	75
150		25l. green	50	75
151		1r. deep magenta	1·00	1·25
148/51	*Set of 4*		1·75	3·25

On 26 July 1965, Maldive Islands became independent and left the Commonwealth, rejoining the organisation on 9 July 1982.

47 Isis (wall carving, Abu Simbel)

48 President Kennedy and Doves

(Des M. and G. Shamir. Litho Harrison)

1965 (1 Sept). Nubian Monuments Preservation. T **47** and similar vert design. W w **12**. P 14½.

152	**47**	2l. bluish green and brown-purple...	15	1·25
153	–	3l. lake and deep green	15	1·25
154	**47**	5l. dull green and brown-purple....	20	15
155	–	10l. steel-blue and orange	35	15
156	**47**	15l. red-brown and deep violet	60	15
		w. Wmk inverted	£100	
157	–	25l. reddish purple and deep blue ..	90	15
158	**47**	50l. yellow-green and sepia	1·10	45
159	–	1r. ochre and myrtle-green	1·50	55
152/9	*Set of 8*		4·50	3·50

Design:—3, 10, 25l., 1r. Rameses II on throne (wall carving, Abu Simbel).

(Photo State Ptg Wks, Vienna)

1965 (10 Oct). Second Death Anniv of President Kennedy. T **48** and similar horiz design. P 12.

160	**48**	2l. black and mauve	10	1·00
161		5l. bistre-brown and mauve	10	10
162		25l. indigo and mauve	20	10
163	–	1r. bright reddish purple, yellow and blue-green	35	25

164	–	2r. bronze-green, yellow and blue-green	50	1·10
160/4	*Set of 5*		1·00	2·25

MS164a 150×130 mm. No. 164 in block of four. Imperf ... 2·75 3·25

Design:—1r., 2r. Pres. Kennedy and hands holding olive-branch.

49 "XX" and UN Flag

50 ICY Emblem

(Des O. Adler. Photo State Ptg Wks, Vienna)

1965 (24 Nov). 20th Anniv of UN. P 12.

165	**49**	3l. turquoise-blue and red-brown..	15	50
166		10l. turquoise-blue and violet	40	10
167		1r. turquoise-blue and bronze-green	1·25	35
165/7	*Set of 3*		1·60	85

(Des M. and G. Shamir. Photo State Ptg Wks, Vienna)

1965 (20 Dec). International Co-operation Year. P 12.

168	**50**	5l. brown and yellow-bistre	40	20
169		15l. brown and slate-lilac	60	20
170		50l. brown and olive-yellow	1·25	30
171		1r. brown and orange-red	1·75	1·50
172		2r. brown and new blue	2·00	5·00
168/72	*Set of 5*		5·50	6·50

MS173 101×126 mm. Nos. 170/2. Imperf ... 7·00 9·50

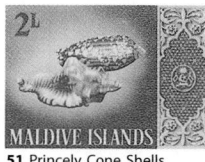

51 Princely Cone Shells

(Des M. and G. Shamir. Photo State Ptg Wks, Vienna)

1966 (1 June). T **51** and similar multicoloured designs. P 12.

174	2l. Type **51**	20	1·75
175	3l. Yellow flowers	20	1·75
176	5l. Reticulate Distorsio and Leopard Cone shells	30	15
177	7l. Camellias	30	15
178	10l. Type **51**	1·00	15
179	15l. Crab Plover and Seagull	3·75	30
180	20l. As 3l.	80	30
181	30l. Type **51**	2·75	35
182	50l. As 15l.	6·00	55
183	1r. Type **51**	4·00	70
184	1r. As 7l.	3·50	70
185	1r.50 As 15l.	3·75	3·75
186	2r. As 7l.	5·00	4·25
187	5r. As 15l.	23·00	17·00
188	10r. As 5l.	23·00	25·00
174/88 *Set of 15*		70·00	50·00

The 3l., 7l., 20l., 1r. (No. 184), 1r.50 and 2r. are diamond-shaped (43½×43½ mm); the others are horizontal designs as T **51**.

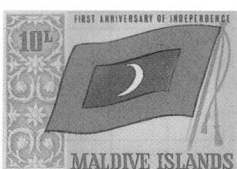

52 Maldivian Flag

(Des M. and G. Shamir. Litho Harrison)

1966 (26 July). First Anniv of Independence. P 14×14½.

189	**52**	10l. green, red and turquoise	4·00	75
190		1r. green, red, brown orange-yellow	10·00	1·25

53 Luna 9 on Moon

(Des M. and G. Shamir. Litho Harrison)

1966 (1 Nov). Space Rendezvous and Moon Landing. T **53** and similar horiz designs. W w **12**. P 15×14.

191	10l. light brown, grey-blue and bright blue	40	10
192	25l. green and carmine	60	10
193	50l. orange-brown and green	90	15
194	1r. turquoise-blue and chestnut	1·50	35
195	2r. green and violet	2·00	65
196	5r. rose-pink and deep turquoise-blue	3·00	1·60
191/6 *Set of 6*		7·50	2·50

MS197 108×126 mm. Nos. 194/6. Imperf ... 3·75

Designs:—25l., 1r., 5r. Gemini 6 and 7 rendezvous in space; 2r. Gemini spaceship as seen from the other spaceship; 50l. Type **53**.

54 UNESCO Emblem, and Owl on Book

55 Sir Winston Churchill and Cortège

(Litho Harrison)

1966 (15 Nov). 20th Anniv of UNESCO T **54** and similar vert designs. W w **12**. Multicoloured. P 15×14.
198		1l. Type **54**	40	2·25
199		3l. UNESCO emblem, and globe and microscope	40	2·25
200		5l. UNESCO emblem, and mask, violin and palette	80	50
201		50l. Type **54**	8·00	75
202		1r. Design as 3l.	9·00	1·00
203		5r. Design as 5l.	26·00	26·00
198/203		*Set of 6*	40·00	30·00

(Des M. and G. Shamir. Litho Harrison)

1967 (1 Jan). Churchill Commemoration. T **55** and similar horiz design. Flag in red and blue. P 14½×13½.
204	**55**	2l. olive-brown	40	3·50
205	–	10l. turquoise-blue	3·25	60
206	**55**	15l. green	4·00	60
207	–	25l. violet	6·00	70
208	–	1r. brown	15·00	1·50
209	**55**	2r.50 crimson	25·00	23·00
204/9		*Set of 6*	48·00	27·00
Design:—10l., 25l.,1r. Churchill and catafalque.

IMPERFORATE STAMPS. From No. 210 onwards some sets and perforated miniature sheets exist imperforate from limited printings.

56 Footballers and Jules Rimet Cup

(Des M. and G. Shamir. Photo Govt Printer, Israel)

1967 (22 Mar). England's Victory in World Cup Football Championship. T **56** and similar horiz designs. Multicoloured. P 14×13½.
210		2l. Type **56**	30	2·00
211		3l. Player in red shirt kicking ball	30	2·00
212		5l. Scoring goal	30	50
213		25l. As 3l.	2·25	50
		a. Emerald (face value and inscr) omitted	£475	
214		50l. Making a tackle	3·00	50
215		1r. Type **56**	4·75	80
216		2r. Emblem on Union Jack	7·00	7·00
210/16		*Set of 7*	16·00	12·00
MS217		100×121 mm. Nos. 214/16. Imperf	16·00	12·00

57 Ornate Butterflyfish

(Des M. and G. Shamir. Photo Govt Printer, Israel)

1967 (1 May). Tropical Fish. T **57** and similar horiz designs. Multicoloured. P 14.
218		2l. Type **57**	15	1·50
219		3l. Black-saddled Pufferfish	20	1·50
220		5l. Blue Boxfish	50	30
221		6l. Picasso Triggerfish	50	40
222		50l. Semicircle Angelfish	4·50	50
223		1r. As 3l.	6·50	1·00
224		2r. As 50l.	10·00	9·50
218/24		*Set of 7*	20·00	13·00

58 Hawker Siddeley H.S.748 over Hulule Airport Building

(Des M. and G. Shamir. Photo Govt Printer, Israel)

1967 (26 July). Inauguration of Hulule Airport. T **58** and similar horiz design. P 14×13½.
225		2l. reddish violet and yellow-olive	25	75
226		5l. deep green and lavender	50	10
227		10l. reddish violet and light turquoise-green	65	10
228		15l. deep green and yellow-ochre	1·00	10
229		30l. deep ultramarine and light blue	1·75	10
230		50l. deep brown and magenta	2·50	20

231		5r. deep ultramarine and yellow-orange	6·00	5·50
232		10r. deep brown and blue	8·00	9·00
225/32		*Set of 8*	18·00	14·00
Designs:—2l., 10l., 30l., 5r. T **58**; 5l., 15l., 50l., 10r. Airport building and Hawker Siddeley H.S.748. Higher values were also issued, intended mainly for fiscal use.

59 "Man and Music" Pavilion

International Tourist Year 1967 (**60**)

(Des M. and G. Shamir. Photo Govt Printer, Israel)

1967 (1 Sept). World Fair Montréal. T **59** and similar horiz design. Multicoloured. P 14×13½.
233		2l. Type **59**	10	1·00
234		5l. "Man and His Community" Pavilion	10	10
235		10l. Type **59**	15	10
236		50l. As 5l.	60	30
237		1r. Type **59**	1·00	50
238		2r. As 5l.	2·00	2·25
233/8		*Set of 6*	3·50	3·75
MS239		102×137 mm. Nos. 237/8. Imperf	2·50	4·50

1967 (1 Dec). International Tourist Year. Nos. 225/32 optd as T **60** (in one or three lines), in gold.
240		2l. reddish violet and yellow-olive	20	1·25
241		5l. deep green and lavender	40	25
242		10l. reddish violet and light turquoise-green	55	25
243		15l. deep green and yellow-ochre	60	25
244		30l. deep ultramarine and light blue	80	30
245		50l. deep brown and magenta	1·00	35
246		5r. deep ultramarine and yellow-orange	4·50	5·50
247		10r. deep brown and blue	5·50	8·00
240/7		*Set of 8*	12·00	14·50

61 Cub signalling and Lord Baden-Powell

62 French Satellite *A 1*

(Litho Harrison)

1968 (1 Jan). Maldivian Scouts and Cubs. T **61** and similar vert design. P 14×14½.
248	**61**	2l. brown, green and yellow	10	1·25
249	–	3l. carmine, bright blue and light blue	10	1·25
250	**61**	25l. bluish violet, lake and orange-red	1·50	40
251	–	1r. blackish green, chestnut and apple-green	3·50	1·60
248/51		*Set of 4*	4·50	4·00
Design:—3l., 1r. Scouts and Lord Baden-Powell.

(Des M. and G. Shamir. Photo Govt Printer, Israel)

1968 (27 Jan). Space Martyrs. Triangular designs as T **62**. P 14.
252		2l. magenta and ultramarine	20	1·00
253		3l. violet and yellow-brown	20	1·00
254		7l. olive-brown and lake	50	1·00
255		10l. deep blue, pale drab and lake	55	20
256		25l. bright emerald and reddish violet	1·25	20
257		50l. blue and orange-brown	1·60	30
258		1r. purple-brown and deep bluish green	2·25	50
259		2r. deep brown, pale blue and black	2·75	2·50
260		5r. magenta, light drab and black	3·50	4·00
252/60		*Set of 9*	11·50	9·50
MS261		110×155 mm. Nos. 258/9. Imperf	6·50	7·00
Designs:—2l., 50l. Type **62**; 3l., 25l. Luna 10; 7l.,1r. Orbiter and Mariner; 10l., 2r. Astronauts White, Grissom and Chaffee; 5r. Cosmonaut V. M. Komarov.

63 Putting the Shot

64 *Adriatic Seascape* (Bonington)

(Des M. Shamir. Litho Harrison)

1968 (1 Feb). Olympic Games, Mexico (1st issue). T **63** and similar vert design. Multicoloured. P 14½.
262		2l. Type **63**	10	90
263		6l. Throwing the discus	25	90
264		10l. Type **63**	40	15
265		15l. As 6l.	55	10
266		1r. Type **63**	1·00	35
267		2r.50 As 6l.	2·25	2·50
262/7		*Set of 6*	4·00	4·50
See also Nos. 294/7.

(Des M. Shamir. Litho Govt Printer, Israel)

1968 (1 Apr). Paintings. T **64** and similar horiz designs. Multicoloured. P 14.
268		50l. Type **64**	2·25	30
269		1r. *Ulysses deriding Polyphemus* (Turner)	2·75	45
270		2r. *Sailing Boat at Argenteuil* (Monet)	3·50	2·75
271		5r. *Fishing Boats at Les Saintes-Maries* (Van Gogh)	6·00	7·00
268/71		*Set of 4*	13·00	9·50

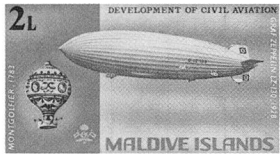

65 LZ-130 *Graf Zeppelin II* and Montgolfier's Balloon

(Des M. Shamir. Photo Govt Printer, Israel)

1968 (1 June). Development of Civil Aviation. T **65** and similar horiz designs. P 14×13½.
272		2l. orange-brown, yellow-green and ultramarine	20	1·25
273		3l. turquoise-blue, violet and orange-brown	20	1·25
274		5l. slate-green, crimson and turquoise-blue	20	20
275		7l. bright blue, purple and red-orange	4·00	1·75
276		10l. brown, turquoise-blue and bright purple	45	20
277		50l. crimson, slate-green and yellow-olive	1·50	30
278		1r. emerald, blue and vermilion	3·25	60
279		2r. maroon, bistre and bright blue	22·00	12·00
272/9		*Set of 8*	28·00	16·00
Designs:—3l., 1r. Boeing 707-420 and Douglas DC-3; 5l., 50l. Wright Type A and Lilienthal's glider; 7l., 2r. Projected Boeing 733 and Concorde; 10l. Type **65**.

66 WHO Building, Geneva

International Boy Scout Jamboree, Farragut Park, Idaho, U.S.A. August 1-9, 1967 (**67**)

(Litho Harrison)

1968 (15 July). 20th Anniv of World Health Organisation. P 14½×13½.
280	**66**	10l. violet, turquoise-blue and light greenish blue	1·50	30
281		25l. bronze-green, yellow-brown and orange-yellow	2·00	30
282		1r. deep brown, emerald and bright green	4·50	1·00
283		2r. bluish violet, magenta and mauve	6·50	8·00
280/3		*Set of 4*	13·00	8·75

1968 (1 Aug). First Anniv of Scout Jamboree, Idaho. Nos. 248/51 optd with T **67**.
284		2l. brown, green and yellow	10	1·00
285		3l. carmine, bright blue and light blue	10	1·00
286		25l. bluish violet, lake and orange-red	1·50	55
287		1r. blackish green, chestnut and apple-green	4·50	2·10
284/7		*Set of 4*	5·50	4·25

68 Curlew and Redshank

1968 (24 Sept). T **68** and similar horiz designs. Photo. Multicoloured. P 14×13½.
288		2l. Type **68**	50	1·25
289		10l. Pacific Grinning Tun and Papal Mitre shells	1·25	20
290		25l. Oriental Angel Wing and Tapestry Turban shells	1·75	25
291		50l. Type **68**	9·50	1·10
292		1r. As 25l.	4·50	1·10
293		2r. As 10l.	5·50	5·00
288/93		*Set of 6*	21·00	8·00

69 Throwing the Discus

(Des M. Shamir. Photo Govt Printer, Israel)

1968 (12 Oct). Olympic Games, Mexico (2nd issue). T **69** and similar multicoloured designs. P 14.
294		10l. Type **69**	10	10
295		50l. Running	20	20
296		1r. Cycling	6·00	1·25
297		2r. Basketball	8·00	4·00
294/7		*Set of 4*	13·00	5·00

INDEPENDENT REPUBLIC
11 November 1968

70 Fishing Dhow

71 The Thinker (Rodin)

(Photo Harrison)

1968 (11 Nov). Republic Day. T **70** and similar horiz design. P 14×14½.

298	10l. brown, ultramarine and light yellow-green	1·50	50
299	1r. green, red and bright blue	11·00	2·00

Design:—1r. National Flag, Crest and map.

(Des M. Shamir. Litho Rosenbaum Brothers, Vienna)

1969 (10 Apr). UNESCO "Human Rights". T **71** and similar vert designs, showing sculptures by Rodin. Multicoloured. P 13½.

300	6l. Type **71**	75	60
301	10l. *Hands*	75	20
302	1r.50 *Eve*	3·75	3·75
303	2r.50 *Adam*	4·00	4·00
300/3 *Set of 4*		8·25	7·75
MS304 112×130 mm. Nos. 302/3. Imperf		13·00	13·00

72 Module nearing Moon's Surface

(Des M. Shamir. Litho Govt Printer, Israel)

1969 (25 Sept). First Man on the Moon. T **72** and similar square designs. Multicoloured. P 14.

305	6l. Type **72**	50	35
306	10l. Astronaut with hatchet	50	20
307	1r.50 Astronaut and module	3·25	2·25
308	2r.50 Astronaut using camera	3·50	2·75
305/8 *Set of 4*		7·00	5·00
MS309 101×130 mm. Nos. 305/8. Imperf		6·50	7·50

Gold Medal Winner
Mohamed Gammoudi
5000 m. run
Tunisia

REPUBLIC OF MALDIVES

(73)

1969 (1 Dec). Gold-medal Winners, Olympic Games, Mexico (1968). Nos. 295/6 optd with T **73**, or similar inscr honouring P. Trentin (cycling) of France.

310	50l. multicoloured	60	60
311	1r. multicoloured	1·40	90

74 Racoon Butterflyfish

(Des M. Shamir. Litho)

1970 (1 Jan). Tropical Fish. T **74** and similar diamond-shaped designs. Multicoloured. P 10½.

312	2l. Type **74**	40	1·00
313	5l. Clown Triggerfish	65	50
314	25l. Broad-barred Lionfish	1·25	50
315	50l. Long-nosed Butterflyfish	1·50	1·00
316	1r. Emperor Angelfish	1·75	1·25
317	2r. Royal Angelfish	2·25	7·00
312/17 *Set of 6*		7·00	10·00

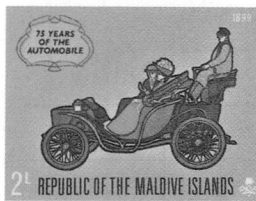
75 Columbia Dauman Victoria, 1899

(Des M. Shamir. Litho)

1970 (1 Feb). 75 Years of the Automobile. T **75** and similar horiz designs. Multicoloured. P 12.

318	2l. Type **75**	30	75
319	5l. Duryea Phaeton, 1902	45	40
320	7l. Packard S-24, 1906	60	40
321	10l. Autocar Runabout, 1907	60	40
322	25l. Type **75**	1·40	40
323	50l. As 5l.	1·60	70
324	1r. As 7l.	1·75	1·00
325	2r. As 10l.	1·90	6·50
318/25 *Set of 8*		7·75	9·50
MS326 95×143 mm. Nos. 324/5. P 11½		3·25	7·50

76 UN Headquarters, New York

77 Ship and Light Buoy

(Des M. Shamir. Litho Rosenbaum Brothers, Vienna)

1970 (26 June). 25th Anniv of United Nations. T **76** and similar horiz designs. Multicoloured. P 13½.

327	2l. Type **76**	10	1·00
328	10l. Surgical operation (WHO)	2·25	40
329	25l. Student, actress and musician (UNESCO)	3·75	50
330	50l. Children at work and play (UNICEF)	2·00	70
331	1r. Fish, corn and farm animals (FAO)	2·00	1·00
332	2r. Miner hewing coal (ILO)	7·50	7·50
327/32 *Set of 6*		16·00	10·00

(Des M. Shamir. Litho)

1970 (26 July). Tenth Anniv of Inter-governmental Maritime Consultative Organization. T **77** and similar vert design. Multicoloured. P 13½.

333	50l. Type **77**	1·25	50
334	1r. Ship and lighthouse	6·50	1·50

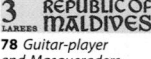
78 Guitar-player and Masqueraders (A. Watteau)

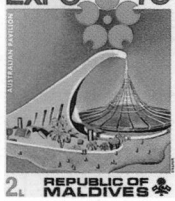
79 Australian Pavilion

(Des M. Shamir. Litho Govt Printer, Israel)

1970 (1 Aug). Famous Paintings showing the Guitar. T **78** and similar vert designs. Multicoloured. P 14.

335	3l. Type **78**	15	80
336	7l. *Spanish Guitarist* (E. Manet)	25	80
337	50l. *Costumed Player* (Watteau)	1·25	40
338	1r. *Mandolins-player* (Roberti)	2·00	55
339	2r.50 *Guitar-player and Lady* (Watteau)	3·50	4·00
340	5r. *Mandolins-player* (Frans Hals)	6·50	7·50
335/40 *Set of 6*		12·00	12·50
MS341 132×80 mm. Nos. 339/40. Roul		9·00	11·00

(Des M. Shamir. Litho Rosenbaum Brothers, Vienna)

1970 (1 Aug). EXPO 70 World Fair, Osaka, Japan. T **79** and similar vert designs. Multicoloured. P 13½.

342	2l. Type **79**	15	1·00
343	3l. West German Pavilion	15	1·00
344	10l. USA Pavilion	65	10
345	25l. British Pavilion	2·00	15
346	50l. Soviet Pavilion	2·50	45
347	1r. Japanese Pavilion	2·75	65
342/7 *Set of 6*		7·25	3·00

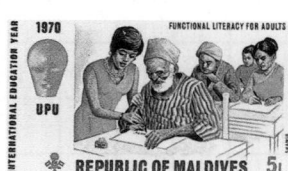
80 Learning the Alphabet

(Des M. Shamir. Litho Govt Printer, Israel)

1970 (7 Sept). International Education Year. T **80** and similar horiz designs. Multicoloured. P 14.

348	5l. Type **80**	50	60
349	10l. Training teachers	60	40
350	25l. Geography lesson	2·75	60
351	50l. School inspector	2·75	80
352	1r. Education by television	3·00	1·00
348/52 *Set of 5*		8·75	3·00

Philympia
London 1970

(81)

82 Footballers

1970 (18 Sep). Philympia 1970 Stamp Exhibition, London. Nos. 306/MS309 optd with T **81**, in silver.

353	10l. multicoloured	20	10
354	1r.50 multicoloured	1·25	1·00
355	2r.50 multicoloured	1·25	1·50
353/5 *Set of 3*		2·40	2·25
MS356 101×130 mm. Nos. 305/8 optd. Imperf		6·50	8·50

(Des M. Shamir. Litho Rosenbaum Brothers, Vienna)

1970 (1 Dec). World Cup Football Championship, Mexico. T **82** and similar vert designs, each showing football scenes and outline of the Jules Rimet Trophy. P 13½.

357	3l. multicoloured	20	1·25
358	6l. multicoloured	35	75
359	7l. multicoloured	35	55
360	25l. multicoloured	1·25	30
361	1r. multicoloured	2·75	1·00
357/61 *Set of 5*		4·25	3·50

Malta

Early records of the postal services under the British Occupation are fragmentary, but it is known that an Island Postmaster was appointed in 1802. A British Packet Agency was established in 1806 and it later became customary for the same individual to hold the two appointments together. The inland posts continued to be the responsibility of the local administration, but the overseas mails formed part of the British GPO system.

The stamps of Great Britain were used on overseas mails from September 1857. Previously during the period of the Crimean War letters franked with Great Britain stamps from the Crimea were cancelled at Malta with a wavy line obliterator. Such postmarks are known between April 1855 and September 1856.

The British GPO relinquished control of the overseas posts on 31 December 1884 when Great Britain stamps were replaced by those of Malta.

Z 1   Z 2

1855–56. Stamps of GREAT BRITAIN cancelled with wavy lines obliteration, Type Z **1**.

Z1	1d. red-brown (1854), Die I, wmk Small Crown, perf 16	£1000
Z2	1d. red-brown (1855), Die II, wmk Small Crown, perf 14	£1000
	a. Very blued paper	
Z3	1d. red-brown (1855), Die II, wmk Large Crown, perf 16	£1000
Z3a	1d. red-brown (1855), Die II, wmk Large Crown, perf 14	£1000
Z4	2d. blue (1855), wmk Large Crown, perf 14. Plate No. 5	£4500
Z5	6d. (1854) embossed	£4500
Z6	1s. (1847) embossed	£5000

It is now established that this obliterator was sent to Malta and used on mail in transit emanating from the Crimea.

1857 (18 Aug)–**59.** Stamps of GREAT BRITAIN cancelled "M", Type Z **2**.

Z7	1d. red-brown (1841), imperf	£2500
Z8	1d. red-brown, Die I, wmk Small Crown, perf 16	£160
Z9	1d. red-brown, Die II, wmk Small Crown, perf 16	£950
Z10	1d. red-brown, Die II (1855), wmk Small Crown, perf 14	£250
Z11	1d. red-brown, Die II (1855), wmk Large Crown, perf 14	80·00
Z11a	1d. rose-red (1857) wmk Large Crown, perf 16	
Z12	1d. rose-red (1857), wmk Large Crown, perf 14	22·00
Z13	2d. blue (1841), imperf	£3750
Z14	2d. blue (1854) wmk Small Crown, perf 16	£850
	Plate No. 4	
Z15	2d. blue (1855), wmk Large Crown, perf 14 *From*. Plate Nos. 5, 6	65·00
Z16	2d. blue (1858), wmk Large Crown, perf 16. Plate No. 6	£350
Z17	2d. blue (1858) (Plate Nos. 7, 8, 9) *From*	45·00
Z18	4d. rose (1857)	40·00
	a. Thick glazed paper	£225
Z19	6d. violet (1854), embossed	£5000
Z20	6d. lilac (1856)	42·00
	a. Thick paper	£250
Z21	6d. lilac (1856) (blued paper)	£900
Z22	1s. green (1856)	£130
	a. Thick paper	£200

Z 3   Z 6

Z 4

Z 5

Z 7

It should be noted that prices given here are for stamps bearing a portion of the "A25" obliterator. Stamps in fine condition bearing only the datestamp are worth a premium.

1859–84. Stamps of GREAT BRITAIN cancelled "A 25" as in Types Z **3/7**.

Z23	½d. rose-red (1870–79) *From*	32·00
	Plate Nos. 4, 5, 6, 8, 9, 10, 11, 12, 13, 14, 15, 19, 20.	
Z24	1d. red-brown (1841), imperf	£3250
Z25	1d. red-brown (1854), wmk Small Crown, perf 16	£375
Z26	1d. red-brown (1855), wmk Large Crown, perf 14	85·00
Z27	1d. rose-red (1857), wmk Large Crown, perf 14	9·00
Z28	1d. rose-red (1861), Alphabet IV	£475
Z30	1d. rose-red (1864–79) *From*	19·00
	Plate Nos. 71, 72, 73, 74, 76, 78, 79, 80, 81, 82, 83, 84, 85, 86, 87, 88, 89, 90, 91, 92, 93, 94, 95, 96, 97, 98, 99, 100, 101, 102, 103, 104, 105, 106, 107, 108, 109, 110, 111, 112, 113, 114, 115, 116, 117, 118, 119, 120, 121, 122, 123, 124, 125, 127, 129, 130, 131, 132, 133, 134, 135, 136, 137, 138, 139, 140, 141, 142, 143, 144, 145, 146, 147, 148, 149, 150, 151, 152, 153, 154, 155, 156, 157, 158, 159, 160, 161, 162, 163, 164, 165, 166, 167, 168, 169, 170, 171, 172, 173, 174, 175, 176, 177, 178, 179, 180, 181, 182, 183, 184, 185, 186, 187, 188, 189, 190, 191, 192, 193, 194, 195, 196, 197, 198, 199, 200, 201, 202, 203, 204, 205, 206, 207, 208, 209, 210, 211, 212, 213, 214, 215, 216, 217, 218, 219, 220, 221, 222, 223, 224.	
Z31	1½d. lake-red (1870–79) (Plate Nos. 1, 3) *From*	£600
Z32	2d. blue (1841), imperf	£4500
Z33	2d. blue (1855) wmk Large Crown perf 14	80·00
Z34	2d. blue (1858–69) *From*	19·00
	Plate Nos. 7, 8, 9, 12, 13, 14, 15.	
Z35	2½d. rosy mauve (1875) (blued paper) *From*	80·00
	Plate Nos. 1, 2.	
Z36	2½d. rosy mauve (1875–76) *From*	35·00
	Plate Nos. 1, 2, 3.	
Z37	2½d. rosy mauve (Error of Lettering)	£3500
Z38	2½d. rosy mauve (1876–79) *From*	17·00
	Plate Nos. 3, 4, 5, 6, 7, 8, 9, 10, 11, 12, 13, 14, 15, 16, 17.	
Z39	2½d. blue (1880–81) *From*	11·00
	Plate Nos. 17, 18, 19, 20.	
Z40	2½d. blue (1881) (Plate Nos. 21, 22, 23) *From*	8·00
Z41	3d. carmine-rose (1862)	£130
Z42	3d. rose (1865) (Plate No. 4)	80·00
Z43	3d. rose (1867–73) *From*	32·00
	Plate Nos. 4, 5, 6, 7, 8, 9, 10.	
Z44	3d. rose (1873–76) *From*	38·00
	Plate Nos. 11, 12, 14, 15, 16, 17, 18, 19, 20.	
Z45	3d. rose (1881) (Plate Nos. 20, 21) *From*	£1000
Z46	3d. on 3d. lilac (1883)	£550
Z47	4d. rose (or rose-carmine) (1857)	40·00
	a. Thick glazed paper	£150
Z48	4d. red (1862) (Plate Nos. 3, 4) *From*	35·00
Z49	4d. vermilion (1865–73) *From*	18·00
	Plate Nos. 7, 8, 9, 10, 11, 12, 13, 14.	
Z50	4d. vermilion (1876) (Plate No. 15)	£225
Z51	4d. sage-green (1877) (Plate Nos. 15, 16) *From*	£110
Z52	4d. grey-brown (1880) wmk Large Garter. Plate No. 17.	£180
Z53	4d. grey-brown (1880) wmk Crown *From*	55·00
	Plate Nos. 17, 18.	
Z54	6d. violet (1854), embossed	£3750
Z55	6d. lilac (1856)	48·00
	a. Thick paper	
Z56	6d. lilac (1862) (Plate Nos. 3, 4) *From*	40·00
Z57	6d. lilac (1865–67) (Plate Nos. 5, 6) *From*	30·00
Z58	6d. lilac (1865–67) (Wmk error)	£1300
Z59	6d. lilac (1867) (Plate No. 6)	38·00
Z60	6d. violet (1867–70) (Plate Nos. 6, 8, 9) *From*	26·00
Z61	6d. buff (1872–73) (Plate Nos. 11, 12) *From*	£100
Z62	6d. chestnut (1872) (Plate No. 11)	35·00
Z63	6d. grey (1873) (Plate No. 12)	75·00
Z64	6d. grey (1873–80) *From*	35·00
	Plate Nos. 13, 14, 15, 16, 17.	
Z65	6d. grey (1881–82) (Plate Nos. 17, 18) *From*	80·00
Z66	6d. on 6d. lilac (1883)	£150
Z67	8d. orange (1876)	£475
Z68	9d. straw (1862)	£700
Z69	9d. bistre (1862)	£650
Z70	9d. straw (1865)	£650
Z71	9d. straw (1867)	£800
Z72	10d. red-brown (1867)	£130
Z73	1s. (1847), embossed	£4000
Z74	1s. green (1856)	80·00
Z75	1s. green (1856) (thick paper)	£275
Z76	1s. green (1862)	70·00
Z77	1s. green ("K" variety)	£2250
Z78	1s. green (1865) (Plate No. 4)	48·00
Z79	1s. green (1867–73) (Plate Nos. 4, 5, 6, 7) *From*	32·00
Z80	1s. green (1873–77) *From*	45·00
	Plate Nos. 8, 9, 10, 11, 12, 13.	
Z81	1s. orange-brown (1880) (Plate No. 13)	£300
Z82	1s. orange-brown (1881) *From*	90·00
	Plate Nos. 13, 14.	
Z83	2s. blue (shades) (1867) *From*	£160
Z84	2s. brown (1880)	£3250
Z85	5s. rose (1867–74) (Plate No. 1, 2) *From*	£425
Z86	5s. rose (1882) (Plate No. 4), blued paper	£2500
Z87	5s. rose (1882) (Plate No. 4), white paper	£1800
Z88	10s. grey-green (1878)	£3500

1880.

Z89	½d. deep green	16·00
Z90	½d. pale green	16·00
Z91	1d. Venetian red	16·00
Z92	1½d. Venetian red	£500
Z93	2d. pale rose	40·00
Z94	2d. deep rose	42·00
Z95	5d. indigo	75·00

1881.

Z96	1d. lilac (14 dots)	35·00
Z97	1d. lilac (16 dots)	9·00

1883–84.

Z98	½d. slate-blue	20·00
Z99	1½d. lilac	
Z100	2d. lilac	£110
Z101	2½d. lilac	13·00
Z102	3d. lilac	
Z103	4d. dull green	£180
Z104	5d. dull green	£150
Z105	6d. dull green	£400
Z106	9d. dull green	
Z107	1s. dull green	£400
Z108	5s. rose (blued paper)	£2000
Z109	5s. rose (white paper)	£1100

POSTAL FISCALS

Z109a	1d. reddish lilac (Type F **8**) (1867) wmk Anchor	
Z110	1d. purple (Type F **12**) (1871) wmk Anchor	£850
Z111	1d. purple (Type F **12**) (1881) wmk Orb	£650

PRICES FOR STAMPS ON COVER TO 1945

Nos. 1/3	from × 5
Nos. 4/17	from × 6
Nos. 18/19	from × 12
Nos. 20/9	from × 6
No. 30	—
Nos. 31/3	from × 4
Nos. 34/7	from × 10
Nos. 38/88	from × 4
Nos. 92/3	from × 5
Nos. 97/103	from × 3
Nos. 104/5	—
Nos. 106/20	from × 3
No. 121	—
Nos. 122/38	from × 3
Nos. 139/40	—
Nos. 141/72	from × 4
Nos. 173/209	from × 3
Nos. 210/31	from × 2
Nos. D1/10	from × 30
Nos. D11/20	from × 15

CROWN COLONY

PRINTERS. Nos. 1/156. Printed by De La Rue; typographed *except where otherwise stated.*

1

Type **1**

The first Government local post was established on 10 June 1853 and, as an experiment, mail was carried free of charge. During 1859 the Council of Government decided that a rate of ½d. per ½ ounce should be charged for this service and stamps in Type **1** were ordered for this purpose. Both the new rate and the stamps were introduced on 1 December 1860. Until 1 January 1885 the ½d. stamps were intended for the local service only; mail for abroad being handled by the British Post Office on Malta, using GB stamps.

Specialists now recognise 29 printings in shades of yellow and one in green during the period to 1884. These printings can be linked to the changes in watermark and perforation as follows:

Ptg 1—Blued paper without wmk. P 14.
Ptgs 2 and 3—White paper without wmk. P 14.
Ptgs 4 to 9, 11, 13 to 19, 22 to 24—Crown CC wmk. P 14.
Ptg 10—Crown CC wmk. P 12½ (rough).
Ptg 12—Crown CC wmk. P 12½ (clean-cut).
Ptgs 20 and 21—Crown CC wmk. P 14×12½.
Ptgs 25 to 28, 30—Crown CA wmk. P 14.
Ptg 29—In green (No. 20).

PRICES. The prices quoted for Nos. 1/19 are for examples in very fine condition, with fresh colour. Unused examples should have original gum, used examples should have neat clear cancels. The many surviving stamps which do not meet these criteria are usually worth only a fraction of the prices quoted, with stamps of poor colour being virtually worthless.

(Des E. Fuchs)

1860 (1 Dec)–**63.** No wmk. P 14.

(a) Blued paper

1	½d. buff (1.12.60)		£1300	£650

(b) Thin, hard white paper

2	½d. brown-orange (11.61)		£1300	£500
3	½d. buff (1.63)		£850	£400
	a. Pale buff		£850	£400

No. 1 is printed in fugitive ink. It is known imperforate but was not issued in that state (Price £12000 unused).

The printing on No. 2 gives a very blurred and muddy impression; on Nos. 3/3a the impression is clear.

Specks of carmine can often be detected with a magnifying glass on Nos. 2/3a, and also on No. 4. Examples also exist on which parts of the design are in pure rose, due to defective mixing of the ink.

1863-81. Wmk Crown CC.

(a) P 14

4	½d. buff (6.63) (shades)	£120	75·00
	w. Wmk inverted	£500	£450
	x. Wmk reversed	£1700	
5	½d. bright orange (11.64)	£900	£250
	w. Wmk inverted	£1700	£1200
6	½d. orange-brown (4.67)	£425	£110
7	½d. dull orange (4.70)	£300	90·00
	w. Wmk inverted	†	£700
	x. Wmk reversed	£2000	
8	½d. orange-buff (5.72)	£190	80·00
9	½d. golden yellow (aniline) (10.74)	£350	£400
10	½d. yellow-buff (9.75) (shades)	85·00	60·00
11	½d. pale buff (3.77)	£190	75·00
	w. Wmk inverted	£1200	£600
12	½d. bright orange-yellow (4.80)	£275	£120
13	½d. yellow (4.81)	£150	75·00
	w. Wmk inverted	†	£600

(b) P 12½ rough (No. 14) or clean-cut (No. 15)

14	½d. buff-brown (11.68)	£160	£110
15	½d. yellow-orange (5.71)	£400	£180

(c) P 14×12½

16	½d. yellow-buff (7.78)	£200	£110
	w. Wmk inverted	†	£1700
17	½d. yellow (2.79)	£275	£110

Examples of No. 4 from the 1863 printing are on thin, surfaced paper; later printings in the same shade were on unsurfaced paper.

The ink used for No. 5 is mineral and, unlike that on No. 9, does not stain the paper.

Some variations of shade on No. 6 may be described as chestnut. The ink of No. 6 is clear and never muddy, although some examples are over-inked. Deeper shades of No. 4, with which examples of No. 6 might be confused, have muddy ink.

Nos. 7/8 and 11 are distinctive shades which should not be confused with variants of No. 10.

It is believed that there are no surviving pairs of the buff-brown imperforate between variety previously listed.

The Royal Collection contains an unused horizontal pair of the yellow-buff perforated 12½×14.

1882 (Mar)-84. Wmk Crown CA. P 14.

18	½d. orange-yellow	40·00	35·00
19	½d. red-orange (9.84)	18·00	50·00

2   **3**

4   **5**

1885 (1 Jan)-90. Wmk Crown CA. P 14.

20	1	½d. green	5·50	50
		w. Wmk inverted	£170	£110
21	2	1d. rose	85·00	26·00
		w. Wmk inverted	£2250	
22		1d. carmine (shades) (1890)	13·00	35
		w. Wmk inverted	†	£1400
23	3	2d. grey	12·00	2·50
24	4	2½d. dull blue	65·00	3·00
25		2½d. bright blue	50·00	1·00
26		2½d. ultramarine	50·00	1·00
27	3	4d. brown	11·00	3·00
		a. Imperf (pair)	£5500	£6500
		w. Wmk inverted	£2500	
28		1s. violet	50·00	12·00
29		1s. pale violet (1890)	60·00	21·00
20/8 Set of 6			£110	17·00
20s/8s Optd "SPECIMEN" Set of 6			£4750	

Although not valid for postage until 1 January 1885 these stamps were available at the GPO, Valletta from 27 December 1884.

Three unused examples of the ½d. green, No. 20, are known line perforated 12. These originated from proof books, the stamp not being issued for use with this perforation.

The Royal Collection includes an example of the 1d. carmine printed on the gummed side.

1886 (1 Jan). Wmk Crown CC. P 14.

30	5	5s. rose	£110	80·00
		s. Optd "SPECIMEN"	£1000	
		w. Wmk inverted	£160	£130

6 Harbour of Valletta   **7** Gozo Fishing Boat   **8** Galley of Knights of St. John

9 Emblematic figure of Malta   **10** Shipwreck of St. Paul

(T 6/10 recess)

1899 (4 Feb)-1901. P 14.

(a) Wmk Crown CA (sideways* on ¼d)

31	6	¼d. brown (4.1.01)	9·00	2·75
		a. Red-brown	1·50	40
		b. Wmk upright	£3000	
		bx. Wmk upright (reversed)	†	£3000
		w. Wmk Crown to left of CA	2·50	75
		ws. Optd "SPECIMEN"	80·00	
		x. Wmk sideways reversed	48·00	25·00
		y. Wmk Crown to left of CA and reversed	80·00	32·00
		ys. Optd "SPECIMEN"	£275	
32	7	4½d. sepia	27·00	16·00
		x. Wmk reversed	£1000	
33	8	5d. vermilion	48·00	19·00
		x. Wmk reversed	£225	£225

(b) Wmk Crown CC

34	9	2s.6d. olive-grey	45·00	16·00
		x. Wmk reversed	£1500	
35	10	10s. blue-black	£100	65·00
		x. Wmk reversed	—	£1200
		y. Wmk inverted and reversed	£900	£700
31/5 Set of 5			£190	£100
31s/5s Optd "SPECIMEN" Set of 5			£300	

*The normal sideways watermark shows Crown to right of CA, as seen from the back of the stamp.

One Penny

(11)   **12**

1902 (4 July). Nos. 24 and 25 surch locally at Govt Ptg Office with T 11.

36		1d. on 2½d. dull blue	1·75	2·25
		a. Surch double	£16000	£3750
		b. "One Pnney" (R. 9/2)	32·00	55·00
		ba. Surch double, with "One Pnney"	£42000	
		s. Optd "SPECIMEN"	70·00	
		w. Wmk inverted	—	£2000
37		1d. on 2½d. bright blue	1·25	2·25
		a. "One Pnney" (R. 9/2)	32·00	55·00

(Des E. Fuchs)

1903 (12 Mar)-04. Wmk Crown CA. P 14.

38	12	½d. green	10·00	85
39		1d. blackish brown and red (7.5.03)	15·00	40
40		2d. purple and grey	29·00	6·00
41		2½d. maroon and blue (1903)	32·00	4·50
42		3d. grey and purple (26.3.03)	2·00	50
43		4d. blackish brown and brown (19.5.04)	26·00	19·00
44		1s. grey and violet (6.4.03)	35·00	9·00
38/44 Set of 7			£130	35·00
38s/44s Optd "SPECIMEN" Set of 7			£190	

1904-14. Wmk Mult Crown CA (sideways* on ¼d.). P 14.

45	6	¼d. red-brown (10.10.05)	9·00	2·50
		a. Deep brown (1910)	9·00	10
		w. Wmk Crown to left of CA	28·00	1·50
		x. Wmk reversed	£350	
		y. Wmk Crown to left of CA and reversed	£250	
47	12	½d. green (6.11.04)	5·50	30
		aw. Wmk inverted		
		b. Deep green (1909)	6·00	10
		bw. Wmk inverted		
48		1d. black and red (24.4.05)	26·00	20
49		1d. red (2.4.07)	3·50	10
50		2d. purple and grey (22.2.05)	17·00	3·75
51		2d. grey (4.10.11)	6·00	6·50
52		2½d. maroon and blue (8.10.04)	38·00	60
53		2½d. bright blue (15.1.11)	5·50	4·25
54		4d. black and brown (1.4.06)	11·00	8·50
		w. Wmk inverted		
55		4d. black and red/yellow (21.11.11)	4·50	5·00
57	7	4½d. brown (27.2.05)	40·00	8·50
		w. Wmk inverted	£550	£375
58		4½d. orange (6.3.12†)	4·75	4·50
59	8	5d. vermilion (20.2.05)	45·00	8·00
60		5d. pale sage-green (1910)	4·75	4·00
		a. Deep sage-green (1914)	11·00	14·00
		y. Wmk inverted and reversed	†	£1100
61	12	1s. grey and violet (14.12.04)	50·00	2·00
62		1s. black/green (15.3.11)	7·50	4·25
63		5s. green and red/yellow (22.3.11)	65·00	75·00
45/63 Set of 17			£300	£110
45as, 47bs, 49s, 51s, 53s, 55s, 58s, 60s, 62s/3s Optd "SPECIMEN" Set of 10			£500	

*The normal sideways watermark shows Crown to right of CA, as seen from the back of the stamp.

†This is the earliest known date of use.

13   **14**   **15**

1914-21. Ordinary paper (¼d. to 2½d., 2s.6d.) or chalk-surfaced paper (others). Wmk Mult Crown CA. P 14.

69	13	¼d. brown (2.1.14)	1·75	10
		a. Deep brown (1919)	3·00	1·75
		x. Wmk reversed	†	£1600
71		½d. green (20.1.14)	3·50	30
		aa. Wmk sideways	†	£11000

---

		a. Deep green (1919)	7·00	1·50
		aw. Wmk inverted	†	£450
73		1d. carmine-red (15.4.14)	1·50	10
		a. Scarlet (1915)	3·00	40
		w. Wmk inverted	†	£500
		y. Wmk inverted and reversed	†	£1600
75		2d. grey (12.8.14)	15·00	8·00
		aw. Wmk inverted	†	£1400
		b. Deep slate (1919)	15·00	19·00
77		2½d. bright blue (11.3.14)	2·75	65
		w. Wmk inverted	†	£225
78	14	3d. purple/yellow (1.5.20)	2·50	21·00
		a. On orange-buff (1915)	75·00	50·00
		bs. On yellow, white back (opt. "SPECIMEN")	£375	
79	6	4d. black (21.8.15)	15·00	7·00
		a. Grey-black (28.10.16)	45·00	10·00
80	13	6d. dull and bright purple (10.3.14)	11·00	21·00
		a. Dull purple and magenta (1918)	16·00	21·00
		w. Wmk inverted		
81	14	1s. black/green (white back) (2.1.14)	17·00	48·00
		a. On green, green back (1915)	13·00	26·00
		ab. Wmk sideways	†	£2500
		as. Optd "SPECIMEN"	70·00	
		b. On blue-green, olive back (1918)	19·00	35·00
		c. On emerald surface (1920)	9·00	48·00
		d. On emerald back (1921)	42·00	90·00
86	15	2s. purple and bright blue/blue (15.4.14)	50·00	38·00
		a. Break in scroll	£375	
		b. Broken crown and scroll	£400	£400
		c. Nick in top right scroll	£375	£375
		f. Damaged leaf at bottom right	£500	£500
		g. Dull purple and blue/grey-blue (1921)	90·00	65·00
		ga. Break in scroll	£650	
		gb. Broken crown and scroll	£700	
		ge. Break in lines below left scroll	£700	
		gf. Damaged leaf at bottom right	£700	£700
87	9	2s.6d. olive-green (1919)	75·00	80·00
		a. Olive-grey (1920)	80·00	£110
88	15	5s. green and red/yellow (21.3.17)	£100	£110
		a. Break in scroll	£550	
		b. Broken crown and scroll	£600	£650
		c. Nick in top right scroll	£600	£650
		e. Break in lines below left scroll	£800	£800
		f. Damaged leaf at bottom right	£750	
69/88 Set of 12			£250	£275
69s/88s (ex 2s.6d.) Optd "SPECIMEN" Set of 11			£550	

The design of Nos. 79/a differs in various details from that of Type 6. We have only seen one example of No. 71aa; it is in used condition.

No. 78bs, the 3d. purple on yellow on white back, was prepared for use in 1914, and "SPECIMEN" examples were distributed to UPU members, but the stamp was never issued.

An example of the 2s.6d. olive-grey with bottom margin attached exists with the "A" omitted from "CA" in the watermark on the margin.

For illustrations of the varieties on Nos. 86 and 88 see above No. 51b of Bermuda.

WAR TAX

(16)   **17**   **18**

1917-18. Optd with T 16 by De La Rue.

92	13	½d. deep green (14.12.17*)	2·25	15
		w. Wmk inverted	£650	
		y. Wmk inverted and reversed	£950	
93	12	3d. grey and purple (15.2.18*)	3·50	16·00
92s/3s Optd "SPECIMEN" Set of 2			£150	

*These are the earliest known dates of use.

(T 17 recess)

1919 (6 Mar). Wmk Mult Crown CA. P 14.

96	17	10s. black	£3250	£4500
		s. Optd "SPECIMEN"	£1000	

Dark flaw on scroll (R. 2/4 1st state)   Lines omitted from scroll (R. 2/4 later state)

1921 (16 Feb)-22. Chalk-surfaced paper (6d., 2s.) or ordinary paper (others). Wmk Mult Script CA. P 14.

97	13	¼d. brown (12.1.22)	6·00	40·00
98		½d. green (19.1.22)	6·50	35·00
99		1d. scarlet (24.12.21)	7·00	2·75
		w. Wmk inverted	£1200	£500
100	18	2d. grey	11·00	1·75
101	13	2½d. bright blue (15.1.22)	7·00	48·00
102		6d. dull purple and bright purple (19.1.22)	35·00	85·00
103	15	2s. purple and blue/blue (shades) (19.1.22)	70·00	£225
		a. Break in scroll	£350	£750
		b. Broken crown and scroll	£375	

		c. Dark flaw on scroll	£3500	
		d. Lines omitted from scroll	£550	
		e. Break in lines below left scroll	£400	
		f. Damaged leaf at bottom right	£400	
		g. Nick in top right scroll	£375	
104	**17**	10s. black (19.1.22)	£350	£800
97/104 Set of 8			£450	£1100
97s/104s Optd "SPECIMEN" Set of 8			£475	

For illustrations of other varieties on No. 103 see above No. 51*b* of Bermuda.

Examples of all values are known showing a forged G.P.O. Malta postmark dated "MY 10 22".

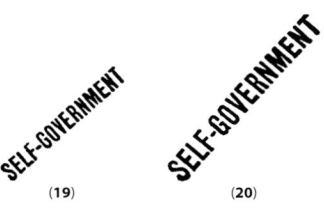

(19)   (20)

1922 (12 Jan–Apr). Optd with T **19** or T **20** (large stamps), at Govt Printing Office, Valletta.

(a) On No. 35. Wmk Crown CC

105	**10**	10s. blue-black (R.)	£250	£400
		x. Wmk reversed	£1800	

(b) On Nos. 71, 77, 78a, 80, 81d, 86c, 87a and 88. Wmk Mult Crown CA

106	**13**	½d. green	2·25	4·00
		w. Wmk inverted	£200	
107		2½d. bright blue	19·00	50·00
108	**14**	3d. purple/*orange-buff*	5·00	27·00
109	**13**	6d. dull and bright purple	7·00	40·00
		x. Wmk reversed	£1500	£1500
110	**14**	1s. black/*emerald*	7·00	29·00
111	**15**	2s. purple and blue/*blue* (R.)	£250	£500
		a. Break in scroll	£1100	
		b. Broken crown and scroll	£1100	
		c. Nick in top right scroll	£1300	
		e. Break in lines below left scroll	£1300	
		f. Damaged leaf at bottom right	£1300	
112	**9**	2s.6d. olive-grey	32·00	55·00
		a. "C" of "CA" missing from wmk	£1400	
113	**15**	5s. green and red/*yellow*	60·00	£100
		a. Break in scroll	£375	
		b. Broken crown and scroll	£375	
		c. Lines omitted from scroll	£375	
		e. Break in lines below left scroll	£475	
		f. Damaged leaf at bottom right	£475	
106/13 Set of 8			£350	£700

(c) On Nos. 97/104. Wmk Mult Script CA

114	**13**	¼d. brown	30	1·00
		w. Wmk inverted		
115		½d. green (29.4)	5·50	15·00
116		1d. scarlet	1·00	20
117	**18**	2d. grey	6·00	45
118	**13**	2½d. bright blue (15.1)	1·10	2·50
119		6d. dull and bright purple (19.4)	25·00	55·00
120	**15**	2s. purple and blue/*blue* (R.) (25.1)	50·00	95·00
		a. Break in scroll	£300	
		b. Broken crown and scroll	£300	
		c. Lines omitted from scroll	£425	
		e. Break in lines below left scroll	£375	
		f. Damaged leaf at bottom right	£375	£600
121	**17**	10s. black (R.) (9.3)	£140	£250
		x. Wmk reversed	£3250	
114/21 Set of 8			£200	£375

Examples of all values are known showing a forged GPO Malta postmark dated "MY 10 22".

One Farthing (21)   22   23

1922 (15 Apr). No. 100 surch with T **21**, at Govt Printing Office, Valletta.

122	**18**	¼d. on 2d. grey	85	30
		a. Dot to "i" of "Farthing" omitted	£425	

No. 122a occurred on R. 4/4 of the lower left pane during part of the printing only. Small or faint dots are found on other positions.

(Des E. C. Dingli (T **22**) and G. Vella (**23**))

1922 (1 Aug)–**26**. Wmk Mult Script CA (sideways* on T **22**, except No. 140). P 14.

(a) Typo. Chalk-surfaced paper

123	**22**	¼d. brown (22.8.22)	2·75	60
		a. Chocolate-brown	7·50	80
		w. Wmk Crown to right of CA	—	£160
124		½d. green	2·50	15
		w. Wmk Crown to right of CA	—	£160
125		1d. orange and purple	7·00	20
		w. Wmk Crown to right of CA	—	£120
126		1d. bright violet (25.4.24)	4·25	80
127		1½d. brown-red (1.10.23)	5·50	15
128		2d. bistre-brown and turquoise (28.8.22)	3·50	1·25
		w. Wmk Crown to right of CA	—	£190
129		2½d. ultramarine (16.2.26)	6·00	19·00
130		3d. cobalt (28.8.22)	9·00	3·25
		a. Bright ultramarine	7·00	2·75
131		3d. black/*yellow* (16.2.26)	5·00	25·00

132		4d. yellow and bright blue (28.8.22)	3·00	6·00
		w. Wmk Crown to right of CA	£375	
133		6d. olive-green and reddish violet	7·00	4·75
134	**23**	1s. indigo and sepia	16·00	4·50
135		2s. brown and blue	14·00	24·00
136		2s.6d. bright magenta and black (28.8.22)	13·00	15·00
137		5s. orange-yellow and bright ultramarine (28.8.22)	21·00	50·00
138		10s. slate-grey and brown (28.8.22)	65·00	£160

(b) Recess

139	**22**	£1 black and carmine-red (wmk sideways) (28.8.22)	£150	£350
140		£1 black and bright carmine (wmk upright) (14.5.25)	£110	£325
123/40 Set of 17			£250	£550
123s/39s Optd "SPECIMEN" Set of 17			£550	

*The normal sideways watermark shows Crown to left of CA, as seen from the back of the stamp.

Two pence halfpenny (24)   **POSTAGE** (25)

1925. Surch with T **24**, at Govt Printing Office, Valletta.

141	**22**	2½d. on 3d. cobalt (3.12)	2·75	9·00
142		2½d. on 3d. bright ultramarine (9.12)	1·75	7·00

1926 (1 Apr). Optd with T **25** at Govt Printing Office, Valletta.

143	**22**	¼d. brown	1·50	8·50
144		½d. green	70	15
		w. Wmk Crown to right of CA	£170	
145		1d. bright violet	1·00	25
146		1½d. brown-red	1·25	60
147		2d. bistre-brown and turquoise	75	2·25
148		2½d. ultramarine	1·25	2·00
149		3d. black/*yellow*	75	1·00
		a. Opt inverted	£170	£500
150		4d. yellow and bright blue	26·00	42·00
		w. Wmk Crown to right of CA	£350	
151		6d. olive-green and violet	2·75	8·00
152	**23**	1s. indigo and sepia	5·50	25·00
153		2s. brown and blue	55·00	£150
154		2s.6d. bright magenta and black	18·00	50·00
155		5s. orange-yellow and bright ultramarine	10·00	50·00
156		10s. slate-grey and brown	7·00	22·00
143/56 Set of 14			£110	£325

26   27 Valletta Harbour

28 St. Publius   29 Mdina (Notabile)

30 Gozo fishing boat   31 Neptune

32 Neolithic temple, Mnajdra   33 St. Paul

(T **26** typo, others recess Waterlow)

1926 (6 Apr)–**27**. T **26**/**33**. Inscr "POSTAGE". Wmk Mult Script CA. P 15×14 (T **26**) or 12½ (others).

157	**26**	¼d. brown	80	15
158		½d. yellow-green (5.8.26)	60	15
		a. Printed on the gummed side	£1700	
		w. Wmk inverted	†	£1600
159		1d. rose-red (1.4.27)	3·00	1·75
160		1½d. chestnut (7.10.26)	2·00	10
161		2d. greenish grey (1.4.27)	4·50	16·00
162		2½d. blue (1.4.27)	4·00	2·75
162a		3d. violet (1.4.27)	4·25	6·00
163		4d. black and red	3·50	18·00
164		4½d. lavender and ochre	3·50	9·00
165		6d. violet and scarlet (5.5.26)	4·25	9·00
166	**27**	1s. black	6·50	5·00
167	**28**	1s.6d. black and green	8·00	22·00
168	**29**	2s. black and purple	8·50	27·00
169	**30**	2s.6d. black and vermilion	21·00	55·00
170	**31**	3s. black and blue	21·00	48·00
171	**32**	5s. black and green (5.5.26)	24·00	75·00
172	**33**	10s. black and carmine (9.2.27)	65·00	£110
157/72 Set of 17			£160	£350
157s/72s Optd "SPECIMEN" Set of 17			£400	

POSTAGE

AIR MAIL (34)	POSTAGE AND REVENUE (35)	POSTAGE AND REVENUE. (36)

1928 (1 Apr). Air. Optd with T **34**.

173	**26**	6d. violet and scarlet	1·75	2·00

1928 (1 Oct–5 Dec). As Nos. 157/72, optd.

174	**35**	¼d. brown	1·50	10
175		½d. yellow-green	1·50	10
176		1d. rose-red	1·75	3·25
177		1d. chestnut (5.12.28)	4·50	10
178		1½d. chestnut	3·00	85
179		1½d. rose-red (5.12.28)	4·25	10
180		2d. greenish grey	4·25	9·00
181		2½d. blue	2·00	10
182		3d. violet	2·00	80
183		4d. black and red	2·00	1·75
184		4½d. lavender and ochre	2·25	1·00
185		6d. violet and scarlet	2·25	1·50
186	**36**	1s. black (R.)	5·50	2·50
187		1s.6d. black and green (R.)	14·00	11·00
188		2s. black and purple (R.)	27·00	70·00
189		2s.6d. black and vermilion (R.)	17·00	21·00
190		3s. black and blue (R.)	23·00	24·00
191		5s. black and green (R.)	38·00	70·00
192		10s. black and carmine (R.)	70·00	£100
174/92 Set of 19			£200	£275
174s/92s Optd "SPECIMEN" Set of 19			£425	

1930 (20 Oct). As Nos. 157/172, but inscr "POSTAGE (&) REVENUE".

193		¼d. brown	60	10
194		½d. yellow-green	60	10
195		1d. chestnut	60	10
196		1½d. rose-red	70	10
197		2d. greenish grey	1·25	50
198		2½d. blue	2·00	10
199		3d. violet	1·50	20
200		4d. black and red	1·25	7·50
201		4½d. lavender and ochre	3·25	1·25
202		6d. violet and scarlet	3·00	2·75
203		1s. black	10·00	24·00
204		1s.6d. black and green	8·50	32·00
205		2s. black and purple	15·00	27·00
206		2s.6d. black and vermilion	17·00	60·00
207		3s. black and blue	50·00	60·00
208		5s. black and green	55·00	75·00
209		10s. black and carmine	£110	£180
193/209 Set of 17			£225	£425
193s/209s Perf "SPECIMEN" Set of 17			£400	

1935 (6 May). Silver Jubilee. As Nos. 91/4 of Antigua, but printed by B.W. P 11×12.

210		½d. black and green	50	70
		a. Extra flagstaff	26·00	48·00
		b. Short extra flagstaff	65·00	
		c. Lightning conductor	40·00	60·00
211		2½d. brown and deep blue	2·50	4·50
		a. Extra flagstaff	£140	£190
		b. Short extra flagstaff	£180	£250
		c. Lightning conductor	£160	£225
212		6d. light blue and olive-green	7·00	13·00
		a. Extra flagstaff	£180	£275
		b. Short extra flagstaff	£325	£375
		c. Lightning conductor	£200	£275
213		1s. slate and purple	19·00	30·00
		a. Extra flagstaff	£425	£550
		b. Short extra flagstaff	£450	£600
		c. Lightning conductor	£400	£550
210/13 Set of 4			26·00	42·00
210s/13s Perf "SPECIMEN" Set of 4			£180	

For illustrations of plate varieties see Omnibus section following Zanzibar.

Sheets from the second printing of the ½d., 6d. and 1s. in November 1935 had the extra flagstaff partially erased from the stamp with a sharp point.

1937 (12 May). Coronation. As Nos. 95/7 of Antigua, but printed by D.L.R. P 14.

214		½d. green	10	20
215		1½d. scarlet	1·50	65
		a. Brown-lake	£650	£650
216		2½d. bright blue	1·50	80
214/16 Set of 3			2·75	1·50
214s/16s Perf "SPECIMEN" Set of 3			£160	

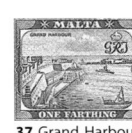

37 Grand Harbour, Valletta   38 H.M.S. *St. Angelo*

39 Verdala Palace   40 Hypogeum, Hal Saflieni

41 Victoria and Citadel, Gozo

42 De L'Isle Adam entering Mdina

43 St. John's Co-Cathedral

44 Ruins at Mnajdra

45 Statue of Manoel de Vilhena

46 Maltese girl wearing faldetta

47 St. Publius

48 Mdina Cathedral

49 Statue of Neptune

50 Palace Square, Valletta

51 St. Paul

1½d. Broken cross (Right pane R. 5/7)

2d. Extra windows (R. 2/7) (corrected in 1945)

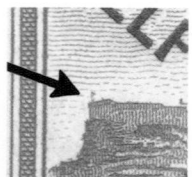

2d. Flag on citadel (R. 5/8)

Damaged value tablet (R. 4/9)

5s. Semaphore flaw (R. 2/7)

(Recess Waterlow)

1938 (17 Feb*)–**43**. T **37/51**. Wmk Mult Script CA (sideways on No. 217). P 12½.

217	**37**	¼d. brown	10	10
218	**38**	½d. green	4·50	30
218a		½d. red-brown (8.3.43)	55	30

219	**39**	1d. red-brown	7·00	40
219a		1d. green (8.3.43)	60	10
220	**40**	1½d. scarlet	3·75	30
		a. Broken cross	£400	90·00
220b		1½d. slate-black (8.3.43)	30	30
		ba. Broken cross	80·00	70·00
221	**41**	2d. slate-black	3·75	2·00
		a. Extra windows	£190	
221b		2d. scarlet (8.3.43)	40	30
		ba. Extra windows	85·00	60·00
		bb. Flag on citadel	£130	£100
222	**42**	2½d. greyish blue	8·50	1·25
222a		2½d. dull violet (8.3.43)	60	10
223	**43**	3d. dull violet	6·00	80
223a		3d. blue (8.3.43)	30	20
224	**44**	4½d. olive-green and yellow-brown	50	30
225	**45**	6d. olive-green and scarlet	3·00	30
226	**46**	1s. black	3·00	30
227	**47**	1s.6d. black and olive-green	8·50	4·00
228	**48**	2s. green and deep blue	5·50	7·50
229	**49**	2s.6d. black and scarlet	9·00	6·00
		a. Damaged value tablet	£400	£225
230	**50**	5s. black and green	5·50	9·00
		a. Semaphore flaw	85·00	£170
231	**51**	10s. black and carmine	19·00	19·00
		217/31 *Set of 21*	75·00	45·00
		217s/31s Perf "SPECIMEN" *Set of 21*	£700	

*This is the local date of issue but the stamps were released in London on 15 February.

1946 (3 Dec). Victory. As Nos. 110/11 of Antigua, but inscr "MALTA" between Maltese Cross and George Cross.

232		1d. green	15	10
		w. Wmk inverted	£1600	
233		3d. blue	75	2·00
		232s/3s Perf "SPECIMEN" *Set of 2*	£120	

SELF-GOVERNMENT

SELF-GOVERNMENT 1947

(**52**)

½d. and **5s.** "NT" joined (R. 4/10)

1½d. "NT" joined (R. 4/6)

2d. Halation flaw (Pl 2 R. 2/5) (ptg of 8 Jan 1953)

2d. Cracked plate (Pl 2 R. 5/1) (ptg of 8 Jan 1953)

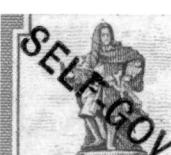

6d. Damaged "F" (R. 3/1)

"F" repaired

(Optd by Waterlow)

1948 (25 Nov)–**53**. New Constitution. As Nos. 217/31 but optd as T **52**; reading up on ½d. and 5s., down on other values, and smaller on ¼d. value.

234	**37**	¼d. brown	30	20
235	**38**	½d. red-brown	30	10
		a. "NT" joined	19·00	25·00
236	**39**	1d. green	30	10
236a		1d. grey (R.) (8.1.53)	75	10
237	**40**	1½d. blue-black (R.)	1·25	10
		aa. Broken cross	£170	75·00
		a. "NT" joined (R. 4/6)		
237b		1½d. green (8.1.53)	30	10
		ba. Albino opt	†	£18000
238	**41**	2d. scarlet	1·25	10
		a. Extra windows	£200	£120
		b. Flag on citadel	£160	£110
238c		2d. yellow-ochre (8.1.53)	30	10
		c. Halation flaw	£200	£225
		cc. Cracked plate	£190	£200
239	**42**	2½d. dull violet (R.)	80	10
239a		2½d. scarlet-vermilion (8.1.53)	75	1·50
240	**43**	3d. blue (R.)	3·00	15
		aa. "NT" joined (R. 4/6)		
240a		3d. dull violet (R.) (8.1.53)	50	15
241	**44**	4½d. olive-green and yellow-brown	2·75	1·00
241a		4½d. olive-green and deep ultramarine (R.) (8.1.53)	50	90

242	**45**	6d. olive-green and scarlet	3·25	15
		a. Damaged "F"	£110	70·00
		b. "F" repaired	95·00	70·00
243	**46**	1s. black	3·75	40
244	**47**	1s.6d. black and olive-green	2·50	50
245	**48**	2s. green and deep blue (R.)	9·00	2·50
246	**49**	2s.6d. black and scarlet	12·00	2·50
		a. Damaged value tablet	£2000	
247	**50**	5s. black and green (R.)	30·00	3·50
		a. "NT" joined	£300	£140
		b. Semaphore flaw	—	£3750
248	**51**	10s. black and carmine	30·00	27·00
		234/48 *Set of 21*	90·00	35·00

1949 (4 Jan). Royal Silver Wedding. As Nos. 112/13 of Antigua, but inscr "MALTA" between Maltese Cross and George Cross and with £1 ptd in recess.

249		1d. green	50	10
250		£1 indigo	38·00	48·00

1949 (10 Oct). 75th Anniv of UPU As Nos. 114/17 of Antigua, but inscr "MALTA" in recess.

251		2½d. violet	30	10
		a. "A" of "CA" omitted from wmk	£1200	£1200
252		3d. deep blue	3·00	1·00
		a. "C" of "CA" omitted from wmk	£1200	
253		6d. carmine-red	60	1·00
254		1s. blue-black	60	2·50
		251/4 *Set of 4*	4·00	4·25

53 Queen Elizabeth II when Princess

54 Our Lady of Mount Carmel (attrib Palladino)

(T **53/4**. Recess B.W.)

1950 (1 Dec). Visit of Princess Elizabeth to Malta. Wmk Mult Script CA. P 12×11½.

255	**53**	1d. green	15	15
256		3d. blue	25	20
257		1s. black	1·00	3·00
		255/7 *Set of 3*	1·25	3·00

1951 (12 July). Seventh Centenary of the Scapular. Wmk Mult Script CA. P 12×11½.

258	**54**	1d. green	20	30
259		3d. violet	50	10
260		1s. black	2·10	2·25
		258/60 *Set of 3*	2·50	2·25

1953 (3 June). Coronation. As No. 120 of Antigua.

261		1½d. black and deep yellow-green	70	10

55 St. John's Co-Cathedral

56 Immaculate Conception (Caruana) (altarpiece, Cospicua)

(Recess Waterlow)

1954 (3 May). Royal Visit. Wmk Mult Script CA. P 12½.

262	**55**	3d. violet	45	10

(Photo Harrison)

1954 (8 Sept). Centenary of Dogma of the Immaculate Conception. Wmk Mult Script CA. Chalk-surfaced paper. P 14×14.

263	**56**	1½d. emerald	15	10
264		3d. bright blue	15	10
265		1s. grey-black	35	20
		263/5 *Set of 3*	60	35

57 Monument of the Great Siege, 1565

58 Wignacourt aqueduct horse trough

59 Victory Church

60 Second World War Memorial

61 Mosta Church

62 Auberge de Castile

63 The King's Scroll

64 Roosevelt's Scroll

65 Neolithic temples Tarxien

66 Vedette (tower)

67 Mdina gate

68 *Les Gavroches* (statue)

69 Monument of Christ the King

70 Grand Master Cottener's monument

71 Grand Master Perello's monument

72 St. Paul

73 Baptism of Christ

(Recess Waterlow (2s.6d. to £1). B.W. (others))

1956 (23 Jan)–**58.** T **57/73.** Wmk Mult Script CA. P 14×13½ (2s.6d. to £1) or 11½ (others).

266	**57**	¼d. violet	20	10
267	**58**	½d. orange	50	10
268	**59**	1d. black (9.2.56)	3·00	10
269	**60**	1½d. bluish green (9.2.56)	30	10
270	**61**	2d. brown (9.2.56)	3·25	10
		a. Deep brown (26.2.58)	8·50	40
271	**62**	2½d. orange-brown	2·25	30
272	**63**	3d. rose-red (22.3.56)	1·50	10
		w. Wmk inverted	†	£1500
273	**64**	4½d. deep blue	2·50	1·00
274	**65**	6d. indigo (9.2.56)	1·25	10
		w. Wmk inverted		£325
275	**66**	8d. bistre-brown	4·50	1·00
276	**67**	1s. deep reddish violet	1·75	
277	**68**	1s.6d. deep turquoise-green	17·00	35
278	**69**	2s. olive-green	13·00	4·75
279	**70**	2s.6d. chestnut (22.3.56)	11·00	2·50
280	**71**	5s. green (11.10.56)	17·00	3·25
281	**72**	10s. carmine-red (19.11.56)	38·00	16·00
282	**73**	£1 yellow-brown (5.1.57)	38·00	35·00
266/82 *Set of 17*			£130	55·00

See also Nos. 314/15.

74 "Defence of Malta"

75 Searchlights over Malta

(Des E. Cremona. Photo Harrison)

1957 (15 Apr). George Cross Commemoration. Cross in silver. T **74/5** and similar design. Wmk Mult Script CA. P 14½×14 (3d.) or P 14×14½ (others).

283	1½d. deep dull green	20	10
284	3d. vermilion	20	10
285	1s. reddish brown	20	10
283/5 *Set of 3*		55	25

Design: Vert—1s. Bombed buildings.

77 "Design"

(Des E. Cremona. Photo Harrison)

1958 (15 Feb). Technical Education in Malta. T **77** and similar designs. W w **12.** P 14×14½ (3d.) or 14½×14 (others).

286	1½d. black and deep green	25	10
287	3d. black, scarlet and grey	25	10
288	1s. grey, bright purple and black............	30	10
286/8 *Set of 3*		70	25

Designs: Vert—3d. "Construction". Horiz—1s. Technical School, Paola.

80 Bombed-out Family

81 Sea Raid on Grand Harbour, Valletta

3d. White flaw on third gun from right appearing as larger gunflash (Pl. 1A R. 5/7)

(Des E. Cremona. Photo Harrison)

1958 (15 Apr). George Cross Commemoration. Cross in first colour, outlined in silver. T **80/1** and similar design. W w **12.** P 14×14½ (3d.) or 14½×14 (others).

289	1½d. blue-green and black	25	10
290	3d. red and black	25	10
	a. "Gunflash" flaw	4·75	
291	1s. reddish violet and black	35	10
	a. Silver (outline) omitted...............	£800	
289/91 *Set of 3*		75	25

Design: Horiz—1s. Searchlight crew.

83 Air Raid Casualties

84 "For Gallantry"

(Des E. Cremona. Photo Harrison)

1959 (15 Apr). George Cross Commemoration. T **83/4** and similar design. W w **12.** P 14½×14 (3d.) or 14×14½ (others).

292	1½d. grey-green, black and gold	30	10
293	3d. reddish violet, black and gold..........	30	10
294	1s. blue-grey, black and gold..............	1·40	1·75
292/4 *Set of 3*		1·75	1·75

Design: Vert—1s. Maltese under bombardment.

86 Shipwreck of St. Paul (after Palombi)

87 Statue of St. Paul, Rabat, Malta

8d. Two white flaws in "PAUL" one giving the "P" the appearance of "R" and other a blob over the "L" (Pl. 1A-1A R.5/2).

(Des E. Cremona. Photo Harrison)

1960 (9 Feb). 19th Centenary of the Shipwreck of St. Paul. T **86/7** and similar designs. W w **12.**

295	1½d. blue, gold and yellow-brown	15	10
	a. Gold (dates and crosses) omitted.....	75·00	£110
296	3d. bright purple, gold and blue..............	15	10
	a. Printed on the gummed side		
297	6d. carmine, gold and pale grey..............	25	10
298	8d. black and gold..............................	40	60
	a. "RAUL" flaw	6·00	
299	1s. maroon and gold	30	10
300	2s.6d. blue, deep bluish green and gold	1·00	2·75
	a. Gold omitted..............................	£1900	£750
295/300 *Set of 6*		2·00	3·25

Designs: Vert as T **86**—3d. Consecration of St. Publius (first Bishop of Malta) (after Palombi); 6d. Departure of St. Paul (after Palombi). Diamond shaped as T **87**—1s. Angel with *Acts of the Apostles*; 2s.6d. St. Paul with *Second Epistle to the Corinthians*.

92 Stamp of 1860

(Centre litho; frame recess. Waterlow)

1960 (1 Dec). Stamp Centenary. W w **12.** P 13½.

301	**92**	1½d. buff, pale blue and green...........	25	10
		a. Buff, pale blue and myrtle (white paper)	9·00	3·50
302		3d. buff pale blue and deep carmine	30	10
		a. Blank corner	£650	
303		6d. buff, pale blue and ultramarine	80	1·00
301/3 *Set of 3*			1·25	1·10

Examples of the 1½d. apparently with the blue omitted are from sheets with a very weak printing of this colour.

No. 302a shows the right-hand bottom corner of the 1860 stamp blank. It occurs on R. 4/7 from early trial plates and sheets containing the error should have been destroyed, but some were sorted into good stock and issued at a post office.

93 George Cross

(Photo Harrison)

1961 (15 Apr). George Cross Commemoration. T **93** and similar designs showing medal. W w **12.** P 15×14.

304	1½d. black, cream and bistre........................	30	10
305	3d. olive-brown and greenish blue	30	10
306	1s. olive-green, lilac and deep reddish violet	1·40	2·50
304/6 *Set of 3*		1·75	2·50

96 "Madonna Damascena"

(Photo Harrison)

1962 (7 Sept). Great Siege Commemoration. T **96** and similar vert designs. W w **12** P 13×12.

307	2d. bright blue	10	10
308	3d. red.......................................	10	10

309		6d. bronze-green	30	10
310		1s. brown-purple	30	40
307/10 Set of 4			70	60

Designs:—3d. Great Siege Monument; 6d. Grand Master La Valette; 1s. Assault on Fort St. Elmo.

1963 (4 June). Freedom from Hunger. As No. 146 of Antigua.

| 311 | | 1s.6d. sepia | 1·50 | 2·50 |

1963 (2 Sept). Red Cross Centenary. As Nos. 147/8 of Antigua.

| 312 | | 2d. red and black | 25 | 15 |
| 313 | | 1s. 6d. red and blue | 1·50 | 4·50 |

1963 (15 Oct)–**64**. As Nos. 268 and 270, but wmk. w **12**.

| 314 | **59** | 1d. black | 50 | 30 |
| 315 | **61** | 2d. deep brown (11.7.64*) | 1·50 | 4·25 |

*This is the earliest known date recorded in Malta.

100 Bruce, Zammit and Microscope **101** Goat and Laboratory Equipment

(Des E. Cremona. Photo Harrison)

1964 (14 Apr). Anti-Brucellosis Congress. W **12**. P 14.

316	**100**	2d. light brown, black and bluish green	10	10
		a. Black (microscope, etc) omitted	£450	
317	**101**	1s.6d. black and maroon	1·25	2·00

102 Nicole Cotoner tending Sick Man (M. Preti)

105 Maltese Cross (Upright)

In this illustration the points of the crosses meet in a vertical line. When the watermark is sideways they meet in a horizontal line.

(Des E. Cremona. Photo Harrison)

1964 (5 Sept). First European Catholic Doctors' Congress, Vienna. T **102** and similar horiz designs. (sideways). W **105**. P 13½×11½.

318		2d. red, black, gold and grey-blue	20	10
319		6d. red, black, gold and bistre	50	15
320		1s.6d. red, black, gold and reddish violet	1·10	1·90
318/20 Set of 3			1·60	1·90

Designs:—6d. St. Luke and Hospital; 1s.6d. Sacra Infermeria, Valletta.

INDEPENDENT

106 Dove and British Crown **109** "The Nativity"

(Des E. Cremona. Photo Harrison)

1964 (21 Sept). Independence. T **106** and similar vert designs. W w **105**. P 14½×13½.

321		2d. olive-brown, red and gold	30	10
		a. Gold omitted	75·00	
322		3d. brown-purple, red and gold	30	10
		a. Gold omitted	75·00	
323		6d. slate, red and gold	60	15
324		1s. blue, red and gold	60	15
325		1s.6d. indigo, red and gold	1·25	1·00
326		2s.6d. deep violet-blue, red and gold	1·50	3·75
321/6 Set of 6			4·00	4·75

Designs:—2d, 1s. Type **106**; 3d., 1s.6d. Dove and Pope's Tiara; 6d., 2s.6d. Dove and UN emblem.

4d. White flaw on Virgin's head-shawl appearing as earring (Pl. 1B-2B. R. 6/1)

(Des E. Cremona. Photo D.L.R.)

1964 (3 Nov). Christmas. W **105** (sideways). P 13×13½.

327	**109**	2d. bright purple and gold	10	10
328		4d. bright blue and gold	20	15
		a. "Earring" flaw	3·00	
329		8d. deep bluish green and gold	45	45
327/9 Set of 3			65	60

110 Neolithic era **111** Punic era **112** Roman era

113 Proto Christian era **114** Saracenic era **115** Siculo Norman era

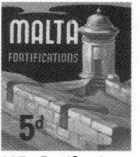

116 Knights of Malta **117** Galleys of Knights of St. John **117a** Fortifications

118 French occupation **119** British rule

119a Naval arsenal **120** Maltese corps of the British army

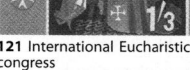

121 International Eucharistic congress **122** Self-government

123 Gozo civic council **124** State of Malta

125 Independence **126** HAFMED (Allied forces, Mediterranean)

127 The Maltese Islands (map) **128** Patron saints

(Des E. Cremona. Photo Harrison)

1965 (7 Jan)–**70**. T **110/28**. W **105**. Chalk-surfaced paper. P 14×14½ (vert) or 14½ (horiz).

330	**110**	½d. multicoloured	10	10
		a. "½d." (white) printed twice†	10·00	
		ab. ditto, once inverted	†	£2250
		b. Rose-pink ("MALTA") printed twice	10·00	
		c. White (face value) omitted	85·00	
331	**111**	1d. multicoloured	10	10
		a. Gold (ancient lettering) omitted	£150	
		b. White (Greek lettering and "PUNIC") omitted	£110	
		c. White ptg double	30·00	
		d. "PUNIC" omitted	£160	
332	**112**	1½d. multicoloured	30	10
333	**113**	2d. multicoloured	10	10
		a. Gold omitted	26·00	
		b. Imperf (pair)	£275	
334	**114**	2½d. multicoloured	1·00	10
		a. Orange omitted*	£110	
		b. Gold ("SARACENIC") omitted	55·00	
		c. Salmon printed twice†	£110	
335	**115**	3d. multicoloured	10	10
		a. Gold (windows) omitted	£100	
		b. "MALTA" (silver) omitted	26·00	
		c. "MALTA" (silver) printed twice	£400	
		d. Bright lilac ("SICULO NORMAN") omitted	£425	
		e. Imperf (pair)	£300	
		f. Value omitted (vert pair with normal)	£1100	
336	**116**	4d. multicoloured	1·00	10
		a. "KNIGHTS OF MALTA" (silver) omitted	45·00	
		b. "MALTA" (silver) omitted	£120	
		c. Black (shield surround) omitted	70·00	
		d. Imperf (pair)	£170	
		e. Gold omitted	£150	
337	**117**	4½d. multicoloured	1·00	75
		a. Silver ("MALTA", etc) omitted	£1900	
337b	**117a**	5d. multicoloured	30	20
		ba. "FORTIFICATIONS" (gold) omitted	£140	
338	**118**	6d. multicoloured	30	10
		a. "MALTA" (silver) omitted	45·00	
		b. Black omitted	£110	
339	**119**	8d. multicoloured	50	10
		a. Gold (centre) omitted	42·00	
		b. Gold (frame) omitted	65·00	
339c	**119a**	10d. multicoloured (1.8.70)	50	1·50
		ca. "NAVAL ARSENAL" (gold) omitted	£325	
340	**120**	1s. multicoloured	30	10
		a. Gold (centre) omitted	£250	
		b. Gold (framework) omitted	48·00	
		c. Gold (framework) doubled		
341	**121**	1s.3d. multicoloured	2·00	1·40
		a. Gold (centre) omitted	65·00	
		b. Gold (framework) omitted	£250	
		c. Imperf (pair)	£400	
342	**122**	1s.6d. multicoloured	60	20
		a. Head (black) omitted	£375	
		b. Gold (centre) omitted	55·00	
		c. Gold (frame) omitted	£150	
343	**123**	2s. multicoloured	70	10
		a. Gold (centre) omitted	£170	
		b. Gold (framework) omitted	70·00	
344	**124**	2s.6d. multicoloured	70	50
345	**125**	3s. multicoloured	1·00	75
		a. Gold (framework) omitted	45·00	
		b. Gold ("1964") omitted	£200	
346	**126**	5s. multicoloured	4·00	1·00
		a. Gold (HAFMED emblem) omitted	£180	
		b. Gold (framework) omitted	£180	
347	**127**	10s. multicoloured	2·00	5·00
		a. Gold (centre) omitted	£425	
348	**128**	£1 multicoloured	2·25	5·50
		a. Pink omitted	32·00	
330/48 Set of 21			16·00	15·00

*The effect of this is to leave the Saracenic pattern as a pink colour.
†On the ½d. the second impression is 6½ mm lower or 3 mm to the left, and on the 2½d. 1 mm lower so that it falls partly across "MALTA" and "2½d." Stamps with almost coincidental double impression are common The ½d. and 1d. had white printing plates. Two silver plates were used on the 4d., one for "KNIGHTS OF MALTA" and the other for "MALTA". Two gold plates were used for the 8d. to 10s., one for the framework and the other for the gold in the central part of the designs.

No. 335f comes from a sheet showing a major shift of the grey-black colour, so that stamps in the top horizontal row are without the face value.

No. 337a comes from a sheet on which the silver printing was so misplaced that it missed the top horizontal row entirely.

The ½d. to 4d., 1s. and 1s.6d. to 5s. values exist with PVA gum as well as gum arabic and the 5d. and 10d. have PVA gum only.

129 Dante (Raphael)

(Des E. Cremona. Photo Govt Ptg Works, Rome)

1965 (7 July). 700th Birth Anniv of Dante. P 14.

349	**129**	2d. indigo	10	10
350		6d. bronze-green	25	10
351		2s. chocolate	1·10	1·50
349/151	*Set of 3*		1·25	1·50

130 Turkish Camp   **131** Turkish Fleet

(Des E. Cremona. Photo Harrison)

1965 (1 Sept). 400th Anniv of Great Siege. T **130/1** and similar designs. W **105** (sideways). P 13 (6d., 1s.) or 14½×14 (others).

352		2d. olive-green, red and black	25	10
		a. Red (flag) omitted	£425	
353		3d. olive-green, red, black and light drab	25	10
354		6d. multicoloured	35	10
		a. Gold (framework and dates) omitted	£375	
		b. Black (on hulls) omitted	£375	
355		8d. red, gold, indigo and blue	70	90
		a. Gold (flag and dates) omitted	£180	
356		1s. red, gold and deep grey-blue	35	10
357		1s.6d. ochre, red and black	70	30
358		2s.6d. sepia, black, red and yellow-olive	1·10	3·00
352/8	*Set of 7*		3·25	4·00

Designs: Square (as T **130**)—3d. Battle scene; 8d. Arrival of relief force; 1s.6d. "Allegory of Victory" (from mural by M. Preti); 2s.8d. Victory medal. Vert (as T **131**)—1s. Grand Master J. de La Valette's Arms.

137 "The Three Kings"   **138** Sir Winston Churchill

(Des E. Cremona. Photo Enschedé)

1965 (7 Oct). Christmas. W **105** (sideways). P 11×11½.

359	**137**	1d. slate-purple and red	10	10
360		4d. slate-purple and blue	30	30
361		1s.3d. slate-purple and bright purple	30	30
359/61	*Set of 3*		65	60

(Des E. Cremona. Photo Harrison)

1966 (24 Jan). Churchill Commemoration. T **138** and similar square design. W **105** (sideways). P 14½×14.

362	**138**	2d. black, red and gold	25	10
363	–	3d. bronze-green, yellow-olive and gold	25	10
		a. Gold omitted	£375	
364	**138**	1s. maroon, red and gold	40	10
		a. Gold (shading) omitted	£170	
365	–	1s.6d. chalky blue, violet-blue and gold	50	1·10
362/5	*Set of 4*		1·25	1·25

Design:—3d., 1s.6d. Sir Winston Churchill and George Cross.

140 Grand Master La Valette   **145** President Kennedy and Memorial

(Des E. Cremona. Photo State Ptg Works, Vienna)

1966 (28 Mar). 400th Anniv of Valletta. T **140** and similar square designs. Multicoloured. W **105** (sideways). P 12.

366		2d. Type **140**	10	10
367		3d. Pope Pius V	15	10
		a. Gold omitted	£850	
368		6d. Map of Valletta	20	10
369		1s. Francesco Laparelli (architect)	20	10
370		2s.6d. Girolamo Cassar (architect)	45	60
366/70	*Set of 5*		1·00	80

(Des E. Cremona. Photo Harrison)

1966 (28 May). President Kennedy Commemoration. W **105** (sideways). P 15×14.

371	**145**	3d. olive, gold and black	10	10
		a. Gold inscr omitted	£300	
372		1s.6d. Prussian blue, gold and black	10	10

146 "Trade"

(Des E. Cremona. Photo D.L.R.)

1966 (16 June). Tenth Malta Trade Fair. W **105** (sideways). P 13½.

373	**146**	2d. multicoloured	10	10
		a. Gold omitted	80·00	
374		8d. multicoloured	50	1·10
375		2s.6d. multicoloured	55	1·10
		a. Gold omitted	85·00	
373/5	*Set of 3*		1·00	2·00

147 "The Child in the Manger"   **148** George Cross

(Des E. Cremona. Photo D.L.R.)

1966 (7 Oct). Christmas. W **105**. P 13½.

376	**147**	1d. black, gold, turquoise-blue and slate-purple	10	10
377		4d. black, gold, ultramarine and slate-purple	10	10
378		1s.3d. black, gold, bright purple and slate purple	10	10
		a. Gold omitted	70·00	
376/8	*Set of 3*		25	25

(Des E. Cremona. Photo Harrison)

1967 (1 Mar). 25th Anniv of George Cross Award to Malta. W **105** (sideways). P 14½×14.

379	**148**	2d. multicoloured	10	10
380		4d. multicoloured	10	10
381		3s. multicoloured	20	40
379/81	*Set of 3*		30	45

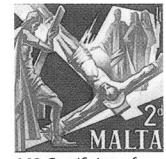

149 Crucifixion of St. Peter

150 Open Bible and Episcopal Emblems

(Des E. Cremona. Photo Harrison)

1967 (28 June). 1900th Anniv of Martyrdom of Saints Peter and Paul. T **149/50** and similar design. W **105** (sideways). P 13½×14½ (8d.) or 14½ (others).

382		2d. chestnut, orange and black	10	10
383		8d. yellow-olive, gold and black	15	10
384		3s. blue, light blue and black	20	20
382/4	*Set of 3*		40	30

Design:—Square as T **149**—3s. Beheading of St. Paul.

152 St. Catherine of Siena   **156** Temple Ruins, Tarxien

(Des E. Cremona. Photo Enschedé)

1967 (1 Aug). 300th Death Anniv of Melchior Gafà (sculptor). T **152** and similar horiz designs. Multicoloured. W **105** (sideways). P 13½×13.

385		2d. Type **152**	10	10
386		4d. *Thomas of Villanova*	10	10
387		1s.6d. Baptism of Christ (detail)	20	10
388		2s.6d. St. John the Baptist (from *Baptism of Christ*)	30	20
385/8	*Set of 4*		55	35

(Des E. Cremona. Photo Harrison)

1967 (12 Sept). 15th International Historical Architecture Congress, Valletta. T **156** and similar square designs. Multicoloured. W **105**. P 15×14½.

389		2d. Type **156**	10	10
390		6d. Facade of Palazzo Falzon, Notabile	10	10

391		1s. Parish Church, Birkirkara	10	10
392		3s. Portal, Auberge de Castille	25	25
389/92	*Set of 4*		40	40

160 "Angels"   **161** "Crib"   **162** "Angels"

(Des E. Cremona. Photo D.L.R.)

1967 (20 Oct). Christmas. W **105** (sideways). P 14.

393	**160**	1d. multicoloured	10	10
		a. Horiz strip of 3. Nos. 393/5	45	25
		b. White stars (red omitted)	£120	
394	**161**	8d. multicoloured	20	10
395	**162**	1s.4d. multicoloured	20	10
393/5	*Set of 3*		45	25

Nos. 393/5 were issued in sheets of 60 of each value (arranged *tête-bêche*), and also in sheets containing the three values *se-tenant*, thus forming a triptych of the Nativity.

163 Queen Elizabeth II and Arms of Malta

(Des E. Cremona. Photo Harrison)

1967 (13 Nov). Royal Visit. T **163** and similar designs. W **105** (sideways on 2d., 3s.). P 14×15 (4d.) or 15×14 (others).

396		2d. multicoloured	10	10
		a. Grey-brown omitted*	£150	
397		4d. black, brown-purple and gold	10	10
398		3s. multicoloured	20	30
396/8	*Set of 3*		35	40

Designs: Vert—4d. Queen in Robes of Order of St. Michael and St. George. Horiz—3s. Queen and outline of Malta.

*This affects the Queen's face.

166 Human Rights Emblem and People **167**

(Des E. Cremona. Photo Harrison)

1968 (2 May). Human Rights Year. W **105** (6d.) or 14½ (others).

399	**166**	2d. multicoloured	10	10
400	**167**	6d. multicoloured	10	10
401		2s. multicoloured	10	15
399/401	*Set of 3*		25	25

The design of the 2s. value is a reverse of Type **166**.

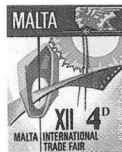

169 Fair "Products"

(Des E. Cremona. Photo Harrison)

1968 (1 June). Malta International Trade Fair. W **105** (sideways). P 14½×14.

402	**169**	4d. multicoloured	10	10
403		8d. multicoloured	10	10
404		3s. multicoloured	20	15
402/4	*Set of 3*		30	25

170 Arms of the Order of St. John and La Valette   **171** La Valette (A. de Favray)

172 La Valette's Tomb   **173** Angels and Scroll bearing Date of Death

(Des E. Cremona. Photo Govt Printer, Israel)

1968 (1 Aug). Fourth Death Centenary of Grand Master La Valette. W **105** (upright, 1s.6d.; sideways, others). P 13×14 (1d., 1s.6d.) or 14×13 (others).

405	**170**	1d. multicoloured	10	10
406	**171**	8d. multicoloured	15	10
407	**172**	1s.6d. multicoloured	15	10
408	**173**	2s.6d. multicoloured	20	25
405/8 Set of 4			55	45

174 Star of Bethlehem and Angel waking Shepherds   **177** "Agriculture"

(Des E. Cremona. Photo Harrison)

1968 (3 Oct). Christmas. T **174** and similar shaped designs. Multicoloured. W **105** (sideways). P 14½×14.

409		1d. Type **174**	10	10
410		8d. Mary and Joseph with shepherd watching over cradle	15	10
411		1s.4d. Three Wise Men and Star of Bethlehem	15	20
409/11 Set of 3			35	35

The shortest side at top and the long side at the bottom both gauge 14½, the other three sides are 14. Nos. 409/11 were issued in sheets of 60 arranged in ten strips of six, alternately upright and inverted.

2s.6d. Large white flaw on chest (left pane, R. 1/10)

1968 (21 Oct). Sixth Food and Agricultural Organization Regional Conference for Europe. T **177** and similar vert designs. Multicoloured. W **105** (sideways). P 12½×12.

412		4d. Type **177**	10	10
413		1s. FAO emblem and coin	10	10
414		2s.6d. "Agriculture" sowing seeds	10	15
		a. White chest	5·00	
412/14 Set of 3			25	30

 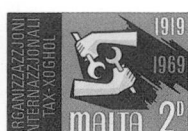

180 Mahatma Gandhi   **181** ILO Emblem

(Des E. Cremona. Photo Enschedé)

1969 (24 Mar). Birth Centenary of Mahatma Gandhi. W **105**. P 12½×12½.

415	**180**	1s.6d. blackish brown, black and gold	65	10

(Des E. Cremona. Photo Harrison)

1969 (26 May). 50th Anniv of International Labour Organization. W **105** (sideways). P 13½×14½.

416	**181**	2d. indigo, gold and turquoise	10	10
417		6d. sepia gold and chestnut	10	10

182 Robert Samut (birth centenary)

183 Dove of Peace, UN Emblem and Sea-Bed (UN Resolution on Oceanic Resources)

184 "Swallows" returning to Malta (Maltese Migrants' Convention)

185 University Arms and Grand Master de Fonseca (founder) (Bicentenary of University)

(Des E. Cremona. Photo D.L.R.)

1969 (26 July). Anniversaries. W **105** (sideways). P 13.

418	**182**	2d. multicoloured	10	10
419	**183**	5d. multicoloured	10	10
420	**184**	10d. black, gold and yellow-olive	10	10
421	**185**	2s. multicoloured	15	20
418/21 Set of 4			25	25

186 1919 Monument   **187** Flag of Malta and Birds

(Des E. Cremona. Photo Enschedé)

1969 (20 Sept). Fifth Anniv of Independence. T **186/7** and similar designs. W **105** (upright on 5d., sideways others). P 13½×12½ (2d.), 12×12½ (5d.), or 12½×12 (others).

422		2d. multicoloured	10	10
423		5d. black, red and gold	10	10
424		10d. black, turquoise-blue and gold	10	10
425		1s.6d. multicoloured	20	40
426		2s.6d. black, olive-brown and gold	25	50
422/6 Set of 5			50	1·00

Designs:—Vert as T **187**—10d. "Tourism"; 1s.6d. UN and Council of Europe emblems; 2s.6d. "Trade and Industry".

191 Peasants playing Tambourine and Bagpipes

(Des E. Cremona. Litho D.L.R.)

1969 (8 Nov). Christmas. Children's Welfare Fund. T **191** and similar horiz designs. Multicoloured. W **105** (sideways). P 12½.

427		1d. +1d. Type **191**	10	20
		a. Gold omitted	£180	
		b. Horiz strip of 3. Nos. 427/9	35	75
428		5d. +1d. Angels playing trumpet and harp	15	20
429		1s.6d. +3d. Choirboys singing	15	45
427/9 Set of 3			35	75

Nos. 427/9 were issued in sheets of 60 of each value, and also in sheets containing the three values se-tenant, thus forming the triptych No. 427b.

194 "The Beheading of St. John" (Caravaggio)

(Des E. Cremona. Photo Enschedé)

1970 (21 Mar). 13th Council of Europe Art Exhibition. T **194** and similar multicoloured designs. W **105** (upright, 10d., 2s.; sideways, others). P 14×13 (1d., 8d.), 12 (10d., 2s.) or 13×13½ (others).

430		1d. Type **194**	10	10
431		2d. St. John the Baptist (M. Preti) (45×32 mm)	10	10
432		5d. Interior of St. John's Co-Cathedral, Valletta (39×39 mm)	10	10
433		6d. Allegory of the Order (Neapolitan School) (45×32 mm)	15	10
434		8d. St. Jerome (Caravaggio)	15	50
435		10d. Articles from the Order of St. John in Malta (63×21 mm)	15	10
436		1s.6d. The Blessed Gerard receiving Godfrey de Bouillon (A. de Favray) (45×35 mm)	25	40
437		2s. Cape and Stolone (16th-century) (63×21 mm)	25	55
		a. Blue omitted	£300	
430/37 Set of 8			1·00	1·50

202 Artist's Impression of Fujiyama

(Des E. Cremona. Photo D.L.R.)

1970 (29 May). World Fair, Osaka. W **105** (sideways). P 15.

438	**202**	2d. multicoloured	10	10
439		5d. multicoloured	10	10
440		3s. multicoloured	15	15
438/40 Set of 3			30	30

203 "Peace and Justice"   **204** Carol-Singers, Church and Star

(Des J. Casha. Litho Harrison)

1970 (30 Sept). 25th Anniv of United Nations. W **105**. P 14×14½.

441	**203**	2d. multicoloured	10	10
442		5d. multicoloured	10	10
443		2s.6d. multicoloured	15	15
441/3 Set of 3			30	30

(Des E. Cremona. Photo Govt Printer, Israel)

1970 (7 Nov). Christmas. T **204** and similar vert designs. Multicoloured. W **105** (sideways). P 14×13.

444		1d. +½d. Type **204**	10	10
445		10d. +2d. Church, star and Angels with Infant	15	20
446		1s.6d. +3d. Church, star and nativity scene	20	40
444/6 Set of 3			40	60

STAMP BOOKLETS

B **1**

1970 (16 May). Brownish black on brownish grey cover as Type B **1** depicting GPO Palazzo Parisio, Valletta. Stitched.

SB1	2s.6d. booklet containing 6×1d. and 12×2d. (Nos. 331, 333) in blocks of 6	5·50	

1970 (18 May). Black on pink cover as Type B **1** depicting Magisterial Palace, Valletta. Stitched.

SB2	2s.6d. booklets containing 6×1d. and 12×2d. (Nos. 331, 333) in blocks of 6	4·00	

POSTAGE DUE STAMPS

D **1**   D **2**

1925 (16 Apr). Typeset by Govt Printing Office, Valletta. Imperf.

D1	D **1**	½d. black	1·25	10·00
		a. Tête-bêche (horiz pair)	5·00	23·00
D2		1d. black	3·25	4·50
		a. Tête-bêche (horiz pair)	10·00	12·00
D3		1½d. black	3·00	3·75
		a. Tête-bêche (horiz pair)	10·00	15·00
D4		2d. black	15·00	25·00
		a. Tête-bêche (horiz pair)	32·00	60·00
D5		2½d. black	2·75	2·75
		a. "2" of "½" omitted	£900	£1300
		b. Tête-bêche (horiz pair)	12·00	15·00
D6		3d. black/grey	9·00	15·00
		a. Tête-bêche (horiz pair)	30·00	48·00
D7		4d. black/buff	5·00	9·50
		a. Tête-bêche (horiz pair)	17·00	38·00
D8		6d. black/buff	5·00	30·00
		a. Tête-bêche (horiz pair)	17·00	65·00
D9		1s. black/buff	6·50	32·00
		a. Tête-bêche (horiz pair)	25·00	65·00
D10		1s.6d. black/buff	19·00	70·00
		a. Tête-bêche (horiz pair)	42·00	£140
D1/10 Set of 10			60·00	£180

Nos. D1/10 were each issued in sheets containing four panes (6×7) printed separately, the impressions in the two left-hand panes being inverted. 14 horizontal tête-bêche pairs occur from the junction of the left and right-hand panes.

No. D5a occurred on R. 4/4 of the last 2½d. pane position to be printed. Forgeries exist, but can be detected by comparison with a normal example under ultra-violet light. They are often found in pair with normal, showing forged cancellations of "VALLETTA AP 20 25" or "G.P.O. MY 7 25".

(Typo B.W.)

1925 (20 July). Wmk Mult Script CA (sideways). P 12.

D11	D **2**	½d. green	1·25	60
D12		1d. violet	1·25	45
D13		1½d. brown	1·50	80
D14		2d. grey	7·00	1·00
D15		2½d. orange	2·00	1·25
		x. Wmk reversed	£160	
D16		3d. blue	4·50	1·25
D17		4d. olive-green	9·00	16·00
D18		6d. purple	4·00	7·50
D19		1s. black	6·00	17·00
D20		1s.6d. carmine	8·50	50·00
D11/20		Set of 10	40·00	85·00
D11s/20s		Optd "SPECIMEN." Set of 10	£275	

1953–63. Chalk-surfaced paper. Wmk Mult Script CA (sideways). P 12.

D21	D **2**	½d. emerald	70	4·00
D22		1d. purple	70	1·25
		a. Deep purple (17.9.63)	75	3·75
D23		1½d. yellow-brown	2·50	17·00
D24		2d. grey-brown (20.3.57)	5·50	9·50
		a. Blackish brown (3.4.62)	29·00	13·00
D25		3d. deep slate-blue	1·00	2·00
D26		4d. yellow-olive	2·50	4·25
D21/6		Set of 6	11·50	35·00

1966 (1 Oct). As No. D24, but wmk w **12** (sideways).

D27	D **2**	2d. grey-brown	12·00	23·00

1967–70. Ordinary paper. W **105** (sideways).

(a) P 12, line (9.11.67)

D28	D **2**	½d. emerald	4·00	9·00
D29		1d. purple	4·00	9·00
D30		2d. blackish brown	6·50	9·00
D31		4d. yellow-olive	45·00	£110
D28/31		Set of 4	55·00	£120

(b) P 12½, comb (30.5.68–70)

D32	D **2**	½d. emerald	35	2·00
D33		1d. purple	30	1·50
D34		1½d. yellow-brown	35	3·25
		a. Orange-brown (23.10.70)	1·25	3·00
D35		2d. blackish brown	85	70
		a. Brownish black (23.10.70)	3·25	3·00
D36		2½d. yellow-orange	60	70
D37		3d. deep slate-blue	60	60
D38		4d. yellow-olive	1·00	80
D39		6d. purple	75	1·75
D40		1s. black	90	1·50
D41		1s.6d. carmine	2·75	7·50
D32/41		Set of 10	7·00	18·00

The above are the local release dates. In the 12½ perforation the London release dates were 21 May for the ½d. to 4d. and 4 June for the 6d. to 1s.6d.

Nos. D34a and D35a are on glazed paper.

Mauritius

GREAT BRITAIN STAMPS USED IN MAURITIUS. We no longer list the Great Britain stamps with obliteration "B 53" as there is no evidence that British stamps were available from the Mauritius Post Office.

See under SEYCHELLES for stamps of Mauritius used at Victoria with "B 64" cancellations between 1861 and 1890.

A similar "B 65" cancellation was used on the island of Rodrigues, a dependency of Mauritius, from 11 December 1861 onwards.

PRICES FOR STAMPS ON COVER TO 1945

Nos. 1/5	from × 2
Nos. 6/9	from × 3
Nos. 10/15	from × 4
Nos. 16/25	from × 5
Nos. 26/9	from × 3
Nos. 30/1	—
Nos. 32/5	from × 4
Nos. 36/44	from × 5
Nos. 46/72	from × 3
Nos. 76/82	from × 5
Nos. 83/91	from × 6
Nos. 92/100	from × 4
Nos. 101/11	from × 3
Nos. 117/24	from × 8
Nos. 127/32	from × 7
No. 133	from × 4
Nos. 134/5	from × 10
No. 136	from × 8
Nos. 137/56	from × 6
Nos. 157/63	from × 5
Nos. 164/221	from × 3
No. 222	—
Nos. 223/41	from × 3
Nos. 242/4	from × 10
Nos. 245/8	from × 3
Nos. 249/63	from × 2
Nos. E1/2	from × 10
No. E3	from × 30
No. E4	—
No. E5	from × 10
No. E6	from × 25
Nos. D1/5	from × 40
Nos. R1/3	from × 15

CROWN COLONY

Nos. 1/25 and 36/44 were printed in Mauritius.

1 ("POST OFFICE") **2** ("POST PAID")

(Engraved on copper by J. O. Barnard)

1847 (21 Sept). Head of Queen on groundwork of diagonal and perpendicular lines. Imperf.

1	**1**	1d. orange-red	—	£1300000
2		2d. deep blue	—	£1500000

A single plate contained one example of each value.

It is generally agreed that 15 examples of No. 1 have survived (including two unused) and 12 of No. 2 (including four unused). Most are now in permanent museum collections.

NOTE. Our prices for early Mauritius are for stamps in very fine condition. Exceptional copies are worth more, poorer copies considerably less.

(Engraved on copper by J. O. Barnard)

1848 (June)–**59**. Imperf.

A. Earliest impressions. Design deep, sharp and clear. Diagonal lines predominate. Thick paper (Period of use: 1d. 1853–54, 2d. 1848–49)

3	**2**	1d. orange-vermilion/yellowish	£70000	£18000
4		2d. indigo-blue/grey to bluish	£65000	£26000
5		2d. deep blue/grey to bluish	£65000	£26000
		a. "PENOE" for "PENCE" (R. 3/1)	£130000	£45000

B. Early impressions. Design sharp and clear but some lines slightly weakened. Paper not so thick, grey to yellowish white or bluish (Period of use: 1d. 1853–55, 2d. 1849–54)

6	**2**	1d. vermilion	£35000	£7500
7		1d. orange-vermilion	£35000	£7000
8		2d. blue	£38000	£9000
		a. "PENOE" for "PENCE" (R. 3/1)	£70000	£17000
9		2d. deep blue	£45000	£9500

C. Intermediate impressions. White patches appear where design has worn. Paper yellowish white, grey or bluish, of poorish quality (Period of use: 1d and 2d. 1854–57)

10	**2**	1d. bright vermilion	£23000	£3000
11		1d. dull vermilion	£23000	£3000
12		1d. red	£23000	£3000
13		2d. deep blue	£30000	£4250
14		2d. blue	£24000	£3500
		a. "PENOE" for "PENCE" (R. 3/1) from	£42000	£8000
15		2d. light blue	£24000	£3500

D. Worn impressions. Much of design worn away but some diagonal lines distinct. Paper yellowish, grey or bluish, of poorish quality (Period of use: 1d. 1857–59, 2d. 1855–58)

16	**2**	1d. red/yellowish or grey	£8000	£950
17		1d. red-brown/yellowish or grey	£8000	£950
18		1d. red/bluish	£7500	£900
		a. Doubly printed		
19		1d. red-brown/bluish	£7500	£900

20		2d. blue (shades)/yellowish or grey	£10000	£1700
		a. "PENOE" for "PENCE" (R. 3/1) from	—	£3500
21		2d. grey-blue/yellowish or grey	£11000	£1600
22		2d. blue (shades)/bluish	£10000	£1600
		a. Doubly printed		

E. Latest impressions. Almost none of design showing except part of Queen's head and frame. Paper yellowish, grey or bluish, of poorish quality (Period of use: 1d. 1859, 2d. 1856–58)

23	**2**	1d. red	£6500	£800
24		1d. red-brown	£6500	£800
25		2d. grey-blue/bluish	£8000	£1200
		a. "PENOE" for "PENCE" (R. 3/1)	£15000	£2250

Earliest known use of the 2d. value is on 19 June 1848, but the 1d. value is not known used before 27 September 1853.

There were separate plates for the 1d. and 2d. values, each of 12 (3×4).

3 **(4)** **5**

(Eng G. Fairman. Recess P.B.)

1858*. Surch with T **4**. Imperf.

26	**3**	4d. green	£1800	£450

*Although originally gazetted for use from 8 April 1854, research into the archives indicates that No. 26 was not actually issued until 1858, when the stamps were mentioned in an ordinance of 30 April. The earliest dated postmark known is 27 March 1858.

PERKINS BACON "CANCELLED". For notes on these handstamps, showing "CANCELLED" between horizontal bars forming an oval, see Catalogue Introduction.

1858–62. No value expressed. Imperf.

27	**3**	(4d.) green	£450	£200
28		(6d.) vermilion	65·00	£120
29		(9d.) dull magenta (1859)	£900	£225
		a. Reissued as (1d.) value (11.62)	†	£170

Prepared for use but not issued

30	**3**	(No value), red-brown	27·00	
31		(No value), blue (H/S "CANCELLED" in oval £13000)	12·00	

Use of the dull magenta as a 1d. value can be confirmed by the presence of the "B 53" cancellation which was first introduced in 1861. Remainders of Nos. 30/1, overprinted "L.P.E. 1890" in red, were perforated at the London Philatelic Exhibition and sold as souvenirs.

(Recess P.B.)

1859–61. Imperf.

32	**5**	6d. blue (H/S "CANCELLED" in oval £15000)	£800	55·00
33		6d. dull purple-slate (1861)	42·00	65·00
34		1s. vermilion (H/S "CANCELLED" in oval £11000)	£3250	70·00
35		1s. yellow-green (1861)	£650	£150

The 1859 printings had the colours transposed by mistake.

6 **7** **8**

(Engraved on copper by J. Lapirot)

1859 (Mar–Nov). Imperf.

(a) Early impressions

36	**6**	2d. deep blue	£20000	£3750
37		2d. blue	£18000	£3250

(b) Intermediate prints. Lines of background, etc, partly worn away (July)

38	**6**	2d. blue	£9500	£1400
		a. Doubly printed	†	—

(c) Worn impressions, bluish paper (Oct)

39	**6**	2d. blue	£4750	£900

(d) Retouched impression (Nov)

39a	**6**	2d. blue	†	—
		ab. "MAURITIUS" (R. 2/4)	†	£130000
		ac. "MAURITUS" (R. 3/1)	†	£130000

Nos. 36/9a were printed from a plate of 12 (4×3).

Research by Mr A. Rudge has established the existence of an initial state of the plate, before the lines were deepened to produce the "Early impression". Only one stamp from this state has so far been identified.

The plate became worn through use, and was eventually extensively re-engraved. Only two pairs (one on cover) have been recorded from this re-touched impression. The errors made in the re-engraving of the inscriptions probably resulted in it being withdrawn from use.

(1848 plate re-engraved by R. Sherwin)

1859 (Oct). Bluish paper. Imperf.

40	**7**	2d. deep blue	£225000	£8000

The 1d. plate was also re-engraved, but was not put into use. Reprints in black were made in 1877 from both 1d. and 2d. re-engraved plates. Coloured autotype illustrations were prepared from these reprints and 600 were included in the R.P.S.L. handbook on British Africa in 1900. Further reprints in black were made in 1911 after the plates had been presented to the R.P.S.L. and defaced.

(Lithographed by L. A. Dardenne)

1859 (12 Dec). White laid paper. Imperf.

41	**8**	1d. deep red	£16000	£2500
41a		1d. red	£12000	£1700
42		1d. dull vermilion	£9500	£1400
43		2d. slate-blue	£10000	£1300
43a		2d. blue	£6000	£950
44		2d. pale blue	£5550	£850
		a. Heavy retouch on neck	—	£2000
		b. Retouched below "TWO"	—	£1200

The neck retouch shows a prominent curved white line running from the base of the chignon to the nape of the neck. No. 44b shows several diagonal lines in the margin below "TWO".

| | 9 | | 10 |

(Typo D.L.R.)

1860 (7 Apr)–**63**. No wmk. P 14.

46	**9**	1d. purple-brown........................	£400	45·00
47		2d. blue.................................	£425	55·00
48		4d. rose.................................	£425	42·00
49		6d. green (1862)......................	£1000	£170
50		6d. slate (1863).......................	£400	£110
51		9d. dull purple........................	£200	42·00
52		1s. buff (1862)........................	£400	95·00
53		1s. green (1863)......................	£900	£200

(Recess P.B.)

1862. Intermediate perf 14 to 16.

54	**5**	6d. slate...............................	40·00	£110
		a. Imperf between (horiz pair).......	£8000	
55		1s. deep green.........................	£2750	£325

(Typo D.L.R.)

1863–72. Wmk Crown CC. P 14.

56	**9**	1d. purple-brown......................	80·00	17·00
		w. Wmk inverted......................	95·00	40·00
		y. Wmk inverted and reversed.......		£150
57		1d. brown..............................	£100	13·00
58		1d. bistre (1872)......................	£140	17·00
59		w. Wmk inverted......................		
		2d. pale blue..........................	75·00	13·00
		a. Imperf (pair).......................	£1800	£2000
		w. Wmk inverted......................	£190	38·00
		x. Wmk reversed.......................	—	£170
		y. Wmk inverted and reversed.......		
60		2d. bright blue........................	95·00	13·00
61		3d. deep red...........................	£170	45·00
61a		3d. dull red............................	90·00	21·00
		aw. Wmk inverted......................	£225	55·00
62		4d. rose................................	95·00	3·75
		w. Wmk inverted......................	£275	30·00
63		6d. dull violet.........................	£425	50·00
		w. Wmk inverted......................		
		x. Wmk reversed.......................		
		y. Wmk inverted and reversed.......	†	£225
64		6d. yellow-green (1865)..............	£325	16·00
65		6d. blue-green........................	£250	6·50
		w. Wmk inverted......................	£400	55·00
		y. Wmk inverted and reversed.......		
66		9d. yellow-green (1872)..............	£190	£400
		w. Wmk inverted......................		
67	**10**	10d. maroon (1872)....................	£375	60·00
		w. Wmk inverted......................		
68	**9**	1s. yellow.............................	£375	30·00
		w. Wmk inverted......................	£550	75·00
69		1s. blue (1866)........................	£130	29·00
		w. Wmk inverted......................	—	90·00
		x. Wmk reversed.......................	—	£300
70		1s. orange (1872).....................	£300	12·00
		w. Wmk inverted......................	£425	70·00
		x. Wmk reversed.......................	—	£225
		y. Wmk inverted and reversed.......	†	£250
71		5s. rosy mauve........................	£275	55·00
		w. Wmk inverted......................	£500	£150
72		5s. bright mauve (1865)..............	£325	55·00
		w. Wmk inverted......................	£500	£140

Most values of the above set, including the 2d. bright blue, exist imperforate, but these are from proof sheets. The 2d. pale blue imperforate (No. 59a) was issued in error.

HALF PENNY $\frac{1}{2}$ d

HALF PENNY (11)	HALF PENNY (12)

1876.

(a) Nos. 51 and 67 surch with T 11 locally.

76	**9**	½d. on 9d. dull purple (2.79)........	26·00	24·00
		a. Surch inverted.....................	£750	
		b. Surch double.......................	—	£2250
77	**10**	½d. on 10d. maroon (10.79)...........	5·50	29·00
		y. Wmk inverted and reversed.......		

(b) Prepared for use, but not issued. No. 51 surch with T 12

78	**9**	½d. on 9d. dull purple (R.)...........	£3250	
		a. "PRNNY"............................		
		b. Black surch........................	£4750	

HALF PENNY (13)	One Penny (14)	One Shilling (15)

1877 (Apr–Dec). Nos. 62, 67 (colour changed) and 71/2 surch T 13 by D.L.R. or T **14/15** locally.

79	**10**	½d. on 10d. rose......................	13·00	50·00
		w. Wmk inverted......................	£120	
80	**9**	1d. on 4d. rose-carmine (6.12)......	27·00	29·00
		w. Wmk inverted......................	£150	£110
81		1s. on 5s. rosy mauve (6.12)........	£350	£120
		w. Wmk inverted......................	£550	£200
82		1s. on 5s. bright mauve (6.12)......	£350	£150
		w. Wmk inverted......................	—	£250

(New Currency. 100 cents = 1 rupee)

"CANCELLED" OVERPRINTS. Following the change of currency in 1878 various issues with face values in sterling were overprinted "CANCELLED" in serifed type and sold as remainders. The stamps involved were Nos. 51, 56/62, 65, 67/8, 71/2, 76, 78/b, 79 and 81/2. Examples of such overprints on stamps between Nos. 51 and 72 are worth about the same as the prices quoted for used, on Nos. 78/b they are worth 5% of the unused price, on No. 79 65% and on Nos. 81/2 20%.

---

2 CENTS · 2 Rs. 50 C.
(16) · (17)

1878 (3 Jan). Surch as T **16** or **17** (No. 91) by De La Rue. Wmk Crown CC. P 14.

83	**10**	2c. dull rose (lower label blank)......	19·00	14·00
		w. Wmk inverted......................	£130	85·00
84	**9**	4c. on 1d. bistre......................	28·00	12·00
85		8c. on 2d. blue.......................	85·00	4·25
		w. Wmk inverted......................	—	£400
86		13c. on 3d. orange-red................	28·00	55·00
87		17c. on 4d. rose......................	£190	4·50
88		25c. on 6d. slate-blue................	£275	8·00
89		38c. on 9d. pale violet...............	50·00	£100
90		50c. on 1s. green.....................	90·00	6·50
		w. Wmk inverted......................		
91		2r.50 on 5s. bright mauve............	23·00	28·00
83/91	*Set of 9*		£700	£200

	18		19		20
	21		22		23
	24		25		26

(Typo D.L.R.)

1879 (Mar)–**80**. Wmk Crown CC. P 14.

92	**18**	2c. Venetian red (1.80)..............	55·00	28·00
93	**19**	4c. orange............................	65·00	3·50
		w. Wmk inverted......................		
94	**20**	8c. blue (1.80)........................	45·00	4·00
		w. Wmk inverted......................	—	£160
95	**21**	13c. slate (1.80).......................	£180	£325
96	**22**	17c. rose (1.80).......................	95·00	10·00
		w. Wmk inverted......................	—	£200
97	**23**	25c. olive-yellow......................	£475	18·00
98	**24**	38c. bright purple (1.80).............	£200	£375
99	**25**	50c. green (1.80)......................	7·50	6·50
		w. Wmk inverted......................	£160	
100	**26**	2r.50 brown-purple (1.80)............	55·00	80·00
92/100	*Set of 9*		£1000	£750

| | 27 |

(Typo D.L.R.)

1883–94. Wmk Crown CA. P 14.

101	**18**	1c. pale violet (1893)................	3·00	45
102		2c. Venetian red.....................	40·00	8·00
103		2c. green (1885)......................	5·50	60
104	**19**	4c. orange............................	95·00	8·00
		w. Wmk inverted......................		
105		4c. carmine (1885)...................	6·50	1·00
		w. Wmk inverted......................	£130	
		x. Wmk reversed.......................	†	£275
106	**20**	8c. blue (1891)........................	6·00	1·50
		w. Wmk inverted......................		
		x. Wmk reversed.......................	†	£275
107	**27**	15c. chestnut (1893)..................	9·50	1·25
		w. Wmk inverted......................	—	£160
108		15c. blue (1894).......................	14·00	1·75
109		16c. chestnut (1885)..................	13·00	2·75
110	**23**	25c. olive-yellow......................	15·00	4·00
		w. Wmk inverted......................	£400	£200
111	**25**	50c. orange (1887)....................	45·00	22·00
		w. Wmk inverted......................		
101/11	*Set of 11*		£225	45·00
101s, 103s, 105s, 107s/9s, 111s Optd "SPECIMEN" *Set of 7*			£750	

---

16 CENTS · 16 CENTS
(28) · (28a)

1883 (26 Feb). No. 96 surch with T **28/a** locally.

112	**22**	16c. on 17c. rose (surch T **28**– 14½ *mm* long)................	£170	55·00
		a. Surch double......................	†	£2750
		b. Horiz pair. Nos. 112/13..........	£850	£750
113		16c. on 17c. rose (surch T **28**– 15½ *mm* long)................	£180	55·00
		a. Surch double......................	—	£3000
114		16c. on 17c. rose (surch T **28a**)....	£375	£140

These stamps were surcharged using two different settings, each of which produced three horizontal rows at a time.

The length of the surcharge in the first setting (Type **28**) is either 14½ mm or 15½ mm and these exist in horizontal *se-tenant* pairs.

In Type **28** the height of the surcharge is 3.25 mm. On the second setting (Type **28a**) the type differs, especially the numerals and "S", with the surcharge measuring 15-15½ mm long and 3 mm high.

SIXTEEN CENTS · 2 CENTS · 2 CENTS
(29) · (30) · (31)

1883 (14 July). Surch with T **29** by D.L.R. Wmk Crown CA. P 14.

115	**22**	16c. on 17c. rose.....................	£110	2·50
		w. Wmk inverted......................		

1886 (11 May). No. 98 surch with T **30** locally.

116	**24**	2c. on 38c. bright purple............	£160	45·00
		a. Without bar.......................	—	£250
		b. Surch inverted....................	£1200	£950
		c. Surch double......................	£1300	

1887 (6 July). No. 95 surch with T **31** locally.

117	**21**	2c. on 13c. slate (R.)................	75·00	£120
		a. Surch inverted....................	£275	£300
		b. Surch double......................	£850	£750
		c. Surch double, one on back of stamp........................	£950	
		d. Surch double, both inverted......	†	£1600

TWO CENTS

TWO CENTS (32) · ▬▬▬ (33)

1891 (10–16 Sept). Nos. 88, 96, 98 and 105 surch locally as T **32** (Nos. 118/19, 121) or T **33** (No. 120).

118	**19**	2c. on 4c. carmine (No. 105) (12.9).	2·75	1·00
		a. Surch inverted....................	85·00	
		b. Surch double......................	90·00	85·00
		c. Surch double, one inverted.......	90·00	85·00
119	**22**	2c. on 17c. rose (No. 96) (16.9).....	£140	£150
		a. Surch inverted....................	£550	£600
		b. Surch double......................	£900	£900
120	**9**	2c. on 38c. on 9d. pale violet (No. 89) (16.9).....	16·00	8·50
		a. Surch inverted....................	£600	
		b. Surch double......................	£800	£800
		c. Surch double, one inverted.......	£190	£200
		w. Wmk inverted......................	†	£400
121	**24**	2c. on 38c. bright purple (No. 98)...	12·00	18·00
		a. Surch inverted....................	£1300	
		b. Surch double......................	£250	£275
		c. Surch double, one inverted.......	£275	£300

Minor varieties are also known with portions of the surcharge missing, due to defective printing.

ONE CENT · ONE CENT
(34) · ▬▬▬ (35)

1893 (1–7 Jan). Surch with T **34** by D.L.R. or T **35** locally. Wmk Crown CA. P 14.

123	**18**	1c. on 2c. pale violet................	2·50	2·00
		s. Optd "SPECIMEN"..................	35·00	
124	**27**	1c. on 16c. chestnut (7.1)............	3·75	5·00
		w. Wmk inverted......................	90·00	

| | 36 | | 37 |

(Typo D.L.R.)

1895–99. Wmk Crown CA. P 14.

127	**36**	1c. dull purple and ultramarine (8.7.97).....................	1·00	1·50
128		2c. dull purple and orange (8.7.97).....................	8·00	50
129		3c. dull purple and deep purple (8.7.97)......	70	50
130		4c. dull purple and emerald (8.7.97).....................	6·00	50
131		6c. green and rose-red (1899)......	7·00	4·00
132		18c. green and ultramarine (8.7.97).....................	23·00	3·50
127/32	*Set of 6*		40·00	9·50
127s/32s Optd "SPECIMEN" *Set of 6*			£150	

(Des L. Duvergé. Typo D.L.R.)

1898 (15 Apr). Diamond Jubilee. Wmk CA over Crown (sideways). P 14.

133	**37**	36c. orange and ultramarine..........	14·00	28·00
		s. Optd "SPECIMEN"..................	55·00	

6 CENTS · 15 CENTS
(38) · (39)

1899 (23–28 May). Nos. 132/3 surcharged with T **38/9** locally.

134	**36**	6c. on 18c. green and ultramarine (R.)....................	1·75	1·00
		a. Surch inverted....................	£700	£300
135	**37**	15c. on 36c. orange and ultramarine (B) (28.5)......	4·00	1·75
		a. Bar of surch omitted..............	£475	

The space between "6" and "CENTS" varies from 2½ to 4½ mm.

40 Admiral Mahé de La Bourdonnais, Governor of Mauritius, 1735–46

4 Cents

(41)

(Recess D.L.R.)

1899 (13 Dec). Birth Bicentenary of La Bourdonnais. Wmk Crown CC. P 14.

136	**40**	15c. ultramarine	35·00	4·75
		s. Optd "SPECIMEN"	80·00	
		w. Wmk inverted	£200	£160

1900. No. 109 surch with T **41** locally.

137	**27**	4c. on 16c. chestnut	17·00	28·00

42

12 CENTS

(43)

(Typo D.L.R.)

1900–05. Ordinary paper. Wmk Crown CC (1r.) or Crown CA (others) (sideways on 2r.50, 5r.). P 14.

138	**36**	1c. grey and black (1901)	50	10
139		2c. dull purple and bright purple (4.01)	1·00	20
140		3c. green and carmine/yellow (1902)	4·25	1·25
141		4c. purple and carmine/yellow	3·25	40
		w. Wmk inverted	—	£150
142		4c. grey-green and violet (1903)	3·25	2·00
		w. Wmk inverted		
143		4c. black and carmine/blue (14.10.04)	18·00	60
		w. Wmk inverted	28·00	17·00
144		5c. dull purple and bright purple/buff (8.10.02)	12·00	£110
145		5c. dull purple and black/buff (2.03)	2·50	2·50
146		6c. purple and carmine/red (1902)	4·75	80
		a. Wmk sideways	£2500	£2500
		w. Wmk inverted	32·00	20·00
147		8c. green and black/buff (16.7.02)	5·00	17·00
148		12c. grey-black and carmine (16.7.02)	3·00	2·25
149		15c. green and orange (1902)	32·00	10·00
		w. Wmk inverted		
150		15c. black and blue/blue (1905)	65·00	1·25
151		25c. green and carmine/green (1902)	32·00	50·00
		a. Chalk-surfaced paper	6·00	29·00
152		50c. dull green and deep green/yellow (1902)	17·00	75·00
153	**42**	1r. grey-black and carmine (1902)	65·00	55·00
		w. Wmk inverted	£140	£150
154		2r.50 green and black/blue (1902)	40·00	£160
155		5r. purple and carmine/red (1902)	£110	£180

138/55 Set of 18 .... £350 £550
138s/55s Optd "SPECIMEN" Set of 18 .... £425

Examples of Nos. 144 and 151/5 are known showing a forged Port Louis postmark dated "SP 29 10".

1902. No. 132 surch with T **43**.

156	**36**	12c. on 18c. green and ultramarine	3·75	12·00

The bar cancelling the original value seems in some cases to be one thick bar and in others two thin ones.

Postage & Revenue.

(44)

1902 (7 July). Various stamps optd with T **44** locally.

157	**36**	4c. purple and carmine/yellow (No. 141)	2·50	20
158		6c. green and rose-red (No. 131)	3·25	3·00
159		15c. green and orange (No. 149)	9·00	1·25
160	**23**	25c. olive-yellow (No. 110)	9·00	3·50
161	**25**	50c. green (No. 99)	27·00	7·50
162	**26**	2r.50 brown-purple (No. 100)	£130	£225

157/62 Set of 6 .... £170 £225

Nos. 157/62 were overprinted to make surplus stocks of postage stamps available for revenue (fiscal) purposes also.

1902 (22 Sept). No. 133 surch as T **43**, but with longer bar.

163	**37**	12c. on 36c. orange and ultramarine	2·75	1·25
		a. Surch inverted	£800	£475

The note below No. 156 also applies to No. 163.
Forged double surcharge errors show a straight, instead of a curved, serif to the "1" of "12".

(Typo D.L.R.)

1904–07. Ordinary paper (2c., 4c., 6c.) or chalk-surfaced paper (others). Wmk Mult Crown CA. P 14.

164	**36**	1c. grey and black (1907)	8·00	4·50
165		2c. dull and bright purple (1905)	35·00	3·00
		a. Chalk-surfaced paper	32·00	1·75
166		3c. green and carmine/yellow	21·00	14·00
167		4c. black and carmine/blue	40·00	1·50
		a. Chalk-surfaced paper	16·00	10
		aw. Wmk inverted	†	£350
168		6c. purple and carmine/red	25·00	30
		a. Chalk-surfaced paper	14·00	10
		aw. Wmk inverted	†	£350
171		15c. black and blue/blue (1907)	4·00	35
174		50c. green and deep green/yellow	3·00	8·50
175	**42**	1r. grey-black and carmine (1907)	50·00	60·00

164/75 Set of 8 .... £130 75·00
Nos. 176 to 180 are vacant.

46   **47**

(Typo D.L.R.)

1910 (17 Jan). Ordinary paper (1c. to 15c.) or chalk-surfaced paper (25c. to 10r.). Wmk Mult Crown CA. P 14.

181	**46**	1c. black	3·00	30
		w. Wmk inverted	†	
182		2c. brown	2·75	10
		w. Wmk inverted	†	£150
183		3c. green	3·00	10
		a. "A" of "CA" missing from wmk	†	—
		w. Wmk inverted	50·00	
184		4c. pale yellow-green and carmine	4·00	10
		w. Wmk inverted	—	75·00
		y. Wmk inverted and reversed	†	£170
185	**47**	5c. grey and carmine	4·00	3·00
186	**46**	6c. carmine-red	7·00	20
		a. Pale red	13·00	2·50
		ab. "A" of "CA" missing from wmk	†	—
187		8c. orange	3·50	2·50
188	**47**	10c. greyish slate	4·25	2·75
189	**46**	15c. blue	19·00	20
190	**47**	25c. black and red/yellow	2·00	12·00
191		50c. dull purple and black	4·50	22·00
192		1r. black/green	21·00	16·00
193		2r.50 black and red/blue	29·00	75·00
194		5r. green and red/yellow	45·00	95·00
195		10r. green and red/green	£170	£325

181/95 Set of 15 .... £275 £500
181s/95s Optd "SPECIMEN" Set of 15 .... £375

On Nos. 185, 191, 192, 193 and 194 the value labels are as in T **48**.

48   **49**

(Typo D.L.R.)

1913–22. Die I. Ordinary paper (5c., 12c.) or chalk-surfaced paper (others). Wmk Mult Crown CA. P 14.

196	**48**	5c. grey and carmine (1913)	4·50	4·25
		a. Slate-grey and carmine	12·00	12·00
198	**49**	12c. greyish slate (1914)	9·00	1·00
199		25c. black and red/yellow (1913)	50	1·40
		a. White back (1914)	3·25	22·00
		aw. Wmk inverted and reversed	65·00	
		b. On orange-buff (1920)	35·00	60·00
		c. On pale yellow (1921)	35·00	40·00
		cs. Optd "SPECIMEN"	55·00	
		cw. Wmk inverted	£180	
		d. Die II. On pale yellow (1921)	1·25	26·00
		ds. Optd "SPECIMEN"	50·00	
200	**48**	50c. dull purple and black (1920)	50·00	£130
201		1r. black/blue-green (olive back) (1917)	10·00	25·00
		a. On emerald (olive back) (1921)	15·00	55·00
		b. Die II. On emerald (emerald back) (1921)	2·25	7·50
		bs. Optd "SPECIMEN"	50·00	
202		2r.50 black and red/blue (1916)	45·00	75·00
203		5r. green and red/orange-buff (1921)	£150	£250
		a. On pale yellow (1921)	£130	£180
		b. Die II. On pale yellow (1922)	90·00	£200
204	**49**	10r. green and red/green (blue-green back) (1913)	£110	£250
		a. On blue-green (olive back) (1919)	£1100	
		b. On emerald (olive back) (1921)	£160	£250
		c. On emerald (emerald back) (1921)	90·00	£225
		d. Die II. On emerald (emerald back) (1922)	55·00	£200
		ds. Optd "SPECIMEN"	70·00	

196/204d Set of 8 .... £225 £550
196s/202s, 203as, 204s Optd "SPECIMEN" Set of 8 .... £300

Examples of Nos. 200/4d are known showing part strikes of the forged Port Louis postmark mentioned after Nos. 138/55.

49a

(Typo D.L.R.)

1921–26. Chalk-surfaced paper (50r.). Wmk Mult Script CA. P 14.

205	**46**	1c. black	1·00	1·00
		w. Wmk inverted	45·00	55·00
206		2c. brown	1·00	10
		w. Wmk inverted		
207		2c. purple/yellow (1926)	4·00	3·00
		w. Wmk inverted	28·00	38·00
208		3c. green (1926)	5·00	4·50
209		4c. pale olive-green and carmine	1·50	1·75
		x. Wmk reversed	£130	
210		4c. green (1922)	1·00	10
		w. Wmk inverted	£100	
		x. Wmk reversed		
211		4c. brown (1926)	7·50	3·50
212		6c. carmine	12·00	6·50
		x. Wmk reversed	95·00	95·00
213		6c. bright mauve (1922)	1·25	10
214		8c. orange (1925)	2·25	27·00
215		10c. grey (1922)	2·00	3·25
216		10c. carmine-red (1926)	14·00	9·00
217		12c. carmine-red (1922)	1·50	40
218		12c. grey (1926)	1·75	7·00
219		15c. blue (1926)	5·50	7·00
		ax. Wmk reversed	£120	£120
		b. Cobalt (1926)	1·00	25
220		20c. blue (1922)	2·00	80
221		20c. purple (1926)	8·50	17·00
222	**49a**	50r. dull purple and green (1924)	£950	£2750
		s. Optd "SPECIMEN"	£400	

205/21 Set of 17 .... 60·00 75·00
205s/21s Optd "SPECIMEN" Set of 17 .... £475

Normal   Open "C" (R. 9/6 of right pane)

A   B

Two types of duty plate in the 12c. In Type B the letters of "MAURITIUS" are larger; the extremities of the downstroke and the tail of the "2" are pointed, instead of square, and the "c" is larger.

(Typo D.L.R.)

1921–34. Die II. Chalk-surfaced paper (25c. to 10r.). Wmk Mult Script CA. P 14.

223	**49**	1c. black (1926)	2·25	3·00
224		2c. brown (1926)	1·25	10
225		3c. green (1926)	2·75	40
226		4c. sage-green and carmine (1926)	3·75	30
		a. Open "C"	80·00	25·00
		b. Die I (1932)	19·00	60·00
		ba. Open "C"	£190	35·00
226c		4c. green (Die I) (1932)	16·00	45
		ca. Open "C"	£180	
227	**48**	5c. grey and carmine (1922)	1·00	10
		a. Die I (1932)	13·00	6·00
228	**49**	6c. sepia (1927)	5·50	60
229		8c. orange (1926)	3·50	19·00
230		10c. carmine-red (1926)	4·75	20
		a. Die I (1932)	17·00	19·00
231		12c. grey (Type A) (1922)	2·00	25·00
232		12c. carmine-red (Type A) (1922)	65	3·50
232a		12c. pale grey (Type A) (1926)	7·00	25·00
		as. Optd "SPECIMEN"	50·00	
232b		12c. grey (Type B) (1934)	21·00	20
233		15c. Prussian blue (1926)	4·75	20
234		20c. purple (1926)	5·50	40
235		20c. Prussian blue (Die I) (1932)	10·00	2·75
		a. Die II (1934)	29·00	40
236		25c. black and red/pale yellow (1922)	1·00	15
		a. Die I (1932)	12·00	70·00
237	**48**	50c. dull purple and black (1921)	7·50	7·50
238		1r. black/emerald (1924)	7·50	1·75
		a. Die I (1932)	29·00	65·00
239		2r.50 black and red/blue (1922)	20·00	18·00
240		5r. green and red/yellow (1924)	50·00	£110
241	**49**	10r. green and red/emerald (1924)	£160	£375

223/41 Set of 20 .... £275 £475
223/41s Optd or Perf (Nos. 226cs, 235s) "SPECIMEN" Set of 20 .... £600

3 Cents

(50)   **51**

1925 (25 Nov). Nos. 210, 217 and 220 surch locally as T **50**.

242	**46**	3c. on 4c. green	9·00	7·00
243		10c. on 12c. carmine-red	45	1·50
244		15c. on 20c. blue	60	1·50

242/4 Set of 3 .... 9·00 9·00
242s/4s Optd "SPECIMEN" Set of 3 .... £100

1935 (6 May). Silver Jubilee. As Nos. 91/4 of Antigua. P 13½×14.

245		5c. ultramarine and grey	50	10
		f. Diagonal line by turret	85·00	30·00
		g. Dot to left of chapel	£140	65·00
		h. Dot by flagstaff	£160	75·00
246		12c. green and indigo	4·50	10
		f. Diagonal line by turret	£150	50·00
		g. Dot to left of chapel	£350	80·00
247		20c. brown and deep blue	5·50	20
		f. Diagonal line by turret	£225	70·00
		g. Dot to left of chapel	£325	90·00
248		1r. slate and purple	29·00	50·00
		h. Dot by flagstaff	£400	£550

245/8 Set of 4 .... 35·00 50·00
245s/8s Perf "SPECIMEN" Set of 4 .... £130

For illustrations of plate varieties see Omnibus section following Zanzibar.

20c. Line through sword (R. 2/2)   **20c.** Line by sceptre (R. 5/3)

1937 (12 May). Coronation. As Nos. 95/7 of Antigua.

249	5c. violet		40	20
250	12c. scarlet		75	2·25
251	20c. bright blue		1·75	1·00
	a. Line through sword		90·00	50·00
	b. Line by sceptre		90·00	50·00
249/51 Set of 3			2·50	3·00
249s/51s Perf "SPECIMEN" Set of 3			£110	

Similar but less pronounced examples of the "Line by sceptre" occur on R. 5/2 and R. 5/6.

3c. Sliced "S" at right (R. 2/2, 3/2, right pane)   **3c.** Split frame (R. 7/6, right pane, Key Plate 1)

4c. Damaged "S" (R. 4/4, right pane).   **10c.** Sliced "S" at top (R. 4/1, left pane and R. 8/4, right pane)

20c., 2r.50 Broken frame under "A" of "MAURITIUS" (R. 9/3 left pane, Key Plate 2)   **25c.** "IJ" flaw (R. 3/6 of right pane)

1r. Battered "A" (R. 6/1 of right pane)

(Typo D.L.R.)

1938–49. T **51** and similar types. Chalk-surfaced paper (25c. to 10r.). Wmk Mult Script CA. P 14.

252	2c. olive-grey (9.3.38)		30	10
	a. Perf 15×14 (1942)		1·00	10
253	3c. reddish purple and scarlet (27.10.38)		2·00	2·00
	a. Sliced "S" at right		85·00	85·00
	b. Split frame		£200	
	c. Reddish lilac and red (4.43)		5·50	4·00
	ca. Sliced "S" at right		£225	£200
254	4c. dull green (26.2.38)		7·50	2·00
	a. Open "C"		£225	£120
	b. Deep dull green (4.43)		2·50	2·25
	ba. Open "C"		£150	£130
	bb. Damaged "S"		£275	
255	5c. slate-lilac (23.2.38)		17·00	85
	a. Pale lilac (shades) (4.43)		3·25	20
	b. Perf 15×14 (1942)		60·00	10
256	10c. rose-red (9.3.38)		2·75	30
	a. Sliced "S" at top		£170	48·00
	b. Deep reddish rose (shades) (4.43)		2·50	20
	ba. Sliced "S" at top		£160	38·00
	c. Perf 15×14. Pale reddish rose (1942)		42·00	3·00
	ca. Sliced "S" at top		£700	£150
257	12c. salmon (shades) (26.2.38)		1·00	20
	a. Perf 15×14 (1942)		55·00	1·25
258	20c. blue (26.2.38)		1·00	10
	a. Broken frame		£1500	£400
259	25c. brown-purple (2.3.38)		22·00	20
	b. Ordinary paper (1942)		9·00	10
	ba. "IJ" flaw		£300	48·00
260	1r. grey-brown (2.3.38)		45·00	3·00
	a. Battered "A"		£900	£250
	b. Ordinary paper (1942)		20·00	1·75
	ba. Battered "A"		£650	£170
	c. Drab (4.49)		55·00	21·00
	ca. Battered "A"		£1000	£475
261	2r.50 pale violet (2.3.38)		60·00	32·00
	a. Ordinary paper (8.4.43)		42·00	30·00
	ab. Broken frame		£1500	£850
	b. Slate-violet (4.48)		70·00	50·00

262	5r. olive-green (2.3.38)		55·00	45·00
	a. Ordinary paper. Sage-green (8.4.43)		38·00	45·00
263	10r. reddish purple (shades) (2.3.38)		80·00	55·00
	a. Ordinary paper (8.4.43)		17·00	48·00
252/63a Set of 12			£120	£110
252s/63s Perf "SPECIMEN" Set of 12			£425	

Less pronounced examples of the "Sliced S" variety on the 3c. occur in other positions the slice on the 10c. at R.4/1 also varies considerably. The prices for the listed varieties being for pronounced examples, as illustrated. The illustration of the "Battered A" on the 1r. value shows the variety as it appears on issues between 1942 and 1949. On early printings of No. 260a the top of the "A" is normal.

The broken frame on the 2r.50 (No. 261ab) differs slightly from that on the 20c. but the distorted frame above "AU" is the same.

The stamps perf 15×14 were printed by Bradbury Wilkinson from De La Rue plates and issued only in the colony in 1942. De La Rue printings of the 2c. to 20c. in 1943–45 were on thin, whiter paper. 1942–45 printings of the 25c. to 10r. were on ordinary paper.

1946 (20 Nov). Victory. As Nos. 110/11 of Antigua.

264	5c. lilac		10	75
265	20c. blue		20	25
264s/5s Perf "SPECIMEN" Set of 2			95·00	

52 1d. "Post Office" Mauritius and King George VI

(Recess B.W.)

1948 (22 Mar). Centenary of First British Colonial Postage Stamp. Wmk Mult Script CA. P 11½×11.

266	**52**	5c. orange and magenta	10	50
267		12c. orange and green	15	25
268	–	20c. blue and light blue	20	10
269	–	1r. blue and red-brown	1·00	30
266/9 Set of 4			1·25	1·00
266s/9s Perf "SPECIMEN" Set of 4			£180	

Design:—20c., 1r. As T **52** but showing 2d. "Post Office" Mauritius.

1948 (25 Oct). Royal Silver Wedding. As Nos. 112/13 of Antigua.

270	5c. violet		10	10
271	10r. magenta		17·00	42·00

1949 (10 Oct). 75th Anniv of UPU As Nos. 114/17 of Antigua.

272	12c. carmine		50	3·50
273	20c. deep blue		2·25	2·50
274	35c. purple		60	1·50
275	1r. sepia		50	20
272/5 Set of 4			3·50	7·00

53 Labourdonnais Sugar Factory   **54** Grand Port

55 Aloe Plant   **56** Tamarind Falls

57 Rempart Mountain   **58** Transporting cane

59 Mauritius Dodo and map   **60** Legend of Paul and Virginie

61 La Bourdonnais Statue   **62** Government House, Reduit

63 Pieter Both Mountain   **64** Timor Deer

65 Port Louis   **66** Beach scene

67 Arms of Mauritius

(Photo Harrison)

1950 (1 July). T **53/67**. Chalk-surfaced paper. Wmk Mult Script CA. P 13½×14½ (horiz), 14½×13½ (vert).

276	**53**	1c. bright purple	10	50
277	**54**	1c. rose-carmine	15	10
278	**55**	3c. yellow-green	60	4·25
279	**56**	4c. green	20	3·00
280	**57**	5c. blue	15	10
281	**58**	10c. scarlet	30	75
282	**59**	12c. olive-green	1·50	3·00
283	**60**	20c. ultramarine	1·00	15
284	**61**	25c. brown-purple	2·50	40
285	**62**	35c. violet	40	10
		w. Wmk inverted	†	£3250
286	**63**	50c. emerald-green	2·75	50
287	**64**	1r. sepia	9·50	10
288	**65**	2r.50 orange	23·00	20·00
289	**66**	5r. red-brown	25·00	48·00
		w. Wmk inverted	†	£3250
290	**67**	10r. dull blue	17·00	48·00
276/290 Set of 15			75·00	85·00

The latitude is incorrectly shown on No. 282.

1953 (2 June). Coronation. As No. 120 of Antigua.

291	10c. black and emerald		1·50	15

68 Tamarind Falls   **69** Historical Museum, Mahebourg

(Photo Harrison)

1953 (3 Nov)–**58**. Designs previously used for King George VI issue but with portrait of Queen Elizabeth II as in T **68/9**. Chalk-surfaced paper. Wmk Mult Script CA. P 13½×14½ (horiz) or 14½×13½ (vert).

293	**54**	2c. bright carmine (1.6.54)	10	10
294	**55**	3c. yellow-green (1.6.54)	30	40
295	**53**	4c. bright purple (1.6.54)	10	1·00
		w. Wmk inverted	£110	
296	**57**	5c. Prussian blue (1.6.54)	10	10
297	**68**	10c. bluish green (1.6.54)	20	10
		a. Yellowish green (9.2.55)	1·00	10
298	**69**	15c. scarlet	10	10
299	**61**	20c. brown-purple	15	20
		w. Wmk inverted	6·00	10·00
300	**60**	25c. bright ultramarine	1·50	10
		a. Bright blue (19.6 57)	7·50	75
301	**62**	35c. reddish violet (1.6.54)	20	10
		w. Wmk inverted	£350	£250
302	**63**	50c. bright green	55	85
302a	**59**	60c. deep green (2.8.54)	10·00	10
		ab. Bronze-green (27.8.58)	14·00	10
303	**64**	1r. sepia	30	10
		a. Deep grey-brown (19.6.57)	4·75	65
		w. Wmk inverted	£400	
304	**65**	2r.50 orange (1.6.54)	14·00	9·00
305	**66**	5r. red-brown (1.6.54)	27·00	10·00
		a. Orange-brown (19.6.57)	60·00	16·00
306	**67**	10r. deep grey-blue (1.6.54)	16·00	2·00
293/306 Set of 15			60·00	21·00

Nos. 296 and 300 exist in coils, constructed from normal sheets. See also Nos. 314/16.

70 Queen Elizabeth II and King George III (after Lawrence)

(Litho Enschedé)

1961 (11 Jan). 150th Anniv of British Post Office in Mauritius. W w **12**. P 13½×14.

307	**70**	10c. black and brown-red	10	10

	w. Wmk inverted		40·00	20·00
308	20c. ultramarine and light blue		30	50
	w. Wmk inverted		70·00	35·00
309	35c. black and yellow		40	50
310	1r. deep maroon and green		60	30
	w. Wmk inverted		£170	
307/10 *Set of 4*			1·25	1·25

1963 (4 June). Freedom from Hunger. As No. 146 of Antigua.

311	60c. reddish violet	40	10

1963 (2 Sept). Red Cross Centenary. As No. 147/8 of Antigua.

312	10c. red and black	15	10
313	60c. red and blue	60	20

1963 (12 Nov)–**65**. As Nos. 297, 302*ab* and 304 but wmk w **12**.

314	**68**	10c. bluish green (1964)	15	10
		a. Yellowish green (21.1.65)	25	10
315	**59**	60c. bronze-green (28.5.64)	4·00	10
316	**65**	2r.50 orange	13·00	8·50
314/16 *Set of 3*			15·00	8·50

71 Bourbon White Eye

72 Rodriquez Fody

73 Mauritius Olive White-eye

74 Mascarene Paradise Flycatcher

75 Mauritius Fody

76 Mauritius Parakeet

77 Mauritius Greybird

78 Mauritius Kestrel

79 Pink Pigeon

80 Réunion Bulbul

81 Mauritius Blue Pigeon (extinct)

82 Mauritius Dodo (extinct)

83 Rodriquez Solitaire (extinct)

84 Mauritius Red Rail (extinct)

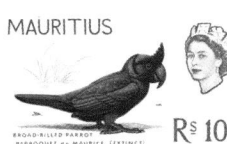

85 Broad-billed Parrot (extinct)

(Des D. M. Reid-Henry. Photo Harrison)

1965 (16 Mar). Horiz designs as T **71/85**. W w **12** (upright). Multicoloured; background colours given. P 14½×14.

317	**71**	2c. lemon	40	15
		a. Grey (leg) omitted	£375	
		w. Wmk inverted	20·00	
318	**72**	3c. brown	1·00	15
		a. Black (eye and beak) omitted	£450	
		w. Wmk inverted	70·00	
319	**73**	4c. light reddish purple	30	15
		a. Mauve-pink omitted*	80·00	
		b. Pale grey omitted	£350	
		c. Orange omitted	£450	
		w. Wmk inverted	9·00	8·00
320	**74**	5c. grey-brown	3·75	10
		w. Wmk inverted	£110	
321	**75**	10c. light grey-green	30	10
		w. Wmk inverted	16·00	
322	**76**	15c. pale grey	2·00	40
		a. Red (beak) omitted	£900	
		w. Wmk inverted	80·00	
323	**77**	20c. light yellow-bistre	2·00	10
		w. Wmk inverted	27·00	
324	**78**	25c. bluish grey	2·00	30
		w. Wmk inverted	11·00	
325	**79**	35c. greyish blue	3·75	10
		w. Wmk inverted	£130	
326	**80**	50c. light yellow-buff	50	40
		w. Wmk inverted	95·00	
327	**81**	60c. light greenish yellow	60	10
		w. Wmk inverted	1·50	75
328	**82**	1r. light yellow-olive	12·00	10
		a. Pale orange omitted	£325	
		b. Light grey (ground) omitted	£475	£475
329	**83**	2r.50 pale stone	5·00	9·50
330	**71**	5r. pale grey-blue	15·00	17·00
		a. Brown-red omitted	£450	£450
331	**85**	10r. pale bluish green	35·00	38·00
317/31 *Set of 15*			70·00	60·00

*On the 4c. the background is printed in two colours so that in No. 319a the background colour is similar to that of the 5c.

On No. 317a it is the deep grey which is missing, affecting the leg, beak and part of the branch. On No. 319c the missing orange affects the under breast of the bird, which appears much paler. On No. 328a the omission affects the legs and part of the body and on No. 330a the whole of the bird appears in the same colour as the legs.

The 50c. and 2r.50 exist with PVA gum as well as gum arabic.

Nos. 320 and 324 exist in coils, constructed from normal sheets.

See also Nos. 340/1 and 370/5.

1965 (17 May). ITU Centenary. As No. 166/7 of Antigua.

332	10c. red-orange and apple-green	20	10
333	60c. yellow and bluish violet	70	20

1965 (25 Oct). International Co-operation Year. As No. 168/9 of Antigua.

334	10c. reddish purple and turquoise-green	15	10
335	60c. deep bluish green and lavender	30	20

1966 (24 Jan). Churchill Commemoration. As No. 170/3 of Antigua.

336	2c. new blue	10	3·75
	w. Wmk inverted	60·00	
337	10c. deep green	50	10
	w. Wmk inverted	45·00	
338	60c. brown	1·60	20
	w. Wmk inverted	18·00	
339	1r. bluish violet	1·60	20
336/9 *Set of 4*		3·25	3·75

1966–67. As Nos. 320, 325 but wmk w **12** sideways*.

340	5c. grey-brown (1966)	70	15
	w. Wmk Crown to right of CA	50·00	
341	35c. greyish blue (27.6.67)	30	15

*The normal sideways watermark shows Crown to left of CA, *as seen from the back of the stamp.*

No. 340 exists in coils, constructed from normal sheets.

1966 (1 Dec). 20th Anniv of UNESCO As No. 196/8 of Antigua.

342	5c. slate-violet, red, yellow and orange	25	30
343	10c. orange-yellow, violet and deep olive	30	10
344	60c. black, bright purple and orange	1·40	15
342/4 *Set of 3*		1·75	50

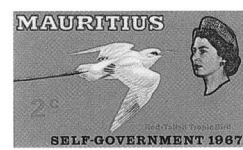

86 Red-tailed Tropicbird

(Des D. M. Reid-Henry. Photo Harrison)

1967 (1 Sept). Self-Government. T **86** and similar horiz designs. Multicoloured. W w **12**. P 14½.

345	2c. Type **86**	25	3·00
	w. Wmk inverted	19·00	
346	10c. Rodriguez Brush Warbler	80	10
347	60c. Rose-ringed Parakeet (extinct)	85	10
348	1r. Grey-rumped Swiftlet	90	10
345/8 *Set of 4*		2·50	3·00

SELF GOVERNMENT 1967
(90)

1967 (1 Dec). Self-Government. As Nos. 317/31 but wmk sideways* on Nos. 352/3 and 357. Optd with T **90**. P 14×14½.

349	2c. lemon	10	50
	w. Wmk inverted	16·00	
350	3c. brown	10	50
	w. Wmk inverted	22·00	
351	4c. light reddish purple	10	50
	a. Orange omitted	£325	
352	5c. grey-brown	10	10
353	10c. light grey-green	10	10
	w. Wmk Crown to right of CA	22·00	
354	15c. pale grey	10	30
355	20c. light yellow-bistre	15	10
	w. Wmk inverted	16·00	
356	25c. bluish grey	15	10
357	35c. greyish blue	20	10
	w. Wmk Crown to right of CA	£100	
358	50c. light yellow-buff	30	15
359	60c. light greenish yellow	30	10
	w. Wmk inverted	12·00	
360	1r. light yellow-olive	1·50	10
361	2r.50 pale stone	1·00	2·25
362	5r. pale grey-blue	6·00	3·25
363	10r. pale bluish green	10·00	15·00
349/63 *Set of 15*		18·00	21·00

*The normal sideways watermark shows Crown to the left of CA, *as seen from the back of the stamp.*

91 Flag of Mauritius

92 Arms and Mauritius Dodo Emblem

(Litho D.L.R.)

1968 (12 Mar). Independence. T **91/2**. P 13½×13.

364	**91**	2c. multicoloured	10	2·25
365	**92**	3c. multicoloured	20	2·25
366	**91**	15c. multicoloured	60	10
367	**92**	20c. multicoloured	60	10
368	**91**	60c. multicoloured	1·10	10
369	**92**	1r. multicoloured	1·10	10
364/9 *Set of 6*			3·25	4·50

1968 (12 July). As Nos. 317/18, 322/3 and 327/8 but background colours changed as below.

370	**71**	2c. olive-yellow	20	4·50
		a. Black printed double	£150	
		b. Grey printed double	£110	
371	**72**	3c. cobalt	1·75	8·50
		w. Wmk inverted	85·00	
372	**76**	15c. cinnamon	55	20
		a. Greenish blue omitted	£500	
373	**77**	20c. buff	3·50	4·00
374	**81**	60c. rose	1·50	1·25
		w. Wmk inverted	50·00	
375	**82**	1r. reddish purple	3·25	1·50
370/5	*Set of 6*		9·50	18·00

93 Dominique rescues Paul and Virginie

(Des V. Whiteley, from prints. Litho Format)

1968 (2 Dec). Bicentenary of Bernardin de St. Pierre's Visit to Mauritius. Multicoloured designs as T **93**. P 13½.

376	2c. Type **93**	10	1·25
377	15c. Paul and Virginie crossing the river..	65	10
378	50c. Visit of La Bourdonnais to Madame de la Tour (*horiz*)	1·25	10
379	60c. Meeting of Paul and Virginie in Confidence (*vert*)	1·25	10
380	1r. Departure of Virginie for Europe (*horiz*)	1·25	20
381	2r.50 Bernardin de St. Pierre (*vert*)	1·75	3·75
376/81	*Set of 6*	5·50	5·00

99 Black-spotted Emperor

(Des J. Vinson (3c., 20c., 1r.) R. Granger Barrett (others). Photo Harrison)

1969 (12 Mar)–73. W w **12** (sideways* on 2, 3, 4, 5, 10, 15, 60 and 75c). Chalk-surfaced paper. P 14.

382	2c. multicoloured	10	2·75
	a. Pale green printed double**	£120	
383	3c. multicoloured	10	3·50
	w. Wmk Crown to right of CA	£150	
384	4c. multicoloured	2·50	4·50
	w. Wmk Crown to right of CA	25·00	
385	5c. multicoloured	30	10
386	10c. scarlet, black and flesh	2·00	10
	w. Wmk Crown to right of CA	35·00	
387	15c. ochre, black and cobalt	30	10
	w. Wmk Crown to right of CA	2·75	
388	20c. multicoloured	65	70
	a. Glazed ordinary paper (20.2.73)	45	13·00
389	25c. red, black and pale apple-green	30	3·75
	a. Glazed ordinary paper (22.1.71)	3·75	6·50
	aw. Wmk inverted	4·00	8·00
390	30c. multicoloured	1·50	1·75
	a. Glazed, ordinary paper (20.3.73)	8·00	18·00
391	35c. multicoloured	1·75	1·25
	a. Glazed ordinary paper (3.2.71)	1·00	3·50
	aw. Wmk inverted	2·50	
392	40c. multicoloured	35	1·25
	a. Glazed ordinary paper (20.2.73)	8·00	18·00
	aw. Wmk inverted	24·00	
393	50c. multicoloured	1·00	10
	a. Red omitted	£190	
	b. Glazed ordinary paper (22.1.71)	1·50	1·25
	ba. Red printed double		
	bw. Wmk inverted	1·50	20
394	60c. black, rose and ultramarine	1·50	10
395	75c. multicoloured	1·50	2·75
	w. Wmk Crown to right of CA	32·00	
396	1r. multicoloured	60	10
	a. Glazed ordinary paper (22.1.71)	2·25	15
	aw. Wmk inverted	95·00	
397	2r. 50 multicoloured	3·00	8·50
	a. Glazed ordinary paper (20.2.73)	2·00	20·00
398	5r. multicoloured	12·00	12·00
	a. Glazed ordinary paper (22.1.71)	12·00	3·50
	aw. Wmk inverted	55·00	
399	10r. multicoloured	2·50	4·75
	w. Wmk inverted (26.1.72)	1·50	1·50
382/99	*Set of 18*	27·00	40·00
388a/98a	*Set of 9*	35·00	75·00

Designs:—3c. Red Reef Crab; 4c. Episcopal Mitre (*Mitra mitra*); 5c. Black-saddled Pufferfish ("Bourse"); 10c. Starfish; 15c. Sea Urchin; 20c. Fiddler Crab 25c. Spiny Shrimp; 30c. Single Harp Shells and Double Harp Shell; 35c. Common Paper Nautilus (*Argonauta argo*); 40c. Spanish Dancer (*Hexabranchus sanguineus*); 50c. Orange Spider Conch (*Lambis crocata*) and Violet Spider Conch (*Lambis violacea*); 60c. Blue Marlin; 75c. *Conus clytospira*; 1r. Dolphin (fish); 2r.50, Spiny Lobster; 5r. Ruby Snapper ("Sacre Chien Rouge"); 10r. Yellowedged Lyretail ("Croissant Queue Jaune").

*The normal sideways watermark shows Crown to left of CA, *as seen from the back of the stamp*.

**No. 382a occurs from a sheet on which a second printing of the pale green appears above the normal.

Nos. 385/6 and 389 exist in coils constructed from normal sheets.

This set was re-issued between 1972 and 1974 with watermark w **12** upright on 2c. to 15c., 60c. and 75c. and sideways on other values. Between 1974 and 1977 it was issued on Multiple Crown CA Diagonal watermark paper.

---

117 Gandhi as Law Student

124 Frangourinier Cane-crusher (18th-cent)

(Des J. W. Litho Format)

1969 (1 July). Birth Centenary of Mahatma Gandhi. T **117** and similar vert designs. Multicoloured. W w **12**. P 13½.

400	2c. Type **117**	30	20
401	15c. Gandhi as stretcher-bearer during Zulu Revolt	65	10
402	50c. Gandhi as Satyagrahi in South Africa	80	50
403	60c. Gandhi at No. 10 Downing Street, London	80	10
404	1r. Gandhi in Mauritius, 1901	90	10
405	2r. 50 Gandhi, the "Apostle of Truth and Non-Violence"	2·00	2·00
400/5	*Set of 6*	5·00	2·75
MS406	153×153 mm. Nos. 400/5	12·00	8·00

(Des V. Whiteley. Photo Enschedé)

1969 (22 Dec*). 150th Anniv of Telfair's Improvements to the Sugar Industry. T **124** and similar multicoloured designs. W w **12** (sideways on 2c. to 1r.), P 11½×11 (2r.50) or 11×11½ (others).

407	2c. Three-roller Vertical Mill	10	20
408	15c. Type **124**	10	10
409	60c. Beau Rivage Factory, 1867	10	10
410	1r. Mon Desert-Alma Factory, 1969	10	10
411	2r.50 Dr. Charles Telfair (*vert*)	25	1·25
407/11	*Set of 5*	60	1·60
MS412	159×88 mm. Nos. 407/11†. Wmk sideways. P 11×11½	1·50	2·25

*This was the local release date but the Crown Agents issued the stamps on 15 December.

†In the miniature sheet the 2r.50 is perf 11 at the top and imperf on the other three sides.

EXPO '70' OSAKA (**128**)

129 Morne Plage, Mountain and Boeing 707

1970 (7 Apr). World Fair, Osaka. Nos. 394 and 396 optd with T **128** by Harrison & Sons.

413	60c. black, rose and ultramarine	10	10
	w. Wmk Crown to right of CA	70·00	
414	1r. multicoloured	20	20

(Des H. Rose. Litho G. Gehringer, Kaiserslautern, Germany)

1970 (2 May). Inauguration of Lufthansa Flight, Mauritius–Frankfurt. T **129** and similar multicoloured design. P 14.

415	25c. Type **129**	30	20
416	50c. Boeing 707 and Map (*vert*)	30	20

131 Lenin as a Student

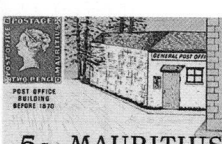

133 2d. "Post Office" Mauritius and original Post Office

(Photo State Ptg Works, Moscow)

1970 (15 May). Birth Centenary of Lenin. T **131** and similar vert design. P 12×11½.

417	15c. blackish green and silver	10	10
418	75c. blackish brown and gold	20	20

Design:—75c. Lenin as Founder of USSR.

(Des and litho D.L.R.)

1970 (15 Oct). Port Louis, Old and New. T **133** and similar horiz designs. Multicoloured. W w **12** (sideways). P 14.

419	5c. Type **133**	20	10
420	15c. GPO Building (built 1870)	20	10
421	50c. Mail Coach (*vert*)	80	15
422	75c. Port Louis Harbour (1970)	95	25
423	2r.50 Arrival of Pierre A. de Suffren (1783)	1·00	2·75
419/23	*Set of 5*	2·75	3·00
MS424	165×95 mm. Nos. 419/23	4·75	8·50

---

138 UN Emblem and Symbols

(Des Jennifer Toombs. Litho Format)

1970 (24 Oct). 25th Anniv of United Nations. W w **12** (sideways). P 14½.

425	**138**	10c. multicoloured	10	10
426		60c. multicoloured	40	10

STAMP BOOKLETS

1953 (10 Oct). Black on white cover. Stapled.

SB1	5r. booklet containing 4×5c., 8×10c. and 8×50c. (Nos. 280, 286, 291) in blocks of 4 and one pane of 4 air mail labels	£225

1954 (23 Sept). Black on white or grey cover. Stapled.

SB2	5r. booklet containing 4×5c., 8×50c. (Nos. 296/7, 302) in blocks of 4 and one pane of 4 air mail labels	40·00

1955. Black on grey cover. Stapled.

SB3	5r. booklet containing 4×5c., 8×10c. and 8×50c. (Nos. 296, 297a, 302) in block of 4 and one pane of 4 air mail labels	50·00

EXPRESS DELIVERY STAMPS

EXPRESS DELIVERY 15 c. (E **1**)

EXPRESS DELIVERY (INLAND) 15 c. (E **2**)

EXPRESS DELIVERY (INLAND) 15 c. (E **3**)

EXPRESS DELIVERY (INLAND) 15 c (E **4**)

Type E **2**. "(INLAND)" was inserted at a second printing on stamps already surcharged with Type E **1** (No. E1).

Type E **3**. New setting made at one printing. More space above and below "(INLAND)".

Type E **4**. New setting with smaller "15c" and no stop.

1903 (10 Aug)–04. No. 136 surch locally in red.

E1	E **1**	15c. on 15c. ultramarine	19·00	48·00
E2	E **2**	15c. on 15c. ultramarine (28.3.04)	65·00	£100
		a. "A" inverted	£1700	£1300
		b. "(INLAND)" inverted	†	£3500
E3	E **3**	15c. on 15c. ultramarine (4.04)	13·00	4·25
		a. Surch inverted	£1300	£850
		aw. Surch and wmk inverted	—	£1200
		b. Surch double, both inverted	£1900	£1900
		c. Imperf between (vert pair)	£8000	
		w. Wmk inverted		
		x. Wmk reversed		
E4	E **4**	15c. on 15c. ultramarine (1904)	£850	£800
		a. Surch inverted	—	£1900
		b. Surch double	—	£3500
		c. Surch double, both inverted	—	£5000
		d. "c" omitted	—	£2500

(FOREIGN) EXPRESS DELIVERY 18 CENTS (E **5**)

1904. T **42** (without value in label), surch with Type E **5** locally. Wmk Crown CC. P 14.

E5	18c. green	4·75	42·00
	a. Exclamation mark for "I" in "FOREIGN"	£750	

1904. T **42** (without value in label) surch with Type E **3** locally.

E6	15c. grey-green (R.)	25·00	8·00
	a. Surch inverted	£1000	£900
	b. Surch double	£750	£750
	c. Surch double, one "LNIAND"	£850	£800

POSTAGE DUE STAMPS

D 1

(Typo Waterlow)

1933–54. Wmk Mult Script CA. P 15×14.

D1	D **1**	2c. black...	1·25	50
D2		4c. violet...	50	65
D3		6c. scarlet..	60	80
D4		10c. green...	70	3·00
D5		20c. bright blue...................................	70	3·50
D6		50c. deep magenta (1.3.54)..............	55	20·00
D7		1r. orange (1.3.54)..........................	70	17·00
D1/7	*Set of 7*		4·50	40·00
D1s/5s	Perf "SPECIMEN" *Set of 5*		£120	

(Typo D.L.R.)

1966–72. Chalk-surfaced paper. Wmk w **12**. P 13½×14 (2c.) or 15×14 (others).

D8	D **1**	2c. black (11.7.67)............................	3·00	5·50
D9		4c. slate-lilac (7.1.69)......................	1·75	8·00
D10		6c. red-orange (7.1.69)....................	6·50	32·00
		a. Perf 13½×14...............................	23·00	65·00
D11		10c. yellow-green (16.2.67)...............	30	2·00
D12		20c. blue (3.1.66)..............................	2·25	7·50
		a. Deep blue (7.1.69)......................	2·25	17·00
D13		50c. deep magenta (7.1.69)..............	1·00	15·00
		a. Magenta (10.1.72)......................	2·00	16·00
D8/13	*Set of 6*		13·00	60·00

FISCALS USED FOR POSTAGE

INLAND REVENUE (F **1**)	INLAND REVENUE (F **2**)	MAURITIUS INLAND REVENUE 4c F **3**

1889. T **19**, wmk Crown CA, optd. P 14.

R1	F **1**	4c. carmine..	35·00	8·50
R2	F **2**	4c. lilac...	12·00	13·00

(Typo D.L.R.)

1896. Wmk Crown CA. P 14.

R3	F **3**	4c. dull purple...................................	50·00	70·00

Montserrat

A local post office operated on Montserrat from 1702, although the first recorded postal marking does not occur until 1791. A branch of the British GPO was established at Plymouth, the island capital, in 1852.

The stamps of Great Britain were used from 1858 until the overseas postal service reverted to local control on 1 April 1860.

In the interim period between 1860 and the introduction of Montserrat stamps in 1876 No. CC1 and a similar "uncrowned" handstamp were again used.

PLYMOUTH

CROWNED-CIRCLE HANDSTAMPS

C 1

CC1	C **1**	MONTSERRAT (R). (15.7.1852)........	*Price on cover*	£4750

No. CC1 was used as an emergency measure, struck in red or black, between 1883 and 1886.

Stamps of GREAT BRITAIN cancelled "A 08" as Type Z **1** of Jamaica.

1858 (8 May)–**60.**

Z1		1d. rose-red (1857), *perf* 14............	£1300
Z2		4d. rose (1857).................................	
Z3		6d. lilac (1856).................................	£550
Z4		1s. green (1856)..............................	£2750

PRICES FOR STAMPS ON COVER TO 1945	
Nos. 1/2	from × 50
No. 3	†
Nos. 4/5	from × 10
Nos. 6/13	from × 12
Nos. 14/22	from × 4
No. 23	—
Nos. 24/33	from × 4
Nos. 35/47	from × 3
No. 48	—
Nos. 49/59	from × 3
Nos. 60/2	from × 15
Nos. 63/83	from × 3
Nos. 84/93	from × 4
Nos. 94/7	from × 3
Nos. 98/100	from × 8
Nos. 101/12	from × 5

1	**MONTSERRAT** (**2**)	3 (Die I)

*(T **1** recess D.L.R.)*

1876 (Aug)–**83.** Stamps of Antigua optd with T **2**. Wmk Crown CC. P 14.

1	**1**	1d. red..	30·00	17·00
		a. Bisected (½d.) (1883) (*on cover*)..	†	£1400
		b. Inverted "S".................................	£1000	£750
		w. Wmk inverted..............................	50·00	45·00
		x. Wmk reversed.............................	35·00	22·00
		y. Wmk inverted and reversed........	50·00	60·00
2		6d. green..	70·00	40·00
		a. Trisected (used as 2d.) (12.83) (*on cover*)......................................	†	£6500
		b. Inverted "S".................................	£1900	£1200
		x. Wmk reversed.............................	—	£110
3		6d. blue-green.................................	£1300	
		a. Inverted "S".................................	£13000	

Nos. 1/3 were overprinted either from a setting of 120 (12×10) or from a setting of 60 (6×10) applied twice to each sheet. This setting of 60 had an inverted "S" on R. 2/3. The same setting was subsequently used for some sheets of Nos. 6 and 8.

No. 1 was bisected and used for a ½d. in 1883. This bisected stamp is found surcharged with a small "½" in *black* and also in *red*; both were unofficial and they did not emanate from the Montserrat P.O. (*Price on cover, from* £500).

The 6d. in blue-green is only known unused.

*(T **3** typo D.L.R.)*

1880 (Jan). Wmk Crown CC. P 14.

4	**3**	2½d. red-brown..................................	£250	£180
5		4d. blue..	£150	30·00
		w. Wmk inverted..............................	—	£250
		x. Wmk reversed.............................	£600	

1883 (Mar). Wmk Crown CA. P 12.

6	**1**	1d. red..	80·00	65·00
		a. Inverted "S".................................	£2000	£1300
		b. Bisected (½d.) (*on cover*)............	†	£1600
		x. Wmk reversed.............................	—	60·00

Top left triangle detached (Pl 2 R. 3/3 of right pane)

1884–85. Wmk Crown CA. P 14.

7	**3**	½d. dull green...................................	1·00	11·00
		a. Top left triangle detached..........	£200	
8	**1**	1d. red..	28·00	16·00
		a. Inverted "S".................................	£1000	£1000
		bx. Wmk reversed............................	—	26·00
		c. Rose-red (1885)...........................	32·00	13·00
		ca. Bisected (½d.) (*on cover*)..........	†	£1300
		cb. Inverted "S"..............................	£1100	£1000
		cx. Wmk reversed............................	35·00	21·00
9	**3**	2½d. red-brown..................................	£275	65·00
10		2½d. ultramarine (1885).....................	30·00	21·00
		a. Top left triangle detached..........	£600	£450
		w. Wmk inverted..............................	£140	£160
11		4d. blue..	£1800	£250
12		4d. mauve (1885)..............................	5·50	3·00
		a. Top left triangle detached..........	£375	£375
10s, 12s	Optd "SPECIMEN" *Set of 2*		£475	

The stamps for Montserrat were superseded by the general issue for Leeward Islands in November 1890, but the following issues were in concurrent use with the stamps inscribed "LEEWARD ISLANDS" until 1 July 1956, when Leeward Islands stamps were withdrawn and invalidated.

4 Device of the Colony   **5**

(Typo D.L.R.)

1903 (Aug).

(a) Wmk Crown CA. P 14

14	**4**	½d. grey-green and green.................	75	19·00
15		1d. grey-black and red.....................	75	40
		w. Wmk inverted..............................	£275	
16		2d. grey and brown..........................	5·50	50·00
17		2½d. grey and blue.............................	1·50	1·75
18		3d. dull orange and deep purple	8·50	50·00
19		6d. dull purple and olive..................	15·00	65·00
20		1s. green and bright purple.............	10·00	26·00
21		2s. green and brown-orange............	42·00	27·00
22		2s.6d. green and black........................	28·00	60·00

(b) Wmk Crown CC. P 14

23	**5**	5s. black and scarlet........................	£160	£225
14/23	*Set of 10*		£225	£450
14s/23s	Optd "SPECIMEN" *Set of 10*............	£225	

1904–08. Ordinary paper (½d., 2d., 3d., 6d.) or chalk-surfaced paper (others). Wmk Mult Crown CA. P 14.

24	**4**	½d. grey-green and green.................	13·00	4·00
		a. Chalk-surfaced paper (3.06).......	1·00	1·25
25		1d. grey-black and red (11.07)........	17·00	24·00
26		2d. grey and brown..........................	3·50	14·00
		a. Chalk-surfaced paper (5.06).......	2·25	1·25
27		2½d. grey and blue (12.05).................	2·50	7·00
28		3d. dull orange and deep purple.....	13·00	8·00
		a. Chalk-surfaced paper (5.08).......	12·00	2·50
29		6d. dull purple and olive..................	13·00	42·00
		a. Chalk-surfaced paper (5.08).......	15·00	6·00
30		1s. green and bright purple (5.08) ..	12·00	7·00
31		2s. green and orange (5.08)............	60·00	55·00
32		2s.6d. green and black (5.08)...............	65·00	60·00
33	**5**	5s. black and red (9.07)...................	£160	£190
24/33	*Set of 10*		£300	£325

1908 (June)–**14.** Ordinary paper (½d. to 2½d.) or chalk-surfaced paper (3d. to 5s.). Wmk Mult Crown CA. P 14.

35	**4**	½d. deep green (4.10).......................	12·00	1·00
36		1d. rose-red......................................	1·40	30
38		2d. greyish slate (9.09)....................	1·75	21·00
39		2½d. blue..	2·25	3·50
40		3d. purple/*yellow* (9.09)..................	1·00	18·00
		a. White back (1.14)........................	4·00	40·00
		as. Optd "SPECIMEN".......................	32·00	
43		6d. dull and deep purple (9.09).......	12·00	55·00
		a. Dull and bright purple (1914)......	19·00	65·00
44		1s. black/*green* (9.09)......................	9·00	45·00
45		2s. purple and bright blue/*blue* (9.09)..	50·00	60·00
46		2s.6d. black and red/*blue* (9.09).........	45·00	80·00
47	**5**	5s. red and green/*yellow* (9.09)........	65·00	85·00
35/47	*Set of 10*		£170	£325
35s/47s	Optd "SPECIMEN" *Set of 10*............	£275	

Examples of most values are known showing forged Montserrat postmarks dated "OC 16 1909" or "NO 26 1910".

WAR STAMP

7	8	(**9**)

(T 7/8 typo D.L.R.)

1914. Chalk-surfaced paper. Wmk Mult Crown CA. P 14.

48	**7**	5s. red and green/*yellow*	90·00	£160
		s. Optd "SPECIMEN"	85·00	

1916 (10 Oct)–**22**. Ordinary paper (½d. to 2½d.) or chalk-surfaced paper (3d. to 5s.). Wmk Mult Crown CA. P 14.

49	**8**	½d. green	30	2·50
50		1d. scarlet	3·00	75
		a. Carmine-red	38·00	9·00
51		2d. grey	3·25	5·00
52		2½d. bright blue	2·00	26·00
53		3d. purple/*yellow*	1·25	23·00
		a. On pale yellow (13.7.22)	1·00	20·00
		as. Optd "SPECIMEN"	30·00	
54		4d. grey-black and red/*pale yellow* (13.7.22)	9·00	42·00
55		6d. dull and deep purple	3·75	38·00
56		1s. black/*blue-green* (olive back)	3·25	42·00
57		2s. purple and blue/*blue*	23·00	60·00
58		2s.6d. black and red/*blue*	40·00	90·00
59		5s. green and red/*yellow*	55·00	95·00
49/59 Set of 11			£130	£375
49s/59s Optd "SPECIMEN" Set of 11			£250	

1917 (8 Oct)–**18**. No. 49 optd with T **9**.

60	**8**	½d. green (R.)	10	1·50
		a. Short opt (right pane R. 10/1)	11·00	
		y. Wmk inverted and reversed	70·00	
61		½d. green (Blk.) (5.18)	4·50	7·50
		a. Short opt (right pane R. 10/1)	50·00	
		b. Deep green (10.18)	15	1·75
		ba. "C" and "A" missing from wmk.	£1200	
		bb. Short opt (right pane R. 10/1)	11·00	
		w. Wmk inverted	£140	

Nos. 60a, 61a, and 61bb show the overprint 2 mm high instead of 2½ mm.

No. 61ba shows the "C" omitted from one impression and the "A" missing from the next. The price quoted is for a horizontal pair.

1919 (4 Mar). T **8**. Special printing in orange. Value and "WAR STAMP" as T **9** inserted in black at one printing.

62		1½d. black and orange	10	30
60s/2s Optd "SPECIMEN" Set of 3			£110	

1922 (13 July)–**29**. Ordinary paper (¼d. to 3d.) (No. 73) or chalk-surfaced paper (others). Wmk Mult Script CA. P 14.

63	**8**	¼d. brown	15	5·50
64		½d. green	30	30
65		1d. bright violet	30	60
66		1d. carmine (1929)	75	1·50
67		1½d. orange-yellow	1·75	9·50
68		1½d. carmine (5.4.23)	45	6·00
69		1½d. red-brown (1929)	3·50	50
70		2d. grey	50	2·00
71		2½d. deep bright blue	8·50	17·00
		a. Pale bright blue (17.8.26)	70	90
		as. Optd "SPECIMEN"	42·00	
72		2½d. orange-yellow (5.4.23)	1·25	19·00
73		3d. dull blue (5.4.23)	75	16·00
74		3d. purple/*yellow* (2.1.27)	1·10	8·00
75		4d. black and red/*pale yellow* (5.4.23)	75	13·00
76		5d. dull purple and olive	6·00	10·00
77		6d. pale and bright purple (5.4.23)	3·00	7·50
78		1s. black/*emerald* (5.4.23)	3·00	7·00
79		2s. purple and blue/*blue*	7·00	24·00
80		2s.6d. black and red/*blue* (5.4.23)	12·00	65·00
81		3s. green and violet	12·00	24·00
82		4s. black and scarlet	15·00	50·00
83		5s. green and red/*pale yellow* (6.23)	38·00	65·00
63/83 Set of 21			95·00	£300
63/83s Optd or Perf (Nos. 66s, 69s) "SPECIMEN" Set of 21			£375	

10 Plymouth

(Recess D.L.R.)

1932 (18 Apr). 300th Anniv of Settlement of Montserrat. Wmk Mult Script CA. P 14.

84	**10**	½d. green	1·75	16·00
85		1d. scarlet	1·75	5·50
86		1½d. red-brown	1·75	3·50
87		2d. grey	2·00	23·00
88		2½d. ultramarine	2·00	21·00
89		3d. orange	1·75	21·00
90		6d. violet	2·25	38·00
91		1s. olive-brown	12·00	50·00
92		2s.6d. purple	48·00	85·00
93		5s. chocolate	£110	£190
84/93 Set of 10			£160	£400
84s/93s Perf "SPECIMEN" Set of 10			£250	

Examples of all values are known showing a forged GPO Plymouth postmark dated "MY 13 32".

1935 (6 May). Silver Jubilee. As Nos. 91/4 of Antigua, but ptd by Waterlow & Sons. P 11×12.

94		1d. deep blue and scarlet	1·00	3·25
95		1½d. ultramarine and grey	2·25	3·50
96		2½d. brown and deep blue	2·25	4·50
97		1s. slate and purple	6·50	18·00
94/7 Set of 4			11·00	26·00
94s/7s Perf "SPECIMEN" Set of 4			£110	

1937 (12 May). Coronation. As Nos. 95/7 of Antigua, but printed by D.L.R. P 14.

98		1d. scarlet	35	1·75
99		1½d. yellow-brown	1·00	40
100		2½d. bright blue	60	1·75
98/100 Set of 3			1·75	3·50
98s/100s Perf "SPECIMEN" Set of 3			80·00	

11 Carr's Bay

12 Sea Island cotton

13 Botanic Station

3d. "Tower" on hill (R. 2/2, later printings)

1s. Plate scratch (R. 10/5)

(Recess D.L.R.)

1938 (2 Aug)–**48**. Wmk Mult Script CA. P 12 (10s., £1) or 13 (others).

101	**11**	½d. blue-green	6·50	2·00
		a. Perf 14 (1942)	15	20
102	**12**	1d. carmine	6·50	40
		a. Perf 14 (1943)	1·75	30
103		1½d. purple	25·00	1·25
		a. Perf 14 (1942)	1·75	50
		ab. "A" of "CA" missing from wmk	£1400	
104	**13**	2d. orange	25·00	1·00
		a. Perf 14 (1942)	2·00	70
105	**12**	2½d. ultramarine	6·00	1·50
		a. Perf 14 (1943)	50	30
106	**11**	3d. brown	10·00	2·00
		a. Perf 14. Red-brown (1942)	3·25	40
		ab. Deep brown (1943)	1·75	7·50
		ac. "Tower" on hill	£300	£400
107	**13**	6d. violet	25·00	1·25
		a. Perf 14 (1943)	4·25	60
108	**11**	1s. lake	29·00	1·25
		aa. Plate scratch	£300	65·00
		a. Perf 14 (1942)	2·50	30
109	**13**	2s.6d. slate-blue	45·00	1·25
		a. Perf 14 (1943)	27·00	4·00
110	**11**	5s. rose-carmine	50·00	12·00
		a. Perf 14 (1942)	30·00	4·00
111	**13**	10s. pale blue (1.4.48)	23·00	24·00
112	**11**	£1 black (1.4.48)	30·00	45·00
101a/12 Set of 12			£110	70·00
101s/12s Perf "SPECIMEN" Set of 12			£325	

Nos. 101/2 exist in coils constructed from normal sheets.

1946 (1 Nov). Victory. As Nos. 110/11 of Antigua.

113		1½d. purple	15	15
114		3d. chocolate	15	15
113s/14s Perf "SPECIMEN" Set of 2			85·00	

1949 (3 Jan). Royal Silver Wedding. As Nos. 112/13 of Antigua.

115		2½d. ultramarine	10	10
116		5s. carmine	6·50	16·00

1949 (10 Oct). 75th Anniv of UPU As Nos. 114/17 of Antigua.

117		2½d. ultramarine	15	1·25
118		3d. brown	2·25	2·00
119		6d. purple	30	2·75
120		1s. purple	30	2·25
117/20 Set of 4			2·75	7·25

(New Currency. 100 cents = 1 West Indies, later Eastern Caribbean dollar)

1951 (16 Feb). Inauguration of B.W.I. University College. As Nos. 118/19 of Antigua.

121		3c. black and purple	20	1·25
122		12c. black and violet	20	1·25

14 Government House

15 Sea Island cotton: cultivation

16 Map of colony

17 Picking tomatoes

17a St. Anthony's Church

18 Badge of Presidency

19 Sea Island cotton: ginning

19a Government House

(Recess B.W.)

1951 (17 Sept). T **14/19a**. Wmk Mult Script CA. P 11½×11.

123	**14**	1c. black	10	2·75
124	**15**	2c. green	15	1·25
125	**16**	3c. orange-brown	40	70
126	**17**	4c. carmine	30	2·75
		a. "A" of "CA" missing from wmk	£850	
127	**17a**	5c. reddish violet	30	1·50
128	**18**	6c. olive-brown	30	30
		a. "A" of "CA" missing from wmk	£850	
129	**19**	8c. deep blue	2·75	2·75
130	**17a**	12c. blue and chocolate	1·00	30
131	**17**	24c. carmine and yellow-green	1·25	40
132	**19**	60c. black and carmine	11·00	6·00
133	**15**	$1·20 yellow-green and blue	9·00	8·50
134	**19a**	$2·40 black and green	18·00	23·00
135	**18**	$4·80 black and purple	30·00	32·00
123/135 Set of 13			65·00	70·00

In the 4c. and 5c. the portrait is on the left and on the 12c. and 24c. it is on the right.

1953 (2 June). Coronation. As No. 120 of Antigua.

136		2c. black and deep green	60	40

20 Government House

Two Types of ½c., 3c., 6c. and $4·80: I. Inscr "PRESIDENCY". II. Inscr "COLONY".

1953 (15 Oct)–**62**. As King George VI issue, but with portrait of Queen Elizabeth II as in T **20**. Wmk Mult Script CA. P 11½×11.

136a	**16**	½c. deep violet (I) (3.7.56)	50	10
136b		½c. deep violet (II) (1.9.58)	80	10
137	**20**	1c. black	10	10
138	**15**	2c. green	15	10
139	**16**	3c. orange-brown (I)	50	10
139a		3c. orange-brown (II) (1.9.58)	1·00	2·00
140	**17**	4c. carmine-red (1.6.55)	30	20
141	**17a**	5c. reddish lilac (1.6.55)	30	1·00
142	**18**	6c. deep bistre-brown (I) (1.6.55)	30	10
142a		6c. deep bistre-brown (II) (1.9.58)	55	15
		ab. Deep sepia-brown (30.7.62)	14·00	6·50
143	**19**	8c. deep bright blue (1.6.55)	1·00	10
144	**17a**	12c. blue and red-brown (1.6.55)	1·50	10
145	**17**	24c. carmine-red and green (1.6.55)	1·50	20
145a	**15**	48c. yellow-olive and purple (15.10.57)	16·00	7·00
146	**19**	60c. black and carmine (1.6.55)	10·00	2·25
147	**15**	$1·20 green and greenish blue (1.6.55)	19·00	12·00
148	**19a**	$2·40 black and bluish green (1.6.55).	26·00	26·00
149	**18**	$4·80 black and deep purple (I) (1.6.55)	6·50	10·00
149a		$4·80 black and deep purple (II) (1.9.58)	30·00	15·00
136a/49 Set of 15			75·00	50·00

See also No. 157.

1958 (22 Apr). Inauguration of British Caribbean Federation. As Nos. 135/7 of Antigua.

150		3c. deep green	1·00	20
151		6c. blue	1·00	75
152		12c. scarlet	1·10	15
150/2 Set of 3			2·75	1·00

1963 (8 July). Freedom from Hunger. As No. 146 of Antigua.

153		12c. reddish violet	30	15

1963 (2 Sept). Red Cross Centenary. As Nos. 147/8 of Antigua.

154		4c. red and black	25	20
155		12c. red and blue	45	50

1964 (23 Apr). 400th Birth Anniv of William Shakespeare. As No. 164 of Antigua.

156		12c. indigo	35	10

1964 (29 Oct). As No. 138 but wmk w **12**.

157		2c. green	1·00	20

1965 (17 May). ITU Centenary. As Nos. 166/7 of Antigua.

158		4c. vermilion and violet	15	10
159		48c. light emerald and carmine	40	20

21 Pineapple

22 Avocado

(Des Sylvia Goaman. Photo Harrison)

1965 (16 Aug). T **21**/2 and similar vert designs showing vegetables, fruit or plants. Multicoloured. W w **12** (upright). P 15×14.

160		1c. Type **21**	10	10
	w.	Wmk inverted	1·00	1·50
161		2c. Type **22**	10	10
162		3c. Soursop	10	10
163		4c. Pepper	10	10
164		5c. Mango	10	10
165		6c. Tomato	10	10
166		8c. Guava	10	10
167		10c. Ochro	10	10
168		12c. Lime	50	75
	w.	Wmk inverted	—	50·00
169		20c. Orange	30	10
170		24c. Banana	20	10
171		48c. Onion	75	60
172		48c. Cabbage	2·00	75
173		60c. Pawpaw	3·00	1·10
174		$1.20 Pumpkin	2·00	6·00
175		$2.40 Sweet Potato	8·00	8·50
176		$4.80 Egg Plant	8·00	12·00
160/76		Set of 17	23·00	26·00

See also Nos. 213/22.

1965 (25 Oct). International Co-operation Year. As Nos. 168/9 of Antigua.

177		2c. reddish purple and turquoise-green	10	20
178		12c. deep bluish green and lavender	25	10

1966 (26 Jan). Churchill Commemoration. As Nos. 170/3 of Antigua.

179		1c. new blue	10	2·50
	a.	Cerise (sky) omitted	£750	
180		2c. deep green	30	20
181		24c. brown	1·00	10
182		42c. bluish violet	1·10	1·25
179/82		Set of 4	2·25	3·75

1966 (4 Feb). Royal Visit. As No. 174 of Antigua.

183		14c. black and ultramarine	1·00	15
184		24c. black and magenta	1·50	15

1966 (20 Sept). Inauguration of WHO Headquarters, Geneva. As Nos. 178/9 of Antigua.

185		12c. black, yellow-green and light blue	20	25
186		60c. black, light purple and yellow-brown	55	75

1966 (1 Dec). 20th Anniv of UNESCO. As Nos. 196/8 of Antigua.

187		4c. slate-violet, red, yellow and orange	10	10
	a.	Orange omitted	£130	
188		60c. orange-yellow, violet and deep olive	70	20
189		$1.80 black, bright purple and orange	2·25	85
187/9		Set of 3	2·75	1·00

On No. 187a the omission of the orange only affects the squares of the lower case letters so that they appear yellow, the same as the capital squares.

25 Yachting   **(26)**

Normal

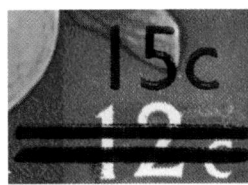

Narrow bars

The gap between the obliterating bars is normally ¾ mm. On Nos. 194a and 195a it is ¼ mm (R. 5/10).

(Des and photo Harrison)

1967 (29 Dec). International Tourist Year. T **25** and similar multicoloured designs. W w **12** (sideways on 15c.). P 14.

190		5c. Type **25**	10	10
191		15c. Waterfall near Chance Mountain (vert)	15	10
192		16c. Fishing, skin-diving and swimming	20	70
193		24c. Playing golf	1·00	45
190/3		Set of 4	1·25	1·25

1968 (6 May). Nos. 168, 170, 172 and 174/6 surch as T **26**. W w **12** (upright).

194		15c. on 12c. Lime	20	15
	a.	Narrow bars	6·00	
195		25c. on 24c. Banana	25	15
	a.	Narrow bars	6·00	
196		50c. on 48c. Cabbage	45	15
197		$1 on $1.20 Pumpkin	1·10	40
198		$2.50 on $2.40 Sweet Potato	1·10	4·25
199		$5 on $4.80 Egg Plant	1·10	4·25
194/9		Set of 6	3·75	8·50

See also Nos. 219 etc.

27 Sprinting

28 Sprinting, and Aztec Pillars

(Des G. Vasarhelyi. Photo Harrison)

1968 (31 July). Olympic Games, Mexico. T **27**/8 and similar designs. W w **12** (sideways on $1). P 14.

200	**27**	15c. deep claret, emerald and gold	10	10
201	–	25c. blue, orange and gold	15	10
202	–	50c. green, red and gold	25	15
203	**28**	$1 multicoloured	35	30
200/3		Set of 4	75	55

Designs: Horiz as T **27**—25c. Weightlifting; 50c. Gymnastics.

31 Alexander Hamilton

(Des and photo Harrison)

1968 (6 Dec*). Human Rights Year. T **31** and similar horiz designs. Multicoloured. W w **12**. P 14×14½.

204		5c. Type **31**	10	10
205		15c. Albert T. Marryshow	10	10
206		25c. William Wilberforce	10	10
207		50c. Dag Hammarskjöld	10	15
208		$1 Dr. Martin Luther King	25	30
204/8		Set of 5	60	65

*Although first day covers were postmarked 2 December, these stamps were not put on sale in Montserrat until 6 December.

32 The Two Trinities (Murillo)

33 The Adoration of the Kings (detail, Botticelli)

(Des and photo Harrison)

1968 (16 Dec). Christmas. W w **12** (sideways). P 14½×14.

209	**32**	5c. multicoloured	10	10
210	**33**	15c. multicoloured	10	10
211	**32**	25c. multicoloured	10	10
212	**33**	50c. multicoloured	25	25
209/12		Set of 4	50	45

1969–70. As Nos. 160/4, 167, 167 and 194/6 but wmk w **12** sideways*.

213		1c. Type **21** (24.6.69)	10	10
214		2c. Type **22** (23.4.70)	1·25	85
215		3c. Soursop (24.6.69)	30	15
	w.	Wmk Crown to right of CA	25·00	
216		4c. Pepper (24.6.69)	60	15
217		5c. Mango (23.4.70)	2·50	85
218		10c. Ochro (24.6.69)	50	15
	w.	Wmk Crown to right of CA	90·00	
219		15c. on 12c. Lime (24.6.69)	60	20
220		20c. Orange (17.3.69)	75	20
221		25c. on 24c. Banana (24.6.69)	1·00	25
222		50c. on 48c. Cabbage (24.6.69)	7·00	14·00
213/22		Set of 10	13·00	13·00

*The normal sideways watermark shows Crown to left of CA, as seen from the back of the stamp.

The 1c., 3c., 4c., 10c., 15c. and 20c. exist with PVA gum as well as gum arabic, but the 2c. and 5c. exist with PVA gum only.

34 Map showing "CARIFTA" Countries

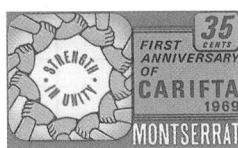

35 "Strength in Unity"

(Des J. Cooter. Photo Harrison)

1969 (27 May). First Anniv of CARIFTA (Caribbean Free Trade Area). W w **12** (sideways* on T **34**). P 14.

223	**34**	15c. multicoloured	10	10
224		20c. multicoloured	10	10
	w.	Wmk Crown to right of CA	1·00	
225	**35**	35c. multicoloured	10	20
226		30c. multicoloured	15	20
223/6		Set of 4	40	55

*The normal sideways watermark shows Crown to left of CA, as seen from the back of the stamp.

36 Telephone Receiver and Map of Montserrat

40 Dolphin (fish)

(Des R. Reid, adapted by V. Whiteley. Litho P.B.)

1969 (29 July). Development Projects. T **36** and similar vert designs. Multicoloured. W w **12**. P 13½.

227		15c. Type **36**	10	10
228		25c. School symbols and map	10	10
229		50c. Hawker Siddeley H.S.748 aircraft and map	15	20
230		$1 Electricity pylon and map	25	75
227/30		Set of 4	55	1·00

(Des Harrison. Photo Enschedé)

1969 (1 Nov). Game Fish. T **40** and similar horiz designs. Multicoloured. P 13×13½.

231		5c. Type **40**	25	10
232		15c. Atlantic Sailfish	30	10
233		25c. Black-finned Tuna	35	10
234		40c. Spanish Mackerel	45	55
231/4		Set of 4	1·25	75

41 King Caspar before the Virgin and Child (detail) (Norman 16th-cent stained glass window)

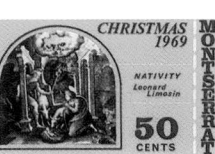

42 Nativity (Leonard Limosin)

(Des J. Cooter. Litho D.L.R.)

1969 (10 Dec). Christmas. Paintings multicoloured; frame colours given. W w **12** (sideways on 50c.). P 13.

235	**41**	15c. black, gold and violet	10	10
236		25c. black and vermilion	10	10
237	**42**	50c. black, ultramarine and yellow-orange	15	15
235/7		Set of 3	30	30

43 "Red Cross Sale"

(Des and litho J. W.)

1970 (13 Apr). Centenary of British Red Cross. T **43** and similar horiz designs. Multicoloured. W w **12** (sideways). P 14½×14.

238		3c. Type **43**	15	25
239		4c. School for deaf children	15	25
240		15c. Transport services for disabled	20	20
241		20c. Workshop	20	60
238/41		Set of 4	65	1·10

44 Red-footed Booby   **45** Madonna and Child with Animals (Brueghel the Elder, after Dürer)

(Des V. Whiteley)

1970 (2 July)–**74**. Birds. T **44** and similar multicoloured designs. W w **12** (sideways* on vert designs and upright on horiz designs). Glazed ordinary paper ($10) or chalk-surfaced paper (others). P 14×14½ (horiz) or 14½×14 (vert).

242		1c. Type **44**	10	10
	w.	Wmk inverted	24·00	
243		2c. American Kestrel (vert)	15	15
	a.	Glazed, ordinary paper (22.1.71)	1·25	3·00
244		3c. Magnificent Frigate Bird (vert)	15	15

	w. Wmk Crown to right of CA		2·00	15
245	4c. Great Egret (vert)		2·00	15
246	5c. Brown Pelican (vert)		2·50	10
	aw. Wmk Crown to right of CA		2·50	
	b. Glazed, ordinary paper (22.1.71)		1·50	2·00
	bw. Glazed, Crown to right of CA			
247	10c. Bananaquit (vert)		40	40
	a. Glazed, ordinary paper (22.1.71)		1·50	2·00
248	15c. Smooth-billed Ani		30	15
	a. Glazed, ordinary paper (22.1.71)		4·50	5·00
	aw. Wmk inverted		4·50	
249	20c. Red-billed Tropicbird		35	15
	a. Glazed, ordinary paper (22.1.71)		1·50	2·00
250	25c. Montserrat Oriole		50	50
	a. Glazed, ordinary paper (22.1.71)		5·00	6·00
251	50c. Green-throated Carib (vert)		10·00	1·50
	a. Glazed, ordinary paper (22.1.71)		4·00	4·50
252	$1 Antillean Crested Hummingbird		12·00	1·00
	aw. Wmk inverted		32·00	
	b. Glazed, ordinary paper (22.1.71)		4·25	5·00
253	$2.50 Little Blue Heron (vert)		5·50	12·00
	a. Glazed, ordinary paper (22.1.71)		8·00	10·00
254	$5 Purple-throated Carib		7·50	20·00
	a. Glazed, ordinary paper (22.1.71)		13·00	18·00
254c	$10 Forest Thrush (30.10.74)		18·00	24·00
242/54c	Set of 14		40·00	50·00

The normal sideways watermark shows Crown to left of CA, as seen from the back of the stamp.

Eight values in this set were subsequently reissued with the watermark sideways on horizontal designs and upright on vertical designs.

(Des G. Drummond. Litho D.L.R.)

1970 (1 Oct*). Christmas. T **45** and similar multicoloured design. W w **12**. P 13½×14.

255	5c. Type **45**	10	10
	w. Wmk inverted	29·00	
256	15c. *The Adoration of the Shepherds* (Domenichino)	10	10
257	20c. Type **45**	10	10
	w. Wmk inverted	3·25	
258	$1 As 15c.	35	1·50
255/8	Set of 4	60	1·60

*This was the local date of issue but the stamps were released by the Crown Agents on 21 September.

46 War Memorial

47 Girl Guide and Badge

(Des V. Whiteley. Litho J.W.)

1970 (30 Nov). Tourism. T **46** and similar horiz designs. Multicoloured. W w **12** (sideways*). P 14½×14.

259	5c. Type **46**	10	10
260	15c. Plymouth from Fort St. George	10	10
261	25c. Carr's Bay	15	15
262	50c. Golf Fairway	1·00	2·25
	w. Wmk Crown to right of CA	7·00	
259/62	Set of 4	1·25	2·40
MS263	135×109 mm. Nos. 259/62	3·25	2·25

The normal sideways watermark shows Crown to left of CA, as seen from the back of the stamp.

(Des V. Whiteley. Litho Questa)

1970 (31 Dec). Diamond Jubilee of Montserrat Girl Guides. T **47** and similar vert design. Multicoloured. W w **12**. P 14.

264	10c. Type **47**	10	10
265	15c. Brownie and Badge	10	10
266	25c. As 15c.	15	15
267	40c. Type **47**	20	80
264/7	Set of 4	50	1·00

Morocco Agencies (British Post Offices)

With the growth of trade and commerce during the 19th-century European powers opened post offices or postal agencies in various ports along the Moroccan coast from the early 1850's onwards. French and, in the north, Spanish influence eventually became predominant, leading to the protectorates of 1912. The British, who had inaugurated a regular postal service between Gibraltar and Tangier or Tetuan in May 1778, established their first postal agency in 1857. German offices followed around the turn of the century.

Before 1892 there was no indigenous postal service and those towns where there was no foreign agency were served by a number of private local posts which continued to flourish until 1900. In November 1892 the Sultan of Morocco established the Cherifian postal service, but this was little used until after its reorganization at the end of 1911. The Sultan's post was absorbed by the French postal service on 1 October 1913. Issues of the local posts and of the Sultan's post can occasionally be found used on cover in combination with stamps of Gibraltar or the Morocco Agencies.

On 1 April 1857 the first British postal agency was established at Tangier within the precincts of the Legation and was run by the official interpreter. From 1 March 1858 all letters for Great Britain sent via the British mail packets from Tangier required franking with Great Britain stamps.

In 1872 the Tangier office was relocated away from the Legation and the interpreter was appointed British Postal Agent and supplied with a stock of British postage stamps which would be cancelled on arrival in Gibraltar with the "A26" obliterator. Such stamps used in Morocco can therefore only be identified when on cover or large piece, also showing the Tangier datestamp. British stamps known to have been used in Morocco are the ½d. of 1870, 1880 and 1884; 1d. of 1864 and 1881; 2d. of 1858; 2½d. of 1876, 1880, 1881 and 1884; 4d. of 1865 and 6d. stamps of 1856, 1865 and 1872. At the same time the agency was placed under the control of the Gibraltar postmaster.

When the colonial posts became independent of the British GPO on 1 January 1886 Gibraltar retained responsibility for the Morocco Agencies. Further offices, each under the control of the local Vice-Consul, were opened from 1886 onwards.

I. GIBRALTAR USED IN MOROCCO

Details of the various agencies are given below. Type C, the "A26" killer, is very similar to postmarks used at Gibraltar during this period. In addition to the town name, postmarks as Types A, B and D from Fez, Mazagan, Saffi and Tetuan were also inscribed "MOROCCO".

Postmark Types used on Gibraltar issues.

Type A Circular datestamp | Type C "A26" killer

Type B Duplex cancellation

Type D Registered oval

BISECTS. The 1886-87 1d. and the 10c., 40c. and 50c. values of the 1889 surcharges and the 1889–96 issue are known bisected and used for half their value from various of the Morocco Agencies (*price on cover from £500*). These bisects were never authorised by the Gibraltar Post Office.

CASABLANCA

The British postal agency opened on 1 January 1887 and was initially supplied with ½d., 4d. and 6d. stamps from the Gibraltar 1886 overprinted on Bermuda issue and 1d., 2d. and 2½d. values from the 1886–87 set.

Stamps of GIBRALTAR cancelled with Types A (without code or code "C"), B (without code or code "A") or D.

1886. Optd on Bermuda (Nos. 1/7).

Z1	½d. dull green	£140
Z2	4d. orange-brown	£500
Z3	6d. deep lilac	£500

1886–87. Queen Victoria £sd issue (Nos. 8/14).

Z4	½d. dull green	75·00
Z5	1d. rose	60·00
Z6	2d. brown-purple	£140

Z7	2½d. blue	75·00
Z8	4d. orange-brown	£200
Z10	1s. bistre	£550

1889. Surch in Spanish currency (Nos. 15/21).

Z11	5c. on ½d. green	95·00
Z12	10c. on 1d. rose	85·00
Z13	25c. on 2d. brown-purple	£120
Z14	25c. on 2½d. bright blue	75·00
Z15	40c. on 4d. orange-brown	£250
Z16	50c. on 6d. bright lilac	£200
Z17	75c. on 1s. bistre	£275

1889–96. Queen Victoria Spanish currency issue (Nos. 22/33).

Z18	5c. green	25·00
Z19	10c. carmine	22·00
Z20	20c. olive-green and brown	70·00
Z21	20c. olive-green	£200
Z22	25c. ultramarine	22·00
Z23	40c. orange-brown	65·00
Z24	50c. bright lilac	50·00
Z25	75c. olive-green	£170
Z26	1p. bistre	£150
Z28	1p. bistre and ultramarine	75·00
Z29	2p. black and carmine	£100

FEZ

The British postal agency in this inland town opened on 13 February 1892 and was initially supplied with stamps up to the 50c. value from the Gibraltar 1889–96 issue.

Stamps of GIBRALTAR cancelled with Types A (without code) or D.

1889–96. Queen Victoria Spanish currency issue (Nos. 22/33).

Z31	5c. green	50·00
Z32	10c. carmine	45·00
Z33	20c. olive-green and brown	£140
Z35	25c. ultramarine	70·00
Z36	40c. orange-brown	£160
Z37	50c. bright lilac	£140

LARAICHE

The British postal agency at Laraiche opened on 3 April 1886, although the first postmark, an "A26" killer, was not supplied until May.

Stamps of GIBRALTAR cancelled with Types B (without code) or D.

1886. Optd on Bermuda (Nos. 1/7).

Z39	½d. dull green	£180
Z40	1d. rose-red	£170
Z41	2½d. ultramarine	£180

1886–87. Queen Victoria £sd issue (Nos. 8/14).

Z42	½d. dull green	£180
Z43	1d. rose	£170
Z45	2½d. blue	£180

1889. Surch in Spanish currency (Nos. 15/21).

Z47	5c. on ½d. green	£150
Z48	10c. on 1d. rose	
Z49	25c. on 2½d. bright blue	

It is believed that the other surcharges in this series were not supplied to Laraiche.

1889–96. Queen Victoria Spanish currency issue (Nos. 22/33).

Z50	5c. green	65·00
Z51	10c. carmine	70·00
Z52	20c. olive-green and brown	£170
Z54	25c. ultramarine	70·00
Z55	40c. orange-brown	£170
Z56	50c. bright-lilac	£170
Z57	1p. bistre and ultramarine	

MAZAGAN

This was the main port for the inland city of Marrakesh. The British postal agency opened on 1 March 1888 and was initially supplied with stamps from the Gibraltar 1886–87 series.

Stamps of GIBRALTAR cancelled with Types A (codes "A" or "C") or D (without code, code "A" or code "C").

1886–87. Queen Victoria £sd issue (Nos. 8/14).

Z58	½d. dull green	60·00
Z59	1d. rose	70·00
Z60	2d. brown-purple	
Z61	2½d. blue	75·00
Z62	4d. orange-brown	£250
Z63	6d. lilac	£300

1889. Surch in Spanish currency (Nos. 15/21).

Z64	5c. on ½d. green	£110
Z65	10c. on 1d. rose	
Z66	25c. on 2½d. bright blue	

It is believed that the other surcharges in this series were not supplied to Mazagan.

1889–96. Queen Victoria Spanish currency issue (Nos. 22/33).

Z67	5c. green	30·00
Z68	10c. carmine	26·00
Z69	20c. olive-green and brown	£110
Z70	25c. ultramarine	60·00
Z71	40c. orange-brown	£130
Z72	50c. bright lilac	£160
Z74	1p. bistre and ultramarine	£180
Z75	2p. black and carmine	£180

MOGADOR

The British postal agency at this port opened on 1 June 1887 and was initially supplied with stamps from the Gibraltar 1886–87 series.

Stamps of GIBRALTAR cancelled with Types A (code "C"), B (code "C") or D.

1886. Optd on Bermuda (Nos. 1/7).

Z75d	4d. orange-brown	£500

1886–87. Queen Victoria £sd issue (Nos. 8/14).

Z76	½d. dull green	55·00
Z77	1d. rose	80·00
Z78	2d. brown-purple	£160
Z79	2½d. blue	65·00
Z79b	6d. lilac	£275

1889. Surch in Spanish currency (Nos. 15/21).
Z80	5c. on ½d. green	95·00
Z81	10c. on 1d. rose	90·00
Z82	25c. on 2½d. bright blue	80·00

It is believed that the other surcharges in this series were not supplied to Mogador.

1889–96. Queen Victoria Spanish currency issue (Nos. 22/33).
Z83	5c. green	25·00
Z84	10c. carmine	25·00
Z85	25c. olive-green and brown	£110
Z87	25c. ultramarine	29·00
Z88	40c. orange-brown	£120
Z89	50c. bright lilac	90·00
Z89a	1p. bistre	£170
Z90	1p. bistre and ultramarine	£120
Z91	2p. black and carmine	£150

RABAT

The British postal agency at this port on the north-west coast of Morocco opened on 6 April 1886, although the first cancellation, an "A26" killer, was not supplied until May. The initial stock of stamps was from the Gibraltar 1886 overprinted on Bermuda issue.

Stamps of GIBRALTAR cancelled with Types B (code "O") or D.

1886. Optd on Bermuda (Nos. 1/7).
Z92	½d. dull green	
Z93	1d. rose-red	
Z94	2½d. ultramarine	£300

1886–87. Queen Victoria £sd issue (Nos. 8/14).
Z95	½d. dull green	65·00
Z96	1d. rose	60·00
Z97	2d. brown-purple	£140
Z98	2½d. blue	75·00
Z101	1s. bistre	£700

1889. Surch in Spanish currency (Nos. 15/21).
Z102	5c. on ½d. green	£100
Z103	10c. on 1d. rose	85·00
Z104	25c. on 2½d. bright blue	90·00

It is believed that the other surcharges in this series were not supplied to Rabat.

1889–96. Queen Victoria Spanish currency issue (Nos. 22/33).
Z105	5c. green	28·00
Z106	10c. carmine	27·00
Z107	20c. olive-green and brown	£120
Z108	25c. ultramarine	27·00
Z109	40c. orange-brown	£120
Z110	50c. bright lilac	90·00
Z110a	1p. bistre and ultramarine	£140

SAFFI

The British postal agency at this port opened on 1 July 1891 and was supplied with stamps from the Gibraltar 1889–96 series.

Stamps of GIBRALTAR cancelled with Types B (code "C") or D (code "C").

1889–96. Queen Victoria Spanish currency issue (Nos. 22/33).
Z111	5c. green	40·00
Z112	10c. carmine	38·00
Z113	20c. olive-green and brown	£100
Z115	25c. ultramarine	45·00
Z116	40c. orange-brown	£140
Z117	50c. bright lilac	£100
Z118	1p. bistre and ultramarine	£130
Z119	2p. black and carmine	£150

TANGIER

The British postal agency in Tangier opened on 1 April 1857 and from 1 March of the following year letters from it sent via the packet service to Great Britain required franking with Great Britain stamps.

No identifiable postmark was supplied to Tangier until 1872 and all earlier mail was cancelled with one of the Gibraltar marks. In April 1872 a postmark as Type A was supplied on which the "N" of "TANGIER" was reversed. A corrected version, with code letter "A", followed in 1878, but both were used as origin or arrival marks and the Great Britain stamps continued to be cancelled with Gibraltar obliterators. The Type A postmarks generally fell into disuse after 1880 and very few identifiable marks occur on mail from Tangier until the introduction of Gibraltar stamps on 1 January 1886.

Type E Horizontal
"A26" killer

New cancellers were not ready on 1 January and, as a temporary measure, the old horizontal "A26" killer was sent from Gibraltar. Strikes of this handstamp on the overprinted Bermuda stamps tend to be blurred but are indicative of use in Tangier. Use of Type E lasted until 4 May, when it was replaced by Type C.

Stamps of GIBRALTAR cancelled with Types A (codes "A" or "C"), B (code "A"), D or E.

1886. Optd on Bermuda (Nos. 1/7).
Z120	½d. dull green	75·00
Z121	1d. rose-red	95·00
Z122	2d. purple-brown	£225
Z123	2½d. ultramarine	85·00
Z124	4d. orange-brown	£300
Z125	6d. deep lilac	£300
Z126	1s. yellow-brown	£650

1886–87. Queen Victoria £sd issue (Nos. 8/14).
Z127	½d. dull green	22·00
Z128	1d. rose	22·00
Z129	2d. brown-purple	75·00
Z130	2½d. blue	30·00
Z131	4d. orange-brown	£120
Z132	6d. lilac	£180
Z133	1s. bistre	£400

1889. Surch in Spanish currency (Nos. 15/21).
Z134	5c. on ½d. green	45·00
Z135	10c. on 1d. rose	29·00
Z136	25c. on 2d. brown-purple	60·00
Z137	25c. on 2½d. bright blue	45·00
Z138	40c. on 4d. orange-brown	£170
Z139	50c. on 6d. bright lilac	£160
Z140	75c. on 1s. bistre	£200

1889–96. Queen Victoria Spanish currency issue (Nos. 22/33).
Z141	5c. green	7·00
Z142	10c. carmine	6·00
Z143	20c. olive-green and brown	26·00
Z144	20c. olive-green	£130
Z145	25c. ultramarine	9·00
Z146	40c. orange-brown	14·00
Z147	50c. bright lilac	13·00
Z148	75c. bright lilac	95·00
Z149	1p. bistre	85·00
Z150	1p. bistre and ultramarine	32·00
Z151	2p. black and carmine	60·00
Z152	5p. slate-grey	£130

TETUAN

The British postal agency in this northern town opened on 4 May 1890 and was supplied with stamps from the Gibraltar 1889–96 series.

Stamps of GIBRALTAR cancelled with Types A (code "C"), B (code "C" often inverted) or D (code "C").

1889–96. Queen Victoria Spanish currency issue (Nos. 22/33).
Z153	5c. green	42·00
Z154	10c. carmine	45·00
Z155	20c. olive-green and brown	95·00
Z157	25c. ultramarine	48·00
Z158	40c. orange-brown	£110
Z159	50c. bright lilac	£110
Z161	1p. bistre and ultramarine	£150
Z162	2p. black and carmine	£160
Z163	5p. slate-grey	£200

PRICES FOR STAMPS ON COVER TO 1945
Nos. 1/16	from × 7
Nos. 17/30	from × 3
Nos. 31/74	from × 3
Nos. 75/6	from × 4
Nos. 112/24	from × 4
No. 125	—
Nos. 126/35	from × 5
Nos. 136/42	from × 2
Nos. 143/59	from × 3
Nos. 160/75	from × 8
Nos. 191/9	from × 5
Nos. 200/1	from × 3
Nos. 202/11	from × 4
Nos. 212/15	from × 5
Nos. 216/24	from × 8
Nos. 225/6	from × 2
Nos. 227/30	from × 8
Nos. 231/52	from × 6

The above prices apply to stamps used on cover from Morocco. Examples of Nos. 31/76 & 231/52 used on cover in G.B. after 1950 have little value.

II. GIBRALTAR ISSUES OVERPRINTED

Following a decision to identify the exact revenue derived from the Morocco postal service, it became necessary to provide separate issues for the Morocco Agencies. The need was reinforced when the Revision of Fees Ordinance in Gibraltar required all fees there to be collected in sterling, while the Morocco Agencies continued to use Spanish currency.

The following were used in all the British postal agencies. Unoverprinted stamps of Gibraltar remained valid for postage until 15 June 1898.

Morocco Agencies	Morocco Agencies
(1)	(2)

Λgencies	Agencies	Morocco
Inverted "V" for "A" (Right-hand pane R. 6/6)	Long tail to "S" (Right-hand pane R. 8/2)	Deformed "M" (Second setting, left-hand pane R. 1/1)

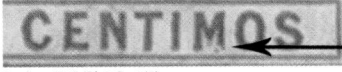

Broken "M" (Pl 2 R. 4/5)

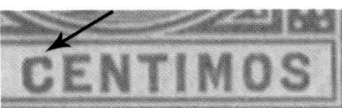

Flat top to "C" (Pl 2 R. 4/4)

Exclamation mark for "I" (Pl 2 R. 8/4)

1898 (1 June)**–1900**. Nos. 22/8 and 31/2 (Queen Victoria) of Gibraltar optd typographically (No. 2e) or by lithography (others) with T **1** (wide "M" and ear of "g" projecting upwards), in black at *Gibraltar Chronicle* office.
1	5c. green	6·00	6·50
	a. Inverted "V" for "A"	60·00	70·00
	b. Long tail to "S"	70·00	80·00
	c. Deformed "M"	90·00	
	d. Broken "M" in "CENTIMOS"	90·00	
2	10c. carmine	11·00	3·00
	a. Inverted "V" for "A"	£225	£275
	b. Long tail to "S"	£225	
	c. Deformed "M"	£110	75·00
	e. Lines of opt 5 mm apart (6.00)	16·00	8·00
	ea. Opt double	£750	£650
	g. Bisected (5c.) (*on cover*)	†	£1100
3	20c. olive-green and brown	23·00	4·25
	a. Inverted "V" for "A"	£120	£120
	b. Long tail to "S"	£130	£130
3c	20c. olive-green	20·00	12·00
	ca. Opt double	£500	£650
	cb. Inverted "V" for "A"	£140	£160
	cc. Long tail to "S"	£150	£170
	cd. Flat top to "C" in "CENTIMOS"	£200	£250
4	25c. ultramarine	9·50	2·50
	a. Inverted "V" for "A"	£150	£130
	b. Long tail to "S"	£160	£140
	c. Deformed "M"	—	£150
5	40c. orange-brown (2.6.98)	6·00	3·50
	a. Inverted "V" for "A"	£180	£200
	b. Long tail to "S"	£190	£225
	c. Deformed "M"	£225	£250
	d. Exclamation mark for "I"	£150	£150
	f. Blue-black opt (7.98)	50·00	32·00
	fa. "Morocco" omitted (R. 1/1)	£1000	
	fc. Deformed "M"	£375	
	fd. Exclamation mark for "I"	£275	
6	50c. bright lilac (2.6.98)	17·00	23·00
	a. Inverted "V" for "A"	£275	£350
	b. Long tail to "S"	£325	£375
	f. Blue-black opt (7.98)	24·00	19·00
	fc. Deformed "M"	£275	
7	1p. bistre and ultramarine (2.6.98)	21·00	32·00
	a. Inverted "V" for "A"	£275	£375
	b. Long tail to "S"	£325	£425
	c. Deformed "M"	£275	
	f. Blue-black opt (7.98)	£170	£250
	fc. Deformed "M"	£275	
8	2p. black and carmine (4.6.98)	35·00	35·00
	a. Inverted "V" for "A"	£375	£425
	b. Long tail to "S"	£425	£475
	c. Deformed "M"	£375	
1/8	Set of 8	£110	95·00

The blue-black overprint can be easily distinguished by looking through the stamp in front of a strong light. The overprint on the 50c. value shows more blue than on the 40c. and 1p. values.

The Inverted "V" for "A" and Long tail to "S" varieties occur from the first 12×10 litho setting. They were not present on the second 12×10 setting of July 1898, which produced further supplies of Nos. 5/8, and included the blue-black overprints, listed as Nos. 5f, 6f, 7f. The same setting was subsequently used to produce additional stocks of Nos. 1/2 and is also recorded on No. 4. This second setting includes the Deformed "M" variety. Numerous more minor varieties exist from both settings.

No. 2e comes from two further printings in 1900 using a third setting (6×10) on which the two lines of the overprint were 5 mm apart instead of the 4 mm space used previously and applied typographically.

Early release of No. 1 is known at Saffi (from 26 May).

Agencies	**Morocco**	**Agencies**
"CD" sideways flaw (Left-hand pane R. 1/5)	Broad top to "M" (Left-hand pane R. 7/3)	Hyphen between "nc" (Right-hand pane R. 3/5)

1899 (Feb–Mar). Nos. 22/3, 25/8 and 31/2 (Queen Victoria) of Gibraltar optd typographically with T **2** (narrow "M" and ear of "g" horizontal), in black by D.L.R., London.
9	5c. green	4·00	3·00
	a. "CD" sideways	42·00	45·00
	b. Broad top to "M"	12·00	19·00
	c. Hyphen between "nc"	12·00	19·00
	d. Broken "M" in "CENTIMOS"	80·00	
10	10c. carmine	6·00	3·00
	a. "CD" sideways	65·00	48·00
	b. Broad top to "M"	15·00	19·00
	c. Hyphen between "nc"	15·00	19·00
	d. Opt double	£850	£800
	e. Bisected (5c.) (*on cover*)	†	£1100
11	20c. olive-green (3.99)	15·00	2·50
	b. Broad top to "M"	65·00	55·00
	c. Hyphen between "nc"	65·00	55·00
	d. Flat top to "C" in "CENTIMOS"	£150	£110
12	25c. ultramarine (3.99)	11·00	90
	a. "CD" sideways	£100	75·00
	b. Broad top to "M"	55·00	55·00
	c. Hyphen between "nc"	55·00	55·00
13	40c. orange-brown (3.99)	50·00	50·00
	b. Broad top to "M"	£275	£300
	c. Hyphen between "nc"	£275	£300
	d. Exclamation mark for "I"	£225	
14	50c. bright lilac (3.99)	16·00	6·50
	b. Broad top to "M"	£130	£130
	c. Hyphen between "nc"	£130	£130
15	1p. bistre and ultramarine (3.99)	29·00	48·00
	b. Broad top to "M"	£180	£300
	c. Hyphen between "nc"	£180	£300
16	2p. black and carmine (3.99)	60·00	48·00
	b. Broad top to "M"	£350	£375
	c. Hyphen between "nc"	£350	£375
9/16	Set of 8	£170	£140
9s/16s	Optd "SPECIMEN" Set of 8		£225

1903–05. As Nos. 46/51 (King Edward VII) of Gibraltar, but with value in Spanish currency, optd with T **2**. Wmk Crown CA. P 14.
17	5c. grey-green and green (1.04)	10·00	3·00
	a. "CD" sideways	80·00	70·00
	b. Broad top to "M"	60·00	65·00
	c. Hyphen between "nc"	60·00	65·00

18	10c. dull purple/*red* (8.03)	9·00	40
	a. "CD" sideways	75·00	45·00
	b. Broad top to "M"	60·00	45·00
	c. Hyphen between "nc"	60·00	45·00
	w. Wmk inverted	70·00	
19	20c. grey-green and carmine (9.04)	21·00	50·00
	a. "CD" sideways	£170	£275
	b. Broad top to "M"	£150	£275
	c. Hyphen between "nc"	£150	£275
	d. Flat top to "C" in "CENTIMOS"	£225	
20	25c. purple and black/*blue* (1.7.03)	8·00	30
	a. "CD" sideways	80·00	48·00
	b. Broad top to "M"	60·00	48·00
	c. Hyphen between "nc"	70·00	48·00
21	50c. purple and violet (3.7.05)	80·00	£250
	a. "CD" sideways	£425	
	b. Broad top to "M"	£375	
	c. Hyphen between "nc"	£375	
22	1p. black and carmine (19.11.05)	35·00	£200
	a. "CD" sideways	£300	
	b. Broad top to "M"	£225	
	c. Hyphen between "nc"	£225	
23	2p. black and blue (19.11.05)	50·00	£180
	a. "CD" sideways	£350	
	b. Broad top to "M"	£275	
	c. Hyphen between "nc"	£275	
17/23 *Set of 7*		£190	£600
17s/23s Optd "SPECIMEN" *Set of 7*		£225	

Examples of Nos. 19 and 21/3 are known showing a forged Registered Mazagan postmark dated "15 SP 10".

1905 (Jan)–**06**. As Nos. 17/23 but wmk Mult Crown CA. Ordinary paper (5, 10, 20c.) or chalk-surfaced paper (others).

24	5c. grey-green and green (4.05)	22·00	12·00
	a. "CD" sideways	£130	85·00
	b. Broad top to "M"	£120	85·00
	c. Hyphen between "nc"	£900	£1200
	d. Chalk-surfaced paper (1.06)	9·00	14·00
	da. "CD" sideways	70·00	£100
	db. Broad top to "M"	70·00	£100
25	10c. dull purple/*red*	24·00	2·00
	a. "CD" sideways	£110	42·00
	b. Broad top to "M"	£100	42·00
	cw. Wmk inverted	35·00	23·00
	d. Chalk-surfaced paper (12.05)	9·00	3·50
	da. "CD" sideways	65·00	45·00
	db. Broad top to "M"	65·00	45·00
26	20c. grey-green and carmine (1.06)	9·50	32·00
	a. "CD" sideways	80·00	£200
	b. Broad top to "M"	80·00	£200
27	25c. purple and black/*blue* (6.06)	70·00	8·50
	a. "CD" sideways	£475	£170
	b. Broad top to "M"	£475	£170
28	50c. purple and violet (7.05)	11·00	65·00
	a. "CD" sideways	£180	£400
	b. Broad top to "M"	£160	£375
29	1p. black and carmine (11.05)	50·00	90·00
	a. "CD" sideways	£300	£475
	b. Broad top to "M"	£275	£475
30	2p. black and blue (11.05)	27·00	38·00
	a. "CD" sideways	£225	£275
	b. Broad top to "M"	£200	£275
24/30 *Set of 7*		£160	£200

Examples of Nos. 26 and 28/30 are known showing a forged Registered Mazagan postmark dated "15 SP 10".

Control of the British postal agencies in Morocco returned to the GPO, London, from 1 January 1907. The Gibraltar overprints remained vaild until 28 February of that year.

All the following issues are overprinted on Great Britain

III. BRITISH CURRENCY

Stamps overprinted "MOROCCO AGENCIES" only were primarily intended for use on parcels (and later, air-mail correspondence), and were on sale at British POs throughout Morocco including Tangier, until 1937.

PRICES. Our prices for used stamps with these overprints are for specimens used in Morocco. These stamps were valid for postal purposes in Great Britain from the summer of 1950 onwards. Examples with GB postmarks are worth 50 per cent of the used prices quoted.

MOROCCO AGENCIES (4)	MOROCCO AGENCIES (5)	MOROCCO AGENCIES (6)

1907 (30 Apr)–**13**. King Edward VII optd as T **4** or **5** (2s.6d.).

(a) De La Rue printings. Ordinary paper (½d., 1d., 4d. (No. 35a) or chalk-surfaced paper (others)

31	½d. pale yellowish green (29.5.07)	2·25	14·00
32	1d. scarlet (5.5.07)	9·50	9·00
33	2d. pale grey-green and carmine-red	10·00	6·00
34	4d. green and chocolate-brown (29.5.07)	3·75	4·25
35	4d. pale orange (3.12)	18·00	24·00
	a. Orange-red	10·00	21·00
36	6d. pale dull purple (5.5.07)	15·00	32·00
	a. Dull purple	22·00	40·00
37	1s. dull green and carmine (5.5.07)	26·00	17·00
38	2s.6d. pale dull purple (5.5.07)	95·00	£170
	a. Dull purple	95·00	£170
31/8 *Set of 8*		£150	£250
37s/8s Optd "SPECIMEN" *Set of 2*		£140	

(b) Harrison printing. Ordinary paper

40	4d. bright orange (No. 286) (1913)	45·00	32·00

Note that No. 40 is perf 15×14, whereas Nos. 35/a are perf 14.

(c) Somerset House printing. Ordinary paper

41	2s.6d. dull reddish purple (No. 316) (1913)	£150	£250

1914–31. King George V.

(a) W 100 (Simple Cypher). Optd with T 4

42	½d. green	8·50	50
43	1d. scarlet	2·25	20
44	1½d. red-brown (1921)	8·00	18·00
45	2d. orange (Die I)	5·50	60
46	3d. bluish violet (1921)	1·75	35
47	4d. grey-green (1921)	9·00	1·50
48	6d. reddish purple (*chalk-surfaced paper*) (1921)	9·50	15·00

49	1s. bistre-brown (1917)	15·00	2·50
	a. Opt triple, two albino	£120	
	(b) W 110 (Single Cypher). Optd with T 6		
50	2s.6d. sepia-brown (*Waterlow ptg*) (No. 400) (1914)	55·00	65·00
	a. Re-entry (R. 2/1)	£800	£1000
	b. Opt double, one albino	£200	
51	2s.6d. yellow-brown (*D.L.R. ptg*) (No. 406) (1917)	55·00	35·00
	a. Opt double	£1600	£1400
	b. Opt triple, two albino	£275	
	c. *Pale brown* (No. 407)	50·00	55·00
53	2s.6d. chocolate-brown (*B.W. ptg*) (No. 414)	50·00	27·00
	a. Opt double, one albino*	£200	
54	5s. rose-red (*B.W. ptg*) (No. 416) (30.6.31)	55·00	£110
	a. Opt triple, two albino	£300	
42/54 *Set of 10*		£140	£150
49s/50s, 54s Optd "*SPECIMEN*" or "SPECIMEN" (No. 54s) *Set of 3*		£225	

*The albino overprint is quite clear, with "MOROCCO" appearing just below "AGENCIES" on the normal overprint and a little to the right as seen from the back. There is also a second faint albino impression just below the normal overprint.

MOROCCO AGENCIES S (7)	MOROCCO AGENCIES S (8)

Type **7**: Opt 14 mm long; ends of "s" cut off diagonally.
Type **8**: Opt 15½ mm long; ends of "s" cut off horizontally

1925–36. King George V (W **111** (Block Cypher)) optd with T **8** (4d.) or **7** (others).

55	½d. green	3·50	50
	aw. Wmk inverted	75·00	
	b. Optd with Type 8	21·00	60·00
56	1½d. chestnut (20.5.31)	12·00	18·00
57	2d. orange	2·25	1·00
58	2½d. blue	9·00	1·50
	a. Optd with Type 8	£100	16·00
59	4d. grey-green (1.36)	15·00	50·00
60	6d. purple (1931)	3·50	8·50
	a. Opt double, one albino	£140	
	b. Optd with Type 8	2·00	60
61	1s. bistre-brown	18·00	6·00
	as. Optd "*SPECIMEN*"	75·00	
	b. Optd with Type 8	55·00	50·00
55/61 *Set of 7*		55·00	65·00

1935 (8 May). Silver Jubilee (Nos. 453/6) optd "MOROCCO AGENCIES" only, as in T **17**.

62	½d. green (B.)	1·50	6·50
63	1d. scarlet (B.)	1·50	12·00
64	1½d. red-brown (B.)	7·00	23·00
65	2½d. blue (R.)	8·00	2·50
62/5 *Set of 4*		16·00	40·00

1935–37. King George V.

(a) Harrison photo ptgs (Nos. 440/5 and 449). W 111 (Block Cypher). Optd with T 8

66	1d. scarlet (11.35)	3·25	23·00
67	1½d. red-brown (14.10.35)	5·50	27·00
68	2d. orange (1.5.36)	1·25	16·00
69	2½d. ultramarine (11.2.36)	1·75	4·25
70	3d. violet (2.3.36)	50	30
71	4d. deep grey-green (14.5.36)	50	30
72	1s. bistre-brown (31.8.36)	1·00	9·50
	s. Optd "*SPECIMEN*"	75·00	

(b) Waterlow re-engraved ptgs. W 110 (Single Cypher) optd with T 6

73	2s.6d. chocolate-brown (No. 450) (14.10.35)	55·00	75·00
	s. Optd "*SPECIMEN*"	85·00	
74	5s. bright rose-red (No. 451) (23.2.37)	28·00	£140
66/74 *Set of 9*		85·00	£250

1936 (26 Oct)–**37**. King Edward VIII, optd "MOROCCO AGENCIES" only, as in T **18** with "MOROCCO" 14¼ mm long.

75	1d. scarlet	10	40
	a. "MOROCCO" 15¼ mm long (5.1.37)	7·00	28·00
76	2½d. bright blue	10	15
	a. "MOROCCO" 15¼ mm long (5.1.37)	1·00	6·50

The first two printings of both values showed all the stamps with the short overprint, Nos. 75/6.

On 5 January 1937 a further printing of both values was placed on sale in London which had the 24 stamps from the bottom two horizontal rows (Rows 19 and 20) with the long overprint, Nos. 75a/6a. Subsequent printings increased the number of long overprints in the sheet to 25 by the addition of R. 8/9, and, finally, to 31 (R. 1/7, R. 7/1, R. 8/1, R. 13/3, 4 and 10, R. 14/6, but without R. 8/9).

For the 1d. value all sheets from cylinder 2 show the first setting. Sheets from cylinder 6 were also used for the first, and for all subsequent settings. The 2½d. value was overprinted on sheets from cylinder 2 throughout.

From 3 June 1937 unoverprinted stamps of Great Britain were supplied to the post offices at Tangier and Tetuan (Spanish Zone) as local stocks of issues overprinted "MOROCCO AGENCIES" were exhausted.

Type E   Type F

Stamps of GREAT BRITAIN cancelled as Types E or F at Tangier.

1937. King George V.

Z170	1½d. red-brown (No. 441)		
Z171	2d. orange (No. 442)		18·00
Z172	3d. violet (No. 444)		18·00
Z173	4d. deep grey-green (No. 445)		11·00

Z174	6d. purple (No. 426a)		10·00
Z175	1s. bistre-brown (No. 449)		35·00
Z176	2s.6d. chocolate-brown (No. 450)		£110
Z177	5s. bright rose-red (No. 451)		£150

1937–39. King George VI (Nos. 462/75).

Z178	½d. green		15·00
Z179	1d. scarlet		15·00
Z180	1½d. red-brown		13·00
Z181	2d. orange		13·00
Z182	2½d. ultramarine		9·50
Z183	3d. violet		9·50
Z184	4d. grey-green		9·50
Z185	5d. brown		13·00
Z186	6d. purple		6·50
Z187	7d. emerald-green		11·00
Z188	8d. bright carmine		20·00
Z189	9d. deep olive-green		14·00
Z190	10d. turquoise-blue		20·00
Z191	1s. bistre-brown		6·50

1939–42. King George VI (Nos. 476/8b).

Z192	2s.6d. brown		70·00
Z193	2s.6d. yellow-blue		16·00
Z194	5s. red		23·00
Z195	10s. dark brown		£140
Z196	10s. ultramarine		50·00

1941–42. King George VI pale colours (Nos. 485/90).

Z197	½d. pale green		9·50
Z198	1d. pale scarlet		9·50
Z199	1½d. pale red-brown		10·00
Z200	2d. pale orange		10·00
Z201	2½d. light ultramarine		9·00
Z202	3d. pale violet		6·50

1946. Victory (Nos. 491/2).

Z203	2½d. ultramarine		9·00
Z204	3d. violet		9·00

Type G

Stamps of GREAT BRITAIN cancelled as Type G or registered oval as Type F at Tetuan.

1937. King George V.

Z208	4d. deep grey-green (No. 445)		25·00
Z209	6d. purple (No. 426a)		23·00
Z210	1s. bistre-brown (No. 449)		

1937–39. King George VI (Nos. 465/75).

Z211	2d. orange		22·00
Z212	2½d. ultramarine		
Z213	3d. violet		
Z214	4d. grey-green		22·00
Z215	6d. purple		13·00
Z216	9d. deep olive-green		28·00
Z216a	10d. turquoise-blue		42·00
Z217	1s. bistre-brown		13·00

1939–42. King George VI (Nos. 476/7).

Z218	2s.6d. brown		
Z219	2s.6d. yellow-green		45·00
Z220	5s. red		60·00

1941. King George VI pale colours (Nos. 485/90).

Z221	½d. pale green		21·00
Z221a	1d. pale scarlet		21·00
Z222	2d. pale orange		
Z223	2½d. light ultramarine		
Z224	3d. pale violet		13·00

Other unoverprinted stamps of Great Britain are known with Morocco Agencies postmarks during this period, but it is believed that only Nos. Z170/224 were sold by the local post offices.

The use of unoverprinted stamps in Tangier ceased with the issue of Nos. 261/75 on 1 January 1949. Stamps overprinted "MOROCCO AGENCIES" replaced the unoverprinted values at Tetuan on 16 August 1949.

MOROCCO AGENCIES (9)	MOROCCO AGENCIES (10)

1949 (16 Aug). King George VI, optd with T **9** or **10** (2s.6d., 5s.).

77	½d. pale green	1·75	8·50
78	1d. pale scarlet	2·75	11·00
79	1½d. pale red-brown	2·75	9·50
80	2d. pale orange	3·00	13·00
81	2½d. light ultramarine	3·25	13·00
82	3d. pale violet	1·50	2·75
83	4d. grey-green	50	1·25
84	5d. brown	3·00	15·00
85	6d. purple	1·50	2·50
86	7d. emerald-green	50	17·00
87	8d. bright carmine	3·00	7·00
88	9d. deep olive-green	50	12·00
89	10d. turquoise-blue	50	10·00
90	11d. plum	70	11·00
91	1s. bistre-brown	3·00	7·00
92	2s.6d. yellow-green	22·00	48·00
93	5s. red	42·00	75·00
77/93 *Set of 17*		80·00	£225

1951 (3 May). King George VI (Nos. 503/7, 509/10), optd with T **9** or **10** (2s.6d., 5s.).

94	½d. pale orange	2·00	1·00
95	1d. light ultramarine	2·00	1·40
96	1½d. pale green	2·00	11·00
97	2d. pale red-brown	2·25	7·00
98	2½d. pale scarlet	2·00	6·50

99	2s.6d. yellow-green (HMS *Victory*)	13·00	21·00
100	5s. red (Dover)	13·00	23·00
94/100	Set of 7	32·00	60·00

1952–55. Queen Elizabeth II. W **153** (Tudor Crown). Optd with T **9**.

101	½d. orange-red (31.8.53)	10	10
102	1d. ultramarine (31.8.53)	15	1·75
103	1½d. green (5.12.52)	15	20
104	2d. red-brown (31.8.53)	20	2·25
105	2½d. carmine-red (5.12.52)	15	1·25
106	4d. ultramarine (1.3.55)	4·00	4·75
107	5d. brown (6.7.53)	60	80
108	6d. reddish purple (1.3.55)	1·25	4·25
109	8d. magenta (6.7.53)	60	70
110	1s. bistre-brown (6.7.53)	60	1·50
101/10	Set of 10	7·00	16·00

1956 (10 Sept). Queen Elizabeth II. W **165** (St. Edward's Crown). Optd with T **9**.

111	2½d. carmine-red (No. 544)	1·75	4·25

Stamps overprinted "MOROCCO AGENCIES" were withdrawn from sale on 31 December 1956.

IV. SPANISH CURRENCY

Stamps surcharged in Spanish currency were sold at British POs throughout Morocco until the establishment of the French Zone and the Tangier International Zone, when their use was confined to the Spanish Zone.

During this period further British postal agencies were opened at Alcazar (1907–1916), Fez–Mellah (Jewish quarter) (1909), Marrakesh (1909), Marrakesh–Mellah (Jewish quarter) (1909–17) and Mequinez (1907–1916).

MOROCCO AGENCIES

MOROCCO AGENCIES

5 CENTIMOS
(11)

6 PESETAS
(12)

1907 (1 Jan)–**12.** King Edward VII surch as T **11** (5c. to 1p.) or **12** (3p. to 12p.).

(a) De La Rue printings. Ordinary paper (Nos. 112/13, 116, 118, 122/3) or chalk-surfaced paper (others).

112	5c. on ½d. pale yellowish green	14·00	20
	a. Yellowish green	14·00	20
113	10c. on 1d. scarlet	22·00	10
	a. Bright scarlet	22·00	10
114	15c. on 1½d. pale dull purple and green	15·00	1·75
	a. Slate-purple and bluish green	9·00	20
	b. "1" of "15" omitted	£7000	
115	20c. on 2d. pale grey-green and carmine-red	7·00	2·75
	a. Pale grey-green and scarlet	9·50	3·00
116	25c. on 2½d. ultramarine	3·50	20
	a. Pale ultramarine	3·00	20
117	40c. on 4d. green and chocolate-brown (29.10.07)	3·25	6·50
	a. Deep green and chocolate-brown	6·00	4·50
118	40c. on 4d. pale orange (12.5.10)	4·00	2·50
	a. Orange-red	1·50	1·75
119	50c. on 5d. dull purple and ultramarine	12·00	9·00
	a. Slate-purple and ultramarine	11·00	9·00
120	1p. on 10d. dull purple and carmine	50·00	25·00
	a. Slate-purple and carmine	23·00	23·00
	b. No cross on crown		
121	3p. on 2s.6d. pale dull purple	25·00	38·00
	a. Dull purple	25·00	38·00
122	6p. on 5s. bright carmine	35·00	45·00
	a. Deep bright carmine	35·00	45·00
123	12p. on 10s. ultramarine (30.4.07)	80·00	80·00
112/23	Set of 12	£200	£180
117s, 123s	Optd "SPECIMEN" Set of 2	£150	

(b) Harrison printing Ordinary paper

124	25c. on 2½d. bright blue (No. 283) (1912)	60·00	50·00
	a. Dull blue	45·00	50·00

(c) Somerset House printing. Ordinary paper

125	12p. on 10s. blue (No. 319) (1912)	£200	£250

No. 114b occurred on stamps from the first vertical row of one sheet.

1912. King George V (W **49** (Imperial Crown)) surch as T **11**.

126	5c. on ½d. green (No. 339)	4·75	20
127	10c. on 1d. scarlet (No. 342)	1·25	10
	a. No cross on crown	£110	55·00

MOROCCO AGENCIES

MOROCCO AGENCIES

3 CENTIMOS
(13)

10 CENTIMOS
(14)

MOROCCO AGENCIES

MOROCCO AGENCIES

15 CENTIMOS
(15)

6 PESETAS
(16)

1914–26. King George V.

(a) W **100** *(Simple Cypher).* Surch as T **11** (5c.), **13** (3c. and 40c.)*, **15** (15c.) and **14** (remainder).

128	3c. on ½d. green (1917)	3·50	13·00
129	5c. on ½d. green	2·75	10

130	10c. on 1d. scarlet	4·50	10
	y. Wmk inverted and reversed	—	£250
131	15c. on 1½d. red-brown (1915)	1·50	10
	a. Surch double, one albino	80·00	
132	20c. on 2d. orange (Die I)	1·50	25
	a. Surch double, one albino	80·00	
133	25c. on 2½d. blue (*shades*)	3·25	25
	a. Surch double, one albino	80·00	
	w. Wmk inverted	£100	
134	40c. on 4d. grey-green (1917)	9·00	4·00
135	1p. on 10d. turquoise-blue	9·00	17·00
	a. Surch double, one albino	90·00	

*The surcharge on Nos. 134, 148 and 158 is as T **13** for the value and T **15** for "MOROCCO AGENCIES".

(b) W **110** *(Single Cypher).* Surch as T **16**

(i) Waterlow printings

136	6p. on 5s. rose-carmine	38·00	50·00
	a. Surch double, one albino	£160	
	b. Surch triple, two albino	£180	
137	6p. on 5s. pale rose-carmine	£150	£200
	a. Surch double, one albino	£225	
	b. Surch triple, two albino	£275	
138	12p. on 10s. indigo-blue (R.)	£110	£200
	a. Surch double, one albino	£250	
136s, 138s	Optd "SPECIMEN" or "SPECIMEN" (No. 138s)		
	Set of 2	£190	

(ii) De La Rue printings

139	3p. on 2s.6d. grey-brown (1918)	50·00	£140
	a. Surch double, one albino	£180	
140	3p. on 2s.6d. yellow-brown	50·00	£170
	a. Surch double, one albino	£170	
141	12p. on 10s. blue (R.)	95·00	£170
	a. Surch double, one albino	£275	

(iii) Bradbury Wilkinson printings

142	3p. on 2s.6d. chocolate-brown (27.4.26)	28·00	75·00
128/42	Set of 11	£170	£275

1925 (12 Oct)–**31.** King George V (W **111** (Block Cypher)), surch as T **11**, **13**, **14** or **15**.

143	5c. on ½d. green (3.1.31)	8·00	30·00
144	10c. on 1d. scarlet (4.11.29)	35·00	35·00
145	15c. on 1½d. red-brown	7·50	23·00
146	20c. on 2d. orange (1931)	3·00	13·00
	a. Surch double, one albino	85·00	
147	25c. on 2½d. blue	7·00	2·50
	a. Surch double, one albino	80·00	
	w. Wmk inverted	65·00	
148	40c. on 4d. grey-green (1930)	7·50	2·50
	a. Surch double, one albino	90·00	
143/8	Set of 6	60·00	95·00

MOROCCO AGENCIES

10 CENTIMOS
(17)

MOROCCO AGENCIES

10 CENTIMOS
(18)

1935 (8 May). Silver Jubilee (Nos. 453/6). Surch as T **17**.

149	5c. on ½d. green (B.)	1·00	1·25
150	10c. on 1d. scarlet (B.)	2·75	2·75
	a. Pair, one with "CENTIMES"	£1700	£2500
151	15c. on 1½d. red-brown (B.)	7·00	24·00
152	25c. on 2½d. blue (B.)	3·50	2·25
149/52	Set of 4	13·00	27·00

No. 150a occurred on R. 5/4 of a small second printing made in June 1935. The error can only be identified when *se-tenant* with a normal No. 150. Beware of forgeries.

1935–37. King George V (Harrison photo ptgs) (Nos. 439/43, 445 and 448). Surch as T **11**, **13**, **14** or **15**. W **111** (Block Cypher).

153	5c. on ½d. green	1·25	23·00
154	10c. on 1d. scarlet (24.11.35)	4·50	22·00
155	15c. on 1½d. red-brown (11.4.35)	12·00	3·25
156	20c. on 2d. orange (26.10.36)	50	35
157	25c. on 2½d. ultramarine (8.9.36)	1·25	11·00
158	40c. on 4d. deep grey-green (18.5.37)	50	8·00
159	1p. on 10d. turquoise-blue (14.4.37)	6·00	3·75
153/9	Set of 7	23·00	65·00

1936 (26 Oct)–**37.** King Edward VIII surch as T **18** with "MOROCCO" 14¼ mm long.

160	5c. on ½d. green	10	10
161	10c. on 1d. scarlet	50	20
	a. "MOROCCO" 15¼ mm long (5.1.37)	2·75	19·00
162	15c. on 1½d. red-brown	10	15
163	25c. on 2½d. bright blue	10	10
160/3	Set of 4	65	2·00

The first three printings of the 10c. on 1d. (from cyls 4, 5 and 6) showed all stamps with the short surcharge (No. 161).

On 5 January 1937 a further printing was placed on sale in London which had 49 stamps in the sheet (R. 1/2 to 11, R. 2/1, 5 and 6, 8 and 9, R. 3/5, R. 4/5, R. 5/4 and 5, 10, R. 6/6 and 7, R. 7/8, R. 9/8, R. 11/7, 9, R. 13/2 to 5, 7 and 8, R. 14/1, 7, R. 15/7, 11, R. 16/5, 10, R. 17/4, 10 and 11, R. 18/1, R. 19/2, R. 20/1 and 2, 3, 7, 9) with long surcharge (No. 161a). The next printing increased the number of long surcharges in the sheet to 50 (R. 10/2), but the final version, although retaining 50 long surcharges, showed them on R. 1/2 to 11, R. 17/5 to 8 and the entire rows 18, 19 and 20. The first two printings with long surcharges were from cylinder 6 and the last from cylinder 13.

MOROCCO AGENCIES

15 CENTIMOS
(19)

1937 (13 May). Coronation (No. 461), surch as T **19**.

164	15c. on 1½d. maroon (B.)	1·00	70

MOROCCO AGENCIES

MOROCCO AGENCIES

10 CENTIMOS
(20)

10 CENTIMOS
(21)

1937 (11 June)–**52.** King George VI (Nos. 462/4, 466, 468, 471 and 474), surch as T **20**.

165	5c. on ½d. green (B.)	1·25	30
166	10c. on 1d. scarlet	1·00	10
167	15c. on 1½d. red-brown (B.) (4.8.37)	3·50	25
168	25c. on 2½d. ultramarine	2·00	1·25
169	40c. on 4d. grey-green (9.40)	40·00	17·00
170	70c. on 7d. emerald-green (9.40)	3·50	23·00
171	1p. on 10d. turquoise-blue (16.6.52)	2·25	10·00
165/71	Set of 7	48·00	45·00

1940 (6 May). Centenary of First Adhesive Postage Stamps (Nos. 479/81 and 483), surch as T **21**.

172	5c. on ½d. green (B.)	30	2·75
173	10c. on 1d. scarlet	3·75	5·00
174	15c. on 1½d. red-brown (B.)	70	6·00
175	25c. on 2½d. ultramarine	80	5·00
172/5	Set of 4	5·00	17·00

25 CENTIMOS

45 PESETAS
MOROCCO AGENCIES

MOROCCO AGENCIES

(22)

(23)

1948 (26 Apr). Silver Wedding (Nos. 493/4), surch with T **22** or **23**.

176	25c. on 2½d. ultramarine	1·25	1·00
177	45p. on £1 brown	17·00	23·00

1948 (29 July). Olympic Games (Nos. 495/8), variously surch as T **22**.

178	25c. on 2½d. ultramarine	50	1·50
179	30c. on 3d. violet	50	1·50
	a. Crown flaw	85·00	£130
180	60c. on 6d. bright purple	50	1·50
181	1p.20c. on 1s. brown	60	1·50
	a. Surch double	£1500	
178/81	Set of 4	1·90	5·50

1951 (3 May)–**52.** King George VI (Nos. 503/5 and 507/8), surch as T **20**.

182	5c. on ½d. pale orange	2·00	7·00
183	10c. on 1d. light ultramarine	3·25	10·00
184	15c. on 1½d. green	1·75	26·00
185	25c. on 2½d. pale scarlet	1·75	24·00
186	40c. on 4d. light ultramarine (26.5.52)	1·00	13·00
182/6	Set of 5	8·75	70·00

1954–55. Queen Elizabeth II. W **153** (Tudor Crown). Surch as T **20**.

187	5c. on ½d. orange-red (1.9.54)	20	4·00
188	10c. on 1d. scarlet (1.3.55)	50	2·75

1956. Queen Elizabeth II. W **165** (St. Edward's Crown). Surch as T **20**.

189	5c. on ½d. orange-red (6.56)	15	4·50
190	40c. on 4d. ultramarine (15.8)	70	4·00

The British postal agency at Laraiche closed on 30 June 1938. Stamps surcharged in Spanish currency were withdrawn from sale when the Tetuan agency closed on 31 December 1956.

V. FRENCH CURRENCY

For use in the British postal agencies at Casablanca (closed 14.8.37), Fez (closed 8.1.38), Fez–Mellah (closed after 1930), Marrakesh (closed 14.8.37), Mazagan (closed 14.8.37), Mogador (closed 31.10.33) and Rabat (closed 8.1.38) and Saffi (closed 14.8.37).

MOROCCO AGENCIES

MOROCCO AGENCIES

25 CENTIMES
(24)

1 FRANC
(25)

1917 (Dec)–**24.** King George V (W **100** (Simple Cypher)), surch as T **24** or **25** (1f.).

191	3c. on ½d. green (R.)	3·00	2·50
192	5c. on ½d. green	75	20
193	10c. on 1d. scarlet	4·50	40
194	15c. on 1½d. red-brown	4·25	20
195	25c. on 2½d. blue	1·50	20
196	40c. on 4d. slate-green	2·00	1·50
	a. Surch double, one albino		
197	50c. on 5d. yellow-brown (24.10.23)	1·00	2·75
198	75c. on 9d. olive-green (1924)	1·00	75
	a. Surch double, one albino	£110	
199	1f. on 10d. turquoise-blue	12·00	4·00
	a. Surch double, one albino	85·00	
191/9	Set of 9	27·00	11·00

1924–32. King George V (B.W. ptg). W **110** (Single Cypher), surch as T **25**, but closer vertical spacing.

200	3f. on 2s.6d. chocolate-brown	5·00	1·50
	a. Major re-entry (R. 1/2)	£500	£500
	b. Surch double, one albino		
	c. Reddish brown	8·00	10·00
201	6f. on 5s. rose-red (23.9.32)	32·00	40·00
200s/1s	Optd "SPECIMEN" or "SPECIMEN" (No. 201s)		
	Set of 2	£160	

1925–34. King George V (W **111** (Block Cypher)), surch as T **24** or **25** (1f.).

202	5c. on ½d. green	30	6·50
203	10c. on 1d. scarlet	30	2·00
	a. Surch double, one albino	95·00	
204	15c. on 1½d. red-brown	2·00	1·75
205	25c. on 2½d. blue	3·50	50
206	40c. on 4d. grey-green	75	80
	a. Surch double, one albino	80·00	
207	50c. on 5d. yellow-brown	1·50	10
	w. Wmk inverted	75·00	
208	75c. on 9d. olive-green	15·00	20
	a. Surch double, one albino	£130	
	w. Wmk inverted	—	£200
209	90c. on 9d. olive-green (8.5.34)	22·00	14·00
210	1f. on 10d. turquoise-blue	1·50	10
	a. Surch double, one albino	£110	
211	1f.50 on 1s. bistre-brown (8.5.34)	20·00	2·25
	s. Optd "SPECIMEN"	65·00	
202/11	Set of 10	60·00	25·00

1935 (8 May). Silver Jubilee (Nos. 453/6), surch as T **17**, but in French currency.

212	5c. on ½d. green (B.)	20	20
213	10c. on 1d. scarlet (B.)	4·25	70
214	15c. on 1½d. red-brown (B.)	1·50	2·25
215	25c. on 2½d. blue (R.)	45	25
212/15	Set of 4	5·75	3·00

1935–37. King George V (Harrison photo ptgs. W **111** (Block Cypher)), surch as T **24** or **25** (1f.).

216	5c. on ½d. green (21.10.35)	75	8·00
217	10c. on 1d. scarlet (2.3.36)	35	30
218	15c. on 1½d. red-brown	12·00	6·00
219	25c. on 2½d. ultramarine (25.9.36)	30	15
220	40c. on 4d. deep grey-green (2.12.36)	30	15
221	50c. on 5d. yellow-brown (15.9.36)	30	15
222	90c. on 9d. deep olive-green (15.2.37)	75	1·75
223	1f. on 10d. turquoise-blue (10.2.37)	30	30
224	1f.50 on 1s. bistre-brown (20.7.37)	75	3·50
	s. Optd "SPECIMEN"	70·00	

1935–36. King George V (Waterlow re-engraved ptgs). W **100** (Single Cypher), surch as T **25**, but closer vertical spacing.

225	3f. on 2s.6d. chocolate-brown (No. 450)	4·75	12·00
226	6f. on 5s. bright rose-red (No. 451) (9.6.36)	9·50	23·00
216/26	Set of 11	27·00	50·00
225s/6s	Optd "SPECIMEN" or "SPECIMEN" (No. 226s) Set of 2	£150	

1936 (26 Oct). King Edward VIII, surch as T **18**, but in French currency.

227	5c. in ½d. green	10	15
	a. Bar through "POSTAGE"	£750	
228	15c. on 1½d. red-brown	10	15

No. 227a involved R. 18/10 to 12 on a total of eight sheets. The bar, probably a printers rule, became progressively longer so that on four of the sheets it extends over all three stamps. Price quoted is for an example with the bar through the entire word.

1937 (13 May). Coronation (No. 461), surch as T **19**, but in French currency.

229	15c. on 1½d. maroon (B.)	40	20

1937 (11 June). King George VI, surch as T **20**, but in French currency.

230	5c. on ½d. green (B.)	4·50	4·00

Stamps surcharged in French currency were withdrawn from sale on 8 January 1938.

VI. TANGIER INTERNATIONAL ZONE

By an agreement between Great Britain, France and Spain, Tangier was declared an international zone in 1924. Stamps overprinted "Morocco Agencies" or surcharged in Spanish currency were used there until replaced by Nos. 231/4.

PRICES. Our note *re* UK usage (at beginning of Section III) also applies to "TANGIER" optd stamps.

TANGIER (26) **TANGIER** (27)

1927 (29 Apr). King George V (W **111** (Block Cypher)), optd with T **26**.

231	½d. green	7·00	20
	a. Opt double, one albino		
232	1d. scarlet	9·50	25
	a. Inverted "Q" for "O" (R. 20/3)	£800	
233	1½d. chestnut	8·50	8·50
234	2d. orange	3·25	20
	a. Opt double, one albino	80·00	
231/4	Set of 4	25·00	8·50

1934 (13 Dec)–**35.** King George V (Harrison photo ptgs. W **111** (Block Cypher)), optd with T **26**.

235	½d. green (16.2.35)	1·25	3·00
236	1d. scarlet	13·00	4·00
237	1½d. red-brown	75	20
235/7	Set of 3	13·50	6·50

1935 (8 May). Silver Jubilee (Nos. 453/5), optd with T **27** in blue.

238	½d. green	2·75	9·00
239	1d. scarlet	25·00	22·00
240	1½d. red-brown	1·25	2·25
238/40	Set of 3	26·00	30·00

1936 (26 Oct). King Edward VIII, optd with T **26**.

241	½d. green	10	20
242	1d. scarlet	10	10
243	1½d. red-brown	15	10
241/3	Set of 3	30	30

TANGIER (28) **TANGIER** (29) **TANGIER**

1937 (13 May). Coronation (No. 461), optd with T **28**.

244	1½d. maroon (B.)	1·50	50

1937. King George VI (Nos. 462/4), optd with T **29**.

245	½d. green (B.) (6.37)	8·50	1·75
246	1d. scarlet (6.37)	27·00	1·75
247	1½d. red-brown (B.) (4.8)	2·75	40
245/7	Set of 3	35·00	3·50

TANGIER (30) **TANGIER** (31)

1940 (6 May). Centenary of First Adhesive Postage Stamps (Nos. 479/81), optd with T **30**.

248	½d. green (B.)	30	8·50
249	1d. scarlet	45	1·00
250	1½d. red-brown (B.)	2·00	12·00
248/50	Set of 3	2·50	19·00

1944. King George VI pale colours (Nos. 485/6), optd with T **29**.

251	½d. pale green (B.)	12·00	5·00
252	1d. pale scarlet	12·00	5·00

1946 (11 June). Victory (Nos. 491/2), optd as T **31**.

253	2½d. ultramarine	1·00	65
254	3d. violet	1·00	2·00

The opt on No. 254 is smaller (23×2½ *mm*).

1948 (26 Apr). Royal Silver Wedding (Nos. 493/4), optd with T **30**.

255	2½d. ultramarine	50	15
	a. Opt omitted (in vert pair with stamp optd at top)	£9000	
256	£1 blue	20·00	25·00

No. 255a comes from a sheet on which the overprint is misplaced downwards resulting in the complete absence of the opt from the six stamps of the top row. On the rest of the sheet the opt falls at the top of each stamp instead of at the foot (*Price £250, unused, £350 used*).

1948 (29 July). Olympic Games (Nos. 495/8), optd with T **30**.

257	2½d. ultramarine	1·00	2·00
258	3d. violet	1·00	2·25
	a. Crown flaw	£100	
259	6d. bright purple	1·00	2·25
260	1s. brown	1·00	2·00
257/60	Set of 4	3·50	8·00

1949 (1 Jan). King George VI, optd with T **29**.

261	2d. pale orange	8·50	10·00
262	2½d. light ultramarine	6·50	10·00
263	3d. pale violet	70	1·25
264	4d. grey-green	11·00	17·00
265	5d. brown	5·50	35·00
266	6d. purple	1·50	30
267	7d. emerald-green	2·50	18·00
268	8d. bright carmine	5·00	16·00
269	9d. deep olive-green	2·50	16·00
270	10d. turquoise-blue	2·75	15·00
271	11d. plum	4·50	24·00
272	1s. bistre-brown	1·50	2·75
273	2s.6d. yellow-green	9·50	27·00
274	5s. red	20·00	48·00
275	10s. ultramarine	55·00	65·00
261/75	Set of 15	£120	£325

1949 (10 Oct). 75th Anniv of UPU (Nos. 499/502), optd with T **30**.

276	2½d. ultramarine	70	4·50
	a. Lake in India	85·00	
277	3d. violet	70	7·50
278	6d. bright purple	70	1·50
279	1s. brown	70	3·25
276/9	Set of 4	2·50	15·00

1950 (2 Oct)–**51.** King George VI, optd with T **29** or **30** (shilling values).

280	½d. pale orange (3.5.51)	1·00	1·50
281	1d. light ultramarine (3.5.51)	1·25	3·00
282	1½d. pale green (3.5.51)	1·25	24·00
283	2d. pale red-brown (3.5.51)	1·25	5·00
284	2½d. pale scarlet (3.5.51)	1·25	11·00
285	4d. light ultramarine	4·50	3·00
286	2s.6d. yellow-grn (HMS *Victory*) (3.5.51)	10·00	15·00
287	5s. red (Dover) (3.5.51)	17·00	15·00
288	10s. ultramarine (St. George) (3.5.51)	32·00	15·00
280/8	Set of 9	60·00	75·00

1952–54. Queen Elizabeth II (W **153** (Tudor Crown)), optd with T **29**.

289	½d. orange-red (31.8.53)	10	50
290	1d. ultramarine (31.8.53)	15	50
291	1½d. green (5.12.52)	10	30
292	2d. red-brown (31.8.53)	20	1·25
293	2½d. carmine-red (5.12.52)	10	1·00
294	3d. deep lilac (B.) (18.1.54)	20	1·25
295	4d. ultramarine (2.11.53)	60	4·25
296	5d. brown (6.7.53)	60	1·00
297	6d. reddish purple (18.1.54)	60	15
298	7d. bright green (18.1.54)	60	4·25
299	8d. magenta (6.7.53)	60	1·50
300	9d. bronze-green (8.2.54)	1·40	1·75
301	10d. Prussian blue (8.2.54)	1·40	2·75
302	11d. brown-purple (8.2.54)	1·40	3·25
303	1s. bistre-brown (6.7.53)	60	70
304	1s.3d. green (2.11.53)	1·00	7·50
305	1s.6d. grey-blue (2.11.53)	1·50	2·25
289/305	Set of 17	10·00	30·00

1953 (3 June). Coronation (Nos. 532/5), optd with T **30**.

306	2½d. carmine-red	50	50
307	4d. ultramarine	2·00	50
308	1s.3d. deep yellow-green	1·75	1·50
309	1s.6d. deep grey-blue	1·75	2·00
306/9	Set of 4	5·50	4·00

1955 (23 Sept). Queen Elizabeth II, Castle high values (W **165** (St. Edward's Crown)), optd with T **30**.

310	2s.6d. black-brown	3·50	10·00
311	5s. rose-red	4·50	23·00
312	10s. ultramarine	17·00	28·00
310/12	Set of 3	23·00	55·00

1956. Queen Elizabeth II (W **165** (St. Edward's Crown)), optd with T **29**.

313	½d. orange-red (21.3)	10	1·00
314	1d. ultramarine (13.4)	20	50
315	1½d. green (22.10)	40	3·00
316	2d. red-brown (25.7)	1·25	1·75
317	2d. light brown (10.12)	70	40
318	2½d. carmine-red (19.12)	40	40
319	3d. deep lilac (B) (22.10)	40	7·50
320	4d. ultramarine (25.6)	65	2·00
321	6d. reddish purple (22.10)	50	7·50
322	1s.3d. green (26.11)	1·75	13·00
313/22	Set of 10	5·75	32·00

1857-1957

TANGIER (32) **1857-1957 TANGIER** (33)

1957 (1 Apr). Centenary of British Post Office in Tangier.

*(a) Nos. 540/2 and 543b/66 (W **165** (St. Edward's Crown)), optd as T **32** or **33** (7d.)*

323	½d. orange-red	10	15
324	1d. ultramarine	10	15
325	1½d. green	10	15
326	2d. light red-brown	10	15
327	2½d. carmine-red	15	1·25
328	3d. deep lilac (B.)	15	40
329	4d. ultramarine	30	30
330	5d. brown	30	35
331	6d. reddish purple	30	35
332	7d. bright green	30	35
333	8d. magenta	30	1·00
334	9d. bronze-green	30	30
	a. "TANGIER" omitted	£7500	
335	10d. Prussian blue	30	30
336	11d. brown-purple	30	30
337	1s. bistre-brown	30	30
338	1s.3d. green	45	5·00
339	1s.6d. grey-blue	50	1·60

*(b) Nos. 536/8 (W **165** (St. Edward's Crown)), optd as T **32***

340	2s.6d. black-brown	2·00	7·00
	a. Hyphen omitted	£100	£180
	b. Hyphen inserted	30·00	
341	5s. rose-red	2·75	13·00
	a. Hyphen omitted	£100	£200
	b. Hyphen inserted	17·00	
342	10s. ultramarine	3·75	13·00
	a. Hyphen omitted	£130	£225
	b. Hyphen inserted	24·00	
323/42	Set of 20	11·50	40·00

Nos. 340a/b, 341a/b and 342a/b occur on R.9/2 in the sheet of 40 (4×10). They are best collected in marginal blocks of four from the bottom left corner of the sheet. Specialists recognise two forms of No. 340b; one where the hyphen on R.9/2 was inserted separately to correct the error, No. 340a; the other from a later printing where a new and corrected overprinting plate was used. (*Price £12 un.*).

All stamps overprinted "TANGIER" were withdrawn from sale on 30 April 1957.

Muscat

An independent Arab Sultanate in Eastern Arabia with an Indian postal administration.

The Indian post office at Muscat town is officially recorded as having opened on 1 May 1864. Stamps of India were provided for its use.

The office was initially included in the Bombay Postal Circle and the first postmark, so far only recorded on stampless covers, was a single circle, 21½ mm in diameter, broken at the top by "MUSCAT" and with the date in two lines across the centre. This was followed by a cancellation showing the post office number, "309", within a diamond of 13, later 16, bars. It is believed that this was used in conjunction with a single-ring date stamp inscribed "MUSCAT".

1864 Diamond

In 1869 the office was transferred to the Sind Circle, assigned a new number, "23", and issued with a duplex cancellation. Major reorganisation of the postal service in 1873 resulted in Muscat becoming office "K-4". For ten years from 1873 the cancellations do not, very confusingly, carry any indication of the year of use.

1869 Duplex

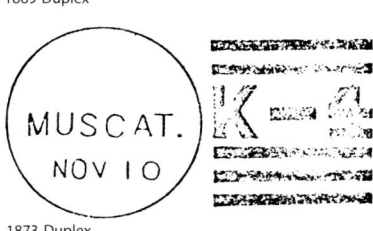

1873 Duplex

Muscat rejoined the Bombay Circle in 1879 and was issued with a cancellation showing a "B" within a square of horizontal bars. The date stamp used at this time was unique in that it carried the inscription "MASKAT", although the spelling reverted to the more usual form by 1882. The square cancellation had been replaced by a similar circular mark by 1884.

Subsequent postmarks were of various circular types, all inscribed "MUSCAT".

There was only one Indian post office in Muscat, but a further office did exist, from 12 April 1868, at the Muscat dependency of Guadur, a port on the Mekran coast of Baluchistan.

Stamps of INDIA cancelled by numeral, duplex or circular types inscribed 'MUSCAT' or 'MASKAT'.

1856–64. (Nos. 37/49).
Z1	½a. blue	85·00
Z3	2a. yellow	£140
Z4	4a. grey-black	£140
Z5	8a. carmine	£275

1865. (Nos. 54/63).
Z7	½a. blue (Die I)	22·00
Z9	1a. pale brown	28·00
Z10	2a. yellow	48·00
Z11	2a. brown-orange	42·00

1866. (Nos. 69/71).
Z13	4a. green (Die I)	65·00
Z14	4a. blue-green (Die II)	70·00

1868. (Nos. 73/4).
Z15	8a. pale rose (Die II)	90·00

1873. (Nos. 75/6).
Z16	½a. blue (Die II)	13·00

1874. (Nos. 77/9).
Z17	9p. bright mauve	£120
Z18	1r. slate	£300

1876. (Nos. 80/2).
Z19	6a. pale brown	42·00
Z20	12a. Venetian red	£180

1882–90. (Nos. 84/101).
Z21	½a. blue green	11·00
Z23	1a. brown-purple	11·00
Z24	1a.6p. sepia	23·00
Z25	2a. blue	14·00
Z26	3a. orange	26·00
Z27	3a. brown-orange	17·00
Z28	4a. olive-green	25·00
Z29	4a.6p. yellow-green	35·00
Z30	8a. dull mauve	35·00

Z31	12a. purple/*red*	75·00
Z32	1r. slate	90·00

1891. (No. 102).
Z33	2½a. on 4½a. yellow-green	30·00

1892–97. (Nos. 103/6).
Z34	2a.6p. yellow-green	11·00
Z35	1r. green and aniline carmine	90·00

1898. (No. 110).
Z37	¼ on ½a. blue-green	35·00

1899. (No. 111).
Z38	3p. carmine	23·00

1900–02. (Nos. 112/18).
Z39	3p. grey	90·00
Z40	½a. pale yellow-green	13·00
Z41	1a. carmine	13·00
Z42	2a. pale violet	30·00
Z43	2a.6p. ultramarine	16·00

1902–11. (Nos. 119/36).
Z44	3p. grey	13·00
Z45	½a. green	7·50
Z46	1a. carmine	8·50
Z47	2a. mauve	12·00
Z48	2a.6p. ultramarine	7·50
Z50	4a. olive	14·00
Z52	8a. purple	29·00
Z54	1r. green and carmine	60·00

1905. (No. 148).
Z57	¼ on ½a. green	29·00

1906–07. (Nos. 149/50).
Z58	½a. green	7·50
Z59	1a. carmine	7·50

1911–22. (Nos. 151/86).
Z60	3p. grey	13·00
Z61	½a. light green	7·50
Z62	1a. carmine	7·50
Z63	1½a. chocolate (No. 163)	29·00
Z64	1½a. chocolate (No. 165)	35·00
Z65	2a. purple	11·00
Z66	2a.6p. ultramarine (No. 170)	19·00
Z67	2a.6p. ultramarine (No. 171)	11·00
Z69	4a. olive-green	22·00
Z70	6a. brown-ochre	29·00
Z71	8a. deep mauve	35·00
Z73	1r. brown and green	45·00

1921. (Nos. 192/4).
Z76	9p. on 1a. rose-carmine	35·00

1922. (Nos. 195/6).
Z77	¼ on 1½a. bright green	35·00

1922–26. (Nos. 197/200).
Z78	1a. chocolate	11·00
Z80	2a.6p. orange	23·00
Z81	3a. ultramarine	28·00

1926–33. (Nos. 201/17).
Z82	3p. slate	5·50
Z83	½a. green	5·50
Z84	1a. chocolate	5·50
Z87	2a.6p. orange	18·00
Z88	3a. blue	12·00
Z89	4a. sage-green (No. 211)	13·00
Z90	8a. reddish purple	18·00
Z91	12a. claret	30·00
Z92	1r. chocolate and green	29·00
Z93	2r. carmine and orange	42·00
Z95	10r. green and scarlet	£140

1929. (Nos. 221/4).
Z97	3a. blue	19·00
Z99	6a. bistre	24·00
Z100	8a. purple	29·00

1931. (Nos. 227/8).
Z103	½a. violet and green	29·00
Z104	1a. mauve and chocolate	29·00

1932–36. (Nos. 232/9).
Z107	½a. green	7·50
Z109	1a. chocolate	7·50
Z110	1a.3p. mauve	7·50
Z112	3a. carmine	18·00
Z114	6a. bistre	40·00

1935. (Nos. 240/6).
Z115	½a. black and yellow-green	14·00
Z116	9p. black and grey-green	18·00
Z117	1a. black and brown	14·00
Z118	1¼a. black and bright violet	18·00
Z119	2½a. black and orange	25·00
Z121	8a. black and purple	48·00

1937–40. (Nos. 247/60).
Z122	3p. slate	5·50
Z123	½a. red-brown	5·50
Z124	9p. green	8·00
Z125	1a. carmine	5·50
Z126	2a. vermilion	11·00
Z127	2a.6p. bright violet	13·00
Z130	4a. brown	14·00
Z131	6a. turquoise-green	29·00
Z132	8a. slate-violet	29·00
Z133	12a. lake	35·00
Z134	1r. grey and red-brown	22·00
Z135	2r. purple and brown	28·00

1940. (Nos. 265/77).
Z138	3p. slate	5·50
Z139	½a. purple	5·50
Z140	9p. green	7·00
Z141	1a. carmine	5·50
Z142	1a.3p. yellow-brown	7·00
Z143	1½a. dull violet	6·50

Z144	2a. vermilion	6·50
Z145	3a. bright violet	6·50
Z146	3½a. bright blue	8·00
Z147	4a. brown	5·50
Z148	6a. turquoise-green	8·50
Z149	8a. slate-violet	6·50
Z150	12a. lake	15·00
Z151	14a. purple	22·00

1946. (Nos. 278/81).
Z152	9p. yellow-green	30·00
Z153	1½a. dull violet	30·00
Z154	3½a. bright blue	42·00
Z155	12a. claret	60·00

1946. (No. 282).
Z156	3p. on 1a.3p. yellow-brown	15·00

OFFICIAL STAMPS

1866–72. (No. O12).
Z158	2a. yellow	£400

1867–73. (Nos. O23/9).
Z160	1a. brown	85·00
Z161	2a. yellow	£120
Z162	4a. green (Die I)	£130

1874. (No. O31).
Z163	½a. blue (Die II)	70·00

1883–99. (Nos. O39/42).
Z165	½a. blue-green	32·00
Z166	1a. brown-purple	32·00
Z167	2a. blue	32·00

1902–09. (No. O59).
Z171	2a. mauve	32·00

1909. (No. O68).
Z174	2r. carmine and yellow-brown	£140

1912–13. (Nos. O76/83*a*).
Z178	½a. light green	16·00
Z179	1a. carmine	16·00
Z180	2a. reddish purple	22·00

1921. (No. O97).
Z183	9p. on 1a. rose-carmine	60·00

1922. (No. O98).
Z184	1a. chocolate	22·00

1926–31. (Nos. O109/16).
Z185	3p. slate	17·00
Z188	2a. purple	22·00
Z189	4a. sage-green	28·00
Z190	8a. reddish purple	28·00
Z191	12a. claret	48·00

1932–36. (Nos. O127/33).
Z195	9p. deep green	22·00
Z197	1a.3p. mauve	27·00
Z199	6a. bistre	60·00

1937–39. (Nos. O137/40).
Z202	1a. carmine	16·00
Z203	1r. grey and red-brown	32·00
Z204	2r. purple and brown	42·00
Z205	5r. green and blue	80·00

1939–42. (Nos. O144/50).
Z207	½a. red-brown	18·00
Z208	1a. carmine	18·00
Z209	1½a. dull violet	18·00
Z210	2a. vermilion	23·00
Z211	4a. brown	29·00
Z212	8a. slate-violet	40·00

GUADUR

No cancellations have been reported from Guadur before its transfer to the Sind Circle in 1869. Cancellations are all similar in style to those for Muscat, Guadur being initially assigned number "24", although an office in Southern India is also known to have used this numeral. The 1869 duplex is interesting in that it is inscribed "GWADUR". Under the 1873 reorganisation the office became "4/K-1", this postmark using the "GUADUR" spelling.

1869 Duplex

Stamps of INDIA cancelled by duplex or circular types inscribed 'GWADUR' or 'GUADUR'.

1865. (Nos. 54/65)
Z301	½a. blue	22·00
Z303	1a. brown	28·00
Z304	2a. orange	42·00

1866. (Nos. 69/72)
Z305	4a. green (Die I)	65·00

1873. (Nos. 75/6)
Z309	½a. blue (Die II)	13·00

1882-90. (Nos. 84/101)
Z312	½a. blue-green	12·00
Z313	9p. rose	
Z314	1a. brown-purple	12·00
Z316	2a. blue	16·00
Z319	4a.6p. yellow-green	40·00

1891. (No. 102)
Z323   2½a. on 4½a. yellow-green .... 35·00

1892-97. (Nos. 103/6)
Z324   2a.6p. yellow-green .... 12·00
Z325   1r. green and carmine .... 95·00

1898. (No. 110)
Z327   ¼ on ½a. blue-green .... 35·00

1899. (No. 111)
Z328   3p. carmine .... 25·00

1900-02. (Nos. 112/8)
Z329   3p. grey ....
Z330   ½a. yellow-green .... 15·00
Z331   1a. carmine .... 15·00

1902-11. (Nos. 119/47)
Z334   3p. grey .... 14·00
Z335   ½a. yellow-green .... 8·00
Z336   1a. carmine .... 9·00
Z339   3a. orange-brown .... 20·00
Z345   3r. brown and green £100

1906-07. (Nos. 149/50)
Z347   ½a. yellow-green .... 8·50
Z348   1a. carmine .... 8·50

1911-22. (Nos. 151/91)
Z349   3p. grey .... 15·00
Z350   ½a. green .... 8·50
Z351   1a. carmine .... 8·50
Z353   1½a. chocolate (No. 165) .... 35·00
Z354   2a. purple .... 12·00
Z357   4a. olive-green .... 24·00

1921. (Nos. 192/4)
Z363   9p. on 1a. carmine .... 35·00

1922-26. (Nos. 197/200)
Z364   1a. chocolate .... 15·00

1926-33. (Nos. 201/19)
Z367   3p. slate .... 6·00
Z369   1a. chocolate .... 7·00
Z371   2a. purple .... 15·00
Z373   4a. sage-green (No.211) .... 15·00
Z374   8a. reddish purple .... 20·00
Z375   12a. claret .... 35·00
Z376   1r. chocolate and green .... 32·00
Z377   2r. carmine and orange .... 45·00

1929. (Nos. 220/5)
Z379   2a. deep blue-green .... 20·00
Z380   3a. blue .... 20·00
Z381   4a. olive-green .... 20·00
Z382   6a. bistre .... 20·00
Z384   12a. rose red .... 75·00

1931. (Nos. 226/31)
Z385   ¼a. olive-green and orange-brown .... 20·00
Z386   ½a. violet and green .... 20·00
Z387   1a. mauve and chocolate .... 20·00
Z388   2a. green and blue .... 20·00
Z389   3a. chocolate and carmine .... 20·00

1932-36. (Nos. 232/9)
Z392   9p. deep green .... 12·00
Z393   1a. chocolate .... 8·00
Z395   1a.3p. mauve .... 8·50
Z396   2a. vermilion (large die) (No. 236b) .... 15·00
Z397   2a. vermilion (small die) (No.236c) .... 15·00

1935. (Nos. 240/6)
Z401   9p. black and grey-green .... 25·00
Z402   1a. black and brown .... 20·00
Z403   1¼a. black and bright violet .... 25·00
Z404   2½a. black and orange .... 30·00
Z405   3½a. black and dull ultramarine .... 40·00

1937-40. (Nos. 247/64)
Z406   3p. slate .... 8·00
Z407   ½a. red-brown .... 6·00
Z409   1a. carmine .... 6·00
Z412   3a. yellow-green .... 15·00
Z414   4a. brown .... 15·00

1940-43. (Nos. 265/77)
Z423   1a.3p. yellow-brown .... 9·00

OFFICIAL STAMPS

1874-82. (Nos. O31/7)
Z430   ½a. blue .... 75·00

1883-99. (Nos. O37a/48)
Z433   3p. carmine .... 45·00
Z434   ½a. blue-green .... 35·00
Z435   1a. brown-purple .... 35·00
Z436   2a. blue .... 35·00

1900. (Nos. O49/52)
Z440   1a. carmine .... 38·00

1902-09. (Nos. O54/65)
Z443   3p. grey .... 35·00
Z444   ½a. green .... 25·00
Z445   1a. carmine .... 25·00
Z446   2a. mauve .... 30·00

1906. (Nos. O66/7)
Z450   ½a. yellow-green .... 25·00
Z451   1a. carmine .... 25·00

1909. (Nos. O68/72)
Z453   5r. ultramarine and violet .... —

1912-13. (Nos. O73/96)
Z456   1a. carmine .... 20·00

1921. (No. O97)
Z472   9p. on 1a. rose carmine .... —

PRICES FOR STAMPS ON COVER	
Nos. 1/15	*from* × 75
Nos. O1/10	*from* × 100

(Currency 12 pies = 1 anna; 16 annas = 1 Indian rupee)

(1)   (2)

1944 (20 Nov). Bicentenary of Al-Busaid Dynasty. Nos. 259/60, 265/8 and 269c/77 (King George VI) of India optd ("AL BUSAID 1363" in Arabic script) as T **1** or **2** (rupee values).

1	3p. slate	50	8·50
	w. Wmk inverted		9·00
2	½a. purple	50	8·50
3	9p. green	50	8·50
4	1a. carmine	50	8·50
5	1½a. dull violet	50	8·50
6	2a. vermilion	50	8·50
	w. Wmk inverted		27·00
7	3a. bright violet	1·00	8·50
	w. Wmk inverted	10·00	18·00
8	3½a. bright blue	1·00	8·50
9	4a. brown	1·25	8·50
10	6a. turquoise-green	1·25	8·50
11	8a. slate-violet	1·50	8·50
12	12a. lake	1·75	8·50
13	14a. green	4·00	14·00
14	1r. grey and red-brown	5·00	13·00
15	2r. purple and brown	12·00	22·00
1/15	Set of 15	29·00	£140

OFFICIAL STAMPS

1944 (20 Nov). Bicentenary of Al-Busaid Dynasty. Nos. O138, O143, O144ba/6 and O146b/50 of India optd as T **1** or **2** (1r.).

O1	3p. slate	60	16·00
O2	½a. purple	1·50	16·00
O3	9p. green	1·00	16·00
O4	1a. carmine	1·00	16·00
O5	1½a. dull violet	1·50	16·00
O6	2a. vermilion	1·50	16·00
O7	2½a. bright violet	7·50	16·00
O8	4a. brown	2·75	16·00
O9	8a. slate-violet	5·00	18·00
O10	1r. grey and red-brown	10·00	30·00
O1/10	Set of 10	29·00	£160

Used prices quoted for Nos. 1/15 and O1/10 are for stamps cancelled with contemporary postmarks of the Indian postal administration. Those with cancellations of the subsequent British post office are worth considerably less. Collectors are warned against forged overprints and cancellations.

From December 1947 there was a Pakistani postal administration and stamps of Pakistan were used until 31 March 1948. The subsequent British administration operated from 1 April 1948 to 29 April 1966 when the stamps of the BRITISH POSTAL AGENCIES IN EASTERN ARABIA were used. Guadur, however, continued to use the stamps of Pakistan until the dependency was finally ceded to that country in 1953.

▌ Natal *see* **South Africa**

Nauru

Stamps of MARSHALL ISLANDS were used in Nauru from the opening of the German Colonial Post Office on 14 July 1908 until 8 September 1914. Following the occupation by Australian forces on 6 November 1914 the "N.W. PACIFIC ISLANDS" overprints on Australia (see NEW GUINEA) were used from 2 January 1915.

PRICES FOR STAMPS ON COVER TO 1945	
Nos. 1/12	*from* × 10
Nos. 13/16	*from* × 4
Nos. 17/25	—
Nos. 26/39	*from* × 6
Nos. 40/3	*from* × 10
Nos. 44/7	*from* × 15

BRITISH MANDATE

NAURU   **NAURU**   **NAURU**
(1)   (2)   (3)

1916 (2 Sept)–**23**. Stamps of Great Britain (1912–22) overprinted at Somerset House.

*(a) With T **1** (12½ mm long) at foot*

1	½d. yellow-green	2·25	11·00
	a. "NAUP.U"	£450	
	b. Double opt, one albino	60·00	
	c. Triple opt, two albino	£400	
2	1d. bright scarlet	2·50	14·00
	a. "NAUP.U"	£700	£1300
	b. Double opt, one albino	£325	
2c	1d. carmine-red	21·00	
	cb. Double opt, one albino	£225	
3	1½d. red-brown (1923)	55·00	85·00
4	2d. orange (Die I)	2·00	13·00
	a. "NAUP.U"	£425	£950
	b. Double opt, one albino	£110	
	c. Triple opt, two albino	£425	
	y. Wmk inverted and reversed	£120	£275
5	2d. orange (Die II) (1923)	70·00	£100
6	2½d. blue	2·75	7·00
	a. "NAUP.U"	£475	£1000
	b. Double opt, one albino	£225	
7	3d. bluish violet	2·00	6·00
	a. "NAUP.U"	£475	£1100
	b. Double opt, one albino	£350	
8	4d. slate-green	2·00	8·50
	a. "NAUP.U"	£700	£1600
	b. Double opt, one albino	£225	
9	5d. yellow-brown	2·25	14·00
	a. "NAUP.U"	£2250	
	b. Double opt, one albino	£180	
10	6d. purple (chalk-surfaced paper)	7·50	10·00
	a. "NAUP.U"	£1600	
	b. Double opt, one albino	£375	
11	9d. agate	8·50	23·00
	a. Double opt, one albino	£350	
12	1s. bistre-brown	7·00	19·00
	a. Double opt, one albino	£400	
	s. Optd "SPECIMEN"	£140	
1/12	Set of 11	85·00	£190

*(b) With T **2** (13½ mm long) at centre (1923)*

13	½d. green	4·00	55·00
14	1d. scarlet	19·00	45·00
15	1½d. red-brown	28·00	55·00
	a. Double opt, one albino	£225	
16	2d. orange (Die II)	30·00	80·00
13/16	Set of 4	70·00	£200

The "NAUP.U" errors occur on R. 6/2 from Control I 16 only. The ink used on this batch of overprints was shiny jet-black.

There is a constant variety consisting of short left stroke to "N" which occurs at R. 1/8 on Nos. 1, 2, 4 (£30 each); 2c (£75); 3 (£175); 5 (£200); 6, 7 (£40 each); 8, 9, 10 (£60 each); 11, 12 (£85 each). All unused prices.

*(c) With T **3***
(i) Waterlow printing

17	5s. rose-carmine	£2500	£2250
	s. Optd "SPECIMEN"	£1800	
18	10s. indigo-blue (R.)	£11000	£5000
	a. Double opt, one albino	£13000	£7000
	s. Optd "SPECIMEN"	£1000	
	sa. Ditto "NAURU" double, one albino ...	£2500	

(ii) De La Rue printing

19	2s.6d. sepia-brown (shades)	£600	£1600
	a. Double opt, one albino	£1700	
	b. Treble opt, two albino	£1800	
	s. Optd "SPECIMEN"	£350	
20	2s.6d. yellow-brown (shades)	70·00	£120
21	2s.6d. brown (shades)	70·00	£120
	a. Re-entry (R. 2/1)	£6000	
22	5s. bright carmine (shades)	£100	£150
	a. Treble opt, two albino	£1500	
	s. Optd "SPECIMEN"	£325	
	sa. Ditto "NAURU" double, one albino ...	£1500	
23	10s. pale blue (R.)	£250	£350
	a. Treble opt (Blk.+R.+albino)	£3750	
	b. Double opt, one albino	£1600	
	c. Treble opt, two albino	£1700	
23d	10s. deep bright blue (R.)	£500	£700

(iii) Bradbury Wilkinson printing (1919)

24	2s.6d. chocolate-brown	90·00	£200
	b. Double opt, one albino	£500	
25	2s.6d. pale brown	80·00	£190
	a. Double opt, one albino	£500	

The initial printing of the 2s.6d. to 10s. values, made in Sept 1915 but not known to have been issued before 2 Sept 1916, comprised one and a half sheets each of the 2s.6d. (No. 19) and 10s. (No. 18) and three sheets of the 5s. (No. 17), as well as the supply of "Specimens", where the 5s. value was mostly from the De La Rue printing (No. 22).

The original supply of the 2s.6d. value (No. 19) included distinct shade variants, covered by "sepia-brown (shades)". The "Specimens" are mostly in a deeper shade than the issued stamp. One half-sheet of 20 was quite deep, and only appears to exist cancelled "SE 2 16", apart from a mint block of four in the Royal Collection. The full sheet of 40 was in a slightly paler shade and included 12 double, one albino and eight treble, two albino varieties. A few sheets in sepia-brown shades were also included in later supplies of the 2s.6d. value, but these were mostly in shades of yellow-brown (No. 20) and brown (No. 21).

Examples of most values between Nos. 1 and 25 are known showing a forged PO. Pleasant Island postmark dated "NO 2 21".

AUSTRALIAN MANDATE

4 *Century* (freighter)

(Des R. A. Harrison. Eng T. S. Harrison. Recess Note Printing Branch of the Treasury, Melbourne and from 1926 by the Commonwealth Bank of Australia)

1924–48. No wmk. P 11.

A. Rough surfaced, greyish paper (1924–34)

26A	**4**	½d. chestnut	2·50	2·75
27A		1d. green	3·50	2·75
28A		1½d. scarlet	4·00	4·00
29A		2d. orange	4·00	19·00
30A		2½d. slate-blue	6·00	25·00
		c. Greenish blue (1934)	18·00	32·00
31A		3d. pale blue	4·00	13·00
32A		4d. olive-green	7·50	27·00
33A		5d. brown	4·25	7·00
34A		6d. dull violet	4·75	20·00
35A		9d. olive-brown	9·50	19·00
36A		1s. brown-lake	6·50	13·00
37A		2s.6d. grey-green	32·00	55·00
38A		5s. claret	50·00	£110
39A		10s. yellow	£130	£190
26A/39A *Set of 14*			£225	£450

B. Shiny surfaced, white paper (1937–48)

26B	**4**	½d. chestnut	4·00	13·00
		c. Perf 14 (1947)	1·60	10·00
27B		1d. green	2·50	3·00
28B		1½d. scarlet	1·00	1·50
29B		2d. orange	6·00	8·00
30B		2½d. dull blue (1948)	4·75	4·00
		a. Imperf between (vert pair)	£17000	£18000
		b. Imperf between (horiz pair)	£17000	£18000
31B		3d. greenish grey (1947)	7·00	22·00
32B		4d. olive-green	7·00	13·00
33B		5d. brown	14·00	4·00
34B		6d. dull violet	11·00	5·00
35B		9d. olive-brown	12·00	22·00
36B		1s. brown-lake	13·00	2·75
37B		2s.6d. grey-green	32·00	35·00
38B		5s. claret	38·00	50·00
39B		10s. yellow	85·00	£100
26B/39B *Set of 14*			£200	£225

HIS MAJESTY'S JUBILEE.

1910 - 1935
(5)

6

1935 (12 July). Silver Jubilee. T **4** (shiny surfaced, white paper) optd with T **5**.

40		1½d. scarlet	75	80
41		2d. orange	1·50	4·25
42		2½d. dull blue	1·50	1·50
43		1s. brown-lake	7·25	3·50
40/3 *Set of 4*			10·00	9·00

2½d. Re-entry (R. 4/4)

(Recess John Ash, Melbourne)

1937 (10 May). Coronation. P 11.

44	**6**	1½d. scarlet	45	1·75
45		2d. orange	45	2·75
46		2½d. blue	45	1·75
		a. Re-entry	35·00	55·00
47		1s. purple	65	2·00
44/7 *Set of 4*			1·75	7·50

Japanese forces invaded Nauru on 26 August 1942 and virtually all the inhabitants were removed to Truk in the Caroline Islands.

The Australian army liberated Nauru on 13 September 1945. After an initial period without stamps, Australian issues were supplied during October 1945 and were used from Nauru until further supplies of Nos. 26/39B became available. The deportees did not return until early in 1946

7 Nauruan Netting Fish

8 Anibare Bay

9 Loading phosphate from cantilever

10 Great Frigate bird

11 Nauruan canoe

12 Domaneab (meeting-house)

13 Palm trees

14 Buada lagoon

15 Map of Nauru

(Recess Note Printing Branch, Commonwealth Bank, Melbourne, and from 1960 by Note Ptg Branch, Reserve Bank of Australia, Melbourne)

1954 (6 Feb)–**65**. T **7**/**15**. Toned paper. P 13½×14½ (horiz) or 14½×13½ (vert).

48	**7**	½d. deep violet	20	2·00
		a. Violet (8.5.61)	30	80
49	**8**	1d. bluish green	30	2·00
		a. Emerald-green (8.5.61)	1·00	55
		b. Deep green (1965)	4·00	3·00
50	**9**	3½d. scarlet	1·75	1·00
		a. Vermilion (1958)	8·50	75
51	**10**	4d. grey-blue	2·75	2·00
		a. Deep blue (1958)	19·00	4·00
52	**11**	6d. orange	70	20
53	**12**	9d. claret	60	20
54	**13**	1s. deep purple	30	30
55	**14**	2s.6d. deep green	2·75	1·00
56	**15**	5s. magenta	8·00	2·25
48a/56 *Set of 9*			15·00	7·00

Nos. 48a, 49a/b, 50a and 51a are on white paper.

16 Micronesian Pigeon

17 Poison Nut

18 "Iyo" (*calophyllum*)

19 Black Lizard

20 Capparis

21a Coral pinnacles

21 White Tern

21b Finsch's Reed Warbler

(Recess (10d., 2s.3d.) or photo (others) Note Ptg Branch, Reserve Bank of Australia, Melbourne)

1963–65. T **16**/**21b**. P 13½×13 (5d.), 13×13½ (8d.), 14×13½ (10d.), 15×14½ (1s.3d.) or 13½ (others).

57	**16**	2d. black, blue, red-brown and orange-yellow (3.5.65)	75	2·25
58	**17**	3d. multicoloured (16.4.64)	40	35
59	**18**	5d. multicoloured (22.4.63)	40	75
60	**19**	8d. black and green (1.7.63)	1·75	80
61	**20**	10d. black (16.4.64)	40	30
62	**21**	1s.3d. blue, black and yellow-green (3.5.65)	1·00	4·75
63	**21a**	2s.3d. ultramarine (16.4.64)	2·00	55
64	**21b**	2s.3d. multicoloured (3.5.65)	1·00	4·25
57/64 *Set of 8*			7·00	12·50

22 *Simpson and his Donkey*

(Des C. Andrew (after statue, Shrine of Remembrance, Melbourne. Photo Note Ptg Branch, Reserve Bank of Australia, Melbourne))

1965 (14 Apr). 50th Anniv of Gallipoli Landing. P 13½.

65	**22**	5d. sepia, black and emerald	15	10

(New Currency. 100 cents = 1 Australian dollar)

24 Anibare Bay

25 "Iyo" (*calophyllum*)

(Recess (1, 2, 3, 5, 8, 19, 25c. and $1) or photo (others))

1966 (14 Feb–25 May). Decimal Currency. Various stamps with values in cents and dollars as T **24**/**5** and some colours changed. Recess printed stamps on Helecon paper.

66	**24**	1c. deep blue	15	10
67	**7**	2c. brown-purple (25.5)	15	50
68	**9**	3c. bluish green (25.5)	30	2·25
69	**25**	4c. multicoloured	20	10
70	**19**	5c. deep ultramarine (25.5)	25	60
71	**19**	7c. black and chestnut	30	10
72	**20**	8c. olive-green	20	10
73	**10**	10c. red (as 4d.)	40	10
74	**21**	15c. blue, black and yellow-green (25.5)	60	3·25
75	**21a**	25c. deep brown (25.5)	30	1·25
76	**17**	30c. multicoloured	45	30
77	**21b**	35c. multicoloured (25.5)	75	35
78	**16**	50c. multicoloured	1·50	80
79	**15**	$1 magenta	75	1·00
66/79 *Set of 14*			5·50	9·50

The 25c. is as No. 63, but larger, 27½×24½ mm.

REPUBLIC

Nauru became independent on 31 January 1968 and was later admitted into special membership of the Commonwealth.

REPUBLIC
OF
NAURU
(26)

1968 (31 Jan–15 May). Nos. 66/79 optd with T **26**.

80	**24**	1c. deep blue (R.)	10	30
81	**7**	2c. brown-purple	10	10
82	**9**	3c. bluish green	15	10
83	**25**	4c. multicoloured (15.5.68)	10	10
84	**13**	5c. deep ultramarine (R.)	10	10
85	**19**	7c. black and chestnut (R.) (15.5.68)	25	10
86	**20**	8c. olive-green (R.)	10	10
87	**10**	10c. red	50	15
88	**21**	15c. blue, black and yellow-green	1·00	2·75
89	**21a**	25c. deep brown (R.)	15	15
90	**17**	30c. multicoloured (15.5.68)	40	15
91	**21b**	35c. multicoloured (15.5.68)	1·25	30
92	**16**	50c. multicoloured	1·00	35
93	**15**	$1 magenta	75	50
80/93 *Set of 14*			5·00	4·25

27 "Towards the Sunrise"

28 Planting Seedling, and Map

(Des H. Fallu (5c.), Note Ptg Branch (10c.). Photo Note Ptg Branch, Reserve Bank of Australia, Melbourne)

1968 (11 Sept). Independence. P 13½.

94	**27**	5c. black, slate-lilac, orange-yellow and yellow-green	10	10
95	**28**	10c. black, yellow-green and new blue	10	10

29 Flag of Independent Nauru

(Des J. Mason. Photo Note Ptg Branch, Reserve Bank of Australia, Melbourne)

1969 (31 Jan). P 13½.

96	**29**	15c. yellow, orange and royal blue	65	15

This is a definitive issue which was put on sale on the first anniversary of Independence.

Nevis *see* St. Kitts-Nevis

New Brunswick *see* Canada

Newfoundland *see* Canada

New Guinea *see after* Australia

New Hebrides

Stamps of NEW SOUTH WALES were used by various Postal Agencies in the New Hebrides from August 1891 onwards. From late 1892 the N.S.W. agency at Port Vila was run by the Australian New Hebrides Company who, from 1897, issued local 1d. and 2d. stamps for the carriage of mail on the Company's ships. These can be found used in combination with N.S.W. issues. Similar Postal Agencies supplying the stamps of NEW CALEDONIA were opened from 1903 onwards. The use of New South Wales and New Caledonia stamps was prohibited after 1 December 1908.

PRICES FOR STAMPS ON COVER TO 1945

Nos. 1/8 (F1/5)	*from* × 10
No. 9	*from* × 2
Nos. 10/16 (F6/10)	*from* × 8
Nos. 18/28 (F11/32)	*from* × 6
Nos. 30/4 (F33/7)	*from* × 4
No. 35 (F32*a*)	—
Nos. 36/9	*from* × 3
Nos. 40/2 (F38/41)	*from* × 4
Nos. 43/51 (F42/52)	*from* × 5
Nos. 52/63 (F53/64)	*from* × 3
Nos. D1/5 (FD53/7)	*from* × 100
Nos. D6/10 (FD65/9)	*from* × 8

ANGLO-FRENCH CONDOMINIUM

The New Hebrides, an island group in the south-west Pacific, were recognised as an area of joint Anglo-French influence in 1878. The position was regularised by the Convention of 20 October 1906 which created a Condominium, the two nations having equal rights and shares in the administration of the islands.

Stamps inscribed in English or French were issued concurrently and had equal validity throughout the islands. A common currency was reflected in the face values from 1938.

Where common designs were used, the main differences between stamps inscribed in English and those in French are as follows:

(a) Inscriptions in English or French.

(b) Position of cyphers. French issues normally have "RF" to the right or above the British royal cypher.

(c) French issues are without watermark, *unless otherwise stated.*

Inscriptions in English

Inscriptions in French

I. STAMPS INSCRIBED IN ENGLISH

NEW HEBRIDES.   **NEW HEBRIDES**

CONDOMINIUM.   **CONDOMINIUM**
(1)   (2)

1908 (29 Oct). T **23** and **24** of Fiji optd with T **1** by Govt Printing Establishment, Suva. On the bicoloured stamps the word "FIJI" obliterated by a bar in the colour of the word. P 14.

(a) Wmk Mult Crown CA. Ordinary paper (½d., 1d.) or chalk-surfaced paper (1s.)

1		½d. green and pale green (No. 115)	17·00	26·00
1*a*		½d. green (No. 118)	40	7·00
2		1d. red	50	40
		a. Opt omitted (in vert pair with normal)	£10000	
3		1s. green and carmine	28·00	3·75

(b) Wmk Crown CA

4		½d. green and grey-green	60·00	85·00
5		2d. dull purple and orange	60	70
6		2½d. dull purple and blue/*blue*	60	70
7		5d. dull purple and green	80	2·00
8		6d. dull purple and carmine	70	1·25
9		1s. green and carmine	£140	£300
1*a*/9 *Set of 9*			£200	£350

1910 (15 Dec). Types as last optd with T **2** by D.L.R. Ordinary paper (½d. to 2½d.) or chalk-surfaced paper (5d., 6d., 1s.). Wmk Mult Crown CA. P 14.

10		½d. green	3·50	32·00
11		1d. red	11·00	8·50
12		2d. grey	70	3·00
13		2½d. bright blue	75	7·50
14		5d. dull purple and olive-green	2·25	5·50
15		6d. dull and deep purple	1·50	8·00
16		1s. black/*green* (R.)	1·50	7·00
10/16 *Set of 7*			19·00	65·00
10s/16s Optd "SPECIMEN" *Set of 7*			£275	

3 Weapons and Idols

1d.
(4)

(Des J. Giraud. Recess D.L.R.)

1911 (25 July). Wmk Mult Crown CA. P 14.

18	**3**	½d. green	85	1·75
19		1d. red	5·50	2·00
20		2d. grey	9·00	3·00

21		2½d. ultramarine	5·00	5·50
24		5d. sage-green	4·50	7·00
25		6d. purple	3·00	5·00
26		1s. black/*green*	2·75	13·00
27		2s. purple/*blue*	48·00	22·00
28		5s. green/*yellow*	48·00	55·00
18/28 *Set of 9*			£110	£100
18s/28s Optd "SPECIMEN" *Set of 9*			£250	

1920 (June)–**21**. Surch with T **4** at Govt Printing Establishment, Suva.

(a) On Nos. 24 and 26/8

30	**3**	1d. on 5d. sage-green (10.3.21)	11·00	65·00
		a. Surch inverted	£4500	
31		1d. on 1s. black/*green*	4·25	13·00
32		1d. on 2s. purple/*blue*	1·75	10·00
33		1d. on 5s. green/*yellow*	1·00	10·00

(b) On No. F16

34	**3**	2d. on 40c. red/*yellow*	1·00	23·00

(c) On No. F27

35	**3**	2d. on 40c. red/*yellow*	£130	£700

1921 (Sept–Oct). Wmk Mult Script CA. P 14.

36	**3**	1d. scarlet	2·50	14·00
37		2d. slate-grey	4·25	45·00
39		6d. purple	14·00	80·00
36/9 *Set of 3*			19·00	£130
36s/9s Optd "SPECIMEN" *Set of 3*			85·00	

1924 (1 May). Surch as T **4**, at Suva.

40	**3**	1d. on ½d. green (No. 18)	4·00	24·00
41		3d. on 1d. scarlet (No. 36)	4·00	11·00
42		5d. on 2½d. ultramarine (No. 21)	7·50	28·00
		a. Surch inverted	£3500	
40/2 *Set of 3*			14·00	55·00

5

(Recess D.L.R.)

1925 (June). Wmk Mult Script CA. P 14.

43	**5**	½d. (5c.) black	1·25	21·00
44		1d. (10c.) green	1·00	19·00
45		2d. (20c.) slate-grey	1·75	2·50
46		2½d. (25c.) brown	1·00	13·00
47		5d. (50c.) ultramarine	3·00	2·75
48		6d. (60c.) purple	4·00	17·00
49		1s. (1.25fr.) black/*emerald*	3·25	19·00
50		2s. (2.50fr.) purple/*blue*	6·00	22·00
51		5s. (6.25fr.) green/*yellow*	6·00	25·00
43/51 *Set of 9*			23·00	£120
43s/51s Optd "SPECIMEN" *Set of 9*			£225	

(New Currency. 100 gold centimes = 1 gold franc)

The currency used for the face values of issues to 1977 was an artificial, rather than an actual, monetary unit. The actual currencies in use were Australian dollars and the local franc.

6 Lopevi Island and Outrigger Canoe

(Des J. Kerhor. Eng J. G. Hall. Recess B.W.)

1938 (1 June). Gold Currency. Wmk Mult Script CA. P 12.

52	**6**	5c. blue-green	2·50	4·50
53		10c. orange	3·50	2·25
54		15c. bright violet	3·50	4·50
55		20c. scarlet	4·00	6·00
56		25c. reddish brown	1·60	3·00
57		30c. blue	4·50	2·75
58		40c. grey-olive	4·50	6·50
59		50c. purple	1·60	2·75
60		1f. red/*green*	10·00	9·00
61		2f. blue/*green*	30·00	24·00
62		5f. red/*yellow*	75·00	55·00
63		10f. violet/*blue*	£225	80·00
52/63 *Set of 12*			£325	£170
52s/63s Perf "SPECIMEN" *Set of 12*			£275	

(Recess Waterlow)

1949 (10 Oct). 75th Anniv of UPU As No. 117 of Antigua. Wmk Mult Script CA. P 13½×14.

64		10c. red-orange	30	1·25
65		15c. violet	30	1·25
66		30c. ultramarine	30	1·25
67		50c. purple	40	1·25
64/7 *Set of 4*			1·10	4·50

7 Outrigger Sailing Canoes

8 Native carving

9 Two natives outside hut

(Des C. Hertenberger (1f. to 5f.), R. Serres (others). Recess Waterlow)

1953 (30 Apr). T **7/9**. Wmk Mult Script CA. P 12½.
68	**7**	5c. green	1·00	2·25
69		10c. scarlet	1·50	1·25
70		15c. yellow-ochre	1·50	20
71		20c. ultramarine	1·50	20
72	**8**	25c. olive	60	20
73		30c. brown	60	20
74		40c. blackish brown	60	20
75		50c. violet	1·00	20
76	**9**	1f. orange	7·00	3·00
77		2f. reddish purple	7·00	8·50
78		5f. scarlet	8·50	22·00
68/78 Set of 11			27·00	32·00

1953 (2 June). Coronation. As No. 120 of Antigua.
79	10c. black and carmine	1·00	50

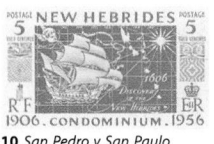

10 San Pedro y San Paulo (Quiros)

11 "Marianne", "Talking Drum" and "Britannia"

(Photo Harrison)

1956 (20 Oct). 50th Anniv of Condominium. T **10/11**. Wmk Mult Script CA. P 14½×14.
80	**10**	5c. emerald	15	10
81		10c. scarlet	40	10
82	**11**	20c. deep bright blue	10	10
83		50c. deep lilac	15	15
80/3 Set of 4			70	40

12 Port Vila: Iririki Islet

13 River scene and spear fisherman

14 Woman drinking from coconut

(Des H. Cheffer (T **12**), P. Gandon (others). Recess Waterlow)

1957 (3 Sept). Wmk Mult Script CA. T **12/14**. P 13½.
84	**12**	5c. green	40	1·50
85		10c. scarlet	30	10
86		15c. yellow-ochre	50	1·50
87		20c. ultramarine	40	10
88	**13**	25c. olive	45	10
89		30c. brown	45	10
90		40c. sepia	45	10
91		50c. violet	45	10
92	**14**	1f. orange	1·00	1·00
93		2f. mauve	4·00	2·50
94		5f. black	9·00	3·75
84/94 Set of 11			15·00	9·50

1963 (2 Sept). Freedom from Hunger. As No. 146 of Antigua.
95	60c. green	50	15

15 Red Cross Emblem

(Des V. Whiteley. Litho B.W.)

1963 (2 Sept). Red Cross Centenary. W w **12**. P 13½.
96	**15**	15c. red and black	40	10
97		45c. red and blue	60	20

16 Exporting Manganese, Forari

17 Cocoa Beans

18 Copra

19 Fishing from Palikulo Point

---

20 Painted Triggerfish

21 New Caledonian Nautilus Shell

22 Lionfish

23 Clown Surgeonfish

24 Cardinal Honeyeater

25 Buff-bellied Flycatcher

26 Thicket Warbler

27 White-collared Kingfisher

(Des V. Whiteley, from drawings by J. White (10c., 20c.), K. Penny (40c.), C. Robin (3f.). Photo Harrison. Des C. Robin (5c., 1f.), J. White (15c.), G. Vasarhelyi (25c., 5f.), A. Larkins, Turrell and Thomas (30c., 50c., 2f.). Recess Govt Printing Works, Paris)

1963 (25 Nov)–**72**. T **16/27**. W w **12** (10c., 20c., 40c., 3f.) or no wmk (others). P 14 (3f.), 12½ (10c., 20c., 40c.) or 13 (others).
98	**16**	5c. lake, purple-brown and greenish blue (15.8.66)	2·00	50
		a. Lake and greenish blue* (29.2.72)	42·00	9·50
99	**17**	10c. light brown, buff and emerald (16.8.65)	15	10
100	**18**	15c. yellow-bistre, red-brown and deep violet	15	10
101	**19**	20c. black, olive-green and greenish blue (16.8.65)	55	10
102	**20**	25c. reddish violet, orange-brown and crimson (15.8.66)	50	70
103	**21**	30c. chestnut, bistre and violet	75	10
104	**22**	40c. vermilion and deep blue (16.8.65)	80	1·40
105	**23**	50c. green, yellow and greenish blue	60	10
106	**24**	1f. red, black and deep bluish green (15.8.66)	2·00	3·00
107	**25**	2f. black, brown-purple and yellow-olive	2·00	1·25
108	**26**	3f. deep violet, orange-brown, emerald and black (16.8.65)	6·00	3·50
		w. Wmk inverted	7·00	
109	**27**	5f. blue, deep blue and black (24.1.67)	6·00	19·00
98/109 Set of 12			19·00	26·00

*In No. 98a the globe is printed in the same colour as the centre, instead of in purple-brown.
See also No. 129.

28 ITU Emblem

(Des M. Goaman. Litho Enschedé)

1965 (17 May). I.T.U. Centenary. W w **12**. P 11×11½.
110	**28**	15c. scarlet and drab	20	10
111		60c. blue and light red	35	20

29 ICY Emblem

(Des V. Whiteley. Litho Harrison)

1965 (24 Oct). International Co-operation Year. W w **12**. P 14½.
112	**29**	5c. reddish purple and turquoise-green	15	10
113		55c. deep bluish green and lavender	20	20

30 Sir Winston Churchill and St. Paul's Cathedral in Wartime

(Des Jennifer Toombs. Photo Harrison)

1966 (24 Jan). Churchill Commemoration. W w **12**. P 14.
114	**30**	5c. black, cerise, gold and new blue	20	15
115		15c. black, cerise, gold and deep green	70	10
116		25c. black, cerise, gold and brown	80	10
117		30c. black, cerise, gold and bluish violet	80	15
114/17 Set of 4			2·25	45

31 Footballer's Legs, Ball and Jules Rimet Cup

(Des V. Whiteley. Litho Harrison)

1966 (1 July). World Cup Football Championship. W w **12** (sideways). P 14.
118	**31**	20c. violet, yellow-green, lake and yellow-brown	30	15
119		40c. chocolate, blue-green, lake and yellow-brown	70	15

32 WHO Building

(Des M. Goaman. Litho Harrison)

1966 (20 Sept). Inauguration of WHO Headquarters, Geneva. W w **12** (sideways). P 14.
120	**32**	25c. black, yellow-green and light blue	15	10
121		60c. black, light purple and yellow-brown	40	20

33 "Education"

(Des Jennifer Toombs. Litho Harrison)

1966 (1 Dec). 20th Anniv of UNESCO. W w **12** (sideways). T **33** and similar horiz designs. P 14.
122		15c. slate-violet, red, yellow and orange	25	10
123		30c. orange-yellow, violet and deep olive	65	10
124		45c. black, bright purple and orange	75	15
122/4 Set of 3			1·50	30

Designs:—30c. "Science"; 45c. "Culture".

36 The Coast Watchers

(Des R. Granger Barrett. Photo Enschedé)

1967 (26 Sept). 25th Anniv of the Pacific War. T **36** and similar horiz designs. Multicoloured. W w **12**. P 14×13.
125		15c. Type **36**	40	15
126		25c. Map of war zone, US marine and Australian soldier	70	25
127		60c. HMAS Canberra (cruiser)	70	40
128		1f. Boeing B-17 Flying Fortress	70	1·25
125/8 Set of 4			2·25	1·90

1967 (5 Dec). New value with W w **12** (sideways).
129	60c. vermilion and deep blue (as No. 104)	40	15

40 Globe and Hemispheres

(Des and eng J. Combet. Recess Govt Printing Works, Paris)

1968 (23 May). Bicentenary of Bougainville's World Voyage. T **40** and similar horiz designs. P 13.
130		15c. emerald, slate-violet and red	20	10
131		25c. deep olive, maroon and ultramarine	45	15
132		60c. bistre-brown, brown-purple and myrtle-green	45	20
130/2 Set of 3			1·00	40

Designs:—25c. Ships La Boudeuse and L'Etoile, and map; 60c. Bougainville, ship's figure-head and bougainvillea flowers.

43 Concorde and Vapour Trails

45 Kauri Pine

(Des S. W. Moss (25c.), R. Granger Barrett (60c.). Litho D.L.R.)

1968 (9 Oct). Anglo-French Concorde Project. T **43** and similar horiz design. W w **12** (sideways). P 14.

133		25c. light blue, orange-red and deep violet-blue	35	30
134		60c. red, black and bright blue	40	45

Design:—60c. Concorde in flight.

(Des V. Whiteley. Litho Format)

1969 (30 June). Timber Industry. W w **12**. P 14½.

135	**45**	20c. multicoloured (shades)	10	10

No. 135 was issued in small sheets of nine (3×3) printed on a simulated wood-grain background and with a decorative border showing various stages of the local timber industry. There is a wide range of shades on the printing.

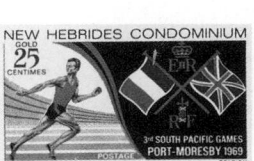

46 Cyphers, Flags and Relay Runner receiving Baton

48 Diver on Platform

(Des C. Haley. Photo Delrieu)

1969 (13 Aug). Third South Pacific Games, Port Moresby. T **46** and similar horiz design. Multicoloured. P 12½.

136		25c. Type **46**	10	10
137		1f. Cyphers, flags and relay runner passing baton	20	20

(Des V. Whiteley. Litho P.B.)

1969 (15 Oct). Pentecost Island Land Divers. T **48** and similar vert designs. Multicoloured. W w **12** (sideways). P 12½.

138		15c. Type **48**	10	10
139		25c. Diver jumping	10	10
140		1f. Diver at end of fall	20	20
138/40	Set of 3		35	35

51 U.P.U. Emblem and New Headquarters Building

52 General Charles de Gaulle

(Des and eng J. Gauthier. Recess Govt Ptg Wks, Paris)

1970 (20 May). Inauguration of New UPU Headquarters Building. P 13.

141	**51**	1f.05 slate, red-orange and bright purple	20	20

(Des V. Whiteley. Photo Govt Ptg Wks, Paris)

1970 (20 July). 30th Anniv of New Hebrides' Declaration for the Free French Government. P 13.

142	**52**	65c. multicoloured	35	70
143		1f.10 multicoloured	45	70

(53)

54 The Virgin and Child (Bellini)

1970 (15 Oct). As No. 101, but W w **12** (sideways) and surch with T **53**.

144		35c. on 20c. black, olive-green and greenish blue	30	30

(Des V. Whiteley. Litho Harrison)

1970 (30 Nov). Christmas. T **54** and similar vert design. Multicoloured. W w **12** (sideways). P 14½×14.

145		15c. Type **54**	10	10
146		50c. The Virgin and Child (Cima)	20	20

POSTAGE DUE STAMPS

POSTAGE DUE **POSTAGE DUE** **POSTAGE DUE**
(D **1**)   (D **2**)   (D **3**)

1925 (June). Optd with Type D **1**, by D.L.R.

D1	**5**	1d. (10c.) green	30·00	1·00
D2		2d. (20c.) slate-grey	32·00	1·50
D3		3d. (30c.) red	32·00	2·75
D4		5d. (50c.) ultramarine	35·00	4·75
D5		10d. (1f.) carmine/blue	40·00	6·00
D1/5	Set of 5		£150	14·00
D1s/5s Optd "SPECIMEN" Set of 5			£180	

1938 (1 June). Optd with Type D **2**, by B.W.

D6	**6**	5c. blue-green	35·00	50·00
D7		10c. orange	35·00	50·00
D8		20c. scarlet	42·00	75·00
D9		40c. grey-olive	48·00	85·00
D10		1f. red/green	48·00	90·00
D6/10	Set of 5		£190	£325
D6s/10s Perf "SPECIMEN" Set of 5			£160	

1953 (30 Apr). Nos. 68/9, 71, 74 and 76 optd with Type D **3**, by Waterlow.

D11		5c. green	5·00	9·00
D12		10c. scarlet	1·75	16·00
D13		20c. ultramarine	5·00	25·00
D14		40c. blackish brown	17·00	45·00
D15		1f. orange	4·50	45·00
D11/15	Set of 5		30·00	£130

1957 (3 Sept). Nos. 84/5, 87, 90 and 92 optd with Type D **3**, by Waterlow.

D16	**12**	5c. green	30	1·50
D17		10c. scarlet	30	1·50
D18		20c. ultramarine	75	1·75
D19		40c. sepia	1·00	2·75
D20	**14**	1f. orange	1·25	3·25
D16/20	Set of 5		3·25	9·50

II. STAMPS INSCRIBED IN FRENCH

(Currency. 100 centimes = 1 French franc)

NOUVELLES HÉBRIDES
(F **1**)

NOUVELLES-HÉBRIDES
(F **2**)

1908 (21 Nov). T **15/17** of New Caledonia. optd with Types F **1** or F **2** (1f.), by Govt Ptg Wks, Paris.

F1		5c. green	13·00	4·75
F2		10c. red	13·00	3·50
F3		25c. blue/greenish (R.)	9·50	2·25
F4		50c. red/orange	8·50	4·75
F5		1f. blue/green (R.)	28·00	20·00
F1/5	Set of 5		65·00	30·00

CONDOMINIUM   **10c.**
(F **3**)   (F **6**)

1910 (Aug)–11. Nos. F1/5 further optd with Type F **3**, or larger (1f.), by Govt Ptg Wks, Paris.

F6		5c. green	9·50	3·00
F7		10c. carmine	9·50	1·25
F8		25c. blue/greenish (R.) (1911)	3·00	4·00
F9		50c. red/orange (1911)	13·00	35·00
F10		1f. blue/green (R.)	30·00	22·00
F6/10	Set of 5		60·00	60·00

All the above were released in Paris on 16 March 1910. The 5c., 10c. and 1f. were issued in New Hebrides in August but the 25c. and 50c. were not received until 1911 after the issue of the definitive stamps and they were placed in reserve, although some may have been issued on request.

1911 (12 July). Wmk Mult Crown CA. P 14.

F11	**3**	5c. green	1·00	3·00
F12		10c. carmine	50	1·00
F13		20c. greyish slate	1·00	2·25
F14		25c. ultramarine	2·75	4·50
F15		30c. brown/yellow	6·50	5·25
F16		40c. red/yellow	1·40	6·00
F17		50c. sage-green	2·00	6·50
F18		75c. orange	7·00	32·00
F19		1f. red/blue	7·00	4·50
F20		2f. violet	12·00	22·00
F21		5f. red/green	12·00	48·00
F11/21	Set of 11		45·00	£120

1913. As last but wmk "R F" in sheet or without wmk.

F22	**3**	5c. green	1·25	5·50
F23		10c. carmine	1·00	6·00
F24		20c. greyish slate	1·00	2·40
F25		25c. ultramarine	1·25	5·00
F26		30c. brown/yellow	2·50	19·00
F27		40c. red/yellow	24·00	80·00
F28		50c. sage-green	19·00	40·00
F29		75c. orange	9·00	42·00
F30		1f. red/blue	9·00	10·00
F31		2f. violet	9·00	50·00
F32		5f. red/green	35·00	60·00
F22/32	Set of 11		£100	£275

The above were placed on sale in Paris on 29 April 1912.

1920–21. Surch as Type F **6**, at Govt Printing Establishment, Suva, Fiji.

(a) On stamps of 1908–11 (June 1920)

F32a		5c. on 50c. red/orange (F4)	£550	£650
F33		5c. on 50c. red/orange (F9)	2·40	22·00
F33a		10c. on 25c. blue/greenish (F8)	50	1·50

(b) On stamps of 1911–13 (10.3.21)

F34	**3**	5c. on 40c. red/yellow (F27)	27·00	£100
F35		20c. on 30c. brown/yellow (F15)	15·00	70·00
F36		20c. on 30c. brown/yellow (F26)	11·00	80·00

(c) On Inscr in English (10.3.21)

F37	**3**	10c. on 5d. sage-green (24)	16·00	60·00

1924 (1 May). Stamps of 1911–13 surch as Type F **6**, at Suva.

F38	**3**	10c. on 5c. green (F22)	1·00	11·00
F39		30c. on 10c. carmine (F23)	1·00	3·00
F40		50c. on 25c. ultramarine (F14)	50·00	£110
F41		50c. on 25c. ultramarine (F25)	2·50	29·00
F38/41	Set of 4		50·00	£140

F **7**   (F **9**)   **France Libre**

(Recess D.L.R.)

1925 (June). Wmk "R F" in sheet or without wmk. P 14.

F42	F **7**	5c. (½d.) black	75	13·00
F43		10c. (1d.) green	1·00	9·00
F44		20c. (2d.) greyish slate	4·00	2·75
F45		25c. (2½d.) brown	1·50	9·00
F46		30c. (3d.) red	1·75	18·00
F47		40c. (4d.) red/yellow	3·00	16·00
F48		50c. (5d.) ultramarine	2·00	1·75
F49		75c. (7½d.) yellow-brown	1·50	23·00
F50		1f. (10d.) carmine/blue	1·50	2·50
F51		2f. (1/8) violet	2·50	38·00
F52		5f. (4s.) carmine/green	3·50	38·00
F42/52	Set of 11		20·00	£150
F42s/52s Optd "SPECIMEN" Set of 11			£250	

In July 1929 a batch of mail was carried by aircraft from Port Vila to the French cruiser *Tourville* for sorting and forwarding at Nouméa, New Caledonia. Stamps of the above issue (including those with English inscriptions) were affixed to covers and handstamped "PAR AVION" before cancellation.

(New Currency. 100 gold centimes = 1 gold franc)

1938 (1 June). Gold Currency. Wmk "R F" in sheet or without wmk. P 12.

F53	**6**	5c. blue-green	5·50	13·00
F54		10c. orange	6·00	3·75
F55		15c. bright violet	6·00	9·50
F56		20c. scarlet	6·00	7·00
F57		25c. reddish brown	12·00	9·00
F58		30c. blue	12·00	9·50
F59		40c. grey-olive	6·50	17·00
F60		50c. purple	6·50	6·50
F61		1f. lake/pale green (shades)	7·50	10·00
F62		2f. blue/pale green (shades)	50·00	50·00
F63		5f. red/yellow	75·00	80·00
F64		10f. violet/blue	£160	£170
F53/64	Set of 12		£300	£350
F53s/64s Perf "SPECIMEN" Set of 12			£350	

1941 (15 Apr). Adherence to General de Gaulle. Optd with Type F **9**, at Nouméa, New Caledonia.

F65	**6**	5c. blue-green	2·00	25·00
F66		10c. orange	6·00	40·00
F67		15c. bright violet	9·50	40·00
F68		20c. scarlet	27·00	32·00
F69		25c. reddish brown	29·00	42·00
F70		30c. blue	30·00	38·00
F71		40c. grey-olive	30·00	40·00
F72		50c. purple	25·00	38·00
F73		1f. lake/pale green	25·00	40·00
F74		2f. blue/pale green	24·00	38·00
F75		5f. red/yellow	19·00	38·00
F76		10f. violet/blue	18·00	38·00
F65/76	Set of 12		£200	£375

1949 (10 Oct). 75th Anniv of UPU As Nos. 64/7. Wmk "R F" in sheet or without wmk. P 13½.

F77		10c. red-orange	3·50	7·50
F78		15c. violet	4·75	12·00
F79		30c. ultramarine	7·50	16·00
F80		50c. purple	8·50	19·00
F77/80	Set of 4		22·00	50·00

1953 (30 Apr). As Nos. 68/78. Wmk "R F" in sheet or without wmk. P 12½.

F81	**7**	5c. green	3·25	8·00
F82		10c. scarlet	6·50	8·00
F83		15c. yellow-ochre	6·50	8·50
F84		20c. ultramarine	6·50	6·50
F85	**8**	25c. olive	3·50	6·50
F86		30c. brown	1·75	6·50
F87		40c. blackish brown	2·00	6·50
F88		50c. violet	2·00	4·50
F89	**9**	1f. orange	15·00	13·00
F90		2f. reddish purple	19·00	50·00
F91		5f. scarlet	19·00	85·00
F81/91	Set of 11		75·00	£170

1956 (20 Oct). 50th Anniv of Condominium. As Nos. 80/3. Wmk "R F" in sheet or without wmk. P 14½×14.

F92	**10**	5c. emerald	2·00	2·25
F93		10c. scarlet	2·25	2·25
F94	**11**	20c. deep bright blue	1·50	2·75
F95		50c. deep lilac	1·50	2·75
F92/5	Set of 4		6·50	9·25

1957 (3 Sept). As Nos. 84/94. Wmk "R F" in sheet or without wmk. P 13½.

F96	**12**	5c. green	1·75	3·00
F97		10c. scarlet	2·25	3·50
F98		15c. orange-yellow	2·50	4·00
F99		20c. ultramarine	2·75	3·50
F100	**13**	25c. yellow-olive	2·50	3·00
F101		30c. brown	2·50	1·75

F102		40c. sepia	2·25	2·00
F103		50c. reddish violet	2·75	1·60
F104	**14**	1f. red-orange	9·00	4·00
F105		2f. mauve	12·00	21·00
F106		5f. black	30·00	38·00
F96/106 *Set of* 11			60·00	75·00

F **14** Emblem and Globe

(Des and eng J. Derrey. Recess Govt Ptg Wks, Paris)

1963 (2 Sept). Freedom from Hunger. P 13.

F107	F **14**	60c. deep bluish green and chestnut	19·00	18·00

F **15** Centenary Emblem

(Des and eng J. Combet. Recess Govt Ptg Wks, Paris)

1963 (2 Sept). Red Cross Centenary. P 13.

F108	F **15**	15c. red, grey and orange	11·00	11·00
F109		45c. red, grey and yellow-bistre	14·00	29·00

1963 (25 Nov)–**72**. As Nos. 98/109 and 129. No wmk. P 12½ (10, 20, 40, 60c.), 14 (3f.) or 13 (others).

F110	**16**	5c. lake, purple-brown and greenish blue (15.8.66)	55	2·00
		a. *Lake and greenish blue* (29.2.72)	65·00	65·00
F111	**17**	10c. lt brown, buff and emerald* (16.8.65)	2·00	4·50
F112		10c. light brown, buff and emerald (5.8.68)	1·00	2·25
F113	**18**	15c. Yellow-bistre, red-brown and deep violet	6·00	1·25
F114	**19**	20c. black, olive-green and greenish blue* (16.8.65)	2·25	5·50
F115		20c. black, olive-green and greenish blue (5.8.68)	2·00	2·50
F116	**20**	25c. reddish violet, orange-brown and crimson (15.8.6)	70	2·00
F117	**21**	30c. chestnut, bistre and violet	7·50	1·25
F118	**22**	40c. vermilion and deep blue* (16.8.65)	3·25	9·00
F119	**23**	50c. green, yellow and greenish blue	8·50	2·50
F120	**22**	60c. vermilion and deep blue (5.12.67)	1·75	3·50
F121	**24**	1f. red, black and deep bluish green (15.8.66)	2·00	5·00
F122	**25**	2f. black, brown purple and yellow-olive	17·00	9·00
F123	**26**	3f. multicoloured* (16.8.65)	8·50	26·00
F124		3f. multicoloured (5.8.68)	8·50	16·00
F125	**27**	5f. blue, deep blue and black (24.1.67)	30·00	27·00
F110/25 *Set of* 16			90·00	£100

*Normally all French New Hebrides issues have the "RF" inscription on the right to distinguish them from the British New Hebrides stamps which have it on the left. The stamps indicated by an asterisk have "RF" wrongly placed on the left.

F **16a** *Syncom* Communications Satellite, Telegraph Poles and Morse Key

(Des and eng J. Combet. Recess Govt Ptg Wks, Paris)

1965 (17 May). Air. ITU Centenary. P 13.

F126	F **16a**	15c. blue, chocolate and emerald	10·00	9·00
F127		60c. carmine, deep bluish green and slate	28·00	35·00

1965 (24 Oct). International Co-operation Year. As Nos. 112/13. P 14½.

F128	**29**	5c. deep reddish purple and turquoise-green	3·00	7·00
F129		55c. deep bluish green and lavender	11·00	12·00

1966 (24 Jan). Churchill Commemoration. As Nos. 114/17. P 14.

F130	**30**	5c. black, cerise, gold and new blue	2·10	8·00

F131		15c. black, cerise, gold and deep green	3·00	3·00
F132		25c. black, cerise, gold and brown	4·00	9·00
F133		30c. black, cerise, gold and bluish violet	4·25	10·00
F130/3 *Set of* 4			12·00	27·00

1966 (1 July). World Cup Football Championship. As Nos. 118/19. P 14.

F134	**31**	20c. violet, yellow-green lake and yellow-brown	2·25	5·50
F135		40c. chocolate, blue-green, lake and yellow-brown	4·00	5·50

1966 (20 Sept). Inauguration of WHO Headquarters, Geneva. As Nos. 120/1. P 14.

F136	**32**	25c. black, yellow-green and light blue	4·00	4·50
F137		60c. black, mauve and yellow-ochre	6·00	10·00

1966 (1 Dec). 20th Anniv of UNESCO. As Nos. 122/4. P 14.

F138	**33**	15c. slate-violet, red, yellow and orange	2·50	3·25
F139	–	30c. orange-yellow, violet and deep olive	3·50	4·75
F140	–	45c. black, bright purple and orange	4·00	6·50
F138/40 *Set of* 3			9·00	13·00

1967 (26 Sept). 25th Anniv of the Pacific War. As Nos. 125/8. P 14×13.

F141		15c. Type **36**	1·40	1·50
F142		25c. Map of war zone, US marine and Australian soldier	2·00	3·00
F143		60c. HMAS *Canberra* (cruiser)	2·00	2·50
F144		1f. Boeing B-17 Flying Fortress	2·25	2·75
F141/4 *Set of* 4			7·00	8·75

1968 (23 May). Bicentenary of Bougainville's World Voyage. As Nos. 130/2. P 13.

F145	**40**	15c. emerald, slate-violet and red	55	1·10
F146	–	25c. deep olive, maroon and ultramarine	65	1·25
F147	–	60c. bistre-brown, brown-purple and myrtle-green	1·10	1·50
F145/7 *Set of* 3			2·10	3·50

1968 (9 Oct). Anglo-French Concorde Project. As Nos. 133/4. P 14.

F148	**43**	25c. light blue, orange-red and deep violet-blue	1·90	2·40
F149	–	60c. red, black and bright blue	2·25	4·25

1969 (30 June). Timber Industry. As No. 135. P 14½.

F150	**45**	20c. multicoloured (*shades*)	45	1·00

1969 (13 Aug). Third South Pacific Games, Port Moresby, Papua New Guinea. As Nos. 136/7. Multicoloured. P 12½.

F151		25c. Type **46**	50	1·40
F152		1f. Runner passing baton, and flags	1·50	2·00

1969 (15 Oct). Pentecost Island Land Divers. As Nos. 138/40. Multicoloured. P 12½.

F153		15c. Type **48**	55	1·25
F154		25c. Diver jumping	45	1·25
F155		1f. Diver at end of fall	1·10	2·00
F153/5 *Set of* 3			1·90	4·00

1970 (20 May). Inauguration of New UPU Headquarters Building, Berne. As No. 141. P 13.

F156	**51**	1f.05 slate, red-orange and bright purple	1·00	2·75

1970 (20 July). 30th Anniv of New Hebrides' Declaration for the Free French Government. As Nos. 142/3. P 13.

F157	**52**	65c. multicoloured	2·75	2·00
F158		1f.10 multicoloured	3·00	2·25

1970 (15 Oct). No. F115 surch with T **53**.

F159		35c. on 20c. black, olive-green and greenish blue	65	1·75

1970 (30 Nov). Christmas. As Nos. 145/6. Multicoloured. P 14½×14.

F160		15c. Type **54**	25	1·00
F161		50c. *The Virgin and Child* (G. Cima)	45	1·25

POSTAGE DUE STAMPS

CHIFFRE TAXE	CHIFFRE TAXE	TIMBRE-TAXE
(FD **1**)	(FD **2**)	(FD **3**)

1925 (June). Optd with Type FD **1**, by D.L.R.

FD53	F **7**	10c. (1d.) green	55·00	4·25
FD54		20c. (2d.) greyish slate	55·00	4·25
FD55		30c. (3d.) red	55·00	4·25
FD56		50c. (5d.) ultramarine	55·00	4·25
FD57		1f. (10d.) carmine/*blue*	55·00	4·25
FD53/7 *Set of* 5			£250	19·00
FD53s/7s Optd "SPECIMEN" *Set of* 5			£250	

Although on sale in Paris, the Postmaster would not issue any in unused condition for about a year and most copies are cancelled-to-order.

1938 (1 June). Optd with Type FD **2**, by Bradbury Wilkinson.

FD65	**6**	5c. blue-green	20·00	75·00
FD66		10c. orange	23·00	75·00
FD67		20c. scarlet	29·00	80·00
FD68		40c. grey-olive	65·00	£160
FD69		1f. lake/*pale green*	65·00	£160
FD65/9 *Set of* 5			£180	£500
FD65s/9s Perf "SPECIMEN" *Set of* 5			£200	

1941 (15 Apr). Nos. FD65/9 optd with Type F **9** at Nouméa, New Caledonia.

FD77	**6**	5c. blue-green	19·00	48·00
FD78		10c. orange	19·00	48·00
FD79		20c. scarlet	19·00	48·00

FD80		40c. grey-olive	24·00	48·00
FD81		1f. lake/*pale green*	22·00	48·00
FD77/81 *Set of* 5			95·00	£200

1953 (30 Apr). Optd with Type FD **3**, by Waterlow.

FD92	**7**	5c. green	11·00	25·00
FD93		10c. scarlet	10·00	24·00
FD94		20c. ultramarine	25·00	40·00
FD95	**8**	40c. blackish brown	18·00	38·00
FD96	**9**	1f. orange	20·00	60·00
FD92/6 *Set of* 5			75·00	£170

1957 (3 Sept). Optd with Type FD **3**, by Waterlow.

FD107	**12**	5c. green	1·50	9·50
FD108		10c. scarlet	2·00	9·50
FD109		20c. ultramarine	3·50	14·00
FD110	**13**	40c. sepia	8·00	27·00
FD111	**14**	1f. red-orange	7·00	35·00
FD107/11 *Set of* 5			20·00	85·00

New Republic *see* South Africa

New South Wales *see* Australia

New Zealand

From 1831 mail from New Zealand was sent to Sydney, New South Wales, routed through an unofficial postmaster at Kororareka.

The first official post office opened at Kororareka in January 1840 to be followed by others at Auckland, Britannia, Coromandel Harbour, Hokianga, Port Nicholson, Russell and Waimate during the same year. New South Wales relinquished control of the postal service when New Zealand became a separate colony on 3 May 1841.

The British GPO was responsible for the operation of the overseas mails from 11 October 1841 until the postal service once again passed under colonial control on 18 November 1848.

CC 1

CC 2

AUCKLAND
CROWNED-CIRCLE HANDSTAMPS
CC1   CC **1**   AUCKLAND NEW ZEALAND (R.) (31.10.1846) .... *Price on cover*   £300

NELSON
CROWNED-CIRCLE HANDSTAMPS
CC2   CC **1**   NELSON NEW ZEALAND (R.) (31.10.1846) .... *Price on cover*   £1100

NEW PLYMOUTH
CROWNED-CIRCLE HANDSTAMPS
CC3   CC **1**   NEW PLYMOUTH NEW ZEALAND (R. or Black) (31.10.1846) .... *Price on cover*   £2750
CC3*a*   CC **2**   NEW PLYMOUTH NEW ZEALAND (R. or Black) (1854) .... *Price on cover*   £3250

OTAGO
CROWNED-CIRCLE HANDSTAMPS
CC4   CC **2**   OTAGO NEW ZEALAND (R.) (1851) .... *Price on cover*   £1900

PETRE
CROWNED-CIRCLE HANDSTAMPS
CC5   CC **1**   PETRE NEW ZEALAND (R.) (31.10.1846) .... *Price on cover*   £1400

PORT VICTORIA
CROWNED-CIRCLE HANDSTAMPS
CC6   CC **2**   PORT VICTORIA NEW ZEALAND (R.) (1851) .... *Price on cover*   £1200

RUSSELL
CROWNED-CIRCLE HANDSTAMPS
CC7   CC **1**   RUSSELL NEW ZEALAND (R.) (31.10.1846) .... *Price on cover*   £7000

WELLINGTON
CROWNED-CIRCLE HANDSTAMPS
CC8   CC **1**   WELLINGTON NEW ZEALAND (R.) (31.10.1846) .... *Price on cover*   £350

A similar mark for Christchurch as Type CC **2** is only known struck, in black, as a cancellation after the introduction of adhesive stamps. No. CC3*a* is a locally-cut replacement with the office name around the circumference, but a straight "PAID AT" in the centre.

PRICES FOR STAMPS ON COVER TO 1945	
Nos. 1/125	from × 2
Nos. 126/36	from × 3
Nos. 137/9	from × 2
No. 140	—
No. 141	from × 2
No. 142	—
Nos. 143/8	from × 2
Nos. 149/51	from × 10
Nos. 152/84	from × 2
Nos. 185/6	
Nos. 187/203	from × 3
Nos. 205/7*e*	
Nos. 208/13	from × 2
Nos. 214/16*j*	
Nos. 217/58	from × 3
No. 259	—
Nos. 260/9	from × 3
No. 270	—
Nos. 271/6	from × 3
Nos. 277/307	from × 2
Nos. 308/16	from × 3
No. 317	—
Nos. 318/28	from × 3
Nos. 329/48	
No. 349	from × 5
Nos. 350/1	
No. 352	from × 5
Nos. 353/69	
Nos. 370/86	from × 4
No. 387	
Nos. 388/99	from × 3
Nos. 400/666	from × 2
Nos. E1/5	from × 5

PRICES FOR STAMPS ON COVER TO 1945	
No. E6	from × 10
Nos. D1/8	from × 3
Nos. D9/16	from × 5
Nos. D17/20	from × 3
Nos. D21/47	from × 6
Nos. O1/34	from × 5
Nos. O59/66	from × 4
Nos. O67/8	—
Nos. O69/81	from × 5
Nos. O82/7	—
Nos. O88/93	from × 20
Nos. O94/9	from × 12
Nos. O100/11	from × 5
Nos. O112/13	—
Nos. O115/19	from × 15
Nos. O120/33	from × 10
Nos. O134/51	from × 4
Nos. P1/7	from × 8
Nos. L1/9	from × 10
Nos. L9a/12	—
Nos. L13/20	from × 15
Nos. L21/3	—
Nos. L24/41	from × 12
No. F1	—
No. F2	from × 5
Nos. F3/144	
Nos. F145/58	from × 3
Nos. F159/68	—
Nos. F169/79	from × 3
Nos. F180/6	—
Nos. F187/90	from × 2
Nos. F191/203	from × 3
Nos. F204/11	—
Nos. F212/18	from × 2
Nos. A1/3	from × 2

CROWN COLONY

PERKINS BACON "CANCELLED". For notes on these handstamps, showing "CANCELLED" between horizontal bars forming an oval, see Catalogue Introduction.

1

2

(Eng by Humphreys. Recess P.B.)

1855 (20 July)–57. Wmk Large Star, W w **1**. Imperf.

1	**1**	1d. dull carmine (*white paper*) (H/S "CANCELLED" in oval £32000)...	£70000	£18000
2		2d. dull blue (*blued paper*) (H/S "CANCELLED" in oval £32000)...	£35000	£650
3		1s. pale yellow-green (*blued paper*) (H/S "CANCELLED" in oval £26000).................................	£45000	£5500
		a. Bisected (6d.) (*on cover*) (1857)	†	£42000

The 2d. and 1s. on white paper formerly listed are now known to be stamps printed on blued paper which have had the bluing washed out. Nos. 3a and 6a were used at Port Chalmers between March 1857, when the rate for ½ oz. letters to Great Britain was reduced to 6d., and August 1859. All known examples are bisected vertically.

(Printed by J. Richardson, Auckland, N.Z.)

1855 (Dec). First printing. White paper. Wmk Large Star. Imperf.

3*b*	**1**	1d. orange	£32000

1855 (Nov)–58. Blue paper. No wmk. Imperf.

4		1d. red	£13000	£2000
5		2d. blue (3.56)	£3000	£300
6		1s. green (9.57)	£40000	£3750
		a. Bisected (6d.) (*on cover*) (1858).	†	£26000

These stamps on blue paper may occasionally be found watermarked double-lined letters, being portions of the papermaker's name.

1857 (Jan). White paper similar to the issue of July 1855. Wmk Large Star.

7	**1**	1d. dull orange	†	£30000

This stamp is in the precise shade of the 1d. of the 1858 printing by Richardson on *no wmk* white paper. An unsevered pair is known with Dunedin cancellation on a cover front showing an Auckland arrival postmark of 19.1.1857.

The paper employed for the local printings was often too small to cover the full printing plate, a problem which was overcome by overlapping two sheets on the press. Depending on how accurately the sheets were overlapped, stamps may be found with portions of the design missing (including a unique example of the 2d. value in the Royal Philatelic Collection with the value tablet missing, formerly listed as No. 5a), or may resemble marginal copies, in spite of coming from the middle of the plate.

1857–63. Hard or soft white paper. No wmk.

(a) Imperf

8	**1**	1d. dull orange (1858)	£3500	£750
8*a*		2d. deep ultramarine (1858)............	£3000	£1000
9		2d. pale blue	£1300	£180
10		2d. blue (12.57)	£1300	£180
11		2d. dull deep blue	£1800	£275
12		6d. bistre-brown (8.59)	£4000	£500
13		6d. brown	£3000	£300
14		6d. pale brown	£3000	£300
15		6d. chestnut	£4750	£600
16		1s. dull emerald-green (1858)........	£20000	£1800
17		1s. blue-green	£17000	£1800

(b) Pin-roulette, about 10 at Nelson (1860)

18	**1**	1d. dull orange	†	£5500
19		2d. blue	†	£3500
20		6d. brown	†	£4250

20*a*		1s. dull emerald-green................	†	£7000
21		1s. blue-green	†	£8000

(c) Serrated perf about 16 or 18 at Nelson (1862)

22	**1**	1d. dull orange	†	£5000
23		2d. blue	†	£3750
24		6d. brown	†	£3500
25		6d. chestnut	†	£7000
26		1s. blue-green	†	£6500

(d) Rouletted 7 at Auckland (April 1859)

27	**1**	1d. dull orange	£10000	£5500
		a. Imperf between (horiz pair)......		
28		2d. blue	£7500	£3250
29		6d. brown	£7500	£2750
		a. Imperf between (pair)	£27000	£13000
30		1s. dull emerald-green................	†	£4750
31		1s. blue-green	†	£5500

(e) P 13 at Dunedin (1863)

31*a*	**1**	1d. dull orange	†	£7500
31*b*		2d. pale blue	£7500	£3500
32		6d. pale brown	†	£6500

(f) "H" roulette 16 at Nelson

32*a*	**1**	2d. blue	†	£4750
32*b*		6d. brown	†	£5000

(g) "Y" roulette 18 at Nelson

32*c*	**1**	1d. dull orange	†	£6000
32*d*		2d. blue	†	£4000
32*e*		6d. brown	†	£4750
32*f*		6d. chestnut	†	£5500
32*g*		1s. blue-green	†	£8000

(h) Oblique roulette 13 at Wellington

32*h*	**1**	1d. dull orange	†	£6500

The various separations detailed above were all applied by hand to imperforate sheets. The results were often poorly cut and badly aligned and examples showing separations on all sides are rare. Nos. 32a/b and 32c/g were produced using roulette wheels fitted with cutting edges in the shape of "H" or "Y", and cannot readily be distinguished from Nos. 22/6 unless the separations are well-preserved.

The separation type described as "Serrated perf" in these listings is technically a form of roulette.

(Printed by John Davies at the GPO, Auckland, N.Z.)

1862 (Feb)–64. Wmk Large Star.

(a) Imperf

33	**1**	1d. orange vermilion......................	£950	£275
34		1d. vermilion (9.62)	£750	£275
35		1d. carmine-vermilion (10.63)..........	£450	£300
36		2d. deep blue (Plate I)..................	£800	95·00
		a. Double print	—	£4000
37		2d. slate-blue (Plate I)	£2000	£200
37*a*		2d. milky blue (Plate I, worn) (1863)..	—	£225
38		2d. pale blue (Plate I, worn)............	£700	90·00
39		2d. blue (*to deep*) (Plate I, very worn) (1864).................................	£700	90·00
40		3d. brown-lilac (Jan 1863)	£600	£160
41		6d. black-brown	£1900	£130
42		6d. brown	£2000	£130
43		6d. red-brown (1863)	£1600	£110
44		1s. green	£2250	£325
45		1s. yellow-green	£2000	£350
46		1s. deep green	£2250	£375

The 2d. in a distinctive deep bright blue on white paper wmkd. Large Star is believed by experts to have been printed by Richardson in 1861 or 1862. This also exists doubly printed and with serrated perf.

No. 37 shows traces of plate wear to the right of the Queen's head. This is more pronounced on Nos. 37a/8 and quite extensive on No. 39.

(b) Rouletted 7 at Auckland (5.62)

47	**1**	1d. orange-vermilion	£4750	£850
48		1d. vermilion	£3500	£800
48*a*		1d. carmine-vermilion	£5000	£1000
49		2d. deep blue	£3750	£475
50		2d. slate-blue	£4500	£850
51		2d. pale blue	£3000	£600
52		3d. brown-lilac	£3750	£800
53		6d. black-brown	£3750	£475
54		6d. brown	£3750	£600
55		6d. red-brown	£3500	£475
56		1s. green	£4000	£900
57		1s. yellow-green	£4000	£900
58		1s. deep green	£5000	£1100

(c) Serrated perf 16 or 18 at Nelson (7.62)

59	**1**	1d. orange-vermilion	£10000	£2250
60		2d. deep blue	†	£1300
61		2d. slate-blue		
62		3d. brown-lilac	£6000	£1800
63		6d. black-brown	†	£1800
64		6d. brown	†	£2250
65		1s. yellow-green	†	£4500

(d) Pin-perf 10 at Nelson (8.62)

66	**1**	2d. deep blue	†	£3000
67		6d. black-brown	†	£4000

(e) "H" roulette 16 at Nelson

67*a*	**1**	2d. deep blue (Plate I)..................	†	£2000
67*b*		6d. black-brown	†	£2250
67*c*		1s. green	†	£4250

(f) "Y" roulette 18 at Nelson (6.62)

67*d*	**1**	1d. orange-vermilion	†	£2500
67*e*		2d. deep blue (Plate I)..................	†	£2000
		a. Imperf between (horiz pair)......	†	£7000
67*f*		2d. slate-blue (Plate I)	†	£2000
67*g*		3d. brown-lilac	†	£2500
67*h*		6d. black-brown	†	£2000
67*i*		6d. brown	†	£2000
67*j*		1s. yellow-green	†	£4250

(g) Oblique roulette 13 at Wellington

67*k*	**1**	2d. deep blue (Plate I)..................	†	£2500
67*l*		2d. slate-blue (Plate I)		
67*m*		3d. brown-lilac	†	£3000
67*n*		6d. brown	†	£2500

(h) Square roulette 14 at Auckland

67*o*	**1**	1d. orange-vermilion	†	£2500
67*p*		2d. deep blue (Plate I)..................	†	£2500
67*q*		3d. brown-lilac	†	£3000
67*r*		6d. red-brown	†	£2500

(i) Serrated perf 13 at Dunedin

67*s*	**1**	1d. orange-vermilion	†	£3000
67*t*		2d. deep blue (Plate I)..................	†	£2000
67*u*		3d. brown-lilac	£4250	£1800

67v		6d. brown	†	£2000
67w		1s. yellow-green	†	£4250

The dates put to the above varieties are the earliest recorded.

1862 (Dec)–**64**. Wmk Large Star. P 13 (at Dunedin).

68	1	1d. orange-vermilion	£3000	£350
		a. Imperf between (horiz pair)	†	£11000
69		1d. carmine-vermilion	£3000	£350
70		2d. deep blue (Plate I)	£1100	£110
71		2d. slate-blue (Plate I)	†	£750
72		2d. blue (Plate I)	£700	80·00
72a		2d. milky blue (Plate I)	—	£500
73		2d. pale blue (Plate I)	£700	80·00
74		3d. brown-lilac	£3000	£500
75		6d. black-brown	£2000	£225
		a. Imperf between (horiz pair)		
76		6d. brown	£1800	£160
77		6d. red-brown	£1500	£120
78		1s. dull green	£3000	£425
79		1s. deep green	£3250	£400
80		1s. yellow-green	£3000	£375

See also Nos. 110/25 and the note that follows these.

1862 (Aug)–**63**. Pelure paper. No wmk.

(a) Imperf

81	1	1d. orange-vermilion (1863)	£12000	£2500
82		2d. ultramarine (10.62)	£6500	£850
83		2d. pale ultramarine	£5500	£800
84		3d. lilac (1863)	£50000	†
85		6d. black-brown	£3500	£250
86		1s. deep green	£14000	£1100

The 3d. is known only unused.

(b) Rouletted 7 at Auckland

87	1	1d. orange-vermilion	†	£6500
88		6d. black-brown	£4000	£475
89		1s. deep green	£15000	£1800

(c) P 13 at Dunedin

90	1	1d. orange-vermilion	£15000	£3500
91		2d. ultramarine	£8500	£800
92		2d. pale ultramarine	£7500	£700
93		6d. black-brown	£7500	£400
94		1s. deep green	£14000	£2000

(d) Serrated perf 16 at Nelson

95	1	6d. black-brown	—	£5500

(e) Serrated perf 13 at Dunedin

95a	1	1d. orange-vermilion	†	£10000

1863 (early). Thick soft white paper. No wmk.

(a) Imperf

96	1	2d. dull deep blue (shades)	£3750	£800

(b) P 13

96a	1	2d. dull deep blue (shades)	£2000	£475

These stamps show slight beginnings of wear of the printing plate in the background to right of the Queen's ear, as one looks at the stamps. By the early part of 1864, the wear of the plate had spread, more or less, all over the background of the circle containing the head. The major portion of the stamps of this printing appears to have been consigned to Dunedin and to have been there perforated 13.

1864. Wmk "N Z", W **2**.

(a) Imperf

97	1	1d. carmine-vermilion	£950	£350
98		2d. pale blue (Plate I worn)	£1600	£275
99		6d. red-brown	£5500	£700
100		1s. green	£2000	£275

(b) Rouletted 7 at Auckland

101	1	1d. carmine-vermilion	£6000	£3000
102		2d. pale blue (Plate I worn)	£2500	£750
103		6d. red-brown	£7000	£3000
104		1s. green	£4500	£1100

(c) P 13 (line) at Dunedin

104a	1	1d. carmine-vermilion	£11000	£5500
105		2d. pale blue (Plate I worn)	£1100	£190
106		1s. green	£2500	£500
		a. Imperf between (horiz pair)	†	£40000
		aa. Perf 6½×13	†	£4250

(d) "Y" roulette 18 at Nelson

106b	1	1d. carmine-vermilion	†	£6500

(e) P 12½ (comb) at Auckland

106c	1	1d. carmine-vermilion	£11000	£4750
107		2d. pale blue (Plate I worn)	£450	75·00
108		6d. red-brown	£650	60·00
109		1s. yellow-green	£7500	£2750

The "NZ" watermark is frequently found inverted.

1864–71. Wmk Large Star. P 12½ (comb or line)* (at Auckland).

110	1	1d. carmine-vermilion (1865)	£225	42·00
111		1d. pale orange-vermilion (1866)	£275	42·00
		a. Imperf (pair)	£4500	£2750
		b. Imperf between (vert pair)	†	—
112		1d. orange (1871)	£600	90·00
113		2d. pale blue (Plate I worn)	£325	30·00
114		2d. deep blue (Plate II) (7.65)	£225	22·00
		a. Imperf vert (horiz pair)	†	£5500
115		2d. blue (Plate II)	£225	22·00
		a. Retouched (Plate II) (1867)	£350	50·00
		c. Imperf (pair) (Plate II)	£3000	£2500
		d. Retouched. Imperf (pair)	£4000	£4250
116		3d. brown-lilac	£2500	£650
117		3d. lilac (1867)	£160	35·00
		a. Imperf (pair)	£4500	£2000
		b. Imperf between (horiz pair)	†	—
118		3d. deep mauve (1867)	£800	75·00
		a. Imperf (pair)	£5000	£2000
119		4d. deep rose (1.6.65)	£3250	£250
120		4d. yellow (1866)	£250	£120
121		4d. orange (1871)	£2250	£1000
122		6d. red-brown	£325	28·00
122a		6d. brown (1867)	£350	42·00
		b. Imperf (pair)	£3000	£3000
123		1s. deep green	£1300	£350
124		1s. green	£750	£140
125		1s. yellow-green	£325	£120

The above issue is sometimes difficult to distinguish from Nos. 68/80 because the vertical perforations usually gauge 12¾ and sometimes a full 13. However, stamps of this issue invariably gauge 12½ horizontally, whereas the 1862 stamps measure a full 13.

* Until late 1866 two comb perforating heads were in use. These were then converted to single-line heads, and all subsequent printings

were line perforated. Some stamps (such as Nos. 110, 113, 116 and 119) only exist with the early comb perforation, while others (such as Nos. 112, 117/8, 121 and 122a) are always line perforated.

Nos. 111a, 115c/d, 117a, 118a and 122b were issued during problems with the perforation machine which occurred in 1866–67, 1869–70 and 1871–73. Imperforate sheets of the 1s. were also released, but these stamps are very similar to Nos. 44/6.

The new plate of the 2d. showed signs of deterioration during 1866 and thirty positions in rows 13 and 16 to 20 were retouched by a local engraver.

The 1d., 2d. and 6d. were officially reprinted, without gum, in 1884 for presentation purposes. They can be distinguished from the errors listed by their shades which are pale orange, dull blue and dull chocolate-brown respectively, and by the worn state of the plates from which they were printed (*Prices £95 each unused*).

1871 (1 Oct)–**73**. Wmk Large Star. New colours (except No. 129/a).

(a) P 10

126	1	1d. brown	£1000	£130

(b) P 12½×10

127	1	1d. deep brown	†	£4750

(c) P 10×12½

128	1	1d. brown	£350	55·00
		a. Perf 12½ comp 10 (1 side)	£700	£200
129		2d. deep blue (Plate II)	†	£14000
		a. Perf 10*	†	£30000
130		2d. vermilion	£300	42·00
		a. Retouched	£450	60·00
		b. Perf 12½ comp 10 (1 side)	£1800	£475
		c. Perf 10*	†	£25000
131		6d. deep blue	£3250	£900
		a. Blue	£1800	£550
		b. Imperf between (vert pair)		
		c. Perf 12½ comp 10 (1 side)	£1600	£450
		ca. Imperf vert (horiz pair)	†	—

(d) P 12½ (1872–73)

132	1	1d. red-brown	£250	48·00
		a. Brown (shades, worn plate) (1873)	£225	42·00
		b. Imperf horiz (vert pair)	—	£6000
133		2d. orange	£170	29·00
		a. Retouched	£275	50·00
134		2d. vermilion	£200	32·00
		a. Retouched	£300	60·00
135		6d. blue	£325	65·00
136		6d. pale blue	£225	55·00

*Only one used copy of No. 129a and two of No. 130c have been reported.

1873 (Aug–Sept). No wmk. P 12½.

137	1	1d. brown	£1200	£275
		a. Watermarked (script letters)*	£4250	£2250
		b. Watermarked (double-lined capitals)*	£2000	£600
138		2d. vermilion	£160	55·00
		a. Retouched	£275	85·00
		b. Watermarked (script letters)*	£4000	£1400
		c. Watermarked (double-lined capitals)*	£1900	£800
139		4d. orange-yellow	£200	£850
		a. Watermarked (double-lined capitals)*	£400	

*1d., 2d. and 4d. stamps were printed on paper showing sheet watermarks of either "W. T. & Co." (Wiggins Teape & Co.) in script letters or "T. H. Saunders" in double-lined capitals (the former appearing once, at the top or bottom of the sheet, and the latter occurring twice in the sheet); portions of these letters are occasionally found on stamps. A third, as yet unidentified script watermark has also been identified on the 1d. and 2d. values.

It seems likely that Nos. 137/9 were printed and issued after Nos. 140/2.

1873 (July?). Wmk "N Z", W **2**. P 12½.

140	1	1d. brown	†	£8000
141		2d. vermilion	£1400	£350
		a. Retouched	£1700	£425

The "NZ" watermark may be found inverted or inverted and reversed.

1873 (Aug). Wmk Lozenges, with "INVICTA" in double-lined capitals four times in the sheet. P 12½.

142	1	2d. vermilion	£3000	£500
		a. Retouched	£4500	£750

3
4

(Des John Davies. Die eng on wood in Melbourne. Printed from electrotypes at Govt Ptg Office, Wellington)

1873 (1 Jan).

(a) Wmk "NZ", W F 5

143	3	½d. pale dull rose (P 10)	£110	60·00
144		½d. pale dull rose (P 12½)	£180	85·00
145		½d. pale dull rose (P 12½×10)	£200	85·00
		a. Perf 10×12½	£350	£150

(b) No wmk

146	3	½d. pale dull rose (P 10)	£200	75·00
147		½d. pale dull rose (P 12½)	£250	£100
148		½d. pale dull rose (P 12½×10)	£275	£110
		a. Perf 10×12½	£550	£190

As the paper used for Nos. 143/5 was originally intended for fiscal stamps which were more than twice as large, about one-third of the impressions fall on portions of the sheet showing no watermark, giving rise to varieties Nos. 146/8. In later printings of No. 151 a few stamps in each sheet are without watermark. These can be distinguished from No. 147 by the shade.

1875 (Jan). Wmk Star, W **4**.

149	3	½d. pale dull rose (P 12½)	29·00	3·00
		a. Imperf horiz (vert pair)	£850	£750
		b. Imperf between (horiz pair)	†	£850
		c. Perf compound of 12½ and 10	†	
150		½d. dull pale rose (P nearly 12)	70·00	13·00

1892 (May). Wmk "NZ and Star". W **12b**. P 12½.

151	3	½d. bright rose (shades)	14·00	2·00
		a. No wmk	25·00	16·00

		w. Wmk inverted	75·00	50·00
		x. Wmk reversed	—	£180

5
6
7
8
9
10
11
12
12a 6 mm
12b 7 mm
12c 4 mm

(T **5**/**10** eng De La Rue. T **11** and **12** des, eng and plates by W. R. Bock. Typo Govt Ptg Office, Wellington)

1874 (2 Jan)–**78**.

*A. White paper. W **12a***

(a) P 12½

152	5	1d. lilac	£120	17·00
		a. Imperf (pair)	—	£1800
		w. Wmk inverted	†	£100
		x. Wmk reversed	†	£450
		y. Wmk inverted and reversed	†	£1000
153	6	2d. rose	£130	8·00
154	7	3d. brown	£170	80·00
155	8	4d. maroon	£300	70·00
		w. Wmk inverted	£800	£250
156	9	6d. blue	£250	12·00
		w. Wmk inverted	—	95·00
157	10	1s. green	£600	38·00
		w. Wmk inverted	£1500	£350

(b) Perf nearly 12 (line)

158	6	2d. rose (1878)	£1200	£190

(c) Perf compound of 12½ and 10

159	5	1d. lilac	£170	45·00
		w. Wmk inverted	—	£120
160	6	2d. rose	£225	85·00
		w. Wmk inverted	†	£160
161	7	3d. brown	£200	85·00
		w. Wmk inverted	†	—
162	8	4d. maroon	£800	£160
163	9	6d. blue	£300	50·00
		w. Wmk inverted	—	£120
164	10	1s. green	£650	£140
		a. Imperf between (vert pair)	†	£7000
		bw. Wmk inverted	†	£475
164c	5	1d. lilac (1875)	£1500	£375
165	6	2d. rose (1878)	£1200	£325

B. Blued paper

(a) P 12½

166	5	1d. lilac	£225	40·00
167	6	2d. rose	£225	40·00
		w. Wmk inverted	—	£120
		x. Wmk reversed	†	£225
168	7	3d. brown	£375	£110
169	8	4d. maroon	£600	£120
170	9	6d. blue	£425	55·00
171	10	1s. green	£1100	£190

(b) Perf compound of 12½ and 10

172	5	1d. lilac	£250	60·00
173	6	2d. rose	£550	£100
174	7	3d. brown	£400	£110
175	8	4d. maroon	£800	£160
176	9	6d. blue	£450	£100
177	10	1s. green	£1100	£250

1875. Wmk Large Star, W w **1**. P 12½.

178	5	1d. deep lilac	£2000	£300
179	6	2d. rose	£800	38·00

1878. W **12a**. P 12×11½ (comb).

180	5	1d. mauve-lilac	65·00	8·00
181	6	2d. rose	70·00	7·00
182	8	4d. maroon	£190	50·00
183	9	6d. blue	£130	12·00
184	10	1s. green	£200	50·00
		w. Wmk inverted	†	£450
185	11	2s. deep rose (1.7)	£375	£300
186	12	5s. grey (1.7)	£375	£300

This perforation is made by a horizontal "comb" machine, giving a gauge of 12 horizontally and about 11¾ vertically. Single examples can be found apparently gauging 11½ all round or 12 all round, but these are all from the same machine. The perforation described above as "nearly 12" was from a single-line machine.

13	**14**	**15**
16	**17**	**18**
19	**20**	**21**
	22	

Description of Watermarks

W **12a**. 6 mm between "NZ" and star; broad irregular star; comparatively wide "N"; "N Z" 11½ mm wide.

W **12b**. 7 mm between "N Z" and star; narrower star; narrow "N"; "N Z" 10 mm wide.

W **12c**. 4 mm between "N Z" and star; narrow star; wide "N"; "N Z" 11½ mm wide.

Description of Papers

1882–88. Smooth paper with horizontal mesh. W **12a**.
1888–98. Smooth paper with vertical mesh. W **12b**.
1890–91. Smooth paper with vertical mesh. W **12c**.
1898. Thin yellowish toned, coarse paper with clear vertical mesh. W **12b**. Perf 11 only.

In 1899–1900 stamps appeared on medium to thick white coarse paper but we do not differentiate these (except where identifiable by shade) as they are more difficult to distinguish.

PAPER MESH. This shows on the back of the stamp as a series of parallel grooves, either vertical or horizontal. It is caused by the use of a wire gauze conveyor-belt during paper-making.

Description of Dies

1d.

Die 1

Die 2

Die 3

1882. Die 1. Background shading complete and heavy.
1886. Die 2. Background lines thinner. Two lines of shading weak or missing left of Queen's forehead.
1889. Die 3. Shading on head reduced; ornament in crown left of chignon clearer, with unshaded "arrow" more prominent.

"Ellipse" flaw (Die 3, lower left pane, R. 9/2)

"Chisel" flaw (Die 3 upper left pane, R. 4/6) (a smaller break occurs in the lower right frame of this stamp)

2d.

Die 1

Die 2

Die 3

1882. Die 1. Background shading complete and heavy.
1886. Die 2. Weak line of shading left of forehead and missing shading lines below "TA".
1889. Die 3. As Die 2 but with comma-like white notch in hair below "&".

6d.

Die 1

Die 2

1882. Die 1. Shading heavy. Top of head merges into shading. Second ornament from the right on the crown shows a line in its left portion.
1892. Die 2. Background lines thinner. Shading on head more regular with clear line of demarcation between head and background shading. Second ornament from the right in the crown has small dots in its left portion. Most examples also show a break in the back line of the neck immediately above its base.

"2" and "1" joined (Upper right pane, R. 9/1)

1s. "Bulbous nose" (Lower right pane, R. 1/1)

HIGH VALUES. From 1882 to 1931 postal requirements for higher value stamps were met by the Queen Victoria "Stamp Duty" adhesives (F5/144).

Truebridge Miller

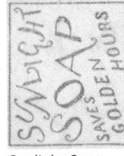
Sunlight Soap

STAMPS WITH ADVERTISEMENTS. During November 1891 the New Zealand Post Office invited tenders for the printing of advertisements on the reverse of the current 1d. to 1s. stamps. The contract was awarded to Messrs Miller, Truebridge & Reich and the first sheets with advertisements on the reverse appeared in February 1893. Different advertisements were applied to the backs of the individual stamps within the sheets of 240 (four panes of 60).

On the first setting those in a vertical format were inverted in relation to the stamps and each of the horizontal advertisements had its base at the left-hand side of the stamp when seen from the back. For the second and third settings the vertical advertisements were the same way up as the stamps and the bases of those in the horizontal format were at the right as seen from the back. The third setting only differs from the second in the order of the individual advertisements.

Examples of the advertisements being printed double are known, but we do not list them.

The experiment was not, however, a success and the contract was cancelled at the end of 1893.

(Des F. W. Sears (½d.), A. E. Cousins (2½d.), A. W. Jones (5d.); others adapted from 1874 issue by W. H. Norris. Dies eng A. E. Cousins (½d., 2½d., 5d.), W. R. Bock (others). Typo Govt Ptg Office)
1882–1900. Inscr "POSTAGE & REVENUE".

		*A. Paper with horiz mesh (1.4.82–86). W **12a***		
		(a) P 12×11½		
187	**14**	1d. rose *to* rose-red (Die 1)	50·00	7·00
		a. Imperf (pair)	£1100	
		b. Imperf between (vert pair)	£1200	
		cw. Wmk inverted		
		d. Die 2. *Pale rose to carmine-rose* (1886)	65·00	8·00
		dw. Wmk inverted	†	£100
		dx. Wmk reversed	£170	80·00
188	**15**	2d. lilac *to* lilac-purple (Die 1)	60·00	4·00
		a. Imperf (pair)	£1100	
		b. Imperf between (vert pair)	£1200	
		cw. Wmk inverted	£160	75·00
		d. Die 2. *Lilac* (1886)	70·00	15·00
189	**17**	3d. yellow	80·00	19·00
190	**18**	4d. blue-green	85·00	11·00
191	**20**	6d. brown (Die 1)	£120	3·75
		w. Wmk inverted	£425	85·00
192	**21**	8d. blue (1885)	£100	65·00
193	**22**	1s. red-brown	£150	16·00
		(b) P 12½ (1884?)		
193a	**14**	1d. rose *to* rose-red (Die 1)	£500	£300
		*B. Paper with vert mesh (1888–95). W **12b***		
		(a) P 12×11½ (1888–95)		
194	**13**	½d. black (1.4.95)	42·00	90·00
195	**14**	1d. rose *to* rosine (Die 2)	50·00	5·00
		aw. Wmk inverted	£225	38·00
		b. Die 3. *Rose to carmine* (1889)	50·00	4·50
		bb. Red-brown advert (1st setting) (2.93)	£250	70·00
		bc. Red advert (1st setting) (3.93)	£250	70·00
		bd. Blue advert (2nd setting) (4.93)	£500	£180
		be. Mauve advert (2nd setting) (5.93)	£250	60·00
		bf. Green advert (2nd setting) (6.93)	†	—
		bg. Brown-red advert (3rd setting) (9.93)	£250	55·00
		bh. "Ellipse" flaw	£140	30·00
		bi. "Chisel" flaw	£140	30·00
		bw. Wmk inverted	£140	38·00
		bx. Wmk reversed	£170	70·00
196	**15**	2d. lilac (Die 2)	60·00	5·50
		a. Die 3. *Lilac to purple* (1889)	60·00	6·50
		ab. Red advert (1st setting) (3.93)	£350	60·00
		ac. Mauve advert (2nd setting) (5.93)	£350	60·00
		ad. Sepia advert (2nd setting) (5.93)	£350	60·00
		ae. Green advert (2nd setting) (6.93)	—	£170
		af. Brown-red advert (3rd setting) (9.93)	£350	60·00
		aw. Wmk inverted	£170	38·00
197	**16**	2½d. pale blue (1891)	80·00	5·50
		a. Brown-red advert (2nd setting) (4.93)	£650	£200
		ax. Wmk reversed	£650	£250
		b. *Ultramarine* (green advert. 2nd setting) (6.93)	£650	£200
198	**17**	3d. yellow	70·00	22·00
		a. Brown-red advert (2nd setting) (4.93)	£650	£225
		b. Sepia advert (2nd setting) (5.93)	—	£350
199	**18**	4d. green *to* bluish green	75·00	4·00
		a. Sepia advert (2nd setting) (5.93)	£375	£200
		aw. Wmk inverted	†	£300
200	**19**	5d. olive-black (1.2.91)	80·00	18·00
		a. Imperf (pair)	£1100	
		b. Brown-purple advert (3rd setting) (9.93)	£750	£180
201	**20**	6d. brown (Die 1)	£100	6·50
		a. Die 2 (1892)	£200	£150
		ab. Sepia advert (2nd setting) (5.93)	—	£750
		ac. Brown-red advert (3rd setting) (9.93)	—	£450
		ax. Wmk reversed	†	
202	**21**	8d. blue	85·00	60·00
203	**22**	1s. red-brown	£130	6·00
		a. Black advert (2nd setting) (5.93)	—	£500
		b. Brown-purple advert (3rd setting) (9.93)	£475	75·00
		w. Wmk inverted	£550	£120
		(b) P 12×11½ (1888–91)		
204	**14**	1d. rose (Die 2)	£375	£500
		a. Die 3 (1889)	†	—
		(c) P 12½ (1888–89)		
205	**14**	1d. rose (Die 3) (1889)	£450	£300
		a. Mauve advert (3rd setting) (5.93)	†	£650
		x. Wmk reversed	†	£750
206	**15**	2d. lilac (Die 2)	£475	£475
		a. Die 3. *Deep lilac* (1889)	£475	£550
		ab. Brown-red advert (3rd setting) (9.93)	£650	£350
207	**16**	2½d. blue (1891)	£550	£350
		(d) Mixed perfs 12×11½ and 12½ (1891–93)		
207a	**14**	1d. rose (Die 3) (brown-red advert. 3rd setting)	£375	£225
207b	**15**	2d. lilac (Die 3)	†	£450
		ba. Brown-red advert (3rd setting) (9.93)	†	—
207c	**18**	4d. green	†	£325
207d	**19**	5d. olive-black	†	£350
207e	**20**	6d. brown (Die 1)	†	£225
		ea. Die 2	†	£250

C. Paper with vert mesh (1890). W 12c

(a) P 12×11½

208	14	1d. rose (Die 3)	£275	32·00
		a. "Ellipse" flaw	£700	£100
		b. "Chisel" flaw	£700	£100
209	15	2d. purple (Die 3)	95·00	20·00
		x. Wmk reversed		
210	16	2½d. ultramarine (27.12)	60·00	14·00
		x. Wmk reversed	†	£225
211	17	3d. yellow	£110	50·00
		a. Lemon-yellow	£110	55·00
212	20	6d. brown (Die 1)	£170	50·00
213	22	1s. deep red-brown	£275	£275

(b) P 12½

214	14	1d. rose (Die 3)	£450	£375
215	15	2d. purple (Die 3)	£550	£650
216	16	2½d. ultramarine	£550	£450

(c) P 12×12½

216a	20	6d. brown (Die 1)	£475	£375

D. Paper with vert mesh (1891–1900). Continuation of W 12b

(a) P 10×12½ (1891–94)

216b	14	1d. rose (Die 3)	£225	£250
		ba. Perf 12½×10	£300	£250
		bb. Red-brown advert (1st setting) (2.93)	£750	£400
		bc. Brown-red advert (2nd setting) (4.93)	£750	£400
		bd. Mauve advert (2nd setting) (5.93)	£750	£400
		be. Green advert (2nd setting) (6.93)	£750	£400
		bf. "Ellipse" flaw	£650	
		bg. "Chisel" flaw	£650	
216c	15	2d. lilac (Die 3)	£450	£300
216d	16	2½d. blue (1893)	£350	£275
		da. Perf 12½×10	£650	£400
		dab. Mauve advert (2nd setting)	†	£400
216e	17	3d. yellow	£500	£600
		ea. Perf 12½×10		
216f	18	4d. green	£500	£450
		fa. Perf 12½×10, brown-purple advert (3rd setting)	†	£1200
216g	19	5d. olive-black (1894)	£300	£275
		ga. Perf 12½×10	£375	£300
216h	20	6d. brown (Die 1)	£550	£600
		i. Die 2 (1892)	£475	£475
		ia. Brown-purple advert (3rd setting) (9.93)		
216j	22	1s. red-brown	£250	£275
		ja. Perf 12½×10	£425	£350

(b) P 10 (1891–95)

217	13	½d. black (1895)	9·50	2·25
		x. Wmk reversed		—
218	14	1d. rose (Die 3)	14·00	1·00
		a. Carmine	14·00	1·50
		b. Imperf (pair)	£1000	£1000
		c. Imperf between (pair)	£1100	
		d. Imperf horiz (vert pair)	£1000	
		e. Mixed perfs 10 and 12½	£300	£250
		f. Red-brown advert (1st setting) (2.93)	50·00	7·00
		g. Red advert (1st setting) (3.93)	50·00	9·00
		h. Brown-red advert (2nd and 3rd settings) (4.93)	42·00	4·00
		i. Blue advert (2nd setting) (4.93)	£130	48·00
		j. Mauve advert (2nd setting) (5.93)	42·00	4·00
		k. Green advert (2nd setting) (6.93)	£100	30·00
		l. Brown-purple advert (3rd setting) (9.93)	42·00	5·50
		m. "Ellipse" flaw	45·00	11·00
		n. "Chisel" flaw	45·00	11·00
		w. Wmk inverted	£170	85·00
		x. Wmk reversed	£275	£170
219	15	2d. lilac (Die 3)	22·00	1·75
		a. Purple	22·00	1·75
		b. Imperf between (pair)	£1200	
		c. Mixed perfs 10 and 12½	£750	£500
		d. Red-brown advert (1st setting) (2.93)	55·00	12·00
		e. Red advert (1st setting) (3.93)	55·00	9·00
		f. Brown-red advert (2nd and 3rd settings) (4.93)	55·00	4·50
		g. Sepia advert (2nd setting) (5.93)	55·00	6·00
		h. Green advert (2nd setting) (6.93)	80·00	15·00
		i. Brown-purple advert (3rd setting) (9.93)	55·00	4·50
		x. Wmk reversed	£170	70·00
220	16	2½d. blue (1892)	65·00	3·50
		a. Ultramarine	65·00	4·00
		b. Mixed perfs 10 and 12½	£425	£225
		c. Mauve advert (2nd setting) (5.93)	£200	16·00
		d. Green advert (2nd setting) (6.93)	£225	23·00
		e. Brown-purple advert (3rd setting) (9.93)	£200	16·00
		ex. Wmk reversed	£300	£110
221	17	3d. pale orange-yellow	65·00	19·00
		a. Orange	65·00	25·00
		b. Lemon-yellow	65·00	25·00
		c. Mixed perfs 10 and 12½	£750	£650
		d. Brown-red advert (2nd and 3rd settings) (4.93)	£160	30·00
		e. Sepia advert (2nd setting) (5.93)	£170	50·00
		f. Brown-purple advert (3rd setting) (9.93)	£160	28·00
222	18	4d. green (1892)	65·00	8·50
		a. Blue-green	65·00	8·50
		b. Mixed perfs 10 and 12½	£300	£200
		c. Brown-red advert (2nd setting) (4.93)	£180	13·00
		d. Brown-purple advert (3rd setting) (9.93)	£180	13·00
223	19	5d. olive-black (1893)	65·00	30·00
		a. Brown-purple advert (3rd setting) (9.93)	£190	50·00
		ab. Mixed perfs 10 and 12½	£450	£325
224	20	6d. brown (Die 1)	£160	45·00
		a. Mixed perfs 10 and 12½		

		b. Die 2 (1892)	80·00	9·00
		ba. Black-brown	80·00	9·00
		bb. Imperf (pair)	£1200	
		bc. Mixed perfs 10 and 12½	£375	£200
		bd. Sepia advert (2nd setting) (4.93)	£400	20·00
		be. Brown-red advert (3rd setting) (9.93)	£400	20·00
		bf. Brown-purple advert (3rd setting) (9.93)	£400	20·00
		bx. Wmk reversed (with brown-purple advert)	†	£140
225	21	8d. blue (brown-purple advert. 3rd setting) (9.93)	90·00	70·00
226	22	1s. red-brown	£120	16·00
		a. Imperf between (pair)	£2000	
		b. Mixed perfs 10 and 12½	£425	£275
		c. Sepia advert (2nd setting) (5.93)	£375	55·00
		d. Black advert (2nd setting) (5.93)	£400	£150
		e. Brown-red advert (3rd setting) (9.93)	£375	55·00
		f. Brown-purple advert (3rd setting) (9.93)	£375	55·00
		g. "Bulbous nose"	£650	£110

(c) P 10×11 (1895–97)

227	13	½d. black (1896)	5·00	60
		a. Mixed perfs 10 and 11	£170	£120
		b. Perf 11×10 (11.95)	42·00	18·00
228	14	1d. rose (Die 3)	13·00	15
		a. Mixed perfs 10 and 11	£180	£250
		b. Perf 11×10 (10.95)	75·00	13·00
		c. "Ellipse" flaw	45·00	12·00
		d. "Chisel" flaw	45·00	12·00
		x. Wmk reversed	£110	80·00
229	15	2d. purple (Die 3)	24·00	30
		a. Mixed perfs 10 and 11	£100	75·00
230	16	2½d. blue (1896)	65·00	3·75
		a. Ultramarine	65·00	4·50
		b. Mixed perfs 10 and 11	—	£150
		c. "2" and "1" joined	£275	30·00
231	17	3d. lemon-yellow (1896)	75·00	22·00
232	18	4d. pale green (1896)	95·00	12·00
		a. Mixed perfs 10 and 11	—	£180
233	19	5d. olive-black (1897)	70·00	15·00
234	20	6d. deep brown (Die 2) (1896)	90·00	19·00
		a. Mixed perfs 10 and 11	†	£325
		b. Perf 11×10	†	
235	22	1s. red-brown (1896)	£100	10·00
		a. Mixed perfs 10 and 11	£300	£150
		b. "Bulbous nose"	£500	90·00

(d) P 11 (1895–1900)

236	13	½d. black (1897)	9·50	15
		aw. Wmk inverted	75·00	32·00
		ax. Wmk reversed	£170	85·00
		b. Thin coarse toned paper (1898)	38·00	6·00
		ba. Wmk sideways	†	£2000
237	14	1d. rose (Die 3) (6.95)	6·00	10
		a. Deep carmine	6·00	1·50
		b. Imperf between (pair)	£1000	
		c. Deep carmine/thin coarse toned (1898)	15·00	3·25
		ca. Wmk sideways	†	£2000
		d. "Ellipse" flaw	35·00	10·00
		e. "Chisel" flaw	35·00	10·00
		w. Wmk inverted	75·00	45·00
		x. Wmk reversed	85·00	55·00
		y. Wmk inverted and reversed	£150	85·00
238	15	2d. mauve (Die 3)	17·00	1·00
		a. Purple	17·00	1·00
		b. Deep purple/thin coarse toned (1898)	24·00	6·00
		ba. Wmk sideways	†	£2000
		w. Wmk inverted	85·00	38·00
		x. Wmk reversed	£180	60·00
239	16	2½d. blue (1897)	55·00	4·00
		a. Thin coarse toned paper (1898)	£110	27·00
		b. "2" and "1" joined	£225	30·00
240	17	3d. pale yellow (1897)	55·00	8·50
		a. Pale dull yellow/thin coarse toned (1898)	£110	26·00
		b. Orange (1899)	55·00	14·00
		c. Dull orange-yellow (1900)	50·00	28·00
241	18	4d. yellowish green (7.96)	60·00	5·00
		a. Bluish green (1897)	55·00	4·50
		w. Wmk inverted	£200	£100
242	19	5d. olive-black/thin coarse toned (1899)	70·00	40·00
243	20	6d. brown (Die 2) (1897)	70·00	6·00
		a. Black-brown	80·00	5·00
		b. Brown/thin coarse toned (1898)	£150	16·00
		x. Wmk reversed	†	£110
244	21	8d. blue (1898)	80·00	60·00
245	22	1s. red-brown (1897)	£100	7·00
		a. Imperf between (vert pair)	£2000	
		b. "Bulbous nose"	£500	80·00

Only the more prominent shades have been included. Stamps perf compound of 10×11 and 12½ and 11 and 12½ exist. For the ½d. and 2d. with double-lined watermark, see Nos. 271/2.

23 Mount Cook or Aorangi   **24** Lake Taupo and Mount Ruapehu   **25** Pembroke Peak, Milford Sound

26 Lake Wakatipu and Mount Earnslaw, inscribed "WAKITIPU"   **27** Lake Wakatipu and Mount Earnslaw, inscribed "WAKATIPU"

28 Huia   **29** White Terrace, Rotomahana   **30** Otira Gorge and Mount Ruapehu

31 Brown Kiwi   **32** Maori War Canoe

33 Pink Terrace, Rotomahana   **34** Kea and Kaka

35 Milford Sound   **36** Mount Cook

(Des H. Young (½d.), J. Gaut (1d.), W. Bock (2d., 3d., 9d., 1s.), E. Howard (4d., 6d., 8d.), E. Luke (others). Eng A. Hill (2½d., 1s.), J. A. C. Harrison (5d.), Rapkin (others). Recess Waterlow)

1898 (5 Apr.). No wmk. P 12 to 16.

246	23	½d. purple-brown	8·50	1·50
		a. Imperf between (pair)	£1700	£1400
		b. Purple-slate	8·50	1·50
		c. Purple-black	8·50	2·75
247	24	1d. blue and yellow-brown	6·00	60
		a. Imperf between (horiz pair)	£1300	£1300
		b. Imperf vert (horiz pair)	£900	£1000
		c. Imperf horiz (vert pair)	£900	£1000
		d. Blue and brown	6·50	80
		da. Imperf between (vert pair)	£1300	£1300
248	25	2d. lake	38·00	25
		a. Imperf vert (horiz pair)	£600	£1000
		b. Rosy lake	38·00	25
		ba. Imperf between (vert pair)	£1400	
		bb. Imperf vert (horiz pair)	£600	
249	26	2½d. sky-blue (inscr "WAKITIPU")	11·00	50·00
		a. Blue	11·00	50·00
250	27	2½d. blue (inscr "WAKATIPU")	50·00	8·50
		a. Deep blue	50·00	8·50
251	28	3d. yellow-brown	27·00	7·50
252	29	4d. bright rose	18·00	19·00
		a. Lake-rose	18·00	23·00
		b. Dull rose	16·00	19·00
253	30	5d. sepia	85·00	£200
		a. Purple-brown	55·00	22·00
254	31	6d. green (to deep green)	65·00	45·00
		a. Grass-green	£200	£225
255	32	8d. indigo	75·00	50·00
		a. Prussian blue	75·00	50·00
256	33	9d. purple	75·00	45·00
257	34	1s. vermilion	80·00	29·00
		a. Dull red	80·00	29·00
		ab. Imperf between (pair)	£5500	
258	35	2s. grey-green	£160	£140
		a. Imperf between (vert pair)	£5500	£5500
259	36	5s. vermilion	£300	£475
246/59 Set of 13			£800	£800

Collectors are warned against faked examples of the imperforate between errors, made from imperforate plate proofs.

37 Lake Taupo and Mount Ruapehu

(Recess Govt Printer, Wellington)

1899 (May)–**03**. Thick, soft ("Pirie") paper. No wmk. P 11.

260	27	2½d. blue (6.99)	24·00	4·75
		a. Imperf between (pair)	£1500	
		b. Imperf horiz (vert pair)	£600	
		c. Deep blue	24·00	4·75
261	28	3d. yellow-brown (5.00)	25·00	2·25
		a. Imperf between (pair)	£1500	
		b. Imperf vert (horiz pair)	£600	
		c. Deep brown	25·00	2·25
		d. Imperf between (horiz pair)	£1500	
262	37	4d. indigo and brown (8.99)	6·00	3·50
		a. Bright blue and chestnut	6·00	3·50
		b. Deep blue and bistre-brown	6·00	3·50

263	30	5d. purple-brown (6.99)	50·00	6·00
		a. Deep purple-brown	50·00	6·00
		ab. Imperf between (pair)	£3250	
264	31	6d. deep green	70·00	75·00
		a. Yellow-green	£100	£130
265		6d. pale rose (5.5.00)	50·00	9·00
		a. Imperf vert (horiz pair)	£550	
		b. Imperf between (horiz pair)	£1200	
		c. Rose-red	50·00	9·00
		ca. Printed double	£800	£850
		cb. Imperf between (vert pair)	£1600	
		cc. Imperf vert (horiz pair)	£450	
		cd. Showing part of sheet wmk (7.02)*	£100	£110
		d. Scarlet	80·00	26·00
		db. Imperf vert (horiz pair)	£750	
266	32	8d. indigo	55·00	21·00
		a. Prussian blue	55·00	21·00
267	33	9d. deep purple (8.99)	60·00	38·00
		a. Rosy purple	50·00	18·00
268	34	1s. red (5.00)	70·00	13·00
		a. Dull orange-red	70·00	7·50
		b. Dull brown-red	70·00	18·00
		c. Bright red	75·00	40·00
269	35	2s. blue-green (7.99)	£150	55·00
		a. Laid paper (1.03)	£225	£250
		b. Grey-green	£150	65·00
270	36	5s. vermilion (7.99)	£275	£375
		a. Carmine-red	£325	£450
260/70		Set of 11	£700	£500

*No. 265cd is on paper without general watermark, but showing the words "LISBON SUPERFINE" wmkd once in the sheet; the paper was obtained from Parsons Bros, an American firm with a branch at Auckland.

38

1900. Thick, soft ("Pirie") paper. Wmk double-lined "NZ" and Star, W 38 (sideways*). P 11.

271	13	½d. black	7·50	19·00
		x. Wmk sideways reversed	£275	£225
272	15	2d. bright purple	32·00	20·00
		w. Wmk sideways inverted	90·00	45·00
		y. Wmk sideways inverted and reversed		£225

*The normal sideways wmk on Nos. 271/2 shows the top of the star pointing to the left, as seen from the back of the stamp.

39 White Terrace, Rotomahana   41

40 Commemorative of the New Zealand Contingent in the South African War

1½d. Major re-entry (R. 2/12)

(Des J. Nairn (1½d.). Recess Govt Printer, Wellington)
1900 (Mar–Dec). Thick, soft ("Pirie") paper. W 38. P 11.

273	23	½d. pale yellow-green (7.3.00)	19·00	7·00
		a. Yellow-green	10·00	2·25
		b. Green	10·00	2·00
		ba. Imperf between (pair)	£600	
		c. Deep green	10·00	2·00
		w. Wmk inverted	50·00	25·00
		y. Wmk inverted and reversed	£110	50·00
274	39	1d. crimson (7.3.00)	13·00	20
		a. Rose-red	13·00	20
		ab. Imperf between (pair)	£1600	£1800
		ac. Imperf vert (horiz pair)	£650	
		b. Lake	50·00	5·00
		w. Wmk inverted	†	£300
		x. Wmk reversed	†	£225
		y. Wmk inverted and reversed	†	£400

275	40	1½d. khaki (7.12.00)	£1200	£750
		a. Brown	60·00	50·00
		ab. Imperf vert (horiz pair)	£1200	
		ac. Imperf (pair)	£1300	
		b. Chestnut	10·00	4·00
		ba. Imperf vert (horiz pair)	£1200	
		bb. Imperf horiz (vert pair)	£1800	
		c. Pale chestnut	10·00	4·00
		ca. Imperf (pair)	£1300	
		d. Major re-entry	£180	£120
276	41	2d. dull violet (3.00)	20·00	65
		a. Imperf between (pair)	£1500	
		b. Mauve	24·00	1·50
		c. Purple	16·00	75
		ca. Imperf between (pair)	£1400	

The above ½d. stamps are slightly smaller than those of the previous printing. A new plate was made to print 240 stamps instead of 120 as previously, and to make these fit the watermarked paper, the border design was redrawn and contracted, the centre vignette remaining design as before. The 2d. stamp is also from a new plate providing smaller designs.

42

(Des G. Bach and G. Drummond. Eng J. A. C. Harrison. Recess Waterlow)
1901 (1 Jan). Universal Penny Postage. No wmk. P 12 to 16.

277	42	1d. carmine	3·50	4·50

All examples of No. 277 show a minute dot above the upper left corner of the value tablet which is not present on later printings.

(Recess Govt Printer, Wellington)
1901 (Feb–Dec). Thick, soft ("Pirie") paper with vertical mesh. W 38.

(a) P 11

278	42	1d. carmine	6·00	25
		a. Imperf vert (horiz pair)	£400	
		b. Deep carmine	6·00	25
		ba. Imperf vert (horiz pair)	£400	
		c. Carmine-lake	24·00	11·00
		x. Wmk reversed	†	80·00
		y. Wmk inverted and reversed	—	£120

(b) P 14

279	23	½d. green (11.01)	24·00	7·50
280	42	1d. carmine	65·00	24·00
		a. Imperf vert (horiz pair)	£325	
		y. Wmk inverted and reversed	£170	80·00

(c) P 14×11

281	23	½d. green	13·00	17·00
		a. Deep green	13·00	17·00
		b. Perf 11×14	14·00	26·00
282	42	1d. carmine	£275	£110
		a. Perf 11×14	£2250	£850

*(d) P 11 and 14 mixed**

283	23	½d. green	55·00	80·00
284	42	1d. carmine	£275	£110

*The term "mixed" is applied to stamps from sheets which were at first perforated 14, or 14×11, and either incompletely or defectively perforated. These sheets were patched on the back with strips of paper, and re-perforated 11 in those parts where the original perforation was defective.
Nos. 278/84 were printed from new plates supplied by Waterlow. These were subsequently used for Nos. 285/307 with later printings on Cowan paper showing considerable plate wear.

WATERMARK VARIETIES. The watermark on the Basted Mills version of the W 38 paper used for Nos. 285/92 occurs indiscriminately normal, reversed, inverted etc.

(Recess Govt Printer, Wellington)
1901 (Dec). Thin, hard ("Basted Mills") paper with vertical mesh. W 38.

(a) P 11

285	23	½d. green	85·00	£110
286	42	1d. carmine	£150	£130

(b) P 14

287	23	½d. green	45·00	45·00
		a. Imperf vert (horiz pair)	£400	
288	42	1d. carmine	20·00	9·50
		a. Imperf vert (horiz pair)	£300	
		b. Imperf horiz (vert pair)	£300	

(c) P 14×11

289	23	½d. green	50·00	65·00
		a. Deep green	50·00	65·00
		b. Perf 11×14	27·00	50·00
290	42	1d. carmine	38·00	20·00
		a. Perf 11×14	10·00	4·50

(d) Mixed perfs

291	23	½d. green	65·00	95·00
292	42	1d. carmine	75·00	80·00

(Recess Govt Printer, Wellington)
1902 (Jan). Thin, hard ("Cowan") paper with horizontal mesh. No wmk.

(a) P 11

293	23	½d. green	£180	£190

(b) P 14

294	23	½d. green	35·00	9·00
295	42	1d. carmine	13·00	4·50

(c) P 14×11

296	23	½d. green	£130	£190
		a. Perf 11×14	£180	£325
297	42	1d. carmine	£110	£130
		a. Perf 11×14	£130	£180

(d) Mixed perfs

298	23	½d. green	£160	£225
299	42	1d. carmine	£120	£160

43 "Single" Wmk

SIDEWAYS WATERMARKS. In its sideways format the single NZ and Star watermark W 43, exists indiscriminately sideways, sideways inverted, sideways reversed and sideways inverted plus reversed.

(Recess Govt Printer, Wellington)
1902 (Apr). Thin, hard ("Cowan") paper. W 43.

(a) P 11

300	23	½d. green	75·00	£110
301	42	1d. carmine	£800	£750

(b) P 14

302	23	½d. green	10·00	1·50
		a. Imperf vert (horiz pair)	£300	
		b. Deep green	9·50	1·50
		ba. Imperf vert (horiz pair)	£300	
		c. Yellow green	12·00	1·50
		d. Pale yellow-green	22·00	4·25
		w. Wmk inverted	50·00	22·00
		x. Wmk reversed	55·00	30·00
		y. Wmk inverted and reversed	85·00	42·00
303	42	1d. carmine	3·00	10
		a. Imperf horiz (vert pair)	£200	
		b. Booklet pane of 6 (21.8.02)	£275	
		c. Pale carmine	3·00	10
		ca. Imperf horiz (vert pair)	£200	
		cb. Booklet pane of 6	£275	
		d. Deep carmine*	32·00	4·00
		w. Wmk inverted	90·00	42·00
		x. Wmk reversed	90·00	42·00
		y. Wmk inverted and reversed	95·00	42·00

(c) P 14×11

304	23	½d. green	32·00	£120
		a. Deep green	35·00	£120
		b. Perf 11×14	32·00	85·00
305	42	1d. carmine	£100	£120
		a. Perf 11×14	£150	£140
		ab. Deep carmine*	£550	£550

(d) Mixed perfs

306	23	½d. green	42·00	70·00
		a. Deep green	50·00	70·00
307	42	1d. carmine	38·00	50·00
		a. Pale carmine	38·00	50·00
		b. Deep carmine*	£275	£300
		y. Wmk inverted and reversed		

*Nos. 303d, 305ab and 307b were printed from a plate made by Waterlow & Sons, known as the "Reserve" plate. The stamps do not show evidence of wearing and the area surrounding the upper part of the figure is more deeply shaded. This plate was subsequently used to produce Nos. 362, 364 and 366/9.
A special plate, made by W. R. Royle & Sons, showing a minute dot between the horizontal rows, was introduced in 1902 to print the booklet pane, No. 303b. A special characteristic of the booklet pane was that the pearl in the top left-hand corner was large. Some panes exist with the outer edges imperforate.

(Recess Govt Printer, Wellington)
1902 (28 Aug)–07. Thin, hard ("Cowan") paper. W 43 (sideways on 3d., 5d., 6d., 8d., 1s. and 5s.).

(a) P 11

308	27	2½d. blue (5.03)	38·00	12·00
		a. Deep blue	38·00	12·00
		w. Wmk inverted	£200	95·00
		x. Wmk reversed	£225	55·00
		y. Wmk inverted and reversed	£350	90·00
309	28	3d. yellow-brown	40·00	3·50
		a. Bistre-brown	48·00	3·50
		b. Pale bistre	55·00	6·00
310	37	4d. deep blue and deep brown/bluish (27.11.02)	6·00	75·00
		a. Imperf vert (horiz pair)	£650	
311	30	5d. red-brown (4.03)	55·00	10·00
		a. Deep brown	50·00	8·00
		b. Sepia	60·00	21·00
312	31	6d. rose (9.02)	40·00	7·50
		a. Rose-red	40·00	7·50
		ab. Wmk upright (?1.03)	£2750	£2000
		b. Rose-carmine	50·00	7·50
		ba. Imperf vert (horiz pair)	£850	
		bb. Imperf horiz (vert pair)		
		c. Bright carmine-pink	60·00	8·00
		d. Scarlet	75·00	18·00
313	32	8d. blue (2.03)	55·00	11·00
		a. Steel-blue	55·00	11·00
		ab. Imperf vert (horiz pair)	£2000	
		ac. Imperf horiz (vert pair)	£2000	
314	33	9d. purple (5.03)	70·00	12·00
		w. Wmk inverted	£250	£140
		x. Wmk reversed	£275	£225
		y. Wmk inverted and reversed	£325	£275
315	34	1s. brown-red (11.02)	75·00	15·00
		a. Bright red	75·00	15·00
		b. Orange-red	75·00	8·50
		ba. Error. Wmk W 12b (inverted)	—	£2000
		c. Orange-brown	70·00	22·00
316	35	2s. green (4.03)	£160	65·00
		a. Blue-green	£150	45·00
		x. Wmk reversed	£750	
		w. Wmk inverted	£450	£180
317	36	5s. deep red (6.03)	£300	£400
		a. Wmk upright	£325	£425
		b. Vermilion	£275	£375
		ba. Wmk upright	£325	£425
		w. Wmk inverted	£1500	£850

(b) P 14

318	40	1½d. chestnut (2.07)	26·00	60·00
		a. Major re-entry	£275	
319	41	2d. grey-purple (12.02)	5·50	2·75
		a. Purple	5·50	2·75
		ab. Imperf vert (horiz pair)	£550	£850
		ac. Imperf horiz (vert pair)	£800	
		b. Bright reddish purple	6·50	3·75
320	27	2½d. blue (1906)	27·00	5·00
		a. Deep blue	27·00	5·00
		w. Wmk inverted	£170	£130
		x. Wmk reversed	†	£300
		y. Wmk inverted and reversed	£375	£200
321	28	3d. bistre-brown (1906)	30·00	8·00
		a. Imperf vert (horiz pair)	£950	
		b. Bistre	30·00	8·00
		c. Pale yellow-bistre	65·00	20·00
322	37	4d. deep blue and deep brown/ bluish (1903)	7·50	4·00
		a. Imperf vert (horiz pair)	£650	
		b. Imperf horiz (vert pair)	£650	
		c. Centre inverted	†	*
		d. Blue and chestnut/bluish	4·00	3·25
		e. Blue and ochre-brown/bluish	4·00	3·25
		w. Wmk inverted	60·00	35·00
		x. Wmk reversed	£140	£100
		y. Wmk inverted and reversed	£225	£180
323	30	5d. black-brown (1906)	60·00	38·00
		a. Red-brown	40·00	16·00
324	31	6d. bright carmine-pink (1906)	60·00	9·50
		a. Imperf vert (horiz pair)	£850	
		b. Rose-carmine	60·00	9·50
325	32	8d. steel-blue (1907)	50·00	11·00
326	33	9d. purple (1906)	48·00	8·50
		w. Wmk inverted	£375	£275
327	34	1s. orange-brown (1906)	80·00	9·00
		a. Orange-red	75·00	9·00
		b. Pale red	£170	65·00
328	35	2s. green (1.06)	£130	32·00
		a. Blue-green	£150	42·00
		aw. Wmk inverted	£800	£250
		ax. Wmk reversed	†	*
		ay. Wmk inverted and reversed	£800	£250
329	36	5s. deep red (1906)	£225	£300
		a. Wmk upright	£225	£375
		b. Dull red	£225	£300
		ba. Wmk upright	£225	£375

(c) Perf compound of 11 and 14

330	40	1½d. chestnut (1907)	£1600	
331	41	2d. purple (1903)	£500	£425
332	28	3d. bistre-brown (1906)	£950	£750
333	37	4d. blue and yellow-brown (1903)	£450	£500
		x. Wmk inverted	—	£850
334	30	5d. red-brown (1906)	£1700	£1400
335	31	6d. rose-carmine (1907)	£450	£450
336	32	8d. steel-blue (1907)	£1400	£1500
337	33	9d. purple (1906)	£1700	£1600
338	36	5s. deep red (wmk sideways) (1906)	£3250	£3250

(d) Mixed perfs

339	40	1½d. chestnut (1907)	£1600	
340	41	2d. purple (1903)	£450	£325
341	28	3d. bistre-brown (1906)	£900	£700
342	37	4d. blue and chestnut/bluish (1904)	£400	£450
		a. Blue and yellow-brown/bluish	£400	£450
		w. Wmk inverted	£950	£850
		x. Wmk reversed	£950	£900
343	30	5d. red-brown (1906)	£1300	£110
344	31	6d. rose-carmine (1907)	£425	£425
		a. Bright carmine-pink	£450	£450
345	32	8d. steel-blue (1907)	£1400	£1400
346	33	9d. purple (1906)	£1500	£1600
347	35	2s. blue-green (1906)	£1700	£1800
348	36	5s. vermilion (Wmk upright) (1906)	£2500	£3000
		w. Wmk inverted	*	

Two sizes of paper were used for the above stamps:—
(1) A sheet containing 240 wmks, with a space of 9 mm between each.
(2) A sheet containing 120 wmks, with a space of 24 mm between each vertical row.

Size (1) was used for the ½d., 1d., 2d. and 4d., and size (2) for 2½d., 5d., 9d. and 2s. The paper in each case exactly fitted the plates, and had the watermark in register, though in the case of the 4d., the plate of which contained only 80 stamps, the paper was cut up to print it. The 3d., 6d., 8d. and 1s. were printed on variety (1), but with watermark sideways: by reason of this, examples from the margins of the sheets show parts of the words "NEW ZEALAND POSTAGE" in large letters, and some have no watermark at all. For the 1½d. and 5s. stamps variety (1) was also used, but two watermarks appear on each stamp.

*The only known example of No. 322c, postmarked at Picton on 21 March 1904, was purchased for the New Zealand Post archive collection in 1998.

(Recess Govt Printer, Wellington)
1904 (Feb). Printed from new "dot" plates made by W. R. Royle & Sons. Thin, hard ("Cowan") paper. W **43**.

(a) P 14

349	42	1d. rose-carmine	11·00	50
		a. Pale carmine	11·00	50
		w. Wmk inverted	£120	38·00
		y. Wmk inverted and reversed	£120	45·00

(b) P 11×14

350	42	1d. rose-carmine	£180	£130

(c) Mixed perfs

351	42	1d. rose-carmine	42·00	55·00
		a. Pale carmine	42·00	55·00

These plates have a dot in the margins between stamps, level with the small pearls at the side of the design, but it is frequently cut out by the perforations. However, they can be further distinguished by the notes below.

In 1906 fresh printings were made from four new plates, two of which, marked in the margin "W1" and "W2", were supplied by Waterlow Bros and Layton, and the other two, marked "R1" and "R2", by W. R. Royle & Son. The intention was to note which pair of plates wore the best and produced the best results. They can be distinguished as follows:—

(a)   *(b)*   *(c)*

(d)   *(e)*   *(f)*

(a) Four o'clock flaw in rosette at top right corner. Occurs in all these plates but not in the original Waterlow plates.
(b) Pearl at right strong.
(c) Pearl at right weak.
(d) Dot at left and S-shaped ornament unshaded.
(e) S-shaped ornament with one line of shading within.
(f) As (e) but with line from left pearl to edge of stamp.
"Dot" plates comprise (a) and (d).
Waterlow plates comprise (a), (b) and (c).
Royle plates comprise (a), (c) and (e) and the line in (f) on many stamps but not all.

(Recess Govt Printer, Wellington)
1906. Thin, hard ("Cowan") paper. W **43**.

(a) Printed from new Waterlow plates

(i) P 14

352	42	1d. deep rose-carmine	55·00	3·75
		a. Imperf horiz (vert pair)	£300	
		b. Aniline carmine	50·00	3·75
		ba. Imperf vert (horiz pair)	£300	
		c. Rose-carmine	50·00	3·75
		y. Wmk inverted and reversed	—	£400

(ii) P 11

353	42	1d. aniline carmine	£700	£850

(iii) P 11×14

354	42	1d. rose-carmine	£475	£900
		a. Perf 14×11	£500	£850

(iv) Mixed perfs

355	42	1d. deep rose-carmine	£425	£650

(b) Printed from new Royle plates

(i) P 14

356	42	1d. rose-carmine	12·00	1·25
		a. Imperf horiz (vert pair)	£250	£325
		b. Bright rose-carmine	13·00	1·40
		w. Wmk inverted	†	£500
		y. Wmk inverted and reversed	—	£250

(ii) P 11

357	42	1d. bright rose-carmine	£110	£225

(iii) P 11×14

358	42	1d. rose-carmine	£100	£200
		a. Perf 14×11	£150	£200

(iv) Mixed perfs

359	42	1d. rose-carmine	£160	£275

(v) P 14×14½ (comb)

360	42	1d. bright rose-carmine	85·00	60·00
		a. Rose-carmine	85·00	60·00

Nos. 360/a are known both with and without the small dot. See also No. 386.

1905 (15 June)–06. Stamps supplied to penny-in-the-slot machines.

(i) "Dot" plates of 1904
(ii) Waterlow "reserve" plate of 1902

(a) Imperf top and bottom; zigzag roulette 9½ on one or both sides, two large holes at sides

361	42	1d. rose-carmine (i)	£200	£300
362		1d. deep carmine (ii)	£225	

(b) As last but rouletted 14½ (8.7.05)

363	42	1d. rose-carmine (i)	£200	£300
364		1d. deep carmine (ii)	£425	

(c) Imperf all round, two large holes each side (6.3.06)

365	42	1d. rose-carmine (i)	£160	
366		1d. deep carmine (ii)	£170	£300

(d) Imperf all round (21.6.06)

367	42	1d. deep carmine (ii)	£180	£300

(e) Imperf all round. Two small indentations on back of stamp (1.06)

368	42	1d. deep carmine (ii)	£225	£300

(f) Imperf all round; two small pin-holes in stamp (21.6.06)

369	42	1d. deep carmine (ii)	£200	£300

No. 365 only exists from strips of Nos. 361 or 363 (resulting from the use of successive coins) which have been separated by scissors. Similarly strips of Nos. 362 and 364 can produce single copies of No. 366 but this also exists in singles from a different machine.

Most used copies of Nos. 361/7 are forgeries and they should only be collected on cover.

44 Maori Canoe, *Te Arawa*

45 Maori art

46 Landing of Cook

46a Annexation of New Zealand

3d. White flaw behind Chieftain (Left pane, R. 4/2)

(Des L. J. Steele. Eng W. R. Bock. Typo Govt Printer, Wellington)
1906 (1–17 Nov). New Zealand Exhibition, Christchurch. W **43** (sideways). P. 14.

370	44	½d. emerald-green	40·00	38·00
371	45	1d. vermilion	16·00	16·00
		a. Claret	£8000	£11000
372	46	3d. brown and blue	55·00	85·00
		a. Flaw behind Chieftain	£350	£450
373	46a	6d. pink and olive-green (17.11)	£200	£275
370/3		Set of 4	£275	£375

The 1d. in claret was the original printing, which was considered unsatisfactory.

47 (T **28** reduced)   **48** (T **31** reduced)   **49** (T **34** reduced)

(New plates (except 4d.), supplied by Perkins Bacon. Recess Govt Printer, Wellington)
1907–08. Thin, hard ("Cowan") paper. W **43**.

(a) P 14 (line)

374	23	½d. green (1907)	42·00	16·00
		a. Imperf (pair)	£350	
		b. Yellow-green	35·00	7·50
		c. Deep yellow-green	35·00	7·50
375	47	3d. brown (6.07)	95·00	28·00
376	48	6d. carmine-pink (3.07)	48·00	13·00
		a. Red	55·00	40·00

(b) P 14×13, 13½ (comb)

377	23	½d. green (1907)	17·00	17·00
		a. Yellow-green	10·00	8·50
		b. Imperf three sides (top stamp of vert pair)	£500	
378	47	3d. brown (2.08)	55·00	50·00
		a. Yellow-brown	55·00	50·00
379	37	4d. blue and yellow-brown/bluish (6.08)	42·00	60·00
380	48	6d. pink (2.08)	£425	£170
381	49	1s. orange-red (12.07)	£140	65·00

(c) P 14×15 (comb)

382	23	½d. yellow-green (1907)	8·50	1·00
		a. Imperf three sides (top stamp of vert pair)	£450	
		y. Wmk inverted and reversed	—	£325
383	47	3d. brown (8.08)	50·00	15·00
		a. Yellow-brown	50·00	15·00
384	48	6d. carmine-pink (8.08)	50·00	11·00
385	49	1s. orange-red (8.08)	£110	24·00
		a. Deep orange-brown	£325	£900

The ½d. stamps of this 1907–8 issue have a minute dot in the margin between the stamps, where not removed by the perforation. (See note after No. 351a.) Those perforated 14 can be distinguished from the earlier stamps, Nos. 302/d, by the absence of plate wear. This is most noticeable on the 1902 printings as a white patch at far left, level with the bottom of the "P" in "POSTAGE". Such damage is not present on the new plates used for Nos. 374/c.

Stamps of T **47**, **48** and **49** also have a small dot as described in note after No. 351a.

TYPOGRAPHY PAPERS.

1908–30. De La Rue paper is chalk-surfaced and has a smooth finish. The watermark is as illustrated. The gum is toned and strongly resistant to soaking.

Jones paper is chalk-surfaced and has a coarser texture, is poorly surfaced and the ink tends to peel. The outline of the watermark commonly shows on the surface of the stamp. The gum is colourless or only slightly toned and washes off readily.

Cowan paper is chalk-surfaced and is white and opaque. The watermark is usually smaller than in the "Jones" paper and is often barely visible.

Wiggins Teape paper is chalk-surfaced and is thin and hard. It has a vertical mesh with a narrow watermark, whereas the other papers have a horizontal mesh and a wider watermark.

50

(Typo Govt Printer, Wellington, from Perkins Bacon plate).
1908 (1 Dec). De La Rue chalk-surfaced paper. W **43**. P 14×15 (comb).

386	50	1d. carmine	23·00	3·25
		w. Wmk inverted	†	£120

The design of Type **50** differs from Type **42** by alterations in the corner rosettes and by the lines on the globe which are diagonal instead of vertical.

51   **52**   **53**

(Eng. P.B. Typo Govt Printer, Wellington)

1909 (8 Nov)–**12**. De La Rue chalk-surfaced paper with toned gum. W **43**. P 14×15 (comb).

387	**51**	½d. yellow-green	5·00	50
		aa. Deep green	5·00	50
		a. Imperf (pair)	£225	
		b. Booklet pane. 5 stamps plus label in position 1 (4.10)	£800	
		c. Ditto, but label in position 6 (4.10)	£800	
		d. Booklet pane of 6 (4.10)	£250	
		e. Ditto, but with coloured bars on selvedge (5.12)	£225	
		w. Wmk inverted	†	£500

Stamps with blurred and heavy appearance are from booklets.

(Eng W. R. Royle & Son, London. Recess Govt Printer, Wellington)

1909 (8 Nov)–**16**. T **52** and similar portraits.

(a) W **43**. P 14×14½ (comb)

388		2d. mauve	9·50	6·50
		a. Deep mauve	18·00	6·50
		w. Wmk inverted	†	
389		3d. chestnut	23·00	1·25
390		4d. orange-red	26·00	27·00
390*a*		4d. yellow (1912)	7·00	9·50
		aw. Wmk inverted	£475	£150
391		5d. brown (1910)	17·00	5·00
		a. Red-brown	17·00	5·00
		w. Wmk inverted	†	
392		6d. carmine (1910)	40·00	2·00
		a. Deep carmine (29.10.13)	50·00	3·50
393		8d. indigo-blue	13·00	3·50
		a. Deep bright blue	13·00	3·50
		w. Wmk inverted	85·00	50·00
394		1s. vermilion (1910)	50·00	5·00
		w. Wmk inverted	£400	£150
388/94 Set of 8			£160	55·00

(b) W **43**. P 14 (line)*

395		3d. chestnut (1910)	50·00	20·00
396		4d. orange (1910)	21·00	15·00
397		5d. brown	26·00	4·50
		a. Red-brown (15.9.11)	26·00	5·00
		w. Wmk inverted		
398		6d. carmine	42·00	10·00
399		1s. vermilion	65·00	14·00
395/9 Set of 5			£180	55·00

(c) W **43** (sideways) (paper with widely spaced wmk as used for Nos. 308 and 320 – see note below No. 348). P 14 (line)*

400		8d. indigo-blue (8.16)	50·00	95·00
		a. No wmk	£120	£200

(d) W **43** P 14×13½ (comb)†

401		3d. chestnut (1915)	75·00	£130
		a. Vert pair. P 14×13½ and 14×14½	£250	£475
		w. Wmk inverted	£400	£130
402		5d. red-brown (1916)	19·00	3·00
		a. Vert pair. P 14×13½ and 14×14½	60·00	£170
403		6d. carmine (1915)	75·00	£130
		a. Vert pair. P 14×13½ and 14×14½	£250	£600
404		8d. indigo-blue (3.16)	50·00	3·25
		b. Deep bright blue	55·00	3·25
		ba. Vert pair. P 14×13½ and 14×14½	80·00	£170
		w. Wmk inverted	£140	50·00
401/4 Set of 4			£190	£225

*In addition to showing the usual characteristics of a line perforation, these stamps may be distinguished by their vertical perforation which measures 13.8. Nos. 388/94 generally measure vertically 14 to 14.3. An exception is 13.8 one vertical side but 14 the other.

†The 3d. and 6d. come in full sheets perf 14×13½. The 3d., 5d. and 6d. values also exist in two combinations: *(a)* five top rows perf 14×13½ with five bottom rows perf 14×14½ and *(b)* four top rows perf 14×13½ with six bottom rows perf 14×14½. The 8d. perf 14×13½ only exists from combination *(b)*.

1d. "Feather" flaw (Plate 12, R. 3/1)

1d. "Globe" flaw (Plate 12, R. 5/24)

1d. "Q" flaw (Plate 13, R. 10/19)

1d. "N" flaw (Plate 12, R. 9/23, *printings from 1925*)

(Eng P.B. Typo Govt Printer, Wellington)

1909 (8 Nov)–**27**. P 14×15 (comb).

(a) W **43**. De La Rue chalk-surfaced paper with toned gum

405	**53**	1d. carmine	1·75	10
		a. Imperf (pair)	£375	
		b. Booklet pane of 6 (4.10)	£200	
		c. Ditto, but with coloured bars on selvedge (5.12)	£160	
		d. "Feather" flaw	30·00	8·50
		e. "Globe" flaw	30·00	8·50
		f. "Q" flaw	60·00	25·00
		w. Wmk inverted	80·00	70·00
		y. Wmk inverted and reversed		

(b) W **43**. Jones chalk-surfaced paper with white gum

406	**53**	1d. deep carmine (6.24)	20·00	9·00
		a. On unsurfaced paper. *Pale carmine*	£400	
		b. Booklet pane of 6 with bars on selvedge (1.12.24)	£160	
		c. "Feather" flaw	90·00	50·00
		d. "Globe" flaw	90·00	50·00
		w. Wmk inverted	£120	60·00

(c) W **43**. De La Rue unsurfaced medium paper with toned gum

407	**53**	1d. rose-carmine (4.25)	42·00	£140
		a. "Feather" flaw	£300	
		b. "Globe" flaw	£300	

(d) W **43** (sideways). De La Rue chalk-surfaced paper with toned gum

408	**53**	1d. bright carmine (4.25)	12·00	50·00
		a. No wmk	24·00	80·00
		b. Imperf (pair)	£160	
		c. "Feather" flaw	80·00	
		d. "Globe" flaw	80·00	

(e) No wmk, but bluish "NZ" and Star lithographed on back. Art paper

409	**53**	1d. rose-carmine (7.25)	2·00	8·00
		a. "NZ" and Star in black	24·00	
		b. "NZ" and Star colourless	24·00	
		c. "Feather" flaw	60·00	95·00
		d. "Globe" flaw	60·00	95·00

(f) W **43**. Cowan thick, opaque, chalk-surfaced paper with white gum

410	**53**	1d. deep carmine (8.25)	12·00	1·00
		a. Imperf (pair)	£140	£180
		b. Booklet pane of 6 with bars and adverts on selvedge	£190	
		c. "Feather" flaw	70·00	40·00
		d. "Globe" flaw	70·00	40·00
		e. "N" flaw	£120	£120
		w. Wmk inverted	65·00	42·00
		x. Wmk reversed (1926)	12·00	4·00
		xa. Booklet pane of 6 with bars and adverts on selvedge (1927)	£180	
		xc. "Feather" flaw	£120	70·00
		xd. "Globe" flaw	£120	70·00
		xe. "N" flaw	£140	£100
		y. Wmk inverted and reversed (1926)	£120	90·00

(g) W **43**. Wiggins Teape thin, hard, chalk-surfaced paper with white gum

411	**53**	1d. rose-carmine (6.26)	40·00	28·00
		a. "Feather" flaw	£180	75·00
		b. "Globe" flaw	£180	75·00
		c. "N" flaw	£180	95·00
		w. Wmk inverted	85·00	55·00

Examples of No. 405 with a blurred and heavy appearance are from booklets.

No. 406a comes from a sheet on which the paper coating was missing from the right-hand half.

Many stamps from the sheets of No. 408 were without watermark or showed portions of "NEW ZEALAND POSTAGE" in double-lined capitals.

AUCKLAND EXHIBITION, 1913.

(59)   **60**

1913 (1 Dec). Auckland Industrial Exhibition. Nos. 387*aa*, 389, 392 and 405 optd with T **59** by Govt Printer, Wellington.

412	**51**	½d. deep green	22·00	55·00
413	**53**	1d. carmine	28·00	50·00
		a. "Feather" flaw	£325	£425
		b. "Globe" flaw	£325	£425
414	**52**	3d. chestnut	£130	£250
415		6d. carmine	£160	£300
412/15 Set of 4			£300	£600

These overprinted stamps were only available for letters in New Zealand and to Australia.

(Des H. L. Richardson. Recess Govt Printer, Wellington, from plates made in London by P.B.)

1915 (30 July)–**30**. W **43**. P 14×13½ (comb) (see notes below).

(a) Cowan unsurfaced paper

416	**60**	1½d. grey-slate	3·25	2·50
		a. Perf 14×14½ (1915)	5·00	1·75
		aw. Wmk inverted	£500	£500
		b. Vert pair. Nos. 416/a	35·00	£100
417		2d. bright violet	12·00	65·00
		a. Perf 14×14½	6·00	50·00
		b. Vert pair. Nos. 417/a	28·00	£140
418		2d. yellow (15.1.16)	7·50	32·00
		a. Perf 14×14½	7·50	32·00
		b. Vert pair. Nos. 418/a	21·00	£250
419		2½d. blue	3·25	7·00
		a. Perf 14×14½ (1916)	9·50	32·00
		b. Vert pair. Nos. 419/a	40·00	£180
420		3d. chocolate	22·00	60·00
		aw. Wmk inverted	£225	£150
		ax. Wmk reversed		
		b. Perf 14×14½	13·00	2·00
		bw. Wmk inverted	£450	£170
		bx. Wmk reversed	£650	
		c. Vert pair. Nos. 420 and 420b	50·00	£140
		cw. Wmk inverted		
		cx. Wmk reversed		
421		4d. yellow	4·25	60·00
		a. Re-entry (Pl 20 R. 1/6)	50·00	
		b. Re-entry (Pl 20 R. 4/10)	60·00	
		c. Perf 14×14½	4·25	60·00
		d. Vert pair. Nos. 421 and 421c	27·00	£250

422		4d. bright violet (7.4.16)	11·00	50
		a. Imperf three sides (top stamp of vertical pair)	£1500	
		b. Re-entry (Pl 20 R. 1/6)	55·00	35·00
		c. Re-entry (Pl 20 R. 4/10)	65·00	40·00
		dx. Wmk reversed	—	£350
		e. Perf 14×14½	7·00	50
		ex. Wmk reversed	—	£350
		f. Vert pair. Nos. 422 and 422e	60·00	£150
		fx. Wmk reversed		
		g. Deep purple (7.26)	50·00	15·00
		h. Ditto. Perf 14×14½	7·00	50
		ha. Imperf three sides (top stamp of vertical pair)	£1500	
		hb. Vert pair. Nos. 422g/h	£2500	
		hw. Wmk inverted	†	£1900
423		4½d. deep green	18·00	28·00
		a. Perf 14×14½ (1915)	12·00	55·00
		b. Vert pair. Nos. 423/a	55·00	£170
424		5d. light blue (4.22)	7·00	1·00
		a. Imperf (pair)	£140	£180
		aa. Imperf (top stamp of vertical pair)	£850	
		bw. Wmk inverted	—	£300
		c. Perf 14×14½	12·00	38·00
		d. Pale ultramarine (5.30)	17·00	13·00
		da. Perf 14×14½	32·00	25·00
		db. Vert pair. Nos. 424d/da	80·00	£250
425		6d. carmine	9·00	50
		a. Imperf three sides (top stamp of vert pair)	£1500	
		bw. Wmk inverted	£200	£160
		bx. Wmk reversed	—	£250
		by. Wmk inverted and reversed	†	£1900
		c. Carmine-lake (11.27)	£500	£400
		d. Perf 14×14½ (1915)	10·00	60
		dw. Wmk inverted	£190	65·00
		e. Vert pair. Nos. 425 and 425d	65·00	£140
426		7½d. red-brown	14·00	30·00
		a. Perf 14×14½ (10.20)	11·00	80·00
		b. Vert pair. Nos. 426/a	50·00	£225
427		8d. indigo-blue (19.4.21)	15·00	60·00
		a. Perf 14×14½	8·50	55·00
		b. Vert pair. Nos. 427/a	38·00	£180
428		8d. red-brown (3.22)	32·00	1·50
429		9d. sage-green	17·00	2·75
		a. Imperf (pair)	£1500	
		b. Imperf three sides (top stamp of vert pair)	£1500	
		c. Yellowish olive (12.25)	20·00	24·00
		dw. Wmk inverted	†	£1900
		e. Perf 14×14½	15·00	32·00
		f. Vert pair. Nos. 429 and 429e	75·00	£225
430		1s. vermilion	21·00	2·25
		a. Imperf (pair)	£2250	
		aa. Imperf (top stamp of vertical pair)	£2000	
		bw. Wmk inverted	£375	£350
		c. Perf 14×14½ (1915)	14·00	50
		ca. Pale orange-red (4.24)	30·00	25·00
		cb. Imperf (pair)	£325	
		cba. Imperf (top stamp of vertical pair)	£750	
		cc. Orange-brown (1.2.28)	£600	£450
		cw. Wmk inverted	£300	
		d. Vert pair. Nos. 430 and 430c	75·00	£275
		dw. Wmk inverted		
416/30c Set of 15			£130	£225

(b) W **43** (sideways on 2d., 3d. and 6d.). Thin paper with widely spaced watermark as used for Nos. 308 and 320 (see note below No. 348). P 14×13½ (comb) (see notes below) (1½d.) or 14 (line) (others)

431	**60**	1½d. grey-slate (3.16)	3·00	11·00
		a. No wmk	5·50	23·00
		b. Perf 14×14½	3·00	11·00
		ba. No wmk	5·50	23·00
		by. Wmk inverted and reversed	£500	£500
		c. Vert pair. Nos. 431 and 431b	26·00	£120
		ca. Vert pair. Nos. 431a and 431ba	60·00	£190
432		2d. yellow (6.16)	6·00	60·00
		a. No wmk	75·00	£160
433		3d. chocolate (6.16)	7·00	50·00
		a. No wmk	75·00	£160
434		6d. carmine (6.16)	11·00	£110
		a. No wmk	£100	£225
431/4 Set of 4			25·00	£200

The 1½d., 2½d., 4½d. and 7½d. have value tablets as shown in Type **60**. For the other values the tablets are shortened and the ornamental border each side of the crown correspondingly extended.

With the exception of Nos. 432/4 stamps in this issue were comb-perforated 14×13½, 14×14½ or a combination of the two.

The 1½d. (No. 416), 2½d., 4d. (both), 4½d., 5d., 6d., 7½d., 8d. red-brown, 9d. and 1s. are known to have been produced in sheets perforated 14×13½ throughout with the 4d. bright violet, 5d., 6d. and 1s. known perforated 14×14½ throughout.

On the sheets showing the two perforations combined, the top four rows are usually perforated 14×13½ and the bottom six 14×14½. Combination sheets are known to have been produced in this form for the 1½d. (Nos. 416 and 431), 2d. (both), 2½d., 4d. (both), 4½d., 6d., 7½d., 8d. indigo-blue, 9d. and 1s. On a late printing of the 4d. deep purple and 5d. pale ultramarine the arrangement is different with the top five rows perforated 14×14½ and the bottom five 14×13½.

With the exception of Nos. 432/4 any with perforations measuring 14×14 or nearly must be classed as 14×14½, this being an irregularity of the comb machine, and not a product of the 14-line machine.

4d Re-entry (Plate 20, R. 1/6)   **4d Re-entry** (Plate 20, R. 4/10)

During the laying-down of plate 20 for the 4d., from the roller-die which also contained dies of other values, an impression of the 4½d. value was placed on R. 1/6 and of the 2½d. on R. 4/10. These errors were subsequently corrected by re-entries of the 4d. impression, but on R. 1/6 traces of the original impression can be found in the right-hand value tablet and above the top frame line, while on R. 4/10 the foot of the "2" is visible in the ½d. left-hand value tablet with traces of "½" to its right.

★ ★

WAR STAMP

61 **62** (**63**)

Type **62** (from local plates) can be identified from Type **61** (prepared by Perkins Bacon) by the shading on the portrait. This is diagonal on Type **62** and horizontal on Type **61**.

(Die eng W. R. Bock. Typo Govt Printer, Wellington, from plates made by P.B. (T **61**) or locally (T **62**))

1915 (30 July)–**33**. W **43**. P 14×15.

(a) De La Rue chalk-surfaced paper with toned gum

435	61	½d. green	1·50	20
		a. Booklet pane of 6 with bars on selvedge	£170	
		b. Yellow-green	4·00	1·75
		ba. Booklet pane of 6 with bars on selvedge	£150	
		c. Very thick, hard, highly surfaced paper with white gum (12.15)	12·00	55·00
		w. Wmk inverted	£100	£140
		x. Wmk reversed	—	£180
		y. Wmk inverted and reversed	—	£225
436	62	1½d. grey-black (4.16)	13·00	1·75
		a. Black	13·00	2·00
		w. Wmk inverted and reversed	—	£350
437	61	1½d. slate (5.9.16)	9·00	20
		w. Wmk inverted	—	£400
438		1½d. orange-brown (9.18)	2·25	20
		w. Wmk inverted	£200	£170
		x. Wmk reversed	†	—
		y. Wmk inverted and reversed	£350	£300
439		2d. yellow (9.16)	2·25	20
		a. Pale yellow	6·00	1·25
		w. Wmk inverted	£150	
440		3d. chocolate (5.19)	7·00	1·50
435/40		Set of 6		3·50

*(b) W **43**. Jones chalk-surfaced paper with white gum*

441	61	½d. green (10.24)	10·00	14·00
		a. Booklet pane of 6 with bars on selvedge (1.12.24)	£160	
		w. Wmk inverted	£110	£110
442		2d. dull yellow (7.24)	10·00	60·00
		w. Wmk inverted	£150	
443		3d. deep chocolate (3.25)	22·00	32·00
441/3		Set of 3	38·00	90·00

(c) No wmk, but bluish "NZ" and Star lithographed on back. Art paper

444	61	½d. apple-green (4.25)	2·75	9·00
		a. "NZ" and Star almost colourless	5·00	
445		2d. yellow (7.25)	12·00	75·00

*(d) W **43**. Cowan thick, opaque, chalk-surfaced paper with white gum*

446	61	½d. green (8.25)	1·75	20
		a. Booklet pane of 6 with bars and adverts on selvedge	£180	
		aa. Imperf 3 sides (top stamp of vertical pair)	£1200	
		ab. Booklet pane of 6 with bars on selvedge (1928)	£425	
		bw. Wmk inverted	£110	£110
		bx. Wmk reversed (1926)	13·00	3·75
		bxa. Booklet pane of 6 with bars and adverts on selvedge (1927)	£150	
		by. Wmk inverted and reversed (1926)	£140	£110
		c. Perf 14 (1927)	2·75	35
		ca. Booklet pane of 6 with bars on selvedge (1928)	£140	
		cb. Booklet pane of 6 with bars and adverts on selvedge (1928)	£140	
		cw. Wmk inverted	£200	£110
447		1½d. orange-brown (P 14) (8.29)	8·50	42·00
		a. Perf 14×15 (7.33)	38·00	90·00
448		2d. yellow (8.25)	11·00	1·50
		ax. Wmk reversed (1927)	35·00	£130
		ay. Wmk inverted and reversed (1927)	£300	£650
		b. Perf 14 (1929)	2·75	20
		bw. Wmk inverted	£140	50·00
449		3d. chocolate (8.25)	7·50	2·00
		aw. Wmk inverted	£110	
		b. Perf 14 (1929)	7·50	4·25
446/9		Set of 4	18·00	42·00

*(e) W **43**. Wiggins Teape thin, hard, chalk-surfaced paper*

450	61	1½d. orange-brown (P 14) (1930)	55·00	£130
451		2d. yellow (5.26)	14·00	25·00
		aw. Wmk inverted	90·00	60·00
		b. Perf 14 (10.27)	15·00	24·00
		bw. Wmk inverted	£110	55·00

The designs of these stamps also differ as described beneath No. 434.

Stamps from booklet panes often have blurred, heavy impressions. Different advertisements can be found on the listed booklet panes.

Examples of No. 446aa, which occur in booklet panes, show the stamps perforated at top.

The ½d. and 2d. (Nos. 446c and 448b) are known showing ½d. and 1d. local surcharges from 1932 applied diagonally in blue to stamps previously stuck on to envelopes or cards at Christchurch (½d.) or Wellington (1d.).

1915 (24 Sept). No. 435 optd with T **63**.

452	61	½d. green	2·25	50

64 "Peace" and Lion   **65** "Peace" and Lion

---

66 **67**

66a **67a**

(Des and typo D.L.R. from plates by P.B., Waterlow and D.L.R.)

1920 (27 Jan). Victory. De La Rue chalk-surfaced paper. W **43** (sideways on ½d., 1½d., 3d. and 1s.). P 14.

453	64	½d. green	3·00	2·50
		a. Pale yellow-green	27·00	28·00
454	65	1d. carmine-red	4·50	60
		a. Bright carmine	7·50	70
		w. Wmk inverted	35·00	22·00
		x. Wmk reversed	£120	60·00
455	66	1½d. brown-orange	3·00	50
456	66a	3d. chocolate	12·00	14·00
457	67	6d. violet	14·00	17·00
		a. Wmk sideways	†	£1000
		w. Wmk inverted	£650	£450
458	67a	1s. orange-red	24·00	50·00
453/8		Set of 6	55·00	75·00

The above stamps were placed on sale in London in November, 1919.

2d. **2d.**

TWOPENCE

(**68**) **69**

1922 (Mar). No. 453 surch with T **68**.

459	64	2d. on ½d. green (R.)	6·00	1·40

(Des and eng W. R. Bock, Typo Govt Printer, Wellington)

1923 (1 Oct)–**25**. Restoration of Penny Postage. W **43**. P 14×15.

(a) De La Rue chalk-surfaced paper with toned gum

460	69	1d. carmine	4·75	60

(b) Jones chalk-surfaced paper with white gum

461	69	1d. carmine (3.24)	14·00	11·00
		a. Wmk sideways	†	£700
		w. Wmk inverted	80·00	60·00

(c) Cowan unsurfaced paper with very shiny gum

462	69	1d. carmine-pink (4.25)	48·00	27·00

The paper used for No. 462 is similar to that of Nos. 416/30.

70 Exhibition Buildings

(Des H. L. Richardson. Eng and typo Govt Printer, Wellington)

1925 (17 Nov). Dunedin Exhibition. Cowan chalk-surfaced paper. W **43**. P 14×15.

463	70	½d. yellow-green/green	3·00	16·00
		w. Wmk inverted	£225	£180
464		1d. carmine/rose	4·25	7·50
		w. Wmk inverted	£325	£200
465		4d. mauve/pale mauve	30·00	75·00
		a. "POSTAGF" at right (R. 10/1)	£100	£180
463/5		Set of 3	32·00	90·00

71 King George V as Field-Marshal   **72** King George V as Admiral

(Des H. L. Richardson; plates by B.W. (1d. from sheets), P.B. (1d. from booklets), Royal Mint, London (others). Typo Govt Printer, Wellington)

1926 (12 July)–**34**. W **43**. P 14.

(a) Jones chalk-surfaced paper with white gum

466	72	2s. deep blue	80·00	70·00
		w. Wmk inverted	65·00	80·00
467		3s. mauve	£110	£200
		w. Wmk inverted	£130	£250

(b) Cowan thick, opaque, chalk-surfaced paper with white gum

468	71	1d. rose-carmine (15.11.26)	75	20
		a. Imperf (pair)	£275	
		ab. Imperf three sides (horiz pair)	£400	£500
		b. Booklet pane of 6 with bars on selvedge (1928)	£150	
		c. Booklet pane of 6 with bars and adverts on selvedge (1928)	£130	
		dw. Wmk inverted	£100	55·00
		e. Perf 14×15 (3.27)	65	50
		ea. Booklet pane of 6 with bars and adverts on selvedge (1934)	£140	

---

		ew. Wmk inverted	£120	55·00
		ex. Wmk reversed		15·00
469	72	2s. light blue (5.27)	75·00	29·00
470		3s. pale mauve (9.27)	£130	£190
468/70		Set of 3	£180	£200

(c) Wiggins Teape thin, hard, chalk-surfaced paper with white gum

471	71	1d. rose-carmine (6.30)	42·00	16·00
		w. Wmk inverted	£225	£110

No. 468ex exists in a range of colours including scarlet and deep carmine to magenta but we have insufficient evidence to show that these were issued.

Following the reduction of the postage rate to ½d. on 1 June 1932 the firm of R. H. White & Co. Ltd. of Stratford returned a quantity of envelopes stamped with 1d. stamps (No. 468) to the New Plymouth post office who surcharged the stamps "HALFPENNY" in purple using a handstamp. The covers were then returned to the firm for normal use. Similar local surcharges were applied diagonally to 1d. stamps stuck onto postcards or lettercards at Dunedin, Greymouth and Invercargill in blue or at Palmerston North in purple. With the exception of the Greymouth provisional, where 40 mint examples were acquired by a stamp dealer, these local surcharges are only found unused, no gum, or used.

Nos. 472 to 543 are vacant.

73 Nurse   **74** Smiling Boy

(Typo Govt Printing Office, Wellington)

1929–30. Anti-Tuberculosis Fund. T **73** and similar design. W **43**. P 14.

(a) Inscribed "HELP STAMP OUT TUBERCULOSIS"

544		1d. +1d. scarlet (11.12.29)	11·00	19·00
		w. Wmk inverted	£375	£275

(b) Inscribed "HELP PROMOTE HEALTH"

545		1d. +1d. scarlet (29.10.30)	20·00	45·00

HIGH VALUES. From 1931 postal requirements for higher values were met by the "Arms" "Stamp Duty" adhesives (F145 etc).

(Des L. C. Mitchell. Dies eng and plates made Royal Mint, London (1d.), Govt Ptg Office, Wellington from W. R. Bock die (2d.). Typo Govt Ptg Office, Wellington)

1931 (31 Oct). Health Stamps. W **43** (sideways). P 14½×14.

546	74	1d. +1d. scarlet	75·00	75·00
547		2d. +1d. blue	75·00	60·00

75 New Zealand Lake Scenery

FIVE PENCE

(**76**)

(Des L. C. Mitchell. Plates, Royal Mint, London. Typo Govt Ptg Office)

1931 (10 Nov)–**35**. Air. W **43**. P 14×14½.

548	75	3d. chocolate	22·00	16·00
		a. Perf 14×15 (4.35)	£130	£425
549		4d. blackish purple	22·00	22·00
550		7d. brown-orange	22·00	9·00
548/50		Set of 3	60·00	42·00

1931 (18 Dec). Air. Surch with T **76**. W **43**. P 14×14½.

551	75	5d. on 3d. green (R.)	10·00	10·00

77 Hygeia, Goddess of Health   **78** The Path to Health

(Des R. E. Tripe and W. J. Cooch. Eng H. T. Peat. Recess Govt Printing Office, Wellington)

1932 (18 Nov). Health Stamp. W **43**. P 14.

552	77	1d. +1d. carmine	25·00	32·00
		w. Wmk inverted	£450	£250
		x. Wmk reversed	†	£600

(Des J. Berry. Eng H. T. Peat. Recess Govt Printing Office, Wellington)

1933 (8 Nov). Health Stamp. W **43**. P 14.

553	78	1d. +1d. carmine	16·00	21·00
		w. Wmk inverted	£325	£200

TRANS-TASMAN AIR MAIL "FAITH IN AUSTRALIA."

(**79**)

80 Crusader

1934 (17 Jan). Air. T **75** in new colour optd with T **79**. W **43**. P 14×14½.

554	**75**	7d. light blue (B.)	35·00	50·00

(Des J. Berry. Recess D.L.R.)

1934 (25 Oct). Health Stamp. W **43** (sideways). P 14×13½.

555	**80**	1d. +1d. carmine	11·00	17·00

81 Collared Grey Fantail

82 Brown Kiwi

83 Maori Woman

84 Maori Carved House

85 Mt. Cook

86 Maori Girl   87 Mitre Peak

88 Striped Marlin   89 Harvesting

90 Tuatara Lizard

91 Maori Panel

92 Parson Bird

93 Capt. Cook at Poverty Bay   94 Mt. Egmont

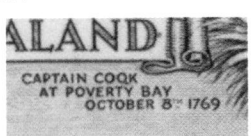
Die I   Die II

AL AND
CAPTAIN COQK
AT POVERTY BAY
OCTOBER 8TH 1769
2s. "CAPTAIN COQK" (R. 1/4)

(Des J. Fitzgerald (½d., 4d.), C. H. and R. J. G. Collins (1d.), M. Matthews (1½d.), H. W. Young (2d.), L. C. Mitchell (2½d., 3d., 8d., 1s., 3s.), W. J. Cooch and R. E. Tripe (5d.), T. I. Archer (6d.), I. F. Calder (9d.) and I. H. Jenkins (2s.). Litho Waterlow (9d.). Recess D.L.R. (remainder))

1935 (1 May)–**36**. W **43** (sideways on. 8d.).

556	**81**	½d. bright green, P 14×13½	3·25	1·50
		w. Wmk inverted (12.35)	6·50	8·00
557	**82**	1d. scarlet (Die I), P 14×13½	3·50	1·50
		aw. Wmk inverted (2.36)	8·50	14·00
		b. Perf 13½×14 (1936)	75·00	65·00
		c. Die II. Perf 14×13½ (18.11.35)	13·00	4·75
		ca. Booklet pane of 6 with adverts on selvedge	60·00	
		cw. Wmk inverted	17·00	7·50
558	**83**	1½d. red-brown, P 14×13½	15·00	21·00
		a. Perf 13½×14 (11.35)	6·50	14·00
		ay. Wmk inverted and reversed (2.36)	20·00	42·00
559	**84**	2d. orange, P 14×13½	3·75	3·25
		w. Wmk inverted	£1200	£600
560	**85**	2½d. chocolate and slate, P 13–14×13½	14·00	40·00
		aw. Wmk inverted	40·00	95·00
		b. Perf 13½×14 (11.35)	10·00	30·00
		bx. Wmk reversed	†	£2750

561	**86**	3d. brown, P 14×13½	12·00	4·00
		w. Wmk inverted	£1100	£500
562	**87**	4d. black and sepia, P 14	4·75	3·50
		w. Wmk inverted	£850	£550
563	**88**	5d. ultramarine, P 13–14×13½	23·00	40·00
		a. Double print, one albino	†	—
		bw. Wmk inverted	†	£750
		c. Perf 13½×14	28·00	50·00
564	**89**	6d. scarlet, P 13½×14	9·00	12·00
		w. Wmk inverted	£650	£475
565	**90**	8d. chocolate, P 14×13½	13·00	20·00
		w. Wmk sideways inverted	£600	£375
566	**91**	9d. scarlet and black, P 14×14½	16·00	7·00
567	**92**	1s. deep green, P 14×13½	24·00	19·00
568	**93**	2s. olive-green, P 13–14×13½	50·00	50·00
		a. "CAPTAIN COQK"	£170	£130
		bw. Wmk inverted	£170	95·00
		c. Perf 13½×14 (1935)	65·00	60·00
		ca. "CAPTAIN COQK"	£170	£130
569	**94**	3s. chocolate and yellow-brown, P 13–14×13½	19·00	55·00
		a. Perf 13½×14 (11.35)	20·00	60·00
		aw. Wmk inverted	†	£1800
		ay. Wmk inverted and reversed (1936)	£450	£475
556/69		Set of 14	£170	£225

Some stamps from sheets perforated 14×13½ by De La Rue sometimes show the horizontal perforations nearer 13½.

In the 2½d., 5d., 2s. and 3s. perf 13–14×13½ the horizontal perforations of each stamp are in two sizes, one half of each horizontal side measuring 13 and the other 14.

See also Nos. 577/90 and 630/1.

95 Bell Block Aerodrome

96 King George V and Queen Mary

(Des J. Berry. Eng Stamp Printing Office, Melbourne. Recess Govt Printing Office, Wellington)

1935 (4 May). Air. W **43**. P 14.

570	**95**	1d. carmine	1·00	70
		w. Wmk inverted	£200	£110
571		3d. violet	4·50	3·00
		w. Wmk inverted	£250	£120
572		6d. blue	8·00	3·00
		w. Wmk inverted	£300	£130
570/2		Set of 3	12·00	6·00

(Frame by J. Berry. Recess B.W.)

1935 (7 May). Silver Jubilee. W **43**. P 11×11½.

573	**96**	½d. green	75	1·00
574		1d. carmine	1·00	80
575		6d. red-orange	20·00	32·00
573/5		Set of 3	20·00	32·00

97 "The Key to Health"

98 "Multiple Wmk"

(Des S. Hall. Recess John Ash, Melbourne)

1935 (30 Sept). Health Stamp. W **43**. P 11.

576	**97**	1d. +1d. scarlet	2·50	3·75

WATERMARKS. In W **43** the wmk units are in vertical columns widely spaced and the sheet margins are unwatermarked or wmkd "NEW ZEALAND POSTAGE" in large letters.

In W **98** the wmk units are arranged alternately in horizontal rows closely spaced and are continued into the sheet margins.

Stamps with W **98** sideways show the top of the star pointing to the right, *as seen from the back*. Sideways inverted varieties have the top of the star to left *as seen from the back*.

(Litho Govt Ptg Office, Wellington (9d). Recess Waterlow or D.L.R. (others))

1936–42. W **98**.

577	**81**	½d. bright green, P 14×13½	3·50	10
		w. Wmk inverted	5·50	10·00
578	**82**	1d. scarlet (Die II), P 14×13½ (4.36)	4·50	10
		w. Wmk inverted	10·00	8·50
579	**83**	1½d. red-brown P 14×13½ (6.36)	20·00	7·00
580	**84**	2d. orange, P 14×13½ (3.36)	30	10
		aw. Wmk inverted	£600	£400
		b. Perf 12½† (6.41)	7·00	20
		bw. Wmk inverted		
		c. Perf 14 (6.41)	38·00	1·25
		d. Perf 14×15 (6.41)	38·00	26·00
581	**85**	2½d. chocolate and slate, P 13–14×13½	11·00	26·00
		aw. Wmk inverted	80·00	£150
		b. Perf 14 (11.36)	10·00	1·50
		bw. Wmk inverted	60·00	95·00
		c. Perf 14×13½ (11.42)	1·00	5·50
582	**86**	3d. brown, P 14×13½	35·00	1·50
		w. Wmk inverted	75·00	75·00
583	**87**	4d. black and sepia, P 14×13½	9·00	1·00
		aw. Wmk inverted	32·00	40·00
		b. Perf 12½* (8.41)	48·00	20·00
		bw. Wmk inverted	†	—
		c. Perf 14, line (11.41)	65·00	£130

		d. Perf 14×14½ comb (7.42)	1·00	20
		dw. Wmk inverted	£600	£375
584	**88**	5d. ultramarine, P 13–14×13½ (8.36)	28·00	3·50
		aw. Wmk inverted	75·00	75·00
		b. Perf 12½*† (7.41)	13·00	10·00
		c. Perf 14×13½ (11.42)	2·00	2·25
		ca. Double print, one albino	£900	
		cw. Wmk inverted	£600	£400
585	**89**	6d. scarlet, P 13½×14 (8.36)	26·00	1·75
		aw. Wmk inverted	£100	80·00
		b. Perf 12½* (10.41)	3·00	5·00
		c. Perf 14½×14 (6.42)	1·25	20
		cw. Wmk inverted	£800	£800
586	**90**	8d. chocolate, P 14×13½ (wmk sideways)	17·00	7·00
		aw. Wmk sideways inverted	60·00	£130
		b. Wmk upright (7.39)	4·00	7·50
		bw. Wmk sideways inverted		
		c. Perf 12½* (wmk sideways) (7.41)	4·00	1·50
		d. Perf 14×14½ (wmk sideways) (7.42)	4·00	1·50
		dw. Wmk sideways inverted	—	£400
587	**91**	9d. red and grey, P 14×15 (wmk sideways)	50·00	4·50
		ay. Wmk sideways inverted and reversed	—	£350
		b. Wmk upright. *Red and grey-black*, P 14×14½ (1.3.38)	65·00	6·00
		bw. Wmk inverted	£225	£160
588	**92**	1s. deep green, P 14×13½	2·50	1·25
		aw. Wmk inverted	£120	£250
		b. Perf 12½* (11.41)	70·00	27·00
589	**93**	2s. olive-green, P 13–14×13½ (8.36)	50·00	11·00
		a. "CAPTAIN COQK"	95·00	42·00
		bw. Wmk inverted	£750	£600
		c. Perf 13½×14 (3.39)	£300	4·00
		ca. "CAPTAIN COQK"	£350	65·00
		d. Perf 12½*† (7.41)	19·00	9·50
		da. "CAPTAIN COQK"	80·00	38·00
		e. Perf 14×13½ (9.42)	4·25	1·50
		ea. "CAPTAIN COQK"	£190	85·00
		ew. Wmk inverted	—	£850
590	**94**	3s. chocolate and yellow-brown, P 13–14×13½	50·00	13·00
		aw. Wmk inverted	£200	£140
		b. Perf 12½* (1941)	80·00	50·00
		c. Perf 14×13½ (9.42)	3·00	3·25
577/90c		Set of 14	£120	22·00

*†Stamps indicated with an asterisk were printed and perforated by Waterlow; those having a dagger were printed by D.L.R. and perforated by Waterlow. No. 580d was printed by D.L.R. and perforated by Harrison and No. 583c was printed by Waterlow and perforated by D.L.R. These are all known as "Blitz perfs" because De La Rue were unable to maintain supplies after their works were damaged by enemy action. All the rest, except the 9d., were printed and perforated by D.L.R.

On stamps printed and perforated by De La Rue the perf 14×13½ varies in the sheet and is sometimes nearer 13½. 2d. perf 14×15 is sometimes nearer 14×14½.

2½d., 5d., 2s. and 3s. in perf 13–14×13½ one half the length of each horizontal perforation measures 13 and the other 14. In perf 14×13½ the horizontal perforation is regular.

4d. No. 583c. is line-perf measuring 14 exactly and has a blackish sepia frame. No. 583d is a comb-perf measuring 14×14.3 or 14×14.2 and the frame is a warmer shade.

2s. No. 589c is comb-perf and measures 13.5×13.75.

For 9d. typographed, see Nos. 630/1.

99 NZ Soldier at Anzac Cove

100 Wool

(Des L. C. Mitchell. Recess John Ash, Melbourne)

1936 (27 Apr). Charity. 21st Anniv of "Anzac" Landing at Gallipoli. W **43**. P 11.

591	**99**	½d. +½d. green	75	1·40
592		1d. +1d. scarlet	1·25	1·10

101 Butter

102 Sheep

103 Apples

104 Exports

(Des L. C. Mitchell. Recess John Ash, Melbourne)

1936 (1 Oct). Congress of British Empire Chambers of Commerce, Wellington. Industries Issue. T **100/104**. W **43** (sideways). P 11½.

593		½d. emerald-green	30	30
594		1d. scarlet	30	20
595		2½d. blue	1·50	8·00
596		4d. violet	1·25	5·50
597		6d. red-brown	4·00	6·00
593/7		Set of 5	6·50	18·00

105 Health Camp

106 King George VI and Queen Elizabeth

(Des J. Berry. Recess John Ash, Melbourne)
1936 (2 Nov). Health Stamp. W **43** (sideways). P 11.
598 **105** 1d. +1d. scarlet .... 2·75 3·75

(Recess B.W.)
1937 (13 May). Coronation. W **98**. P 14×13½.
599 **106** 1d. carmine 30 10
600 2½d. Prussian blue .... 60 2·00
601 6d. red-orange .... 80 1·75
599/601 Set of 3 .... 1·50 3·50

107 Rock climbing

108 King George VI

108a

(Des G. Bull and J. Berry. Recess John Ash, Melbourne)
1937 (1 Oct). Health Stamp. W **43**. P 11.
602 **107** 1d. +1d. scarlet .... 4·00 3·75

Broken ribbon flaw (R. 6/6 of Pl 8)

(Des W. J. Cooch. Recess B.W.)
1938–44. W **98**. P 14×13½.
603 **108** ½d. green (1.3.38) .... 10·00 10
       w. Wmk inverted (from booklets) ... 28·00 6·00
604 ½d. orange-brown (10.7.41) 20 40
       w. Wmk inverted ....
605 1d. scarlet (1.7.38) .... 5·00 10
       a. Broken ribbon £110
       w. Wmk inverted (from booklets) ... 24·00 4·75
606 1d. green (21.7.41) 20 10
       w. Wmk inverted .... £110 60·00
607 **108a** 1½d. purple-brown (26.7.38) ...... 26·00 3·25
       w. Wmk inverted (from booklets) ... 40·00 13·00
608 1½d. scarlet (1.2.44) 20 80
       w. Wmk inverted .... — £170
609 3d. blue (26.9.41) 20 10
       w. Wmk inverted .... — £250
603/9 Set of 7 .... 38·00 4·00
       For other values see Nos. 680/9.

109 Children playing

110 Beach Ball

(Des J. Berry. Recess B.W.)
1938 (1 Oct). Health Stamp. W **98**. P 14×13½.
610 **109** 1d. +1d. scarlet .... 9·50 3·25

(Des S. Hall. Recess Note Printing Branch, Commonwealth Bank of Australia, Melbourne)
1939 (16 Oct). Health Stamps. Surcharged with new value. W **43**. P 11.
611 **110** 1d. on ½d. +½d. green .... 4·75 6·00
612 2d. on 1d. +1d. scarlet .... 5·50 6·00

111 Arrival of the Maoris, 1350

112 *Endeavour*, Chart of NZ and Capt. Cook

113 British Monarchs

114 Tasman with his ship and chart

115 Signing Treaty of Waitangi, 1840

116 Landing of immigrants, 1840

117 Road, rail, sea and air transport

118 HMS *Britomart* at Akaroa, 1840

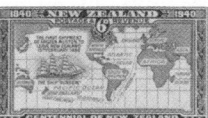

119 *Dunedin* and "frozen mutton route" to London

120 Maori council

121 Gold mining in 1861 and 1940

122 Giant Kauri tree

(Des L. C. Mitchell (½d., 3d., 4d.); J. Berry (others). Recess B.W.)
1940 (2 Jan–8 Mar). Centenary of Proclamation of British Sovereignty. T **111/122**. W **98**. P 14×13½ (2½d.), 13½×14 (5d.) or 13½ (others).
613 **111** ½d. blue-green 60 10
614 **112** 1d. chocolate and scarlet .... 4·00 10
615 **113** 1½d. light blue and mauve 30 60
616 **114** 2d. blue-green and chocolate ...... 1·50 10
617 **115** 2½d. blue-green and blue .... 2·00 1·00
618 **116** 3d. purple and carmine .... 4·00 1·25
619 **117** 4d. chocolate and lake .... 14·00 1·50
620 **118** 5d. pale blue and brown .... 10·00 3·75
621 **119** 6d. emerald-green and violet ...... 11·00 1·25
622 **120** 7d. black and red .... 2·25 4·00
623 8d. black and red (8.3) .... 11·00 6·00
624 **121** 9d. olive-green and orange .... 8·00 2·00
625 **122** 1s. sage-green and deep green .... 13·00 4·25
613/25 Set of 13 .... 70·00 23·00

1940 (1 Oct). Health Stamps. As T **110**, but without extra surcharge. W **43**. P 11.
626 **110** 1d. +½d. blue-green .... 11·00 14·00
627 2d. +1d. brown-orange .... 11·00 14·00

1ᴰ 1ᴰ 2ᴰ

■ ■ ■ **2ᴰ** 1941
(123) (123a) Inserted "2" (124)

1941. Nos. 603 and 607 surch as T **123/a**.
628 **108** 1d. on ½d. green (1.5.41) .... 1·75 10
629 **108a** 2d. on 1½d. purple-brown (4.41) ..... 1·75 10
       a. Inserted "2" £650 £450
       The variety "Inserted 2" occurs on the 10th stamp, 10th row. It is identified by the presence of remnants of the damaged "2", and by the spacing of "2" and "D" which is variable and different from the normal.

(Typo Govt Printing Office, Wellington)
1941. As T **91**, but smaller (17½×20½ mm). Chalk-surfaced paper. P 14×15.
                  (a) W **43**
630 **91** 9d. scarlet and black (5.41) .... 95·00 32·00
       w. Wmk inverted .... † £450
                  (b) W **98**
631 **91** 9d. scarlet and black (29.9.41) .... 3·00 5·00
       w. Wmk inverted £500 £375

1941 (4 Oct). Health Stamps. Nos. 626/7 optd with T **124**.
632 **110** 1d. +½d. blue-green .... 50 2·25
633 2d. +1d. brown-orange .... 50 2·25

125 Boy and Girl on Swing

126 Princess Margaret

127 Queen Elizabeth II as Princess

(Des S. Hall. Recess Note Printing Branch, Commonwealth Bank of Australia, Melbourne)
1942 (1 Oct). Health Stamps. W **43**. P 11.
634 **125** 1d. +1d. blue-green .... 30 1·25
635 2d. +1d. orange-red .... 30 1·25

(Des J. Berry. Recess B.W.)
1943 (1 Oct). Health Stamps. T **126/7**. W **98**. P 12.
636 1d. +½d. green .... 30 1·50
       a. Imperf between (vert pair) £15000
637 2d. +1d. red-brown 30 25
       a. Imperf between (vert pair) £18000 £18000
       The watermark is at an angle in relation to the design on single stamps.

✚ **TENPENCE** ✚
(128)

1944 (1 May). No. 615 surch with T **128**.
662 10d. on 1½d. light blue and mauve 15 30

129 Queen Elizabeth II as Princess and Princess Margaret

130 Statue of Peter Pan, Kensington Gardens

(Recess B.W.)
1944 (9 Oct). Health Stamps. W **98**. P 13½.
663 **129** 1d. +½d. green 30 40
664 2d. +1d. blue 30 30

(Des J. Berry. Recess B.W.)
1945 (1 Oct). Health Stamps. W **98**. P 13½.
665 **130** 1d. +½d. green and buff 15 20
       w. Wmk inverted £110 £130
666 2d. +1d. carmine and buff 15 20
       w. Wmk inverted £350 £170

131 Lake Matheson

132 King George VI and Parliament House, Wellington

133 St. Paul's Cathedral

134 The Royal Family

135 RNZAF badge and aircraft

136 Army badge, tank and plough

137 Navy badge, HMNZS *Achilles* (cruiser) and *Dominion Monarch* (liner)

138 NZ coat of arms, foundry and farm

139 "St. George" (Wellington College War Memorial Window)

140 Southern Alps and Franz Joseph Glacier

141 National Memorial Campanile

½d. Printer's guide mark (R. 12/3)

3d. Completed rudder (R. 2/4 of Pl 42883 and R. 3/2 of Pl 42796)

5d. Trailing aerial (R. 8/1 of Pl 42794)

9d. Guide mark (R. 3/3 of Pl 42723)

(Des J. Berry. Photo Harrison (1½d. and 1s.). Recess B.W. (1d. and 2d.) and Waterlow (others))

1946 (1 Apr). Peace issue. T **131/41**. W **98** (sideways on 1½d.). P 13 (1d., 2d.), 14×14½ (1½d., 1s.), 13½ (others).

667	131	½d. green and brown	20	65
		a. Printer's guide mark	23·00	38·00
		w. Wmk inverted	£120	80·00
668	132	1d. green	10	10
		w. Wmk inverted	85·00	50·00
669	133	1½d. scarlet	10	50
		w. Wmk sideways inverted	10	50
670	134	2d. purple	15	10
671	135	3d. ultramarine and grey	45	15
		a. Completed rudder	19·00	22·00
		b. Ultramarine omitted	£15000	
672	136	4d. bronze-green and orange	50	20
		w. Wmk inverted	£200	90·00
673	137	5d. green and ultramarine	1·25	1·75
		a. Trailing aerial	38·00	48·00
674	138	6d. chocolate and vermilion	20	30
675	139	8d. black and carmine	20	30
676	140	9d. blue and black	20	30
		a. Guide mark	29·00	40·00
677	141	1s. grey-black	1·00	40
667/77	*Set of 11*		3·50	4·00

Only one example of No. 671b is known. It was caused by a paper fold.

142 Soldier helping Child over Stile

2d. +1d. Feathers in hat (R. 8/8 of Pl 43010)

(Des J. Berry. Recess Waterlow)

1946 (24 Oct). Health Stamps. W **98**. P 13½.

678	142	1d. +½d. green and orange-brown	15	15
		a. *Yellow-green and orange-brown*	6·00	12·00
		w. Wmk inverted	80·00	70·00
679		2d. +1d. chocolate and orange-brown	15	15
		a. Feathers in hat	35·00	35·00

144 King George VI

145 Statue of Eros

Plate 1

Plate 2

(Des W. J. Cooch. Recess T **108a**, B.W.; T **144**, D.L.R.)

1947 (1 May)–**52**. W **98** (sideways on "shilling" values).

(a) P 14×13½

680	108a	2d. orange	30	10
		w. Wmk inverted	£225	£300
681		4d. bright purple	80	1·00
682		5d. slate	1·00	1·00
683		6d. carmine	1·00	10
		w. Wmk inverted	£325	£140
684		8d. violet	1·25	1·25
685		9d. purple-brown	2·00	60
		w. Wmk inverted	£100	28·00

(b) P 14

686	144	1s. red-brown and carmine (Plate 1)	2·00	1·50
		aw. Wmk sideways inverted	23·00	17·00
		b. Wmk upright (Plate 1)	60	80
		c. Wmk upright (Plate 2) (1950)	2·25	1·25
		cw. Wmk inverted	£180	55·00
687		1s.3d. red-brown and blue (Plate 2)	2·75	1·25
		aw. Wmk sideways inverted	22·00	10·00
		b. Wmk upright (14.1.52)	2·25	4·50
		bw. Wmk inverted	†	—
688		2s. brown-orange and green (Plate 1)	8·50	2·50
		aw. Wmk sideways inverted	38·00	26·00
		b. Wmk upright (Plate 1)	13·00	20·00
689		3s. red-brown and grey (Plate 2)	4·50	3·50
		aw. Wmk sideways inverted	50·00	29·00
680/9	*Set of 10*		20·00	11·00

In head-plate 2 the diagonal lines of the background have been strengthened and result in the upper corners and sides appearing more deeply shaded.
For details of the sideways watermarks, see above No. 577.

(Des J. Berry. Recess Waterlow)

1947 (1 Oct). Health Stamps. W **98** (sideways). P 13½.

690	145	1d. +½d. green	15	15
		w. Wmk sideways inverted	£110	85·00
691		2d. +1d. carmine	15	15
		w. Wmk sideways inverted	£150	£130

146 Port Chalmers, 1848

147 Cromwell, Otago

148 First Church, Dunedin

149 University of Otago

(Des J. Berry. Recess B.W.)

1948 (23 Feb). Centennial of Otago. T **146/9**. W **98** (sideways inverted on 3d.). P 13½.

692	146	1d. blue and green	25	35
		w. Wmk inverted	95·00	85·00
693	147	2d. green and brown	25	35
694	148	3d. purple	30	60
695	149	6d. black and rose	30	60
		w. Wmk inverted	—	£400
692/5	*Set of 4*		1·00	1·75

150 Boy Sunbathing and Children Playing

151 Nurse and Child

(Des E. Linzell. Recess B.W.)

1948 (1 Oct). Health Stamps. W **98**. P 13½.

696	150	1d. +½d. blue and green	15	20
		w. Wmk inverted	£130	60·00
697		2d. +1d. purple and scarlet	15	20

1949 ROYAL VISIT ISSUE. Four stamps were prepared to commemorate this event: 2d. Treaty House, Waitangi; 3d. HMS *Vanguard*; 5d. Royal portraits; 6d. Crown and sceptre. The visit did not take place and the stamps were destroyed, although a few examples of the 3d. later appeared on the market. A similar set was prepared in 1952, but was, likewise, not issued.

(Des J. Berry. Photo Harrison)

1949 (3 Oct). Health Stamps. W **98**. P 14×14½.

698	151	1d. +½d. green	25	20
699		2d. +1d. ultramarine	25	20
		a. No stop below "D" of "1D." (R. 1/2)	7·00	21·00

1½d.
POSTAGE
(152)

153 Queen Elizabeth II as Princess and Prince Charles

1950 (28 July). As Type F **6**, but without value, surch with T **152**. Chalk-surfaced paper. W **98** (inverted). P 14.

700	F 6	1½d. carmine	40	30
		w. Wmk upright	5·50	6·50

(Des J. Berry and R. S. Phillips. Photo Harrison)

1950 (2 Oct). Health Stamps. W **98**. P 14×14½.

701	153	1d. +½d. green	25	20
		w. Wmk inverted	8·00	9·00
702		2d. +1d. plum	25	20
		w. Wmk inverted	95·00	95·00

154 Christchurch Cathedral

155 Cairn on Lyttleton Hills

156 John Robert Godley

157 Canterbury University College

158 Aerial view of Timaru

(Des L. C. Mitchell (2d.), J. A. Johnstone (3d.) and J. Berry (others). Recess B.W.)

1950 (20 Nov). Centennial of Canterbury, NZ T **154/8**. W **98** (sideways inverted on 1d. and 3d.). P 13½.

703	**154**	1d. green and blue	40	85
704	**155**	2d. carmine and orange	40	1·00
705	**156**	3d. dark blue and blue	45	1·25
706	**157**	6d. brown and blue	50	1·00
707	**158**	1s. reddish purple and blue	50	1·60
703/7		Set of 5	2·00	5·00

159 Takapuna class Yachts

(Des J. Berry and R. S. Phillips. Recess B.W.)

1951 (1 Nov). Health Stamps. W **98**. P 13½.

708	**159**	1½d. +½d. scarlet and yellow	50	1·00
709		2d. +1d. deep green and yellow	50	25
		w. Wmk inverted	95·00	£100

160 Princess Anne **161** Prince Charles

3D

(162)

(From photographs by Marcus Adams. Photo Harrison)

1952 (1 Oct). Health Stamps. W **98**. P 14×14½.

710	**160**	1½d. +½d. carmine-red	15	30
711	**161**	2d. +1d. brown	15	20

1952–53. Nos. 604 and 606 surch as T **162**.

712	**108**	1d. on ½d. brown-orange (11.9.53) .	50	1·00
		a. "D" omitted	†	£4500
713		3d. on 1d. green (12.12.52)	10	10

163 Buckingham Palace **164** Queen Elizabeth II

165 Coronation State Coach **166** Westminster Abbey

167 St. Edward's Crown and Royal Sceptre

(Des L. C. Mitchell (1s.6d.), J. Berry (others). Recess D.L.R. (2d., 4d.), Waterlow (1s.6d.) Photo Harrison (3d., 8d.))

1953 (25 May). Coronation. T **163/7**. W **98**. P 13 (2d., 4d.), 13½ (1s.6d.) or 14×14½ (3d., 8d.).

714	**163**	2d. deep bright blue	40	30
715	**164**	3d. brown	30	10
716	**165**	4d. carmine	1·40	2·50
717	**166**	8d. slate-grey	1·00	1·60
718	**167**	1s.6d. purple and ultramarine	2·75	3·25
714/18		Set of 5	5·00	7·00

168 Girl Guides **169** Boy Scouts

(Des J. Berry. Photo Harrison)

1953 (7 Oct). Health Stamps. W **98**. P 14×14½.

719	**168**	1½d. +½d. blue	15	10
720	**169**	2d. +1d. deep yellow-green	15	40
		a. Imperf 3 sides (block of 4)	£3500	

No. 720a shows the left-hand vertical pair imperforate at right and the right-hand pair imperforate at left, top and bottom.

170 Queen Elizabeth II **171** Queen Elizabeth II and Duke of Edinburgh

(Des L. C. Mitchell. Recess Waterlow)

1953 (9 Dec). Royal Visit. W **98**. P 13×14 (3d.) or 13½ (4d.).

721	**170**	3d. dull purple	15	10
		w. Wmk inverted	—	£170
722	**171**	4d. deep ultramarine	15	60

172 **173** Queen Elizabeth II **174**

Die I Die II

(Des L. C. Mitchell (T **172/3**), J. Berry (T **174**). Recess D.L.R. (T **173**), B.W. (others))

1953 (15 Dec)–59. W **98**. P 14×13½ (T **172**), 14 (T **173**) or 13½ (T **174**).

723	**172**	½d. slate-black (1.3.54)	15	30
724		1d. orange (1.3.54)	15	10
		w. Wmk inverted	40	2·25
725		1½d. brown-lake	20	10
		w. Wmk inverted	†	£500
726		2d. bluish green (1.3.54)	20	10
		w. Wmk inverted	†	£500
727		3d. vermilion (1.3.54)	20	10
		w. Wmk inverted (from booklets)..	40	2·25
728		4d. blue (1.3.54)	40	50
		w. Wmk inverted	†	£750
729		6d. purple (1.3.54)	70	1·75
		w. Wmk inverted	£550	£350
730		8d. carmine (1.3.54)	60	60
		w. Wmk inverted	£950	£700
731	**173**	9d. brown and bright green (1.3.54)	60	60
		w. Wmk inverted	£500	£375
732		1s. black and carmine-red (Die I) (1.3.54)	65	10
		aw. Wmk inverted	£550	£425
		b. Die II (1958)	£180	20·00
733		1s.6d. black and bright blue (1.3.54)	1·50	60
		aw. Wmk inverted	£475	£375
733b		1s.9d. black and red-orange (1.7.57)	5·50	1·50
		bw. Wmk inverted	£750	£450
		c. White opaque paper (2.2.59)	3·50	1·50
733d	**174**	2s.6d. brown (1.7.57)	13·00	5·00
734		3s. bluish green (1.3.54)	14·00	50
		w. Wmk inverted	£800	£500
735		5s. carmine (1.3.54)	30·00	3·25
736		10s. deep ultramarine (1.3.54)	50·00	17·00
723/36		Set of 16	£100	28·00

1s. Dies I and II. The two dies of the Queen's portrait differ in the shading on the sleeve at right. The long lines running upwards from left to right are strong in Die I and weaker in Die II. In the upper part of the shading the fine cross-hatching is visible in Die I only between the middle two of the four long lines, but in Die II it extends clearly across all four lines.

In the lower part of the shading the strength of the long lines in Die I makes the cross-hatching appear subdued, whereas in Die II the weaker long lines make the cross-hatching more prominent.

Centre plates 1A, 1B and 2B are Die I; 3A and 3B are Die II.

For stamps as T **172** but with larger figures of value see Nos. 745/51.

WHITE OPAQUE PAPER. A new white opaque paper first came into use in August 1958. It is slightly thicker than the paper previously used, but obviously different in colour (white, against cream) and opacity (the previous paper being relatively transparent).

175 Young Climber and Mts Aspiring and Everest

(Des J. Berry. Recess; vignette litho B.W.)

1954 (4 Oct). Health Stamps. W **98**. P 13½.

737	**175**	1½d. +½d. sepia and deep violet	15	30
738		2d. + 1d. sepia and blue-black	15	30

176 Maori Mail Carrier **177** Queen Elizabeth II

178 Douglas DC-3 Airliner

(Des R. M. Conly (2d.), J. Berry (3d.), A. G. Mitchell (4d.). Recess D.L.R.)

1955 (18 July). Centenary of First New Zealand Postage Stamps. W **98**. P 14 (2d.) 14×14½ (3d.) or 13 (4d.)

739	**176**	2d. sepia and deep green	10	10
		w. Wmk inverted	—	£325
740	**177**	3d. brown-red	10	10
741	**178**	4d. black and bright blue	70	1·00
739/41		Set of 3	80	1·00

179 Children's Health Camps Federation Emblem **180**

(Des E. M. Taylor. Recess B.W.)

1955 (3 Oct). Health Stamps. W **98** (sideways). P 13½×13.

742	**179**	1½d. +½d. sepia and orange-brown	10	60
743		2d. +1d. red-brown and green	10	35
744		3d. +1d. sepia and deep rose-red ...	15	15
		a. Centre omitted	£15000	
742/4		Set of 3	30	1·00

Only one example of No. 744a is known. It was caused by a paper fold.

1955–59. As Nos. 724/30 but larger figures of value with stars omitted from lower right corner and new colour (8d.).

745	**180**	1d. orange (12.7.56)	50	10
		aw. Wmk inverted	1·50	3·50
		b. White opaque paper (2.6.59)	50	75
		bw. Wmk inverted	1·50	4·25
746		1½d. brown-lake (1.12.55)	60	60
747		2d. bluish green (19.3.56)	40	10
		a. White opaque paper (10.11.59)	55	10
748		3d. vermilion (1.5.56)	50	50
		aw. Wmk inverted	1·50	2·50
		b. White opaque paper (20.6.59)	30	10
		bw. Wmk inverted	2·00	4·25
749		4d. blue (3.2.58)	1·00	80
		a. White opaque paper (9.9.59)	1·00	2·50
750		6d. purple (20.10.55)	5·00	20
751		8d. chestnut (white opaque paper) (1.12.59)	3·50	4·25
745/51		Set of 7	10·00	5·50

See note re white opaque paper after No. 736.

181 "The Whalers of Foveaux Strait" **182** "Farming"

183 Takahe

(Des E. R. Leeming (2d.), L. C. Mitchell (3d.), M. R. Smith (8d.). Recess D.L.R.)

1956 (16 Jan). Southland Centennial. T **181/3**. W **98**. P 13½×13 (8d.) or 13×12½ (others).

752	**181**	2d. deep blue-green	30	15
753	**182**	3d. sepia	10	10
		w. Wmk inverted	—	£275
754	**183**	8d. slate-violet and rose-red	1·25	1·50
752/4		Set of 3	1·50	1·50

184 Children picking Apples

(Des L. C. Mitchell, after photo by J. F. Louden. Recess B.W.)

1956 (24 Sept). Health Stamps. W **98**. P 13×13½.

755	**184**	1½d. +½d. purple-brown	15	70
		a. *Blackish brown*	2·00	7·00
756		2d. +1d. blue-green	15	55
757		3d. +1d. claret	15	15
755/7	*Set of 3*		40	1·25

185 New Zealand Lamb and Map

186 Lamb, *Dunedin* and *Port Brisbane* (refrigerated freighter)

(Des M. Goaman. Photo Harrison)

1957 (15 Feb). 75th Anniv of First Export of NZ Lamb. W **98** (sideways inverted on 4d.). P 14×14½ (4d.) or 14½×14 (8d.).

758	**185**	4d. blue	50	1·00
		w. Wmk sideways	14·00	22·00
759	**186**	8d. deep orange-red	75	1·00

187 Sir Truby King

(Des M. R. Smith. Recess B.W.)

1957 (14 May). 50th Anniv of Plunket Society. W **98**. P 13.

760	**187**	3d. bright carmine-red	10	10
		w. Wmk inverted	£150	

188 Life-savers in Action

189 Children on Seashore

(Des L. Cutten (2d.), L. C. Mitchell (3d.). Recess Waterlow)

1957 (25 Sept). Health Stamps. W **98** (sideways). P 13½.

761	**188**	2d. +1d. black and emerald	15	70
762	**189**	3d. +1d. ultramarine and rose-red	15	10
MS762*b*	Two sheets each 112×96 mm with Nos. 761 and 762 in blocks of 6 (2×3)			
			Per pair 6·00	23·00
MS762*c*	As last but with wmk upright	*Per pair* 10·00	45·00

2d

(190)

1958 (6 Jan–Mar). No. 746 surch as T **190**.

763	**180**	2d. on 1½d. brown-lake	70	10
		a. Smaller dot in surch	15	10
		b. Error. Surch on No. 725 (3.58)	£130	£170

Diameter of dot on No. 763 is 4¼ mm; on No. 763a 3¾ mm. Forgeries of No. 763b are known.

Almost all examples of No. 763b have the 4¼ mm dot, but examples with the smaller dot are known.

191 Girls' Life Brigade Cadet

192 Boys' Brigade Bugler

(Des J. Berry. Photo Harrison)

1958 (20 Aug). Health Stamps. W **98**. P 14×14½.

764	**191**	2d. +1d. green	20	40
765	**192**	3d. +1d. blue	20	40
MS765*a*	Two sheets each 104×124 mm with Nos. 764/5 in blocks of 6 (3×2)			
			Per pair 8·00	20·00

193 Sir Charles Kingsford-Smith and Fokker F.VIIa/3m *Southern Cross*

194 Seal of Nelson

(Des J. E. Lyle. Eng F. D. Manley. Recess Commonwealth Bank of Australia Note Ptg Branch)

1958 (27 Aug). 30th Anniv of First Air Crossing of the Tasman Sea. W **98** (sideways). P 14×14½.

766	**193**	6d. deep ultramarine	50	75

(Des M. J. Macdonald. Recess B.W.)

1958 (29 Sept). Centenary of City of Nelson. W **98**. P 13½×13.

767	**194**	3d. carmine	10	10

195 Pania Statue, Napier

196 Australian Gannets on Cape Kidnappers

(Des M. R. Smith (2d.), J. Berry (3d.), L. C. Mitchell (8d.). Photo Harrison)

1958 (3 Nov). Centenary of Hawke's Bay Province. T **195/6** and similar design. W **98** (sideways on 3d.). P 14½×14 (3d.) or 13½×14½ (others).

768	**195**	2d. yellow-green	10	10
769	**196**	3d. blue	30	10
770		8d. red-brown	70	1·00
768/70	*Set of 3*		1·00	1·00

Design: Vert—8d. Maori sheep-shearer.

197 "Kiwi" Jamboree Badge

198 Careening HMS *Endeavour* at Ship Cove

(Des Mrs. S. M. Collins. Recess B.W.)

1959 (5 Jan). Pan-Pacific Scout Jamboree, Auckland. W **98**. P 13½×13.

771	**197**	3d. sepia and carmine	30	10

(Des G. R. Bull and G. R. Smith. Photo Harrison)

1959 (2 Mar). Centenary of Marlborough Province. T **198** and similar horiz designs. W **98** (sideways). P 14½×14.

772	**198**	3d. green	30	10
773		3d. deep blue	30	10
774		8d. light brown	1·10	1·00
772/4	*Set of 3*		1·40	1·00

Designs:—3d. Shipping wool, Wairau Bar, 1857; 8d. Salt industry, Grassmere.

201 Red Cross Flag

(Photo Harrison)

1959 (3 June). Red Cross Commemoration. W **98** (sideways). P 14½×14.

775	**201**	3d. +1d. red and ultramarine	20	10
		a. Red Cross omitted	£2250	

202 Grey Teal   **203** New Zealand Stilt

(Des Display Section, G.P.O. Photo Harrison)

1959 (16 Sept). Health Stamps. W **98** (sideways). P 14×14½.

776	**202**	2d. +1d. greenish yellow, olive and rose-red	50	65
777	**203**	3d. +1d. black, pink and light blue.	50	65
		a. Pink omitted	£180	
		bw. Wmk sideways inverted	18·00	28·00
MS777*c*	Two sheets, each 95×109 mm with Nos. 776/7 in blocks of 6 (3×2)			
			Per pair 9·00	26·00

204 "The Explorer"   **205** "The Gold Digger"

(Des G. R. Bull and G. R. Smith. Photo Harrison)

1960 (16 May). Centenary of Westland Province. T **204/5** and similar vert design. W **98**. P 14×14½.

778	**204**	2d. deep dull green	20	10
779	**205**	3d. orange-red	30	10
780		8d. grey-black	90	2·00
778/80	*Set of 3*		1·25	2·00

Design:—8d. "The Pioneer Woman".

   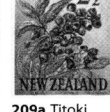

207 Manuka (Tea Tree)   **208** Karaka   **209** Kowhai Ngutu-kaka (Kaka-Beak)   **209a** Titoki

210 Kowhai   **211** Puarangi (Hibiscus)   **211a** Matua Tikumu (Mountain Daisy)   **212** Pikiarero

212a Koromiko   **213** Rata   **214** National Flag

215 Timber Industry   **216** Rainbow Trout   **217** Tiki

218 Aerial Top Dressing   **218a** Aerial Top Dressing   **219** Taniwha (Maori Rock Drawing)

220 Butter Making   **221** Tongariro National Park and Château

221a Tongariro National Park and Château   **222** Sutherland Falls

223 Tasman Glacier

224 Pohutu Geyser

NEW ZEALAND

2d. "F" for "E" in "ZEALAND". (R. 3/1, black Pl. 2)

(Des Harrison (½d.), G. F. Fuller (1d., 3d., 6d.), A. G. Mitchell (2d., 4d., 5d., 8d., 3s., 10s., £1), P.O. Public Relations Division (7d.), P.O. Publicity Section (9d.), J. Berry (1s., 1s.6d.), R. E. Barwick (1s.3d.), J. C. Boyd (1s.9d.), D. F. Kee (2s.), L. C. Mitchell (2s.6d., 5s.). Photo D.L.R. (½d., 1d., 2d., 3d., 4d., 6d., 8d.) or Harrison (others))

1960 (11 July)–66. T **207/224**. Chalk-surfaced paper (2½d., 5d., 7d., 1s.9d. (No. 795), 3s. (No. 799). W **98** (sideways on 5d., 1s.3d., 1s.6d., 2s.6d., 3s. and 10s. or sideways inverted (2½d.)). P 14×14½ (1s.3d., 1s.6d., 2s., 5s., £1) or 14½×14 (others).

781	**207**	½d. pale blue, green and cerise (1.9.60)	10	10
		a. Pale blue omitted	£325	£250
		b. Green omitted	£450	
782	**208**	1d. orange, green, lake and brown (1.9.60)	10	10
		a. Orange omitted	£650	£375
		b. Coil. Perf 14½×13. Wmk sideways (11.63)	1·40	2·75
		c. Chalk-surfaced paper (1965?)	10	2·00
783	**209**	2d. carmine, black, yellow and green	10	10
		a. Black omitted	£550	£400
		b. Yellow omitted	£600	
		c. "ZFALAND"	85·00	
784	**209a**	2½d. red, yellow, black and green (1.11.61)	1·00	10
		a. Red omitted	£850	£600
		b. Yellow omitted	£325	
		c. Green omitted	£400	
		d. Red and green omitted	£1100	
		w. Wmk sideways	£120	90·00
785	**210**	3d. yellow, green, yellow-brown and deep greenish blue (1.9.60)	30	10
		a. Yellow omitted	£200	£170
		b. Green omitted	£325	£225
		c. Yellow-brown omitted	£225	
		e. Coil. Perf 14½×13. Wmk sideways (3.10.63)	1·40	2·75
		f. Chalk-surfaced paper (1965?)	30	2·25
		fa. Yellow-brown omitted	£650	
786	**211**	4d. purple, buff, yellow-green and light blue	40	10
		a. Purple omitted	£650	£500
		b. Buff omitted	£900	
		d. Chalk-surfaced paper (1966)..	£950	18·00
787	**211a**	5d. yellow, deep green, black and violet (14.5.62)	1·00	10
		a. Yellow omitted	£425	£425
		w. Wmk sideways inverted	£170	£100
788	**212**	6d. lilac, green and deep bluish green (1.9.60)	50	10
		a. No wmk	55·00	
		b. Lilac omitted	£425	
		c. Green omitted	£425	£425
		d. Chalk-surfaced paper (1966?)	65	4·50
788e	**212a**	7d. red, green, yellow and pale red (16.3.66)	1·00	1·10
		ew. Wmk inverted	4·50	12·00
789	**213**	8d. rose-red, yellow, green and grey (1.9.60)	40	10
790	**214**	9d. red and ultramarine (1.9.60) ..	40	10
		a. Red omitted	£550	
791	**215**	1s. brown and deep green	30	10
792	**216**	1s.3d. carmine, sepia and bright blue	2·50	70
		a. Carmine omitted	£850	
		b. Carmine, sepia and greyish blue	1·50	25
		w. Wmk sideways inverted	£325	£200
793	**217**	1s.6d. olive-green and orange-brown	75	10
794	**218**	1s.9d. bistre-brown	12·00	15
795	**218a**	1s.9d. orange-red, blue, green and yellow (4.11.63)	2·50	1·00
		a. Wmk sideways	£950	
		w. Wmk inverted	£750	£750
796	**219**	2s. black and orange-buff	2·00	10
		a. Chalk-surfaced paper (1966)..	1·00	2·75
797	**220**	2s.6d. yellow and light brown	1·00	1·00
		a. Yellow omitted	£1400	£850
798	**221**	3s. blackish brown	17·00	1·00
799	**221a**	3s. bistre, blue and green (1.4.64)	1·50	1·75
		w. Wmk sideways inverted	90·00	90·00
800	**222**	5s. blackish green	1·50	60
		a. Chalk-surfaced paper (1966)..	1·25	5·50
801	**223**	10s. steel-blue	3·50	2·75
		a. Chalk-surfaced paper (1966)..	2·50	10·00
802	**224**	£1 deep magenta	10·00	7·00
781/802	*Set of 23*		48·00	15·00

Nos. 782b and 785e were replaced by coils with upright watermark perf 14½×14 in 1966.

Examples of the 3d., perf 14×14½ with watermark sideways inverted (top of star pointing to the left, *as seen from the back of the stamp*) are known. They are believed to come from a trial printing.

CHALKY PAPER. The chalk-surfaced paper is not only whiter but also thicker, making the watermark difficult to see. Examples of the 4d. value can be found on a thick surfaced paper. These should not be confused with the rare chalk-surfaced printing, No. 786d, which can be identified by its positive reaction to the silver test and fluoresces brightly, both front and back, under ultraviolet light.

---

225 Sacred Kingfisher

226 New Zealand Pigeon

(Des Display Section, G.P.O. Recess B.W.)

1960 (10 Aug). Health Stamps. W **98**. P 13½.

803	**225**	2d. +1d. sepia and turquoise-blue..	50	75
804	**226**	3d. +1d. deep purple-brown and orange	50	75
MS804b	Two sheets each 95×107 mm with Nos. 803 and 804 in blocks of 6. P 11½×11	*Per pair*	24·00	38·00

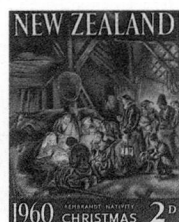

227 The Adoration of the Shepherds (Rembrandt)

(Photo Harrison)

1960 (1 Nov). Christmas. W **98**. P 12.

805	**227**	2d. red and deep brown/*cream*	15	10
		a. Red omitted	£425	£425

228 Great Egret

229 New Zealand Falcon

(Des Display Section, G.P.O. Recess B.W.)

1961 (2 Aug). Health Stamps. W **98**. P 13½.

806	**228**	2d. +1d. black and purple	50	70
807	**229**	3d. +1d. deep sepia and yellow-green	50	70
MS807a	Two sheets each 97×121 mm with Nos. 806/7 in blocks of 6 (3×2)	*Per pair*	24·00	35·00

$2\frac{1}{2}$d $2\frac{1}{2}$d

232 Adoration of the Magi (Dürer)

≡   ≡
(**230**)   (**231**)

1961 (1 Sept). No. 748 surch with T **230** (wide setting).

808	**180**	2½d. on 3d. vermilion	25	30
		a. Narrow setting (T **231**)	15	30
		b. Pair, wide and narrow	16·00	35·00

The difference in the settings is in the overall width of the new value, caused by two different spacings between the "2", "½" and "d".

(Photo Harrison)

1961 (16 Oct). Christmas. W **98** (sideways). P 14½×14.

809	**232**	2½d. multicoloured	10	10
		w. Wmk sideways inverted	80·00	48·00

233 Morse Key and Port Hills, Lyttelton

3d. Damage to the plate resulted in a vertical green dotted line below the fingers (R. 14/1)

(Des A. G. Mitchell (3d.) and L. C. Mitchell (8d.). Photo Harrison)

1962 (1 June). Telegraph Centenary. T **233** and similar horiz design. W **98** (sideways). P 14½×14.

810		3d. sepia and bluish green	10	10
		a. Bluish green omitted	£3000	
		b. Dotted line flaw	15·00	
811		8d. black and brown-red	90	90
		a. Imperf (pair)	£2500	
		b. Black omitted	£2250	

Design:—8d. Modern teleprinter.

No. 811a comes from a sheet with the two top rows imperforate and the third row imperforate on three sides.

235 Red-fronted Parakeet

236 Tieke Saddleback

(Des Display Section, G.P.O. Photo D.L.R.)

1962 (3 Oct). Health Stamps. W **98**. P 15×14.

812	**235**	2½d. +1d. multicoloured	50	70
		a. Orange omitted	£1600	
		b. Printed on the gummed side	£1300	
		w. Wmk inverted	£160	£150
813	**236**	3d. +1d.multicoloured	50	70
		a. Orange omitted	£2750	
MS813b	Two sheets each 96×101 mm with Nos. 812/13 in blocks of 6 (3×2)	*Per pair*	40·00	50·00

No. 812b comes from a miniature sheet.

237 Madonna in Prayer (Sassoferrato)

1962 (15 Oct). Christmas. W **98**. P 14½×14.

814	**237**	2½d. multicoloured	10	10

238 Prince Andrew

239

3d.+1d. A prominent flaw on the middle finger of the Prince's right hand appears as a bloodstain. Later attempts to remove the flaw met with only partial success (Pl. 1B, R. 3/5)

(Design after photographs by Studio Lisa, London. Recess D.L.R.)

1963 (7 Aug). Health Stamps. W **98**. P 14.

815	**238**	2½d. +1d. dull ultramarine	30	70
		a. Ultramarine	40	80
		b. Deep blue	30	40
816	**239**	3d. +1d. carmine	30	10
		a. Bloodstained finger	90·00	50·00
MS816b	Two sheets each 93×100 mm with Nos. 815/16 in blocks of 6 (3×2)	*Per pair*	20·00	35·00

The price for No. 816a is for the flaw in its original state, as illustrated. Examples with the flaw partially removed are worth less.

240 The Holy Family (Titian)

An orange flaw over the donkey's nose appears as a nosebag (Pl. 1B, R. 3/8)

(Photo Harrison)

1963 (14 Oct). Christmas. W 98 (sideways). P 12½.

817	240	2½d. multicoloured		10	10
		a. Imperf (pair)		£275	
		b. Yellow omitted		£300	
		c. Nosebag flaw		5·00	2·00
		w. Wmk sideways inverted		40	40

241 Steam Locomotive *Pilgrim* (1863) and Class DG Diesel Locomotive   **242** Diesel Express and Mt Ruapehu

(Des Commercial Art Section, NZ Railways. Photo D.L.R.)

1963 (25 Nov). Railway Centenary. W 98 (sideways on 3d., sideways inverted on 1s.9d). P 14.

818	241	3d. multicoloured		40	10
		a. Blue (sky) omitted		£550	
819	242	1s.9d. multicoloured		1·75	1·25
		a. Red (value) omitted		£2500	

243 "Commonwealth Cable"

(Des P. Morriss. Photo Note Printing Branch, Reserve Bank of Australia)

1963 (3 Dec). Opening of COMPAC (Trans-Pacific Telephone Cable). No wmk. P 13½.

820	243	8d. red, blue and yellow		50	1·00

244 Road Map and Car Steering-wheel   **245** Silver Gulls

3d. Flaw between "W" and "Z" of "NEW ZEALAND" resembling an apostrophe (R. 3/2)

(Des L. C. Mitchell. Photo Harrison)

1964 (1 May). Road Safety Campaign. W 98. P 15×14.

821	244	3d. black, ochre-yellow and blue		30	10
		a. "Apostrophe" flaw		13·00	

(Des Display Section G.P.O., after Miss T. Kelly. Photo Harrison)

1964 (5 Aug). Health Stamps. T 245 and similar horiz design. Multicoloured. W 98. P 14½.

822		2½d. +1d. Type 245		40	50
		a. Red (beak and legs) omitted		£350	£250
		w. Wmk inverted		†	£475
823		3d. +1d. Little Penguin		40	50
		aw. Wmk inverted		£200	
MS823b	Two sheets each 171×84 mm with Nos. 822/3 in blocks of 8 (4×2)		*Per pair*	40·00	65·00
		bw. Wmk inverted (No. 823 only)			

246 Rev. S. Marsden taking first Christian service at Rangihoua Bay, 1814

7ᴰ

POSTAGE

(247)

(Des L. C. Mitchell. Photo Harrison)

1964 (12 Oct). Christmas. W 98 (sideways). P 14×13½.

824	246	2½d. multicoloured		10	10

1964 (14 Dec). As Type F 6, but without value, surch with T 247. W 98. Unsurfaced paper. P 14×13½.

825	F 6	7d. carmine-red		50	1·00

248 Anzac Cove

(Des R. M. Conly. Photo Harrison)

1965 (14 Apr). 50th Anniv of Gallipoli Landing. T 248 and similar horiz design. W 98. P 12½.

826	248	4d. yellow-brown		10	10
827		5d. green and red		10	60

Design:—5d. Anzac Cove and poppy.

249 ITU Emblem and Symbols   **250** Sir Winston Churchill

(Photo Harrison)

1965 (17 May). ITU Centenary. W 98. P 14½×14.

828	249	9d. blue and pale chocolate		55	35

(Des P. Morriss from photograph by Karsh. Photo Note Ptg Branch, Reserve Bank of Australia)

1965 (24 May). Churchill Commemoration. P 13½.

829	250	7d. black, pale grey and light blue		30	50

251 Wellington Provincial Council Building

(Des from painting by L. B. Temple (1867). Photo Harrison)

1965 (26 July). Centenary of Government in Wellington. W 98 (sideways). P 14½×14.

830	251	4d. multicoloured		10	10

252 Kaka   **253** Collared Grey Fantail (after Miss T. Kelly)

(Des Display Section, G.P.O. Photo Harrison)

1965 (4 Aug). Health Stamps. W 98. P 14×14½.

831	252	3d. +1d. multicoloured		40	65
		w. Wmk inverted		†	£100
832	253	4d. +1d. multicoloured		40	65
		a. Green ("POSTAGE HEALTH" and on leaves) omitted		£2250	
		bw. Wmk inverted		80·00	£130
MS832c	Two sheets each 100×109 mm with Nos. 831/2 in blocks of 6 (3×2)		*Per pair*	32·00	48·00
		cw. Wmk inverted (No. 831 only)		†	—

254 ICY Emblem   **255** The Two Trinities (Murillo)

(Litho D.L.R.)

1965 (28 Sept). International Co-operation Year. W 98 (sideways inverted). P 14.

833	254	4d. carmine-red and light yellow-olive		20	10
		w. Wmk sideways		4·25	4·00

(Photo Harrison)

1965 (11 Oct). Christmas. W 98. P 13½×14.

834	255	3d. multicoloured		10	10
		a. Gold (frame) omitted		£1500	

256 Arms of New Zealand   **259** "Progress" Arrowhead

(Des Display Section, G.P.O. Photo D.L.R.)

1965 (30 Nov). 11th Commonwealth Parliamentary Conference. T 256 and similar horiz designs. Multicoloured. P 14.

835		4d. Type 256		15	10
		a. Blue (incl value) omitted		£1100	
		b. Printed on the gummed side		£1000	
836		9d. Parliament House, Wellington and Badge		30	35
837		2s. Wellington from Mt Victoria		1·40	2·50
		a. Carmine omitted		£1000	
835/7	*Set of 3*			1·60	2·50

There is invariably a faint impression of the crossed regalia at upper left on No. 837a.

(Des Display Section, G.P.O. Photo Harrison)

1966 (5 Jan). Fourth National Scout Jamboree, Trentham. W 98. P 14×15.

838	259	4d. gold and myrtle-green		15	10
		a. Gold (arrowhead) omitted		£1200	£1100

260 New Zealand Bell Bird   **262** The Virgin with Child (Maratta)

(Des Display Section, G.P.O. Photo Harrison)

1966 (3 Aug). Health Stamps. T 260 and similar vert design. Multicoloured. W 98 (sideways). P 14×14½.

839		3d. +1d. Type 260		40	65
		w. Wmk sideways inverted		£120	
840		4d. +1d. Weka Rail		40	65
		a. Deep brown (values and date) omitted		£2500	
		w. Wmk sideways inverted		£110	
MS841	Two sheets each 107×91 mm. Nos. 839/40 in blocks of 6 (3×2)		*Per pair*	15·00	50·00

In No. 840a besides the value, "1966" and "Weka" are also omitted and the bird, etc. appears as light brown.

(Photo Harrison)

1966 (3 Oct). Christmas. W 98 (sideways). P 14½.

842	262	3d. multicoloured		10	10
		a. Red omitted		£350	

263 Queen Victoria and Queen Elizabeth II   **264** Half-sovereign of 1867 and Commemorative Dollar Coin

(Des Display Section, G.P.O. Photo Harrison)

1967 (3 Feb). Centenary of New Zealand Post Office Savings Bank. W 98 (sideways on 4d.). P 14×14½.

843	263	4d. black, gold and maroon		10	10
		w. Wmk sideways inverted		85·00	29·00
844	264	9d. gold, silver, black, light blue and deep green		10	20
		w. Wmk inverted		£600	

(New Currency. 100 cents = 1 New Zealand Dollar)

265 Manuka (Tea Tree)   **266** Pohutu Geyser

(Photo D.L.R. (½c. to 3c., 5c. and 7c.) or Harrison (others))

1967 (10 July). Decimal Currency. Designs as 1960–66 issue, but with values inscr in decimal currency as T **265/6**. Chalky paper. W **98** (sideways on 8c., 10c., 20c., 50c. and $2). P 13½×14 (½c. to 3c., 5c. and 7c.), 14½×14 (4c., 6c., 8c., 10c., 25c. and $1) or 14×14½ (15c., 20c., 50c. and $2).

845	**265**	½c. pale blue, yellow-green and cerise	10	10
846	**208**	1c. yellow, carmine, green and light brown (as 1d.)	10	10
		a. Booklet pane. Five stamps plus one printed label	2·25	
847	**209**	2c. carmine, black, yellow and green (as 2d.)	10	10
848	**210**	2½c. yellow, green, yellow-brown and deep bluish green (as 3d.)	10	10
		a. Deep bluish green omitted*	£3750	
		b. Imperf (pair)†	£150	
849	**211**	3c. purple, buff, yellow-green and light greenish blue (as 4d.)	10	10
850	**211a**	4c. yellow, deep green, black and violet (as 5d.)	30	10
851	**212**	5c. lilac, yellow-olive and bluish green (as 6d.)	50	1·00
852	**212a**	6c. red, green, yellow and light pink (as 7d.)	50	1·00
853	**213**	7c. rose-red, yellow, green and grey (as 8d.)	60	1·50
		w. Wmk inverted	60	
854	**214**	8c. red and ultramarine	60	60
		a. Red omitted	£1200	
855	**215**	10c. brown and deep green (as 1s.)	60	1·00
		w. Wmk sideways inverted	£650	£550
856	**217**	15c. olive-green and orange-brown (as 1s.6d.)	2·50	2·25
		w. Wmk inverted	2·75	10·00
857	**219**	20c. black and buff	1·00	20
858	**220**	25c. yellow and light brown	1·00	2·00
859	**221a**	30c. olive-yellow, green and greenish blue	1·25	25
		w. Wmk inverted	£130	85·00
860	**222**	50c. blackish green (as 5s.)	1·75	50
861	**223**	$1 Prussian blue (as 10s.)	9·00	1·00
		w. Wmk inverted	£375	£200
862	**266**	$2 deep magenta	4·25	6·00
845/62		Set of 18	21·00	15·00

*This occurred on one horizontal row of ten, affecting the background colour so that the value is also missing. In the row above and the row below, the colour was partially omitted. The price is for a vertical strip.

The 2½c. value has been seen with the yellow omitted, but only on a used example.

†This comes from a sheet of which the six right-hand vertical rows were completely imperforate and the top, bottom and left-hand margins had been removed.

The 4c., 30c. and 50c. exist with PVA gum as well as gum arabic.
For $4 to $10 in the "Arms" type, see under Postal Fiscal stamps.
For other versions of 15c., 30c. and $2 see Nos. 870/9.

268 Running with Ball

(Des L. C. Mitchell. Photo Harrison)

1967 (2 Aug). Health Stamps. Rugby Football. T **268** and similar multicoloured design. W **98** (sideways on 2½c.). P 14½×14 (2½c.) or 14×14½ (3c.)

867		2½c. +1c. Type **268**	15	15
868		3c. +1c. Positioning for a place-kick (horiz)	15	15
MS869		Two sheets; (a) 76×130 mm (867); (b) 130×76 mm (868). Containing blocks of 6 ...... Per pair	15·00	32·00

270 Kaita (trawler) and Catch   **271** Brown Trout

272 Apples and Orchard   **273** Forest and Timber

274 Sheep and the "Woolmark"   **275** Consignments of Beef and Herd of Cattle

276 Dairy Farm, Mt Egmont and Butter Consignment   **277** Fox Glacier, Westland National Park

(Des Display Section, G.P.O. (7, 8, 10, 18, 20, 25c. and 28c. from photo), R. M. Conly (7½c.). Litho B.W. (7, 8, 18, 20c.) or photo D.L.R. (7½c.) and Harrison (10, 25, 28c.). Others (15, 30c., $2) as before)

1967–70. T **270/7**. Chalky paper (except 7, 8, 18, 20c.). No wmk (7, 8, 20, 30c.) or W **98** (sideways inverted on 7½c., sideways on 10, 15, 25c., upright on 18, 28c., $2). P 13½ (7, 7½c.), 13×13½ (8, 18, 20c.), 14½×14 (10, 25, 30c.) or 14×14½ (15, 28c., $2).

870	**270**	7c. multicoloured (3.12.69)	1·00	1·00
871	**271**	7½c. multicoloured* (29.8.67)	50	70
		a. Wmk upright (10.68)	50	1·00
872	**272**	8c. multicoloured (8.7.69)	75	70
873	**273**	10c. multicoloured (2.4.68)	50	10
		a. Green (background) omitted	£950	
		w. Wmk sideways inverted	†	£1100
874	**217**	15c. apple-green, myrtle-green and carmine (as No. 856†) (19.3.68)	1·00	1·00
		w. Wmk sideways inverted	†	£170
875	**274**	18c. multicoloured (8.7.69)	1·00	55
		a. Printed on the gummed side	£800	
876	**275**	20c. multicoloured (8.7.69)	1·00	20
877	**276**	25c. multicoloured (10.12.68)	1·00	1·50
878	**277**	28c. multicoloured (30.7.68)	60	10
		a. Yellow omitted	£750	
		bw. Wmk inverted	†	£1200
878c	**221a**	30c. olive-green, green and greenish blue (as No. 859) (2.6.70)	3·75	5·00
879	**266**	$2 black, ochre and pale blue (as No. 862) (10.12.68)	13·00	13·00
870/9		Set of 11	22·00	22·00

*No. 871 was originally issued to commemorate the introduction of the brown trout into New Zealand.

†No. 874 is slightly larger than No. 856, measuring 21×25 mm and the inscriptions and numerals differ in size.

278 The Adoration of the Shepherds (Poussin)   **279** Mount Aspiring, Aurora Australis and Southern Cross   **280** Sir James Hector (founder)

(Photo Harrison)

1967 (3 Oct). Christmas. W **98** (sideways). P 13½×14.

880	**278**	2½c. multicoloured	10	10

4c. A large white flaw to the right of the fern (a multipositive flaw affecting all plates, R. 1/10)

(Des J. Berry. Litho D.L.R.)

1967 (10 Oct). Centenary of the Royal Society of New Zealand. W **98** (sideways on 4c.). P 14 (4c.) or 13×14 (8c.).

881	**279**	4c. multicoloured	25	20
		a. Fern flaw	6·00	
		w. Wmk sideways inverted	8·00	9·00
882	**280**	8c. multicoloured	25	80

281 Open Bible   **282** Soldiers and Tank

(Des Display Section, G.P.O. Litho D.L.R.)

1968 (23 Apr). Centenary of Maori Bible. W **98**. P 13½.

883	**281**	3c. multicoloured	10	10
		a. Gold (inscr etc.) omitted	£160	£110
		w. Wmk sideways inverted	35·00	35·00

(Des L. C. Mitchell. Litho D.L.R.)

1968 (7 May). New Zealand Armed Forces. T **282** and similar horiz designs. Multicoloured. W **98** (sideways). P 14×13½.

884		4c. Type **282**	25	10
		w. Wmk sideways inverted	9·50	14·00

885		10c. Airmen, Fairey Firefly and English Electric Canberra aircraft	40	50
886		28c. Sailors and HMNZS Achilles, 1939, and HMNZS Waikato, 1968	70	1·60
		w. Wmk sideways inverted	1·50	5·00
884/6		Set of 3	1·25	2·00

285 Boy breasting Tape, and Olympic Rings   **287** Placing Votes in Ballot Box

(Des L. C. Mitchell. Photo Harrison)

1968 (7 Aug). Health Stamps. T **285** and similar horiz design. Multicoloured. P 14½×14.

887		2½c. . +1c. Type **285**	20	15
888		3c. +1c. Girl swimming and Olympic rings	20	15
		a. Red (ring) omitted	£3500	
		b. Blue (ring) omitted	£2250	
MS889		Two sheets each 145×95 mm. Nos. 887/8 in blocks of six ...... Per pair	13·00	40·00

No. 888a occurred in one miniature sheet. Six examples are known, one being used. No. 888b occurred from a second miniature sheet.

(Des J. Berry. Photo Japanese Govt Ptg Bureau, Tokyo)

1968 (19 Sept). 75th Anniv of Universal Suffrage in New Zealand. P 13.

890	**287**	3c. ochre, olive-green and light blue	10	10

288 Human Rights Emblem   **289** Adoration of the Holy Child (G. van Honthorst)

(Photo Japanese Govt Ptg Bureau, Tokyo)

1968 (19 Sept). Human Rights Year. P 13.

891	**288**	10c. scarlet, yellow and deep green.	10	30

(Photo Harrison)

1968 (1 Oct). Christmas. W **98** (sideways). P 14×14½.

892	**289**	2½c. multicoloured	10	10

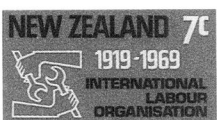

290 ILO Emblem

(Photo Harrison)

1969 (11 Feb). 50th Anniv of International Labour Organization. W **98** (sideways inverted). P 14½×14.

893	**290**	7c. black and carmine-red	15	30

291 Supreme Court Building, Auckland   **292** Law Society's Coat of Arms

(Des R. M. Conly. Litho B.W.)

1969 (8 Apr). Centenary of New Zealand Law Society. T **291/2** and similar design. P 13½×13 (3c.) or 13×13½ (others).

894	**291**	3c. multicoloured (shades)	10	10
895	**292**	10c. multicoloured (shades)	20	35
896		18c. multicoloured (shades)	30	95
894/6		Set of 3	55	1·25

Design: Vert—18c. "Justice" (from Memorial Window in University of Canterbury, Christchurch).

295 Student being conferred with Degree

(Des R. M. Conly. Litho B.W.)

1969 (3 June). Centenary of Otago University. T **295** and similar multicoloured design. P 13½×13 (3c.) or 13½×13 (10c.).

897		3c. Otago University (vert)	15	10
898		10c. Type **295**	30	25

296 Boys playing Cricket

298 Dr. Elizabeth Gunn (founder of First Children's Health Camp)

(Des R. M. Conly (4c.); L. C. Mitchell (others). Litho B.W.)

1969 (6 Aug). Health Stamps. T **296** and similar horiz design and T **298**. P 12½×13 (No. 901) or 13×12½ (others).

899	**296**	2½c. +1c. multicoloured	40	65
900	—	3c. +1c. multicoloured	40	65
901	**298**	4c. +1c. brown and ultramarine	40	1·50
899/901	*Set of 3*		1·10	2·50

MS902 Two sheets each 144×84 mm. Nos. 899/900
in blocks of six.............................*Per pair* 16·00 50·00
Design:—3c. Girls playing cricket.

299 Oldest existing House in New Zealand, and Old Stone Mission Store, Kerikeri

(Litho D.L.R.)

1969 (18 Aug). Early European Settlement in New Zealand, and 150th Anniv of Kerikeri. T **299** and similar horiz design. Multicoloured. W **98** (sideways inverted). P 13×13½.

903	4c. Type **299**		20	25
904	6c. View of Bay of Islands		30	1·75

301 *The Nativity* (Federico Fiori (Barocci))

302 Captain Cook, Transit of Venus and "Octant"

(Photo Harrison)

1969 (1 Oct). Christmas. W **98**. P 13×14.

905	**301**	2½c. multicoloured	10	10
		a. No wmk	10	15

(Des Eileen Mayo. Photo; portraits embossed Harrison)

1969 (9 Oct). Bicentenary of Captain Cook's Landing in New Zealand. T **302** and similar horiz designs. P 14½×14.

906	4c. black, cerise and blue		30	15
	a. Imperf (pair)			£425
907	6c. slate-green, purple-brown and black		40	1·00
908	18c. purple-brown, slate-green and black		60	40
909	28c. cerise, black and blue		1·00	1·25
906/9	*Set of 4*		2·10	2·50

MS910 109×90 mm. Nos. 906/9 .... 14·00 25·00
Designs:—6c. Sir Joseph Banks (naturalist) and outline of HMS *Endeavour*; 18c. Dr. Daniel Solander (botanist) and his plant; 28c. Queen Elizabeth II and Cook's chart 1769.
The miniature sheet exists additionally inscribed on the selvedge at bottom. "A SOUVENIR FROM NEW ZEALAND STAMP EXHIBITION, NEW PLYMOUTH 6TH–11TH OCTOBER. 1969". These were not sold from Post Offices.

306 Girl, Wheat Field and CORSO Emblem

307 Mother feeding her Child, Dairy Herd and CORSO Emblem

(Des L. C. Mitchell. Photo Japanese Govt Printing Bureau, Tokyo)

1969 (18 Nov). 25th Anniv of CORSO (Council of Organizations for Relief Services Overseas). P 13.

911	**306**	7c. multicoloured	35	85
912	**307**	8c. multicoloured	35	90

308 "Cardigan Bay" (champion trotter)

(Des L. C. Mitchell. Photo Courvoisier)

1970 (28 Jan). Return of "Cardigan Bay" to New Zealand. P 11½.

913	**308**	10c. multicoloured	30	30

309 *Vanessa gonerilla* (Red Admiral)

310 Queen Elizabeth II and New Zealand Coat of Arms

(Des Enid Hunter (½c., 1c., 2c., 18c., 20c.), Eileen Mayo (2½c. to 7c.), D. B. Stevenson (7½c., 8c.), M. Cleverley (10, 15, 25, 30c., $1, $2), M. V. Askew (23, 50c.). Photo Harrison (½c. to 20c.), Enschedé (23, 50c.), Courvoisier ($1, $2) or Litho B.W. (25, 30c.))

1970 (12 Mar)–**76**. Various designs as T **309/10**. W **98** (sideways on 10c., or sideways inverted on 15, 20c.) or No wmk (23c. to $2).

*(a) Size as T **309**. P 13½×13*

914	½c. multicoloured (2.9.70)	10	20
	w. Wmk inverted	—	£200
915	1c. multicoloured (2.9.70)	10	10
	aw. Wmk inverted	50·00	35·00
	b. Wmk sideways inverted (booklets) (6.7.71)	80	2·50
	ba. Booklet pane. No. 915bx3 with three se-tenant printed labels	2·25	
	bb. Red omitted	£275	
	bc. Blue omitted (booklets)	£250	£200
	bw. Wmk sideways	£120	
916	2c. multicoloured (2.9.70)	10	10
	a. Black (inscr, etc) omitted	£400	
	w. Wmk inverted	4·00	1·50
917	2½c. multicoloured (2.9.70)	30	20
918	3c. black, brown and orange (2.9.70)	15	10
	aw. Wmk inverted	2·50	2·75
	b. Wmk sideways inverted (booklets) (6.7.71)	55	1·50
	bw. Wmk sideways	32·00	32·00
919	4c. multicoloured (2.9.70)	15	10
	aw. Wmk inverted	3·00	1·75
	b. Wmk sideways inverted (booklets) (6.7.71)	55	1·75
	ba. Bright green (wing veins) omitted ...	£250	£110
	bw. Wmk sideways	85·00	75·00
	c. Bright green (wing veins) omitted ...	†	£250
920	5c. multicoloured (4.11.70)	30	10
	w. Wmk inverted	†	—
921	6c. blackish green, yellow-green and carmine (4.11.70)	30	1·00
	w. Wmk inverted	†	£250
922	7c. multicoloured (4.11.70)	50	1·00
	w. Wmk inverted	—	£300
923	7½c. multicoloured (4.11.70)	75	2·00
	w. Wmk inverted	†	—
924	8c. multicoloured (4.11.70)	50	1·00
	w. Wmk inverted	†	£250

*(b) Size as T **310**. Various perfs*

925	10c. multicoloured (P 14½×14)	50	10
	w. Wmk sideways inverted	8·00	3·75
926	15c. black, flesh and pale brown (P 13½×13) (20.1.71)	75	30
	a. Pale brown omitted	£700	
	w. Wmk sideways	50·00	45·00
927	18c. chestnut, black and apple-green (P 13×13½) (20.1.71)	75	30
	w. Wmk inverted	55·00	45·00
928	20c. black and yellow-brown (P 13½×13) (20.1.71)	75	10
929	23c. multicoloured (P 13½×12½) (1.12.71)	60	15
930	25c. multicoloured (P 13×13½) (1.9.71)	1·00	35
	a. Printed on the gummed side	£750	
	b. Perf 14 (11.76?)	50	75
931	30c. multicoloured (P 13½×13) (1.9.71)	50	15
	a. Perf 14 (9.76?)	1·00	1·75
932	50c. multicoloured (P 13½×12½) (1.9.71)	50	20
	a. Apple green (hill on right) omitted..	28·00	24·00
	b. Buff (shore) omitted	55·00	
	c. Dark green (hill on left) omitted	£350	
933	$1 multicoloured (P 11½) (14.4.71)	1·00	1·00
934	$2 multicoloured (P 11½) (14.4.71)	2·50	1·00
914/34	*Set of 21*	10·00	8·00

Designs: Vert—½c. *Lycaena salustius* (Glade Copper Butterfly); 2c. *Argyrophenga antipodum* (Tussock Butterfly); 2½c. *Nyctemera annulata* (Magpie Moth); 3c. *Detunda egregia* (Lichen Moth); 4c. *Charagia virescens* (Puriri Moth); 5c. Scarlet Wrasse ("Scarlet Parrot Fish"); 6c. Big-bellied Sea Horses; 7c. Leather jacket (fish); 7½c. Intermediate Halfbeak ("Garfish"); 8c. John Dory (fish); 18c. Maori club; 25c. Hauraki Gulf Maritime Park; 30c. Mt Cook National Park. Horiz—10c. Type **310**: 15c. Maori fish hook; 20c. Maori tattoo Pattern; 23c. Egmont National Park; 50c. Abel Tasman National Park; $1 Geothermal Power; $2 Agricultural Technology.
Although issued as a definitive No. 925 was put on sale on the occasion of the Royal Visit to New Zealand.
Used examples of No. 931 are known showing the sky in light blue instead of the normal stone colour. It was suggested by the printer involved that this was caused by a residue of ink used for another stamp remaining in the ink ducts when a printing of the 30c. commenced. Most authorities, however, agree that the "blue sky" stamps are colour changelings.
The 1c., 2c., 3c. to 7c. and 8c. to 20c. values were re-issued between 1973 and 1976 on unwatermarked paper.

311 Geyser Restaurant

312 UN HQ Building

(Des M. Cleverley. Photo Japanese Govt Printing Bureau, Tokyo)

1970 (8 Apr). World Fair, Osaka. T **311** and similar horiz designs. Multicoloured. P 13.

935	7c. Type **311**		20	55
936	8c. New Zealand Pavilion		20	55
937	18c. Bush Walk		40	55
935/7	*Set of 3*		70	1·50

(Des R. M. Conly (3c.), L. C. Mitchell (10c.). Litho D.L.R.)

1970 (24 June). 25th Anniv of United Nations. T **312** and similar vert design. P 13½.

938	3c. multicoloured	10	10
939	10c. scarlet and yellow	20	20

Design:—10c. Tractor on horizon.

313 Soccer

(Des L. C. Mitchell. Litho D.L.R.)

1970 (5 Aug). Health Stamps. T **313** and similar multicoloured design. P 13½.

940	2½c. +1c. Netball (*vert*)	25	70
941	3c. +1c.Type **313**	25	70

MS942 Two sheets: (a) 102×125 mm
(940); (b) 125×102 mm (941), containing
blocks of 6 ....*Per pair* 16·00 50·00

314 *The Virgin adoring the Child* (Correggio)

315 *The Holy Family* (stained glass window, Invercargill Presbyterian Church)

(Litho D.L.R.)

1970 (1 Oct). Christmas. T **314/15** and similar design. P 12½.

943	2½c. multicoloured	10	10
944	3c. multicoloured	10	10
	a. Green (inscr and value) omitted	£300	£200
945	10c. black, orange and silver	30	75
943/5	*Set of 3*	35	75

Design: Horiz—10c. Tower of Roman Catholic Church, Sockburn. No. 943 exists as an imperforate proof with the country inscription and face value omitted.

316 Chatham Islands Lily

(Des Eileen Mayo. Photo Japanese Govt Printing Bureau, Tokyo)

1970 (2 Dec). Chatham Islands. T **316** and similar horiz design. Multicoloured. P 13.

946	1c. Type **316**	10	35
947	2c. Shy Albatross	30	40

STAMP BOOKLETS

Nos. SB1 to SB24 are stapled.
Nos. SB1/5 were sold at ½d. above the face value of the stamps to cover the cost of manufacture.

1901 (1 Apr). White card covers with postage rates.

SB1	1s.½d. booklet containing 12×1d. (No. 278) in blocks of 6	£2250
SB2	2s. 6½d. booklet containing 30×1d. (No. 278) in blocks of 6	£3000

Original printings of Nos. SB1/2 showed the face value on the cover in small figures. Subsequent printings show large figures of value on the covers and the prices quoted are for this type.

1902 (21 Aug)–**05**. White card covers with postage rates.

SB3	1s.½d. booklet containing 12×1d. in panes of 6 (Nos. 303b or 303cb)	£1800
SB4	2s.½d. booklet containing 24×1d. in panes of 6 (Nos. 303b or 303cb) (21.3.05)	£2250
SB5	2s. 6½d. booklet containing 30×1d. in panes of 6 (Nos. 303b or 303cb)	£2750

1910 (Apr). White card cover with postage rates.

SB6	2s. booklet containing 11×½d. in pane of 5 with 1 label (Nos. 387b or 387c) and pane of 6 (No. 387d), and 18×1d. in three panes of 6 (No. 405b)	£5000

1912 (May). White card cover.

SB7	2s. booklet containing 12×½d. and 18×1d. in panes of 6 with bars on the selvedge (Nos. 387e, 405c)	£3000

1915 (Feb). Red card cover.

SB8	2s. booklet containing 12×½d. and 18×1d. in panes of 6 with bars on the selvedge (Nos. 435a or 435ba, 405c)	£1800
	a. Grey cover	
	b. Blue cover	
	c. Yellow-buff cover	
	d. Purple-buff cover	

1924 (1 Dec)–**25**. Cover inscription within frame.

SB9	2s. booklet containing 12×½d. and 18×1d. in panes of 6 with bars on the selvedge (Nos. 441a, 406b) (lilac cover)	£2000	
	a. Grey cover		
	b. Pale blue cover	£2250	
SB10	2s. booklet containing 12×½d. and 18×1d. in panes of 6 with bars and advertisements on the selvedge (Nos. 446a, 410b) (yellow-buff cover) (1925)	£2500	
	a. Grey-green cover	£2500	
	b. Grey-buff cover	£2500	
	c. Grey-pink cover	£2500	

1928–34.

SB11	2s. booklet containing 12×½d. (P 14×15) and 18×1d. in panes of 6 with bars on the selvedge (Nos. 446aab, 468b)	£3000	
	a. As No. SB11, but ½d. (P 14) (Nos. 446ca, 468b)	£1800	
	b. As No. SB11 but panes with bars and advertisements on the selvedge (Nos. 446cb, 468c)	£2000	
SB12	2s. booklet containing 24×1d. (P 14) in panes of 6 with bars and advertisements on the selvedge (No. 468c) (1930)	£1800	
	a. As No. SB12, but 1d. (P 14×15) (No. 468ea) (1934)	£1700	

1935 (18 Nov).

SB15	2s. booklet containing 24×1d., in panes of 6 with advertisements on the selvedge (No. 557ca)	£375	

1936 (Nov).

SB16	2s. booklet containing 24×1d. (No. 578) in blocks of 6	£300	

B **1**

1938 (1 July). Cream cover as Type B **1**.

SB17	2s. booklet containing 24×1d. (No. 605) in blocks of 6	£375	

1938 (Nov). Cream (No. SB18) or blue (No. SB19) covers as Type B **1**.

SB18	2s. booklet containing 12×½d. and 18×1d. (Nos. 603, 605) in blocks of 6	£500	
SB19	2s.3d. booklet containing 18×1½d. (No. 607) in blocks of 6	£400	

B **2**

1954 (1 Apr)–**55**. Black and green on cream cover as Type B **2**.

SB20	4s. booklet containing 12×1d. and 12×3d. (Nos. 724, 727), each in blocks of 6	4·00	
	a. Contents as SB20 but with one pane of air mail labels (9.55)	21·00	

1956 (1 May). Black and green on cream cover as Type B **2**.

SB21	4s. booklet containing 12×1d. and 12×3d. (Nos. 724, 748), each in blocks of 6, and one pane of air mail labels	10·00	

1957 (5 Sept). Black and green on cream cover as Type B **2**.

SB22	4s. booklet containing 12×1d. and 12×3d. (Nos. 745, 748), each in blocks of 6, and one pane of air mail labels	9·00	

B **3**

1960 (1 Sept). Black and red on cream cover as Type B **3**.

SB23	4s. booklet containing 12×1d. and 12×3d. (Nos. 782, 785), each in blocks of 6, and one pane of air mail labels	14·00	

1962 (21 May). Black and red on cream cover as Type B **3**.

SB24	4s.6d. booklet containing 12×½d., 12×1d. and 12×3d. (Nos. 781, 782, 785), each in blocks of 6, and one pane of air mail labels	50·00	

1964. Black and carmine on cream cover as Type B **3**. Stitched.

SB25	4s.3d. booklet containing 6×1½d. and 12×1d. and 12×3d. (Nos. 781/2, 785) each in blocks of 6, and one pane of air mail labels	16·00	

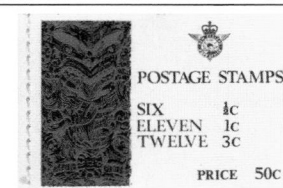

B **4** Maori Art

1967 (10 July). Black and carmine on pale lemon cover as Type B **4**. Stitched.

SB26	50c. booklet containing ½c. (No. 845) in block of 6, 11×1c. in block of 6 (No. 846) and pane of 5 stamps and 1 label (No. 846a), and 12×3c. (No. 849) in blocks of 6	6·50	

EXPRESS DELIVERY STAMPS

E **1**

(Typo Govt Printing Office, Wellington)

1903 (9 Feb). Value in first colour. W **43** (sideways). P 11.

E1	E **1**	6d. red and violet	38·00	23·00

1926–36. Thick, white, opaque chalk-surfaced "Cowan" paper. W **43**.

(a) P 14×14½

E2	E **1**	6d. vermilion and bright violet	50·00	26·00
		w. Wmk inverted	£300	

(b) P 14×15 (1936)

E3	E **1**	6d. carmine and bright violet	70·00	60·00

1937–39. Thin, hard, chalk-surfaced "Wiggins Teape" paper.

(a) P 14×14½

E4	E **1**	6d. carmine and bright violet	£110	50·00

(b) P 14×15 (4.39)

E5	E **1**	6d. vermilion and bright violet	£180	£350

E **2** Express Mail Delivery Van

(Des J. Berry. Eng Stamp Ptg Office, Melbourne. Recess Govt Ptg Office, Wellington)

1939 (16 Aug). W **43**. P 14.

E6	E **2**	6d. violet	1·50	1·75
		w. Wmk inverted	90·00	

No. E6 was withdrawn on 30 June 1948, when the Express Delivery Service ceased.

POSTAGE DUE STAMPS

D **1**   (I)   (II)

3D.   **5**D.

(a) Large "D"   *(b)* Small "D"

(Typo Govt Printing Office, Wellington)

1899 (1 Dec). Coarse paper. W **12b**. P 11.

I. Type I. Circle of 14 ornaments 17 dots over "N.Z.", "N.Z." large

(a) Large "D"

D1	D **1**	½d. carmine and green	35·00	45·00
		a. No stop after "D" (Right pane R. 2/3)	£200	£250
D2		8d. carmine and green	60·00	85·00
		a. Carmine "8D." printed double		
D3		1s. carmine and green	70·00	95·00
D4		2s. carmine and green	£120	£150
D1/4	*Set of 4*		£250	£325

To avoid further subdivision the 1s. and 2s. are placed with the *pence* values, although the two types of "D" do not apply to the higher values.

(b) Small "D"

D6	D **1**	5d. carmine and green	35·00	50·00
D7		6d. carmine and green	48·00	50·00
D8		10d. carmine and green	75·00	£100
D6/8	*Set of 3*		£130	£180

II. Type II. Circle of 13 ornaments, 15 dots over "N.Z.", "N.Z." small

(a) Large "D"

D9	D **1**	½d. vermilion and green	4·25	16·00
		a. No stop after "D" (Right pane R. 2/3)	65·00	£120
D10		1d. vermilion and green	22·00	3·75
D11		2d. vermilion and green	55·00	9·00
D12		3d. vermilion and green	17·00	7·00
D9/12	*Set of 4*		85·00	32·00

(b) Small "D"

D14	D **1**	1d. vermilion and green	21·00	3·75
D15		2d. vermilion and green	55·00	9·50
D16		4d. vermilion and green	40·00	21·00
D14/16	*Set of 3*		£100	30·00

Nos. D9/16 were printed from a common frame plate of 240 (4 panes of 60) used in conjunction with centre plates of 120 (2 panes of 60) for the ½d. and 4d. or 240 for the other values. Sheets of the 1d. and 2d. each contained two panes with large "D" and two panes with small "D".

D **2**   D **3**

(Des W. R. Bock. Typo Govt Printing Office)

1902 (28 Feb). No wmk. P 11.

D17	D **2**	½d. red and deep green	3·25	9·00

1904–08. "Cowan" unsurfaced paper. W **43** (sideways).

(a) P 11

D18	D **2**	½d. red and green (4.04)	3·25	3·00
		a. Imperf between (horiz pair)	£1400	
D19		1d. red and green (5.12.05)	23·00	3·50
D20		2d. red and green (5.4.06)	£110	£120
D18/20	*Set of 3*		£120	£120

(b) P 14

D21	D **2**	1d. carmine and green (12.06)	26·00	1·50
		a. *Rose-pink and green* (9.07)	15·00	1·50
D22		2d. carmine and green (10.06)	15·00	11·00
		a. *Rose-pink and green* (6.08)	9·00	3·00

The note regarding sideways watermark varieties below No. 299 applies here also.

1919 (Jan)–**20**. "De La Rue" chalky paper. Toned gum. W **43**. P 14×15.

D23	D **2**	½d. carmine and green (6.19)	3·75	6·00
D24		1d. carmine and green	9·00	50
D25		w. Wmk inverted	†	—
		2d. carmine and green (8.20)	26·00	4·50
D23/5	*Set of 3*		35·00	9·50

1925 (May). "Jones" chalky paper. White gum. W **43**. P 14×15.

D26	D **2**	½d. carmine and green	45·00	55·00

1925 (July). No wmk, but bluish "N Z" and Star lithographed on back. P 14×15.

D27	D **2**	½d. carmine and green	2·00	25·00
D28		2d. carmine and green	3·50	35·00

1925 (Nov)–**35**. "Cowan" thick, opaque chalky paper. W **43**.

(a) P 14×15

D29	D **2**	½d. carmine and green (12.26)	1·75	14·00
D30		1d. carmine and green	3·75	80
D31		2d. carmine and green (6.26)	29·00	4·25
		x. Wmk reversed	55·00	28·00
D32		3d. carmine and green (6.35)	50·00	55·00
D29/32	*Set of 4*		75·00	65·00

(b) P 14

D33	D **2**	½d. carmine and green (10.28)	50·00	32·00
D34		1d. rose and pale yellow-green (6.28)	4·00	1·25
D35		2d. carmine and green (10.29)	7·00	3·00
D36		3d. carmine and green (5.28)	15·00	50·00
D33/6	*Set of 4*		70·00	75·00

1937–38. "Wiggins Teape" thin, hard chalky paper. W **43**. P 14×15.

D37	D **2**	½d. carmine and yellow-green (2.38)	45·00	45·00
D38		1d. carmine and yellow-green (1.37)	18·00	4·25
D39		2d. carmine and yellow-green (6.37)	55·00	21·00
D40		3d. carmine and yellow-green (11.37)	£100	75·00
D37/40	*Set of 4*		£190	£130

(Des J. Berry. Typo Govt Printing Office, Wellington)

1939–49. P 15×14.

(a) W **43** *(sideways inverted) (16.8.39)*

D41	D **3**	½d. turquoise-green	5·00	5·00
D42		1d. carmine	4·00	4·25
		w. Wmk sideways	£200	9·50
D43		2d. bright blue	6·00	2·75
		w. Wmk sideways	£250	
D44		3d. orange-brown	35·00	25·00
		w. Wmk sideways	£190	
D41/4	*Set of 4*		45·00	32·00

(b) W **98** *(sideways (1d.), sideways inverted (2d.) or upright (3d.)*

D45	D **3**	1d. carmine (4.49)	20·00	7·50
D46		2d. bright blue (12.46)	11·00	5·00
		w. Wmk sideways (4.49)	2·75	12·00
D47		3d. orange-brown (1943)	60·00	50·00
		a. Wmk sideways inverted (6.45)	32·00	17·00
		aw. Wmk sideways (28.11.49)	9·00	22·00
D45/7aw	*Set of 3*		29·00	26·00*

*The use of Postage Due stamps ceased on 30 September 1951, our used price for No. D45 being for stamps postmarked after this date (*price for examples clearly cancelled 1949–51, £30).

OFFICIAL STAMPS

1891 (Dec)–**1906**. Contemporary issues handstamped "O.P.S.O." in 3½mm capital letters.

(a) Stamps of 1873 type optd in violet. P 12½

O1	**3**	½d. pale dull rose (W **4**) (No. 149)	—	£1400
O2		½d. bright rose (W **12b**) (No. 151)	—	£900

(b) Stamps of 1882–97 optd in rose/magenta. W **12b**

O3	**13**	½d. black (P 10) (No. 217)	—	£800
		a. Violet opt		£950
O4		½d. black (P 10×11) (No. 227)	—	£800
O5		1d. rose (P 12×11½) (No. 195b)	—	£800
		a. Violet opt		
O6		1d. rose (P 10) (violet opt) (No. 218)		
O7		1d. rose (P 11) (No. 237)	—	£800
		a. Violet opt		
O8		2d. purple (P 11) (No. 238)	—	£850
		a. Violet opt		
O9		2d. mauve-lilac (P 10) (No. 219)	—	£850
		a. Advert on back (3rd setting)		
		b. Violet opt		£1200
		ba. Advert on back		
O10		2½d. blue (P 12×11½) (violet opt) (No. 197)	—	
O11		2½d. blue (P 11) (violet opt) (No. 239)	—	£850

O12	2½d. ultramarine (P 10) (No. 220)	—	£850
	a. Advert on back	—	
	b. Violet opt	—	
	ba. Green advert (2nd setting)	—	
	bb. Mauve advert (3rd setting)	—	
O13	2½d. ultramarine (P 10×11) (No. 230)	—	£850
	a. Violet opt	—	
O14	5d. olive-black (P 12×11½) (No. 200)	—	£1100
	a. violet opt	—	
O15	6d. brown (P 12½×11½) (No. 201)	—	£1300

(c) Stamps of 1898–1903 optd in violet. P 11

(i) No wmk

O16	½d. green (P 14) (No. 294)	—	£800
	a. Rose or magenta opt	—	
O17	2½d. blue (P 12-16) (No. 249)	—	£1200
O18	2½d. blue (No. 260)	—	£950
	a. Rose/magenta opt	—	
O19	4d. indigo and brown (No. 262)	—	£1100
O20	5d. purple-brown (No. 263)	—	£1100
	a. Rose/magenta opt	—	
	b. Greenish blue opt	—	
O21	8d. Indigo (No. 266)	—	£1300
O22	1s. red (No. 268)	—	£2500

(ii) W 38

O23	½d. green (No. 273b)	—	
O24	1d. carmine (No. 278)	—	£850
	a. Blue opt	—	

(iii) W 43 (sideways on 3d. 5d., 1s.)

O25	½d. green (P 14) (No. 302)	—	
	a. Rose or magenta opt	—	
O26	1d. carmine (P 14) (No. 303)	—	£850
	a. Green opt	—	
O27	1d. carmine (P 14) (No. 349)	—	£850
O28	1d. carmine (P 14) (No. 356)	—	£850
O29	1d. carmine (P 14) (No. 357) (black opt)	—	
O30	2½d. blue (No. 308)	—	£900
O31	3d. yellow-brown (No. 309)	—	£1100
O32	5d. red-brown (No. 311)	—	
O33	1s. orange-red (No. 315b)	—	£2500
O34	2s. green (No. 316)	—	£3750

The letters signify "On Public Service Only" and stamps so overprinted were used exclusively at the General Post Office, Wellington, on official correspondence to foreign countries between December 1891 and 31 December 1906.

Four different handstamps were used, differing slightly in the length of the overprint. The handstamp was normally applied diagonally reading upwards but other positions are known.

The stamps were not available unused and such examples with the "O.P.S.O." handstamp are generally considered to be reprints.

OFFICIAL.

(O **3**)

1907–11. Stamps of 1902–6 optd with Type O **3** (vertically, upwards). W **43** (sideways on 3d., 6d., 1s. and 5s.). P 14.

O59	23	½d. yellow-green	18·00	75
		a. Perf 11×14	£350	
		b. Mixed perfs	£350	£350
O60	42	1d. carmine (No. 303) (1.7.07*)	14·00	22·00
		a. Booklet pane of 6	55·00	
		ab. Imperf horiz (booklet pane of 6)	£2750	
O60b		1d. rose-carmine (Waterlow) (No. 352)	30·00	70
		ba. Perf 11×14	—	£550
		bb. Mixed perfs	—	£550
		bc. Mixed perfs	—	£1000
O60c		1d. carmine (Royle)	60·00	70
		ca. Perf 11×14	£375	£600
		cb. Mixed perfs	£375	£475
O61	41	2d. purple	18·00	1·75
		a. Bright reddish purple	8·50	1·60
		ab. Mixed perfs	£550	£425
O63	28	3d. bistre-brown	50·00	1·75
		a. Mixed perfs	—	£1600
O64	31	6d. bright carmine-pink	£250	25·00
		a. Imperf vert (horiz pair)	£1500	
		b. Mixed perfs	£1000	£750
		c. Opt inverted (reading downwards)	†	£4250
O65	34	1s. orange-red	£110	22·00
O66	35	2s. blue-green	85·00	£140
		a. Imperf between (pair)	£4000	
		b. Imperf vert (horiz pair)	£2750	
		w. Wmk inverted	£750	£550
O67	36	5s. deep red	£170	£190
		a. Wmk upright (1911)	£1200	£1200

*Though issued in 1907 a large quantity of booklets was mislaid and not utilized until they were found in 1930.

1908–09. Optd as Type O **3**. W **43**.

O69	23	½d. green (P 14×15)	19·00	6·00
O70	50	1d. carmine (P 14×15)	70·00	5·50
O71	48	6d. pink (P 14×13, 13½)	£200	48·00
O72		6d. pink (P 14×15) (1909)	£225	35·00
O72a	F 4	£1 rose-pink (P 14) (No. F89)	£650	450

1910. No. 387 optd with Type O **3**.

O73	51	½d. yellow-green	18·00	40
		a. Opt inverted (reading downwards)	†	£3000

1910–16. Nos. 389 and 392/4 optd with Type O **3**. P 14×14½.

O74	52	3d. chestnut	14·00	80
		a. Perf 14×13½ (1915)	65·00	£130
		ab. Vert pair. Nos. O74/a	£350	£750
O75	—	6d. carmine	19·00	5·50
		a. Perf 14 (line) (No. 398)	†	£3750
		b. Deep carmine	25·00	6·00
		w. Wmk inverted		
O76		8d. indigo-blue (R.) (5.16)	12·00	29·00
		aw. Wmk inverted	75·00	85·00
		b. Perf 14×13½	12·00	29·00
		bw. Wmk inverted	75·00	85·00

	c. Vert pair, Nos. O76 and O76b	70·00	£140
	cw. Wmk inverted	£275	£325
O77		1s. vermilion	55·00	20·00
O74/7 Set of 4			90·00	50·00

1910–26. Optd with Type O **3**.

*(a) W **43**. De La Rue chalk-surfaced paper with toned gum*

O78	53	1d. carmine (No. 405)	5·50	10
		a. "Feather" flaw	70·00	12·00
		b. "Globe" flaw	70·00	12·00
		c. "Q" flaw	75·00	45·00
		y. Wmk inverted and reversed		

*(b) W **43**. Jones chalk-surfaced paper with white gum*

O79	53	1d. deep carmine (No. 406) (1925)	16·00	11·00
		a. "Feather" flaw	£160	80·00
		b. "Globe" flaw	£160	80·00

(c) No wmk, but bluish "NZ" and Star lithographed on back. Art paper

O80	53	1d. rose-carmine (No. 409) (1925)	7·00	22·00
		a. "Feather" flaw	75·00	

*(d) W **43**. Cowan thick, opaque, chalk-surfaced paper with white gum*

O81	53	1d. deep carmine (No. 410) (1925)	8·00	1·25
		a. "Feather" flaw	75·00	32·00
		b. "Globe" flaw	75·00	32·00
		c. "N" flaw	£180	£100
		x. Wmk reversed (1926)	50·00	38·00
		xa. "Feather" flaw	£325	£225
		xb. "Globe" flaw	£325	£225
		xc. "N" flaw	£325	£225

1913–25. Postal Fiscal stamps optd with Type O **3**.

(i) Chalk-surfaced De La Rue paper

(a) P 14 (1913–14)

O82	F 4	2s. blue (30.9.14)	65·00	50·00
O83		5s. yellow-green (13.6.13)	90·00	£130
O84		£1 rose-carmine (1913)	£650	£550
O82/4 Set of 3			£750	£650

(b) P 14½×14, comb (1915)

O85	F 4	2s. deep blue (Aug)	65·00	50·00
		a. No stop after "OFFICIAL" (R. 2/5)	£180	£160
O86		5s. yellow-green (1.15)	90·00	£130
		a. No stop after "OFFICIAL" (R. 2/5)	£275	£350

(ii) Thick, white, opaque chalk-surfaced Cowan paper. P 14½×14 (1925)

O87	F 4	2s. blue	85·00	£100
		a. No stop after "OFFICIAL" (R. 2/5)	£250	£300

The overprint on these last, and on Nos. O69 and O72a is from a new set of type, giving a rather sharper impression than Type O **3**, but otherwise resembling it closely.

1915 (12 Oct)**–34.** Optd with Type O **3**. P 14×15.

(a) On Nos. 435/40 (De La Rue chalk-surfaced paper with toned gum)

O88	61	½d. green	1·25	20
O89	62	1½d. grey-black (6.16)	8·50	2·75
O90	61	1½d. slate (12.16)	5·50	1·00
O91		1½d. orange-brown (4.19)	5·00	30
O92		2d. yellow (4.17)	13·00	20
O93		3d. chocolate (11.19)	12·00	1·00
O88/93 Set of 6			40·00	5·00

(b) On Nos. 441 and 443 (Jones chalk-surfaced paper with white gum)

O94	61	½d. green (1924)	4·50	3·50
O95		3d. deep chocolate (1924)	50·00	9·50

(c) On Nos. 446/7 and 448a/9 (Cowan thick, opaque, chalk surfaced paper with white gum)

O96	61	½d. green (1925)	6·00	10
		ax. Wmk reversed (1927)	85·00	27·00
		ay. Wmk inverted and reversed (1927)	£325	65·00
		b. Perf 14 (1929)	3·75	70
		ba. No stop after "OFFICIAL"	35·00	40·00
O97		1½d. orange-brown (P 14) (1929)	15·00	17·00
		a. No stop after "OFFICIAL"	£110	£110
		b. Perf 14×15 (1934)	50·00	45·00
O98		2d. yellow (P 14) (1931)	2·50	50
		a. No stop after "OFFICIAL"	75·00	80·00
O99		3d. chocolate (1925)	7·00	70
		a. No stop after "OFFICIAL"	75·00	55·00
		b. Perf 14 (1930)	70·00	15·00
		ba. No stop after "OFFICIAL"	£275	£200
O96/9 Set of 4			25·00	17·00

1915 (Dec)**–27.** Optd with Type O **3**. P 14×13½.

(a) Nos. 420, 422, 425, 428 and 429/30 (Cowan unsurfaced paper)

O100	60	3d. chocolate	4·50	1·50
		aw. Wmk inverted	32·00	7·00
		b. Perf 14×14½	4·50	1·75
		bw. Wmk inverted	50·00	12·00
		c. Vert pair, Nos. O100 and O100b	40·00	£120
		cw. Wmk inverted	£140	£225
		d. Opt double	†	£1400
O101		4d. bright violet (4.25)	14·00	7·50
		a. Re-entry (Pl 20 R. 1/6)	85·00	60·00
		b. Re-entry (Pl 20 R. 4/10)	90·00	70·00
		c. Perf 14×14½ (Deep purple) (4.27)	40·00	1·25
O102		6d. carmine (6.16)	5·00	75
		aw. Wmk inverted	£140	
		b. Perf 14×14½	5·00	2·00
		c. Vert pair, Nos. O102 and O102b	55·00	£140
O103		8d. red-brown (8.22)	65·00	£190
O104		9d. sage-green (4.25)	42·00	38·00
O105		1s. vermilion (9.16)	24·00	14·00
		aw. Wmk inverted	£275	£170
		ax. Wmk reversed	†	
		b. Perf 14×14½	7·00	2·00
		ba. Pale orange-red	15·00	20·00
		bw. Wmk inverted	£250	£275
		c. Vert pair. Nos. O105 and O105b.	65·00	£190
		cw. Wmk inverted	£650	
O100/5 Set of 6			£120	£200

(b) No. 433 (Thin paper with widely spaced sideways wmk)

O106	60	3d. chocolate (P 14) (7.16)	3·00	15·00
		a. No wmk	50·00	80·00

1927–33. Optd with Type O **3**. W **43**. P 14.

O111	71	1d. rose-carmine (No. 468)	2·00	20
		a. No stop after "OFFICIAL" (R. 1/2, 5/24)	42·00	£110

	bw. Wmk inverted	†	50·00	20
		8·00	20
O112	72	2s. light blue (No. 469) (2.28)	85·00	£130
O113	F 6	5s. green (1933)	£325	£375
O111/13 Set of 3			£375	£475

Unused examples of No. O111 are known printed on Cowan unsurfaced paper.

Official   Official

(O **4**)   (O **5**)

1936–61. Pictorial issue optd horiz or vert (2s.) with Type O **4**.

*(a) W **43** (Single "N Z" and Star)*

O115	82	1d. scarlet (Die I) (21.3.36)	10·00	1·25
		a. Perf 13½×14	£140	85·00
O116	83	1½d. red-brown (P 13½×14) (3.36)	45·00	35·00
		a. Perf 14×13½	£20000	
O118	92	1s. deep green (P 14×13½) (3.36)	50·00	65·00
O119	F 6	5s. green (P 14) (12.38)	£160	65·00
		w. Wmk inverted	†	£650
O115/19 Set of 4			£225	£160

The watermark of No. O119 is almost invisible.

Only four examples of No. O116a exist. The error occurred when a sheet of No. 558a was found to have a block of four missing. This was replaced by a block of No. 558 and the sheet was then sent for overprinting.

*(b) W **98** (Mult "N Z" and Star)*

O120	81	½d. bright green, P 14×13½ (7.37)	7·50	4·50
		w. Wmk inverted	48·00	55·00
O121	82	1d. scarlet (Die II), P 14×13½ (11.36)	12·00	50
		w. Wmk inverted (P 14×13½)	48·00	55·00
O122	83	1½d. red-brown, P 14×13½ (7.36)	35·00	4·75
O123	84	2d. orange, P 14×13½ (1.38)	13·00	10
		aw. Wmk inverted	—	£400
		b. Perf 12½ (1941)	£200	60·00
		c. Perf 14 (1941)	65·00	16·00
O124	85	2½d. chocolate and slate, P 13-14×13½ (26.7.38)	70·00	£110
		a. Perf 14 (1938)	14·00	21·00
O125	86	3d. brown, P 14×13½ (1.3.38)	48·00	3·50
		w. Wmk inverted	—	£400
O126	87	4d. black and sepia, P 14×13½ (8.36)	22·00	1·10
		a. Perf 14 (8.41)	24·00	4·50
		b. Perf 12½ (12.41)	24·00	10·00
		c. Perf 14×14½ (10.42)	1·00	1·00
		cw. Wmk inverted	—	£800
O127	89	6d. scarlet, P 13½×14 (12.37)	40·00	80
		aw. Wmk inverted	†	£750
		b. Perf 12½ (1941)	15·00	10·00
		c. Perf 14½×14 (7.42)	17·00	40
O128	90	8d. chocolate, P 12½ (wmk sideways) (8.42)	23·00	17·00
		a. Perf 14×14½ (wmk sideways) (8.45)	8·50	16·00
		b. Perf 14×13½ (1942)	†	£3750
O129	91	9d. red and grey-black (G.) (No. 587a), P 13½×14 (1.3.38)	90·00	40·00
O130		9d. scarlet and black (chalk-surfaced paper) (Blk.) (No. 631), P 14×15 (10.43)	20·00	22·00
O131	92	1s. deep green, P 14×13½ (2.37)	50·00	1·50
		aw. Wmk inverted	—	£750
		b. Perf 12½ (4.42)	40·00	3·00
O132	93	2s. olive-green, P 13–14×13½ (5.37)	80·00	42·00
		a. "CAPTAIN COQK"	£225	£120
		b. Perf 13½×14 (5.39)	£250	11·00
		ba. "CAPTAIN COQK"	£350	85·00
		c. Perf 12½ (3.42)	80·00	22·00
		ca. "CAPTAIN COQK"	£225	85·00
		d. Perf 14×13½ (1944)	50·00	11·00
		da. "CAPTAIN COQK"	£500	£225
O133	F 6	5s. green (chalk-surfaced paper), P 14 (3.43)	50·00	6·00
		aw. Wmk inverted	40·00	6·00
		b. Perf 14×13½. Yellow-green (ordinary paper) (10.61)	14·00	30·00
O120/33 Set of 14			£350	£120

The opt on No. O127b was sometimes applied at the top of the stamp, instead of always at the bottom as on No. O127.

All examples of No. O128b were used by a government office in Whangarei.

The 5s. value on ordinary paper perforated 14×13½ does not exist without the "Official" overprint.

See notes on perforations after No. 590b.

1938–51. Nos. 603 etc., optd with Type O **4**.

O134	108	½d. green (1.3.38)	28·00	2·25
O135		½d. brown-orange (1946)	2·75	4·25
O136		1d. scarlet (1.7.38)	38·00	15
O137		2d. orange (10.7.41)	7·00	10
O138	108a	1½d. purple-brown (26.7.38)	75·00	25·00
O139		1½d. scarlet (2.4.51)	17·00	12·00
O140		3d. blue (16.10.41)	7·50	10
O134/40 Set of 7			£160	38·00

1940 (2 Jan–8 Mar). Centennial. Nos. 613, etc., optd with Type O **5**.

O141		½d. blue-green (R.)	3·00	35
		a. "ff" joined, as Type O **4**	55·00	65·00
O142		1d. chocolate and scarlet	7·50	10
		a. "ff" joined, as Type O **4**	50·00	60·00
O143		1½d. light blue and mauve	6·50	2·00
O144		2d. blue-green and chocolate	9·50	10
		a. "ff" joined, as Type O **4**	65·00	65·00
O145		2½d. blue-green and ultramarine	5·00	2·75
		a. "ff" joined, as Type O **4**	50·00	75·00
O146		3d. purple and carmine (R.)	8·00	1·00
		a. "ff" joined, as Type O **4**	45·00	55·00
O147		4d. chocolate and lake	42·00	1·50
		a. "ff" joined, as Type O **4**	£120	£100
O148		6d. emerald-green and violet	35·00	1·50
		a. "ff" joined, as Type O **4**	80·00	75·00
O149		8d. black and red (8.3)	35·00	17·00
		a. "ff' joined, as Type O **4**	80·00	£120
O150		9d. olive-green and vermilion	14·00	4·00
O151		1s. sage-green and deep green	50·00	9·00
O141/51 Set of 11			£190	30·00

For this issue the Type O **4** overprint occurs on R. 4/3 of the 2½d. and on R. 1/10 of the other values.

1947 (1 May)–**51**. Nos. 680, etc., optd with Type O **4**.

O152	**108a**	2d. orange	7·00	10
O153		4d. bright purple	4·75	4·25
O154		6d. carmine	21·00	50
O155		8d. violet	8·00	7·50
O156		9d. purple-brown	9·00	6·50
O157	**144**	1s. red-brown and carmine (wmk upright) (Plate 1)	17·00	1·00
		a. Wmk sideways (Plate 1) (6.49)	8·50	12·00
		aw. Wmk sideways inverted	45·00	25·00
		b. Wmk upright (Plate 2) (4.51)	24·00	7·50
		bw. Wmk inverted	£150	50·00
O158		2s. brown-orange and green (wmk sideways) (Plate 1)	42·00	16·00
		a. Wmk upright (Plate 1)	35·00	48·00
O152/8	*Set of 7*		80·00	32·00

O **6** Queen Elizabeth II (O **7**)

(Des J. Berry. Recess B.W.)

1954 (1 Mar)–**63**. W **98**. P 14×13½.

O159	**06**	1d. orange	75	1·00
		a. White opaque paper (8.7.59)	50	1·00
O160		1½d. brown-lake	2·75	3·50
O161		2d. bluish green	50	50
		a. White opaque paper (11.12.58)	40	60
O162		2½d. olive (*white opaque paper*) (1.3.63)	3·00	1·50
O163		3d. vermilion	70	10
		a. White opaque paper (1960)	40	10
		aw. Wmk inverted	40·00	30·00
O164		4d. blue	1·50	75
		a. Printed on the gummed side	£200	
		b. White opaque paper (1.9.61)	1·00	50
O165		9d. carmine	7·50	3·25
O166		1s. purple	1·75	30
		a. White opaque paper (2.10.61)	2·50	1·00
O167		3s. slate (*white opaque paper*) (1.3.63)	24·00	40·00
O159/67	*Set of 9*		38·00	48·00

See note *re* white opaque paper after No. 736.
No. O164a shows the watermark inverted and reversed.

1959 (1 Oct). No. O160 surch with Type O **7**.

O168	O **6**	6d. on 1½d. brown-lake	50	1·10

1961 (1 Sept). No. O161 surch as Type O **7**.

O169	O **6**	2½d. on 2d. bluish green	1·25	2·50

Owing to the greater use of franking machines by Government Departments, the use of official stamps was discontinued on 31 March 1965, but they remained on sale at the GPO until 31 December 1965.

STAMP BOOKLET

1907 (1 July). White card cover.

OB1	10s. booklet containing 120×1d. in panes of 6 (No. 060a)		£1200

PROVISIONALS ISSUED AT REEFTON AND USED BY THE POLICE DEPARTMENT

1907 (Jan). Current stamps of 1906, optd "Official", in red manuscript and handstamped with a circular "Greymouth—PAID—3". P 14.

P1	**23**	½d. green	£1300	£1600
P2	**40**	1d. carmine	£1300	£1500
P3	**38**	2d. purple	£1500	£2000
P4	**28**	3d. bistre	£2250	
P5	**31**	6d. pink	£2250	
P6	**34**	1s. orange-red	£3000	
P7	**35**	2s.	£8500	

Only the ½d., 1d. and 2d. are known postally used, cancelled with the Reefton squared circle postmark. The 3d. and 6d. were later cancelled by favour at Wanganui.

LIFE INSURANCE DEPARTMENT

L **1** Lighthouse L **2** Lighthouse

2d. "Z" flaw (R. 1/6, upper right pane)

(Des W. B. Hudson and J. F. Rogers; Eng. A. E. Cousins. Typo Govt Printing Office, Wellington)

1891 (2 Jan)–**98**.

A. W 12c. P 12×11½

L1	L **1**	½d. bright purple	£110	6·00
		a. Mixed perf 12×11 and 12½	†	—
		x. Wmk reversed	†	£190

L2		1d. blue	90·00	4·00
		ax. Wmk reversed	†	£190
		ay. Wmk inverted and reversed	†	£110
		b. Wmk **12b**	£180	28·00
		bx. Wmk reversed	†	£500
L3		2d. brown-red	£170	15·00
		ax. Wmk reversed	†	£160
		b. Wmk **12b**	£190	22·00
L4		3d. deep brown	£325	38·00
L5		6d. green	£400	80·00
L6		1s. rose	£600	£150
L1/6	*Set of 6*		£1500	£250

B. W 12b (1893–98)

(a) P 10 (1893)

L7	L **1**	½d. bright purple	£110	22·00
L8		1d. blue	90·00	1·75
L9		2d. brown-red	£150	3·75
		a. "Z" flaw	—	£110
L7/9	*Set of 3*		£300	25·00

(b) P 11×10

L10	L **1**	½d. bright purple (1896)	£120	28·00
		a. Perf 10×11	£300	£110
L11		1d. blue (1897)	†	90·00
		a. Perf 10×11	£110	14·00

(c) Mixed perfs 10 and 11 (1897)

L12	L **1**	2d. brown-red	£1400	£1000

(d) P 11 (1897–98)

L13	L **1**	½d. bright purple	95·00	4·00
		a. Thin coarse toned paper (1898)	£180	15·00
L14		1d. blue	90·00	75
		a. Thin coarse toned paper (1898)	£190	6·50
		x. Wmk reversed	£275	55·00
		y. Wmk inverted and reversed	£275	60·00
L15		2d. brown-red	£170	3·50
		a. Chocolate	£190	25·00
		b. Thin coarse toned paper (1898)	£300	6·00
		c. "Z" flaw	—	£110
L13/15	*Set of 3*		£300	7·50

1902–04. W **43** (sideways).

(a) P 11

L16	L **1**	½d. bright purple (1903)	£110	14·00
L17		1d. blue (1902)	90·00	3·25
L18		2d. brown-red (1904)	£225	22·00
L16/18	*Set of 3*		£375	35·00

(b) P 14×11

L19	L **1**	½d. bright purple (1903)	£2500	£1500
L20		1d. blue (1904)	£160	14·00

Nos. L16/17 and L20 are known without watermark from the margins of the sheet. Note that the Type W **43** watermark may be found both sideways and sideways inverted.

1905–06. Redrawn, with "V.R." omitted. W **43** (sideways).

(a) P 11

L21	L **2**	2d. brown-red (12.05)	£1500	£130

(b) P 14

L22	L **2**	1d. blue (7.06)	£275	30·00

(c) P 14×11

L23	L **2**	1d. blue (7.06)	£850	£225
		a. Mixed perfs	†	£750

Between January 1907 and the end of 1912 the Life Insurance Department used ordinary Official stamps.

1913 (2 Jan)–**37**. New values and colours. W **43**.

(a) "De La Rue" paper. P 14×15

L24	L **2**	½d. green	22·00	2·50
		a. Yellow-green	22·00	2·50
L25		1d. carmine	20·00	1·25
		a. Carmine-pink	23·00	1·75
L26		1½d. black (1917)	50·00	8·50
L27		1½d. chestnut-brown (1919)	1·50	3·00
L28		2d. bright purple	60·00	35·00
		w. Wmk inverted	†	£350
L29		2d. yellow (1920)	12·00	4·00
L30		3d. yellow-brown	55·00	38·00
L31		6d. carmine-pink	48·00	35·00
L24/31	*Set of 8*		£225	£110

(b) "Cowan" paper

(i) P 14×15

L31a	L **2**	½d. yellow-green (1925)	45·00	4·50
		aw. Wmk inverted	†	—
L31b		1d. carmine-pink (1925)	42·00	3·50
		bw. Wmk inverted	£200	75·00

(ii) P 14

L32	L **2**	½d. yellow-green (1926)	24·00	4·00
		w. Wmk inverted	†	90·00
L33		1d. scarlet (1931)	8·50	2·00
		w. Wmk inverted	£100	50·00
L34		2d. yellow (1937)	7·00	13·00
		w. Wmk inverted	£100	£130
L35		3d. brown-lake (1931)	14·00	24·00
		a. "HREE" for "THREE" (R. 7/11)	£375	
L36		6d. pink (1925)	55·00	60·00
L32/6	*Set of 5*		95·00	90·00

(c) "Wiggins Teape" paper. P 14×15

L36a	L **2**	½d. yellow-green (3.37)	8·00	12·00
L36b		1d. scarlet (3.37)	22·00	3·25
L36c		6d. pink (7.37)	35·00	40·00
L36a/c	*Set of 3*		60·00	50·00

For descriptions of the various types of paper, see after No. 385. In the 1½d. the word "POSTAGE" is in both the side-labels instead of at left only.

1944–47. W **98**. P 14×15.

L37	L **2**	½d. yellow-green (7.47)	8·50	9·00
L38		1d. scarlet (6.44)	3·25	2·00
L39		2d. yellow (1946)	17·00	38·00
L40		3d. brown-lake (10.46)	32·00	40·00
		a. "HREE" for "THREE" (R. 7/11)	£400	
L41		6d. pink (7.47)	20·00	50·00
L37/41	*Set of 5*		70·00	£120

L **3** Castlepoint lighthouse   L **4** Taiaroa lighthouse

L **5** Cape Palliser lighthouse

L **6** Cape Campbell   L **7** Eddystone   L **8** Stephens
lighthouse   lighthouse   Island lighthouse

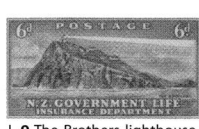

L **9** The Brothers lighthouse   L **10** Cape Brett lighthouse

(Des J. Berry. Recess B.W.).

1947 (1 Aug)–**65**. Type L **3/10**. W **98** (sideways inverted on 1d., 2d., sideways on 2½d.). P 13½.

L42	L **3**	½d. grey-green and orange-red	1·75	70
L43	L **4**	1d. olive-green and pale blue	1·75	1·25
L44	L **5**	2d. deep blue and grey-black	3·75	1·00
L45	L **6**	2½d. black and bright blue (*white opaque paper*) (4.11.63)	9·50	13·00
L46	L **7**	3d. mauve and pale blue	4·50	1·25
L47	L **8**	4d. brown and yellow-orange	4·25	1·75
		a. Wmk sideways (*white opaque paper*) (13.10.65)	3·00	14·00
L48	L **9**	6d. chocolate and blue	4·50	2·75
L49	L **10**	1s. red-brown and blue	5·00	4·00
L42/49	*Set of 8*		30·00	23·00

(L **11**)   (L **12**)

1967 (10 July)–**68**. Decimal currency. Stamps of 1947–65, surch as Type L **12** or L **11** (2c.).

L50		1c. on 1d. (No. L43)	1·75	4·25
		a. Wmk upright (*white opaque paper*) (10.5.68)	1·00	7·00
L51		2c. on 2½d. (No. L45)	7·00	14·00
L52		2½c. on 3d. (No. L46)	1·25	4·00
		a. Horiz pair, one without surcharge	£4250	
		b. Wmk sideways (*white opaque paper*) (4.68?)	1·90	4·75
L53		3c. on 4d. (No. L47a)	2·75	5·00
		w. Wmk sideways inverted	£1600	£750
L54		5c. on 6d. (No. L48)	75	6·50
		a. White opaque paper	1·00	6·50
L55		10c. on 1s. (No. L49)	1·00	8·00
		a. Wmk sideways (*white opaque paper*)	75	4·00
		aw. Wmk sideways inverted	†	£475
L50/5a	*Set of 6*		12·00	32·00

See note *re* white paper below No. 736.

L **13** Moeraki Point   L **14** Puysegur Point lighthouse
lighthouse

L **14a** Baring Head   L **14b** Cape Egmont lighthouse
lighthouse

L **14c** East Cape   L **14d** Farewell Spit   L **15** Dog Island lighthouse

(Des J. Berry. Litho B.W.)

1969 (27 Mar)–**76**. Types L **13/15**. No wmk. Chalk-surfaced paper (8, 10c.), ordinary paper (others). P 14 (8, 10c.) or 13½ (others).

L56	L **13**	½c. greenish yellow, red and deep blue	65	1·50
L57	L **14**	2½c. ultramarine, green and pale buff	50	1·00
L58	L **14a**	3c. reddish brown and yellow	50	60
		a. Chalk-surfaced paper (1974)	50	2·75
L59	L **14b**	4c. light new blue, yellowish green and apple-green	50	75
		a. Chalk-surfaced paper (1975)	50	2·25
L60	L **14c**	8c. multicoloured (17.11.76)	40	2·00
L61	L **14d**	10c. multicoloured (17.11.76)	40	2·00
L62	L **15**	15c. black, light yellow and ultramarine	40	1·25
		a. Chalk-surfaced paper (3.75)	20·00	22·00
		ab. Perf 14 (24.12.76)	90	3·50
L56/62		Set of 7	3·00	8·00

The ordinary paper stamps have shiny gum and fluoresce brightly under UV light. The chalk-surfaced paper stamps have matt, PVA gum and the front of the stamps give a dull reaction under UV light.

POSTAL FISCAL STAMPS

As from 1 April 1882 fiscal stamps were authorised for postal use and conversely postage stamps became valid for fiscal use. Stamps in the designs of 1867 with "STAMP DUTY" above the Queen's head were withdrawn and although some passed through the mail quite legitimately they were mainly "philatelic" and we no longer list them. The issue which was specifically authorised in 1882 was the one which had originally been put on sale for fiscal use in 1880.

There is strong evidence that the authorities used up existing low value revenue stamps for postage, delaying the general release of the new "Postage and Revenue" low values (T **14**, **15** and **18-22**) to achieve this. Used prices for such stamps are for examples with 1882-3 postal cancellations.

Although all fiscal stamps were legally valid for postage, only values between 2s. and £1 were stocked at ordinary post offices. Other values could only be obtained by request from the GPO, Wellington or from offices of the Stamp Duties Department. From 1884 these stamps were also supplied to major telegraph offices in values between £1 and £10, where they were cancelled with postal datestamps until specific 'Telegraph office' cancellers were provided in the late 1890s. Later the Arms types above £1 could also be obtained from the head post offices in Auckland, Christchurch, Dunedin and also a branch post office at Christchurch North where there was a local demand for them.

It seems sensible to list under Postal Fiscals the Queen Victoria stamps up to the £1 value and the Arms types up to the £5 because by 1931 the higher values were genuinely needed for postal purposes. The £10 was occasionally used on insured airmail parcels and is therefore also listed.

Although 2s. and 5s. values were included in the 1898 pictorial issue, it was the general practice for the Postal Department to limit the postage issues to 1s. until 1926 when the 2s. and 3s. appeared. These were then dropped from the fiscal issues and when in turn the 5s. and 10s. were introduced in 1953 and the £1 in 1960 no further printings of these values occurred in the fiscal series.

FORGED POSTMARKS. Our prices are for stamps with genuine postal cancellations. Beware of forged postmarks on stamps from which fiscal cancellations have been cleaned off.

Many small post offices acted as agents for government departments and it was the practice to use ordinary postal date-stamps on stamps used fiscally, so that when they are removed from documents they are indistinguishable from postally used specimens unless impressed with the embossed seal of the Stamp Duties Department.

Date-stamps very similar to postal date-stamps were sometimes supplied to offices of the Stamp Duties Department and it is not clear when this practice ceased. Prior to the Arms types the only sure proof of the postal use of off-cover fiscal stamps is when they bear a distinctive duplex, registered or parcel post cancellation, but beware of forgeries of the first two.

F **1**   F **2**   F **3**

(Die eng W. R. Bock. Typo Govt Ptg Office)

1882 (Feb). W **12a**. P 12×11½.

F1	F **1**	1d. lilac	£1200	£600
F2		1d. blue	£275	45·00
		w. Wmk inverted	—	£250

The 1d. fiscal was specifically authorised for postal use in February 1882 owing to a shortage of the 1d. Type **5** and pending the introduction of the 1d. Type **14** on 1 April.

The 1d. lilac fiscal had been replaced by the 1d. blue in 1878 but postally used copies with 1882 duplex postmarks are known although most postally used examples are dated from 1890 and these must have been philatelic.

1882 (early). W **12a**. P 12×11½.

F3	F **2**	1s. grey-green		
F4	F **3**	1s. grey-green and red		
F4a		2s. rose and blue		

Examples of these are known postally used in 1882 and although not specifically authorised for postal use it is believed that their use was permitted where there was a shortage of the appropriate postage value.

WMK TYPE F 5. The balance of the paper employed for the 1867 issue was used for early printings of Type F **4** introduced in 1880 before changing over to the "N Z" and Star watermark. The values we list with this watermark are known with 1882–83 postal date stamps. Others have later dates and are considered to be philatelic but should they be found with 1882–83 postal dates we would be prepared to add them to the list.

F **4**   F **5**

The 12s.6d. value has the head in an oval (as Type **10**), and the 15s. and £1 values have it in a broken circle (as Type **7**).

(Dies eng W.R. Bock. Typo Govt Ptg Office)

1882 (1 Apr)–**1930**. Type F **4** and similar types. "De La Rue" paper.

*A. W **12a** (6 mm)*

(a) P 12 (1882)

F5	4d. orange-red (Wmk F **5**)	—	£425
F6	6d. lake-brown	—	£325
	a. Wmk F **5**	—	£850
F7	8d. green (Wmk F **5**)	—	£850
F8	1s. pink	—	£400
	a. Wmk F **5**		
F9	2s. blue	£140	9·50
	a. Wmk F **5**		
F10	2s.6d. grey-brown	£190	9·50
	a. Wmk F **5**		
F11	3s. mauve	£250	13·00
F12	4s. brown-rose	£300	20·00
	a. Wmk F **5**		
F13	5s. green	£350	19·00
	a. Yellow-green	£350	19·00
F14	6s. rose	£375	50·00
	a. Wmk F **5**		
F15	7s. ultramarine	£400	90·00
	a. Wmk F **5**		
F16	7s.6d. bronze-grey	£1500	£300
F17	8s. deep blue	£475	£110
	a. Wmk F **5**		
F18	9s. orange	£550	£120
F19	10s. brown-red	£350	30·00
	a. Wmk F **5**		
F20	15s. green	£1100	£250
F21	£1 rose-pink	£550	£90

(b) P 12½ (1886)

F22	2s. blue	£140	9·50
F23	2s.6d. grey-brown	£190	9·50
F24	3s. mauve	£275	13·00
F25	4s. purple-claret	£300	20·00
	a. Brown-rose	£300	20·00
F26	5s. green	£350	19·00
	a. Yellow-green	£350	19·00
F27	6s. rose	£425	50·00
F28	7s. ultramarine	£425	90·00
F29	8s. deep blue	£475	£110
F30	9s. orange	£550	£120
F31	10s. brown-red	£350	30·00
F32	15s. green	£1100	£250
F33	£1 rose-pink	£550	£90

*B. W **12b** (7 mm). P 12½ (1888)*

F34	2s. blue	£140	9·50
F35	2s.6d. grey-brown	£190	9·50
F36	3s. mauve	£250	13·00
F37	4s. brown-rose	£275	20·00
	a. Brown-red	£275	20·00
F38	5s. green	£325	19·00
	a. Yellow-green	£325	19·00
F39	6s. rose	£425	50·00
F40	7s. ultramarine	£450	90·00
F41	7s.6d. bronze-grey	£1500	£300
F42	8s. deep blue	£475	£110
F43	9s. orange	£550	£120
F44	10s. brown-red	£350	29·00
	a. Maroon	£350	29·00
F45	£1 pink	£550	£90

*C. W **12c** (4 mm). P 12½ (1890)*

F46	2s. blue	£200	22·00
F46a	2s.6d. grey-brown	£300	24·00
F47	3s. mauve	£400	55·00
F48	4s. brown-red	£350	35·00
F49	5s. green	£375	24·00
F50	6s. rose	£475	60·00
F51	7s. ultramarine	£550	£110
F52	8s. deep blue	£550	£130
F53	9s. orange	£600	£150
F54	10s. brown-red	£450	40·00
F55	15s. green	£1400	£300

*D. Continuation of W **12b**. P 11 (1895–1901)*

F56	2s. blue	90·00	9·50
F57	2s.6d. grey-brown	£180	9·00
	a. Inscr "COUNTERPART" (1901)*	£200	£300
F58	3s. mauve	£225	12·00
F59	4s. brown-red	£275	18·00
F60	5s. yellow-green	£325	19·00
F61	6s. rose	£375	50·00
F62	7s. pale blue	£425	£90
F63	7s.6d. bronze-grey	£1500	£300
F64	8s. deep blue	£475	£100
F65	9s. orange	£550	£140
	a. Imperf between (horiz pair)	£3500	
F66	10s. brown-red	£350	28·00
	a. Maroon	£350	28·00
F67	15s. green	£1100	£250
F68	£1 rose-pink	£550	£90

*The plate normally printed in yellow and inscribed "COUNTERPART" just above the bottom value panel, was for use on the counterparts of documents but was issued in error in the colour of the normal fiscal stamp and accepted for use.

---

*E. W **43** (sideways)*

(i) Unsurfaced "Cowan" paper

(a) P 11 (1903)

F69	2s.6d. grey-brown	£225	9·00
F70	3s. mauve	£275	13·00
F71	4s. orange-red	£275	18·00
F72	6s. rose	£350	50·00
F73	7s. pale blue	£450	95·00
F74	8s. deep blue	£475	£100
F75	10s. brown-red	£350	30·00
	a. Maroon	£350	30·00
F76	15s. green	£1200	£250
F77	£1 rose-pink	£500	90·00

(b) P 14 (1906)

F78	2s.6d. grey-brown	£150	9·00
F79	3s. mauve	£200	12·00
F80	4s. orange-red	£200	16·00
F81	5s. yellow-green	£225	16·00
F82	6s. rose	£325	50·00
F83	7s. pale blue	£375	90·00
F84	7s.6d. bronze-grey	£1400	£275
F85	8s. deep blue	£450	£100
F86	9s. orange	£475	£110
F87	10s. maroon	£325	29·00
F88	15s. green	£1200	£250
F89	£1 rose-pink	£475	90·00

(c) P 14½×14, comb (clean-cut) (1907)

F90	2s. blue	90·00	8·50
F91	2s.6d. grey-brown	£180	9·00
F92	3s. mauve	£225	13·00
F93	4s. orange-red	£225	17·00
F94	6s. rose	£350	50·00
F95	10s. maroon	£325	28·00
F96	15s. green	£1200	£250
F97	£1 rose-pink	£475	90·00

(ii) Chalk-surfaced "De La Rue" paper

(a) P 14 (1913)

F98	2s. blue	70·00	8·00
	a. Imperf horiz (vert pair)	£2000	
F99	2s.6d. grey-brown	85·00	9·00
F100	3s. purple	£170	12·00
F101	4s. orange-red	£170	14·00
F102	5s. yellow-green	£180	15·00
F103	6s. rose	£300	32·00
F104	7s. pale blue	£325	55·00
F105	7s.6d. bronze-grey	£1500	£300
F106	8s. deep blue	£425	65·00
F107	9s. orange	£500	£110
F108	10s. maroon	£325	27·00
F109	15s. green	£1200	£250
F110	£1 rose-carmine	£450	90·00

(b) P 14½×14, comb (1913–21)

F111	2s. deep blue	70·00	8·00
F112	2s.6d. grey-brown	85·00	9·00
F113	3s. purple	£170	11·00
F114	4s. orange-red	£170	14·00
F115	5s. yellow-green	£180	15·00
F116	6s. rose	£300	32·00
F117	7s. pale blue	£325	55·00
F118	8s. deep blue	£425	65·00
F119	9s. orange	£475	£110
F120	10s. maroon	£325	27·00
F121	12s.6d. deep plum (1921)	£18000	£7500
F122	15s. green	£1200	£250
F123	£1 rose-carmine	£450	90·00

The "De La Rue" paper has a smooth finish and has toned gum which is strongly resistant to soaking.

(iii) Chalk-surfaced "Jones" paper. P 14½×14, comb (1924)

F124	2s. deep blue	£100	11·00
F125	2s.6d. deep grey-brown	£110	12·00
F126	3s. purple	£225	15·00
F127	5s. yellow-green	£225	19·00
F128	10s. brown-red	£375	30·00
F129	12s.6d. deep purple	£18000	£7500
F130	15s. green	£1000	£275

The "Jones" paper has a coarser texture, is poorly surfaced and the ink tends to peel. The outline of the watermark commonly shows on the surface of the stamp. The gum is colourless or only slightly toned and washes off readily.

(iv) Thick, opaque, chalk-surfaced "Cowan" paper. P 14½×14, comb (1925–30)

F131	2s. blue	75·00	9·50
F132	2s.6d. deep grey-brown	90·00	10·00
F133	3s. mauve	£225	19·00
F134	4s. orange-red	£170	19·00
F135	5s. yellow-green	£180	21·00
	x. Wmk reversed (1927)	£275	42·00
F136	6s. rose	£300	38·00
F137	7s. pale blue	£325	60·00
F138	8s. deep blue	£500	70·00
	a. Blue (1930)	£550	
F139	10s. brown-red	£325	32·00
	x. Wmk reversed (1927)	£400	£275
F140	12s.6d. blackish purple	£18000	£7500
F141	15s. green	£1100	£275
F142	£1 rose-pink	£425	95·00

The "Cowan" paper is white and opaque and the watermark, which is usually smaller than in the "Jones" paper, is often barely visible.

(v) Thin, hard, chalk-surfaced "Wiggins Teape" paper. P 14½×14, comb (1926)

F143	4s. orange-red	£190	26·00
F144	£1 rose-pink	£475	£170

The "Wiggins Teape" paper has a horizontal mesh, in relation to the design, with narrow watermark, whereas other chalk-surfaced papers with this perforation have a vertical mesh and wider watermark.

F **6**   (F **7**)   35/-

(Des H. L. Richardson. Typo Govt Ptg Office)

1931–40. As Type F **6** (various frames). W **43**. P 14.

(i) Thick, opaque, chalk-surfaced "Cowan" paper, with horizontal mesh (1931–35)

F145	1s.3d. lemon (4.31)	6·50	50·00
F146	1s.3d. orange-yellow	18·00	21·00
F147	2s.6d. deep brown	16·00	4·50
F148	4s. red	15·00	12·00
F149	5s. green	42·00	16·00
F150	6s. carmine-rose	32·00	16·00
F151	7s. blue	28·00	27·00
F152	7s6d. olive-grey	85·00	£110
F153	8s. slate-violet	32·00	35·00
F154	9s. brown-orange	32·00	29·00
F155	10s. carmine-lake	24·00	10·00
F156	12s.6d. deep plum (9.35)	£170	£170
F157	15s. sage-green	95·00	£100
F158	£1 pink	85·00	19·00
F159	25s. greenish blue	£700	£950
F160	30s. brown (1935)	£425	£250
F161	35s. orange-yellow	£5500	£6500
F162	£2 bright purple	£425	85·00
F163	£2 10s. red	£500	£650
F164	£3 green	£700	£350
F165	£3 10s. rose (1935)	£2250	£2750
F166	£4 light blue (1935)	£600	£250
F167	£4 10s. deep olive-grey (1935)	£2000	£2250
F168	£5 indigo-blue	£500	£150
F168*a*	£10 deep blue	£1600	£500

(ii) Thin, hard 'Wiggins Teape' paper with vertical mesh (1936–40)

(a) Chalk-surfaced (1936–39)

F169	1s.3d. pale orange-yellow	50·00	5·50
F170	2s.6d. dull brown	£130	4·00
F171	4s. pale red-brown	£170	22·00
F172	5s. green	£170	7·00
	w. Wmk inverted	—	£750
F173	6s. carmine-rose	£180	55·00
F174	7s. pale blue	£300	60·00
F175	8s. slate-violet	£325	85·00
F176	9s. brown-orange	£375	£120
F177	10s. pale carmine-lake	£300	7·00
F178	15s. sage-green	£475	90·00
F179	£1 pink	£300	42·00
F180	30s. brown (1.39)	£850	£275
F181	35s. orange-yellow	£8000	£7500
F182	£2 bright purple (1937)	£1300	£170
	w. Wmk inverted		£3500
F183	£3 green (1937)	£1700	£500
F184	£5 indigo-blue (1937)	£2250	£425

(b) Unsurfaced (1940)

F185	7s.6d. olive-grey	£250	90·00

Not all values listed above were stocked at ordinary post offices as some of them were primarily required for fiscal purposes but all were valid for postage.

1939. No. F161 and F168*a* surch as Type F **7**.

F186	35/- on 35s. orange-yellow	£900	£400
F186*a*	£10 on £10 deep blue	£2250	£500
	aw. Wmk inverted		

Because the 35s. orange-yellow could so easily be confused with the 1s.3d. and the £10 with the £5 in similar colours, they were surcharged.

1940 (June). New values surch as Type F **7**. "Wiggins Teape" chalk-surfaced paper. W **43**. P 14.

F187	3/6 on 3s.6d. grey-green	80·00	40·00
F188	5/6 on 5s.6d. lilac	£140	75·00
F189	11/- on 11s. yellow	£275	£225
F190	22/- on 22s. scarlet	£700	£500
F187/90 *Set of 4*		£1100	£750

These values were primarily needed for fiscal use.

1940–58. As Type F **6** (various frames). W **98**. P 14.

(i) "Wiggins Teape" chalk-surfaced paper with vertical mesh (1940–56)

F191	1s.3d. orange-yellow	25·00	4·25
	w. Wmk inverted	—	£350
F192	1s.3d. yellow and black (wmk inverted) (14.6.55)	9·00	4·50
	aw. Wmk upright (9.9.55)	35·00	35·00
	b. Error. Yellow and blue (wmk inverted) (7.56)	4·75	4·50
F193	2s.6d. deep brown	17·00	1·40
	w. Wmk inverted (3.49)	19·00	1·50
F194	4s. red-brown	38·00	2·00
	w. Wmk inverted (3.49)	45·00	2·75
F195	5s. green	24·00	1·25
	w. Wmk inverted (1.5.50)	30·00	1·25
F196	6s. carmine-rose	55·00	3·75
	w. Wmk inverted (1948)	65·00	3·75
F197	7s. pale blue	55·00	6·00
F198	7s.6d. olive-grey (wmk inverted) (21.12.50)	90·00	£100
F199	8s. slate-violet	95·00	17·00
	w. Wmk inverted (6.12.50)	£110	22·00
F200	9s. brown-orange (1.46)	50·00	60·00
	w. Wmk inverted (9.1.51)	£100	50·00
F201	10s. carmine-lake	60·00	2·50
	w. Wmk inverted (4.50)	70·00	2·50
F202	15s. sage-green	90·00	26·00
	w. Wmk inverted (8.12.50)	£110	26·00
F203	£1 pink	32·00	3·75
	w. Wmk inverted (1.2.50)	65·00	5·50
F204	25s. greenish blue (1946)	£800	£800
	w. Wmk inverted (7.53)	£1000	£1000
F205	30s. brown (1946)	£475	£190
	w. Wmk inverted (9.49)	£400	£170
F206	£2 bright purple (1946)	£225	32·00
	w. Wmk inverted (17.6.52)	£200	22·00
F207	£2 10s. red (wmk inverted) (9.8.51)	£475	£500
F208	£3 green (1946)	£300	60·00
	w. Wmk inverted (17.6.52)	£350	65·00
F209	£3 10s. rose (11.48)	£3500	£2250
	w. Wmk inverted (5.52)	£3500	£2250
F210	£4 light blue (wmk inverted) (12.2.52)	£350	£200
	w. Wmk upright	†	£1700
F211	£5 indigo-blue	£700	£100
	w. Wmk inverted (11.9.50)	£400	70·00
F191/211 *Set of 21*		£6250	£3750

3s.6d.

Type I. Broad serifed capitals

Type II. Taller capitals, without serifs

Surcharged as Type F **7**.

F212	3/6 on 3s.6d. grey-green (I) (1942)	21·00	8·50
	w. Wmk inverted (12.10.50)	48·00	23·00
F213	3/6 on 3s.6d. grey-green (II) (6.53)	17·00	50·00
	w. Wmk inverted (6.53)	55·00	55·00
F214	5/6 on 5s.6d. lilac (1944)	70·00	28·00
	w. Wmk inverted (13.9.50)	80·00	19·00
F215	11/- on 11s. yellow (1942)	£100	48·00
F216	22/- on 22s. scarlet (1945)	£450	£200
	aw. Wmk inverted (1.3.50)	£475	£225
F216*b*	£10 on £10 deep blue	£1700	£450
	bw. Wmk inverted	£1700	£450
F212/16 *Set of 5*		£600	£275

(ii) P 14×13½. "Wiggins Teape" unsurfaced paper with horizontal mesh (1956–58)

F217	1s.3d. yellow and black (11.56)	4·75	5·00
	w. Wmk inverted	48·00	48·00
F218	£1 pink (20.10.58)	40·00	12·00

No. F192b had the inscription printed in blue in error but as many as 378,000 were printed.

From 1949–53 inferior paper had to be used and for technical reasons it was necessary to feed the paper into the machine in a certain way which resulted in whole printings with the watermark inverted for most values.

F **8**

1967 (10 July)–**84.** Decimal currency. W **98** (sideways inverted). Unsurfaced paper. P 14 (line).

F219	F **8**	$4 deep reddish violet	7·00	7·00
		a. Perf 14 (comb) (wmk sideways) (17.9.68)	2·00	1·50
		aw. Wmk sideways inverted (6.7.84)	3·25	11·00
F220		$6 emerald	10·00	21·00
		a. Perf 14 (comb) (wmk sideways) (17.9.68)	2·50	3·50
		aw. Wmk sideways inverted (6.7.84)	3·75	13·00
F221		$8 light greenish blue	26·00	35·00
		a. Perf 14 (comb) (wmk sideways) (20.6.68)	3·00	4·50
		aw. Wmk sideways inverted (6.7.84)		
F222		$10 deep ultramarine	24·00	20·00
		a. Perf 14 (comb) (wmk sideways) (20.6.68)	3·00	3·50
		aw. Wmk sideways inverted (6.7.84)	25·00	30·00
F219/22 *Set of 4*			60·00	75·00
F219a/22a *Set of 4*			9·50	11·50

The original printings were line perforated on paper with the watermark sideways inverted (top of star pointing to left, *when viewed from the back*). In 1968 the stamps appeared comb perforated with the watermark sideways (top of star to right). A further comb perforated printing in July 1984 showed the sideways inverted watermark.

ANTARCTIC EXPEDITIONS

VICTORIA LAND

These issues were made under authority of the New Zealand Postal Department and, while not strictly necessary, they actually franked correspondence to New Zealand. They were sold to the public at a premium.

(A **1**)

1908 (15 Jan). Shackleton Expedition. T **42** of New Zealand (P 14), optd with Type A **1**, by Coulls, Culling and Co., Wellington.

A1		1d. rose-carmine (No. 356 Royle) (G.)	£475	42·00
		a. Opt double	†	£1600
A1*b*		1d. rose-carmine (No. 352c Waterlow) (G.)	£1600	£850

Nos. A1/1*b* were used on board the expedition ship, *Nimrod*, and at the Cape Royds base in McMurdo Sound. Due to adverse conditions Shackleton landed in Victoria Land rather than King Edward VII Land, the intended destination.

VICTORIA LAND.   VICTORIA LAND.
(A **2**)   (A **3**)

1911 (9 Feb)–**13.** Scott Expedition. Stamps of New Zealand optd with Types A **2** (½d.) or A **3** (1d.) by Govt Printer, Wellington.

A2	**51**	½d. deep green (No. 387*aa*) (18.1.13)	£750	£850
A3	**53**	1d. carmine (No. 405)	55·00	£120
		a. No stop after "LAND" (R. 7/5)	£425	£850
		b. "Q" flaw	£650	

Nos. A2/3 were used at the Cape Evans base on McMurdo Sound or on the *Terra Nova*.

ROSS DEPENDENCY

This comprises a sector of the Antarctic continent and a number of islands. It was claimed by Great Britain on 30 July 1923 and soon afterward put under the jurisdiction of New Zealand.

1 HMS *Erebus*

2 Shackleton and Scott

3 Map of Ross Dependency and New Zealand   **4** Queen Elizabeth II

(Des E. M. Taylor (3d.), L. C. Mitchell (4d.), R. Smith (8d.), J. Berry (1s.6d.). Recess D.L.R.)

1957 (11 Jan). W **98** of New Zealand (Mult N Z and Star). P 13 (1s.6d.) or 14 (others).

1	**1**	3d. indigo	1·00	60
2	**2**	4d. carmine-red	1·00	60
3	**3**	8d. bright carmine-red and ultramarine	1·00	60
		a. Bright carmine-red and blue	4·25	3·75
4	**4**	1s.6d. slate-purple	1·00	60
1/4 *Set of 4*			3·50	2·25

(New Currency. 100 cents = 1 New Zealand dollar)

5 HMS *Erebus*

1967 (10 July). Decimal currency. As Nos. 1/4 but with values inscr in decimal currency as T **5**. Chalky paper (except 15c.). W **98** of New Zealand (sideways on 7c.). P 13 (15c.) or 14 (others).

5	**5**	2c. indigo	9·00	8·00
		a. Deep blue	18·00	9·50
6	**2**	3c. carmine-red	2·50	4·25
		w. Wmk inverted	75·00	
7	**3**	7c. bright carmine-red and ultramarine	2·75	5·00
8	**4**	15c. slate-purple	2·00	10·00
		w. Wmk inverted	£100	
5/8 *Set of 4*			14·50	25·00

TOKELAU ISLANDS

Formerly known as the Union Islands, and administered as part of the Gilbert & Ellice Islands Colony, Tokelau was transferred to New Zealand on 4 November 1925 and administered with Western Samoa. The Islands were finally incorporated in New Zealand on 1 January 1949 and became a dependency. The name Tokelau was officially adopted on 7 May 1946.

Stamps of GILBERT AND ELLICE ISLANDS were used in Tokelau from Febuary 1911 until June 1926 when they were replaced by those of SAMOA. These were current until 1948.

The post office on Atafu opened in 1911, but the cancellations for the other two islands, Fakaofo and Nukunono, did not appear until 1926.

NEW ZEALAND ADMINISTRATION

1 Atafu Village and Map   **2** Nukunono hut and map

3 Fakaofo village and map

(Des J. Berry from photographs by T. T. C. Humphrey. Recess B.W.)

1948 (22 June). T **1**/3. Wmk T **98** of New Zealand (Mult N Z and Star). P 13½.

1	**1**	½d. red-brown and purple	15	75
2	**2**	1d. chestnut and green	15	50
		w. Wmk inverted	£275	
3	**3**	2d. green and ultramarine	15	50
1/3 Set of 3			40	1·60

Covers are known postmarked 16 June 1948, but this was in error for 16 July.

1953 (16 June*). Coronation. As No. 715 of New Zealand, but inscr "TOKELAU ISLANDS".

4	**164**	3d. brown	2·00	1·75

*This is the date of issue in Tokelau. The stamps were released in New Zealand on 25 May.

ONE SHILLING

TOKELAU ISLANDS
(4)   (5)

1956 (27 Mar). No. 1 surch with T **4** by Govt Printer, Wellington.

5	**1**	1s. on ½d. red-brown and purple	75	1·25

1966 (8 Nov). Postal fiscal stamps of New Zealand (Type F **6**), but without value, surch as T **5** by Govt Printer, Wellington. W **98** of New Zealand. P 14.

6		6d. light blue	25	80
7		8d. light emerald	25	80
8		2s. light pink	30	80
6/8 Set of 3			70	2·25

(New Currency. 100 cents = 1 New Zealand dollar)

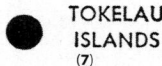

1c
(6)

5c
TOKELAU ISLANDS
(7)

1967 (4 Sept*)–68. Decimal currency.

(a) Nos. 1/3 surch in decimal currency as T **6** by Govt Printer, Wellington

9		1c. on 1d.	20	1·00
10		2c. on 2d.	30	1·50
11		10c. on ½d.	70	2·00

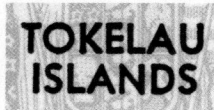

R. 7/1

TOKELAU ISLANDS

Normal

On R. 7/1 of Nos. 12/15 the words "TOKELAU" and "ISLANDS" are ½ mm apart instead of 1½ mm.

(b) Postal Fiscal stamps of New Zealand (Type F **6**), but without value, surch as T **7** by Govt Printer, Wellington. W **98** of New Zealand (sideways). P 14 (line or comb)

12	F **6**	3c. reddish lilac	30	20
		a. Narrow setting	10·00	10·00
13		5c. light blue	30	20
		a. Narrow setting	10·00	10·00
		b. *Pale blue* (second setting) (18.9.68)	2·00	2·50
14		7c. light emerald	30	20
		a. Narrow setting	10·00	10·00
15		20c. light pink	30	30
		a. Narrow setting	10·00	10·00
9/15 Set of 7			2·25	4·75

*This is the date of issue in Tokelau. The stamps were released in New Zealand on 10 July.

In the second setting of the 5c. the words "TOKELAU" and "ISLANDS" are in thinner letters and almost 2 mm apart.

1877
Tokelau Islands became a British Protectorate
TOKELAU ISLANDS

8 British Protectorate (1877)

(Des New Zealand P.O. artists from suggestions by Tokelau Administration. Litho B.W.)

1969 (8 Aug). History of Tokelau. T **8** and similar horiz designs. W **98** of New Zealand. P 13×12½.

16		5c. ultramarine, yellow and black	15	10
17		10c. vermilion, yellow and black	15	10
18		15c. green, yellow and black	20	15
19		20c. yellow-brown, yellow and black	25	15
16/19 Set of 4			65	45

Designs:—10c. Annexed to Gilbert and Ellice Islands, 1916: 15c. New Zealand Administration, 1925: 20c. New Zealand Territory, 1948.

1969 (14 Nov*). Christmas. As T **301** of New Zealand, but inscr "TOKELAU ISLANDS". W **98** of New Zealand. P 13½×14½.

20		2c. multicoloured	10	15

*This is the date of issue in Tokelau. The stamps were released in New Zealand on 1 October.

1970 (15 Nov*). Christmas. As T **314** of New Zealand, but inscr "TOKELAU ISLANDS". P 12½.

21		2c. multicoloured	10	20

*This is the date of issue in Tokelau. The stamps were released in New Zealand on 1 October.

NIUE

Niue became a British Protectorate on 20 April 1900 and was transferred to New Zealand control on 11 June 1901. There was considerable local resentment at attempts to incorporate Niue into the Cook Islands and, in consequence, the island was recognised as a separate New Zealand dependency from 1902.

PRICES FOR STAMPS ON COVER TO 1945

No. 1	from × 3
Nos. 2/5	from × 8
Nos. 6/7	—
Nos. 8/9	from × 30
Nos. 10/12	—
Nos. 13/31	from × 3
Nos. 32/7c	—
Nos. 38/47	from × 5
Nos. 48/9	—
No. 50	from × 15
Nos. 51/4	—
Nos. 55/61	from × 8
Nos. 62/8	from × 12
Nos. 69/71	from × 3
Nos. 72/4	from × 10
Nos. 75/8	from × 8
Nos. 79/88	—
Nos. 89/97	from × 2

NEW ZEALAND DEPENDENCY

Stamps of New Zealand overprinted

NIUE
(1)

1902 (4 Jan). Handstamped with T **1** in green or bluish green. Pirie paper. Wmk double-lined "N Z" and Star, W **38** of New Zealand. P 11.

1		1d. carmine	£300	£300

A few overprints were made with a *greenish violet* ink. These occurred only in the first vertical row and part of the second row of the first sheet overprinted owing to violet ink having been applied to the pad (*Price* £1500 *un*).

NIUE.
½ PENI.
(2)

NIUE.
TAHA PENI.
(3) 1d.

NIUE.
2½ PENI.
(4)

1902 (4 Apr). Type-set surcharges. T **2**, **3**, and **4**.

(i) Pirie paper. No wmk. P 11

2	**27**	2½d. blue (R.)	1·50	4·25
		a. No stop after "PENI"	28·00	55·00
		b. Surch double	£2500	

*(ii) Basted Mills paper. Wmk double-lined "N Z" and Star, W **38** of New Zealand*

(a) P 14

3	**23**	½d. green (R.)	5·50	7·00
		a. Spaced "U" and "E" (R. 3/3, 3/6, 8/3, 8/6)	23·00	35·00
		b. Surch inverted	£325	£600
		c. Surch double	£1200	
4	**42**	1d. carmine (B.)	50·00	55·00
		a. Spaced "U" and "E" (R. 3/3, 3/6, 8/6)	£190	£225
		b. No stop after "PENI" (R. 9/3)	£500	£600
		c. Varieties a. and b. on same stamp (R. 8/3)	£500	£600

(b) P 11×14

5	**42**	1d. carmine (B.)	1·75	4·00
		b. Spaced "U" and "E" (R. 3/3, 3/6, 8/6)	14·00	27·00
		c. No stop after "PENI" (R. 9/3)	50·00	70·00
		d. Varieties b. and c. on same stamp (R. 8/3)	50·00	70·00

(c) Mixed perfs

6	**23**	½d. green (R.)	£1900	
7	**42**	1d. carmine (B.)	£1000	

1902 (2 May). Type-set surcharges, T **2**, **3**. Cowan paper. Wmk single-lined "N Z" and Star, W **43** of New Zealand.

(a) P 14

8	**23**	½d. green (R.)	1·50	1·50
		a. Spaced "U" and "E" (R. 3/3, 3/6, 8/3, 8/6)	9·00	13·00
9	**42**	1d. carmine (B.)	60	1·00
		a. Surch double	£1800	£2000
		b. Spaced "U" and "E" (R. 3/3, 3/6, 8/6)	11·00	20·00
		c. No stop after "PENI" (R. 5/3, 7/3, 9/3, 10/3, 10/6)	9·00	17·00
		d. Varieties b. and c. on same stamp (R. 8/3)	42·00	65·00
		e. "I" of "NIUE" omitted (R. 6/5 from end of last ptg)	£1000	

(b) P 14×11

10	**23**	½d. green (R.)		

(c) Mixed perfs

11	**23**	½d. green (R.)	£1800	
12	**42**	1d. carmine (B.)	£200	£250
		a. Spaced "U" and "E" (R. 3/3, 3/6, 8/3, 8/6)	£600	
		b. No stop after "PENI" (R. 5/3, 7/3, 9/3, 10/3, 10/6)	£550	

NIUE.
(5)

Tolu e Pene.
(6) 3d.

Ono e Pene.
(7) 6d.

Taha e Sileni.
(8) 1s.

1903 (2 July). Optd with name at top, T **5**, and values at foot, T **6**/8, in blue. W **43** of New Zealand (sideways). P 11.

13	**28**	3d. yellow-brown	9·50	5·00
14	**31**	6d. rose-red	15·00	11·00
15	**34**	1s. brown-red ("Tahae" joined)	£650	†
		a. Surch double, one albino	£850	†
16		1s. bright red	40·00	48·00
		a. *Orange-red*	45·00	48·00
13/16 Set of 3			55·00	60·00

No. 15/a with "Tahae" joined as one word comes from the small first printing, which was withdrawn when it was discovered that the absence of a space between "Taha" and "e" gave the meaning "thief" rather than "one". One sheet had been sold in Auckland, but no supplies were ever sent to Niue. Other examples emanate from record sheets retained in New Zealand, later distributed in presentation sets.

NIUE.
½ PENI.
(9)

NIUE.
2½ PENI.
(9a)

NIUE.
(10)

1911 (30 Nov). ½d. surch with T **9**, others optd at top as T **5** and values at foot as T **7**, **8**. W **43** of New Zealand. P 14×15 (½d.) or 14×14½ (others).

17	**51**	½d. green (C.)	50	50
18	**52**	6d. carmine (B.)	2·00	7·00
19		1s. vermilion (B.)	6·50	48·00
17/19 Set of 3			8·00	50·00

1915 (Sept). Surch with T **9a**. W **43** of New Zealand. P 14.

20	**27**	2½d. deep blue (C.)	26·00	55·00

1917 (Aug). 1d. surch as T **3**, 3d. optd as T **5** with value as T **6**. W **43** of New Zealand.

21	**53**	1d. carmine (P 14×15) (Br.)	24·00	5·50
		a. No stop after "PENI" (R. 10/16)	£850	
22	**60**	3d. chocolate (P 14×14½) (B.)	50·00	£100
		a. No stop after "Pene" (R. 10/4)	£850	
		b. Perf 14×13½	65·00	£120
		c. Vert pair, Nos. 22/b	£180	

1917–21. Optd with T **10**. W **43** of New Zealand.

(a) P 14×15

23	**61**	½d. green (R.) (2.20)	70	3·00
24	**53**	1d. carmine (R.) (10.17)	10·00	15·00
25	**61**	1½d. slate (R.) (1.17)	1·00	2·50
26		1½d. orange-brown (R.) (2.19)	70	8·50
27		3d. chocolate (R.) (6.19)	1·60	38·00

(b) P 14×13½

28	**60**	2½d. blue (R.) (10.20)	4·50	18·00
		a. Perf 14×14½	1·25	15·00
		ab. Opt double, one albino	£500	
		b. Vert pair, Nos. 28/a	18·00	70·00
29		3d. chocolate (B.) (10.17)	3·25	2·00
		a. Perf 14×14½	1·25	1·75
		b. Vert pair, Nos. 29/a	22·00	50·00
30		6d. carmine (B.) (8.21)	10·00	24·00
		a. Perf 14×14½	4·75	24·00
		b. Vert pair, Nos. 30/a	32·00	£120
31		1s. vermilion (B.) (10.18)	16·00	38·00
		a. Perf 14×14½	5·50	27·00
		b. Vert pair, Nos. 31/a	45·00	£130
23/31a Set of 9			24·00	£120

1918–29. Postal Fiscal stamps as Type F **4** of New Zealand optd with T **10**. W **43** of New Zealand (sideways).

(i) Chalk-surfaced "De La Rue" paper

(a) P 14

32		5s. yellow-green (R.) (7.18)	£110	£120

(b) P 14½×14, comb

33		2s. deep blue (R.) (9.18)	16·00	32·00
34		2s.6d. grey-brown (B.) (2.23)	24·00	48·00
35		5s. yellow-green (R.) (10.18)	25·00	55·00
36		10s. maroon (B.) (2.23)	£140	£180
37		£1 rose-carmine (B.) (2.23)	£180	£275
33/7 Set of 5			£350	£550

(ii) Thick, opaque, white chalk-surfaced "Cowan" paper. P 14½×14

37a		5s. yellow-green (R.) (10.29)	27·00	65·00
37b		10s. brown-red (B.) (2.27)	95·00	£160
37c		£1 rose-pink (B.) (2.28)	£160	£275
37a/c Set of 3			£250	£450

11 Landing of Captain Cook

12 Landing of Captain Cook

1d. R. 2/8   R. 3/6   R. 5/2

Double derrick flaws

(Des, eng and recess P.B.)

1920 (23 Aug). T **11** and similar designs. No wmk. P 14.

38		½d. black and green	3·75	4·50
39		1d. black and dull carmine	2·00	1·25
	a.	Double derrick flaw (R. 2/8, 3/6 or 5/2)	7·00	7·00
40		1½d. black and red	2·75	18·00
41		3d. black and blue	1·75	16·00
42		6d. red-brown and green	5·00	18·00
43		1s. black and sepia	6·00	18·00
38/43 *Set of 6*			19·00	65·00

Designs as Cook Islands Types **10/14**: Vert—1d. Wharf at Avarua; 1½d. "Capt Cook (Dance)"; 3d. Palm tree. Horiz—6d. Huts at Arorangi; 1s. Avarua Harbour.

Examples of the 6d. with inverted centre were not supplied to the Post Office (*Price, £850, unused*).

1925–27. As Nos. 38/9 and new values. W **43** of New Zealand (sideways on 4d.) P 14.

44		½d. black and green (1927)	3·00	12·00
45		1d. black and deep carmine (1925)	1·75	1·00
	a.	Double derrick flaw (R. 2/8, 3/6 or 5/2)	5·50	4·75
46		2½d. black and blue (10.27)	4·25	15·00
47		4d. black and violet (10.27)	7·50	20·00
44/7 *Set of 4*			15·00	42·00

Designs as Cook Islands Types **16/17**: Vert—2½d. Te Po, Rarotongan chief. Horiz—4d. Harbour, Rarotonga, and Mount Ikurangi.

1927–28. Admiral type of New Zealand optd as T **10**. W **43** of New Zealand. P 14.

(a) "Jones" paper (wmk inverted)

48	**72**	2s. deep blue (2.27) (R.)	15·00	48·00

(b) "Cowan" paper

49	**72**	2s. light blue (R.) (2.28)	18·00	32·00

1931 (1 Apr). No. 40 surch as T **18** of Cook Is.

50		2d. on 1½d. black and red	5·00	1·00

1931 (12 Nov). Postal Fiscal stamps as Type F **6** of New Zealand optd as T **10**. W **43** of New Zealand. Thick, opaque, chalk-surfaced "Cowan" paper. P 14.

51		2s.6d. deep brown (B.)	4·00	11·00
52		5s. green (R.)	35·00	70·00
53		10s. carmine-lake (B.)	35·00	£110
54		£1 pink (B.)	75·00	£160
51/4 *Set of 4*			£140	£325

See also Nos. 79/82 for different type of overprint.

(Des L. C. Mitchell. Recess P.B.)

1932 (16 Mar). T **12** and similar designs inscr "NIUE" and "COOK ISLANDS". No wmk. P 13.

55		½d. black and emerald	14·00	25·00
	a.	Perf 13×14×13×13	£250	
56		1d. black and deep lake	1·00	50
57		2d. black and red-brown	7·50	4·25
	a.	Perf 14×13×13×13	£140	£180
58		2½d. black and slate-blue	8·00	80·00
59		4d. black and greenish blue	14·00	65·00
		Perf 14	16·00	60·00
60		6d. black and orange-vermilion	2·50	2·00
61		1s. black and purple (P 14)	3·75	5·50
55/61 *Set of 7*			45·00	£160

Designs as Cook Islands Types **21/6**: Vert—1d. Capt Cook; 1s. King George V. Horiz—2d. Double Maori canoe; 2½d. Islanders working cargo; 4d. Port of Avarua; 6d. RMS *Monowai*.

Examples of the 2½d. with inverted centre were not supplied to the Post Office (*Price, £300, unused*).

Nos. 55a and 57a are mixed perforations, each having one side perforated 14 where the original perforation, 13, was inadequate.

(Recess from Perkins Bacon's plates at Govt Ptg Office, Wellington, N.Z.)

1932 (May)–**36**. As Nos. 55/61, but W **43** of New Zealand. P 14.

62		½d. black and emerald (10.8.32)	50	3·50
63		1d. black and deep lake (10.8.32)	50	2·25
	w.	Wmk inverted	50·00	
64		2d. black and yellow-brown (1.4.36)	50	1·75
	w.	Wmk inverted	32·00	55·00
65		2½d. black and slate-blue	50	4·25
	w.	Wmk inverted	50·00	
66		4d. black and greenish blue	1·75	4·25
	w.	Wmk inverted	£160	
67		6d. black and red-orange (1.4.36)	70	75
68		1s. black and purple (1.4.36)	9·00	26·00
62/8 *Set of 7*			12·00	38·00

Imperforate proofs of No. 65 are known used on registered mail from Niue postmarked 30 August 1945 or 29 October 1945.

See also Nos. 89/97.

Normal Letters **B K E N**

Narrow Letters **B K E N**

1935 (7 May). Silver Jubilee. Designs as Nos. 63, 65 and 67 (colours changed) optd with T **13** (wider vertical spacing on 6d.). W **43** of New Zealand. P 14.

69		1d. red-brown and lake	60	3·50
	a.	Narrow "K" in "KING"	2·75	9·00
	b.	Narrow "B" in "JUBILEE"	8·50	21·00
70		2½d. dull and deep blue (R.)	4·25	13·00
	a.	Narrow first "E" in "GEORGE"	4·25	13·00
71		6d. green and orange	6·50	10·00
	a.	Narrow "N" in "KING"	15·00	35·00
69/71 *Set of 3*			10·00	24·00

Examples of No. 70 imperforate horizontally are from proof sheets not issued through the Post and Telegraph Department (*Price £250 for vert pair*).

NIUE
NIUE (14)

Short opt (R. 9/4)

1937 (13 May). Coronation. Nos. 599/601 of New Zealand optd with T **14**.

72		1d. carmine	30	10
	a.	Short opt	15·00	

73		2½d. Prussian blue	40	1·50
	a.	Short opt	17·00	
74		6d. red-orange	40	20
	a.	Short opt	17·00	
72/4 *Set of 3*			1·00	1·60

15 King George VI

16 Tropical Landscape

1938 (2 May). T **15** and similar designs inscr "NIUE COOK ISLANDS". W **43** of New Zealand. P 14.

75		1s. black and violet	18·00	8·00
76		2s. black and red-brown	12·00	18·00
	w.	Wmk inverted	£225	£350
77		3s. blue and yellowish green	35·00	17·00
75/7 *Set of 3*			60·00	38·00

Designs as Cook Islands Types **30/1**: Vert—2s. Island village. Horiz—3s. Cook Islands canoe.

1940 (2 Sept). Unissued stamp surch as in T **16**. W **98** of New Zealand. P 13½×14.

78		3d. on 1½d. black and purple	75	60

Type **16** was not issued without surcharge but archival examples exist. (*Price, £250, unused*).

NIUE.
(17)

1941–67. Postal Fiscal stamps as Type F **6** of New Zealand with thin opt, T **17**. P 14.

(i) Thin, hard, chalk-surfaced "Wiggins Teape" paper with vertical mesh (1941–43)

*(a) W **43** of New Zealand*

79		2s.6d. deep brown (B.) (4.41)	£110	£120
80		5s. green (R.) (4.41)	£400	£400
81		10s. pale carmine-lake (B.) (6.42)	£140	£325
82		£1 pink (B.) (2.43?)	£200	£500
79/82 *Set of 4*			£750	£1200

*(b) W **98** of New Zealand (1944–54)*

83		2s.6d. deep brown (B.) (3.45)	4·50	10·00
	w.	Wmk inverted (11.51)	24·00	40·00
84		5s. green (R.) (11.44)	15·00	16·00
	w.	Wmk inverted (19.5.54)	9·50	24·00
85		10s. carmine-lake (B.) (11.45)	60·00	£130
	w.	Wmk inverted	75·00	£140
86		£1 pink (B.) (6.42)	65·00	75·00
83/6 *Set of 4*			£120	£200

*(ii) Unsurfaced "Wiggins Teape" paper with horizontal mesh. W **98** of New Zealand (1957–67).*

87		2s.6d. deep brown (P 14×13½) (1.11.57)	17·00	12·00
88		5s. pale yellowish green (wmk sideways) (6.67)	16·00	75·00

No. 88 came from a late printing made to fill demands from Wellington, but no supplies were sent to Niue. It exists in both line and comb perf.

1944–46. As Nos. 62/7 and 75/7, but W **98** of New Zealand (sideways on ½d., 1d., 1s. and 2s.).

89	**12**	½d. black and emerald	50	5·00
90	–	1d. black and deep lake	1·00	4·50
91	–	2d. black and red-brown	12·00	14·00
92	–	2½d. black and slate-blue (1946)	60	3·25
93	–	4d. black and greenish blue	4·25	1·00
	y.	Wmk inverted and reversed	23·00	
94	–	6d. black and red-orange	2·25	1·40
95	**15**	1s. black and violet	1·50	1·25
96	–	2s. black and red-brown (1945)	8·50	4·50
97	–	3s. blue and yellowish green (1945)	15·00	9·50
89/97 *Set of 9*			40·00	40·00

1946 (4 June). Peace. Nos. 668, 670, 674/5 of New Zealand optd as T **17** without stop (twice, reading up and down on 2d.).

98		1d. green (Blk.)	40	10
99		2d. purple (Blk.)	40	10
100		6d. chocolate and vermilion (Blk.)	40	80
	a.	Opt double, one albino	£550	
101		8d. black and carmine (B.)	50	80
98/101 *Set of 4*			1·50	1·60

Nos. 102/112 are vacant.

18 Map of Niue

19 HMS *Resolution*

20 Alofi landing

20a Native hut

21 Arch at Hikutavake

21a Alofi Bay

---

22 Spearing fish

22a Cave, Makefu

23 Bananas

24 Matapa Chasm

(Des J. Berry. Recess B.W.)

1950 (3 July). W **98** of New Zealand (sideways inverted on 1d., 2d., 3d., 4d., 6d. and 1s.). P 13½×14 (horiz) or 14×13½ (vert).

113	**18**	½d. orange and blue	20	1·75
114	**19**	1d. brown and blue-green	2·25	3·00
115	**20**	2d. black and carmine	1·25	3·00
116	**20a**	3d. blue and violet-blue	10	20
117	**21**	4d. olive-green and purple-brown	10	20
118	**21a**	6d. green and brown-orange	1·00	1·25
119	**22**	9d. orange and brown	15	1·40
120	**22a**	1s. purple and black	15	20
121	**23**	2s. brown-orange and dull green	6·00	6·00
122	**24**	3s. blue and black	5·50	5·50
113/22 *Set of 10*			15·00	20·00

1953 (25 May). Coronation. As Nos. 715 and 717 of New Zealand, but inscr "NIUE".

123		3d. brown	80	40
124		6d. slate-grey	95	40

(New Currency. 100 cents = 1 New Zealand dollar)

(25)

26

1967 (10 July). Decimal currency.

*(a) No. 113/22 surch as T **25***

125		½c. on ½d.	10	10
126		1c. on 1d.	1·10	15
127		2c. on 2d.	10	10
128		2½c. on 3d.	10	10
129		3c. on 4d.	10	10
130		5c. on 6d.	10	10
131		8c. on 9d.	10	10
132		10c. on 1s.	10	10
133		20c. on 2s.	35	2·00
134		30c. on 3s.	65	1·50
125/34 *Set of 10*			2·00	3·50

*(b) Arms type of New Zealand without value, surch as in T **26**. W **98** of New Zealand (sideways). P 14*

135	**26**	25c. deep yellow-brown	30	55
	a.	Rough perf 11	6·00	18·00
136		50c. pale yellowish green	70	80
	a.	Rough perf 11	6·00	19·00
137		$1 magenta	45	1·25
	a.	Rough perf 11	7·50	13·00
138		$2 light pink	50	2·00
	a.	Rough perf 11	8·50	14·00
135/8 *Set of 4*			1·75	4·25
135/8a *Set of 4*			25·00	55·00

The 25c., $1 and $2 perf 14 exist both line and comb perforated. The 50c. is comb perforated only. The perf 11 stamps resulted from an emergency measure in the course of printing.

1967 (3 Oct). Christmas. As T **278** of New Zealand, but inscr "NIUE". W **98** (sideways) of New Zealand. P 13½×14.

139		2½c. multicoloured	10	10
	w.	Wmk sideways inverted	15	30

1969 (1 Oct). Christmas. As T **301** of New Zealand, but inscr "NIUE". W **98** of New Zealand. P 13½×14½.

140		2½c. multicoloured	10	10

27 "Pua"

37 Kalahimu

(Des Mrs. K. W. Billings. Litho Enschedé)

1969 (27 Nov). T **27** and similar vert designs. Multicoloured. P 12½×13½.

141		½c. Type **27**	10	10
142		1c. "Golden Shower"	10	10
143		2c. Flamboyant	10	10
144		2½c. Frangipani	10	10
145		3c. Niue Crocus	10	10
146		5c. Hibiscus	10	10
147		8c. "Passion Fruit"	10	10
148		10c. "Kampui"	10	10
149		20c. Queen Elizabeth II (after Anthony Buckley)	35	1·75
150		30c. Tapeu Orchid	1·10	2·25
141/150 *Set of 10*			1·60	4·00

(Des G. F. Fuller. Photo Enschedé)

1970 (19 Aug). Indigenous Edible Crabs. T **37** and similar horiz designs. Multicoloured. P 13½×12½.

151	3c. Type **37**	10	10
152	5c. Kalavi	10	10
153	30c. Unga	30	25
151/3 Set of 3		45	40

1970 (1 Oct). Christmas. As T **314** of New Zealand, but inscr "NIUE".

154	2½c. multicoloured	10	10

38 Outrigger Canoe and Fokker F.27 Friendship Aircraft over Jungle

(Des L. C. Mitchell. Litho B.W.)

1970 (9 Dec). Opening of Niue Airport. T **38** and similar horiz designs. Multicoloured. P 13½.

155	3c. Type **38**	10	20
156	5c. Tofua II (cargo liner) and Fokker F.27 Friendship over harbour	15	20
157	8c. Fokker F.27 Friendship over Airport	15	30
155/7 Set of 3		35	65

Nigeria

LAGOS

A British Consul was established at Lagos during 1853 as part of the anti-slavery policy, but the territory was not placed under British administration until occupied by the Royal Navy in August 1861. From 19 February 1866 Lagos was administered with Sierra Leone and from July 1874 as part of Gold Coast. It became a separate colony on 13 January 1886.

Although a postal service had been established by the British G...in April 1852 no postal markings were supplied to Lagos until 1859. The British GPO retained control of the postal service until June 1863, when it became the responsibility of the colonial authorities.

CROWNED-CIRCLE HANDSTAMPS

CC **1**

CC1   CC **1** LAGOS (19.12.1859).................*Price on cover* £4000
First recorded use of No. CC **1** is 12 December 1871. It is later known used as a cancellation.

PRICES FOR STAMPS ON COVER

Nos. 1/9	*from* × 15
Nos. 10/26	*from* × 12
Nos. 27/9	—
Nos. 30/8	*from* × 12
Nos. 39/41	—
No. 42	*from* × 40
Nos. 44/50	*from* × 10
Nos. 51/3	—
Nos. 54/60	*from* × 10
Nos. 61/3	—

PRINTERS. All the stamps of Lagos were typographed by D.L.R.

1

1874 (10 June)–**75**. Wmk Crown CC. P 12½.

1	**1**	1d. lilac-mauve	80·00	50·00
2		2d. blue	80·00	45·00
3		3d. red-brown (2.75)	£130	42·00
5		4d. carmine	£150	50·00
6		6d. blue-green	£150	20·00
8		1s. orange (value 15½ mm) (2.75)	£700	£150
		a. Value 16½ mm long (7.75)	£425	70·00
1/8a Set of 6			£900	£225

1876–79. Wmk Crown CC. P 14.

10	**1**	1d. lilac-mauve	50·00	20·00
11		2d. blue	80·00	15·00
12		3d. red-brown	£120	18·00
		w. Wmk inverted	†	£350
13		3d. chestnut	£130	42·00
14		4d. carmine	£225	12·00
		a. Wmk sideways	£1700	£130
15		6d. green	£130	6·50
16		1s. orange (value 16½ mm long) (1879)	£950	85·00
10/16 Set of 6			£1400	£130

1882 (June). Wmk Crown CA. P 14.

17	**1**	1d. lilac-mauve	40·00	28·00
18		2d. blue	£200	8·50
19		3d. chestnut	30·00	8·50
		w. Wmk inverted	†	£350
20		4d. carmine	£225	12·00
17/20 Set of 4			£450	50·00

1884 (Dec)–**86**. New values and colours. Wmk Crown CA. P 14.

21	**1**	½d. dull green (1885)	2·00	80
22		1d. rose-carmine	2·00	80
		w. Wmk inverted	£180	£120
23		2d. grey	£100	9·50
24		4d. pale violet	£160	12·00
		w. Wmk inverted	—	£300
		y. Wmk inverted and reversed	†	£400
25		6d. olive-green	8·00	55·00
26		1s. orange (3.85)	21·00	24·00
27		2s.6d. olive-black (1886)	£350	£275
28		5s. blue (1886)	£700	£500
29		10s. purple-brown (1886)	£1600	£1100
21/9 Set of 9			£2500	£1800
27s/9s Optd "SPECIMEN" Set of 3			£425	

We would warn collectors against clever forgeries of Nos. 27 to 29 on genuinely watermarked paper.

2½ PENNY

A

2½ PENNY

B

1887 (Mar)–**1902**. Wmk Crown CA. P 14.

30	**1**	2d. dull mauve and blue	8·50	2·00
31		2½d. ultramarine (A) (1891)	8·00	1·75
		a. Larger letters of value (B)	22·00	17·00
		b. *Blue* (A)	80·00	50·00
32		3d. dull mauve and chestnut (4.91)	2·50	3·25
33		4d. dull mauve and black	2·25	1·75
34		5d. dull mauve and green (2.94)	2·25	11·00
35		6d. dull mauve and mauve	4·75	3·00
		a. Dull mauve and carmine (10.02)	5·00	10·00
36		7½d. dull mauve and mauve (2.94)	4·25	38·00
37		10d. dull mauve and yellow (2.94)	4·50	13·00
38		1s. yellow-green and brown	5·50	28·00
		a. Blue-green and black	7·00	38·00
39		2s.6d. green and carmine	23·00	80·00
40		5s. green and blue	48·00	£150
41		10s. green and brown	£120	£250
30/41 Set of 12			£200	£500
30s/41s Optd "SPECIMEN" Set of 12			£325	

HALF PENNY

(2)   **3**

1893 (2 Aug). No. 33 surch with T **2** locally.

42	**1**	½d. on 4d. dull mauve and black	11·00	3·75
		a. Surch double	70·00	55·00
		b. Surch treble	£170	
		c. Error. ½d. on 2d. (No. 30)	—	£25000

There were two separate settings of No. 42. The most common, of which there were five separate printings, shows "HALF PENNY" 16 mm long and was applied as a horizontal pair or triplet. The scarcer setting, also applied as a triplet, shows "HALF PENNY" 16½ mm long.

Three examples of No. 42c are known, two unused and one used. Only the latter is in private hands.

1904 (22 Jan–Nov). Wmk Crown CA. P 14.

44	**3**	½d. dull green and green	3·00	5·50
45		1d. purple and black/*red*	1·25	15
46		2d. dull purple and blue	6·00	4·00
47		2½d. dull purple and blue/*blue* (B)	1·50	1·50
		b. Smaller letters of value as A	4·50	8·50
		bw. Wmk inverted	£200	£180
48		3d. dull purple and brown	3·25	1·75
49		6d. dull purple and mauve	35·00	9·00
50		1s. green and black	35·00	42·00
51		2s.6d. green and carmine	£160	£325
52		5s. green and blue	£130	£325
53		10s. green and brown (11.04)	£350	£950
44/53 Set of 10			£650	£1500
44s/53s Optd "SPECIMEN" Set of 10			£225	

1904–06. Ordinary paper. Wmk Mult Crown CA. P 14.

54	**3**	½d. dull green and green (12.10.04)	18·00	3·00
		a. Chalk-surfaced paper (12.3.06)	13·00	1·75
		w. Wmk inverted		
55		1d. purple and black/*red* (22.10.04)	10·00	10
		a. Chalk-surfaced paper (21.9.05)	1·50	10
		aw. Wmk inverted	—	£120
56		2d. dull purple and blue (2.05)	6·00	3·25
		a. Chalk-surfaced paper (25.9.06)	21·00	11·00
		aw. Wmk inverted	£180	
57		2½d. dull purple and blue/*blue* (B) (chalk-surfaced paper) (13.10.05)	1·75	16·00
		a. Smaller letters of value as A	55·00	£120
58		3d. dull purple and brown (27.4.05)	3·50	1·25
		a. Chalk-surfaced paper (2.8.06)	15·00	1·75
		w. Wmk inverted		
59		6d. dull purple and mauve (31.10.04)	6·50	7·00
		a. Chalk-surfaced paper (1.3.06)	4·25	1·50
60		1s. green and black (15.10.04)	23·00	32·00
		a. Chalk-surfaced paper (4.06)	28·00	2·25
		w. Wmk inverted		
61		2s.6d. green and carmine (3.12.04)	28·00	75·00
		a. Chalk-surfaced paper (21.10.06)	50·00	70·00
62		5s. green and blue (1.05)	26·00	£110
		a. Chalk-surfaced paper (21.10.06)	80·00	£180
63		10s. green and brown (3.12.04)	£100	£275
		a. Chalk-surfaced paper (12.3.06)	90·00	£250
54/63 Set of 10			£170	£400

Lagos was incorporated into the Colony and Protectorate of Southern Nigeria, previously formed from Niger Coast Protectorate and part of the Niger Company territories, on 16 February 1906. Stamps of Lagos were then authorised for use throughout Southern Nigeria.

NIGER COAST PROTECTORATE

OIL RIVERS PROTECTORATE

A British consulate for the Bights of Benin and Biafra was established in 1849 on the off-shore Spanish island of Fernando Po. In 1853 the appointment was divided with a consul for the Bight of Benin at Lagos. The consulate for the Bight of Biafra was transferred to Old Calabar in 1882.

A British protectorate was proclaimed over the coastal area, with the exceptions of the colony of Lagos and the centre of the Niger delta, on 5 June 1885. It was not, however, until July 1891 that steps were taken to set up an administration with a consul-general at Old Calabar and vice-consuls at some of the river ports.

The consulate-general at Old Calabar and the vice-consulates at Benin, Bonny, Brass, Forcados and Opobo acted as collection and distribution centres for mail from November 1891, but were not recognised as post offices until 20 July 1892.

For a few months from July 1892 local administrative handstamps, as Type Z **1**, were in use either as obliterators or in conjunction with the c.d.s.

Z 1

These oval handstamps are usually found on the 1892–94 overprinted issue, but the following are known on unoverprinted stamps of Great Britain:

1892.

BENIN

Stamps of GREAT BRITAIN cancelled with oval postmark, Type Z **1**, inscribed "BENIN".

Z1	2½d. purple/*blue* (V.)	£1500

BONNY

Stamps of GREAT BRITAIN cancelled with oval postmark, Type Z **1**, inscribed "BONNY".

Z2	2½d. purple/*blue* (V.)	£1100

BRASS RIVER

Stamps of GREAT BRITAIN cancelled with oval postmark, Type Z **1**, inscribed "BRASS".

Z3	2½d. purple/*blue* (Blk.)	£1000

OLD CALABAR RIVER

Stamps of GREAT BRITAIN cancelled with oval postmark, Type Z **1**, inscribed "OLD CALABAR".

Z4	2½d. purple/*blue* (Blk.)	£1000

Stamps of GREAT BRITAIN cancelled with "BRITISH VICE-CONSULATE OLD CALABAR" within double-lined circle.

Z5	2½d. purple/*blue* (V.)	£750
Z6	5d. dull purple and blue (V.)	

For later use of Type Z **1** and the circular Vice-Consulate marks see note beneath No. 6.

Z 2

Unoverprinted stamps of Great Britain remained officially valid for postage in the Protectorate until 30 September 1892, but were available from post offices in the Niger Company Territories up to the end of 1899. The two areas were so closely linked geographically that offices in the Protectorate continued to accept letters franked with Great Britain stamps until the reorganisation of 1900. The listing below covers confirmed examples, known on cover or piece, the prices quoted being for the latter.

1892–99.

Stamps of GREAT BRITAIN cancelled with circular postmarks as Type Z **2**.

BENIN RIVER

Z7	2d. green and carmine	
Z8	2½d. purple/*blue*	£1000
Z9	3d. purple/*yellow*	£1500
Z10	5d. dull purple and blue	
Z11	1s. green	

BONNY RIVER

Z12	½d. vermilion	£500
Z12a	1d. lilac	£450
Z13	2½d. purple/*blue*	£400
Z14	5d. dull purple and blue	£500
Z15	6d. deep purple/*red*	£850

BRASS RIVER

Z16	1½d. dull purple and green	£1000
Z17	2½d. purple/*blue*	£850
Z17a	2½d. purple/*blue* (squared-circle cancellation)	£1000
Z18	6d. purple/*red*	£900

FORCADOS RIVER

Z19	1d. lilac	£750
Z20	2½d. purple/*blue*	
Z21	5d. dull purple and blue (m/s cancellation)	£1000
Z22	10d. dull purple and carmine	

OLD CALABAR RIVER

Z23	½d. vermilion	£400
Z24	1d. lilac	£375
Z25	1½d. dull purple and green	£500
Z26	2d. green and vermilion	£500
Z27	2½d. purple/*blue*	£375
Z28	5d. dull purple and blue	£475
Z29	6d. purple/*red*	£475
Z30	1s. green	£700

OPOBO RIVER

Z31	2½d. purple/*blue*	£450
Z32	10d. dull purple and carmine	£750

Some later covers are known franked with GB stamps, but the origin of the stamps involved is uncertain.

PRICES FOR STAMPS ON COVER	
Nos. 1/6	from × 15
Nos. 7/37	from × 6
Nos. 38/44	
Nos. 45/50	from × 15
Nos. 51/6	from × 20
Nos. 57/65	from × 5
Nos. 66/72	from × 15
Nos. 73/4	—

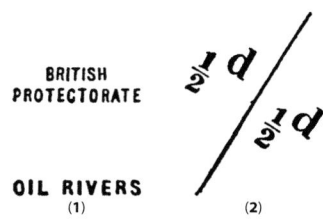

BRITISH PROTECTORATE

OIL RIVERS

(1)   (2)

1892 (20 July)–**94.** Nos. 172, 197, 200/1, 207*a* and 211 of Great Britain optd by D.L.R. with T **1**.

1	½d. vermilion	21·00	13·00
2	1d. lilac	13·00	11·00
	a. Opt reversed "OIL RIVERS" at top	£9000	
	b. Bisected (½d.) (*on cover*)	†	£2000
3	2d. grey-green and carmine	35·00	9·00
	a. Bisected (1d.) (*on cover*)	†	£2000
4	2½d. purple/*blue*	10·00	2·50
5	5d. dull purple and blue (Die II) (No. 207*a*)	19·00	6·50
6	1s. dull green	70·00	90·00
1/6 Set of 6		£150	£120
1s/6s H/S "SPECIMEN" *Set* of 6		£300	

Nos. 2b and 3a were used at Bonny River during August and September 1894.

OVAL HANDSTAMPS. In addition to Nos. Z1/4 postmarks as Type Z **1** are also known used on the 1892–94 overprinted issue from the following offices:

Bakana (Nos. 2, 4/6)
Benin (Nos. 1/6)
Bonny (No. 2)
Brass (Nos. 3/5)
Buguma (Nos. 4 and 6)
Old Calabar (No. 4)
Opobo (Nos. 1/3)
Sombreiro River (Nos. 1/6)

The Vice-Consulate marks, as Nos. Z5/6, are also known struck on examples of No. 4 from Bonny, Forcados or Old Calabar.

Nos. 2 to 6 surcharged locally

1893 (3 Sept). Issued at Old Calabar. Surch with T **2** and then bisected.

7	½d. on half of 1d. (R.)	£160	£140
	a. Unsevered pair	£500	£450
	ab. Surch inverted and dividing line reversed (unsevered pair)	—	£25000
	b. Surch reversed (dividing line running from left to right) (unsevered pair)	—	£17000
	c. Straight top to "1" in "½"	£350	£350
	d. "½" omitted	†	—
	e. Surch double (unsevered pair with normal)	—	£1800
	f. Vert se-tenant pair. Nos. 7a/8a	—	£23000
8	½d. on half of 1d. (V.)	£7000	£5000
	a. Unsevered pair	£18000	£16000
	b. Surch double (pair)	£25000	

The surcharge was applied in a setting covering one horizontal row at a time. Violet ink was used for the top row in the first sheet, but was then replaced with red.

HALF PENNY.   HALF PENNY.
(3)   (4)

In T **3** "HALF" measures 9½ mm and "PENNY" 12½ mm with space 1½ mm between the words. Bar 14½ mm ending below the stop. The "F" is nearly always defective.

In T **4** "HALF" is 8½ mm, "PENNY" 12½ mm, spacing 2½ mm, and bar 16 mm, extending beyond the stop.

HALF PENN.Y   HALF PENNY
5 (Stop after "N")   **6** (No stop after "N")

In T **5** the "P" and "Y" are raised, and the space between the words is about 4 mm. Bar is short, approx 13½ mm. T **6** is similar but without the stop after "N".

Half Penny   Half Penny
(7)   (8)

In T **7** the "a" and "e" are narrow and have a short upward terminal hook. The "1" has a very small hook. The letters "nny" have curved serifs, and the distance between the words is 5½ mm.

In T **8** the "a" and "e" are wider. The "1" has a wider hook. The letters "nny" have straight serifs, and the distance between the words is 4¼ mm.

HALF PENNY.   HALF PENNY
(9)   (10)

1893 (Dec). Issue at Old Calabar. Nos. 3/4 handstamped.

*(a) With T **3***

9	½d. on 2d. (V.)	£500	£350
	a. Surch inverted	£17000	
	b. Surch diagonal (up or down)	£7000	
	c. Surch vertical (up or down)	£9000	
10	½d. on 2½d. (Verm.)	£14000	
10a	½d. on 2½d. (C.)	£35000	

*(b) With T **4***

11	½d. on 2½d. (G.)	£300	£250
	a. Surch double	£2750	£2750
	b. Surch diagonally inverted		
12	½d. on 2½d. (Verm.)	£1200	£300
13	½d. on 2½d. (C.)	£425	£450
	a. Surch omitted (in pair)		
14	½d. on 2½d. (B.)	£425	£475
15	½d. on 2½d. (Blk.)	£4250	
	a. Surch inverted	£15000	
	b. Surch diagonal inverted (up or down)	£13000	
16	½d. on 2½d. (B.-Blk.)	£4750	

*(c) With T **5***

17	½d. on 2½d. (Verm.)	£1300	£200
	a. Surch double	†	£2250
	b. Surch vertical (up)	†	£10000

*(d) With T **6***

18	½d. on 2d. (V.)	£1100	£500
19	½d. on 2½d. (Verm.)	£600	£325
	a. Surch inverted	£10000	
	b. Surch double	—	£2500
	c. Surch diagonal (up or down)	£4500	
	d. Surch omitted (in vert strip of 3)	£35000	
	e. Surch vertical (up or down)	£13000	
	f. Surch diagonal, inverted (up or down)	£7500	
20	½d. on 2d. (V.)	£475	£250
	a. Surch double	†	£6500
	b. Surch vertical (up or down)	£7500	
	c. Surch diagonal (up or down)	£7500	
	d. Surch diagonal (inverted)	£17000	
	e. Surch inverted	£17000	
21	½d. on 2½d. (Verm.)	£375	£180
	a. Surch double	†	£7500
	b. Surch vertical (up or down)	£8000	
	c. Surch inverted	£12000	
	d. Surch diagonal (up or down)	£5500	
	e. Surch diagonal, inverted (up)	£14000	
22	½d. on 2½d. (B.)	£35000	
23	½d. on 2½d. (C.)		
24	½d. on 2½d. (V.)	£12000	

*(f) With T **8***

25	½d. on 2½d. (Verm)	£550	£650
	a. Surch diagonal (up)	£7500	
26	½d. on 2½d. (B.)	£35000	
27	½d. on 2½d. (G.)	£500	
28	½d. on 2½d. (C.)	£22000	£22000

*(g) With T **9***

29	½d. on 2d. (V.)	£500	£375
30	½d. on 2d. (B.)	£2000	£750
	a. Surch double		
31	½d. on 2½d. (Verm.)	£600	£700
	a. Surch double		
32	½d. on 2½d. (B.)	£425	£400
33	½d. on 2½d. (G.)	£450	£500
	a. Surch double (G.)	£2000	
	b. Surch double (G.+Verm.)		
34	½d. on 2½d. (V.)	£7000	

*(h) With T **10***

35	½d. on 2½d. (G.)	£500	£450
36	½d. on 2½d. (V.)	£9000	

Various types of surcharges on Nos. 9 to 36 were printed on the same sheet, and different types in different colours may be found *se-tenant* (Prices, from £5000 per pair, unused).

Unused examples of Nos. 11, 12 and 31 with surcharge omitted in pair with normal (No. 11) or as the first and third stamps in a strip of three (Nos. 12 and 31) exist in the Royal collection.

One Shilling   5/-
(11)   (12)

1893 (Dec). Issued at Old Calabar. Nos. 3 and 5/6 handstamped.

*(a) With T **11***

37	1s. on 2d. (V.)	£450	£375
	a. Surch inverted	£12000	
	b. Surch vertical (up or down)	£7000	
	c. Surch diagonal (up or down)	£9000	
	d. Surch diagonal, inverted (up or down)	£12000	
	e. Pair, Nos. 37 and 38	£6000	
38	1s. on 2d. (Verm.)	£750	£4000
	a. Surch inverted	£18000	
	b. Surch diagonal (up or down)	£10000	
	c. Surch vertical (up or down)	£15000	
39	1s. on 2d. (Blk.)	£6000	
	a. Surch inverted	£20000	
	b. Surch vertical (up or down)	£15000	
	c. Surch diagonal (up)	£15000	

*(b) As T **12***

40	5s. on 2d. (V.)	£9000	£11000
	a. Surch inverted	£50000	
	b. Surch vertical (up or down)	£45000	£45000
	c. Surch diagonal (down)	£35000	
41	10s. on 5d. (Verm.)	£6500	£10000
	a. Surch inverted	£50000	
	b. Surch vertical (up or down)	£45000	
	c. Surch diagonal (down)	£35000	

42	20s. on 1s. (V.)	£140000	
	a. Surch inverted	£180000	
43	20s. on 1s. (Verm.)	£120000	
44	20s. on 1s. (Blk.)	£120000	

There are two main settings of the "One Shilling" surcharge:—

Type A. The "O" is over the "hi" of "Shilling" and the downstrokes on the "n" in "One", if extended, would meet the "ll" of "Shilling". The "g" is always raised. Type A is known in all three colours from one sheet of 120.

Type B. The "O" is over the first "i" of "Shilling" and the downstrokes of the "n" would meet the "li" of "Shilling". Type B is known in violet (two sheets) and vermilion (one sheet).

An example of No. 38 with surcharge diagonal, inverted exists in the Royal collection.

NIGER COAST PROTECTORATE

The protectorate was extended into the interior and the name changed to Niger Coast Protectorate on 12 May 1893.

PERFORATION. There are a number of small variations in the perforation of the Waterlow issues of 1893 to 1898 which were due to irregularity of the pins rather than different perforators.

In the following lists, stamps perf 12, 12½, 13 or compound are described as perf 12–13, stamps perf 13½, 14 or compound are described as perf 13½–14 and those perf 14½, 15 or compound are listed as perf 14½–15. In addition the 13½–14 perforation exists compound with 14½–15 and with 12–13, whilst perf 15½–16 comes from a separate perforator.

13   **14**

(Des G. D. Drummond. Recess Waterlow)

1894 (1 Jan). T **13** (with "OIL RIVERS" obliterated and "NIGER COAST" in top margin). Various frames. Thick and thin papers. No wmk. P 14½–15.

45	½d. vermilion	10·00	11·00
	a. Perf 13½–14	7·00	12·00
46	1d. pale blue	6·00	5·00
	a. Bisected (½d.) (on cover)	†	£750
	b. Dull blue	8·50	4·50
	ba. Bisected (½d.) (on cover)	†	£650
	c. Perf 13½–14	5·00	4·75
	d. Perf 13½–14, comp 12–13	30·00	25·00
	e. Perf 12–13	£150	£120
47	2d. green	48·00	48·00
	a. Imperf between (horiz pair)	†	£17000
	b. Bisected (1d.) (on cover)	†	£900
	c. Perf 14½–15, comp 12–13		
	d. Perf 13½–14	19·00	18·00
	e. Perf 13½–14, comp 12–13	50·00	42·00
	f. Perf 12–13	£300	£190
48	2½d. carmine-lake	19·00	4·25
	a. Perf 13½–14	27·00	12·00
	b. Perf 13½–14, comp 12–13	38·00	38·00
	c. Perf 12–13	£275	£250
49	5d. grey-lilac	23·00	17·00
	a. Lilac (1894)	16·00	23·00
	b. Perf 13½–14	23·00	13·00
	c. Perf 13½–14, comp 12–13	70·00	
50	1s. black	14·00	15·00
	a. Perf 14½–15, comp 12–13	£110	90·00
	b. Perf 13½–14	35·00	22·00
	c. Perf 13½–14, comp 12–13	50·00	40·00
	d. Perf 14½–15, comp 13½–14	55·00	38·00
45/50	Set of 6	70·00	60·00

There were three printings of each value, in November 1893, January 1894 and March 1894.

Nos. 46a, 46ba and 47b were used at Bonny River during August and September 1894.

(Recess Waterlow)

1894 (May). T **14** (various frames). No wmk. P 14½–15.

51	½d. yellow-green	5·00	5·00
	a. Deep green	5·50	6·00
	b. Perf 14½–15, comp 13½–14		
	c. Perf 13½–14	17·00	17·00
	d. Perf 13½–14, comp 12–13	40·00	35·00
52	1d. orange-vermilion	23·00	17·00
	a. Vermilion	13·00	8·50
	b. Bisected diagonally (½d.) (on cover)	†	£800
	c. Perf 15½–16	—	85·00
	d. Perf 13½–14	40·00	
	e. Perf 13½–14, comp 12–13	70·00	23·00
53	2d. lake	32·00	6·50
	a. Bisected diagonally (1d.) (on cover)	†	
	b. Perf 13½–14	42·00	9·00
	c. Perf 13½–14, comp 12–13	85·00	22·00
54	2½d. blue	20·00	4·50
	a. Pale blue	8·50	7·50
	b. Perf 13½–14	42·00	15·00
55	5d. purple	15·00	5·50
	a. Deep violet	12·00	5·50
56	1s. black	80·00	26·00
	a. Perf 13½–14	60·00	7·00
	b. Perf 13½–14, comp 12–13	80·00	50·00
51/6	Set of 6	£110	32·00

Nos. 52b and 53a were used at Bonny River during August and September 1894.

1—
2
(15)   **1**
(16) **ONE**
HALF PENNY
(17)

1894. Provisionals. Issued at Opobo.

*(a) Nos. 46b and 46 bisected vertically and surch with T **15*** *(May–June)*

57	"½" on half of 1d. dull blue (R.) (5.94)	£2250	£650
	a. Surch inverted (in strip of 3 with normals)	£20000	
58	"½" on half of 1d. pale blue (R.) (6.94)	£1200	£375
	a. Surch tête-bêche (pair)	£14000	
	b. Surcharge inverted	—	£350
	c. Perf 13½–14	—	£350
	d. Perf 13½–14, comp 12–13	—	£400

(b) No. 3 bisected vertically and surch
*(i) With T **16** (12 mm high) (June–Oct)*

59	"1" on half of 2d. (Verm.)	£1700	£375
	a. Surch double	£6500	£1200
	b. Surch inverted	†	£2000
	c. Unsevered pair	†	£4000

(ii) Smaller "1" (4¾ mm high)

60	"1" on half of 2d. (C.)	†	£10000

(iii) Smaller "1" (3¾ mm high)

61	"1" on half of 2d. (C.)	†	—

Nos. 60 and 61 exist se-tenant. (Price £40,000 used).

*(c) No. 52a (Perf 14½–15) bisected, surch with T **15*** *(Aug–Sept)*

62	"½" on half of 1d. vermilion (Blk.)	£5500	£1000
63	"½" on half of 1d. vermilion (V.)	£4000	£700
64	"½" on half of 1d. vermilion (B.)	£3500	£500
	a. "½" double		
	b. Perf 13½–14	£3500	£500
	c. Perf 13½–14, comp 12–13	—	£600

The stamp is found divided down the middle and also diagonally.

1894 (10 Aug). Issued at Old Calabar. No. 54 surch with T **17** and two bars through value at foot.

65	½d. on 2½d. blue	£425	£250
	a. Surch double	£8000	£2000
	b. "OIE" for "ONE"	£2000	£1200
	c. Ditto. Surch double	†	£10000

There are eight types in the setting of Type **17**, arranged as a horizontal row. No. 65b occurred on No. 8 in the setting at some point during surcharging.

(Recess Waterlow)

1897 (Mar)–**98**. As T **14** (various frames). Wmk Crown CA. P 14½–15.

66	½d. green (7.97)	8·50	1·50
	a. Sage-green	8·50	2·75
	b. Perf 13½–14	3·25	3·00
	by. Wmk inverted and reversed	—	£275
	c. Perf 15½–16	19·00	6·50
	d. Perf 13½–14, comp 12–13	42·00	26·00
	x. Wmk reversed	—	£170
67	1d. orange-vermilion	4·50	1·50
	a. Vermilion	6·50	1·50
	b. Imperf vert (horiz pair)	£16000	
	c. Perf 15½–16	11·00	7·50
	d. Perf 13½–14	2·50	2·75
	e. Perf 13½–14, comp 12–13	22·00	16·00
	f. Perf 13½–14, comp 14½–15	—	22·00
	x. Wmk reversed	†	—
68	2d. lake (7.97)	5·00	2·00
	a. Perf 15½–16	5·00	3·00
	b. Perf 13½–14	4·75	3·75
	c. Perf 13½–14, comp 12–13	50·00	35·00
	x. Wmk reversed	£130	£120
69	2½d. slate-blue (8.97)	7·50	2·75
	a. Deep bright blue	18·00	3·00
	b. Perf 13½–14	6·50	4·00
	c. Perf 15½–16	—	60·00
	w. Wmk inverted	—	£300
	x. Wmk reversed	£750	£350
70	5d. red-violet (P 13½–14) (1898)	23·00	90·00
	a. Purple	13·00	95·00
	b. Perf 13½–14, comp 12–13	42·00	£200
	c. Perf 14½–15	—	£225
71	6d. yellow-brown (6.98)	7·00	10·00
	a. Perf 13½–14	8·50	13·00
	b. Perf 15½–16	70·00	42·00
	x. Wmk reversed	£275	
72	1s. black (1898)	15·00	29·00
	a. Perf 13½–14	14·00	30·00
	b. Perf 13½–14, comp 12–13	75·00	
73	2s.6d. olive-bistre (6.98)	95·00	£170
	a. Perf 15½–16	80·00	£180
	b. Perf 13½–14	23·00	90·00
74	10s. deep violet (6.98)	£180	£300
	a. Bright violet	£225	£375
	b. Perf 13½–14	£130	£225
	ba. Bright violet	£120	£200
	bx. Wmk reversed	£600	
	c. Perf 13½–14, comp 12–13	£275	£425
66/74	Set of 9	£170	£375
71s, 73s/4s	Optd "SPECIMEN" Set of 3	£275	

Owing to temporary shortages in Southern Nigeria, the above issue was again in use at various times from 1902 until 1907.

On 1 January 1900 the Niger Coast Protectorate together with the southern portion of the Niger Company Territories became the protectorate of Southern Nigeria.

NIGER COMPANY TERRITORIES

Following the development of trade along the Niger, British commercial interests formed the United African Company in 1879 which became the National African Company in 1882 and the Royal Niger Company in 1886. A charter was granted to the Company in the same year to administer territory along the Rivers Niger and Benue over which a British protectorate had been proclaimed in June 1885. The Company's territories extended to the Niger delta to provide access to the interior.

Post Offices were opened at Akassa (1887), Burutu (1896), Lokoja (1899) and Abutshi (1899). The stamps of Great Britain were used from 1888.

On the establishment of postal services in 1887 the Company arranged with the British GPO that unstamped mail marked with their handstamps would be delivered in Great Britain, the recipients only being charged the normal rate of postage from West Africa. This system was difficult to administer, however, so the British authorities agreed in 1888 to the supply of GB stamps for use at the Company post offices.

Initially the stamps on such covers were left uncancelled until the mail arrived in the United Kingdom, the Company handstamp being struck elsewhere on the address side. This method continued to be used until early 1896, although a number of covers from the 12 months prior to that date do show the Company handstamp cancelling the stamps. Some of these covers were later recancelled on arrival in Great Britain. From May 1896 the postage stamps were cancelled in the Niger Territories.

In the following listings no attempt has been made to cover the use of the Company marks on the reverse of envelopes.

Dates given are those of earliest known postmarks. Colour of postmarks in brackets. Where two or more colours are given, price is for cheapest.

Stamps of GREAT BRITAIN cancelled as indicated below.

ABUTSHI

1899. Cancelled as T **8**, but inscribed "THE ROYAL NIGER CO. C. & L. ABUTSHI" with "CUSTOMS (date) OFFICE" in central oval.

Z1	½d. vermilion (V.)		£1000
Z2	1d. lilac (V.)		£700
Z3	2½d. purple/blue (V.)		£1000
Z4	5d. dull purple and blue (V.)		£1100
Z5	10d. dull purple and carmine (V.)		£1300
Z6	2s.6d. deep lilac (V.)		£1700

AKASSA

The listings for Nos. Z7/15a are for covers on which the Akassa handstamp appears on the front, but is not used as a cancellation for the GB stamps. Examples of Nos. Z16/26 occur, from 1895–96, with the handstamp struck on the front of the cover away from the stamps, or, from 1896, used as a cancellation. The prices quoted are for single stamps showing the cancellation; covers from either period being worth considerably more. On Nos. Z29/42b the handstamp was used as a cancellation and the prices quoted are for single stamps.

1

1888–90. Cancelled as T **3**, but with Maltese cross each side of "AKASSA". Size 36×22 mm.

Z7	6d. deep purple/red (V.)		£2500

1889–94. Size 39×24 mm.

Z8	**1**	2½d. purple/blue (V.)		£900
Z9		3d. purple/yellow (V.)		£1000
Z10		5d. dull purple and blue (V.)		£1000
Z11		6d. deep purple/red (V.)		£700
Z12		10d. dull purple and carmine (V.)		£1000
Z12a		1s. green (V.)		£1800
Z13		2s.6d. lilac (V.)		£1300

1894–95.

Z14	**2**	1d. lilac (V.)		£1200
Z15		2½d. purple/blue (V.)		£1200
Z15a		2s.6d. lilac (V.)		

3

1895. Size 39×25 mm.

Z16	**3**	2½d. purple/blue (V.)		£3000

1895–99.

Z17	**4**	½d. vermilion (V.)		£130
Z18		1d. lilac (V.)		£120

THE ROYAL NIGER COMPANY
CHARTERED & LIMITED.
7 – AUG. 98
POST OFFICE
AKASSA.

4

Z19		2d. green and carmine (V.)		£600
Z20		2½d. purple/*blue* (V.)		70·00
Z21		3d. purple/*yellow* (V.)		£425
Z22		5d. dull purple and blue (V.)		£100
Z23		6d. deep purple/*red* (V.)		£475
Z24		9d. dull purple and blue (V.)		£900
Z25		10d. dull purple and carmine (V.)		£160
Z26		2s.6d. deep lilac (V.)		£375

5

1897–99.

Z29	5	½d. vermilion (V.)		£100
Z30		1d. lilac (V.)		70·00
		a. "RECD" for year in postmark		£1000
Z31		2d. green and carmine (V.)		£400
Z32		2½d. purple/*blue* (V.)		80·00
		a. "RECD" for year in postmark (1898)		£1200
Z33		3d. purple/*yellow* (V.)		£350
Z34		4d. green and brown (V.)		£550
Z35		4½d. green and carmine (V.)		£1700
Z36		5d. dull purple and blue (V.)		95·00
Z37		6d. deep purple/*red* (V.)		£425
Z38		9d. dull purple and blue (V.)		£900
Z39		10d. dull purple and carmine (V.)		£250
Z40		1s. green (V.)		£1700
Z41		2s.6d. deep lilac (V.)		£500

1899. Cancelled as T **7** but inscribed "AKASSA".

Z42		5d. dull purple and blue (V.)		£1500

1899. Cancelled as T **4**, but "CUSTOMS DEPT" in place of "POST OFFICE".

Z42a		1d. lilac (V.)		£1000
Z42b		2½d. purple/*blue* (V.)		£1000

BURUTU

6

1896–99. Cancelled as T **6**, "BURUTU" in sans-serif caps. Size 44×24 mm.

Z43	6	½d. vermilion (V., Blk.)		£150
Z44		1d. lilac (V.)		£100
Z45		1½d. dull purple and green (V.)		£800
Z46		2d. green and carmine (V., Blk.)		£325
Z47		2½d. purple/*blue* (V., Blk.)		50·00
Z48		3d. purple/*yellow* (V., Blk.)		£350
Z49		4d. green and brown (V. Blk.)		£450
Z50		5d. dull purple and blue (V., Blk.)		£120
Z51		6d. deep purple/*red* (V.)		£450
Z52		9d. dull purple and blue (V.)		£900
Z53		10d. dull purple and carmine (V., Blk.)		£180
Z54		1s. green (V.)		£1400
Z55		2s.6d. lilac (V.)		£425

1898–99. Cancelled as T **4**, but inscribed "BURUTU" in serifed caps. Size 44×27 mm.

Z56		½d. vermilion (V., Blk.)		85·00
Z57		1d. lilac (V.)		55·00
Z58		2d. green and carmine (V.)		£450
Z59		2½d. purple/*blue* (V., Blk.)		65·00
Z60		3d. purple/*yellow* (V.)		£425
Z61		4d. green and brown (V.)		£550
Z62		4½d. green and carmine (V.)		£1700
Z63		5d. dull purple and blue (V.)		£120
Z64		6d. deep purple/*red* (V.)		£450
Z65		9d. dull purple and blue (V.)		£900
Z66		10d. dull purple and carmine (V., Blk.)		£160
Z67		2s.6d. lilac (V., Blk.)		£425

7

1898–99.

Z68	7	1d. lilac (V.)		
Z69		2½d. purple/*blue* (V.)		£350

1899. Cancelled as T **4**, but inscribed "CUSTOM DEPT. BURUTU".

Z70		1d. lilac (V.)		

LOKOJA

8

1899.

Z71	8	½d. vermilion (V.)		£170
Z72		1d. lilac (V.)		£110
Z73		2½d. purple/*blue* (V.)		£350
Z74		5d. dull purple and blue (V.)		£650
Z75		10d. dull purple and carmine (V.)		£800
Z76		2s.6d. deep lilac (V.)		£1200

AGENT GENERAL NIGER TERRITORIES

The listings for Nos. Z78/81 are for covers showing a handstamp struck on the address side, but not used as a cancellation for the GB stamp.

1894–99. Cancelled as T **8**, but inscribed "AGENT GENERAL NIGER TERRITORIES".

Z77		1d. lilac (V.)		
Z78		2½d. purple/*blue* (V.)		£2500

1895–96. Cancelled as T **7**, but inscribed as Nos. Z77/8.

Z79		2½d. purple/*blue* (V.)		£2500
Z80		5d. dull purple and blue (V.)		£2500
Z81		10d. dull purple and carmine (V.)		£2500
Z82		2s.6d. deep lilac (V.)		

It is now believed that these cancellations may have been used at Asaba. They all occur on covers with Akassa handstamps, often of different dates.

The British Government purchased the Royal Niger Company territories and from 1 January 1900 they were incorporated into the protectorates of Northern and Southern Nigeria. Of the post offices listed above, only Lokoja was then situated in Northern Nigeria, the remainder joining Niger Coast in forming Southern Nigeria.

Issues for Northern Nigeria did not reach Lokoja until sometime in March 1900 and the post office there continued to use unoverprinted stamps of Great Britain until these supplies arrived.

NORTHERN NIGERIA

The protectorate of Northern Nigeria was formed on 1 January 1900 from the northern part of the Niger Company Territories. Only one post office existed in this area, at Lokoja, and this continued to use unoverprinted stamps of GREAT BRITAIN until the arrival of Nos. 1/9 during April 1900.

PRICES FOR STAMPS ON COVER	
Nos. 1/7	from × 6
Nos. 8/9	—
Nos. 10/16	from × 5
Nos. 17/19	—
Nos. 20/6	from × 5
No. 27	—
Nos. 28/37	from × 5
Nos. 38/9	—
Nos. 40/9	from × 5
Nos. 50/2	—

PRINTERS. All issues were typographed by De La Rue & Co.

1   **2**

1900 (Apr). Wmk Crown CA. P 14.

1	1	½d. dull mauve and green	8·50	21·00
2		1d. dull mauve and carmine	5·50	5·50
3		2d. dull mauve and yellow	16·00	60·00
4		2½d. dull mauve and ultramarine	13·00	45·00
5	2	5d. dull mauve and chestnut	30·00	70·00
6		6d. dull mauve and violet	30·00	50·00
7	1	1s. green and black	30·00	85·00
8		2s.6d. green and ultramarine	£180	£550
9		10s. green and brown	£325	£900
1/9 *Set of 9*			£550	£1600
1s/9s Optd "SPECIMEN" *Set of 9*			£225	

Examples of all values are known showing a forged Northern Nigeria postmark dated "AU 14 1900".

3   **4**

1902 (1 July). Wmk Crown CA. P 14.

10	3	½d. dull purple and green	2·00	1·75
		w. Wmk inverted	—	£375
11		1d. dull purple and carmine	4·75	1·00
12		2d. dull purple and yellow	2·00	3·00
13		2½d. dull purple and ultramarine	1·75	12·00
14	4	5d. dull purple and chestnut	7·00	8·50
15		6d. dull purple and violet	19·00	8·00
16	3	1s. green and black	8·50	8·50
17		2s.6d. green and ultramarine	19·00	75·00

18		10s. green and brown	50·00	55·00
10/18 *Set of 9*			£100	£150
10s/18s Optd "SPECIMEN" *Set of 9*			£170	

1904 (Apr). Wmk Mult Crown CA. P 14.

19	4	£25 green and carmine		£60000

No. 19, although utilising the "POSTAGE & REVENUE" Key type, was intended to pay the fiscal fee for liquor licences.

1905 (Aug)–07. Ordinary paper. Wmk Mult Crown CA. P 14.

20	3	½d. dull purple and green (10.05)	30·00	8·00
		a. Chalk-surfaced paper (1906)	5·50	5·00
21		1d. dull purple and carmine	21·00	1·50
		a. Chalk-surfaced paper (1906)	5·50	1·00
22		2d. dull purple and yellow (10.05)	26·00	32·00
		a. Chalk-surfaced paper (1907)	19·00	32·00
23		2½d. dull purple and ultramarine (10.05)	6·50	12·00
24	4	5d. dull purple and chestnut (10.05)	40·00	85·00
		a. Chalk-surfaced paper (1907)	38·00	80·00
25		6d. dull purple and violet (10.05)	27·00	65·00
		a. Chalk-surfaced paper (1906)	55·00	55·00
26	3	1s. green and black (10.05)	70·00	£110
		a. Chalk-surfaced paper (1906)	22·00	55·00
27		2s.6d. green and ultramarine (10.05)	60·00	70·00
		a. Chalk-surfaced paper (1906)	45·00	60·00
20a/7a *Set of 8*			£200	£275

1910 (30 Jan)–11. Ordinary paper (½d. to 2½d.) or chalk-surfaced paper (others). Wmk Mult Crown. CA. P 14.

28	3	½d. green (15.4.10)	2·00	1·25
29		1d. carmine	5·50	1·25
30		2d. grey (26.10.11)	9·00	6·00
31		2½d. blue (10.10)	4·00	10·00
32	4	3d. purple/*yellow* (10.9.11)	4·00	1·00
34		5d. dull purple and olive-green (26.2.11)	6·00	18·00
35		6d. dull purple and purple (10.11.10)	6·00	27·00
		a. Dull and bright purple (1911)	5·00	6·00
36	3	1s. black/*green* (10.11.10)	5·00	75
37		2s.6d. black and red/*blue* (15.3.11)	18·00	48·00
38	4	5s. green and red/*yellow* (10.9.11)	28·00	75·00
39		10s. green and red/*green* (15.3.11)	55·00	48·00
28/39 *Set of 11*			£120	£190
28s/39s Optd "SPECIMEN" *Set of 11*			£350	

5   **6**

1912 (Sept). Ordinary paper (½d., 1d., 2d.) or chalk-surfaced paper (others). Wmk Mult Crown CA. P 14.

40	5	½d. deep green	4·25	1·25
41		1d. red	4·50	60
42		2d. grey	6·50	17·00
43	6	3d. purple/*yellow*	2·50	1·25
44		4d. black and red/*yellow*	1·25	2·25
45		5d. dull purple and olive-green	4·00	19·00
46		6d. dull and bright purple	4·00	4·25
47		9d. dull purple and carmine	2·25	12·00
48	5	1s. black/*green*	4·75	2·75
49		2s.6d. black and red/*blue*	10·00	55·00
50	6	5s. green and red/*yellow*	25·00	85·00
51		10s. green and red/*green*	45·00	48·00
52	6	£1 purple and black/*red*	£180	£110
40/52 *Set of 13*			£250	£325
40s/52s Optd "SPECIMEN" *Set of 13*			£225	

Examples of most values are known showing forged postmarks of Lokoja dated "MR 22 12" or Minna dated "JN 16 1913". These forged postmarks have also been seen on examples of earlier issues.

On 1 January 1914 Northern Nigeria became part of Nigeria.

SOUTHERN NIGERIA

The Colony and Protectorate of Southern Nigeria was formed on 1 January 1900 by the amalgamation of Niger Coast Protectorate with the southern part of the Niger Territories. Lagos was incorporated into the territory on 1 May 1906.

The stamps of NIGER COAST PROTECTORATE were used in Southern Nigeria until the introduction of Nos. 1/9, and also during a shortage of these values in mid-1902. The issues of LAGOS were utilized throughout Southern Nigeria after 1 May 1906 until supplies were exhausted.

PRICES FOR STAMPS ON COVER	
Nos. 1/7	from × 8
Nos. 8/9	—
Nos. 10/18	from × 4
Nos. 19/20	—
Nos. 21/30	from × 4
Nos. 31/2	—
Nos. 33/42	from × 4
Nos. 43/4	—
Nos. 45/53	from × 4
Nos. 55/6	—

PRINTERS. All issues of Southern Nigeria were typographed by De La Rue & Co, Ltd, London.

1   **2**   **3**

1901 (Mar)–02. Wmk Crown CA. P 14.

1	1	½d. black and pale green	1·75	3·00
		a. *Sepia and green* (1902)	2·50	2·75
2		1d. black and carmine	3·00	2·75
		a. *Sepia and carmine* (1902)	4·25	1·75
3		2d. black and red-brown	3·50	7·00
4		4d. black and sage-green	3·50	29·00
5		6d. black and purple	4·75	12·00
6		1s. green and black	10·00	32·00
7		2s.6d. black and brown	48·00	95·00
8		5s. black and orange-yellow	65·00	£130
9		10s. black and purple/*yellow*	£150	£300
1/9 *Set of 9*			£250	£550
1s/9s Optd "SPECIMEN" *Set of 9*			£225	

1903 (Mar)–04. Wmk Crown CA. P 14.

10	2	½d. grey-black and pale green	1·00	30
		w. Wmk inverted		
11		1d. grey-black and carmine	1·25	70
12		2d. grey-black and chestnut	17·00	1·50
13		2½d. grey-black and blue (1904)	2·00	2·50
14		4d. grey-black and olive-green	5·50	5·50
15		6d. grey-black and purple	9·00	8·00
16		1s. green and black	42·00	19·00
17		2s.6d. grey-black and brown	42·00	75·00
18		5s. grey-black and yellow	90·00	£225
19		10s. grey-black and purple/*yellow*	45·00	£150
20		£1 green and violet	£475	£1000
10/20 *Set of 11*			£650	£1300
10s/20s Optd "SPECIMEN" *Set of 11*			£325	

Two Dies of Head Plate:

A   B

In Head A the fifth line of shading on the king's cheek shows as a line of dots and the lines of shading up to the king's hair are broken in places. In Head B the lines of shading are more regular, especially the fifth line.

1904 (June)–09. Head Die A. Ordinary paper. Wmk Mult Crown CA. P 14.

21	2	½d. grey-black and pale green	60	10
		a. Chalk-surfaced paper (1905)	2·25	90
22		1d. grey-black and carmine	18·00	20
		a. Chalk-surfaced paper (1905)	12·00	10
23		2d. grey-black and chestnut (1905)	2·75	45
		a. *Pale grey and chestnut* (Head Die B) (1907)	4·50	40
24		2½d. grey-black and bright blue (9.09)	1·00	1·00
25		3d. orange-brown and bright purple (chalk-surfaced paper) (Head Die B) (18.8.07)	9·50	1·25
		s. Optd "SPECIMEN"	27·00	
26		4d. grey-black and olive-green (12.05)	14·00	25·00
		a. Chalk-surfaced paper (1906)	26·00	30·00
		ab. *Grey-black and pale olive-green* (Head Die B) (1907)	50·00	50·00
27		6d. grey-black and bright purple (9.05)	13·00	9·50
		a. Chalk-surfaced paper (1906)	13·00	15·00
		ab. Head Die B (1907)	18·00	2·25
28		1s. grey-green and black (19.9.07)	3·25	3·50
		a. Chalk-surfaced paper (Head Die B) (1907)	42·00	3·25
29		2s.6d. grey-black and brown (30.4.06)	24·00	29·00
		a. Chalk-surfaced paper (1906)	55·00	20·00
		ab. Head Die B (1907)	65·00	29·00
30		5s. grey-black and yellow (10.12.07)	60·00	90·00
		a. Chalk-surfaced paper (Head Die B) (1908)	85·00	£100
31		10s. grey-black and purple/*yellow* (chalk-surfaced paper) (Head Die B) (9.08)	£170	£225
32		£1 green and violet (19.3.06)	£350	£425
		a. Chalk-surfaced paper (1906)	£325	£425
		ab. Head Die B (1907)	£325	£400
21/32ab *Set of 12*			£550	£700

I   II

Die I. Thick "1", small "d". (double working plate).
Die II. Thinner "1", larger "d" (single working plate).

1907–11. Colours changed. Head Die B. Ordinary paper (½d. to 2½d.) or chalk-surfaced paper (others). Wmk Mult Crown CA. P 14.

33	2	½d. grey-green (1907)	7·00	20
		a. Head Die A	16·00	3·25
		b. *Blue-green* (1910)	2·25	20
34		1d. carmine (I) (12.8.07)	4·00	60
		a. Head Die A	28·00	3·25
		ab. Die II. *Carmine-red* (1910)	1·00	10
35		2d. greyish slate (9.09)	2·75	70
36		2½d. blue (9.09)	8·00	3·75
37		3d. purple/*yellow* (7.09)	2·00	30
38		4d. black and red/*yellow* (9.09)	2·25	80
39		6d. dull purple and purple (9.09)	50·00	3·25
		a. *Dull purple and bright purple* (1911)	28·00	3·25
		aw. Wmk inverted	†	£275

40		1s. black/*green* (7.09)	7·00	40
41		2s.6d. black and red/*blue* (9.09)	18·00	3·25
42		5s. green and red/*yellow* (9.09)	40·00	48·00
43		10s. green and red/*green* (9.09)	£100	£140
44		£1 purple and black/*red* (9.09)	£250	£300
33/44 *Set of 12*			£400	£450
33s/44s Optd "SPECIMEN" *Set of 12*			£400	

1912. Wmk Mult Crown CA. P 14.

45	3	½d. green	2·25	10
46		1d. red	2·25	10
		w. Wmk inverted	£225	£170
		y. Wmk inverted and reversed	†	£300
47		2d. grey	75	85
48		2½d. bright blue	5·50	2·75
49		3d. purple/*yellow*	1·00	30
50		4d. black and red/*yellow*	1·25	2·00
51		6d. dull and bright purple	3·00	1·25
52		1s. black/*green*	2·75	75
53		2s.6d. black and red/*blue*	9·00	50·00
54		5s. green and red/*yellow*	20·00	80·00
55		10s. green and red/*green*	48·00	£100
56		£1 purple and black/*red*	£200	£275
45/56 *Set of 12*			£250	£450
45s/56s Optd "SPECIMEN" *Set of 12*			£275	

STAMP BOOKLETS

1904. Black on red cover. Stapled.

SB1 2s.1d. booklet containing 24×1d (No. 11) in blocks of 6.

1905 (1 June)–06. Black on red cover. Stapled.

SB2	2s.1d. booklet containing 24×1d. (No. 22) in blocks of 6	£2000
	a. As No. SB2 but containing No. 22a (1906)	£1800

1907 (7 Oct). Black on red cover. Stapled.

SB3	2s.1d. booklet containing 24×1d (No. 34) in blocks of 6	£2250

1910 (19 Sept). Black on red cover. Stapled.

SB4	2s. booklet containing 11×½d. and 18×1d. (Nos. 33b, 34ab) in blocks of 6 or 5	

1912 (Oct). Black on red cover. Stapled.

SB5	2s. booklet containing 12×½d. and 18×1d. (Nos. 45/6) in blocks of 6	£2000

On 1 January 1914 Southern Nigeria became part of Nigeria.

NIGERIA

Nigeria was formed on 1 January 1914 from the former protectorates of Northern and Southern Nigeria.

PRICES FOR STAMPS ON COVER TO 1945	
Nos. 1/10	*from* × 3
Nos. 11/12	—
Nos. 15/28	*from* × 3
Nos. 29/a	—
Nos. 30/3	*from* × 3
Nos. 34/59	*from* × 2

CROWN COLONY

1   2

(Typo D.L.R.)

1914 (1 June)–29. Die I. Ordinary paper (½d. to 2½d.) or chalk-surfaced paper (others). Wmk Mult Crown CA. P 14.

1	1	½d. green	5·50	70
2		1d. carmine-red	4·75	10
		a. *Scarlet* (1916)	15·00	20
		w. Wmk inverted	£160	£120
3		2d. grey	8·00	1·75
		a. *Slate-grey* (1918)	9·00	75
4		2½d. bright blue	10·00	7·50
		a. *Dull blue* (1915)	27·00	11·00
5	2	3d. purple (white back)	2·75	12·00
		a. *Lemon back* (19.8.15)	1·50	2·75
		b. *On deep yellow (yellow back)* (thick paper) (1915)	50·00	7·50
		bs. Optd "SPECIMEN"	48·00	
		c. *On orange-buff* (1920)	9·00	22·00
		d. *On buff* (1920)	12·00	
		e. *On pale yellow* (1921)	14·00	15·00
6		4d. black and red/*yellow* (white back)	1·40	10·00
		a. *Lemon back* (19.8.15)	1·00	5·00
		b. *On deep yellow (yellow back)* (thick paper) (1915)	50·00	8·50
		bs. Optd "SPECIMEN"	48·00	
		c. *On orange-buff* (1920)	14·00	14·00
		d. *On buff* (1920)	14·00	
		e. *On pale yellow* (1921)	10·00	18·00
7		6d. dull purple and bright purple	9·00	10·00
8	1	1s. black/*blue-green* (white back)	1·50	23·00
		a. *On yellow-green (white back)* (1915)	£225	
		b. *Yellow-green back* (19.8.15)	60·00	60·00
		c. *Blue-green back* (1915)	3·50	9·50
		cs. Optd "SPECIMEN"	48·00	
		d. *Pale olive back* (1917)	38·00	50·00
		dw. Wmk inverted		
		e. *On emerald (pale olive back)* (1920)	8·00	50·00
		f. *On emerald (emerald back)* (1920)	1·25	15·00
9		2s.6d. black and red/*blue*	16·00	6·50

10	2	5s. green and red/*yellow* (white back)	24·00	65·00
		a. *Lemon back* (19.8.15)	21·00	60·00
		b. *On deep yellow (yellow back)* (thick paper) (1915)	60·00	75·00
		bs. Optd "SPECIMEN"	55·00	
		c. *On orange-buff* (1920)	70·00	£110
		d. *On buff* (1920)	80·00	
		e. *On pale yellow* (1921)	£130	£180
11	1	10s. green and red/*blue-green* (white back)	50·00	£180
		a. *Blue-green back* (19.8.15)	70·00	£100
		as. Optd "SPECIMEN"	65·00	
		b. *Pale olive back* (1917)	£1100	£1800
		c. *On emerald (pale olive back)* (1920)	£160	£250
		d. *On emerald (emerald back)* (1921)	35·00	£120
12	2	£1 deep purple and black/*red*	£190	£275
		a. *Purple and black/red* (1917)	£225	£250
		b. Die II. *Deep purple and black/red* (19.1.27)	£275	£350
		ba. *Purple and black/red* (1929)	£225	£325
1/12 *Set of 12*			£275	£400
1s/12s Optd "SPECIMEN" *Set of 12*			£325	

The ½d. and 1d. were printed in sheets of 240 using two plates one above the other.

1921–32. Ordinary paper (½d. to 3d.) or chalk-surfaced paper (others). Wmk Mult Script CA. P 14.

15	1	½d. green (Die I) (1921)	1·25	55
		aw. Wmk inverted	£160	£120
		b. Die II (1925)	6·50	85
		c. Vert gutter pair. Die I and Die II. Nos. 15/b (1925)	£475	
16		1d. rose-carmine (Die I) (1921)	3·25	30
		aw. Wmk inverted	£140	£100
		b. Die II (1925)	1·75	35
		c. Vert gutter pair. Die I and Die II. Nos. 16/b (1925)	£425	
17	2	1½d. orange (Die II) (1.4.31)	9·00	15
18		2d. grey (Die I) (1921)	1·50	8·00
		a. Die II (1924)	10·00	40
19		2d. chestnut (Die II) (1.10.27)	4·50	1·00
20		2d. chocolate (Die II) (1.7.28)	4·50	15
		a. Die I (1932)	5·50	75
21		2½d. bright blue (Die I) (1921)	1·25	14·00
22	2	3d. bright violet (Die I) (1924)	6·00	4·75
		a. Die II (1925)	10·00	4·75
23		3d. bright blue (Die I) (1.4.31)	10·00	1·00
24		4d. black and red/*pale yellow* (Die II) (1923)	65	55
		a. Die I (1932)	4·00	4·75
25		6d. dull purple and bright purple (Die I) (1921)	13·00	42·00
		a. Die II (1923)	7·00	8·00
		aw. Wmk inverted	£180	
26		1s. black/*emerald* (Die II) (1924)	7·00	2·00
27		2s.6d. black and red/*blue* (Die II) (1925)	6·50	50·00
		a. Die I (1932)	50·00	85·00
28	2	5s. green and red/*pale yellow* (Die II) (1926)	15·00	80·00
		a. Die I (1932)	75·00	£250
29	1	10s. green and red/*green* (Die II) (1925)	65·00	£225
		a. Die I (1932)	£130	£500
15/29 *Set of 15*			£120	£350

15s/29s (ex 2d. chocolate) Optd or Perf (1½d., 3d. blue) "SPECIMEN" *Set of 14* ... £450

The ½d. and 1d., together with the 1½d. from 1932, were printed in sheets of 240 using two plates one above the other. Nos. 15c and 16c come from printings in November 1924 which combined Key Plate No. 7 (Die I) above Key Plate No. 12 (Die II).

1935 (6 May). Silver Jubilee. As Nos. 91/4 of Antigua, but ptd by Waterlow. P 11×12.

30		1½d. ultramarine and grey	1·00	1·50
31		2d. green and indigo	2·00	2·00
		k. Kite and vertical log	£130	£110
32		3d. brown and deep blue	3·25	19·00
33		1s. slate and purple	10·00	45·00
30/3 *Set of 4*			14·50	60·00
30s/3s Perf "SPECIMEN" *Set of 4*			£120	

For illustration of plate variety see Omnibus section following Zanzibar.

3 Apapa Wharf   **4** Cocoa   **5** Tin dredger

6 Timber industry   **7** Fishing Village   **8** Cotton ginnery

9 Habe Minaret   **10** Fulani cattle

11 Victoria-Buea Road

12 Oil Palms

13 River Niger at Jebba

14 Canoe Pulling

(Recess D.L.R.)
1936 (1 Feb). T **3/14**. Wmk Mult Script CA.

(a) P 11½×13

34	**3**	½d. green	1·50	1·40
35	**4**	1d. carmine	50	40
36	**5**	1½d. brown	2·00	40
		a. Perf 12½×13½	85·00	4·00
37	**6**	2d. black	50	80
38	**7**	3d. blue	2·00	1·50
		a. Perf 12½×13½	£150	24·00
39	**8**	4d. red-brown	2·25	2·00
40	**9**	6d. dull violet	50	60
41	**10**	1s. sage-green	1·75	4·75

(b) P 14

42	**11**	2s.6d. black and ultramarine	8·50	42·00
43	**12**	5s. black and olive-green	21·00	60·00
44	**13**	10s. black and grey	90·00	£140
45	**14**	£1 black and orange	£130	£200
34/45 *Set of 12*			£225	£400
34s/45s Perf "SPECIMEN" *Set of 12*			£300	

1937 (12 May). Coronation. As Nos. 95/7 of Antigua. P 11×11½.

46		1d. carmine	1·00	2·50
47		1½d. brown	3·00	3·00
48		3d. blue	3·00	6·00
46/8 *Set of 3*			6·25	10·50
46s/8s Perf "SPECIMEN" *Set of 3*			£110	

15 King George VI

16 Victoria-Buea Road

(Recess B.W. (T **15**), D.L.R. (others))
1938 (1 May)–**51**. Designs as T **15/16**. Wmk Mult Script CA. P 12 (T **15**) or 13×11½ (others).

49	**15**	½d. green	10	10
		a. Perf 11½ (15.2.50)	2·25	1·75
50		1d. carmine	19·00	2·50
		a. Rose-red (shades) (1940)	75	30
		ab. "A" of "CA" missing from wmk.	£2250	
50b		1d. bright purple (1.12.44)	10	20
		ba. Perf 11½ (15.2.50)	1·00	60
		bw. Wmk inverted (P 12)	†	—
51		1½d. brown	20	10
		a. Perf 11½ (15.11.50)	30	10
52		2d. black	10	3·25
52a		2d. rose-red (1.12.44)	10	3·50
		ab. Perf 11½ (15.2.50)	1·25	70
		aba. Wmk sideways	†	—
52b		2½d. orange (4.41)	10	3·00
53		3d. blue	10	10
		a. Wmk sideways	†	£5500
53b		3d. black (1.12.44)	15	3·25
54		4d. orange	50·00	3·75
54a		4d. blue (1.12.44)	15	4·50
55		6d. blackish purple	40	10
		a. Perf 11½ (17.4.51)	2·75	60
56		1s. sage-green	60	10
		a. Perf 11½ (15.2.50)	1·75	10
57		1s.3d. light blue (1940)	1·00	30
		a. Perf 11½ (14.6.50)	4·25	70
		ab. Wmk sideways	†	£5000
58	**16**	2s.6d. black and blue	60·00	25·00
		a. Perf 13½ (6.42)	4·50	8·50
		ab. Black and deep blue (1947)	55·00	55·00
		b. Perf 14 (1942)	3·50	3·50
		bw. Wmk inverted	£3250	£4500
		c. Perf 12 (15.8.51)	2·25	4·75
59	**13**	5s. black and orange	£110	22·00
		a. Perf 13½ (8.42)	7·50	4·50
		b. Perf 14 (1948)	11·00	3·00
		c. Perf 12 (19.5.49)	11·00	4·00
49/59c *Set of 16*			55·00	23·00
49s/59s (ex 2½d.) Perf "SPECIMEN" *Set of 15*			£450	

The 1d., No. 50ba, exists in coils constructed from normal sheets.

1946 (21 Oct). Victory. As Nos. 110/11 of Antigua.

60		1½d. chocolate	50	10
61		4d. blue	50	2·50
60s/1s Perf "SPECIMEN" *Set of 2*			85·00	

1948 (20 Dec). Royal Silver Wedding. As Nos. 112/13 of Antigua.

62		1d. bright purple	35	40
63		5s. brown-orange	17·00	26·00

1949 (10 Oct). 75th Anniv of UPU As Nos. 114/17 of Antigua.

64		1d. bright reddish purple	15	30
65		3d. deep blue	1·25	3·75
66		6d. purple	30	3·75
67		1s. olive	50	2·00
64/7 *Set of 4*			2·00	9·00

1953 (2 June). Coronation. As No. 120 of Antigua but ptd by B.W.

68		1½d. black and emerald	50	10
		w. Wmk inverted	†	—

18 Old Manilla Currency

19 Bornu horsemen

1d. Die I Flat-bed   Die Ia Rotary

Two types of 1d.:
The Belgian rotary printings have thicker lines of shading giving blotches of black colour instead of fine lines, particularly in the stirrups.

20 "Groundnuts"

21 "Tin"

2d. Major re-entry showing duplication of steps of the terraces (Pl 3, R. 1/5)

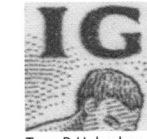
2d. Type A Gap in row of dots   Type B Unbroken row of dots

Two types of 2d. slate-violet:
Nos. 72c/f. The original cylinder used was Type A (July 1956); later Type B (Sept 1957). The above illustrations will help classification, but two stamps per sheet of 60 of Type A show faint dots. Shades are distinctive.

"2d" re-entry. Partial doubling of the "2d" and dot (Type A, R. 5/2 and 3). Also known on booklet panes.

2d. A flaw resembles an extra figure (Type A, R. 5/4)

22 Jebba Bridge and River Niger

23 "Cocoa"

3d. Die I Flat-bed

Die Ia Rotary

Two types of 3d.:
As in the 1d. the Belgian rotary printings have thicker lines of shading and this is particularly noticeable in the dark hills in the background.

24 Ife Bronze   **25** "Timber"

26 Victoria Harbour

27 "Palm-oil"

28 "Hides and skins"

29 New and Old Lagos

(Des M. Fievet. Recess Waterlow)
1953 (1 Sept)–**58**. T **18/29**. Wmk Mult Script CA. P 14.

69	**18**	½d. black and orange	15	30
70	**19**	1d. black and bronze-green (Die I)	20	10
		a. Die Ia (1.9.58)	20	20
71	**20**	1½d. blue-green	50	40
72	**21**	2d. black and yellow-ochre	4·00	30
		a. Black and ochre (18.8.54)	5·00	30
		b. Re-entry	£150	
72c		2d. slate-violet (Type A) (23.7.56)	3·00	2·00
		ca. "2d." re-entry	40·00	
		cb. Extra figure	40·00	
		d. Slate-blue (shades) (Type A)	9·00	40
		da. "2d." re-entry	80·00	
		db. Extra figure	85·00	
		e. Bluish grey (Type B) (25.9.57)	4·75	40
		f. Grey (shades) (Type B)	6·50	30
73	**22**	3d. black and purple (Die I)	55	10
		a. Die Ia. Black and reddish purple (1.9.58)	55	10
		b. Imperf (pair)	£400	
74	**23**	4d. black and blue	2·50	20
75	**24**	6d. orange-brown and black	30	10
		a. Chestnut and black (18.8.54)	2·75	10
76	**25**	1s. black and maroon	50	10
77	**26**	2s.6d. black and green	19·00	1·25
		a. Black and deep green (18.8.54)	30·00	1·25
78	**27**	5s. black and red-orange	6·50	1·40

79	**28**	10s. black and red-brown	24·00	3·25
80	**29**	£1 black and violet	35·00	19·00
69/80		*Set of 13*	80·00	24·00

Nos. 70a, 72c/db and 73a were printed on rotary machines by a subsidiary company, Imprimerie Belge de Sécurité, in Belgium.

Nos. 72d and 72f were only available in Nigeria.

The ½d. and 1d. (Die I) exist in coils constructed from sheets. Coils containing the 1d. (Die Ia) and 2d. (Type A) appeared in 1958 from continuously printed reels.

ROYAL VISIT 1956
(30)

1956 (28 Jan). Royal Visit. No. 72a optd with T **30**.

| 81 | **21** | 2d. black and ochre | 40 | 30 |
| | | a. Opt inverted | £350 | |

31 Victoria Harbour

(Recess Waterlow)

1958 (1 Dec). Centenary of Victoria. W w **12**. P 13½×14.

| 82 | **31** | 3d. black and purple | 40 | 30 |

32 Lugard Hall

33 Kano Mosque

(Recess Waterlow)

1959 (14 Mar). Attainment of Self–Government, Northern Region of Nigeria. T **32/3**. W w **12**. P 13½ (3d.) or 13½×14 (1s.).

| 83 | **32** | 3d. black and purple | 30 | 10 |
| 84 | **33** | 1s. black and green | 95 | 60 |

INDEPENDENT FEDERATION

34

35 Legislative Building

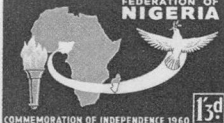

38 Dove, Torch and Map

(Des L. J. Wittington (1d.), R. Crawford (3d.), R. D. Baxter (6d.), J. White (1s.3d.), Photo Waterlow)

1960 (1 Oct). Independence. T **35**, **38** and similar horiz designs. W **34**. P 13½ (1s.3d.) or 14 (others).

85		1d. black and scarlet	10	10
86		3d. black and greenish blue	15	10
87		6d. green and red-brown	20	20
88		1s.3d. bright blue and yellow	40	20
85/8		*Set of 4*	70	50

Designs: (As T **35**)—3d. African paddling canoe; 6d. Federal Supreme Court.

39 Groundnuts

40 Coal mining

41 Adult education

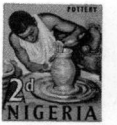

42 Pottery

43 Oyo carver

44 Weaving

---

45 Benin mask

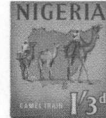

46 Yellow-casqued Hornbill

47 Camel train

48 Central Bank

49 Nigeria Museum

50 Kano Airport

51 Lagos railway station

1961 (1 Jan). T **39/51**. W **34**. P 15×14 (½d. to 1s.3d.) or 14½ (others).

89	**39**	½d. emerald	10	60
90	**40**	1d. reddish violet	80	10
91	**41**	1½d. carmine-red	80	2·25
92	**42**	2d. deep blue	30	10
		w. Wmk inverted	†	—
93	**43**	3d. deep green	40	10
94	**44**	4d. blue	40	2·00
95	**45**	6d. yellow and black	80	10
		a. Yellow omitted	£3250	£1500
96	**46**	1s. yellow-green	4·50	10
97	**47**	1s.3d. orange	1·50	10
98	**48**	2s.6d. black and yellow	2·75	15
99	**49**	5s. black and emerald	65	1·25
		w. Wmk inverted	†	—
100	**50**	10s. black and ultramarine	3·75	4·25
101	**51**	£1 black and carmine-red	14·00	18·00
		w. Wmk inverted	†	—
89/101		*Set of 13*	27·00	26·00

PRINTERS. The above and all following issues to No. 206 were printed in photogravure by Harrison & Sons, *except where otherwise stated.*

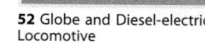

52 Globe and Diesel-electric Locomotive

56 Coat of Arms

(Des M. Goaman)

1961 (25 July). Admission of Nigeria into UPU. T **52** and similar horiz designs. W **34**. P 14½.

102		1d. red-orange and blue	30	10
103		3d. olive-yellow and black	30	10
104		1s.3d. blue and carmine-red	80	20
105		2s.6d. deep green and blue	85	2·00
102/5		*Set of 4*	2·00	2·00

Designs:—3d. Globe and mail-van; 1s.3d. Globe and Bristol 175 Britannia aircraft; 2s.6d. Globe and liner.

(Des S. Bodo (3d.), R. Hopeman (4d.), C. Adesina (6d.), M. Shamir (1s.6d.), B. Endwonwu (2s.6d.))

1961 (1 Oct). First Anniv of Independence. T **56** and similar designs. W **34**. P 14½.

106		3d. multicoloured	10	10
107		4d. yellow-green, yellow-orange and dull vermilion	30	75
108		6d. emerald-green	40	10
109		1s.3d. grey, emerald and blue	45	10
110		2s.6d. green, grey-blue and blackish brown	55	1·75
106/10		*Set of 5*	1·60	2·50

Designs: Horiz—4d. Natural resources and map; 6d. Nigerian Eagle; 1s.3d. Eagles in flight; 2s.6d. Nigerians and flag.

A used copy of No. 106 has been seen with both the silver (large "Y" appearing grey) and the yellow (appearing white) omitted.

61 "Health"

66 Malaria Eradication Emblem and Parasites

(Des M. Shamir)

1962 (25 Jan). Lagos Conference of African and Malagasy States. T **61** and similar vert designs. W **34**. P 14×14½.

111		1d. yellow-bistre	10	10
112		3d. deep reddish purple	10	10
113		6d. deep green	15	10
114		1s. brown	20	10
115		1s.3d. blue	25	20
111/15		*Set of 5*	65	40

Designs:—3d. "Culture"; 6d. "Commerce"; 1s. "Communications"; 1s.3d. "Co-operation".

1962 (7 Apr). Malaria Eradication. T **66** and similar horiz designs. W **34**. P 14½.

116		3d. green and orange-red	15	10
		w. Wmk inverted	†	
117		6d. blue and bright purple	20	10
118		1s.3d. magenta and violet-blue	30	10
119		2s.6d. blue and yellow-brown	45	90
116/19		*Set of 4*	1·00	1·00

Designs:—6d. Insecticide spraying; 1s.3d. Aerial spraying; 2s.6d. Mother, child and microscope.

70 National Monument

71 Benin Bronze

(Des S. Bodo (3d.), B. Endwonwu (5s.))

1962 (1 Oct). Second Anniv of Independence. W **34**. P 14½×14 (3d.) or 14×14½ (5s.).

120	**70**	3d. emerald and blue	10	10
		a. Emerald omitted	£800	£475
121	**71**	5s. red, emerald and violet	1·00	1·00

72 Fair Emblem

73 "Cogwheels of Industry"

(Des M. Goaman (1d., 2s.6d.), J. O. Gbagbeolu and M. Goaman (6d.), R. Hegeman (1s.))

1962 (27 Oct). International Trade Fair, Lagos. W **34**. T **72/3** and similar designs. P 14½.

122	**72**	1d. olive-brown and orange-red	10	10
123	**73**	6d. carmine-red and black	15	10
124		1s. orange-brown and black	15	10
125		2s.6d. ultramarine and yellow	60	20
122/5		*Set of 4*	85	30

Designs: Horiz as T **73**—1s. "Cornucopia of Industry"; 2s.6d. Oilwells and tanker.

76 "Arrival of Delegates"

77 Mace as Palm Tree

(Des S. Akosile (2½d.), M. Goaman (others))

1962 (5 Nov). Eighth Commonwealth Parliamentary Conference, Lagos. T **76/77** and similar design. W **34**. P 14½.

126	**76**	2½d. greenish blue	15	1·10
127		4d. indigo and rose-red	15	30
128	**77**	1s.3d. sepia and lemon	20	20
126/8		*Set of 3*	45	1·50

Design: Horiz—4d. National Hall.

80 Tractor and Maize **81** Mercury Capsule and Kano Tracking Station

(Des M. Goaman)

1963 (21 Mar). Freedom from Hunger. T **80** and similar design. W **34**. P 14.
| 129 | 3d. olive-green | 2·00 | 20 |
| 130 | 6d. magenta | 2·25 | 20 |

Design: Vert—3d. Herdsman.

(Des R. Hegeman)

1963 (21 June). "Peaceful Use of Outer Space". T **81** and similar vert design. W **34**. P 14½×14.
| 131 | 6d. blue and yellow-green | 25 | 10 |
| 132 | 1s.3d. black and blue-green | 35 | 20 |

Design:—1s.3d. Satellite and Lagos Harbour.

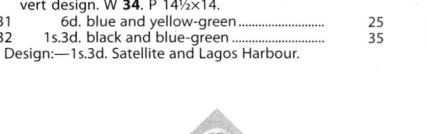

83 Scouts shaking Hands

(Des S. Apostolou (3d), G. Okiki (1s.))

1963 (1 Aug). 11th World Scout Jamboree, Marathon. T **83** and similar triangular-shaped design. W **34**. P 14.
133	3d. red and bronze-green	30	20
134	1s. black and red	95	80
MS134a	93×95 mm. Nos. 133/4	1·75	1·75
	ab. Red omitted (on 3d. value)	£1400	

Design:—1s. Campfire.

85 Emblem and First Aid Team **88** President Azikiwe and State House

(Des M. Goaman)

1963 (1 Sept). Red Cross Centenary. T **85** and similar horiz designs. W **34**. P 14½.
135	3d. red and deep ultramarine	60	10
136	6d. red and deep green	80	10
137	1s.3d. red and deep sepia	1·00	70
135/7 Set of 3		2·25	80
MS137a	102×102 mm. No. 137 (block of 4)	8·50	11·00

Designs:—6d. Emblem and "Hospital Services"; 1s.3d. Patient and emblem.

(Des M. Shamir. Photo Govt Printer, Israel)

1963 (1 Oct). Republic Day. T **88** and similar vert designs showing administrative buildings and President Azikiwe. P 14×13.
138	3d. yellow-olive and grey-green	10	10
139	1s.3d. yellow-brown and sepia	10	10
	a. Yellow-brown (portrait) omitted		
140	2s.6d. turquoise-blue and deep violet-blue	15	15
138/40 Set of 3		30	30

Designs:—1s.3d. Federal Supreme Court Building; 2s.6d. Parliament Building.

89 Charter and Broken Whip **90** "Freedom of Worship"

(Des S. Apostolou (3d.), Mrs. F. P. Effiong (others). Photo D.L.R.)

1963 (10 Dec). 15th Anniv of Declaration of Human Rights. T **89/90** and similar designs. W **34**. P 13.
141	**89**	3d. vermilion	10	10
142	**90**	6d. blue-green	15	10
143		1s.3d. ultramarine	30	10
144		2s.6d. bright purple	45	30
141/4 Set of 4			85	35

Designs: Vert as T **90**—1s.3d. "Freedom from want"; 2s.6d. "Freedom of speech".

93 Queen Nefertari **94** Rameses II

(Des M. Shamir)

1964 (8 Mar). Nubian Monuments Preservation. W **34**. P 14½.
| 145 | **93** | 6d. yellow-olive and emerald | 50 | 10 |
| 146 | **94** | 2s.6d. brown, deep olive and emerald | 1·75 | 2·25 |

95 President Kennedy

(Des M. Shamir (1s.3d), M. Goaman (2s.6d), Mr. Bottiau (5s.). Photo Govt Printer, Israel (1s.3d.); litho Lewin-Epstein, Bat Yam, Israel (others))

1964 (27 Aug). President Kennedy Memorial Issue. T **95** and similar horiz designs. P 13×14 (1s.3d.) or 14 (others).
147	1s.3d. light violet and black	30	15
148	2s.6d. black, red, blue and green	40	65
149	5s. black, deep blue, red and green	70	1·75
147/9 Set of 3		1·25	2·25
MS149a	154×135 mm. No. 149 (block of 4). Imperf	6·00	12·00

Designs:—2s.6d. President Kennedy and flags; 5s. President Kennedy (US coin head) and flags.

98 President Azikiwe **99** Herbert Macaulay

(Des S. Apostolou (3d), W. H. Irvine (others). Photo Govt Printer, Israel (3d); Harrison (others))

1964 (1 Oct). First Anniv of Republic. T **98** or **99** and similar vert design. P 14×13 (3d.) or 14½ (others).
150	**98**	3d. red-brown	10	10
151	**99**	1s.3d. green	35	10
152		2s.6d. deep grey-green	70	1·25
150/2 Set of 3			1·00	1·25

Design:—2s.6d. King Jaja of Opobo.

101 Boxing Gloves

102 Hurdling

(Des A. Adalade (3d), S. Medahunsi (6d.), M. Shamir (1s.3d.), M. Goaman (2s.6d.))

1964 (10 Oct). Olympic Games, Tokyo. T **101** and similar designs, and T **102**. W **34**. P 14 (2s. 6d) or 14½ (others).
153	3d. sepia and olive green	45	10
154	6d. emerald and indigo	60	10
155	1s.3d. sepia and yellow-olive	1·00	15
156	2s.6d. sepia and chestnut	1·75	3·75
153/6 Set of 4		3·50	3·75
MS156a	102×102 mm. No. 156 (block of 4). Imperf	3·00	4·25

Designs: Horiz—6d. High jumping. Vert—1s.3d. Running.

105 Scouts on Hill-top

(Des S. Apostolou (1d., 1s.3d), H. N. G. Cowham and Eagle Scout N. A. Lasisi (3d.), W. H. Irvine (6d.))

1965 (1 Jan). 50th Anniv of Nigerian Scout Movement. T **105** and similar vert designs. P 14×14½.
157	1d. brown	10	1·25
158	3d. red, black and emerald	20	10
159	6d. red, sepia and yellow-green	30	20
160	1s.3d. bistre-brown, greenish yellow and black-green	55	55
157/60 Set of 4		1·00	1·75
MS160a	76×104 mm. No. 160 (block of 4). Imperf	5·00	8·50

Designs:—3d. Scout badge on shield; 6d. Scout badges; 1s.3d. Chief Scout and Nigerian scout.

109 Telstar **110** Solar Satellite

(Des M. Shamir. Photo Govt Printer, Israel)

1965 (1 Apr). International Quiet Sun Years. P 14×13.
| 161 | **109** | 6d. reddish violet and turquoise-blue | 15 | 15 |
| 162 | **110** | 1s.3d. green and reddish lilac | 15 | 15 |

111 Native Tom-tom and Modern Telephone

(Des C. Botham (5s.), H. N. G. Cowham (others). Photo Enschedé)

1965 (2 Aug). ITU Centenary. T **111** and similar designs. P 11½×11 (1s.3d.) or 11×11½ (others).
163	3d. black, carmine and yellow-brown	30	10
164	1s.3d. black, blue-green and chalky blue	2·75	1·00
165	5s. black, carmine, blue and bright greenish blue	7·00	7·00
163/5 Set of 3		9·00	7·25

Designs: Vert—1s.3d. Microwave aerial. Horiz—5s. Telecommunications satellite and part of globe.

114 ICY Emblem and Diesel-hydraulic Locomotive **117** Carved Frieze

(Des W. H. Irvine. Photo D.L.R.)

1965 (1 Sept). International Co-operation Year. T **114** and similar horiz designs. W **34**. P 14×15.
166	3d. green, red and orange	4·00	20
167	1s. black, bright blue and lemon	3·00	40
168	2s.6d. green, bright blue and yellow	9·50	7·00
166/8 Set of 3		15·00	7·00

Designs:—1s. Students and Lagos Teaching Hospital; 2s.6d. Kainji (Niger) Dam.

(Des S. Apostolou (3d.), W. H. Irvine (others). Photo D.L.R.)

1965 (1 Oct). Second Anniv of Republic. T **117** and similar designs. P 14×15 (3d.) or 15×14 (others).
169	3d. black, red and orange-yellow	10	10
170	1s.3d. red-brown, deep green and light ultramarine	25	10
171	5s. brown, blackish brown and light green	60	1·25
169/71 Set of 3		85	1·25

Designs: Vert—1s.3d. Stone images at Ikom; 5s. Tada bronze.

120 Lion and Cubs **121** African Elephants

122 Splendid Sunbird

123 Village Weaver and Red-headed Malimbe

124 Cheetah

125 Leopards

126 Saddle-bill Stork

127 Grey Parrots

128 Blue-breasted Kingfishers

129 Crowned Cranes

130 Kobs

131 Giraffes

132 Hippopotamus

133 African Buffalo

(Des M. Fievet. Photo Harrison (1d., 2d., 3d., 4d. (No. 177a), 9d.) or Delrieu (others))

1965 (1 Nov)–**66**. T **120/33**. Without printer's imprint. Chalk-surfaced paper (1d., 2d., 3d., 4d., 9d.). P 12×12½ (½d., 6d.), 12½×12 (1½d., 4d.), 14×13½ (1d., 2d., 3d., 9d.) or 12½ (others).

172	120	½d. multicoloured (1.11.65)	1·00	2·75
173	121	1d. multicoloured (1.11.65)	50	15
174	122	1½d. multicoloured (2.5.66)	7·00	10·00
175	123	2d. multicoloured (1.4.66)	3·75	15
176	124	3d. multicoloured (17.10.66)	1·25	30
177	125	4d. multicoloured (2.5.66)	1·75	4·25
		a. Perf 14×13½ (1966)	30	10
178	126	6d. multicoloured (2.5.66)	1·50	40
179	127	9d. Prussian blue and orange-red (17.10.66)	2·50	60
180	128	1s. multicoloured (2.5.66)	5·00	2·00
181	129	1s.3d. multicoloured (2.5.66)	8·50	2·00

182	130	2s.6d. orange-brown, buff and brown (2.5.66)	75	2·50
183	131	5s. chestnut, light yellow and brown (2.5.66)	2·00	3·50
		a. Pale chestnut, yellow and brown-purple (1966)	5·50	3·50
184	132	10s. multicoloured (2.5.66)	6·50	4·00
185	133	£1 multicoloured (2.5.66)	21·00	9·00
172/85		*Set of 14*	55·00	35·00

The 2d. and 3d. exist with PVA gum as well as gum arabic. See also Nos. 220, etc.

The 1d., 3d., 4d. (No. 177a), 1s., 1s.3d., 2s.6d., 5s. and £1 values exist overprinted "F.G.N." (Federal Government of Nigeria) twice in black. They were prepared during 1968 at the request of one of the State Governments for use as official stamps, but the scheme was abandoned and meter machines were used instead. Some stamps held at Lagos Post Office were sold over the counter in error and passed through the post in October 1968. The Director of Posts made limited stocks of all values, except the 1s., available from the Philatelic Bureau from 11 April 1969 "in order not to create an artificial scarcity", but they had no postal validity. Covers do, however, exist showing the 4d. value used by Lagos Federal Income Tax Office in April 1969, the 1s.3d. on commercial mail to Britain in May 1969 and others from the Office of the Secretary to the Military Government in 1973 carry the 3d., 4d. and 2s.6d. values.

COMMONWEALTH P. M. MEETING 11. JAN. 1966 (**134**)

135 YWCA Emblem and HQ, Lagos

1966 (11 Jan). Commonwealth Prime Ministers Meeting, Lagos. No. 98 optd with T **134** by the Nigerian Security Printing and Minting Co, Lagos, in red.

186	48	2s.6d. black and yellow	30	30

(Des S. B. Ajayi. Litho Nigerian Security Printing & Minting Co Ltd)

1966 (1 Sept). Nigerian YWCA's Diamond Jubilee. P 14.

187	135	4d. yellow-orange, ultramarine, orange brown and yellow-green	15	10
188		9d. yellow-orange, ultramarine, brown and turquoise-green	15	60

137 Telephone Handset and Linesman

139 "Education, Science and Culture"

(Des S. B. Ajayi (4d.), N. Lasisi (1s.6d.), B. Endwonwu (2s.6d))

1966 (1 Oct). Third Anniv of Republic. T **137** and similar designs. W **34**. P 14½×14.

189		4d. green	10	10
190		1s.6d. black, brown and reddish violet	30	50
191		2s.6d. indigo, blue, yellow and green	1·00	2·25
189/91		*Set of 3*	1·25	2·50

Designs: Vert—4d. Dove and flag. Horiz—2s.6d. North Channel Bridge over Niger, Jebba.

(Des V. Whiteley from sketch by B. Salisu)

1966 (4 Nov). 20th Anniv of UNESCO. W **34** (sideways). P 14½×14.

192	139	4d. black, lake and orange-yellow	65	20
193		1s.6d. black, lake and turquoise-green	3·00	3·50
194		2s.6d. black, lake and rose-pink	4·00	9·50
192/4		*Set of 3*	7·00	12·00

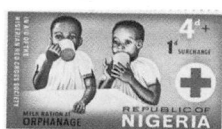

140 Children drinking

(Des V. Whiteley, after M. O. Afamefuna (4d.), I. U. Anawanti (1s.6d.) and S. Adeyemi (2s.6d.))

1966 (1 Dec). Nigerian Red Cross. T **140** and similar designs. W **34**. P 14×14½ (1s.6d.) or 14½×14 (others).

195		4d. +1d. black, reddish violet and red	30	30
196		1s.6d. +3d. multicoloured	55	3·75
197		2s.6d. +3d. multicoloured	65	4·25
195/7		*Set of 3*	1·25	7·50

Designs: Vert—1s.6d. Tending patient. Horiz—2s.6d. Tending casualties, and badge.

143 Surveying

(Des M. Goaman)

1967 (1 Feb). International Hydrological Decade. T **143** and similar multicoloured design. W **34**. P 14½×14 (4d.) or 14×14½ (2s.6d.).

198		4d. Type **143**	10	10
199		2s.6d. Water gauge on dam (*vert*)	40	2·25

145 Globe and Weather Satellite

147 Eyo Masqueraders

(Des M. Shamir (4d.), S. Bodo (1s.6d.))

1967 (23 Mar). World Meteorological Day. T **145** and similar horiz design. W **34**. P 14½×14.

200		4d. magenta and blue	15	10
201		1s.6d. black, yellow and blue	65	90

Design:—1s.6d. Passing storm and sun.

(Des G. A. Okiki (4d.), A. B. Saka Lawal (1s.6d.), S. Bodo (2s.6d.). Photo Enschedé)

1967 (1 Oct). Fourth Anniv of Republic. T **147** and similar multicoloured designs. P 11½×11 (2s.6d.) or 11×11½ (others).

202		4d. Type **147**	15	10
203		1s.6d. Crowd watching acrobat	50	1·50
204		2s.6d. Stilt dancer (*vert*)	75	3·50
202/4		*Set of 3*	1·25	4·50

150 Tending Sick Animal

151 Smallpox Vaccination

(Des G. Drummond)

1967 (1 Dec). Rinderpest Eradication Campaign. P 14½×14.

205	150	4d. multicoloured	15	10
206		1s.6d. multicoloured	55	1·50

PRINTERS AND PROCESS. Nos. 207/55 were printed in photogravure by the Nigerian Security Printing and Minting Co Ltd, *unless otherwise stated*.

(Des J. Owei. Litho)

1968 (7 Apr). 20th Anniv of World Health Organization. T **151** and similar horiz design. P 14.

207		4d. magenta and black	15	10
208		1s.6d. orange, lemon and black	55	1·00

Design:—1s.6d. African and mosquito.

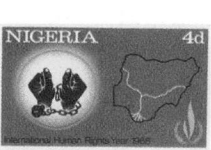

153 Chained Hands and Outline of Nigeria

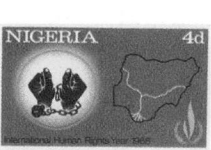

155 Hand grasping at Doves of Freedom

(Des Jennifer Toombs)

1968 (1 July). Human Rights Year. T **153** and similar design. P 14.

209		4d. greenish blue, black and yellow	15	10
210		1s.6d. myrtle-green, orange-red and black	85	1·00

Design: Vert—1s.6d. Nigerian flag and Human Rights emblem.

(Des G. Vasarhelyi)

1968 (1 Oct). Fifth Anniv of Federal Republic. P 13½×14.

211	155	4d. multicoloured	10	10
212		1s.6d. multicoloured	20	75

156 Map of Nigeria and Olympic Rings

158 GPO, Lagos

(Des J. Owei)

1968 (14 Oct). Olympic Games, Mexico. T **156** and similar horiz design. P 14.

213		4d. black, green and scarlet	20	10
214		1s.6d. multicoloured	80	30

Design:—1s.6d. Nigerian athletes, flag and Olympic rings.

(Des D.L.R.)

1969 (11 Apr). Inauguration of Philatelic Service. P 14.

215	158	4d. black and green	10	10
216		1s.6d. black and blue	20	50

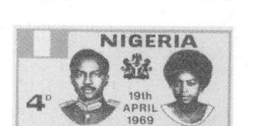

159 Yakubu Gowon and Victoria Zakari

(Des adapted from photo by Jackie Phillips. Litho)

1969 (20 Sept). Wedding of General Gowon. P 13×13½.

217	159	4d. chocolate and emerald	10	10
218		1s.6d. black and emerald	90	30

1969–72.
(a) As No. 173 etc, but printed by Nigerian Security Printing and Minting Co Ltd. With printer's imprint "N.S.P. & M. CO. LTD." P 13½ (6d.) or P 13×13½ (others)

220	**121**	1d. multicoloured	3·00	2·25
222	**123**	2d. multicoloured	4·50	2·75
		a. Smaller imprint* (13.1.71)	1·00	1·75
223	**124**	3d. multicoloured (7.71)	65	2·00
		a. Larger imprint* (22.10.71)	1·00	1·50
224	**125**	4d. multicoloured	8·50	10
		a. Smaller imprint†	90·00	20·00
225	**126**	6d. multicoloured (1971)	2·25	20
226	**127**	9d. Prussian blue and orange-red (1970)	6·00	50
		a. "TD" of "LTD" omitted from imprint (Pl. 1B, R. 10/2)	70·00	
227	**128**	1s. multicoloured (8.71)	2·50	20
228	**129**	1s.3d. multicoloured (1971)	11·00	4·50
229	**130**	2s.6d. multicoloured (1972)	22·00	7·00
230	**131**	5s. multicoloured (1972)	3·25	27·00
220/30	*Set of 10*		55·00	40·00

*On No. 222a the designer's name measures 4¾ mm. On No. 223a the imprints measure 9 and 8½ mm respectively. The normal imprints on Nos. 222/3 both measure 5½ mm.

The date given for Nos. 222a and 223a are for the earliest known used copies.

†No. 224 has the left-hand imprint 6 mm long and the right-hand 5½ mm. On No. 224a the imprints are 5½ mm and 4½ mm respectively. The width of the design is also ½ mm smaller.

Postal forgeries of the 2s.6d. exist printed by lithography and roughly perforated 11–12.

Imperforate proofs of similar 10s. and £1 values are known.

(b) As Nos. 222 and 224, but redrawn, and printed by Enschedé. No printer's imprint; designer's name at right. P 14½×13

231	**123**	2d. multicoloured (9.70)	50·00	2·00
232	**125**	4d. multicoloured (3.71)	2·00	30

In the 2d. the face value is white instead of yellow, and in the 4d. the white lettering and value are larger.

160 Bank Emblem and "5th Anniversary" **161** Bank Emblem and Rays

(Des J. Owei (4d.), B. Salisu (1s.6d.). Litho)

1969 (18 Oct). Fifth Anniv of African Development Bank. P 14.

233	160	4d. orange, black and blue	10	10
234	161	1s.6d. lemon, black and plum	20	1·25

162 ILO Emblem **164** Olumo Rock

(Des D. West)

1969 (15 Nov). 50th Anniv of International Labour Organisation. T **162** and similar horiz design. P 14.

235		4d. black and bright reddish violet	10	10
236		1s.6d. emerald and black	75	1·50

Design:—1s.6d. World map and ILO emblem.

(Des A. Onwudimegwu)

1969 (30 Dec). International Year of African Tourism. T **164** and similar designs. P 14.

237		4d. multicoloured	15	10
238		1s. black and bright emerald	20	10
239		1s.6d. multicoloured	1·25	95
237/9	*Set of 3*		1·40	1·00

Designs: Vert—1s. Traditional musicians; 1s.6d. Assob Falls.

167 Symbolic Tree **168** UPU HQ Building

(Des E. Emokpae (4d., 1s., 2s.), B. Onobrakpeya (1s.6d.). Photo Enschedé)

1970 (28 May). Stamp of Destiny; End of Civil War. T **167** and similar designs. P 11×11½ (2s.) or 11½×11 (others).

240		4d. gold, new blue and black	10	10
241		1s. multicoloured	10	10
242		1s.6d. yellow-green and black	15	10
243		2s. multicoloured	20	20
240/3	*Set of 4*		40	30

Designs: Vert—1s. Symbolic Wheel 1s.6d. United Nigerians supporting Map. Horiz—2s. Symbolic Torch.

(Des A. Onwudimegwu)

1970 (29 June). New UPU Headquarters Building. P 14.

244	168	4d. reddish violet and greenish yellow	10	10
245		1s.6d. light greenish blue and deep blue	40	20

169 Scroll **170** Oil Rig

(Des A. Onwudimegwu)

1970 (1 Sept). 25th Anniv of United Nations. T **169** and similar vert design. P 14.

246		4d. orange-brown, buff and black	10	10
247		1s.6d. steel-blue, cinnamon and gold	30	20

Design:—1s.6d. UN Building.

(Des E. Emokpae. Litho Enschedé)

1970 (30 Sept). Tenth Anniv of Independence. T **170** and similar vert designs. Multicoloured. P 13½×13.

248		2d. Type **170**	25	25
249		4d. University Graduate	15	10
250		6d. Durbar Horsemen	30	10
251		9d. Servicemen raising Flag	40	10
252		1s. Footballer	40	10
253		1s.6d. Parliament Building	40	40
254		2s. Kainji Dam	70	1·40
255		2s.6d. Agricultural Produce	70	2·25
248/55	*Set of 8*		3·00	4·00

STAMP BOOKLETS

1915. Black on crimson cover, inscribed "NIGERIA".
SB1 2s. booklet containing 12×½d. and 18×1d. (Nos. 1/2) in blocks of 6 ... £2750

1921–26. Black on scarlet cover, inscribed "NIGERIA".
SB2 4s. booklet containing 12×1d. and 18×2d. grey (both Die I) (Nos. 16, 18) in blocks of 6 ... £2750
a. Containing Nos. 16 and 18a (1924) ... £2500
b. Containing Nos. 16b and 18a (1926) ... £2500

1926(?). Black on scarlet cover, inscribed "STAMPS BOOKLET/ NIGERIA".
SB3 4s. booklet containing 12×1d. and 18×2d. grey (both Die II) (Nos. 16b, 18a) in blocks of 6 ... £2750

1928. Black on scarlet cover, inscribed "STAMPS BOOKLET/ NIGERIA".
SB5 4s. booklet containing 12×1d. (Die II) and 18×2d. chestnut (Nos. 16b, 19) in blocks of 6 ... £2750

1929. Black on scarlet cover, inscribed "STAMPS BOOKLET/ NIGERIA".
SB6 4s. booklet containing 12×1d. (Die II) and 18×2d. chocolate (Nos. 16b, 20) in blocks of 6 ... £2250

1931 (Jan). Black on scarlet cover, inscribed "STAMPS BOOKLET/ NIGERIA".
SB7 4s. booklet containing 12×1d. and 24×1½d. (Nos. 16b, 17) in blocks of 6 ... £2750

1957 (Aug). Black on green cover. Stitched.
SB8 2s. booklet containing 4×1d. and 8×½d. and 8×2d. (Nos. 69/70, 72c) in blocks of 4 ... 24·00
a. Contents as No. SB8, but containing No. 72d . 60·00

1957 (Oct). Black on buff cover. Stitched.
SB9 10s. booklet containing 8×3d. and 8×1s. (Nos. 73, 76) in blocks of 4 and a pane of air mail labels ... 32·00

1963. Black on green (No. SB10) or buff (No. SB11) covers. Stitched.
SB10 2s. booklet containing 1d. and 3d. (Nos. 90, 93) in blocks of 6 ... 5·50
SB11 10s.6d. booklet containing 6×1s.3d. and 12×3d. (Nos. 93, 103) in blocks of 6 and two panes of air mail labels ... 16·00

1966. Black on green cover. Stitched.
SB12 3s. booklet containing 4×1d. and 4×4d. and 8×2d. (Nos. 173, 175, 177a) in blocks of 4 ... 50·00

POSTAGE DUE STAMPS

D **1**

(Litho BW.)

1959 (4 Jan). Wmk Mult Script CA. P 14½×14.

D1	D **1**	1d. red-orange	15	1·00
D2		2d. red-orange	20	1·00
D3		3d. red-orange	25	1·50
D4		6d. red-orange	25	5·50
D5		1s. grey-black	50	7·50
D1/5	*Set of 5*		1·25	15·00

1961 (1 Aug). W **34**. P 14½×14.

D6	D **1**	1d. red	15	40
D7		2d. light blue	20	45
D8		3d. emerald	25	60
D9		6d. yellow	30	1·40
D10		1s. blue (*shades*)	50	2·25
D6/10	*Set of 5*		1·25	4·50

BIAFRA

The Eastern Region of Nigeria declared its independence on 30 May 1967 as the Republic of Biafra. Nigerian military operations against the breakaway republic commenced in July 1967.

The Biafran postal service continued to use Nigerian stamps and when supplies of these became low in July 1967 "Postage Paid" cachets were used pending the issue of Nos. 1/3.

1 Map of Republic **2** Arms, Flag and Date of Independence **3** Mother and Child

(Typo and litho Mint, Lisbon)

1968 (5 Feb). Independence. P 12½.

1	**1**	2d. multicoloured	25	70
2	**2**	4d. multicoloured	25	70
3	**3**	1s. multicoloured	25	2·00
1/3	*Set of 3*		65	3·00

(4)

1968 (1 Apr). Nos. 172/5 and 177/85 of Nigeria optd as T **4** (without "SOVEREIGN" on 10s.) by Govt Printer at Enugu.

4		½d. multicoloured (No. 172)	2·25	6·50
5		1d. multicoloured (No. 173)	3·50	9·50
		a. Opt double	£200	
		b. Opt omitted (in pair with normal)	£550	
6		1½d. multicoloured (No. 174)	12·00	19·00
7		2d. multicoloured (No. 175)	38·00	55·00
8		4d. multicoloured (No. 177a)	19·00	55·00
9		6d. multicoloured (No. 179)	9·00	18·00
10		9d. Prussian blue and orange-red (No. 179)	3·75	4·25
11		1s. multicoloured (Blk.+R.) (No. 180)	65·00	£130
12		1s.3d. multicoloured (Blk.+R.) (No. 181)	35·00	60·00
		a. Black opt omitted	£400	
		b. Red opt omitted	£375	
13		2s.6d. orange-brown, buff and brown (Blk.+R.) (No. 182)	4·75	19·00
		a. Red opt omitted	£300	
14		5s. chestnut, light yellow and brown (Blk.+R.) (No. 183)	3·75	18·00
		a. Red opt omitted	£300	
		b. Black opt omitted	£300	
		c. Red opt omitted	£350	
		d. Pale chestnut, yellow and brown-purple (No. 183a)	4·50	13·00
15		10s. multicoloured (No. 184)	10·00	42·00
16		£1 multicoloured (Blk.+R.) (No. 185)	10·00	42·00
		a. Black ("SOVEREIGN BIAFRA") opt omitted	£300	
		b. Red (Coat of Arms) opt omitted	£300	
4/16	*Set of 13*		£190	£400

Nos. 172/3 of Nigeria also exist surcharged "BIAFRA– FRANCE FRIENDSHIP 1968 SOVEREIGN BIAFRA", clasped hands and "+5/-" (½d.) or "+£1" (1d.). There is no evidence that these two surcharges were used for postage within Biafra (*Price for set of 2 £20 mint*).

5 Flag and Scientist **8** Biafran Arms and Banknote **9** Orphaned Child

(Des S. Okeke. Litho Mint, Lisbon)

1968 (30 May). First Anniv of Independence. T **5**, **8/9** and similar vert designs. P 12½.

17	**5**	4d. multicoloured	25	20
18		1s. multicoloured	25	30
19		2s.6d. multicoloured	70	5·50
20	**8**	5s. multicoloured	80	6·00
		a. Indigo (banknote) omitted	£110	
		b. Red (from flag) omitted	£100	
21	**9**	10s. multicoloured	1·10	6·50
		a. Bright green (from flag) omitted	60·00	
17/21	*Set of 5*		2·75	16·00

Designs:—1s. Victim of atrocity; 2s.6d. Nurse and refugees.

Nos. 17/21 also exist surcharged "HELP BIAFRAN CHILDREN" and different charity premium ranging from 2d. on the 4d. to 2s.6d. on the 10s. There is no evidence that these surcharges were used for postage within Biafra (*Price for set of 5 £2 mint*).

In September 1968 a set of four values, showing butterflies and plants, was offered for sale outside Biafra. The same stamps also exist overprinted "MEXICO OLYMPICS 1968" and Olympic symbol. There is no evidence that either of these issues were used for postage within Biafra (*Price for set of 4 £4 (Butterflies and Plants) or £5 (Olympic overprints), both mint*).

CANCELLED-TO-ORDER. Many issues of Biafra, including the three unissued sets mentioned above, were available cancelled-to-order with a special "UMUAHIA" handstamp. This was the same diameter as postal cancellations, but differed from them by having larger letters, 3 mm. high, and the year date set in full. Where such cancellations exist on issued stamps the used prices quoted are for c-t-o examples. Postally used stamps are worth considerably more.

16 Child in Chains and Globe

17 Pope Paul VI, Map of Africa and Papal Arms

1969 (30 May). Second Anniv of Independence. Multicoloured; frame colours given. Litho (in Italy). P 13×13½.

35	**16**	2d. yellow-orange	1·25	4·25
36		4d. red-orange	1·25	4·25
		a. Green (wreath) and orange (Sun) omitted	£375	
37		1s. new blue	1·75	7·50
38		2s.6d. emerald	2·00	15·00
35/8 *Set of 4*			5·75	28·00

A miniature sheet with a face value of 10s. was also released.

1969 (1 Aug). Visit of Pope Paul to Africa. T **17** and similar vert designs. Multicoloured. Litho (in Italy). P 13×13½.

39		4d. Type **17**	1·25	3·00
40		6d. Pope Paul VI, map of Africa and Arms of the Vatican	1·50	7·50
41		9d. Pope Paul VI, map of Africa and St. Peter's Basilica, Vatican	1·75	8·50
42		3s. Pope Paul VI, map of Africa and Statue of St. Peter	3·25	16·00
39/42 *Set of 4*			7·00	32·00

A miniature sheet with a face value of 10s. was also released.

No. 42 has a magenta background. This value is also known with the background in brown-red or brown.

On 17 December the French Agency released a Christmas issue consisting of Nos. 39/42 overprinted "CHRISTMAS 1969 PEACE ON EARTH AND GOODWILL TO ALL MEN" together with the miniature sheet overprinted "CHRISTMAS 1969" and surcharged £1. Later Nos. 35/38 were released overprinted in red "SAVE BIAFRA 9TH JAN 1970" with a premium of 8d., 1s.4d., 4s., and 10s. respectively together with the miniature sheet with a premium of £1. We have no evidence that these issues were actually put on sale in Biafra before the collapse, but it has been reported that the 4d. Christmas issue and 2d.+8d. Save Biafra exist genuinely used before capitulation.

Nos. 40/41 have been seen surcharged "+ 10/-HUMAN RIGHTS" and the United Nations emblem but it is doubtful if they were issued.

No. 81 of Nigeria has also been reported with the original "ROYAL VISIT 1956" overprint, together with "NIGERIA" from the basic stamp, obliterated and a "SERVICE" overprint added. Such stamps were not used for official mail in Biafra, although an example is known with the "UMUAHIA" c-t-o mark.

Biafra was overrun by Federal troops in January 1970 and surrender took place on 15 January.

■ **Niue** *see after* **New Zealand**

■ **Norfolk Island** *see after* **Australia**

North Borneo

PRICES FOR STAMPS ON COVER TO 1945	
No. 1	from × 100
Nos. 2/3	from × —
Nos. 4/5	—
Nos. 6/19	from × 10
No. 21b	—
Nos. 22/8	from × 50
Nos. 29/35	—
Nos. 36/44	from × 100
Nos. 45/50	—
Nos. 51/2	from × 10
No. 54	—
Nos. 55/65	from × 10
Nos. 66/79	from × 4
Nos. 81/6	—
Nos. 87/91	from × 12
Nos. 92/111	from × 4
Nos. 112/26	from × 10
Nos. 127/40	from × 6
Nos. 141/5	—
Nos. 146/57	from × 5
Nos. 158/79	from × 8
Nos. 181/5	—
Nos. 186/8	from × 10
Nos. 189/230	from × 4
Nos. 231/4	—
Nos. 235/49	from × 3
Nos. 250/2	—
Nos. 253/75	from × 12
Nos. 276/92	from × 7
Nos. 293/4	—
Nos. 295/300	from × 6
Nos. 301/2	—
Nos. 303/17	from × 3
Nos. 318/19	from × 20
Nos. 320/34	from × 3
Nos. F1/3	—
Nos. D1/30	from × 25
Nos. D31/6	from × 12
No. D37	—
Nos. D38/84	from × 40
Nos. D85/9	from × 8

BRITISH NORTH BORNEO COMPANY ADMINISTRATION

PRINTERS. The stamps of this country up to 1894 were designed by T. Macdonald and printed in lithography by Blades, East and Blades, London.

1   8 Cents. **(2)**   EIGHT CENTS **(3)**

1883 (Mar). P 12.

1	**1**	2c. red-brown	50·00	75·00
		a. Imperf between (horiz pair)	£15000	

The figure "2" varies in size.

1883 (June). No. 1 surch as T **2** or **3**.

2	**2**	8c. on 2c. red-brown	£1400	£850
3	**3**	8c. on 2c. red-brown	£500	£190
		a. Surch double	†	£6000

Type **2** was handstamped and stamps without stop are generally forgeries. Type **3** was a setting of 50 (10×5) providing ten varieties; it normally has a stop which sometimes failed to print.

> **CANCELLED-TO-ORDER**—Prices are separately indicated in a third price column, for stamps showing the recognisable black bars remainder cancellation. The issues since 1916 have not been thus cancelled.
>
> It should be noted, however, that a postmark of this form was in use for postal purposes up to this period, and was used at one or two of the smaller post-offices until 1949. A small oval with five bars was used to mark railway mail during 1945/55 and also as a paquebot mark at Jesselton *c.* 1950.

4   **5**   and Revenue **(6)**

1883. P 14.

4	**4**	50c. violet	£225	£275	40·00
		a. Inverted "L" for first "F" in "FIFTY" (R. 5/2)	£2000	—	£350
5	**5**	$1 scarlet	£180	£250	18·00

1883 (July). P 12.

6	**1**	4c. pink	65·00	70·00
		a. Imperf between (horiz pair)	£5500	
7		8c. green	85·00	60·00

1886. P 14.

8	**1**	½c. magenta	£120	£200
9		1c. orange	£200	£325

		a. Imperf (pair)	£275	£275
		b. Imperf horiz (vert pair)	£1500	
10		2c. brown	50·00	42·00
		a. Imperf between (horiz pair)	£700	
11		4c. pink	19·00	55·00
		a. Imperf between (horiz pair)	†	£1700
12		8c. green	22·00	50·00
		a. Imperf between (horiz pair)	£850	
13		10c. blue	55·00	65·00
		a. Imperf (pair)	£350	
8/13 *Set of 6*			£400	£650

1886 (Sept). Nos. 8 and 13 optd with T **6**.

14		½c. magenta	£250	£325
15		10c. blue	£300	£375

3 CENTS (7)   **5 CENTS (8)**   **3 CENTS** Small "3" variety (R. 3/1, 3/4, 3/7)

(Surch by *North Borneo Herald*, Sandakan)

1886 (Sept). T **1** surch as T **7/8**.

(a) P 12

16	**7**	3c. on 4c. pink	£325	£375
		a. Small "3"	—	£16000
17	**8**	5c. on 8c. green	£325	£375

(b) P 14

18	**7**	3c. on 4c. pink	£130	£150
		a. Small "3"	£1500	
19	**8**	5c. on 8c. green	£140	£150
		a. Surch inverted	£2750	

No. 16 is known fiscally used with error surcharge double.

9

10

11

12   **13**

1886–87.

(a) P 14

21b	**9**	½c. magenta	21·00	50·00
22		½c. rose	4·50	21·00
		a. Imperf (pair)	65·00	
23		1c. orange-yellow	19·00	42·00
		a. Imperf between (vert pair)	£425	
		b. Imperf (pair)	75·00	
24		1c. orange	2·00	16·00
		a. Imperf (pair)	50·00	
25		2c. brown	2·00	14·00
		a. Imperf (pair)	50·00	
26		4c. pink	6·50	20·00
		a. Imperf (pair)	60·00	
		b. Imperf between (horiz or vert pair)	£400	
		c. Imperf vert (horiz pair)	£325	
		d. Error. 1c. pink (R. 2/3) (centre stamp of strip of 3)	£350	£1300
		da. Imperf vert (strip of 3)	£7500	
		db. Imperf (strip of 3)	£6500	
27		8c. green	30·00	28·00
		a. Imperf (pair)	55·00	
28		10c. blue	15·00	45·00
		a. Imperf between (vert pair)	£425	
		b. Imperf (pair)	55·00	
29	**10**	25c. indigo	£475	25·00
		a. Imperf between (vert pair)	£425	
		b. Imperf (pair)	£425	50·00
30	**11**	50c. violet	£475	26·00
		a. Imperf (pair)	£550	50·00
31	**12**	$1 scarlet	£400	25·00
		a. Imperf (pair)	£600	50·00
32	**13**	$2 sage-green	£700	30·00
		a. Imperf (pair)	£600	55·00
22/32 *Set of 10*			£1900	£200

(b) P 12

34	**9**	½c. magenta	£400	£700
35		1c. orange	£250	£400

Nos. 21b/32 are known to have been sold as cancelled remainders, but these are difficult to distinguish from postally used. Values above 10c. are infrequently found postally used so that the used prices quoted are for the remainders.

14

15

16

17

18

1888–92. T **14** (as T **9** but inscr "POSTAGE & REVENUE")
and T **15/18** (T **10/13** redrawn). P 14.

36	14	½c. magenta (1889)	4·00	30·00	2·50
		a. Imperf vert (horiz pair)	†	†	£250
		b. Rose	1·50	9·00	60
		ba. Imperf between (horiz pair)	£400		
		c. Imperf (pair)	50·00	—	11·00
37		1c. orange (1892)	7·50	8·00	50
		a. Imperf vert (horiz pair)	£375		
		b. Imperf (pair)	50·00	—	10·00
38		2c. brown (1889)	20·00	27·00	90
		a. Imperf between (horiz pair)	†	†	£400
		b. Lake-brown	9·00	27·00	50
		c. Imperf (pair)	50·00	—	9·50
39		3c. violet (1889)	2·50	13·00	50
		b. Imperf (pair)	35·00	—	9·50
40		4c. rose-pink (1889)	15·00	50·00	50
		a. Imperf vert (horiz pair)	†	†	£250
		b. Imperf (pair)	55·00	—	10·00
41		5c. slate (1889)	2·75	30·00	50
		a. Imperf between (pair)	55·00		10·00
		b. Imperf (pair)	55·00	—	10·00
42		6c. lake (1892)	19·00	32·00	50
		a. Imperf (pair)	55·00	—	14·00
43		8c. blue-green (1891)	45·00	50·00	1·00
		a. Yellow-green	30·00	40·00	50
		c. Imperf (pair)	55·00	—	13·00
44		10c. blue (1891)	9·00	40·00	1·00
		a. Imperf between (vert pair)	†	†	£300
		b. Dull blue	7·00	22·00	50
		ba. Imperf between (horiz pair)			
		c. Imperf (pair)	50·00	—	11·00
45	15	25c. indigo	£110	£110	75
		a. Imperf (pair)	£500	†	22·00
		b. Imperf vert (horiz pair)	†	†	£300
46	16	50c. violet	£130	£150	75
		a. Imperf (pair)	£600	†	22·00
		b. Chalky blue	£140	£150	†
47	17	$1 scarlet	70·00	£110	75
		a. Imperf (pair)	£475	†	22·00
48	18	$2 dull green	£250	£250	1·50
		a. Imperf (pair)	£750	†	25·00
36b/48 Set of 13			£600	£750	7·50

Nos. 39, 43 and 44 showing stamps printed double or triple, one inverted, are from waste sheets subsequently sold by the British North Borneo Company to collectors.

These stamps to the 10c. value were forged on several occasions. Most forgeries of the ½c. value can be identified by the presence of a diagonal line joining the top two horizontal strokes of the uppermost Chinese character.

The new 25c. has the inscription "BRITISH NORTH BORNEO" in taller capitals. In the 50c. the "0" of the numerals "50" in the two upper corners is square-shaped at the top and bottom instead of being oval. The 1 dollar has 14 pearls instead of 13 at each side, and on the 2 dollars the word "BRITISH" measures 10½ to 11 mm in length in place of 12 mm.

19

20

1889. P 14.

49	19	$5 bright purple	£375	£400	8·50
		a. Imperf (pair)	£1000	†	75·00
50	20	$10 brown	£375	£400	12·00
		a. Imperf (pair)	£1200	†	85·00

---

		b. "DOLLAPS" for "DOLLARS" at foot (R. 2/1)	£1500	£2000	£375
		ba. Ditto. Imperf (pair)	£4750	†	£750

Two 6 1
Cents. cents. cent.
(21)   (22)   (23)

1890 (Dec). Surch as T **21**, in red.

51	15	2c. on 25c. indigo	85·00	95·00	
		a. Surch inverted	£450	£450	
52		8c. on 25c. indigo	£130	£140	

The first printing of Nos. 51/2 had the two lines of the surcharge 3.5 mm apart. On a second printing of both values this gap widened to 5 mm.

1891–92. Surch with T **22**.

54	9	6c. on 8c. green (1892)	£9000	£5000	
		a. Large "s" in "cents"	£16000		
55	14	6c. on 8c. yellow-green	29·00	10·00	
		a. Surch inverted	£475	£500	
		b. Inverted "c" in "cents" (R. 5/4)	£700	£750	
		c. "cetns." for "cents" (R. 3/7)	£700	£750	
		d. Large "s" in "cents" (R. 2/9 or 3/7)	£250	£200	
56	9	6c. on 10c. blue	60·00	23·00	
		a. Surch inverted	£300	£350	
		b. Surch double	£1400		
		c. Surch treble	£550		
		d. Large "s" in "cents"	£325	£180	
57	14	6c. on 10c. blue	£200	26·00	
		a. Large "s" in "cents"	£850	£225	

Unused examples of Nos. 55 and 57 are normally without gum.
There were three settings of the surcharge for No. 55. On the first two the large "s" in "cents" occurred on R. 2/9 with the other two listed varieties also included. Nos. 55b/c were corrected on the third setting and the large "s" in cents occurred on R. 3/7.

1892 (Mar–Nov). Surch as T **23** ("Cents." with capital "C" as in T **21** on No. 65), in red.

63	14	1c. on 4c. rose-pink	27·00	14·00	
		a. Surch double	£1600		
		b. Surch on back and on front	†	£600	
64		1c. on 5c. slate (11.92)	7·00	6·00	
65	15	8c. on 25c. indigo (date?)	£180	£190	

Unused examples of Nos. 63/5 are normally without gum.

24 Dyak Chief

25 Sambar Stag (*Cervus unicolor*)

26 Sago Palm

27 Great Argus Pheasant

28 Arms of the Company

29 Malay Dhow

30 Estuarine Crocodile

31 Mount Kinabalu

32 Arms of the Company with Supporters

PERFORATION. There are a number of small variations in the perforation of the Waterlow issues of 1894 to 1922 which we believe were due to irregularity of the pins rather than different perforators.

In the following lists, stamps perf 12, 12½, 13 or compound are described as perf 12–13, stamps perf 13½, 14 or compound are described as perf 13½–14 and those perf 14½, 15 or compound are listed as perf 14½–15. In addition the 13½–14 perforation exists compound with 14½–15 and with 12–13, whilst perf 15½–16 comes from a separate perforator.

(Recess Waterlow)

1894 (Feb). P 14½–15.

66	24	1c. black and olive-bistre	1·25	9·50	50
		a. Imperf between (horiz or vert pair)	£950		
		b. Perf 13½–14	1·75	15·00	50
		c. Perf 13½–14, comp 14½–15	50·00	60·00	—
		d. Perf 13½–14, comp 12–13	29·00	60·00	
		e. Perf 12–13			
67		1c. black and bistre-brown	4·00	23·00	50
		a. Perf 13½–14	5·00	23·00	1·00
		b. Perf 13½–14, comp 12–13	38·00	70·00	
		c. Perf 12–13			

68	25	2c. black and rose-lake	5·50	2·00	50
		a. Imperf between (horiz or vert pair)	£1500	£1500	†
		b. Perf 13½–14	55·00	55·00	75
		c. Perf 13½–14, comp 14½–15			
69		2c. black and lake	5·50	2·50	50
		a. Perf 13½–14	50·00	50·00	2·25
		b. Perf 13½–14, comp 12–13	42·00	45·00	—
		c. Imperf between (horiz pair)			
70	26	3c. olive-green and dull purple	2·75	8·50	50
		a. Imperf between (horiz pair)	£1200	£1100	†
		ab. Imperf between (vert pair)	£1400		
		b. Perf 13½–14, comp 14½–15			
		c. Bronze-green and dull purple	5·50		50
		d. Perf 13½–14			
71		3c. olive-green and violet (P 13½–14)	45·00	60·00	2·25
		a. Imperf between (horiz pair)	†	£1500	†
72	27	5c. black and vermilion	14·00	11·00	60
		a. Imperf between (horiz or vert pair)	£900		
		b. Perf 13½–14	50·00	60·00	1·25
		c. Perf 13½–14, comp 12–13	—	65·00	5·50
		d. Perf 13½–14, comp 14½–15			
		e. Perf 12–13			
73	28	6c. black and bistre-brown	65·00	85·00	60
		a. Perf 13½–14	4·50	18·00	60
		b. Perf 13½–14, comp 12–13	—	65·00	5·50
		c. Perf 13½–14, comp 14½–15	65·00		
		d. Imperf between (horiz pair)			
74	29	8c. black and dull purple	6·50	11·00	60
		a. Imperf between (vert pair)	£800		
		b. Perf 13½–14	10·00	42·00	1·00
		ba. Imperf between (vert pair)	£550	†	£300
		d. Perf 13½–14, comp 12–13			
75	30	12c. black and blue	40·00	85·00	2·50
		a. Perf 13½–14	29·00	80·00	2·50
		b. Imperf between (horiz pair)	£1800	†	£700
		c. Perf 13½–14, comp 14½–15			5·00
76		12c. black and ultramarine	50·00	85·00	3·00
		a. Perf 13½–14	50·00	85·00	3·00
		b. Imperf between (pair)			
78	31	18c. black and deep green	28·00	85·00	2·00
		a. Perf 13½–14	48·00	50·00	2·00
		b. Perf 13½–14, comp 14½–15	—		5·00
		c. Perf 13½–14 comp 12–13	—		5·00
79	32	24c. blue and rose-lake	23·00	85·00	2·00
		a. Imperf between (vert pair)			£500
		b. Imperf between (vert strip of 3)	†	†	£650
		c. Perf 13½–14	23·00	70·00	2·00
		d. Perf 13½–14, comp 14½–15			
66/79 Set of 9			£100	£225	9·00

32a   **32b**

32c   **32d**

32e   **32f**

(Litho Blades, East & Blades, London)

1894 (Jan). T **32a** to **32f**. P 14.

81	32a	25c. indigo	9·50	30·00	1·00
		a. Imperf (pair)	70·00	†	12·00
		b. Imperf between (horiz or vert pair)	£900	—	£110
82	32b	50c. deep slate-purple	50·00	65·00	2·00
		a. Imperf (pair)	—	†	12·00
		b. Imperf between (horiz pair)			
		d. Chalky blue	—	65·00	—
83	32c	$1 scarlet	14·00	30·00	1·25
		a. Perf 14×11	£300		
		b. Imperf (pair)	50·00	†	13·00

84	**32d**	$2 dull green	28·00	80·00	2·50
		a. Imperf (pair)	—	†	18·00
85	**32e**	$5 bright purple	£275	£350	17·00
		a. Imperf (pair)	£900	†	65·00
		b. Dull purple	£325	£375	11·00
86	**32f**	$10 brown	£325	£400	16·00
		a. Imperf (pair)	£950	†	65·00
81/6 *Set of 6*			£650	£850	30·00
81s/6s Optd "SPECIMEN" *Set of 6*			£170		

For Nos. 81 to 83 in other colours, see Labuan 80a, 81a and 82a.

Nos. 81/4 showing stamps printed double, double, one inverted, or on both sides, are from waste sheets subsequently sold by the British North Borneo Company to collectors.

No. 83a comes from a sheet (10×5) in which columns 3 to 10 were perf 14×11, column 2 perf compound of 14 and 11 (at right only) and column 1 perf 14 all round.

4
CENTS
(33) *(3½ mm between lines of surcharge)*

(Surcharged by Waterlow)

1895 (June). No. 83 surch as T **33**.

87	**32c**	4c. on $1 scarlet	7·00	1·50	50
		a. Surch double, one diagonal		£950	
88		10c. on $1 scarlet	27·00	1·75	50
89		20c. on $1 scarlet	55·00	17·00	50
90		30c. on $1 scarlet	50·00	40·00	1·75
91		40c. on $1 scarlet	60·00	65·00	1·75
87/91 *Set of 5*			£180	£110	4·50
87s/91s Optd "SPECIMEN" *Set of 5*			90·00		

For 4c. on $1 with wider spacing see No. 121.

No. 88 exists with the figures of the surcharge 2½ mm away from "CENTS". The normal setting has a space of 3½ mm. Examples of the narrow setting have, so far, only been seen on cancelled-to-order stamps.

34

35

36

37 Orang-Utan

38

39

40

41 Sun Bear

42

43 Borneo Railway Train

44

45

(Recess Waterlow)

1897 (Mar)–**1902**. T **34** to **45**. New frames. P 13½–14.

92	**34**	1c. black and bistre-brown	38·00	5·50	40
		aa. Perf 16			
		a. Perf 14½–15	11·00	2·75	40
		b. Perf 13½–14, comp 12–13	70·00	50·00	—
		c. Imperf between (horiz pair)	†	†	£650
		d. Perf 12–13			£250
93		1c. black and ochre	65·00	15·00	50
		a. Perf 14½–15	50·00	15·00	50
		ab. Imperf between (horiz pair)	†	†	£650
		b. Perf 13½–14 comp 12–13			
		c. Perf 16			£250
94	**35**	2c. black and lake	65·00	3·50	40
		a. Perf 14½–15	25·00	1·50	40
		ab. Imperf between (horiz pair)	†	†	£650
		b. Perf 13½–14, comp 12–13	—	21·00	2·00
		c. Perf 12–13			£250
		d. Imperf between (vert pair)	†	†	£850
		e. Perf 13½–14, comp 14½–15		—	3·75

95		2c. black and green (1900)	70·00	2·00	60
		a. Perf 14½–15	£150	3·00	3·00
		b. Perf 13½–14, comp 12–13	£180	40·00	—
		c. Perf 12–13			
		d. Imperf between (horiz pair)	—	£1200	†
96	**36**	3c. green and rosy mauve	75·00	22·00	40
		a. Perf 14½–15	75·00	55·00	1·00
		b. Perf 13½–14, comp 12–13	£120	75·00	
97		3c. green and dull mauve (P 14½–15)	38·00	3·00	50
98	**37**	4c. black and green (1900)	13·00		1·50
		b. Perf 13½–14, comp 12–13			
99		4c. black and carmine (1900)	40·00	12·00	50
		a. Perf 16	£140	50·00	50
		b. Perf 14½–15	90·00	1·75	50
		c. Perf 13½–14, comp 12–13	60·00	50·00	3·25
		d. Perf 12–13			
100	**38**	5c. black and orange-vermilion	£120	3·50	70
		a. Perf 14½–15	£120	2·00	70
		ab. Imperf between (horiz pair)	†	£1700	†
		b. Perf 13½–14, comp 12–13	£160	14·00	80
		c. Perf 12–13			
101	**39**	6c. black and bistre-brown	95·00	38·00	50
		a. Perf 14½–15	55·00	4·25	50
		b. Perf 13½–14, comp 12–13	—		3·75
102	**40**	8c. black and brown-purple	90·00	50·00	1·00
		a. Perf 16	£110	25·00	70
		ab. Imperf between (vert pair)	£475	£600	£350
		b. Perf 14½–15	55·00	2·75	60
103		8c. black and brown	16·00	48·00	1·00
		a. Perf 14½–15	65·00	80·00	1·00
		b. Perf 16			
104	**41**	10c. brown and slate-lilac (1902)	£150	55·00	4·50
		a. Imperf between (vert pair)	†	†	£1100
105		10c. brown and slate-blue (1902)	£425	£110	1·50
106	**42**	12c. black and dull blue	£225	50·00	2·00
		a. Imperf between (vert pair)	†	†	£750
		b. Perf 14½–15	£150	35·00	1·50
		c. Perf 13½–14, comp 12–13	£250	55·00	—
107	**43**	16c. green and chestnut (1902)	£140	90·00	3·25
		a. Perf 14½–15	£275	£150	10·00
108	**44**	18c. black and green (P 16)	38·00	80·00	4·00
		a. Imperf vert (horiz pair)	†	†	85·00
		b. Imperf between (vert pair)	†	†	£350
		c. Imperf (pair)	†	†	£180
		d.		—	10·00
109	**45**	24c. blue and lake	48·00	95·00	4·00
		a. Perf 13½–14, comp 12–13	55·00	£100	4·00
		b. Perf 12–13	£325		
92/109 *(one of each value)* Set of 12			£700	£325	16·00
92s/109s *(excl 93, 97, 103, 105)* Optd "SPECIMEN" *Set of 14*			£325		

No. 98 was printed in an incorrect frame colour and it is doubtful if it was issued for postal purposes in North Borneo. Used examples come from dealers' stock sent to the territory for cancellation.

In the above Nos. the 18c. has "POSTAL REVENUE" instead of "POSTAGE & REVENUE" and the 24c. has those words omitted. These stamps were replaced by others with corrected inscriptions; see Nos. 110 and 111.

46

47

1897. Corrected inscriptions. P 13½–14.

110	**46**	18c. black and green	£225	48·00	4·50
		a. Imperf between (horiz pair)	†	†	£700
		b. Perf 14½–15	£130	12·00	1·50
		c. Perf 13½–14, comp 12–13	—	—	3·50
111	**47**	24c. blue and lake	£130	50·00	2·25
		a. Perf 16	£225	£120	2·00
		b. Perf 14½–15	60·00	55·00	3·75
		c. Perf 13½–14, comp 12–13	—	—	5·50
		d. Perf 12–13			
110s/11s Optd "SPECIMEN" *Set of 2*			55·00		

BRITISH
4
CENTS
(48) *(4½ mm between lines of surcharge)*

PROTECTORATE.
(49)

4
cents
(50)

1899 (22 July–Oct). Surch with T **48**. P 14½–15 (Nos. 112/17) or 14 (Nos. 118/26).

(a) 4½ mm between lines of surch

112		4c. on 5c. (No. 100a)	60·00	50·00	
		a. Perf 13½–14	50·00	10·00	
		asa. Surch inverted, optd "SPECIMEN"	£800		
		b. Perf 13½–14, comp 12–13	60·00	32·00	
113		4c. on 6c. (No. 101a) (date?)	19·00	24·00	
		a. Perf 13½–14		27·00	50·00
		b. Perf 13½–14 comp 14½–15			
114		4c. on 8c. (No. 102b) (10.99)	17·00	10·00	
115		4c. on 12c. (No. 106b) (10.99)	48·00	13·00	
		a. Imperf between (horiz pair)	£850		
		b. Imperf between (vert pair)	£950	£950	
		c. Perf 12–13		60·00	65·00
		d. Perf 12–13			
		e. Perf 13½–14, comp 12–13	55·00	45·00	
116		4c. on 18c. (No. 110b) (10.99)	22·00	14·00	
		a. Perf 13½–14	50·00	50·00	

117		4c. on 24c. (No. 111b) (Oct)	48·00	23·00	
		a. Perf 16	60·00	60·00	
		b. Perf 13½–14	30·00	38·00	
		c. Perf 13½–14, comp 12–13	50·00	50·00	
		d. Perf 12–13		£160	£170
118		4c. on 25c. indigo (No. 81)	5·50	8·50	
		a. Imperf between (horiz strip of 3)	£1400		
119		4c. on 50c. deep slate-purple (No. 82)	27·00	16·00	
		a. Chalky blue	29·00	38·00	
121		4c. on $1 scarlet (No. 83)	5·50	12·00	
122		4c. on $2 dull green (No. 84)	5·50	13·00	
123		4c. on $5 bright purple (No. 85)	£180	£250	
		a. Dull purple	£325	£350	
124		4c. on $10 brown (No. 86)	£130	£250	
112/24 *Set of 12*			£450	£550	
112s/24s Optd "SPECIMEN" *Set of 12*			£225		

(b) 8½ mm between lines of surch. P 14

125		4c. on $5 (No. 85)	8·00	18·00	
126		4c. on $10 (No. 86)	8·00	18·00	

No. 121 differs only from No. 87 in having the "4" and "cents" wider apart.

Examples of the Kudat postmark dated "AU 15 1899" struck on Nos. 112/26 are generally considered to be faked.

A new setting of the surcharge, with 2½ mm between "4" and "CENTS" for values to $2 and 3½ mm on the $5 and $10, was used for the SPECIMEN overprints, including unissued surcharges on the 1c., 2c. and 3c. values (price £130 *the set of three*).

(Optd by Waterlow)

1901 (8 Oct)–**05**. Optd as T **49**.

(a) P 13½–14

127		1c. (No. 92) (R.)	3·50	1·50	30
		a. Perf 14½–15	2·50	1·75	30
128		2c. (No. 95) (R.)	10·00	1·00	30
		a. Perf 16	3·50	21·00	40
		b. Perf 14½–15	18·00	12·00	30
129		3c. (No. 96)	1·75	5·50	30
		a. Imperf between (vert pair)	†	†	£1500
		b. Perf 14½–15	15·00	2·75	30
		c. Perf 13½–14, comp 14½–15	60·00		2·00
130		4c. (No. 99) (G.)	9·00	1·00	30
		a. Perf 14½–15	38·00	1·00	50
131		5c. (No. 100) (G.)	70·00	4·75	30
		a. Perf 14½–15	14·00	3·25	30
132		6c. (No. 101) (R.)	65·00	70·00	1·25
		a. No stop after "Protectorate"	90·00	90·00	1·25
		b. Perf 16	4·00	15·00	70
133		8c. (No. 103) (B.)	6·00	3·75	50
		a. No stop after "Protectorate"	3·00	27·00	1·50
		b. Perf 13½–14, comp 12–13	80·00	35·00	—
		c. Imperf horiz (vert pair)	†	†	£350
134		10c. (No. 104) (R.) (7.02)	£100	5·00	2·00
		a. Perf 14½–15	£180	32·00	2·75
		c. Perf 13½–14. No stop after "Protectorate"	£325	—	14·00
		d. Opt double	£1000	†	£325
		e. (No. 105)	£375	£225	1·00
		f. Imperf vert (horiz pair)	†	†	£850
135		12c. (No. 106) (R.)	70·00	12·00	1·50
136		16c. (No. 107) (7.02)	£225	38·00	2·25
		a. Perf 14½–15	£190	55·00	2·25
		b. Perf 13½–14 comp 12–13	£425	90·00	—
137		18c. (No. 110) (R.)	20·00	26·00	1·25
		a. No stop after "Protectorate"			
		b. Perf 13½–14, comp 12–13	85·00	—	1·50
138		24c. (No. 111)	18·00	40·00	1·50
		a. Perf 14½–15	70·00	95·00	1·75
		ab. Imperf between (horiz pair)	†	†	£1700

(b) P 14

139		25c. (No. 81) (R.)	2·00	10·00	50
		a. No stop after "Protectorate"	£250	£300	27·00
		b. Overprints tête-bêche (horiz pair)			
		c. Overprint inverted	£750		
140		50c. (No. 82) (R.)	2·75	11·00	55
		a. No stop after "Protectorate"	£130	£180	—
		b. Chalky blue			
141		$1 (No. 83) (R.) (1.04)	6·00	65·00	—
142		$1 (No. 83)	4·50	38·00	2·00
		a. Imperf horiz (vert pair)	£800		
		b. Opt double	†	†	£375
		c. Opt treble			
143		$2 (No. 84) (R.) (1903)	50·00	£100	2·75
		a. Opt double	£1700	†	£550
144		$5 (No. 85b) (R.) (2.05)	£425	£550	9·00
145		$10 (No. 86) (R.) (2.05)	£750	£1100	11·00
		a. Opt inverted	£3250	†	£550
127/45 *Set of 18*			£1400	£1800	30·00
127/40s Optd "SPECIMEN" *Set of 14*			£350		

There was more than one setting of the overprint for some of the values. Full sheets of the 6c. and 8c. are known, without stop throughout.

See also Nos. 184/5.

1904–05. Surch locally with T **50**.

(a) P 14½–15

146		4c. on 5c. (No. 100a)	50·00	55·00	12·00
147		4c. on 6c. (No. 101a)	7·00	21·00	12·00
		a. Surch inverted	£225		
148		4c. on 8c. (No. 102b)	21·00	26·00	12·00
		a. Surch inverted	£325		
149		4c. on 12c. (No. 106b)	55·00	40·00	12·00
		a. Perf 13½–14	65·00	65·00	12·00
		b. Perf 13½–14 comp 12–13	55·00	65·00	—
150		4c. on 18c. (No. 110b)	14·00	38·00	12·00
		a. Perf 13½–14			
151		4c. on 24c. (No. 111b)	45·00	55·00	12·00
		a. Perf 16	25·00	50·00	12·00
		b. Perf 13½–14	45·00	55·00	12·00
		c. Perf 12–13			

(b) P 14

152		4c. on 25c. (No. 81)	6·00	26·00	12·00
153		4c. on 50c. (No. 82)	6·00	38·00	12·00
154		4c. on $1 (No. 83)	6·00	48·00	12·00
155		4c. on $2 (No. 84)	6·00	48·00	12·00
156		4c. on $5 (No. 85)	15·00	48·00	12·00
		a. Surch on No. 85b	35·00	50·00	—
157		4c. on $10 (No. 86)	12·00	48·00	12·00
		a. Surch inverted	£3000		
146/57 *Set of 12*			£200	£425	£130

51 Malayan Tapir

52 Travellers' Tree

53 Jesselton Railway Station

54 The Sultan of Sulu, his staff and W. C. Cowie, Managing Director of the Company

55 Indian Elephant

56 Sumatran Rhinoceros

57 Ploughing with Buffalo

58 Wild Boar

59 Palm Cockatoo

60 Rhinoceros Hornbill

61 Banteng

62 Dwarf Cassowary

(Recess Waterlow)

1909 (1 July)–**23**. Centres in black. P 13½–14.

158	**51**	1c. chocolate-brown	7·00	2·75	30
		a. Perf 14½–15	60·00	18·00	40
159		1c. brown	30·00	1·25	30
		a. Perf 14½–15	55·00	4·50	30
		b. Imperf between (vert pair)	£2750		
160	**52**	2c. green	1·00	70	30
		a. Imperf between (pair)			
		b. Perf 14½–15	4·75	70	30
161	**53**	3c. lake	4·50	2·75	30
162		3c. rose-lake	5·50	2·75	50
		a. Perf 14½–15	50·00	—	55
163		3c. green (1923)	55·00	1·50	†
164	**54**	4c. scarlet	3·50	30	30
		a. Imperf between (vert pair)			
		b. Perf 14½–15	27·00	2·00	35
165	**55**	5c. yellow-brown	18·00	4·00	40
		a. Perf 14½–15			
166		5c. dark brown	48·00	5·50	—
167	**56**	6c. olive-green	13·00	1·50	30
		a. Perf 14½–15	80·00	6·50	60
168		6c. apple-green	45·00	2·00	60
169	**57**	8c. lake	4·00	1·00	60
		a. Perf 14½–15	—	—	13·00
170	**58**	10c. greyish blue	45·00	8·00	1·25
		a. Perf 14½–15	£100	50·00	—
171		10c. blue	55·00	2·25	—
172		10c. turquoise-blue	50·00	1·50	1·50
		a. Perf 14½–15	70·00	4·50	—
173	**59**	12c. deep blue	55·00	1·50	1·00
		a. Perf 14½–15	—	—	12·00
		b. Imperf vert (horiz pair)	†	†	£800
173c		12c. deep bright blue			
174	**60**	16c. brown-lake	26·00	3·00	1·00
175	**61**	18c. blue-green	£160	35·00	1·00
176	**62**	24c. deep rose-lilac	28·00	2·00	1·75
		a. Deep lilac	55·00	6·50	—

158/76 *Set of 13* .... £375 50·00

158s/76s Optd "SPECIMEN" *Set of 13* £350

For this issue perf 12½ see Nos. 277, etc.

20
CENTS
(63)

64 **65**

1909 (7 Sept). No. 175 surch with T **63** by Waterlow. P 13½–14.

177		20c. on 18c. blue-green (R.)	7·00	1·00	30
		a. Perf 14½–15	£250	70·00	—
		s. Optd "SPECIMEN."	50·00		

Re-entry. Doubled oars and dots behind lion (R. 4/9).

(Recess Waterlow)

1911 (7 Mar). P 13½–14.

178	**64**	25c. black and yellow-green	25·00	5·50	2·00
		a. Perf 14½–15	28·00	48·00	—
		b. Imperf (pair) (no gum)	55·00		
		c. Re-entry	90·00	32·00	
178d		25c. black and blue-green	60·00		
		e. Re-entry	£180		
179		50c. black and steel-blue	22·00	6·00	2·25
		a. Perf 14½–15	32·00	35·00	—
		ab. Imperf between (horiz pair)	£4000	£5000	
		c. Imperf (pair) (no gum)	90·00		
		d. Re-entry	85·00	35·00	
180		$1 black and chestnut	20·00	4·00	4·50
		a. Perf 14½–15	65·00	16·00	9·00
		b. Imperf (pair) (no gum)	£190		
		c. Re-entry	85·00	30·00	
181		$2 black and lilac	85·00	19·00	7·50
		a. Re-entry	£275	80·00	
182	**65**	$5 black and lake	£200	£140	35·00
		a. Imperf (pair) (no gum)	£225		
183		$10 black and brick-red	£750	£800	£100
		a. Imperf (pair) (no gum)	£550		

178/83 *Set of 6* £1000 £900 £140

178s/83s Optd "SPECIMEN." *Set of 6* £375

BRITISH

2

PROTECTORATE   **cents**
(66)   (67)   (68)

1912 (July). Nos. 85b and 86 optd with T **66**.

184		$5 dull purple (R.)	£2000	£2250	11·00
185		$10 brown (R.)	£2250	—	11·00
		a. Opt inverted	†	†	—

1916 (Feb). Nos. 162, 167 and 173 surch as T **67** by Govt Printing Office, Sandakan. P 13½–14.

186	**53**	2c. on 3c. black and rose-lake	30·00	15·00	
		a. "s" inverted (R. 2/5)	£110	£100	
		b. Surch double	£2500		
187	**56**	4c. on 6c. black and olive-green (R.)	32·00	25·00	
		a. "s" inverted (R. 2/5)	£110	£110	
		b. "s" inserted by hand	—	£1800	
		c. Perf 14½–15	£200	£200	
		ca. "s" inverted			
188	**59**	10c. on 12c. black and deep blue (R.)	60·00	70·00	
		a. "s" inverted (R. 2/5)	£180	£200	
		b. "s" inserted by hand	£1700		
		c. Perf 14½–15	£110	95·00	

186/8 *Set of 3* .... £110 95·00

186s/8s Optd "SPECIMEN" *Set of 3* £120

Nos. 186/8 were surcharged from a setting of 25 (5×5) on which the required face values were inserted.

1916 (May). Stamps of 1909–11 optd with T **68** by Waterlow. Centres in black. P 13½–14.

(a) Cross in vermilion (thick shiny ink)

189	**51**	1c. brown	10·00	35·00	
190	**52**	2c. green	70·00	85·00	
		a. Perf 14½–15	32·00	85·00	
		ab. Opt double, one albino	£425		
191	**53**	3c. rose-lake	27·00	50·00	
		a. Nos. 191 and 204 se-tenant (vert pair)	£5000		
192	**54**	4c. scarlet	5·50	32·00	
		a. Perf 14½–15	£300	£200	
193	**55**	5c. yellow-brown	60·00	60·00	
		a. Perf 14½–15			
194	**56**	6c. apple-green	75·00	75·00	
		a. Perf 14½–15	£250	£250	

195	**57**	8c. lake	24·00	60·00	
196	**58**	10c. blue	65·00	75·00	
197	**59**	12c. deep blue	£110	£110	
198	**60**	16c. brown-lake	£120	£120	
199	**61**	20c. on 18c. blue-green	70·00	£110	
200	**62**	24c. dull mauve	£150	£150	
201	**64**	25c. green (P 14½–15)	£400	£500	
		a. Re-entry	£1600		
189/201 *Set of 13*			£1000	£1300	

(b) Cross in shades of carmine (matt ink)

202	**51**	1c. brown	26·00	65·00	
		a. Perf 14½–15	£300		
203	**52**	2c. green	30·00	50·00	
		b. Perf 14½–15	£225		
		ba. Opt double	†	£2500	
204	**53**	3c. rose-lake	55·00	70·00	
204a	**54**	4c. scarlet	£850	£950	
		ab. Perf 14½–15	†		
205	**55**	5c. yellow-brown	70·00	80·00	
206	**56**	6c. apple-green	65·00	80·00	
		a. Perf 14½–15	£225	£250	
207	**57**	8c. lake	29·00	55·00	
208	**58**	10c. blue	70·00	80·00	
209	**59**	12c. deep blue	£110	£120	
210	**60**	16c. brown-lake	£110	£120	
211	**61**	20c. on 18c. blue-green	£110	£120	
212	**62**	24c. dull mauve	£130	£140	
		a. Imperf between (vert pair)	£4250		
213	**64**	25c. green	£950		
		a. Perf 14½–15	£450	£475	
		b. Re-entry	£1800		
202/13a (ex 4c.) *Set of 12*			£1100	£1300	

The British North Borneo Company donated a proportion of the above issue to be sold by the National Philatelic War Fund for the benefit of the Red Cross and St. John's Ambulance Brigade.

RED CROSS

TWO CENTS   **FOUR CENTS**
(69)   (70)

1918 (Aug). Stamps of 1909–11 surch as T **69**. P 13½–14.

(a) Lines of surcharge 9 mm apart

214	**51**	1c. +2c. brown	3·50	17·00	
		a. Imperf between (horiz pair)	£3250		
		b. Imperf between (vert pair)	£3250		
215	**52**	2c. +2c. green	1·00	8·50	
		a. Imperf between (horiz or vert pair)	£4250		
		b. Imperf (pair)			
		c. Perf 14½–15			
216	**53**	3c. +2c. rose-red	14·00	19·00	
		a. Imperf between (horiz pair)	£5000		
		b. Perf 14½–15	40·00	70·00	
217		3c. +2c. dull rose-carmine	£150		
		a. Perf 14½–15	£190		
218	**54**	4c. +2c. scarlet	70	5·00	
		a. Surch inverted	£450		
		b. "TWO CENTS" omitted	£1100		
219	**55**	5c. +2c. deep brown	8·00	38·00	
220		5c. +2c. pale brown	15·00	28·00	
221	**56**	6c. +2c. olive-green	5·00	38·00	
		a. Perf 14½–15	£225	£250	
221b		6c. +2c. apple-green	5·00	29·00	
		c. Perf 14½–15	£275	£300	
222	**57**	8c. +2c. lake	5·50	11·00	
		a. Inverted figure "3" for "C" in "CENTS"			
223	**58**	10c. +2c. blue	8·00	32·00	
224	**59**	12c. +2c. deep bright blue	21·00	55·00	
		a. Surch inverted	£600		
225	**60**	16c. +2c. brown-lake	22·00	45·00	
226	**62**	24c. +2c. mauve	22·00	45·00	

(b) Lines of surch 13–14 mm apart

227	**52**	2c. +2c. green	55·00	£120	
228	**56**	6c. +2c. olive-green	£475	£900	
229	**64**	25c. +2c. green	10·00	45·00	
		a. Re-entry	60·00	£180	
230		50c. +2c. steel-blue	12·00	45·00	
		a. Re-entry	70·00		
231		$1 +2c. chestnut	50·00	55·00	
		a. Surcharge double, one albino	£375		
		b. Re-entry	£170	£200	
232		$2 +2c. lilac	75·00	95·00	
		a. Re-entry	£275	£325	
233	**65**	$5 +2c. lake	£500	£800	
234		$10 +2c. brick-red	£600	£850	
214/34 *Set of 17*			£1200	£2000	

The above stamps were dispatched from London in three consignments, of which two were lost through enemy action at sea.

No. 218a normally shows a second inverted albino surcharge.

No. 218b occurs from the top row of a sheet on which the surcharge was misplaced downwards. Stamps from the other rows show the lines of the surcharge transposed (with "TWO CENTS" above "RED CROSS"). Only one sheet was found of No. 228.

These stamps were sold at a premium of 2c. per stamp, which went to the Red Cross Society.

1918 (Oct). Stamps of 1909–11 surch with T **70**, in red. P 13½–14.

235	**51**	1c. +4c. chocolate	60	5·00	
		a. Imperf between (horiz pair)	£3000		
236	**52**	2c. +4c. green	65	8·00	
237	**53**	3c. +4c. rose-lake	1·00	3·75	
238	**54**	4c. +4c. scarlet	40	4·75	
239	**55**	5c. +4c. brown	2·00	25·00	
240	**56**	6c. +4c. apple-green	1·90	12·00	
		a. Imperf between (vert pair)	£2750		
241	**57**	8c. +4c. lake	1·25	9·50	
242	**58**	10c. +4c. turquoise-blue	2·25	12·00	
242a		10c. +4c. greenish blue	9·00	45·00	
243	**59**	12c. +4c. deep blue	12·00	14·00	
		a. Surch double	£2000		
244	**60**	16c. +4c. brown-lake	7·00	16·00	
245	**62**	24c. +4c. mauve	9·00	20·00	

246	64	25c. +4c. yellow-green	12·00	50·00
		a. Re-entry	60·00	
247		25c. +4c. blue-green	25·00	75·00
		a. Re-entry	90·00	
248		50c. +4c. steel-blue	15·00	45·00
		a. Perf 14½–15	60·00	
		b. Re-entry	75·00	
249		$1 +4c. chestnut	29·00	65·00
		a. Perf 14½–15	£200	
		b. Re-entry	95·00	
250		$2 +4c. lilac	60·00	85·00
		a. Re-entry	£190	
251	65	$5 +4c. lake	£300	£400
252		$10 +4c. brick-red	£400	£475
235/52 Set of 17			£750	£1100

Nos. 235/52 were sold at face, plus 4c. on each stamp for Red Cross Funds.

Examples of a double-ring "SANDAKAN N. BORNEO" postmark dated "1 NOV 1918" on these stamps are generally considered to be faked.

THREE

MALAYA-BORNEO

EXHIBITION

1922.

(71)

■CENTS■

(72)

1922 (31 Mar). Malaya–Borneo Exhibition, Singapore. Stamps of 1909–22 some in different shades, optd as T **71** by Govt Printing Office, Sandakan. P 13½–14.

253	51	1c. brown (R.)	26·00	90·00
		a. "BORHEO"	£325	£900
		b. "BORNEQ"	£500	£1000
		c. Stop after "EXHIBITION."	£120	
		d. Raised stop after "1922"	£950	£1400
		e. "EXHIBITICN." with stop	£950	
		f. Perf 14½–15	50·00	75·00
		fa. "BORHEO"	£550	£1000
		fb. "BORNEQ"	£850	£1400
		fc. Raised stop after "1922"	£800	
		fd. "EXHIBITICN." with stop	£800	
		fe. "MHLAYA" and "EXHIBITICN." with stop	£8000	
		ff. Stop after "EXHIBITION."	£250	
253g		1c. brown (B.) (P 14½–15)	£1700	
		ga. Vert pair, with and without opt	£8500	
		gb. Raised stop after "1922"	£9500	
		gc. "BORHEO"	£6500	
		gd. "BORNEQ"	£9500	
		gg. "MHLAYA" and "EXHIBITICN." with stop	£9500	
		gh. "EXHIBITIOH"	£9500	
254		1c. orange-brown (R.)	65·00	95·00
255	52	2c. green (R.)	3·75	30·00
		a. Stop after "EXHIBITION."	42·00	£170
		b. No hyphen	£110	
256	53	3c. rose-lake (B.)	16·00	65·00
		a. Stop after "EXHIBITION."	80·00	£275
		b. "EXHIBITICN." with stop	£5000	
		c. Raised stop after "1922"	£5000	
257	54	4c. scarlet (B.)	3·75	50·00
		a. Stop after "EXHIBITION."	55·00	£250
		b. Perf 14½–15	£130	
		ba. Stop after "EXHIBITION."	£800	
258	55	5c. orange-brown (B.)	10·00	70·00
		a. Imperf between (vert pair)	£2000	£2500
		b. Stop after "EXHIBITION."	85·00	£275
		c. Opt double	£2500	
		d. Opt double (with stop)	£8500	
259		5c. chestnut (B.)	23·00	75·00
		a. Stop after "EXHIBITION."	£110	
260	56	6c. apple-green (R.)	10·00	70·00
		a. Stop after "EXHIBITION."	65·00	£250
		b. Opt double	£2500	
		c. Opt double (with stop)	£8500	
261	57	8c. dull rose (B.)	11·00	50·00
		a. Stop after "EXHIBITION."	£100	
262		8c. deep rose-lake (B.)	9·50	50·00
		a. Stop after "EXHIBITION."	£100	
263	58	10c. turquoise-blue (R.)	21·00	70·00
		a. Stop after "EXHIBITION."	£130	£300
		b. Perf 14½–15	50·00	£140
		ba. Stop after "EXHIBITION."	£425	
264		10c. greenish blue (R.)	30·00	85·00
		a. Stop after "EXHIBITION."	£150	
265	59	12c. deep blue (R.)	13·00	21·00
		a. Stop after "EXHIBITION."	95·00	£170
266		12c. deep bright blue (R.)	50·00	
		a. Stop after "EXHIBITION."	£300	
267	60	16c. brown-lake (R.)	29·00	75·00
		a. Stop after "EXHIBITION."	£140	£350
		b. Opt in red	£11000	
268	61	20c. on 18c. blue-green (B.)	29·00	95·00
		a. Stop after "EXHIBITION."	£225	
269		20c. on 18c. blue-green (R.)	29·00	£170
		a. Stop after "EXHIBITION."	£375	£1200
270	62	24c. mauve (R.)	55·00	80·00
		a. Stop after "EXHIBITION."	£250	£350
271		24c. lilac (R.)	55·00	80·00
		a. Stop after "EXHIBITION."	£250	£350
272		24c. reddish lilac (R.)	70·00	£110
		a. Stop after "EXHIBITION."	£375	
273	64	25c. blue-green (R.)	48·00	95·00
		a. Stop after "EXHIBITION."	£425	
		b. Re-entry	£325	
274		25c. yellow-green (R.)	14·00	75·00
		a. Stop after "EXHIBITION."	£275	
		b. Re-entry	£140	
		c. Opt double	£4500	
		d. Perf 14½–15	19·00	80·00
		da. Stop after "EXHIBITION."	£250	£475
		db. Re-entry	£200	
275		50c. steel-blue (R.)	19·00	75·00
		a. Stop after "EXHIBITION."	£250	£550
		b. Re-entry	£200	£550

		c. Perf 14½–15	30·00	90·00
		ca. Stop after "EXHIBITION."	£250	
		cb. Re-entry	£225	
253/75 Set of 14			£225	£800
253s/75s Optd "SPECIMEN" Set of 14			£475	

These overprints were applied from a number of settings covering 10, 20, 25 or 30 stamps at a time.

Of the ten settings known for the horizontal stamps the earliest were only used for the 1c. on which most of the varieties occur. Of the others the vast majority come from settings of 20 (10×2) with the stop after "EXHIBITION" variety on R. 2/7 or R. 2/9, or 25 (5×5) on which the same variety can be found on R. 5/4. In addition the 3c. comes from a different setting of 20 (10×2) on which there is a raised stop after "1922" on R. 2/8 and "EXHIBITICN." on R. 2/9.

The 1c. sequence is complicated, but additionally includes a setting of 10 with "BORHEO" on stamps 3 and 10, "BORNEQ" on stamp 4, raised stop on stamp 8 and "EXHIBITICN." on stamp 9. A setting of 20 repeats this sequence on its bottom line as does one of 30, although in this instance "MHLAYA" joins "EXHIBITICN." as the variety on stamp 9.

For the vertical stamps (2, 6, 10, 12, 16 and 20c. on 18c.) the settings were of 20 (10×2) or 25 (5×5). The stop after "EXHIBITION" occurs on R. 2/7 or R. 2/9 of the former and R. 5/4 of the latter.

The 25c. and 50c. high values were overprinted from a setting of 10×1 or 25 (5×5), with the stop after "EXHIBITION" on R. 5/4 of the latter.

1923 (Oct). T **54** surch with T **72**.

276		3c. on 4c. black and scarlet	4·50	6·00
		a. Surch double	£1300	
		s. Optd "SPECIMEN"	55·00	

1925–28. Designs as 1909–22 issue with centres in black and some frame colours changed. P 12½.

277	51	1c. chocolate-brown	1·00	70
		a. Imperf between (horiz pair)	£1700	
278	52	2c. claret	85	60
		a. Imperf between (vert pair)	—	£1900
		b. Imperf between (horiz pair)		
279	53	3c. green	3·00	75
		a. Imperf between (horiz pair)	†	£2750
280	54	4c. scarlet	50	10
		a. Imperf between (vert pair)	£275	£450
		b. Imperf between (horiz pair)	£750	
		c. Imperf between (vert strip of 3)	£1200	
281	55	5c. yellow-brown	6·50	2·25
		a. Imperf between (vert pair)	£1200	
282	56	6c. olive-green	15·00	90
283	57	8c. carmine	7·50	50
		a. Imperf between (vert pair)	£600	
		b. Imperf between (horiz pair)		
		c. Imperf between (vert strip of 4)	£2000	
284	58	10c. turquoise-blue	4·25	90
		a. Imperf between (horiz pair)	£1700	£2500
		b. Imperf between (vert pair)	£2000	
285	59	12c. deep blue	30·00	80
286	60	16c. red-brown	50·00	£250
287	61	20c. on 18c. blue-green (R.)	20·00	3·00
288	62	24c. violet	80·00	£250
289	64	25c. green	22·00	4·25
		a. Re-entry	£100	32·00
290		50c. steel-blue	32·00	14·00
		a. Re-entry	£130	70·00
291		$1 chestnut	38·00	£900
		a. Re-entry	£150	
292		$2 mauve	95·00	£1100
		a. Re-entry	£300	
293	65	$5 lake (1928)	£225	£1800
294		$10 orange-red (1928)	£650	£2000
277/94 Set of 18			£1100	£5500

Examples of No. 278 were supplied for UPU distribution punched with a 3½ mm diameter hole.

Examples of the 24c., $1, $2, $5 and $10 in this perforation were not supplied to the territory for postal purposes. Used examples exist from covers prepared by stamp dealers and the prices quoted above are for stamps with verified contemporary cancels.

73 Head of a Murut

74 Orang-Utan

75 Dyak warrior

76 Mount Kinabalu

77 Clouded Leopard

78 Badge of the Company

79 Arms of the Company

80 Arms of the Company

(Eng J. A. C. Harrison. Recess Waterlow)

1931 (1 Jan). 50th Anniv of British North Borneo Company. T **73/80**. P 12½.

295	73	3c. black and blue-green	1·50	80
296	74	6c. black and orange	20·00	2·75
297	75	10c. black and scarlet	5·50	13·00
298	76	12c. black and ultramarine	5·50	8·00
299	77	25c. black and violet	48·00	35·00
300	78	$1 black and yellow-green	27·00	£110
301	79	$2 black and chestnut	50·00	£110
302	80	$5 black and purple	£180	£700
295/302 Set of 8			£300	£900
295s/302s Optd "SPECIMEN" Set of 8			£350	

Examples of all values are known showing a forged Jesselton postmark dated "22 AUG 1931".

81 Buffalo Transport

82 Palm Cockatoo

83 Native

84 Proboscis Monkey

85 Mounted Bajaus

86 Eastern Archipelago

87 Orang-Utan

88 Murut with blowpipe

89 Dyak

90 River scene

91 Native boat

92 Mt. Kinabalu

93 Badge of the Company

94 Arms of the Company

95 Arms of the Company

1c. "Ant trail" (R. 8/8)

(Eng J. A. C. Harrison. Recess Waterlow)

1939 (1 Jan). T **81/95**. P 12½.

303	81	1c. green and red-brown	4·75	2·75
		a. Ant trail	£110	65·00
304	82	2c. purple and greenish blue	5·00	3·75
305	83	3c. slate-blue and green	6·00	3·75
306	84	4c. bronze-green and violet	20·00	1·00
307	85	6c. deep blue and claret	14·00	20·00
308	86	8c. scarlet	25·00	2·25
309	87	10c. violet and bronze-green	42·00	9·00
310	88	12c. green and royal blue	50·00	12·00
		a. Green and blue	70·00	18·00
311	89	15c. blue-green and brown	35·00	17·00
312	90	20c. violet and slate-blue	29·00	10·00
313	91	25c. green and chocolate	45·00	20·00
		a. Vignette printed double, one albino	£350	£350
314	92	50c. chocolate and violet	48·00	18·00
315	93	$1 brown and carmine	£150	23·00
316	94	$2 violet and olive-green	£300	£180
317	95	$5 indigo and pale blue	£850	£425
303/17 Set of 15			£1400	£600
303s/17s Perf "SPECIMEN" Set of 15			£650	

Examples of most values are known showing forged Jesselton postmarks dated "22 AUG 1941" or "15 JA 48".

No. 313a has the albino impression sideways.

WAR TAX

 WAR TAX (96)

 WAR TAX (97)

1941 (24 Feb). Nos. 303/4 optd at Sandakan with T **96/7**.

318	1c. green and red-brown	2·75	7·00
	a. Optd front and back	£850	
	b. Ant trail	75·00	£130
319	2c. purple and greenish blue	12·00	7·50

The 1c. was for compulsory use on internal mail and the 2c. on overseas mail, both in addition to normal postage.

BRITISH MILITARY ADMINISTRATION

North Borneo, including Labuan, was occupied by the Japanese in January 1942. Australian forces landed on Labuan on 10 June 1945 and by the end of the war against Japan on 14 August had liberated much of western North Borneo. Prior to the issue of Nos. 320/34 Australian stamps were made available for civilian use. The territory was placed under British Military Administration on 5 January 1946.

BMA (98)

(99)

1945 (17 Dec). Nos. 303/17 optd with T **98**.

320	81	1c. green and red-brown	23·00	3·00
		a. Ant trail	£225	65·00
321	82	2c. purple and greenish blue	14·00	2·00
		a. Opt double	£9500	
322	83	3c. slate-blue and green	1·25	1·25
323	84	4c. bronze-green and violet	26·00	16·00
324	85	6c. deep blue and claret	1·25	1·25
325	86	8c. scarlet	3·00	75
326	87	10c. violet and bronze-green	3·00	40
327	88	12c. green and blue	6·00	6·50
		a. Green and royal blue	20·00	6·50
328	89	15c. blue-green and brown	3·50	1·00
329	90	20c. violet and slate-blue	9·00	3·25
330	91	25c. green and chocolate	8·50	2·00
		a. Vignette printed double, one albino	£400	
331	92	50c. chocolate and violet	8·50	3·50
332	93	$1 brown and carmine	65·00	42·00
333	94	$2 violet and olive-green	75·00	50·00
		a. Opt double	£4250	
334	95	$5 indigo and pale blue	40·00	22·00
320/34 Set of 15			£250	£130

These stamps and the similarly overprinted stamps of Sarawak were obtainable at all post offices throughout British Borneo (Brunei, Labuan, North Borneo and Sarawak), for use on local and overseas mail.

CROWN COLONY

North Borneo became a Crown Colony on 15 July 1946.

Lower bar broken at right (R. 8/3)

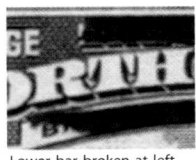

Lower bar broken at left (R. 8/4 and R. 8/8)

1947 (1 Sept–22 Dec). Nos. 303 to 317 optd with T **99** and bars obliterating words "THE STATE OF" and "BRITISH PROTECTORATE".

335	81	1c. green and red-brown (15.12)	30	1·00
		b. Lower bar broken at right	22·00	40·00
		c. Lower bar broken at left (R. 8/4)	22·00	40·00
		d. Ant trail and lower bar broken at left (R. 8/8)	27·00	48·00
336	82	2c. purple and greenish blue (22.12)	2·25	1·00

337	83	3c. slate-blue and green (R.) (22.12)	30	1·00
338	84	4c. bronze-green and violet	1·00	1·00
339	85	6c. deep blue and claret (R.) (22.12)	40	20
340	86	8c. scarlet	1·00	20
		b. Lower bar broken at right	28·00	22·00
341	87	10c. violet and bronze-green (15.12)	1·50	40
342	88	12c. green and royal blue (22.12)	5·50	2·75
		a. Green and blue	20·00	15·00
343	89	15c. blue-green and brown (22.12)	2·25	30
344	90	20c. violet and slate-blue (22.12)	4·75	85
		b. Lower bar broken at right	80·00	35·00
345	91	25c. green and chocolate (22.12)	3·00	50
		a. Vignette printed double, one albino		
		b. Lower bar broken at right	80·00	35·00
346	92	50c. chocolate and violet (22.12)	4·25	85
		b. Lower bar broken at right	90·00	38·00
		c. Lower bar broken at left	80·00	35·00
347	93	$1 brown and carmine (22.12)	17·00	1·75
348	94	$2 violet and olive-green (22.12)	22·00	18·00
349	95	$5 indigo and pale blue (R.) (22.12)	42·00	32·00
		b. Lower bar broken at right	£350	£300
335/49 Set of 15			95·00	55·00
335s/49s Perf "SPECIMEN" Set of 15			£325	

1948 (1 Nov). Royal Silver Wedding. As Nos. 112/13 of Antigua.

350	8c. scarlet	30	80
351	$10 mauve	32·00	40·00

1949 (10 Oct). 75th Anniv of UPU. As Nos. 114/17 of Antigua.

352	8c. carmine	60	30
353	10c. brown	3·25	2·00
354	30c. orange-brown	1·50	2·00
355	55c. blue	1·50	3·00
352/5 Set of 4		6·00	6·50

100 Mount Kinabalu

101 Native musical instrument

102 Coconut Grove

103 Hemp drying

104 Cattle at Kota Belud

105 Map

106 Log pond

107 Malay prau, Sandakan

108 Bajau Chief

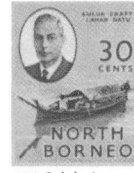

109 Suluk river canoe, Lahad Datu

110 Clock Tower Jesselton

111 Bajau horsemen

112 Murut with blowpipe

113 Net-fishing

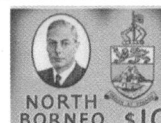

114 Arms of North Borneo

(Photo Harrison)

1950 (1 July)–**52**. T **100/114**. Chalk-surfaced paper. Wmk Mult Script CA. P 13½×14½ (horiz), 14½×13½ (vert).

356	100	1c. red-brown	15	1·25
357	101	2c. blue	15	50
358	102	3c. green	30	15
359	103	4c. bright purple	1·00	10
360	104	5c. violet	1·00	10
361	105	8c. scarlet	2·75	85
362	106	10c. maroon	2·25	15
363	107	15c. ultramarine	2·25	65
364	108	20c. brown	3·50	10
365	109	30c. olive-brown	5·50	30
366	110	50c. rose-carmine ("JESSLETON")	2·75	7·50
366a		50c. rose-carmine ("JESSELTON") (1.5.52)	17·00	3·25
		aw. Wmk inverted	£1000	
367	111	$1 red-orange	10·00	2·00
368	112	$2 grey-green	17·00	23·00
369	113	$5 emerald-green	28·00	38·00
370	114	$10 dull blue	70·00	95·00
356/70 Set of 16			£140	£150

1953 (3 June). Coronation. As No. 120 of Antigua.

371	10c. black and bright scarlet	2·50	1·00

115 Log Pond

10c. Vertical line appears as an extra chimney (R. 1/10)

(Photo Harrison)

1954 (1 Mar)–**59**. Designs previously used for King George VI issue, but with portrait of Queen Elizabeth II as in T **115**. Chalk-surfaced paper. Wmk Mult Script CA. P 14½×13½ (vert) or 13½×14½ (horiz).

372	100	1c. red-brown (1.10.54)	10	30
373	101	2c. blue (1.6.56)	2·00	15
374	102	3c. green (1.2.57)	4·50	2·00
		a. Deep green (14.1.59)	10·00	4·50
375	103	4c. bright purple (16.5.55)	2·00	20
376	104	5c. reddish violet (1.7.54)	1·00	10
377	105	8c. scarlet (1.10.54)	1·25	30
378	115	10c. maroon	30	10
		a. Extra chimney	38·00	12·00
379	107	15c. bright blue (16.5.55)	1·00	10
380	108	20c. brown (3.8.54)	50	15
381	109	30c. olive-brown (3.8.54)	3·25	20
382	110	50c. rose-carmine ("JESSELTON") (10.2.56)	6·00	20
		a. Rose (9.12.59)	25·00	1·75
		aw. Wmk inverted	£1000	£475
383	111	$1 red-orange (1.4.55)	6·50	20
384	112	$2 deep green (1.10.55)	17·00	1·50
		a. Grey-green (22.1.58)	48·00	7·00
385	113	$5 emerald-green (1.2.57)	14·00	35·00
386	114	$10 deep blue (1.2.57)	30·00	42·00
372/86 Set of 15			75·00	70·00

Plate 2 of the 30c., released 10 August 1960, had a finer, 250 screen, instead of the previous 200 (price £4 mint).

116 Borneo Railway, 1902

117 Malay prau

118 Mount Kinabalu

119 Arms of Chartered Company

(Recess Waterlow)

1956 (1 Nov). 75th Anniv of British North Borneo Co. T **116/19**. Wmk Mult Script CA. P 13×13½ (horiz) or 13½×13 (vert).

387	116	10c. black and rose-carmine	1·25	40
388	117	15c. black and red-brown	1·50	30

389	**118**	35c. black and bluish green	1·00	2·00
390	**119**	$1 black and slate	1·25	3·00
387/90		*Set of 4*	4·50	5·00

120 Sambar Stag

121 Sun Bear

122 Clouded Leopard

123 Dusun woman with gong

124 Map of Borneo

125 Banteng

126 Butterfly orchid

127 Sumatran Rhinoceros

128 Murut with blow-pipe

129 Mount Kinabalu

130 Dusun and buffalo transport

131 Bajau horsemen

132 Orang-Utan

133 Rhinoceros Hornbill

134 Crested Wood Partridge

135 Arms of North Borneo

(Des Chong Yun Fatt. Recess Waterlow (until 1962), then D.L.R.)

1961 (1 Feb). T **120/35**. W w **12**. P 13.

391	**120**	1c. emerald and brown-red	20	10
392	**121**	4c. bronze-green and orange	1·25	90
393	**122**	5c. sepia and violet	1·25	10
394	**123**	6c. black and blue-green	1·25	40
395	**124**	10c. green and red	1·75	10
396	**125**	12c. brown and grey-green	1·00	10
397	**126**	20c. blue-green and ultramarine	4·00	10
398	**127**	25c. grey-black and scarlet	1·75	1·50
399	**128**	30c. sepia and olive	2·00	20
400	**129**	35c. slate-blue and red-brown	2·75	2·50
401	**130**	50c. emerald and yellow-brown	2·75	20
402	**131**	75c. grey-blue and bright purple	19·00	90
403	**132**	$1 brown and yellow-green	18·00	2·00
404	**133**	$2 brown and slate	35·00	4·00
405	**134**	$5 emerald and maroon	38·00	24·00
406	**135**	$10 carmine and blue	55·00	50·00
391/406		*Set of 16*	£160	75·00

(Des M. Goaman. Photo Harrison)

1963 (4 June). Freedom from Hunger. As No. 146 of Antigua.

407		12c. ultramarine	1·75	75

POSTAL FISCALS

Three Cents. Revenue
(F **1**) (Raised stop)

Ten Cents. Revenue
(F **2**)

1886. Regular issues surch as Type F **1** or F **2**.

F1	**1**	3c. on 4c. pink (No. 6)	£140	£190
		a. Raised stop after "Cents"	£120	£180
F2		5c. on 8c. green (No. 7)	£140	£190
		a. Raised stop after "Cents"	£120	£180
F3	**4**	10c. on 50c. violet (No. 4)	£225	£250
		a. Surch double	—	£1700
		b. No stop after "Cents" and stop after "Revenue."	£600	£650
		c. Inverted "L" for first "F" in "FIFTY" (R. 5/2)	£1500	£1500

It is believed that Nos. F1/2 were each surcharged from a horizontal setting of five so that the raised stop variety occurs on every stamp in the first, second, third, sixth, seventh and eighth vertical columns in the sheets of 50 (10×5).

No. F1 is known fiscally used with error surcharge inverted.

POSTAGE DUE STAMPS

POSTAGE DUE
(D **1**)

1895 (1 Aug)–**97**. Nos. 68/79 optd with Type D **1** horizontally (8, 12, 18 and 24c.) or vertically, reading upwards (others). P 14½–15.

D1	**25**	2c. black and rose-lake	42·00	50·00	4·25
		a. Opt double*	†	†	£350
		b. Opt vertical, reading downwards*	†	†	£550
D2		2c. black and lake	28·00	24·00	3·75
		a. Perf 13½–14			
		b. Perf 13½–14, comp 12–13*	†	†	14·00
		c. Opt omitted (in vert pair with normal)*	†	†	£2000
D3	**26**	3c. olive-green and dull purple	6·00	16·00	1·25
		a. Bronze-green and dull purple	10·00	20·00	
		b. Opt vertical, reading downwards*	†	†	£600
D4		3c. olive-green and violet			
		a. Perf 13½–14			
		b. Opt double*	†	†	£425
D5	**27**	5c. black and vermilion	70·00	38·00	4·00
		a. Printed double	—	†	—
		b. With stop after "DUE" in opt (1897)	£400		
		c. Opt double*	£800	£900	†
		d. Perf 13½–14	—	80·00	2·50
		da. Opt double*	†	†	£600
		e. Perf 13½–14, comp 12–13	—	£100	10·00
D6	**28**	6c. black and bistre-brown	90·00	75·00	3·75
		a. Perf 13½–14	25·00	50·00	3·75
		b. Perf 12–13*	†	†	—
		c. Perf 13½–14, comp 12–13	†	†	14·00
		d. Opt vertical, reading downwards*	†	†	£550
D7	**29**	8c. black and dull purple*	65·00	50·00	4·00
		a. Opt double*	†	†	£375
		b. Perf 13½–14	†	†	5·00
		ba. Opt inverted*	†	†	£200
		c. Perf 13½–14, comp 12–13	£130	†	15·00
D8	**30**	12c. black and blue	—	60·00	4·25
		a. Opt double*	†	†	£400
		b. Perf 13½–14	70·00	50·00	4·25
		c. Perf 13½–14, comp 14½–15	£100		
D9		12c. black and ultramarine (P 13½–14)	95·00	75·00	—
D10	**31**	18c. black and deep green	75·00	65·00	6·00
		a. Opt inverted	£375	£400	†
		b. Perf 13½–14	£150	£120	6·00
		ba. Opt double*	†	†	£325
		c. Opt vertical, reading upwards (1897)	80·00	95·00	†
		ca. Opt vertical, reading downwards	£600	£375	†
D11	**32**	24c. blue and rose-lake	£130	£110	4·25
		a. Opt double*	†	†	£350
		b. Perf 13½–14	32·00	55·00	4·25
		c. Perf 13½–14, comp 14½–15	55·00	—	—

D3s, D5s, D8s, D10cs, D11s Optd "SPECIMEN"
Set of 5 .... £160

There were two local overprintings of these stamps which show variations in the distance between the two words. Further overprints were produced in London for sale to dealers by the British North Borneo Company. Those listings marked with an * only exist from the London overprinting and are usually only known cancelled-to-order.

No. D5b comes from at least one sheet which was included in a later overprinting.

The 18c. with vertical opt (No. D10c) is P 14½–15. It also exists P 13½–14 and P 13½–14, comp 12–13, but only with "SPECIMEN" opt (*Prices from* £100 *each*).

1897–99. Nos. 94/7, 99/103, 106, 108/11 optd with Type D **1** horizontally (8c.) or vertically reading upwards (others). P 14½–15.

D12	**35**	2c. black and lake (1898)	13·00	9·00	1·50
		a. Perf 13½–14	90·00		
		b. Opt horizontal*	£325		
		s. Optd "SPECIMEN"	35·00		
D13		2c. black and green (P 13½–14)*	£110	†	70
		a. Perf 13½–14, comp 12–13*	£160	†	1·00
		b. Perf 16*			

		c. Perf 12–13*	£375		
		d. Opt vertical, reading downwards*			£350
		e. Opt horizontal*			£350
D14	**36**	3c. green and rosy mauve*	55·00	†	50
		a. Perf 13½–14*	75·00	†	2·75
		b. Perf 13½–14, comp 14½–15*			
		c. Opt double*			†
D15		3c. green and dull mauve	48·00	55·00	†
D16	**37**	4c. black and carmine*	—	†	2·25
		a. Perf 13½–14	95·00	†	50
		b. Perf 13½–14, comp 12–13	†	†	5·00
D17	**38**	5c. black and orange-vermilion (1899)	90·00	65·00	1·00
		a. Perf 13½–14	28·00	65·00	1·75
		b. Perf 13½–14, comp 12–13		60·00	
D18	**39**	6c. black and bistre-brown	10·00	50·00	70
		a. Perf 13½–14	†	75·00	50
		b. Perf 13½–14, comp 12–13*	†	†	3·25
		s. Optd "SPECIMEN"	35·00		
D19	**40**	8c. black and brown-purple (1898)	65·00	90·00	†
		a. Opt vertical, reading upwards (P 16)*	†	†	£500
		s. Optd "SPECIMEN"	35·00		
D20		8c. black and brown (opt vert, reading upwards)*	15·00	†	50
		a. Opt vertical, reading downwards*	†	†	£700
		b. Perf 13½–14*	£500	†	†
		c. Perf 16			
D21	**42**	12c. black and dull blue*	—	†	7·50
		a. Perf 13½–14	£170	†	4·25
D22	**44**	18c. black and green (P 16)*	†	†	£1200
D23	**46**	18c. black and green (P 13½–14)*	£110	†	4·75
		a. Perf 13½–14, comp 12–13*	£180	†	4·75
D24	**45**	24c. blue and lake (P 13½–14)*		†	£900
D25	**47**	24c. blue and lake*	75·00	†	3·25
		a. Perf 13½–14*		†	£900

In addition to local overprints, stamps from the 1897–1902 series were also overprinted by Waterlow on two occasions for sale by the British North Borneo Company to dealers from London. These Waterlow overprints were not supplied to North Borneo for postal purposes and are indicated by an * in the above listing.

1901–02. Nos. 96/7, 100 and 102/3 optd locally as Type D **1**, but with stop after "DUE", horizontally (8c.) or vertically reading upwards (others). P 13½–14.

D26	**36**	3c. green and rosy mauve (1902)	80·00	75·00
		a. Opt double	£325	
D27		3c. green and dull mauve (P 14½–15) (1902)	50·00	55·00
		a. Opt double	£275	£325
		b. Stop after "DUE" omitted (in pair with normal)	£250	
D28	**38**	5c. black and orange-vermilion	£150	
		a. Perf 14½–15	£110	£190
D29	**40**	8c. black and brown-purple (P 14½–15)	23·00	75·00
D30		8c. black and brown (P 14½–15)	£325	£350

The "stop omitted" variety on the 3c. occurs on R. 6/10, but has also been recorded on other positions.

1902 (10 Oct)–**12**. Stamps of 1901–05 (optd "BRITISH PROTECTORATE") further optd with Type D **1** locally (No. D31) or by Waterlow (others). P 13½–14.

(a) Optd horizontally showing stop after "DUE"

D31	**34**	1c. black and bistre-brown	7·50	65·00
		a. With raised stop after "DUE"	8·50	70·00

(b) Optd vertically reading upwards

D32	**35**	2c. black and green (P 16)	£700	£350
D33	**36**	3c. green and rosy mauve	£200	£170
D34	**38**	5c. black and orange-vermilion (P 14½–15)	£350	£190
D35	**40**	8c. black and brown	£275	£110
D36	**47**	24c. blue and lake	£450	£190

(c) Optd horizontally at centre of stamp

D37	**34**	1c. black and bistre-brown*		†	38·00
		a. Perf 14½–15*	£325	†	38·00
D38	**35**	2c. black and green (1909)	38·00	4·50	30
		a. Perf 14½–15 (1903)	85·00	35·00	†
D39	**36**	3c. green and rosy mauve (1912)	9·00	5·00	30
		a. Perf 14½–15 (1904)	50·00	48·00	†
		ab. Type D **1** opt double	£475		
D40	**37**	4c. black and carmine (1912)	30·00	8·00	30
		a. Type D **1** opt double*	£600	†	£225
		b. Perf 14½–15 (1.3.03)	12·00	20·00	3·00
D41	**38**	5c. black and orange-vermilion (1905)	60·00	5·50	30
		a. No stop after "PROTECTORATE"	†	£250	†
		b. Perf 14½–15 (1905)	£110	48·00	4·00
D42	**39**	6c. black and bistre-brown (1912)	30·00	11·00	40
		a. Type D **1** opt inverted*	£550	†	£140
		b. Type D **1** opt double*	£850		
		c. No stop after "PROTECTORATE" (1912)			
		d. Perf 16 (1906)	£100	40·00	
D43	**40**	8c. black and brown (1912)	40·00	5·00	40
		a. No stop after "PROTECTORATE" (1903)	48·00	25·00	†
D44	**41**	10c. brown and slate-lilac (1906)	£425	£130	9·00
		a. No stop after "PROTECTORATE" (1906)			†

No.	Type	Description			
D45		10c. brown and slate-blue (1912)	£110	25·00	1·60
D46	42	12c. black and dull blue (2.12.10)	55·00	25·00	4·25
D47	43	16c. green and chestnut (2.12.10)	£110	38·00	4·25
D48	46	18c. black and green (2.12.10)	23·00	26·00	1·50
		a. Type D **1** opt double*	£550	†	85·00
		b. Imperf between (vert pair)	—	†	£1100
D49	47	24c. blue and lake (1905)	26·00	45·00	4·25
		a. Perf 14½–15 (1909)	60·00	85·00	†
		b. Type D **1** opt double*	£375	†	£110

(d) Optd horizontally at top of stamp

D50	35	2c. black and green (P 16) (1906)	£110	55·00	
		a. Perf 14½–15 (1908)	80·00	50·00	
D51	37	4c. black and carmine (1906)	65·00	30·00	

Items marked * only occur in stocks obtained from the British North Borneo Company in London.

POSTAGE DUE   POSTAGE DUE
(D **2**)   (D **3**)

Type D **2**. Thick letters. Ends of "S" and top of "G" straight. Pointed beard to "G".
Type D **3**. Thinner letters. Ends of "S" and top of "G" slanted. Square beard to "G".

1918–30. Opt with Type D **2** locally.

(a) On stamps of 1909–23. P 13½–14

D52	52	2c. black and green (opt at foot) (1.24)	12·00	80·00
		a. Perf 14½–15	35·00	£100
		s. Optd "SPECIMEN"	38·00	
D53	53	3c. black and green (opt at foot) (1.9.23)	4·75	50·00
D54	54	4c. black and scarlet (opt at top) (10.18)	£150	17·00
D55		4c. black and scarlet (opt at foot) (1.22)	1·00	1·25
D56		4c. black and scarlet (opt in centre) (5.23)	£190	29·00
D57	55	5c. black and yellow-brown (opt at foot) (1.22)	10·00	40·00
D58		5c. black and yellow-brown (opt in centre) (1.23)	50·00	42·00
D59	56	6c. black and olive-green (opt at foot) (1.9.23)	25·00	25·00
D60		6c. black and olive-green (opt in centre) (6.23)	50·00	7·50
D61	–	6c. black and apple-green (opt at foot) (1.9.23)	14·00	16·00
D62	57	8c. black and rose-lake (opt at foot) (1.9.23)	1·50	1·50
		a. Opt double	£1400	
D63	58	10c. black and turquoise-blue (opt at foot) (1.8.24)	22·00	19·00
		a. Perf 14½–15	£150	£250
D64	59	12c. black and deep blue (1.8.24)	80·00	55·00
		a. Horiz pair, one without opt	£14000	
D65	60	16c. black and brown-lake (2.29)	35·00	60·00
		a. Black and red-brown		

(b) On stamps of 1925–28 with opt at foot. P 12½ (1926–30)

D66	52	2c. black and claret (3.30)	1·50	2·00
D67	53	3c. black and green (1926)	12·00	45·00
D68	54	4c. black and scarlet (1926)	1·50	2·75
D69	55	5c. black and yellow-brown (1926)	8·50	£100
D70	56	6c. black and olive-green (3.28)	30·00	2·75
D71	57	8c. black and carmine (2.28)	40·00	45·00
D72	58	10c. black and turquoise-blue (1926)	19·00	90·00
D73	59	12c. black and deep blue (1926)	35·00	£180

Dates given as month and year only indicate first known postmark where recorded.

1930–38. Optd with Type D **3**, locally, at foot of stamp.

(a) On stamps of 1909–23. P 13½–14

D74	57	8c. black and carmine (1931)	20·00	2·00
D75	60	16c. black and brown-lake (11.31)	17·00	75·00
		a. Black and red-brown	6·50	
		s. Optd "SPECIMEN"	45·00	

(b) On stamps of 1925–28. P 12½

D76	52	2c. black and claret (5.31)	50	2·00
D77	53	3c. black and green (11.38)	18·00	42·00
D78	54	4c. black and scarlet (6.36)	60·00	5·00
D79	55	5c. black and yellow-brown	23·00	
D80	56	6c. black and olive-green (12.30)	9·50	2·50
D81	57	8c. black and carmine (9.31)	3·75	30·00
D82	58	10c. black and turquoise-blue (12.32)	35·00	£130
D83	59	12c. black and deep blue	75·00	
D84	60	16c. black and red-brown	65·00	£225

Dates given are those of earliest postmark where recorded.

D **4** Crest of the Company

(Recess Waterlow)

1939 (1 Jan). P 12½.

D85	D **4**	2c. brown	7·00	80·00
D86		4c. scarlet	12·00	£110
D87		6c. violet	40·00	£160
D88		8c. green	48·00	£300
D89		10c. blue	80·00	£475
D85/9		*Set of 5*	£160	£1000
D85s/9s		Perf "SPECIMEN" *Set of 5*	£200	

The stamps of North Borneo were withdrawn on 30 June 1964. For later issues see Malaysia/Sabah.

LABUAN

CROWN COLONY

The island of Labuan, off the northern coast of Borneo, was ceded to Great Britain by the Sultan of Brunei in December 1846.

Stamps of STRAITS SETTLEMENTS were used from 1867 until 1879. Covers of 1864 and 1865 are known from Labuan franked with stamps of INDIA or HONG KONG.

PRICES FOR STAMPS ON COVER	
Nos. 1/4	
Nos. 5/10	*from × 40*
Nos. 11/13	
Nos. 14/21	*from × 40*
Nos. 22/5	—
Nos. 26/35	*from × 50*
Nos. 36/8	
Nos. 39/47	*from × 100*
Nos. 49/50	*from × 15*
Nos. 51/7	*from × 60*
Nos. 62/74	*from × 15*
Nos. 75/9	*from × 40*
Nos. 80/8	*from × 20*
Nos. 89/97	*from × 15*
Nos. 98/116	*from × 10*
Nos. 117/28	*from × 30*
Nos. 129/37	*from × 10*
Nos. 138/42	—
Nos. D1/9	*from × 30*

1   (2)   (3)

Normal   6c. No dot at upper left (R. 2/4)

Normal   12c. No right foot to second Chinese character (R. 2/3)

(Recess D.L.R.)

1879 (May). Wmk CA over Crown W w **7**, sideways. P 14.

1	**1**	2c. blue-green	£1600	£900
2		6c. orange-brown	£225	£250
		a. No dot at upper left	£600	£600
3		12c. carmine	£1900	£800
		a. No right foot to second Chinese character	£4000	£1600
4		16c. blue	70·00	£200

This watermark is always found sideways and may be sideways inverted or reversed. It extends over two stamps, a single specimen showing only a portion of the Crown or the letters CA, these being tall and far apart. This paper was chiefly used for long fiscal stamps.

Normal   8c. No dot at lower left (R. 2/5)

Normal   10c. "Stolen jewel" (R. 1/1)

1880 (Jan)–**82.** Wmk Crown CC (reversed on 8c.). P 14.

5	**1**	2c. yellow-green	32·00	55·00
		w. Wmk inverted	£170	
		x. Wmk reversed	60·00	80·00
		y. Wmk inverted and reversed	£130	£140
6		6c. orange-brown	£140	£150
		a. No dot at upper left	£325	£350
		w. Wmk inverted	£325	£350
7		8c. carmine (4.82)	£130	£130
		a. No dot at lower left	£325	£325
		x. Wmk normal (not reversed)	£375	£375
		y. Wmk inverted and reversed	†	£450

8		10c. brown	£200	£100
		a. "Stolen jewel"	£400	£250
		w. Wmk inverted	£160	£130
		x. Wmk reversed		
9		12c. carmine	£300	£400
		a. No right foot to second Chinese character	£600	£750
		w. Wmk inverted	£550	
		x. Wmk reversed	£375	£400
		y. Wmk inverted and reversed	£600	
10		16c. blue (1881)	£100	£130
		w. Wmk inverted	£225	£275
		x. Wmk reversed	£170	£200
		y. Wmk inverted and reversed	£325	£375
5/10		*Set of 6*	£750	£850

1880 (Aug).

*(a) No. 9 surch with T **2** in black and with the original value obliterated by manuscript bar in red or black*

11		8c. on 12c. carmine	£1800	£850
		a. Type **2** inverted	£2000	£1000
		b. "12" not obliterated	£3500	£1800
		c. As b. with Type **2** inverted	£4000	
		d. No right foot to second Chinese character	£3750	£1700
		x. Wmk reversed	£2000	£850

*(b) No. 4 surch with two upright figures and No. 9 surch with two at right angles as T **3***

12		6c. on 16c. blue (R.)	£4000	£1300
		a. With one "6" only	—	£1500
13		8c. on 12c. carmine	£2250	£1200
		a. Both "8's" upright	—	£1500
		b. Upright "8" inverted	£2250	£1300
		c. No right foot to second Chinese character	£4000	£2000
		w. Wmk inverted	†	£2000
		x. Wmk reversed	£2250	£1200
		y. Wmk inverted and reversed		

EIGHT CENTS   Eight Cents
(4)   (5)   (6)

1881 (Mar). No. 9 handstamped with T **4.**

14		8c. on 12c. carmine	£475	£500
		a. No right foot to second Chinese character	£1100	£1100
		w. Wmk inverted	£700	
		x. Wmk reversed	£425	£450

1881 (June). No. 9 surch with T **5.**

15		8c. on 12c. carmine	£150	£160
		a. Surch double	£2750	£2250
		b. Surch inverted	£12000	
		c. "Eighr"	£20000	
		d. No right foot to second Chinese character	£325	£375
		w. Wmk inverted	£400	£400
		x. Wmk reversed	£150	£160

The error "Eighr" occurred on R. 2/1 of the first printing, but was soon corrected.

Only one sheet of ten existed of No. 15b, which also shows wmk inverted and reversed.

1883. Wmk Crown CA (reversed on 8c.). P 14.

17	**1**	2c. yellow-green	30·00	55·00
		a. Imperf between (horiz pair)	£18000	
		w. Wmk inverted	90·00	
		x. Wmk reversed	32·00	60·00
		y. Wmk inverted and reversed	£130	
18		8c. carmine	£325	£110
		a. No dot at lower left	£650	£250
		x. Wmk normal (not reversed)	—	£300
19		10c. yellow-brown	60·00	55·00
		a. "Stolen jewel"	£150	£150
		w. Wmk inverted	£110	£110
		x. Wmk reversed	£110	£110
20		16c. blue	£100	£200
21		40c. amber	30·00	£140
		x. Wmk reversed	35·00	£120
17/21		*Set of 5*	£475	£475

1883 (May). No. 10 surch "One Dollar A.S.H." by hand as T **6.**

22	**1**	$1 on 16c. blue (R.)	£4500	

The initials are those of the postmaster, Mr. A. S. Hamilton.

2 CENTS   2 Cents   2 Cents
(7)   (8)   (9)

1885 (June). Nos. 18 and 10 handstamped as T **7.**

23	**1**	2c. on 8c. carmine	£225	£550
		a. No dot at lower left	£450	
		x. Wmk normal (not reversed)	£400	
24		2c. on 16c. blue	£950	£900
		w. Wmk inverted	£1100	
		x. Wmk reversed	£1200	£900
		y. Wmk inverted and reversed	£1100	

No. 23 is known with handstamped surcharge applied diagonally rather than horizontally, and also with surcharge double.

1885 (July). No. 20 surch as T **8.**

25	**1**	2c. on 16c. blue	£110	£160
		a. Surch double	†	£7000
		b. "2" inserted	£1800	
		w. Wmk inverted		

No. 25b shows a second "2" applied by a separate handstamp to correct indistinct impressions of Type **8.**

1885 (Sept). No. 18 handstamped diag as T **9**.

26	**1**	2c. on 8c. carmine	80·00	£130
		a. No dot at lower left	£180	£325
		x. Wmk normal (not reversed)		£225

1885 (Sept)–**86**. Wmk Crown CA. P 14.

30	**1**	2c. rose-red	4·00	19·00
		a. *Pale rose-red* (1886)	4·50	17·00
		w. Wmk inverted	95·00	
		x. Wmk reversed	17·00	
		xs. Ditto, optd "SPECIMEN"	£200	
31		8c. deep violet	50·00	9·00
		a. No dot at lower left	£110	24·00
		bxs. Wmk reversed, optd "SPECIMEN"	£200	
		c. *Mauve* (1886)	48·00	13·00
		ca. No dot at lower left	£100	28·00
		cw. Wmk inverted	£130	
		cx. Wmk reversed	90·00	
32		10c. sepia (1886)	40·00	70·00
		a. "Stolen jewel"	85·00	£140
		w. Wmk inverted	80·00	
		x. Wmk reversed	45·00	
33		16c. grey (1886)	£170	
		30/3x Set of 4	£120	£180
		30s/3s Optd "SPECIMEN" Set of 4	£550	

ISSUES OF BRITISH NORTH BORNEO COMPANY

From 1 January 1890 while remaining a Crown Colony, the administration of Labuan was transferred to the British North Borneo Co, which issued the following stamps.

6
Cents
(10)

Two Cents
(11)

Six Cents
(12)

1891 (July)–**92**. Handstamped with T **10**.

34	**1**	6c. on 8c. deep violet (No. 31)	£225	£200
		a. Surch inverted	£300	£275
		b. Surch double	£600	
		c. Surch double, one inverted	£1000	
		d. "Cents" omitted	£475	£500
		da. Surch inverted with "Cents" omitted	£600	
		f. Pair, one without surch, one surch inverted	£2000	
		g. No dot at lower left	£450	£425
35		6c. on 8c. mauve (No. 31c)	16·00	16·00
		a. Surch inverted	80·00	75·00
		b. Surch double, one inverted	£900	
		c. Surch double, both inverted	£900	
		d. "6" omitted	£600	
		e. Pair, one without surcharge	£2000	£2000
		f. "Cents" omitted	—	£550
		fa. Surch inverted with "Cents" omitted	£550	
		g. Pair, one without surch, one surch inverted	£2250	£2250
		h. Surch double	£350	
		i. No dot at lower left	38·00	35·00
		j. Imperf between (horiz pair)	£18000	
		w. Wmk inverted	90·00	90·00
		x. Wmk reversed	45·00	
36		6c. on 8c. mauve (R.) (No. 31c) (2.92)	£1500	£850
		a. Surch inverted	£1800	£1000
		b. No dot at lower left	£3000	
37		6c. on 16c. blue (No. 4) (3.92)	£2750	£2500
		a. Surch inverted	£15000	£8000
38		6c. on 40c. amber (No. 21)	£14000	£5000
		a. Surch inverted	£12000	£8000

There are two different versions of Type **10** with the lines of the surcharge either 1 mm or 2 mm apart.

Normal

10c. Missing stroke at left of third Chinese character (R. 2/3)

Normal

10c. Short tail to upper Jawi character (R. 4/4)

2c. Scar over eyebrow (R. 4/1)

(Recess D.L.R.)

1892–93. No wmk. P 14.

39	**1**	2c. rose-lake	6·50	3·50
		a. Scar over eyebrow	30·00	20·00
40		6c. bright green	14·00	4·50
		a. No dot at upper left	30·00	15·00
41		8c. violet	13·00	19·00
		a. *Pale violet* (1893)	9·00	19·00
43		10c. brown	32·00	8·00
		a. *Sepia-brown* (1893)	26·00	19·00
		b. Missing stroke to Chinese character	£110	35·00
		c. Short tail to Jawi character	£110	35·00
45		12c. bright blue	15·00	6·50
		a. No right foot to second Chinese character	30·00	18·00
46		16c. grey	15·00	18·00
47		40c. ochre	23·00	45·00
		a. *Brown-buff* (1893)	50·00	25·00
		39/47 Set of 7	£100	75·00

The 6c., 12c., 16c. and 40c. are in sheets of ten, as are all the earlier issues. The other values are in sheets of 30.

1892 (Dec). Nos. 47 and 46 surch locally as T **11** or **12**.

49	**1**	2c. on 40c. ochre (13.12)	£170	£100
		a. Surch inverted	£450	£600
50		6c. on 16c. grey (20.12)	£375	£150
		a. Surch inverted	£550	£300
		b. Surch sideways	£550	£300
		c. Surch "Six Cents"	£1900	

There are ten slightly different versions of each of these surcharges which were applied in settings of 5×2, although instances of single handstamps are known.

A "SIX CENTS" handstamp with Roman "I" in "SIX" (without dot) is a clandestine surcharge, although it can be found with genuine postmarks. It also exists sideways or inverted.

The "Six Cents" surcharge of No. 50c was handstamped onto examples where the Type **12** surcharge had failed to print or where it was partially or completely albino.

> **CANCELLED-TO-ORDER.** Prices are separately indicated, in a third price column, for stamps showing the recognisable black bars remainder cancellation. Earlier issues of the Company administration were also so treated, but, as similar postal cancellations were used, these cannot be identified.

(Litho D.L.R.)

1894 (Apr). No wmk. P 14.

51	**1**	2c. carmine-pink	2·00	18·00	50
52		6c. bright green	28·00	65·00	50
		a. Imperf between (horiz pair)	£11000		
		b. No dot at upper left	55·00	£140	1·25
53		8c. bright mauve	29·00	70·00	50
54		10c. brown	55·00	90·00	50
		a. Missing stroke to Chinese character	£200		4·00
		b. Short tail to Jawi character	£200		4·00
55		12c. pale blue	38·00	£110	70
		a. No right foot to second Chinese character	70·00	£250	2·00
56		16c. grey	40·00	£190	50
57		40c. orange-buff	60·00	£225	50
		51/7 Set of 7	£225	£700	3·25
		51s/7s H/S "SPECIMEN" Set of 7	£130		

Collectors are warned against forgeries of this issue.

PERFORATION. There are a number of small variations in the perforation of the Waterlow issues of 1894 to 1905 which we believe to be due to irregularity of the pins rather than from different perforators.

In the following lists, stamps perf 12, 12½, 13 or compound are described as perf 12–13, stamps perf 13½, 14 or compound are described as perf 13½–14 and those perf 14½, 15 or compound are listed as perf 14½–15. In addition the 13½–14 perforation exists compound with 14½–15 and with 12–13, whilst perf 16 comes from a separate perforator.

LABUAN
40
CENTS
(14)
13

1894 (May)–**96**. T **24/32** of North Borneo (colours changed), with "LABUAN" engraved on vignette plate as T **13** (8, 12, 24c.) or horizontally (others). P 14½–15.

(a) Name and central part of design in black

62	**24**	1c. grey-mauve	1·50	14·00	50
		a. Imperf between (vert pair)	†	†	£650
		b. Perf 13½–14	17·00	10·00	—
		ba. Imperf between (vert pair)	£1200	—	£500
		c. Perf 13½–14, comp 14½–15	40·00		
		d. Perf 13½–14, comp 12–13	42·00	17·00	1·00
		e. Perf 12–13			
63	**25**	2c. blue	2·50	15·00	50
		a. Imperf (pair)	£600		
		b. Perf 13½–14	8·50	15·00	—
		c. Perf 13½–14, comp 14½–15	42·00		
		d. Perf 13½–14, comp 12–13			
		e. Perf 12–13	£190		
64	**26**	3c. ochre	3·75	25·00	50
		a. Perf 13½–14	18·00	9·00	—
		b. Perf 13½–14, comp 14½–15			
		c. Perf 13½–14, comp 12–13	50·00		
		d. Perf 12–13			

65	**27**	5c. green	32·00	42·00	1·00
		a. Perf 13½–14	50·00	24·00	—
		ab. Imperf between (horiz pair)	£1500		
		b. Perf 13½–14, comp 12–13	65·00		
		c. Perf 12–13	£225		
67	**28**	6c. brown-lake	2·50	24·00	50
		a. Imperf (pair)	£600	†	£300
		b. Perf 13½–14	—		3·00
		c. Perf 13½–14, comp 14½–15	—		2·50
		d. Perf 13½–14, comp 12–13			
		e. Perf 12–13			
68	**29**	8c. rose-red	35·00	45·00	2·25
		a. Perf 13½–14	45·00	55·00	—
69		8c. pink (1896)	12·00	35·00	50
		a. Perf 13½–14	48·00	32·00	1·00
70	**30**	12c. orange-vermilion	23·00	55·00	50
		a. Imperf between (vert pair)	†	†	£3250
		b. Perf 13½–14	65·00	90·00	2·75
		c. Perf 12–13	£250		
		d. Perf 13½–14, comp 12–13	80·00	£110	—
71	**31**	18c. olive-brown	27·00	60·00	50
		a. Perf 13½–14	70·00		
72		18c. olive-bistre (1896)	55·00	75·00	50
		a. Perf 13½–14	27·00	70·00	—
		b. Perf 13½–14, comp 12–13			
		c. Imperf between (vert pair)	†	†	£2000
		d. Perf 13½–14, comp 14½–15	†	†	2·25
		(b) Name and central part in blue			
73	**32**	24c. pale mauve	42·00	65·00	50
		a. Perf 13½–14	42·00	65·00	—
		b. Perf 13½–14 comp 14½–15			
74		24c. dull lilac (1896)	22·00	55·00	1·25
		a. Perf 13½–14	21·00	55·00	1·25
		62/74 Set of 9	£110	£250	4·50
		62s/74s Optd "SPECIMEN" Set of 9	£160		

1895 (June). No. 83 of North Borneo ($1 inscr "STATE OF NORTH BORNEO") surch as T **14**.

75	**32c**	4c. on $1 scarlet	4·50	5·00	40
76		10c. on $1 scarlet	11·00	1·40	40
77		20c. on $1 scarlet	50·00	14·00	50
78		30c. on $1 scarlet	55·00	65·00	1·50
79		40c. on $1 scarlet	55·00	55·00	1·50
		75/9 Set of 5	£160	£120	3·75
		75s/9s Optd "SPECIMEN" Set of 5	80·00		

No. 76 exists with the figures of the surcharge 2½ mm away from "CENTS". The normal setting has a space of 4 mm. Examples of the narrow setting have, so far, only been seen on cancelled-to-order stamps (*Price* £20 *c.t.o.*).

1846
JUBILEE
LABUAN 1896
(15) **(16)**

4
CENTS
(17)

1896. T **32a** to **32c** of North Borneo (as Nos. 81 to 83, but colours changed) optd with T **15**.

80		25c. green	42·00	50·00	60
		a. Opt omitted	35·00	—	2·00
		b. Imperf (pair)			60·00
		ba. Opt omitted	50·00		
81		50c. maroon	42·00	50·00	60
		a. Opt omitted	32·00	—	2·00
		b. Imperf (pair)			60·00
		ba. Opt omitted	50·00		
82		$1 blue	80·00	75·00	1·25
		a. Opt omitted	48·00	—	2·75
		b. Imperf (pair)			60·00
		ba. Opt omitted	55·00		
		80s/2s Optd "SPECIMEN" Set of 3	70·00		

Nos. 80/1 showing stamps either printed double or double, one inverted, are from waste sheets subsequently sold by the British North Borneo Company to collectors.

1896 (24 Sept). Jubilee of Cession of Labuan to Gt Britain. Nos. 62 to 68 optd with T **16**. P 14½–15.

83		1c. black and grey-mauve	25·00	25·00	1·75
		b. Opt in orange	£200	£200	20·00
		c. "JEBILEE" (R. 8/7)	£1200	£650	£300
		d. "JUBILE" (R. 3/10)	£2750		
		e. Perf 13½–14	35·00	26·00	—
		ea. Opt double	£375	£375	—
		eb. Opt in orange	£325	£200	†
		f. Perf 13½–14, comp 12–13	48·00	23·00	—
		fa. Opt in orange	—	£200	†
		fb. Opt double	£475	£475	
		g. Perf 12–13			
84		2c. black and blue	50·00	35·00	1·75
		a. Imperf horiz (vert pair)	£1500	£1600	†
		b. "JEBILEE" (R. 8/7)	£1800	£1200	—
		c. "JUBILE" (R. 3/10)	£3000	£3000	—
		d. Perf 13½–14	50·00	24·00	—
		e. Perf 13½–14, comp 14½–15	—	45·00	—
		f. Perf 13½–14 comp 12–13	60·00		
85		3c. black and ochre	50·00	22·00	1·50
		a. "JEBILEE" (R. 8/7)	£2000	£1700	£700
		b. "JUBILE" (R. 3/10)			
		d. Perf 13½–14	55·00	35·00	1·50
		da. Opt double	—	—	£150
		db. Opt treble	£650		
		e. Perf 13½–14, comp 14½–15			
		f. Perf 13½–14, comp 12–13			
		fa. Opt double	£375	£375	£160
		fb. Opt treble	£650		
86		5c. black and green	70·00	16·00	1·50
		a. Opt double	£950	£700	

		b. Perf 13½–14	70·00	22·00	1·50
		c. Perf 13½–14, comp 12–13	95·00		
		d. Perf 13½–14, comp 14½–15	—	—	3·50
87		6c. black and brown-lake	48·00	35·00	80
		a. Opt double	£850	£650	†
		b. "JEBILEE" (R.8/7)	†	†	£2750
		c. "JUBILE" (R. 3/10)	£3500	—	£2750
		d. Perf 13½–14, comp 14½–15			
		e. Perf 13½–14	—	£100	—
88		8c. black and pink	55·00	18·00	80
		a. Opt double	†	£3500	†
		b. Perf 13½–14	55·00	15·00	1·00
		c. Perf 13½–14, comp 14½–15	55·00	22·00	—
83/8		Set of 6	£250	£110	7·25
		83s/8s Optd "SPECIMEN" *Set of 6.*	£150		

The normal overprint on the 1c. varies in appearance from pure black to brownish black due to a mixing of the inks. The orange overprint on this value is in a clear, bright, unadulterated ink.

No. 84b is known in a vertical strip of three imperf horizontally except at the base of the bottom stamp (*Price £7500 unused*).

Nos. 87b and 87c are known with additional "SPECIMEN" overprint. (*Price £2000 each*).

1897 (Apr)–**1901**. T **34/45** of North Borneo (colours changed), with "LABUAN" engraved on vignette plate as T **13** (8, 12, 24c.) or horizontally (others). Name and central part in black (24c. in blue). P 13½–14.

89	34	1c. dull claret (P 14½–15)..	7·50	4·75	50
		a. Perf 13½–14, comp 14½–15			2·00
		ab. Perf 16	—	—	2·00
		b. Brown (1901)	26·00	28·00	65
		ba. Perf 14½–15	3·00		
		bb. Perf 16	24·00	21·00	—
90	35	2c. blue	27·00	6·00	65
		a. Imperf between (vert pair)	†	†	£1100
		b. Imperf between (horiz pair)	†	†	£1500
		c. Perf 14½–15	35·00	—	1·00
		d. Perf 13½–14, comp 12–13	60·00	25·00	—
		e. Perf 16	—	—	7·00
91	36	3c. ochre	9·00	30·00	50
		a. Imperf between (vert pair)	£1300	†	£650
		b. Perf 14½–15	9·00	7·00	50
		c. Perf 13½–14, comp 12–13	21·00	48·00	2·25
		d. Perf 12–13	£100		
92	38	5c. green	70·00	60·00	70
		a. Perf 14½–15	65·00	60·00	70
		b. Perf 13½–14, comp 12–13			
93	39	6c. brown-lake	6·50	50·00	1·50
		a. Perf 14½–15	15·00	21·00	50
		ba. Imperf between (vert pair)	†	†	£750
		c. Perf 13½–14, comp 12–13	—	—	8·00
94	40	8c. rose-red	55·00	—	1·00
		a. Perf 14½–15	27·00	12·00	—
		b. Perf 13½–14, comp 12–13	55·00	—	2·75
		c. Vermilion	12·00	—	75
		ca. Perf 16	—	—	7·00
95	42	12c. vermilion	£140	£160	3·00
		a. Perf 14½–15	32·00	55·00	2·50
96	44	18c. olive-bistre	£130	£130	2·25
		a. Perf 16	12·00	45·00	50
		ab. Imperf between (vert pair)	†	†	£3250
97	45	24c. grey-lilac	55·00	£110	2·25
		a. Perf 14½–15	12·00	55·00	50
89/97a		Set of 9	£160	£225	6·50
		89s/97s Optd "SPECIMEN" *Set of 9*	£180		

The 12, 18 and 24c. above were errors; in the 12c., "LABUAN" is over the value at the top; the 18c. has "POSTAL REVENUE" instead of "POSTAGE & REVENUE", and the 24c. is without "POSTAGE & REVENUE".

1897 (Nov)–**98.**

(a) Types of North Borneo (colours changed), with "LABUAN" engraved on the vignette plate as in T **13**. P 13½–14

98	42	12c. black and vermilion (3.98)	†	—	3·50
		a. Perf 14½–15	55·00	55·00	—
		b. Perf 13½–14, comp 14½–15			
		c. Perf 16	80·00	80·00	—
99	46	18c. black and olive-bistre .			
		a. Perf 14½–15	90·00	60·00	2·00
		b. Perf 13½–14, comp 12–13	£140		
		c. Perf 16	†	—	10·00
100	47	24c. blue and lilac-brown	55·00	70·00	2·00
		a. Perf 14½–15	50·00	60·00	—
		b. Perf 13½–14, comp 12–13	—	70·00	—
		c. Perf 16	60·00	60·00	—
		d. Blue and ochre (P 14½–15)	—	—	5·00

In the 12c., "LABUAN" is now correctly placed at foot of stamp. The 18c. and 24c. have the inscriptions on the stamps corrected, but the 18c. still has "LABUAN" *over* the value at foot, and was further corrected as follows:

(b) As No. 99, but "LABUAN" at top

101	46	18c. black and olive-bistre (3.98)	70·00	60·00	—
		a. Perf 14½–15	42·00	75·00	3·50
		b. Perf 13½–14, comp 12–13	55·00	60·00	—
		c. Perf 12–13			
		98s, 100s/1as Optd "SPECIMEN" *Set of 3*	70·00		

1899 (July). Surch with T **17**.

(a) P 14½–15

102	38	4c. on 5c. (No. 92a)	60·00	26·00	
103	39	4c. on 6c. (No. 93b)	32·00	19·00	
		a. Perf 13½–14	45·00	40·00	
		b. Perf 13½–14 comp 12–13	55·00	65·00	

104	40	4c. on 8c. (No. 94a)	65·00	50·00	
		a. Perf 13½–14	50·00	38·00	
		b. Perf 13½–14, comp 12–13	40·00	50·00	
		c. Perf 12–13	40·00	50·00	
105	42	4c. on 12c. (No. 98a)	65·00	35·00	
		a. Perf 13½–14	65·00	45·00	
		b. Perf 16	65·00	42·00	
		c. Perf 13½–14, comp 12–13	75·00	80·00	
106	46	4c. on 18c. (No. 101a)	40·00	18·00	
		a. Surch double	£550	£650	
107	47	4c. on 24c. (No. 100a)	42·00	38·00	
		a. Perf 13½–14	27·00	25·00	
		b. Perf 13½–14, comp 12–13	50·00	30·00	
		c. Perf 16	55·00	55·00	

(b) P 14

108	32a	4c. on 25c. (No. 80)		6·00	7·50
109	32b	4c. on 50c. (No. 81)		8·50	7·50
110	32c	4c. on $1 (No. 82)		8·50	7·50
102/10		Set of 9		£250	£160
		102s/10s Optd "SPECIMEN" *Set of 9*		£170	

A new setting of the surcharge with closer spacing (2½ mm) between "4" and "CENTS" was used for the Specimen overprints, including unissued surcharges on the 1c., 2c. and 3c. values (*Price £140 for the set of 3*).

1900–02. Types of North Borneo with "LABUAN" engraved on the vignette plate as in T **13** (10, 16c.) or horizontally (others), in brown on 10c. and in green on 16c. P 13½–14.

111	35	2c. black and green	3·75	2·50	30
		a. Imperf between (horiz pair)	£3000	†	£1500
		b. Perf 13½–14, comp 12–13			
112	37	4c. black and yellow-brown	8·50	75·00	60
		a. Imperf between (vert pair)	£1400		
		b. Perf 13½–14, comp 12–13	55·00		
113		4c. black and carmine (8.1900)	25·00	3·50	75
		a. Perf 14½–15	5·00	17·00	50
		b. Perf 13½–14, comp 12–13	50·00	12·00	1·50
		c. Perf 16			
114	38	5c. black and pale blue	20·00	23·00	65
		a. Perf 13½–14, comp 12–13	—	90·00	—
		b. Perf 12–13	£225		
115	41	10c. brown and slate-lilac (P 14½–15) (1902)	60·00	£100	60
116	43	16c. green and chestnut (1902)	50·00	£140	2·50
		a. Perf 13½–14, comp 12–13	£110	£170	—
		b. Perf 12–13	£450		
		c. Perf 14½–15	£200		
		sa. Opt "SPECIMEN", double, one albino	£250		
111/16		Set of 6	£130	£300	4·75
		111s/16s Optd "SPECIMEN" *Set of 6*	£180		

No. 112 was printed in an incorrect frame colour and was not issued for postal purposes in Labuan. Used examples come from dealers' stock sent to the island for cancellation.

18   Line through "B" (R. 5/10)

(Recess Waterlow)

1902 (Sept)–**03.** P 13½–14.

117	18	1c. black and purple (10.03)	7·00	7·00	50
		a. Perf 14½–15	£100	9·00	—
		b. Perf 13½–14 comp 12–13	90·00	50·00	
		c. Line through "B"	£120	£130	12·00
118		2c. black and green	4·50	6·50	30
		a. Perf 14½–15	£120	5·50	—
		b. Perf 13½–14, comp 12–13	£120	55·00	
		c. Line through "B"	95·00	£120	12·00
119		3c. black and sepia (10.03)	3·25	23·00	30
		a. Line through "B"	90·00	£200	12·00
120		4c. black and carmine	3·25	4·00	30
		a. Perf 14½–15	11·00	18·00	—
		b. Perf 13½–14 comp 12–13	80·00	50·00	—
		c. Line through "B"	90·00	£100	12·00
121		8c. black and vermilion	14·00	9·00	75
		a. Perf 14½–15	8·00		
		b. Line through "B"	£130	£140	13·00
122		10c. brown and slate-blue .	3·25	19·00	30
		b. Perf 14½–15	11·00	19·00	50
		ba. Imperf between (vert pair)	†	†	£1000
		c. Line through "B"	£100	£190	12·00
123		12c. black and yellow	16·00	26·00	30
		a. Imperf between (vert strip of 3)	†	†	£3500
		b. Perf 16	17·00	26·00	50
		c. Line through "B"	£160	£250	12·00
124		16c. green and brown	4·75	38·00	30
		a. Imperf between (vert pair)	†	†	£2000
		b. Line through "B"	£120	£350	12·00
125		18c. black and pale brown	3·25	38·00	30
		a. Line through "B"	95·00	£350	12·00
126		25c. green and greenish blue	7·50	28·00	50
		a. Perf 14½–15	15·00	50·00	1·00

		b. Error. Black and greenish blue	—	†	£600
		c. Line through "B"	£150	£300	13·00
127		50c. dull purple and lilac	11·00	50·00	2·75
		a. Perf 13½–14 comp 12–13	16·00	60·00	
		b. Line through "B"	£200	£550	27·00
128		$1 claret and orange	9·50	50·00	2·50
		a. Perf 14½–15	10·00	—	2·25
		b. Line through "B"	£200	£550	27·00
117/28		Set of 12	65·00	£275	8·00
		117s/28s Optd "SPECIMEN" *Set of 12*	£200		

4 cents
(19)

1904 (Dec). Issues of 1896, 1897–8 and 1897/1901 surch with T **19**.

(a) P 14½–15

129	38	4c. on 5c. (No. 92a)	55·00	50·00	14·00
130	39	4c. on 6c. (No. 93b)	12·00	50·00	14·00
131	40	4c. on 8c. (No. 94a)	25·00	55·00	14·00
132	42	4c. on 12c. (No. 98a)	48·00	50·00	14·00
		a. Perf 16	50·00	50·00	—
133	46	4c. on 18c. (No. 101) (P 13½–14)	23·00	50·00	14·00
		a. Perf 13½–14, comp 12–13	42·00	50·00	—
		b. Perf 12–13			
134	47	4c. on 24c. (No. 100a)	16·00	50·00	14·00
		a. Perf 13½–14	42·00	42·00	—
		b. Perf 13½–14, comp 12–13	50·00	50·00	—
		c. Perf 16	35·00	50·00	14·00

(b) P 14

135	32a	4c. on 25c. (No. 80)	8·50	40·00	14·00
136	32b	4c. on 50c. (No. 81)	8·50	40·00	14·00
		a. Surch double	£375		
137	32c	4c. on $1 (No. 82)	13·00	40·00	14·00
129/37		Set of 9	£170	£350	£110

No. 136a usually shows one complete surcharge and parts of two further surcharges due to the position of the misplaced second impression.

The barred cancels can be found used on "philatelic" covers of this issue.

LABUAN
(20)

LABUAN
(21)

1901 (?)–**05.** Nos. 81, 83 (in Labuan colour), and 84/6 of North Borneo optd locally with T **20** (25c. $2) or **21** (others).

138	32a	25c. indigo (2.05)	£1200	†	£900
		a. Opt double	—	†	†
139	32c	$1 blue (2.05)	†	†	£1000
140	32d	$2 dull green	£3500	£3750	—
141	32e	$5 bright purple	£6000	†	£1800
		a. Dull purple	£6000	£7500	—
142	32f	$10 brown	£60000	†	£15000

Dangerous forgeries exist.
The overprint on No. 140 is 12 mm long.

POSTAGE DUE STAMPS

POSTAGE DUE
(D 1)

1901. Optd with Type D **1**, reading vertically upwards. P 13½–14.

D1	35	2c. black and green (111)	27·00	45·00	50
		a. Opt double	£275		
		b. Perf 13½–14, comp 12–13	£130	£150	11·00
D2	36	3c. black and ochre (91)	35·00	£130	1·00
		a. Perf 13½–14, comp 12–13	£120	—	4·00
D3	37	4c. black and carmine (113)	60·00	—	3·00
		a. Opt double	†	†	£850
		b. Perf 14½–15	50·00	£110	50
D4	38	5c. black and pale blue (114)	55·00	£170	1·75
		a. Perf 14½–15	—	—	2·25
		b. Perf 13½–14, comp 12–13	£130	£325	—
D5	39	6c. black and brown-lake (93)	45·00	£120	1·00
		a. Perf 14½–15	60·00	£140	—
		b. Perf 16	90·00		1·75
D6	40	8c. black and vermilion (94c)	£120	£130	2·75
		a. Perf 14½–15	£100	£160	85
		ba. Frame inverted	†	†	£8500
		c. Perf 16	£110	£120	—
		d. Black and rose-red (94)	95·00	£140	—
		da. Perf 14½–15	£150	—	9·00
		db. Perf 13½–14, comp 12–13	£160		
D7	42	12c. black and vermilion (98)	£160	—	6·50
		a. Opt reading downwards	†	†	£1300
		b. Perf 14½–15	£120	£170	14·00
D8	46	18c. black and olive-bistre (101) (P 14½–15)	40·00	£140	1·75
D9	47	24c. blue and lilac-brown (100)	80·00	£180	7·50
		a. Perf 13½–14, comp 12–13	£110		
		b. Perf 14½–15	60·00		
		ba. Blue and ochre	£100	—	2·25
		c. Perf 16	65·00	£130	—
		d. Opt double, one albino	£225		
D1/9		Set of 9	£450	£1000	14·00

No. D6ba only exists cancelled-to-order.

The administration of Labuan reverted to Colonial Office control, as part of an agreement with Brunei on 1 January 1906. By Letters Patent dated 30 October 1906 Labuan was incorporated with Straits Settlements and ceased issuing its own stamps. In 1946 it became part of the Colony of North Borneo.

JAPANESE OCCUPATION OF NORTH BORNEO

Japanese forces landed in Northern Borneo on 15 December 1941 and the whole of North Borneo had been occupied by 19 January 1942.

Brunei, North Borneo, Sarawak and, after a short period, Labuan, were administered as a single territory by the Japanese. Until 12 December 1942, previous stamp issues, without overprint, continued to be used in conjunction with existing postmarks. From November 1942 onwards unoverprinted stamps of Japan were made available and examples can be found used from the area for much of the remainder of the War. Japanese Occupation issues for Brunei, North Borneo and Sarawak were equally valid throughout the combined territory but not, in practice, equally available.

PRICES FOR STAMPS ON COVER	
Nos. J1/17	from × 5
Nos. J18/19	from × 6
Nos. J20/32	from × 25
Nos. J33/4	from × 2
Nos. J35/48	from × 12

(1)	
2 Mt. Kinabalu	**3** Borneo Scene

1942 (30 Sept). Stamps of North Borneo handstamped with T **1**.

(a) In violet on Nos. 303/17

J1	1c. green and red-brown	£180	£250
	a. Black opt	£400	£200
	ab. Pair, one without opt	£6000	
J2	2c. purple and greenish blue	£200	£275
	a. Black opt	£650	£300
J3	3c. slate-blue and green	£170	£300
	a. Black opt	£700	£375
J4	4c. bronze-green and violet	£300	£375
	a. Black opt	65·00	£140
J5	6c. deep blue and claret	£190	£350
	a. Black opt	£700	£450
J6	8c. scarlet	£250	£200
	a. Pair, one without opt	£6000	
	b. Black opt	£325	£200
J7	10c. violet and bronze-green	£225	£350
	a. Black opt	£650	£400
J8	12c. green and bright blue	£250	£500
	a. Black opt	£1000	£550
J9	15c. blue-green and brown	£225	£500
	a. Pair, one without opt	£6000	
	b. Black opt	£1100	£550
J10	20c. violet and slate-blue	£325	£650
	a. Black opt	£1300	£800
J11	25c. green and chocolate	£300	£650
	a. Black opt	£1300	£800
J12	50c. chocolate and violet	£350	£700
	a. Black opt	£1500	£900
J13	$1 brown and carmine	£425	£900
	a. Black opt	£1700	£1300
J14	$2 violet and olive-green	£600	£1100
	a. Pair, one without opt	£8000	
	b. Black opt	£2750	£1500
J15	$5 indigo and pale blue	£700	£1200
	a. Black opt	£3500	£2250

(b) In black on Nos. 318/19 ("WAR TAX")

J16	1c. green and red-brown	£700	£325
	a. Pair, one without opt	†	£6000
	b. Violet opt	—	£1200
J17	2c. purple and greenish blue	£2000	£650
	a. Pair, one without opt	†	£9000
	b. Violet opt	—	£1500

(Litho Kolff & Co., Batavia)

1943 (29 Apr). P 12½.

J18	**2**	4c. red	32·00	60·00
J19	**3**	8c. blue	28·00	55·00

(4)	(5)

("Imperial Japanese Postal Service North Borneo")

1944 (30 Sept). Nos. 303/15 of North Borneo optd with T **4** at Chinese Press, Kuching.

J20	1c. green and red-brown	8·00	12·00
	a. Ant trail		
J21	2c. purple and greenish blue	8·00	9·00
	a. Optd on No. J2	£450	
J22	3c. slate-blue and green	8·00	10·00
	a. Optd on No. J3	£450	
J23	4c. bronze-green and violet	17·00	25·00
J24	6c. deep blue and claret	11·00	6·50
J25	8c. scarlet	10·00	17·00
	a. Optd on No. J6	£450	
J26	10c. violet and bronze-green	8·50	13·00
	a. Optd on No. J7	£450	
	b. Optd on No. J7a	£250	£475

J27	12c. green and bright blue	17·00	13·00
	a. Optd on No. J8	£450	
J28	15c. blue-green and brown	17·00	16·00
	a. Optd on No. J9	£450	
J29	20c. violet and slate-blue	40·00	50·00
	a. Optd on No. J10	£3750	
J30	25c. green and chocolate	40·00	50·00
	a. Optd on No. J11	£3750	
J31	50c. chocolate and violet	90·00	£130
	a. Optd on No. J12	£4500	
J32	$1 brown and carmine	£100	£150
J20/32 *Set of 13*		£325	£450

The spacing between the second and third lines of the overprint is 12 mm on the horizontal stamps, and 15 mm on the upright.

1944 (11 May). No. J1 surch with T **5**.

J33	**81**	$2 on 1c green and red-brown	£6000	£5000

(6)	**7** Girl War-worker	(8) ("North Borneo")

1944 (11 May). North Borneo No. 315 surch with T **6**.

J34	$5 on $1 brown and carmine	£5000	£3750
	a. Surch on No. J13	£10000	£6000

1944 (2 Oct)–**45**. Contemporary stamps of Japan as T **7** (various subjects) optd with T **8** at Chinese Press, Kuching.

J35	1s. red-brown (No. 391) (1.45)	9·00	42·00
J36	2s. scarlet (No. 392b) (10.44)	7·50	35·00
J37	3s. emerald-green (No. 316) (8.45)	9·00	42·00
J38	4s. yellow-green (No. 395) (10.44)	18·00	28·00
J39	5s. claret (No. 396) (1.45)	15·00	38·00
J40	6s. orange (No. 319) (8.45)	24·00	40·00
	a. Opt double, one inverted	£650	£650
J41	8s. violet (No. 321) (11.44)	6·50	40·00
	a. Opt double	£350	
J42	10s. carmine and pink (No. 399) (1.45)	15·00	42·00
J43	15s. blue (No. 401) (11.44)	14·00	42·00
J44	20s. blue-slate (No. 325) (11.44)	85·00	90·00
J45	25s. brown and chocolate (No. 326) (2.45)	70·00	90·00
J46	30s. turquoise-blue (No. 327)	£180	95·00
J47	50s. olive and bistre (No. 328) (8.45)	80·00	85·00
J48	1y. red-brown and chocolate (No. 329) (5.45)	95·00	£120
J35/48 *Set of 14*		£550	£700

Designs:—2s. General Nogi; 3s. Hydro-electric Works; 4s. Hyuga Monument and Mt Fuji; 5s. Admiral Togo; 6s. Garambi Lighthouse, Formosa; 8s. Meiji Shrine; 10s. Palms and map of S.E. Asia; 15s. Airman; 20s. Mt Fuji and cherry blossoms; 25s. Horyu Temple; 30s. Torii, Itsukushima Shrine at Miyajima; 50s. Kinkaku Temple; 1y. Great Buddha, Kamakura.

Examples of some values have been found with hand-painted forged overprints.

POSTAGE DUE STAMPS

1942 (30 Sept). Nos. D85/6 and D88 of North Borneo handstamped with T **1** in black.

JD1	D **2**	2c. brown	—	£5500
JD2		4c. scarlet	—	£5500
JD3		8c. green	—	£5500

Northern Nigeria *see* Nigeria

Northern Rhodesia

The north-eastern and north-western provinces of Rhodesia, previously administered by the British South Africa Company, became a Crown Colony on 1 April 1924.

The current stamps of Rhodesia (the "Admiral" design first issued in 1913) remained in use until 31 March 1925 and continued to be valid for postal purposes until 30 September of that year.

PRICES FOR STAMPS ON COVER TO 1945	
Nos. 1/21	from × 3
Nos. 22/4	from × 6
Nos. 25/45	from × 3
Nos. D1/2	from × 30
Nos. D3/4	from × 15

1	2

(Des W. Fairweather. Eng J. A. C. Harrison. Recess Waterlow)

1925 (1 Apr)–**29**. Wmk Mult Script CA. P 12½.

1	**1**	½d. green	1·75	80
2		1d. brown	1·75	10
3		1½d. carmine-red	4·25	30
4		2d. yellow-brown	4·50	10
5		3d. ultramarine	4·50	1·25
6		4d. violet	7·50	50
7		6d. slate-grey	9·00	40
8		8d. rose-purple	9·00	55·00
9		10d. olive-green	9·00	50·00
10	**2**	1s. yellow-brown and black	4·50	1·75
11		2s. brown and ultramarine	30·00	48·00
12		2s.6d. black and green	25·00	15·00
13		3s. violet and blue (1929)	48·00	27·00
14		5s. slate-grey and violet	55·00	19·00
15		7s.6d. rose-purple and black	£190	£300
16		10s. green and black	£120	£100
17		20s. carmine-red and rose-purple	£350	£375
1/17 *Set of 17*			£800	£900
1s/17s Optd or Perf (3s.) "SPECIMEN" *Set of 17*			£1200	

A used example of the 4d. exists imperforate between the stamp and a fragment of another below it.

1935 (6 May). Silver Jubilee. As Nos. 91/4 of Antigua. P 13½×14.

18		1d. light blue and olive-green	1·50	1·50
	f. Diagonal line by turret	£120	£130	
	g. Dot to left of chapel	£375	£400	
	h. Dot by flagstaff	£275	£300	
	i. Dash by turret	£300	£325	
19		2d. green and indigo	3·75	2·75
	f. Diagonal line by turret	£180	£180	
	g. Dot to left of chapel	£325	£350	
20		3d. brown and deep blue	4·75	12·00
	f. Diagonal line by turret	£275	£375	
	g. Dot to left of chapel	£425	£550	
21		6d. slate and purple	12·00	1·75
	a. Frame printed double, one albino	£3000	£3250	
	f. Diagonal line by turret	£275	£375	
	h. Dot by flagstaff	£650	£375	
18/21 *Set of 4*			20·00	16·00
18s/21s Perf "SPECIMEN" *Set of 4*			£225	

For illustrations of plate varieties see Omnibus section following Zanzibar.

Hyphen between "NORTHERN" and "RHODESIA" (R. 9/6)

1937 (12 May). Coronation. As Nos. 95/7 of Antigua. P 11×11½.

22		1½d. carmine	30	50
23		2d. buff	40	1·75
24		3d. blue	60	1·25
	a. Hyphen flaw	£400		
22/4 *Set of 3*			1·10	3·25
22s/4s Perf "SPECIMEN" *Set of 3*			£180	

Fakes of No. 24a exist.

3	4	**½d.** Re-entry to giraffe (Plate 2, R. 12/2)

1d. "Extra boatman" (Pl 4 R. 3/2)	**1½d.** "Tick bird" flaw (Pl 1 R. 7/1 of ptgs from Sept 1938 onwards)

(Recess Waterlow)

1938 (1 Mar)–**52.** Wmk Mult Script CA. P 12½.

25	**3**	½d. green	10	10
		a. "C" of "CA" missing from wmk....	£2250	
		b. Re-entry to giraffe	85·00	60·00
26		½d. chocolate (15.11.51)	2·25	1·50
		a. Perf 12½×14 (22.10.52)	1·40	6·00
27		1d. brown	20	20
		a. Chocolate (1948)	2·00	1·00
		ab. "Extra boatman"	£375	£300
28		1d. green (15.11.51)	1·50	2·25
		a. "Extra boatman"	£375	£425
29		1½d. carmine-red	50·00	75
		a. Imperf between (horiz pair)	£30000	
		b. "Tick bird" flaw	£6500	£450
30		1½d. yellow-brown (10.1.41)	75	10
		b. "Tick bird" flaw	£200	70·00
31		2d. yellow-brown	50·00	1·75
32		2d. carmine-red (10.1.41)	1·75	50
33		2d. purple (1.12.51)	60	1·50
34		3d. ultramarine	70	30
35		3d. scarlet (1.12.51)	60	3·00
36		4d. dull violet	40	40
37		4½d. blue (5.5.52)	3·25	12·00
38		6d. grey	40	10
39		9d. violet (5.5.52)	3·25	14·00
40	**4**	1s. yellow-brown and black	4·00	60
41		2s.6d. black and green	15·00	7·50
42		3s. violet and blue	28·00	18·00
43		5s. grey and dull violet	28·00	18·00
44		10s. green and black	30·00	35·00
45		20s. carmine-red and rose-purple	70·00	80·00
25/45 *Set of 21*			£250	£170
25s/45s Perf "SPECIMEN" *Set of 15*			£750	

Nos. 26a and 28 exist in coils, constructed from normal sheets.

1946 (26 Nov). Victory. As Nos. 110/11 of Antigua. P 13½×14.

46		1½d. red-orange	1·00	1·75
		a. Perf 13½	14·00	12·00
47		2d. carmine	10	50
46s/7s Perf "SPECIMEN" *Set of 2*			£150	

The decimal perforation gauge for Nos. 46/7 is 13.7×14.1 and for No. 46a 13.7×13.4.

1948 (1 Dec). Royal Silver Wedding. As Nos. 112/13 of Antigua, but 20s. ptd entirely in recess.

48		1½d. orange	30	10
49		20s. brown-lake	£110	£100

1949 (10 Oct). 75th Anniv of UPU. As Nos. 114/17 of Antigua.

50		2d. carmine	20	1·50
51		3d. deep blue	2·00	3·00
52		6d. grey	2·00	4·00
53		1s. red-orange	75	2·50
50/3 *Set of 4*			4·50	10·00

5 Cecil Rhodes and Victoria Falls

(Recess D.L.R.)

1953 (30 May). Birth Centenary of Cecil Rhodes. Wmk Mult Script CA. P 12×11½.

54	**5**	½d. brown	55	2·25
55		1d. green	45	2·25
56		2d. mauve	1·00	30
57		4½d. blue	45	4·75
58		1s. orange and black	1·50	5·00
54/8 *Set of 5*			3·50	13·00

1953 (30 May). Rhodes Centenary Exhibition. As No. 171 of Nyasaland.

59	**6**	6d. violet	70	1·50

1953 (2 June). Coronation. As No. 120 of Antigua but des and eng B.W. Recess D.L.R.

60		1½d. black and yellow-orange	1·00	20

7   **8**

(Recess Waterlow)

1953 (15 Sept). Wmk Mult Script CA. P 12½×14 (pence values) or 12½×13½ (shilling values).

61	**7**	½d. deep brown	65	10
62		1d. bluish green	65	10
63		1½d. orange-brown	1·25	10
64		2d. reddish purple	1·25	10
65		3d. scarlet	80	10
66		4d. slate-lilac	1·25	2·00
67		4½d. deep blue	1·50	5·00
68		6d. grey-black	1·25	10
		w. Wmk inverted	£5000	£7000
69		9d. violet	1·25	4·25
70	**8**	1s. orange-brown and black	1·00	10
71		2s.6d. black and green	16·00	8·50
72		5s. grey and dull purple	18·00	15·00
73		10s. green and black	14·00	40·00
74		20s. rose-red and rose-purple	32·00	42·00
61/74 *Set of 14*			80·00	£100

No. 62 is known bisected vertically and endorsed "½d" in red at Mkushi between 17 and 20 November 1953.

For issues from 1954 to 1963, see RHODESIA AND NYASALAND.

9 Arms   **10** Arms   Parting in hair
(Right pane,
R. 4/11)

(Photo Harrison)

1963 (10 Dec). Arms black, orange and blue; portrait and inscriptions black; background colours below. P 14½ (T **9**) or 13½×13 (T **10**).

75	**9**	½d. bright violet	70	1·25
		a. Value omitted	£1100	
		b. Orange (eagle) omitted	£1400	
		c. Parting in hair		
76		1d. light blue	1·50	10
		a. Value omitted	6·00	£100
77		2d. brown	70	10
		c. Parting in hair		
78		3d. yellow	1·25	10
		a. Value omitted	£120	
		b. Value and orange (eagle) omitted	£250	£1000
		c. Eagle printed double	£4500	
		d. Orange (eagle) omitted	£1200	
		e. Parting in hair		
79		4d. green	1·00	30
		a. Value omitted	£130	£500
		c. Parting in hair		
80		6d. light olive-green	1·00	10
		a. Value omitted	£850	
		c. Parting in hair		
81		9d. yellow-brown	70	1·60
		a. Value omitted	£600	
		b. Value and orange (eagle) omitted	£600	
		c. Parting in hair		
82		1s. slate-purple	50	10
		c. Parting in hair		
83		1s.3d. bright purple	2·25	10
		c. Parting in hair		
84	**10**	2s. orange	2·50	8·00
85		2s.6d. lake-brown	3·50	3·00
86		5s. magenta	12·00	9·00
		a. Value omitted	£3000	
87		10s. bright magenta	21·00	24·00
88		20s. blue	22·00	45·00
		a. Value omitted	£1200	
75/88 *Set of 14*			60·00	80·00

Nos. 75/6 exist in coils, constructed from normal sheets.

STAMP BOOKLET

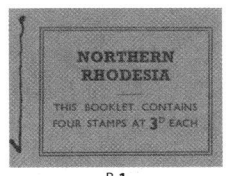

B 1

1964. Black on blue cover as Type B **1**. Stitched.

SB1	1s. booklet containing 3d. (No. 78) in block of 4.		16·00

POSTAGE DUE STAMPS

D 1   **D 2**

(Typo D.L.R.)

1929 (June)–**52.** Wmk Mult Script CA. Ordinary paper. P 14.

D1	**D 1**	1d. grey-black	3·00	2·50
		a. Chalk-surfaced paper. Black (22.1.52)	30·00	85·00
		ab. Error. St. Edward's Crown, W **9b**	£7000	
D2		2d. grey-black	9·00	3·00
		a Bisected (1d.) (on cover)	†	£900
D3		3d. grey-black	3·00	26·00
		a. Chalk-surfaced paper. Black (22.1.52)	8·00	75·00
		ab. Error. Crown missing, W **9a**	£700	
		ac. Error. St. Edward's Crown, W **9b**	£425	
D4		4d. grey-black	13·00	45·00
D1/4 *Set of 4*			25·00	70·00
D1s/4s Perf "SPECIMEN" *Set of 4*			£190	

The 2d. is known bisected and used as a 1d. at Luanshya, Ndola or Nkana on various dates between 1937 and 1951 and on understamped letters from South Africa at Chingola in May 1950. One example of the 1d. bisected as a ½d. is known at Kitwe in 1944. Various offices are known to have used definitive stamps in lieu of postage dues between 1932 and 1963.

Following an increase in the internal letter rate from 1½d. to 2d. on 1 July 1953 stocks of postage due stamps at Mkushi became exhausted. As an emergency measure the sub-postmaster was authorised to surcharge examples of No. 28 "POSTAGE DUE (or Postage Due, or "postage due") 1d." in red by typewriter. No. 55, the 1d. Rhodes Centenary stamp was also surcharged. Examples properly used on cover between 23 July and 15 September 1953 are of considerable scarcity (*Price on cover from £4750*). No unused examples exist.

(Des D. Smith. Litho Govt Ptr, Lusaka)

1963 (10 Dec). P 12½.

D5	**D 2**	1d. orange	3·25	7·00
D6		2d. deep blue	3·25	5·50
D7		3d. lake	3·25	9·00
D8		4d. ultramarine	3·25	16·00
D9		6d. purple	10·00	12·00
D10		1s. light emerald	12·00	38·00
		a. Imperf (vert pair)	£350	
		b. Block of four imperf horiz and imperf between vert	£1600	
D5/10 *Set of 6*			32·00	75·00

In all values the stamps in the right-hand vertical row of the sheet are imperforate on the right.

The stamps of Northern Rhodesia were withdrawn on 23 October 1964 when the territory attained independence as the Republic of Zambia.

North-West Pacific Islands
see **New Guinea** *after* **Australia**

Nova Scotia *see* **Canada**

Nyasaland

PRICES FOR STAMPS ON COVER TO 1945	
Nos. 1/9*a*	from × 15
Nos. 10/19	
No. 20	from × 10
Nos. 21/6	from × 5
Nos. 27/31	
Nos. 32/7	from × 6
Nos. 38/42	—
Nos. 43/7	from × 12
Nos. 48/52	
No. 53	from × 15
No. 54	from × 2
No. 55	from × 4
Nos. 55*b*/7*a*	from × 7
Nos. 57*d*/63	from × 6
Nos. 64/71	—
Nos. 72/9	from × 5
Nos. 80/2	—
Nos. 83/95	from × 4
Nos. 96/9	—
Nos. 100/57	from × 2

By 1891 the territory west of Lake Nyasa was recognised as being under British protection and the southern, eastern and northern borders had been delineated with the Portuguese and German governments.

BRITISH CENTRAL AFRICA

A protectorate under the name "Nyassaland Districts" was declared on 14 May 1891, the title being changed to the "British Central Africa Protectorate" on 22 February 1893. Such a description had been in use for some time previously and the handwritten notice of 20 July 1891, announcing the introduction of postal services, described the area as "British Central Africa".

Until 1895 the British South Africa Company contributed to the revenues of the protectorate administration which, in return governed North-eastern Rhodesia. Stamps of the British South Africa Company overprinted "B.C.A.", in addition to use in British Central Africa, were issued to post offices at Fife, Fort Rosebery, Katwe, Johnston Falls, Rhodesia (later Kalungwisi) and Tanganyika (later Abercorn) in North-eastern Rhodesia from 1893 until 1899.

B.C.A.	B.C.A. FOUR SHILLINGS.	ONE PENNY.
(1)	**(2)**	**(3)**

1891 (20 July)–**95**. Stamps of Rhodesia optd as T **1**. P 14, 14½.

1	**1**	1d. black	12·00	13·00
2	**4**	2d. sea-green and vermilion	13·00	5·00
		a. Bisected (1d.) (on cover) (1895)	†	£7500
3		4d. reddish chestnut and black	16·00	7·50
4	**1**	6d. ultramarine	60·00	20·00
5		6d. deep blue	20·00	11·00
6	**4**	8d. rose-lake and ultramarine	19·00	32·00
6*a*		8d. red and ultramarine	42·00	50·00
7	**1**	1s. grey-brown	30·00	19·00
8		2s. vermilion	50·00	60·00
9		2s.6d. grey-purple	90·00	£100
9*a*		2s.6d. lilac	95·00	£100
10	**4**	3s. brown and green (1895)	90·00	90·00
11		4s. grey-black and vermilion (2.93)	£100	£110
12	**1**	5s. orange-yellow	£110	£120
13		10s. deep green	£200	£225
14	**2**	£1 deep blue	£1300	£700
15		£2 rose-red	£1400	£1600
16		£5 sage-green	£2000	
17		£10 brown	£4500	£6500
1/13 *Set of 12*			£650	£700

Sheet watermarks 1 to 4, as listed under Rhodesia No. 13 are known on this issue.

The overprint varies on values up to 10s. Sets may be made with *thin* or *thick* letters.

Specialists have identified four separate settings; either of 30 (10×3) or 60 (10×6) impressions.

The bisected 2d, No. 2a, was authorised for use at Blantyre, Chiromo and Zomba in July and October 1895.

1892 (Aug)–**93**. Stamps of Rhodesia surch as T **2**.

18	**4**	3s. on 4s. grey-black and vermilion (10.93)	£375	£375
19	**1**	4s. on 5s. orange-yellow	£100	£100

1895. No. 2 surch at Cape Town with T **3**.

20	**4**	1d. on 2d. sea-green and vermilion	42·00	65·00
		a. Surch double	£11000	£8000

Examples are known with double surcharge, without stop after "PENNY". These are from a trial printing made at Blantyre, but it is believed that they were not issued to the public (*Price* £650 un.).

5 Arms of the Protectorate	**6** Arms of the Protectorate

(Des Sir Harry Johnston. Litho D.L.R.)

1895. No wmk. P 14.

21	**5**	1d. black	22·00	17·00
22		2d. black and green	55·00	12·00

23		4d. black and reddish buff	90·00	50·00
24		6d. black and blue	95·00	8·00
25		1s. black and rose	£120	35·00
26	**6**	2s.6d. black and bright magenta	£375	£375
27		3s. black and yellow	£225	65·00
28		5s. black and olive	£300	£275
29		£1 black and yellow-orange	£1200	£600
30		£10 black and orange-vermilion	£8000	£5500
31		£25 black and blue-green	£16000	£16000
21/8 *Set of 8*			£1200	£750
21s/9s Optd "SPECIMEN" *Set of 9*			£450	

Cancellations inscribed "BRITISH CENTRAL AFRICA" within a double-circle and with the name of a town across the centre or at foot were intended for use on stamps presented for the payment of the hut tax. Such marks can be found in black, violet or blue and are without date. Stamps with such fiscal obliterations are of little value. Prices quoted are for postally used.

1896 (Feb). Wmk Crown CA (T **5**) or CC (sideways) (T **6**). P 14.

32	**5**	1d. black	3·25	12·00
		x. Wmk reversed	£950	£950
		y. Wmk inverted and reversed	†	£750
33		2d. black and green	23·00	6·00
34		4d. black and orange-brown	40·00	17·00
35		6d. black and blue	50·00	18·00
36		1s. black and rose	50·00	27·00
37	**6**	2s.6d. black and magenta	£200	£150
38		3s. black and yellow	£200	75·00
39		5s. black and olive	£275	£275
40		£1 black and blue	£1200	£650
41		£10 black and orange	£11000	£6000
		s. Optd "SPECIMEN"	£275	
42		£25 black and green	£26000	
		s. Optd "SPECIMEN"	£425	
32/9 *Set of 8*			£750	£500
32s/40s Optd "SPECIMEN" *Set of 9*			£450	

(Typo D.L.R.)

1897 (Aug)–**1900**. T **7** (wmk Crown CA) and **8** (wmk Crown CC). P 14.

43	**7**	1d. black and ultramarine	3·25	1·25
		w. Wmk inverted	£170	£350
44		2d. black and yellow	4·00	2·00
45		4d. black and carmine	6·50	1·50
46		6d. black and green	60·00	4·25
47		1s. black and dull purple	11·00	7·00
48	**8**	2s.6d. black and ultramarine	£110	50·00
49		3s. black and sea-green	£350	£375
50		4s. black and carmine	£130	£100
50*a*		10s. black and olive-green (1900)	£325	£350
51		£1 black and dull purple	£500	£275
		w. Wmk inverted	£3250	£3000
52		£10 black and yellow	£8500	£2750
		s. Optd "SPECIMEN"	£300	
43/51 *Set of 10*			£1300	£1100
43s/51s Optd "SPECIMEN" *Set of 10*			£425	

ONE PENNY	
(9)	**10**

1897 (31 Dec). No. 49 surch with T **9**, in red.

53	**8**	1d. on 3s. black and sea-green	13·00	22·00
		a. "PNNEY" (R. 4/2)	£10000	£7500
		b. "PENN"	£5500	£4500
		c. Surch double	£750	£1300

No. 53b shows an albino impression of the "Y".

1898 (11 Mar). Imperf.

(a) Setting I. The vertical frame lines of the stamps cross the space between the two rows of the sheet

(i) With the initials "J.G." or "J.T.G." on the back in black ink

54	**10**	1d. vermilion and grey-blue	£16000	£1100
		a. Without the initials	£8000	
		b. Without the initials and centre inverted	£32000	

(ii) With a control number and letter or letters, printed in plain relief at the back

55	**10**	1d. vermilion and grey-blue	—	£750

(b) Setting II. The vertical frame lines do not cross the space between the rows except at the extreme ends of the sheet. Control as No. 55.

55*b*	**10**	1d. vermilion and pale ultramarine	—	£140
		c. Control on face	—	£3500
		d. Centre omitted (pair with normal)	£32000	
56		1d. vermilion and deep ultramarine	—	£150
		a. Without Control at back	£7000	£200
		b. Control doubly impressed	—	£450

1898 (June). Setting II. Control as No. 55. P 12.

57	**10**	1d. vermilion and pale ultramarine	£6500	35·00
57*a*		1d. vermilion and deep ultramarine	—	45·00

		ab. Without Control at back	£6000	£110
		ac. Two different Controls on back	—	£750
		ad. Control printed in black	£9000	

The two different settings of these stamps are each in 30 types, issued without gum.

1901. Wmk Crown CA. P 14.

57*d*	**7**	1d. dull purple and carmine-rose	2·75	50
57*e*		4d. dull purple and olive-green	15·00	11·00
58		6d. dull purple and brown	13·00	6·00
57*d*/8 *Set of 3*			28·00	16·00
57*d*s/8s Optd "SPECIMEN" *Set of 3*			90·00	

11

12

(Typo D.L.R.)

1903–04. T **11** (Wmk Crown CA) and **12** (Wmk Crown CC). P 14.

59	**11**	1d. grey and carmine	8·00	1·75
60		2d. dull and bright purple	3·50	1·00
61		4d. grey-green and black	2·50	9·00
62		6d. grey and reddish buff	3·75	2·00
		aw. Wmk inverted	£225	
62*b*		1s. grey and blue	4·75	17·00
63	**12**	2s.6d. grey-green and green	70·00	£110
64		4s. dull and bright purple	90·00	90·00
		w. Wmk inverted	£1500	
65		10s. grey-green and black	£200	£300
66		£1 grey and carmine	£325	£225
67		£10 grey and black	£8000	£4750
		s. Optd "SPECIMEN"	£500	
59/66 *Set of 9*			£650	£650
59s/66s Optd "SPECIMEN" *Set of 9*			£425	

1907. Chalk-surfaced paper. Wmk Mult Crown CA. P 14.

68	**11**	1d. grey and carmine	11·00	2·75
69		2d. dull and bright purple	£19000	
70		4d. grey-green and black	£19000	
71		6d. grey and reddish buff	50·00	55·00

Nos. 69/70 were prepared, but not issued in Nyasaland due to the Protectorate's name being changed. It is estimated that no more than a dozen examples of each remain in collectors' hands. Dangerous fakes, made from Nos. 60/1, are in circulation, but note that genuine examples are on chalk-surfaced paper, whereas the previous issue was on ordinary paper.

NYASALAND PROTECTORATE

The title of the Protectorate was changed again from 6 July 1907.

13

14

£1 Serif on "G" (R. 4/5. All ptgs of £1 Duty plate)

(Typo D.L.R.)

1908 (22 July)–**11**. P 14.

(a) Wmk Crown CA. Chalk-surfaced paper

72	**13**	1s. black/*green*	6·50	18·00

(b) Wmk Mult Crown CA. Ordinary paper (½d., 1d.) or chalk-surfaced paper (others)

73	**13**	½d. green	2·00	2·25
74		1d. carmine	9·50	1·00
75		3d. purple/*yellow*	2·00	4·25
		w. Wmk inverted	£400	£425
76		4d. black and red/*yellow*	2·25	1·50
		w. Wmk inverted	£150	£180
77		6d. dull purple and bright purple	6·50	11·00
78	**14**	2s.6d. brownish black and carmine-red/*blue*	75·00	£110
		a. Brownish black and deep rose-red/*pale blue* (1911)	£300	£375
79		4s. carmine and black	£110	£180
80		10s. green and red/*green*	£200	£325
81		£1 purple and black/*red*	£650	£275
		c. Serif on "G"	£3000	£3250
82		£10 purple and ultramarine	£12000	£8000
		s. Optd "SPECIMEN"	£1100	
72/81 *Set of 10*			£950	£1250
72s/81s Optd "SPECIMEN" *Set of 10*			£600	

15   **16**

"Bullet holes" flaw (R. 5/2. March 1919 ptgs)

Triangle flaw (R. 3/5. March 1919 ptg of 4s.)

1913 (1 Apr)–**21**. Wmk Mult Crown CA. Ordinary paper (½d. to 2½d.) or chalk-surfaced paper (others). P 14.

83	**15**	½d. green	2·00	2·25
84		½d. blue-green (1918)	4·00	2·75
		w. Wmk inverted	†	£600
85		1d. carmine-red	4·00	2·00
86		1d. scarlet (1916)	8·00	1·00
87		2d. grey (1916)	10·00	1·00
88		2d. slate	22·00	6·50
89		2½d. bright blue	2·50	8·50
90		3d. purple/*yellow* (1914)	8·00	4·50
		a. On pale yellow	6·00	10·00
		w. Wmk inverted		
91		4d. black and red/*yellow* (*shades*)	2·00	2·50
		a. On pale yellow	6·50	8·50
92		6d. dull and bright purple	5·50	10·00
92*a*		6d. dull purple and bright violet	16·00	12·00
93		1s. black/*green*	2·00	8·50
		a. On blue-green, olive back	5·50	1·50
		aw. Wmk inverted	£200	£225
		b. On emerald back (1921)	4·75	6·50
		bs. Optd "SPECIMEN"	75·00	
94	**16**	2s.6d. black and red/*blue*	12·00	29·00
		a. Break in scroll	£200	
		b. Broken crown and scroll	£300	
		c. Nick in top right scroll	£225	£325
		f. Damaged leaf at bottom right	£275	
		h. "Bullet-holes" flaw	£550	£650
		x. Wmk reversed	—	£3250
95		4s. carmine and black	50·00	95·00
		a. Break in scroll	£350	
		b. Broken crown and scroll	£375	
		d. Nick in top right scroll	£350	£500
		f. Damaged leaf at bottom right	£375	
		h. "Bullet-holes" flaw	£550	£850
		i. Triangle flaw	£500	
96		10s. pale green and deep scarlet/*green*	£130	£160
		d. Nick in top right scroll	£500	
		e. Green and deep scarlet/green (1919)	£150	£190
		ea. Break in scroll	£600	
		eb. Broken crown and scroll	£650	
		ef. Damaged leaf at bottom right	£700	
		eh. "Bullet holes" flaw	£1000	
98		£1 purple and black/*red*	£200	£170
		a. Break in scroll	£900	£750
		b. Broken crown and scroll	£900	£750
		c. Nick in top right scroll	£900	
		e. Break in lines below left scroll	£1000	
		f. Damaged leaf at bottom right	£900	
		h. "Bullet holes" flaw	£1700	
		i. Serif on "G"	£1100	£850
		w. Wmk inverted		
99		£10 purple and dull ultramarine	£8000	
		c. Nick in top right scroll	£10000	
		e. Purple and royal blue (1919) (f.c. £150)	£4000	£2000
		ea. Break in scroll	£8000	£4000
		eb. Broken crown and scroll	£8000	£4000
		ef. Damaged leaf at bottom right	£8500	
		eh. "Bullet holes" flaw	£9500	
		s. Optd "SPECIMEN"	£700	
83/98 *Set of* 12			£375	£425
83s/98s Optd "SPECIMEN" *Set of* 12			£600	

For illustrations of the other varieties on Nos. 94/9 see above Bermuda No. 51*b*.

Only single unused and used examples have so far been reported of No. 94x.

For stamps overprinted "N.F." see TANGANYIKA.

Damaged crown (R. 4/1. 2s.6d. ptg of June 1924)

Lines omitted from scroll (R. 2/4)

1921–33. Wmk Mult Script CA. Ordinary paper (½d. to 2d.) or chalk-surfaced paper (others). P 14.

100	**15**	½d. green	3·25	50
		w. Wmk inverted	—	£450
		y. Wmk inverted and reversed	—	£550
101		1d. carmine	3·75	50
102		1½d. orange	3·25	17·00
103		2d. grey	3·75	50
105		3d. purple/*pale yellow*	21·00	3·25
106		4d. black and red/*yellow*	6·50	11·00
107		6d. dull and bright purple	6·50	3·25
108		1s. black/*emerald* (1930)	14·00	4·50
109	**16**	2s. purple and blue/*pale blue* (1926)	21·00	12·00
		a. Break in scroll	£180	£160
		b. Broken crown and scroll	£180	£160
		c. Nick in top right scroll	£180	£160
		e. Break in lines below left scroll	£180	£160
		f. Damaged leaf at bottom right	£180	£160
		g. Purple and blue/grey-blue (10.33)	55·00	26·00
		ga. Break in scroll	£450	£300
		gb. Broken crown and scroll	£450	£300
		gd. Break through scroll	£450	£300
		ge. Break in lines below left scroll	£450	£300
		gf. Damaged leaf at bottom right	£450	£300
		gg. Gash in fruit and leaf	£450	£300
		gh. Breaks in scrolls at right	£450	£300
110		2s.6d. black and carmine-red/*pale blue* (30.9.24)	27·00	40·00
		a. Break in scroll	£200	£250
		b. Broken crown and scroll	£200	£250
		c. Nick in top right scroll	£200	£250
		e. Break in lines below left scroll	£200	£250
		f. Damaged leaf at bottom right	£200	£250
		i. Damaged crown	£400	£425
		j. Grey-black and scarlet-vermilion/pale blue (10.26)	48·00	19·00
		ja. Break in scroll	£375	£180
		jb. Broken crown and scroll	£375	£180
		je. Break in lines below left scroll	£375	£180
		jf. Damaged leaf at bottom right	£375	£180
		k. Black and scarlet-vermilion/grey-blue (10.33)	60·00	38·00
		ka. Break in scroll	£450	£325
		kb. Broken crown and scroll	£450	£325
		kd. Break through scroll	£450	£350
		ke. Break in lines below left scroll	£450	£325
		kf. Damaged leaf at bottom right	£450	£325
		kg. Gash in fruit and leaf	£450	£350
		kh. Breaks in scrolls at right	£450	£350
		ki. "C" of "CA" omitted from watermark		
111		4s. carmine and black (1927)	27·00	45·00
		a. Break in scroll	£225	£325
		b. Broken crown and scroll	£225	
		c. Nick in top right scroll	£225	
		e. Break in lines below left scroll	£225	£325
		f. Damaged leaf at bottom right	£225	£325
112		5s. green and red/*yellow* (1929)	55·00	85·00
		a. Break in scroll	£375	
		b. Broken crown and scroll	£375	
		c. Nick in top right scroll	£375	
		e. Break in lines below left scroll	£375	
		f. Damaged leaf at bottom right	£375	
113		10s. green and red/*pale emerald* (1926)	£120	£120
		a. Break in scroll	£550	£600
		b. Broken crown and scroll	£550	£600
		c. Nick in top right scroll	£550	£600
		e. Break in lines below left scroll	£550	£600
		f. Damaged leaf at bottom right	£750	
		g. Lines omitted from scroll	£550	£600
		h. Green and scarlet/emerald (1927)	£750	£850
		ha. Break in scroll	£2250	
		hb. Broken crown and scroll	£2250	
		he. Break in lines below left scroll	£2250	£3750
		hf. Damaged leaf at bottom right	£2250	
100/13 *Set of* 13			£275	£275
100s/13s Optd or Perf (1s., 5s.) "SPECIMEN" *Set of* 13			£600	

For illustrations of the other varieties on Nos. 109/13 see above Bermuda No. 51*b*.

17 King George V and Symbol of the Protectorate

(Des Major H. E. Green. Recess Waterlow)

1934 (June)–**35**. Wmk Mult Script CA. P 12½.

114	**17**	½d. green	75	1·25
115		1d. brown	75	75
116		1½d. carmine	75	3·00
117		2d. pale grey	1·00	1·25
118		3d. blue	3·00	1·75
119		4d. bright magenta (20.5.35)	8·00	3·50
120		6d. violet	2·75	50
121		9d. olive-bistre (20.5.35)	9·00	16·00
122		1s. black and orange	23·00	14·00
114/22 *Set of* 9			45·00	38·00
114s/22s Perf "SPECIMEN" *Set of* 9			£350	

1935 (6 May). Silver Jubilee. As Nos. 91/4 of Antigua, but ptd by Waterlow. P 11×12.

123		1d. ultramarine and grey	1·00	2·00
		k. Kite and vertical log	£170	£250
		m. "Bird" by turret	£250	£300
124		2d. green and indigo	1·00	2·25
		m. "Bird" by turret	£225	£275
125		3d. brown and deep blue	12·00	22·00
		k. Kite and vertical log	£400	£550
126		1s. slate and purple	29·00	55·00
		k. Kite and vertical log	£450	£700
123/6 *Set of* 4			38·00	70·00
123s/6s Perf "SPECIMEN" *Set of* 4			£140	

For illustrations of plate varieties see Omnibus section following Zanzibar.

1937 (12 May). Coronation. As Nos. 95/7 of Antigua. P 11×11½.

127		½d. green	30	2·25
128		1d. brown	50	1·50
129		2d. grey-black	50	3·25
127/9 *Set of* 3			1·10	6·25
127s/9s Perf "SPECIMEN" *Set of* 3			£150	

18 Symbol of the Protectorate   **19**

(T **18** recess Waterlow; T **19** typo D.L.R.)

1938 (1 Jan)–**44**. Chalk-surfaced paper (2s. to £1). P 12½ (T **18**) or 14 (T **19**).

(a) Wmk Mult Script CA

130	**18**	½d. green	1·00	2·50
130*a*		½d. brown (12.12.42)	10	2·50
131		1d. brown	4·00	30
		a. "A" of "CA" omitted from watermark	†	£1300
131*b*		1d. green (12.12.42)	30	2·25
132		1½d. carmine	11·00	8·50
132*a*		1½d. grey (12.12.42)	30	8·50
		ab. "A" of "CA" missing from wmk	£1600	
133		2d. grey	8·00	1·25
		aa. "A" of "CA" missing from wmk	†	£1300
133*a*		2d. carmine (12.12.42)	30	1·75
		b. "A" of "CA" missing from wmk	£1600	
134		3d. blue	1·00	1·50
135		4d. bright magenta	3·00	2·00
136		6d. violet	2·75	2·00
137		9d. olive-bistre	3·00	5·00
138		1s. black and orange	3·50	3·25
139	**19**	2s. purple and blue/*blue*	10·00	17·00
140		2s.6d. black and red/*blue*	16·00	22·00
141		5s. pale green and red/*yellow*	55·00	35·00
		a. Ordinary paper. *Green and red/pale yellow* (3.44)	80·00	£140
142		10s. emerald and deep red/*pale green*	55·00	80·00
		a. Ordinary paper. *Bluish green and brown-red/pale green* (1.38)	£425	£450

(b) Wmk Mult Crown CA

143	**19**	£1 purple and black/*red*	50·00	50·00
		c. Serif on "G"	£1100	£1200
130/43 *Set of* 18			£200	£200
130s/43s Perf "SPECIMEN" *Set of* 18			£200	

No. 141*a* has a yellow surfacing often applied in horizontal lines giving the appearance of laid paper

The printer's archives record the despatch of No. 142*a* to Nyasaland in January 1938, but no examples have been reported used before 1945. The paper coating on this printing varied considerably across the sheet. It is reported that some examples show a faint reaction to the silver test.

20 Lake Nyasa   **21** King's African Rifles

22 Tea estate **23** Map of Nyasaland

24 Fishing village **25** Tobacco

25a Badge of Nyasaland

(Recess B.W.)

1945 (1 Sept). T **20/25a**. Wmk Mult Script CA (sideways on horiz designs). P 12.

144	**20**	½d. black and chocolate	50	10
145	**21**	1d. black and emerald	20	70
146	**22**	1½d. black and grey-green	30	50
147	**23**	2d. black and scarlet	1·50	85
148	**24**	3d. black and light blue	60	30
149	**25**	4d. black and claret	2·25	80
150	**22**	6d. black and violet	3·75	90
151	**20**	9d. black and olive	4·25	3·00
152	**23**	1s. indigo and deep green	3·75	20
153	**24**	2s. emerald and maroon	10·00	6·00
154	**25**	2s.6d. emerald and blue	10·00	7·50
155	**25a**	5s. purple and blue	7·00	8·50
156	**23**	10s. claret and emerald	25·00	19·00
157	**25a**	20s. scarlet and black	29·00	42·00
144/57 *Set of 14*			85·00	80·00
144s/57s Perf "SPECIMEN" *Set of 14*			£550	

1946 (16 Dec). Victory. As Nos. 110/11 of Antigua.

158		1d. green	20	30
159		2d. red-orange	30	30
158s/9s Perf "SPECIMEN" *Set of 2*			£140	

26 Symbol of the Protectorate **27** Arms in 1891 and 1951

(Recess B.W.)

1947 (20 Oct). Wmk Mult Script CA. P 12.

160	**26**	1d. red-brown and yellow-green	50	30
		s. Perf "SPECIMEN"	90·00	

1948 (15 Dec). Royal Silver Wedding. As Nos. 112/13 of Antigua.

161		1d. green	15	10
162		10s. mauve	18·00	35·00

1949 (21 Nov). 75th Anniv of UPU. As Nos. 114/17 of Antigua.

163		1d. blue-green	30	30
		a. "A" of "CA" missing from wmk	£900	
164		3d. greenish blue	2·25	4·50
165		6d. purple	50	1·25
166		1s. ultramarine	30	1·00
163/6 *Set of 4*			3·00	6·25

(Des C. Twynam. Recess B.W.)

1951 (15 May). Diamond Jubilee of Protectorate. Wmk Mult Script CA. P 11×12.

167	**27**	2d. black and scarlet	1·25	1·50
168		3d. black and turquoise-blue	1·25	1·50
169		6d. black and violet	1·50	2·50
170		5s. black and indigo	9·00	10·00
167/70 *Set of 4*			11·50	14·00

28 Arms of Rhodesia and Nyasaland **29** Grading Cotton

(Recess Waterlow)

1953 (30 May). Rhodes Centenary Exhibition. Wmk Mult Script CA. P 14×13½.

171	**28**	6d. violet	50	30

1953 (2 June). Coronation. As No. 120 of Antigua but des and recess B.W.

172		2d. black and brown-orange	70	80

(Recess B.W.)

1953 (1 Sept)–**54**. Designs previously used for King George VI issue, but with portrait of Queen Elizabeth II. Wmk Mult Script CA. P 12.

173	**20**	½d. black and chocolate	10	1·75
		a. Perf 12×12½ (8.3.54)	10	1·75
174	**26**	1d. brown and bright green	65	65
175	**22**	1½d. black and deep grey-green	30	1·90
176	**23**	2d. black and yellow-orange	85	40
		a. Perf 12×12½ (8.3.54)	70	30
177	**29**	2½d. green and black	30	50
178	**25**	3d. black and scarlet	30	20
179	**24**	4½d. black and light blue	1·00	60
180	**22**	6d. black and violet	1·00	1·50
		a. Perf 12×12½ (8.3.54)	2·00	1·00
181	**20**	9d. black and deep olive	1·25	3·50
182	**23**	1s. deep blue and slate-green	3·75	50
183	**24**	2s. deep green and brown-red	3·50	4·75
184	**25**	2s.6d. deep emerald and deep blue	4·25	9·00
185	**25a**	5s. purple and Prussian blue	13·00	9·00
186	**23**	10s. carmine and deep emerald	16·00	26·00
187	**25a**	20s. red and black	28·00	45·00
173/87 *Set of 15*			65·00	90·00

Stamps perf 12×12½ come from sheets comb-perforated 11.8×12.25. They were also issued in coils of 480 stamps made up from sheets.

For issues between 1954 and 1963, see RHODESIA AND NYASALAND.

30 (**31**)

(Recess B.W.)

1963 (1 Nov). Revenue stamps optd "POSTAGE", as in T **30**, or additionally surch as T **31**. P 12.

188	½d. on 1d. greenish blue	30	30
189	1d. green	30	10
190	2d. scarlet	30	30
191	3d. blue	30	10
192	6d. brown-purple	30	10
193	9d. on 1s. cerise	40	25
194	1s. purple	45	10
195	2s.6d. black	1·25	2·75
196	5s. chocolate	3·25	3·50
197	10s. yellow-olive	5·50	8·50
	a. Greenish olive	21·00	18·00
198	£1 deep violet	5·50	11·00
188/98 *Set of 11*		16·00	24·00

32 Mother and Child **33** Chambo (fish)

34 Tea Industry **35** Nyala

(Des V. Whiteley. Photo Harrison)

1964 (1 Jan). Designs as T **32/5**. P 14½.

199	**32**	½d. reddish violet	10	30
200	**33**	1d. black and green	10	10
201		2d. light red-brown	10	10
202		3d. red-brown, yellow-green and bistre-brown	10	10
203		4d. indigo and orange-yellow	20	30
204	**34**	6d. purple, yellow-green and light blue	85	70
205		1s. brown, turquoise-blue and pale yellow	15	10
206		1s.3d. bronze-green and chestnut	3·75	10
207		2s.6d. brown and blue	3·25	50
208		5s. blue, green, yellow and black	1·50	1·75
209		10s. green, orange-brown and black	2·50	3·25
210	**35**	£1 deep reddish purple and yellow	10·00	14·00
199/210 *Set of 12*			20·00	19·00

Designs: As T **32/3**—2d. Zebu Bull; 3d. Groundnuts; 4d. Fishing. As T **34**—1s. Timber; 1s.3d. Turkish tobacco industry; 2s.6d. Cotton industry; 5s. Monkey Bay, Lake Nyasa; 10s. Forestry, Afzelia. Nos. 199 and 200 exist in coils constructed from normal sheets.

STAMP BOOKLETS

1954 (1 Jan). Black on green cover, stitched (No. SB1) or buff cover, stapled (No. SB2). R.W. Gunson (Seeds) Ltd. advertisement on front.

SB1	2s.6d. booklet containing 4×½d., 4×1d., and 12×2d. (Nos. 173/4, 176), each in blocks of 4	29·00	
SB2	5s. booklet containing 8×½d., 8×1d., 8×6d. and 12×2d. (Nos. 173/4, 176, 180), each in blocks of 4	35·00	

POSTAGE DUE STAMPS

D 1

(Typo D.L.R.)

1950 (1 July). Wmk Mult Script CA. P 14.

D1	**D 1**	1d. scarlet	4·25	32·00
D2		2d. ultramarine	20·00	32·00
D3		3d. green	17·00	6·00
D4		4d. purple	30·00	60·00
D5		6d. yellow-orange	42·00	£160
D1/5 *Set of 5*			£100	£250

Nyasaland attained independence on 5 July 1964 when the country was renamed Malawi.

Orange Free State *see* South Africa

Pakistan

(Currency. 12 pies = 1 anna; 16 annas = 1 rupee)

DOMINION

PAKISTAN   **PAKISTAN**
(1)   (2)

1947 (1 Oct). Nos. 259/68 and 269b/77 (King George VI) of India optd by litho at Nasik, as T **1** (3p. to 12a.) or T **2** (14a. and rupee values).

1	3p. slate	30	10
2	½a. purple	30	10
	w. Wmk inverted	—	55·00
3	9p. green	30	10
4	1a. carmine	30	10
5	1½a. dull violet	2·00	10
	w. Wmk inverted	—	30·00
6	2a. vermilion	30	20
7	3a. bright violet	35	20
8	3½a. bright blue	1·00	2·25
9	4a. brown	35	20
10	6a. turquoise-green	1·00	1·25
11	8a. slate-violet	45	60
12	12a. lake	1·00	20
13	14a. purple	3·25	4·50
14	1r. grey and red-brown	9·00	1·25
	w. Wmk inverted	80·00	55·00
15	2r. purple and brown	3·50	5·50
16	5r. green and blue	10·00	9·00
17	10r. purple and claret	10·00	14·00
18	15r. brown and green	90·00	£150
19	25r. slate-violet and purple	95·00	£100
1/19 Set of 19		£200	£250

Numerous provisional "PAKISTAN" overprints, both handstamped and machine-printed, in various sizes and colours, on Postage and Official stamps, also exist.

These were made under authority of Provincial Governments, District Head Postmasters or Local Postmasters and are of considerable philatelic interest.

The 1a.3p. (India No. 269) exists only as a local issue (Price, Karachi opt £3 unused; £4 used).

The 12a., as No. 12 but overprinted at Karachi, exists with overprint inverted (Price £70 unused).

The 1r. value with Karachi local overprint exists with overprint inverted (Price £250 unused) or as a vertical pair with one stamp without overprint (Price £1000 unused).

3 Constituent Assembly Building, Karachi

4 Karachi Airport entrance

5 Gateway to Lahore Fort   **6** Crescent and Stars

(Des A. Chughtai (1r.). Recess D.L.R.)

1948 (9 July). Independence. T **3/6** . P 13½×14 or 11½ (1r.).

20	1½a. ultramarine	1·25	2·25
21	2½a. green	1·25	20
22	3a. purple-brown	1·25	35
23	1r. scarlet	1·25	70
	a. Perf 14×13½	4·75	26·00
20/3 Set of 4		4·50	3·25

7 Scales of Justice   **8** Star and Crescent   **9** Lloyds Barrage

10 Karachi Airport   **11** Karachi Port Trust

12 Salimullah Hostel, Dacca   **13** Khyber Pass

(Des M. Suharwardi (T **8**). Recess Pakistan Security Ptg Corp Ltd, Karachi (P 13 and 13½), D.L.R. (others))

1948 (14 Aug)–57. T **7/13**.

24	**7**	3p. red (P 12½)	10	10
		a. Perf 13½ (5.54)	3·75	1·00
25		6p. violet (P 12½)	1·25	10
		a. Perf 13½ (1954)	8·00	5·50
26		9p. green (P 12½)	50	10
		a. Perf 13½ (1954)	9·50	1·75
27	**8**	1a. blue (P 12½)	30	50
28		1½a. grey-green (P 12½)	30	10
29		2a. red (P 12½)	7·00	70
30	**9**	2½a. green (P 14×13½)	9·00	13·00
31	**10**	3a. green (P 14)	7·50	1·00
32	**9**	3½a. bright blue (P 14×13½)	9·00	5·50
33		4a. reddish brown (P 12½)	1·25	10
34	**11**	6a. blue (P 14×13½)	2·00	50
35		8a. black (P 12)	1·50	1·50
36	**10**	10a. scarlet (P 14)	8·50	12·00
37	**11**	12a. scarlet (P 14×13½)	10·00	1·00
38	**12**	1r. ultramarine (P 14)	25·00	10
		a. Perf 13½ (1954)	22·00	12·00
39		2r. chocolate (P 14)	20·00	75
		a. Perf 13½ (5.54)	26·00	10·00
40		5r. carmine (P 14)	24·00	2·75
		a. Perf 13½ (7.53)	17·00	25
41	**13**	10r. magenta (P 14)	22·00	45·00
		a. Perf 12	£140	12·00
		b. Perf 13 (1951)	19·00	3·50
42		15r. blue-green (P 12)	18·00	30·00
		a. Perf 14	25·00	£100
		b. Perf 13 (27.7.57)	27·00	38·00
43		25r. violet (P 14)	55·00	£130
		a. Perf 12	42·00	42·00
		b. Perf 13 (1.11.54)	50·00	48·00
24/43a Set of 20			£160	£100

For 25r. with W **98**, see No. 210.
The 6p. (No. 25) exists from coils made up from normal sheets.

14 Star and Crescent   **15** Karachi Airport

15a Karachi Port Trust

(Recess Pakistan Security Ptg Corp (P 13½), D.L.R. (others)).

1949 (Feb)–53. Redrawn. Crescent moon with points to left as T **14/15a**.

44	**14**	1a. blue (P 12½)	4·00	85
		a. Perf 13½ (1952)	13·00	10
45		1½a. grey-green (P 12½)	3·75	85
		a. Perf 13½ (1953)	3·50	10
		ab. Printed on the gummed side	65·00	
46		2a. red (P 12½)	4·50	10
		a. Perf 13½ (1952)	7·00	10
47	**15**	3a. green (P 14)	16·00	1·00
48	**15a**	6a. blue (as No. 34) (P 14×13½)	23·00	2·50
49		8a. black (as No. 35) (P 12½)	23·00	2·50
50	**15**	10a. scarlet (P 14)	27·00	4·00
51	**15a**	12a. scarlet (as No. 37) (P 14×13½)	29·00	60
44/51 Set of 8			£110	9·50

The 1a. (No. 44) exists from coils made up from normal sheets.

16   **16a**

(Recess D.L.R.)

1949 (11 Sept). First Death Anniv of Mohammed Ali Jinnah. T **16/a** . P 14.

52	**16**	1½a. brown	3·25	2·00
53		3a. green	3·25	1·50
54	**16a**	10a. black	9·00	8·00
52/4 Set of 3			14·00	10·50

17 Pottery   **18** Stylised aeroplane and Hourglass

Two Types of 3½a.:

I   II

---

19 Saracenic Leaf Pattern   **20** Archway and Lamp

(Des A. Chughtai. Recess D.L.R., later printings, Pakistan Security Ptg Corp)

1951 (14 Aug)–56. Fourth Anniv of Independence. P 13.

55	**17**	2½a. carmine	1·75	1·25
56	**18**	3a. purple	1·00	10
57	**17**	3½a. blue (I)	1·25	8·50
57a		3½a. blue (II) (12.56)	4·75	6·00
58	**19**	4a. green	2·00	10
59		6a. brown-orange	2·00	10
60	**20**	8a. sepia	4·50	25
61		10a. violet	2·00	2·25
62	**18**	12a. slate	2·75	10
55/62 Set of 9			20·00	16·00

The above and the stamps issued on the 14 August 1954, 1955 and 1956, are basically definitive issues, although issued on the Anniversary date of Independence.

21 "Scinde Dawk" stamp and Ancient and Modern Transport

(Recess D.L.R.)

1952 (14 Aug). Centenary of "Scinde Dawk" Issue of India. P 13.

63	**21**	3a. deep olive/yellow-olive	1·00	85
64		12a. deep brown/salmon	1·25	15

PRINTERS. All issues up to No. 219 were recess-printed by the Pakistan Security Printing Corporation, unless otherwise stated.

22 Kaghan Valley   **23** Mountains, Gilgit

24 Bahshahi Mosque, Lahore   **25** Mausoleum of Emperor Jehangir, Lahore

26 Tea Plantation, East Pakistan   **27** Cotton plants, West Pakistan

28 Jute fields and River, East Pakistan

1954 (14 Aug). Seventh Anniv of Independence. T **22/8**. P 13½ (14a., 1r., 2r.) or 13 (others).

65	**22**	6p. reddish violet	25	10
66	**23**	9p. blue	3·75	3·00
67	**24**	1a. carmine	30	10
68	**25**	1½a. red	30	10
69	**26**	14a. deep green	6·00	10
70	**27**	1r. green	11·00	10
71	**28**	2r. red-orange	3·00	10
65/71 Set of 7			22·00	3·00

29 View of K 2

1954 (25 Dec). Conquest of K 2 (Mount Godwin-Austen). P 13.
72   **29**   2a. deep violet.................................. 40   40

30 Karnaphuli Paper Mill, Type I (Arabic fraction on left)   **31** Textile Mill, West Pakistan

32 Jute Mill, East Pakistan   **33** Main Sui gas plant

Type II (Arabic fraction on right)

1955 (14 Aug)–**56**. Eighth Anniv of Independence. T **30/3**. P 13.
73   **30**   2½a. scarlet (I)............................... 1·00   1·40
73a   2½a. scarlet (II) (12.56)............... 2·75   1·40
74   **31**   6a. deep ultramarine.................... 1·75   10
75   **32**   8a. deep reddish violet................ 3·75   10
76   **33**   12a. carmine and orange............... 4·00   10
73/6 Set of 5 .... 12·00   2·75

TENTH ANNIVERSARY UNITED NATIONS

24.10.55.

(34)

35 Map of West Pakistan

TENTH ANNIVERSARY UNITED NATIONS

24.10.55.

"UNITED NATIONS" shifted 1 mm to left
(1½a. R. 7/10; 12a. R. 1/8, 3/8, 5/8, 7/8, 9/8)

1955 (24 Oct). Tenth Anniv of United Nations. Nos. 68 and 76 optd as T **34**.
77   1½a. red (B.)............................... 1·50   5·00
     a. "UNITED NATIONS" 1 mm to left ...... 28·00   40·00
78   12a. carmine and orange (B.) 50   3·50
     a. "UNITED NATIONS" 1 mm to left ...... 7·00   16·00

Forgeries exist of the overprint on No. 77. These are in very uneven thin type and measure 20×18 mm instead of the genuine 19½×19 mm.

1955 (7 Dec). West Pakistan Unity. P 13½.
79   **35**   1½a. myrtle-green....................... 1·25   2·25
80   2a. sepia..................................... 1·00   35
81   12a. deep rose-red....................... 1·50   50
79/81 Set of 3 .... 3·25   2·75

REPUBLIC

36 Constituent Assembly Building, Karachi

(Litho D.L.R.)

1956 (23 Mar). Republic Day. P 13.
82   **36**   2a. myrtle-green......................... 80   10

---

37   **38** Map of East Pakistan

1956 (14 Aug). Ninth Anniv of Independence. P 13½.
83   **37**   2a. scarlet 65   10
     a. Printed on the gummed side .... 7·00

1956 (15 Oct). First Session of National Assembly of Pakistan at Dacca. P 13½.
84   **38**   1½a. myrtle-green....................... 50   1·50
85   2a. sepia..................................... 50   10
86   12a. deep rose-red....................... 55   1·25
84/6 Set of 3 .... 1·40   2·50

39 Karnaphuli Paper Mill, East Bengal   **40** Pottery

41 Orange Tree

1957 (23 Mar). First Anniv of Republic. P 13.
87   **39**   2½a. scarlet 25   10
88   **40**   3½a. blue.................................... 30   10
89   **41**   10r. myrtle-green and yellow-
        orange................................... 1·00   25
87/9 Set of 3 .... 1·40   35
The above and No. 95 are primarily definitive issues, although issued on the Anniversary of Republic Day.
For 10r. with W **98**, see No. 208.

42 Pakistani Flag   **43** Pakistani Industries

(Des Ahsan. Litho D.L.R.)

1957 (10 May). Centenary of Struggle for Independence (Indian Mutiny). P 13.
90   **42**   1½a. bronze-green 50   40
91   12a. light blue............................ 1·25   10

(Litho D.L.R.)

1957 (14 Aug). Tenth Anniv of Independence. P 14.
92   **43**   1½a. ultramarine....................... 20   45
93   4a. orange-red........................... 45   1·75
94   12a. mauve................................. 45   50
92/4 Set of 3 .... 1·00   2·40

44 Coconut Tree   **45**

1958 (23 Mar). Second Anniv of Republic. P 13.
95   **44**   15r. red and deep reddish purple .... 2·50   1·50
This is a definitive issue, see note below No. 89.
See No. 209 for this stamp with W **98**.

(Photo Harrison)

1958 (21 Apr). 20th Death Anniv of Mohammed Iqbal (poet). P 14½×14.
96   **45**   1½a. yellow-olive and black 55   1·00
97   2a. orange-brown and black............ 55   25
98   14a. turquoise-blue and black........... 90   10
96/8 Set of 3 .... 1·75   1·25

 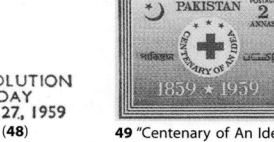

46 UN Charter and Globe   **PAKISTAN BOY SCOUT 2nd NATIONAL JAMBOREE CHITTAGONG Dec. 58–Jan. 59** (47)

1958 (10 Dec). Tenth Anniv of Declaration of Human Rights. P 13.
99   **46**   1½a. turquoise-blue..................... 10   10
100   14a. sepia................................... 45   10

1958 (28 Dec). Second Pakistan Boy Scouts National Jamboree, Chittagong. Nos. 65 and 75 optd with T **47**.
101   6p. reddish violet........................ 20   10
102   8a. deep reddish violet 40   10

REVOLUTION DAY Oct. 27, 1959
(48)   **49** "Centenary of An Idea"

1959 (27 Oct). Revolution Day. No. 74 optd with T **48** in red.
103   6a. deep ultramarine.................... 80   10

1959 (19 Nov). Red Cross Commemoration. Recess; cross typo. P 13.
104   **49**   2a. red and green......................... 30   10
105   10a. red and deep blue.................. 55   10

50 Armed Forces Badge   **51** Map of Pakistan

(Litho D.L.R.)

1960 (10 Jan). Armed Forces Day. P 13½×13.
106   **50**   2a. red, ultramarine and blue-
        green..................................... 50   10
107   14a. red and bright blue............... 1·00   10

1960 (23 Mar). P 13×13½.
108   **51**   6p. deep purple........................... 40   10
109   2a. brown-red............................. 60   10
110   8a. deep green............................ 1·25   10
111   1r. blue..................................... 2·00   10
     a. Printed on the gummed side ....
108/11 Set of 4 .... 3·75   20

52 Uprooted Tree   **53** Punjab Agricultural College

1960 (7 Apr). World Refugee Year. P 13.
112   **52**   2a. rose-carmine......................... 20   10
113   10a. green.................................. 30   10

1960 (10 Oct). Golden Jubilee of Punjab Agricultural College, Lyallpur. T **53** and similar horiz design. P 12½×14.
114   2a. slate-blue and carmine-red........ 15   10
115   8a. bluish green and reddish violet........ 40   10
Design:—8a. College Arms.

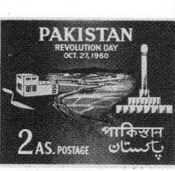

55 "Land Reforms, Rehabilitation and Reconstruction"   **56** Caduceus

(Des M. Hanjra. Photo D.L.R.)

1960 (27 Oct). Revolution Day. P 13×13½.
116   **55**   2a. green, pink and brown 10   10
     a. Green and pink omitted............ 26·00
     b. Pink omitted........................... 7·50
117   14a. green, yellow and ultramarine... 50   75

(Photo D.L.R.)

1960 (16 Nov). Centenary of King Edward Medical College, Lahore. P 13.
118   **56**   2a. yellow, black and blue 50   10
119   14a. emerald, black and carmine....... 1·75   1·00

57 "Economic Co-operation"

58 Zam-Zama Gun, Lahore ("Kim's Gun," after Rudyard Kipling)

1960 (5 Dec). International Chamber of Commerce CAFEA Meeting, Karachi. P 13.

120	**57**	14a. orange-red	75	20

(Centre typo, background recess Pakistan Security Ptg Corp)

1960 (24 Dec). Third Pakistan Boy Scouts National Jamboree, Lahore. P 12½×14.

121	**58**	2a. carmine, yellow and deep bluish green	80	30

(New Currency. 100 paisa = 1 rupee)

1 PAISA

(59)

1961 (1 Jan–14 Feb). Nos. 24a, 67/8, 83 and 108/9, surch as T **59**. Nos. 123/4 and 126 surch by Pakistan Security Ptg Corp and others by the Times Press, Karachi.

122		1p. on 1½a. red (10.1)	40	10
		a. Printed and surch on the gummed side	60·00	
123		2p. on 3p. red	10	10
124		3p. on 6p. deep purple	15	10
		a. "PASIA" for "PAISA"	10·00	
125		7p. on 1a. carmine (14.2)	40	10
126		13p. on 2a. brown-red (14.2)	40	10
		a. "PAIS" for "PAISA"	10·00	
127		13p. on 2a. scarlet (14.2)	30	10
122/7	*Set of 6*		1·60	30

No. 122. Two settings were used, the first with figure "1" 2½ mm tall and the second 3 mm.

On the 1p. with tall "1" and the 13p. (No. 127), the space between the figures of value and "P" of "PAISA" varies between 1½ mm and 3 mm. See also Nos. 262/4.

ERRORS. In the above issue and the corresponding official stamps we have listed errors in the stamps surcharged by the Pakistan Security Printing Corp but have not included the very large number of errors which occurred in the stamps surcharged by the less experienced Times Press. This was a very hurried job and there was no time to carry out the usual checks. It is also known that some errors were not issued to the public but came on the market by other means.

NOTE. Stamps in the old currency were also handstamped with new currency equivalents and issued in various districts but these local issues are outside the scope of this catalogue.

60 Khyber Pass

61 Shalimar Gardens, Lahore

62 Chota Sona Masjid (gateway)

(a) (b) (c)

Types (a) and (b) show the first letter in the top right-hand inscription; (a) wrongly engraved, "SH" (b) corrected to "P".

On Nos. 131/2 and 134 the corrections were made individually on the plate, so that each stamp in the sheet may be slightly different. Type (c) refers to No. 133a only.

1961–63. No wmk. P 13 (T **62**) or 14 (others).

(a) Inscribed "SHAKISTAN" in Bengali

128	**60**	1p. violet (1.1.61)	1·50	30
129		2p. rose-red (12.1.61)	1·50	10
130		5p. ultramarine (23.3.61)	3·00	10

(b) Inscribed "PAKISTAN" in Bengali

131	**60**	1p. violet	1·00	10
		a. Printed on the gummed side		
132		2p. rose-red	1·00	10
133		3p. reddish purple (27.10.61)	75	10
		a. Re-engraved. First letter of Bengali inscription as Type (c) (1963)	9·00	4·00
134		5p. ultramarine	7·50	10
		a. Printed on the gummed side		
135		7p. emerald (23.3.61)	2·00	10
136	**61**	10p. brown (14.8.61)	25	10
137		13p. slate-violet (14.8.61)	25	10
138		25p. deep blue (1.1.62)	5·50	10
139		40p. deep purple (1.1.62)	1·50	10

140		50p. deep bluish green (1.1.62)	45	10
141		75p. carmine-red (23.3.62)	1·00	70
142		90p. yellow-green (1.1.62)	1·25	70
143	**62**	1r. vermilion (7.1.63)	9·50	10
		a. Imperf (pair)		
144		1r.25 reddish violet (27.10.61)	1·25	1·75
144a		2r. orange (7.1.63)	5·50	15
144b		5r. green (7.1.63)	6·00	3·00
128/44b	*Set of 19*		45·00	6·00

See also Nos. 170/81 and 204/7.

(63)

64 Warsak Dam and Power Station

1961 (12 Feb). Lahore Stamp Exhibition. No. 110 optd with T **63**.

145	**51**	8a. deep green (R.)	1·00	1·75

(Des A. Ghani)

1961 (1 July). Completion of Warsak Hydro-Electric Project. P 12½×14.

146	**64**	40p. black and blue	60	10

65 Narcissus

66 Ten Roses

(Des A. Ghani)

1961 (2 Oct). Child Welfare Week. P 14.

147	**65**	13p. turquoise-blue	50	10
148		90p. bright purple	1·25	20

(Des A. Ghani)

1961 (4 Nov). Co-operative Day. P 13.

149	**66**	13p. rose-red and deep green	40	10
150		90p. rose-red and blue	85	90

67 Police Crest and "Traffic Control"

68 Locomotive *Eagle*, 1861

(Photo D.L.R.)

1961 (30 Nov). Police Centenary. P 13.

151	**67**	13p. silver, black and blue	50	10
152		40p. silver, black and red	1·00	20

(Des M. Thoma. Photo D.L.R.)

1961 (31 Dec). Railway Centenary. T **68** and similar horiz design. P 14.

153		13p. green, black and yellow	75	80
154		50p. yellow, black and green	1·00	1·50

Design:—50p. Diesel locomotive No. 20 and tracks forming "1961".

(70)

71 *Anopheles* sp (mosquito)

1962 (6 Feb). First Karachi-Dacca Jet Flight. No. 87 surch with T **70**.

155	**39**	13p. on 2½a. scarlet (R.)	1·75	1·25

(Photo D.L.R.)

1962 (7 Apr). Malaria Eradication. T **71** and similar horiz design. P 14.

156		10p. black, yellow and red	35	10
157		13p. black, greenish yellow and red	35	10

Design:—13p. Mosquito pierced by blade.

73 Pakistan Map and Jasmine

(Photo Courvoisier)

1962 (8 June). New Constitution. P 12.

158	**73**	40p. yellow-green, bluish green and grey	1·00	10

74 Football

78 Marble Fruit Dish and Bahawalpuri Clay Flask

(Des A. Ghani and M. Bhatti)

1962 (14 Aug). Sports. T **74** and similar horiz designs. P 12½×14.

159		7p. black and blue	10	10
160		13p. black and green	60	2·25
161		25p. black and purple	20	10
162		40p. black and orange-brown	2·00	2·25
159/62	*Set of 4*		2·50	4·00

Designs:—13p. Hockey; 25p. Squash; 40p. Cricket.

(Des A. Ghani and M. Bhatti)

1962 (10 Nov). Small Industries. T **78** and similar vert designs. P 13.

163		7p. brown-lake	10	10
164		13p. deep green	2·50	2·75
165		25p. reddish violet	10	10
166		40p. yellow-green	10	10
167		50p. deep red	10	10
163/7	*Set of 5*		2·50	2·75

Designs:—13p. Sports equipment; 25p. Camel-skin lamp and brassware; 40p. Wooden powderbowl and basket-work; 50p. Inlaid cigarette-box and brassware.

83 "Child Welfare"

(Des M. Thoma. Photo D.L.R.)

1962 (11 Dec). 16th Anniv of UNICEF. P 14.

168	**83**	13p. black, light blue and maroon	35	10
169		40p. black, yellow and turquoise-blue	35	10

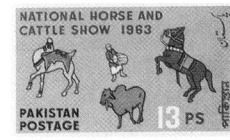

Nos. 170, etc.   Nos. 131/42

1962–70. As T **60/1** but with redrawn Bengali inscription at top right. No wmk.

170	**60**	1p. violet (1963)	10	10
171		2p. rose-red (1964)	2·75	10
		a. Imperf (pair)	3·00	
172		3p. reddish purple (1970)	16·00	7·50
173		5p. ultramarine (1963)	1·00	
		a. Printed on the gummed side	13·00	
174		7p. emerald (1964)	7·00	3·50
175	**61**	10p. brown (1963)	20	10
		a. Printed on the gummed side	13·00	
176		13p. slate-violet	20	10
176a		15p. bright purple (31.12.64)	30	10
		ab. Imperf (pair)	4·50	
		ac. Printed on the gummed side	15·00	
176b	**61**	20p. myrtle-green (26.1.70)	40	10
		ba. Imperf (pair)	3·50	
		bb. Printed on the gummed side	15·00	
177		25p. deep blue (1963)	11·00	10
		a. imperf (pair)	10·00	
178		40p. deep purple (1964)	30	30
		a. Imperf (pair)	6·50	
179		50p. deep bluish green (1964)	30	10
		a. Printed on the gummed side		
180		75p. carmine-red (1964)	70	70
		a. Printed on the gummed side	13·00	
181		90p. yellow-green (1964)	70	1·00
170/81	*Set of 14*		35·00	12·00

Other values in this series and the high values (Nos. 204/10) are known imperforate but we are not satisfied as to their status.

(84)

85 "Dancing" Horse, Camel and Bull

1963 (15 Feb). Pakistan UN Force in West Irian. No. 176 optd with T **84**.

182	**61**	13p. slate-violet (R.)	10	2·00

(Des S. Jahangir. Photo Courvoisier)

1963 (13 Mar). National Horse and Cattle Show. P 11½.

183	**85**	13p. blue, sepia and cerise	10	10

86 Wheat and Tractor

(Des B. Mirza)

1963 (21 Mar). Freedom from Hunger. T **86** and similar horiz design. P 12½×14.
184   13p. orange-brown .... 3·00   10
185   50p. bistre-brown .... 4·50   55
Design:—50p. Rice.

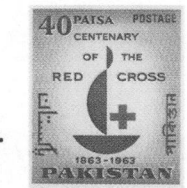

13 PAISA

INTERNATIONAL DACCA STAMP EXHIBITION 1963

(**88**)   **89** Centenary Emblem

1963 (23 Mar). Second International Stamp Exhibition, Dacca. No. 109 surch with T **88**.
186   **51**   13p. on 2a. brown-red 50   50

1963 (25 June). Centenary of Red Cross. Recess; cross typo. P 13.
187   **89**   40p. red and deep olive .... 2·25   15

90 Paharpur   (**94**)

(Des A. Ghani)

1963 (16 Sept). Archaeological Series. T **90** and similar designs. P 14×12½ (13p.) or 12½×15 (others).
188   7p. ultramarine 55   10
189   13p. sepia 55   10
190   40p. carmine 90   10
191   50p. deep reddish violet 95   10
188/91 Set of 4 .... 2·75   35
Designs: Vert—13p. Moenjodaro; Horiz—40p. Taxila; 50p. Mainamati.

1963 (7 Oct). Centenary of Public Works Department. No. 133 surch with T **94** by typography.
192   **60**   13p. on 3p. reddish purple 10   10
Forged surcharges applied in lithography exist.

95 Atatürk's Mausoleum

(Des A. Ghani)

1963 (10 Nov). 25th Death Anniv of Kemal Atatürk. P 13½.
193   **95**   50p. red 50   10

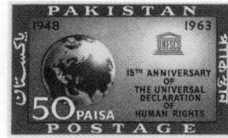

96 Globe and UNESCO Emblem

(Photo D.L.R.)

1963 (10 Dec). 15th Anniv of Declaration of Human Rights. P 14.
194   **96**   50p. brown, red and ultramarine 40   10

97 Thermal Power Installations

(Des A. Ghani)

1963 (25 Dec). Completion of Multan Thermal Power Station. P 12½×14.
195   **97**   13p. ultramarine 10   10

98 Multiple Star and Crescent

99 Temple of Thot, Queen Nefertari and Maids

1963–79. As Nos. 43b, 89, 95 and 143/4b, but W **98** (sideways* on 15r.).
204   **62**   1r. vermilion .... 1·50   10
    a. Printed on the gummed side .... 13·00

b. Imperf (pair) .... 7·50
w. Wmk inverted .... 2·00
205   1r.25 reddish violet (1964) .... 3·00   2·25
aw. Wmk inverted .... 3·50
b. Purple (1975?) .... 6·50   2·50
ba. Imperf (pair) .... 6·00
206   2r. orange (1964) .... 1·50   15
a. Imperf (pair) .... 8·00
w. Wmk inverted .... 2·25
207   5r. green (1964) .... 7·50   1·00
a. Imperf (pair) .... 11·00
w. Wmk inverted .... 7·50
208   **41**   10r. myrtle-green and yellow-orange (1968) .... 8·00   7·00
a. Imperf (pair) .... 8·00
bw. Wmk inverted ....
c. Wmk sideways .... 4·75   5·00
209   **44**   15r. red and deep reddish purple (20.3.79) .... 2·50   4·50
a. Imperf (pair) .... 13·00
w. Wmk tips of crescent pointing downwards ....
210   **13**   25r. violet (1968) .... 17·00   23·00
aw. Wmk inverted .... 19·00
b. Wmk sideways .... 8·00   12·00
ba. Imperf (pair) .... 15·00
204/10b Set of 7 .... 26·00   22·00

MULTIPLE STAR AND CRESCENT WATERMARKED PAPER. When viewed from the back with the stamp upright, upright and sideways reversed watermarks show the tips of the crescents pointing upwards and to the right; reversed and sideways watermarks show the tips pointing upwards and to the left; inverted and sideways inverted and reversed watermarks show the tips pointing downwards and to the left, while sideways inverted and upright inverted and reversed watermarks show them pointing downwards and to the left. Upright and sideways reversed watermarks may be differentiated by the angle of the row of stars which is approximately 60° for the upright and 30° for the sideways reversed.

(Des A. Ghani)

1964 (30 Mar). Nubian Monuments Preservation. T **99** and similar horiz design. P 13×13½.
211   13p. turquoise-blue and red 30   10
212   50p. bright purple and black 70   10
Design:—50p. Temple of Abu Simbel.

101 "Unisphere" and Pakistan Pavilion

103 Shah Abdul Latif's Mausoleum

(Des A. Ghani)

1964 (22 Apr). New York World's Fair. T **101** and similar design. P 12½×14 (13p.) or 14×12½ (1r.25).
213   13p. ultramarine 10   10
214   1r.25 ultramarine and red-orange 40   20
Design: Vert—1r.25 Pakistan Pavilion on "Unisphere".

(Des A. Ghani)

1964 (25 June). Death Bicentenary of Shah Abdul Latif of Bhit. P 13½×13.
215   **103**   50p. bright blue and carmine-lake.... 1·00   10

104 Mausoleum of Quaid-i-Azam

105 Mausoleum

(Des A. Ghani)

1964 (11 Sept). 16th Death Anniv of Mohammed Ali Jinnah (Quaid-i-Azam). P 13½ (15p.) or 13 (50p.).
216   **104**   15p. emerald-green .... 1·00   10
217   **105**   50p. bronze-green .... 2·25   10

106 Bengali and Urdu Alphabets

107 University Building

(Des N. Rizvi)

1964 (5 Oct). Universal Children's Day. P 13.
218   **106**   15p. brown 10   10

(Des N. Rizvi)

1964 (21 Dec). First Convocation of the West Pakistan University of Engineering and Technology, Lahore. P 12½×14.
219   **107**   15p. chestnut 10   10

PROCESS. All the following issues were lithographed by the Pakistan Security Printing Corporation, *unless otherwise stated.*

108 "Help the Blind"   **109** ITU Emblem and Symbols

(Des A. Chughtai)

1965 (28 Feb). Blind Welfare. P 13.
220   **108**   15p. ultramarine and yellow 20   10

(Des N. Rizvi. Recess)

1965 (17 May). ITU Centenary. P 12½×14.
221   **109**   15p. reddish purple .... 1·50   30

110 ICY Emblem

1965 (26 June). International Co-operation Year. P 13×13½.
222   **110**   15p. black and light blue .... 1·00   15
223   50p. green and yellow .... 1·75   40

111 "Co-operation"

112 Globe and Flags of Turkey, Iran and Pakistan

1965 (21 July). First Anniv of Regional Development Co-operation Pact. P 13½×13 (15p.) or 13 (50p.).
224   **111**   15p. multicoloured 20   10
225   **112**   50p. multicoloured .... 1·10   10

113 Soldier and Tanks

(Des S. Ghori (7p.), N. Rizvi (15p.), A. Ghani (50p.))

1965 (25 Dec). Pakistan Armed Forces. T **113** and similar horiz designs. Multicoloured. P 13½×13.
226   7p. Type **113** 75   70
227   15p. Naval officer and *Tughril* (destroyer)   1·50   10
228   50p. Pilot and Lockheed F-104C Star fighters .... 2·50   30
226/8 Set of 3 .... 4·25   1·00

116 Army, Navy and Air Force Crests

117 Atomic Reactor, Islamabad

(Des A. Ghani)

1966 (13 Feb). Armed Forces Day. P 13½×13.
229   **116**   15p. royal blue, dull green, bright blue and buff .... 1·00   10

(Des A. Ghani. Recess)

1966 (30 Apr). Inauguration of Pakistan's First Atomic Reactor. P 13.
230   **117**   15p. black 10   10

118 Bank Crest

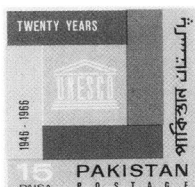
119 Children

(Des A. Ghani)

1966 (25 Aug). Silver Jubilee of Habib Bank. P 12½×14.
231	**118**	15p. blue-green, yellow-orange and sepia	10	10

(Des S. Nagi)

1966 (3 Oct). Universal Children's Day. P 13½.
232	**119**	15p. light brown, black, red and pale yellow	10	10

120 UNESCO Emblem

1966 (24 Nov). 20th Anniv of UNESCO. P 14.
233	**120**	15p. multicoloured	3·75	30

121 Flag, Secretariat Building and President Ayub

(Des A. Ghani)

1966 (29 Nov). Islamabad (new capital). P 13.
234	**121**	15p. deep bluish green, chestnut, light blue and bistre-brown	35	10
235		50p. deep bluish green, chestnut, light blue and black	65	10

122 Avicenna

123 Mohammed Ali Jinnah

(Des A. Ghani)

1966 (3 Dec). Foundation of Health and Tibbi Research Institute. P 13×13½.
236	**122**	15p. dull green and salmon	40	10
		a. Imperf (pair)	75·00	

(Des A. Ghani. Recess and litho)

1966 (25 Dec). 90th Birth Anniv of Mohammed Ali Jinnah. T **123** and similar design bearing same portrait, but in different frame. P 13.
237	**123**	15p. black, orange and greenish blue	15	10
238	–	50p. black, purple and ultramarine	35	10

124 Tourist Year Emblem

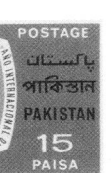
125 Emblem of Pakistan TB Association

(Des A. Ghani)

1967 (1 Jan). International Tourist Year. P 13½×13.
239	**124**	15p. black, light blue and yellow-brown	10	10

1967 (10 Jan). Tuberculosis Eradication Campaign. P 13½×13.
240	**125**	15p. red, sepia and chestnut	10	10

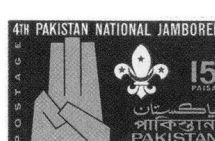
126 Scout Salute and Badge

127 "Justice"

(Des A. Rauf. Photo)

1967 (29 Jan). Fourth National Scout Jamboree. P 12½×14.
241	**126**	15p. light orange-brown and maroon	15	10

(Des A. Rauf)

1967 (17 Feb). Centenary of West Pakistan High Court. P 13.
242	**127**	15p. black, slate, light red and slate-blue	10	10

128 Dr. Mohammed Iqbal (philosopher)

(Des A. Rauf)

1967 (21 Apr). Iqbal Commemoration. P 13.
243	**128**	15p. sepia and light red	15	10
244		1r. sepia and deep green	35	10

129 Hilal-i-Isteqlal Flag

(Des A. Rahman)

1967 (15 May). Award of Hilal-i-Isteqlal (for Valour) to Lahore, Sialkot, and Sargodha. P 13.
245	**129**	15p. multicoloured	10	10

130 "20th Anniversary"

(Des F. Karim. Photo)

1967 (14 Aug). 20th Anniv of Independence. P 13.
246	**130**	15p. red and deep bluish green	10	10

131 "Rice Exports"

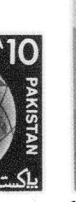
132 Cotton Plant, Yarn and Textiles

(Des S. Nagi (10p.), F. Karim (others). Photo)

1967 (26 Sept). Pakistan Exports. T **131/2** and similar design. P 13×13½.
247	**131**	10p. yellow, deep bluish green and deep blue	10	15
248	**132**	15p. multicoloured	10	10
		a. Pale orange (top panel) omitted	26·00	
249		50p. multicoloured	20	15
247/9	*Set of 3*		35	35

Design: Vert as T **132**—50p. Raw jute, bale and bags.

134 Clay Toys

135 Shah and Empress of Iran and Gulistan Palace, Teheran

1967 (2 Oct). Universal Children's Day. P 13.
250	**134**	15p. multicoloured	10	10

(Des F. Karim)

(Des S. Ghori. Recess and litho)

1967 (26 Oct). Coronation of Shah Mohammed Riza Pahlavi and Empress Farah of Iran. P 13.
251	**135**	50p. purple, blue and light yellow-ochre	1·25	10

136 "Each For All—All For Each"

(Des A. Rauf)

1967 (4 Nov). Co-operative Day. P 13.
252	**136**	15p. multicoloured	10	10

137 Mangla Dam

(Des S. Nagi)

1967 (23 Nov). Indus Basin Project. P 13.
253	**137**	15p. multicoloured	10	10

138 Crab pierced by Sword

139 Human Rights Emblem

(Des F. Karim)

1967 (26 Dec). The Fight against Cancer. P 13.
254	**138**	15p. red and black	70	10

1968 (31 Jan). Human Rights Year. Photo. P 14×13.
255	**139**	15p. red and deep turquoise-blue	10	15
256		50p. red, yellow and silver-grey	10	15

140 Agricultural University, Mymensingh

141 WHO Emblem

(Des S. Ghori. Photo)

1968 (28 Mar). First Convocation of East Pakistan Agricultural University. P 13½×13.
257	**140**	15p. multicoloured	10	10

(Des A. Salahuddin. Photo)

1968 (7 Apr). 20th Anniv of World Health Organization. P 14×13.
258	**141**	15p. green and orange-red	10	15
		a. "PAIS" for "PAISA" (R. 4/5)	3·75	
259		50p. red-orange and indigo	10	15

142 Kazi Nazrul Islam (poet, composer and patriot)

(Des F. Karim. Recess and litho)

1968 (25 June). Nazrul Islam Commemoration. P 13.
260	**142**	15p. sepia and pale yellow	35	15
261		50p. sepia and pale rose-red	65	15

Nos. 260/1 with a two-line inscription giving the wrong date of birth ("1889") were prepared but not issued. Some are known to have been released in error.

4 PAISA
(143)

1968 (18 July–Aug). Nos. 56, 74 and 61 surch as T **143**.
262	4p. on 3a. purple	1·00	1·75
263	4p. on 6a. deep ultramarine (R.) (8.68)	1·25	1·75
264	60p. on 10a. violet (R.)	1·00	35
	a. Surch in black	40	2·50
	b. Surch triple	50·00	
262/4 Set of 3		3·00	3·50

144 Children running with Hoops

(Des A. Rauf)

1968 (7 Oct). Universal Children's Day. P 13.
265	**144**	15p. multicoloured	10	10

145 "National Assembly"

(Des M. Khatoon)

1968 (27 Oct). "A Decade of Development". T **145** and similar horiz designs. P 13.
266	10p. multicoloured	10	35
267	15p. multicoloured	10	10
268	50p. multicoloured	2·00	30
269	60p. light blue, dull purple and vermilion	50	1·25
266/9 Set of 4		2·40	1·75

Designs:—15p. Industry and agriculture; 50p. Army, Navy and Air Force; 60p. Minaret and atomic reactor plant.

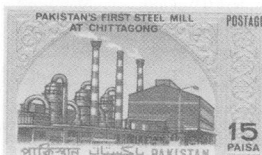

149 Chittagong Steel Mill

(Des M. Khatoon)

1969 (7 Jan). Pakistan's First Steel Mill, Chittagong. P 13.
270	**149**	15p. grey, light blue and pale yellow-olive	10	10

150 "Family"   **151** Olympic Gold Medal and Hockey Player

(Des M. Khatoon)

1969 (14 Jan). Family Planning. P 13½×13.
271	**150**	15p. bright purple and pale greenish blue	10	10

(Des S. Ghori. Photo)

1969 (30 Jan). Olympic Hockey Champions. P 13½.
272	**151**	15p. black, gold, deep green and pale blue	75	50
273		1r. black, gold, deep green and flesh-pink	2·25	1·00

152 Mirza Ghalib and Lines of Verse

(Des A. Rauf)

1969 (15 Feb). Death Centenary of Mirza Ghalib (poet). P 13.
274	**152**	15p. multicoloured	20	15
275		50p. multicoloured	50	15

The lines of verse on No. 275 are different from those in T **152**.

153 Dacca Railway Station

(Des F. Karim)

1969 (27 Apr). First Anniv of New Dacca Railway Station. P 13.
276	**153**	15p. multicoloured	65	10

154 ILO Emblem and "1919–1969"   **155** "Lady on Balcony" (18th-cent Mogul)

(Des R-ud Din)

1969 (15 May). 50th Anniv of International Labour Organization. P 13½.
277	**154**	15p. buff and bluish green	10	10
278		50p. cinnamon and cerise	40	10

(Des S. Ghori, A. Rauf, F. Karim, A. Salahuddin, N. Mohammad and M. Khatoon)

1969 (21 July). Fifth Anniv of Regional Co-operation for Development. T **155** and similar vert designs showing miniatures. Multicoloured. P 13.
279	20p. Type **155**	15	10
280	50p. "Kneeling Servant" (17th-cent Persian)	15	10
281	1r. "Suleiman the Magnificent holding Audience" (16th-cent Turkish)	20	10
279/81 Set of 3		45	25

158 Eastern Refinery, Chittagong

(Des M. Khatoon. Photo)

1969 (14 Sept). First Oil Refinery in East Pakistan. P 13½×13.
282	**158**	20p. multicoloured	10	10

159 Children playing outside "School"

(Des M. Khatoon. Photo)

1969 (6 Oct). Universal Children's Day. P 13.
283	**159**	20p. multicoloured	10	10

160 Japanese Doll and PIA Air Routes

(Des N. Mohammad)

1969 (1 Nov). Inauguration of PIA Pearl Route, Dacca–Tokyo. P 13½×13.
284	**160**	20p. multicoloured	40	10
		a. Yellow and pink omitted	11·00	
285		50p. multicoloured	60	40
		a. Yellow and pink omitted	11·00	

161 "Reflection of Light" Diagram

(Des A. Rauf. Photo)

1969 (4 Nov). Millenary Commemorative of Ibn-al-Haitham (physicist). P 13.
286	**161**	20p. black, lemon and light blue	10	10

162 Vickers Vimy and Karachi Airport   **163** Flags, Sun Tower and Expo Site Plan

(Des N. Mohammad. Photo)

1969 (2 Dec). 50th Anniv of First England–Australia Flight. P 13½×13.
287	**162**	50p. multicoloured	1·50	35

(Des R-ud Din)

1970 (15 Mar). World Fair, Osaka. P 13.
288	**163**	50p. multicoloured	20	30

164 New UPU HQ Building

(Des R-ud Din)

1970 (20 May). New UPU Headquarters Building. P 13½×13.
289	**164**	20p. multicoloured	15	10
290		50p. multicoloured	25	25

The above, in a miniature sheet, additionally inscr "U.P.U. Day 9th Oct, 1971", were put on sale on that date in very limited numbers.

165 UN HQ Building

(Des A. Rauf)

1970 (26 June). 25th Anniv of United Nations. T **165** and similar horiz design. Multicoloured. P 13×13½.
291		20p. Type **165**	10	10
292		50p. UN emblem	15	20

167 IEY Emblem, Book and Pen

(Des M. Khatoon)

1970 (6 July). International Education Year. P 13.
293	**167**	20p. multicoloured	10	10
294		50p. multicoloured	20	20

168 Saiful Malook Lake (Pakistan)

1970 (21 July). Sixth Anniv of Regional Co-operation for Development. T **168** and similar square designs. Multicoloured. P 13.

295	20p. Type **168**	25	10
296	50p. Seeyo-Se-Pol Bridge, Esfahan (Iran)	35	10
297	1r. View from Fethiye (Turkey)	50	15
295/7	*Set of 3*	1·00	30

171 Asian Productivity Symbol

172 Dr. Maria Montessori

1970 (18 Aug). Asian Productivity Year. Photo. P 12½×14.

| 298 | **171** | 50p. multicoloured | 20 | 20 |

(Des M. Khatoon)

1970 (31 Aug). Birth Centenary of Dr. Maria Montessori (educationist). P 13.

| 299 | **172** | 20p. multicoloured | 15 | 10 |
| 300 | | 50p. multicoloured | 15 | 30 |

173 Tractor and Fertilizer Factory

1970 (12 Sept). Tenth Near East FAO Regional Conference, Islamabad. P 13.

| 301 | **173** | 20p. bright green and orange-brown | 15 | 50 |

174 Children and Open Book

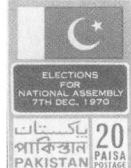

175 Pakistan Flag and Text

(Des F. Karim. Photo)

1970 (5 Oct). Universal Children's Day. P 13.

| 302 | **174** | 20p. multicoloured | 15 | 10 |

(Des A. Salahuddin)

1970 (7 Dec). General Elections for National Assembly. P 13½×13.

| 303 | **175** | 20p. green and bluish violet | 15 | 10 |

(Des A. Salahuddin)

1970 (17 Dec). General Elections for Provincial Assemblies. As No. 303, but inscr "PROVINCIAL ASSEMBLIES 17TH DEC., 1970".

| 304 | **175** | 20p. green and pale magenta | 15 | 10 |

176 Conference Crest and burning Al-Aqsa Mosque

(Des R-ud Din)

1970 (26 Dec). Conference of Islamic Foreign Ministers, Karachi. P 13.

| 305 | **176** | 20p. multicoloured | 75 | 15 |

STAMP BOOKLETS

1956 (23 Mar). Black on green cover. Stapled.

| SB1 | 1r. 08 booklet containing 12×6p. and 12×1½a. (Nos. 65, 68) in blocks of 4 | 9·00 |

OFFICIAL STAMPS

PAKISTAN

PAKISTAN (O **1**)   **SERVICE** (O **1a**)

1947. Nos. O143, O144b, O145/6, O146b/50 and 259/62 (King George VI) of India, optd as Type O **1** (Nos. O1/9) or as T **1a** (Nos. O10/13), both in litho by Nasik.

O1		3p. slate	3·50	2·75
O2		½a. purple	60	10
O3		9p. green	5·50	4·50
O4		1a. carmine	60	10
		w. Wmk inverted	—	28·00
O5		1½a. dull violet	60	10
		w. Wmk inverted	30·00	17·00
O6		2a. vermilion	60	1·00
O7		2½a. bright violet	7·50	16·00
O8		4a. brown	1·50	1·75
O9		8a. slate-violet	2·25	3·25
O10		1r. grey and red-brown	1·25	4·25
O11		2r. purple and brown	14·00	13·00
O12		5r. green and blue	35·00	65·00
O13		10r. purple and claret	90·00	£180
O1/13	*Set of 13*		£140	£250

See note after No. 19. The 1a.3p. (India No. O146a) exists as a local issue (*Price*, Karachi opt, £16 *mint*, £42 *used*).

Whereas the Nasik overprints on the Rupee values were applied to the Indian postage stamps (Nos. 259/62). Those applied at Karachi were on the official stamps (O138/41). The two overprints may be identified by the relative positions of the two words and the shape of the "R" of "SERVICE".

SERVICE (O **2**)   SERVICE (O **3**)   SERVICE (O **4**)

NOTE. Apart from a slight difference in size, Types O **2** and O **3** can easily be distinguished by the difference in the shape of the "c". Type O **4** is taller and thinner in appearance.

PRINTERS. Type O **2** was overprinted by De La Rue and Type O **3** by the Pakistan Security Ptg Corp.

1948 (14 Aug)–**54**? Optd with Type O **2**.

O14	**7**	3p. red (No. 24)	10	10
O15		6p. violet (No. 25) (R.)	10	10
O16		9p. green (No. 26) (R.)	30	10
O17	**8**	1a. blue (No. 27) (R.)	3·75	10
O18		1½a. grey-green (No. 28) (R.)	3·50	10
O19		2a. red (No. 29)	1·50	10
O20	**10**	3a. green (No. 31)	26·00	20·00
O21	**9**	4a. reddish brown (No. 33)	2·75	10
O22	**11**	8a. black (No. 35) (R.)	2·75	10·00
O23	**12**	1r. ultramarine (No. 38)	1·50	10
O24		2r. chocolate (No. 39)	14·00	10·00
O25		5r. carmine (No. 40)	65·00	29·00
O26	**13**	10r. magenta (No. 41)	26·00	80·00
		a. Perf 12 (10.10.51)	38·00	85·00
		b. Perf 13 (1954?)	26·00	90·00
O14/26	*Set of 13*		£130	£130

1949. Optd with Type O **2**.

O27		1a. blue (No. 44)	7·00	10
O28		1½a. grey-green (No. 45) (R.)	5·00	10
		a. Opt inverted	£375	60·00
O29		2a. red (No. 46)	10·00	10
		a. Opt omitted (in pair with normal)	—	£180
O30		3a. green (No. 47)	42·00	8·50
O31		8a. black (No. 49) (R.)	65·00	25·00
O27/31	*Set of 5*		£110	30·00

1951 (14 Aug). Fourth Anniv of Independence. As Nos. 56, 58 and 60, but inscr "SERVICE" instead of "PAKISTAN POSTAGE".

O32	**18**	3a. purple	10·00	10·00
O33	**19**	4a. green	2·50	20
O34	**20**	8a. sepia	11·00	11·00
O32/4	*Set of 3*		21·00	19·00

1953. Optd with Type O **3**.

O35		3p. red (No. 24a)	10	10
O36		6p. violet (No. 25a) (R.)	10	10
O37		9p. green (No. 26a) (R.)	10	10
O38		1a. blue (No. 44a) (R.)	10	10
O39		1½a. grey-green (No. 45a) (R.)	10	10
O40		2a. red (No. 46a) (1953?)	20	10
O41		1r. ultramarine (No. 38a)	10·00	7·50
O42		2r. chocolate (No. 39a)	8·50	1·25
O43		5r. carmine (No. 40a)	90·00	35·00
O44		10r. magenta (No. 41b) (date?)	28·00	90·00
O35/44	*Set of 10*		£120	£120

1954 (14 Aug). Seventh Anniv of Independence. Nos. 65/71 optd with Type O **3**.

O45		6p. reddish violet (R.)	15	4·00
O46		9p. blue (R.)	3·50	14·00
O47		1a. carmine	20	2·50
O48		1½a. red	20	2·50
O49		14a. deep green (R.)	2·25	14·00
O50		1r. green (R.)	1·00	10
O51		2r. red-orange	7·50	15
O45/51	*Set of 7*		13·50	32·00

1955 (14 Aug). Eighth Anniv of Independence. No. 75 optd with Type O **3**.

| O52 | | 8a. deep reddish violet (R.) | 1·25 | 10 |

1957 (Jan)–**59**. Nos. 65/71 optd with Type O **4**.

O53		6p. reddish violet (R.)	10	10
		a. Opt inverted	†	—
O54		9p. blue (R.) (1.59)	15	10
		a. Opt inverted	26·00	
O55		1a. carmine	15	10
		a. Opt inverted	—	60·00
		b. Printed on the gummed side		
O56		1½a. red	15	10
		a. Opt double		
		b. Printed on the gummed side		
O57		14a. deep green (R.) (2.59)	75	6·50
O58		1r. green (R.) (4.58)	75	10
O59		2r. red-orange (4.58)	6·00	10
O53/9	*Set of 7*		7·25	6·50

1958 (Jan)–**61**. Optd with Type O **4**.

| O60 | **7** | 3p. red (No. 24a) | 10 | 10 |

O61	—	5r. carmine (No. 40a) (7.59)	8·00	15
O62	**41**	10r. myrtle-green and yellow-orange (No. 89) (R.) (1961)	7·00	12·00
		a. Opt inverted	17·00	
O60/2	*Set of 3*		14·00	12·00

1958 (Jan)–**61**. Nos. 74/5 optd with Type O **4**.

| O63 | | 6a. deep ultramarine (R.) (4.61) | 50 | 10 |
| O64 | | 8a. deep reddish violet (R.) | 1·25 | 10 |

1959 (Aug). No. 83 optd with Type O **4**.

| O65 | **37** | 2a. scarlet | 20 | 10 |

1961 (Apr). Nos. 110/11 optd with Type O **4**.

O66	**51**	8a. deep green	50	10
O67		1r. blue	50	10
		a. Opt inverted	13·00	

NEW CURRENCY. In addition to the local handstamped surcharges mentioned in the note above No. 122, the following typographed surcharges were made at the Treasury at Mastung and issued in the Baluchi province of Kalat: 6p. on 1a. (No. O55), 9p. on 1½a. (No. O56) and 13p. on 2a. (No. O65). They differ in that the surcharges are smaller and "PAISA" is expressed as "Paisa". Being locals they are outside the scope of this catalogue.

1961. Optd with Type O **4**.

O68		1p. on 1½a. (No. 122)	10	10
		a. Optd with Type O **3**	9·00	2·00
O69		2p. on 3p. (No. 123) (1.1.61)	10	10
		a. Surch double		
		b. Optd with Type O **3**	25·00	6·50
O70		3p. on 6p. (No. 124)	10	10
O71		7p. on 1a. (No. 125)	10	10
		a. Optd with Type O **3**	25·00	20·00
O72		13p. on 2p. (No. 126)	10	10
O73		13p. on 2a. (No. 127)	10	10
O68/73	*Set of 6*		55	30

No. O68 exists with small and large "1" (see note below Nos. 122/7, etc.).

ERRORS. See note after No. 127.

SERVICE (O **5**)

1961–63. Nos. 128/44b optd with Type O **4** (rupee values) or O **5** (others).

(a) Inscribed "SHAKISTAN"

O74		1p. violet (R.) (1.1.61)	10	10
O75		2p. rose-red (R.) (12.1.61)	10	10
O76		5p. ultramarine (R.) (23.3.61)	15	10
		a. Opt inverted		

(b) Inscribed "PAKISTAN"

O77		1p. violet (R.)	9·00	10
		a. Printed on the gummed side		
		b. Opt inverted		
O78		2p. rose-red (R.)	1·00	10
		a. Printed on the gummed side		
O79		3p. reddish purple (R.) (27.10.61)	10	10
O80		5p. ultramarine (R.)	8·00	10
O81		7p. emerald (R.) (23.3.61)	10	10
O82		10p. brown (R.)	10	10
		a. Opt inverted		
O83		13p. slate-violet (R.) (14.2.61)	10	10
O85		40p. deep purple (R.) (1.1.62)	15	10
O86		50p. deep bluish green (R.) (1.1.62)	15	10
		a. Opt double		
O87		75p. carmine-red (R.) (23.3.62)	20	10
		a. Opt double		
O88		1r. vermilion (7.1.63)	35	10
		a. Opt double	25·00	
		b. Opt as Type O **3**	50·00	35·00
		c. Opt inverted	17·00	
O89		2r. orange (7.1.63)	1·50	20
O90		5r. green (7.1.63)	4·25	9·50
O74/90	*Set of 16*		22·00	9·50

1963–78?. Nos. 170, etc., optd with Type O **5**, in red.

O91		1p. violet	10	10
O92		2p. rose-red (1965)	10	10
		a. Opt inverted	3·25	
		b. Albino opt		
		c. Opt double, one albino		
O93		3p. reddish purple (1967)	3·75	1·50
		a. Opt double	20·00	
		b. Opt inverted	3·75	
		c. Printed on the gummed side		
O94		5p. ultramarine	10	10
		a. Opt inverted	2·00	
		ab. Vert pair, top stamp without opt, lower with opt inverted		
O95		7p. emerald (date?)	50·00	17·00
O96		10p. brown (1965)	10	10
		a. Opt inverted	3·75	
O97		13p. slate-violet	10	10
O98		15p. bright purple (31.12.64)	10	2·50
O99		20p. myrtle-green (26.1.70)	10	40
		a. Opt double	26·00	
O100		25p. deep blue (1977)	22·00	5·50
O101		40p. deep purple (1972?)	28·00	13·00
O102		50p. deep bluish green (1965)	15	15
O103		75p. carmine-red (date?)	40·00	32·00
O104		90p. yellow-green (5.78?)	17·00	13·00
O91/104	*Set of 14*		£130	75·00

1968?. Nos. 204, 206 and 207 optd with Type O **4**.

O105	**62**	1r. vermilion	4·75	1·25
		a. Opt inverted	13·00	
		b. Printed and overprinted on the gummed side	17·00	
		w. Wmk inverted	13·00	
O107		2r. orange (date?)	22·00	2·25
		a. Opt inverted	13·00	
O108		5r. green (R.) (date?)	50·00	14·00
		a. Opt inverted	18·00	
O105/8	*Set of 3*		65·00	16·00

BAHAWALPUR

Bahawalpur, a former feudatory state situated to the west of the Punjab, was briefly independent following the partition of India on 15 August 1947 before acceding to Pakistan on 3 October of the same year.

East India Company and later Indian Empire post offices operated in Bahawalpur from 1854. By a postal agreement of 1879 internal mail from the state administration was carried unstamped, but this arrangement was superseded by the issue of Official stamps in 1945.

These had been preceded by a series of pictorial stamps prepared in 1933–34 on unwatermarked paper. It was intended that these would be used as state postage stamps, but permission for such use was withheld by the Indian Government so they were used for revenue purposes. The same designs were utilised for the 1945 Official series, Nos. O1/6, on paper watermarked Star and Crescent. Residual stocks of the unwatermarked 1a., 8a., 1r. and 2r. were used for the provisional Officials, Nos. O7 and O11/13.

A commemorative 1a. Receipt stamp was produced to mark the centenary of the alliance with Great Britain. This may not have been ready until 1935, but an example of this stamp is known used on cover from Deh Rawal to Sadiq Garh and postmarked 14 August 1933. Both this 1a. and the same value from the unwatermarked set also exist with Official Arabic overprint in black. These were not issued for postal purposes although one used example of the latter has been recorded postmarked 22 February 1933 also from Deh Rawal.

Stamps of India were overprinted in the interim period between 15 August and 3 October 1947. After the state joined Pakistan postage stamps were issued for internal use until 1953.

> **PRICES FOR STAMPS ON COVER**
> The postage and Official stamps of Bahawalpur are rare used on cover.

Nawab (from 1947 Amir) Sadiq Mohammad Khan Abbasi V, 1907–1966

(1)

1947 (15 Aug). Nos. 265/8, 269b/77 and 259/62 (King George VI) of India optd locally with T **1**.

1		3p. slate (R.)		45·00
2		½a. purple		45·00
3		9p. green (R.)		45·00
4		1a. carmine		45·00
5		1½a. dull violet (R.)		45·00
6		2a. vermilion		45·00
		a. Opt double		£4750
7		3a. bright violet (R.)		45·00
8		3½a. bright blue (R.)		45·00
9		4a. brown		45·00
10		6a. turquoise-green (R.)		45·00
		a. Opt double		£4750
11		8a. slate-violet (R.)		45·00
12		12a. lake		45·00
13		14a. purple		90·00
14		1r. grey and red-brown		60·00
		a. Opt double, one albino		£550
15		2r. purple and brown (R.)		£4750
16		5r. green and blue (R.)		£4750
17		10r. purple and claret		£4750
1/17 *Set of 17*				£14000

Nos. 1/17 were issued during the interim period, following the implementation of the Indian Independence Act, during which time Bahawalpur was part of neither of the two Dominions created. The Amir acceded to the Dominion of Pakistan on 3 October 1947 and these overprinted stamps of India were then withdrawn.

The stamps of Bahawalpur only had validity for use within the state. For external mail Pakistan stamps were used.

PRINTERS. All the following issues were recess-printed by De La Rue & Co, Ltd, London.

2 Amir Muhammad Bahawal Khan I Abbasi

3

1947 (1 Dec). Bicentenary Commemoration. W **3** (sideways). P 12½×11½.

18	**2**	½a. black and carmine	3·75	11·00

4 H.H. the Amir of Bahawalpur

5 The Tombs of the Amirs

6 Mosque in Sadiq-Garh

7 Fort Derawar from the Lake

8 Nur-Mahal Palace

9 The Palace, Sadiq-Garh

10 H.H. the Amir of Bahawalpur

11 Three Generations of Rulers; H.H. the Amir in centre

1948 (1 Apr). W **3** (sideways on vert designs). P 12½ (T **4**), 11½×12½ (T **5**, **7**, **8** and **9**), 12½×11½ (T **6** and **10**) or 13½×14 (T **11**).

19	**4**	3p. black and blue	3·00	20·00
20		½a. black and claret	2·75	20·00
21		9p. black and green	2·75	20·00
22		1a. black and carmine	2·75	20·00
23		1½a. black and violet	4·00	16·00
24	**5**	2a. green and carmine	4·00	20·00
25	**6**	4a. orange and brown	4·00	20·00
26	**7**	6a. violet and blue	4·00	20·00
27	**8**	8a. carmine and violet	5·50	20·00
28	**9**	12a. green and carmine	7·00	30·00
29	**10**	1r. violet and brown	7·00	45·00
30		2r. green and claret	3·00	80·00
31		5r. black and violet	3·00	£100
32	**11**	10r. scarlet and black	32·00	£130
19/32 *Set of 14*			75·00	£500

12 H.H. The Amir of Bahawalpur and Mohammed Ali Jinnah

13 Soldiers of 1848 and 1948

1948 (3 Oct). First Anniv of Union of Bahawalpur with Pakistan. W **3**. P 13.

33	**12**	1½a. carmine and blue-green	1·75	7·50

1948 (15 Oct). Multan Campaign Centenary. W **3**. P 11½.

34	**13**	1½a. black and lake	1·25	16·00

1948. As Nos. 29/32, but colours changed.

35	**10**	1r. deep green and orange	1·00	20·00
36		2r. black and carmine	1·00	24·00
37		5r. chocolate and ultramarine	1·00	42·00
38	**11**	10r. red-brown and green	1·00	55·00
35/8 *Set of 4*			3·50	£130

14 Irrigation

15 Wheat

16 Cotton

17 Sahiwal bull

1949 (3 Mar). Silver Jubilee of Accession of H.H. the Amir of Bahawalpur. T **14/17**. W **3**. P 14.

39		3p. black and ultramarine	10	8·00
40		½a. black and brown-orange	10	8·00
41		9p. black and green	10	8·00
42		1a. black and carmine	10	8·00
39/42 *Set of 4*			35	29·00

Nos. 39/42 exist imperforate (*Prices, £28 per pair, unused*).

18 UPU Monument, Berne

1949 (10 Oct). 75th Anniv of Universal Postal Union. W **3**. P 13.

43	**18**	9p. black and green	20	2·75
		a. Perf 17½×17	3·00	24·00
44		1a. black and magenta	20	2·75
		a. Perf 17½×17	3·00	24·00
45		1½a. black and orange	20	2·75
		a. Perf 17½×17	3·00	24·00
46		2½a. black and blue	20	2·75
		a. Perf 17½×17	3·00	24·00
43/6 *Set of 4*			70	10·00
43a/6a *Set of 4*			11·00	85·00

Nos. 43/6 exist imperforate (*Prices, £5 per pair, unused*).

OFFICIAL STAMPS

O 1 Panjnad Weir

O 2 Dromedary and Calf

O 3 Blackbuck

O 4 Eastern White Pelicans

O 5 Friday Mosque, Fort Derawar

O 6 Temple at Pattan Munara

Normal

"Sarkark": Part of the overprint at left is missing, altering the word from "Sarkari" (Official) to "Sarkark" (R. 6/3)

1945 (1 Jan). Various horizontal pictorial designs, with red Arabic opt. W **3**. P 14.

O1	O **1**	½a. black and green	14·00	15·00
O2	O **2**	1a. black and carmine	3·75	18·00
		a. Opt omitted	†	£1400
		b. "Sarkark"	£170	
O3	O **3**	2a. black and violet	3·25	17·00
		a. "Sarkark"	£120	
O4	O **4**	4a. black and olive-green	18·00	35·00
O5	O **5**	8a. black and brown	40·00	22·00
		a. "Sarkark"	£425	
O6	O **6**	1r. black and orange	42·00	22·00
O1/6 *Set of 6*			£110	£120

Examples of No. O2a come from a sheet used at Rahimya Khan.

It is believed that examples of Nos. O1/2 in different shades and with white gum appeared in 1949 and were included in the Silver Jubilee Presentation Booklet.

O **7** Baggage Camels   (O **8**)

1945 (10 Mar). Revenue stamp with red Arabic opt. No wmk. P 14.
O7	O **7**	1a. black and brown	£120	85·00

1945 (Mar–May). Surch as Type O **8** (at Security Printing Press, Nasik) instead of red Arabic opt. No wmk. P 14.
O11	O **5**	½a. on 8a. black and purple	11·00	7·00
O12	O **6**	1½a. on 1r. black and orange	42·00	11·00
O13	O **1**	1½a. on 2r. black and blue (1.5)	£140	8·50
O11/13 Set of 3			£170	24·00

The stamps used as a basis for Nos. O7 and O11/13 were part of the Revenue series issued in 1933–34.

(O **9**)   O **10** H.H. the Amir of Bahawalpur

1945 (June). Optd with Type O **9** (by D.L.R.) instead of red Arabic opt. No wmk. P 14.
O14	O **1**	½a. black and carmine	1·25	11·00
O15	O **2**	1a. black and carmine	2·00	13·00
O16	O **3**	2a. black and orange	4·00	55·00
O14/16 Set of 3			6·50	70·00

1945 (Sept). P 14.
O17	O **10**	3p. black and blue	8·00	18·00
O18		1½a. black and violet	27·00	8·00

O **11** Allied Banners

(Des E. Meronti. Recess, background litho)

1946 (1 May). Victory. P 14.
O19	O **11**	1½a. green and grey	6·00	7·00

1948. Nos. 19, 22, 24/5 and 35/8 optd as Nos. O1/6.
O20	**4**	3p. black and blue (R.)	55	13·00
O21		1a. black and carmine (Blk.)	55	12·00
O22	**5**	2a. green and carmine (Blk.)	55	13·00
O23	**6**	4a. orange and brown (Blk.)	55	18·00
O24	**10**	1r. deep green and orange (R.)	55	20·00
O25		2r. black and carmine (R.)	55	26·00
O26		5r. chocolate and ultramarine (R.)	55	42·00
O27	**11**	10r. red-brown and green (R.)	55	42·00
O20/7 Set of 8			4·00	£170

1949 (10 Oct). 75th Anniv of Universal Postal Union. Nos. 43/6 optd as Nos. O1/6.
O28	**18**	9p. black and green	15	4·50
		aw. Wmk inverted	†	£500
		b. Perf 17½×17	2·50	32·00
O29		1a. black and magenta	15	4·50
		b. Perf 17½×17	2·50	32·00
O30		1½a. black and orange	15	4·50
		b. Perf 17½×17	2·50	32·00
O31		2½a. black and blue	15	4·50
		b. Perf 17½×17	2·50	32·00
O28/31 Set of 4			55	16·00
O28b/31b Set of 4			9·00	£110

Nos. O28/31 exist imperforate (Prices, £5 per pair, unused).

From 1947 stamps of Pakistan were used on all external mail. Bahawalpur issues continued to be used on internal mail until 1953.

Palestine

The stamps of TURKEY were used in Palestine from 1865.
In addition various European Powers, and Egypt, maintained post offices at Jerusalem (Austria, France, Germany, Italy, Russia), Jaffa (Austria, Egypt, France, Germany, Russia) and Haifa (Austria, France) using their own stamps or issues specially prepared for Levant post offices. All foreign post offices had closed by the time of the British Occupation.

PRICES FOR STAMPS ON COVER TO 1945
No. 1/b	from × 6
No. 2	from × 4
Nos. 3/4	from × 5
Nos. 5/15	from × 4
Nos. 16/29	from × 3
Nos. 30/42	from × 4
No. 43	—
No. 44	from × 10
No. 44a	—
Nos. 45/6	from × 10
Nos. 47/57	from × 3
Nos. 58/9	—
Nos. 60/8	from × 3
Nos. 69/70	—
Nos. 71/89	from × 3
Nos. 90/100	from × 4
No. 101	from × 15
Nos. 102/3	from × 10
Nos. 104/9	from × 10
Nos. 110/11	from × 100
Nos. D1/5	from × 40
Nos. D6/11	from × 100
Nos. D12/20	from × 20

BRITISH MILITARY OCCUPATION

British and allied forces invaded Palestine in November 1917 capturing Gaza (7 November), Jaffa (16 November) and Jerusalem (9 December). The front line then stabilised until the second British offensive of September 1918.

Nos. 1/15 were issued by the British military authorities for use by the civilian population in areas they controlled previously, part of the Ottoman Empire. Before the issue of Nos. 1/2 in February 1918, civilian mail was carried free. In addition to Palestine the stamps were available from E.E.F. post offices in Syria (including what subsequently became Transjordan) from 23 September 1918 to 23 February 1922, Lebanon from 21 October 1918 to September 1920 and Cilicia from 2 September 1919 to 16 July 1920. Use in the following post offices outside Palestine is recorded in *British Empire Campaigns and Occupations in the Near East, 1914–1924* by John Firebrace:

Adana, Cilicia	Hajjin ("Hadjin"), Cilicia Hama, Syria
Akkari ("Akkar"), Syria	
Aleih ("Alie"), Lebanon	Hasbaya, Lebanon
Aleppo ("Alep, Halep"), Syria	Hasine, Cilicia
Alexandretta, Syria	Hommana, Lebanon
Antakie, Syria	Homs, Syria
Baalbek, Lebanon	Kozan, Cilicia
Bab, Syria	Lattakia ("Laskie, Lattaquie"), Syria
Babitoma, Syria	
Ba'abda, Lebanon	Massel el Chouf ("Moussalc"), Lebanon
Behamdoun, Lebanon	
Beit Mery, Beyrouth Lebanon	Merdjajoun Lebanon
Beit ed Dine, Lebanon	Mersina ("Mersine"), Cilicia
Bekaa, Lebanon	Mounboudje, Syria
Beyrouth, Lebanon	Nabatti, Lebanon
Bouzanti, Syria	Nebk ("Nebik"), Syria
Broumana, Lebanon	Payass, Syria
Damascus ("Damas"), Syria	Racheya, Lebanon
Damour ("Damor"), Lebanon	Safita, Syria
Der'a ("Deraa"), Syria	Savour, Tyre, Lebanon
Deurt-Yol, Syria	Selimie, Syria
Djey Han, Syria	Sidan ("Saida (Echelle)"), Lebanon
Djezzin ("Djezzine"), Lebanon	Suweidiya ("Suvedie"), Syria
Djon, Lebanon	Talia, Syria
Djounie, Lebanon	Tarsous, Cilicia
Djubeil, Lebanon	Tartous, Syria
Douma, Syria	Tibnin, Lebanon
Edleb, Syria	Tripoli, Syria
Feke, Turkey	Zahle, Lebanon
Habib Souk, Syria	Zebdani, Syria

This information is reproduced here by permission of the publishers, Robson Lowe Publications.

(Currency. 10 milliemes = 1 piastre)

1   (2)   3

"E.E.F." = Egyptian Expeditionary Force

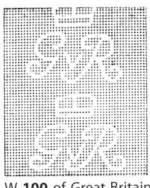

W **100** of Great Britain

(Des G. Rowntree. Litho Typographical Dept, Survey of Egypt, Giza, Cairo)

1918 (10 Feb). Wmk Royal Cypher in column (W **100** of Great Britain). Ungummed. Roul 20.
1	**1**	1p. indigo	£200	£110
		a. Deep blue	£160	£100
		b. Blue	£160	£100
		s. Optd "SPECIMEN"	£300	

Control: A 18 (Prices, corner block of 4; No. 1 £900. No. 1a, £800. No. 1b, £850).

1918 (16 Feb). As last (ungummed) surch with T **2**.
2	**1**	5m. on 1p. cobalt-blue	£110	£500
		a. "MILLILMES" (R. 1/10)	£3750	£9500
		s. Optd "SPECIMEN"	£300	

Control: B 18 A (Corner block, £1200).

1918 (5 Mar). As No. 1 but colour changed. With gum.
3	**1**	1p. ultramarine (shades)	2·00	2·00
		a. Crown missing from wmk	60·00	65·00
		b. Printed on the gummed side		
		w. Wmk inverted	£250	£300

Control: C 18. (Corner block, £85).

1918 (5 Mar–13 May). No. 3 surch with T **2**.
4	**1**	5m. on 1p. ultramarine	8·00	2·75
		a. Arabic surch wholly or partly missing (R. 1/11)	£375	£425
		b. Crown missing from wmk	95·00	
		w. Wmk inverted	£325	

Controls: C 18 B (3.18). (Corner block, £1000).
D 18 C (5.18). (Corner block, £225).

4m. Arabic "40" (R. 10/3 and 18/3)

(Typo Stamping Dept, Board of Inland Revenue, Somerset House, London)

1918 (16 July–27 Dec). Wmk Royal Cypher in column (W **100** of Great Britain). P 15×14.
5	**3**	1m. sepia	30	40
		a. Deep brown	60	40
6		2m. blue-green	30	45
		a. Deep green	2·00	1·00
7		3m. yellow-brown (17.12)	50	35
		a. Chestnut	15·00	6·00
8		4m. scarlet	35	40
		a. Arabic "40"	12·00	13·00
9		5m. yellow-orange (25.9)	4·50	50
		a. Orange	65	30
		b. Crown missing from wmk	£180	
		w. Wmk inverted	†	£1600
10		1p. deep indigo (9.11)	50	25
		a. Crown missing from wmk	£150	£170
		w. Wmk inverted	£225	£250
11		2p. pale olive	3·50	60
		a. Olive	3·50	1·10
12		5p. purple	3·75	2·50
13		9p. ochre (17.12)	12·00	7·50
14		10p. ultramarine (17.12)	12·00	4·50
		w. Wmk inverted	£600	
15		20p. pale grey (27.12)	18·00	20·00
		a. Slate-grey	24·00	27·00
5/15 Set of 11			45·00	32·00

Nos. 5/15 exist imperforate, from imprimatur sheets sold by the National Postal Museum in 2013.

There are two sizes of the design of this issue:
19×23 mm. 1, 2, and 4m., and 2 and 5p.
18×21½ mm. 3 and 5m., and 1, 9, 10 and 20p.

There are numerous minor plate varieties in this issue, such as stops omitted in "E.E.F.", malformed Arabic characters, etc.

CIVIL ADMINISTRATION UNDER BRITISH HIGH COMMISSIONER

Palestine was placed under civil administration by a British High Commissioner on 1 July 1920.

(4)   (5)   (6)

Differences:—
T **5**. 20 mm vert and 7 mm between English and Hebrew.
T **6**. 19 mm and 6 mm respectively.

Two settings of Type **4**:
Setting I (used for Nos. 16/26). This consisted of two horizontal rows of 12 of which the first setting row appeared on Rows 1, 3/7, 15, 17/18 and 20 of the sheet and the second on Rows 2, 8/14, 16 and 19.

On the first position in the top setting row the Arabic "t" (third character from the left) is incorrectly shown as an Arabic "z" by the addition of a dot to its right. On the eleventh position in the same row the first two letters in the Hebrew overprint were transposed so that " character appears first. On row 12 stamp 1 the final "E" of "PALESTINE" appears as a "B" on certain values. Once the errors were noticed vertical columns one and eleven were removed from the remaining sheets.

ولفسطين

PALESTIN B

פלשתינה א"י

"PALESTINB" (Setting I)

فلسطين

PALESTIN B

פלשתינה א"י

"PALESTINB" (Setting II)

Setting II (used for Nos. 16/29). This consisted of a single horizontal row of 12 reproduced to overprint the complete sheet of 240. The order in which the horizontal rows were used was changed several times during overprinting. During one such re-arrangement a damaged impression was replaced by one from Setting I showing the Arabic "z" error. (R. 14/8 for 1, 2, 3, 4, 5m (P 14), 20p.). The "B" error also occurs in the second setting, once in each sheet on either R. 17/8, 18/8 or 19/8.

TRIAL OVERPRINT. Before the issue of Nos. 16/26 (from Setting I), a trial overprint was prepared, resembling Type 4 but with the two Hebrew words in the bottom line transposed, the short word appearing on the right. This overprint was rejected for political reasons, but one sheet of each value existed, with the opt in gold on the 1p.
Price from £250, per stamp.

(Optd at Greek Orthodox Convent, Jerusalem)

1920 (1 Sept). Optd with T **4** (Arabic 8 mm long).

(a) P 15×14

16	**3**	1m. sepia	9·50	1·90
		b. Arabic "z" (Settings I and II)	£2750	
		c. Hebrew characters transposed (I)	£1400	
		d. "PALESTINB" (II)	£130	
17		2m. blue-green	14·00	6·00
		b. "Arabic "z" (Settings I and II)	£1000	
		c. Hebrew characters transposed (I)	£1000	
		d. "PALESTINB" (II)	£150	
18		3m. chestnut	18·00	8·50
		a. Opt inverted	£550	£700
		b. Arabic "z" (Settings I and II)	£2250	
		c. Hebrew characters transposed (I)	£2250	
		d. "PALESTINB" (II)	£100	
19		4m. scarlet	5·00	1·75
		b. Arabic "z" (Settings I and II)	£2500	
		c. Hebrew characters transposed (I)	£2500	
		d. PALESTINB" (II)	80·00	
		e. Arabic "40"	48·00	38·00
20		5m. yellow-orange	25·00	4·25
		c. Hebrew characters transposed (I)	†	£5500
		d. "PALESTINB" (II)	£160	
21		1p. deep indigo (Sil.)	5·50	1·00
		d. "PALESTINB" (II)	60·00	
		w. Wmk inverted	£160	£170
22		2p. deep olive	7·00	2·50
		a. Crown missing from wmk	£600	
		b. Arabic "z" (I)	£250	
		c. Hebrew characters transposed (I)	£250	£250
		d. "PALESTINB" (Settings I and II)	£140	
23		5p. deep purple	27·00	30·00
		b. Arabic "z" (I)	£1100	
		c. Hebrew characters transposed (I)	£650	
		d. "PALESTINB" (Setting I and II)	£250	
24		9p. ochre	15·00	20·00
		b. Arabic "z" (I)	£500	
		c. Hebrew characters transposed (I)	£600	
		d. "PALESTINB" (Settings I and II)	£250	
25		10p. ultramarine	13·00	17·00
		b. Arabic "z" (I)	£400	
		c. Hebrew characters transposed (I)	£500	
		d. "PALESTINB" (Settings I and II)	£300	
26		20p. pale grey	35·00	50·00
		b. Arabic "z" (Settings I and II)	£1000	
		c. Hebrew characters transposed (I)	£1000	
		d. "PALESTINB" (Settings I and II)	£1900	
16/26		Set of 11	£150	£130

(b) P 14

27	**3**	2m. blue-green	4·50	1·75
		d. "PALESTINB" (II)	60·00	
28		3m. chestnut	£130	65·00
29		5m. orange	8·00	75
		b. Arabic "z" (II)	£300	£250
		d. "PALESTINB" (II)	£150	

Faulty registration of the overprint in this issue has resulted in numerous misplaced overprints, either vertically or horizontally. All values exist with the overprint out of sequence, i.e. Hebrew/Arabic/English or English/Arabic/Hebrew. Also all values are known with Arabic/English or English/Hebrew only.

1920 (Dec)–**21**. Optd with T **5*** (Arabic 10 mm long).

(a) P 15×14

30	**3**	1m. sepia (27.12.20)	2·50	1·00
		a. Opt inverted	£450	†
31		2m. blue-green (27.12.20)	11·00	4·00
		a. Opt double	£450	
32		3m. yellow-brown (27.12.20)	4·00	1·00
33		4m. scarlet (27.12.20)	6·00	1·50
		a. Arabic "40"	65·00	40·00
34		5m. yellow-orange	4·25	75
35		1p. deep indigo (Silver) (21.6.21)	£550	38·00
36		2p. olive (21.6.21)	85·00	40·00
37		5p. deep purple (21.6.21)	50·00	10·00

(b) P 14

38	**3**	1m. sepia	£850	£950
39		2m. blue-green	5·50	5·50
40		4m. scarlet	90·00	£120
		a. Arabic "40"	£375	£425
41		5m. orange	85·00	9·00
		a. Yellow-orange	11·00	1·25
42		1p. deep indigo (Silver)	65·00	1·75
43		5p. purple	£225	£500

*In this setting the Arabic and Hebrew characters are badly worn and blunted, the Arabic "S" and "T" are joined (i.e. there is no break in the position indicated by the arrow in our illustration); the letters of "PALESTINE" are often irregular or broken; and the space between the two groups of Hebrew characters varies from 1 mm to over 1¾ mm. The " character in the left-hand Hebrew word extends above the remainder of the line (For clear, sharp overprint, see Nos. 47/59.).
The dates of issue given are irrespective of the perforations, i.e. one or both perfs could have been issued on the dates shown.
Nos. 31 and 39 exist with any one line of the overprint partly missing.

1920 (6 Dec). Optd with T **6**.

(a) P 15×14

44	**3**	3m. yellow-brown	60·00	32·00
44a		5m. yellow-orange	£15000	£12000

(b) P 14

45	**3**	1m. sepia	60·00	35·00
46		5m. orange	£450	30·00

فلسطين   فلسطين   فلسطين

PALESTINE **PALESTINE** **PALESTINE**

פלשתינה א"י פלשתינה א"י פלשתינה א"י

(6a)   **(7)**   **(8)**

1921 (29 May–4 Aug). Optd as T **6a**.

(a) P 15×14

47	**3**	1m. sepia (23.6)	20·00	4·00
48		2m. blue-green (18.6)	32·00	6·00
49		3m. yellow-brown (23.6)	45·00	3·00
50		4m. scarlet (23.6)	48·00	3·50
		a. Arabic "40"	£225	65·00
51		5m. yellow-orange	80·00	1·00
52		1p. deep indigo (Silver) (1.7)	32·00	1·50
53		2p. olive (4.8)	25·00	6·50
54		5p. purple (4.8)	25·00	8·00
55		9p. ochre (4.8)	70·00	£120
56		10p. ultramarine (4.8)	85·00	15·00
57		20p. pale grey (4.8)	£130	70·00
47/57		Set of 11	£500	£200

(b) P 14

58	**3**	1m. sepia	†	£2250
59		20p. pale grey	£12000	£2500

In this setting the Arabic and Hebrew characters are sharp and pointed and there is usually a break between the Arabic "S" and "T", though this is sometimes filled with ink. The space between the two groups of Hebrew characters is always 1¾ mm. The top of the " character in the Hebrew aligns with the remainder of the word.
The 3m. with "PALESTINE" omitted is an essay (Price £2500 unused).

1921 (26 Sept)–**22**. Optd with T **7** ("PALESTINE" in sans-serif letters) by Stamping Dept, Board of Inland Revenue, Somerset House, London. Wmk Royal Cypher in column (W **100** of Great Britain). P 15×14.

60	**3**	1m. sepia (5.10.21)	2·00	30
61		2m. blue-green (11.10.21)	3·00	30
62		3m. yellow-brown (17.10.21)	3·25	30
63		4m. scarlet (15.10.21)	3·75	60
		a. Arabic "40"	50·00	14·00
64		5m. yellow-orange	3·50	20
65		1p. bright turquoise-blue (14.11.21)	2·75	35
		w. Wmk inverted	†	—
66		2p. olive (7.12.21)	4·75	30
67		5p. deep purple (11.12.21)	12·00	6·00
		a. Opt double, one albino	£1000	
68		9p. ochre (10.3.22)	25·00	14·00
69		10p. ultramarine (10.3.22)	28·00	£650
		w. Wmk inverted	†	
70		20p. pale grey (10.3.22)	80·00	£1500
60/70		Set of 11	£150	

Dates quoted are of earliest known postmarks.

(Printed and optd by Waterlow & Sons from new plates)

1922 (Sept–Nov). T **3** (redrawn), optd with T **8**. Wmk Mult Script CA.

(a) P 14

71	**3**	1m. sepia	2·25	30
		a. Deep brown	2·75	30
		b. Opt inverted	†	£12000
		c. Opt double	£250	£450
		w. Wmk inverted	55·00	42·00
72		2m. yellow	3·00	30
		a. Orange-yellow	5·00	50
		b. Wmk sideways	†	£2000
		w. Wmk inverted	45·00	40·00
73		3m. greenish blue	3·25	15
		w. Wmk inverted	48·00	40·00
74		4m. carmine-pink	3·25	20
		w. Wmk inverted	70·00	55·00
75		5m. orange	3·50	20
		w. Wmk inverted	90·00	60·00
76		6m. blue-green	2·75	30
		w. Wmk inverted	65·00	70·00
77		7m. yellow-brown	2·75	30
		w. Wmk inverted	£325	£325
78		8m. scarlet	2·75	30
		w. Wmk inverted	75·00	80·00
79		1p. grey	3·25	30
		w. Wmk inverted	90·00	80·00
80		13m. ultramarine	4·00	15
		w. Wmk inverted	45·00	35·00
		x. Wmk reversed	†	£750
81		2p. olive	4·00	35
		a. Opt inverted	£325	£550
		b. Ochre	£130	6·50
		w. Wmk inverted	£325	£325
82		5p. deep purple	6·00	1·25
		aw. Wmk inverted	†	£750
82b		9p. ochre	£1100	£250
83		10p. light blue	90·00	17·00
		a. "E.F.F." for "E.E.F." in bottom panel (R. 10/3)	£2000	£550
84		20p. bright violet	£200	£120

(b) P 15×14

86	**3**	5p. deep purple	65·00	7·00
87		9p. ochre	10·00	9·00
88		10p. light blue	8·50	4·00
		a. "E.F.F." for "E.E.F." in bottom panel (R. 10/3)	£450	£300
		w. Wmk inverted	£550	£325
89		20p. bright violet	12·00	5·50
71s/89s		Optd "SPECIMEN" Set of 15	£450	

Most values can be found on thin paper.
All known examples of the 1m. with inverted opt (No. 71b) also have inverted wmk.
In this issue the design of all denominations is the same size, 18×21½ mm. Varieties may be found with one or other of the stops between "E.F.F." missing.

BRITISH MANDATE TO THE LEAGUE OF NATIONS

The League of Nations granted a mandate to Great Britain for the administration of Palestine on 29 September 1923.

(New Currency. 1,000 mils = 1 Palestine pound)

9 Rachel's Tomb

10 Dome of the Rock

11 Citadel, Jerusalem

12 Sea of Galilee

(Des F. Taylor. Typo Harrison)

1927 (1 June)–**45**. Wmk Mult Script CA. P 13½×14½ (2m. to 20m.) or 14.

90	**9**	2m. greenish blue (14.8.27) (a) (b) (c) (d)	2·75	10
		w. Wmk inverted	†	£550
91		3m. yellow-green (a) (b) (c) (d)	1·75	10
		w. Wmk inverted	†	£325
92	**10**	4m. rose-pink (14.8.27) (a) (b)	9·00	1·50
93	**11**	5m. orange (14.8.27) (a) (b) (c) (d)	4·25	10
		a. From coils. Perf 14½×14 (1936)	16·00	20·00
		ac. Yellow. From coils. Perf 14½×14 (1945)	45·00	35·00
		aw. Wmk inverted	22·00	26·00
		b. Yellow (12.44)	3·00	15
		w. Wmk inverted	40·00	40·00
94	**10**	6m. pale green (14.8.27) (a) (b)	6·00	1·75
		a. Deep green	1·50	20
95	**11**	7m. scarlet (14.8.27) (a) (b)	11·00	60
96	**10**	8m. yellow-brown (14.8.27) (a) (b)	18·00	6·50
97	**9**	10m. slate (14.8.27) (a) (b) (c) (d)	2·00	10
		a. Grey. From coils. Perf 14½×14 (11.38)	20·00	27·00
		aw. Wmk inverted		
		b. Grey (1944)	2·25	10
98	**10**	13m. ultramarine (14.8.27) (a) (b)	17·00	30
99	**11**	20m. dull olive-green (14.8.27) (a) (b) (d)	3·50	15
		a. Bright olive-green (12.44)	2·25	15
		w. Wmk inverted	†	£550
100	**12**	50m. deep dull purple (14.8.27) (a) (b) (d)	3·25	30
		a. Bright purple (12.44)	6·00	30
		x. Wmk reversed	†	£650

101		90m. bistre (14.8.27) (a) (b).....................	85·00	60·00
102		100m. turquoise-blue (14.8.27) (a) (b)		
		(d)..	2·25	70
103		200m. deep violet (14.8.27) (a) (b) (d)..	8·00	5·00
		a. Bright violet (1928)........................	38·00	17·00
		b. Blackish violet (12.44)...................	13·00	3·75
90/103 Set of 14			£150	65·00
90s/103s Handstamped "SPECIMEN" Set of 14				£450

Nos 90/103 were printed on four distinct papers. The original issue in 1927 was on thin semi-transparent paper ('a'). In 1928 a special thick paper with vertical ribbing ('b') was introduced, the purpose of the ribbing being to prevent curling of the sheets. A similar paper with horizontal ribbing ('c') was used for an experimental printing C.1937. From 1936 paper 'b' was replaced by ordinary opaque white wove paper ('d'). The papers known for each value are indicated in the above listing by letters in brackets.

2m. stamps in the grey colour of the 10m., including an example postmarked in 1935, exist as do 50m. stamps in blue, but it has not been established whether they were issued.

Nos. 90/1 and 93 exist in coils, constructed from normal sheets.

1932 (1 June)–44. New values and colours. Wmk Mult Script CA. P 13½×14½ (4m. to 15m.) or 14.

104	**10**	4m. purple (1.11.32) (b) (d)...................	3·00	10
		w. Wmk inverted.............................	†	£650
105	**11**	7m. deep violet (b) (c) (d)...................	1·00	10
106	**10**	8m. scarlet (b) (c) (d).........................	1·25	20
		w. Wmk inverted.............................	†	£800
107		13m. bistre (1.8.32) (b) (c) (d)............	3·50	10
108		15m. ultramarine (1.8.32) (b) (c) (d) ...	6·50	10
		a. Grey-blue (12.44)........................	5·50	40
		b. Greenish blue.............................	5·50	40
		w. Wmk inverted.............................	†	£800
109	**12**	250m. brown (15.1.42) (d)....................	7·50	3·50
110		500m. scarlet (15.1.42) (d)..................	8·50	3·50
111		£P1 black (15.1.42) (d)........................	12·00	3·50
104/11 Set of 8			38·00	10·00
104s/11s Perf "SPECIMEN" Set of 8				£475

No. 108 exists in coils, constructed from normal sheets.

Nos 104/11 were printed on papers 'b', 'c' and 'd', as defined in the note after Nos 90/103.

STAMP BOOKLETS

1929. Blue cover inscr "PALESTINE POSTAGE STAMP BOOKLET" and contents in English. Without advertisements on front. Stitched.
SB1	150m. booklet containing 12×2m., 12×3m.		
	18×5m. (Nos. 90/1, 93) in blocks of 6................	£2500	
	a. As No. SB1, but stapled.....................................	£2500	

1933. Blue cover inscr "PALESTINE POSTS & TELEGRAPHS POSTAGE STAMP BOOKLET" and contents all in English, Arabic and Hebrew. Without advertisements on front. Stapled.
SB2	150m. booklet. Contents as No. SB1....................	£3000	

1937–38. Red cover inscr "POSTAGE STAMP BOOKLET" and contents in English, Hebrew and Arabic. With advertisements on front. Stapled.
SB3	150m. booklet containing 2m., 3m., 5m. and 15m.		
	(Nos. 90/1, 93, 108) in blocks of 6......................	£2750	
	a. Blue cover (1938)...	£2500	

1939. Pink cover inscr "POSTAGE STAMP BOOKLET" and contents in English, Hebrew and Arabic. With advertisements on front. Stapled.
SB4	120m. booklet containing 6×10m. and 12×5m.		
	(Nos. 93, 97) in blocks of 6.................................	£2500	

POSTAL FISCALS

Type-set stamps inscribed "O.P.D.A." (= Ottoman Public Debt Administration) or "H.J.Z." (Hejaz Railway); British 1d. stamps of 1912–24 and Palestine stamps overprinted with one or other of the above groups of letters, or with the word "Devair", with or without surcharge of new value, are fiscal stamps. They are known used as postage stamps, alone, or with other stamps to make up the correct rates, and were passed by the postal authorities, although they were not definitely authorised for postal use.

POSTAGE DUE STAMPS

D **1**   D **2** (MILLIEME)   D **3** (MIL)

(Typo Greek Orthodox Convent Press, Jerusalem)
1923 (1 Apr). P 11.
D1	D **1**	1m. yellow-brown..............................	26·00	38·00
		a. Imperf (pair).................................	£325	
		b. Imperf between (horiz pair)........	£1300	
D2		2m. blue-green..................................	21·00	10·00
		a. Imperf (pair).................................	£450	
D3		4m. scarlet..	10·00	13·00
D4		8m. mauve...	7·50	7·00
		a. Imperf (pair).................................	£140	
		b. Imperf between (horiz pair)........	†	£2250
D5		13m. steel blue..................................	7·50	8·00
		a. Imperf between (horiz pair)........	£1100	
D1/5 Set of 5			65·00	70·00

Perfectly centred and perforated stamps of this issue are worth considerably more than the above prices, which are for average examples.

(Types D **2**/3. Typo D.L.R.)
1924 (3 Oct). Wmk Mult Script CA. P 14.
D6	D **2**	1m. deep brown.................................	1·00	2·00
D7		2m. yellow...	4·00	1·75
		w. Wmk inverted.............................	†	£500
D8		4m. green...	2·00	1·25
D9		8m. scarlet...	3·00	90
D10		13m. ultramarine...............................	3·25	2·50
D11		5p. violet...	14·00	1·75
D6/11 Set of 6			24·00	9·00
D6s/11s Optd "SPECIMEN" Set of 6				£300

1928 (1 Feb)–44. Wmk Mult Script CA. P 14.
D12	D **3**	1m. brown	2·50	85
		a. Perf 15×14 (1944).........................	42·00	80·00
D13		2m. yellow..	3·50	60
		w. Wmk inverted.............................	†	£550
D14		4m. green...	4·00	1·60
		a. Perf 15×14 (1942).........................	75·00	£110
D15		6m. orange-brown (10.33)..................	18·00	5·00
D16		8m. carmine.......................................	2·75	1·75
D17		10m. pale grey....................................	1·75	60
D18		13m. ultramarine...............................	4·50	2·75
D19		20m. pale olive-green.........................	4·50	1·25
D20		50m. violet...	4·75	2·25
D12/20 Set of 9			42·00	15·00
D12s/20s Optd or Perf (6m.) "SPECIMEN" Set of 9				£350

Nos. D12a and D14a were printed and perforated by Harrison and Sons following bomb damage to the De La Rue works on 29 December 1940.

The British Mandate terminated on 14 May 1948. Later issues of stamps and occupation issues will be found listed under Gaza, Israel and Jordan in the Stanley Gibbons *Middle East Catalogue*.

Papua *see after* **Australia**

Penrhyn Island
see after **Cook Islands**

CROWN COLONY

The settlement of Pitcairn Island by the *Bounty* mutineers in 1790 was not discovered until the American whaler *Topaz*, Capt. Mayhew Folger, called there in 1808. A visit by two Royal Navy frigates followed in 1814 and reports from their captains resulted in considerable interest being taken in the inhabitants' welfare by religious and philanthropic circles in Great Britain.

Due to overcrowding the population was resettled on Tahiti in 1831, but many soon returned to Pitcairn which was taken under British protection in 1838. The island was again evacuated in 1856, when the inhabitants were moved to Norfolk Island, but a number of families sailed back to their original home in 1859 and 1864.

The earliest surviving letter from the island is dated 1849. Before 1921 the mail service was irregular, as it depended on passing ships, and mail for the island was often sent via Tahiti. Some covers, purportedly sent from Pitcairn between 1883 and 1890 are known handstamped "Pitcairn Island" or "PITCAIRN ISLAND", but these are now believed to be forgeries.

In 1920 a regular mail service was introduced. As there were no stamps available, letters were allowed free postage as long as they carried a cachet, or manuscript endorsement, indicating their origin. Illustrations of Cachets I/VI, VIII, VIIIa, X and XIII are taken from *Pitcairn Islands Postal Markings 1883–1991*, published by the Pitcairn Islands Study Group, and are reproduced by permission of the author, Mr. Cy Kitching. Cachets I to XIII are shown three-quarter size.

POSTED IN PITCAIRN
NO STAMPS AVAILABLE
Cachet I

Cat No.		*Value on cover*
C1	**1920–25.** Cachet I (62×8 mm) (*violet or black*)............	£3250

POSTED AT PITCAIRN ISLAND
NO STAMPS AVAILABLE.
Cachet II

C2	**1921–25.** Cachet II (*violet or red*)	£2750

POSTED AT PITCAIRN ISLAND
NO STAMPS AVAILABLE.
Cachet III

C3	**1922–28.** Cachet III (49×8½ mm) (*vio, pur or blk*).........	£2000

POSTED IN PITCAIRN ISLAND
1923 NO STAMPS AVAILABLE
Cachet IV

C4	**1923.** Cachet IV (*black*)................................	£2750

Posted at Pitcairn
Island no Stamps
Available
Cachet IVa

C4a	**1923.** Cachet IVa (73½×22 mm) (*red*)............................	£2750

POSTED AT PITCAIRN ISLAND
NO STAMPS AVAILABLE
Cachet V

C5	**1923–28.** (Aug). Cachet V (47×9 mm) (*red, violet or black*)..	£2500
C5a	**1925–26.** As Cachet V, but second line shown as "No Stamps Available" (*black*)	£3250

POSTED AT PITCAIRN ISLAND.
NO STAMPS AVAILABLE.
NOT TO BE SURCHARGED.

Cachet VI

C6	**1923.** Cachet VI (*blue-green or red*)	£3000
C7	**1923.** As Cachet V, but in three lines (*red*)	

POSTED IN PITCAIRN.
NO STAMPS AVAILABLE
Cachet VIa

C7a	**1923–24.** Cachet VIa (66×10 mm) (*blue-black or violet*)	£2250

POSTED AT PITCAIRN ISLAND
NO STAMPS AVAILABLE.
Cachet VII

C8	**1923–27.** Cachet VII (*violet or black*)	£1900
C9	**1924.** As Cachet IV, but dated "1924" (*black*)	£2500

POSTED AT PITCAIRN ISLAND.

NO STAMPS AVAILABLE.

Cachet VIII

C10   **1924–26.** Cachet VIII (36×8 mm) (vio, blk or red) £2500

POSTED AT PITCAIRN
NO STAMPS AVAILABLE

Cachet VIIIa

C10a   **1924–26.** Cachet VIIIa (36×8¾ mm) (vio or blk) £2250

POSTED AT PITCAIRN ISLAND
NO STAMPS AVAILABLE.

Cachet IX

C11   **1923–26.** Cachet IX (63×7 mm) (vio or blk) £2750
C12   **1925.** (Sept). As Cachet IV, but dated "1925" (blk).. £2750

POSTED IN PITCAIRN
NO STAMPS AVAILABLE.

Cachet X

C13   **1925.** Cachet X (48×5 mm) ....

POSTED AT PITCAIRN ISLAND,
NO STAMPS AVAILABLE.

Cachet XI

C14   **1925–26.** Cachet XI (50×10 mm) (violet or blk) £2500

Posted at PITCAIRN ISLAND
No Stamps Available

Cachet XII

C15   **1925.** Cachet XII (55×7½ mm) (violet).....................
C15a   As Cachet XII but "POSTED AT" in capital letters.....

POSTED IN PITCAIRN
NO STAMPS AVAILABLE.

Cachet XIII

C16   **1926.** (Jan). Cachet XIII (64×8 mm) (pur or blk) £3000

The New Zealand Government withdrew the free postage concession on 12 May 1926, but after representations from the islanders, opened a postal agency on Pitcairn using New Zealand stamps cancelled with Type Z **1**. Some impressions of this postmark appear to show a double ring, but this is the result of heavy or uneven use of the handstamp. The postal agency operated from 7 June 1927 until 14 October 1940.

The Earlier New Zealand stamps are known cancelled with Type Z **1**, but these were not supplied to the postal agency and their use is considered to be contrived.

PRICES. Those quoted for Nos. Z1/72 and ZF1 are for examples showing a virtually complete strike of Type Z **1**. Due to the size of the cancellation such examples will usually be on piece.

Z **1**

Stamps of New Zealand cancelled with Type Z **1**.

1915–29. King George V (Nos. 419, 422/6, 428/31 and 446/9).
Z1	½d. green..................	30·00
Z2	1½d. grey-slate.............	65·00
Z3	1½d. orange-brown...........	50·00
Z4	2d. yellow	48·00
Z5	2½d. blue...................	85·00
Z6	3d. chocolate..............	90·00
Z7	4d. bright violet..........	85·00
Z8	4½d. deep green............	£120
Z9	5d. light blue.............	90·00
Z10	6d. carmine...............	£100
Z11	7½d. red-brown............	£130
Z12	8d. red-brown.............	£170
Z13	9d. yellowish olive.......	£170
Z14	1s. vermilion.............	£160

1923. Map of New Zealand (No. 460).
Z14a	1d. carmine...............	£100

1925. Dunedin Exhibition (No. 464).
Z14b	½d. yellow-green/green.....	£150
Z14c	1d. carmine/rose...........	£120

1926–27. King George V in Field-Marshal's or Admiral's uniform (Nos. 468/9).
Z15	1d. rose-carmine..........	30·00
Z16	2s. light blue............	£350

1929. Anti-Tuberculosis Fund (No. 544).
Z17	1d. +1d. scarlet..........	£160

1931. Air (Nos. 548/9).
Z18	3d. chocolate.............	£300
Z19	4d. blackish purple.......	£350

1932. Health (No. 552).
Z21	1d. +1d. carmine..........	£170

1935. Pictorials (Nos. 556/8 and 560/9). W **43**.
Z22	½d. bright green..........	65·00
Z23	1d. scarlet...............	40·00
Z24	1½d. red-brown............	£100
Z26	2½d. chocolate and slate..	85·00
Z27	3d. brown.................	£100
Z28	4d. black and sepia.......	£130
Z29	5d. ultramarine...........	£150
Z30	6d. scarlet...............	£130
Z31	8d. chocolate.............	£150
Z32	9d. scarlet and black.....	£150
Z33	1s. deep green............	£130
Z34	2s. olive-green...........	£350
Z35	3s. chocolate and yellow-brown..	£400

1935. Silver Jubilee (Nos. 573/5).
Z36	½d. green.................	50·00
Z37	1d. carmine...............	50·00
Z38	6d. red-orange............	£100

1935. Health (No. 576).
Z39	1d. +1d. scarlet..........	75·00

1936. Pictorials (Nos. 577/82). W **98**.
Z40	½d. bright green..........	50·00
Z41	1d. scarlet...............	17·00
Z42	1½d. red-brown............	85·00
Z43	2d. orange................	70·00
Z44	2½d. chocolate and slate..	75·00
Z45	3d. brown.................	80·00

1936. 21st Anniversary of "Anzac" Landing at Gallipoli (Nos. 591/2).
Z46	½d. +½d. green............	50·00
Z47	1d. +1d. scarlet..........	50·00

1936. Congress of British Empire Chambers of Commerce (Nos. 593/7).
Z48	½d. emerald-green.........	48·00
Z49	1d. scarlet...............	48·00
Z50	2½d. blue.................	65·00
Z51	4d. violet................	95·00
Z52	6d. red-brown.............	95·00

1936. Health (No. 598).
Z53	1d. +1d. scarlet..........	75·00

1937. Coronation (Nos. 599/601).
Z54	1d. carmine...............	40·00
Z55	2½d. Prussian blue........	45·00
Z56	6d. red-orange............	45·00

1937. Health (No. 602).
Z57	1d. +1d. scarlet..........	75·00

1938. King George VI (Nos. 603, 605, 607).
Z58	½d. green.................	75·00
Z59	1d. scarlet...............	75·00
Z60	1½d. purple-brown.........	85·00

1939. Health (Nos. 611/12).
Z60a	1d. on ½d.+½d. green......	75·00
Z60b	2d. on 1d.+1d. scarlet....	75·00

1940. Centenary of British Sovereignty (Nos. 613/22, 624/5).
Z61	½d. blue-green............	38·00
Z62	1d. chocolate and scarlet.	42·00
Z63	1½d. light blue and mauve.	50·00
Z64	2d. blue-green and chocolate.	45·00
Z65	2½d. blue-green and blue..	50·00
Z66	3d. purple and carmine....	50·00
Z67	4d. chocolate and lake....	85·00
Z68	5d. pale blue and brown...	95·00
Z69	6d. emerald-green and violet.	95·00
Z70	7d. black and red.........	£130
Z71	9d. olive-green and orange.	£130
Z72	1s. sage-green and deep green.	£130

POSTAL FISCAL STAMPS

1932. Arms (No. F147).
ZF1	2s.6d. deep brown.........	£400

PRICES FOR STAMPS ON COVER TO 1945	
Nos. 1/8	from × 10

1 Cluster of Oranges

2 Christian on *Bounty* and Pitcairn Island

3 John Adams and his house

4 Lt. Bligh and H.M.S. *Bounty*

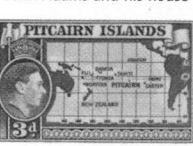

5 Pitcairn Islands and the Pacific Ocean

5a *Bounty* Bible

6 HMS *Bounty*

6a School, 1949

7 Fletcher Christian and Pitcairn Island

8 Christian on HMS *Bounty* and Pitcairn Coast

(Recess B.W. (1d., 3d., 4d., 8d. and 2s.6d.), and Waterlow (others))

1940 (15 Oct)–**51.** T **1/8.** Wmk Mult Script CA. P 11½×11 (1d., 3d., 4d., 8d. and 2s.6d.) or 12½ (others).
1	**1**	½d. orange and green........	1·25	1·25
2	**2**	1d. mauve and magenta.......	1·50	80
3	**3**	1½d. grey and carmine.......	1·50	50
4	**4**	2d. green and brown.........	2·50	1·40
5	**5**	3d. yellow-green and blue...	1·25	1·40
		aw. Wmk inverted............	£5000	
5b	**5a**	4d. black and emerald-green (1.9.51)........	23·00	12·00
6	**6**	6d. brown and deep greenish grey..	7·00	1·50
6a	**6a**	8d. olive-green and magenta (1.9.51)........	24·00	8·00
7	**7**	1s. violet and grey........	6·50	3·50
8	**8**	2s.6d. green and brown.....	17·00	4·00
1/8		Set of 10..................	75·00	30·00
1s/8s (ex 4d., 8d.) Perf "SPECIMEN" Set of 8			£1400	

2d. Flaw by launch (R. 6/3, subsequently retouched)

3d. Flagstaff flaw (R. 8/2)

1946 (2 Dec). Victory. As Nos. 110/11 of Antigua.
9		2d. brown.................	70	30
		a. Flaw by launch........	70·00	
10		3d. blue..................	1·00	30
		a. Flagstaff flaw........	60·00	60·00
9s/10s Perf "SPECIMEN" Set of 2............			£425	

1949 (1 Aug). Royal Silver Wedding. As Nos. 112/13 of Antigua.
11		1½d. scarlet..............	2·00	1·50
12		10s. mauve................	40·00	50·00

1949 (10 Oct). 75th Anniversary of UPU. As Nos. 114/17 of Antigua.
13		2½d. red-brown............	2·25	4·25
14		3d. deep blue.............	7·00	4·25
15		6d. deep blue-green.......	3·50	4·25
16		1s. purple................	3·50	4·25
13/16 Set of 4.............			14·50	15·00

1953 (2 June). Coronation. As No. of 120 Antigua, but ptd by B.W.
17		4d. black and deep bluish green............	2·00	3·75

9 *Cordyline terminalis*

10 Pitcairn Island Map

11 John Adams and *Bounty* bible

12 Handicrafts: Bird model

13 Bounty Bay

14 Pitcairn School

15 Pacific Ocean map

16 Island scene

17 Handicrafts: Ship model

18 Island wheelbarrow

19 Lauching new whaleboat

(Recess D.L.R.)

1957 (2 July)–**63**. T **9/19**. Wmk Mult Script CA. P 13×12½ (horiz) or 12½×13 (vert).

18	**9**	½d. green and reddish lilac	80	1·50
		a. Green and reddish purple (9.3.63) ..	1·25	3·25
19	**10**	1d. black and olive-green	4·50	2·25
		a. Black and yellow-olive (19.2.59)	21·00	21·00
		b. Black and light olive-green (24.2.60)	65·00	27·00
20	**11**	2d. brown and greenish blue	2·25	60
21	**12**	2½d. deep brown and red-orange	75	40
22	**13**	3d. emerald and deep ultramarine	80	40
23	**14**	4d. scarlet and deep ultramarine (I)	90	40
23a		4d. carmine-red and deep ultramarine (II) (5.11.58)	4·00	1·50
24	**15**	6d. pale buff and indigo	3·50	55
25	**16**	8d. deep olive-green and carmine-lake	75	40
26	**17**	1s. black and yellowish brown.....	2·25	40
27	**18**	2s. green and red-orange	11·00	10·00
28	**19**	2s.6d. ultramarine and lake	26·00	12·00
		a. Blue and deep lake (10.2.59)......	48·00	14·00
18/28 Set of 12			50·00	27·00

Nos. 23/a. Type I is inscribed "PITCAIRN SCHOOL"; Type II "SCHOOL TEACHER'S HOUSE".
See also No. 33.

20 Pitcairn Island and Simon Young

21 Norfolk Island and Pitcairn Islands

22 Migrant brigantine *Mary Ann*

6d. Right-angle over crown (R. 4/2)

(Des H. E. Maud. Photo Harrison)

1961 (15 Nov). Centenary of Return of Pitcairn Islanders from Norfolk Island. T **20/2**. W w **12**. P 14½×13½.

29	**20**	3d. black and yellow...............	50	45
30	**21**	6d. red-brown and blue...........	1·00	75
		a. Right-angle over crown	23·00	
31	**22**	1s. red-orange and blue-green	1·00	75
29/31 Set of 3			2·25	1·75

1963 (4 June). Freedom from Hunger. As No. 146 of Antigua.

32		2s.6d. ultramarine	3·50	1·50

1963 (4 Dec). As No. 18a, but wmk w **12**.

33	**9**	½d. green and reddish purple...........	65	60

1963 (9 Dec). Red Cross Centenary. As Nos. 147/8 of Antigua.

34		2d. red and black	1·00	1·00
35		2s.6d. red and blue......................	2·00	3·00

23 Pitcairn Is. Longboat   **24** Queen Elizabeth II (after Anthony Buckley)

(Des M. Farrar Bell. Photo Harrison)

1964 (5 Aug)–**65**. T **23/4** and similar horiz designs. Multicoloured. W w **12**. P 14×14½.

36		½d. Type **23**	10	30
		a. Blue omitted	£750	
37		1d. HMS *Bounty*	30	30
38		2d. "Out from Bounty Bay".........	30	30
39		3d. Great Frigatebird	75	30
40		4d. White Tern	75	30
41		6d. Pitcairn Warbler	75	30
42		8d. Red-footed Booby	75	30
		a. Pale blue (beak) omitted..........	£600	
		b. Pale blue (beak) printed double.......		
43		10d. Red-tailed Tropicbirds	60	30
44		1s. Henderson Island Crake.........	60	30
45		1s.6d. Stephen's Lory	1·50	1·25
46		2s.6d. Murphy's Petrel	1·50	1·50
47		4s. Henderson Island Fruit Dove ...	2·00	1·50
48		8s. Type **24** (5.4.65)	1·25	2·00
36/48 Set of 13			10·00	8·00

1965 (17 May). ITU Centenary. As Nos. 166/7 of Antigua.

49		1d. mauve and orange-brown..........	50	40
50		2s.6d. turquoise-green and bright blue	1·50	2·00
		w. Wmk inverted	£200	

1965 (25 Oct). International Co-operation Year. As Nos. 168/9 of Antigua.

51		1d. reddish purple and turquoise-green	50	40
		a. "TRISTAN DA CUNHA" offset on back in reddish purple	£800	
52		1s.6d. deep bluish green and lavender	1·50	2·00

No. 51a was caused by the back of one sheet of stamps coming into contact with the blanket plate used for applying the Tristan da Cunha inscription to the same basic design.

1966 (24 Jan). Churchill Commemoration. As Nos. 170/3 of Antigua.

53		2d. new blue	70	85
54		3d. deep green	1·25	1·00
55		6d. brown	1·25	1·75
56		1s. bluish violet	1·25	2·50
53/6 Set of 4			4·00	5·50

1966 (1 Aug). World Cup Football Championship. As Nos. 176/7 of Antigua.

57		4d. violet, yellow-green, lake and yellow-brown.................	75	1·00
58		2s.6d. chocolate, blue-green, lake and yellow-brown.................	1·25	1·25

1966 (20 Sept). Inauguration of WHO Headquarters, Geneva. As Nos. 178/9 of Antigua.

59		8d. black, yellow-green and light blue...	2·00	3·25
60		1s.6d. black, light purple and yellow-brown	3·50	3·75

1966 (1 Dec). 20th Anniversary of UNESCO. As Nos. 196/8 of Antigua.

61		½d. slate-violet, red, yellow and orange	20	1·00
62		10d. orange-yellow, violet and deep olive	1·25	75
63		2s. black, bright purple and orange	2·50	2·25
61/3 Set of 3			3·50	3·50

36 Mangarevan Canoe, *circa* 1325

(Des V. Whiteley. Photo Harrison)

1967 (1 Mar). Bicentenary of Discovery of Pitcairn Islands. T **36** and similar horiz designs. Multicoloured. W w **12**. P 14½.

64		½d. Type **36**	10	20
65		1d. P. F. de Quiros and *San Pedro y San Pablo*, 1606	20	20
66		8d. *San Pedro y San Pablo* and *Los Tres Reyes*, 1606	25	20
67		1s. Carteret and HMS *Swallow*, 1767.......	25	25
68		1s.6d. *Hercules*, 1819	25	25
64/8 Set of 5			1·00	1·00

(New Currency. 100 cents = 1 New Zealand dollar)

½c

(41 Bounty Anchor)

1967 (10 July). Decimal currency. Nos. 36/48 surch in decimal currency by die-stamping in gold as T **41**.

69		½c. on ½d. multicoloured..................	10	10
		a. Deep brown omitted............................	£1500	
		b. Surch double, one albino.....................	£200	
70		1c. on 1d. multicoloured...................	30	1·25
71		2c. on 2d. multicoloured...................	25	1·25
72		2½c. on 3d. multicoloured..................	25	1·25
73		3c. on 4d. multicoloured...................	25	20
74		5c. on 6d. multicoloured...................	30	1·25
75		10c. on 8d. multicoloured.................	50	30
		a. "10c." omitted..............................	£2000	
		b. Pale blue (beak) omitted................	£900	
76		15c. on 10d. multicoloured...............	1·50	40
77		20c. on 1s. multicoloured.................	1·50	55
78		25c. on 1s.6d. multicoloured.............	1·50	1·25
79		30c. on 2s.6d. multicoloured.............	1·75	1·25
80		40c. on 4s. multicoloured.................	1·75	1·25
81		50c. on 8s. multicoloured.................	1·50	1·50
69/81 Set of 13			10·00	10·50

On No. 75a the anchor emblem is still present. Several examples of this variety have been identified as coming from R9/1.
The ½c. and 1c. exist with PVA gum as well as gum arabic.

42 Bligh and *Bounty*'s Launch

(Des Jennifer Toombs. Litho D.L.R.)

1967 (7 Dec). 150th Death Anniversary of Admiral Bligh. T **42** and similar horiz designs. P 13½×13.

82		1c. turquoise-blue, black and royal blue (*shades*)	10	10
83		8c. black, yellow and magenta...........	25	50
84		20c. black, brown and pale buff............	25	55
82/4 Set of 3...			55	1·00

Designs:—8c. Bligh and followers cast adrift; 20c. Bligh's tomb.

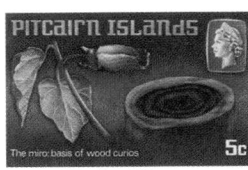
45 Human Rights Emblem

(Des G. Hamori. Litho D.L.R.)

1968 (4 Mar). Human Rights Year. P 13½×13.

85	**45**	1c. multicoloured................................	10	10
86		2c. multicoloured................................	10	10
87		25c. multicoloured..............................	35	35
85/7 Set of 3..			50	50

46 Miro Wood and Flower

(Des Jennifer Toombs. Photo Harrison)

1968 (19 Aug). Handicrafts. T **46** and similar designs. W w **12** (sideways* on vert designs). P 14×13½ (5, 10c.) or 13½×14 (others).

88		5c. multicoloured............................	20	30
89		10c. bronze-green, brown and orange	20	40
90		15c. deep bluish violet, chocolate and salmon.........................	25	40
91		20c. multicoloured............................	25	45
		w. Wmk Crown to right of CA	£225	
88/91 Set of 4			80	1·40

Designs: Horiz—10c. Flying Fish model. Vert—15c. "Hand" vases; 20c. Woven baskets.
*The normal sideways watermark shows Crown to left of CA, *as seen from the back of the stamp*.

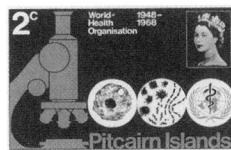
50 Microscope and Slides

(Des Jennifer Toombs. Litho D.L.R.)

1968 (25 Nov). 20th Anniversary of World Health Organisation. T **50** and similar horiz design. W w **12** (sideways). P 14.

92		2c. black, turquoise-blue and ultramarine.................................	10	20
93		20c. black, orange and bright purple	40	50

Design:—20c. Hypodermic syringe and jars of tablets.

52 Pitcairn Island

62 "Flying Fox" Cable System

(Des Jennifer Toombs. Litho Questa (50c., $1), D.L.R. (others))

1969 (17 Sept)–**75**. T **52**, **62** and similar designs. Chalk–surfaced paper. W w **12** (upright on 3c., 25c. sideways* on $1 and horiz designs). P 14½×14 (50c.), 14 ($1) or 13 (others).

94	1c. multicoloured	2·25	2·00
	a. Glazed, ordinary paper (9.8.71)	1·25	2·00
	aw. Wmk Crown to right of CA	2·25	2·00
95	2c. multicoloured	25	15
96	3c. multicoloured	25	15
97	4c. multicoloured	2·50	15
98	5c. multicoloured	70	15
	a. Gold (Queens head) omitted	£2000	
99	6c. multicoloured	30	20
100	8c. multicoloured	2·00	20
101	10c. multicoloured	2·00	85
	a. Glazed, ordinary paper (9.8.71)	2·00	3·50
	aw. Wmk Crown to right of CA	6·00	6·50
102	15c. multicoloured	2·25	1·75
	a. Queen's head omitted	£1000	
103	20c. multicoloured	60	40
104	25c. multicoloured	70	40
	w. Wmk inverted		
105	30c. multicoloured	55	45
106	40c. multicoloured	75	60
106a	50c. multicoloured (glazed, ordinary paper) (2.1.73)	2·00	12·00
106b	$1 multicoloured (glazed, ordinary paper) (21.4.75)	5·50	17·00
94/106b Set of 15		20·00	32·00

Designs: Horiz—2c. Captain Bligh and *Bounty* chronometer; 4c. Plans and drawing of *Bounty*; 5c. Breadfruit containers and plant; 6c. Bounty Bay; 8c. Pitcairn longboat; 10c. Ship landing point; 15c. Fletcher Christian's Cave; 20c. Thursday October Christian's House; 30c. Radio Station, Taro Ground; 40c. *Bounty* Bible; 50c. Pitcairn Coat of Arms. Vert—3c. *Bounty* anchor; $1 Queen Elizabeth II.

*The normal sideways watermark shows Crown to left of CA, as seen from the back of the stamp.

The 1c. was reissued in 1974, W w **12** upright.

65 Lantana

69 Band-tailed Hind

(Des Jennifer Toombs. Litho D.L.R.)

1970 (23 Mar). Flowers. T **65** and similar vert designs. Multicoloured. W w **12**. P 14.

107	1c. Type **65**	15	50
108	2c. "Indian Shot"	20	60
109	5c. Pulau	25	70
110	25c. Wild Gladiolus	60	1·00
107/10 Set of 4		1·10	2·50

(Des Jennifer Toombs. Photo Harrison)

1970 (12 Oct). Fish. T **69** and similar horiz designs. Multicoloured. W w **12**. P 14.

111	5c. Type **69**	1·25	1·00
	w. Wmk inverted	8·00	3·00
112	10c. High-finned Rudderfish	1·25	1·00
	w. Wmk inverted	16·00	3·50
113	15c. Elwyn's Wrasse	1·25	1·50
	w. Wmk inverted	9·00	3·50
114	20c. Yellow Wrasse ("Whistling Daughter")	1·75	1·50
	w. Wmk inverted	25·00	8·50
111/14 Set of 4		5·00	4·50

STAMP BOOKLET

1940 (15 Oct). Black on deep green cover. Stapled.

SB1   4s.8d. booklet containing one each ½d., 1d., 1½d., 2d., 3d., 6d., 1s. and 2s.6d. (Nos. 1/5, 6, 7/8) ... £3250

Genuine examples of No. SB1 are interleaved with ordinary kitchen wax-paper, which frequently tones the stamps, and are secured with staples 17 mm long.

The status of other booklets using different size staples or paper fasteners is uncertain although it is believed that some empty booklet covers were available on the island.

Prince Edward Island *see* **Canada**

Qatar

1957. 100 Naye Paise = 1 Rupee 1966. 100 Dirhams = 1 Riyal

The Arab Sheikhdom of Qatar consists of a large peninsula jutting into the Persian Gulf. In 1868, after Qatar had been invaded by Bahrain, a member of the leading Al Thani family was installed as Sheikh and an agreement was made by which he referred to the British Resident all disputes in which the sheikhdom was involved. Qatar was under nominal Turkish suzerainty, and Turkish troops were stationed there from 1871 until August 1915, when the Royal Navy forced them to abandon Doha, the capital, to the sheikh. On 3 November 1916 the sheikhdom entered into special treaty relations with the United Kingdom giving it British naval and military protection from attack. Oil was discovered on the peninsula in January 1940 and was first shipped to Europe at the end of 1949. On the withdrawal of British forces from the Gulf, Qatar declined to join the United Arab Emirates, terminated the Treaty with Great Britain and became fully independent on 3 September 1971.

There was no postal service from Qatar until 18 May 1950. Prior to this date the few foreign residents made their own arrangements for their mail to be carried to Bahrain for onward transmission through the postal service.

The first organised post from the capital, Doha, was an extension of the work in the state by the British Political Officer. From 18 May 1950 British residents were able to send mail via his office. The first three sendings had the Bahrain or British Postal Agencies in Eastern Arabia stamps cancelled by a circular date stamp, but later batches, up to the introduction of the first Doha postmark in July 1950, had the stamps cancelled on arrival at Bahrain.

(two circular DOHA postmark illustrations)

July 1950 Cancellation

1956 Cancellation

The Post Office became a seperate entity in August 1950 when its services were made available to the general public. After initially using the Bahrain surcharges on Great Britain the supply of stamps for the Qatar office was switched to the British Postal Agencies in Eastern Arabia surcharges.

The circular cancellation, dating from July 1950, continued to be used until replaced by a slightly smaller version in early 1956.

A further post office was opened on 1 February 1956 at the Umm Said oil terminal, using its own cancellation.

Both offices were issued with standard oval Registered handstamps, Doha in 1950 and Umm Said in 1956.

1956. Umm Said Cancellation

All stamps to 1960 surcharged on Queen Elizabeth II issues of Great Britain.

QATAR NP 1 NP	QATAR NP 3 NP	QATAR 75 NP
(1)	(2)	(3)

1957 (1 Apr)–**59**.

(a) Nos. 540/2, 543b/8, 551 and 555/6 (St. Edward's Crown wmk), surch as T **1** to **3**

1	**1**	1n.p. on 5d. brown	20	20
2	**2**	3n.p. on ½d. orange-red	40	50
3		6n.p. on 1d. ultramarine	40	30
4		9n.p. on 1½d. green	1·00	25
5		12n.p. on 2d. light red-brown	55	4·00
6		15n.p. on 2½d. carmine-red (I)	15	10
7	**2**	20n.p. on 3d. deep lilac (B.)	15	10
8		25n.p. on 4d. ultramarine	2·75	4·00
9		40n.p. on 6d. reddish purple	15	30
		a. Deep claret (21.7.59)	2·00	10
10		50n.p. on 9d. bronze-green	80	4·00
11	**3**	75n.p. on 1s.3d. green	1·00	6·50
12		1r. on 1s.6d. grey-blue	19·00	10
1/12 Set of 12			23·00	18·00

Designs:—Nos. 1/12, Various portraits of Queen Elizabeth II.

QATAR 2 RUPEES	
QATAR 2 RUPEES	
(4) II	

QATAR 5 RUPEES	
QATAR 5 RUPEES	
(5) II	
QATAR 10 RUPEES	
QATAR 10 RUPEES	
(6) II	

Type I (**4/6**). Type-set overprints. Bold thick letters with sharp corners and straight edges. Bars close together and usually slightly longer than in Type II.

Type II (**4/6**). Plate-printed overprints by Harrison. Thinner letters, rounded corners and rough edges. Bars wider apart.

(b) Nos. 536/8 (St. Edward's Crown wmk) surcharged with T **4/6**

13	2r. on 2s.6d. black-brown (I) (1.4.57)	7·00	7·00
	a. Type II (18.9.57)	15·00	8·00
14	5r. on 5s. rose-red (1) (1.4.57)	7·00	10·00
	a. Type II (18.9.57)	16·00	28·00
15	10r. on 10s. ultramarine (I) (1.4.57)	7·00	16·00
	a. Type II (18.9.57)	55·00	£150
13/15 Set of 3		19·00	30·00
13a/15a Set of 3		75·00	£160

Designs:—No. 13, Carrickfergus Castle; 14, Caernarvon Castle; 15, Edinburgh Castle.

QATAR 15 NP

(7)

1957 (1 Aug). World Scout Jubilee Jamboree. Nos. 557/9 surch in two lines as T **7** (15n.p.) or in three lines (others).

16	15n.p. on 2½d. carmine-red	35	70
17	25n.p. on 4d. ultramarine	35	45
18	75n.p. on 1s.3d. green	40	50
16/18 Set of 3		1·00	1·50

Designs:—No. 16, Scout badge and "Rolling Hitch"; 17, "Scouts coming to Britain"; 18, Globe within a Compass.

1960 (26 Apr–28 Sept). Nos. 570/5 and 579 (Mult Crown wmk) surcharged as T **1** or **2**.

20	**2**	3n.p. on ½d. orange-red (28.9)	1·00	1·75
21		6n.p. on 1d. ultramarine (21.6)	4·50	2·75
22		9n.p. on 1½d. green (28.9)	1·00	1·50
23		12n.p. on 2d. light red-brown (28.9)	7·00	6·50
24	**1**	15n.p. on 2½d. carmine-red (11)	3·50	10
25	**2**	20n.p. on 3d. deep lilac (B.) (28.9)	75	10
26	**1**	40n.p. on 6d. deep claret (21.6)	4·50	2·00
20/6 Set of 7			20·00	13·00

Designs:—Various portraits of Queen Elizabeth II.

Sheikh Ahmad bin Ali al-Thani
24 October 1960–22 February 1972

8 Sheikh Ahmad bin Ali al-Thani

9 Peregrine Falcon

10 Dhow

11 Oil Derrick

12 Mosque

(Des O. C. Meronti (T **8**), M. Goaman (T **9**), M. Farrar Bell (T **10**), J. Constable and O. C. Meronti (T **11/12**). Photo Harrison, (T **8/10**). Recess D.L.R. (T **11/12**))

1961 (2 Sept). P 14½ (5n.p. to 75n.p.) or 13 (1r. to 10r.).

27	**8**	5n.p. carmine	30	15
28		15n.p. black	30	25

29		20n.p. reddish purple	30	15
30		30n.p. deep green	35	30
31	**9**	40n.p. red	4·25	30
32		50n.p. sepia	4·50	40
33	**10**	75n.p. ultramarine	1·60	4·50
34	**11**	1r. scarlet	5·50	35
35		2r. ultramarine	5·50	3·25
36	**12**	5r. bronze-green	38·00	13·00
37		10r. black	75·00	21·00
27/37 Set of 11			£120	40·00

The Qatar Post Department took over the postal services on 23 May 1963.

■ Queensland *see* Australia

■ Rarotonga *see* Cook Islands

Rhodesia

Stamps of BECHUANALAND were used in Matabeleland on the runner post between Gubulawayo and Mafeking (Bechuanaland) from 9 August 1888 until 5 May 1894. Such stamps were cancelled "GUBULAWAYO" or by the barred oval "678" obliteration.

Between 27 June 1890 and 13 May 1892 external mail from Mashonaland was franked with that territory's stamps. A similar arrangement, using the stamps of MOZAMBIQUE existed for the route via Beira inaugurated on 29 August 1891. In both instances the stamps were cancelled by the post offices receiving the mail from Mashonaland. From 14 May until 31 July 1892 letters via Bechuanaland were franked with a combination of B.S.A Company and Bechuanaland issues.

Rhodesia joined the South African Postal Union on 1 August 1892 when its stamps became valid for international mail. Combination frankings with Mozambique stamps continued to be required until April 1894.

For the use of British Central Africa overprints in North-eastern Rhodesia from 1893 to 1899 see NYASALAND.

PRICES FOR STAMPS ON COVER TO 1945	
Nos. 1/7	from × 6
Nos. 8/13	—
Nos. 14/17	from × 2
Nos. 18/24	from × 10
Nos. 25/6	—
Nos. 27/8	from × 7
Nos. 29/35	from × 10
Nos. 36/7	—
Nos. 41/6	from × 6
Nos. 47/50	—
Nos. 51/3	from × 2
Nos. 58/64	from × 3
Nos. 66/72	from × 8
Nos. 73/4	—
Nos. 75/87	from × 6
Nos. 88/93a	—
Nos. 94/9	from × 3
Nos. 100/10	from × 5
Nos. 111/13e	—
Nos. 114/18	from × 7
Nos. 119/21	from × 15
No. 122	from × 3
Nos. 123/5	from × 10
No. 126	from × 20
No. 127	—
Nos. 128/30	from × 15
Nos. 131/3	from × 6
Nos. 134/54	from × 10
Nos. 154a/6b	—
Nos. 167/78	from × 6
Nos. 179/81a	—
Nos. 182/5a	from × 4
Nos. 186/208	from × 8
Nos. 209/41	from × 8
Nos. 242/54a	—
Nos. 255/77	from × 8
Nos. 278/9c	—
Nos. 280/1	from × 15
Nos. 282/310	from × 8
Nos. 311/22	—

A. ISSUES FOR THE BRITISH SOUTH AFRICA COMPANY TERRITORY

    1   **2**   **(3)**

(Recess B.W.)

1892 (2 Jan*)–**93**. Thin wove paper. P 14, 14½.

1	**1**	1d. black	18·00	4·25
2		6d. ultramarine	80·00	26·00
3		6d. deep blue (1893)	50·00	4·25
4		1s. grey-brown	50·00	16·00
5		2s. vermilion	75·00	42·00
6		2s.6d. grey-purple	48·00	55·00
7		2s.6d. lilac (1893)	65·00	55·00
8		5s. orange-yellow	90·00	60·00
9		10s. deep green	£130	£100
10	**2**	£1 deep blue	£325	£170
11		£2 rose-red** (f.c. £20)	£550	£170
12		£5 sage-green (f.c. £50)	£1600	£450
13		£10 brown (f.c. £70)	£2750	£700
1/10 Set of 8			£700	£400

Great caution is needed in buying the high values in either used or unused condition, many stamps offered being revenue stamps cleaned and re-gummed or with forged postmarks.

*Printing of stamps in Types **1**, **2** and **4** commenced in 1890, although none were used for postal purposes before 2 January 1892 when the route to the East Coast was inaugurated.

**For later printings of the £2 see No. 74.

The following sheet watermarks are known on Nos. 1/26: (1) William Collins, Sons & Co's paper watermarked with the firm's monogram, and "PURE LINEN WOVE BANK" in double-lined capitals (1890 and 1891 ptgs). (2) As (1) with "EXTRA STRONG" and "139" added (1892 ptgs). (3) Paper by Wiggins Teape & Co, watermarked "W T & Co" in script letters in double-lined wavy border (1893 ptgs). (4) The same firm's paper, watermarked "1011" in double-lined figures (1894 ptgs except ½d.). (5) "WIGGINS TEAPE & CO LONDON" in double-lined block capitals (1894 ptg of No. 18). Many values can also be found on a slightly thicker paper without wmk, but single specimens are not easily distinguishable.

1892 (2 Jan). Nos. 2 and 4 surch as T **3**.

14	**1**	½d. on 6d. ultramarine	£140	£500
15		2d. on 6d. ultramarine	£190	£700
16		4d. on 6d. ultramarine	£200	£800
17		8d. on 1s. grey-brown	£225	£850
14/17 Set of 4			£650	£2500

Caution is needed in buying these surcharges as both forged surcharges and forged postmarks exist.

   4   **5** (Ends of scrolls behind legs of springboks)

(T **4**. Centre recess; value B.W.)

1892 (2 Jan)–**94**. Thin wove paper (wmks as note after No. 13). P 14, 14½.

18	**4**	½d. dull blue and vermilion	4·50	4·75
19		½d. deep blue and vermilion (1893)	5·00	7·00
20		2d. deep dull green and vermilion	28·00	8·00
21		3d. grey-black and green (8.92)	25·00	4·75
22		4d. chestnut and black	48·00	6·50
23		8d. rose-lake and ultramarine	22·00	24·00
24		8d. red and ultramarine (1892)	17·00	24·00
25		3s. brown and green (1894)	£190	90·00
26		4s. grey-black and vermilion (1893)	48·00	55·00
18/26 Set of 7			£325	£170

(Recess P.B. from the Bradbury Wilkinson plates)

1895. Thick soft wove paper. P 12½.

27	**4**	2d. green and red	32·00	19·00
28		4d. yellow-brown and black	32·00	21·00
		a. Imperf (pair)	£2000	

(T **5**. Centre recess; value typo P.B.)

1896–97. Wove paper. P 14.

(a) Die I. Plates 1 and 2. Small dot to the right of the tail of the right-hand supporter in the coat of arms. Body of lion only partly shaded

29	**5**	1d. scarlet and emerald	40·00	5·50
		a. Carmine-red and emerald		
30		2d. brown and mauve	40·00	2·75
		a. Yellow-brown and mauve	40·00	3·50
31		3d. chocolate and ultramarine	10·00	2·25
32		4d. ultramarine and mauve	55·00	
		a. Imperf between (pair)		
		b. Blue and mauve	45·00	26·00
33		6d. mauve and pink	85·00	27·00
34		8d. green and mauve/buff	19·00	60
		a. Imperf between (pair)		
		b. Imperf (pair)	£4250	
35		1s. green and blue	28·00	3·50
36		3s. green and mauve/blue	90·00	42·00
		a. Imperf (pair)	£13000	
37		4s. orange-red and blue/green	75·00	3·00
29/37 Set of 9			£375	£100

(b) Die II. Plates 3 and 4. No dot. Body of lion heavily shaded all over

41	**5**	½d. slate and violet	4·50	4·00
42		1d. scarlet and emerald	14·00	5·00
43		2d. brown and mauve	30·00	12·00
		a. Yellow-brown and mauve	35·00	14·00
44		4d. ultramarine and mauve	75·00	13·00
		a. Blue and mauve	24·00	50
46		6d. mauve and rose	18·00	1·25
47		2s. indigo and green/buff	55·00	14·00
48		2s.6d. brown and purple/yellow	90·00	65·00
49		5s. chestnut and emerald	65·00	15·00
50		10s. slate and vermilion/rose	£150	75·00
41/50 Set of 9			£400	£160

One Penny   THREE

                         PENCE.

    (6)   **(7)**

(Surch by Bulawayo Chronicle)

1896 (Apr–May). Matabele Rebellion provisionals. Surch with T **6** and **7**.

51	**6**	1d. on 3d. (No. 21)	£600	£750
		a. "P" in "Penny" inverted	£48000	
		b. "y" in "Penny" inverted		
52		1d. on 4s. (No. 26)	£300	£350
		a. "P" in "Penny" inverted	£35000	
		b. "y" in "Penny" inverted	£35000	
		c. Single bar through original value	£1100	£1200
53	**7**	3d. on 5s. (No. 8) (5.96)	£190	£250
		a. "R" in "THREE" inverted	£35000	
		b. "T" in "THREE" inverted	£48000	

Nos. 51 and 52 occur in two settings, one with 9¾ mm between value and upper bar, the other with 11 mm between value and upper bar.

Nos. 54 to 57 are vacant.

BRITISH

SOUTH AFRICA

COMPANY.

    (8)   **9** (Ends of scrolls between legs of springboks)

1896 (22 May–Aug). Cape of Good Hope stamps optd by Argus Printing Co, Cape Town, with T **8**. Wmk Anchor (3d. wmk Crown CA). P 14.

58	**6**	½d. grey-black (No. 48a)	19·00	24·00
59	**17**	1d. rose-red (No. 58)	22·00	28·00
60	**6**	2d. deep bistre (No. 50a)	28·00	14·00
61		3d. pale claret (No. 40)	55·00	75·00
62		4d. blue (No. 51)	35·00	26·00
		a. "COMPANY." omitted	£9500	
63	**4**	6d. deep purple (No. 52a)	70·00	80·00
64	**6**	1s. yellow-ochre (No. 65) (8.96)	£150	£150
58/64 Set of 7			£325	£350

No. 62 also exists with "COMPANY" partially omitted. Examples with the word completely omitted, as No. 62a, are known from positions 1 to 6 of the setting.

Forgeries of this overprint show a narrow final "A" in "AFRICA" and have a rectangular full stop. On the genuine overprint both "As" are the same and the stop is oval.

(T **9**. Eng J. A. C. Harrison (vignette), Bain or Rapkin (£1) (frames). Recess Waterlow.)

1897. P 13½ to 16.

66	**9**	½d. grey-black and purple	7·50	9·50
67		1d. scarlet and emerald	12·00	11·00
68		2d. brown and mauve	26·00	4·25
69		3d. brown-red and slate-blue	10·00	50
		a. Imperf between (vert pair)	£4750	
70		4d. ultramarine and claret	32·00	4·00
		a. Imperf between (horiz pair)	£18000	£18000
71		6d. dull purple and pink	22·00	3·50
72		8d. green and mauve/*buff*	32·00	50
		a. Imperf between (horiz pair)	†	£3750
73		£1 black and red-brown/*green*	£450	£225
66/73 Set of 8			£500	£225

(T **2**. Recess Waterlow.)

1897 (Jan). P 15.

74	**2**	£2 rosy red	£1900	£475

10   **11**

12   **£2.** Re-entry (R. 6/5)

(Recess Waterlow.)

1898–1908. P 13½ to 15½.

75	**10**	½d. dull bluish green	18·00	3·75
		a. Yellow green (1904)	7·00	3·75
		aa. Imperf vert (horiz pair)	£850	
		ab. Imperf (pair)	£900	
		ac. Imperf between (vert pair)	£1600	
76		½d. deep green (shades) (1908)	40·00	4·00
77		1d. rose (shades)	16·00	1·00
		a. Imperf (pair)	£700	£750
		b. Imperf between (vert pair)	£550	
		c. Imperf between (horiz pair)	—	£950
78		1d. red (shades) (1905)	12·00	70
		a. Imperf vert (horiz pair)	£400	£450
		ab. Imperf horiz (vert pair)	£1000	
		b. Imperf (pair)	£600	£600
		c. Imperf between (horiz pair)	£800	£500
		d. Imperf between (vert strip of 4)	£2750	
79		2d. brown	14·00	2·75
80		2½d. dull blue (shades)	25·00	2·00
		a. Imperf vert (horiz pair)	£950	£1100
		b. Grey-blue (shades) (1903)	25·00	1·75
81		3d. claret	22·00	80
		a. Imperf between (vert pair)	£700	
82		4d. olive	20·00	55
		a. Imperf between (vert pair)	£700	
83		6d. reddish purple	27·00	3·50
		a. Reddish mauve (1902)	32·00	7·50
84	**11**	1s. bistre	40·00	5·50
		a. Imperf between (vert pair)	£3250	
		ab. Imperf between (horiz pair)	£3750	
		b. Deep olive-bistre (1907)	£350	
		bc. Imperf (pair)	£3250	
		bd. Imperf between (horiz pair)	£4500	
		c. Bistre-brown (1908)	75·00	18·00
		d. Brownish yellow (1908)	40·00	15·00
85		2s.6d. bluish grey (11.06)	75·00	2·25
		a. Imperf between (vert pair)	£1100	£500
86		3s. deep violet (1902)	40·00	4·25
		a. Deep bluish violet (1908)	85·00	17·00
87		5s. brown-orange	70·00	28·00
88		7s.6d. black (11.01)	£110	35·00
89		10s. grey-green	65·00	2·75
90	**12**	£1 greyish red-purple (P 15½) (7.01)	£375	£170
		a. Perf 14. Blackish purple (1902)	£650	£160
91		£2 brown (5.08)	£130	6·50
		a. Re-entry	£650	£400
92		£5 deep blue (7.01) (f.c. £25)	£3250	£2500
93		£10 lilac (7.01) (f.c. £50)	£3500	£2250
93a		£20 yellow-bistre (1901?) (f.c. £100)	£16000	
75/90 Set of 14			£750	£200
80s/1s, 85s/6s, 88s/93s Perf "SPECIMEN" Set of 10			£900	

A £100 cherry-red, perf 13½, was ordered in June 1901, a number of mint, together with several examples showing fiscal cancellations being known (*Price, £1500 with fiscal cancellation*).

---

13 Victoria Falls   **5d.** Bird in tree (R. 2/5)

RHODESIA.

(14)

(Recess Waterlow)

1905 (13 July). Visit of British Association and Opening of Victoria Falls Bridge. P 14½ to 15 (5d.), 14 (others).

94	**13**	1d. red	9·00	11·00
		a. Perf 14½ to 15	22·00	22·00
95		2½d. deep blue	19·00	12·00
		a. Perf 14½ to 15	32·00	20·00
96		5d. claret	42·00	60·00
		a. Bird in tree	£225	
		b. Perf 14	80·00	£100
		ba. Bird in tree	£350	
		sa. Optd "SPECIMEN"	£170	
97		1s. blue-green	45·00	50·00
		a. Imperf (pair)	£28000	
		b. Imperf between (horiz pair)	£35000	
		c. Imperf between (vert pair)	£38000	
		d. Imperf vert (horiz pair)	£29000	
		e. Perf 14½ to 15	£550	£475
98		2s.6d. black	£140	£170
99		5s. violet	£140	48·00
		a. Perf 14½ to 15	£550	
94/9 Set of 6			£350	£325
94s/9s Optd or Perf (5d.) "SPECIMEN" Set of 6			£425	

Nos. 96a and 96ba are as illustrated. Lesser variations in a similar position exist on all stamps in row 3.

1909 (15 Apr)–**12**. Optd as T **14**. P 13½ to 15.

100	**10**	½d. green to deep green	6·00	3·25
		a. No stop	75·00	48·00
		b. Yellow-green (1911)	45·00	32·00
101		1d. carmine-rose	11·00	1·50
		a. No stop	90·00	35·00
		b. Imperf between (horiz pair)	£450	
		c. Deep carmine-rose	12·00	1·50
		cd. Imperf between (horiz pair)	£450	
102		2d. brown	7·00	9·00
		a. No stop	£140	£110
103		2½d. pale dull blue	4·75	2·00
		a. No stop	65·00	30·00
104		3d. claret	4·75	2·50
		a. No stop	£170	75·00
		b. Opt inverted	†	18·00
		c. Opt double	†	£1100
105		4d. olive	17·00	4·00
		a. No stop	£100	65·00
		b. Opt inverted	†	15·00
106		6d. reddish purple	11·00	11·00
		a. No stop	90·00	90·00
		b. Reddish mauve		
		c. Dull purple	27·00	11·00
		ca. No stop	£140	75·00
107	**11**	1s. bistre	38·00	
		a. No stop	£170	
		b. Bistre-brown		
		ba. No stop		
		c. Deep brownish bistre	18·00	11·00
		ca. No stop	£110	60·00
108		2s.6d. bluish grey	40·00	13·00
		a. No stop	£140	75·00
		b. Opt inverted	†	24·00
109		3s. deep violet	29·00	13·00
110		5s. orange	55·00	85·00
		a. No stop	£180	£275
111		7s.6d. black	£110	38·00
112		10s. dull green	75·00	23·00
		a. No stop	£400	£250
113	**12**	£1 grey-purple	£200	£110
		a. Vert pair, lower stamp without opt	£38000	
		b. Opt in violet	£375	£190
113c		£2 brown (f.c. £50)	£5000	£325
		ca. Re-entry	—	£1200
113d		£2 rosy brown (bluish paper) (P 14½×15) (1912) (f.c. £50)	£4000	£300
		da. Imperf between (horiz pair)	£10000	£1200
113e		£5 deep blue (bluish paper) (f.c. £100)	£9000	£5000
100/13 Set of 14			£500	£275
100s/13s Perf "SPECIMEN" Set of 14			£425	

In some values the no stop variety occurs on every stamp in a vertical row of a sheet, in other values only once in a sheet. Other varieties, such as no serif to the right of apex of "A", no serif to top of "E", etc., exist in some values.

No. 113a comes from a sheet with the overprint omitted from the bottom row.

RHODESIA.
5d
(15)

RHODESIA.
TWO SHILLINGS.
(16)

1909 (Apr)–**11**. Surch as T **15** and **16** (2s.) in black.

114	**10**	5d. on 6d. reddish purple	15·00	22·00
		a. Surcharge in violet	90·00	
		b. Reddish mauve		
		c. Dull purple	26·00	22·00
116	**11**	7½d. on 2s.6d. bluish grey	6·50	3·75
		a. Surcharge in violet	26·00	10·00
		ab. Surch double	†	£6500
117		10d. on 3s. deep violet	18·00	19·00
		a. Surcharge in violet	8·50	4·25

118		2s. on 5s. orange	16·00	8·00
114/18 Set of 4			40·00	35·00
114s/18s Perf "SPECIMEN" Set of 4			£180	

In the 7½d. and 10d. surcharges the bars are spaced as in T **16**.

17   **18**

(Recess Waterlow)

1910 (11 Nov)–**13**.

(a) P 14

119	**17**	½d. yellow-green	15·00	2·25
		a. Imperf between (horiz pair)	£28000	
120		½d. bluish green	38·00	4·75
		a. Imperf (pair)	£15000	£7500
121		½d. olive-green	45·00	5·50
122		½d. dull green	70·00	80·00
123		1d. bright carmine	35·00	5·50
		a. Imperf between (vert pair)	£22000	£14000
		b. Imperf between (horiz pair)	£22000	£14000
124		1d. carmine-lake	80·00	4·00
125		1d. rose-red	50·00	3·75
126		2d. black and grey	65·00	4·00
127		2d. black-purple and slate-grey	£160	£750
128		2d. black and slate-grey	65·00	7·50
129		2d. black and slate	80·00	10·00
130		2d. black and grey-black	95·00	24·00
131		2½d. ultramarine	35·00	12·00
131a		2½d. bright ultramarine	27·00	12·00
132		2½d. dull blue	35·00	16·00
133		2½d. chalky blue	28·00	24·00
134		3d. purple and ochre	50·00	55·00
135		3d. purple and yellow-ochre	65·00	22·00
136		3d. magenta and yellow-ochre	£200	17·00
137		3d. violet and ochre	£150	£100
138		4d. greenish black and orange	£120	£120
139		4d. brown-purple and orange	90·00	70·00
140		4d. black and orange	50·00	28·00
141		5d. purple-brown and olive-green	65·00	75·00
141a		5d. purple-brown and olive-yellow	50·00	65·00
		ab. Error. Purple-brown and ochre	£650	£150
143		5d. lake-brown and olive	£325	65·00
143a		5d. lake-brown and green (9.12)	£24000	£1600
144		6d. red-brown and mauve	50·00	50·00
145		6d. brown and mauve	65·00	26·00
145a		6d. bright chestnut and mauve	£700	70·00
146		8d. black and purple	£6500	
147		8d. dull purple and purple	£180	£120
148		8d. greenish black and purple	£180	£100
149		10d. scarlet and reddish mauve	50·00	50·00
150		10d. carmine and deep purple	£650	60·00
151		1s. grey-black and deep blue-green	65·00	40·00
151a		1s. black and deep blue-green	£250	55·00
152		1s. black and pale blue-green	70·00	24·00
152a		1s. purple-black and blue-green	£250	80·00
153		2s. black and ultramarine	£120	75·00
154		2s. black and dull blue	£1200	85·00
154a		2s. purple-black and ultramarine	£3000	£225
155		2s.6d. black and lake	£400	£450
155a		2s.6d. black and crimson	£350	£300
156		2s.6d. sepia and deep crimson	£425	£375
156a		2s.6d. bistre-brown and crimson	£1100	£700
157		2s.6d. black and rose-carmine	£350	£425
158		3s. green and violet (shades)	£250	£200
158a		3s. bright green and magenta	£1300	£850
159		5s. vermilion and deep green	£325	£425
160		5s. scarlet and pale yellow-green	£350	£200
160a		5s. crimson and yellow-green	£300	£200
160b		7s.6d. carmine and pale blue	£650	£425
161		7s.6d. carmine and light blue	£900	£1200
		sa. Opt "SPECIMEN." double	£3500	
162		7s.6d. carmine and bright blue	£4500	£1400
163		10s. deep myrtle and orange	£650	£300
164		10s. blue-green and orange	£425	£500
165		£1 carmine-red and bluish black	£1700	£700
166		£1 rose-scarlet and bluish black	£1600	£375
166a		£1 crimson and slate-black	£2000	£2000
		b. Scarlet and reddish mauve (prepared for use but not issued)	£10000	

(b) P 15

167	**17**	½d. blue-green	£300	13·00
168		½d. yellow-green	£350	11·00
169		½d. apple-green	£600	30·00
170		1d. carmine	£300	8·50
170a		1d. carmine-lake	£450	20·00
170b		1d. rose-carmine	£350	12·00
171		2d. black and grey-black	£900	50·00
171a		2d. black and grey	£900	50·00
171b		2d. black and slate	£1000	50·00
172		2½d. ultramarine (shades)	75·00	42·00
173		3d. purple and yellow-ochre	£9000	90·00
173a		3d. claret and pale yellow-ochre	£4000	75·00
174		4d. black and orange (shades)	60·00	75·00
175		5d. lake-brown and olive	£800	80·00
176		6d. brown and mauve	£425	60·00
177		1s. black and blue-green (shades)	£1300	60·00
178		2s. black and dull blue	£2500	£350
179		£1 red and black	£18000	£3250

(c) P 14×15 (½d., 3d., 1s.) or 15×14 (1d., 4d.)

179a	**17**	½d. yellow-green	†	£3500
179b		1d. carmine	†	£7000
180		3d. purple and ochre	£7500	£300
181		4d. black and orange	£450	
181a		1s. black and blue-green	£30000	£2750

(d) P 13½

182	**17**	½d. yellow-green	£300	55·00
182a		½d. green	£350	60·00
183		1d. bright carmine	£2000	50·00
184		2½d. ultramarine (shades)	38·00	70·00
185		8d. black and purple	60·00	£250
185a		8d. grey-purple and dull purple	£375	£450
119s/85s Optd "SPECIMEN." (all perf 14 except 2½d. and 8d. perf 13½) Set of 18			£3500	

Plate varieties in T **17** are:—½d., double dot below "D" in right-hand value tablet (R. 3/9) (from £550 un. £375 used); 2d. to £1 excluding 2½d., straight stroke in Queen's right ear known as the "gash in ear" variety (R. 1/2) (from 3 to 5 times normal).

Stamps from the above and the next issue are known compound perf with 14 or 15 on one side only or on adjoining sides but we no longer list them.

Examples of some values are known with a forged registered Bulawayo postmark dated "JA 10 11".

(Recess Waterlow)

1913 (1 Sept)–**19**. No wmk.

(i) From single working plates

(a) P 14

186	**18**	½d. blue-green	13·00	2·25
187		½d. deep green	10·00	2·25
		a. Imperf horiz (vert pair)	£950	
		b. Imperf between (vert strip of 5)	£4000	
		c. Imperf between (vert strip of 6)	£4750	
188		½d. yellow-green	23·00	2·25
		a. Imperf between (horiz pair)	£1100	
188b		½d. dull green	14·00	2·25
		ba. Imperf vert (horiz pair)	£1000	£1000
		bb. Imperf between (horiz pair)	£1300	
189		½d. bright green	28·00	2·25
		a. Imperf between (vert pair)	£1800	
190		1d. rose-carmine	8·50	2·25
		a. Imperf between (horiz pair)	£1200	£950
191		1d. carmine-red (shades)	14·00	2·75
		a. Imperf between (pair)	£1700	
192		1d. brown-red	4·75	3·75
193		1d. red	9·00	2·25
		a. Imperf between (horiz pair)	£1100	
194		1d. scarlet	25·00	2·50
		a. Imperf between (horiz pair)	£1400	
195		1d. rose-red	13·00	2·25
		a. Imperf between (horiz pair)	£1000	£1000
		b. Imperf between (vert pair)	£3000	
196		1d. rosine	£500	20·00
197		1½d. brown-ochre (1919)	5·50	2·25
		a. Imperf between (horiz pair)	£850	£850
198		1½d. bistre-brown (18.5.17)	7·00	2·25
		a. Imperf between (horiz pair)	£850	£850
199		1½d. drab-brown (1917)	8·00	2·25
		a. Imperf between (horiz pair)	£850	
		b. Imperf between (vert pair)	£2500	
200		2½d. deep blue	10·00	48·00
201		2½d. bright blue	10·00	42·00

(b) P 15

202	**18**	½d. blue-green	9·50	30·00
203		½d. green	14·00	24·00
204		1d. rose-red	£600	22·00
		a. Imperf between (horiz pair)	£18000	
205		1d. brown-red	7·50	10·00
206		1½d. bistre-brown (1919)	50·00	7·00
		a. Imperf between (horiz pair)	£24000	
206b		1½d. brown-ochre (1917)	50·00	14·00
207		2½d. deep blue	24·00	70·00
208		2½d. bright blue	16·00	65·00

(c) P 14×15

208a	**18**	½d. green	£7500	£200

(d) P 15×14

208b	**18**	½d. green	£8000	£350
208c		1½d. drab-brown		

(e) P 13½

208d	**18**	1d. red (1914)	†	£550

Die I   Die II   Die III

The remaining values were printed from double, i.e. head and duty, plates. There are at least four different head plates made from three different dies, which may be distinguished as follows:—

Die I. The King's left ear is neither shaded nor outlined; no outline to top of cap. Shank of anchor in cap badge is complete.

Die II. The ear is shaded all over, but has no outline. The top of the cap has a faint outline. Anchor as Die I.

Die III. The ear is shaded and outlined; a heavy continuous outline round the cap. Shank of anchor is broken just below the lowest line which crosses it.

(ii) Printed from double plates. Head Die I

(a) P 14

209	**18**	2d. black and grey	24·00	12·00
210		3d. black and yellow	85·00	24·00
211		4d. black and orange-red	15·00	45·00
212		4d. black and green	8·00	25·00
213		6d. black and mauve	£250	32·00
213a		8d. violet and green	£5500	
214		2s. black and brown	£160	£120

(b) P 15

215	**18**	3d. black and yellow	10·00	28·00
216		4d. black and orange-red	£170	30·00
217		6d. black and mauve	13·00	14·00
217a		8d. violet and green	£22000	£22000
218		2s. black and brown	21·00	65·00

(iii) Head Die II

(a) P 14

219	**18**	2d. black and grey	25·00	9·50
220		2d. black and brownish grey	75·00	15·00
221		3d. black and deep yellow	60·00	14·00
222		3d. black and yellow	85·00	14·00
223		3d. black and buff	17·00	14·00
224		4d. black and orange-red	40·00	17·00
225		4d. black and deep orange-red	25·00	17·00
226		5d. black and grey-green	28·00	55·00
227		5d. black and bright green	26·00	55·00
228		6d. black and mauve	50·00	7·50
229		6d. black and purple	85·00	8·50
230		8d. violet and green	22·00	75·00
231		10d. blue and carmine-red	32·00	55·00

232		1s. black and greenish blue	60·00	55·00
233		1s. black and turquoise-blue	21·00	22·00
234		2s. black and brown	£100	19·00
235		2s. black and yellow-brown	£375	50·00
236		2s.6d. indigo and grey-brown	85·00	60·00
236a		2s.6d. pale blue and brown	£1300	80·00
236b		3s. brown and blue	£120	£140
237		3s. chestnut and bright blue	£130	£170
238		5s. blue and yellow-green	£170	£120
239		5s. blue and blue-green	95·00	£100
240		7s.6d. blackish purple and slate-black	£350	£400
241		10s. crimson and yellow-green	£200	£350
242		£1 black and purple	£425	£650
243		£1 black and violet	£450	£600

(b) P 15

244	**18**	2d. black and grey	17·00	30·00
245		4d. black and deep orange-vermilion	£1600	£300
246		8d. violet and green	£200	£170
247		10d. blue and red	18·00	50·00
248		1s. black and greenish blue	75·00	26·00
249		2s.6d. indigo and grey-brown	55·00	£100
250		3s. chocolate and blue	£750	£300
251		5s. blue and yellow-green	£225	£250
251a		5s. blue and blue-green	£2250	
252		7s.6d. blackish purple and slate-black	£160	£275
253		10s. red and green	£225	£375
		a. Frame double, one albino	£650	
254		£1 black and purple	£1800	£1600
254a		£1 black and deep purple	£3000	£2500

186s, 190s, 198s, 208s, 209s, 211s/12s, 215s, 217s/18s, 230s, 232s, 237s/8s, 240s/2s, 247s, 249s Optd "SPECIMEN" Set of 19 ... £2750

(iv) Head Die III (1919). Toned paper, yellowish gum

(a) P 14

255	**18**	2d. black and brownish grey	22·00	6·50
256		2d. black and grey-black	15·00	3·50
		a. Imperf between (horiz pair)	£7000	
		b. Imperf between (horiz strip of 3)	£16000	£16000
		c. Imperf vert (horiz pair)	£6500	£6500
257		2d. black and grey	21·00	15·00
258		2d. black and sepia	70·00	17·00
259		3d. black and yellow	21·00	4·25
260		3d. black and ochre	24·00	5·00
261		4d. black and orange-red	27·00	13·00
262		4d. black and dull red	25·00	18·00
263		5d. black and pale green	13·00	50·00
		a. Imperf between (horiz strip of 3)	£38000	
264		5d. black and green	13·00	50·00
265		6d. black and reddish mauve	22·00	8·50
		a. Imperf between (horiz pair)	£26000	
266		6d. black and dull mauve		8·50
267		8d. mauve and dull blue-green	30·00	70·00
268		8d. mauve and greenish blue	27·00	70·00
		a. Imperf vert (horiz pair)	£16000	
269		10d. indigo and carmine	25·00	55·00
270		10d. blue and red	23·00	60·00
271		1s. black and greenish blue	21·00	23·00
272		1s. black and pale blue-green	15·00	17·00
272a		1s. black and light blue	21·00	27·00
272b		1s. black and green	85·00	60·00
273		2s. black and brown	26·00	22·00
		aa. Imperf between (vert pair)	†	£42000
273a		2s. black and yellow-brown	£4250	£180
274		2s.6d. dp ultramarine and grey-brn	55·00	80·00
274a		2s.6d. pale blue and pale bistre-brown (shades)	£130	80·00
274b		3s. chestnut and light blue	£275	£180
275		5s. deep blue and blue-green (shades)	£150	85·00
276		5s. blue and blue-grn (shades)	£150	85·00
276a		7s.6d. maroon and slate-black	£900	£1400
277		10s. carmine-lake and yellow-green	£400	£275
278		£1 black and bright purple	£550	£700
279		£1 black and deep purple	£600	£700
279a		£1 black and violet-indigo	£700	£800
279b		£1 black and deep violet	£650	£700

(b) P 15

279c	**18**	2d. black and brownish grey	£5500	£400

Half Penny (19)   Half-Penny. (20)

1917 (15 Aug). No. 190 surch at the Northern Rhodesian Administrative Press, Livingstone, with T **19**, in violet or violet-black.

280	**18**	½d. on 1d. rose-carmine (shades)	2·50	10·00
		a. Surch inverted	£1200	£1400
		b. Letters "n n" spaced wider	11·00	38·00
		c. Letters "n y" spaced wider	7·50	28·00

The setting was in two rows of ten repeated three times in the sheet. The two colours of the surcharge occur on the same sheet.

1917 (22 Sept). No. 190 surch as T **20** (new setting with hyphen, and full stop after "Penny"), in deep violet.

281	**18**	½d. on 1d. rose-carmine (shades)	2·75	9·50

1922–24. New printings on white paper with clear white gum.

(i) Single working plates

(a) P 14

282	**18**	½d. dull green (1922)	5·50	11·00
		a. Imperf between (vert pair)	£3000	£2000
283		½d. deep blue-green (1922)	5·50	12·00
284		1d. bright rose (1922)	13·00	10·00
285		1d. bright rose-scarlet (1923)	13·00	10·00
		a. Imperf between (horiz pair)	£2000	
		b. Imperf between (vert pair)	£3000	
286		1d. aniline red (8.24) (toned paper)	20·00	24·00
287		1½d. brown-ochre (1923)	12·00	7·50
		a. Imperf between (vert pair)	£3000	£1900

(b) P 15

288	**18**	½d. dull green (1923)	50·00	
289		1d. bright rose-scarlet (1923)	50·00	
290		1½d. brown-ochre (1923)	50·00	

(ii) Double plates. Head Die III

(a) P 14

291	**18**	2d. black and grey-purple (1922)	18·00	11·00
292		2d. black and slate-purple (1923)	13·00	16·00
293		3d. black and yellow (1922)	20·00	48·00
294		4d. black and orange-vermilion (1922–3)	29·00	60·00
295		6d. jet-black and lilac (1922–3)	11·00	12·00
296		8d. mauve and pale blue-green (1922)	45·00	90·00
297		8d. violet and grey-green (1923)	55·00	90·00
298		10d. bright ultramarine and red (1922)	24·00	70·00
299		10d. bright ultramarine and carmine-red (1923)	35·00	70·00
300		1s. black and dull blue (1922–3)	18·00	25·00
		a. Imperf between (horiz pair)	£30000	
		b. Imperf between (vert pair)	£25000	
301		2s. black and brown (1922–3)	27·00	60·00
302		2s.6d. ultramarine and sepia (1922)	65·00	£100
303		2s.6d. violet-blue and grey-brown (1923)	80·00	£110
304		3s. red-brown and turquoise-blue (1922)	£130	£170
305		3s. red-brown and grey-blue (1923)	£140	£190
306		5s. bright ultramarine and emerald (1922)	£160	£190
307		5s. deep blue and bright green (1923)	£170	£190
308		7s.6d. brown-purple and slate (1922)	£250	£425
309		10s. crimson and bright yellow-green (1922)	£275	£325
310		10s. carmine and yellow-green (1923)	£300	£375
311		£1 black and magenta (1922)	£700	£900
311a		£1 black and deep magenta (1923)	£1000	£1300

(b) P 15 (1923)

312	**18**	2d. black and slate-purple	55·00	
313		4d. black and orange-vermilion	55·00	
314		6d. jet-black and lilac	70·00	
315		8d. violet and grey-green	75·00	
316		10d. bright ultramarine and carmine-red	85·00	
317		1s. black and dull blue	95·00	
318		2s. black and brown		£140
319		2s.6d. violet-blue and grey-brown		£150
320		3s. red-brown and grey-blue		£190
321		5s. deep blue and bright green		£325
322		£1 black and deep magenta		£1100

The 1922 printing shows the mesh of the paper very clearly through the gum. In the 1923 printing the gum is very smooth and the mesh of the paper is not so clearly seen. Where date is given as "(1922–23)" two printings were made, which do not differ sufficiently in colour to be listed separately.

Nos. 288/90 and 312/22 were never sent out to Rhodesia, but were issued in London. Any used copies could, therefore, only have been obtained by favour.

Southern Rhodesia, that part of the Company's territory south of the River Zambesi, became a self-governing colony on 1 October 1923. British South Africa Company rule continued in Northern Rhodesia until the administration was transferred to the Colonial Office on 1 April 1924.

The current stamps of Rhodesia, the Admiral series first issued in 1913, continued to be used in Southern Rhodesia until 1 April 1924 (invalidated 1 May 1924) and in Northern Rhodesia until 1 April 1925 (invalidated 30 September 1925).

TELEGRAPH STAMPS

Stamps were prepared by the Reuters agent in Bulawayo, Capt. C.L. Norris-Newman to cover the cost of sending messages to the northern end of the telegraph line, then under construction from Tati towards Bulawayo.

T **1**

T **2**

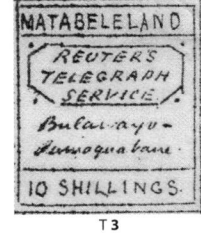

T **3**

1894 (28 Mar). Cyclostyled. Imperf.

T1	T **1**	2s.6d. black	£550	£850
		a. Vert se-tenant strip of 3	£2750	†
T2		5s. black	£550	£950
T3	T **3**	10s. black	£500	£1100

These stamps were produced from a hand-drawn stencil in sheets of 18 (6×3) with the three values se-tenant. The 10s. value (top row, inscribed "Bulawayo-Ramaguabane") was issued first, while the distance to the construction point was 96 miles. The 5s. value (middle row, inscribed "Bulawayo-Mangwe") came into use when the distance was reduced to 60 miles. The 2s.6d. value (bottom row, inscribed "Bulawayo-Fig Tree") was used only in the last phase, as the line neared Bulawayo, Fig Tree being 29 miles from Bulawayo. In June 1894 the Post Office took over the service and the stamps were withdrawn.

Used stamps were cancelled in blue crayon or ink with Capt. Norris-Newman's initials and the date.

For issues from 1924 to 1964 see SOUTHERN RHODESIA.

In October 1964 Southern Rhodesia was renamed Rhodesia.

RHODESIA

59 "Telecommunications" **60** Bangala Dam

(Des V. Whiteley. Photo Harrison)

1965 (17 May). ITU Centenary. P 14½.

351	**59**	6d. violet and light yellow-olive	1·75	45
352		1s.3d. violet and lilac	1·75	45
353		2s.6d. violet and light brown......	6·00	6·50
351/3	*Set of 3*		8·50	6·75

(Des V. Whiteley. Photo Harrison)

1965 (19 July). Water Conservation. T **60** and similar vert designs. Multicoloured. P 14.

354		3d. Type **60**	30	10
355		4d. Irrigation canal	1·50	2·00
356		2s.6d. Cutting sugar cane	2·25	4·50
354/6	*Set of 3*		3·50	6·00

63 Sir Winston Churchill, Quill, Sword and Houses of Parliament

(Des H. Baxter. Photo Harrison)

1965 (16 Aug). Churchill Commemoration. P 14½.

357	**63**	1s.3d. black and bright blue..................	70	35

UNILATERAL DECLARATION OF INDEPENDENCE

Independence was declared by Rhodesia on 11 November 1965 but this was not recognised by the British Government. Following a conference in London during 1979 it was agreed that the British Government should resume control, pending elections to he held in February 1980.

After the elections Rhodesia became an independent republic within the Commonwealth on 18 April 1980, as ZIMBABWE.

64 Coat of Arms

(Des C. Hartley. Litho Mardon Printers, Salisbury)

1965 (8 Dec). "Independence". P 11.

358	**64**	2s.6d. multicoloured..................................	15	15
		a. Imperf (pair).................................	£900	

**INDEPENDENCE
11th November
1965**

**INDEPENDENCE
11th November 1965** = **5/-**
(**65**) (**66**)

1966 (17 Jan).

*(a) Nos. 92/105 of Southern Rhodesia optd with T **65** or larger (5s. to £1) by Mardon Printers, Salisbury*

359		½d. yellow, yellow-green and light blue	10	10
		a. Pair, one stamp without opt...............	£7500	
360		1d. reddish violet and yellow-ochre......	10	10
361		2d. violet and deep violet......	10	10
362		3d. chocolate and pale blue......	10	10
363		4d. yellow-orange and deep green......	15	10
364		6d. carmine-red, yellow and deep dull green......	15	10
		a. Vertical strip of 6, bottom 3 stamps without opt	£4500	
365		9d. red-brown, yellow and olive-green..	30	10
		a. Opt double......	£800	
		b. Vertical strip of 6, bottom 2 stamps without opt	£4500	
366		1s. blue-green and ochre......	40	10
		a. Opt double......	£800	
		b. Vertical strip of 6, bottom 4 stamps without opt	£4500	
367		1s.3d. red, violet and yellow-green......	50	50
368		2s. blue and ochre......	60	3·25
		a. Dot over "IA"......	12·00	
369		2s.6d. ultramarine and vermilion......	60	1·00
370		5s. light brown, bistre-yellow and light blue......	2·00	5·50
		a. Opt double......	£850	
371		10s. black, yellow-ochre, light blue and carmine-red......	4·00	2·25
		a. Extra "feather"......	40·00	
372		£1 brown, yellow-green, buff and salmon-pink......	1·25	2·25
		*(b) No. 357 surch with T **66***		
373		5s. on 1s.3d. black and bright blue (R.)......	6·50	14·00
		a. "5/-" omitted......		
359/73	*Set of 15*		15·00	26·00

Owing to the existence of forgeries, the errors should only be purchased when accompanied by a certificate of genuineness. Unique pairs of the 1d and 3d exist with the overprint omitted from one stamp, but both are defective. Other overprint errors exist from the clandestine use of the original settings.

67 Emeralds **68** Zeederberg Coach, *circa* 1895

(Des V. Whiteley. Photo Harrison)

1966 (9 Feb). As Nos. 92/105, but inscr "RHODESIA" as T **67**. Some designs and colours changed. P 14½ (1d. to 4d.), 13½×13 (6d. to 2s.6d) or 14½×14 (5s. to £1).

374		1d. reddish violet and yellow-ochre......	10	10
375		2d. yellow-orange and deep green (as No. 96)......	10	10
		a. Yellow-orange omitted..............	£3250	
376		3d. chocolate and pale blue......	10	10
		a. Chocolate omitted......	£7000	
		b. Pale blue omitted......	£5000	
377	**67**	4d. emerald and sepia......	1·75	10
378	**50**	6d. carmine-red, yellow and deep dull green......	15	10
379	—	9d. yellow and deep violet (as No. 94)......	60	20
380	**45**	1s. yellow, yellow-green and light blue......	15	10
381	—	1s.3d. blue and ochre (as No. 101)......	25	15
		a. Ochre omitted......	£4000	
382	—	1s.6d. red-brown, yellow and olive-green (as No. 98)......	2·25	25
383	—	2s. red, violet and yellow-green (as No. 100)......	60	2·50
384	—	2s.6d. blue, vermilion and turquoise-blue......	1·50	20
385	**56**	5s. light brown, bistre-yellow and light blue......	1·00	90
386	—	10s. black, yellow-ochre, light blue and carmine-red......	4·25	3·75
387	**58**	£1 brown, yellow-green, buff and salmon-pink......	3·25	7·50
374/87	*Set of 14*		14·00	14·00

Nos. 379/80 are in larger format, as T **50**.
No. 374 exists in coils constructed from normal sheets. Coil-vending machines were withdrawn from service in 1967.
No. 375a occurred on single rows from two separate sheets, No. 376a in the bottom row of a sheet and No. 376b in the top two rows of a sheet and No. 381a in the third vertical row on two sheets.
For stamps printed by lithography, see Nos. 397/407.

PRINTERS. All the following stamps were printed by lithography by Mardon Printers, Salisbury.

(Des V. Whiteley (Nos. 388/90))

1966 (2 May). 28th Congress of Southern Africa Philatelic Federation ("Rhopex"). T **68** and similar horiz designs. P 14½.

388	3d. multicoloured......	20	10
389	9d. grey-buff, sepia and grey-green........	20	25
390	1s.6d. pale blue and black......	30	35
391	2s.6d. salmon-pink, pale dull grn and blk...	40	1·00
388/91	*Set of 4*	1·00	1·50
MS392	126×84 mm. Nos. 388/91 (*toned paper*)......	4·00	11·00
	a. White paper.................................	6·50	13·00

Designs:—9d. Sir Rowland Hill; 1s.6d. The Penny Black; 2s.6d. Rhodesian stamp of 1892 (No. 12).
The 3d., 2s.6d. and miniature sheet exist imperforate from sheets prepared for presentation purposes.

69 de Havilland DH.89 Dragon Rapide (1946) **70** Kudu

1966 (1 June). 20th Anniversary of Central African Airways. T **69** and similar horiz designs. P 14½×14.

393	6d. black, blue, blue and green............	1·00	35
394	1s.3d. blue, yellow-orange, black and green	1·00	40
395	2s.6d. blue, yellow, black and green......	1·25	1·50
396	5s. black and blue......	1·75	4·50
393/6	*Set of 4*	4·50	6·00

Aircraft:—1s.3d. Douglas DC-3 (1953); 2s.6d. Vickers Viscount 748 Matopos (1956); 5s. BAC One Eleven 200.
The 6d., 2s.6d. and 5s. values exist imperforate from sheets prepared for presentation purposes.

1966–68. As Nos. 374/87 but litho. P 14½ (1d. to 2s.) or 14½×14 (others).

397	1d. reddish violet and yellow-ochre (*shades*) (2.6.66)......	15	10
398	2d. orange and green (1.11.67)......	1·00	65
399	3d. chocolate-brown and pale greenish blue (29.1.68)......	2·25	10
400	4d. emerald, bistre-brown and drab (21.9.66)......	65	10
401	6d. carmine-red, yellow and olive-grey (1.11.66)......	60	50
402	9d. yellow and light violet (20.11.67)......	2·25	10
403	1s.3d. blue and ochre (9.11.66)......	1·00	30
404	2s. dull red, violet and sage-green (18.7.66)......	1·00	3·50
405	5s. yellow-brown, deep bistre-yellow and light blue (25.6.66)......	1·50	4·00
406	10s. black, buff, light blue and carmine-red (10.8.66)......	6·00	13·00
407	£1 pale brown, yellow-green, brown-ochre and salmon (10.8.66)......	6·00	19·00
397/407	*Set of 11*	20·00	35·00

In addition to the change in printing process from photogravure to lithography and the difference in perforation in the 6d. to 2s. values (14½ instead of 13½×13) and shade variations, the oval portrait frame is larger (and in some values thicker) in the 1d. to 2s., and in the 1s.3d. the Queen's head is also larger.
Trial printings, made in June 1966, exist of the 5s., 10s. and £1 values on a slightly thinner paper. These are rare.
The 1d., 3d. and 5s. values exist imperforate from sheets prepared for presentation purposes.

1967–68. Dual Currency Issue. As Nos. 376, 380 and 382/4 but value in decimal currency in addition as in T **70**. P 14½. White gum (No. 408) or cream gum (others).

408		3d./2½c. chocolate-brown and pale greenish blue (14.3.67)......	50	15
409		1s./10c. yellow, green and greenish blue (1.11.67)......	50	25
410		1s.6d./15c. red-brown, yellow and yellow-green (11.3.68)......	4·75	40
411		2s./20c. dull red, violet and sage-green (11.3.68)......	4·50	4·50
412		2s.6d./25c. ultramarine-blue, vermilion and bright turquoise-blue (9.12.68)......	20·00	26·00
408/12	*Set of 5*......		27·00	28·00

71 Dr. Jameson (administrator)

(Des from painting by F. M. Bennett)

1967 (17 May). Famous Rhodesians (1st issue) and 50th Death Anniversary of Dr. Jameson. P 14½.

413	**71**	1s.6d. multicoloured..............................	20	35

See also Nos. 426, 430 and 457. Further stamps in this series appeared after 1970.

72 Soapstone Sculpture (Joram Mariga)

1967 (12 July). Tenth Anniversary of Opening of Rhodes National Gallery. T **72** and similar vert designs. P 14½×14 (3d., 9d.) or 14 (others).

414		3d. reddish chestnut, yellow-olive and black......	10	10
415		9d. light greenish blue, deep olive-brown and black......	20	20
		a. Perf 13½......	4·75	13·00
416		1s.6d. multicoloured......	20	25
417		2s.6d. multicoloured......	25	60
414/17	*Set of 4*		65	1·00

Designs: 9d. *The Burgher of Calais* (detail, Rodin); 1s.3d. *The Knight* (stamp design wrongly inscr) (Roberto Crippa); 2s.6d. *John the Baptist* (M. Tossini).

73 Baobab Tree

1967 (6 Sept). Nature Conservation. T **73** and similar designs. P 14½.

418		4d. light brown and black......	10	20
419		4d. yellow-olive and black......	25	20
420		4d. deep grey and black......	25	20
421		4d. yellow-orange and black......	10	20
418/21	*Set of 4*		60	70

Designs: Horiz—No. 418, Type **73**; 419, White Rhinoceros; 420, African Elephants. Vert—No. 421, Wild Gladiolus.

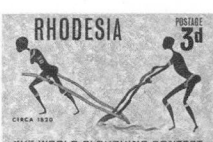

74 Wooden Hand Plough

(Des Rose Martin)

1968 (26 Apr). 15th World Ploughing Contest, Norton, Rhodesia. T **74** and similar horiz designs. P 14½.

422		3d. pale orange, orange-vermilion and lake-brown......	10	10
423		9d. multicoloured......	15	20
424		1s.6d. multicoloured......	20	55
425		2s.6d. multicoloured......	20	75
422/5	*Set of 4*		60	1·40

Designs: 9d. Early wheel plough; 1s.6d. Steam powered tractor, and ploughs; 2s.6d. Modern tractor, and plough.

75 Alfred Beit (national benefactor)

76 Raising the Flag, Bulawayo, 1893

(Des from painting by A. Haywood)

1968 (15 July). Famous Rhodesians (2nd series). P 14½.
426	**75**	1s.6d. pale orange, black and brown ..	20	30

(Des Rose Martin)

1968 (4 Nov). 75th Anniversary of Matabeleland. T **76** and similar vert designs. P 14½.
427	3d. pale orange, red-orange and black..	15	10
428	9d. multicoloured	15	20
429	1s.6d. pale turquoise-green, deep emerald and blackish green	20	60
427/9 *Set of 3*		45	80

Designs:—9d. View and Coat of Arms of Bulawayo; 1s.6d. Allan Wilson (combatant in the Matabele War).

77 Sir William Henry Milton (administrator)

(Des from painting by S. Kendrick)

1969 (15 Jan). Famous Rhodesians (3rd issue). P 14½.
430	**77**	1s.6d. multicoloured	30	40

78 2ft Gauge Steam Locomotive No. 15, 1897

(Des Rose Martin)

1969 (22 May). 70th Anniversary of Opening of Beira-Salisbury Railway. T **78** and similar horiz designs showing locomotives. Multicoloured. P 14½.
431	3d. Type **78**	30	10
432	9d. 7th Class steam locomotive No. 43, 1903	60	30
433	1s.6d. Beyer Peacock 15th Class steam locomotive No. 413, 1951	75	60
434	2s.6d. Class DE2 diesel-electric locomotive No. 1203, 1955	1·10	3·00
431/4 *Set of 4*		2·50	3·50

79 Low Level Bridge

(Des Rose Martin)

1969 (18 Sept). Bridges of Rhodesia. T **79** and similar horiz designs. Multicoloured. P 14½.
435	3d. Type **79**	20	10
436	9d. Mpudzi bridge	40	20
437	1s.6d. Umniati bridge	60	60
438	2s.6d. Birchenough bridge	80	1·25
435/8 *Set of 4*		1·75	1·90

(New Currency. 100 cents = 1 dollar)

80 Harvesting Wheat

81 Devil's Cataract, Victoria Falls

(Des from colour-transparencies (3, 6c.), Rose Martin (others))

1970 (17 Feb)–73. Decimal Currency. T **80/1** and similar horiz designs. P 14½.
439	1c. multicoloured	10	10
	a. Booklet pane of 4	30	
440	2c. multicoloured	10	10
441	2½c. multicoloured	10	10
	a. Booklet pane of 4	35	
441c	3c. multicoloured (1.1.73)	1·25	10
	ca. Booklet pane of 4	4·50	
442	3½c. multicoloured	10	10
	a. Booklet pane of 4	65	
442b	4c. multicoloured (1.1.73)	2·50	1·00
	ba. Booklet pane of 4	8·50	
443	5c. multicoloured	15	10
443b	6c. multicoloured (1.1.73)	4·25	6·50

443c	7½c. multicoloured (1.1.73)	8·50	60
444	8c. multicoloured	75	20
445	10c. multicoloured	60	10
446	12½c. multicoloured	1·75	10
446a	14c. multicoloured (1.1.73)	12·00	70
447	15c. multicoloured	1·25	15
448	20c. multicoloured	1·00	15
449	25c. multicoloured	4·00	60
450	50c. turquoise and ultramarine	1·25	55
451	$1 multicoloured	6·00	3·00
452	$2 multicoloured	8·50	15·00
439/52 *Set of 19*		48·00	26·00

Designs: Size as T **80**—2c. Pouring molten metal; 2½c. Zimbabwe Ruins; 3c. Articulated lorry; 3½c. and 4c. Statute of Cecil Rhodes; 5c. Mine headgear. Size as T **81**—6c. Hydrofoil *Seaflight*; 7½c. As 8c.; 10c. Yachting on Lake McIlwaine; 12½c. Hippopotamus in river; 14c. and 15c. Kariba Dam; 20c. Irrigation canal. As T **80/1** *but larger* (31×26 *mm*)—25c. Bateleurs; 50c. Radar antenna and Vickers Viscount 810; $1 "Air Rescue"; $2 Rhodesian flag.
Booklet panes Nos. 439a, 441a, 441ca, 442a and 442ba have margins all round.

82 Despatch Rider, *circa* 1890

(Des Rose Martin)

1970 (1 July). Inauguration of Posts and Telecommunications Corporation. T **82** and similar horiz designs. Multicoloured. P 14½.
453	2½c. Type **82**	40	10
454	3½c. Loading mail at Salisbury airport	45	50
455	15c. Constructing telegraph line, *circa* 1890	50	1·25
456	25c. Telephone and modern telecommunications equipment	55	2·00
453/6 *Set of 4*		1·75	3·50

83 Mother Patrick (Dominican nurse and teacher)

(Des Rose Martin from photograph)

1970 (16 Nov). Famous Rhodesians (4th issue). P 14½.
457	**83**	15c. multicoloured	45	50

STAMP BOOKLETS

1967 (Feb). Black on orange cover, size 57×45 mm. Stitched.
SB7	1s. booklet containing 3d. (No. 376) in block of 4		3·75

Although not issued in Rhodesia until February 1967, No. SB7 was released in London in June 1966.

1968 (21 Dec). Black on yellow cover, size 51×94 mm. Stapled.
SB8	5s. booklet containing 12×1d. and 12×3d., and 6×2d. (Nos. 397/9) in blocks of 6		18·00

1970 (17 Feb). Red on yellow cover. Stapled.
SB9	46c. booklet containing 12×1c., 8×2½c. and 4×3½c. in panes of 4 (Nos. 439a, 441a, 442a)		5·00

POSTAGE DUE STAMPS

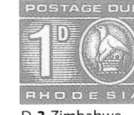

D 2

D 3 Zimbabwe Bird (soapstone sculpture)

(Des E.W. Jones Typo Printing and Stationery Dept, Salisbury)

1965 (17 June). Roul 9.
D8	**D 2**	1d. orange-red (roul 5)	50	12·00
		a. Roul 9	6·00	12·00
D9		2d. deep blue	40	8·00
D10		4d. green	50	8·00
D11		6d. plum	50	6·00
D8/11 *Set of 4*			1·75	30·00

The 2d. has a stop below the "D".

(Litho Mardon Printers, Salisbury)

1966 (15 Dec). P 14½.
D12	**D 3**	1d. red	60	4·25
D13		2d. bluish violet	75	2·50
D14		4d. pale green	75	4·75
D15		6d. reddish violet	75	1·50
D16		1s. red-brown	75	1·50
D17		2s. black	1·00	6·00
D12/17 *Set of 6*			4·25	18·00

1970 (17 Feb)–73. Decimal Currency. As Type D **3**, but larger (26×22½ *mm*). P 14½.
D18	**D 3**	1c. bright green	60	1·25
D19		2c. ultramarine	60	60
		a. Printed on the gummed side	50·00	
D20		5c. bright reddish violet	1·00	1·75
D21		6c. pale lemon (7.5.73)	5·50	4·00
D22		10c. cerise	1·00	4·00
D18/22 *Set of 5*			8·00	10·50

Rhodesia & Nyasaland

Stamps for the Central Africa Federation of Northern and Southern Rhodesia and Nyasaland Protectorate.

1

2

3 Queen Elizabeth II

(Recess Waterlow)

1954 (1 July)–56. P 13½×14 (T **1**), 13½×13 (T **2**) or 14½×13½ (T **3**).
1	**1**	½d. orange-red	15	10
		a. Coil stamp. Perf 12½×14. *Reddish orange* (6.2.56)	30	2·75
2		1d. ultramarine	15	10
		a. Coil stamp. Perf 12½×14. *Deep blue* (9.55)	1·50	21·00
		ab. *Ultramarine* (1.10.55)	4·75	19·00
3		2d. bright green	15	10
3a		2½d. ochre (15.2.56)	6·50	10
4		3d. carmine-red	20	10
5		4d. red-brown	60	20
6		4½d. blue-green	30	1·75
7		6d. bright reddish purple	2·25	10
		a. *Bright purple* (5.5.56)	6·00	10
8		9d. violet	2·50	1·00
9		1s. grey-black	2·50	10
10	**2**	1s.3d. red-orange and ultramarine	8·00	40
11		2s. deep blue and yellow-brown	9·00	6·50
12		2s.6d. black and rose-red	9·00	2·25
13		5s. violet and olive-green	26·00	8·50
14	**3**	10s. dull blue-green and orange	26·00	11·00
15		£1 olive-green and lake	45·00	32·00
1/15 *Set of 16*			£120	55·00

Nos. 1a and 2a printed on rotary machines by subsidiary company, Imprimerie Belge de Securité, in Belgium.

4 de Havilland DH.106 Comet 1 over Victoria Falls

5 Livingstone and Victoria Falls

3d. Wing flaw (R. 3/3)

(Des J. E. Hughes (3d.), V. E. Horne (1s.). Recess Waterlow)

1955 (15 June). Centenary of Discovery of Victoria Falls. P 13½ (3d.) or 13 (1s.).
16	**4**	3d. ultramarine and deep turquoise-green	1·00	30
		a. Wing flaw	24·00	13·00
17	**5**	1s. purple and deep blue	55	70

6 Tea Picking

7 VHF mast

8 Copper mining

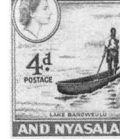

9 Fairbridge Memorial

10 Rhodes's Grave

11 Lake Bangweulu

12 Eastern Cataract, Victoria Falls

12a Rhodesian Railway Trains

13 Tobacco

14 Lake Nyasa

15 Chirondu Bridge

16 Salisbury Airport

17 Rhodes Statue

18 Mlanje

19 Federal Coat of Arms

1d. Pylon re-entry. The diagonal lines representing the pylon arms are doubled (R. 3/6)

(Des M. Kinsella (9d.). Recess Waterlow (½d., 1d., 2d., 1s.) until 1962, then D.L.R.; D.L.R. (2½d., 4d., 6d., 9d., 2s., 2s.6d.) and B.W. (others))

1959 (12 Aug)–**62**. T **6/19**. P 13½×14 (½d., 1d., 2d.), 14½ (2½d., 4d., 6d., 9d., 2s., 2s.6d.), 14×13½ (3d.), 13½×13 (1s.), 14 (1s.3d.) or 11 (others).

18	6	½d. black and light emerald	1·25	2·25
		a. Coil stamp. Perf 12½×14	3·50	6·50
19	7	1d. carmine-red and black	30	10
		aa. Pylon re-entry	15·00	
		a. Coil stamp. Perf 12½×14	3·50	13·00
		ab. Carmine-red and grey-black	8·50	19·00
		ac. Carmine-red (centre) omitted	£200	
20	8	2d. violet and yellow-brown	2·50	50
21	9	2½d. purple and grey-blue	2·00	2·25
22	10	3d. black and blue	1·00	10
		a. Black (centre) omitted	£30000	
		b. Printed on the gummed side	£450	
23	11	4d. maroon and olive	1·50	10
24	12	6d. ultramarine and deep myrtle-green	2·75	10
24a	12a	9d. orange-brown and reddish violet (15.5.62)	9·00	3·50
25	13	1s. light green and ultramarine	1·25	10
26	14	1s.3d. emerald and deep chocolate	5·50	10
27	15	2s. grey-green and carmine	4·25	60
28	16	2s.6d. light blue and yellow-brown	12·00	1·00
29	17	5s. deep chocolate and yellow-green	16·00	2·75
30	18	10s. olive-brown and rose-red	28·00	26·00
31	19	£1 black and deep violet	48·00	65·00
18/31		Set of 15	£110	90·00

Only three examples from two different sheets, all unused, are believed to exist of No. 22a, although further stamps from the same sheets can be found with the centre partially omitted.

20 Kariba Gorge, 1955

Gorge flaw (R. 4/6)

1s.3d. Earring flaw (R. 1/4)

(Photo Harrison (3d., 6d.), D.L.R. (others))

1960 (17 May). Opening of Kariba Hydro-Electric Scheme. T **20** and similar horiz designs. P 14½×14 (3d., 6d.) or 13 (others).

32		3d. blackish green and red-orange	70	10
		a. Red-orange omitted	£6000	
		b. Gorge flaw	30·00	8·50
33		6d. brown and yellow-brown	1·00	20
34		1s. slate-blue and green	2·50	4·00
35		1s.3d. light blue and orange-brown	2·75	3·50
		aa. Earring flaw	55·00	
		a. Blue and deep orange-brown	15·00	11·00
36		2s.6d. deep slate-purple and orange-red	4·00	8·50
37		5s. reddish violet and turquoise-blue	11·00	12·00
32/7		Set of 6	20·00	25·00

Designs:—6d. 330 kV power lines; 1s. Barrage wall; 1s.3d. Barrage and lake; 2s.6d. Interior of power station; 5s. Barrage wall and Queen Mother (top left).

No. 35aa comes only on the first shade only.

26 Miner Drilling

(Des V. Whiteley. Photo Harrison)

1961 (8 May). Seventh Commonwealth Mining and Metallurgical Congress. T **26** and similar horiz design. P 15×14.

38		6d. olive-green and orange-brown	1·00	20
39		1s.3d. black and light blue	1·25	80

Design:—1s.3d. Surface installations, Nchanga Mine.

Imperforate examples of the 6d. are believed to be printer's waste.

28 de Havilland DH.66 Hercules *City of Basra* on Rhodesian Airstrip

31 Tobacco Plant

2s.6d. Extra landing light (Cyl. B, R. 9/2)

1962 (6 Feb). 30th Anniv of First London-Rhodesia Airmail Service. T **28** and similar horiz designs. P 14½×14.

40		6d. bronze-green and vermilion	2·50	75
41		1s.3d. light blue, black and yellow	1·75	50
42		2s.6d. rose-red and deep violet	2·50	6·50
		a. Extra landing light	45·00	
40/2		Set of 3	6·00	7·00

Designs:—1s.3d. Short S.23 flying boat *Canopus* taking off from Zambesi; 2s.6d. Hawker Siddeley Comet 4 at Salisbury airport.

(Des V. Whiteley. Photo Harrison)

1963 (18 Feb). World Tobacco Congress, Salisbury. T **31** and similar vert designs. P 14×14½.

43		3d. green and olive-brown	30	10
44		6d. green, brown and blue	40	35
45		1s.3d. chestnut and indigo	1·50	45
46		2s.6d. yellow and brown	1·75	3·25
43/6		Set of 4	3·50	3·75

Designs:—6d. Tobacco field; 1s.3d. Auction floor; 2s.6d. Cured tobacco.

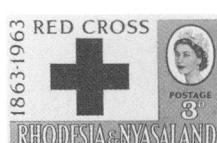

35 Red Cross Emblem

(Photo Harrison)

1963 (6 Aug). Red Cross Centenary. P 14½×14.

47	35	3d. red	1·50	10

36 African "Round Table" Emblem

(Des V. Whiteley. Photo Harrison)

1963 (11 Sept). World Council of Young Men's Service Clubs, Salisbury. P 14½×14.

48	36	6d. black, gold and yellow-green	75	1·50
49		1s.3d. black, gold, yellow-green and lilac	1·00	1·25

STAMP BOOKLETS

1955 (1 Jan). Black on yellow cover. Stitched.

SB1	5s. booklet containing 12×½d. and 18×1d. and 18×2d. (Nos. 1/3) in blocks of 6	35·00

1963 (4 Apr). Black on yellow cover. Stitched.

SB2	1s. booklet containing 3d. (No. 22) in block of 4.	2·00

POSTAGE DUE STAMPS

After Federation in 1954 existing stocks of Postage Due Stamps from Northern Rhodesia, Nyasaland and Southern Rhodesia continued to be used and were sometimes distributed throughout the federation.

Increased postal rates in July 1956 and in 1959 led to the exhaustion of certain values, in particular the 1d., and various offices then used Rhodesia and Nyasaland postage issues for postage due purposes. There were isolated instances of such stamps being cancelled "POSTAGE DUE" from December 1956 onwards.

Some of these handstamps may have been applied at Bulawayo while others, in violet or black, originate from the Salisbury Delivery Room at Kingsway Post Office. Only the 1d. and 2d. (Nos. 2/3) are known with such handstamps. After mint examples began to appear the Postmaster General suppressed the use of the handstamps in August 1959.

D 1

(Des E.W. Jones. Typo Federal Printing and Stationery Dept, Salisbury)

1961 (19 Apr). P 12½.

D1	D **1**	1d. vermilion	3·75	5·50
		a. Imperf between (horiz pair)	£800	£900
D2		2d. deep violet-blue	3·00	3·00
D3		4d. green	3·50	9·50
D4		6d. purple	4·50	7·50
		a. Imperf between (horiz pair)	£1900	
D1/4		Set of 4	13·00	23·00

The 2d. has a stop below the "D".

The stamps of the Federation were withdrawn on 19 February 1964 when all three constituent territories had resumed issuing their own stamps.

St. Helena

CROWN COLONY

PRICES FOR STAMPS ON COVER TO 1945	
Nos. 1/5	from × 12
Nos. 6/30	from × 10
Nos. 34/45	from × 15
Nos. 46/52	from × 6
Nos. 53/67	from × 5
No. 71	—
Nos. 72/86	from × 5
Nos. 87/8	from × 12
Nos. 89/95	from × 5
No. 96	—
Nos. 97/110	from × 5
Nos. 111/13	—
Nos. 114/40	from × 4

PERKINS BACON "CANCELLED". For notes on these handstamps, showing "CANCELLED" between horizontal bars forming an oval, see Catalogue Introduction.

ONE PENNY   FOUR PENCE
(2)   (3)
1

(Recess P.B.)

1856 (1 Jan). Wmk Large Star, W w **1**. Imperf.
| 1 | 1 | 6d. blue (H/S "CANCELLED" in oval £10000) | £500 | £180 |

1861 (Apr?). Wmk Large Star, W w **1**.
(a) Clean-cut perf 14 to 16
| 2 | 1 | 6d. blue | £1700 | £275 |
(b) Rough perf 14 to 16
| 2a | 1 | 6d. blue | £425 | £130 |

NOTE: The issues which follow consist of 6d. stamps, T **1**, printed in various colours and (except in the case of the 6d. values) surcharged with a new value, as T **2** to **10**, e.g. stamps described as "1d." are, in fact, 1d. on 6d. stamps, and so on.
The numbers in the Type column below refer to the *types of the lettering* of the surcharged value.

(Printed by D.L.R. from P.B. plate)

Two Types of Bar on 1d. value:
A. Bar 16–17 mm long.
B. Bar 18½–19 mm long.

1863 (July). Surch as T **2/3** with thin bar approximately the same length as the words. Wmk Crown CC. Imperf.
3	2	1d. lake (Type A)	£150	£250
		a. Surch double	£6500	£4250
		b. Surch omitted	£21000	
		w. Wmk inverted	£750	
4		1d. lake (Type B)	£160	£275
		a. Vert pair. Nos. 3/4	£11000	
5	3	4d. carmine (bar 15½–16½ mm)	£500	£250
		a. Surch double	£15000	£7500

ONE PENNY   ONE PENNY   ONE PENNY
(4 (A))   (4 (B))   (4 (C))

TWO PENCE   THREE PENCE   FOUR PENCE
(5)   (6)   (7)

ONE SHILLING   FIVE SHILLINGS
(8)   (9)

Three Types of Bar:
A. Thin bar (16½ to 17 mm) nearly the same length as the words.
B. Thick bar (14 to 14½ mm) much shorter than the words, except on the 2d. (Nos. 9, 22, 28) where it is nearly the same length.
C. Long bar (17 to 18 mm) same length as the words.

1864–80. 6d. as T **1**, without surcharge. Wmk Crown CC.
(a) P 12½ (1864–73)
6	4	1d. lake (Type A) (1864)	70·00	29·00
		a. Surch double	£12000	
7		1d. lake (Type B) (1868)	£225	60·00
		a. Surch double	£1000	
		b. Imperf	£3000	
		w. Wmk inverted	—	£225
		x. Wmk reversed	—	£160
8	4	1d. lake (Type C) (1871)	£140	17·00
		a. Surch in blue-black	£1000	£550
		x. Wmk reversed	£300	55·00
		y. Wmk inverted and reversed	£400	
9	5	2d. yellow (Type B) (1868)	£180	60·00
		a. Imperf	£10000	
		x. Wmk reversed	£475	
10		2d. yellow (Type C) (1873)	£160	45·00
		a. Surch in blue-black	£4000	£2250
		b. Surch double, one albino	£2000	
		x. Wmk reversed	£225	80·00
11	6	3d. deep dull purple (Type B) (1868)	£120	50·00
		a. Surch double	—	£7500
		b. Imperf	£850	
		c. Light purple	£3000	£750
		x. Wmk reversed	£300	

12		3d. deep dull purple (Type A) (1873)	£150	65·00
13	7	4d. carmine (Type A) (words 17 mm long) (1864)	£170	50·00
		a. Surch double	†	£6000
14		4d. carmine (Type B) (words 18 mm long) (1868)	£150	60·00
		a. Surch double	†	£6000
		b. Surch double (18+19 mm widths)	£26000	£12000
		c. Imperf	£12000	
		x. Wmk reversed	£350	£150
15		4d. carmine-rose (Type B) (words 19 mm long) (1868)	£325	£120
		a. Surch omitted	†	£6000
		x. Wmk reversed	—	£225
16		6d. dull blue (1871)	£850	£120
		a. Ultramarine (1873)	£550	85·00
		x. Wmk reversed	£1600	£250
17	8	1s. deep yellow-green (Type A) (1864)	£450	28·00
		a. Surch double	†	£24000
		w. Wmk inverted	—	£100
18		1s. deep yellow-green (Type B) (1868)	£750	£130
		a. Surch double	£21000	
		b. Imperf	£18000	
		c. Surch omitted*	£21000	
19		1s. deep green (Type C) (1871)	£750	16·00
		a. Surch in blue-black	£1000	75·00
		x. Wmk reversed	£1000	
20	9	5s. orange (Type B) (1868)	60·00	70·00
		a. Yellow	£450	£450
		w. Wmk inverted	£550	£600
		x. Wmk reversed	£170	£190
		y. Wmk inverted and reversed		
(b) P 14×12½ (1876)
21	4	1d. lake (Type B)	85·00	15·00
		w. Wmk inverted	£325	
22	5	2d. yellow (Type B)	£140	50·00
23		3d. purple (Type B)	£350	70·00
24		4d. carmine (Type B) (words 16½ mm long)	£170	60·00
		y. Wmk inverted and reversed	£170	75·00
25	—	6d. milky blue	£550	50·00
26	8	1s. deep green (Type C)	£900	24·00
(c) P 14 (1880)
27	4	1d. lake (Type B)	£120	20·00
		w. Wmk inverted	£400	
28	5	2d. yellow (Type B)	£150	42·00
29	—	6d. milky blue	£550	50·00
		x. Wmk reversed	†	£180
30	8	1s. yellow-green (Type B)	21·00	12·00
		y. Wmk inverted and reversed	—	£160

Two used examples of No. 15a are known, one being in the Royal Collection and the other damaged at bottom right. The price is for the latter.
*No. 18c is from a sheet of the 1s. with surcharge misplaced, the fifth row of 12 stamps being thus doubly surcharged and the tenth row without surcharge.

2½d
(10)   11   12

FOUR PENCE
Additional thin bar
in surch (R. 7/2)

1884–94. T **1** surch. Bars similar to Type B above (except 2½d., T **10**, and the 1s., in which the bar is nearly the same length as the words). The 6d. as before without surcharge. Wmk Crown CA. P 14.
34	—	½d. emerald (words 17 mm) (1884)	19·00	25·00
		a. "N" and "Y" spaced	£1100	£1200
		b. Surch double	£1300	£1400
		ba. Ditto. "N" and "Y" spaced	£11000	
		w. Wmk inverted	—	75·00
		y. Wmk inverted and reversed	—	75·00
35	—	½d. green (words 17 mm) (1885)	13·00	21·00
		a. "N" and "Y" spaced	£475	£700
		x. Wmk reversed	12·00	23·00
36	—	½d. green (words 14½ mm) (1893)	2·50	2·75
		a. "N" and "Y" spaced	£1600	
37	4	1d. red (1887)	4·75	3·25
		x. Wmk reversed	5·50	4·50
38		1d. pale red (1890)	8·50	3·25
		x. Wmk reversed	15·00	7·00
39	5	2d. yellow (1894)	3·00	8·00
40	10	2½d. ultramarine (1893)	3·75	5·50
		a. Surch double	£25000	
		b. Stamp doubly printed	£10000	
		w. Wmk inverted	32·00	
		x. Wmk reversed	40·00	
41	6	3d. deep mauve (1887)	7·50	11·00
		a. Surch double	—	£10000
42		3d. deep reddish lilac (1887)	9·00	5·00
		a. Surch double	£10000	£6000
		w. Wmk reversed	10·00	6·00
43	7	4d. pale brown (words 16½ mm) (1890)	45·00	40·00
		by. Wmk inverted and reversed	65·00	
43c		4d. sepia (words 17 mm) (1894)	27·00	17·00
		ca. Additional thin bar in surch (R. 7/2)	£850	£850
		cx. Wmk reversed	40·00	29·00
44	—	6d. grey (1887)	42·00	5·00
		a. Surch double	55·00	5·00
		x. Wmk inverted and reversed	—	£110
45	8	1s. yellow-green (1894)	65·00	30·00
		a. Surch double	£4750	
36/45 Set of 8			£130	70·00
40s/1s, 43bys, 44s Optd "SPECIMEN" Set of 4			£200	

Examples of the above are sometimes found showing no watermark; these are from the bottom row of the sheet, which had escaped the watermark, the paper being intended for stamps of a different size to Type **1**.

Some are found without bar and others with bar at top of stamp, due to careless overprinting.
Nos. 34a and 35a occur on R. 18/12 and show a minimum space between the letters of 0.8 mm. Normal examples are spaced 0.5 mm, but some stamps show intermediate measurements due to loose type. On No. 34ba only one impression of the surcharge shows "N" and "Y" spaced. On the reset surcharge, No. 36, a similar variety occurs on R. 5/9.
Of the 2½d. with double surcharge only six copies exist, and of the 2½d. doubly printed, one row of 12 stamps existed on one sheet only.

CANCELLATIONS. Nos. 40/5 and No. 20 were sold as remainders in 1904 defaced with a violet diamond-shaped grill with four interior bars extending over two stamps. These cannot be considered as *used* stamps, and they are consequently not priced in the list.
This violet obliteration is easily removed and many of these remainders have been cleaned and offered as unused; some are repostmarked with a date and name in thin type rather larger than the original, a usual date being "Ap.4.01."

(Typo D.L.R.)

1890–97. Die I for the 1½d. Die II for the other values (for differences see Seychelles). Wmk Crown CA. P 14.
46	11	½d. green (1897)	2·75	7·00
47		1d. carmine (1896)	19·00	2·75
48		1½d. red-brown and green (1890)	4·50	14·00
49		2d. orange-yellow (1896)	5·00	13·00
50		2½d. ultramarine (1896)	18·00	12·00
51		5d. mauve (1896)	11·00	35·00
52		10d. brown (1896)	26·00	70·00
46/52 Set of 7			75·00	£130
46s/52s Optd "SPECIMEN" Set of 7			£350	

The note below No. 45a re violet diamond-shaped grill cancellation also applies to Nos. 48/52.

1902. Wmk Crown CA. P 14.
53	12	½d. green (3.02)	2·00	2·75
54		1d. carmine (24.02.02)	13·00	70
53s/4s Optd "SPECIMEN" Set of 2			£100	

13 Government House   14 The Wharf

(Typo D.L.R.)

1903 (May). Wmk Crown CC. P 14.
55	13	½d. brown and grey-green	2·00	3·25
		w. Wmk inverted	£200	£275
56	14	1d. black and carmine	1·50	35
		w. Wmk inverted	—	£700
		x. Wmk reversed	£700	
57	13	2d. black and sage-green	13·00	1·25
58	14	8d. black and brown	23·00	32·00
59	13	1s. brown and brown-orange	26·00	40·00
60	14	2s. black and violet	65·00	95·00
55/60 Set of 6			£110	£150
55s/60s Optd "SPECIMEN" Set of 6			£275	

(Typo D.L.R.)

1908 (May)–**11.** Ordinary paper (2½d.) or chalk-surfaced paper (4d., 6d.). P 14.
(a) Wmk Mult Crown CA
64	15	2½d. blue	2·00	1·50
66		4d. black and red/yellow	17·00	38·00
		a. Ordinary paper (1911)	7·50	18·00
67		6d. dull and deep purple	48·00	55·00
		a. Ordinary paper (1911)	13·00	14·00
(b) Wmk Crown CA. Chalk-surfaced paper
70	15	10s. green and red/green	£275	£325
64/70 Set of 4			£275	£325
64s/70s Optd "SPECIMEN" Set of 4			£300	

Examples of Nos. 58/60 and 66/70 are known showing a forged St. Helena postmark dated "JY 28 1".

1911. Wmk Mult Crown CA. P 14. Prepared for use but not issued.
| 71s | 14 | 1d. red (optd "SPECIMEN") | £425 | |

This stamp was printed in error, as a result of a misunderstanding between the Postmaster and De La Rue, but withdrawn and destroyed. The supply was sent to St. Helena, but withdrawn and destroyed. Specimen examples were sent to UPU member countries.

16   17

(Typo D.L.R.)

1912–16. Wmk Mult Crown CA. P 14.
72	16	½d. black and green	2·25	10·00
73	17	1d. black and carmine-red	4·75	1·75
		a. Black and scarlet (1916)	10·00	9·00

74		1½d. black and dull orange (1913).....	3·50	9·00
75	**16**	2d. black and greyish slate.................	7·00	1·75
76	**17**	2½d. black and bright blue.................	3·50	7·00
77	**16**	3d. black and purple/*yellow* (1913)...	3·50	5·00
78	**17**	8d. black and dull purple...................	12·00	60·00
79	**16**	1s. black/*green*...................	9·00	35·00
80	**17**	2s. black and blue/*blue*...................	55·00	£100
81		3s. black and violet (1913).................	75·00	£160
72/81 *Set of 10*........................			£150	£350
72s/81s Optd "SPECIMEN" *Set of 10*...........			£375	

No. 73a is on thicker paper than 73.

18 **19**

Split "A"
(R. 8/3 of
left pane)

(Typo D.L.R.)

1912. Chalk-surfaced paper. Wmk Mult Crown CA. P 14.

83	**18**	4d. black and red/*yellow*...................	15·00	28·00
84		6d. dull and deep purple...................	4·25	5·50
83s/4s Optd "SPECIMEN" *Set of 2*...........			£140	

1913. Wmk Mult Crown CA. P 14.

85	**19**	4d. black and red/*yellow*...................	8·00	2·75
		a. Split "A"...........................	£400	£300
86		6d. dull and deep purple...................	14·00	28·00
		a. Split "A"...........................	£650	£1000
85s/6s Optd "SPECIMEN" *Set of 2*...........			£140	

WAR TAX

WAR TAX

WAR TAX

ONE PENNY
(20)

1d.
(21)

1916 (Sept). As No. 73a, on thin paper, surch with T **20**.

87	**17**	1d.+1d. black and scarlet...........................	3·50	3·25
		a. Surch double...........................	†	£18000
		s. Optd "SPECIMEN"...........................	70·00	

1919. No. 73 on thicker paper, surch with T **21**.

88	**17**	1d.+1d. black and carmine-red		
		(*shades*)...........................	2·00	4·50
		s. Optd "SPECIMEN"...........................	70·00	

1922 (Jan). Printed in one colour. Wmk Mult Script CA. P 14.

89	**17**	1d. green...........................	3·25	55·00
		w. Wmk inverted...........................	£700	
		y. Wmk inverted and reversed.......	£350	
90		1½d. rose-scarlet...........................	12·00	50·00
91	**16**	3d. bright blue...........................	25·00	95·00
		y. Wmk inverted and reversed.......	£325	£650
89/91 *Set of 3*........................			35·00	£180
89s/91s Optd "SPECIMEN" *Set of 3*...........			£200	

22 Badge of St. Helena

PLATE FLAWS ON THE 1922–37 ISSUE. Many constant plate varieties exist on both the vignette and duty plates of this issue. The major varieties are illustrated and listed below.

a.   Broken mainmast. Occurs on R. 2/1 of all sheets from the second printing onwards. It does not appear on Nos. 93/6 and 111/13 as these stamps only exist from the initial printing invoiced in May 1922.

1936 and subsequent printings show additional minor varieties to the vignette of this stamp; a dent in the lower left frame and breaks in the bottom frame.

b.   Torn flag. Occurs on R. 4/6 of all sheets from printings up to and including that invoiced in December 1922. The flaw was retouched for the printing invoiced in December 1926 and so does not occur on Nos. 97h, 99f, 103/d, 107/10 and 111d.

c.   Cleft rock. Occurs on R. 5/1 of all sheets from the second printing onwards. It does not appear on Nos. 93/6 and 111/13 as these stamps only exist from the initial printing invoiced in May 1922.

"Storm over rock"
(R. 3/5, December 1922
printings only)

Damaged value tablet
(R. 1/4 of first printing
and part of second
(1932) printing)

(Des T. Bruce. Typo D.L.R.)

1922 (June)–**37**. P 14

(a) Wmk Mult Crown CA. Chalk-surfaced paper

92	**22**	4d. grey and black/*yellow* (2.23)	15·00	6·00
		a. Broken mainmast...........................	£275	£300
		b. Torn flag...........................	£275	£300
		c. Cleft rock...........................	£250	£275
		d. "Storm over rock"...........................	£275	£300
93		1s.6d. grey and green/*blue-green*...........	22·00	70·00
		b. Torn flag...........................	£550	£1200
94		2s.6d. grey and red/*yellow*...........	28·00	75·00
		b. Torn flag...........................	£650	£1300
95		5s. grey and green/*yellow*...........	50·00	£130
		b. Torn flag...........................	£950	£1700
96		£1 grey and purple/*red*...........	£450	£700
		b. Torn flag...........................	£4250	
92/6 *Set of 5*........................			£500	£900
92s/6s Optd "SPECIMEN" *Set of 5*...........			£650	

The paper of No. 93 is bluish on the surface with a full green back.

(b) Wmk Mult Script CA. Ordinary paper (1s.6d., 2s.6d., 5s.) or chalk-surfaced paper (others)

97	**22**	½d. grey and black (2.23)	4·50	4·25
		a. Broken mainmast...........................	85·00	£120
		b. Torn flag...........................	£275	£325
		c. Cleft rock...........................	75·00	£120
		d. "A" of "CA" missing from wmk....	†	£1500
		e. Damaged value tablet...........	£275	
		f. "Storm over rock"...........................	£275	£325
		gw. Wmk inverted...........................	£500	£550
		h. Grey-black and black (6.36).......	13·00	4·25
		ha. Broken mainmast...........................	£300	£200
		hc. Cleft rock...........................	£300	£200
98		1d. grey and green...........................	4·00	1·60
		a. Broken mainmast...........................	85·00	95·00
		b. Torn flag...........................	£250	£300
		c. Cleft rock...........................	75·00	95·00
		d. Wmk sideways...........................		
99		1½d. rose-red (*shades*) (2.23)...........	4·00	13·00
		a. Broken mainmast...........................	£100	£200
		b. Torn flag...........................	£100	£200
		c. Cleft rock...........................	95·00	£200
		d. "Storm over rock"...........................	£120	£200
		ew. Wmk inverted...........................	£1600	
		ex. Wmk reversed...........................	£2000	£1800
		f. Deep carmine-red (1937)...........	90·00	85·00
		fa. Broken mainmast...........................	£1600	£1400
		fc. Cleft rock...........................	£1600	£1400
100		2d. grey and slate (2.23)...........	4·50	2·00
		a. Broken mainmast...........................	£160	£180
		b. Torn flag...........................	£325	£375
		c. Cleft rock...........................	£150	£180
		d. "Storm over rock"...........................	£325	£375
101		3d. bright blue (2.23)...........	2·25	4·00
		a. Broken mainmast...........................	£130	£200
		b. Torn flag...........................	£130	£200
		c. Cleft rock...........................	£110	£190

		d. "Storm over rock"...........................	£130	£200
		x. Wmk reversed...........................	£800	
103		5d. green and deep carmine/*green*		
		(1927)...........................	6·00	5·50
		a. Broken mainmast...........................	£275	£350
		c. Cleft rock...........................	£250	£350
		d. Green and carmine-red/green		
		(1936)...........................	12·00	7·50
		da. Broken mainmast...........................	£425	£450
		dc. Cleft rock...........................	£400	£450
104		6d. grey and bright purple...........	7·00	9·00
		a. Broken mainmast...........................	£300	£425
		b. Torn flag...........................	£300	£425
		c. Cleft rock...........................	£275	£400
105		8d. grey and bright violet (2.23)...	4·50	8·00
		a. Broken mainmast...........................	£200	£375
		b. Torn flag...........................	£200	£375
		c. Cleft rock...........................	£180	£375
		d. "Storm over rock"...........................	£200	£375
		w. Wmk inverted...........................	†	£2750
106		1s. grey and brown...........	7·00	9·00
		a. Broken mainmast...........................	£375	£500
		b. Torn flag...........................	£500	£650
		c. Cleft rock...........................	£350	£500
107		1s.6d. grey and green/*green* (1927)	16·00	60·00
		a. Broken mainmast...........................	£475	£950
		c. Cleft rock...........................	£450	£950
108		2s. purple and blue/*blue* (1927)	25·00	55·00
		a. Broken mainmast...........................	£550	£900
		c. Cleft rock...........................	£500	
109		2s.6d. grey and red/*yellow* (1927)........	20·00	75·00
		a. Broken mainmast...........................	£450	£1400
		c. Cleft rock...........................	£425	£1400
110		5s. grey and green/*yellow* (1927)	45·00	90·00
		a. Broken mainmast...........................	£750	£1500
		c. Cleft rock...........................	£700	£1500
111		7s.6d. grey-brown and yellow-orange	£150	£225
		b. Torn flag...........................	£1300	£2750
		d. Brownish grey and orange		
		(1937)...........................	£1300	£2000
		da. Broken mainmast...........................	£27000	
		dc. Cleft rock...........................	£27000	
112		10s. grey and olive-green...........	£170	£250
		b. Torn flag...........................	£1800	£3250
113		15s. grey and purple/*blue*...........	£1100	£2750
		b. Torn flag...........................	£8500	£15000
97/112 *Set of 15*........................			£425	£750
97s/113s Optd "SPECIMEN" *Set of 16*...........			£1600	

Examples of all values are known showing a forged St. Helena postmark dated "DE 18 27".

23 Lot and Lot's Wife

24 The "Plantation"

25 Map of St. Helena

26 Quay at Jamestown

27 James Valley

28 Jamestown

29 Munden's Promontory

30 St. Helena

31 High Knoll

32 Badge of St. Helena

(Recess B.W.)

1934 (23 Apr). Centenary of British Colonisation. T **23/32**. Wmk Mult Script CA. P 12.

114	**23**	½d. black and purple...........................	1·25	80
115	**24**	1d. black and green...........................	75	85
116	**25**	1½d. black and scarlet...........................	2·50	3·25
117	**26**	2d. black and orange...........................	4·25	1·25
118	**27**	3d. black and blue...........................	1·40	4·50
119	**28**	6d. black and light blue...........................	3·25	3·00
120	**29**	1s. black and chocolate...........................	6·50	18·00
121	**30**	2s.6d. black and lake...........................	50·00	60·00
122	**31**	5s. black and chocolate...........................	£100	£100
123	**32**	10s. black and purple...........................	£300	£350
114/23 *Set of 10*........................			£425	£475
114s/23s Perf "SPECIMEN" *Set of 10*...........			£475	

Examples of all values are known showing a forged St. Helena postmark dated "MY 12 34".

1935 (6 May). Silver Jubilee. As Nos. 91/4 of Antigua. P 13½×14.

124		1½d. deep blue and carmine	1·50	5·50
		f. Diagonal line by turret	£100	£200
125		2d. ultramarine and grey	3·75	90
		f. Diagonal line by turret	£180	£225
		g. Dot to left of chapel	£350	
126		6d. green and indigo	9·50	3·25
		a. Frame printed double, one albino	£3500	
		f. Diagonal line by turret	£500	£550
		g. Dot to left of chapel	£800	
		h. Dot by flagstaff	£750	
127		1s. slate and indigo	26·00	29·00
		h. Dot by flagstaff	£950	£1000
		i. Dash by turret	£1200	
124/7		Set of 4	35·00	35·00
124s/7s		Perf "SPECIMEN" Set of 4	£190	

For illustrations of plate varieties see Omnibus section following Zanzibar.

1937 (19 May). Coronation. As Nos. 95/7 of Antigua, but ptd by D.L.R. P 14.

128		1d. green	40	75
129		2d. orange	55	45
130		3d. bright blue	80	50
128/30		Set of 3	1·60	1·50
128s/30s		Perf "SPECIMEN" Set of 3	£160	

33 Badge of St. Helena

(Recess Waterlow)

1938 (12 May)–44. Wmk Mult Script CA. P 12½.

131	**33**	½d. violet	15	65
132		1d. green	13·00	3·50
132a		1d. yellow-orange (8.7.40)	30	30
133		1½d. scarlet	30	40
134		2d. red-orange	30	15
135		3d. ultramarine	80·00	18·00
135a		3d. grey (8.7.40)	30	30
135b		4d. ultramarine (8.7.40)	2·50	2·50
136		6d. light blue	2·25	2·75
136a		8d. sage-green (8.7.40)	4·50	2·25
		b. Olive-green (24.5.44)	7·00	4·25
137		1s. sepia	1·25	1·75
138		2s.6d. maroon	20·00	7·50
139		5s. chocolate	20·00	17·00
140		10s. purple	20·00	20·00
131/40		Set of 14	£140	65·00
131s/40s		Perf "SPECIMEN" Set of 14	£600	

See also Nos. 149/51.

1946 (21 Oct). Victory. As Nos. 110/11 of Antigua.

141		2d. red-orange	40	50
142		4d. blue	60	30
141s/2s		Perf "SPECIMEN" Set of 2	£150	

1948 (20 Oct). Royal Silver Wedding. As Nos. 112/13 of Antigua.

143		3d. black	30	30
144		10s. violet-blue	28·00	45·00

1949 (10 Oct). 75th Anniv of UPU. As Nos. 114/17 of Antigua.

145		3d. carmine	25	1·25
146		4d. deep blue	3·00	3·00
147		6d. olive	1·50	4·00
148		1s. blue-black	35	1·10
145/8		Set of 4	4·50	8·50

1949 (1 Nov). Wmk Mult Script CA. P 12½.

149	**33**	1d. black and green	1·50	1·50
150		1½d. black and carmine	1·50	1·50
151		2d. black and scarlet	1·50	1·50
149/51		Set of 3	4·00	4·00

1953 (2 June). Coronation. As No. 120 of Antigua.

152		3d. black and deep reddish violet	1·75	1·50

34 Badge of St. Helena

34a Flax plantation

35 Heart-shaped Waterfall

35a Lace-making

36 Drying flax

37 St. Helena Sand Plover

38 Flagstaff and The Barn

39 Donkeys carrying flax

40 Island map

41 The Castle

42 Cutting flax

43 Jamestown

44 Longwood House

(Recess D.L.R.)

1953 (4 Aug)–59. T **34/44**. Wmk Mult Script CA. P 14.

153	**34**	½d. black and bright green	30	30
154	**34a**	1d. black and deep green	15	20
155	**35**	1½d. black and reddish purple	4·75	1·50
		a. Black and deep reddish purple (14.1.59)	12·00	4·25
156	**35a**	2d. black and claret	1·00	30
157	**36**	2½d. black and red	40	30
158	**37**	3d. black and brown	3·25	30
159	**38**	4d. black and deep blue	40	1·00
160	**39**	6d. black and deep lilac	40	30
161	**40**	7d. black and grey-black	1·75	1·75
162	**41**	1s. black and carmine	40	70
163	**42**	2s.6d. black and violet	20·00	8·50
164	**43**	5s. black and deep brown	25·00	11·00
165	**44**	10s. black and yellow-orange	40·00	14·00
153/65		Set of 13	85·00	35·00

45 Stamp of 1856

46 Arms of East India Company

47 East Indiaman *London* off James Bay

48 Commemoration Stone

(Recess D.L.R.)

1956 (3 Jan). St. Helena Stamp Centenary. Wmk Mult Script CA. P 11½.

166	**45**	3d. Prussian blue and carmine	15	10
167		4d. Prussian blue and reddish brown	15	20
168		6d. Prussian blue and deep reddish purple	15	25
166/8		Set of 3	40	50

(Recess Waterlow)

1959 (5 May). Tercentenary of Settlement. T **46/48**. W w **12**. P 12½×13.

169	**46**	3d. black and scarlet	20	15
170	**47**	6d. light emerald and slate-blue	75	75
171	**48**	1s. black and orange	50	75
169/71		Set of 3	1·25	1·50

ST. HELENA
Tristan Relief
9d +

(49)

1961 (12 Oct). Tristan Relief Fund. Nos. 46 and 49/51 of Tristan da Cunha surch as T **49** by Govt Printer, Jamestown.

172	2½c. +3d. black and brown-red	£1500	£650
173	5c. +6d. black and blue	£1800	£700
174	7½c. +9d. black and rose-carmine	£3000	£1300
175	10c. +1s. black and light brown	£2250	£1300
172/5	Set of 4	£8000	£3500

The above stamps were withdrawn from sale on 19 October, 434 complete sets having been sold.

50 St. Helena Butterflyfish

51 Yellow Canary

53 Queen Elizabeth II

63 Queen Elizabeth II with Prince Andrew (after Cecil Beaton)

(Des V. Whiteley. Photo Harrison)

1961 (12 Dec)–**65**. T **50/1**, **53**, **63** and similar designs. W w **12**. P 11½×12 (horiz), 12×11½ (vert) or 14½×14 (£1).

176	**50**	1d. bright blue, dull violet, yellow and carmine	40	20
		a. Chalk-surfaced paper (4.5.65)	1·75	30
177	**51**	1½d. yellow, green, black and light drab	50	20
178		2d. scarlet and grey	15	20
179	**53**	3d. light blue, black, pink and deep blue	1·25	20
		a. Chalk-surfaced paper (30.11.65)	8·00	1·50
180		4½d. yellow-green, green, brown and grey	60	60
181		6d. red, sepia and light yellow-olive	5·50	70
		a. Chalk-surfaced paper (30.11.65)	10·00	70
182		7d. red-brown, black and violet	35	70
183		10d. brown-purple and light blue	35	70
184		1s. greenish yellow, bluish green and brown	55	1·25
185		1s.6d. grey, black and slate-blue	11·00	4·75
186		2s.6d. red, pale yellow and turquoise (*chalk-surfaced paper*)	2·50	2·50
187		5s. yellow, brown and green	14·00	5·50
188		10s. orange-red, black and blue	13·00	10·00
189	**63**	£1 chocolate and light blue	22·00	24·00
		a. Chalk-surfaced paper (30.11.65)	55·00	50·00
176/89		Set of 14	60·00	45·00

Designs: Horiz (as T **50**)—2d. Brittle Starfish; 7d. Trumpetfish; 10d. Feather Starfish; 2s.6d. Orange Starfish; 10s. Deep-water Bullseye. Vert (as T **51**)—4½d. Red-wood Flower; 6d. Madagascar Red Fody; 1s. Gum-wood Flower; 1s.6d. White Tern; 5s. Night-blooming Cereus.

1963 (4 June). Freedom from Hunger. As No. 146 of Antigua.

190	1s. 6d. ultramarine	75	40

1963 (2 Sept). Red Cross Centenary. As Nos. 147/8 of Antigua.

191	3d. red and black	30	50
192	1s.6d. red and blue	70	2·00

FIRST LOCAL POST
4th JANUARY 1965
(**64**)

65 Badge of St. Helena

1965 (4 Jan). First Local Post. Nos. 176, 179, 181 and 185 optd with T **64**.

193	1d. bright blue, dull violet, yellow and carmine	10	25
194	3d. light blue, black, pink and deep blue	10	25
195	6d. red, sepia and light yellow-olive	40	30
196	1s.6d. grey, black and slate-blue	60	35
193/6	Set of 4	1·10	1·00

1965 (17 May). ITU Centenary. As Nos. 166/7 of Antigua.

197	3d. blue and grey-brown	25	25
198	6d. bright purple and bluish green	35	25

1965 (15 Oct). International Co-operation. Year. As Nos. 168/9 of Antigua.

199	1d. reddish purple and turquoise-green	30	15
200	6d. deep bluish green and lavender	30	15
	w. Wmk inverted		

1966 (24 Jan). Churchill Commemoration. As Nos. 170/3 of Antigua.

201		1d. new blue	15	25
202		3d. deep green	25	25
203		6d. brown	40	30
204		1s.6d. bluish violet	45	85
201/4 Set of 4			1·10	1·50

1966 (1 July). World Cup Football Championships. As Nos. 176/7 of Antigua.

205		3d. violet, yellow-green, lake and yellow-brown	45	35
206		6d. chocolate, blue-green, lake and yellow-brown	55	35

1966 (20 Sept). Inauguration of WHO Headquarters, Geneva. As Nos. 178/9 of Antigua.

207		3d. black, yellow-green and light blue	75	20
208		1s.6d. black, light purple and yellow-brown	2·25	1·00

1966 (1 Dec). 20th Anniversary of UNESCO. As Nos. 196/8 of Antigua.

209		3d. slate-violet, red, yellow and orange	1·00	25
210		6d. orange-yellow, violet and deep olive	1·25	90
211		1s.6d. black, bright purple and orange	2·25	2·50
209/11 Set of 3			4·00	3·25

(Des W. H. Brown. Photo Harrison)

1967 (5 May). New Constitution. W w **12** (sideways). P 14½×14.

212	**65**	1s. multicoloured	10	10
213		2s.6d. multicoloured	20	20
		a. Red (ribbon, etc.) omitted	£1500	

66 Fire of London

(Des M. Goaman. Recess D.L.R.)

1967 (4 Sept). 300th Anniv of Arrival of Settlers after Great Fire of London. T **66** and similar horiz designs. W w **12**. P 13.

214		1d. carmine-red and black	15	10
		a. Carmine and black	2·25	2·50
215		3d. ultramarine and black	20	10
216		6d. slate-violet and black	20	15
217		1s.6d. olive-green and black	20	20
214/17 Set of 4			65	50

Designs:—3d. East Indiaman *Charles*; 6d. Settlers landing at Jamestown; 1s.6d. Settlers clearing scrub.

70 Interlocking Maps of Tristan and St. Helena

(Des Jennifer Toombs. Photo Harrison)

1968 (4 June). 30th Anniv of Tristan da Cunha as a Dependency of St. Helena. T **70** and similar horiz design. W w **12**. P 14×14½.

218	**70**	4d. purple and chocolate	10	10
219	–	8d. olive and brown	10	30
220	**70**	1s.9d. ultramarine and chocolate	15	40
221	–	2s.3d. greenish blue and brown	20	40
218/21 Set of 4			50	1·10

Design:—8d., 2s.3d. Interlocking maps of St. Helena and Tristan.

72 Queen Elizabeth and Sir Hudson Lowe

(Des M. Farrar Bell. Litho D.L.R.)

1968 (4 Sept). 150th Anniv of the Abolition of Slavery in St. Helena. T **72** and similar horiz design. Multicoloured. W w **12** (sideways). P 13×12½.

222		3d. Type **72**	10	15
223		9d. Type **72**	10	20
224		1s.6d. Queen Elizabeth and Sir George Bingham	15	30
225		2s.6d. As 1s. 6d.	25	45
222/5 Set of 4			55	1·00

74 Blue Gum Eucalyptus and Road Construction

(Des Sylvia Goaman. Litho P.B.)

1968 (4 Nov). Horiz designs as T **74**. Multicoloured. W w **12** (sideways*). P 13½.

226		½d. Type **74**	10	20
227		1d. Cabbage-tree and electricity development	10	20
		w. Wmk Crown to right of CA	9·00	
228		1½d. St. Helena Redwood and dental unit	15	20
229		2d. Scrubweed and pest control	15	20
230		3d. Tree-fern and flats in Jamestown	30	20
231		4d. Blue gum Eucalyptus, pasture and livestock improvement	20	20
232		6d. Cabbage-tree and schools broadcasting	50	20
233		8d. St. Helena Redwood and country cottages	30	20
234		10d. Scrubweed and new school buildings	30	20
235		1s. Tree-fern and reafforestation	30	20
236		1s.6d. Blue gum Eucalyptus and heavy lift crane	70	3·00
237		2s.6d. Cabbage-tree and Lady Field Children's Home	70	3·50
238		5s. St. Helena Redwood and agricultural training	70	3·50
239		10s. Scrubweed and New General Hospital	2·00	4·50
240		£1 Tree-fern and lifeboat *John Dutton*	10·00	15·00
226/40 Set of 15			15·00	28·00

*The normal sideways watermark shows Crown to left of CA, *as seen from the back of the stamp.*

A distinct shade of the £1 value was issued in 1971, with the decimal currency definitives.

89 Brig *Perseverance*

93 W.O. and Drummer of the 53rd Foot, 1815

(Des J.W. Litho P.B.)

1969 (19 Apr). Mail Communications. T **89** and similar horiz designs. Multicoloured. W w **12** (sideways). P 13½.

241		4d. Type **89**	20	20
242		8d. *Phoebe* (screw steamer)	25	40
243		1s.9d. *Llandovery Castle* (liner)	25	60
244		2s.3d. *Good Hope Castle* (cargo liner)	25	75
241/4 Set of 4			85	1·75

No. 242 is inscribed "DANE" in error.

(Des R. North. Litho Format)

1969 (3 Sept). Military Uniforms. T **93** and similar vert designs. Multicoloured. W w **12**. P 14.

245		6d. Type **93**	15	25
		w. Wmk inverted	£180	
246		8d. Officer and Surgeon, 20th Foot, 1816	15	25
247		1s.8d. Drum Major, 66th Foot, 1816, and Royal Artillery Officer, 1820	20	45
248		2s.6d. Private, 91st Foot, and 2nd Corporal, Royal Sappers and Miners, 1832	20	55
245/8 Set of 4			65	1·40

97 Dickens, Mr. Pickwick and Job Trotter (*Pickwick Papers*)

(Des Jennifer Toombs. Litho P.B.)

1970 (9 June). Death Centenary of Charles Dickens. T **97** and similar horiz designs each incorporating a portrait of Dickens. Multicoloured. Chalk-surfaced paper. W w **12** (sideways*). P 13½×13.

249		4d. Type **97**	80	15
		a. Shiny unsurfaced paper	30	1·40
		b. Yellow omitted	£600	
		w. Wmk Crown to right of CA	60·00	
250		8d. Mr. Bumble and Oliver (*Oliver Twist*)	90	15
		a. Shiny unsurfaced paper	30	1·60
251		1s.6d. Sairey Gamp and Mark Tapley (*Martin Chuzzlewit*)	1·00	20
		a. Shiny unsurfaced paper	40	2·25
252		2s.6d. Jo and Mr. Turveydrop (*Bleak House*)	1·00	25
		a. Shiny unsurfaced paper	40	2·50
249/52 Set of 4			3·25	65
249a/52a Set of 4			1·25	7·00

*The normal sideways watermark shows Crown to left of CA, *as seen from the back of the stamp.*

Supplies sent to St. Helena were on paper with a dull surface which reacts to the chalky test and with PVA gum. Crown Agents supplies were from a later printing on shiny paper which does not respond to the chalky test and with gum arabic.

98 "Kiss of Life"

99 Officer's Shako Plate (20th Foot)

(Des Jennifer Toombs. Litho J.W.)

1970 (15 Sept). Centenary of British Red Cross. T **98** and similar horiz designs. W w **12** (sideways). P 14.

253		6d. bistre, vermilion and black	15	15
254		9d. turquoise-green, vermilion and black	15	20
255		1s.9d. pale grey, vermilion and black	20	30
256		2s.3d. pale lavender, vermilion and black	20	45
253/6 Set of 4			65	1·00

Designs:—9d. Nurse with girl in wheelchair; 1s.9d. Nurse bandaging child's knee; 2s.3d. Red Cross emblem.

(Des J.W. Litho Questa)

1970 (2 Nov). Military Equipment (1st issue). T **99** and similar vert designs. Multicoloured. W w **12**. P 12.

257		4d. Type **99**	20	20
258		9d. Officer's Breast-plate (66th Foot)	25	30
259		1s.3d. Officer's Full Dress Shako (91st Foot)	25	40
260		2s.11d. Ensign's Shako (53rd Foot)	40	60
257/60 Set of 4			1·00	1·40

Further stamps in this series appeared after 1970.

STAMP BOOKLETS

1962 (2 Mar). Black on green cover. Stitched.

SB1	4s.6d. booklet containing 1d., 1½d., 2d., 3d. and 6d. (Nos. 176/9, 181), each in block of 4	55·00	

1969. Black on grey-green cover. Stapled.

SB2	5s.4d. booklet containing 1d., 2d., 3d., 4d. and 6d. (Nos. 227, 229/32), each in block of 4	30·00	

St. Kitts-Nevis

ST. CHRISTOPHER

From 1760 the postal service for St. Christopher was organised by the Deputy Postmaster General on Antigua. It was not until May 1779 that the first postmaster was appointed to the island and the use of postmarks on outgoing mail commenced.

Stamps of Great Britain were used between May 1858 and the end of March 1860 when control of the postal services passed to the local authorities. In the years which followed, prior to the introduction of St. Christopher stamps in April 1870, a circular "PAID" handstamp was used on overseas mail.

BASSETERRE

Stamps of GREAT BRITAIN cancelled "A 12" as Type Z **1** of Jamaica.

1858–60.

Z1	1d. rose-red (1857), perf 14	£750
Z2	2d. blue (1858) (Plate No. 7)	£1500
Z3	4d. rose (1857)	£500
Z4	6d. lilac (1856)	£250
Z5	1s. green (1856)	£2250

PRICES FOR STAMPS ON COVER	
Nos. 1/9	from × 25
Nos. 11/21	from × 30
Nos. 22/6	from × 25
No. 27	—
No. 28	from × 30
Nos. R1/6	—

1

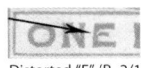

Distorted "E" (R. 2/1)

1870 (1 Apr)–**82**. Wmk Crown CC.

(a) P 12½

1	**1**	1d. dull rose	90·00	50·00
		a. Wmk sideways	£225	£160
		w. Wmk inverted	—	£250
2		1d. magenta *(shades)* (1871)	80·00	32·00
		a. Wmk sideways	†	£950
		w. Wmk inverted	£170	80·00
		x. Wmk reversed		
4		6d. yellow-green	£120	19·00
		w. Wmk inverted		
5		6d. green (1871)	£120	7·50
		w. Wmk inverted	—	£130
		x. Wmk reversed	£475	£300

(b) P 14

6	**1**	1d. magenta *(shades)* (1875)	80·00	7·00
		a. Bisected diag or vert (½d.) *(on cover)* (3.82)	†	£2500
		w. Wmk inverted	£250	£110
7		2½d. red-brown (11.79)	£190	£250
8		4d. blue (11.79)	£200	15·00
		a. Wmk sideways	£1700	£225
		w. Wmk inverted	£425	60·00
9		6d. green (1876)	60·00	5·00
		a. Imperf between (pair)		
		b. Wmk sideways	£1000	£250
		w. Wmk inverted	—	£130
		x. Wmk reversed	£400	

The magenta used for the 1d. was a fugitive colour which reacts to both light and water.

No. 1a is known with both Crown to left of CC and Crown to right of CC, *as seen from the back of the stamp.*

No. 6a was authorised for use between March and June 1882 to make up the 2½d. letter rate and for ½d. book post.

1882 (June)–**90**. Wmk Crown CA. P 14.

11	**1**	½d. dull green	6·50	4·25
		a. Wmk sideways	£300	
		x. Wmk reversed	£300	
12		1d. dull magenta	£550	70·00
		a. Bisected diagonally (½d.) *(on cover)*	†	—
		w. Wmk inverted	£1000	£200
13		1d. carmine-rose (2.84)	3·50	2·25
		a. Bisected (½d.) *(on cover)*	†	—
		b. Distorted "E"	35·00	
		w. Wmk inverted	£200	
		x. Wmk reversed	£250	
14		2½d. pale red-brown	£180	60·00
15		2½d. deep red-brown	£190	65·00
16		2½d. ultramarine (2.84)	5·50	1·50
		x. Wmk reversed	£300	
17		4d. blue	£550	16·00
		w. Wmk inverted		
18		4d. grey (10.84)	1·75	1·00
		w. Wmk inverted	£200	
19		6d. olive-brown (3.90)	90·00	£400
		w. Wmk inverted		
20		1s. mauve (6.86)	£100	65·00
		w. Wmk inverted	—	£190
21		1s. bright mauve (1890)	90·00	£180
19s/20s Optd "SPECIMEN" *Set of* 2			£120	

FOUR PENCE
(2)

Halfpenny
(3)

1884 (Dec). No. 9 surch with T **2** by The Advertiser Press.

22	**1**	4d. on 6d. green	70·00	50·00
		a. Full stop after "PENCE"	70·00	50·00

---

		b. Surch double	—	£2750
		w. Wmk inverted	—	£300

No. 22a occurred on alternate stamps.

1885 (Mar). No. 13 bisected and each half diagonally surch with T **3**.

23	**1**	½d. on half of 1d. carmine-rose	29·00	42·00
		a. Unsevered pair	£120	£120
		ab. Ditto, one surch inverted	£425	£300
		b. Surch inverted	£225	£110
		ba. Ditto, unsevered pair	£1000	
		c. Surch double		

ONE PENNY.
(4)

4d.
(5)

1886 (June). No. 9 surch with T **4** or **5** each showing a manuscript line through the original value.

24	**1**	1d. on 6d. green	20·00	50·00
		a. Surch inverted	£9000	
		b. Surch double	—	£2500
25		4d. on 6d. green	60·00	95·00
		a. No stop after "d"	£225	£325
		b. Surch double	£2500	£2750

No. 24b is only known penmarked with dates between 21 July and 3 August 1886, or with violet handstamp.

1887 (May). No. 11 surch with T **4** showing a manuscript line through the original value.

26	**1**	1d. on ½d. dull green	50·00	60·00

The genuine surcharge on No. 26 is from worn type and always shows a stop after "PENNY". A similar surcharge from fresh type and without stop is of clandestine origin.

ONE PENNY.
(7)

1888 (May). No. 16 surch.

(a) With T **4**. *Original value unobliterated.*

27	**1**	1d. on 2½d. ultramarine	£22000	£14000

(b) With T **7** *showing a manuscript line through the original value*

28	**1**	1d. on 2½d. ultramarine	70·00	70·00
		a. Surch inverted	£25000	£11000

The 1d. of Antigua was used provisionally in St. Christopher between January and March 1890 during a shortage of 1d. stamps. Such use can be distinguished by the postmark, which is "A 12" in place of "A02" (*price from* £130 *used*).

REVENUE STAMPS USED FOR POSTAGE

SAINT KITTS NEVIS REVENUE

Saint Christopher
(R **1**)

SAINT KITTS NEVIS REVENUE
(R **2**)

1883. Nos. F6 and F8 of Nevis optd with Type R **1**, in violet. Wmk Crown CA. P 14.

R1		1d. lilac-mauve	£375	
R2		6d. green	£130	£170

1885. Optd with Type R **2**. Wmk Crown CA. P 14.

R3	**1**	1d. rose	2·75	18·00
		a. Distorted "E"	27·00	
R4		3d. mauve	16·00	65·00
R5		6d. orange-brown	21·00	50·00
R6		1s. olive	4·00	42·00

Other fiscal stamps with overprints as above also exist, but none of these were ever available for postal purposes.

The stamps for St. Christopher were superseded by the general issue for Leeward Islands on 31 October 1890.

NEVIS

Little is known concerning the early postal affairs of Nevis, although several covers exist from the island in the 1660s. It is recorded that the British GPO was to establish a branch office on the island under an Act of Parliament of 1710, although arrangements may not have been finalised for a number of years afterwards. Nevis appears as "a new office" in the PO Accounts of 1787.

Stamps of Great Britain were used on the island from May 1858 until the colonial authorities assumed control of the postal service on 1 May 1860. Between this date and the introduction of Nevis stamps in 1862 No. CC1 was again used on overseas mail.

CHARLESTOWN

CROWNED-CIRCLE HANDSTAMPS

CC **1**

CC1		CC **1** NEVIS (R.) (9.1852)	*Price on cover*	£4500

No. CC1, struck in red, was in use between 1854 and 1858, and again between 1860 and 1862, prior to the introduction of Nevis stamps. Later examples, struck in black (Nov 1870 and Jan 1871) or red (Jan 1882), date from periods of stamp shortage.

Stamps of GREAT BRITAIN cancelled "A 09" as Type Z **1** of Jamaica.

1858 (May)–**60**.

Z1	1d. rose-red (1857), perf 14	£650
Z2	2d. blue (1858) (Plate No. 8)	£2000
Z3	4d. rose (1857)	£550
Z4	6d. lilac (1856)	£300
Z5	1s. green (1856)	

PRICES FOR STAMPS ON COVER	
No. 1	—
Nos. 2/3	from × 30
No. 4	—
Nos. 9/10	from × 30
Nos. 11/14	from × 30
Nos. 15/17	from × 100
No. 18	from × 20
Nos. 19/21	from × 20
No. 22	from × 40
No. 23	from × 20
No. 24	—
Nos. 25/7	from × 20
Nos. 28/9	—
No. 30	from × 40
No. 31	from × 60
Nos. 32/3	—
No. 34	from × 15
Nos. 35/6	from × 10
Nos. F1/8	from × 30

1   **2**

3   **4**

The design on the stamps refers to a medicinal spring on the island, and is taken from the Great Seal of the colony.

(Recess Nissen & Parker, London)

1862 (19 July). Greyish paper. P 13.

1	**1**	1d. dull lake	£110	55·00
2	**2**	4d. rose	£160	75·00
3	**3**	6d. grey-lilac	£170	60·00
4	**4**	1s. green	£350	90·00

Types **1/4** were printed in sheets of 12 (3×4). Each position on the original engraved plates was individually engraved by hand.

The greyish paper used for Nos. 1/4 sometimes shows a degree of blueing, but there was only one printing of each value.

Crossed lines on hill

1867 (Jan)–**76**. White paper. P 15.

9	**1**	1d. pale red	65·00	50·00
10		1d. deep red	65·00	50·00
11	**2**	4d. orange	£150	23·00
12		4d. deep orange	£150	23·00
13	**4**	1s. blue-green	£300	40·00
14		1s. yellow-green (1876)	£850	£110
		a. Vertically laid paper	—	£5000
		b. No. 9 on sheet with crossed lines on hill	£3500	£500
		c. Ditto. On laid paper	†	£16000

Examples of the 4d. exist showing part of a papermakers watermark reading "A. COWAN & SONS EXTRA SUPERFINE".

(Lithographed by transfer from the engraved plates Nissen and Parker, London)

1871–78.

(a) P 15

15	**1**	1d. pale rose-red	32·00	25·00
		a. Imperf (pair)	£1800	
16		1d. deep rose-red	45·00	29·00
17		1d. vermilion-red (1877)	42·00	42·00
		a. Bisected (½d.) *(on cover)*	†	—
18	**2**	4d. orange-yellow (1878)	£170	38·00
		a. Imperf between (vert pair)	£11000	
19	**3**	6d. grey (1878)	£225	£200
20	**4**	1s. pale green (1878)	90·00	£110
		a. Imperf		
		b. Imperf between (horiz strip of 3)	£16000	
		c. No. 9 on sheet with crossed lines on hill	£250	
21		1s. deep green	£120	£160
		c. No. 9 on sheet with crossed lines on hill	£1000	

(b) P 11½

22	**1**	1d. vermilion-red (1878)	60·00	55·00
		a. Bisected (½d.) *(on cover)*	†	—
		b. Imperf (pair)		
		c. Imperf between (horiz pair)	£1100	
		d. Perf compound of 11½ and 15		

A total of 24 different transfers were used for the 1d. value, in a sequence of seven printings between June 1871 and Feb 1878. The retouches listed below occurred in the group of four transfers used for the 31 Dec 1876 printing.

Four different transfers were used for the 4d. value, but only one for the 6d. The two printings of the 1s. value, in Feb 1878 (pale green) and Nov 1878 (deep green) were from different transfers. The "crossed lines on hill" variety was retouched early in the second printing, so that No. 21c is only found on a small number of sheets.

RETOUCHES. 1d. Vermilion-red Lithograph (No. 17).

i.	No. 1 on sheet (Pane "A"). Top of hill over kneeling figure redrawn by five thick lines and eight small slanting lines	£150	£160
ii.	No. 1 on sheet (Pane "C"). Another retouch. Three series of short vertical strokes behind the kneeling figure	£150	£160
iii.	No. 3 on sheet (Pane "A"). Right upper corner star and border below star retouched	£150	£160
iv.	No. 9 on sheet (Pane "B"). Retouch in same position as on No. 3 but differing in detail	£170	£180
v.	No. 12 on sheet (Pane "C"). Dress of standing figure retouched by a number of horizontal and vertical lines	£150	£160

5 (Die I) **(6)**

(Typo D.L.R.)

1879–80. Wmk Crown CC. P 14.

23	**5**	1d. lilac-mauve (1880)	80·00	50·00
		a. Bisected (½d.) (*on cover*)	†	£1000
		w. Wmk inverted		
24		2½d. red-brown	£160	90·00

1882–90. Wmk Crown CA. P 14.

25	**5**	½d. dull green (11.83)	14·00	27·00
		a. Top left triangle detached	£425	
26		1d. lilac-mauve	£110	48·00
		a. Bisected (½d.) on cover (1883)	†	£700
27		1d. dull rose (11.83)	42·00	35·00
		a. Carmine (1884)	20·00	20·00
		ab. Top left triangle detached	£600	
28		2½d. red-brown	£120	50·00
29		2½d. ultramarine (11.83)	23·00	27·00
		a. Top left triangle detached	£800	
30		4d. blue	£350	50·00
31		4d. grey (1884)	24·00	9·00
		a. Top left triangle detached	£800	£450
32		6d. green (11.83)	£450	£350
33		6d. chestnut (10.88)	24·00	75·00
		a. Top left triangle detached	£850	
34		1s. pale violet (3.90)	£110	£200
		a. Top left triangle detached	£1600	
33s/4s Optd "SPECIMEN" *Set of 2*			£110	

For illustration of the "top left triangle detached" variety, which occurs on Plate 2 R. 3/3 of the right pane, see above No. 21 of Antigua.

1883 (4 Sept). No. 26 bisected vertically and surch with T **6**, reading upwards or downwards.

35		½d. on half 1d. lilac-mauve (V.)	£1100	55·00
		a. Surch double	—	£350
		b. Surch on half "REVENUE" stamp No. F6	—	£550
36		½d. on half 1d. lilac-mauve	£1100	50·00
		a. Surch double		£325
		b. Unsevered pair	£6500	£750
		c. Surch on half "REVENUE" stamp No. F6	—	£550

FISCALS USED FOR POSTAGE

Revenue   REVENUE
(F 1)   (F 2)

1882.

(a) Stamps of 1876–78 optd with Type F **1** *by Nissen & Parker, London*

F1	**1**	1d. bright red	£150	£100
F2		1d. rose	85·00	40·00
F3	**2**	4d. orange	£170	
F4	**3**	6d. grey	£325	
F5	**4**	1s. green	£350	
		a. No. 9 on sheet with crossed lines on hill		

(b) Nos. 26, 30 and 32 optd with Type F **2** *by D.L.R.*

F6	**5**	1d. lilac-mauve	80·00	55·00
		a. Bisected (½d.) (*on cover*)	†	—
F7		4d. blue	55·00	60·00
F8		6d. green	29·00	65·00

Nos. F1/5 were produced from fresh transfers. Similar "Revenue." handstamps, with stop, were also applied to postage issues.

The stamps of Nevis were superseded by the general issue for Leeward Islands on 31 October 1890.

ST. KITTS-NEVIS

CROWN COLONY

Stamps for the combined colony were introduced in 1903, and were used concurrently with the general issues of Leeward Islands until the latter were withdrawn on 1 July 1956.

PRICES FOR STAMPS ON COVER TO 1945	
Nos. 1/9	*from × 3*
No. 10	
Nos. 11/20	*from × 3*
No. 21	
Nos. 22/3	*from × 15*
Nos. 24/34	*from × 3*
Nos. 35/6	
Nos. 37/47	*from × 2*
Nos. 47a/b	

PRICES FOR STAMPS ON COVER TO 1945	
Nos. 48/57	*from × 2*
Nos. 58/60	
Nos. 61/4	*from × 2*
Nos. 65/7	*from × 5*
Nos. 68/77	*from × 2*

1 Christopher Columbus   **2** Medicinal Spring

(Typo D.L.R.)

1903. Wmk Crown CA. P 14.

1	**1**	½d. dull purple and deep green	1·75	70
2	**2**	1d. grey-black and carmine	4·75	20
3	**1**	2d. dull purple and brown	4·25	11·00
4		2½d. grey-black and blue	19·00	5·50
5	**2**	3d. deep green and orange	24·00	30·00
6	**1**	6d. grey-black and bright purple	8·00	48·00
7		1s. grey-green and orange	7·50	11·00
8	**2**	2s. deep green and grey-black	12·00	20·00
9	**1**	2s.6d. grey-black and violet	18·00	50·00
10	**2**	5s. dull purple and sage-green	70·00	60·00
1/10 *Set of 10*			£150	£200
1s/10s Optd "SPECIMEN" *Set of 10*			£160	

1905–18. Chalk-surfaced paper (1d. (No. 13), 5s.) or ordinary paper (others). Wmk Mult Crown CA. P 14.

11	**1**	½d. dull purple and deep green	16·00	8·00
12		½d. grey-green (1907)	1·00	1·00
		a. Dull blue-green (1916)	1·00	3·75
13	**2**	1d. grey-black and carmine (1906)	9·50	25
14		1d. carmine (1907)	2·25	15
		a. Scarlet (1916)	1·25	20
15	**1**	2d. dull purple and brown	11·00	8·00
		a. Chalk-surfaced paper (1906)	6·50	8·00
16		2½d. grey-black and blue (1907)	40·00	6·00
17		2½d. bright blue (1907)	2·50	50
18	**2**	3d. deep green and orange	38·00	20·00
		a. Chalk-surfaced paper (1906)	3·50	2·75
19	**1**	6d. grey-black and deep violet	42·00	55·00
		a. Chalk-surfaced paper. Grey-black and deep purple (1908)	25·00	25·00
		ab. Grey-black and bright purple (1916)	12·00	35·00
20		1s. grey-green and orange (1909)	50·00	65·00
		a. Chalk-surfaced paper	3·50	35·00
21	**2**	5s. dull purple and sage-green (11.18)	45·00	£120
11/21 *Set of 11*			£130	£180
12s, 14s, 17s Optd "SPECIMEN" *Set of 3*			70·00	

WAR TAX   WAR STAMP
(3)   **(3a)**

1916 (Oct). Optd with T **3**. Wmk Mult Crown CA. P 14.

22	**1**	½d. dull blue-green (No. 12a)	2·50	50
		a. Deep green	1·00	50
		s. Optd "SPECIMEN"	50·00	
		x. Wmk reversed	55·00	

No. 22a was a special printing produced for this overprint.

1918 (26 July). Optd with T **3a**. Wmk Mult Crown CA. P 14.

23	**1**	1½d. orange	1·75	1·00
		a. Short opt (right pane R. 10/1)	26·00	
		s. Optd "SPECIMEN"	55·00	

No. 23 was a special printing produced for this overprint. No. 23a shows the overprint 2 mm high instead of 2½ mm.

4   **5**

(Typo D.L.R.)

1920–22. Ordinary paper (½d. to 2½d.) or chalk-surfaced paper (others). Wmk Mult Crown CA (sideways*). P 14.

24	**4**	½d. blue-green	3·75	5·50
		a. "C" of "CA" missing from wmk	£500	
25	**5**	1d. scarlet	3·75	6·00
26	**4**	1½d. orange-yellow	1·25	1·75
		x. Wmk sideways reversed	£150	
		y. Wmk sideways inverted and reversed	£200	
27	**5**	2d. slate-grey	3·25	7·50
28	**4**	2½d. ultramarine	8·00	9·00
		a. "A" of "CA" missing from wmk	£600	
29	**5**	3d. purple/yellow	1·75	11·00
30	**4**	6d. dull purple and bright mauve	3·50	11·00
31	**5**	1s. grey and black/green	3·50	4·00
32	**4**	2s. dull purple and blue/blue	27·00	55·00
		x. Wmk sideways reversed	£325	
33	**5**	2s.6d. grey and red/blue	5·00	42·00
		x. Wmk sideways reversed	£350	
		y. Wmk sideways inverted and reversed	£325	
34	**4**	5s. green and red/pale yellow	5·00	42·00
		x. Wmk sideways reversed	£250	
35	**5**	10s. green and red/green	12·00	48·00
36	**4**	£1 purple and black/red (1922)	£300	£375
24/36 *Set of 13*			£350	£550
24s/36s Optd "SPECIMEN" *Set of 13*			£350	

*The normal sideways watermark shows Crown to left of CA, as seen from the back of the stamp.

Examples of most values are known showing a forged St. Kitts postmark dated "8 DE 23".

1921–29. Chalk-surfaced paper (2½d. (No. 44), 3d. (No. 45a) and 6d. to 5s.) or ordinary paper (others). Wmk Mult Script CA (sideways*).

37	**4**	½d. blue-green	2·50	1·50
		a. Yellow-green (1922)	3·75	15
38	**5**	1d. rose-carmine	1·25	15
		sa. Perf "SPECIMEN" (1929)	70·00	
39		1d. deep violet (1922)	7·50	1·00
		a. Pale violet (1929)	12·00	1·75
		sa. Opt "SPECIMEN" double	£500	
40	**4**	1½d. red (1925)	7·50	1·00
40a		1½d. red-brown (1929)	2·25	30
41	**5**	2d. slate-grey (1922)	1·00	60
42	**4**	2½d. pale bright blue (1922)	4·50	2·00
43		2½d. brown (1922)	4·50	12·00
44		2½d. ultramarine (1927)	1·50	1·00
45	**5**	3d. dull ultramarine (1922)	1·50	3·00
45a		3d. purple/yellow (1927)	2·25	2·00
46	**4**	6d. dull and bright purple (1924)	8·50	6·00
		aw. Wmk Crown to right of CA	8·00	6·50
46b	**5**	1s. black (1929)	6·50	3·25
47	**4**	2s. purple and blue/blue (1922)	15·00	38·00
		asa. Opt "SPECIMEN" double	£700	
47b	**5**	2s.6d. black and red/blue (1927)	24·00	29·00
47c	**4**	5s. green and red/yellow (1929)	55·00	£100
37/47c *Set of 16*			£130	£170
37s/47cs Optd or Perf (1½d. red-brown, 1s., 5s.) "SPECIMEN" *Set of 16*			£400	

*The normal watermark shows Crown to left of CA, as seen from the back of the stamp.

6 Old Road Bay and Mount Misery   **1d.** Damaged second "E" of "REVENUE"

(Typo D.L.R.)

1923 (1 Jan). Tercentenary of Colony. Chalk-surfaced paper. P 14.

(a) Wmk Mult Script CA (sideways)

48	**6**	½d. black and green	2·25	9·00
49		1d. black and bright violet	4·50	3·00
		a. Damaged second "E" of "REVENUE"	£160	£200
50		1½d. black and scarlet	4·50	10·00
51		2d. black and slate-grey	3·75	1·75
52		2½d. black and brown	6·00	35·00
53		3d. black and ultramarine	6·00	15·00
54		6d. black and bright purple	9·50	32·00
55		1s. black and sage-green	14·00	15·00
56		2s. black and blue/blue	50·00	85·00
57		2s.6d. black and red/blue	50·00	£100
58		10s. black and red/emerald	£325	£600

(b) Wmk Mult Crown CA (sideways)

59	**6**	5s. black and red/pale yellow	90·00	£250
60		£1 black and purple/red	£800	£1600
48/60 *Set of 13*			£1200	£2250
48s/60s Optd "SPECIMEN" *Set of 13*			£800	

Examples of all values are known showing a forged St. Kitts postmark dated "8 DE 23".

1935 (6 May). Silver Jubilee. As Nos. 91/4 of Antigua, but ptd by Waterlow. P 11×12.

61		1d. deep blue and scarlet	1·00	70
		k. Kite and vertical log	£160	£170
		l. Kite and horizontal log	£250	£250
62		1½d. ultramarine and grey	75	1·00
		k. Kite and vertical log	£130	£140
63		2½d. brown and deep blue	1·00	1·00
		k. Kite and vertical log	£130	£140
64		1s. slate and purple	16·00	17·00
		k. Kite and vertical log	£500	
		l. Kite and horizontal log	£475	£550
61/4 *Set of 4*			17·00	18·00
61s/4s Perf "SPECIMEN" *Set of 4*			£100	

For illustrations of plate varieties see Omnibus section following Zanzibar.

1937 (12 May). Coronation. As Nos. 95/7 of Antigua, but ptd by D.L.R. P 14.

65		1d. scarlet	30	25
66		1½d. buff	40	10
67		2½d. bright blue	60	1·60
65/7 *Set of 3*			1·10	1·75
65s/7s Perf "SPECIMEN" *Set of 3*			90·00	

Nos. 61/7 are inscribed "ST. CHRISTOPHER AND NEVIS".

7 King George VI   **8** King George VI and Medicinal Spring

9 King George VI and Christopher Columbus   **10** King George VI and Anguilla Island

Break in value tablet (R. 12/5) (1947 ptg only)

6d. Break in oval (R. 12/1) (1938 ptg only)

Break in value tablet frame (R. 3/2)

Break in value tablet frame (R. 12/3) (ptgs between 1941 and 1945)

5s. Break in frame above ornament (R. 2/4) (ptgs between 1941 and 1950)

5s. Break in oval at foot (R. 12/5) (ptgs between 1941 and 1945 only). Sometimes touched-in by hand painting

5s. Break in oval at left (R. 7/1) (ptgs between 1941 and 1945 only)

(Typo; centre litho (T **10**). D.L.R.)

1938 (15 Aug)–**50.** Chalk-surfaced paper (10s., £1). Wmk Mult Script CA (sideways on T **8** and **9**). P 14 (T **7** and **10**) or 13×12 (T **8/9**).

68	**7**	½d. green	4·25	20
		a. *Blue-green (5.4.43)*	10	10
69		1d. scarlet	7·50	70
		a. *Carmine (5.43)*	2·75	50
		b. *Carmine-pink (4.47)*	65·00	16·00
		c. *Rose-red (7.47)*	4·00	80
70		1½d. orange	20	30
71	**8**	2d. scarlet and grey	32·00	2·75
		a. Chalk-surfaced paper. *Carmine and deep grey (18.2.41*)*	55·00	12·00
		b. *Perf 14. Scarlet and pale grey (6.43*)*	1·50	1·25
		ba. *Scarlet and deep grey (6.42*)*	28·00	2·25
		c. Perf 14. Chalk-surfaced paper. *Scarlet and pale grey (2.50*)*	9·00	5·50
72	**7**	2½d. ultramarine	10·00	30
		a. *Bright ultramarine (5.4.43)*	70	30
73	**8**	3d. dull reddish purple and scarlet	28·00	8·00
		a. Chalk-surfaced paper. *Brown-purple and carmine-red (1940)*	40·00	11·00
		b. Perf 14. Chalk-surfaced paper. *Dull reddish purple and carmine-red (6.43*)*	50·00	5·50
		c. Perf 14. Ordinary paper. *Reddish lilac and scarlet (8.46*)*	4·50	45·00
		d. Perf 14. Ordinary paper. *Purple and bright scarlet (1.46*)*	38·00	19·00
		da. Break in value tablet	£350	£400
		e. Perf 14. Chalk-surfaced paper. *Deep purple and scarlet (12.47*)*	£100	45·00
		f. Perf 14. Ordinary paper. *Rose-lilac and bright scarlet (1.49*)*	25·00	17·00
		g. Perf 14. Chalk-surfaced paper. *Deep reddish purple and bright scarlet (8.50*)*	15·00	15·00
74	**9**	6d. green and bright purple	12·00	3·00
		a. Break in oval	£200	
		b. Perf 14. Chalk-surfaced paper. *Green and deep claret (17.5.43*)*	55·00	14·00
		c. Perf 14. Ordinary paper. *Green and purple (10.44*)*	10·00	1·50
		d. Perf 14. Chalk-surfaced paper. *Green and purple (11.48*)*	10·00	6·00
75	**8**	1s. black and green	12·00	2·00
		a. Break in value tablet frame	£250	
		b. Perf 14 (8.43*)	4·75	85
		ba. Break in value tablet frame	£140	90·00
		c. Perf 14. Chalk-surfaced paper (7.50*)	17·00	12·00
		ca. Break in value tablet frame	£275	£400
76		2s.6d. black and scarlet	32·00	9·00
		a. Perf 14. Chalk-surfaced paper (12.43*)	29·00	6·00
		ab. Ordinary paper (5.45*)	12·00	4·50
77	**9**	5s. grey-green and scarlet	65·00	25·00
		a. Perf 14. Chalk-surfaced paper (25.10.43*)	£140	50·00
		ab. Break in value tablet frame	£800	£500
		ac. Break in frame above ornament	£800	£500
		ad. Break in oval at foot	£800	£500
		ae. Break in oval at left	£800	£500
		b. Perf 14. Ordinary paper. *Bluish green and scarlet (7.11.45*)*	28·00	12·00

		ba. Break in value tablet frame	£350	£250
		bb. Break in frame above ornament	£350	£250
		bc. Break in oval at foot	£350	£250
		bd. Break in oval at left	£350	£250
		c. Perf 14. Chalk-surfaced paper. *Green and scarlet-vermilion (10.50*)*	55·00	70·00
		cb. Break in frame above ornament	£500	
77e	**10**	10s. black and ultramarine (1.9.48)	14·00	19·00
77f		£1 black and brown (1.9.48)	18·00	23·00
68a/77f		*Set of 12*	85·00	60·00
68s/77s		Perf "SPECIMEN" *Set of 10*	£325	

*Earliest postmark date. Many printings were supplied to St. Kitts-Nevis considerably earlier. Details of many of the dates are taken, with permission, from *A Study of the King George VI Stamps of St. Kitts-Nevis* by P. L. Baldwin (2nd edition 1997).

1946 (1 Nov). Victory. As Nos. 110/11 of Antigua.

78		1½d. red-orange	10	10
79		3d. carmine	10	10
78s/9s		Perf "SPECIMEN" *Set of 2*	90·00	

1949 (3 Jan). Royal Silver Wedding. As Nos. 112/13 of Antigua.

80		2½d. ultramarine	10	50
81		5s. carmine	9·50	10·00

1949 (10 Oct). 75th Anniv of UPU. As Nos. 114/17 of Antigua.

82		2½d. ultramarine	15	30
83		3d. carmine-red	2·10	2·75
84		6d. magenta	20	2·00
85		1s. blue-green	20	40
		a. "A" of "CA" missing from wmk	—	£800
82/5		*Set of 4*	2·40	5·00

ANGUILLA

ANGUILLA

TERCENTENARY

TERCENTENARY

TERCENTENARY 1650-1950	TERCENTENARY 1650—1950
(11)	(12)

1950 (10 Nov). Tercentenary of British Settlement in Anguilla. Nos. 69c, 70 and 72a (perf 14) optd as T **11** and new ptgs of T **8/9** on chalk-surfaced paper perf 13×12½ optd as T **12**.

86	**7**	1d. rose-red	10	20
87		1½d. orange	10	50
		a. Error. Crown missing, W **9a**	£3250	
		b. Error. St. Edward's Crown, W **9b**	£1400	
88		2½d. bright ultramarine	25	20
89	**8**	3d. dull purple and scarlet	80	75
90	**9**	6d. green and bright purple	45	20
91	**8**	1s. black and green (R.)	1·40	25
		a. Break in value tablet frame	20·00	20·00
86/91		*Set of 6*	2·75	1·90

Nos. 87a/b occur on a row in the watermark, in which the crowns and letters "CA" alternate.

(New Currency. 100 cents = 1 West Indian dollar)

1951 (16 Feb). Inauguration of BWI University College. As Nos. 118/19 of Antigua.

92		3c. black and yellow-orange	30	15
93		12c. turquoise-green and magenta	30	2·00

ST. CHRISTOPHER, NEVIS AND ANGUILLA

LEGISLATIVE COUNCIL

13 Bath House and Spa, Nevis

14 Warner Park

 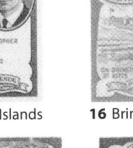

15 Map of the Islands

16 Brimstone Hill

17 Nevis from the Sea, North

18 Pinney's Beach

 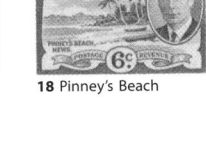

19 Sir Thomas Warner's Tomb

20 Old Road Bay

21 Sea Island Cotton

22 The Treasury

23 Salt Pond, Anguilla

24 Sugar Factory

(Recess Waterlow)

1952 (14 June). T **13/24**. Wmk Mult Script CA. P 12½.

94	**13**	1c. deep green and ochre	15	3·00
95	**14**	2c. green	1·00	1·00
96	**15**	3c. carmine-red and violet	30	1·25
97	**16**	4c. scarlet	20	20
98	**17**	5c. bright blue and grey	30	10
99	**18**	6c. ultramarine	30	15
100	**19**	12c. deep blue and reddish brown	1·25	10
101	**20**	24c. black and carmine-red	1·25	10
102	**21**	48c. olive and chocolate	3·50	6·00
103	**22**	60c. ochre and deep green	2·25	4·50
104	**23**	$1.20 deep green and ultramarine	7·50	6·50
105	**24**	$4.80 green and carmine	16·00	20·00
94/105		*Set of 12*	30·00	38·00

1953 (2 June). Coronation. As No. 120 of Antigua.

106		2c. black and bright green	30	30

25 Sombrero Lighthouse

26 Map of Anguilla and Dependencies

(Recess Waterlow (until 1961), then D.L.R.)

1954 (1 Mar)–**63.** Designs previously used for King George VI issue, but with portrait of Queen Elizabeth II as in T **25/6** or new values and designs (½c., 8c., $2.40). Wmk Mult Script CA. P 12½.

106a	**23**	½c. deep olive (3.7.56)	50	10
107	**13**	1c. deep green and ochre	20	10
		a. *Deep green and orange-ochre (13.2.62)*	1·25	3·75
		b. *Imperf vert (horiz strip of 3)*	†	£9000
108	**14**	2c. green	1·00	10
		a. *Yellow-green (31.7.63)*	5·00	8·50
109	**15**	3c. carmine-red and violet	65	10
		a. *Carmine and deep violet (31.7.63)*	5·00	9·00
110	**16**	4c. scarlet	15	10
111	**17**	5c. bright blue and grey	15	10
112	**18**	6c. ultramarine	70	10
		a. *Blue (19.2.63)*	1·75	1·00
112b		8c. grey-black (1.2.57)	3·00	25
113	**19**	12c. deep blue and red-brown	30	10
114	**20**	24c. black and carmine-red (1.12.54)	30	10
115	**21**	48c. olive-bistre and chocolate (1.12.54)	2·25	1·50
116	**22**	60c. ochre and deep green (1.12.54)	6·50	7·50
117	**23**	$1.20 deep green and ultramarine (1.12.54)	26·00	4·00
		a. *Deep green and violet-blue (19.2.63)*	55·00	19·00
117b	**26**	$2.40 black and red-orange (1.2.57)	26·00	18·00
118	**24**	$4.80 green and carmine (1.12.54)	26·00	11·00
106a/18		*Set of 15*	85·00	38·00

27 Alexander Hamilton and View of Nevis

(Des Eva Wilkin. Recess Waterlow)

1957 (11 Jan). Birth Bicentenary of Alexander Hamilton. Wmk Mult Script CA. P 12½.

119	**27**	24c. green and deep blue	60	25

1958 (22 Apr). Inauguration of British Caribbean Federation. As Nos. 135/7 of Antigua.

120		3c. deep green	1·25	15
121		6c. blue	1·25	2·50
122		12c. scarlet	1·25	35
120/2		*Set of 3*	3·25	2·75

MINISTERIAL GOVERNMENT

28 One Penny Stamp of 1862

(Recess Waterlow)

1961 (15 July). Nevis Stamp Centenary. T **28** and similar horiz designs. W w **12**. P 14.

123		2c. red-brown and green	30	1·00
124		8c. red-brown and deep blue	35	15
125		12c. black and carmine-red	40	20
126		24c. deep bluish green and red-orange	60	30
123/6 *Set of 4*			1·50	1·50

It is now accepted that the first stamps of Nevis were issued in 1862. Designs:— 8c. 4d. stamp of 1862; 12c. 6d. stamp of 1862; 24c. 1s. stamp of 1862.

1963 (2 Sept). Red Cross Centenary. As Nos. 147/8 of Antigua.

127		3c. red and black	20	20
128		12c. red and blue	40	60

32 New Lighthouse, Sombrero

33 Loading Sugar Cane, St. Kitts

34 Pall Mall Square, Basseterre

35 Gateway, Brimstone Hill Fort, St Kitts

36 Nelson's Spring, Nevis

37 Grammar School, St. Kitts

38 Crater, Mt Misery, St. Kitts

39 Hibiscus

40 Sea Island cotton, Nevis

41 Boat building, Anguilla

42 White-crowned Pigeon

43 St. George's Church Tower, Basseterre

44 Alexander Hamilton

45 Map of St. Kitts-Nevis

46 Map of Anguilla

47 Arms of St. Christopher, Nevis and Anguilla

(Des V. Whiteley. Photo Harrison)

1963 (20 Nov)–**69**. T **32/47**. W w **12** (upright). P 14.

129	**32**	½c. sepia and light blue	10	10
		w. Wmk inverted	£225	
130	**33**	1c. multicoloured	10	10
131	**34**	2c. multicoloured	10	10
		a. Yellow omitted (White fountain and church)	£300	
		w. Wmk inverted	†	£110
132	**35**	3c. multicoloured	10	10
		w. Wmk inverted	†	£100
133	**36**	4c. multicoloured	10	10
		w. Wmk inverted		
134	**37**	5c. multicoloured	3·75	10
135	**38**	6c. multicoloured	10	10
		w. Wmk inverted (19.12.69)	30	30
136	**39**	10c. multicoloured	15	10
137	**40**	15c. multicoloured	70	10
		w. Wmk inverted		
138	**41**	20c. multicoloured	30	10
139	**42**	25c. multicoloured	2·25	10
		a. Turquoise-green background (13.4.65)	13·00	1·75
		w. Wmk inverted	—	80·00
140	**43**	50c. multicoloured	75	25
141	**44**	60c. multicoloured	1·00	30
142	**45**	$1 greenish yellow and blue	2·50	40
143	**46**	$2.50 multicoloured	3·50	4·00
144	**47**	$5 multicoloured	12·00	13·00
129/44 *Set of 16*			24·00	16·00

The 1, 4, 5, 6, 10 and 20c. values exist with PVA gum as well as gum arabic.

See also Nos. 166/71.

ARTS FESTIVAL ST KITTS 1964
(48)

49 Festival Emblem

1964 (14 Sept). Arts Festival. Nos. 132 and 139 optd as T **48**.

145		3c. Gateway, Brimstone Hill Fort, St. Kitts	10	15
		a. Opt double	£400	
146		25c. White-crowned Pigeon	20	15
		a. "FESTIVAI" (R. 1/10)	75·00	
		w. Wmk inverted	—	8·50

1965 (17 May). ITU Centenary. As Nos. 166/7 of Antigua.

147		2c. bistre-yellow and rose-carmine	10	10
148		50c. turquoise-blue and yellow-olive	40	50

1965 (15 Oct). International Co-operation Year. As Nos. 168/9 of Antigua.

149		2c. reddish purple and turquoise-green	10	20
150		25c. deep bluish green and lavender	65	10

1966 (24 Jan). Churchill Commemoration. As Nos. 170/3 of Antigua.

151		½c. new blue	10	3·00
		a. Value omitted	£500	
		b. Value at left instead of right	£140	
152		3c. deep green	35	10
153		15c. brown	80	20
154		25c. bluish violet	85	20
151/4 *Set of 4*			1·75	3·25

1966 (4 Feb). Royal Visit. As Nos. 174/5 of Antigua.

155		3c. black and ultramarine	25	30
156		25c. black and magenta	30	30

1966 (1 July). World Cup Football Championship. As Nos. 176/7 of Antigua.

157		6c. violet, yellow-green, lake and yellow-brown	40	20
158		25c. chocolate, blue-green, lake and yellow-brown	60	10

(Photo Harrison)

1966 (15 Aug). Arts Festival. P 14×14½.

159	**49**	3c. black, buff, emerald-green and gold	10	10
160		25c. black, buff, emerald-green and silver	20	10

1966 (20 Sept). Inauguration of WHO Headquarters, Geneva. As Nos. 178/9 of Antigua.

161		3c. black, yellow-green and light blue	10	10
162		40c. black, light purple and yellow-brown	30	20

1966 (1 Dec). 20th Anniv of UNESCO. As Nos. 196/8 of Antigua.

163		3c. slate-violet, red, yellow and orange	10	10
164		6c. orange-yellow, violet and deep olive	10	10
165		40c. black, bright purple and orange	30	35
163/5 *Set of 3*			45	50

ASSOCIATED STATEHOOD

1967–69. As Nos. 129, 131/2, 137, 139 and 142 but wmk sideways.

166	**32**	½c. sepia and light blue (9.1.69)	20	2·75
167	**34**	2c. multicoloured (27.6.67)	1·75	10
168	**35**	3c. multicoloured (16.7.68)	20	10
169	**40**	15c. multicoloured (16.7.68)	70	30
170	**42**	25c. multicoloured (16.7.68)	2·50	20
171	**45**	$1 greenish yellow and blue (16.7.68)	5·00	4·00
		a. Greenish yellow and ultramarine-blue (19.12.69)	13·00	6·50
166/71 *Set of 6*			9·25	6·50

The 2c. and $1 values exist with PVA gum as well as gum arabic.

Nos. 172/81 are vacant.

50 Government Headquarters, Basseterre

53 John Wesley and Cross

(Des V. Whiteley. Photo Harrison)

1967 (1 July). Statehood. T **50** and similar horiz designs. Multicoloured. W w **12**. P 14½×14.

182		3c. Type **50**	10	10
183		10c. National Flag	10	10
		w. Wmk inverted	28·00	
184		25c. Coat of Arms	15	15
182/4 *Set of 3*			30	30

(Litho D.L.R.)

1967 (1 Dec). West Indies Methodist Conference. T **53** and similar vert designs. P 13×13½.

185		3c. black, cerise and reddish violet	10	10
186		25c. black, light greenish blue and blue	15	10
187		40c. black, yellow and orange	15	15
185/7 *Set of 3*			35	30

Designs:—25c. Charles Wesley and Cross; 40c. Thomas Coke and Cross.

56 Handley Page H.P.R.7 Dart Herald Aircraft over *Jamaica Producer* (freighter)

57 Dr. Martin Luther King

(Des and litho D.L.R.)

1968 (30 July). Caribbean Free Trade Area. W w **12** (sideways). P 13.

188	**56**	25c. multicoloured	40	10
189		50c. multicoloured	40	20

(Des G. Vasarhelyi. Litho Enschedé)

1968 (30 Sept). Martin Luther King Commemoration. W w **12**. P 12×12½.

190	**57**	50c. multicoloured	15	10

58 *Mystic Nativity* (Botticelli)

60 Tarpon Snook

(Des and photo Harrison)

1968 (27 Nov). Christmas. Paintings. T **58** and similar vert design. Multicoloured. W w **12** (sideways). P 14½×14.

191	12c. Type **58**	10	10
192	25c. *The Adoration of the Magi* (Rubens)..	10	10
193	40c. Type **58**	15	10
194	50c. As 25c.	15	10
191/4 *Set of 4*		45	35

(Des G. Drummond. Photo Harrison)

1969 (25 Feb). Fish. T **60** and similar horiz designs. W w **12**. P 14×14½.

195	6c. multicoloured	10	10
196	12c. black, turquoise-green and greenish blue	15	10
197	40c. multicoloured	25	10
198	50c. multicoloured	30	15
195/8 *Set of 4*		70	40

Designs:—12c. Needlefish; 40c. Horse-eyed Jack; 50c. Blackfinned Snapper.

64 The Warner Badge and Islands

67 *The Adoration of the Kings* (Mostaert)

(Des V. Whiteley. Litho Format)

1969 (1 Sept). Sir Thomas Warner Commemoration. T **64** and similar horiz designs. Multicoloured. W w **12** (sideways). P 13½×14.

199	20c. Type **64**	10	10
200	25c. Sir Thomas Warner's tomb	10	10
201	40c. Charles I's commission	15	15
199/201 *Set of 3*		30	30

(Des Enschedé. Litho B.W.)

1969 (17 Nov). Christmas. Paintings. T **67** and similar vert design. Multicoloured. W w **12** (sideways). P 13½.

202	10c. Type **67**	10	10
203	25c. Type **67**	10	10
204	40c. *The Adoration of the Kings* (Geertgen)	10	10
205	50c. As 40c.	10	10
202/5 *Set of 4*		35	35

73 Portuguese Caravels (16th- cent)

(Des and litho J.W.)

1970 (2 Feb)–**74**. Designs as T **73** in black, pale orange and emerald (½c.) or multicoloured (others). W w **12** (upright on vert designs, sideways* on horiz designs). P 14.

206	½c. Pirates and treasure at Frigate Bay (vert)	10	10
	w. Wmk inverted (15.3.71)	20	20
207	1c. English two-decker warship, 1650 (vert)	30	10
208	2c. Naval flags of colonising nations (vert)	15	10
209	3c. Rapier hilt (17th-century) (vert)	15	10
210	4c. Type **73**	20	10
	w. Wmk Crown to right of CA (24.7.74)	70	50
211	5c. Sir Henry Morgan and fireships, 1669	60	60
	w. Wmk Crown to right of CA (24.7.74)	40	60
212	6c. L'Ollonois and pirate carrack (16th-century)	30	10
	w. Wmk Crown to right of CA (24.7.74)	40	50
213	10c. 17th-century smugglers' ship	30	10
	w. Wmk Crown to right of CA (24.7.74)	40	15
214	15c. "Piece-of-eight" (vert) (I)	2·50	40
214*a*	15c. "Piece-of-eight" (vert) (II) (8.9.70)	5·00	10
215	20c. Cannon (17th-century)	35	10
	w. Crown to right of CA (24.7.74)	50	20
216	25c. Humphrey Cole's *Astrolabe*, 1574 (vert)	40	10
217	50c. Flintlock pistol (17th-century)	85	80
	w. Wmk Crown to right of CA (24.7.74)	1·25	80
218	60c. Dutch flute (17th-century) (vert)	1·50	70
219	$1 Captain Bartholomew Roberts and his crew's death warrant (vert)	1·50	75
220	$2.50 Railing piece (16th-century)	1·25	5·50
	w. Wmk Crown to right of CA (24.7.74)	2·00	5·50
221	$5 Drake, Hawkins and sea battle	1·50	4·50
	w. Wmk Crown to right of CA (24.7.74)	3·25	5·00
206/21 *Set of 17*		15·00	12·00

Nos. 214/*a*. Type I, coin inscribed "HISPANIANUM"; Type II corrected to "HISPANIARUM". No. 214*a* also differs considerably in shade from No. 214.

*The normal sideways watermark shows Crown to left of CA, *as seen from the back of the stamp*.

Values from this set were subsequantly reissued with W w **12** sideways on vertical designs and upright on horizontal designs. Later values were issued on paper watermarked W w **14**.

85 Graveyard Scene (*Great Expectations*)

(Des Jennifer Toombs. Litho B. W.)

1970 (1 May). Death Centenary of Charles Dickens. T **85** and similar designs. W w **12** (sideways on horiz designs). P 13.

222	4c. bistre-brown, gold and deep blue-green	10	90
223	20c. bistre-brown, gold and reddish purple	15	20
224	25c. bistre-brown, gold and olive-green	15	20
225	40c. bistre-brown, gold and ultramarine	25	35
222/5 *Set of 4*		55	1·50

Designs: Horiz—20c. Miss Havisham and Pip (*Great Expectations*). Vert—25c. Dickens's Birthplace; 40c. Charles Dickens.

86 Local Steel Band

(Des V. Whiteley. Litho Enschedé)

1970 (1 Aug). Festival of Arts. T **86** and similar horiz designs. Multicoloured. W w **12** (sideways). P 13½.

226	20c. Type **86**	10	10
227	25c. Local String Band	10	10
228	40c. Scene from *A Midsummer Night's Dream*	15	15
226/8 *Set of 3*		30	30

87 1d. Stamp of 1870 and Post Office, 1970

88 *Adoration of the Shepherds* (detail) (Frans van Floris)

(Des J. Cooter. Litho J.W.)

1970 (14 Sept). Stamp Centenary. T **87** and similar horiz designs. W w **12** (sideways). P 14½.

229	½c. green and rose	10	10
230	20c. deep blue, green and rose	10	10
231	25c. brown-purple, green and rose	10	10
232	50c. scarlet, green and black	30	45
229/32 *Set of 4*		55	65

Designs:—20c., 25c., 1d. and 6d. Stamps of 1870; 50c., 6d. Stamp of 1870 and early postmark.

(Des Enschedé. Litho Format)

1970 (16 Nov). Christmas. T **88** and similar vert design. Multicoloured. W w **12**. P 14.

233	3c. Type **88**	10	10
234	20c. *The Holy Family* (Van Dyck)	10	10
235	25c. As 20c.	10	10
236	40c. Type **88**	15	50
235/6 *Set of 4*		40	70

St. Lucia

Although a branch office of the British GPO was not opened at Castries, the island capital, until 1844 some form of postal arrangements for overseas mails existed from at least 1841 when the issue of a Ship Letter handstamp is recorded.

The stamps of Great Britain were used on the island from May 1858 until the end of April 1860 when the local authorities assumed responsibility for the postal service. No. CC1 was again used on overseas mail between 1 May and the introduction of St. Lucia stamps in December 1860.

CASTRIES

CROWN-CIRCLE HANDSTAMPS

CC **1**

CC1	CC **1** ST. LUCIA (R.) (1.5.1844)	*Price on cover*	£900

No. CC1 was utilised, struck in black, during a shortage of 1d. stamps in late April and early May 1904. *Price on cover* £325.

Stamps of GREAT BRITAIN cancelled "A 11" as Type Z **1** of Jamaica.

1858–60.

Z1	1d. rose-red (1857), perf 14		£1300
Z2	2d. blue (1855)		
Z3	4d. rose (1857)		£475
Z4	6d. lilac (1856)		£275
Z5	1s. green (1856)		£2250

PRICES FOR STAMPS ON COVER TO 1945	
Nos. 1/3	*from* × 60
Nos. 5/8	*from* × 30
Nos. 9/10	†
Nos. 11/24	*from* × 15
Nos. 25/30	*from* × 10
Nos. 31/6	*from* × 6
Nos. 39/42	*from* × 10
Nos. 43/50	*from* × 15
Nos. 51/2	—
Nos. 53/62	*from* × 6
No. 63	*from* × 15
Nos. 64/75	*from* × 4
Nos. 76/7	—
Nos. 78/88	*from* × 3
No. 89	*from* × 4
No. 90	*from* × 20
Nos. 91/112	*from* × 3
Nos. 113/24	*from* × 2
Nos. 125/7	*from* × 10
Nos. 128/41	*from* × 2
Nos. D1/6	*from* × 10
Nos. F1/28	—

CROWN COLONY

PERKINS BACON "CANCELLED". For notes on these handstamps, showing "CANCELLED" between horizontal bars forming an oval, see Catalogue Introduction.

Half penny

1 (**2**)

(Recess P.B.)

1860 (18 Dec). Wmk Small Star, W w **2**. P 14 to 16.

1	**1**	(1d.) rose-red (H/S "CANCELLED" in oval £8500)	£100	65·00
		a. Imperf vert (horiz pair)	£2500	
		b. Double impression		
2		(4d.) blue (H/S "CANCELLED" in oval £9000)	£225	£150
		a. Deep blue		
		b. Imperf vert (horiz pair)		
3		(6d.) green (H/S "CANCELLED" in oval £12000)	£300	£200
		a. Imperf vert (horiz pair)		
		b. Deep green	£350	£225

(Recess D.L.R.)

1863. Wmk Crown CC. P 12½.

5	**1**	(1d.) lake	95·00	£110
		ax. Wmk reversed	70·00	90·00
		b. Brownish lake	£110	£110
		bx. Wmk reversed	85·00	90·00
7		(4d.) indigo	£130	£140
		x. Wmk reversed		
8		(6d.) emerald-green	£225	£225
		w. Wmk inverted		
		x. Wmk reversed	£190	£180

All three values exist imperforate from proof sheets.

Prepared for use, but not issued. Surch as T **2**

9	**1**	½d. on (6d.) emerald-green	70·00
		x. Wmk reversed	£110

10		6d. on (4d.) indigo	£1100	
		a. Surch "Sex pence"	£3500	

Nos. 9/10 were first recorded in 1885. They may have been prepared in 1876.

1864 (19 Nov)–**76**. Wmk Crown CC.

(a) P 12½

11	**1**	(1d.) black	32·00	13·00
		a. Intense black	32·00	13·00
		x. Wmk reversed	38·00	16·00
		y. Wmk inverted and reversed	£120	
12		(4d.) yellow	£200	50·00
		b. Lemon-yellow	£1500	
		c. Chrome-yellow	£200	42·00
		d. Olive-yellow	£375	90·00
		w. Wmk inverted		
		x. Wmk reversed	£170	50·00
		y. Wmk inverted and reversed	£60	
13		(6d.) violet	£130	42·00
		a. Mauve	£190	32·00
		b. Deep lilac	£160	42·00
		w. Wmk inverted	—	£120
		x. Wmk reversed	£160	60·00
14		(1s.) brown-orange	£325	30·00
		b. Orange	£250	30·00
		c. Pale orange	£225	30·00
		ca. Imperf between (horiz pair)	£275	60·00

(b) P 14

15	**1**	(1d.) black (6.76)	50·00	22·00
		a. Imperf between (horiz pair)		
		x. Wmk reversed	50·00	22·00
16		(4d.) yellow (6.76)	£130	24·00
		a. Olive-yellow	£325	£100
		w. Wmk inverted		
		x. Wmk reversed	£130	24·00
17		(6d.) mauve (6.76)	£120	42·00
		a. Pale lilac	£120	22·00
		b. Violet	£250	70·00
		x. Wmk reversed	—	55·00
18		(1s.) orange (10.76)	£250	24·00
		a. Deep orange	£170	16·00
		w. Wmk inverted		£110
		x. Wmk reversed	£190	25·00

All four values exist imperforate from proof sheets.

HALFPENNY **2½ PENCE**
(3) (4) 5

1881 (Sept). Surch with T **3** or **4**. Wmk Crown CC. P 14.

23	**1**	½d. green	85·00	£120
		x. Wmk reversed	—	£190
24		2½d. brown-red	60·00	28·00

The (1d.) black is known surcharged "1d." in violet ink by hand, but there is no evidence that this was done officially.

1882–84. Surch as T **3**. Wmk Crown CA.

(a) P 14

25	**1**	½d. green (1882)	35·00	48·00
26		1d. black (C.)	50·00	16·00
		a. Bisected (on cover)	†	—
27		4d. yellow	£300	24·00
28		6d. violet	50·00	50·00
29		1s. orange	£275	£170

(b) P 12

30	**1**	4d. yellow	£275	28·00

Deep blue stamps, wmk Crown CA, perf 14 or 12 are fiscals from which the overprint "THREE PENCE—REVENUE", or "REVENUE", has been fraudulently removed.

(Typo D.L.R.)

1883 (6 July)–**86**. Die I. Wmk Crown CA. P 14.

31	**5**	½d. dull green	18·00	11·00
		a. Top left triangle detached	£450	
32		1d. carmine-rose	55·00	19·00
33		2½d. blue	75·00	3·00
		a. Top left triangle detached	£1000	£190
34		4d. brown (1885)	50·00	1·25
		a. Top left triangle detached	£850	£140
35		6d. lilac (1885)	£300	£200
36		1s. orange-brown (1886)	£400	£160
	31/6	Set of 6	£800	£350

The 4d. and 6d. exist imperforate from proof sheets.
For illustration of "top left triangle detached" variety on this and the following issue see above No. 21 of Antigua.

1886–87. Die I. Wmk Crown CA. P 14.

39	**5**	1d. dull mauve	17·00	6·00
		a. Top left triangle detached	£400	£225
40		3d. dull mauve and green	£120	22·00
		a. Top left triangle detached	£1200	£475
41		6d. dull mauve and blue (1887)	8·50	21·00
		a. Top left triangle detached	£275	£400
42		1s. dull mauve and red (1887)	£120	50·00
		a. Top left triangle detached	£1300	£750
	39/42	Set of 4	£225	85·00
	39s/42s	Optd "SPECIMEN" Set of 4	£225	

The 1d. exists imperforate from proof sheets.

1891–98. Die II. Wmk Crown CA. P 14.

43	**5**	½d. dull green	4·00	1·00
		w. Wmk inverted	£500	
44		1d. dull mauve	70	30
45		2d. ultramarine and orange (1898)	6·50	1·75
46		2½d. ultramarine	13·00	1·00
47		3d. dull mauve and green	10·00	5·50
48		4d. brown	9·00	3·75
49		6d. dull mauve and blue	45·00	26·00
50		1s. dull mauve and red	15·00	6·00
51		5s. dull mauve and orange	55·00	£160
52		10s. dull mauve and black	95·00	£160
	43/52	Set of 9	£200	£325
	45s, 51s/2s	Optd "SPECIMEN" Set of 3	£120	

For description and illustration of differences between Die I and Die II see Introduction.

ONE HALF PENNY **½d** **ONE PENNY**
(6) (7) (8)

N N
Normal "N" Thick "N"

Three types of T **8**

I. All letters "N" normal.
II. Thick diagonal stroke in first "N" of "PENNY".
III. Thick diagonal stroke in second "N" of "PENNY".

1891–92.

(a) Stamps of Die I surch

53	**6**	½d. on 3d. dull mauve and green	£150	70·00
		a. Small "A" in "HALF"	£375	£150
		b. Small "O" in "ONE"	£375	£150
		c. Top left triangle detached	£1400	
54	**7**	½d. on half 6d. dull mauve and blue	32·00	3·25
		a. No fraction bar	£300	£130
		b. Surch sideways	£1700	
		c. Surch double	£650	£650
		d. "2" in fraction omitted	£500	£500
		e. Thick "1" with sloping serif	£200	£130
		f. Surch triple	£1300	
		g. Figure "1" used as fraction bar	£475	£275
		h. Top left triangle detached	—	£375
55	**8**	1d. on 4d. brown (I) (12.91)	9·00	4·50
		a. Surch double	£250	
		b. Surch inverted	£950	£850
		c. Type II	30·00	24·00
		ca. Surch double	£475	
		cb. Surch inverted	—	£1500
		d. Type III	30·00	24·00
		e. Top left triangle detached	£275	£190
56	**6**	½d. on 3d. dull mauve and green	85·00	29·00
		a. Surch double	£900	£700
		b. Surch inverted	£1900	£650
		c. Surch both sides	£1100	£750
		d. Small "O" in "ONE" (R. 2/6)	£225	90·00
		e. Small "A" in "HALF"	£225	90·00
		f. "ONE" misplaced ("O" over "H") (R. 4/6)	£225	90·00

Nos. 53 and 56 were surcharged with a setting of 30 (6×5). No. 55 was surcharged by a vertical setting of ten, repeated six times across each pane, with Type II (thick first "N") at pos. 1 and Type III (thick second "N") at pos. 9.

9 10

(Typo D.L.R.)

1902–03. Wmk Crown CA. P 14.

58	**9**	½d. dull purple and green	4·00	1·50
59		1d. dull purple and carmine	6·50	50
60		2½d. dull purple and ultramarine	38·00	8·50
61	**10**	3d. dull purple and yellow	10·00	8·50
62		1s. green and black	17·00	50·00
	58/62	Set of 5	65·00	60·00
	58s/62s	Optd "SPECIMEN" Set of 5	£120	

11 The Pitons

(Recess D.L.R.)

1902 (15 Dec). 400th Anniv of Discovery by Columbus. Wmk Crown CC (sideways). P 14.

63	**11**	2d. green and brown	18·00	1·75
		s. Optd "SPECIMEN"	65·00	

This stamp was formerly thought to have been issued on 16 December but it has been seen on a postcard clearly postmarked 15 December.

1904–10. Chalk-surfaced paper (Nos. 71, 73/5 and 77) or ordinary paper (others). Wmk Mult Crown CA. P 14.

64	**9**	½d. dull purple and green	12·00	60
		a. Chalk-surfaced paper	12·00	60
65		½d. green (1907)	1·75	1·00
66		1d. dull purple and carmine	8·50	1·25
		a. Chalk-surfaced paper	11·00	1·25
		aw. Wmk inverted	£225	
67		1d. carmine (1907)	4·25	30
68		2½d. dull purple and ultramarine	38·00	2·75
		a. Chalk-surfaced paper	17·00	4·50
69		2½d. blue (1907)	3·75	2·25
70	**10**	3d. dull purple and yellow	13·00	3·00
71		3d. purple/yellow (1909)	4·50	20·00
72		6d. dull purple and violet (1905)	27·00	40·00
		a. Chalk-surfaced paper	20·00	50·00
		ab. Dull purple and bright purple (1907)	8·50	50·00
73		6d. dull purple (1910)	75·00	95·00
74		1s. green and black (1905)	50·00	38·00
75		1s. black/green (1909)	5·00	8·00
76		5s. green and carmine (1905)	85·00	£200
77		5s. green and red/yellow (1907)	60·00	70·00
	64/77	Set of 14	£300	£425
	65s, 67s, 69s, 71s/2s, 72abs and 75s/7s Optd "SPECIMEN" Set of 9		£325

Examples of Nos. 71/7 are known with a forged Castries postmark dated "JA 21 09".

12 13 14

15 16

(Typo D.L.R.)

1912–21. Die I. Chalk-surfaced paper (3d. to 5s.). Wmk Mult Crown CA. P 14.

78	**12**	½d. deep green	70	50
		a. Yellow-green (1916)	3·25	30
79		1d. carmine-red	1·90	10
		a. Scarlet (1916)	8·50	10
		b. Rose-red	9·00	1·00
80	**13**	2d. grey	1·50	4·25
		a. Slate-grey (1916)	23·00	17·00
81	**12**	2½d. ultramarine	3·75	2·75
		a. Bright blue	4·25	2·75
		b. Deep bright blue (1916)	17·00	10·00
82	**15**	3d. purple/yellow	1·25	2·25
		b. Die II. On pale yellow (1921)	30·00	60·00
		bw. Wmk inverted		
83	**14**	4d. black and red/yellow	1·00	2·50
		a. White back	70	1·50
		as. Optd "SPECIMEN"	30·00	
84	**15**	6d. dull and bright purple	2·00	21·00
		a. Grey-purple and purple (1918)	16·00	28·00
85		1s. black/green	8·00	6·00
		a. On blue-green (olive back) (1918)	17·00	23·00
86		1s. orange-brown (1920)	20·00	45·00
87	**16**	2s.6d. black and red/blue	27·00	55·00
88	**15**	5s. green and red/yellow	25·00	85·00
	78/88	Set of 11	80·00	£200
	78s/88s	Optd "SPECIMEN" Set of 11	£225	

WAR TAX **WAR TAX**
(17) (18)

1916 (1 June). No. 79a optd locally with T **17**.

89	**12**	1d. scarlet	15·00	24·00
		a. Opt double	£550	£650
		b. Carmine-red	65·00	55·00

For overprinting with Type **17** the sheets were vertically divided to the left of the centre margin and the top margin of the sheet was folded beneath the top row of stamps so that the marginal examples from this row show an inverted albino impression of the overprint in the top margin.
Examples are also recorded of similar albino overprints in the right-hand and bottom margins but it is unclear if some sheets had all margins folded under before overprinting.

1916 (Sept). No. 79a optd in London with T **18**.

90	**12**	1d. scarlet	1·75	30
		s. Optd "SPECIMEN"	55·00	

1921–30. Die II. Chalk-surfaced paper (3d. (No. 100) to 5s.). Wmk Mult Script CA. P 14.

91	**12**	½d. green	1·50	50
92		1d. rose-carmine	16·00	22·00
93		1d. deep brown (1922)	1·40	15
94	**14**	1½d. dull carmine (1922)	75	2·50
95	**13**	2d. slate-grey	75	15
96	**12**	2½d. bright blue	8·50	2·75
97		2½d. orange (1925)	16·00	60·00
98		2½d. dull blue (1926)	11·00	2·75
99	**15**	3d. bright blue (1922)	8·50	22·00
		a. Dull blue (1924)	8·50	11·00
100		3d. purple/pale yellow (1926)	3·75	12·00
		a. Deep purple/pale yellow (1930)	38·00	12·00
101	**14**	4d. black and red/yellow (1924)	1·25	3·50
102	**15**	6d. grey-purple and purple	2·00	4·75
103		1s. orange-brown	7·00	3·25
104	**16**	2s.6d. black and red/blue (1924)	18·00	38·00
105	**15**	5s. green and red/pale yellow (1923)	60·00	95·00
	91/105	Set of 15	£140	£225
	91s/105s	Optd "SPECIMEN" Set of 15	£325	

1935 (6 May). Silver Jubilee. As Nos. 91/4 of Antigua. P 13½×14.

109		½d. black and green	30	2·50
		f. Diagonal line by turret	55·00	£100
		g. Dot to left of chapel	£110	
110		2d. ultramarine and grey	1·50	1·75
		f. Diagonal line by turret	£110	£130
111		2½d. brown and deep blue	1·75	1·75
		a. Frame printed double, one albino	†	—
		f. Diagonal line by turret	£130	
		g. Dot to left of chapel	£180	£190
112		1s. slate and purple	18·00	23·00
		h. Dot by flagstaff	£500	
	109/12	Set of 4	19·00	26·00
	109s/12s	Perf "SPECIMEN" Set of 4	95·00	

For illustrations of plate varieties see Omnibus section following Zanzibar.

19 Port Castries   **20** Columbus Square, Castries (inscr "COLUMBUS SQUARE" in error)

21 Ventine Falls

22 Fort Rodney, Pigeon Island

23 Inniskilling monument

24 Government House

25 The Badge of the Colony

(Recess D.L.R.)

1936 (1 Mar–Apr). T **19/25**. Wmk Mult Script CA. P 14 or 13×12 (1s. and 10s.).

113	19	½d. black and bright green	30	50
		a. Perf 13×12 (8.4.36)	6·50	28·00
114	20	1d. black and brown	40	10
		a. Perf 13×12 (8.4.36)	11·00	4·50
115	21	1½d. black and scarlet	70	30
		a. Perf 12×13	18·00	2·25
116	19	2d. black and grey	60	20
117	20	2½d. black and blue	60	15
118	21	3d. black and dull green	1·50	70
119	19	4d. black and red-brown	2·75	1·25
120	20	6d. black and orange	2·75	1·25
121	22	1s. black and light blue	4·25	2·50
122	23	2s.6d. black and ultramarine	17·00	14·00
123	24	5s. black and violet	21·00	20·00
124	25	10s. black and carmine	65·00	£100
113/24 Set of 12			£100	£130
113s/24s Perf "SPECIMEN" Set of 12			£300	

Examples of most values are known with a forged Castries postmark dated "1 MR 36".

1937 (12 May). Coronation. As Nos. 95/7 of Antigua. P 11×11½.

125		1d. violet	30	35
126		1½d. carmine	55	20
127		2½d. blue	55	1·25
125/7 Set of 3			1·25	1·60
125s/7s Perf "SPECIMEN" Set of 3			90·00	

26 King George VI

27 Columbus Square

28 Government House

29 The Pitons

30 *Lady Hawkins* loading bananas

31 Device of St. Lucia

(Des Miss M. Byer and E. Crafer (T **26**), H. Fleury (5s.). Recess Waterlow (½d. to 3½d., 8d., 3s., 5s., £1), D.L.R. (6d., 1s.) and B.W. (2s., 10s.))

1938 (22 Sept)–**48**. T **26/31**. Wmk Mult Script CA (sideways on 2s.).

128	26	½d. green (P 14½×14)	2·00	10
		a. Perf 12½	10	10
129		1d. violet (P 14½×14)	7·50	75
		a. Perf 12½	30	15
129b		1d. scarlet (P 12½) (8.4.47)	1·50	10
		c. Perf 14½×14 (20.9.48)	10	10
130		1½d. scarlet (P 14½×14)	3·50	40
		a. Perf 12½ (22.5.43)	1·50	2·75
131		2d. grey (P 14½×14)	5·50	2·00
		a. Perf 12½ (22.5.43)	15	10

132		2½d. ultramarine (P 14½×14)	8·00	15
		a. Perf 12½ (22.5.43)	40	10
132b		2½d. violet (P 12½) (8.4.47)	1·00	10
133		3d. orange (P 14½×14)	4·00	10
		a. Perf 12½ (22.5.43)	30	10
133b		3½d. ultramarine (P 12½) (1.4.47)	1·00	15
134	27	6d. claret (P 13½)	16·00	1·50
		a. Carmine-lake (P 13½) (30.7.45)	7·00	35
		b. Perf 12. Claret (23.2.48)	3·75	2·50
134c	26	8d. brown (P 12½) (4.2.46)	3·50	30
135	28	1s. brown (P 13½)	3·50	30
		a. Perf 12 (23.2.48)	2·00	30
136	29	2s. blue and purple (P 12)	13·00	1·25
136a	26	3s. bright purple (P 12½) (4.2.46)	8·00	1·75
137	30	5s. black and mauve (P 12½)	24·00	16·00
138	31	10s. black/yellow (P 12)	18·00	9·00
141	26	£1 sepia (P 12½) (4.2.46)	16·00	13·00
128a/41 Set of 17			80·00	38·00
128s/41s Perf "SPECIMEN" Set of 17			£475	

1946 (8 Oct). Victory. As Nos. 110/11 of Antigua.

142		1d. lilac	10	30
143		3½d. blue	10	30
142s/3s Perf "SPECIMEN" Set of 2			80·00	

1948 (26 Nov). Royal Silver Wedding. As Nos. 112/13 of Antigua.

144		1d. scarlet	15	10
145		£1 purple-brown	17·00	35·00

(New Currency. 100 cents = 1 West Indian dollar)

32 King George VI

33 Device of St. Lucia

(Recess Waterlow (**32**), B.W. (**33**))

1949 (1 Oct)–**50**. Value in cents or dollars. Wmk Mult Script CA. P 12½ (1c. to 16c.), 11×11½ (others).

146	32	1c. green	25	10
		a. Perf 14 (1949)	3·75	40
147		2c. magenta	1·00	10
		a. Perf 14½×14 (1949)	6·50	1·50
148		3c. scarlet	1·75	3·25
149		4c. grey	2·00	65
		a. Perf 14½×14 (1950)	†	£17000
150		5c. violet	1·75	10
151		6c. orange	1·50	4·00
152		7c. ultramarine	4·00	3·50
153		12c. claret	5·50	4·75
		a. Perf 14½×14 (1950)	£800	£550
154		16c. brown	5·00	50
155	33	24c. light blue	50	10
156		48c. olive-green	2·00	1·25
157		$1.20 purple	5·50	13·00
158		$2.40 blue-green	9·50	21·00
159		$4.80 rose-carmine	14·00	18·00
146/159 Set of 14			48·00	60·00

Most examples of Nos. 146a and 147a were produced as coils, but a few sheets in these perforations were distributed and blocks of four are scarce.

No genuine mint example of No. 149a is known. Photographic forgeries do, however, exist.

1949 (10 Oct). 75th Anniv of UPU. As Nos. 114/17 of Antigua.

160		5c. violet	15	1·00
161		6c. orange	1·60	3·00
		a. "A" of "CA" missing from wmk	£650	
162		12c. magenta	20	30
163		24c. blue-green	30	30
160/3 Set of 4			2·00	4·25

1951 (16 Feb). Inauguration of BWI University College. As Nos. 118/19 of Antigua.

164		3c. black and scarlet	45	1·50
165		12c. black and deep carmine	65	1·50

34 Phoenix rising from Burning Buildings

N E W
1951
CONSTITUTION
(**35**)

(Flames typo, rest recess B.W.)

1951 (19 June). Reconstruction of Castries. Wmk Mult Script CA. P 13½×13.

166	34	12c. red and blue	35	1·00

1951 (25 Sept). New Constitution. Nos. 147, 149/50 and 153 optd with T **35** by Waterlow. P 12½.

167	32	2c. magenta	20	80
168		4c. grey	20	60
169		5c. violet	25	80
170		12c. claret	1·00	60
167/70 Set of 4			1·50	2·50

1953 (2 June). Coronation. As No. 120 of Antigua.

171		3c. black and scarlet	70	10

---

36 Queen Elizabeth II

37 Device of St. Lucia

(Recess Waterlow (T **36**), until 1960, then D.L.R. B.W. (T **37**))

1953 (28 Oct)–**63**. Wmk Mult Script CA. P 14½×14 (T **36**) or 11×11½ (T **37**).

172	36	1c. green (1.4.54)	10	10
173		2c. magenta	10	10
174		3c. red (2.9.54)	10	10
175		4c. slate (7.1.54)	10	10
176		5c. violet (1.4.54)	10	10
		a. Slate-violet (19.2.63)	25·00	4·75
177		6c. orange (2.9.54)	15	1·00
		a. Brown-orange (26.9.61)	22·00	3·00
178		8c. lake (2.9.54)	30	10
179		10c. ultramarine (2.9.54)	10	10
		a. Blue (14.8.62)	50	10
180		15c. red-brown (2.9.54)	30	10
		a. Brown (30.10.57)	2·50	10
181	37	25c. deep turquoise-blue (2.9.54)	30	10
182		50c. deep olive-green (2.9.54)	4·50	3·75
183		$1 bluish green (2.9.54)	4·00	6·50
184		$2.50 carmine (2.9.54)	6·50	6·50
172/84 Set of 13			15·00	16·00

1958 (22 Apr). Inauguration of British Caribbean Federation. As Nos. 135/7 of Antigua.

185		3c. deep green	1·00	20
186		6c. blue	1·00	1·75
187		12c. scarlet	1·00	80
185/7 Set of 3			2·75	2·50

MINISTERIAL GOVERNMENT

38 Columbus's *Santa Maria* off the Pitons

39 Stamp of 1860

(Recess Waterlow)

1960 (1 Jan). New Constitution for the Windward and Leeward Islands. W w **12**. P 13.

188	38	8c. carmine-red	40	45
189		10c. red-orange	40	45
190		25c. deep blue	60	50
188/90 Set of 3			1·25	1·25

(Eng H. Bard. Recess Waterlow)

1960 (18 Dec). Stamp Centenary. W w **12**. P 13½.

191	39	5c. rose-red and ultramarine	25	10
192		16c. deep blue and yellow-green	45	90
193		25c. green and carmine-red	45	15
191/3 Set of 3			1·00	1·00

1963 (4 June). Freedom from Hunger. As No. 146 of Antigua.

194		25c. bluish green	40	10

1963 (2 Sept). Red Cross Centenary. As Nos. 147/8 of Antigua.

195		4c. red and black	20	1·50
196		25c. red and blue	50	1·50

40

41

Queen Elizabeth II (after A.C. Davidson-Houston)

42 Fishing Boats

43 Pigeon Island

44 Reduit Beach

45 Castries Harbour

46 The Pitons

47 Vigie Beach

48 Queen Elizabeth II

(Des V. Whiteley. Photo Harrison)

1964 (1 Mar)–**69**. Designs as T **40**/**8**, W w **12**. P 14½ (T **40**), others 14½×14 (vert) or 14×14½ (horiz).

197	**40**	1c. crimson	10	10
		w. Wmk inverted	75	1·50
198		2c. bluish violet	30	1·00
		w. Wmk inverted	—	6·50
199		4c. turquoise-green	1·00	30
		a. Deep turquoise (5.8.69)	8·50	3·00
		w. Wmk inverted	—	7·50
200		5c. Prussian blue	30	10
		w. Wmk inverted		6·50
201		6c. yellow-brown	1·00	2·50
202	**41**	8c. multicoloured	10	10
203		10c. multicoloured	1·00	10
204	**42**	12c. multicoloured	50	1·75
205	**43**	15c. multicoloured	20	10
206	**44**	25c. multicoloured	20	10
207	**45**	35c. blue and buff	3·00	10
208	**46**	50c. multicoloured	2·50	10
209	**47**	$1 multicoloured	1·25	2·50
210	**48**	$2.50 multicoloured	3·00	2·25
197/210 *Set of 14*			13·00	9·50

See also No. 249.

1964 (23 Apr). 400th Birth Anniv of William Shakespeare. As No. 164 of Antigua.

211	10c. blue-green	30	10

1965 (17 May). ITU Centenary. As Nos. 166/7 of Antigua.

212	2c. mauve and magenta	10	10
213	50c. lilac and light olive-green	70	90

1965 (25 Oct). International Co-operation Year. As Nos. 168/9 of Antigua.

214	1c. reddish purple and turquoise-green	10	50
215	25c. deep bluish green and lavender	20	20

1966 (24 Jan). Churchill Commemoration. As Nos. 170/3 of Antigua.

216	4c. new blue	15	10
217	6c. deep green	70	4·00
218	25c. brown	80	15
219	35c. bluish violet	85	20
216/19 *Set of 4*		2·25	4·00

1966 (4 Feb). Royal Visit. As Nos. 174/5 of Antigua.

220	4c. black and ultramarine	65	25
221	25c. black and magenta	1·25	75

1966 (1 July). World Cup Football Championship, England. As Nos. 176/7 of Antigua.

222	4c. violet, yellow-green, lake and yellow-brown	25	10
223	25c. chocolate, blue-green, lake and yellow-brown	75	30

1966 (20 Sept). Inauguration of WHO Headquarters, Geneva. As Nos. 178/9 of Antigua.

224	4c. black, yellow-green and light blue	25	30
225	25c. black, light purple and yellow-brown	75	40

1966 (1 Dec). 20th Anniv of UNESCO. As Nos. 196/8 of Antigua.

226	4c. slate-violet, red, yellow and orange	20	10
227	12c. orange-yellow, violet and deep olive	40	65
228	25c. black, bright purple and orange	75	35
226/8 *Set of 3*		1·25	1·00

ASSOCIATED STATEHOOD

STATEHOOD 1st MARCH 1967 (**49**)

STATEHOOD 1st MARCH 1967 (**50**)

51 Map of St. Lucia

(Optd by Art Printery, Castries from dies supplied by Harrison. Photo Harrison (No. 240))

1967 (7 Mar). Statehood.

*(a) Postage. Nos. 198 and 200/9 optd with T **49** (2, 5, 6c.) or T **50** (others) in red*

229	2c. bluish violet		20	20
	a. Horiz pair, one without opt			
230	5c. Prussian blue		20	10
	a. Opt inverted		50·00	
231	6c. yellow-brown		20	20
232	8c. multicoloured		1·00	10
	a. Opt double		£1500	
233	10c. multicoloured		40	30
234	12c. multicoloured		40	10
235	15c. multicoloured		75	1·25
236	25c. multicoloured		40	2·00
237	35c. blue and buff		2·00	1·00
238	50c. multicoloured		1·50	2·25
239	$1 multicoloured		65	1·25
229/39 *Set of 11*			7·00	7·75

Overprinted 1c. and $2.50 stamps were prepared for issue but were not put on sale over the post office counter. Later, however, they were accepted for franking (*Price for set of 2 £2 mint, £8 used*).

The 1c., 6c. and $2.50 also exist with overprint in black, instead of red, and the 25c. UNESCO value is also known with a similar overprint in blue or black.

(b) Air. P 14½×14

240	**51**	15c. new blue	10	10

52 Madonna and Child with the Infant Baptist (Raphael)

53 Batsman and Sir Frederick Clarke (Governor)

(Des and photo Harrison)

1967 (16 Oct). Christmas. W w **12** (sideways). P 14½.

241	**52**	4c. multicoloured	10	10
242		25c. multicoloured	30	10

(Des V. Whiteley. Photo Harrison)

1968 (8 Mar). MCC's West Indies Tour. W w **12** (sideways). P 14½×14.

243	**53**	10c. multicoloured	20	30
244		35c. multicoloured	45	55

54 The Crucified Christ with the Virgin Mary, Saints and Angels (Raphael)

55 Noli me tangere (detail by Titian)

(Des and photo Harrison)

1968 (25 Mar). Easter. W w **12** (sideways). P 14×14½.

245	**54**	10c. multicoloured	10	10
246	**55**	15c. multicoloured	10	10
247	**54**	25c. multicoloured	15	10
248	**55**	35c. multicoloured	15	10
		a. Yellow (sunset) omitted	£200	
245/8 *Set of 4*			45	35

1968 (14 May*). As No. 205 but W w **12** (sideways).

249	**43**	15c. multicoloured	40	30

*This is the London release date. Stamps from this printing were available some months earlier on St. Lucia.

56 Dr. Martin Luther King

57 Virgin and Child in Glory (Murillo)

(Des V. Whiteley. Litho D.L.R.)

1968 (4 July). Martin Luther King Commemoration. W w **12**. P 13½×14.

250	**56**	25c. blue, black and flesh	15	15
251		35c. violet-black, black and flesh	15	15

(Des and photo Harrison)

1968 (17 Oct). Christmas. Paintings. T **57** and similar vert design. Multicoloured. W w **12** (sideways). P 14½×14.

252	5c. Type **57**		10	10
253	10c. *Madonna with Child* (Murillo)		10	10
254	25c. Type **57**		15	10
255	35c. As 10c.		15	10
252/5 *Set of 4*			45	35

59 Purple-throated Carib

(Des V. Whiteley. Litho Format)

1969 (10 Jan). Birds. T **59** and similar horiz design. Multicoloured. W w **12** (sideways). P 14.

256	10c. Type **59**		30	35
257	15c. St. Lucia Amazon		35	40
258	25c. Type **59**		40	45
259	35c. As 15c.		60	50
256/9 *Set of 4*			1·50	1·50

61 Head of Christ Crowned with Thorns (Reni)

62 Resurrection of Christ (Sodoma)

(Des and photo Harrison)

1969 (20 Mar). Easter. W w **12** (sideways). P 14½×14.

260	**61**	10c. multicoloured	10	10
261	**62**	15c. multicoloured	10	10
262	**61**	25c. multicoloured	15	15
263	**62**	35c. multicoloured	15	15
260/3 *Set of 4*			45	45

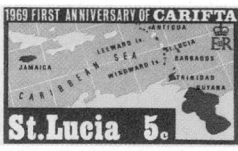

63 Map showing "CARIFTA" Countries

(Des J. Cooter. Photo Harrison)

1969 (29 May). First Anniv of CARIFTA (Caribbean Free Trade Area). T **63** and similar horiz design. Multicoloured. W w **12**. P 14.

264	5c. Type **63**		10	15
265	10c. Type **63**		10	15
266	25c. Handclasp and names of CARIFTA countries		15	15
267	35c. As 25c.		15	15
264/7 *Set of 4*			45	55

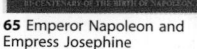

65 Emperor Napoleon and Empress Josephine

66 Virgin and Child (P. Delaroche)

(Des and litho Enschedé)

1969 (22 Sept). Birth Bicentenary of Napoleon Bonaparte. P 14×13.

268	**65**	15c. multicoloured	10	10
269		25c. multicoloured	10	10
270		35c. multicoloured	10	10
271		50c. multicoloured	15	55
268/71 *Set of 4*			40	75

(Des J. W. Photo Harrison)

1969 (27 Oct). Christmas. Paintings. T **66** and similar vert design. Multicoloured. W w **12** (sideways). P 14½×14.

272	5c. Type **66**		10	10
273	10c. *Holy Family* (Rubens)		10	10
274	25c. Type **66**		20	10
275	35c. As 10c.		20	10
272/5 *Set of 4*			55	35

68 House of Assembly

(Des J. Cooter ($10), Sylvia and M. Goaman (others). Litho Questa ($10), Format (others))

1970 (2 Feb)–**73**. T **68** and similar designs. Multicoloured. W w **12** (sideways* on 1c. to 35c. and $10). P 14.

276	1c.	Type **68**	10	10
277	2c.	Roman Catholic Cathedral	15	10
278	4c.	The Boulevard, Castries	1·00	10
		w. Wmk Crown to right of CA	6·50	
279	5c.	Castries Harbour	1·50	10
280	6c.	Sulphur springs	15	10
281	10c.	Vigie Airport	2·00	10
282	12c.	Reduit Beach	20	10
283	15c.	Pigeon Island	30	10
284	25c.	The Pitons and yacht	80	10
		w. Wmk Crown to right of CA	20·00	
285	35c.	Marigot Bay	40	10
		w. Wmk Crown to right of CA	20·00	
286	50c.	Diamond Waterfall (*vert*)	70	80
287	$1	Flag of St. Lucia (*vert*)	40	70
288	$2.50	St. Lucia Coat of Arms (*vert*)	55	1·75
289	$5	Queen Elizabeth II (*vert*)	1·00	4·00
289a	$10	Map of St. Lucia (*vert*) (3.12.73)	6·00	9·00
276/89a		Set of 15	13·50	15·00

*The normal sideways watermark shows Crown to left of CA, *as seen from the back of the stamp.*

The 2c. and 4c. were subsequently reissued with W w **12** upright and the 4c., 5c., 10c. and 13c. on W w **14**.

69 The Sealing of the Tomb (Hogarth)

(Des V. Whiteley. Litho Enschedé)

1970 (7 Mar). Easter. Triptych by Hogarth. T **69** and similar multicoloured designs. W w **12** (sideways). Roul. 9×P 12½.

290	25c.	Type **69**	15	20
		a. Strip of 3. Nos. 290/2	55	70
291	35c.	The Three Marys at the Tomb	15	20
292	$1	The Ascension (39×55 mm)	30	40
290/2		Set of 3	55	70

Nos. 290/2 were issued in sheets of 30 (6×5) containing the Hogarth Triptych spread over all three values of the set. This necessitated a peculiar arrangement with the $1 value (which depicts the centre portion of the triptych) 10 mm higher than the other values in the *se-tenant* strip.

72 Charles Dickens and Dickensian Characters

(Des V. Whiteley. Litho B.W.)

1970 (8 June). Death Centenary of Charles Dickens. W w **12** (sideways). P 14.

293	**72**	1c. multicoloured	10	10
294		25c. multicoloured	20	10
295		35c. multicoloured	25	10
296		50c. multicoloured	35	1·25
293/6		Set of 4	80	1·40

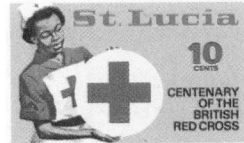

73 Nurse and Emblem

(Des R. Granger Barrett. Litho J.W.)

1970 (18 Aug). Centenary of British Red Cross. T **73** and similar horiz designs. Multicoloured. W w **12** (sideways*). P 14.

297		10c. Type **73**	15	15
298		15c. Flags of Great Britain, Red Cross and St. Lucia	25	25
299		25c. Type **73**	35	40
300		35c. As 15c.	40	40
		w. Wmk Crown to right of CA	28·00	
297/300		Set of 4	1·00	1·10

*The normal sideways watermark shows Crown to left of CA, *as seen from the back of the stamp.*

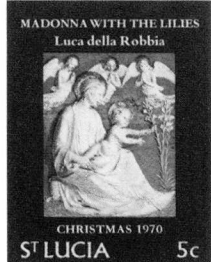

74 Madonna with the Lilies (Luca della Robbie)

(Des P. B. Litho and embossed Walsall)

1970 (16 Nov). Christmas. P 11.

301	**74**	5c. multicoloured	10	10
302		10c. multicoloured	15	10
303		35c. multicoloured	30	10
304		40c. multicoloured	30	30
301/4		Set of 4	75	55

POSTAGE DUE STAMPS

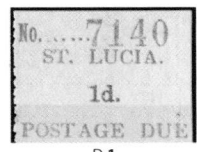

D 1

No. No.

Normal   Wide fount

(Type-set Government Printing Office)

1930. Each stamp individually handstamped with different number. No gum. Rough perf 12.

(a) Horizontally laid paper

D1	D **1**	1d. black/*blue*	11·00	23·00
		b. Wide, wrong fount "No."	25·00	50·00
		c. Missing stop after "ST"	£325	£475
		d. Missing stop after "LUCIA"	£275	£475
		e. Handstamped number double	£900	£1100
		f. Handstamped number triple	£2000	
		g. Incorrect number with correction above		
		h. Two different numbers on same stamp	£2000	
		i. Number omitted	£4000	

(b) Wove paper

D2	D **1**	2d. black/*yellow*	23·00	50·00
		a. Imperf between (vert pair)	£8000	
		b. Wide, wrong fount "No."	48·00	£100
		c. Missing stop after "ST"	£650	£950
		d. Missing stop after "LUCIA"	£900	
		e. Handstamped number double	†	£1900
		g. Incorrect number with correction above	£2000	£2250
		h. Two different numbers on same stamp		£2250

Nos. D1/2 were produced in sheets of 60 (6×10) usually with imperforate outer edges at the top, at right and at foot. It would appear that the sheets were bound into books from which they could be detached using the line of perforations along the left-hand side.

There were three printings of each value, utilising the same basic type. The paper for the first two printings of the 1d. and the first printing of the 2d. showed papermaker's watermarks, that for the 1d. being "KINGSCLERE" in double-lined capitals below a crown with parts occurring on between ten and fourteen stamps in *some sheets*. Details of the printings are as follows:

1d.
First printing. On paper with sheet watermark. Shows wide fount "No." on R. 10/3–6 and missing stop after "ST" on R. 5/3.

Second printing. On paper with sheet watermark. Shows wide fount "No." on R. 10/2–6 and missing stop after "ST" on R. 5/3. The first two printings of the 1d. were numbered together as 1 to 12000.

Third printing. On paper without watermark. Shows wide fount "No." on all stamps in Row 10. Missing stop after "ST" on R. 5/3 corrected, but missing stop after "LUCIA" occurs on R. 9/2. Numbered 12001 to 24000.

2d.
First printing. On paper with sheet watermark. Shows wide fount "No." on R. 10/2–6 and missing stop after "ST" on R. 5/3 (as 1d. second printing). Numbered 1 to 4800.

Second printing. On paper without watermark. Shows wide fount "No." on all stamps in Row 10. Missing stop after "ST" corrected (printed *before* 1d. third printing). Numbered 4801 to 14400.

Third printing. On paper without watermark. Shows wide fount "No." on all stamps in Row 10. Missing stop after "ST" corrected, but missing stop after "LUCIA" occurs on R. 4/4 and 9/2 (printed *after* 1d. third printing). Numbered 14401 to 16800.

The handstamped numbers were applied at the Post Office using a numbering machine. Mistakes in the numbering on the 1d. were sometimes partially erased and then corrected with a second strike, either of the complete number or of incorrect digits, using a machine with a smaller fount.

D **2**   D **3**

(Typo D.L.R.)

1933–47. Wmk Mult Script CA. P 14.

D3	D **2**	1d. black	6·00	8·50
D4		2d. black	24·00	11·00
D5		4d. black (28.6.47)	13·00	55·00
D6		8d. black (28.6.47)	15·00	65·00
D3/6		Set of 4	50·00	£120
D3s/6s		Perf "SPECIMEN" Set of 4	£150	

1949 (1 Oct)–**52**. Value in cents. Typo. Wmk Mult Script CA. P 14.

D7	D **3**	2c. black	2·75	30·00
		a. Chalk-surfaced paper (27.11.52)	10	9·50
		ab. Error. Crown missing, W **9a**	£200	
		ac. Error. St. Edward's Crown, W **9b**.	38·00	
D8		4c. black	3·50	24·00
		a. Chalk-surfaced paper (27.11.52)	50	14·00
		ab. Error. Crown missing, W **9a**	£275	
		ac. Error. St. Edward's Crown, W **9b**.	55·00	
D9		8c. black	3·25	30·00
		a. Chalk-surfaced paper (27.11.52)	3·00	50·00
		ac. Error. St. Edward's Crown, W **9b**.	£350	
D10		16c. black	15·00	70·00
		a. Chalk-surfaced paper (27.11.52)	4·50	65·00
		ac. Error. St. Edward's Crown, W **9b**.	£475	
D7/10		Set of 4	22·00	£140
D7a/10a		Set of 4	7·25	£120

1965 (9 Mar). As Nos. D7/8, but wmk w **12**. Ordinary paper. P 14.

D11	D **3**	2c. black	50	14·00
D12		4c. black	1·00	15·00

Nos. D9a, D10a and D11/12 exist with a similar overprint to Type **49** in red (*Price for set of 4 £100 mint*).

POSTAL FISCAL STAMPS

Nos. F1/28 were authorised for postal use from 14 April 1885.

CANCELLATIONS. Many used examples of the Postal Fiscal stamps have had previous pen cancellations removed before being used postally.

SHILLING STAMP (F **1**)	One Penny Stamp (F **2**)	Stamp (F **3**)

1881. Wmk Crown CC. P 14.

F1	**1**	ONE PENNY STAMP, black (C.)	80·00	50·00
		a. Surch inverted	£750	£750
		b. Surch double	£650	£700
F2		FOUR PENNY STAMP, yellow	£130	80·00
		a. Bisected (2d.) (on cover)	†	
F3		SIX PENCE STAMP, mauve	£200	£150
F4		SHILLING STAMP, orange	£150	85·00
		a. "SHILEING"	£1100	£750
		b. "SHILDING"	£700	£650

*(b) Surch as Type F **2***

F7	**1**	One Penny Stamp, black (R.)	80·00	55·00
		a. Surch double	£750	
		w. Wmk inverted		
F8		Four Pence Stamp, yellow	£120	65·00
		x. Wmk reversed		
F9		Six Pence Stamp, mauve	£150	65·00
F10		Shilling Stamp, orange	£160	85·00

*(c) Nos. 23 and 29 Surch as Type F **3***

F11	**1**	HALFPENNY Stamp, green	75·00	55·00
		a. "Stamp" double	£450	£450
F12		ONE SHILLING Stamp, orange (wmk Crown CA)	£150	75·00
		a. "Stamp" double	£450	£500

Fiscally used examples are known of No. F1b showing one red and one black surcharge and No. F9 with surcharge double.

FOUR PENCE REVENUE (F **4**)	Revenue (F **5**)	REVENUE (F **6**)

1882. Surch as Type F **4** by D.L.R. Wmk Crown CA.

(a) P 14

F13	**1**	1d. black (C.)	55·00	25·00
F14		2d. pale blue	50·00	12·00
F15		3d. deep blue (C.)	£100	50·00
F16		4d. yellow	50·00	4·00
F17		6d. mauve	75·00	40·00
		x. Wmk reversed		

(b) P 12

F18	**1**	1d. black (C.)	55·00	30·00
F19		3d. deep blue (C.)	80·00	20·00
F20		1s. orange	80·00	13·00

The 1d. and 2d. exist as imperforate proofs.

1883. Nos. 25, 26, 30 and 32 optd locally as Type F **5**.

(a) Word 11 mm long

F21		1d. black (C.)	50·00	50·00
		a. Opt inverted		
		b. Opt double	£375	£350

(b) Word 13 mm

F22		1d. black (C.)	—	65·00

(c) Word 15½ mm

F23		½d. green	—	60·00
		a. "Revenue" double		£275
F24		1d. black (C.)	50·00	10·00
		a. "Revenue" double	£170	
		b. "Revenue" triple	£325	
		c. "Revenue" double, one inverted	£300	£300
F25		1d. rose (No. 32)	—	70·00
F26		4d. yellow		£100

1884–85. Optd with Type F **6**. Wmk Crown CA. P 14.

F27	**5**	1d. slate (C.)	45·00	25·00
F28		1d. dull mauve (Die I) (1885)	45·00	14·00

No. F27 exists as an imperforate proof.

St. Vincent

Although postal markings for St. Vincent are recorded as early as 1793 it was not until 1852 that the British GPO opened a branch office at Kingstown, the island's capital.

The stamps of Great Britain were used between May 1858 and the end of April 1860. From 1 May in that year the local authorities assumed responsibility for the postal services and fell back on the use of No. CC 1 until the introduction of St. Vincent stamps in 1861.

KINGSTOWN
CROWNED-CIRCLE HANDSTAMPS

CC 1

CC1   CC **1** ST. VINCENT (R.) (30.1.1852) .... *Price on cover*   £950

Stamps of GREAT BRITAIN cancelled "A 10" as Type Z **1** of Jamaica.

1858–60.

Z1	1d. rose-red (1857), perf 14		£700
Z2	2d. blue (1855)		
Z3	4d. rose (1857)		£425
Z4	6d. lilac (1856)		£325
Z5	1s. green (1856)		£2000

PRICES FOR STAMPS ON COVER TO 1945	
No. 1	*from* × 50
No. 2	*from* × 15
Nos. 4/5	*from* × 40
Nos. 6/7	*from* × 20
No. 8	—
No. 9	*from* × 12
No. 10	—
No. 11	*from* × 15
Nos. 12/13	*from* × 20
No. 14	*from* × 10
No. 15	*from* × 50
No. 16	*from* × 15
No. 17	*from* × 10
No. 18	*from* × 100
No. 19	*from* × 20
Nos. 20/21	*from* × 7
No. 22	*from* × 100
No. 23	*from* × 25
No. 24	*from* × 15
No. 25	*from* × 25
No. 26	—
No. 26a	*from* × 50
Nos. 27/28	—
No. 29	*from* × 100
Nos. 30/31	*from* × 30
Nos. 32/34	—
No. 35	*from* × 30
Nos. 36/7	*from* × 50
No. 38	*from* × 10
Nos. 39/40	*from* × 100
No. 41	*from* × 25
Nos. 42/5	*from* × 8
No. 46	*from* × 15
Nos. 47/54	*from* × 4
Nos. 55/8	*from* × 8
No. 59	*from* × 10
No. 60	*from* × 6
Nos. 61/3	*from* × 8
Nos. 67/75	*from* × 2
Nos. 76/84	*from* × 2
Nos. 85/92	*from* × 3
No. 93	—
Nos. 94/8	*from* × 3
Nos. 99/107	*from* × 2
Nos. 108/19	*from* × 3
No. 120	—
No. 121	*from* × 3
No. 122	*from* × 5
No. 123	—
No. 124	*from* × 5
Nos. 126/9	*from* × 10
Nos. 131/45	*from* × 3
Nos. 146/8	*from* × 6
Nos. 149/59	*from* × 2

CROWN COLONY

1

(2)

3

(T **1**, **3** and **7** recess P.B.)

1861 (8 May). No Wmk. Rough to intermediate perf 14 to 16.

1	**1**	1d. rose-red	50·00	14·00
		a. Imperf vert (horiz pair)	£350	
		b. Imperf (pair)	£275	
2		6d. deep yellow-green	£7500	£200

The perforations on the 1d. are usually rough, but individual examples can be found on which some, or all, of the holes have the appearance of the intermediate perforations. All examples of the 6d. show intermediate perforations.

Imperforate examples, possibly proofs, exist of the 1d. rose-red and 6d. deep green handstamped "CANCELLED" in oval of bars (see note on Perkins Bacon "CANCELLED" in Catalogue Introduction). (*Price* 1d. £8500, 6d. £9500).

1862 (Sept). No wmk. Rough perf 14 to 16.

4	**1**	6d. deep green	60·00	19·00
		a. Imperf between (horiz pair)	£13000	£14000
		b. Imperf (pair)	£1100	

1862 (Dec)–**68**. No wmk.

(a) P 11 to 12½

5	**1**	1d. rose-red	42·00	20·00
6		4d. deep blue (*shades*) (1866)	£275	£110
		a. Imperf between (horiz pair)	†	—
7		6d. deep green (7.68)	£225	75·00
8		1s. slate-grey (8.66)	£2500	£900

(b) P 14 to 16

9		1s. slate-grey (*shades*) (8.66)	£375	£140

(c) P 11 to 12½×14 to 16

10	**1**	1d. rose-red (1866)	£6000	£1100
11		1s. slate-grey (8.66)	£275	£120

1869 (Apr–Sept). Colours changed. No wmk. P 11 to 12½.

12	**1**	4d. yellow (9.69)	£350	£160
13		1s. indigo	£375	90·00
14		1s. brown (9.69)	£500	£160

1871 (Apr). Wmk Small Star, W w **2**. Rough perf 14 to 16.

15	**1**	1d. black	60·00	15·00
		a. Imperf between (vert pair)	£17000	
16		6d. deep green	£325	70·00
		a. Wmk sideways	—	90·00

1872 (June). Colour changed. W w **2** (sideways). P 11 to 12½.

17	**1**	1s. deep rose-red	£750	£140

1872–75. W w **2** (sideways).

(a) Perf about 15

18	**1**	1d. black (*shades*) (11.72)	60·00	15·00
		a. Wmk upright	70·00	16·00
19		6d. dull blue-green (*shades*) (1873) ..	£2000	50·00
		b. Deep blue-green (1875)	£1500	50·00
		c. Wmk upright	£2250	

(b) P 11 to 12½×15

20	**1**	1s. lilac-rose (1873)	£5500	£350

1875. Colour changed. W w **2** (sideways). P 11 to 12½.

21		1s. claret	£600	£250

1875–78. W w **2** (sideways).

(a) P 11 to 12½×15

22	**1**	1d. black (*shades*) (4.75)	85·00	16·00
		a. Imperf between (horiz pair)	†	£23000
		b. Wmk upright	£150	50·00
23		6d. pale green (1877)	£650	50·00
24		1s. vermilion (2.77)	£1000	85·00
		a. Imperf vert (horiz pair)		

(b) P 11 to 12½

25	**1**	4d. deep blue (7.77)	£550	90·00

(c) Perf about 15

26	**1**	6d. pale green (3.77)	£1600	£450
		a. Wmk upright. *Lt yellow-green* (1878)	£700	29·00
27		1s. vermilion (1878?)	†	£40000

Only two examples of No. 27 have been recorded. The 1s vermilion is also known apparently imperforate and used.

1880 (May). No. 19*b* divided vertically by a line of perforation gauging 12, and surch locally with T **2** in red.

28		1d. on half 6d. deep blue-green	£550	£375
		a. Unsevered pair	£2000	£1200

1880 (June). W w **2** (sideways on 1d., 6d. and 1s.). P 11 to 12½.

29	**1**	1d. olive-green	£180	5·00
30		6d. bright green	£475	70·00
31		1s. bright vermilion	£800	60·00
		a. Imperf between (horiz pair)	£25000	
32	**3**	5s. rose-red	£1100	£1500
		a. Imperf	£7500	

(4)

ONE PENNY

(5)

4d

(6)

1881. Nos. 30/1 surch locally. No. 33 is divided vertically as No. 28.

33	**4**	½d. on half 6d. bright green (R.) (1.9)	£160	£170
		a. Unsevered pair	£475	£500
		b. Fraction bar omitted (pair with and without bar)	£4250	£5000
34	**5**	1d. on 6d. bright green (30.11)	£475	£350
35	**6**	4d. on 1s. bright vermilion (28.11)	£1600	£800
		a. 3mm space between "4d." and bar	£3000	£2250

No. 33 exists showing the "1" of "½" with a straight serif. Some examples come from a constant variety on R. 6/20, but others are the result of faulty type.

It is believed that Type **4** was applied as a setting of 36 (6×6) surcharges repeated three times on each sheet across rows 1 to 9. The missing fraction bar occurs on R. 6/3 of the setting.

The tenth vertical row of stamps appears to have been surcharged from a separate setting of 12 (2×6) on which a constant "straight serif" flaw occurs on the bottom right half-stamp.

Three unused single copies of No. 33 are known with the surcharge omitted.

It is believed that Nos. 34 and 35 were surcharged in settings of 30 (10×3).

No. 34 was only on sale between the 30 November and 3 December when supplies of No. 37 became available.

2½ PENCE

(7)   (8)   (9)

1881 (3 Dec). W w **2**. P 11 to 12½.

36	**7**	½d. orange (*shades*)	8·00	11·00
37	**1**	1d. drab (*shades*)	£700	15·00
38		4d. bright blue	£1200	£120
		a. Imperf between (horiz pair)		

(Recess D.L.R. from Perkins Bacon plates)

1882 (Nov)–**83**. No. 40 is surch with T **8**. Wmk Crown CA. P 14.

39	**1**	1d. drab	75·00	3·00
		x. Wmk reversed	95·00	10·00
40		2½d. on 1d. lake (1883)	29·00	1·50
		w. Wmk inverted	85·00	120
		x. Wmk reversed	42·00	5·00
		y. Wmk inverted and reversed		
41		4d. ultramarine	£650	75·00
		a. Dull ultramarine (wmk reversed)	£1000	£350
		w. Wmk inverted		
		x. Wmk reversed	£450	40·00
		y. Wmk inverted and reversed		

1883–84. Wmk Crown CA. P 12.

42	**7**	½d. green (1884)	£110	38·00
		x. Wmk reversed	—	£160
43	**1**	4d. ultramarine-blue	£750	50·00
		a. Grey-blue	£2250	£250
		w. Wmk inverted		
		x. Wmk reversed	£450	24·00
		y. Wmk inverted and reversed	†	£200
44		6d. bright green	£150	£300
		x. Wmk reversed	£400	
45		1s. orange-vermilion	£150	60·00
		x. Wmk reversed	£400	£130

The ½d. orange, 1d. rose-red, 1d. milky blue (without surcharge) and 5s. carmine-lake which were formerly listed are now considered to be colour trials. They are, however, of great interest (*Prices un.* ½d. £950, 1d. red £1000, 1d. blue £1300, 5s. £2500).

1885 (Mar). No. 40 further surch locally as in T **9**.

46	**1**	1d. on 2½d. on 1d. lake	40·00	32·00
		w. Wmk inverted	£100	
		x. Wmk reversed	40·00	32·00

Stamps with three cancelling bars instead of two are considered to be proofs.

1885–93. No. 49 is surch with T **8**. Wmk Crown CA. P 14.

47	**7**	½d. green	1·00	60
		a. Deep green	2·50	60
		w. Wmk inverted	50·00	17·00
		x. Wmk reversed	17·00	20·00
48	**1**	1d. rose-red	4·00	1·00
		a. Rose (1886)	6·00	1·75
		b. Red (1887)	4·00	85
		c. Carmine-red (1889)	24·00	3·75
		w. Wmk inverted		
		x. Wmk reversed	7·00	1·50
49		2½d. on 1d. milky blue (1889)	30·00	10·00
		x. Wmk reversed		
50		4d. red-brown	£950	22·00
		x. Wmk reversed	—	£110
51		4d. purple-brown (1886)	£100	75
		a. Chocolate (1887)	£100	1·40
		w. Wmk inverted	—	65·00
		x. Wmk reversed	£190	12·00
		y. Wmk inverted and reversed		
52		6d. violet (1888)	£180	£225
		w. Wmk inverted	£225	£275
		ws. Optd "SPECIMEN"	85·00	
		x. Wmk reversed		£650
53	**3**	5s. lake (1888)	30·00	55·00
		a. Printed both sides	£7500	
		b. Brown-lake (1893)	35·00	55·00
		w. Wmk inverted	£500	

49s, 51s/2s Optd "SPECIMEN" Set of 3 .... £200

2½d.

(10)

5 PENCE

(11)

1890 (Aug). No. 51*a* surch locally with T **10**.

54	**1**	2½d. on 4d. chocolate	80·00	£120
		a. No fraction bar (R. 1/7, 2/4)	£400	£500

1890–93. No. 55 is surch with T **8**. Colours changed. Wmk Crown CA. P 14.

55	**1**	2½d. on 1d. grey-blue (1890)	25·00	55
		a. Blue (1893)	1·75	35
		b. Surch double	†	£3250
		w. Wmk inverted	†	£100
		x. Wmk reversed		35·00
56		4d. yellow (1893)	1·75	15·00
		s. Optd "SPECIMEN"	35·00	
57		6d. dull purple (1891)	3·75	25·00
58		1s. orange (1891)	5·50	18·00
		a. Red-orange (1892)	14·00	23·00
		ax. Wmk reversed	£100	

Apart from the shades, Nos. 49 and 55/*a* can be differentiated by the perforations, which are always comb on No. 49 and line on Nos. 55/*a*.

1892 (Nov). No. 51*a* surch locally with T **11**, in purple.
59	**1**	5d. on 4d. chocolate	42·00	60·00
		s. Optd *"specimen"*	50·00	
		sa. Error. *"spicemen"* (R.3/3)	£1300	

The overprint also included two ornaments in the upper corners of the stamp.

Some letters are known double due to loose type, the best known being the first "E", but they are not constant.

FIVE PENCE
(12)   13   14

Short "F" (R. 5/1)

1893–94. Surch with T **12**. Wmk Crown CA. P 14.
60	**1**	5d. on 6d. carmine-lake	21·00	30·00
		a. Deep lake (1893)	3·00	2·00
		b. Lake (1894)	3·50	4·25
		c. Surch double	£6000	£3000
		d. Short "F"	42·00	45·00
		s. Optd "SPECIMEN"	50·00	

(Recess D.L.R.)

1897 (13 July). New values. Wmk Crown CA. P 14.
61	**1**	2½d. blue	13·00	2·25
62		5d. sepia	11·00	32·00
61s/2s Optd "SPECIMEN" Set of 2			70·00	

1897 (6 Oct). Surch as T **12**. Wmk Crown CA. P 14.
63	**1**	3d. on 1d. mauve	5·00	26·00
		a. Red-mauve	16·00	50·00
		s. Optd "SPECIMEN"	45·00	

(Typo D.L.R.)

1899 (1 Jan). Wmk Crown CA. P 14.
67	**13**	½d. dull mauve and green	2·75	2·50
68		1d. dull mauve and carmine	4·50	1·50
		w. Wmk inverted	£300	£250
69		2½d. dull mauve and blue	8·50	2·75
70		3d. dull mauve and olive	4·00	22·00
71		4d. dull mauve and orange	7·00	26·00
72		5d. dull mauve and black	8·00	22·00
73		6d. dull mauve and brown	13·00	50·00
74	**14**	1s. green and carmine	17·00	60·00
75		5s. green and blue	£100	£170
67/75 Set of 9			£150	£325
67s/75s Optd "SPECIMEN" Set of 9			£170	

15   16

(Typo D.L.R.)

1902. Wmk Crown CA. P 14.
76	**15**	½d. dull purple and green	4·25	70
77		1d. dull purple and carmine	4·25	30
78	**16**	2d. dull purple and black	6·50	7·00
79	**15**	2½d. dull purple and blue	5·00	3·75
80		3d. dull purple and olive	5·00	8·00
81		6d. dull purple and brown	11·00	50·00
82	**16**	1s. green and carmine	32·00	65·00
83	**15**	2s. green and violet	25·00	60·00
84	**16**	5s. green and blue	80·00	£140
76/84 Set of 9			£150	£300
76s/84s Optd "SPECIMEN" Set of 9			£170	

1904–11. Ordinary paper (½d., 1d., 1s.) or chalk-surfaced paper (others). Wmk Mult Crown CA. P 14.
85	**15**	½d. dull purple and green (1905)	7·50	9·00
		a. Chalk-surfaced paper	1·25	1·25
86		1d. dull purple and carmine	28·00	1·50
		a. Chalk-surfaced paper	28·00	1·50
88		2½d. dull purple and blue (1906)	17·00	50·00
89		6d. dull purple and brown (1905)	16·00	50·00
90	**16**	1s. green and carmine (1906)	35·00	60·00
		a. Chalk-surfaced paper	15·00	70·00
91	**15**	2s. purple and bright blue/*blue* (3.09?)	23·00	50·00
92	**16**	5s. green and red/*yellow* (3.09?)	17·00	55·00
93		£1 purple and black/*red* (22.7.11)	£275	£350
85/93 Set of 8			£350	£500
91s/3s Optd "SPECIMEN" Set of 3			£190	

Examples of most values are known showing a forged Kingstown postmark code letter "O", dated "JA 7 10" or a forged Calliaqua postmark dated "SP 20 09". Both have also been seen on some values of the 1899 and 1902 issues.

17   18

(Recess D.L.R.)

1907–08. Wmk Mult Crown CA. P 14.
94	**17**	½d. green (2.7.07)	3·50	2·50
95		1d. carmine (26.4.07)	4·00	15
96		2d. orange (5.08)	1·50	6·50

97		2½d. blue (8.07)	42·00	8·50
98		3d. violet (1.6.07)	8·00	17·00
94/8 Set of 5			55·00	30·00
94s/8s Optd "SPECIMEN" Set of 5			£130	

1909. No dot below "d". Wmk Mult Crown CA. P 14.
99	**18**	1d. carmine (3.09)	1·50	30
100		6d. dull purple (16.1.09)	9·00	48·00
101		1s. black/*green* (16.1.09)	4·25	10·00
99/101 Set of 3			13·00	50·00
99s/101s Optd "SPECIMEN" Set of 3			80·00	

1909 (Nov)–**11**. T **18**, redrawn (dot below "d", as in T **17**). Wmk Mult Crown CA. P 14.
102		½d. green (31.10.10)	4·00	60
		w. Wmk inverted	£150	
103		1d. carmine	5·00	20
104		2d. grey (3.8.11)	6·50	14·00
105		2½d. ultramarine (25.7.10)	8·00	3·75
106		3d. purple/*yellow*	2·50	15·00
107		6d. dull purple	21·00	16·00
102/7 Set of 6			42·00	45·00
102s, 104s/6s Optd "SPECIMEN" Set of 4			90·00	

ONE
PENNY.
19   (20)

(Recess D.L.R.)

1913 (1 Jan)–**17**. Wmk Mult Crown CA. P 14.
108	**19**	½d. green	75	20
109		1d. red	80	50
		a. Rose-red	1·00	75
		b. Scarlet (1.17)	19·00	5·00
		w. Wmk inverted	£120	
		y. Wmk inverted and reversed	£120	
110		2d. grey	8·00	38·00
		a. Slate	3·00	38·00
111		2½d. ultramarine	75	75
		x. Wmk reversed	£225	
112		3d. purple/*yellow*	80	5·00
		a. On lemon	2·75	12·00
		aw. Wmk inverted	£160	
		ax. Wmk reversed	£160	
		b. On pale yellow	2·50	9·50
		ba. "A" of "CA" missing from wmk	£500	
113		4d. red/*yellow*	80	2·00
114		5d. olive-green (7.11.13)	2·25	16·00
		x. Wmk reversed	£170	
115		6d. claret	2·00	4·50
116		1s. black/*green*	1·50	3·75
117		1s. bistre (1.5.14)	4·00	32·00
118	**18**	2s. blue and purple	4·75	40·00
119		5s. carmine and myrtle	13·00	60·00
		x. Wmk reversed	£250	
120		£1 mauve and black	£120	£180
108/20 Set of 13			£140	£350
108s/20s Optd "SPECIMEN" Set of 13			£250	

Nos. 118/20 are from new centre and frame dies, the motto "PAX ET JUSTITIA" being slightly over 7 mm long, as against just over 8 mm in Nos. 99 to 107. Nos. 139/41 are also from the new dies.

Examples of several values are known showing part strikes of the forged postmarks mentioned below Nos. 85/93.

1915 (30 Jan). No. 116 surch locally with T **20**.
121	**19**	1s. black/*green* (R.)	10·00	40·00
		a. "ONE" omitted	£1400	£1200
		b. "ONE" double	£650	
		c. "PENNY" and bar double	£650	£650
		d. "PENNY" and bar omitted	£1300	

The two lines of the surcharge were applied in separate operations, so that the spacing between them varies considerably.

WAR   **WAR**
STAMP.   **STAMP.**   **WAR STAMP**
(21)   (22)   (24)

1916 (June). No. 109 optd locally with T **21**.
(a) First and second settings; words 2 to 2½ mm apart
122	**19**	1d. red	12·00	23·00
		a. Opt double	£180	£180
		b. Comma for stop	12·00	29·00
		w. Wmk inverted		

In the first printing every second stamp has the comma for stop. The second printing of this setting has full stops only. These two printings can therefore only be distinguished in blocks or pairs.

(b) Third setting; words only 1½ mm apart
123	**19**	1d. red		£120
		a. Opt double		£1300

Stamps of the first setting are offered as this rare one. Care must be taken to see that the distance between the lines is not over 1½ mm.

*(c) Fourth setting; optd with T **22**. Words 3½ mm apart*
124	**19**	1d. carmine-red	3·00	25·00
		a. Opt double	£250	
		w. Wmk inverted		
		y. Wmk inverted and reversed		

1916 (Aug)–**18**. T **19**, from new printings, optd with T **24** by De La Rue.
126		1d. carmine-red	1·50	2·25
		s. Optd "SPECIMEN"	60·00	
		w. Wmk inverted		
		x. Wmk reversed		
		y. Wmk inverted and reversed	£150	
127		1d. pale rose-red	1·50	2·25
		w. Wmk inverted	£100	
		x. Wmk reversed	—	£200
128		1d. deep rose-red	1·75	2·25
129		1d. pale scarlet (1918)	3·50	4·50
		y. Wmk inverted and reversed	—	£200

1921–32. Wmk Mult Script CA. P 14.
131	**19**	½d. green (3.21)	1·75	30
132		1d. carmine (6.21)	1·00	80
		a. Red	2·50	15
		x. Wmk reversed	—	£250
132b		1½d. brown (1.12.32)	6·50	15
133		2d. grey (3.22)	2·50	1·00
133a		2½d. bright blue (12.25)	1·25	1·50
134		3d. bright blue (3.22)	1·00	6·00
		x. Wmk reversed	†	£250
135		3d. purple/*yellow* (1.12.26)	1·00	1·50
135a		4d. red/*yellow* (9.30)	1·75	6·00
136		5d. sage-green (8.3.24)	1·00	11·00
137		6d. claret (1.11.27)	1·50	3·50
138		1s. bistre-brown (9.21)	6·00	30·00
		a. Ochre (1927)	8·00	17·00
139	**18**	2s. blue and purple (8.3.24)	7·50	13·00
140		5s. carmine and myrtle (8.3.24)	18·00	42·00
141		£1 mauve and black (9.28)	£120	£140
131/41 Set of 14			£150	£200
131s/41s Optd or Perf (1½d., 4d., £1) "SPECIMEN" Set of 14			£350	

Examples of Nos. 140/1 are known with forged postmarks, including part strikes of those mentioned above, and others from Kingstown dated "6 MY 35" and "16 MY 41".

1935 (6 May). Silver Jubilee. As Nos. 91/4 of Antigua, but ptd by Waterlow. P 11×12.
142		1d. deep blue and scarlet	50	3·50
143		1½d. ultramarine and grey	1·00	4·75
144		2½d. brown and deep blue	2·00	6·00
145		1s. slate and purple	8·00	14·00
		l. Kite and horizontal log	£500	£600
142/5 Set of 4			10·50	25·00
142s/5s Perf "SPECIMEN" Set of 4			£100	

For illustration of plate variety see Omnibus section following Zanzibar.

1937 (12 May). Coronation. As Nos. 95/7 of Antigua. P 11×11½.
146		1d. violet	35	1·25
147		1½d. carmine	40	1·25
148		2½d. blue	45	4·25
146/8 Set of 3			1·10	
146s/8s Perf "SPECIMEN" Set of 3			80·00	

25   26 Young's Island and Fort Duvernette

27 Kingstown and Fort Charlotte   28 Bathing Beach at Villa

NEW CONSTITUTION 1951
(29a)

29 Victoria Park, Kingstown

(Recess B.W.)

1938 (11 Mar)–**47**. Wmk Mult Script CA. P 12.
149	**25**	½d. blue and green	20	10
150	**26**	1d. blue and lake-brown	20	10
151	**27**	1½d. green and scarlet	20	10
152	**25**	2d. green and scarlet	40	35
153	**28**	2½d. blue-black and blue-green	20	40
153a	**29**	2½d. green and purple-brown (14.1.47)	40	20
154	**25**	3d. orange and brown	20	10
154a	**28**	3½d. blue-black and blue-green (1.4.47)	75	2·50
155	**25**	6d. black and lake	1·50	40
156	**29**	1s. purple and green	1·50	80
157	**25**	2s. blue and purple	7·00	75
157a		2s.6d. red-brown and blue (14.1.47)	1·25	3·50
158		5s. scarlet and deep green	19·00	2·50
158a		10s. violet and brown (14.1.47)	7·50	9·00
		aw. Wmk inverted	£12000	£4250
159		£1 purple and black	28·00	15·00
149/59 Set of 15			60·00	32·00
149s/59s Perf "SPECIMEN" Set of 15			£325	

1946 (15 Oct). Victory. As Nos. 110/11 of Antigua.
160		1½d. carmine	10	10
161		3½d. blue	10	10
		sa. "SPECIMEN" double	£500	
160s/1s Perf "SPECIMEN" Set of 2			75·00	

1948 (30 Nov). Royal Silver Wedding. As Nos. 112/13 of Antigua.
162		1½d. scarlet	10	10
163		£1 bright purple	27·00	40·00

No. 163 was originally printed in black, but later changed to bright purple. The only surviving examples in the original colour are in the Royal Philatelic Collection.

(New Currency. 100 cents = 1 West Indian dollar)

1949 (26 Mar)–**52**. Value in cents and dollars. Wmk Mult Script CA. P 12.
164	**25**	1c. blue and green	20	1·75
164a		1c. green and black (10.6.52)	50	2·50
165	**26**	2c. blue and lake-brown	15	50
166	**27**	3c. green and scarlet	50	1·00

166a	25	3c. orange and purple (10.6.52)	1·00	2·50
167		4c. green and black	35	20
167a		4c. blue and green (10.6.52)	1·00	20
168	29	5c. green and purple-brown	15	10
169	25	6c. orange and purple	50	1·25
169a	27	6c. orange and scarlet (10.6.52)	60	2·25
170	28	7c. blue-black and blue-green	6·50	1·50
170a		10c. blue-black and blue-green (10.6.52)	1·00	20
171	25	12c. black and lake	35	15
172	29	24c. purple and green	35	55
173	25	48c. blue and purple	7·00	8·50
174		60c. red-brown and blue	5·00	8·00
175		$1.20 scarlet and deep green	6·00	4·50
176		$2.40 violet and brown	6·00	10·00
177		$4.80 purple and black	15·00	20·00
164/77 Set of 19			45·00	55·00

1949 (10 Oct). 75th Anniv of UPU. As Nos. 114/17 of Antigua.

178		5c. blue	20	20
179		6c. purple	1·50	2·25
180		12c. magenta	20	2·25
181		24c. blue-green	20	1·00
		a. "C" of "CA" missing from wmk	—	£750
178/81 Set of 4			1·90	5·25

1951 (16 Feb). Inauguration of BWI University College. As Nos. 118/19 of Antigua.

182		3c. deep green and scarlet	30	65
183		12c. black and purple	30	1·75

1951 (21 Sept). New Constitution. Optd with T **29a** by B.W.

184	27	3c. green and scarlet	20	1·75
185	25	4c. green and black	20	60
186	29	5c. green and purple-brown	20	60
187	25	12c. black and lake	1·25	1·25
184/7 Set of 4			1·60	3·75

1953 (2 June). Coronation. As No. 120 of Antigua.

188		4c. black and green	30	20

30

31

(Recess Waterlow (until 1961), then D.L.R.)

1955 (16 Sept)–**63**. Wmk Mult Script CA. P 13½×14 (T **30**) or 14 (T **31**).

189	30	1c. orange	10	10
		a. Deep orange (11.12.62)	11·00	7·00
190		2c. ultramarine	10	10
		a. Blue (26.9.61)	4·25	2·25
191		3c. slate	30	10
192		4c. brown	20	10
193		5c. scarlet	60	10
194		10c. reddish violet	20	65
		a. Deep lilac (12.2.58)	2·50	10
195		15c. deep blue	2·50	1·00
196		20c. green	60	10
197		25c. black-brown	50	10
198	31	50c. red-brown	5·00	3·75
		a. Chocolate (11.6.58)	5·50	1·50
		aw. Wmk inverted	†	£1000
199		$1 myrtle-green	9·00	1·00
		a. Deep myrtle-green (11.6.58)	22·00	4·25
		b. Deep yellowish green (15.1.63)	55·00	20·00
200		$2.50 deep blue	11·00	12·00
		a. Indigo-blue (30.7.62)	60·00	22·00
189/200 Set of 12			27·00	14·00
See also Nos. 207/20.				

1958 (22 Apr). Inauguration of British Caribbean Federation. As Nos. 135/7 of Antigua.

201		3c. deep green	70	20
202		6c. blue	75	1·25
203		12c. scarlet	80	50
201/3 Set of 3			2·00	1·75

MINISTERIAL GOVERNMENT

1963 (4 June). Freedom from Hunger. As No. 146 of Antigua.

204		8c. reddish violet	45	50

1963 (2 Sept). Red Cross Centenary. As Nos. 147/8 of Antigua.

205		4c. red and black	15	20
206		8c. red and blue	35	50

(Recess D.L.R.)

1964–65. As 1955–63 but wmk **12**.

(a) P 12½ (14 Jan–Feb 1964)

207	30	10c. deep lilac	30	20
208		15c. deep blue	30	50
209		20c. green (24.2.64*)	1·75	25
210		25c. black-brown	30	3·00
211	31	50c. chocolate	3·00	5·00
207/11 Set of 5			5·00	8·00

*(b) P 13×14 (T **30**) or 14 (T **31**)*

212	30	1c. orange (15.12.64)	15	10
213		2c. blue (15.12.64)	15	10
214		3c. slate (15.12.64)	50	10
215		5c. scarlet (15.12.64)	15	10
216		10c. deep lilac (15.12.64)	1·00	10
217		15c. deep blue (9.11.64)	1·00	30
218		20c. green (1964)	45	10
		w. Wmk inverted		
219		25c. black-brown (20.10.64)	1·00	15
220	31	50c. chocolate (18.1.65)	9·00	7·00
212/20 Set of 9			12·00	7·00

*This is the earliest known date recorded in St. Vincent although it may have been put on sale on 14.1.64.

32 Scout Badge and Proficiency Badges

33 Tropical Fruits

(Des V. Whiteley. Litho Harrison)

1964 (23 Nov). 50th Anniv of St. Vincent Boy Scouts Association. W w **12**. P 14½.

221	32	1c. yellow-green and chocolate	10	10
222		4c. blue and brown-purple	10	10
223		20c. yellow and black-violet	30	10
224		50c. red and bronze-green	45	70
221/4 Set of 4			85	90

(Des V. Whiteley. Photo Harrison)

1965 (23 Mar). Botanic Gardens Bicentenary. T **33** and similar multicoloured designs. W w **12**. P 14½×13½ (horiz) or 13½×14½ (vert).

225		1c. Type 33	10	10
226		4c. Breadfruit and HMS *Providence* (sloop), 1793	10	10
227		25c. Doric Temple and pond (*vert*)	15	10
228		40c. Talipot Palm and Doric Temple (*vert*)	30	1·25
225/8 Set of 4			60	1·40

1965 (17 May). ITU Centenary. As Nos. 166/7 of Antigua.

229		4c. light blue and light olive-green	15	10
230		48c. ochre-yellow and orange	35	45

37 Boat-building, Bequia (inscr "BEOUIA")

(Des M. Goaman. Photo Harrison)

1965 (16 Aug)–**67**. T **37** and similar multicoloured designs. W w **12**. P 14½×13½ (horiz designs) or 13½×14½ (vert).

231		1c. Type 37 ("BEOUIA")	10	1·00
231a		1c. Type 37 ("BEQUIA") (27.6.67)	65	40
232		2c. Friendship Beach, Bequia	10	10
233		3c. Terminal Building, Amos Vale Airport	1·00	10
		w. Wmk inverted	6·00	
234		4c. Woman with bananas (*vert*)	1·00	30
		w. Wmk inverted		
235		5c. Crater Lake	15	10
236		6c. Carib Stone (*vert*)	15	40
237		8c. Arrowroot (*vert*)	30	10
238		10c. Owia Salt Pond	30	10
239		12c. Deep water wharf	70	10
		w. Wmk inverted	†	£100
240		20c. Sea Island cotton (*vert*)	30	10
		w. Wmk inverted	—	50·00
241		25c. Map of St. Vincent and islands (*vert*)	35	10
		w. Wmk inverted	50·00	
242		50c. Breadfruit (*vert*)	50	30
243		$1 Baleine Falls (*vert*)	3·00	30
244		$2.50 St. Vincent Amazon (*vert*)	20·00	11·00
245		$5 Arms of St. Vincent (*vert*)	3·00	14·00
231/45 Set of 16			26·00	25·00

The 1c. (No. 231a), 2c., 3c., 5c. and 10c. exist with PVA gum as well as gum arabic.
See also No. 261.

1966 (24 Jan). Churchill Commemoration. As Nos. 170/3 of Antigua.

246		1c. new blue	10	10
247		4c. deep green	25	10
248		20c. brown	45	30
249		40c. bluish violet	55	1·00
246/9 Set of 4			1·25	1·25

1966 (4 Feb). Royal Visit. As Nos. 174/5 of Antigua.

250		4c. black and ultramarine	50	20
251		25c. black and magenta	1·50	80

1966 (20 Sept). Inauguration of WHO Headquarters, Geneva. As Nos. 178/9 of Antigua.

252		4c. black, yellow-green and light blue	30	10
253		25c. black, light purple and yellow-brown	70	80

1966 (1 Dec). 20th Anniv of UNESCO. As Nos. 196/8 of Antigua.

254		4c. slate-violet, red, yellow and orange	25	20
255		8c. orange-yellow, violet and deep olive	50	35
256		25c. black, bright purple and orange	1·25	1·00
254/6 Set of 3			1·75	1·40

38 Coastal View of Mount Coke Area

(Des and photo Harrison)

1967 (1 Dec). Autonomous Methodist Church. T **38** and similar horiz designs. Multicoloured. W w **12**. P 14×14½.

257		2c. Type 38	10	80
258		8c. Kingstown Methodist Church	10	10
259		25c. First Licence to perform marriages	25	10
260		35c. Conference Arms	25	10
257/60 Set of 4			60	1·00

1968 (20 Feb). As No. 234, but W w **12** sideways.

261		4c. Woman with bananas	30	30
The above exists with PVA gum as well as gum arabic.				

39 Meteorological Institute

(Des G. Vasarhelyi. Photo Harrison)

1968 (28 May). World Meteorological Day. W w **12**. P 14×14½.

262	39	4c. multicoloured	10	10
263		25c. multicoloured	10	10
264		35c. multicoloured	15	15
262/4 Set of 3			30	30

40 Dr. Martin Luther King and Cotton Pickers

(Des V. Whiteley. Litho D.L.R.)

1968 (28 Aug). Martin Luther King Commemoration. W w **12** (sideways). P 13.

265	40	5c. multicoloured	10	10
266		25c. multicoloured	10	10
267		35c. multicoloured	15	15
265/7 Set of 3			30	30

41 Speaker addressing Demonstrators

42 Scales of Justice and Human Rights Emblem

(Des V. Whiteley. Photo Enschedé)

1968 (1 Nov). Human Rights Year. P 13×14 (3c.) or 14×13 (35c.).

268	41	3c. multicoloured	10	10
269	42	35c. royal blue and turquoise-blue	20	10

43 Male Masquerader

44 Steel Bandsman

(Des V. Whiteley. Litho Format)

1969 (17 Feb). St. Vincent Carnival. T **43/4** and similar designs. P 14.

270		1c. multicoloured	10	20
271		5c. red and deep chocolate	10	10
272		8c. multicoloured	10	10
273		25c. multicoloured	15	10
270/3 Set of 4			40	45
Designs: Horiz—8c. Carnival Revellers. Vert—25c. Queen of Bands.				

METHODIST CONFERENCE MAY 1969
(47)

1969 (14 May). Methodist Conference. Nos. 257/8, 241 and 260 optd with T **47**.

274		2c. multicoloured	10	15
275		8c. multicoloured	15	25
276		25c. multicoloured	15	25
277		35c. multicoloured	75	2·00
274/7 Set of 4			1·00	2·40

48 "Strength in Unity"   **49** Map of "CARIFTA" Countries

53 "Children's Nursery"   **54** Angel and the Two Marys at the Tomb (stained-glass window)

Samoa

(Des J. Cooter. Litho D.L.R.)

1969 (1 July). First Anniv of CARIFTA (Caribbean Free Trade Area). W w **12** (sideways on T **48**). P 13.

278	**48**	2c. black, pale buff and red	10	10
279	**49**	5c. multicoloured	15	10
280	**48**	8c. black, pale buff and pale green	10	10
281	**49**	25c. multicoloured	35	15
278/81	*Set of 4*		60	40

ASSOCIATED STATEHOOD

50 Flag of St. Vincent

(Des V. Whiteley, based on local designs. Photo Harrison)

1969 (27 Oct). Statehood. T **50** and similar horiz designs. W w **12**. P 14×14½.

282	4c. multicoloured	10	10
283	10c. multicoloured	10	10
284	50c. grey, black and orange	35	20
282/4	*Set of 3*	50	35

Designs: 10c. Battle scene with insets of Petreglyph and Carib chief Chatoyer; 50c. Carib House with maces and scales.

51 Green Heron

(Des J.W. Photo Harrison)

1970 (12 Jan)–**71**. T **51** and similar multicoloured designs. Chalk-surfaced paper. W w **12** (sideways* on 1, 2, 3, 6, 8, 20, 25c., $1, 2.50 and upright on others). P 14.

285	½c. House Wren (*vert*)	10	1·75
286	1c. Type **51**	35	3·25
	a. Glazed, ordinary paper (9.8.71)	30	1·50
	aw. Wmk Crown to right of CA	1·00	1·75
287	2c. Lesser Antillean Bullfinches	15	40
	w. Wmk Crown to right of CA	23·00	
288	3c. St. Vincent Amazons	15	30
289	4c. Rufous-throated Solitaire (*vert*)	20	30
290	5c. Red-necked Pigeon (*vert*)	2·50	30
	a. Glazed, ordinary paper (9.8.71)	1·00	30
291	6c. Bananaquits	30	40
292	8c. Purple-throated Carib	40	30
	w. Wmk Crown to right of CA	48·00	
293	10c. Mangrove Cuckoo (*vert*)	30	10
294	12c. Common Black Hawk (*vert*)	40	10
295	20c. Bare-eyed Thrush	40	15
296	25c. Hooded Tanager	50	20
297	50c. Blue Hooded Euphonia	2·00	75
	w. Wmk inverted	75·00	
298	$1 Barn Owl (*vert*)	8·00	1·50
299	$2.50 Yellow-bellied Elaenia (*vert*)	3·50	6·00
300	$5 Ruddy Quail Dove	2·50	6·50
285/300	*Set of 16*	17·00	18·00

*The normal sideways watermark shows Crown to left of CA, *as seen from the back of the stamp.*

Values in this set (and three additional values) were subsequently issued W w **12** upright on 2c., 3c., 6c., 20c. and 30c. and sideways on others.

52 de Havilland DHC-6 Twin Otter 100

(Des R. Granger Barrett. Litho Enschedé)

1970 (13 Mar). 20th Anniv of Regular Air Services. T **52** and similar horiz designs. Multicoloured. W w **12** (sideways). P 14×13.

301	5c. Type **52**	10	10
302	8c. Grumman G.21 Goose	15	10
303	10c. Hawker Siddeley H.S.748	20	10
304	25c. Douglas DC-3	65	30
301/4	*Set of 4*	1·00	55

(Des R. Granger Barrett. Photo Harrison)

1970 (1 June). Centenary of British Red Cross. T **53** and similar horiz designs. Multicoloured. W w **12**. P 14.

305	3c. Type **53**	10	10
306	5c. "First Aid"	15	10
	w. Wmk inverted	75·00	
307	12c. "Voluntary Aid Detachment"	35	1·00
	w. Wmk inverted	2·25	
308	25c. "Blood Transfusion"	55	50
305/8	*Set of 4*	1·00	1·50

(Des L. Curtis. Litho J.W.)

1970 (7 Sept). 150th Anniv of St. George's Cathedral, Kingstown. T **54** and similar multicoloured designs. W w **12** (sideways* on horiz designs). P 14.

309	½c. Type **54**	10	10
310	5c. St. George's Cathedral (*horiz*)	10	10
	w. Wmk Crown to right of CA	60·00	
311	25c. Tower, St. George's Cathedral	10	10
312	35c. Interior, St. George's Cathedral (*horiz*)	15	10
313	50c. Type **54**	20	30
309/13	*Set of 5*	45	60

*The normal sideways watermark shows Crown to left of CA, *as seen from the back of the stamp.*

55 The Adoration of the Shepherds (Le Nain)

(Des J. Cooter. Litho Questa)

1970 (23 Nov). Christmas. T **55** and similar vert design. Multicoloured. W w **12** (sideways* on 25c., 50c.). P 14.

314	8c. *The Virgin and Child* (Bellini)	10	10
315	25c. Type **55**	10	10
	w. Wmk Crown to right of CA	1·00	
316	35c. As 8c.	10	10
317	50c. Type **55**	15	20
	w. Wmk Crown to right of CA	1·50	
314/17	*Set of 4*	40	45

*The normal sideways watermark shows Crown to left of CA, *as seen from the back of the stamp.*

Samoa

PRICES FOR STAMPS ON COVER TO 1945	
Nos. 1/20 are very rare used on cover.	
Nos. 21/40	from × 20
Nos. 41/8	from × 100
Nos. 49/51	—
No. 52	from × 20
Nos. 53/6	—
Nos. 57/64	from × 12
Nos. 65/70	from × 3
Nos. 71/97	from × 20
Nos. 101/9	from × 4
Nos. 110/14	—
Nos. 115/21	from × 4
Nos. 122/32	—
Nos. 134/64	from × 4
Nos. 165/76	—
Nos. 177/214	from × 2

INDEPENDENT KINGDOM OF SAMOA

The first postal service in Samoa was organised by C. L. Griffiths, who had earlier run the *Fiji Times* Express post in Suva. In both instances the principal purpose of the service was the distribution of newspapers of which Griffiths was the proprietor. The first issue of the *Samoa Times* (later the *Samoa Times and South Sea Gazette*) appeared on 6 October 1877 and the newspaper continued in weekly publication until 27 August 1881.

Mail from the Samoa Express post to addresses overseas was routed via New South Wales, New Zealand or USA and received additional franking with stamps of the receiving country on landing.

Cancellations, inscribed "APIA SAMOA", did not arrive until March 1878 so that examples of Nos. 1/9 used before that date were cancelled in manuscript. The Samoa Express stamps may also be found cancelled at Fiji, Auckland and Sydney.

1

A 2nd State (Nos. 4/9)

B 3rd State (Nos. 10/19)

(Des H. H. Glover. Litho S. T. Leigh & Co, Sydney, N.S.W.)

1877 (1 Oct)–**80**.

A. 1st state: white line above "X" in "EXPRESS" not broken. P 12½

1	**1**	1d. ultramarine	£375	£275
2		3d. deep scarlet	£450	£250
3		6d. bright violet	£475	£250
		a. Pale lilac	£500	£250

B. 2nd state: white line above "X" usually broken by a spot of colour, and dot between top of "M" and "O" of "SAMOA". P 12½ (1878–79)

4	**1**	1d. ultramarine	£160	£250
5		3d. bright scarlet	£550	£650
6		6d. bright violet	£700	£700
7		1s. dull yellow	£325	£120
		b. Perf 12 (1879)	£100	£275
		c. Orange-yellow	£325	£130
8		2s. red-brown	£375	£600
		a. Chocolate	£400	£600
9		5s. green	£4000	£1300

C. 3rd state: line above "X" repaired, dot merged with upper right serif of "M" (1879)

(a) P 12½

10	**1**	1d. ultramarine	£300	£120
11		3d. vermilion	£450	£200
12		6d. lilac	£550	£140

13		2s. brown	£400	£425
		a. Chocolate	£400	£425
14		5s. green	£2250	£800
		a. Line above "X" not repaired (R. 2/3)	£3250	

(b) P 12

15	1	1d. blue	40·00	£700
		a. Deep blue	45·00	
		b. Ultramarine	40·00	£700
16		3d. vermilion	70·00	£750
		a. Carmine-vermilion	70·00	
17		6d. bright violet	65·00	£500
		a. Deep violet	60·00	
18		2s. deep brown	£275	
19		5s. yellow-green	£600	
		a. Deep green	£800	
		b. Line above "X" not repaired (R. 2/3)	£900	

D. 4th state: spot of colour under middle stroke of "M". P 12 (1880)

20	1	9d. orange-brown	80·00	£400

Originals exist imperf, but are not known used in this state.

On sheets of the 1d., 1st state, at least eight stamps have a stop after "PENNY". In the 2nd state, three stamps have the stop, and in the 3rd state, only one.

In the 1st state, all the stamps, 1d., 3d. and 6d., were in sheets of 20 (5×4) and also the 1d. in the 3rd state.

All values in the 2nd state, all values except the 1d. in the 3rd state and No. 20 were in sheets of ten (5×2).

As all sheets of all printings of the originals were imperf at the outer edges, the only stamps which can have perforations on all four sides are Nos. 1 to 3a, 10 and 15 to 15b, all other originals being imperf on one or two sides.

The perf 12 stamps, which gauge 11.8, are generally very rough but later the machine was repaired and the 1d., 3d. and 6d. are known with clean-cut perforations.

Remainders of the 1d., unissued 2d. rose, 6d. (in sheets of 21 (7×3), 3d., 9d., 5s. (in sheets of 12 (4×3)) and of the 1s. and 2s. (sheet format unknown) were found in the Samoan post office when the service closed down in 1881. The remainders are rare in complete sheets.

Reprints of all values, in sheets of 40 (8×5), were made after the originals had been withdrawn from sale. These are practically worthless.

The majority of both reprints and remainders are in the 4th state as the 9d. with the spot of colour under the middle stroke of the "M", but a few stamps (both remainders and reprints) do not show this, while on some it is very faint.

There are six known types of forgery, one of which is rather dangerous, the others being crude.

The last mail despatch organised by the proprietors of the *Samoa Express* took place on 31 August 1881, although one cover is recorded postmarked 24 September 1881.

After the withdrawal of the *Samoa Express* service it would appear that the Apia municipality appointed a postmaster to continue the overseas post. Covers are known franked with USA or New Zealand stamps in Samoa, or routed via Fiji.

In December 1886 the municipal postmaster, John Davis, was appointed Postmaster of the Kingdom of Samoa by King Malietoa. Overseas mail sent via New Zealand was subsequently accepted without the addition of New Zealand stamps, although letters to the USA continued to require such franking until August 1891.

2 Palm Trees | **3** King Malietoa Laupepa | **4a** 6 mm

4b 7 mm | **4c** 4 mm

Description of Watermarks

(These are the same as W **12a/c** of New Zealand)

W **4a.** 6 mm between "N Z" and star; broad irregular star; comparatively wide "N"; "N Z" 11½ mm wide, with horizontal mesh.

W **4b.** 7 mm between "N Z" and star; narrower star; narrow "N"; "N Z" 10 mm wide, with vertical mesh.

W **4c.** 4 mm between "N Z" and star; narrow star; wide "N"; "N Z" 11 mm wide, with vertical mesh.

(Des A. E. Cousins (T **3**). Dies eng W. R. Bock and A. E. Cousins (T **2**) or A. E. Cousins (T **3**). Typo Govt Ptg Office, Wellington)

1886–1900.

*(i) W **4a***

(a) P 12½ (15 Oct–Nov 1886)

21	2	½d. purple-brown	35·00	55·00
22		1d. yellow-green	21·00	16·00
23		2d. dull orange	45·00	17·00
24		4d. blue	50·00	13·00
25		1s. rose-carmine	65·00	13·00
		a. Bisected (2½d.) (on cover)*	†	£350
26		2s.6d. reddish lilac	65·00	75·00

(b) P 12×11½ (6 July–Nov 1887)

27	2	½d. purple-brown	70·00	85·00
28		1d. yellow-green	£110	35·00
29		2d. yellow	95·00	£140
30		4d. blue	£275	£225
31		6d. brown-lake	50·00	20·00
32		1s. rose-carmine	—	£200
33		2s.6d. reddish lilac	£1500	

*(ii) W **4c**. P 12×11½ (9 May 1890)*

34	2	½d. purple-brown	80·00	42·00
35		1d. green	55·00	50·00
36		2d. brown-orange	80·00	50·00
37		4d. blue	£140	5·00
38		6d. brown-lake	£300	11·00
39		1s. rose-carmine	£350	14·00
		x. Wmk reversed	£600	£180
40		2s.6d. reddish lilac	£450	8·50

*(iii) W **4b***

(a) P 12×11½ (9 May 1890–92)

41	2	½d. pale purple-brown	7·50	6·50
		a. Blackish purple	8·00	6·50
42		1d. myrtle-green	38·00	2·50
		a. Green	38·00	2·50
		b. Yellow-green	38·00	2·50
43		2d. dull orange	45·00	1·75
		x. Wmk reversed	£190	£190
44	3	2½d. rose (22.11.92)	75·00	6·00
		a. Pale rose	75·00	6·00
45	2	4d. blue	£225	27·00
46		6d. brown-lake	£110	12·00
47		1s. rose-carmine	£250	6·00
48		2s.6d. slate-lilac	£325	12·00

(b) P 12½ (Mar 1891–92)

49	2	½d. purple-brown		
50		1d. green		
51		2d. orange-yellow	—	£1500
52	3	2½d. rose (7.1.92)	38·00	4·50
53	2	4d. blue	£4500	£1500
54		6d. brown-purple	£4500	£2500
55		1s. rose-carmine	£1200	£1500
56		2s.6d. slate-lilac	£5000	

(c) P 11 (May 1895–1900)

57	2	½d. purple-brown	8·00	2·75
		a. Deep purple-brown	5·00	1·75
		b. Blackish purple (1900)	3·75	35·00
58		1d. green	13·00	2·25
		a. Bluish green (1897)	12·00	2·50
		b. Deep green (1900)	4·25	26·00
		w. Wmk inverted	£750	£300
59		2d. pale yellow	45·00	45·00
		a. Orange (1896)	25·00	25·00
		b. Bright yellow (1.97)	18·00	12·00
		c. Pale ochre (10.97)	7·00	12·00
		d. Dull orange (1900)	9·00	
60	3	2½d. rose-carmine	6·50	10·00
		a. Deep rose-carmine (1900)	3·00	42·00
61	2	4d. blue	18·00	10·00
		a. Deep blue (1900)	2·75	50·00
62		6d. brown-lake	19·00	3·00
		a. Brown-purple (1900)	1·75	60·00
63		1s. rose	17·00	3·75
		a. Dull rose-carmine/toned (5.98)	5·00	38·00
		b. Carmine (1900)	1·50	
64		2s.6d. purple	55·00	10·00
		a. Reddish lilac (wmk inverted) (1897)	18·00	14·00
		b. Deep purple/toned (wmk reversed) (17.5.98)	4·75	9·50
		ba. Imperf between (vert pair)	£450	
		c. Slate-violet	£120	

*Following a fire on 1 April 1895 which destroyed stocks of all stamps except the 1s. value perf 12½, this was bisected diagonally and used as a 2½d. stamp for overseas letters between 24 April and May 1895, and was cancelled in blue. Fresh supplies of the 2½d. did not arrive until July 1895, although other values were available from 23 May.

Examples of the 1s. rose perforated 11, No. 63, were subsequently bisected and supplied cancelled-to-order by the post office to collectors, often with backdated cancellations. Most of these examples were bisected vertically and all were cancelled in black (*Price £7*).

The dates given relate to the earliest dates of printing in the various watermarks and perforations and not to issue dates.

The perf 11 issues (including those later surcharged or overprinted), are very unevenly perforated owing to the large size of the pins. Evenly perforated copies are extremely hard to find.

For the 2½d. black, see Nos. 81/2 and for the ½d. green and 1d. red-brown, see Nos. 88/9.

FIVE PENCE (5) | **FIVE PENCE** (6) | **5d** (7)

1893 (Nov–Dec). Handstamped singly, at Apia.

(a) In two operations

65	5	5d. on 4d. blue (37)	75·00	50·00
66		5d. on 4d. blue (45)	65·00	£100
67	6	5d. on 4d. blue (37)	£100	£110
68		5d. on 4d. blue (45)	80·00	

(b) In three operations (Dec)

69	7	5d. on 4d. blue (37) (R.)	45·00	38·00
70		5d. on 4d. blue (45) (R.)	50·00	50·00

In Types **5** and **6** the bars obliterating the original value vary in length from 13½ to 16½ mm and can occur with either the thick bar over the thin one or vice versa. Examples can be found with the bars omitted.

Double handstamps exist but we do not list them.

A surcharge as Type **7** but with stop after "d" is now considered to be a trial. It exists in black and in red. Where the "d" was applied separately its position in relation to the "5" naturally varies.

 Surcharged 1½d. (9) | **R 3d.** (10)

(8)

The "R" in Type **10** indicates use for registration fee.

(Des and die eng A. E. Cousins. Typo New Zealand Govt Ptg Office)

1894 (26 Feb)–**1900**. W **4b** (sideways).

(a) P 11½×12

71	8	5d. dull vermilion	35·00	3·50
		a. Dull red	35·00	3·75
		ab. Mixed perfs 11½×12 and 12½ ..		

(b) P 11

72	8	5d. dull red (1895)	48·00	14·00
		a. Deep red (1900)	6·00	23·00

No. 72 (like Nos. 71/a) shows wmk sideways to left (*as seen from the back of the stamp*), whereas No. 72a shows wmk sideways to right.

1895–1900. W **4b**.

*(i) Handstamped with T **9** or **10***

(a) P 12×11½ (28.1.95)

73	2	1½d. on 2d. dull orange (B.)	26·00	17·00
74		3d. on 2d. dull orange	55·00	22·00

(b) P 11 (6.95)

75	2	1½d. on 2d. dull orange (B.)	7·50	7·50
		a. Pair, one without handstamp	£650	
		b. On 2d. yellow	9·00	7·50
76		3d. on 2d. dull orange	9·50	14·00
		a. On 2d. yellow	11·00	14·00

*(ii) Handstamped as T **9** or **10**. P 11 (1896)*

78	2	1½d. on 2d. orange-yellow (B.)	4·25	28·00
79		3d. on 2d. orange-yellow	5·50	50·00
		a. Imperf between (vert pair)	£700	
		b. Pair, one without handstamp		

*(iv) Surch typo as T **10**. P 11 (7 Feb 1900)*

80	3	2d. on 2d. deep red-orange (G.)	2·00	£130

In No. 78 the "2" has a serif and the handstamp is in pale greenish blue instead of deep blue. In No. 79 the "R" is slightly narrower. In both instances the stamp is in a different shade.

A special printing in a distinctly different colour was made for No. 80 and the surcharge is in green.

Most of the handstamps exist double.

1896 (Aug). Printed in the wrong colour. W **4b**.

(a) P 10×11

81	3	2½d. black	3·00	3·50

(b) P 11

82	3	2½d. black	80·00	70·00
		a. Mixed perfs 10 and 11	£425	

Surcharged 2½d. (11) | **PROVISIONAL GOVT.** (12)

1898–99. W **4b**. P 11.

*(a) Handstamped as T **11** (10.98)*

83	2	2½d. on 1d. dull rose-carmine/toned	50·00	50·00

*(b) Surch as T **11** (1899)*

84	2	2½d. on 1d. bluish green (R.)	75	3·00
		a. Surch inverted	£850	£425
85		2½d. on 1s. dull rose-carmine/toned (R.)	8·50	16·00
		a. Surch double	£400	
86		2½d. on 1s. dull rose-carmine/toned (Blk.)	13·00	13·00
		a. Surch double	£500	
87		2½d. on 2s.6d. deep purple/toned (wmk reversed)	13·00	24·00

The typographed surcharge was applied in a setting of nine, giving seven types differing in the angle and length of the fractional line, the type of stop, etc.

1899 (18 July). Colours changed. W **4b**. P 11.

88		½d. dull blue-green	3·50	5·50
		a. Deep green	3·50	5·50
89		1d. deep red-brown	4·50	5·00

1899 (20 Sept)–**1900**. Provisional Government. New printings optd with T **12** (longer words and shorter letters on 5d.). W **4b**. P 11.

90	2	½d. dull blue-green (R.)	3·75	5·00
		a. Yellowish green (1900)	4·75	10·00
91		1d. chestnut (B.)	4·50	7·00
92		2d. dull orange (R.)	2·50	12·00
		a. Orange-yellow (1900)	4·50	14·00
93		4d. deep dull blue (R.)	70	16·00
94	8	5d. dull vermilion (B.)	3·75	15·00
		a. Red (1900)	5·00	15·00
95	2	6d. brown-lake (B.)	1·50	14·00
96		1s. rose-carmine (B.)	1·50	48·00
97		2s.6d. reddish purple (R.)	4·75	30·00
90/7		Set of 8	21·00	£150

The Samoan group of islands was partitioned on 1 March 1900. Western Samoa (Upolu, Savaii, Apolima and Manono) to Germany and Eastern Samoa (Tutuila, the Manu'a Is and Rose Is) to the United States. German issues of 1900–14 will be found listed in the Stanley Gibbons *Germany Catalogue*, there were no US issues.

The Samoan Kingdom post office run by John Davis was suspended in March 1900.

NEW ZEALAND OCCUPATION

The German Islands of Samoa surrendered to the New Zealand Expeditionary Force on 30 August 1914 and were administered by New Zealand until 1962.

G.R.I. (13) | **G.R.I. 1d. 1 Shillings.** (14)

SETTINGS. Nos. 101/9 were surcharged by a vertical setting of ten, repeated ten times across the sheet. Nos. 110/14 were from a horizontal setting of four repeated five times in the sheet.

Nos. 101b, 102a and 104a occurred on position 6. The error was corrected during the printing of No. 102.
Nos. 101c, 102c, 104d and 105b are from position 10.
Nos. 101d, 102e and 104b are from position 1.
No. 108b is from position 9.

(Surch by *Samoanische Zeitung*, Apia)

1914 (3 Sept). German Colonial issue (ship) (no wmk) inscr "SAMOA" surch as T **13** or **14** (mark values).

101	½d. on 3pf. brown	60·00	16·00
	a. Surch double	£750	£600
	b. No fraction bar	90·00	42·00
	c. Comma after "I"	£700	£425
	d. "1" to left of "2" in "½"	85·00	40·00
102	½d. on 5pf. green	65·00	21·00
	a. No fraction bar	£140	60·00
	c. Comma after "I"	£425	£180
	d. Surch double	£750	£600
	e. "1" to left of "2" in "½"	£110	45·00
103	1d. on 10pf. carmine	£100	40·00
	a. Surch double	£800	£650
104	2½d. on 20pf. ultramarine	60·00	14·00
	a. No fraction bar	95·00	42·00
	b. "1" to left of "2" in "½"	90·00	42·00
	c. Surch inverted	£1100	£1000
	d. Comma after "I"	£550	£350
	e. Surch double	£750	£650
105	3d. on 25pf. black and red/*yellow*	80·00	40·00
	a. Surch double	£1100	£800
	b. Comma after "I"	£5000	£1100
106	4d. on 30pf. black and orange/*buff*	£130	60·00
107	5d. on 40pf. black and carmine	£130	70·00
108	6d. on 50pf. black and purple/*buff*	65·00	35·00
	a. Surch double	£1100	£1000
	b. Inverted "9" for "6"	£180	£100
109	9d. on 80pf. black and carmine/*rose*	£200	£100
110	"1 shillings" on 1m. carmine	£3250	£3500
111	"1 shilling" on 1m. carmine	£11000	£7000
112	2s. on 2m. blue	£3500	£3000
113	3s. on 3m. violet-black	£1400	£1200
	a. Surch double	£10000	£11000
114	5s. on 5m. carmine and black	£1200	£1000
	a. Surch double	£13000	£14000

No. 108b is distinguishable from 108, as the "d" and the "9" are not in a line, and the upper loop of the "9" turns downwards to the left.

UNAUTHORISED SURCHARGES. Examples of the 2d. on 20pf., 3d. on 30pf., 3d. on 40pf., 4d. on 40pf., 6d. on 80pf., 2s. on 3m. and 2s. on Marshall Islands 2m., together with a number of errors not listed above, were produced by the printer on stamps supplied by local collectors. These were not authorised by the New Zealand Military Administration.

SAMOA.

(**15**)

1914 (29 Sept)–**15**. Stamps of New Zealand. T **53**, **51**, **52** and **27**, optd as T **15**, but opt only 14 mm long on all except 2½d. Wmk "N Z" and Star, W **43** of New Zealand.

115	½d. yellow-green (R.) (P 14×15)	1·75	30
116	1d. carmine (B.) (P 14×15)	1·25	10
117	2d. mauve (R.) (P 14×14½) (10.14)	1·25	1·00
118	2½d. deep blue (R.) (P 14) (10.14)	1·75	1·75
	w. Wmk inverted		
119	6d. carmine (B.) (P 14×14½) (10.14)	2·00	1·75
	a. Perf 14×13½	17·00	23·00
	b. Vert pair. Nos. 119/a (1915)	55·00	£100
	c. Pale carmine (P 14×14½)	11·00	10·00
121	1s. vermilion (B.) (P 14×14½) (10.14)	14·00	23·00
115/21	Set of 6	20·00	25·00

1914–24. Postal Fiscal stamps as Type F **4** of New Zealand optd with T **15**. W **43** of New Zealand (sideways). Chalk-surfaced "De La Rue" paper.

(a) P 14 (Nov 1914–17)

122	2s. blue (R.) (9.17)	£100	£100
123	2s.6d. grey-brown (B.) (9.17)	6·00	18·00
124	5s. yellow-green (B.)	25·00	11·00
125	10s. maroon (B.)	40·00	28·00
126	£1 rose-carmine (B.)	90·00	45·00

(b) P 14½×14, comb (1917–24)

127	2s. deep blue (R.) (3.18)	8·50	5·50
128	2s.6d. grey-brown (B.) (10.24)	£425	£170
129	3s. purple (R.) (6.23)	16·00	65·00
130	5s. yellow-green (R.) (9.17)	28·00	17·00
131	10s. maroon (B.) (11.17)	85·00	48·00
132	£1 rose-carmine (B.) (3.18)	£110	70·00

We no longer list the £2 value as it is doubtful this was used for postal purposes.
See also Nos. 165/6e.

1916–19. King George V stamps of New Zealand optd as T **15**, but 14 mm long.

(a) Typo. P 14×15

134	**61**	½d. yellow-green (R.)	1·25	1·25
135		1½d. slate (R.) (1917)	50	25
136		1½d. orange-brown (R.) (1919)	30	50
137		2d. yellow (14.2.18)	2·00	25
138		3d. chocolate (B.) (1919)	4·50	23·00

(b) Recess. P 14×13½

139	**60**	2½d. blue (B.)	2·25	50
		a. Perf 14×14½	1·25	60
		b. Vert pair. Nos. 139/a	17·00	27·00
140		3d. chocolate (B.) (1917)	65	1·50
		a. Perf 14×14½	65	1·00
		b. Vert pair. Nos. 140/a	17·00	30·00
141		6d. carmine (B.) (5.5.17)	4·00	3·25
		a. Perf 14×14½	1·50	1·50
		b. Vert pair. Nos. 141/a	19·00	40·00
142		1s. vermilion (B.)	6·50	1·50
		a. Perf 14×14½	6·50	9·00
		b. Vert pair. Nos. 142/a	29·00	55·00
134/42	Set of 9	17·00	27·00

LEAGUE OF NATIONS MANDATE

Administered by New Zealand.

1920 (July). Victory. Nos. 453/8 of New Zealand optd as T **15**, but 14 mm long.

143	½d. green (R.)	6·50	18·00
144	1d. carmine (R.)	3·25	23·00
145	1½d. brown-orange (R.)	2·00	12·00
146	3d. chocolate (B.)	8·00	11·00
147	6d. violet (R.)	4·50	7·50
148	1s. orange-red (B.)	13·00	11·00
143/8	Set of 6	32·00	75·00

16 Native Hut

 are not in this area

SILVER JOBILEE
OF
KING GEORGE V
1910–1935.

(**17**)

(Eng B.W. Recess-printed at Wellington, NZ)

1921 (23 Dec). W **43** of New Zealand.

(a) P 14×14½

149	**16**	½d. green	6·50	16·00
150		1d. lake	11·00	2·00
151		1½d. chestnut	1·75	22·00
152		2d. yellow	3·00	3·25
149/52	Set of 4	20·00	40·00

(b) P 14×13½

153	**16**	½d. green	4·75	1·75
154		1d. lake	7·00	20
155		1½d. chestnut	23·00	14·00
156		2d. yellow	14·00	80
157		2½d. grey-blue	1·75	10·00
158		3d. sepia	1·75	6·50
159		4d. violet	1·75	3·75
160		5d. light blue	1·75	9·50
161		6d. bright carmine	1·75	8·50
162		8d. red-brown	1·75	16·00
163		9d. olive-green	2·00	30·00
164		1s. vermilion	1·75	24·00
153/64	Set of 12	55·00	£110

1925–28. Postal Fiscal stamps as Type F **4** of New Zealand optd with T **15**. W **43** of New Zealand (sideways). P 14½×14.

(a) Thick, opaque, white chalk-surfaced "Cowan" paper

165	2s. blue (R.) (12.25)	£200	£225
166	2s.6d. deep grey-brown (B.) (10.28)	55·00	£110
166a	5s. mauve (R.) (9.25)	70·00	£120
166b	5s. yellow-green (R.) (11.26)	40·00	55·00
	ba. Opt at top of stamp	£2000	£2250
166c	10s. brown-red (B.) (12.25)	£200	£150
166d	£1 rose-pink (B.) (11.26)	£110	£120
165/6d	Set of 6	£600	£700

(b) Thin, hard, chalk-surfaced "Wiggins Teape" paper

166e	£1 rose-pink (B.) (1928)	£2750	£1200

1926–27. T **72** of New Zealand, optd with T **15**, in red.

(a) "Jones" paper

167	2s. deep blue (11.26)	5·00	18·00
	w. Wmk inverted	—	27·00
168	3s. mauve (10.26)	28·00	50·00
	w. Wmk inverted	35·00	55·00

(b) "Cowan" paper.

169	2s. light blue (10.11.27)	6·00	45·00
170	3s. pale mauve (10.11.27)	60·00	£110

1932 (Aug). Postal Fiscal stamps as Type F **6** of New Zealand optd with T **15**. W **43** of New Zealand. Thick, opaque, white chalk-surfaced "Cowan" paper. P 14.

171	2s.6d. deep brown (B.)	16·00	50·00
172	5s. green (B.)	26·00	55·00
173	10s. carmine-lake (B.)	50·00	£100
174	£1 pink (B.)	75·00	£150
175	£2 bright purple (R.)	£1000	
176	£5 indigo-blue (R.)	£2500	

The £2 and £5 values were primarily for fiscal use.

1935 (7 May). Silver Jubilee. Optd with T **17**. P 14×13½.

177	**16**	1d. lake	30	30
		a. Perf 14×14½	95·00	£170
178		2½d. grey-blue	60	65
179		6d. bright carmine	2·75	5·75
177/9	Set of 3	3·25	6·00

18 Samoan Girl

19 Apia

20 River scene

21 Chief and Wife

22 Canoe and house

23 R. L. Stevenson's home *Vailima*

---

24 Stevenson's tomb

25 Lake Lanuto'o

26 Falefa Falls

(Recess D.L.R.)

1935 (7 Aug). T **18/26**. W **43** of New Zealand ("N Z" and Star). P 14×13½ (½d., 2½d., 2s., 3s.), 14 (2d.) or 13½×14 (others).

180	½d. green	10	35
	w. Wmk inverted		
181	1d. black and carmine	10	10
	w. Wmk inverted	£100	
182	2d. black and orange	3·50	4·75
	aw. Wmk inverted		
	b. Perf 13½×14	4·00	4·25
	bw. Wmk inverted		
183	2½d. black and blue	10	10
184	4d. slate and sepia	70	15
185	6d. bright magenta	50	10
186	1s. violet and brown	30	10
187	2s. green and purple-brown	1·00	50
188	3s. blue and brown-orange	4·00	3·50
180/8	Set of 9	9·00	8·00

See also Nos. 200/3.

WESTERN SAMOA.

(**27**)

1935–42. Postal Fiscal stamps as Type F **6** of New Zealand optd with T **27**. W **43** of New Zealand. P 14.

(a) Thick, opaque chalk-surfaced "Cowan" paper (7.8.35)

189	2s.6d. deep brown (B.)	6·00	16·00
190	5s. green (B.)	26·00	38·00
191	10s. carmine-lake (B.)	70·00	90·00
192	£1 pink (R.)	60·00	£110
193	£2 bright purple (R.)	£160	£400
194	£5 indigo-blue (R.)	£225	£475

(b) Thin, hard chalk-surfaced "Wiggins Teape" paper (1941–42)

194a	5s. green (6.42)	£180	£225
194b	10s. pale carmine-lake (B.) (6.41)	£150	£200
194c	£2 bright purple (2.42)	£550	£1000
194d	£5 indigo-blue (R.) (2.42)	£3000	£3750

The £2 and £5 values were primarily for fiscal use. A £10 deep blue (on "Cowan" paper) was also issued, and exists with postal cancellations.
See also Nos. 207/14.

28 Coastal Scene

29 Map of Western Samoa

30 Samoan dancing party

31 Robert Louis Stevenson

(Des J. Berry (1d. and 1½d.). L. C. Mitchell (2½d. and 7d.). Recess B.W.)

1939 (29 Aug). 25th Anniv of New Zealand Control. T **28/31**. W **98** of New Zealand. P 13½×14 or 14×13½ (7d.).

195	**28**	1d. olive-green and scarlet	1·00	25
196	**29**	1½d. light blue and red-brown	1·75	75
197	**30**	2½d. red-brown and blue	3·00	1·00
198	**31**	7d. violet and slate-green	8·00	4·00
195/8	Set of 4	12·00	5·50

32 Samoan Chief

33 Apia Post Office

(Recess B.W.)

1940 (2 Sept). W **98** of New Zealand (Mult "N Z" and Star). P 14×13½.

199	**32**	3d. on 1½d. brown	75	20

T **32** was not issued without surcharge but archival examples exist (*Price, £200 unused*).

(T **33**. Des L. C. Mitchell. Recess B.W.)

1944–49. As Nos. 180, 182/3 and T **33**. W **98** of New Zealand (Mult "N Z" and Star) (sideways on 2½d.). P 14 or 13½×14 (5d.)

200		½d. green	30	21·00
202		2d. black and orange	3·50	7·50
203		2½d. black and blue (1948)	8·50	45·00
205		5d. sepia and blue (8.6.49)	2·75	1·25
200/5 *Set of 4*			13·50	65·00

1945–53. Postal Fiscal stamps as Type F **6** of New Zealand optd with T **27**. W **98** of New Zealand. Thin hard, chalk-surfaced "Wiggins Teape" paper. P 14.

207	2s.6d. deep brown (B.) (6.45)	22·00	38·00
	w. Wmk inverted	38·00	50·00
208	5s. green (5.45)	21·00	13·00
	w. Wmk inverted	38·00	48·00
209	10s. carmine-lake (B.) (4.46)	20·00	15·00
	w. Wmk inverted	60·00	60·00
210	£1 pink (B.) (6.48)	£140	£200
211	30s. brown (8.48)	£200	£300
212	£2 bright purple (R.) (11.47)	£200	£275
	w. Wmk inverted	£600	£750
213	£3 green (8.48)	£300	£375
214	£5 indigo-blue (R) (1946)	£425	£500
	w. Wmk inverted (5.53)	£425	£500
207/10 *Set of 4*		£180	£225

Values over £1 were mainly used for fiscal purposes.

WESTERN SAMOA
(34)

1946 (4 June). Peace Issue. Nos. 668, 670 and 674/5 of New Zealand optd with T **34** (reading up and down at sides on 2d.).

215		1d. green	40	15
		w. Wmk inverted	£180	
216		2d. purple (B.)	40	15
217		6d. chocolate and vermilion	80	15
218		8d. black and carmine (B.)	40	15
215/18 *Set of 4*			1·75	55

UNITED NATIONS TRUST TERRITORY
Administered by New Zealand.

35 Making Siapo Cloth

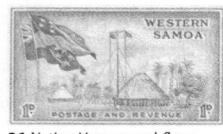

36 Native Houses and flags

37 Seal of Samoa

38 Malifa Falls (wrongly inscribed "Aleisa Falls")

39 Tooth-billed Pigeon

40 Bonito fishing canoe

41 Cacao harvesting

42 Thatching a Native Hut

43 Preparing Copra

44 Samoan Chieftainess

1952 (10 Mar). T **35/44**. W **98** of New Zealand (sideways on 1s. and 3s.). P 13 (½d., 2d. and 1s.) or 13½ (others).

219	**35**	½d. claret and orange-brown	10	2·25
220	**36**	1d. olive-green and green	30	50
221	**37**	2d. carmine-red	30	10
222	**38**	3d. pale ultramarine and indigo	50	20
223	**39**	5d. brown and deep green	10·00	1·50
224	**40**	6d. pale ultramarine and rose-magenta	1·00	10
225	**41**	8d. carmine	30	30
226	**42**	1s. sepia and blue	20	10
227	**43**	2s. yellow-brown	1·00	25
228	**44**	3s. chocolate and brown-olive	3·50	2·75
219/28 *Set of 10*			15·00	7·00

1953 (25 May). Coronation. Designs as Nos. 715 and 717 of New Zealand, but inscr "WESTERN SAMOA".

229	2d. brown	1·25	15
230	6d. slate-grey	1·25	35

WESTERN
SAMOA
(45)

1955 (14 Nov). Postal Fiscal stamps as Type F **6** of New Zealand optd with T **45**. W **98** (inverted). Chalk-surfaced "Wiggins, Teape" paper. P 14.

232	5s. green (B.)	8·00	29·00
233	10s. carmine-lake (B.)	8·00	50·00
234	£1 pink (B.)	15·00	60·00
235	£2 bright purple (R.)	70·00	£160
232/5 *Set of 4*		90·00	£275

The £2 value was mainly used for fiscal purposes.

46 Native Houses and Flags

47 Seal of Samoa

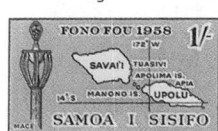

48 Map of Samoa and the Mace

(Recess B.W.)

1958 (21 Mar). Inauguration of Samoan Parliament. T **46/8**. W **98** of New Zealand (sideways). P 13½×13 (6d.) or 13½ (others).

236	**46**	4d. cerise	35	30
237	**47**	6d. deep reddish violet	35	30
238	**48**	1s. deep ultramarine	85	50
236/8 *Set of 3*			1·40	1·00

INDEPENDENT
Samoa became independent on 1 January 1962.

49 Samoan Fine Mat

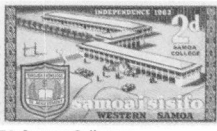

50 Samoa College

(Litho B.W.)

1962 (2 July). Independence. T **49/50** and similar designs. W **98** of New Zealand (sideways on horiz stamps). P 13½.

239		1d. brown and rose-carmine	10	10
240		2d. brown, green, yellow and red	10	10
241		3d. brown, blue-green and blue	10	10
242		4d. magenta, yellow, blue and black	15	60
243		6d. yellow and blue	80	10
244		8d. bluish green, yellow-green and blue	80	10
245		1s. brown and bluish green	20	10
246		1s.3d. yellow-green and blue	1·00	70
247		2s.6d. red and ultramarine	2·25	2·00
248		5s. ultramarine, yellow, red and drab	2·50	2·75
239/48 *Set of 10*			7·00	6·00

Designs: Horiz—3d. Public library; 4d. Fono House; 6d. Map of Samoa; 8d. Airport; 1s.3d. *Vailima*; 2s.6d. Samoan flag; 5s. Samoan Seal. Vert—1s. Samoan orator.
See Nos. 257/62.

59 Seal and Joint Heads of State

60 Signing the Treaty

(Des L. C. Mitchell. Photo Harrison)

1963 (1 Oct). First Anniv of Independence. W **98** of New Zealand. P 14.

249	**59**	1d. deep sepia and green	10	10
250		4d. deep sepia and blue	10	10
251		8d. deep sepia and rose-pink	15	10
252		2s. deep sepia and orange	20	15
249/52 *Set of 4*			45	40

(Des L. C. Mitchell. Photo Enschedé)

1964 (1 Sept). Second Anniv of New Zealand-Samoa Treaty of Friendship. P 13½.

253	**60**	1d. multicoloured	10	10
254		8d. multicoloured	10	10
255		2s. multicoloured	20	10
256		3s. multicoloured	25	30
253/6 *Set of 4*			55	55

61 Kava Bowl

1965 (4 Oct)–**66?**. As Nos. 239, 241/5, but W **61** (sideways on horiz designs).

257		1d. brown and rose-carmine	20	1·00
258		3d. brown, blue-green and blue (1966?)	28·00	3·75
259		4d. magenta, yellow, blue and black	25	60
260		6d. yellow and blue	75	50
261		8d. bluish green, yellow-green and blue	30	10
262		1s. brown and bluish green	25	60
257/62 *Set of 6*			28·00	6·00

62 Red-tailed Tropicbird   **63** Flyingfish

(Des L. C. Mitchell. Photo Harrison)

1965 (29 Dec). Air. W **61** (sideways). P 14½.

263	**62**	8d. black, red-orange and blue	50	10
264	**63**	2s. black and blue	75	20

64 Aerial View of Deep Sea Wharf

(Des Tecon Co (USA). Photo Enschedé)

1966 (3 Mar). Opening of First Deep Sea Wharf Apia. T **64** and similar horiz design. Multicoloured. W **61** (sideways). P 13½.

265		1d. Type **64**	10	10
266		8d. Aerial view of wharf and bay	15	10
267		2s. As 8d.	25	25
268		3s. Type **64**	30	35
265/8 *Set of 4*			70	70

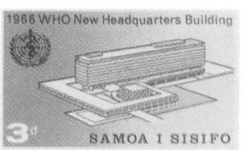

66 WHO Building

(Des M. Goaman. Photo D.L.R.)

1966 (4 July). Inauguration of WHO Headquarters. Geneva. T **66** and similar horiz design. W **61** (sideways*). P 14.

269		3d. yellow-ochre, blue and light slate-lilac	35	10
270		4d. blue, yellow, green and light orange-brown	50	90
271		6d. reddish lilac, emerald and yellow-olive	50	60
		w. Wmk legs to left	1·75	
272		1s. blue, yellow, green and turquoise-green	1·25	65
269/72 *Set of 4*			2·40	2·00

Designs:—3d., 6d. Type **66**; 4d., 1s. WHO Building on flag. *The normal sideways watermark has the legs of the bowl pointing to the right, *as seen from the back of the stamp*.

HURRICANE RELIEF
6ᵈ
(68)

1966 (1 Sept). Hurricane Relief Fund. No. 261 surch with T **68** by Bradbury Wilkinson.

273	8d. +6d. bluish green, yellow-green and blue	10	10

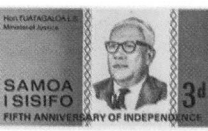

69 Hon. Tuatagaloa L. S. (Minister of Justice)

(Des and Photo Harrison)

1967 (16 Jan). Fifth Anniv of Independence. T **69** and similar horiz designs. W **61** (sideways). P 14½×14.

274		3d. sepia and emerald	10	10
275		8d. sepia and light new blue	10	10
276		2s. sepia and olive	10	10
277		3s. sepia and magenta	15	15
274/7 *Set of 4*			40	40

Designs:—8d. Hon F. C. F. Nelson (minister of Works, Marine and Civil Aviation); 2s. Hon To'omata T. L. (minister of Lands); 3s. Hon Fa'alava'au G. (minister of Post Office, Radio and Broadcasting).

73 Samoan Fales (houses), 1890

(Des V. Whiteley. Photo Harrison)

1967 (16 May). Centenary of Mulinu'u as Seat of Government. T **73** and similar horiz design. Multicoloured. W **61**. P 14½×14.
278	8d. Type **73**	15	10
279	1s. Fono (Parliament) House, 1967	15	10

(New Currency. 100 sene or cents=1 tala or dollar)

75 Carunculated Honeyeater

76 Black-breasted Honeyeater

(Des V. Whiteley. Litho Format ($2, $4). Photo Harrison (others))

1967 (10 July)–**69**. Decimal currency Multicoloured designs as T **75** (1s. to $1) or **76** ($2, $4). W **61** (sideways). P 13½ ($2, $4) or 14×14½ (others).
280	1s. Type **75**	10	10
281	2s. Pacific Pigeon	10	10
282	3s. Samoan Starling	10	10
283	5s. White-vented Flycatcher	10	10
284	7s. Red-headed Parrot Finch	10	10
285	10s. Purple Swamphen	15	10
286	20s. Barn Owl	1·25	40
287	25s. Tooth-billed Pigeon	50	15
288	50s. Island Thrush	50	30
289	$1 Samoan Fantail	75	1·75
289a	$2 Type **76** (14.7.69)	2·00	4·00
289b	$4 Savaii White Eye (6.10.69)	25·00	13·00
280/9b	Set of 12	27·00	18·00

85 Nurse and Child

(Des G. Vasarhelyi. Photo D.L.R.)

1967 (1 Dec). South Pacific Health Service. T **85** and similar horiz designs. Multicoloured. P 14.
290	3s. Type **85**	15	15
291	7s. Leprosartum	20	15
292	20s. Mobile X-ray Unit	35	30
293	25s. Apia Hospital	40	35
290/3	Set of 4	1·00	85

89 Thomas Trood

93 Cocoa

(Des M. Farrar-Bell. Litho B.W.)

1968 (15 Jan). Sixth Anniv of Independence. T **89** and similar horiz designs. Multicoloured. P 13½.
294	2s. Type **89**	10	10
295	7s. Dr Wilhelm Solf	10	10
296	20s. J. C. Williams	10	10
297	25s. Fritz Marquardt	15	10
294/7	Set of 4	40	35

(Des Jennifer Toombs. Photo Enschedé)

1968 (15 Feb). Agricultural Development. T **93** and similar vert designs. W **61**. P 13×12½.
298	3s. deep red-brown, yellow-green and black	10	10
299	5s. myrtle-green, greenish yellow and light brown	10	10
300	10s. scarlet, blackish brown and olive-yellow	10	10
301	20s. yellow-bistre, yellow and blackish olive	15	15
298/301	Set of 4	40	40
Designs:— 5s. Breadfruit; 10s. Copra; 20s. Bananas.

97 Women weaving Mats

(Des G. Vasarhelyi. Photo Harrison)

1968 (22 Apr). 21st Anniv of the South Pacific Commission. T **97** and similar horiz designs. Multicoloured. W **61**. P 14½×14.
302	7s. Type **97**	10	10
303	20s. Palm trees and bay	15	10
304	25s. Sheltered cove	15	15
302/4	Set of 3	35	30

1928-1968 KINGSFORD-SMITH TRANSPACIFIC FLIGHT

(100)

1968 (13 June). 40th Anniv of Kingsford Smith's Trans-Pacific Flight. No. 285 surch with T **100**.
305	20s. on 10s. Purple Swamphen	10	30

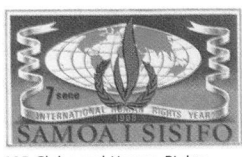

101 Bougainville's Route

(Des Jennifer Toombs. Litho B.W.)

1968 (17 June). Bicentenary of Bougainville's Visit to Samoa. T **101** and similar horiz designs. W **61** (sideways). P 14.
306	3s. new blue and black	10	20
307	7s. light ochre and black	15	20
308	20s. multicoloured	45	30
309	25s. multicoloured	60	40
306/9	Set of 4	1·10	1·00
Designs:—7s. Louis de Bougainville; 20s. Bougainvillea flower; 25s. Ships La Boudeuse and L'Etoile.

105 Globe and Human Rights Emblem

106 Dr. Martin Luther King

(Des G. Vasarhelyi. Photo Harrison)

1968 (26 Aug). Human Rights Year. W **61**. P 14.
310	**105** 7s. greenish blue, brown and gold	10	10
311	20s. orange, green and gold	10	15
312	25s. violet, green and gold	15	15
310/12	Set of 3	30	35

(Des and litho D.L.R.)

1968 (23 Sept). Martin Luther King Commemoration. W **61**. P 14½×14.
313	**106** 7s. black and olive-green	15	10
314	20s. black and bright purple	15	10

107 Polynesian Version of Madonna and Child

108 Frangipani-Plumeria acuminata

(Des and litho D.L.R.)

1968 (14 Oct). Christmas. W **61**. P 14.
315	**107** 1s. multicoloured	10	10
316	3s. multicoloured	10	10
317	20s. multicoloured	10	10
318	30s. multicoloured	15	15
315/18	Set of 4	30	30

(Des J.W. Litho Format)

1969 (20 Jan). Seventh Anniv of Independence. T **108** and similar multicoloured designs. P 14½.
319	2s. Type **108**	10	10
320	7s. Hibiscus (vert)	10	10
321	20s. Red-Ginger (vert)	15	10
322	30s. "Moso'oi"	20	80
319/22	Set of 4	50	1·00

109 R. L. Stevenson and Treasure Island

110 Weightlifting

(Des Jennifer Toombs. Litho D.L.R.)

1969 (21 Apr). 75th Death Anniv of Robert Louis Stevenson. Horiz designs, each showing portrait as in T **109**. Multicoloured. W **61** (sideways). P 14.
323	3s. Type **109**	15	10
324	7s. Kidnapped	20	10
325	20s. Dr. Jekyll and Mr. Hyde	20	50
326	22s. Weir of Hermiston	20	50
323/6	Set of 4	65	1·10

(Des J. Mason. Photo Note Ptg Branch, Reserve Bank of Australia)

1969 (21 July). Third South Pacifc Games, Port Moresby. T **110** and similar vert designs. P 13½.
327	3s. black and sage-green	10	10
328	20s. black and light blue	15	15
329	22s. black and dull orange	15	15
327/9	Set of 3	30	30
Designs:—20s. Yachting; 22s. Boxing.

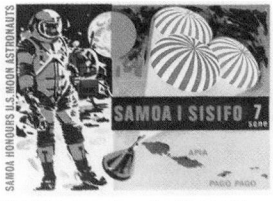

113 US Astronaut on the Moon and the Splashdown near Samoan Islands

(Des J. Mason. Photo Note Ptg Branch, Reserve Bank of Australia)

1969 (24 July). First Man on the Moon. P 13½.
330	**113** 7s. multicoloured	15	15
331	20s. multicoloured	15	15

114 Virgin with Child (Murillo)

(Des and photo Heraclio Fournier)

1969 (13 Oct). Christmas. T **114** and similar vert designs. Multicoloured.
332	1s. Type **114**	10	10
333	3s. The Holy Family (El Greco)	10	10
334	20s. The Nativity (El Greco)	20	10
335	30s. The Adoration of the Magi (detail, Velazquez)	25	15
332/5	Set of 4	45	40
MS336	116×126 mm. Nos. 332/5	75	1·25

115 Seventh Day Adventists' Sanatorium, Apia

(Des V. Whiteley. Litho Format)

1970 (19 Jan). Eighth Anniv of Independence. T **115** and similar designs. W **61** (sideways on 2, 7 and 22s.). P 14.
337	2s. yellow-brown, pale slate and black	10	15
338	7s. violet, buff and black	10	10
339	20s. rose, lilac and black	15	10
340	22s. olive-green, cinnamon and black	15	15
337/40	Set of 4	45	40
Designs: Horiz—7s. Rev. Father Violette and Roman Catholic Cathedral, Apia; 22s. John Williams, 1797–1839 and London Missionary Society Church, Sapapali'I. Vert—20s. Mormon Church of Latter Day Saints, Tuasivi-on-Safotulafai.

119 Wreck of Adler (German steam gunboat)

(Des J.W. Litho Questa)

1970 (27 Apr). "Great Apia Hurricane of 1889". T **119** and similar horiz designs. Multicoloured. W **61** (sideways). P 13½.

341	5s. Type **119**		30	10
342	7s. USS *Nipsic* (steam sloop)		30	10
343	10s. HMS *Calliope* (screw corvette)		30	25
344	20s. Apia after the hurricane		50	75
341/4 *Set of 4*			1·25	1·10

120 Sir Gordon Taylor's Short 825
Sandringham 7 Flying Boat *Frigate Bird III*

(Des R. Honisett. Photo Note Ptg Branch, Reserve Bank of Australia)

1970 (27 July). Air. Aircraft. T **120** and similar horiz designs. Multicoloured. P 13½×13.

345	3s. Type **120**		45	45
346	7s. Polynesian Airlines Douglas DC-3		55	20
347	20s. Pan-American Sikorsky S-42A flying boat *Samoan Clipper*		75	60
348	30s. Air Samoa Britten Norman Islander		75	2·25
	a. Pale purple omitted		£400	
345/8 *Set of 4*			2·25	3·25

121 Kendal's
Chronometer and
Cook's Sextant

122 *Peace for the World*
(F. B. Eccles)

(Des J. Berry, adapted J. Cooler. Litho Questa)

1970 (14 Sept). Cook's Exploration of the Pacific. T **121** and similar designs. W **61** (sideways on 30s.). P 14.

349	1s. carmine, silver and black		10	15
350	2s. multicoloured		10	15
351	20s. black, bright blue and gold		25	25
352	30s. multicoloured		75	80
349/52 *Set of 4*			1·00	1·25

Designs: Vert—2s. Cook's statue, Whitby; 20s. Cook's head. Horiz (83×25 *mm*)—30s. Cook, HMS *Endeavour* and island.

(Des from paintings. Photo Heraclio Fournier)

1970 (26 Oct). Christmas. T **122** and similar vert designs. Multicoloured. P 13.

353	2s. Type **122**		10	10
354	3s. *The Holy Family* (W. E. Jahnke)		10	10
355	20s. *Mother and Child* (F. B. Eccles)		15	10
356	30s. *Prince of Peace* (Meleane Fe'ao)		20	15
353/6 *Set of 4*			35	40
MS357 111×158 mm. Nos. 353/6			60	1·25

123 Pope Paul VI

(Des J. Cooter. Litho Format)

1970 (20 Nov). Visit of Pope Paul to Samoa. W **61**. P 14×14½.

358	**123**	8s. black and grey-blue	15	15
359		20s. black and plum	35	15

STAMP BOOKLETS

1958. Blue on yellow (No. SB1) and blue (No. SB3) or black on pink (No. SB2). Stapled.

SB1 2s.7d. booklet containing ½d. and 2d. (Nos. 219, 221), each in block of 6, 1d. and 3d. (Nos. 220, 222), each in block of 4

SB2 6s. booklet containing 1d., 3d., 6d. and 8d. (Nos. 220, 222, 224/5), each in block of 4

SB3 9s.9d. booklet containing ½d., 2d., 5d. and 1s. (Nos. 219, 221, 223, 226), each in block of 6

	Set of 3	£500

1960 (1 Apr). Contents as Nos. SB1/3, but Arms and inscription in black, and colour of covers changed. Stapled.

SB4 2s.7d. Green cover
a. Buff cover
SB5 6s. Grey cover
a. Blue cover
SB6 9s.9d. Yellow cover
a. White cover

Set of 3 (Nos. SB4, SB5, SB6)		£200
Set of 3 (Nos. SB4a, SB5a, SB6a)		£200

1962 (1 Sept). Black on buff (No. SB7) or green (No. SB8) covers. Inscr "POSTAGE STAMP BOOKLET NO. 1" (1s.9d.) or "NO. 2" (6s.9d.). Stapled.

SB7 6s.9d. booklet containing one each of 1d., 2d., 3d., 4d., 6d., 8d., 1s., 1s.3d. and 2s.6d. (Nos. 239/47) (loose in cellophane bag) ...... 48·00

SB8 11s.9d. booklet containing one each of 1d., 2d., 3d., 4d., 6d., 8d., 1s., 1s.3d., 2s.6d. and 5s. (Nos. 239/48) (loose in cellophane bag) ...... 48·00

1962 (1 Sept)–**64**. Black on pink (No. SB9) or blue (No. SB10) covers. Inscr "POSTAGE STAMP BOOKLET NO. 3" (12s.) or "NO. 4" (6s.). Stapled.

SB9 6s. booklet containing 1d., 3d., 6d. and 8d. (Nos. 239 241, 243/4), each in block of 4 ...... 42·00

SB10 12s. booklet containing 1d., 2d., 3d., 4d., 6d., 8d. and 1s. (Nos. 239/45), each in block of 4 ...... 42·00

1964 (1 Sept)–**67**. As Nos. SB9/10 but containing stamps with mixed wmks (W **98** of New Zealand or W **61** of Samoa). Stapled.

SB11 6s. As No. SB9 ...... *From* 45·00
a. Including block of 3d. W **61** (No. 258) £130

SB12 12s. As No. SB10 ...... *From* 50·00
a. Including block of 3d. W **61** (No. 258) £130

The composition of Nos. SB11/12 can vary as to the watermark and we do not attempt to list them in detail.

1965 (1 Feb)–**67**. As Nos. SB7/8, but containing stamps with mixed wmks (W **98** of New Zealand or W **61** of Samoa). Stapled.

SB13 6s.9d. As No. SB7 ...... *From* 42·00
SB14 11s.9d. As No. SB8 ...... *From* 50·00

The composition of Nos. SB13/14 can vary as to the watermark. Since the precise contents can only be established by dismantling the booklets, it is not possible to give a more detailed listing.

Sarawak

Sarawak was placed under British protection in 1888. It was ceded to Great Britain on 1 July 1946 and was administered as a Crown Colony until 16 September 1963 when it became a state of the Federation of Malaysia.

From 1859 letters from Sarawak to overseas addresses, other than to other British possessions in Borneo and Singapore, were franked by stamps of INDIA and, after 1867, STRAITS SETTLEMENTS, a stock of which was kept by the Sarawak Post Office. The stamps of Sarawak continued to have this limited validity until 1 July 1897 when the country joined the U.P.U.

PRICES FOR STAMPS ON COVER TO 1945	
No. 1	—
Nos. 2/7	*from* × 50
Nos. 8/21	*from* × 8
Nos. 22/6	*from* × 6
No. 27	*from* × 40
Nos. 28/35	*from* × 6
Nos. 36/47	*from* × 8
No. 48	†
No. 49	*from* × 10
Nos. 50/61	*from* × 6
No. 62	†
Nos. 63/71	*from* × 4
Nos. 72/3	*from* × 8
Nos. 74/5	—
Nos. 76/90	*from* × 7
Nos. 91/105	*from* × 5
Nos. 106/25	*from* × 3
Nos. 126/45	*from* × 2

BROOKE FAMILY ADMINISTRATION
Sir James Brooke. 1842–11 June 1868
Sir Charles Brooke. 11 June 1868–17 May 1917

UNUSED PRICES. Nos. 1/7, 27 and 32/5 in unused condition are normally found without gum. Prices in the unused column are for stamps in this state. Examples of these issues with original gum are worth considerably more.

1 Sir James
Brooke

2 Sir Charles
Brooke

The initials in the corners of T **1** and **2** stand for "James (Charles) Brooke, Rajah (of) Sarawak".

(T **1** and **2**. Die eng Wm. Ridgeway. Litho Maclure, Macdonald & Co, Glasgow)

1869 (1 Mar). P 11.

1	**1**	3c. brown/*yellow*	55·00	£225

Similar stamps are known printed from the engraved die in orange-brown on orange surface-coloured paper, and perf 12. These are specimens submitted to the Sarawak authorities and exist both with and without obliterations.

1871 (1 Jan). P 11 (irregular).

2	**2**	3c. brown/*yellow*	3·50	3·75
		a. Stop after "THREE"	70·00	85·00
		b. Imperf between (vert pair)	£550	
		c. Imperf between (horiz pair)	£950	

The "stop" variety, No. 2a, which occurs on R. 10/7 of one printing stone is of no more philatelic importance than any of the numerous other variations, such as narrow first "A" in "SARAWAK" (R. 2/7) and "R" with long tail in left lower corner (R. 9/10), but it has been accepted by collectors for many years, and we therefore retain it. The papermaker's wmk "L N L" appears once or twice in sheets of No. 2.

Examples are known, recess-printed, similar to those mentioned in the note after No. 1.

TWO CENTS

Examples of No. 2 surcharged as above were first reported in 1876 but following the discovery of dies for forgeries and faked postmarks in 1891 it was concluded that the issue was bogus, especially as the availability of the 2c. of 1875 made it unnecessary to issue a provisional. It has now been established that a 2c. postal rate was introduced from 1 August 1874 for the carriage of newspapers. Moreover four examples are known with a stop after "CENTS." and showing other minor differences from the forgery illustrated. This version could be genuine and if others come to light we will reconsider listing it.

1875 (1 Jan). P 11½–12.

3	**2**	2c. mauve/*lilac* (*shades*)	27·00	17·00
4		4c. red-brown/*yellow*	7·00	3·00
		a. Imperf between (vert pair)	£800	£900
5		6c. green/*green*	5·50	5·50
6		8c. bright blue/*blue*	6·00	8·00
7		12c. red/*pale rose*	13·00	6·50
3/7 *Set of 5*			50·00	35·00

Nos. 3, 4, 6 and 7 have the watermark "L N L" in the sheet, as No. 2. No. 5 is watermarked "L N T".

All values exist imperf and can be distinguished from the proofs by shade and impression. Stamps rouletted, pin-perf, or roughly perf 6½ to 7 are proofs clandestinely perforated.

The 12c. "laid" paper, formerly listed, is not on a true laid paper, the "laid" effect being accidental and not consistent.

The lithographic stones for Nos. 3 to 7 were made up from strips of five distinct impressions hence there are five types of each value differing mainly in the lettering of the tablets of value. There are flaws on nearly every individual stamp, from which they can be plated.

4 Sir Charles Brooke

(Typo D.L.R.)

1888 (10 Nov)–**97**. No wmk. P 14.

8	**4**	1c. purple and black (6.6.92)	6·50	1·50
9		2c. purple and carmine (11.11.88)	7·00	3·25
		a. Purple and rosine (1897)	17·00	6·50
10		3c. purple and blue (11.11.88)	12·00	5·50
11		4c. purple and yellow	45·00	65·00
12		5c. purple and green (12.6.91)	42·00	5·00
13		6c. purple and brown (11.11.88)	32·00	65·00
14		8c. green and carmine (11.11.88)	23·00	5·50
		a. Green and rosine (1897)	38·00	18·00
15		10c. green and purple (12.6.91)	60·00	15·00
16		12c. green and blue (11.11.88)	19·00	15·00
17		16c. green and orange (28.12.97)	70·00	90·00
18		25c. green and brown (19.11 88)	80·00	50·00
19		32c. green and black (28.12.97)	60·00	75·00
20		50c. green (26.7.97)	85·00	£130
21		$1 green and black (2.11.97)	£120	£130
8/21		Set of 14	£600	£600

	Prepared for use but not issued		
21a	$2 green and blue	£1200	
21b	$5 green and violet	£1300	
21c	$10 green and carmine	£1300	

On No. 21c the value is on an uncoloured ground.

The tablet of value in this and later similar issues is in the second colour given.

One Cent. (5) **one cent.** (6)

2^c. (7) **5**^{c} (8) **5c.** (9)

1889 (3 Aug)–**92**. T **4** surch by Government Printing Office, Kuching. P 14.

22	**5**	1c. on 3c. purple and blue (12.1.92)	80·00	50·00
		a. Surch double	£750	£650
23	**6**	1c. on 3c. purple and blue (2.92)	3·50	2·75
		a. No stop after "cent" (R. 2/6, 7/6)	£250	£275
24	**7**	2c. on 8c. green and carmine (3.8.89)	4·25	12·00
		a. Surch double	£475	
		b. Surch inverted	£4250	
		c. Surch omitted (in pair with normal)	£8000	
25	**8**	5c. on 12c. green and blue (with stop after "C") (17.2.91)	38·00	60·00
		a. No stop after "C"	50·00	75·00
		b. "C" omitted (in pair with normal)	£900	£1000
		c. Surch double	£1400	
		d. Surch double, one vertical	£4000	
		e. Surch omitted (in pair with normal)	£12000	
26	**9**	5c. on 12c. green and blue (17.2.91)	£325	£350
		a. No stop after "C"	£190	£200
		b. "C" omitted (in pair with normal)	£1300	£1400
		c. Surch double	£1500	

Nos. 22/3 were surcharged with settings of 60 (6×10). Nos. 24/6/a were produced with handstamps.

ONE CENT

―――――――― (10)

1892 (23 May). No. 2 surch with T **10**.

27	**2**	1c. on 3c. brown/yellow	1·40	2·00
		a. Stop after "THREE."	55·00	65·00
		b. Imperf between (vert pair)	£750	
		c. Imperf horiz (vert pair)	£750	
		d. Bar omitted (1st ptg)	£225	£250
		e. Bar at top and bottom (1st ptg)	£375	
		f. Surch double (2nd ptg)	£450	£500

No. 27 was surcharged with a setting of 100 (10×10). It was originally intended that there should be no bar at foot, but this was then added at a second operation before the stamps were issued. Subsequent supplies were surcharged with "ONE CENT" and bar at one operation.

Varieties with part of the surcharge missing are due to gum on the face of the unsurcharged stamps receiving part of the surcharge, which was afterwards washed off.

11

12

13

14

Sir Charles Brooke

(Die eng Wm. Ridgeway. Recess P.B.)

1895 (12 Feb–Sept). No wmk. P 11½–12.

28	**11**	2c. brown-red	17·00	9·00
		a. Imperf between (vert pair)	£600	
		b. Imperf between (horiz pair)	£450	£500
		c. Second ptg. Perf 12½ (9.95)	26·00	5·50
		ca. Perf 12½. Imperf between (horiz pair)	£700	
29	**12**	4c. black	17·00	3·50
		a. Imperf between (horiz pair)	£850	
30	**13**	6c. violet	20·00	9·00
31	**14**	8c. green	45·00	6·00
28/31		Set of 4	90·00	22·00

Stamps of these types, printed in wrong colours, are trials and these, when surcharged with values in "pence", are from waste sheets that were used by Perkins Bacon & Co as trial paper when preparing the 1896–97 issue of stamps for British South Africa Company (Rhodesia).

4 CENTS. (15)

16

1899 (29 June–16 Nov). Surch as T **15**.

32	**2**	2c. on 3c. brown/yellow (19.9)	4·00	1·75
		a. Stop after "THREE"	90·00	90·00
		b. Imperf between (vert pair)	£900	
33		2c. on 12c. red/pale rose	3·75	5·50
		a. Surch inverted	£900	£1400
34		4c. on 6c. green/green (R.) (16 Nov)	60·00	£120
35		4c. on 8c. bright blue/blue (R.)	9·50	16·00
32/5		Set of 4	70·00	£120

A variety of surcharge with small "S" in "CENTS" may be found in the 2c. on 12c. and 4c. on 8c. (R. 1/2, 1/8 and 3/1, first setting) and a raised stop after "CENTS" on the 4c. on 6c. (R. 1/5).

The omission of parts of the surcharge is due to gum on the surface of the stamps (see note after No. 27).

No. 35 is known with compound perforation, perf 12.7 on one or two sides, from the margins of sheets. Examples are rare. (Price, £225 unused)

(Typo D.L.R.)

1899 (10 Nov)–**1908**. Inscribed "POSTAGE POSTAGE". No wmk. P 14.

36	**4**	1c. grey-blue and rosine (1.1.01)	1·50	1·25
		a. Grey-blue and red	6·50	2·75
		b. Ultramarine and rosine	12·00	3·75
		c. Dull blue and rosine	19·00	6·00
37		2c. green (16.12.99)	2·00	90
38		3c. dull purple (1.2.08)	26·00	65
39		4c. rose-carmine (10.11.99)	17·00	2·50
		a. Aniline carmine	3·00	15
40		8c. yellow and black (6.12.99)	2·75	80
41		10c. ultramarine (10.11.99)	7·50	1·00
42		12c. mauve (16.12.99)	7·00	4·50
		a. Bright mauve (1905)	50·00	14·00
43		16c. chestnut and green (16.12.99)	8·50	1·75
44		20c. bistre and bright mauve (4.00)	8·50	7·50
45		25c. brown and blue (16.12.99)	11·00	7·00
46		50c. sage-green and carmine (16.12.99)	35·00	40·00
47		$1 rose-carmine and green (16.12.99)	£100	£130
		a. Rosine and pale green	£120	£140
36/47		Set of 12	£180	£170

	Prepared for use but not issued		
48	**4**	5c. olive-grey and green	15·00	

The figures of value in the $1 are in colour on an uncoloured ground.

1902. Inscribed "POSTAGE POSTAGE". W **16**. P 14.

49	**4**	2c. green	60·00	22·00

Sir Charles Vyner Brooke. 17 May 1917–1 June 1946

17 Sir Charles Vyner Brooke

ONE cent ―――――――― (18)

(Typo D.L.R.)

1918 (24 Mar–Apr). Chalk-surfaced paper. No wmk. P 14.

50	**17**	1c. slate-blue and red	2·25	3·25
		a. Dull blue and carmine	2·25	4·00
51		2c. green	2·50	1·50
52		3c. brown-purple (4.18)	3·25	2·75
53		4c. rose-carmine (4.18)	9·50	4·25
		a. Rose-red	14·00	3·00
54		8c. yellow and black (4.18)	18·00	75·00
55		10c. blue (shades) (4.18)	7·00	6·50
56		12c. purple (4.18)	24·00	55·00
57		16c. chestnut and green (4.18)	5·50	7·50
58		20c. olive and violet (shades) (4.18)	9·50	6·50
59		25c. brown and bright blue (4.18)	4·00	24·00
60		50c. olive-green and carmine (4.18)	10·00	15·00
61		$1 bright rose and green (4.18)	42·00	30·00
50/61		Set of 12	£120	£200
50s/61s		Optd "SPECIMEN" Set of 12	£400	

	Prepared for use but not issued		
62	**17**	1c. slate-blue and slate	22·00	

On the $1 the figures of value are in colour on an uncoloured ground.

Most values are known with part strikes of a forged Kuching postmark dated "12 MAR 90".

1922 (Jan)–**23**. New colours and values. Chalk-surfaced paper. No wmk. P 14.

63	**17**	2c. purple (5.3.23)	2·00	2·75
64		3c. dull green (23.3.22)	5·00	1·25
65		4c. brown-purple (10.4.23)	2·50	2·50
66		5c. yellow-orange	3·00	2·75
67		6c. claret	2·25	1·40
68		8c. bright rose-red (1922)	4·50	32·00
69		10c. black (1923)	4·50	5·00
70		12c. bright blue (12.22)	15·00	18·00
		a. Pale dull blue	12·00	27·00
71		30c. ochre-brown and slate	3·75	4·25
63/71		Set of 9	35·00	60·00

1923 (Jan). Surch as T **18**.

	(a) First printing. Bars 1¼ mm apart			
72	**17**	1c. on 10c. dull blue	10·00	65·00
		a. "cnet" for "cent" (R. 9/5)	£425	£900
73		2c. on 12c. purple	7·00	55·00
		a. Thick, narrower "W" in "TWO"	23·00	£120

	(b) Second printing. Bars ¾ mm apart			
74	**17**	1c. on 10c. dull blue	£600	
		b. "cnet" for "cent" (R. 9/5)	£24000	
		c. Bright blue	£180	£500
		ca. "en" of "cent" scratched out and "ne" overprinted (R. 9/5)	£9000	
75		2c. on 12c. purple	90·00	£350
		a. Thick, narrower "W" in "TWO"	£160	

In the 2c. on 12c. the words of the surcharge are about 7½ mm from the bars.

The "cnet" error occurred on R. 9/5 of all sheets from the first printing of the 1c. on 10c. A single example of the error, No. 74b, is known from the second printing, but the error was then corrected, as shown by the evidence of a surviving plate block, only to have the correct spelling scratched out by a local employee, and "ne" substituted (No. 74ca).

The thick "W" variety occurs on all stamps of the last two horizontal rows of the first printing (12 stamps per sheet), and in the last two vertical rows of the second (20 stamps per sheet).

1928 (7 Apr)–**29**. Chalk-surfaced paper. W **16** (Multiple). P 14.

76	**17**	1c. slate-blue and carmine	1·50	1·00
77		2c. bright purple	2·25	2·00
78		3c. green	4·50	5·50
79		4c. brown-purple	1·75	10
80		5c. yellow-orange (7.8.29)	12·00	5·00
81		6c. claret	1·25	30
82		8c. bright rose-red	3·25	35·00
83		10c. black	1·75	2·00
84		12c. bright blue	3·25	45·00
85		16c. chestnut and green	3·75	4·25
86		20c. olive-bistre and violet	3·75	11·00
87		25c. brown and bright blue	7·00	8·50
88		30c. bistre-brown and slate	4·50	10·00
89		50c. olive-green and carmine	16·00	25·00
90		$1 bright rose and green	21·00	25·00
76/90		Set of 15	75·00	£160
76s/90s		Optd or Perf (5c.) "SPECIMEN" Set of 15	£425	

In the $1 the value is as before.

19 Sir Charles Vyner Brooke

20

(Recess Waterlow)

1932 (1 Jan). W **20**. P 12½.

91	**19**	1c. indigo	80	1·00
92		2c. green	1·00	2·25
		w. Wmk inverted	—	£500
93		3c. violet	4·00	1·00
94		4c. red-orange	13·00	75
95		5c. deep lake	6·50	1·00
96		6c. scarlet	7·00	11·00
97		8c. orange-yellow	11·00	8·50
98		10c. black	2·25	3·25
99		12c. deep ultramarine	4·00	9·50
100		15c. chestnut	6·50	13·00
101		20c. red-orange and violet	6·50	8·00
102		25c. orange-yellow and chestnut	10·00	27·00
103		30c. sepia and vermilion	9·50	45·00
104		50c. carmine-red and olive-green	14·00	13·00
105		$1 green and carmine	22·00	35·00
91/105		Set of 15	£100	£160
91s/105s		Perf "SPECIMEN" Set of 15	£425	

21 Sir Charles Vyner Brooke

B M A (22)

(Recess B.W.)

1934 (1 May)–**41**. No wmk. P 12.

106	**21**	1c. purple	1·25	10
107		2c. green	1·50	10
107a		2c. black (1.3.41)	4·75	1·60
108		3c. black	1·25	10
108a		3c. green (1.3.41)	7·50	4·50
109		4c. bright purple	2·00	15
110		5c. violet	2·00	10
111		6c. carmine	2·75	60
111a		6c. lake-brown (1.3.41)	8·50	8·00
112		8c. red-brown	2·25	10
112a		8c. carmine (1.3.41)	9·00	10
113		10c. scarlet	5·00	40
114		12c. blue	3·00	25

114a		12c. orange (1.3.41)	7·50	4·75
115		15c. orange	8·00	10·00
115a		15c. blue (1.3.41)	9·00	15·00
116		20c. olive-green and carmine	8·00	1·25
117		25c. violet and orange	8·00	1·50
118		30c. red-brown and violet	8·00	2·50
119		50c. violet and scarlet	12·00	75
120		$1 scarlet and sepia	7·00	75
121		$2 bright purple and violet	30·00	35·00
122		$3 carmine and green	50·00	55·00
123		$4 blue and scarlet	50·00	80·00
124		$5 scarlet and red-brown	75·00	85·00
125		$10 black and yellow	35·00	85·00
106/25 Set of 26			£325	£350
106s/25s Perf "SPECIMEN" Set of 26				£850

The original set of 20 (excluding Nos. 107a, 108a, 111a, 112a, 114a, 115a) exist imperforate from proof sheets. (Price for set of 20 imperforate pairs, £1300 unused)

For the 3c. green, wmkd Mult Script CA, see No. 152a.

BRITISH MILITARY ADMINISTRATION

Following the Japanese surrender, elements of the British Military Administration reached Kuching on 11 September 1945. From 5 November 1945 current Australian 1d., 3d., 6d. and 1s. stamps were made available for civilian use until replaced by Nos. 126/45. Other Australian stamps were also accepted as valid for postage during this period.

1945 (17 Dec). Optd with T **22**.

126	**21**	1c. purple	1·25	60
127		2c. black (R.)	5·00	1·50
		a. Opt double	£8500	£5500
128		3c. green	1·25	2·00
129		4c. bright purple	4·75	1·75
		a. Opt double, one albino	£2250	
130		5c. violet (R.)	6·50	2·25
131		6c. lake-brown	6·00	75
132		8c. carmine	19·00	27·00
133		10c. scarlet	2·75	70
134		12c. orange	7·00	3·75
135		15c. blue	11·00	40
136		20c. olive-green and carmine	7·00	7·00
137		25c. violet and orange (R.)	7·50	4·25
138		30c. red-brown and violet	12·00	5·00
139		50c. violet and scarlet	2·50	50
140		$1 scarlet and sepia	3·50	6·50
141		$2 bright purple and violet	15·00	27·00
142		$3 carmine and green	48·00	£100
143		$4 blue and scarlet	42·00	70·00
144		$5 scarlet and red-brown	£200	£300
145		$10 black and yellow (R.)	£225	£275
126/45 Set of 20			£550	£750

These stamps, and the similarly overprinted stamps of North Borneo, were obtainable at all post offices throughout British Borneo (Brunei, Labuan, North Borneo and Sarawak), for use on local and overseas mail.

The administration of Sarawak was returned to the Brooke family on 15 April 1946, but the Rajah, after consulting the inhabitants, ceded the territory to Great Britain on 1 June 1946. Values from the 1934–41 issue were used until replaced by Nos. 150/64.

23 Sir James Brooke, Sir Charles Vyner Brooke and Sir Charles Brooke

(**24**)

(Recess B.W.)

1946 (18 May). Centenary Issue. P 12.

146	**23**	8c. lake	4·75	1·75
147		15c. blue	5·00	2·25
148		50c. black and scarlet	5·00	5·00
149		$1 black and sepia	5·00	42·00
146/9 Set of 4			18·00	45·00
146s/9s Perf "SPECIMEN" Set of 4				£225

Nos. 146/9 exist imperforate from proof sheets. (Price for set of 4 imperforate pairs, £300 unused)

CROWN COLONY

1947 (16 Apr). Optd with T **24**, typo by B.W. in blue-black or red. Wmk Mult Script CA. P 12.

150	**21**	1c. purple	20	30
151		2c. black (R.)	25	15
152		3c. green (R.)	25	15
		a. Albino opt	£9500	
153		4c. bright purple	30	15
154		6c. lake-brown	50	90
155		8c. carmine	1·00	10
156		10c. scarlet	50	20
157		12c. orange	70	1·00
158		15c. blue (R.)	50	40
159		20c. olive-green and carmine (R.)	2·25	50
160		25c. violet and orange (R.)	65	30
161		50c. violet and scarlet (R.)	1·25	40
162		$1 scarlet and sepia	1·50	90
163		$2 bright purple and violet	4·00	8·00
164		$5 scarlet and red-brown	12·00	3·25
150/64 Set of 15			23·00	15·00
150s/64s Perf "SPECIMEN" Set of 15				£400

No. 152a shows an uninked impression of T **24**.

1948 (25 Oct). Royal Silver Wedding. As Nos. 112/13 of Antigua.

165		8c. scarlet	30	30
166		$5 brown	48·00	60·00

1949 (10 Oct). 75th Anniv of UPU. As Nos. 114/17 of Antigua.

167		8c. carmine	1·25	60
168		15c. deep blue	3·50	2·50
169		25c. deep blue-green	2·00	2·00
170		50c. violet	2·00	7·00
167/70 Set of 4			8·00	11·00

25 Trogonoptera brookiana   **26** Western Tarsier

27 Kayan tomb   **28** Kayan girl and boy

29 Bead work   **30** Dyak dancer

31 Malayan Pangolin   **32** Kenyan boys

33 Fire making   **34** Kelemantan rice barn

35 Pepper vines   **36** Iban woman

37 Kelabit Smithy   **38** Map of Sarawak

39 Arms of Sarawak

(Recess; $5 Arms typo B.W.)

1950 (3 Jan). T **25**/**39**. Wmk Mult Script CA. P 11½×11 (horiz) or 11×11½ (vert).

171	**25**	1c. black	75	30
172	**26**	2c. red-orange	45	40
173	**27**	3c. green	60	1·25
174	**28**	4c. chocolate	1·00	90
175	**29**	6c. turquoise-blue	75	20
176	**30**	8c. scarlet	1·00	30
177	**31**	10c. orange	3·25	6·00
178	**32**	12c. violet	3·50	1·50
179	**33**	15c. blue	4·50	15
180	**34**	20c. purple-brown and red-orange	3·00	30
181	**35**	25c. green and scarlet	3·75	30
182	**36**	50c. brown and violet	8·50	45
183	**37**	$1 green and chocolate	27·00	4·50
184	**38**	$2 blue and carmine	45·00	17·00
185	**39**	$5 black, yellow, red and purple	35·00	20·00
171/85 Set of 15			£120	48·00

40 Map of Sarawak

(Recess B.W.)

1952 (1 Feb). Wmk Mult Script CA. P 11½×11.

186	**40**	10c. orange	1·75	50

1953 (3 June). Coronation. As No. 120 of Antigua.

187		10c. black and deep violet-blue	2·25	1·75

41 Logging   **42** Young Orang-utan   **43** Kayan dancing

44 Malabar Pied Hornbill

45 Shield with spears   **46** Kenyah ceremonial carving

47 Barong panau (sailing prau)   **48** Turtles

49 Melanau basket-making   **50** Astana, Kuching

51 Queen Elizabeth II   **52** Queen Elizabeth II (after Annigoni)

(Des M. Thoma (1, 2c.), R. Turrell (4c.), J. D. Hughes (6, 12c.) A. Hakim bin Moliti (8c.), J. Woodcock (10c.), J. Browning (15c.), G. Gundersen (20c.), K. Munich (25c.), Recess, Arms typo ($5). B.W.)

1955 (1 June)–**59**. T **41**/**52**. Wmk Mult Script CA. P 11×11½ (1c., 2c., 4c.), 12×13 (30c., 50c., $1, $2) or 11½×11 (others).

188	**41**	1c. green (1.10.57)	10	30
189	**42**	2c. red-orange (1.10.57)	30	55
190	**43**	4c. lake-brown (1.10.57)	1·50	60
		a. Brown-purple (18.3.59)	12·00	7·00
191	**44**	6c. greenish blue (1.10.57)	3·75	3·25
192	**45**	8c. rose-red (1.10.57)	40	30
193	**46**	10c. deep green (1.10.57)	30	10
194	**47**	12c. plum (1.10.57)	3·75	55
195	**48**	15c. ultramarine (1.10.57)	2·25	30
196	**49**	20c. olive and brown (1.10.57)	1·00	10
197	**50**	25c. sepia and green (1.10.57)	6·50	20
198	**51**	30c. red-brown and deep lilac (1.10.57)	9·00	30
199	**52**	50c. black and carmine (1.10.57)	2·50	30
200	**52**	$1 myrtle-green and orange-brown (1.10.57)	16·00	1·75
201		$2 violet and bronze-green (1.10.57)	26·00	3·00
202	—	$5 multicoloured (1.10.57)	42·00	20·00
188/202 Set of 15			£100	28·00

1963 (4 June). Freedom from Hunger. As No. 146 of Antigua.

203		12c. sepia	1·75	1·75

STATE OF MALAYSIA

1964–65. As 1955–57 but wmk w **12**. Perfs as before.

204	**41**	1c. green (8.9.64)	15	75
205	**42**	2c. red-orange (11.10.65)	1·25	16·00
206	**44**	6c. greenish blue (8.9.64)	6·50	5·00
207	**46**	10c. deep green (8.9.64)	2·25	1·00
208	**47**	12c. plum (8.9.64)	5·00	15·00
209	**48**	15c. ultramarine (17.8.65)	1·25	14·00
210	**49**	20c. olive and brown (9.6.64)	1·25	1·00
211	**50**	25c. deep sepia and bluish green (8.9.64)	5·50	5·50
204/11 *Set of 8*			21·00	50·00

53 Vanda hookeriana

1965 (15 Nov). As Nos. 166/72 of Johore but with Arms of Sarawak inset as in T **53**.

212		1c. multicoloured	10	1·10
		c. Grey omitted	£150	
213		2c. multicoloured	1·25	2·50
		a. Black (country name and shield) omitted	£300	
		c. Yellow-olive (stems) omitted	£200	
214		5c. multicoloured	1·75	10
215		6c. multicoloured	1·25	2·00
		a. Black (country name and shield) omitted	£400	
216		10c. multicoloured	1·25	10
		a. Red omitted	£180	
		b. *Intense black*	2·00	20
217		15c. multicoloured	1·50	10
218		20c. multicoloured	2·00	20
212/18 *Set of 7*			8·00	5·75

The 1c., 6c., 10c. and 15c. exist with PVA gum as well as gum arabic.

No. 213a was formerly listed with Trengganu No. 101 but there is evidence that it was issued in Sarawak.

A used example of No. 218 is known with the bright purple (blooms) omitted.

The higher values used with this issue were Nos. 20/7 of Malaysia (National Issues).

TELEGRAPH STAMPS

(T **1**)   (T **1a**)

1933 (1 Jan). Revenue stamps of 1927 opt at Government Printing Office, Kuching as T T **1/a**. No wmk. Chalk-surfaced paper. Perf 14.

*(a) Opt T T **1**, inscr "TELEGRAPHS"*

T1		3c. purple and carmine	†	£800
T2		5c. purple and green	†	£425
T3		10c. purple and violet	†	£425
T4		25c. purple and blue	†	£325
T5		50c. purple and black	†	£600

*(b) Opt T T **1a**, inscr "TELEGRAPH"*

T9		5c. purple and green	†	£400
T10		$1 yellow-green and green	†	£900

Higher values up to $10 are believed to have been issued, but no examples have been seen. The values listed above are only known in used condition, with circular datestamps of Trusan or Sarikei.

Telegraph

(T **2**)

Telegraph   **Telegraph**

50 Cts.   **$2.**

(T **3**)   (T **4**)

1934(?). Postage stamps of 1932 (Nos. 91, 93/100, 102, 105) optd or surch as T T **2/4**.

T12	**2**	1c. indigo	17·00
T13		3c. violet	8·50
T14		5c. deep lake	8·50
T15		10c. black	9·50
T16		25c. orange-yellow and chestnut	9·50
T17	**3**	50c. on 4c. red-orange	12·00
		a. "5" with straight top and "Cts" sans-serif	£100
T18	**2**	$1 green and carmine	14·00
T19	**4**	$2 on 6c. scarlet	14·00
T20		$3 on 12c. deep ultramarine	17·00
T21		$4 on 15c. chestnut	17·00
T22		$5 on 8c. orange-yellow	17·00
T12/22 *Set of 11*			£130

No. T17a occurs at R. 1/5–8 in the setting of 100 (10×10). No used examples of Nos. T12/22 have been seen.

JAPANESE OCCUPATION OF SARAWAK

Japanese forces landed in North Borneo on 16 December 1941 and Sarawak was attacked on 23 December 1941.

Brunei, North Borneo, Sarawak and after a short period, Labuan, were administered as a single territory by the Japanese. Until September–October 1942, previous stamp issues, without overprint, continued to be used in conjunction with existing postmarks. From 1 October 1942 onwards unoverprinted stamps of Japan were made available and examples can be found used from the area for much of the remainder of the War. Japanese Occupation issues for Brunei, North Borneo and Sarawak were equally valid throughout the combined territory but not, in practice, equally available.

PRICES FOR STAMPS ON COVER	
Nos. J1/21	*from* × 8
Nos. J22/6	—

帝政国本本日大

(**1**) ("Imperial Japanese Government")

1942 (Oct). Stamps of Sarawak handstamped with T **1** in violet.

J1	**21**	1c. purple	48·00	95·00
		a. Pair, one without opt	£5500	
J2		2c. green	£190	£250
		a. Black opt	£130	
J3		2c. black	£180	£200
		a. Black opt	£350	£400
J4		3c. black	£650	£650
J5		3c. green	£100	£130
		a. Black opt	£300	
J6		4c. bright purple	£140	£160
		a. Black opt	£300	
J7		5c. violet	£170	£180
		a. Black opt	£275	
J8		6c. carmine	£225	£225
J9		6c. lake-brown	£170	£180
		a. Black opt	£300	£325
J10		8c. red-brown	£600	£600
		a. Black opt	£1000	
J11		8c. carmine	75·00	£130
		a. Black opt	£475	£600
J12		10c. scarlet	£140	£160
		a. Black opt	£300	
J13		12c. blue	£250	£250
		a. Black opt	£500	
J14		12c. orange	£200	£200
J15		15c. orange	£600	£650
		a. Black opt	£950	
J16		15c. blue	£200	£225
J17		20c. olive-green and carmine	95·00	£140
		a. Black opt	£300	
J18		25c. violet and orange	£140	£180
		a. Black opt	£325	
J19		30c. red-brown and violet	£100	£150
		a. Black opt	£325	
J20		50c. violet and scarlet	95·00	£140
		a. Black opt	£600	
		b. Blue opt	£1000	
J21		$1 scarlet and sepia	£190	£225
		a. Blue opt	£550	
J22		$2 bright purple and violet	£350	£550
		a. Black opt	£600	
J23		$3 carmine and green	£4500	£4500
		a. Black opt	£6500	
J24		$4 blue and scarlet	£350	£650
J25		$5 scarlet and red-brown	£350	£650
J26		$10 black and yellow	£350	£650

The overprint, being handstamped, exists inverted or double on some values. Those on Nos. J20b, J21a and J22a are diagonal. The remainder are horizontal.

Stamps of T **21** optd with Japanese symbols within an oval frame are revenue stamps, while the same stamps overprinted with three Japanese characters between two vertical double rules, were used as seals.

Nos. J1/26 have been extensively forged. Recent research indicates that complete or part sets *on cover* cancelled by Japanese circular postmarks in violet dated "17 11 21" (21 Nov 1942) or "18 3 1" (1 Mar 1943) have forged overprints.

Seychelles

Seychelles was administered as a dependency of Mauritius from 1810 until 1903, although separate stamp issues were provided from April 1890 onwards.

The first post office was opened, at Victoria on Mahé, on 11 December 1861 and the stamps of Mauritius were used there until 1890. No further post offices were opened until 1901.

Z **1**

Stamps of MAURITIUS cancelled with Type Z **1**.

1859–61.

Z2	6d. blue (No. 32)		£900
Z3	6d. dull purple-slate (No. 33)		£2250
Z4	1s. vermilion (No. 34)		£1400

1860–63. (Nos. 46/53).

Z5	1d. purple-brown		£225
Z6	2d. blue		£275
Z7	4d. rose		£250
Z8	6d. green		£1000
Z9	6d. slate		£650
Z10	9d. dull purple		£120
Z11	1s. buff		£325
Z12	1s. green		£800

1862.

Z13	6d. slate (No. 54)		£800

1863–72. (Nos. 56/72).

Z14	1d. purple-brown		£130
Z14a	1d. brown		£110
Z15	1d. bistre		£120
Z16	2d. pale blue		£130
Z17	2d. bright blue		£130
Z18	3d. deep red		£160
Z19	3d. dull red		95·00
Z20	4d. rose		48·00
Z21	6d. dull violet		£250
Z22	6d. yellow-green		£110
Z23	6d. blue-green		80·00
Z24	9d. yellow-green		£1800
Z25	10d. maroon		£325
Z26	1s. yellow		£110
Z27	1s. blue		£325
Z28	1s. orange		£110
Z29	5s. rosy mauve		£950
Z30	5s. bright mauve		£950

1876. (Nos. 76/7).

Z31	½d. on 9d. dull purple		£325
Z32	½d. on 10d. maroon		£300

1877. (Nos. 79/82).

Z33	½d. on 10d. rose		£650
Z34	1d. on 4d. rose-carmine		
Z35	1s. on 5s. rosy mauve		
Z36	1s. on 5s. bright mauve		

1878. (Nos. 83/91).

Z37	2c. dull rose (lower label blank)		£100
Z38	4c. on 1d. bistre		£375
Z39	8c. on 2d. blue		40·00
Z40	13c. on 3d. orange-red		£120
Z41	17c. on 4d. rose		40·00
Z42	25c. on 6d. slate-blue		£120
Z43	38c. on 9d. pale violet		£600
Z44	50c. on 1s. green		£120
Z45	2r.50 on 5s. bright mauve		£500

1879–80. (Nos. 92/100).

Z46	2c. Venetian red		£130
Z47	4c. orange		£130
Z48	8c. blue		40·00
Z49	13c. slate		£1500
Z50	17c. rose		95·00
Z51	25c. olive-yellow		£200
Z52	38c. bright purple		£1800
Z53	50c. green		£850
Z54	2r.50 brown-purple		£850

1883–90.

Z55	2c. Venetian red (No. 102)		£100
Z56	2c. green (No. 103)		£200
Z57	4c. orange (No. 104)		70·00
Z58	4c. carmine (No. 105)		95·00
Z59	16c. chestnut (No. 109)		55·00
Z60	25c. olive-yellow (No. 110)		£110
Z61	50c. orange (No. 111)		£950

1883.

Z62	16c. on 17c. rose (No. 112)		£120

1883.

Z63	16c. on 17c. rose (No. 115)		48·00

1885.

Z64	2c. on 38c. bright purple (No. 116)		

1887.

Z65	2c. on 13c. slate (No. 117)		

POSTAL FISCAL

1889.
ZR1   4c. lilac (No. R2).................................... £1800

Mauritius stamps are occasionally found cancelled with the "SEYCHELLES" cds. Examples are known dated between 25 and 29 February 1884 when it seems that Type Z **1** may have been mislaid (*Price from £500*).

We no longer list the GB 1862 6d. lilac with this obliteration as there is no evidence that the stamps of Great Britain were sold by the Victoria post office.

PRICES FOR STAMPS ON COVER TO 1945	
Nos. 1/8	from × 20
Nos. 9/24	from × 30
No. 25	from × 10
No. 26	from × 20
No. 27	from × 10
Nos. 28/32	from × 20
No. 33	from × 5
No. 34	from × 30
Nos. 35/6	—
Nos. 37/40	from × 40
Nos. 41/2	from × 25
Nos. 43/5	from × 10
Nos. 46/50	from × 30
Nos. 51/4	from × 10
Nos. 55/6	—
Nos. 57/9	from × 10
Nos. 60/7	from × 20
Nos. 68/70	—
Nos. 71/81	from × 10
Nos. 82/131	from × 5
Nos. 132/4	from × 10
Nos. 135/49	from × 3

(Currency: 100 cents = 1 Mauritius, later Seychelles rupee)

DEPENDENCY OF MAURITIUS

PRINTERS. Nos. 1 to 123 were typographed by De La Rue & Co.

1

Die I   Die II

In Die I there are lines of shading in the middle compartment of the diadem which are absent from Die II.

Normal   Malformed "S"   Repaired "S"

The malformed "S" occurs on R. 7/3 of the left pane from Key Plate 2. It is believed that the repair to it took place in mid-1898. Both states may occur on other stamps in Types **1** and **4**. Stamps subsequently printed from Key Plate 3 showed the "S" normal.

1890 (5 Apr)–**92**. Wmk Crown CA. P. 14.

(i) Die I
1	**1**	2c. green and carmine	9·00	20·00
2		4c. carmine and green	48·00	20·00
3		8c. brown-purple and blue	18·00	3·50
4		10c. ultramarine and brown	18·00	40·00
5		13c. grey and black	6·00	20·00
6		16c. chestnut and blue	16·00	4·25
7		48c. ochre and green	27·00	10·00
8		96c. mauve and carmine	70·00	48·00
1/8 *Set of 8*			£190	£150
1s/8s Optd "SPECIMEN" *Set of 8*			£225	

(ii) Die II (1892)
9	**1**	2c. green and rosine	2·50	1·00
10		4c. carmine and green	2·50	1·75
11		8c. brown-purple and ultramarine	16·00	1·75
12		10c. bright ultramarine and brown ..	16·00	3·25
13		13c. grey and black	8·00	2·25
14		16c. chestnut and ultramarine	45·00	11·00
		a. Malformed "S"	£750	
9/14 *Set of 6*			80·00	19·00

The 10c. Die I also exists in ultramarine and chestnut, but has so far only been found with "SPECIMEN" overprint (*Price £800*).

---

3 cents
(2)

18 CENTS
(3)

4

1893 (1 Jan). Surch locally as T **2**.
15		3c. on 4c. (No. 10)............................	1·10	1·50
		a. Surch inverted	£300	£375
		b. Surch double	£475	
		c. Surch omitted (in horiz pair with normal)	£14000	
16		12c. on 16c. (No. 6)...........................	8·50	9·50
		a. Surch inverted	£500	
		b. Surch double	£15000	£9000
17		12c. on 16c. (No. 14).........................	22·00	2·50
		a. Surch double	£4500	£4500
		b. Surch omitted (in pair with normal)		
18		15c. on 16c. (No. 6)...........................	17·00	13·00
		a. Surch inverted	£325	£300
		b. Surch double	£1300	£1300
19		15c. on 16c. (No. 14).........................	27·00	3·00
		a. Surch inverted	£900	£1000
		b. Surch double	£700	£750
		c. Surch triple	£4500	
20		45c. on 48c. (No. 7)..........................	35·00	8·50
21		90c. on 96c. (No. 8)..........................	70·00	50·00
		a. Wide "O" (3½ *mm* wide instead of 3 *mm*) (R. 1/1, 2/1 of setting).............	£400	£375
15/21 *Set of 7*			£160	75·00

Nos. 15/21 were each produced from settings of 30.

Nos. 15, 16, 18, 19 and 20 exist with "cents" omitted and with "cents" above value due to misplacement of the surcharge.

Some examples of No. 15b occur in the same sheet as No. 15c with the double surcharge on stamps from the last vertical row of the left pane and the surcharge omitted on stamps from the last vertical row of the right pane.

Most examples of the inverted surcharge error No. 16a were officially defaced with a red vertical ink line (*Price £200, unused*). Similarly examples of No. 19a exist defaced with a horizontal ink line (*Price £400, unused*).

1893 (Nov). New values. Die II. Wmk Crown CA. P. 14.
22	**1**	3c. dull purple and orange...............	1·50	50
23		12c. sepia and green	2·50	1·25
24		15c. sage-green and lilac..................	9·50	2·00
25		45c. brown and carmine...................	25·00	35·00
22/5 *Set of 4*			35·00	35·00
22s/5s Optd "SPECIMEN" *Set of 4*			£100	

1896 (1 Aug). No. 25 surch locally as T **3**.
26	**1**	18c. on 45c. brown and carmine	11·00	3·75
		a. Surch double	£1500	£1500
		b. Surch triple	£2250	
27		36c. on 45c. brown and carmine	11·00	60·00
		a. Surch double	£1800	
26s/7s Optd "SPECIMEN" *Set of 2*			70·00	

1897–1900. Colours changed and new values. Die II. Wmk Crown CA. P. 14.
28	**1**	2c. orange-brown and green (1900)	2·00	3·50
		a. Repaired "S"	£350	£375
29		6c. carmine (1900)	4·50	50
		a. Repaired "S"	£450	£300
30		15c. ultramarine (1900)	12·00	9·00
		a. Repaired "S"	£550	£400
31		18c. ultramarine	15·00	1·50
32		36c. brown and carmine	48·00	8·00
33	**4**	75c. yellow and violet (1900)	55·00	70·00
		a. Repaired "S"	£650	£850
34		1r. bright mauve and deep red........	17·00	9·00
35		1r.50 grey and carmine (1900).........	85·00	95·00
		a. Repaired "S"	£800	£1000
36		2r.25 bright mauve and green (1900)	£110	85·00
		a. Repaired "S"	£1000	
28/36 *Set of 9*			£300	£250
28s/36s Optd "SPECIMEN" *Set of 9*			£275	

---

3 cents

6 cents

(5)   (5a)

1901 (21 June–Sept). Surch locally with T **5** or **5a**.
37		3c. on 10c. bright ultramarine and brown (No. 12) (9.01)	3·50	75
		a. Surch double	£900	
		b. Surch triple	£3250	
38		3c. on 16c. chestnut and ultramarine (No. 14) (8.01)........	8·00	11·00
		a. Surch inverted	£700	£700
		b. Surch double	£500	£550
		c. "3 cents" omitted	£550	£550
		d. Malformed "S"	£275	£425
39		3c. on 36c. brown and carmine (No. 32)	2·50	80
		a. Surch double	£750	£850
		b. "3 cents" omitted	£650	£700
40		6c. on 8c. brown-purple and ultramarine (No. 11) (7.01)	8·00	3·75
		a. Surch inverted	£650	£750
37/40 *Set of 4*			20·00	14·50
37s/40s H/S "Specimen" (No. 37) or "SPECIMEN" *Set of 4*			£110	

1902 (June). Surch locally as T **5**.
41	**1**	2c. on 4c. carmine and green (No. 10)..	5·50	2·75
42	**4**	30c. on 75c. yellow and violet (No. 33)..	3·25	7·50
		a. Narrow "0" in "30" (R. 3/6, 5/2-4)..	9·50	48·00
		b. Repaired "S"	£350	£550

43		30c. on 1r. bright mauve and deep red (No. 34)	19·00	50·00
		a. Narrow "0" in "30" (R. 3/6, 5/2-4)..	40·00	£120
		b. Surch double	£1500	
44		45c. on 1r. bright mauve and deep red (No. 34)	10·00	50·00
45		45c. on 2r.25 bright mauve and green (No. 36)	50·00	£110
		a. Narrow "5" in "45" (R. 4/1)	£200	£375
		b. Repaired "S"	£750	£1200
41/5 *Set of 5*			75·00	£200
41s/5s Optd "Specimen" *Set of 5*			£140	

6   7

3 cents

(8)

Dented frame (R. 1/6 of left pane)

1903 (26 May). Wmk Crown CA. P. 14.
46	**6**	2c. chestnut and green.....................	1·75	2·00
		a. Dented frame	£160	£190
47		3c. dull green	1·00	1·25
		a. Dented frame	£140	£170
48		6c. carmine......................................	3·75	1·25
		a. Dented frame	£275	£170
49		12c. olive-sepia and dull green.........	6·00	2·50
		a. Dented frame	£325	£250
50		15c. ultramarine	7·50	3·50
		a. Dented frame	£375	£250
51		18c. sage-green and carmine	5·00	5·50
		a. Dented frame	£325	£400
52		30c. violet and dull green	10·00	19·00
		a. Dented frame	£425	£650
53		45c. brown and carmine	7·00	19·00
		a. Dented frame	£425	£650
		w. Wmk inverted	£500	£650
54	**7**	75c. yellow and violet	10·00	38·00
		a. Dented frame	£550	
55		1r.50 black and carmine	55·00	70·00
		a. Dented frame	£950	£1100
56		2r.25 purple and green	50·00	90·00
		a. Dented frame	£1000	£1400
46/56 *Set of 11*			£130	£225
46s/56s Optd "SPECIMEN" *Set of 11*			£225	

1903. Surch locally with T **8**.
57	**6**	3c. on 15c. ultramarine (3.7)	1·00	3·75
		a. Dented frame	£275	£325
58		3c. on 18c. sage-green and carmine (2.9)	2·75	48·00
		a. Dented frame	£400	£1000
59		3c. on 45c. brown and carmine (21.7)	3·00	4·50
		a. Dented frame	£350	£350
57/9 *Set of 3*			6·00	50·00
57s/9s H/S "Specimen" *Set of 3*			90·00	

CROWN COLONY

The Seychelles became a Separate Crown Colony by Letters Patent dated 31 August 1903.

1906. Wmk Mult Crown CA. P. 14.
60	**6**	2c. chestnut and green.....................	1·50	4·25
		a. Dented frame	£130	£225
61		3c. dull green	1·50	1·50
		a. Dented frame	£150	£170
62		6c. carmine......................................	2·25	80
		a. Dented frame	£180	£130
63		12c. olive-sepia and dull green.........	3·00	3·25
		a. Dented frame	£275	£300
64		15c. ultramarine	3·00	2·00
		a. Dented frame	£275	£220
65		18c. sage-green and carmine	3·00	6·50
		a. Dented frame	£300	£400
66		30c. violet and dull green	6·00	8·00
		a. Dented frame	£350	£450
67		45c. brown and carmine	4·25	15·00
		a. Dented frame	£425	£550
68	**7**	75c. yellow and violet	8·50	55·00
		a. Dented frame	£550	
69		1r.50 black and carmine	60·00	65·00
		a. Dented frame	£950	£950
70		2r.25 purple and green	55·00	65·00
		a. Dented frame	£950	£1000
60/70 *Set of 11*			£130	£200

9   10

Split "A" (R. 8/3 of left pane)

1912 (Apr)–**16**. Wmk Mult Crown CA. P 14.

71	**9**	2c. chestnut and green	1·00	8·50
		a. Split "A"	£130	£300
72		3c. green	6·50	60
		a. Split "A"	£275	£130
73		6c. Carmine-red (6.13)	4·25	3·00
		a. Aniline-carmine (1916)	13·00	4·50
		b. Split "A"	£325	£170
74		12c. olive-sepia and dull green (1.13)	1·50	7·50
		a. Split "A"	£180	£325
75		15c. ultramarine	5·00	2·75
		a. Split "A"	£325	£180
76		18c. sage-green and carmine (1.13)	3·25	14·00
		a. Split "A"	£225	£425
77		30c. violet and green (1.13)	15·00	3·25
		a. Split "A"	£375	£190
78		45c. brown and carmine (1.13)	2·75	50·00
		a. Split "A"	£275	
79	**10**	75c. yellow and violet (1.13)	2·75	7·00
		a. Split "A"	£300	£400
80		1r.50 black and carmine (1.13)	13·00	1·50
		a. Split "A"	£475	£150
81		2r.25 deep magenta and green (shades) (1.13)	75·00	3·25
		a. Split "A"	£1100	£250
71/81 Set of 11			£110	90·00
71s/81s Optd "SPECIMEN" Set of 11			£250	

11	**12**	**13**

1917–22. Die I. Chalk-surfaced paper (18c. to 5r.). Wmk Mult Crown CA. P 14.

82	**11**	2c. chestnut and green	50	2·75
83		3c. green	2·00	1·25
84	**12**	5c. deep brown (1920)	4·75	15·00
85	**11**	6c. carmine	1·50	1·00
		a. Rose (1919)	12·00	2·50
86		12c. grey (1919)	2·50	2·25
87		15c. ultramarine	2·00	1·50
88		18c. purple/yellow (1919)	5·00	48·00
		a. On orange-buff (1920)	17·00	60·00
		b. On buff (1920)		
		c. Die II. On pale yellow (1922)	4·50	28·00
89	**13**	25c. black and red/buff (1920)	4·25	50·00
		a. On orange buff (1920)	40·00	75·00
		b. Die II. On pale yellow (1922)	5·50	19·00
90	**11**	30c. dull purple and olive (1918)	1·50	16·00
91		45c. dull purple and orange (1919)	4·50	48·00
92	**13**	50c. dull purple and black (1920)	14·00	60·00
93		75c. black/blue-green (olive back) (1918)	2·00	30·00
		a. Die II. On emerald back (1922)	1·40	25·00
94		1r. dull purple and red (1920)	23·00	70·00
95		1r.50 reddish purple and blue/blue (1918)	9·00	55·00
		a. Die II. Blue-purple and blue/blue (1922)	22·00	32·00
96		2r.25 yellow-green and violet (1918)	50·00	£160
97		5r. green and blue (1920)	£140	£275
82/97 Set of 16			£225	£650
82s/97s Optd "SPECIMEN" Set of 16			£325	

Examples of most values are known showing forged postmarks. These include part strikes of Seychelles postmarks dated "24 AP 93" and "AU 6 1903", and Victoria postmarks dated "NO 27" or "MY 6 35".

1921–32. Die II. Chalk-surfaced paper (18c. and 25c. to 5r.). Wmk Mult Script CA. P 14.

98	**11**	2c. chestnut and green	25	15
99		3c. green	1·75	15
100		3c. black (1922)	1·25	30
101		4c. green (1922)	1·00	2·50
102		4c. sage-green and carmine (1928)	6·50	21·00
103	**12**	5c. deep brown	75	5·50
104	**11**	6c. carmine	5·00	9·00
		w. Wmk inverted	£250	
		6c. deep mauve (1922)	1·50	10
106	**13**	9c. red (1927)	4·50	4·25
107	**11**	12c. grey	2·75	20
		a. Die I (1932)	30·00	65
108		12c. carmine-red (1922)	2·25	30
110		15c. bright blue	2·00	65·00
111		15c. yellow (1922)	1·00	2·75
112		18c. purple/pale yellow (1925)	2·50	21·00
113	**13**	20c. bright blue (1922)	1·50	35
		a. Dull blue (1924)	8·50	55
114		25c. black and red/pale yellow (1925)	2·75	27·00
115	**11**	30c. dull purple and olive	1·25	15·00
		w. Wmk inverted		
116		45c. dull purple and orange	1·25	7·00
117	**13**	50c. dull purple and black	2·50	2·25
118		75c. black/emerald (1924)	8·00	22·00
119		1r. dull purple and red	28·00	18·00
		a. Die I (1932)	12·00	35·00
121		1r.50 purple and blue/blue (1924)	17·00	22·00
122		2r.25 yellow-green and violet	21·00	15·00
123		5r. yellow-green and blue	£120	£170
98/123 Set of 24			£190	£375
98s/123s Optd "SPECIMEN" Set of 24			£400	

The 3c. green and 12c. grey (Die II) were reissued in 1927. "SPECIMEN" overprints on these printings are 15.5×1.75 mm instead of the 14.5×2.5 mm of the original issue. (Price, 3c. £550, 12c. £100).

Examples of most values are known showing the forged postmarks mentioned above.

1935 (6 May). Silver Jubilee. As Nos. 91/4 of Antigua, but ptd by B.W. P 11×12.

128		6c. ultramarine and grey-black	1·25	2·50
		a. Extra flagstaff	£250	£425
		b. Short extra flagstaff	£275	£400
		c. Lightning conductor	£375	
		d. Flagstaff on right-hand turret	£425	£450
		e. Double flagstaff	£475	£500
129		12c. green and indigo	5·50	1·50
		a. Extra flagstaff	£3500	£3750
		b. Short extra flagstaff	£450	£300
		c. Lightning conductor	£2500	
		d. Flagstaff on right-hand turret	£700	£700
		e. Double flagstaff	£700	£700
130		20c. brown and deep blue	4·00	5·50
		a. Extra flagstaff	£400	£500
		b. Short extra flagstaff	£325	
		c. Lightning conductor	£500	£550
		d. Flagstaff on right-hand turret	£550	£650
		e. Double flagstaff	£600	
131		1r. slate and purple	7·50	35·00
		a. Extra flagstaff	£225	£450
		b. Short extra flagstaff	£425	£700
		c. Lightning conductor	£325	£550
		d. Flagstaff on right-hand turret	£650	£850
		e. Double flagstaff	£650	
128/31 Set of 4			16·00	40·00
128s/31s Perf "SPECIMEN" Set of 4			£170	

For illustrations of plate varieties see Omnibus section following Zanzibar.

Examples are known showing forged Victoria "B MY 6 35" postmarks.

1937 (12 May). Coronation. As Nos. 95/7 of Antigua.

132		6c. sage-green	1·00	15
133		12c. orange	1·00	50
134		20c. blue	1·00	1·00
132/4 Set of 3			2·75	1·50
132s/4s Perf "SPECIMEN" Set of 3			£110	

14 Coco-de-mer Palm   **15** Giant Tortoise

16 Fishing Pirogue

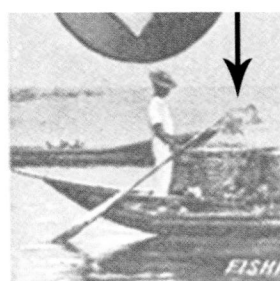

"Handkerchief" on oar flaw (R. 6/2)

(Photo Harrison)

1938 (1 Jan)–**49**. Wmk Mult Script CA. Chalk-surfaced paper. P 14½×13½ (vert) or 13½×14½ (horiz).

135	**14**	2c. purple-brown (10.2.38)	1·50	40
		a. Ordinary paper (18.11.42)	30	1·75
136	**15**	3c. green	12·00	2·75
136a		3c. orange (8.8.41)	1·25	1·00
		ab. Ordinary paper (18.11.42)	55	1·50
137	**16**	6c. orange	17·00	3·50
137a		6c. greyish green (8.8.41)	6·00	1·25
		aw. Wmk inverted	£1500	
		b. Ordinary paper. Green (18.11.42)	3·00	2·25
		c. Green (5.4.49)	20·00	1·25
138	**14**	9c. scarlet (10.2.38)	18·00	4·25
138a		9c. grey-blue (8.8.41)	38·00	40
		ab. Ordinary paper (18.11.42)	25·00	1·50
		ac. Ordinary paper. Dull blue (19.11.45)	8·00	3·25
		ad. Dull blue (5.4.49)	30·00	6·00
		aw. Wmk inverted	£5000	
139	**15**	12c. reddish violet	50·00	1·25
139a		15c. brown-carmine (8.8.41)	28·00	40
		ab. Ordinary paper. Brown-red (18.11.42)	10·00	4·75
139c	**14**	18c. carmine (8.8.41)	14·00	60
		ca. Ordinary paper (18.11.42)	9·00	3·50
		cb. Rose-carmine (5.4.49)	42·00	18·00
140	**16**	20c. blue	45·00	6·00
140a		20c. brown-ochre (8.8.41)	28·00	65
		ab. "Handkerchief" flaw	£600	£160
		b. Ordinary paper (18.11.42)	3·25	3·00
		ba. "Handkerchief" flaw	£275	£180
141	**14**	25c. brown-ochre (8.8.41)	50·00	14·00
142	**15**	30c. carmine (10.2.38)	50·00	11·00
142a		30c. blue (8.8.41)	45·00	50
		ab. Ordinary paper (18.11.42)	2·50	6·50
143	**16**	45c. chocolate (10.2.38)	42·00	4·50

---

		a. Ordinary paper. Purple-brown (18.11.42)	6·00	3·25
		b. Purple-brown (5.4.49)	48·00	23·00
144	**14**	50c. deep reddish violet (10.2.38)	20·00	60
		a. Ordinary paper (18.11.42)	1·75	3·25
144b		50c. bright lilac (13.6.49)	5·50	4·00
145	**15**	75c. slate-blue (10.2.38)	85·00	50·00
145a		75c. deep slate-lilac (8.8.41)	30·00	9·50
		ab. Ordinary paper (18.11.42)	4·50	9·50
146	**16**	1r. yellow-green (10.2.38)	£160	90·00
146a		1r. grey-black (8.8.41)	75·00	6·00
		ab. Ordinary paper (18.11.42)	6·00	7·50
147	**14**	1r.50 ultramarine (10.2.38)	48·00	8·50
		a. Ordinary paper (18.11.42)	9·00	18·00
		aw. Wmk inverted	£5000	
148	**15**	2r.25 olive (10.2.38)	75·00	19·00
		a. Ordinary paper (18.11.42)	32·00	42·00
149	**16**	5r. red (10.2.38)	32·00	17·00
		a. Ordinary paper (18.11.42)	35·00	48·00
135/49 Set of 25			£550	£225
135s/49s (ex 50c. bright lilac) Perf "SPECIMEN" Set of 24			£170	

Examples of most values are known showing forged Victoria postmarks dated "NO 27", "SP 17 41", "DE 12 41", "SP 14 42", "DE 21 42" or "NO 16 43".

Lamp on mast flaw (R. 1/5)

1946 (23 Sept). Victory. As Nos. 110/11 of Antigua.

150		9c. light blue	10	10
151		30c. deep blue	30	20
		a. Lamp on mast flaw	50·00	42·00
150s/1s Perf "SPECIMEN" Set of 2			95·00	

Line by crown (R. 1/3)

1948 (5 Nov). Royal Silver Wedding. As Nos 112/13 of Antigua.

152		9c. ultramarine	15	60
		a. Line by crown	48·00	65·00
153		5r. carmine	15·00	48·00

Examples are known showing forged Victoria "C 11 NOV 48" postmarks.

1949 (10 Oct). 75th Anniv of UPU. As Nos 114/17 of Antigua, but inscribed "SEYCHELLES" in recess.

154		18c. bright reddish purple	20	25
155		50c. purple	1·75	3·75
156		1r. grey	50	60
157		2r.25 olive	35	1·50
154/7 Set of 4			2·50	5·50

17 Sailfish   **18** Map of Indian Ocean

(Photo Harrison)

1952 (3 Mar). Various designs as T **14/16** but with new portrait and crown as in T **17/18**. Chalk-surfaced paper. Wmk Mult Script CA. P 14½×13½ (vert) or 13½×14½ (horiz).

158	**17**	2c. lilac	75	70
		a. Error. Crown missing, W **9a**	£850	
		b. Error. St. Edward's Crown, W **9b**	£140	£190
159	**15**	3c. orange	1·25	30
		a. Error. Crown missing, W **9a**	£650	£700
		b. Error. St. Edward's Crown, W **9b**	£180	£180
160	**14**	9c. chalky blue	60	1·75
		a. Error. Crown missing, W **9a**	£1400	
		b. Error. St. Edward's Crown, W **9b**	£375	£500
161	**16**	15c. deep yellow-green	50	1·00
		a. Error. Crown missing, W **9a**	£900	
		b. Error. St. Edward's Crown, W **9b**	£325	£400
162	**18**	18c. carmine-lake	1·75	20
		a. Error. Crown missing, W **9a**	£1300	
		b. Error. St. Edward's Crown, W **9b**	£375	£425
163	**16**	20c. orange-yellow	3·00	1·75
		a. Error. Crown missing, W **9a**	£1400	£1200
		b. Error. St. Edward's Crown, W **9b**	£450	£600
164	**15**	25c. vermilion	70	4·00
		a. Error. Crown missing, W **9a**	£1800	
		b. Error. St. Edward's Crown, W **9b**	£450	
165	**17**	40c. ultramarine	1·25	3·00
		a. Error. Crown missing, W **9a**	£1900	
		b. Error. St. Edward's Crown, W **9b**	£850	
166	**16**	45c. purple-brown	2·00	30
		a. Error. Crown missing, W **9a**	£2250	
		b. Error. St. Edward's Crown, W **9b**	£475	£475
167	**14**	50c. reddish violet	1·50	1·75
		a. Error. Crown missing, W **9a**	£1700	

		b. Error. St. Edward's Crown, W **9b**	£600	£700
168	**18**	1r. grey-black	6·50	4·50
		a. Error. Crown missing, W**9a**	£4250	
		b. Error. St. Edward's Crown, W **9b**	£1400	
169	**14**	1r.50 blue	14·00	18·00
		b. Error. St. Edward's Crown, W **9b**	£3500	
170	**15**	2r.25 brown-olive	19·00	21·00
		b. Error. St. Edward's Crown, W **9b**	£1600	
171	**18**	5r. red	21·00	22·00
		b. Error. St. Edward's Crown, W **9b**	£1100	£1100
172	**17**	10r. green	28·00	50·00
158/72 *Set of 15*			90·00	£110

See *Introduction* re the watermark errors.

1953 (2 June). Coronation. As No. 120 of Antigua.

173		9c. black and deep bright blue	60	70

19 Sailfish

20 Seychelles Flying Fox

(Photo Harrison)

1954 (1 Feb)–**61**. Designs previously used for King George VI issue, but with portrait of Queen Elizabeth II, as in T **19** and T **20**. Chalk-surfaced paper. Wmk Mult Script CA. P 14½×13½ (vert) or 13½×14½ (horiz).

174	**19**	2c. lilac	10	10
175	**15**	3c. orange	10	10
175a	**20**	5c. violet (25.10.57)	2·75	30
176	**14**	9c. chalky blue	10	10
176a		10c. chalky blue (15.9.56)	1·50	2·25
		ab. Blue (11.7.61)	13·00	5·50
177	**16**	15c. deep yellow-green	2·50	30
178	**18**	18c. crimson	30	10
179	**16**	20c. orange-yellow	1·50	20
180	**15**	25c. vermilion	2·25	1·00
180a	**18**	35c. crimson (15.9.56)	6·50	1·75
181	**19**	40c. ultramarine	1·00	25
182	**16**	45c. purple-brown	20	15
183	**14**	50c. reddish violet	30	80
183a	**16**	70c. purple-brown (15.9.56)	6·50	2·25
184	**18**	1r. grey-black	1·75	40
185	**14**	1r.50 blue	11·00	16·00
186	**15**	2r.25 brown-olive	11·00	11·00
187	**18**	5r. red	18·00	9·00
188	**19**	10r. green	28·00	18·00
174/88 *Set of 19*			80·00	55·00

21 "La Pierre de Possession"

(22)

(Photo Harrison)

1956 (15 Nov). Bicentenary of "La Pierre de Possession". Wmk Mult Script CA. P 14½×13½.

189	**21**	40c. ultramarine	20	20
190		1r. black	30	40

e *e* *s* *s* *c* *c*
191 191a 191 191b 191 191c

1957 (16 Sept). No. 182 surch with T **22**.

191		5c. on 45c. purple-brown	15	10
		a. Italic "e"	15·00	15·00
		b. Italic "s"	6·00	6·50
		c. Italic "c"	3·75	3·75
		d. Thick bars omitted	£1100	
		e. Surch double	£550	

There were two settings of this surcharge. The first setting contained No. 191a on R. 3/1, No. 191b on R. 5/3, No. 191c on R. 6/1 and 9/2, and No. 191d on R. 5/2. Nos. 191a and 191d did not occur on the second setting which shows No. 191b on R. 1/4, and No. 191c on R. 5/1 and R. 10/4.

23 Mauritius 6d. Stamp with Seychelles "B 64" Cancellation

(Recess: cancellation typo B.W.)

1961 (11 Dec). Centenary of First Seychelles Post Office. W **12**. P 11½.

193	**23**	10c. blue, black and purple	25	10
194		35c. blue, black and myrtle-green	40	10
195		2r.25 blue, black and orange-brown	70	70
193/5 *Set of 3*			1·25	75

24 Black Parrot

25 Vanilla vine

26 Fisherman

27 Denis Island Lighthouse

28 Clock Tower, Victoria

29 Anse Royale Bay

30 Government House

31 Fishing pirogue

32 Cascade church

33 Sailfish

34 Coco-de-Mer palm

35 Cinnamon

36 Copra

37 Map

38 Land Settlement

39 Regina Mundi Convent

40 Colony's Badge

(Des V. Whiteley. Photo Harrison)

1962 (21 Feb)–**68**. T **24/40**. W w **12** (upright). P 13½×14½ (horiz designs and 10r.) or 14½×13½ (others).

196	**24**	5c. multicoloured	3·25	10
197	**25**	10c. multicoloured	1·50	10
198	**26**	15c. multicoloured	30	10
199	**27**	20c. multicoloured	2·00	10
200	**28**	25c. multicoloured	50	10
200a		30c. multicoloured (15.7.68)	8·50	6·50
201	**29**	35c. multicoloured	1·75	1·50
202	**30**	40c. multicoloured	20	10
203	**31**	45c. multicoloured (1.8.66)	3·50	5·00
204	**32**	50c. multicoloured	40	25
205	**33**	70c. ultramarine and light blue	7·00	2·50
206	**34**	75c. multicoloured (1.8.66)	2·75	4·25
207	**35**	1r. multicoloured	1·00	10
208	**36**	1r.50 multicoloured	5·50	6·50
209	**37**	2r.25 multicoloured	5·50	12·00
210	**38**	3r.50 multicoloured	2·25	6·50
211	**39**	5r. multicoloured	9·00	2·50
212	**40**	10r. multicoloured	16·00	4·00
196/212 *Set of 18*			60·00	45·00

The 1r. exists with PVA gum as well as gum arabic, but the 30c. exists with PVA gum only.

See also Nos. 233/7.

For stamps of the above issue overprinted "B.I.O.T." see under British Indian Ocean Territory.

1963 (4 June). Freedom from Hunger. As No. 146 of Antigua.

213		70c. reddish violet	60	25

1963 (16 Sept). Red Cross Centenary. As Nos. 147/8 of Antigua.

214		10c. red and black	25	10
215		75c. red and blue	75	1·75

(41)

42 Seychelles Flying Fox

1965 (15 Apr). Nos. 201 and 205 surch as T **41**.

216		45c. on 35c. multicoloured	15	15
217		75c. on 70c. ultramarine and light blue	35	15

No. 216 was surcharged in photogravure; for No. 217 the surcharge was applied typographically.

1965 (1 June). ITU Centenary. As Nos. 166/7 of Antigua.

218		5c. orange and ultramarine	10	10
219		1r.50 mauve and apple-green	50	25

1965 (25 Oct). International Co-operation Year. As Nos. 168/9 of Antigua.

220		5c. reddish purple and turquoise-green	15	10
221		40c. deep bluish green and lavender	35	30

1966 (24 Jan). Churchill Commemoration. As Nos. 170/3 of Antigua.

222		5c. new blue	15	75
223		15c. deep green	45	45
224		75c. brown	1·25	45
225		1r.50 bluish violet	1·40	4·25
222/5 *Set of 4*			3·00	5·00

(Des V. Whiteley. Litho Harrison)

1966 (1 July). World Cup Football Championship. As Nos. 176/7 of Antigua.

226		15c. violet, yellow-green, lake and yellow-brown	20	25
		a. "50 c GRENADA" on front of stamp	£375	
227		1r. chocolate, blue-green, lake and yellow-brown	35	50

No. 226a shows a positive offset of the Grenada duty plate from the blanket on the front and a negative offset on the reverse.

Des M. Goaman. Litho Harrison.

1966 (20 Sept). Inauguration of WHO Headquarters, Geneva. As Nos. 178/9 of Antigua.

228		20c. black, yellow-green and light blue	35	10
229		50c. black, light purple and yellow-brown	65	20

1966 (1 Dec). 20th Anniv of UNESCO. As Nos. 196/8 of Antigua.

230		15c. slate-violet, red, yellow and orange	20	10
231		1r. orange-yellow, violet and deep olive	35	10
232		5r. black, bright purple and orange	80	1·00
230/2 *Set of 3*			1·25	1·00

1967–69. As Nos. 196/7, 204 and new values as T **42** but wmk w **12** (sideways).

233	**24**	5c. multicoloured (7.2.67)	35	2·75
234	**25**	10c. multicoloured (4.6.68)	30	40
235	**32**	50c. multicoloured (13.5.69)	2·25	3·75
236	**42**	60c. red, blue and blackish brown (15.7.68)	2·00	45
237	**33**	85c. ultramarine and light blue (15.7.68)	1·00	40
233/7 *Set of 5*			5·50	7·00

The 10c. exists with PVA gum as well as gum arabic, but the 50c. to 85c. exist with PVA gum only.

UNIVERSAL
ADULT
SUFFRAGE
1967
(43)

44 Money Cowrie, Mole Cowrie and Tiger Cowrie

1967 (18 Sept). Universal Adult Suffrage. As Nos. 198 and 206, but W w **12** (sideways), and Nos. 203 and 210 (wmk upright), optd with T **43**.

238	15c. multicoloured	10	10
	a. Opt double	£425	
239	45c. multicoloured	10	10
240	75c. multicoloured	10	10
241	3r.50 multicoloured	20	50
238/41	Set of 4	30	65

(Des V. Whiteley. Photo Harrison)

1967 (4 Dec). International Tourist Year. T **44** and similar horiz designs. W w **12**. P 14×13.

242	15c. Type **44**	20	10
243	40c. Beech Cone, Textile or Cloth of Gold Cone and Virgin Cone	25	10
244	1r. Arthritic Spider Conch	35	10
245	2r.25 Subulate Auger and Trumpet Triton Shells	60	1·25
242/5	Set of 4	1·25	1·25

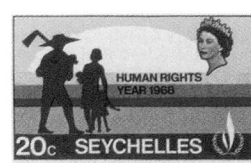

= 30
(48)

49 Farmer with Wife and Children at Sunset

1968 (16 Apr). Nos. 202/3 and as No. 206 surch as T **48** (30c.) or with "CENTS" added, and three bars (others). W w **12** (sideways on No. 248)

246	30c. on 40c. multicoloured	15	50
247	60c. on 45c. multicoloured	20	30
248	85c. on 75c. multicoloured	20	30
246/8	Set of 3	50	1·00

(Des Mary Hayward. Litho Harrison)

1968 (2 Sept). Human Rights Year. W w **12**. P 14½×13½.

249	**49** 20c. multicoloured	10	10
250	50c. multicoloured	10	10
251	85c. multicoloured	10	10
252	2r.25 multicoloured	25	1·60
249/52	Set of 4	40	1·60

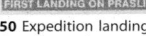

50 Expedition landing at Anse Possession

54 Apollo Launch

(Des Mary Hayward. Litho and die-stamped Harrison)

1968 (30 Dec). Bicentenary of First Landing on Praslin. T **50** and similar multicoloured designs. W w **12** (sideways on 50c., 85c.). P 14.

253	20c. Type **50**	35	10
254	50c. French warships at anchor (vert)	40	15
255	85c. Coco-de-Mer and Black Parrot (vert)	90	25
256	2r.25 French warships under sail	90	3·50
253/6	Set of 4	2·25	3·50

(Des V. Whiteley. Litho Format)

1969 (9 Sept). First Man on the Moon. T **54** and similar horiz designs. Multicoloured. W w **12** (sideways on horiz designs). P 13½.

257	5c. Type **54**	10	50
258	20c. Module leaving Mother-ship for Moon	15	10
259	50c. Astronauts and Space Module on Moon	20	15
260	85c. Tracking station	25	15
261	2r.25 Moon craters with Earth on the "Horizon"	45	1·60
257/61	Set of 5	1·00	2·25

59 Picault's Landing, 1742

60 Badge of Seychelles

(Des Mary Hayward. Litho Enschedé)

1969 (3 Nov)–**75**. Horiz designs as T **59/60**. Multicoloured. W w **12** (sideways*). Slightly toned paper. P 13×12½.

262	5c. Type 59	10	10
	w. Wmk Crown to right of CA	2·75	
263	10c. US satellite-tracking station	10	10
	a. Whiter paper (8.3.73)	70	75
264	15c. *Königsberg* (German cruiser) at Aldabra, 1914	3·00	2·00
	a. Whiter paper (8.3.73)	5·50	9·00
265	20c. Fleet re-fuelling off St. Anne, 1939–45	1·75	10
	a. Whiter paper (13.6.74)	1·25	2·00
266	25c. Exiled Ashanti King Prempeh	20	10
	a. Whiter paper (8.3.73)	65	2·75
267	30c. Laying Stone of Possession, 1756	1·00	4·00
268	40c. As 30c. (11.12.72)	3·25	1·25
	a. Whiter paper (13.6.74)	1·60	1·60
269	50c. Pirates and treasure	30	15
	a. Whiter paper (13.6.74)	1·50	1·75
270	60c. Corsairs attacking merchantman	1·00	1·50
271	65c. As 60c. (11.12.72)	6·00	8·00
	aw. Wmk Crown to left of CA	6·00	
	b. Whiter paper (13.8.75)	6·50	9·50
272	85c. Impression of proposed airport	3·50	1·75
273	95c. As 85c. (11.12.72)	6·50	4·25
	a. Whiter paper (13.6.74)	6·50	3·25
	aw. Wmk Crown to left of CA		
274	1r. French Governor capitulating to British naval officer, 1794	35	15
	a. Whiter paper (8.3.73)	1·00	1·75
275	1r.50 HMS *Sybille* (frigate) and *Chiffone* (French frigate) in battle, 1801	1·75	2·00
	a. Whiter paper (8.3.73)	3·50	11·00
276	3r.50 Visit of the Duke of Edinburgh, 1956	1·00	2·25
	a. Whiter paper (13.8.75)	5·50	17·00
277	5r. Chevalier Queau de Quincy	1·00	2·75
278	10r. Indian Ocean chart, 1574	2·75	8·00
279	15r. Type **60**	4·00	14·00
262/79	Set of 18	28·00	48·00
263a/76a	Set of 11	30·00	50·00

*The normal sideways watermark shows Crown to right of CA on the 40, 65 and 95c. and to left of CA on the others, *as seen from the back of the stamp*.

The stamps on the whiter paper are highly glazed, producing shade variations and are easily distinguishable from the original printings on toned paper.

74 White Terns, French Warship and Island

(Des A. Smith; adapted V. Whiteley. Litho D.L.R.)

1970 (27 Apr). Bicentenary of First Settlement, St. Anne Island. T **74** and similar horiz designs. Multicoloured. W w **12** (sideways). P 14.

280	20c. Type **74**	1·40	10
281	50c. Spot-finned Flyingfish, ship and island	45	10
282	85c. Compass and chart	45	10
283	3r.50 Anchor on sea-bed	70	1·50
280/3	Set of 4	2·75	1·60

78 Girl and Optician's Chart

79 Pitcher Plant

(Des A. Smith. Litho Questa)

1970 (4 Aug). Centenary of British Red Cross. T **78** and similar multicoloured designs. W w **12** (sideways on horiz designs). P 14.

284	20c. Type **78**	30	10
285	50c. Baby, scales and milk bottles	30	10
286	85c. Woman with child and umbrella (vert)	30	10
287	3r.50 Red Cross local HQ building	1·25	2·75
284/7	Set of 4	2·00	2·75

(Des G. Drummond. Litho J.W.)

1970 (29 Dec). Flowers. T **79** and similar vert designs. Multicoloured. W w **12**. P 14.

288	20c. Type **79**	25	15
289	50c. Wild Vanilla	30	15
290	85c. Tropicbird Orchid	80	30
291	3r.50 Vare Hibiscus	1·00	2·25
288/91	Set of 4	2·10	2·50
MS292	81×133 mm. Nos. 288/91. Wmk inverted	2·75	13·00

POSTAGE DUE STAMPS

D **1**

(Frame recess, value typo B.W.)

1951 (1 Mar). Wmk Mult Script CA. P 11½.

D1	D **1**	2c. scarlet and carmine	80	1·50
D2		3c. scarlet and green	3·50	1·50
D3		6c. scarlet and bistre	2·25	1·25
D4		9c. scarlet and orange	2·50	1·25
D5		15c. scarlet and violet	2·25	12·00
D6		18c. scarlet and blue	2·25	13·00
D7		20c. scarlet and brown	2·25	13·00
D8		30c. scarlet and claret	2·25	8·50
D1/8	Set of 8		16·00	48·00

1964 (7 July)–**65**. As 1951 but W w **12**.

D9	D **1**	2c. scarlet and carmine	2·50	15·00
D10		3c. scarlet and green (14.9.65)	1·25	17·00

Sierra Leone

PRICES FOR STAMPS ON COVER TO 1945	
Nos. 1/15	from × 10
Nos. 16/26	from × 15
Nos. 27/34	from × 20
Nos. 35/7	from × 10
No. 38	—
No. 39	from × 15
Nos. 41/52	from × 8
No. 53	—
No. 54	from × 40
Nos. 55/63	from × 5
Nos. 64/71	—
Nos. 73/84	from × 4
No. 85	—
Nos. 86/97	from × 4
No. 98	—
Nos. 99/110	from × 4
No. 111	—
Nos. 112/26	from × 2
Nos. 127/30	—
Nos. 131/45	from × 2
Nos. 146/8	—
Nos. 155/66	from × 2
No. 167	—
Nos. 168/78	from × 2
Nos. 179/80	—
Nos. 181/4	from × 6
Nos. 185/7	from × 5
Nos. 188/200	from × 2

CROWN COLONY AND PROTECTORATE

The first settlement in Sierra Leone intended as a home for repatriated Africans, and subsequently those released by the Royal Navy from slave ships, was established in 1787. The Sierra Leone Company was created by Act of Parliment in 1791, but its charter was surrendered in 1808 and the coastal settlements then became a Crown Colony. The inland region was proclaimed a British protectorate on 21 August 1896.

A post office was established in 1843 but, until the inclusion of Freetown in the British Post Office packet system in 1850, overseas mail was carried at irregular intervals by passing merchant or naval vessels.

The stamps of GREAT BRITAIN were not sold at Sierra Leone post offices, although examples from ships of the West African Squadron do exist with local cancellations.

PRINTERS. All issues of Sierra Leone until 1932 were typographed by De La Rue & Co. Ltd, London.

HALF PENNY

| 1 | 2 | (3) |

Dot after "SIX" and break in octagonal frame (R. 19/11)

1859 (21 Sept)–**74**. No wmk. P 14 (comb).

1	1	6d. dull purple	£250	50·00
		a. Dot after "SIX"	£1800	£550
2		6d. grey-lilac (1865)	£300	42·00
		a. Dot after "SIX"	£2500	£475
3		6d. reddish violet (P 12½, line) (1872)	£425	60·00
		a. Dot after "SIX"	—	£650
4		6d. reddish lilac (1874)	70·00	27·00
		a. Dot after "SIX"	£650	£300

Imperforate proofs exist.

The paper used for the 6d. value often shows varying degrees of blueing, caused by a chemical reaction.

The 6d. plate contained 240 stamps arranged in panes of 20 (4×5) with the sheets containing 12 such panes in four horizontal rows of three.

A second plate flaw, consisting of a dot after the "E" of "PENCE" occurs at R. 11/8. It may be found on all printings of the 6d. from 1872 onwards.

1872–73. Wmk Crown CC. P 12½.

(a) Wmk sideways (Apr 1872)

7	2	1d. rose-red	85·00	50·00
		w. Wmk Crown to left of CC	—	£130
8		3d. buff	£160	45·00
9		4d. blue	£200	40·00
10		1s. green	£500	60·00

*The normal sideways watermark shows Crown to right of CC, as seen from the back of the stamp.

(b) Wmk upright (Sept 1873)

11	2	1d. rose-red	£130	30·00
		w. Wmk inverted	£300	£120
12		2d. magenta	£140	50·00
13		3d. saffron-yellow	£500	85·00
14		4d. blue	£350	60·00
15		1s. green	£650	90·00

1876. Wmk Crown CC. P 14.

16	2	½d. brown	7·00	17·00
		w. Wmk inverted		£250
17		1d. rose-red	60·00	15·00
18		1½d. lilac (11.76)	50·00	10·00
19		2d. magenta	75·00	4·50
20		3d. buff	65·00	8·50
		w. Wmk inverted		

21		4d. blue	£225	6·50
		w. Wmk inverted	90·00	6·50
22		1s. green	£500	60·00
16/22		Set of 7		

1883 (May–13 Sept). Wmk Crown CA. P 14.

23	2	½d. brown	48·00	65·00
24		1d. rose-red (13.9.83*)	£200	35·00
25		2d. magenta	75·00	8·50
26		4d. blue	£1100	28·00
		x. Wmk reversed	†	£500

*Earliest known postmark date.

1884 SIERRA 5s. LEONE SURCHARGE. From 2 June 1884 the administration decided that, as a temporary measure, revenue and fiscal duties were to be paid with ordinary postage stamps. At that time there was no postage value higher than 1s., so a local surcharge, reading "SIERRA 5s. LEONE", was applied to No. 22 (*Price* £225 *unused*). Until withdrawal on 1 March 1885 this surcharge was valid for both fiscal and postal purposes, although no genuine postal cover or piece has yet been found. One mint example is known with overprint inverted (*Price* £1200).

Remainders of the surcharge were cancelled by a horizontal red brush stroke (*Price* £32 *with upright surcharge,* £160 *with inverted surcharge*).

1884 (July)–**91.** Wmk Crown CA. P 14.

27	2	½d. dull green	3·00	3·00
		w. Wmk inverted	£250	£180
28		1d. carmine	17·00	1·75
		a. Rose-carmine (1885?)	30·00	8·50
		aw. Wmk inverted	†	£200
29		1½d. pale violet (1889)	3·50	9·00
30		2d. grey (1889)	60·00	4·50
31		2½d. ultramarine (1891)	19·00	2·00
		w. Wmk inverted	†	£250
32		3d. yellow (1889)	3·50	15·00
33		4d. brown	2·50	4·00
		w. Wmk inverted		£425
		ws. Ditto, optd "SPECIMEN"		£400
34		1s. red-brown (1888)	27·00	22·00
27/34		Set of 8	£120	55·00
27s/34s		(ex 1½d., 3d.) Optd "SPECIMEN" Set of 6		£950
27sa/8sa, 30sa, 33sa Optd "SPECIMEN" (perf 12) Set of 4				£2500

1885–96. Wmk Crown CC. P 14.

35	1	6d. dull violet (1885)	70·00	26·00
		a. Dot after "SIX"	—	£275
36		6d. brown-purple (1890)	28·00	14·00
		a. Dot after "SIX"	£375	£180
		s. Optd "SPECIMEN"	85·00	
		w. Wmk inverted		
37		6d. purple-lake (1896)	2·75	10·00
		a. Dot after "SIX"	£110	£170

Proofs of the 6d. brown-purple exist from 1889 on Crown CA watermark and perforated 12 (*Price* £1800, *unused*).

1893 (8 Jan). Surch with T **3** by Govt Printer, Freetown.

(a) On No. 18. Wmk Crown CC

38	2	½d. on 1½d. lilac	£550	£750
		a. "PFNNY" (R.3/1)	£3750	£4500

(b) On No. 29. Wmk Crown CA

39	2	½d. on 1½d. pale violet	9·50	4·50
		a. Surch double	£120	£120
		b. "PFNNY" (R. 3/1)	85·00	75·00
		ba. Ditto. Surch inverted	£3750	£5000

On Nos. 38/9 the surcharge and the cancelling bars were often applied separately using a separate forme. When the bar missed its intended position across the value tablet, second, or even third bars were added, sometimes by pen or brush. No. 39a exists with the bars either normal or inverted with the rest of the surcharge.

Forged surcharges with "HALF PENNY" shown on one line were prepared by employees of the printer. It is believed that only two examples of this forgery still exist.

The 6d. fiscal, inscribed "STAMP DUTY" as Type **6** surcharged "ONE-PENNY" is known used for postage between May and August 1894, but no official sanction for such usage has been found.

| 4 | 5 |

1896–97. Wmk Crown CA. P 14.

41	4	½d. dull mauve and green (1897)	2·50	3·00
42		1d. dull mauve and carmine	5·00	1·75
43		1½d. dull mauve and black (1897)	4·00	22·00
44		2d. dull mauve and orange	2·50	5·00
45		2½d. dull mauve and ultramarine	2·50	1·25
46	5	3d. dull mauve and slate	8·50	7·00
47		4d. dull mauve and carmine (1897)	9·50	13·00
48		5d. dull mauve and black (1897)	13·00	15·00
49		6d. dull mauve (1897)	8·00	28·00
		w. Wmk inverted	—	£350
50		1s. green and black	6·00	27·00
51		2s. green and ultramarine	32·00	80·00
52		5s. green and carmine	90·00	£250
53		£1 purple/*red*	£325	£600
41/53		Set of 13	£450	£900
41s/53s Optd "SPECIMEN" Set of 13			£300	

Examples of most values are known showing forged oval registered postmarks dated "16 JUL 11" or "4 SP 11".

POSTAGE AND REVENUE

| 6 | (7) |

2½d. 2½d. 2½d.

| (8) | (9) | (10) |

2½d. 2½d. 2½d.

| (11) | (12) | (13) |

POSTAGE AND REVENUE (14)   **REVENUE** Italic "N" (R. 3/4 of the setting)

1897. Fiscal stamps as T **6**. Wmk CA over Crown, w **7**. P 14.

*(a) Optd with T **7** (26 Feb*)*

54		1d. dull purple and green	9·00	3·75
		a. Opt double	£2000	£2000

*(b) Optd with T **7** and surch T **8**, **10**, **11** (with square stop) or **12** with six thin bars across the original face value (27 Feb*)*

55	8	2½d. on 3d. dull purple and green	11·00	21·00
		a. Surch double	£40000	
		b. Surch double (Types 8+10)	£32000	
		c. Surch double (Types 8+11)	£55000	
		d. Bars omitted	£2250	
56	10	2½d. on 3d. dull purple and green	70·00	95·00
57	11	2½d. on 3d. dull purple and green	£200	£250
58	12	2½d. on 3d. dull purple and green	£400	£500
59	8	2½d. on 6d. dull purple and green	8·50	22·00
60	10	2½d. on 6d. dull purple and green	55·00	85·00
61	11	2½d. on 6d. dull purple and green	£150	£190
62	12	2½d. on 6d. dull purple and green	£325	£400

*Earliest known postmark date.

Nos. 55/8 and 59/62 were surcharged from a setting of 30 (10×3) which contained 22 examples of Type **8** (including three with square stops), five of Type **10**, two of Type **11** and one of Type **12**.

Two examples are known of No. 55a, five of No. 55b (of which two are in the Royal Collection) and two of No. 55c (one in the Royal Collection). A unique example of a double surcharge on No. 55 showing Types **8+12** is also in the Royal Collection.

No. 55d comes from the top row of a setting and was caused by the downward displacement of the overprint. Stamps in the lower rows show the overprint transposed with the obliterating bars at the top of the stamp.

*(c) Optd with T **14** and surch T **8**, **9**, **10**, **11** (with round stop) or **13** with five thin bars across the original face value (1 Mar*)*

63	8	2½d. on 1s. dull lilac	£110	70·00
64	9	2½d. on 1s. dull lilac	£1800	£1300
65	10	2½d. on 1s. dull lilac	£950	£750
66	11	2½d. on 1s. dull lilac	£550	£425
		a. Italic "N"	£1800	£1400
66b	13	2½d. on 1s. dull lilac	£1800	£1300
67	8	2½d. on 2s. dull lilac	£2000	£3000
68	9	2½d. on 2s. dull lilac	£50000	£55000
69	10	2½d. on 2s. dull lilac	£20000	
70	11	2½d. on 2s. dull lilac	£12000	£17000
		a. Italic "N"	£50000	£55000
71	13	2½d. on 2s. dull lilac	£45000	†

The setting of 30 (10×3) used for both Nos. 63/6b and 67/71 contained 22 examples of Type **8** (including one with square stop), one of Type **9**, two of Type **10**, four of Type **11** (including one with italic "N") and one of Type **13**.

Most examples of Nos. 63/6b are water-stained. Stamps in this condition are worth about 25% of the price quoted.

| 15 | 16 |

1903. Wmk Crown CA. P 14.

73	15	½d. dull purple and green	3·00	6·50
74		1d. dull purple and rosine	2·00	1·00
75		1½d. dull purple and black	1·50	23·00
76		2d. dull purple and brown-orange	3·75	16·00
77		2½d. dull purple and ultramarine	4·50	8·00
78	16	3d. dull purple and grey	17·00	15·00
79		4d. dull purple and rosine	7·00	21·00
80		5d. dull purple and black	10·00	50·00
81		6d. dull purple	12·00	42·00
82		1s. green and black	26·00	80·00
83		2s. green and ultramarine	55·00	80·00
84		5s. green and carmine	80·00	£140
85		£1 purple/*red*	£275	£350
73/85		Set of 13	£450	£750
73s/85s Optd "SPECIMEN" Set of 13			£250	

1904–05. Ordinary paper (1d.) or chalk-surfaced paper (others). Wmk Mult Crown CA. P 14.

86	15	½d. dull purple and green (1905)	5·00	4·50
87		1d. dull purple and rosine	1·50	1·50
		a. Chalk-surfaced paper (1905)	7·00	1·50
88		1½d. dull purple and black (1905)	3·00	19·00
89		2d. dull purple and brown-orange (1905)	4·25	4·00
90		2½d. dull purple and ultramarine (1905)	8·50	2·75
91	16	3d. dull purple and grey (1905)	55·00	4·50
		w. Wmk inverted	40·00	45·00
92		4d. dull purple and rosine (1905)	14·00	8·00
		w. Wmk inverted		£140
93		5d. dull purple and black (1905)	16·00	38·00
94		6d. dull purple (1905)	9·00	3·75
95		1s. green and black (1905)	7·50	9·00
96		2s. green and ultramarine (1905)	38·00	40·00
97		5s. green and carmine (1905)	50·00	65·00
98		£1 purple/*red* (1905)	£300	£350
86/98		Set of 13	£425	£475

1907–12. Ordinary paper (½d. to 2½d.) or chalk-surfaced paper (others). Wmk Mult Crown CA. P 14.

99	15	½d. green	1·25	50
100		1d. carmine	21·00	75
		a. Red	18·00	60
101		1½d. orange (1910)	3·75	2·00

102		2d. greyish slate (1909)	3·25	1·50
103		2½d. blue	3·75	3·00
104	**16**	3d. purple/*yellow* (1909)	16·00	2·75
		a. Ordinary paper (1912)	28·00	12·00
105		4d. black and red/*yellow* (1908)	2·25	1·60
106		5d. purple and olive-green (1908)	26·00	8·00
107		6d. dull and bright purple (1908)	23·00	8·00
108		1s. black/*green* (1908)	6·00	5·00
109		2s. purple and bright blue/*blue* (1908)	26·00	19·00
110		5s. green and red/*yellow* (1908)	50·00	70·00
111		£1 purple and black/*red* (1911)	£300	£250
99/111 *Set of* 13			£425	£325
99s/111s Optd "SPECIMEN" *Set of* 13			£500	

Most values from the 1903, 1904–05 and 1907–12 issues are known with forged postmarks. These include oval registered examples dated "16 JUL 11" or "4 SP 11".

USED HIGH VALUES. The £2 and £5 values of the King George V series were intended for fiscal use only. Before the introduction of the airmail service at the end of 1926 there was no postal rate for which they could be used. Under the airmail rates used between 1926 and 1932 it is just possible that a very heavy letter may have required a £2 value. Postmarks on the £5 and on the £2 before December 1926 can only have been applied "by favour" or, in the case of the cds type, are on stamps removed from telegraph forms. Used prices quoted for Nos. 129/30 and 147/8 are for "by favour" cancellations.

17   **18**

19   **20**

1912–21. Die I. Chalk-surfaced paper (3d. and 6d. to £5). Wmk Mult Crown CA. P 14.

112	**17**	½d. blue-green	4·75	3·50
		a. Yellow-green (1914)	7·00	2·50
		aw. Wmk inverted	†	£275
		b. Deep green (1919)	8·50	4·50
113		1d. carmine-red	2·25	30
		a. Scarlet (1916)	10·00	1·00
		b. Rose-red (1918)	10·00	80
		bw. Wmk inverted	†	£250
		bx. Wmk reversed	£225	£200
114		1½d. orange (1913)	2·00	2·50
		a. Orange-yellow (1919)	8·00	1·00
115		2d. greyish slate	1·25	20
		a. "A" of "CA" missing from wmk		
		w. Wmk inverted	40·00	40·00
116		2½d. deep blue	20·00	4·00
		a. Ultramarine (1917)	1·25	1·00
116*b*	**20**	3d. purple/*yellow*	6·00	3·25
		a. On pale yellow (1921)	6·00	3·25
117	**18**	4d. black and red/*yellow*	2·75	17·00
		a. On lemon (1915)	5·00	14·00
		b. Die II. On pale yellow (1921)	7·00	5·50
118		5d. purple and olive-green	2·00	7·00
		sa. Opt "SPECIMEN" double	£325	
119		6d. dull and bright purple	5·00	6·00
120	**19**	7d. purple and orange	3·00	13·00
121		9d. purple and black	5·00	12·00
122	**18**	10d. purple and red	3·00	21·00
124	**20**	1s. black/*green*	4·00	4·75
		a. On blue-green, green back	11·00	3·50
		w. Wmk inverted	70·00	60·00
125		2s. blue and purple/*blue*	30·00	7·00
126		5s. red and green/*yellow*	28·00	42·00
127		10s. red and green/*yellow*	£110	£160
		a. Carmine and blue-green/*green*	£140	£200
		b. Carmine and yellow-green/*green*	£150	£225
128		£1 black and purple/*red*	£250	£325
129		£2 blue and dull purple	£950	£1400
		s. Optd "SPECIMEN"	£200	
130		£5 orange and green (f.c. £225)	£3750	£5000
		s. Optd "SPECIMEN"	£475	
112/28 *Set of* 17			£400	£550
112s/28s Optd "SPECIMEN" *Set of* 17			£450	

Examples of Nos. 127/8 are known with part strikes of the forged postmarks mentioned after Nos. 99/111.

1921–27. Die II. Chalk-surfaced paper (6d. to £5). Wmk Mult Script CA. P 14.

131	**17**	½d. dull green	2·75	1·00
		a. Bright green	6·50	2·00
132		1d. bright violet (Die I) (1924)	7·00	2·25
		a. Die II (1925)	9·00	20
133		1½d. scarlet (1925)	2·00	1·25
134		2d. grey (1922)	1·75	20
135		2½d. ultramarine	3·50	21·00
		a. bright blue (1922)	2·50	1·25
136	**18**	3d. bright blue (1922)	2·50	1·25
137		4d. black and red/*pale yellow* (1925)	6·50	3·25
138		5d. purple and olive-green	1·50	1·25
139		6d. grey-purple and bright purple	1·50	2·75
		y. Wmk inverted and reversed		
140	**19**	7d. purple and orange (1927)	5·50	30·00
141		9d. purple and black (1922)	6·50	26·00
142	**18**	10d. purple and red (1925)	6·50	38·00
143	**20**	1s. black/*emerald* (1925)	17·00	6·00
144		2s. blue and dull purple/*blue*	12·00	10·00
		w. Wmk inverted	£200	£225
145		5s. red and green/*yellow* (1927)	12·00	60·00
146		10s. red and green/*green* (1927)	£170	£350

147		£2 blue and dull purple (1923)	£900	£1300
		s. Optd "SPECIMEN"	£200	
148		£5 orange and green (1923) (f.c. £180)	£3500	£4750
		s. Optd "SPECIMEN"	£475	
131/46 *Set of* 16			£225	£475
131s/46s Optd "SPECIMEN" *Set of* 16			£500	

21 Rice Field   **22** Palms and Cola Tree

(Eng J.A.C. Harrison (T **21**))

1932 (1 Mar). Wmk Mult Script CA.

(a) Recess Waterlow. P 12½

155	**21**	½d. green	25	1·00
156		1d. violet	40	30
157		1½d. carmine	75	2·75
		a. Imperf between (horiz pair)		
158		2d. brown	50	30
159		3d. blue	2·25	3·00
160		4d. orange	1·75	16·00
161		5d. bronze-green	3·00	9·00
162		6d. light blue	2·00	5·50
163		1s. lake	8·00	16·00

(b) Recess B.W. P 12

164	**22**	2s. chocolate	7·50	9·50
165		5s. deep blue	21·00	28·00
166		10s. green	90·00	£140
167		£1 purple	£180	£275
155/67 *Set of* 13			£275	£450
155s/67s Perf "SPECIMEN" *Set of* 13			£325	

23 Arms of Sierra Leone   **23a** "Freedom"

23b Map of Sierra Leone   **24** Old Slave Market, Freetown

25 Native fruit seller   **25a** Government sanatorium

25b Bullom canoe   **26** Punting near Banana Islands

26a Government buildings, Freetown   **26b** Bunce Island

27 African Elephant   **28** King George V

29 Freetown harbour

(Des Father F. Welch. Recess B.W.)

1933 (2 Oct). Centenary of Abolition of Slavery and of Death of William Wilberforce. T **23/29**. Wmk Mult Script CA (sideways on horiz designs). P 12.

168	**23**	½d. green	1·00	1·25
169	**23a**	1d. black and brown	65	10
170	**23b**	1½d. chestnut	8·50	4·50
171	**24**	2d. purple	3·25	20
172	**25**	3d. blue	6·50	1·75
173	**25a**	4d. brown	6·50	8·00
174	**25b**	5d. green and chestnut	7·00	8·00
175	**26**	6d. black and brown-orange	13·00	6·00
176	**26a**	1s. violet	6·50	19·00
177	**26b**	2s. brown and light blue	42·00	50·00
178	**27**	5s. black and purple	£160	£190
179	**28**	10s. black and sage-green	£300	£500
180	**29**	£1 violet and orange	£650	£850
168/80 *Set of* 13			£1100	£1500
168s/80s Perf "SPECIMEN" *Set of* 13			£850	

1935 (6 May). Silver Jubilee. As Nos. 91/4 of Antigua, but ptd by B.W. P 11×12.

181		1d. ultramarine and grey-black	2·25	2·50
		a. Extra flagstaff	80·00	£120
		b. Short extra flagstaff	£250	£325
		c. Lightning conductor	£100	
182		3d. brown and deep blue	3·50	8·50
		a. Extra flagstaff	£110	£170
		b. Short extra flagstaff	£500	
		c. Lightning conductor	£150	£225
183		5d. green and indigo	5·00	25·00
		a. Extra flagstaff	£180	£375
		b. Short extra flagstaff	£600	
		c. Lightning conductor	£225	
184		1s. slate and purple	25·00	25·00
		a. Extra flagstaff	£475	£475
		b. Short extra flagstaff	£550	£600
		c. Lightning conductor	£475	£475
181/4 *Set of* 4			32·00	55·00
181s/4s Perf "SPECIMEN" *Set of* 4			£140	

For illustrations of plate varieties see Omnibus section following Zanzibar.

1937 (12 May). Coronation. As Nos. 95/7 of Antigua. P 11×11½.

185		1d. orange	70	1·00
186		2d. purple	1·00	1·25
187		3d. blue	2·00	5·50
185/7 *Set of* 3			3·25	7·00
185s/7s Perf "SPECIMEN" *Set of* 3			£130	

30 Freetown from the Harbour   **31** Rice Harvesting

(Des Father F. Welch. Recess Waterlow)

1938 (1 May)–**44**. Wmk Mult Script CA (sideways). P 12½.

188	**30**	½d. black and blue-green	15	40
189		1d. black and lake	40	60
		a. Imperf between (vert pair)	†	—
190	**31**	1½d. scarlet	20·00	1·00
190*a*		1½d. mauve (1.2.41)	30	60
191		mauve	50·00	3·00
191*a*		2d. scarlet (1.2.41)	30	2·00
192	**30**	3d. black and ultramarine	65	50
193		4d. black and red-brown (20.6.38)	2·50	4·50
194	**31**	5d. olive-green (20.6.38)	3·25	4·25
195		6d. grey (20.6.38)	1·50	50
196	**30**	1s. black and olive-green (20.6.38)	3·75	70
196*a*	**31**	1s.3d. yellow-orange (1.7.44)	75	60
197	**30**	2s. black and sepia (20.6.38)	4·75	2·75
198	**31**	5s. red-brown (20.6.38)	14·00	17·00
199		10s. emerald-green (20.6.38)	38·00	19·00
200	**30**	£1 deep blue (20.6.38)	21·00	35·00
188/200 *Set of* 16			£140	80·00
188s/200s Perf "SPECIMEN" *Set of* 16			£475	

1946 (1 Oct). Victory. As Nos. 110/11 of Antigua.

201		1½d. lilac	20	10
202		3d. ultramarine	20	30
201s/2s Perf "SPECIMEN" *Set of* 2			£110	

1948 (1 Dec). Royal Silver Wedding. As Nos. 112/13 of Antigua.

203		1½d. bright purple	15	15
204		£1 indigo	20·00	35·00

1949 (10 Oct). 75th Anniv of UPU As Nos. 114/17 of Antigua.

205		1½d. purple	20	50
206		3d. deep blue	2·00	5·50
207		6d. grey	50	7·50
208		1s. olive	35	1·00
205/8 *Set of* 4			2·75	13·00

1953 (2 June). Coronation. As No. 120 of Antigua, but ptd by B.W.

209		1½d. black and purple	75	30

32 Cape Lighthouse   **33** Queen Elizabeth II Quay

34 Piassava workers

35 Cotton Tree, Freetown

36 Rice harvesting

37 Iron ore production

38 Whale Bay, York Village

39 Bullom canoe

40 Bristol 170 freighter Mk 31 aircraft and map

41 Orugu Railway Bridge

42 Kuranco Chief

43 Law Courts, Freetown

44 Government House

(Recess Waterlow)

1956 (2 Jan)–61. T **32/44**. Wmk Mult Script CA. P 13½×13 (horiz) or 14 (vert).

210	**32**	½d. black and deep lilac	1·00	2·75
211	**33**	1d. black and olive	90	40
212	**34**	1½d. black and ultramarine	1·60	6·50
213	**35**	2d. black and brown	70	40
214	**36**	3d. black and bright blue	1·25	10
		a. Perf 13×13½	2·50	17·00
215	**37**	4d. black and slate-blue	2·50	2·25
216	**38**	6d. black and violet	1·00	30
217	**39**	1s. black and scarlet	1·25	50
218	**40**	1s.3d. black and sepia	11·00	30
219	**41**	2s.6d. black and chestnut	19·00	13·00
220	**42**	5s. black and deep green	8·50	3·75
221	**43**	10s. black and bright reddish purple	4·25	3·00
		a. Black and purple (19.4.61)	14·00	38·00
222	**44**	£1 black and orange	29·00	42·00
210/22 Set of 13			70·00	65·00

Nos. 210/11 and 214 exist in coils, constructed from normal sheets.

INDEPENDENT

45 Palm Fruit Gathering

46 Licensed Diamond Miner

47 Bunda Mask

48 Bishop Crowther and Old Fourah Bay College

49 Sir Milton Margai

50 Lumley Beach, Freetown

51 Forces bugler

52

(Des K. Penny (½d., 1s.), Messrs Thorns, Turrell and Larkins (1d., 3d., 6d., 2s.6d.), W. G. Burnley (1½d., 5s.), J. H. Vandi (2d., 10s.), R. A. Sweet (4d., 1s 3d.), J. White (£1). Recess B. W.)

1961 (27 Apr). Independence. T **45/51**. W **52**. P 13½.

223	**45**	½d. chocolate and deep bluish green	20	30
224	**46**	1d. orange-brown and myrtle-green	1·50	10
225	**47**	1½d. black and emerald	20	30
226	**48**	2d. black and ultramarine	20	10
227	**49**	3d. orange-brown and blue	20	10
228	**50**	4d. turquoise-blue and scarlet	20	10
229	**49**	6d. black and purple	20	10
230	**45**	1s. chocolate and yellow-orange	20	10
231	**50**	1s.3d. turquoise-blue and violet	20	10
232	**46**	2s.6d. deep green and black	2·75	50
233	**47**	5s. black and red	1·00	1·25
234	**48**	10s. black and green	1·00	1·25
235	**51**	£1 carmine-red and yellow	9·00	23·00
223/235 Set of 13			15·00	24·00

53 Royal Charter, 1799

54 King's Yard Gate, Freetown

55 Old House of Representatives, Freetown, 1924

56 Royal Yacht *Britannia* at Freetown

(Des C. P. Rang (3d., 4d.), F. H. Burgess (1s.3d.). Recess B.W.)

1961 (25 Nov). Royal Visit. T **53/6**. W **52**. P 13½.

236	**53**	3d. black and rose-red	20	10
237	**54**	4d. black and violet	50	2·00
238	**55**	6d. black and yellow-orange	25	15
239	**56**	1s.3d. black and blue	3·50	2·00
236/9 Set of 4			4·00	3·75

57 Campaign Emblem

(Recess B.W.)

1962 (7 Apr). Malaria Eradication. W **52**. P 11×11½.

240	**57**	3d. carmine-red	10	10
241		1s.3d. deep green	20	10

58 Fireball Lily

59 Jina-gbo

(Des M. Goaman. Photo Harrison)

1963 (1 Jan). Flowers. Vert designs as T **58** (½d., 1½d., 3d., 4d., 1s., 2s.6d., 5s., 10s.) or horiz as T **59** (others). Multicoloured. W **52** (sideways on vert designs). P 14.

242		½d. Type **58**	10	50
243		1d. Type **59**	10	10
244		1½d. *Stereospermum*	20	25
245		2d. Black-eyed Susan	20	10
246		3d. Beniseed	20	10
247		4d. Blushing Hibiscus	20	30
248		6d. Climbing Lily	30	10
249		1s. Beautiful Crinum	40	10
250		1s.3d. Blue Bells	1·50	20
251		2s.6d. Broken Hearts	1·25	50
252		5s. Ra-ponthi	1·25	80
253		10s. Blue Plumbago	4·00	1·50
254		£1 African Tulip Tree	6·00	14·00
242/254 Set of 13			14·00	16·00

71 Threshing Machine and Corn Bins

72 Girl with onion crop

(Des V. Whiteley. Recess B.W.)

1963 (21 Mar). Freedom from Hunger. T **71/2**. W **52**. P 11½×11.

255	**71**	3d. black and yellow-ochre	30	10
256	**72**	1s.3d. sepia and emerald-green	35	10

2ND YEAR OF INDEPENDENCE 19 PROGRESS 63 DEVELOPMENT	2nd Year Independence Progress Development 1963
3d.	**10d.**
(73)	**(74)**

(Optd by Govt Printer, Freetown)

1963 (27 Apr). Second Anniv of Independence. Surch or optd as T **73/4**.

(a) Postage

257	3d. on ½d. black and deep lilac (No. 210) (R.)	40	10
	a. Small "c" in "INDEPENDENCE" (R. 4/5)	7·00	7·00
258	4d. on 1½d. black and ultramarine (No. 212) (Br.)	15	10
259	6d. on ½d. black and deep lilac (No. 210) (O.)	30	10
	a. Small "c" in "INDEPENDENCE" (R. 4/5)	7·50	7·50
260	10d. on 3d. black and bright blue (No. 214) (R.)	50	10
261	1s.6d. on 3d. black and bright blue (No. 214) (V.)	30	20
262	3s.6d. on 3d black and bright blue (No. 214) (Ult.)	40	20

(b) Air. Additionally optd "AIR MAIL"

263	7d. on 1½d. black and ultramarine (No. 212) (C.)	20	10
264	1s.3d. on 1½d. black and ultramarine (No. 212) (R.)	20	10
265	2s.6d. on 3d black and chestnut (No. 219) (V.)	2·50	40
266	3s. on 3d black and bright blue (No. 214) (B.)	40	20
267	6s. on 3d black and bright blue (No. 214) (R.)	1·00	20
268	11s. on 10s. black and bright reddish purple (No. 221) (C.)	2·75	4·00
	a. Black and purple	6·50	7·50
269	11s. on £1 black and orange (No. 222) (C.)	£750	£250
257/268 Set of 12		8·25	5·00

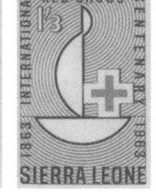

75 Centenary Emblem **76** Red Cross Emblem **77** Centenary Emblem

(Des M. Goaman. Recess B.W.)

1963 (1 Nov). Centenary of Red Cross. T **75/7**. W **52**. P 11×11½.

270	**75**	3d. red and violet	50	10
271	**76**	6d. red and black	50	15
272	**77**	1s.3d. red and deep bluish green	65	20
270/2 *Set of 3*			1·50	40

1853–1859–1963 Oldest Postal Service Newest G.P.O. in West Africa 1s.
(**78**)

1853–1859–1963 Oldest Postage Stamp Newest G.P.O. in West Africa AIRMAIL
(**79**)

1963 (4 Nov). Postal Commemorations. Optd or surch by Govt Printer, Freetown.

*(a) Postage. As T **78***

273		3d. black and bright blue (No. 214)	10	10
		a. "1895" for "1859" (R. 3/3)	3·00	
		b. "1853/1859/1963" (R. 2/3)	3·00	
		ba. As No. 273b, but showing "S vice" also (R. 2/3)		
274		4d. on 1½d. black and ultramarine (No. 212) (C.)	10	10
		a. "1895" for "1859" (R. 1/2)	4·00	
		b. "1853•1859•1963" (R.2/2, 11/4)	3·25	3·75
		c. "1853 1859•1963" (R. 11/4)	4·25	4·75
		d. No stop after "O", but stop after "Africa" (R. 10/1)	3·50	4·00
275		9d. on 1½d. black and ultramarine (No. 212) (V.)	10	10
		a. "1853"1859"1963"(R. 3/2,11/4)	3·50	
		b. No stop after "O" (R. 7/5)	60·00	
		c. No stop after "O", but stop after "Africa" (R. 10/1)	3·50	
276		1s. on 1s.3d. turquoise-blue and violet (No. 231) (C.)	10	10
		a. "1853"1859"1963" (R. 3/4, 10/2)	3·50	4·00
277		1s.6d. on ½d. black and deep lilac (No. 210) (Mag.)	15	10
		a. "1853"1859"1963" (R. 11/1.)	5·50	5·50
		b. "1853*1859 1963" (R. 4/5)	17·00	
278		2s. on 3d. black and bright blue (No. 214) (Br.)	15	10
		a. "1895" for "1859" (R. 4/10)	17·00	18·00
		b. "1853/1859/1963" (R. 2/3)	13·00	

*(b) Air. As T **79***

279		7d. on 3d. black and rose-red (No. 236) (Br.)	20	1·50
		a. "1895" for "1859" (R.3/6, 4/4)	3·25	5·50
		b. "1853-1859-1963" (R.2/3, 4/10)	2·50	4·75
		c. No stop after "O" (R.1/2)	4·00	
280		1s.3d. black and blue (No. 239) (C.)	2·00	1·50
		a. "1895" for "1859" (R.7/3)	30·00	
		b. "1853*1859*1963" (R.3/2,10/4)	10·00	
		c. No stop after "O" (R.8/3)	22·00	
281		2s.6d. on 4d. turquoise-blue and scarlet (No. 228)	1·25	1·50
		a. "1895" for "1859" (R.7/3)	65·00	
		b. "1853*1859*1963" (R.3/2, 10/4)	6·50	8·00
		c. No stop after "O" (R.8/3)	27·00	
282		3s. on 3d. black and rose-red (No. 236) (V.)	2·50	3·75
		a. "1895" for "1859" (R.3/3)	£500	
		b. "1853·1859·1963" (R.2/3, 4/10)	14·00	
		c. No stop after "O" (R.1/2)	27·00	
283		6s. on 6d. black and yellow-orange (No. 238) (Ult.)	1·00	2·75
		a. "1895" for "1859" (R.1/1)	65·00	
		b. "1853*1859*1963" (R.3/2, 10/4)	8·00	11·00
		c. No stop after "O" (R.8/3)	14·00	18·00
284		£1 black and orange (No. 222) (R.)	38·00	45·00
		a. "1895" for "1859" (R.11/4)	£500	
		b. "1853*1859*1963" (R.4/5, 11/1)	£100	
273/84 *Set of 12*			40·00	50·00

The events commemorated are: 1853, "First Post Office"; 1859, "First Postage Stamps"; and 1963 "Newest G.P.O." in West Africa. Nos. 273, 278 have the overprint in five lines; Nos. 279, 282 in six lines (incl "AIRMAIL"). Some of the overprint varieties were corrected during printing.

80 Lion Emblem and Map **81** Globe and Map

Kabala

Extended "A" in "SIERRA" (R. 3/3, later corrected on the 4d. value)

(Thermography and litho Walsall Lithographic Co. Ltd)

1964 (10 Feb). World's Fair, New York. Imperf. Self-adhesive.

(a) Postage

285	**80**	1d. multicoloured	10	10
286		3d. multicoloured	10	10
		a. Lion omitted	£500	
287		4d. multicoloured	10	10
		b. Extended "A"	2·75	
288		6d. multicoloured	10	10
		b. Extended "A"	2·75	
289		1s. multicoloured	15	10
		a. "POSTAGE 1/-" omitted	55·00	
		b. Extended "A"	2·75	
290		2s. multicoloured	40	30
		b. Extended "A"	4·50	
291		5s. multicoloured	60	85
		a. "POSTAGE 5/-" omitted	60·00	
		b. Extended "A"	7·00	

(b) Air

292	**81**	7d. multicoloured	10	10
293		9d. multicoloured	10	10
		a. "AIR MAIL 9d." omitted		
294		1s.3d. multicoloured	30	10
		a. "AIR MAIL 1/3" omitted	60·00	
295		2s.6d. multicoloured	40	15
		a. "AIR MAIL 2/6" omitted		
296		3s.6d. multicoloured	40	25
		a. "AIR MAIL 3/6" omitted		
297		6s. multicoloured	65	85
		a. "AIR MAIL 6/-" omitted	85·00	
298		11s. multicoloured	80	1·75
		a. "AIR MAIL 11/-" omitted	95·00	
285/98 *Set of 14*			3·75	4·25

Nos. 285/98 were issued in sheets of 30 (6×5) on green (postage) or yellow (airmail) backing paper with the emblems of Samuel Jones & Co. Ltd, self-adhesive paper-makers, on the back.

WARNING. These and later self-adhesive stamps should be kept on their backing paper except commercially used, which should be retained *on cover* or *piece*.

"POSTAGE" or "AIR MAIL" and value omitted: We only list examples where these are completely missing. This error also exists on other values but the only examples we have seen have the missing wording on the back of the backing paper due to a paper fold before printing.

82 Inscription and Map **83** Pres Kennedy and Map

(Thermography and litho Walsall)

1964 (11 May). President Kennedy Memorial Issue. Imperf. Self-adhesive.

(a) Postage. Green backing paper

299	**82**	1d. multicoloured	10	10
300		3d. multicoloured	10	10
301		4d. multicoloured	10	10
302		6d. multicoloured	10	10
		b. Extended "A"	2·75	
303		1s. multicoloured	15	10
		b. Extended "A"	2·75	
304		2s. multicoloured	50	1·75
		b. Extended "A"	5·00	
305		5s. multicoloured	75	2·75
		b. Extended "A"	8·00	

(b) Air. Yellow backing paper

306	**83**	7d. multicoloured	15	10
307		9d. multicoloured	15	10
308		1s.3d. multicoloured	35	10
309		2s.6d. multicoloured	50	50
310		3s.6d. multicoloured	50	65
311		6s. multicoloured	75	2·00
312		11s. multicoloured	1·00	3·25
299/312 *Set of 14*			4·50	10·00

(New Currency. 100 cents = 1 leone)

3c **AIRMAIL 7c** **Le 1·00**
(**84**) (**85**) (**86**)

1964–66. Decimal currency. Various stamps surch locally.

(i) First issue (4.8.64)

*(a) Postage. Surch as T **84***

313	–	1c. on 6d. multicoloured (No. 248) (R.)	10	10
		a. Surch inverted		
314	**53**	2c. on 3d. black and rose-red	10	10
315	–	3c. on 3d. multicoloured (No. 246)	10	10
		a. Surch inverted	£160	
316	**45**	5c. on ½d. chocolate and deep bluish green (B.)	10	10
317	**71**	8c. on 3d. black and yellow-ochre (R.)	15	10
318	–	10c. on 1s.3d. mult (No. 250) (R.)	15	10
319	–	15c. on 1s. multicoloured (No. 249)	1·00	10
320	**55**	25c. on 6d. black and yellow-orange (V.)	30	35
321	–	50c. on 2s.6d. deep green and black (No. 232) (O.)	2·75	2·00

---

*(b) Air. As T **85** or **86** (Nos. 326/7)*

322	–	7c. on 1s.3d. sepia and emerald-green (No. 256) (B.)	15	10
		a. Surch omitted (in horiz pair with normal)	£425	
		b. Surch double	85·00	
323	–	20c. on 4d. turquoise-blue and scarlet (No. 228)	25	20
324	–	30c. on 10s. black and green (R.)	40	50
325	–	40c. on 5s. black and red (No. 233)	50	65
326	**83**	1l. on 1s.3d. multicoloured (R.)	75	2·75
327		2l. on 11s. multicoloured (R.)	1·25	4·25
313/27 *Set of 15*			7·00	9·50

TWO LEONES

1c **Le 2·00**
(**87**) (**88**)

*(ii) Second issue (20.1.65). Surch as T **87** or **88** (Nos. 332/3)*

(a) Postage

328	–	1c. on 3d. orange-brown and blue (No. 227)	10	30
329	**82**	1c. on 1d. multicoloured	10	30
330		4c. on 3d. multicoloured (No. 246)	10	30
		a. Error. 4c. on 1d	£170	£250
		b. Stamp omitted (in pair with normal)		
331	–	5c. on 2d. multicoloured (No. 245)	10	10
332	–	1l. on 5s. multicoloured (No. 252) (Gold)	1·75	4·00
333	–	2l. on £1 carmine-red and yellow (No. 235) (B.)	4·00	6·50
		a. Surch double (B.+Blk.)	£200	£110

(b) Air

334	**83**	7c. on 7d. multicoloured (R.)	15	10
335		60c. on 9d. multicoloured	1·00	2·00
328/35 *Set of 8*			6·50	12·00

On No. 330b the stamp became detached before the surcharge was applied so that "4c" appears on the backing paper.

1c **1c**
Normal Small "c" (R. 3/3)

(iii) Third issue (4.65). Surch in figures (various sizes)

(a) Postage

336	–	1c. on 1½d. black and emerald (No. 225) (R.)	10	20
		a. Small "c"	4·00	
337	**82**	2c. on 3d. multicoloured	10	25
338	**80**	2c. on 4d. multicoloured	10	25
		b. Extended "A"	2·75	
339	**59**	3c. on 1d. multicoloured	10	25
340	–	3c. on 2d. black and ultramarine (No. 226) (R.)	10	25
		a. Small "c" (R. 3/3)	4·00	
341	–	5c. on 1s.3d. turquoise-blue and violet (No. 231) (R.)	10	10
		a. Surch inverted		
342	**82**	15c. on 6d. multicoloured	1·00	50
		b. Extended "A"	10·00	
343		15c. on 1s. multicoloured (R.)	1·50	90
		b. Extended "A"	13·00	
344	–	20c. on 6d. black and purple (No. 229) (R.)	40	15
345	–	25c. on 6d. multicoloured (No. 248) (R.)	45	20
346	–	50c. on 3d. orange-brown and blue (No. 227) (R.)	1·25	70
347	**80**	60c. on 6d. multicoloured (V.)	4·25	2·50
		b. Extended "A"	45·00	
348	**82**	1l. on 4d. multicoloured (R.)	4·50	5·50
349	–	2l. on £1 carmine-red and yellow (No. 235) (B.)	14·00	14·00

(b) Air

350	**81**	7c. on 9d. multicoloured	25	10
336/50 *Set of 15*			25·00	23·00

TWO 2c Leones
(**89**) (**90**)

*(iv) Fourth issue (9.11.65). Surch as T **89***

(a) Postage

351	**80**	1c. on 6d. multicoloured (V.)	3·50	9·00
		a. Stamp omitted (in pair with normal)		
		b. Extended "A"	35·00	
352		1c. on 2s. multicoloured (V.)	3·50	9·00
		b. Extended "A"	35·00	
353	**82**	1c. on 2s. multicoloured (V.)	3·50	9·00
		b. Extended "A"	35·00	
354		1c. on 5s. multicoloured (V.)	3·50	9·00
		b. Extended "A"	35·00	

(b) Air

355	**81**	2c. on 1s.3d. multicoloured	3·50	9·00
356	**83**	2c. on 1s.3d. multicoloured	3·50	9·00
		a. Stamp omitted (in pair with normal)		
357		2c. on 3s.6d. multicoloured	3·50	9·00
358	**81**	3c. on 7d. multicoloured	3·50	9·00
359	**83**	3c. on 9d. multicoloured	3·50	9·00
360	**81**	5c. on 2s.6d. multicoloured	3·50	9·00
361	**83**	5c. on 2s.6d. multicoloured	3·50	9·00

362	**81**	5c. on 3s.6d. multicoloured............	3·50	9·00
363		5c. on 6s. multicoloured.................	3·50	9·00
364	**83**	5c. on 6s. multicoloured.................	3·50	9·00
351/64 Set of 14..			42·00	£110

(v) Fifth issue (28.1.66). Air. No. 374 further surch with T 90

365	–	2l. on 30c. on 6d. multicoloured	2·00	2·50

IN MEMORIAM
TWO GREAT LEADERS

SIR MILTON MARGAI 1895-1964   SIR WINSTON CHURCHILL 1874-1965

91 Margai and Churchill

1965 (19 May). Sir Milton Margai and Sir Winston Churchill Commemoration. Nos. 242/3, 245/50 and 252/4 surch as T **91** on horiz designs or with individual portraits on vert designs as indicated.

(a) Postage

366		2c. on 1d. Type **59**.................	75	30
	a.	Horiz pair, one with "2 c" omitted.....	£500	
	b.	Surch and portraits omitted (in horiz pair with normal)........	£500	
367		3c. on 3d. Beniseed (Margai)............	10	20
	a.	Portrait and "3 c" double.............	£190	
	b.	Portrait and "3 c" double, one inverted.........	£150	
	c.	"3 c" omitted...................	£190	
368		10c. on 1s. Beautiful Crinum (Churchill).....	1·90	20
	a.	"10 c" omitted................	£375	
369		20c. on 1s.3d. Blue Bells...............	2·00	20
	a.	Portraits and "20 c" double, one inverted..........	£190	
	b.	"20 c" omitted................	£500	
	c.	"20 c" double, one inverted..........	£150	
370		50c. on 4d. Blushing Hibiscus (Margai)....	90	45
	a.	Portrait inverted..............	£140	
	ab.	Portrait inverted and "50 c" omitted....	£225	
371		75c. on 5s. Ra-ponthi (Churchill).........	4·75	1·25
	a.	Surch value inverted............	£225	

(b) Air. Additionally optd "AIRMAIL"

372		7c. on 2d. Black-eyed Susan............	1·50	20
	a.	"AIRMAIL" and "7c." omitted.......	£150	
	b.	"AIRMAIL" and "7 c" double, one inverted........	£150	
373		15c. on ½d. Type **58** (Margai).........	45	20
	a.	"AIRMAIL" and "15 c" double, one inverted........	£160	
	b.	Portrait double, one inverted........	£150	
374		30c. on 6d. Climbing Lily (O. and W.).......	2·75	35
	a.	"AIRMAIL" and "30 c" double, one inverted........	£140	
	b.	"AIRMAIL" and "30 c" omitted......	£130	
375		1l. on £1 African Tulip Tree...........	6·50	1·50
	a.	"AIRMAIL" and "1 l" double, one inverted........	£140	
	b.	"AIRMAIL" and "1 l" omitted.......	£500	
376		2l. on 10s. Blue Plumbago (Churchill).....	13·00	5·50
	a.	Surch value omitted..............	£200	
366/76 Set of 11.......................................			30·00	9·00

On Nos. 366/76 the portraits and commemorative inscription were applied in a separate operation from the surcharge and, on Nos. 372/6, the word "AIRMAIL".

92 Cola Plant and Nut

93 Arms of Sierra Leone

94 Inscription and Necklace

(Des M. Meers. Manufactured by Walsall Lithographic Co, Ltd)

1965 (17 Dec*). Imperf. Self-adhesive.

A. Embossed on silver foil, backed with paper bearing advertisements. Emerald, olive-yellow and carmine; denominations in colours given. Postage

377	**92**	1c. emerald............	25	10
378		2c. carmine............	25	10
379		3c. olive-yellow..........	25	10
380		4c. silver/emerald..........	30	10
381		5c. silver/carmine..........	30	10

B. Typo and embossed on cream paper backed with advertisements

(a) Postage

382	**93**	20c. multicoloured...........	2·25	60
383		50c. multicoloured...........	4·00	4·00

(b) Air

384	**93**	40c. multicoloured...........	4·00	4·00

C. Die-stamped and litho, with advertisements on white paper backing (see footnote). Air

385	**94**	7c. multicoloured............	80	15
	a.	Bright green and gold (inscr and face value) omitted....	£120	
386		15c. multicoloured............	1·50	90
377/86 Set of 10...			12·00	9·00

*It is believed that some values may have been released as early as 22 November.

The above stamps were issued in single form with attached tabs to remove the backing paper, with the exception of No. 385 which was in sheets of 25 bearing a single large advertisement on the back. No. 385a shows the die-stamping omitted.

For other stamps in Type **92** see Nos. 421/31 and 435/42a.

For 10c. stamps in Type **93** see Nos. 433/b.

2c 15c

AIRMAIL

FIVE YEARS	FIVE YEARS
INDEPENDENCE	INDEPENDENCE
1961-1966	1961-1966
(95)	(96)

1966 (27 Apr). Fifth Anniv of Independence. Various stamps surch.

(a) Postage. As T 95

387		1c. on 6d. multicoloured (No. 248)......	10	40
388		2c. on 4d. multicoloured (No. 247)......	10	40
389		3c. on 1½d. black and ultramarine (No. 212) (B.).........	10	40
390		8c. on 1s. multicoloured (No. 249) (B.)..	1·50	40
391		10c. on 2s.6d. multicoloured (No. 251) (B.)	25	10
392		20c. on 2d. black and brown (No. 213) (B.)	40	10

(b) Air. As T 96

393		7c. on 3d. red and violet (No. 270).......	25	10
394		15c. on 1s. multicoloured (No. 249)........	1·75	30
395		25c. on 2s.6d. multicoloured (No. 251)....	75	70
396		50c. on 1½d. multicoloured (No. 244)......	1·75	1·75
397		1l. on 4d. multicoloured (No. 247).........	2·00	3·25
387/397 Set of 11...			7·75	7·00

The inscription on No. 387 is in larger type.

97 Lion's Head

98 Map of Sierra Leone

(Des and embossed Walsall)

1966 (12 Nov). First Sierra Leone Gold Coinage Commemoration. Circular designs, embossed on gold foil, backed with paper bearing advertisements. Imperf.

(a) Postage

(i) ¼ golde coin. Diameter 1½ in

398	**97**	2c. magenta and yellow-orange	10	10
399	**98**	3c. emerald and bright purple.........	10	10

(ii) ½ golde coin. Diameter 2⅛ in

400	**97**	5c. vermilion and ultramarine........	10	10
401	**98**	8c. turquoise-blue and black..........	20	20

(iii) 1 golde coin. Diameter 3¼ in

402	**97**	25c. violet and emerald................	40	35
403	**98**	1l. orange and cerise...............	2·75	3·25

(b) Air. (i) ¼ golde coin. Diameter 1½ in

404	**98**	7c. red-orange and cerise	15	10
405	**97**	10c. cerise and greenish blue..........	20	25

(ii) ½ golde coin. Diameter 2⅛ in

406	**98**	15c. orange and cerise	35	35
407	**97**	30c. bright purple and black	50	60

(iii) 1 golde coin. Diameter 3¼ in

408	**98**	50c. bright green and purple............	1·00	1·00
409	**97**	2l. black and emerald.................	4·00	4·50
398/409 Set of 12..			8·75	9·75

(99)   (100)   (101)

1967 (2 Dec). Decimal Currency Provisionals. Surch as T **99** (Nos. 410/13), T **100** (Nos. 415/17) or T **101** (others).

(a) Postage

410	–	6½c. on 75c. on 5s. multicoloured (No. 371) (R.).........	50	25
411	–	7½c. on 75c. on 5s. multicoloured (No. 371) (S.).........	50	25
412	–	9½c. on 50c. on 4d. multicoloured (No. 370) (G.).........	35	25
413	–	12½c. on 20c. on 1s.3d. multicoloured (No. 369) (V.).....	65	35
414	**93**	17½c. on 50c. multicoloured.......	2·50	3·50
415	**82**	17½c. on 1l. on 4d. multicoloured (No. 348) (B.).........	2·50	3·50
416		18½c. on 1l. on 4d. multicoloured (No. 348)........	2·50	3·50
417	**80**	18½c. on 60c. on 5s. multicoloured (No. 347).........	6·50	9·50
	b.	Extended "A".................	60·00	
418	**93**	25c. on 50c. multicoloured.........	1·00	1·50

(b) Air

419	**93**	11½c. on 40c. multicoloured.........	45	40
420	**93**	25c. on 40c. multicoloured.........	1·00	1·50
410/20 Set of 11..			17·00	22·00

(Manufactured by Walsall)

1967 (2 Dec)–**69**. Decimal Currency. Imperf. Self-adhesive.

(a) Postage. As T 92, but embossed on white paper, backed with paper bearing advertisements. Background colours given first, and value tablet colours in brackets

421	**92**	½c. carmine-red (carmine/white)	10	75
422		1c. carmine (carmine/white).........	15	25
423		1½c. orange-yellow (green/white)	25	40
424		2c. carmine-red (green/white)........	45	10
425		2½c. apple-green (yellow/white)	75	75
426		3c. carmine-red (white/carmine)......	50	10
427		3½c. reddish purple (white/green).....	70	75
428		4c. carmine-red (white/green)........	70	15
429		4½c. dull green (green/white)........	70	75
430		5c. carmine (yellow/white).........	70	15
431		5½c. brown-red (green/white)........	70	1·00

(b) Air. T 102 embossed on black paper, backed with paper bearing advertisements; or, (No. 433), as T 93, typo and embossed on cream paper, also with advertisements

432	**102**	9½c. red and gold/black	90	1·00
432a		9½c. blue and gold/black (10.9.69).....	11·00	11·00
433	**93**	10c. multicoloured (red frame).........	90	80
	a.	Face value omitted..............		
433b		10c. mult (black frame) (10.9.69)........	12·00	12·00
434	**102**	15c. green and gold/black	1·50	1·25
434a		15c. red and gold/black (10.9.69)........	13·00	13·00
421/34a Set of 17..			40·00	40·00

The ½, 1½, 2, 2½, 3, 3½ and 5c. also exist without advertisements. The footnote below Nos. 377/86 also applies here.

Although only released for collectors on 2 December, the 5c. was known to be in use locally in February and the 3c. in March. The 1c. and 2c. were also released locally some months earlier.

See also Nos. 538/44.

1968. No advertisements on back, and colours in value tablet reversed. Background colours given first, and value tablet colours in brackets.

435	**92**	½c. carmine-red (white/green).........	10	1·00
436		1c. carmine (white/carmine)............	20	1·00
437		2c. carmine (white/green).............	6·50	9·00
438		2½c. apple-green (white/yellow)........	7·00	9·50
439		3c. carmine-red (carmine/white)......	3·25	

On Nos. 435 and 438, the figure "½" is larger than in Nos. 421 and 425.

It is believed that the ½c. was released in February, the 2½c. in April and the others in March.

The 1c. also exists with advertisements on the backing paper. The footnote below Nos. 377/86 also applies here.

1968–69. No advertisements on back, colours changed and new value (7c.). Background colours given first, and value tablet colours in brackets.

(a) Postage

440	**92**	2c. pink (white/brown-lake).............	3·00	3·50
441		2½c. deep bluish green (white/orange).........	3·00	3·50
442		3½c. olive-yellow (blue/white).........	3·25	4·50

(b) Air

442a	**92**	7c. yellow (carmine/white) (10.9.69)..	9·50	4·50
435/42a Set of 9...			32·00	32·00

On Nos. 441/2 the fraction "½" is larger than in Nos. 425 and 427.

It is believed that the 3½c. was released in March 1968 and the 2 and 2½c. in May 1968.

The 2c. also exists with advertisements on the backing paper. The footnote below Nos. 377/86 also applies here.

103 Outline Map of Africa

(Litho Walsall)

1968 (25 Sept). Human Rights Year. Each value comes in six types, showing different territories in yellow, as below. Imperf. self-adhesive.

A. Portuguese Guinea. D. Rhodesia.
B. South Africa. E. South West Africa.
C. Mozambique. F. Angola.

To indicate yellow territory use above letters as suffix to the following catalogue numbers.

(a) Postage

443	**103**	½c. multicoloured		10	10
444		2c. multicoloured		10	10
445		2½c. multicoloured		10	10
446		3½c. multicoloured		10	10
447		10c. multicoloured		25	15
448		11½c. multicoloured		30	20
449		15c. multicoloured		40	25

(b) Air

450	**103**	7½c. multicoloured		25	15
451		9½c. multicoloured		30	20
452		14½c. multicoloured		40	25
453		18½c. multicoloured		50	30
454		25c. multicoloured		60	40
455		1l. multicoloured		3·25	5·50
456		2l. multicoloured		9·00	12·00
443/56		Each territory *Set of 14*		14·00	18·00
443/56		Six territories *Set of 84*		14·00	18·00

Nos. 443/56 were issued in sheets of 30 (6×5) on backing paper depicting diamonds or the Coat of Arms on the reverse. The six types occur once in each horizontal row.

(104)

1968 (30 Nov). Mexico Olympics Participation.

(a) Postage. No. 383 surch or optd (No. 461) as T **104**

457	**93**	6½c. on 50c. multicoloured		40	30
458		17½c. on 50c. multicoloured		45	35
459		22½c. on 50c. multicoloured		65	50
		a. Surch double		£225	
460		28½c. on 50c. multicoloured		85	1·50
461		50c. multicoloured		1·25	2·50

(b) Air. No. 384 surch or optd (No. 466) as T **104** *in red*

462	**93**	6½c. on 40c. multicoloured		45	30
		a. Surch double		£225	
463		17½c. on 40c. multicoloured		55	35
464		22½c. on 40c. multicoloured		70	50
465		28½c. on 40c. multicoloured		85	1·50
466		40c. multicoloured		1·25	2·50
457/66		*Set of 10*		6·50	9·00

105 1859 6d.

111 1965 15c. Self-adhesive

(Litho Walsall)

1969 (1 Mar). Fifth Anniv of World's First Self-adhesive Postage Stamps. Reproductions of earlier issues. Multicoloured. Imperf. Self-adhesive.

(a) Postage. Vert designs

467		1c. Type **105**		10	10

468		2c. 1965 2c. self-adhesive		10	10
469		3½c. 1961 Independence £1		10	10
470		5c. 1965 20c. self-adhesive		10	10
471		12½c. 1948 Royal Silver Wedding £1		30	15
472		1l. 1923 £2		2·50	1·50

(b) Air. Horiz designs

473		7½c. Type **111**		20	10
474		9½c. 1967 9½c. self-adhesive		20	10
475		20c. 1964 1s.3d. self-adhesive		40	25
476		30c. 1964 President Kennedy Memorial 6s. commemorative self-adhesive		55	35
477		50c. 1933 Centenary of Abolition of Slavery £1 commemorative		1·50	75
478		2l. 1963 2nd Anniversary of Independence 11s. commemorative		9·00	8·00
467/478		*Set of 12*		13·00	10·00

Nos. 467 and 473 were issued with tabs as note under Nos. 377/86 and No. 474 exists with tabs and also in the normal version on backing paper.

All values are on white backing paper with advertisements printed on the reverse.

117 Ore Carrier, Globe and Flags of Sierra Leone and Japan

118 Ore Carrier, Map of Europe and Africa and Flags of Sierra Leone and Netherlands

The 3½c., 9½c., 2l. and 10c., 50c., 1l. are as T **118** but show respectively the flags of Great Britain and West Germany instead of the Netherlands.

(Litho Walsall)

1969 (10 July). Pepel Port Improvements. Imperf. Self-adhesive, backed with paper bearing advertisements.

(a) Postage

479	**117**	1c. multicoloured		25	10
480	**118**	2c. multicoloured		35	10
481	–	3½c. multicoloured		45	10
482	–	10c. multicoloured		70	10
483	**118**	18½c. multicoloured		1·00	25
484	–	50c. multicoloured		1·75	1·00

(b) Air

485	**117**	7½c. multicoloured		80	10
486	–	9½c. multicoloured		80	10
487	**117**	15c. multicoloured		1·00	25
488	**118**	25c. multicoloured		1·50	35
489	–	1l. multicoloured		2·25	2·00
490	–	2l. multicoloured		2·75	4·50
479/90		*Set of 12*		12·00	8·00

119 African Development Bank Emblem

(Litho and embossed Walsall)

1969 (10 Sept). Fifth Anniv of African Development Bank. Self adhesive, backed with paper bearing advertisements. Imperf.

(a) Postage

491	**119**	3½c. deep green, gold and blue		25	1·00

(b) Air

492	**119**	9½c. bluish violet, gold and apple green		35	70

120 Boy Scouts Emblem in "Diamond"

(Litho Walsall)

1969 (6 Dec). Boy Scouts Diamond Jubilee. T **120** and similar design. Imperf. Self-adhesive, backed with paper bearing advertisements.

(a) Postage

493	**120**	1c. multicoloured		10	10
494		2c. multicoloured		10	10
495		3½c. multicoloured		15	10
496		4½c. multicoloured		15	15
497		5c. multicoloured		15	15
498		75c. multicoloured		5·50	2·75

(b) Air

499	–	7½c. multicoloured		35	20
500	–	9½c. multicoloured		45	25
501	–	15c. multicoloured		70	50
502	–	22c. multicoloured		90	70
503	–	55c. multicoloured		4·00	2·00
504	–	3l. multicoloured		50·00	38·00
493/504		*Set of 12*		55·00	40·00

Design: *Octagonal Shape (65×51 mm)*—Nos. 499/504 Scout saluting, Baden-Powell and badge.

(121)

1970 (28 Mar). Air. No. 443 surch as T **121**.

505	**103**	7½c. on ½c. multicoloured (G.)		60	20
506		9½c. on ½c. multicoloured (P.)		60	20
507		15c. on ½c. multicoloured (B.)		1·00	40
508		28c. on ½c. multicoloured (G.)		1·50	75
509		40c. on ½c. multicoloured (B.)		2·00	2·00
510		2l. on ½c. multicoloured (Sil.)		7·50	19·00
505/10		Each Territory *Set of 6*		12·00	20·00
505/10		Six Territories *Set of 36*		65·00	£110

122 Expo Symbol and Maps of Sierra Leone and Japan

(Litho Walsall)

1970 (22 June). World Fair, Osaka. T **122** and similar design. Imperf. Self-adhesive, backed with paper bearing advertisements.

(a) Postage

511	**122**	2c. multicoloured		10	10
512		3½c. multicoloured		15	10
513		10c. multicoloured		25	10
514		12½c. multicoloured		25	10
515		20c. multicoloured		30	10
516		45c. multicoloured		60	45

(b) Air

517	–	7½c. multicoloured		20	10
518	–	9½c. multicoloured		25	10
519	–	15c. multicoloured		30	10
520	–	25c. multicoloured		55	20
521	–	50c. multicoloured		75	50
522	–	3l. multicoloured		2·00	5·50
511/22		*Set of 12*		5·00	6·50

Design: *Chrysanthemum shape (43×42 mm)*—Nos. 517/22 Maps of Sierra Leone and Japan.

123 Diamond   **124** Palm Nut

(Litho and embossed Walsall)

1970 (3 Oct). Imperf. Self-adhesive, backed with paper bearing advertisements.

523	**123**	1c. multicoloured		55	40
524		1½c. multicoloured		55	40
525		2c. multicoloured		55	10
526		2½c. multicoloured		55	10
527		3c. multicoloured		65	10
528		3½c. multicoloured		65	10
529		4c. multicoloured		70	10
530		5c. multicoloured		80	20
531	**124**	6c. multicoloured		50	20
532		7c. multicoloured		55	20
533		8½c. multicoloured		70	25
534		9c. multicoloured		70	25
535		10c. multicoloured		75	25
536		11½c. multicoloured		1·25	30
537		18½c. multicoloured		2·25	85

1970 (3 Oct). Air. As T **102**, but embossed on white paper. Backed with paper bearing advertisements.

538	**102**	7½c. gold and red	60	10
539		9½c. rose and bright green	70	10
540		15c. pink and greenish blue	2·00	20
541		25c. gold and purple	3·00	50
542		50c. bright green and orange	6·50	3·50
543		1l. royal blue and silver	13·00	16·00
544		2l. ultramarine and gold	20·00	32·00
523/44 *Set of 22*			50·00	50·00

126 "Jewellery Box" and Sewa Diadem

(Litho and embossed Walsall)

1970 (30 Dec). Diamond Industry. T **126** and similar design. Imperf (backing paper roll 20). Self-adhesive, backed with paper bearing advertisements.

(a) Postage

545	**126**	2c. multicoloured	45	20
546		3½c. multicoloured	45	20
547		10c. multicoloured	70	20
548		12½c. multicoloured	1·00	30
549		40c. multicoloured	2·50	1·25
550		1l. multicoloured	12·00	11·00

(b) Air

551	–	7½c. multicoloured	75	20
552	–	9½c. multicoloured	85	20
553	–	15c. multicoloured	1·50	35
554	–	25c. multicoloured	2·00	60
555	–	75c. multicoloured	7·00	6·00
556	–	2l. multicoloured	27·00	27·00
545/556 *Set of 12*			50·00	42·00

Design: Horiz (63×61 *mm*)—Nos. 551/6, Diamond and curtain.

STAMP BOOKLETS

1929 (22 Jan).

SB1	1s. booklet containing 12×1d. (No. 132a)	
SB2	2s. booklet containing twelve 2d. (No. 134)	

Singapore

A Crown Colony until the end of 1957. From 1 August 1958, an internally self-governing territory designated the State of Singapore. From 16 September 1963, part of the Malaysian Federation until 9 August 1965, when it became an independent republic within the Commonwealth.

Stamps in the Crown Colony Victory design with face values of 8c. and 15c. were prepared for Singapore in 1946, but were not issued.

(Currency. 100 cents = 1 Malayan, dollar)

CROWN COLONY

(Typo D.L.R.)

1948 (1 Sept)–**52**. As T **58** of Malaysia (Straits Settlements), but inscribed "SINGAPORE" at foot. Chalk-surfaced paper. Wmk Mult Script CA.

(a) P 14

1	1c. black	30	1·50
2	2c. orange	20	1·00
3	3c. green	50	2·25
4	4c. brown	20	2·25
5	6c. grey	1·00	1·00
6	8c. scarlet (1.10.48)	50	1·00
7	10c. purple	30	10
8	15c. ultramarine (1.10.48)	11·00	10
9	20c. black and green (1.10 48)	5·50	1·25
10	25c. purple and orange (1.10.48)	7·00	60
11	40c. red and purple (1.10.48)	9·50	7·50
12	50c. black and blue (1.10.48)	3·25	10
13	$1 blue and purple (1.10.48)	14·00	4·25
14	$2 green and scarlet (25.10.48)	48·00	7·50
15	$5 green and brown (1.10.48)	£110	9·00
1/15 *Set of 15*		£180	35·00

(b) P 17½×18

16	1c. black (21.5.52)	2·00	4·75
17	2c. orange (31.10.49)	2·00	2·75
19	4c. brown (1.7.49)	2·25	10
19a	5c. bright purple (1.9.52)	6·50	2·75
20	6c. grey (10.12.52)	3·25	4·50
21a	8c. green (1.9.52)	11·00	6·00
22	10c. purple (9.2.50)	1·25	10
22a	12c. scarlet (1.9.52)	14·00	20·00
23	15c. ultramarine (9.2.50)	27·00	1·00
24	20c. black and green (31.10.49)	13·00	4·50
24a	20c. bright blue (1.9.52)	13·00	10
25	25c. purple and orange (9.2.50)	5·50	10
25a	35c. scarlet and purple (9.2.52)	12·00	1·00
26	40c. red and purple (30.4.51*)	50·00	22·00
27	50c. black and blue (9.2.50)	8·50	10
28	$1 blue and purple (31.10.49)	17·00	20
	a. Error. St. Edward's Crown, W **9b**	£16000	£6000
29	$2 green and scarlet (24.5.51)	90·00	1·25
	a. Error. St. Edward's Crown. W **9b**	£20000	
	w. Wmk inverted	†	£7500
30	$5 green and brown (19.12.51)	£190	1·50
	w. Wmk inverted	†	£5000
16/30 *Set of 18*		£400	60·00

*Earliest known postmark date.

Single-colour values were from single plate printings (Die II) and all bi-colour, except the 25c., from separate head and duty plates (Die I). For differences between the Dies see after Nos. 278/98 of Malaysia (Straits Settlements). The 25c. is unique in this series in that it combines a Die II frame with a separate head plate.

Nos. 28a and 29a occur on rows in the watermark in which the crowns and letters "CA" alternate. The only unused examples seen show the wmk error in the top sheet margin.

Postal forgeries of the 50c., $1 and $2 exist on unwatermarked paper and perforated 14×14½.

1948 (25 Oct). Royal Silver Wedding. As Nos. 112/13 of Antigua.

31	10c. violet	75	1·00
32	$5. brown	£110	50·00

1949 (10 Oct). 75th Anniv of UPU As Nos. 114/17 of Antigua.

33	10c. purple	75	70
34	15c. deep blue	4·50	5·50
	a. "A" of "CA" missing from wmk	—	£1000
35	25c. orange	4·50	3·00
36	50c. blue-black	4·50	3·25
33/6 *Set of 4*		13·00	11·00

1953 (2 June). Coronation. As No. 120 of Antigua.

37	10c. black and reddish purple	3·00	30

1 Chinese Sampan

2 Malay kolek

3 Twa-kow lighter

4 Lombok sloop

5 Trengganu pinas

6 Palari schooner

7 Timber tongkong

8 Hainan junk

9 Cocos-Keeling schooner

10 Douglas DC-4M2 "Argonaut" aircraft

11 Oil tanker

12 *Chusan III* (liner)

13 Raffles Statue

14 Singapore River

15 Arms of Singapore

1c. A flaw between the two Sampans resembles a reflection in the water of one of the figures (Pl. 1B, R. 9/1)

(Des Dr. C. A. Gibson-Hill, except 25c., 30c., 50c. and $5 (from photographs, etc.). Photo Harrison (1c. to 50c.). Recess (centre typo on $5) B.W. (others)

1955 (4 Sept)–**59**. T **1/15**. Wmk Mult Script CA. P 13½×14½ (1c. to 50c.) or 14 (others).

38	**1**	1c. black	10	1·00
		a. Reflection in water	5·00	
39	**2**	2c. yellow-orange	2·50	1·50
40	**3**	4c. brown	2·25	15
		w. Wmk inverted	£375	£375
41	**4**	5c. bright purple	65	50
42	**5**	6c. deep grey-blue	65	70
43	**6**	8c. turquoise-blue	1·25	2·00
44	**7**	10c. deep lilac	3·00	10
45	**8**	12c. rose-carmine	5·00	3·00
46	**9**	20c. ultramarine	2·25	10
		a. Blue (13.3.58)	8·50	30
47	**10**	25c. orange-red and bluish violet	7·00	1·50
		a. Orange-red and purple (21.1.59)	32·00	4·25
48	**11**	30c. violet and brown-purple	3·75	10
49	**12**	50c. blue and black	2·25	10
50	**13**	$1 blue and deep purple	40·00	30
		a. Deep purple (Queen's head) omitted	£32000	
51	**14**	$2 blue-green and scarlet	42·00	1·75
52	**15**	$5 yellow, red, brown and slate-black	42·00	5·00
38/52 *Set of 15*			£130	15·00

Plate 2A and 2B of the 10c. (12 April 1960) and the blue "3A" and "3B" plates of the 50c. "3A-2A" "3B-2B" (part of the 24 January 1961 issue and later printings) were printed with a finer screen (250 dots per inch, instead of the normal 200) (*Price* 10c. £3.75 *un*, 20p *us*. 50c. £3.50 *un*, 10p *us*).

No. 50a was caused by a paper fold.

INTERNAL SELF-GOVERNMENT

16 The Singapore Lion

17 State Flag

(Photo Harrison)

1959 (1 June). New Constitution. W w **12**. P 11½×12.

53	**16**	4c. yellow, sepia and rose-red.........	65	75
54		10c. yellow, sepia and reddish purple	1·00	40
55		20c. yellow, sepia and bright blue....	2·25	3·00
56		25c. yellow, sepia and green............	2·50	2·25
57		30c. yellow, sepia and violet............	2·50	3·25
58		50c. yellow, sepia and deep slate......	3·25	3·25
53/8 *Set of 6*..............................			11·00	11·50

(Litho Enschedé)

1960 (3 June). National Day. W w **12** (sideways*). P 13½.

59	**17**	4c. red, yellow and blue	1·50	2·25
		w. Wmk Crown to right of CA	£110	
60		10c. red, yellow and grey...................	2·75	30
		w. Wmk Crown to right of CA	£100	£100

*The normal sideways watermark shows Crown to left of CA, *as seen from the back of the stamp.*

18 Clasped Hands

(Photo Enschedé)

1961 (3 June). National Day. W w **12** P 13½.

61	**18**	4c. black, brown and pale yellow ...	1·00	2·00
62		10c. black, deep green and pale yellow	1·25	10

19 *Arachnis* "Maggie Oei" (orchid)

20 Yellow Seahorse

21 Tiger Barb

22 Orange Clownfish

23 Archerfish

24 *Vanda* "Tan Chay Yan" (orchid)

25 Harlequinfish

26 *Grammatophyllum speciosum* (orchid)

26a Black-naped Tern

27 Copper-banded Butterflyfish

28 Three-spotted Gorami

29 *Vanda* "Miss Joaquim" (orchid)

30 White-rumped Shama

31 White-breasted Kingfisher

32 Yellow-bellied Sunbird

33 White-bellied Sea Eagle

20c. Nick in fin (R. 1/1)

(Photo Harrison orchids, fish and 15c. bird) D.L.R. (birds, except 15c.)

1962 (31 Mar)–**66**. T **19/33**. W w **12**. P 12½ (i), 14½×13½ (ii), 13½×14½ (iii), 13½×13 (iv) or 13×13½ (v).

63	**19**	1c. multicoloured (i)...................	30	1·00
64	**20**	2c. brown and green (ii).............	30	2·00
65	**21**	4c. black and orange-red (iii).........	30	1·25
		a. Black omitted.............................	£1500	
66	**22**	5c. red and black (iii).................	20	10
		a. Red omitted	£1000	
67	**23**	6c. black and greenish yellow (ii)...	55	1·25
68	**24**	8c. multicoloured (i) (10.3.63)......	1·25	3·50
69	**25**	10c. red-orange and black (iii).........	40	140
		a. Red-orange omitted................	£475	£425
		b. Black omitted...........................	£8000	
70	**26**	12c. multicoloured (i) (10.3.63)......	1·25	3·50
70a	**26a**	15c. multicoloured (i) (9.11.66)......	4·50	10
		ab. Orange (eye) omitted.............	75·00	
		ac. Stone (shading in wings) omitted	£325	
		aw. Wmk inverted.........................	38·00	
71	**27**	20c. orange and blue (ii).............	1·25	10
		a. Orange omitted........................	£1300	
		b. Nick in fin	18·00	
72	**28**	25c. black and orange (iii)...........	75	10
		a. Black omitted...........................	£1500	

73	**29**	30c. multicoloured (i) (10.3.63).........	1·25	40
		a. Yellow (flowers) omitted...............	£130	
		w. Wmk inverted.............................	£110	
74	**30**	50c. multicoloured (iv) (10.3.63)	1·25	10
75	**31**	$1 multicoloured (iv) (10.3.63).......	21·00	60
76	**32**	$2 multicoloured (iv) (10.3.63).......	9·00	1·00
77	**33**	$5 multicoloured (v) (10.3.63).......	20·00	9·00
		w. Wmk inverted.............................	£300	
63/77 *Set of 16*.............................			55·00	21·00

The 10c. exists in coils, constructed from normal sheets.
The 15c., 30c., $2 and $5 exist with PVA gum as well as gum arabic.
The errors, Nos. 70ab, 70ac and 73a, also exist with both gums.
See also Nos. 83/8.

34 "The Role of Labour in Nation-Building"

35 Blocks of Flats, Singapore

(Photo Courvoisier)

1962 (3 June). National Day. P 11½×12.

78	**34**	4c. yellow, rose-carmine and black	1·25	2·25
79		10c. yellow, blue and black.................	1·50	75

(Photo Harrison)

1963 (3 June). National Day. W w **12**. P 12½.

80	**35**	4c. orange-red, black, blue and turquoise-blue.............................	50	1·75
81		10c. orange-red, black, yellow-olive and turquoise-blue.....................	1·75	20
		w. Wmk inverted	75·00	

36 Dancers in National Costume

37 Workers

(Photo Harrison)

1963 (8 Aug). South East Asia. Cultural Festival. W w **12**. P 14×14½.

82	**36**	5c. multicoloured	50	50

INDEPENDENT REPUBLIC

1966 (1 Mar)–**67**. As Nos. 63, 66, 69, 72, 74/5, but W w **12** (sideways*).

83		1c. multicoloured (16.6.67).............	10	2·00
84		5c. red and black (30.5.67).............	4·75	3·25
85		10c. red-orange and black (19.5.67†)	3·00	3·25
86		25c. black and orange (9.66†)............	70	2·00
		w. Wmk Crown to right of CA	3·75	5·50
87		50c. multicoloured (11.1.66†)...........	4·50	2·50
		a. Imperf (pair)...............................	£650	
88		$1 multicoloured (18.5.67).............	16·00	15·00
83/8 *Set of 6*..............................			26·00	25·00

*The normal sideways watermark show Crown to left of CA, *as seen from the back of the stamp.*

†The 25 and 50c. values were not released in London until 30.5.67 and 9.6.66. The 25c. value, however, is known used in September 1966 and the 50c. on 11.1.66. The 10c., released in London on 30 May 1967, is known used locally on 19 May.

The 1c. and 25c. exist with PVA gum as well as gum arabic.

(Photo D.L.R.)

1966 (9 Aug). First Anniv of Republic. (30c.) or no wmk (others). W w **12**. P 12½×13.

89	**37**	15c. multicoloured	75	30
90		20c. multicoloured	1·00	1·25
91		30c. multicoloured	1·25	2·00
89/91 *Set of 3*..............................			2·75	3·25

38 Flag Procession

(Photo D.L.R.)

1967 (9 Aug). National Day. P 14×14½.

92	**38**	6c. rosine, brown and slate	50	90
93		15c. reddish purple, brown and slate	80	10
94		50c. bright blue, brown and slate.....	1·50	1·60
92/4 *Set of 3*..............................			2·50	2·25

Nos. 92/4 are respectively inscribed "Build a Vigorous Singapore" in Chinese, Malay and Tamil in addition to the English inscription.

39 Skyscrapers and Afro-Asian Map

40 Symbolical Figure wielding Hammer, and Industrial Outline of Singapore

(Photo D.L.R.)

1967 (7 Oct). Second Afro-Asian Housing Congress. P 14×13.

95	**39**	10c. multicoloured	30	10
		a. Opt omitted	£1600	£1600
96		25c. multicoloured	75	1·00
97		50c. multicoloured	1·40	1·60
95/7	*Set of 3*		2·25	2·40

The above were originally scheduled for release in 1966, and when finally issued were overprinted with the new date and a black oblong obliterating the old date.

(Photo Harrison)

1968 (9 Aug). National Day. Inscription at top in Chinese (6c.), Malay (15c.) or Tamil (50c.). P 13½×14.

98	**40**	6c. orange-red, black and gold	35	1·75
99		15c. apple-green, black and gold	45	15
100		50c. greenish blue, black and gold	1·00	1·25
98/100	*Set of 3*		1·60	2·75

41 Half check Pattern

42 Scrolled "S" multiple

43 Mirudhangam

44 Pi Pa

45 Sword Dance **51** Dragon Dance

(Photo D.L.R. (5c. to $1), Japanese Govt Printing Bureau, Tokyo

1968 (1 Dec)–**73**. T **43/5**, **51** and similar designs. (5c. to $1) or W **42** (upright on 1c., $5; sideways on 4c., $2, $10). Chalk-surfaced paper (5c. to $1). W **41**. P 14 (5c. to $1) or 13½ (others).

101	1c. multicoloured (10.11.69)	15	2·25
102	4c. multicoloured (10.11.69)	60	4·25
103	5c. multicoloured (29.12.68)	60	1·75
	a. Glazed unsurfaced paper (16.12.70)	14·00	23·00
	b. Perf 13 (27.6.73)	7·50	10·00
104	6c. black, lemon and orange	1·75	2·25
105	10c. multicoloured (29.12.68)	20	10
	a. Glazed unsurfaced paper (16.12.70)	15·00	14·00
	b. Perf 13 (14.7.73*)	24·00	9·50
106	15c. multicoloured (29.12.68)	60	10
107	20c. multicoloured	1·00	1·75
	a. Perf 13 (12.9.73)	13·00	23·00
108	25c. multicoloured (29.12.68)	1·25	1·75
	a. Perf 13 (27.6.73)	8·00	13·00
109	30c. multicoloured	40	1·50
	a. Perf 13 (12.9.73)	13·00	22·00

110	50c. black, orange-red and light yellow-brown	50	1·00
	a. Perf 13 (12.9.73)	14·00	40·00
111	75c. multicoloured	3·00	2·50
112	$1 multicoloured (29.12.68)	4·50	1·25
	a. Perf 13 (12.9.73)	25·00	30·00
113	$2 multicoloured (10.11.69)	3·50	1·00
114	$5 multicoloured (10.11.69)	14·00	1·50
115	$10 multicoloured (6.12.69)	38·00	15·00
101/15	*Set of 15*	60·00	35·00
103b/12a	*Set of 7*	90·00	£130

Designs: Vert (as T **45**)—6c. Lion dance; 10c. Bharatha Natyam; 15c. Tari Payong; 20c. Kathak Kali; 25c. Lu Chih Shen and Lin Chung; 50c. Tari Lilin; 75c. Tarian Kuda Kepang; $1 Yao Chi. (As T **44**—$2, Rebab; $10 Ta Ku. Horiz (as T **43**)—$5 Vina.

*Earliest known date of use.

58 ECAFE Emblem **59** "100000" and Slogan as Block of Flats

(Des Eng Sisk Loy. Photo Japanese Govt Ptg Bureau, Tokyo)

1969 (15 Apr). 25th Plenary Session of the UN Economic Commission for Asia and the Far East. P 13.

116	**58**	15c. black, silver and pale blue	35	20
117		30c. black, silver and red	65	1·25
118		75c. black, silver and violet-blue	1·00	2·50
116/18	*Set of 3*		1·75	3·50

(Des Tay Siew Chiah. Litho B. W.)

1969 (20 July). Completion of "100,000 Homes for the People" Project. P 13½.

119	**59**	25c. black and emerald	1·00	50
120		50c. black and deep blue	1·25	1·25

60 Aircraft over Silhouette of Singapore Docks **61** Sea Shells

(Des Eng Siak Loy and Han Kuan Cheng. Litho B.W.)

1969 (9 Aug). 150th Anniv of Founding of Singapore. T **60** and similar vert designs. P 14×14½.

121	15c. black, vermilion and yellow	2·50	70
122	30c. black, blue and new blue	2·50	1·00
123	75c. multicoloured	4·00	1·00
124	$1 black and vermilion	8·00	10·00
125	$5 vermilion and black	15·00	45·00
126	$10 black and bright green	23·00	45·00
121/6	*Set of 6*	50·00	90·00
MS127	120×120 mm. Nos. 121/6. P 13½	£375	£400

Designs:—30c. UN emblem and outline of Singapore; 75c. Flags and outline of Malaysian Federation; $1 Uplifted hands holding crescent and stars; $5 Tail of Japanese aircraft and searchlight beams; $10 Bust from statue of Sir Stamford Raffles.

(Des Tay Siew Chiah (15c.), Eng Siak Loy (others). Litho Rosenbaum Bros, Vienna)

1970 (15 Mar). World Fair, Osaka. T **61** and similar vert designs. Multicoloured. P 13½.

128	15c. Type **61**	1·00	15
129	30c. Veil-tailed Guppys	1·50	70
130	75c. Greater Flamingo and Helmeted Hornbill	4·00	2·75
131	$1 Orchid	4·50	6·50
128/31	*Set of 4*	10·00	9·00
MS132	94×154 mm. Nos. 128/31	24·00	24·00

62 "Kindergarten" **63** Soldier charging

(Des Choy Weng Yang. Litho B.W.)

1970 (1 July). Tenth Anniv of People's Association. T **62** and similar square designs. P 13½.

133	15c. agate and bright orange	60	20
134	50c. ultramarine and yellow-orange	1·40	2·00
135	75c. bright, purple and black	2·25	3·50
133/5	*Set of 3*	3·75	5·25

Designs:—50c. "Sport"; 75c. "Culture".

(Des Choy Weng Yang. Litho Rosenbaum Bros, Vienna)

1970 (9 Aug). National Day. T **63** and similar vert designs. Multicoloured. P 13½.

136	15c. Type **63**	1·25	20
137	50c. Soldier on assault course	3·00	2·75
138	$1 Soldier jumping	4·00	9·50
136/8	*Set of 3*	7·50	11·00

64 Sprinters

(Des Choy Weng Yang. Photo Japanese Govt Ptg Bureau, Tokyo)

1970 (23 Aug). Festival of Sports. T **64** and similar horiz designs. P 13×13½.

139	10c. magenta, black and ultramarine	1·50	3·25
	a. Horiz strip of 4. Nos. 139/42	7·50	13·00
140	15c. black, ultramarine and red-orange	2·00	3·50
141	25c. black, red-orange and bright green	2·25	3·25
142	50c. black, bright green and magenta	2·50	3·75
139/42	*Set of 4*	7·50	13·00

Designs:—15c. Swimmers; 25c. Tennis-players; 50c. Racing cars. Nos. 139/42 were issued together *se-tenant* in horizontal strips of four within the sheet.

65 *Neptune Aquamarine* (freighter)

(Des W. Lee. Litho Rosenbaum Bros, Vienna)

1970 (1 Nov). Singapore Shipping. T **65** and similar horiz designs. P 12.

143	15c. multicoloured	2·50	65
144	30c. yellow-ochre and ultramarine	4·50	4·25
145	75c. yellow-ochre and vermilion	8·00	10·00
143/5	*Set of 3*	13·50	13·50

Designs:—30c. Container berth; 75c. Shipbuilding.

STAMP BOOKLET

1969 (1 Nov). Black on green cover. Stapled.

SB1	$1.80 booklet containing twelve 15c. (No. 106) in blocks of 4		55·00

POSTAGE DUE STAMPS

The postage due stamps of Malayan Postal Union were in use in Singapore until replaced by the following issues.

D 1

(Litho B.W.)

1968 (1 Feb)–**69**. Toned paper. W w **12**. P 9.

D1	**D 1**	1c. green	60	2·00
D2		2c. red	1·60	2·50
D3		4c. yellow-orange	2·00	5·50
D4		8c. chocolate	1·00	2·00
D5		10c. magenta	1·00	90
		a. White paper (16.12.69)	2·25	8·00
D6		12c. slate-violet	2·75	3·25
		a. White paper (16.12.69)	7·00	20·00
D7		20c. new blue	2·00	3·50
		a. White paper (16.12.69)	10·00	15·00
D8		50c. drab	11·00	5·50
D1/8	*Set of 8*		20·00	22·00

In 1973 the 10c. and 50c. were reissued on whiter paper, perf 13×13½. In 1977–8 the 1c., 4c., 10c., 20c. and 50c. were issued on unwatermarked paper, perf 13×13½.

Somaliland Protectorate

Egyptian post offices were opened in Somaliland during 1876 and the stamps of Egypt were used there until the garrisons were withdrawn in 1884.

Cancellations for these offices have been identified as follows (for illustrations of postmark types see SUDAN).

BARBARA (Berbera). Open 1876 to 1 November 1884. Circular datestamp as Sudan Type I.

ZEILA. Open 1876 to 1 November 1884. Circular datestamp as Sudan Types G and I, sometimes inscr ZEJLA. One example with seal type cancellation as Sudan Type B is also known.

Stamps of India were used at the two post offices from 1 January 1887 until 1903 usually cancelled with circular datestamps or the "B" obliterator used by all offices controlled from Bombay.

The Protectorate Post Office was established on 1 June 1903, when control of British Somaliland was transferred from the Indian Government to the British Foreign Office.

PRICES FOR STAMPS ON COVER TO 1945	
Nos. 1/11	from × 25
Nos. 12/13	
Nos. 18/22	from × 12
Nos. 23/4	
Nos. 25/30	from × 30
Nos. 32/59	from × 12
Nos. 60/92	from × 6
Nos. 93/104	from × 3
Nos. 105/16	from × 4
Nos. O1/13	from × 20
Nos. O4/9f	—
Nos. O10/13	from × 20
Nos. O14/15	—

(Currency. 12 pies = 1 anna; 16 annas = 1 rupee)

BRITISH SOMALILAND (1)

2   3

SETTINGS OF TYPE 1

In all printings the ½, 1, 2, 2½, 3, 4, 8, 12a. and 1r. values were overprinted from a setting of 240 (2 panes 12×10, one above the other), covering the entire sheet at one operation.

The 6a., which was in sheets of 320 (4 panes, each 8×10), had a modified setting of 160, applied twice to each sheet.

The high values were overprinted in sheets of 96 (8 panes, each 4×3).

The settings for the low value stamps contained two slightly different styles of overprint, identified by the position of "B" of "BRITISH". Type A shows this letter over the "M" of "SOMALILAND" and Type B over the "OM".

For the first printing with the overprint at the top of the design the 240 position setting showed all the stamps in the upper pane and 63 in the lower as Type A, with the remaining 57 as Type B. When the setting was used for the printing with overprint at foot it was amended slightly so that one of the Type A examples in the upper pane became a Type B.

The 6a. value with overprint at top shows 250 examples of Type A and 70 as Type B in each sheet. This proportion altered in the printing with overprint at foot to 256 as Type A and 64 as Type B.

OVERPRINT VARIETIES

Missing second "I" in "BRITISH"—Occurs on the stamps with overprint at top from R. 2/6 of the upper pane and R. 5/1 of the lower, although it is believed that the example on the 2½a. (No. 4a) only occurs from the second position. On the later printing with overprint at foot a similar error can be found on R. 7/12 of the upper pane. Some examples of both these errors show traces of the letter remaining, but the prices quoted are for stamps with it completely omitted.

BRITISH SOMALILAND i

Figure "1" for first "I" in "BRITISH" (i)—Occurs on R. 6/4 of the upper pane for all printings of the 240 impression setting. In addition it has been reported from R. 7/12 of the Queen Victoria 8a., 12a. and 1r. with overprint at foot. Both versions of the 6a. show the variety on R. 6/4 of the upper left and upper right panes.

BRITISH SOMALILAND ii

Curved overprint (ii)—Occurs on R. 3/4 of the top right-hand pane of the high values.

SOMALILAND iii   **SOMALILAND** iv

"SOMALILAND"—Occurs on R. 2/9 of the upper pane for all low values with the overprint at foot, except the 6a. (iii). A similar variety occurs on the high values from the same series on R. 1/3 of the top left pane (iv).

"SOMAL.LAND"—Occurs on R. 7/5 of the lower pane from the 240 impression setting with the overprint at foot. In addition the Edwardian values of this series also have an example on R. 6/7. The 6a. has examples of the flaw on R. 6/9 and R. 7/5 of both the lower right and left panes. A similar variety occurs on the high values from the same series at R. 3/4 of the third pane in the right-hand column.

1903 (1 June). Nos. 80, 94, 96, 98, 100, 106/9, 114/16 and 118 of India (Queen Victoria) optd with T **1**, at top of stamp, in Calcutta. Wmk Elephant Head (6a.) or Star (others).

1		½a. yellow-green	2·75	4·25
	a.	"BRIT SH"	£170	£275
	b.	"BR1TISH"	£200	£275
2		1a. carmine	2·75	3·75
	a.	"BRIT SH"	£200	£275
	b.	"BR1TISH"	£200	
3		2a. pale violet	2·25	1·50
	a.	"BRIT SH"	£400	£500
	b.	"BR1TISH"	£325	
	c.	Opt double	£800	
4		2½a. ultramarine	2·00	1·75
	a.	"BRIT SH"	£650	
	b.	"BR1TISH"	£400	
5		3a. brown-orange	3·25	3·00
	a.	"BRIT SH"	£800	
	b.	"BR1TISH"	£400	£450
6		4a. slate-green	3·50	2·75
	a.	"BR1TISH"	£425	£475
7		6a. olive-bistre	7·50	4·50
	a.	"BR1TISH"	£300	£350
8		8a. dull mauve	4·00	5·00
	a.	"BR1TISH"	£425	£550
9		12a. purple/red	7·00	7·00
	a.	"BR1TISH"	£500	£600
10		1r. green and aniline carmine	7·50	10·00
	a.	"BR1TISH"	£475	£650
11		2r. carmine and yellow-brown	32·00	42·00
	a.	Curved opt	£750	
12		3r. brown and green	30·00	55·00
	a.	Curved opt	£750	
13		5r. ultramarine and violet	48·00	65·00
	a.	Curved opt	£750	
1/13	Set of 13		£130	£190

1903 (1 Sept–2 Nov). Stamps of India optd with T **1**, at bottom of stamp, in Calcutta.

(a) On Nos. 80, 100, 106/9 and 118 (Queen Victoria)

18		2½a. ultramarine (2.11)	7·50	8·50
	a.	"BR1TISH"	£200	
	b.	"SUMALILAND"	£250	
	c.	"SOMAL.LAND"	£275	
	d.	"BRIT SH"	£1500	
19		6a. olive-bistre (2.11)	9·00	7·00
	a.	"BR1TISH"	£300	
	b.	"SOMAL.LAND"	£180	
20		12a. purple/red (2.11)	10·00	14·00
	a.	"BR1TISH"	£425	
	b.	"SUMALILAND"	£325	£500
	c.	"SOMAL.LAND"	£375	
21		1r. green and aniline carmine (2.11)	10·00	11·00
	a.	"BR1TISH"	£475	
	b.	"SUMALILAND"	£475	
	c.	"SOMAL.LAND"	£500	
22		2r. carmine and yellow-brown (2.11)	£130	£200
	a.	Curved opt	£850	£1300
	b.	"SUMALILAND"	£850	
	c.	"SOMAL.LAND"	£850	
23		3r. brown and green (2.11)	£140	£200
	a.	Opt double, both inverted with one albino	£950	
	b.	Curved opt	£950	
	c.	"SUMALILAND"	£950	
	d.	"SOMAL.LAND"	£950	
	e.	Opt. double, one albino	£1200	
24		5r. ultramarine and violet (2.11)	£130	£200
	a.	Curved opt	£950	
	b.	"SUMALILAND"	£950	
	c.	"SOMAL.LAND"	£950	

(b) On Nos. 122/4, 127/8 and 133 (King Edward VII)

25		½a. green	2·25	55
	a.	"BRIT SH"	£550	
	b.	"BR1TISH"	£130	
	c.	"SUMALILAND"	£130	£140
	d.	"SOMAL.LAND"	80·00	95·00
26		1a. carmine (8.10)	1·25	30
	a.	"BRIT SH"	£350	
	b.	"BR1TISH"	£130	£140
	c.	"SUMALILAND"	£130	£140
	d.	"SOMAL.LAND"	60·00	70·00
27		2a. violet (2.11)	2·50	1·75
	a.	"BRIT SH"	£1300	
	b.	"BR1TISH"	£250	
	c.	"SUMALILAND"	£225	
	d.	"SOMAL.LAND"	£120	
28		3a. orange-brown (2.11)	2·50	1·75
	a.	"BR1TISH"	£275	£350
	b.	"SUMALILAND"	£225	
	c.	"SOMAL.LAND"	£140	£170
29		4a. olive (2.11)	1·50	1·75
	a.	"BR1TISH"	£225	
	b.	"SUMALILAND"	£200	
	c.	"SOMAL.LAND"	£150	
30		8a. purple (2.11)	3·50	1·75
	a.	"BR1TISH"	£375	
	b.	"SUMALILAND"	£375	
	c.	"SOMAL.LAND"	£225	
18/30	Set of 13		£400	£600

(Typo D.L.R.)

1904 (15 Feb–3 Sept).

(a) Wmk Crown CA. P 14

32	**2**	½a. dull green and green	2·75	4·25
33		1a. grey-black and red	19·00	3·25
34		2a. dull and bright purple (3.9)	2·25	2·50
35		2½a. bright blue (3.9)	3·50	3·75
36		3a. chocolate and grey-green (3.9)	2·50	6·50
37		4a. green and black (3.9)	4·00	9·00
38		6a. green and violet (3.9)	11·00	17·00
39		8a. grey-black and pale blue (3.9)	9·50	9·50
40		12a. grey-black and orange-buff (3.9)	14·00	11·00

(b) Wmk Crown CC. P 14

41	**3**	1r. green (3.9)	21·00	40·00
42		2r. dull and bright purple (3.9)	60·00	90·00
43		3r. green and black (3.9)	70·00	£130
44		5r. grey-black and red (3.9)	70·00	£140
32/44	Set of 13		£250	£425
32s/44s Optd "SPECIMEN" Set of 13			£250	

1905 (July)–**11**. Ordinary paper. Wmk Mult Crown CA. P 14.

45	**2**	½a. dull green and green	1·25	7·50
46		1a. grey-black and red (10.7.05)	27·00	10·00
	a.	Chalk-surfaced paper (1906)	23·00	1·60
47		2a. dull and bright purple	9·00	21·00
	a.	Chalk-surfaced paper (1909)	22·00	17·00
48		2½a. bright blue	3·00	10·00
49		3a. chocolate and grey-green	2·00	16·00
	a.	Chalk-surfaced paper (1911)	21·00	50·00
50		4a. green and black	4·25	25·00
	a.	Chalk-surfaced paper (1911)	24·00	55·00
51		6a. green and violet	3·00	25·00
	a.	Chalk-surfaced paper (1911)	40·00	80·00
52		8a. grey-black and pale blue	8·00	11·00
	a.	Chalk-surfaced paper. *Black and blue* (27.1.11)	27·00	70·00
53		12a. grey-black and orange-buff	6·50	10·00
	a.	Chalk-surfaced paper. *Black and orange-brown* (9.11.11)	17·00	70·00

1909 (30 Apr–May). Wmk Mult Crown CA. P 14.

58	**2**	½a. bluish green (5.09)	45·00	40·00
59		1a. red	2·50	2·00
	s.	Optd "SPECIMEN"	40·00	
45/59	Set of 11		95·00	£140

4   5

(Typo D.L.R.)

1912 (Sept)–**19**. Chalk-surfaced paper (2a. and 3a. to 5r.). Wmk Mult Crown CA. P 14.

60	**4**	½a. green (11.13)	65	13·00
	w.	Wmk inverted	15·00	65·00
61		1a. red	2·50	50
	a.	*Scarlet* (1917)	3·00	1·25
62		2a. dull and bright purple (12.13)	3·50	16·00
	a.	*Dull purple and violet-purple* (4.19)	27·00	50·00
63		2½a. bright blue (10.13)	1·00	8·50
64		3a. chocolate and grey-green (10.13)	2·25	13·00
	w.	Wmk inverted	£120	
65		4a. green and black (12.12)	2·50	10·00
66		6a. green and violet (4.13)	2·50	11·00
67		8a. grey-black and pale blue (10.13)	3·50	15·00
68		12a. grey-black and orange-buff (10.13)	3·50	21·00
69	**5**	1r. green (11.12)	23·00	27·00
70		2r. dull purple and purple (4.19)	29·00	80·00
71		3r. green and black (4.19)	85·00	£170
72		5r. black and scarlet (4.19)	95·00	£250
60/72	Set of 13		£225	£550
60s/72s Optd "SPECIMEN" Set of 13			£325	

1921. Chalk-surfaced paper (2a. and 3a. to 5r.). Wmk Mult Script CA. P 14.

73	**4**	½a. blue-green	2·75	17·00
74		1a. carmine-red	3·50	70
75		2a. dull and bright purple	4·25	1·00
76		2½a. bright blue	1·00	10·00
77		3a. chocolate and green	2·50	7·50
78		4a. green and black	2·50	16·00
79		6a. green and violet	1·50	13·00
80		8a. grey-black and pale blue	2·00	13·00
81		12a. grey-black and orange-buff	8·50	15·00
82	**5**	1r. dull green	8·50	50·00
83		2r. dull purple and purple	27·00	55·00
84		3r. dull green and black	42·00	£120
85		5r. black and scarlet	95·00	£200
73/85	Set of 13		£180	£450
73s/85s Optd "SPECIMEN" Set of 13			£300	

Examples of most values are known showing a forged Berbera postmark dated "21 OC 1932".

1935 (6 May). Silver Jubilee. As Nos. 91/4 of Antigua, but ptd by Waterlow. P 11×12.

86		1a. deep blue and scarlet	2·50	4·25
	m.	"Bird" by turret	£160	£200
87		2a. ultramarine and grey	2·75	4·25
	k.	Kite and vertical log	£150	£200
88		3a. brown and deep blue	2·50	22·00
	k.	Kite and vertical log	£180	£325
	l.	Kite and horizontal log	£180	£325
89		1r. slate and purple	10·00	26·00
	k.	Kite and vertical log	£225	£375
	l.	Kite and horizontal log	£190	£350
86/9	Set of 4		16·00	50·00
86s/9s Perf "SPECIMEN" Set of 4			£110	

For illustrations of plate varieties see Omnibus section following Zanzibar.

1937 (13 May). Coronation. As Nos. 95/7 of Antigua, but ptd by D.L.R. P 14.

90		1a. scarlet	15	50
91		2a. grey-black	55	2·00
92		3a. bright blue	1·10	1·25
90/2	Set of 3		1·60	3·25
90s/2s Perf "SPECIMEN" Set of 3			£100	

6 Berbera Blackhead Sheep   7 Greater Kudu

8 Somaliland Protectorate

(Des H. W. Claxton. Recess Waterlow)

1938 (10 May). Portrait to left. Wmk Mult Script CA. P 12½.

93	**6**	½a. green	2·50	8·50
94		1a. scarlet	1·50	3·00
95		2a. maroon	4·00	4·75
96		3a. bright blue	18·00	21·00
97	**7**	4a. sepia	6·00	15·00
98		6a. violet	16·00	12·00
99		8a. grey	8·00	15·00
100		12a. red-orange	19·00	45·00
101	**8**	1r. green	15·00	90·00
102		2r. purple	26·00	90·00
103		3r. bright blue	25·00	55·00
104		5r. black	32·00	55·00
		a. Imperf between (horiz pair)	£34000	
93/104 *Set of 12*			£150	£350
93s/104s Perf "SPECIMEN" *Set of 12*			£350	

Examples of most values are known showing a forged Berbera postmark dated "15 AU 38".

Italian forces occupied the Protectorate between 19 August 1940 and 16 March 1941. From 1 July of that year until 26 April 1942 contemporary Aden stamps and datestamps were in use.

9 Berbera Blackhead Sheep

5 Cents
(10)

1 Shilling
(11)

(Recess Waterlow)

1942 (27 Apr). As T **6/8** but with full-face portrait of King George VI, as in T **9**. Wmk Mult Script CA. P 12½.

105	**9**	½a. green	25	55
106		1a. scarlet	25	10
107		2a. maroon	70	20
108		3a. bright blue	2·25	20
109	**7**	4a. sepia	3·00	30
110		6a. violet	3·00	20
111		8a. grey	4·00	20
112		12a. red-orange	3·25	3·00
113	**8**	1r. green	3·75	3·25
114		2r. purple	6·00	11·00
115		3r. bright blue	11·00	20·00
116		5r. black	17·00	12·00
105/16 *Set of 12*			48·00	45·00
105s/16s Perf "SPECIMEN" *Set of 12*			£300	

1946 (15 Oct). Victory. As Nos. 110/11, of Antigua.

117		1a. carmine	10	10
		a. Perf 13½	14·00	50·00
118		3a. blue	10	10
117s/18s Perf "SPECIMEN" *Set of 2*			85·00	

1949 (28 Jan). Royal Silver Wedding. As Nos. 112/13 of Antigua.

119		1a. scarlet	10	10
120		5r. black	4·75	7·00

1949 (24 Oct*). 75th Anniv of U.P.U. As Nos. 114/17 of Antigua. Surch with face values in annas.

121		1a. on 10c. carmine	20	50
122		3a. on 30c. deep blue (R.)	1·25	5·50
123		6a. on 50c. purple	35	4·50
124		12a. on 1s. red-orange	90	1·75
121/4 *Set of 4*			2·40	11·00

*This is the local date of issue. The Crown Agents released these stamps in London on 10 October.

(New Currency. 100 cents = 1 shilling)

1951 (1 Apr). 1942 issue surch as T **10/11**.

125		5c. on ½a. green	40	3·25
126		10c. on 2a. maroon	40	2·00
127		15c. on 3a. bright blue	1·75	3·25
128		20c. on 4a. sepia	2·00	30
129		30c. on 6a. violet	2·00	2·75
130		50c. on 8a. grey	2·50	30
131		70c. on 12a. red-orange	4·25	12·00
132		1s. on 1r. green	2·50	2·25
133		2s. on 2r. purple (21.4.51)*	5·50	25·00
134		2s. on 3r. bright blue	17·00	12·00
135		5s. on 5r. black (R.)	25·00	16·00
125/35 *Set of 11*			55·00	70·00

*Earliest reported date.

1953 (2 June). Coronation. As No. 120 of Antigua.

136		15c. black and green	30	20

12 Camel and Gurgi

13 Sentry, Somaliland Scouts

---

14 Somali Stock Dove

15 Martial Eagle

16 Berbera Blackhead Sheep

17 Sheikh Isaaq's Tomb, Mait

18 Taleh Fort

(Recess B.W.)

1953 (15 Sept)–**58**. T **12/18**. Wmk Mult Script CA. P 12½.

137	**12**	5c. slate-black	15	60
138	**13**	10c. red-orange	2·25	1·50
		a. Salmon (20.3.58)	17·00	3·50
139	**12**	15c. blue-green	60	70
140		20c. scarlet	60	40
141	**13**	30c. reddish brown	2·25	40
142	**14**	35c. blue	5·50	1·75
143	**15**	50c. brown and rose-carmine	6·50	55
144	**16**	1s. light blue	1·25	30
145	**17**	1s.30 ultramarine and black (1.9.58)	26·00	4·25
146	**14**	2s. brown and bluish violet	28·00	7·50
147	**15**	5s. red-brown and emerald	35·00	11·00
148	**18**	10s. brown and reddish violet	32·00	45·00
137/48 *Set of 12*			£120	65·00

OPENING OF THE LEGISLATIVE COUNCIL 1957
(19)

LEGISLATIVE COUNCIL UNOFFICIAL MAJORITY, 1960
(20)

1957 (21 May). Opening of Legislative Council. Nos. 140 and 144 optd with T **19**.

149		20c. scarlet	10	15
150		1s. light blue	30	15

1960 (5 Apr). Legislative Council's Unofficial Majority. Nos. 140 arid 145 optd as T **20**.

151		20c. scarlet	50	15
152		1s.30 ultramarine and black	1·50	15

OFFICIAL STAMPS

SERVICE

BRITISH SOMALILAND
(O 1)

BRITISH SOMALILAND
(O 2)

SETTING OF TYPE O 1

The 240 impression setting used for the Official stamps differs considerably from that on the contemporary postage issue with overprint at foot, although the "BR1TISH" error can still be found on R. 6/4 of the upper pane. The Official setting is recorded as consisting of 217 overprints as Type A and 23 as Type B.

OVERPRINT VARIETIES

Figure "1" for first "I" in "BRITISH"—Occurs on R. 6/4 of the upper pane as for the postage issue.

"BRITIS H"—Occurs on R. 8/4 of the lower pane.

1903 (1 June). Nos. O45, O48, O49a and O50/1 of India (Queen Victoria optd "O.H.M.S".) additionally optd with Type O **1** in Calcutta.

O1		½a. yellow-green	7·00	55·00
		a. "BR1TISH"	£475	
		b. "BRITIS H"	£350	£850
O2		1a. carmine	15·00	18·00
		a. "BR1TISH"	£475	£550
		b. "BRITIS H"	£350	£450
O3		2a. pale violet	15·00	55·00
		a. "BR1TISH"	£650	
		b. "BRITIS H"	£500	
O4		8a. dull mauve	12·00	£475
		a. "BR1TISH"	£1700	
		b. "BRITIS H"	£1400	
		c. Stop omitted after "M" of "O.H.M.S." (lower pane R. 10/12)	£4250	
O5		1r. green and carmine	12·00	£750
		a. "BR1TISH"	£1900	
		b. "BRITIS H"	£1600	
O1/5 *Set of 5*			55·00	£1200

No. O4c was caused by an attempt to correct a minor spacing error of the "O.H.M.S." overprint which is known on the equivalent India Official stamp.

SETTING OF TYPE O 2

This 240 impression setting of "BRITISH SOMALILAND" also differs from that used to prepare the postage issue with overprint at foot, although many of the errors from the latter still occur in the same positions for the Official stamps. The setting used for Nos. O6/9f contained 180 overprints as Type A and 60 as Type B.

OVERPRINT VARIETIES

Missing second "I" in "BRITISH"—Occurs R. 7/12 of upper pane as for the postage issue.

Figure "1" for first "I" in "BRITISH"—Occurs R. 6/4 of upper pane as for the postage issue.

"SUMALILAND"—Occurs R. 2/9 of the upper pane as for the postage issue.

"SOMAL.LAND"—Occurs R. 6/7 of the lower pane as for the postage issue.

SERVICE
(O 2a)

"SERVICE" in wrong fount (Type O 2a)—Occurs R. 1/7 of lower pane.

1903. Prepared for use but not issued. Nos. 106, 122/4 and 133 of India (1r. Queen Victoria, rest King Edward VII), optd with Type O **2** in Calcutta.

O6		½a. green	40
	a.	"BRIT SH"	95·00
	b.	"BR1TISH"	85·00
	c.	"SUMALILAND"	85·00
	d.	"SOMAL.LAND"	85·00
	e.	"SERVICE" as Type O **2a**	85·00
O7		1a. carmine	40
	a.	"BRIT SH"	95·00
	b.	"BR1TISH"	85·00
	c.	"SUMALILAND"	85·00
	d.	"SOMAL.LAND"	85·00
	e.	"SERVICE" as Type O **2a**	85·00
O8		2a. violet	70
	a.	"BRIT SH"	£130
	b.	"BR1TISH"	£120
	c.	"SUMALILAND"	£120
	d.	"SERVICE" as Type O **2a**	£120
O9		8a. purple	8·00
	a.	"BRIT SH"	£3000
	b.	"BR1TISH"	£2500
	c.	"SUMALILAND"	£2500
	d.	"SERVICE" as Type O **2a**	£2500
O9f		1r. green and aniline carmine	18·00
	fa.	"BRIT SH"	£3000
	fb.	"BR1TISH"	£2500
	fc.	"SUMALILAND"	£2500
	fd.	"SOMAL.LAND"	£2500
	fe.	"SERVICE" as Type O **2a**	£2500
O6/9f *Set of 5*			25·00

Used examples of Nos. O6/9f are known, but there is no evidence that such stamps did postal duty.

O.H.M.S.
(O 3)

O.H.M.S.
(O 4)

1904 (1 Sept)–05. Stamps of Somaliland Protectorate optd with Type O **3** or O **4** (No. O15).

(a) Wmk Crown CA. P 14

O10	**2**	½a. dull green and green	11·00	48·00
		a. No stop after "M"	£300	
O11		1a. grey-black and carmine	5·00	7·00
		a. No stop after "M"	£200	£300
O12		2a. dull and bright purple	£300	70·00
		a. No stop after "M"	£3250	£900
O13		8a. grey-black and pale blue	60·00	£140
		a. No stop after "M"	£600	£950
		(b) Wmk Mult Crown CA		
O14	**2**	2a. dull and bright purple, (7.05?)	£120	£1100
		a. No stop after "M"	£2500	
		(c) Wmk Crown CC		
O15	**3**	1r. purple	£275	£1100
O10s/13s, O15s Optd "SPECIMEN" *Set of 5*			£160	

SETTING OF TYPE O 3

The anna values were overprinted in sheets of 120 (2 panes 6×10) from a setting matching the pane size. The full stop after the "M" on the fifth vertical column was either very faint or completely omitted. The prices quoted are for stamps with the stop missing; examples with a partial stop are worth much less.

The 1r. value was overprinted with type O **4** from a setting of 60.

All Somaliland Protectorate stamps were withdrawn from sale on 25 June 1960 and until the unification on 1 July, issues of Italian Somalia together with Nos. 353/5 of Republic of Somalia were used. Later issues will be found listed in the Stanley Gibbons *North East Africa Catalogue*.

Empire Philatelists

British Commonwealth and Great Britain Stamps
All Countries ~ All Reigns
1840 ~ 1970

Queen Victoria ~ King Edward VII ~ King George V ~ King George VI ~ Queen Elizabeth II

Quality mint & used, sets, singles and collections, at the most competitive prices
Browse our extensive online stock of stamps all with large high resolution images
We have thousands of items available for immediate purchase

Box Files/Cartons

- Buy one of our Commonwealth or GB Box Files
- A real treasure trove for sorting
- Probably the best value box files on the market

New Stock

Sign up to our exclusive twice a month newsletter to be the first to see new stock

Stamp Finder

Use our Stamp Finder to search all stock
- By Country
- By Reign
- By S.G. Number

Discount Code

Enter this code **EPSGC18** on checkout to recieve 10% discount off your next order

Tel: 0118 947 4114 • Email: stuart@empirephilatelists.com
• www.empirephilatelists.com • www.stores.ebay.co.uk/just-posh-art

Empire Philatelists is part of Just Posh Art Ltd
Members of Philatelic Traders Society

South Africa

South Africa as a nation, rather than a geographical term, came into being with the creation of the Union of South Africa on 31 May 1910.

The development, both political and philatelic, of the area is very complex and the method adopted by the catalogue is to first list, in alphabetical order, the various colonies and republics which formed this federation, followed by stamps for the Union of South Africa.

The section is divided as follows:

I. CAPE OF GOOD HOPE.
   British Kaffraria. Mafeking Siege Stamps. Vryburg.
II. GRIQUALAND WEST.
III. NATAL.
IV. NEW REPUBLIC.
V. ORANGE FREE STATE.
   Orange River Colony.
VI. TRANSVAAL.
   Pietersburg. Local British Occupation Issues
VII. ZULULAND.
VIII. BRITISH ARMY FIELD OFFICES
   DURING SOUTH AFRICAN WAR.
IX. UNION OF SOUTH AFRICA.
X. REPUBLIC OF SOUTH AFRICA.

I. CAPE OF GOOD HOPE

PRICES FOR STAMPS ON COVER	
Nos. 1/4	from × 4
Nos. 5/14	from × 3
Nos. 18/21	from × 5
No. 22	—
Nos. 23/6	from × 5
Nos. 27/31	from × 8
Nos. 32/3	from × 10
No. 34	from × 25
No. 35	from × 20
No. 36	from × 10
Nos. 37/8	from × 25
Nos. 39/45	from × 10
Nos. 46/7	from × 12
Nos. 48/54	from × 10
Nos. 55/6	from × 25
No. 57	from × 50
Nos. 58/69	from × 10
Nos. 70/8	from × 6

PRICES. Our prices for early Cape of Good Hope are for stamps in very fine condition. Exceptional copies are worth more, poorer copies considerably less.

1 Hope

2

(Des Charles Bell, Surveyor-General. Eng W. Humphrys. Recess P.B.)

1853 (1 Sept). W **2**. Imperf.

(a) Paper deeply blued

1	**1**	1d. pale brick-red	£4500	£450
		a. Deep brick-red	£6000	£475
		b. Wmk sideways	†	£500
2		4d. deep blue	£3500	£275
		a. Wmk sideways	£4000	£375

Plate proofs of the 4d. in a shade similar to the issued stamp exist on ungummed watermarked paper. (*Price* £550) The blueing on the reverse of these proofs is uneven giving a blotchy appearance.

(b) Paper slightly blued (blueing not pronounced at back)

3	**1**	1d. brick-red	£3500	£350
		a. Brown-red	£3750	£375
		b. Wmk sideways		£425
4		4d. deep blue	£1900	£170
		a. Blue	£2000	£200
		b. Wmk sideways	†	£375

PERKINS BACON "CANCELLED". For notes on these handstamps showing "CANCELLED" between horizontal bars forming an oval, see Catalogue Introduction.

1855–63. W **2**.

(a) Imperf.

5	**1**	1d. brick-red/cream toned paper (1857)	£5000	£900
		a. Rose (1858) (H/S "CANCELLED" in oval £20000)	£800	£300
		ab. Wmk sideways	—	£650
		b. Deep rose-red	£1200	£375
		ba. Wmk sideways		£650
6		4d. deep blue/white paper (1855)	£1400	95·00
		a. Blue (H/S "CANCELLED" in oval £20000)	£1100	90·00
		b. Bisected (on cover)	†	£35000
		c. Wmk sideways	£3500	£325

7		6d. pale rose-lilac (shades)/white paper (18.2.58) (H/S "CANCELLED" in oval £16000)	£1200	£300
		a. Wmk sideways	†	£1500
		b. Deep rose-lilac/white paper	£2250	£400
		c. Slate-lilac/blued paper (1862)	£4500	£500
		d. Slate-purple/blued paper (1863)	£4000	£1000
		e. Bisected (on cover)	†	
8		1s. bright yellow-green/white paper (18.2.58) (H/S "CANCELLED" in oval £20000)	£3500	£300
		a. Wmk sideways	†	£1500
		b. Deep dark green (1859)	£450	£550

The method adopted for producing the plate of the 4d., 6d. and 1s. stamps involved the use of two dies, so that there are two types of each of these values differing slightly in detail, but produced in equal numbers.

The 1d. value in dull rose on ungummed watermarked paper with the watermark sideways is a plate proof. (*Price* £425)

The 4d. is known bisected in 1858 and used with two other 4d. values to pay the inland registered fee. The 6d. is known bisected and used with 1d. for 4d. rate.

The paper of No. 5 is similar to that of Nos. 1/4, but without the blueing. It is much thicker than the white paper used for later printings of the 1d. The evolution of the paper on these Cape of Good Hope stamps is similar to that of the line-engraved issues of Great Britain. Examples of the 6d. slate-lilac apparently on white paper have had the blueing washed out.

The 4d. value is known printed in black on white watermarked paper. 12 authenticated copies have been recorded, the majority of which show cancellations or, at least, some indication that they have been used.

It was, at one time, believed that these stamps came from a small supply printed in black to mark the death of the Prince Consort, but references to examples can be found in the philatelic press before news of this event reached Cape Town.

It is now thought that these stamps represent proof sheets, possibly pressed into service during a shortage of stamps in 1861.

There is, however, no official confirmation of this theory. (*Price* £45000 *un*, £35000 *with obliteration*).

(b) Unofficially rouletted

9	**1**	1d. brick-red	†	£3000
10		4d. blue	†	£2250
11		6d. rose-lilac	†	£1500
12		1s. bright yellow-green	†	£3250
		a. Deep dark green	†	£3500

These rouletted stamps are best collected on cover.

3 Hope

(Local provisional (so-called "wood-block") issue. Engraved on steel by C. J. Roberts. Printed from stereotyped plates by Saul Solomon & Co, Cape Town)

1861 (Feb–Apr). Laid paper. Imperf.

13	**3**	1d. vermilion (27 Feb)	£17000	£2750
		a. Carmine (7 Mar)	£30000	£3500
		b. Brick-red (10 Apr)	£50000	£5000
		c. Error. Pale milky blue	£200000	£30000
		ca. Pale bright blue	—	£32000
14		4d. pale milky blue (23 Feb)	£25000	£2000
		aa. Retouch or repair to rt-hand corner	—	£9000
		a. Pale grey-blue (March?)	£26000	£2000
		b. Pale bright blue (March?)	£26000	£2250
		ba. Retouch or repair to rt-hand corner	—	£9000
		c. Deep bright blue (12 Apr)	£120000	£5000
		d. Blue	£32000	£3250
		e. Error. Vermilion	£200000	£40000
		ea. Carmine	—	£95000
		f. Sideways tête-bêche (pair)	†	£200000

Nos. 13/14 were each issued in *tête-bêche* pairs normally joined at edges bearing the same inscription ("POSTAGE" against "POSTAGE", etc). No. 14f, of which only one used example is known, comes from the first printing and shows the right-hand stamp misplaced so that "FOUR PENCE" adjoins "POSTAGE".

Nos. 13c/ca and 14e/ea were caused by the inclusion of incorrect clichés in the plates of the 1d. and 4d. values.

Both values were officially reprinted in March 1883, on wove paper. The 1d. is in deep red, and the 4d. in a deeper blue than that of the deepest shade of the issued stamp.

Examples of the reprints have done postal duty, but their use thus was not intended. There are no reprints of the errors or of the retouched 4d.

Further reprints were made privately but with official permission, in 1940/41, in colours much deeper than those of any of the original printings, and on thick carton paper.

Examples of the 4d. are known unofficially rouletted.

Early in 1863, Perkins Bacon Ltd handed over the four plates used for printing the triangular Cape of Good Hope stamps to De La Rue & Co, Ltd, who made all the subsequent printings.

(Printed from the P.B. plates by D.L.R.)

1863–64. Imperf.

*(a) W **2***

18	**1**	1d. deep carmine-red (1864)	£325	£325
		a. Wmk sideways	£700	£600
		b. Deep brown-red	£650	£350
		ba. Wmk sideways	£750	£400
		c. Brownish red	£650	£325
		ca. Wmk sideways	£750	£375
19		4d. deep blue (1864)	£300	£130
		a. Blue	£325	£140
		b. Slate-blue	£2500	£500
		c. Steel-blue	£2250	£275
		d. Wmk sideways	£1100	£375
20		6d. bright mauve (1864)	£425	£600
		a. Wmk sideways	†	£2500
21		1s. bright emerald-green	£650	£700
		a. Pale emerald-green	£1400	

(b) Wmk Crown CC (sideways)

22	**1**	1d. deep carmine-red	£25000	

No. 22 was a trial printing, and is only known unused.

Our prices for the 4d. blue are for stamps which are blue by comparison with the other listed shades. An exceptionally pale shade is used by specialists and is rare.

With the exception of the 4d., these stamps may be easily distinguished from those printed by Perkins Bacon by their colours, which are quite distinct.

The De La Rue stamps of all values are less clearly printed, the figure of Hope and the lettering of the inscriptions standing out less boldly, while the fine lines of the background appear blurred and broken when examined under a glass. The background as a whole often shows irregularity in the apparent depth of colour, due to wear of the plates.

For note regarding the two dies of the 4d., 6d., and 1s. values, see after No. 8.

All the triangular stamps were demonetised as from 1 October 1900.

Four Pence.

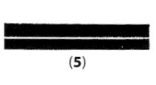

(5)

4 "Hope" seated, with vine and ram. (With outer frame-line)

(Des Charles Bell. Die engraved on steel and stamps typo by D.L.R.)

1864–77. With outer frame-line surrounding the design. Wmk Crown CC. P 14.

23	**4**	1d. carmine-red (5.65)	£130	45·00
		a. Rose-red	£130	42·00
		w. Wmk inverted	£500	£225
24		4d. pale blue (8.65)	£225	4·50
		a. Blue	£225	4·50
		b. Ultramarine	£375	55·00
		c. Deep blue (1872)	£300	4·50
		w. Wmk inverted	£750	£225
25		6d. pale lilac (before 21.3.64)	£225	28·00
		a. Deep lilac	£400	8·00
		b. Violet (to bright) (1877)	£250	1·50
		w. Wmk inverted	†	£475
		x. Wmk reversed	†	£700
26		1s. deep green (1.64)	£850	22·00
		a. Green	£250	4·75
		ax. Wmk reversed	†	£750
		b. Blue-green	£275	6·00
		w. Wmk inverted	£1000	£275

The 1d. rose-red, 6d. lilac, and 1s. blue-green are known imperf, probably from proof sheets.

The 1d. and 4d. stamps of this issue may be found with side and/or top outer frame-lines missing, due to wear of the plates.

See also Nos. 44 and 52/3.

(Surch by Saul Solomon & Co, Cape Town)

1868 (17 Nov). No. 25a surch with T **5**.

27	**4**	4d. on 6d. deep lilac (R.)	£600	18·00
		a. "Peuce" for "Pence"	£2500	£700
		b. "Fonr" for "Four"	—	£700
		w. Wmk inverted	—	£600

Examples may also be found with bars omitted or at the top of the stamp, due to misplacement of the sheet.

The space between the words and bars varies from 12½ to 16 mm, stamps with spacing 15½ and 16 mm being rare. There were two printings, one of 120,000 in November 1868 and another of 1,000,000 in December. Stamps showing widest spacings are probably from the earlier printing.

6 (No outer frame-line)

(Die re-engraved. Typo D.L.R.)

1871–76. Outer frame-line removed. Wmk Crown CC. P 14.

28	**6**	½d. grey-black (shades) (12.75)	40·00	18·00
		w. Wmk inverted	£500	£200
29		1d. carmine-red (shades) (2.72)	60·00	1·25
		w. Wmk inverted	£500	£200
30		4d. dull blue (shades) (12.76)	£225	75
		b. Ultramarine	£375	55·00
		w. Wmk inverted	£650	£160
31		5s. yellow-orange (25.8.71)	£700	25·00
		w. Wmk inverted	†	£550

The ½d., 1d. and 5s. are known imperf, probably from proof sheets.

See also Nos. 36, 39, 40/3, 48/51, 54, 61/2 and 64/8.

ONE PENNY   THREE PENCE

(7)   **(8)**

(Surch by Saul Solomon & Co, Cape Town)

1874–76. Nos. 25a and 26a surch with T **7**.

32	**4**	1d. on 6d. deep lilac (R.) (1.9.74)	£900	£140
		a. "E" of "PENNY" omitted	†	£1800
33		1d. on 1s. green (11.76)	£150	80·00

These provisionals are found with the bar only, either across the centre of the stamp or at top, with value only; or with value and bar close together, either at top or foot. Such varieties are due to misplacement of sheets during surcharging.

1879 (1 Nov). No. 30 surch with T **8**.

34	**6**	3d. on 4d. blue (R.)	£190	2·25
		a. "PENCB" for "PENCE"	£3500	£225
		b. "THE.EE" for "THREE"	£4000	£275
		c. Surch double	£13000	£4500
		d. Variety b. double		

The double surcharge must also have existed showing variety a. but only variety b. is known.

There are numerous minor varieties, including letters broken or out of alignment, due to defective printing and use of poor type.

The spacing between the bar and the words varies from 16½ to 18 mm.

THREEPENCE

 (9) **3** (10) **3** (11)

(Surch by D.L.R.)

1880 (Feb). Special printing of the 4d. in new colour, surch, with T **9**. Wmk Crown CC.
35	**6**	3d. on 4d. pale dull rose	£150	3·25
		w. Wmk inverted		£425

A minor constant variety exists with foot of "P" in "PENCE" broken off, making the letter appear shorter.

1880 (1 July). Wmk Crown CC. P 14.
36	**6**	3d. pale dull rose	£375	42·00
		w. Wmk inverted		£475

(Surch by Saul Solomon & Co, Cape Town)

1880 (Aug). No. 36 surch.
37	**10**	"3" on 3d. pale dull rose	£140	2·25
		a. Surch inverted	£1700	45·00
		b. Vert pair. Nos. 37/8	£2500	£700
		w. Wmk inverted	—	£300
38	**11**	"3" on 3d. pale dull rose	£425	12·00
		a. Surch inverted	£13000	£1600
		w. Wmk inverted	—	£750

The "3" (T **10**) is sometimes found broken. Vert pairs are known showing the two types of surcharge *se-tenant*, and vertical strips of three exist, the top stamp having surcharge T **10**, the middle stamp being without surcharge, and the lower stamp having surcharge T **11** (*Price for strip of 3 £5500 un.*).

1881 (Jan). Wmk Crown CC. P 14.
39	**6**	3d. pale claret	£250	5·00
		a. Deep claret	£190	4·50
		w. Wmk inverted		

This was a definite colour change made at the request of the Postmaster-General owing to the similarity between the colours of the 1d. stamp and the 3d. in pale dull rose. Imperf copies are probably from proof sheets.

Proofs of this value were printed in brown, on unwatermarked wove paper and imperf, but the colour was rejected as unsuitable.

1882 (July)–**83**. Wmk Crown CA. P 14.
40	**6**	½d. black (1.9.82)	48·00	3·00
		a. Grey-black	45·00	3·00
		w. Wmk inverted	—	£250
41		1d. rose-red	90·00	2·50
		a. Deep rose-red	90·00	2·50
		w. Wmk inverted	—	£275
42		2d. pale bistre (1.9.82)	£150	1·75
		a. Deep bistre	£160	1·75
		w. Wmk inverted	—	£300
43		3d. pale claret	13·00	1·75
		a. Deep claret	21·00	75
		aw. Wmk inverted	—	£200
		ax. Wmk reversed		
44	**4**	6d. mauve (to bright) (8.82)	£170	80
45	**5**	5s. orange (8.83)	£1000	£300

Imperf pairs of the ½d., 1d. and 2d. are known, probably from proof sheets.

One Half-penny.

(12) 13 "Cabled Anchor"

(Surch by Saul Solomon & Co, Cape Town)

1882 (July). Nos. 39*a* and 43*a* surch with T **12**.
46	**6**	½d. on 3d. deep claret (Wmk CC)	£5000	£180
		a. Hyphen omitted	—	£4000
47		½d. on 3d. deep claret (Wmk CA)	60·00	8·00
		a. "p" in "penny" omitted	£2500	£800
		b. "y" in "penny" omitted	£2000	£800
		c. Hyphen omitted	£900	£375
		w. Wmk inverted	—	£500

Varieties also exist with broken and defective letters, and with the obliterating bar omitted or at the top of the stamp. The surcharge particularly on No. 46. is also frequently found misplaced.

1884–90. W **13**. P 14.
48	**6**	½d. black (1.86)	12·00	10
		a. Grey-black	12·00	10
		w. Wmk inverted	—	£600
49		1d. rose-red (12.85)	16·00	10
		a. Carmine-red	16·00	10
		w. Wmk inverted	—	£300
50		2d. pale bistre (12.84)	45·00	1·75
		a. Deep bistre	16·00	10
		w. Wmk inverted	—	£250
51		4d. blue (6.90)	26·00	50
		a. Deep blue	26·00	50
52	**4**	6d. reddish purple (12.84)	65·00	1·75
		a. Purple (shades)	23·00	20
		b. Bright mauve	17·00	50
		w. Wmk inverted	—	£500
53		1s. green (12.85)	£250	8·50
		a. Blue-green (1889)	£180	1·25
		w. Wmk inverted	—	£600
54	**6**	5s. orange (7.87)	£170	9·50
48/54 Set of 7			£375	10·50

All the above stamps are known in imperf pairs, probably from proof sheets.

For later shade and colour changes, etc., see Nos. 61, etc.

2½d (14)   15 **ONE PENNY.** (16)

(Surch by D.L.R.)

1891 (Mar). Special printing of the 3d. in new colour, surch with T **14**.
55	**6**	2½d. on 3d. pale magenta	18·00	2·25
		a. Deep magenta	9·00	20
		b. "1" with horiz serif	95·00	35·00

No. 55b occurs on two stamps (Nos. 8 and 49) of the pane of 60. Two types of "d" are found in the surcharge, one with square end to serif at top, and the other with pointed serif.

1892 (June). W **13**. P 14.
56	**15**	2½d. sage-green	28·00	10
		a. Olive-green	28·00	55

See also No. 63.

(Surch by W. A. Richards & Sons, Cape Town)

1893 (Mar). Nos. 50/*a* surch with T **16**.
57	**6**	1d. on 2d. pale bistre	18·00	3·00
		a. Deep bistre	6·00	50
		b. No stop after "PENNY"	£100	27·00
		c. Surch double		£600

No. 57b occurs on R. 7/6 of the upper left-hand pane, and on R. 1/6 of the lower right-hand pane.

Minor varieties exist showing broken letters and letters out of alignment or widely spaced. Also with obliterating bar omitted, due to misplacement of the sheet during surcharging.

17 "Hope" standing. Table Bay in background

18 Table Mountain and Bay with Arms of the Colony

(Des Mr. Mountford. Typo D.L.R.)

1893 (Oct)–**1902**. W **13**. P 14.
58	**17**	½d. green (9.98)	11·00	20
59		1d. rose-red	14·00	3·00
		a. Carmine	4·25	10
		aw. Wmk inverted	†	£225
60		3d. magenta (3.02)	8·00	3·75

The 1d. is known in imperf pairs, probably from proof sheets.

1893–98. New colours, etc. W **13**. P 14.
61	**6**	½d. yellow-green (12.96)	1·50	75
		a. Green	2·75	75
62		2d. chocolate-brown (3.97)	5·00	3·75
63	**15**	2½d. pale ultramarine (3.96)	15·00	15
		a. Ultramarine	15·00	10
64	**6**	3d. bright magenta (9.98)	21·00	1·50
65		4d. sage-green (3.97)	13·00	4·25
66		1s. blue-green (12.93)	£110	9·00
		a. Deep blue-green	£150	15·00
67		1s. yellow-ochre (5.96)	21·00	3·25
		w. Wmk inverted	†	£600
68		5s. brown-orange (6.96)	£150	5·50
61/8 Set of 8			£300	25·00

(Des E. Sturman. Typo D.L.R.)

1900 (Jan). W **13**. P 14.
69	**18**	1d. carmine	9·00	10
		w. Wmk inverted	—	£250

 19   20   21

 22   23   24

 25 26   27

(Typo D.L.R.)

1902 (Dec)–**04**. W **13**. P 14.
70	**19**	½d. green	3·75	10
71	**20**	1d. carmine	3·25	10
		w. Wmk inverted		
		y. Wmk inverted and reversed		
72	**21**	2d. brown (10.04)	25·00	80
		w. Wmk inverted		
73	**22**	2½d. ultramarine (3.04)	5·50	14·00
74	**23**	3d. magenta (4.03)	18·00	1·25
75	**24**	4d. olive-green (2.03)	21·00	65
76	**25**	6d. bright mauve (3.03)	32·00	30

77	**26**	1s. yellow-ochre	18·00	1·25
78	**27**	5s. brown-orange (2.03)	£160	28·00
70/8 Set of 9			£250	42·00

All values exist in imperf pairs, from proof sheets.

The ½d. exists from coils constructed from normal sheets for use in stamp machines introduced in 1911.

STAMP BOOKLET

1905 (Dec). Black on red cover. Stapled.
SB1	2s.7d. booklet containing 30×1d. (No. 71) in blocks of 6		£3000

OFFICIAL STAMPS

The following stamps, punctured with a double triangle device, were used by the Stationery and Printed Forms Branch of the Cape of Good Hope Colonial Secretary's Department between 1904 and 1906. Later South Africa issues may have been similarly treated, but this has not been confirmed.

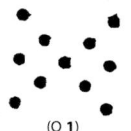

(O **1**)

1904. Various issues punctured as Type O **1**.

(a) Nos. 50 and 52a
O1	**6**	2d. pale bistre	32·00
O2	**4**	6d. purple	40·00

(b) Nos. 58 and 60
O3	**17**	½d. green	42·00
O4		3d. magenta	35·00

(c) Nos. 62 and 64/5
O5	**6**	2d. chocolate-brown	32·00
O6		3d. bright magenta	42·00
O7		4d. sage-green	42·00

(d) No. 69
O8	**18**	1d. carmine	30·00

(e) Nos. 70/2 and 74/8
O9	**19**	½d. green	42·00
O10	**20**	1d. carmine	24·00
O11	**21**	2d. brown	40·00
O12	**23**	3d. magenta	32·00
O13	**24**	4d. olive-green	35·00
O14	**25**	6d. bright mauve	38·00
O15	**26**	1s. yellow-ochre	50·00
O16	**27**	5s. brown-orange	£110

Nos. O1/16 are only known used. They are best collected on piece.

Cape of Good Hope became a province of the Union of South Africa on 31 May 1910. Stamps used during the Interprovincial Period (1 June 1910 – 31 August 1913) will be found listed under South Africa.

BRITISH KAFFRARIA

The history of the Cape eastern frontier was punctuated by a series of armed conflicts with the native population, known as the Kaffir Wars. After a particularly violent outbreak in 1846 the Governor, Sir Harry Smith, advanced the line of the Cape frontier to the Keikama and Tyumie Rivers. In the area between the new frontier and the Kei River a buffer state, British Kaffraria, was established on 17 December 1847. This area was not annexed to the Cape, but was administered as a separate Crown dependency by the Governor of Cape Colony in his capacity as High Commissioner for South Africa.

The territory, with its administration based on King William's Town, used the stamps of the Cape of Good Hope from 1853 onwards, the mail being sent via Port Elizabeth or overland from the Cape. Covers from British Kaffraria franked with the triangular issues are rare.

The first postal marking known from British Kaffraria is the 1849 type octagonal numeral No 47 from Port Beaufort. Oval post-marks of the 1853 type were used at Alice, Aliwal North, Bedford, Fort Beaufort, King William's Town and Queenstown. In 1864 numeral cancellations were issued to all post offices within the Cape system and it is known that the following numbers were initially assigned to post towns in Kaffraria: 4 (King William's Town), 7 (Bedford), 11 (Queenstown), 29 (East London), 32 (Fort Beaufort), 38 (Aliwal North) and 104 (Cathcart).

It is believed that post offices may have also existed at Adelaide, Barkly East, Sterkstoom and Stutterheim, but, to date, no examples of handstamps or cancellations are known from them during the British Kaffraria period.

Following the decimation by famine of the Xhosa tribes in 1857 British Kaffraria was annexed to Cape Colony in 1865.

MAFEKING SIEGE STAMPS

PRICES FOR STAMPS ON COVER	
Nos. 1/16	*from* × 12
Nos. 17/18	*from* × 25
Nos. 19/20	*from* × 15
Nos. 21/2	*from* × 12

23 MARCH to 17 MAY 1900

There are numerous forgeries of the Mafeking overprints, many of which were brought home by soldiers returning from the Boer War.

MAFEKING, 3d. BESIEGED. (1) **MAFEKING 3d. BESIEGED.** (2)

(Surcharged by Townsend & Co, Mafeking)

1900 (23 Mar–28 Apr). Various stamps surch as T **1** and **2**.

(a) Cape of Good Hope stamps surch as T **1** *(23 Mar)*
1	**6**	1d. on ½d. green	£325	85·00
2	**17**	1d. on ½d. green (24.3)	£375	£120

3		3d. on 1d. carmine	£325	65·00
4	**6**	6d. on 3d. magenta (24.3)	£45000	£350
5		1s. on 4d. sage-green (24.3)	£8000	£425

A variety in the setting of each value exists without comma after "MAFEKING".

*(b) Nos. 59 and 61/3 of Bechuanaland Protectorate (previously optd on Great Britain) surch as T **1***

6		1d. on ½d. vermilion (28.3)	£325	80·00
		a. Surch inverted	†	£8000
		b. Vert pair, surch tête-bêche	†	£40000
7		3d. on 1d. lilac (4.4)	£1000	£150
		a. Surch double	†	£38000
8		6d. on 2d. green and carmine (6.4)	£3000	£120
9		6d. on 3d. purple/yellow (30.3)	£7500	£425
		a. Surch inverted	†	£42000
		b. Surch double		

*(c) Nos. 12, 35 and 37 of British Bechuanaland (4d. and 1s. previously optd on Great Britain) surch as T **1***

10		6d. on 3d. lilac and black (27.3)	£550	95·00
11		1s. on 4d. green and purple-brown (29.3)	£1600	£110
		a. Surch double (both Type **1**)	†	£30000
		ab. Surch double (Type **1** and Type **2**)	£14000	£8000
		b. Surch treble	†	£30000
		c. Surch double, one inverted	†	£30000
11d		2s. on 1s. green	†	£38000

*(d) Nos. 61/2 and 65 of Bechuanaland Protectorate (previously optd on Great Britain) surch as T **2***

12		3d. on 1d. lilac (1.4)	£1100	£100
		a. Surch double	†	£11000
13		6d. on 2d. green and carmine (1.4)	£1600	£100
14		1s. on 6d. purple/rose-red (12.4)	£7500	£130

*(e) Nos. 36/7 of British Bechuanaland (previously optd on Great Britain) surch as T **2***

15		1s. on 6d. purple/rose-red (28.4)	£35000	£850
16		2s. on 1s. green (13.4)	£7500	£650

On the stamps overprinted "BECHUANALAND PROTECTORATE" and "BRITISH BECHUANALAND" the local surcharge is so adjusted as not to overlap the original overprint.

3 Cadet Sergt.-Major Goodyear	**4** General Baden-Powell

(Des Dr. W. A. Hayes (T **3**), Capt. H. Greener (T **4**))

1900 (6–10 Apr). Produced photographically by Dr. D. Taylor. Horiz laid paper with sheet wmk "OCEANA FINE". P 12.

(a) 18½ mm wide. (b) 21 mm wide

17	**3**	1d. pale blue/blue (7.4)	£1200	£325
18		1d. deep blue/blue	£1200	£325
19	**4**	3d. pale blue/blue (a)	£1700	£475
		a. Reversed design	£100000	£55000
20		3d. deep blue/blue (a)	£1700	£425
		a. Imperf between (horiz pair)	†	£100000
		b. Double print	†	£25000
21		3d. pale blue/blue (b) (10.4)	£12000	£1200
		a. Vert laid paper	£20000	£6000
22		3d. deep blue/blue (b) (10.4)	£14000	£1400

These stamps vary a great deal in colour from deep blue to pale grey.

No. 18 imperforate and without gum is believed to be a proof (*Price for unused pair £25000*).

No. 19a comes from a sheet of 12 printed in reverse of which ten, three mint and seven used, are known to have survived.

VRYBURG

PRICES FOR STAMPS ON COVER	
Nos. 1/4	from × 5
Nos. 11/12	from × 2

BOER OCCUPATION

Vryburg was occupied by Boer forces on 15 October 1899. Unoverprinted stamps of Transvaal were used initially. Nos. 1/4 were only available from 25 to 29 November. The Boers evacuated the town on 7 May 1900.

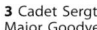

½ PENCE

Z.A.R.

(1)

1899 (25 Nov). Cape stamps surch as T **1** at the offices of *De Stellalander*. Surch 12.5 mm high on No. 3 and 10.5 mm on all other values.

1	**6**	½ PENCE green	£225	80·00
		a. Italic "Z"	£2250	£800
		b. Surch 12.5 mm high	£2250	£800
2	**17**	1 PENCE rose	£250	£100
		a. Italic "Z"	£2500	£900
		b. Surch 12.5 mm high	£2500	£900
		c. "I" for "1"	£1600	£550
3	**4**	2 PENCE on 6d. mauve	£2000	£500
		a. Italic "Z"	£15000	£4500
4	**15**	2½ PENCE on 2½d. blue	£1700	£425
		a. Italic "Z"	£15000	£4500
		b. Surch 12.5 mm high	£15000	£4500

On the "2 PENCE" on 6d. the space between the lines of the surcharge is 7.3 mm. It is possible that this was the first value surcharged, as the remaining three show the space reduced to 5.3 mm, with the exception of R. 4/2 which remained at 7.3 mm. The "Italic 'Z'" variety occurs on R. 3/6 of the setting of 60.

Nos. 1-4 were subsequently declared valid for postage within Transvaal.

BRITISH REOCCUPATION

V.R.
SPECIAL
POST

(2)

1900 (16 May). Provisionals issued by the Military Authorities. Stamps of Transvaal handstamped with T **2**.

11	**30**	½d. green	—	£3500
11a		1d. rose-red (No. 206)		
12		1d. rose-red and green (No. 217)	£14000	£6000
13		2d. brown and green	†	£48000
14		2½d. dull blue and green	†	£48000

No. 11 is known used with double handstamp and Nos. 11/12 with the overprint reading downwards.

II. GRIQUALAND WEST

Griqualand West was situated to the North of Cape Colony, bounded on the north by what became British Bechuanaland and on the east by the Orange Free State.

The area was settled in the early 19th-century by the Griqua tribal group, although many members of the tribe, including the paramount chief, migrated to Griqualand East (between Basutoland and the east coast of South Africa) in 1861–63. There was little European involvement in Griqualand West before 1866, but in that year the diamond fields along the Vaal River were discovered. Sovereignty was subsequently claimed by the Griqua Chief, the Orange Free State and the South African Republic (Transvaal). In 1871 the British authorities arbitrated in favour of the Griqua Chief who promptly ceded his territory to Great Britain. Griqualand West became a separate Crown Colony in January 1873.

During the initial stages of the prospecting boom, mail was passed via the Orange Free State, but a post office connected to the Cape Colony postal system was opened at Klip Drift (subsequently Barkly) in late 1870. Further offices at De Beer's New Rush (subsequently Kimberley), Douglas and Du Toit's Pan (subsequently Beaconsfield) were open by September 1873.

Cape of Good Hope stamps to the 5s. value were in use from October 1871, but those originating in Griqualand West can only be identified after the introduction of Barred Oval Diamond Numeral cancellations in 1873. Numbers known to have been issued in the territory are:

1 De Beers N.R. (New Rush) (subsequently Kimberley)
3 Junction R. & M. (Riet and Modder Rivers)
4 Barkly
6 or 9 Du Toit's Pan (subsequently Beaconsfield)
8 Langford (transferred to Douglas)
10 Thornhill

PRICES FOR STAMPS ON COVER. The stamps of Griqualand West are worth from ×10 the price quoted for used stamps, when on cover from the territory.

FORGED OVERPRINTS. Many stamps show forged overprints. Great care should be taken when purchasing the scarcer items.

Stamps of the Cape of Good Hope, Crown CC, perf 14, overprinted.

1d

(1)

1874 (Sept). No. 24a of Cape of Good Hope surch "1d." in red manuscript as Type **1** by the Kimberley postmaster.

1		1d. on 4d. blue	£1800	£2500

G. W.

(1aa)

1877 (1 Mar). Nos. 29/30 of Cape of Good Hope optd with T **1aa**.

2		1d. carmine-red	£750	£110
		a. Opt double	†	£3000
3		4d. dull blue (R.)	£400	80·00
		w. Wmk inverted	£1300	£275

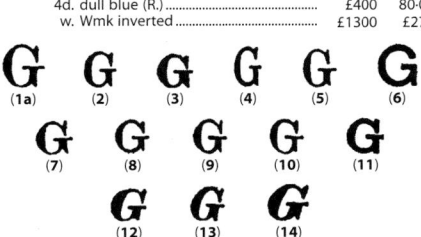

G (1a)	**G** (2)	**G** (3)	**G** (4)	**G** (5)	**G** (6)
G (7)	**G** (8)	**G** (9)	**G** (10)	**G** (11)	
G (12)	**G** (13)	**G** (14)			

1877 (Mar)–78. Nos. 24a, 25a, 26a and 28/31 Cape of Good Hope optd with capital "G".

*(a) First printing. Optd with T **1a/6** and **8** in black (1d.) or red (others)*

4		½d. grey-black		
		a. Opt Type **1a**	42·00	45·00
		b. Opt Type **2**	£100	£120
		c. Opt Type **3**	60·00	70·00
		d. Opt Type **4**	£100	£120
		e. Opt Type **5**	£110	£130
		f. Opt Type **6**	55·00	60·00
		g. Opt Type **8**	†	£800
5		1d. carmine-red		
		a. Opt Type **1a**	42·00	28·00
		b. Opt Type **2**	£110	65·00
		c. Opt Type **3**	60·00	40·00
		d. Opt Type **4**	£110	65·00
		e. Opt Type **5**	£120	80·00
		f. Opt Type **6**	42·00	28·00

		g. Opt Type **8**		*
6		4d. blue (with frame-line) (No. 24a)		
		a. Opt Type **1a**	£450	70·00
		b. Opt Type **2**	£1100	£180
		c. Opt Type **3**	£750	£100
		d. Opt Type **4**	£1100	£180
		e. Opt Type **5**	£1200	£225
		f. Opt Type **6**	£550	90·00
		g. Opt Type **8**	£3500	£950
7		4d. dull blue (without frame-line) (No. 30)		
		a. Opt Type **1a**	£400	48·00
		b. Opt Type **2**	£850	£140
		c. Opt Type **3**	£550	70·00
		d. Opt Type **4**	£850	£140
		e. Opt Type **5**	£900	£160
		f. Opt Type **6**	£500	60·00
		g. Opt Type **8**	£3250	£750
8		6d. deep lilac		
		a. Opt Type **1a**	£300	55·00
		b. Opt Type **2**	£600	£150
		c. Opt Type **3**	£400	75·00
		cw. Wmk inverted	†	£550
		d. Opt Type **4**	£600	£150
		e. Opt Type **5**	£700	£170
		f. Opt Type **6**	£375	75·00
		g. Opt Type **8**	£3000	£900
9		1s. green		
		a. Opt Type **1a**	£350	45·00
		ab. Opt inverted	—	£950
		b. Opt Type **2**	£750	£110
		ba. Opt inverted	—	£1500
		c. Opt Type **3**	£550	60·00
		d. Opt Type **4**	£750	£110
		da. Opt inverted	—	£1500
		e. Opt Type **5**	£850	£140
		f. Opt Type **6**	£500	55·00
		fa. Opt inverted	—	£1100
		g. Opt Type **8**	£4500	£900
10		5s. yellow-orange		
		a. Opt Type **1a**	£1100	55·00
		b. Opt Type **2**	£1800	£130
		c. Opt Type **3**	£1500	75·00
		cw. Wmk inverted	†	£1200
		d. Opt Type **4**	£1800	£130
		dw. Wmk inverted	†	£1700
		e. Opt Type **5**	£2750	£160
		f. Opt Type **6**	£1400	65·00
		fw. Wmk inverted	†	£1300
		g. Opt Type **8**	£4500	£1000

*The 1d. with overprint Type **8** from this setting can only be distinguished from that of the second printing when *se-tenant* with overprint Type **3**.

Nos. 4/10 were overprinted by a setting of 120 covering two panes of 60 (6×10). This setting contained 41 examples of Type **1a**, ten of Type **2**, 23 of Type **3**, ten of Type **4**, eight of Type **5**, 27 of Type **6** and one of Type **8**. Sub-types of Types **1a** and **2** exist. The single example of Type **8** occurs on R. 7/4 of the right-hand pane.

It is believed that there may have been an additional setting used for the 5s. which was in considerable demand to cover the postage and registration on diamond consignments. It is also possible that single panes of this value and of the 1s. were overprinted using the right-hand half of the normal 120 setting.

*(b) Second printing. Optd with T **6/14** in black (1878)*

11		1d. carmine-red		
		a. Opt Type **6**		*
		b. Opt Type **7**	48·00	30·00
		c. Opt Type **8**	£110	52·00
		d. Opt Type **9**	55·00	32·00
		e. Opt Type **10**	£140	90·00
		f. Opt Type **11**	£120	70·00
		g. Opt Type **12**	£120	80·00
		h. Opt Type **13**	£190	£130
		i. Opt Type **14**	£600	£400
12		4d. dull blue (without frame-line) (No. 30)		
		a. Opt Type **6**	£600	95·00
		b. Opt Type **7**	£275	45·00
		c. Opt Type **8**	£550	85·00
		d. Opt Type **9**	£300	45·00
		e. Opt Type **10**	£700	£110
		f. Opt Type **11**	£600	£100
		g. Opt Type **12**	£600	£100
		h. Opt Type **13**	£950	£180
		i. Opt Type **14**	£2750	£600
13		6d. deep lilac		
		a. Opt Type **6**	£850	£140
		b. Opt Type **7**	£450	80·00
		ba. Opt double		
		c. Opt Type **8**	£800	£130
		d. Opt Type **9**	£500	90·00
		da. Opt double	—	£1500
		e. Opt Type **10**	£950	£180
		ea. Opt double	—	£1600
		f. Opt Type **11**	£850	£150
		g. Opt Type **12**	£850	£150
		h. Opt Type **13**	£1300	£275
		i. Opt Type **14**	£3500	£850

*The 1d. with overprint Type **6** from this setting can only be distinguished from that of the first printing when *se-tenant* with Types **11**, **12** or **13**.

Nos. 11/13 were overprinted by another double-pane setting of 120 in which only Types **6** and **8** were repeated from that used for the first printing. The second printing setting contained 12 examples of Type **6**, 30 of Type **7**, 13 of Type **8**, 27 of Type **9**, nine of Type **10**, 11 of Type **11**, 11 of Type **12**, six of Type **13** and one of Type **14**. Sub-types of Types **7** and **12** exist.

G (15)	**G** (16)	**G** (17)

1878 (June). Nos. 24a, 25a and 28/30 of Cape of Good Hope optd with small capital "G", T **15/16**.

14	**15**	½d. grey-black (R.)	27·00	27·00
		a. Opt inverted	29·00	29·00
		b. Opt double	80·00	95·00
		c. Opt double, both inverted	£160	£180
		d. Black opt	£350	£180
		da. Opt inverted	£375	
		db. Opt double, one inverted in red	£600	

		dc. Opt double, one inverted (Type **16**) in red	£325	
15	**16**	½d. grey-black (R.)	28·00	28·00
		a. Opt inverted	28·00	29·00
		b. Opt double	£130	£130
		c. Opt double, both inverted	£100	£120
		d. Black opt	80·00	80·00
		da. Opt inverted	£170	£120
		db. Opt double, one inverted (Type **15**) in red	£325	
16	**15**	1d. carmine-red	28·00	19·00
		a. Opt inverted	28·00	28·00
		b. Opt double	£350	85·00
		c. Opt double, both inverted	£350	£110
		d. Opt double, both inverted with one in red	£100	£100
		e. Opt double, both inverted with one (Type **16**) in red	28·00	20·00
17	**16**	1d. carmine-red	28·00	20·00
		a. Opt inverted	£140	48·00
		b. Opt double	—	£150
		c. Opt double, both inverted	—	£180
		d. Opt double, both inverted with one in red	£180	£180
18	**15**	4d. blue (with frame-line) (No. 24a)	—	£275
19	**16**	4d. blue (with frame-line) (No. 24a)	—	£275
20	**15**	4d. dull blue (without frame-line) (No. 30)	£250	48·00
		a. Opt inverted	£400	£140
		b. Opt double	—	£375
		c. Opt double, both inverted	—	£450
		d. Red opt	£600	£160
		da. Opt inverted	£650	£130
21	**16**	4d. dull blue (without frame-line) (No. 30)	£275	26·00
		a. Opt inverted	£425	48·00
		b. Opt double	—	£350
		c. Opt double, both inverted	—	£425
		d. Red opt	—	£140
		da. Opt inverted	£600	£140
22	**15**	6d. deep lilac	£275	48·00
23	**16**	6d. deep lilac	£275	48·00

Nos. 14/23 were also overprinted using a double-pane setting of 120. Based on evidence from surviving ½d. and 1d. sheets all overprints in the left-hand pane were roman, Type **15**, and all those in the right-hand pane italic, Type **16**, except for R. 1/6, 4/5, 6/6, 7/6, 8/6, 9/6 and 10/6 which were Type **15**. There is considerable evidence to suggest that after the ½d. value had been overprinted the setting was amended to show a Type **15**, instead of a Type **16**, on R. 10/5 of the right-hand pane. Two strikes of the setting were required to overprint the sheets of 240 and it would appear that on many sheets the bottom two panes had the overprints inverted.

1879. Nos. 25b, 26b and 28/31 of Cape of Good Hope optd with small capital "G", T **17**.

24		½d. grey-black	32·00	11·00
		a. Opt double	£500	£325
25		1d. carmine-red	35·00	8·50
		a. Opt inverted	—	£110
		b. Opt double	—	£160
		c. Opt treble	—	£300
		w. Wmk inverted	†	£450
26		4d. dull blue	65·00	8·50
		a. Opt double	—	£140
27		6d. violet	£275	14·00
		a. Opt inverted	—	60·00
		b. Opt double	£1100	£200
28		1s. green	£250	9·00
		a. Opt double	£600	£130
29		5s. yellow-orange	£800	26·00
		a. Opt double	£1000	£130
		b. Opt treble	—	£400

Nos. 24/9 were also overprinted using a setting of 120 which contained a number of minor type varieties.

Griqualand West was merged with Cape Colony in October 1880. The remaining stock of the overprinted stamps was returned from Kimberley to Cape Town and redistributed among various post offices in Cape Colony where they were used as ordinary Cape stamps.

III. NATAL

PRICES FOR STAMPS ON COVER

No.	
No. 1	from × 2
Nos. 2/3	from × 3
Nos. 4/7	from × 2
Nos. 9/25	from × 3
Nos. 26/49	from × 5
Nos. 50/6	from × 4
No. 57	
No. 58	from × 10
Nos. 59/60	from × 5
Nos. 61/3	from × 8
No. 65	from × 10
Nos. 66/70	from × 8
Nos. 71/3	
Nos. 76/82	from × 6
Nos. 83/4	from × 5
Nos. 85/90	from × 5
Nos. 96/103	from × 6
Nos. 104/5	from × 10
Nos. 106/7	from × 6
No. 108	from × 50
Nos. 109/25	from × 6
Nos. 127/42	from × 4
Nos. 143/5b	
Nos. 146/57	from × 4
No. 162	—
Nos. 165/71	from × 3
No. F1	—
Nos. O1/6	from × 10

(Embossed in plain relief on coloured wove paper by May and Davis, Pietermaritzburg)

1857 (26 May)–**61.** Imperf.

1	**1**	1d. blue (9.59)	—	£1200
2		1d. rose (1861)	—	£1900
3		1d. buff (1861)	—	£1400
4	**2**	3d. rose	—	£400
		a. *Tête-bêche* (pair)	—	£50000
5	**3**	6d. green	—	£1100
		a. Bisected (3d.) (on cover)	†	£15000
6	**4**	9d. blue	—	£7500
7	**5**	1s. buff	—	£5500

All the above have been reprinted more than once, and the early reprints of some values cannot always be distinguished with certainty from originals.

For the 1d. stamp on yellow surfaced paper, perf 12½, see No. F1. Stamps on surface-coloured paper with higher face values and perforated 12½ are fiscals.

NOTE. The value of the above stamps depends on their dimensions, and the clearness of the embossing, but our prices are for fine used.

It should be noted that, at the time they were current, only Pietermaritzburg, Ladysmith and Durban were supplied with handstamps. Stamps used in other offices were usually cancelled in manuscript.

PERKINS BACON "CANCELLED". For notes on these handstamps showing "CANCELLED" between horizontal bars forming an oval, see Catalogue Introduction.

6   **7**

(Eng C. H. Jeens. Recess P.B.)

1859–60. No wmk. P 14.

9	**6**	1d. rose-red (1860) (H/S "CANCELLED" in oval £13000)	£180	85·00
10		3d. blue	£225	55·00
		a. Imperf between (vert pair)	†	£13000

No. 10a is only known from a cover of 1867 franked with two such pairs.

The 3d. also exists with "CANCELLED" in oval, but no examples are believed to be in private hands.

1861. No wmk. Intermediate perf 14 to 16.

11	**6**	3d. blue	£350	65·00

1861–62. No wmk. Rough perf 14 to 16.

12	**6**	3d. blue	£170	40·00
		a. Imperf between (horiz pair)	£6000	
13		6d. grey (3.62)	£275	70·00

1862. Wmk Small Star. Rough perf 14 to 16.

15	**6**	1d. rose-red	£170	65·00

The 1d. without watermark and the 3d. watermark Small Star, both imperforate, are proofs.

(Recess D.L.R.)

1863. Thick paper. No wmk. P 13.

18	**6**	1d. lake	£130	29·00
19		1d. carmine-red	£130	29·00

Nos. 18/19 were printed on paper showing a papermakers watermark of "TH SAUNDERS 1862", parts of which can be found on individual stamps. Examples are rare and command a premium.

1863–65. Wmk Crown CC. P 12½.

20	**6**	1d. brown-red	£190	48·00
		y. Wmk inverted and reversed	—	£160
21		1d. rose	£130	38·00
		w. Wmk inverted	†	£170
		x. Wmk reversed	£130	38·00
		y. Wmk inverted and reversed	†	£160
22		1d. bright red	£140	45·00
		x. Wmk reversed	£140	45·00
23		6d. lilac	£120	17·00
		w. Wmk inverted	£600	
		y. Wmk inverted and reversed		
24		6d. violet	90·00	35·00
		w. Wmk inverted	£400	
		x. Wmk reversed	90·00	35·00

The 1d. stamp in yellow and the 6d. in rose are both fiscals.

(Typo D.L.R.)

1867 (Apr). Wmk Crown CC. P 14.

25	**7**	1s. green	£250	50·00
		w. Wmk inverted	†	£400

Stamps as T **7** in purple-brown or deep blue are fiscals.

POSTAGE (7a)   **Postage.** (7b)   **Postage.** (7c)

Postage. (7d)   **POSTAGE.** (7e)

1869 (23 Aug). Optd horiz in Natal. No opt (3d.), wmk Crown CC (others). P 14 or 14–16 (3d.), 12½ (1d., 6d) or 14 (1s.).

(a) With T **7a** *(tall capitals without stop)*

26	**6**	1d. rose	£650	£120
		x. Wmk reversed	£600	£110
27		1d. bright red	£550	£110
		x. Wmk reversed	—	£100
28		3d. blue (No. 10)	£4000	£900
28a		3d. blue (No. 11)	£1200	£375
28b		3d. blue (No. 12)	£800	£120
29		6d. lilac	£850	£100
30		6d. violet	£800	£120
		x. Wmk reversed	£800	£120
31	**7**	1s. green	£35000	£1800

(b) With T **7b** *(12¾ mm long)*

32	**6**	1d. rose	£550	£110
		w. Wmk inverted	†	£400
		x. Wmk reversed	—	£100
33		1d. bright red	£500	95·00
		x. Wmk reversed	£475	90·00
34		3d. blue (No. 10)	—	£700
34a		3d. blue (No. 11)	£1000	£325
34b		3d. blue (No. 12)	£700	£110
35		6d. lilac	£750	85·00
36		6d. violet	£650	£110
		x. Wmk reversed	£650	£100
37	**7**	1s. green	£29000	£1900

(c) With T **7c** *(13¾ mm long)*

38	**6**	1d. rose	£1200	£300
39		1d. bright red	£1200	£275
		x. Wmk reversed	—	£250
40		3d. blue (No. 10)		
40a		3d. blue (No. 11)	—	£1000
40b		3d. blue (No. 12)	£2750	£500
41		6d. lilac	£2750	£225
42		6d. violet	£2500	£225
		x. Wmk reversed	—	£225
43	**7**	1s. green	—	£3000

(d) With T **7d** *(14½ to 15½ mm long)*

44	**6**	1d. rose	£1000	£225
		x. Wmk reversed	£1000	
45		1d. bright red	£1000	£190
		x. Wmk reversed	£1000	£190
46		3d. blue (No. 10)	†	
46a		3d. blue (No. 11)	—	£750
46b		3d. blue (No. 12)	—	£425
47		6d. lilac	—	£150
48		6d. violet	£2000	£140
		x. Wmk reversed	£2000	£140
49	**7**	1s. green	£29000	£2500

(e) With T **7e** *(small capitals with stop)*

50	**6**	1d. rose	£150	50·00
		x. Wmk reversed	£150	50·00
		y. Wmk inverted and reversed	†	£250
51		1d. bright red	£200	50·00
		x. Wmk reversed	£200	50·00
52		3d. blue (No. 10)	£400	85·00
53		3d. blue (No. 11)	£225	50·00
54		3d. blue (No. 12)	£250	50·00
		a. Opt double	†	£1600
54b		6d. lilac	£275	85·00
55		6d. violet	£200	70·00
		x. Wmk reversed	£200	70·00
56	**7**	1s. green	£350	80·00

There were two settings of these overprints. The first setting, probably of 240, contained 60 examples of Type **7a**, 72 of Type **7b**, 20 of Type **7c**, 28 of Type **7d** and 60 of Type **7e**. The second, probably of 60 (6×10), contained Type **7e** only.

In the first setting the overprint is in the bottom half of the stamp on the 1d. and 1s. and in the top half on the 3d. and 6d. In the second setting the overprints were at the top of the 1d. and 1s. and at the bottom of the 3d. and 6d. Prices for Nos. 50/6 are for stamps from the second setting.

A single used example of No. 33 with overprint double is in the Royal Philatelic Collection.

(8)

1870. No. 25 optd with T **8** by De La Rue.

57	**7**	1s. green (C.)	†	£8500
58		1s. green (Blk.)	†	£1600
		a. Opt double	†	£3500
59		1s. green (G.)	£150	10·00

For 1s. orange, see No. 108.

POSTAGE (9)   **POSTAGE** (10)   **POSTAGE** (11)

1870–73. Optd with T **9** by De La Rue. Wmk Crown CC. P 12½.

60	**6**	1d. bright red	£120	13·00
		w. Wmk inverted	†	£250
		x. Wmk reversed	£120	13·00
61		3d. bright blue (R.) (1872)	£130	13·00
		x. Wmk reversed	£130	13·00
62		6d. mauve (1873)	£250	45·00
		x. Wmk reversed	£300	

1873 (July). Fiscal stamp optd locally with T **10**. Wmk Crown CC. P 14.

63	**7**	1s. purple-brown	£425	35·00
		w. Wmk inverted	—	£450

1874 (Apr). No. 21 optd locally with T **11**.

65	**6**	1d. rose	£375	85·00
		w. Wmk inverted		
		x. Wmk reversed		85·00

Two examples of No. 65 with overprint double are known. Both are in permanent museum collections.

12	**13**	**14**

15	**16**

(Typo D.L.R.)

1874 (Jan)–**99**. Wmk Crown CC (sideways on 5s.). P 14.

66	**12**	1d. dull rose	60·00	8·50
67		1d. bright rose	60·00	8·50
68	**13**	3d. blue	£190	42·00
		a. Perf 14×12½	£2500	£1100
69	**14**	4d. brown (1878)	£200	19·00
		aw. Wmk inverted	£550	£180
		b. Perf 12½	£375	70·00
70	**15**	6d. bright reddish violet	£110	7·50
		w. Wmk inverted	†	£250
71	**16**	5s. maroon (1882)	£400	£110
		a. Perf 15½×15 (1874)	£475	£110
72		5s. rose	£140	45·00
73		5s. carmine (1899)	£110	38·00
		s. Handstamped "*SPECIMEN*"	£225	

POSTAGE **POSTAGE** **½ HALF**
  (17)   (18)   (19)

1875–76. Wmk Crown CC. P 14 (1s.) or 12½ (others).

(a) Optd locally with T **17**

76	**6**	1d. rose	£170	65·00
		a. Opt double	£1800	£600
		x. Wmk reversed	£170	65·00
77		1d. bright red	£160	75·00
		x. Wmk reversed	£160	75·00

(b) Optd by Davis and Sons with T **18** *(14½ mm long, without stop)*

81	**6**	1d. rose (1876)	£130	80·00
		a. Opt inverted	£2000	£500
		w. Wmk inverted		
		x. Wmk reversed	£130	80·00
		y. Wmk inverted and reversed		
82		1d. yellow (1876)	90·00	90·00
		a. Opt double, one albino	£250	
		x. Wmk reversed	95·00	95·00
83		6d. violet (1876)	85·00	8·00
		a. Opt double	†	£950
		b. Opt inverted	£750	£150
		w. Wmk inverted	—	£160
		x. Wmk reversed	85·00	8·00
		y. Wmk inverted and reversed	†	£190
84	**7**	1s. green (1876)	£140	7·50
		a. Opt double	†	£325

TYPE 19. There are several varieties of this surcharge, of which T **19** is an example. They may be divided as follows:

(a) "½" 4½ mm high, "2" has straight foot.
(b) As last but "½" is 4 mm high.
(c) As last but "2" has curled foot.
(d) "½" 3½ mm. high, "2" has straight foot.
(e) As last but "2" has curled foot.
(f) As last but "2" smaller.

As the "½" and "HALF" were overprinted separately, they vary in relative position, and are frequently overlapping.

1877 (13 Feb). No. 66 surch locally as T **19**.

85	**12**	½d. on 1d. rose (a)	45·00	75·00
86		½d. on 1d. rose (b)	£170	
87		½d. on 1d. rose (c)	£150	
88		½d. on 1d. rose (d)	85·00	£120
89		½d. on 1d. rose (e)	90·00	
90		½d. on 1d. rose (f)	£100	

The Royal Philatelic Collection contains a single example of No. 85 with "½" double.

POSTAGE

Half-penny

(21)	**23**	(24)

ONE HALF-PENNY.

1877 (7 Oct)–**79**. T **6** (wmk Crown CC. P 12½) surch locally as T **21**.

91		½d. on 1d. yellow	13·00	25·00
		a. Surch inverted	£375	£225
		b. Surch double	£375	£200

---

	c. Surch omitted (lower stamp, vertical pair)	£4250	£2750
	d. "POSTAGE" omitted (in pair with normal)	£2250	
	e. "S" of "POSTAGE" omitted (R. 8/3)	£325	£225
	f. "T" of "POSTAGE" omitted	£325	£300
	x. Wmk reversed	13·00	25·00
	y. Wmk inverted and reversed	£110	
92	1d. on 6d. violet (10.10.77)	75·00	11·00
	a. "S" of "POSTAGE" omitted (R. 8/3)	£600	£150
	x. Wmk reversed	—	11·00
93	1d. on 6d. rose (12.2.79)	£140	55·00
	a. Surch inverted	£1700	£600
	b. Surch double	†	£325
	c. Surch double, one inverted	£375	£200
	d. Surch four times	£500	£275
	e. "S" of "POSTAGE" omitted (R. 8/3)	£950	£375
	x. Wmk reversed	—	55·00

No. 93c. is known with one surcharge showing variety "S" of "POSTAGE" omitted.

Other minor varieties exist in these surcharges.

Nos. 94 and 95 are vacant.

(Typo D.L.R.)

1880 (13 Oct). Wmk Crown CC. P 14.

96	**23**	½d. blue-green	29·00	38·00
		a. Imperf between (vert pair)		

1882 (20 Apr)–**89.** Wmk Crown CA. P 14.

97	**23**	½d. blue-green (23.4.84)	£100	21·00
		a. Dull green (10.4.85)	6·50	1·25
		aw. Wmk inverted	£350	£225
99	**12**	1d. rose (shades) (17.12.83*)	8·00	25
		a. Carmine	8·00	35
		w. Wmk inverted	†	£200
100	**13**	3d. blue (23.4.84)	£160	17·00
101		3d. grey (11.89)	12·00	5·50
		w. Wmk inverted	†	£300
102	**14**	4d. brown	17·00	1·75
103	**15**	6d. mauve	14·00	2·50
		w. Wmk inverted	†	£180
97a/103 Set of 6			£190	25·00
97s, 99s, 101s/3s H/S "*SPECIMEN*" Set of 5			£350	

*Earliest recorded date.

1885 (26 Jan). No. 99 surch locally with T **24**.

104	**12**	½d. on 1d. rose	24·00	15·00
		a. No hyphen after "HALF"	£120	55·00

TWO PENCE (25)

26

TWOPENCE HALFPENNY (27)

1886 (7 Jan). No. 101 surch with T **25** by D.L.R.

105	**13**	2d. on 3d. grey	40·00	5·50

(Typo D.L.R.)

1887 (Sept)–**89.** Wmk Crown CA. P 14.

106	**26**	2d. olive-green (Die I)	55·00	2·25
		a. Top left triangle detached	£650	£250
		s. Optd "*SPECIMEN*"	£100	
		x. Wmk reversed	†	£350
107		2d. olive-green (Die II) (1889)	5·50	1·40
		s. Handstamped "*SPECIMEN*"	80·00	

The differences between Dies I and II are shown in the introduction. For illustration of "top left triangle detached" variety see above No. 21 of Antigua.

1888 (16 Mar). As No. 25, but colour changed and wmk Crown CA, optd with T **8** by D.L.R.

108	**7**	1s. orange (C.)	13·00	1·75
		a. Opt double	†	£2750
		s. Handstamped "*SPECIMEN*"	£120	

1891 (22 Apr). Surch locally with T **27**.

109	**14**	2½d. on 4d. brown	16·00	18·00
		a. "TWOPENGE"	70·00	
		b. "HALFPENN"	£300	£275
		c. Surch double	£375	£325
		d. Surch inverted	£550	£450
		e. Vert pair, one normal, one surch double	£650	£650
		f. Surch tête-bêche (vert pair)	£2000	£2000
		s. Handstamped "*SPECIMEN*"	75·00	

The overprint setting comprised two rows of six stamps and was applied five times to each pane of 60. The "TWOPENGE" variety occurred on stamp 10 of the setting. The "HALFPENN" variety was not present on all sheets, its position is unknown.

POSTAGE.

2½d (28)

·Half-Penny (29)

POSTAGE.
Varieties of long-tailed letters

(Typo D.L.R.)

1891 (June). Wmk Crown CA. P 14.

113	**28**	2½d. bright blue	12·00	1·50
		s. Handstamped "*SPECIMEN*"	75·00	

1895 (12 Mar). No. 24 surch locally with T **29** in carmine.

114		½d. on 6d. violet	3·00	9·50
		a. "Ealf-Penny"	26·00	70·00
		b. "Half-Penny" and long "P"	26·00	70·00
		ba. "Half Penny" and long "T" and "A"	26·00	70·00
		c. No stop after "POSTAGE" and long "P", "T" and "A"	26·00	70·00
		d. Long "P"	3·25	12·00
		e. Long "T"	3·25	12·00
		f. Long "A"	4·00	14·00

---

	g. Long "P" and "T"	3·25	12·00
	h. Long "P" and "A"	3·25	12·00
	i. Long "T" and "A"	3·75	13·00
	k. Long "P", "T" and "A"	3·75	15·00
	ka. Long "P", "T" and "A" with comma after "POSTAGE"	16·00	40·00
	l. Surch double	£325	
	la. Surch double, one vertical	£325	
	m. "POSTAGE" omitted (in pair with normal)	£2000	
	s. Handstamped "*SPECIMEN*"	60·00	
	x. Wmk reversed	3·00	9·50

The surcharge was applied as a setting of 60 (12×5) which contained 17 normals, one each of Nos. 114a, 114b, 114ba, 114c, six of No. 114d, six of 114e, three of 114f, six of 114g, seven of 114h, five of No. 114i, four of No. 114k and two of No. 114ka.

HALF
(30)

31

32

1895 (18 Mar). No. 99 surch locally with T **30**.

125		HALF on 1d. rose (shades)	3·00	2·25
		a. Surch double	£475	£500
		b. "H" with longer left limb	40·00	
		c. Pair, one without surcharge		
		s. Handstamped "*SPECIMEN*"	65·00	

No. 125b, in which the "A" also has a short right leg, occurs on the second, fourth, sixth etc., stamps of the first vertical column of the right-hand pane of the first printing only.

In the second printing what appears to be a broken "E" (with the top limb removed) was used instead of "L" in "HALF" on the last stamp in the sheet (*Price* £40), No. 125c also comes from this second printing.

(Typo D.L.R)

1902–03. Inscr "POSTAGE REVENUE". Wmk Crown CA. P 14.

127	**31**	½d. blue-green	7·50	50
128		1d. carmine	13·00	15
129		1½d. green and black	4·00	7·00
130		2d. red and olive-green	6·50	40
131		2½d. bright blue	2·00	5·50
132		3d. purple and grey	1·50	2·50
133		4d. carmine and cinnamon	13·00	27·00
134		5d. black and orange	4·75	3·75
		w. Wmk inverted	£300	£150
135		6d. green and brown-purple	4·75	4·50
136		1s. carmine and pale blue	6·00	4·75
		w. Wmk inverted	†	£550
137		2s. green and bright violet	55·00	9·00
138		2s.6d. purple	50·00	12·00
139		4s. deep rose and maize	95·00	95·00
127/39 Set of 13			£225	£150
127s/39s Optd "SPECIMEN" Set of 13			£275	

No. 139 exists imperforate and partly perforated, from a proof sheet.

(Typo D.L.R.)

1902. Wmk Crown CC. P 14.

140	**32**	5s. dull blue and rose	65·00	12·00
141		10s. deep rose and chocolate	£130	48·00
142		£1 black and bright blue	£350	80·00
143		£1.10s. green and violet	£600	£130
		s. Optd "SPECIMEN"	£130	
144		£5 mauve and black	£5500	£1400
		s. Optd "SPECIMEN"	£275	
145		£10 green and orange	£14000	£6500
		as. Optd "SPECIMEN"	£450	
145b		£20 red and green	£28000	£19000
		bs. Optd "SPECIMEN"	£650	
140s/2s Optd "SPECIMEN" Set of 3			£190	

USED HIGH VALUES. Collectors are warned against fiscally used high value Natal stamps with penmarks cleaned off and forged postmarks added.

1904–08. Chalk-surfaced paper (£1. 10s.). Wmk Mult Crown CA. P 14.

146	**31**	½d. blue-green	12·00	15
147		1d. rose-carmine	12·00	15
		a. Booklet pane of 6, one stamp optd "NOT FOR USE" (1907)	£475	
		b. deep carmine	16·00	30
		w. Wmk inverted	†	£150
149		2d. red and olive-green	18·00	3·25
152		4d. carmine and cinnamon	3·00	1·25
153		5d. black and orange (1908)	6·00	4·00
155		1s. carmine and pale blue	85·00	7·00
156		2s. dull green and bright violet	70·00	50·00
157		2s.6d. purple	65·00	50·00
162	**32**	£1. 10s. brown-orange and deep purple (1908)	£1800	£4750
		s. Optd "SPECIMEN"	£375	
146/57 Set of 8			£250	£100

1908–09. Inscr "POSTAGE POSTAGE". Wmk Mult Crown CA. P 14.

165	**31**	6d. dull and bright purple	4·50	3·00
166		1s. black/green	6·00	3·00
167		2s. purple and bright blue/blue	15·00	3·00
		w. Wmk inverted	†	£550
168		2s.6d. black and red/blue	25·00	3·00
169	**32**	5s. green and red/yellow	30·00	50·00
170		10s. green and red/green	£130	£130
171		£1 purple and black/red	£425	£375
165/71 Set of 7			£550	£500
165s/71s Optd "SPECIMEN" Set of 7			£425	

STAMP BOOKLETS

1906. Black on red cover. Stapled.

SB1	2s.7d. booklet containing thirty 1d. (No. 147) in blocks of 6		£3750

1907. Black on red cover. Stapled.

SB2	2s.6d. booklet containing thirty 1d. (No. 147) in blocks of 6		£3750

The first or third stamp of the first pane in No. SB2 was overprinted "NOT FOR USE" (No. 147a), the additional penny being used to defray the cost of production.

FISCALS USED FOR POSTAGE

1869. Embossed on coloured wove, surfaced paper. P 12½.

F1	**1**	1d. yellow	55·00	85·00

Examples of 1d. yellow and 6d. rose values as Type **6**, 1s. purple-brown as Type **7** and various values between 5s. and £10 in the design illustrated above are believed to exist postally used, but, as such use was not authorised, they are not now listed.

OFFICIAL STAMPS

OFFICIAL

(O **1**)

1904. T **31**, wmk Mult Crown CA, optd with Type O **1** by De La Rue. P 14.

O1		½d. blue-green	3·25	1·00
O2		1d. carmine	15·00	1·25
O3		2d. red and olive-green	45·00	22·00
O4		3d. purple and grey	27·00	7·00
O5		6d. green and brown-purple	85·00	80·00
O6		1s. carmine and pale blue	£250	£275
O1/6 Set of 6			£375	£350

Nos. O4 and O5 were from special printings of the 3d. and 6d. stamps, which were not issued on wmk Mult Crown CA paper without opt.

The use of stamps overprinted as above was discontinued after 30 May 1907, although later use has been reported. Stamps perforated with the letters "N.G.R." were for use on Government Railways.

TELEGRAPH STAMPS

T **1**

(Typo D.L.R.)

1881. Wmk Crown CA (sideways). P 14.

T1	T **1**	1d. red-brown	16·00	19·00
T2		3d. rose-carmine	22·00	24·00
T3		6d. brown-olive	22·00	19·00
T4		1s. deep blue-green	27·00	25·00
T5		2s. purple	55·00	48·00
T6		5s. blue	85·00	90·00
T7		10s. slate	£160	£180
T8		£1 chocolate	£450	£250
T9		£5 orange	£5500	£3250

Nos. T4 and T7 are known imperforate, from proof sheets.

TELEGRAPH

T **2**

1888. No. 24 optd locally with T T **2**.

T10		6d. violet		
		a. Opt double		£2000

TELEGRAPH   **TELEGRAPH**

THREE PENCE.   THREE PENCE

(T **3**)   (T **4**)

TELEGRAPH

Three Pence

(T **5**)

1902. Fiscal stamps of 1886–90 (as £10 stamp illustrated below No. F1) surch as T T **3/5** by Davis & Son. Wmk Crown CA. P 14.

T11		3d. on 4d. dull mauve (surch T T **3**)	40·00	45·00
		a. Narrow spacing	30·00	35·00
		ab. Small "P" in "PENCE" (R. 2/4)	£180	£200
T12		3d. on 4d. dull mauve (surch T T **4**, narrow spacing)	35·00	40·00
T13		3d. on 4d. dull mauve (surch T T **5**, narrow spacing)	45·00	55·00
		a. Antique "e" in "Three" (R. 5/6)	£180	£200
T14		6d. on 9d. dull mauve (surch as T T **3**)	85·00	95·00
		a. Narrow spacing	38·00	45·00
		b. Surcharged both sides (inverted on reverse)	£475	
T15		1s. on 9s. dull mauve and carmine (surch as T T **3**)	65·00	80·00
		a. Narrow spacing	35·00	40·00
		b. Large "SHILLING" (narrow spacing)	70·00	80·00
T16		1s. on 9s. dull mauve and carmine (surch as T T **4**, narrow spacing) (R. 5/6)	£200	£225
T17		1s. on £1 dull blue-green (surch as T T **3**)	70·00	80·00
		a. Narrow spacing	38·00	45·00
		b. Large "SHILLING" (narrow spacing)	80·00	95·00
T18		1s. on £1 dull blue-green (surch as T T **4**, narrow spacing) (R. 5/6)	£250	£275

T19		1s. on £1.10s. dull mauve and blue (surch as T T **3**)	85·00	95·00
		a. Narrow spacing	45·00	50·00
		b. Large "SHILLING" (narrow spacing)	95·00	£110
T20		1s. on £1.10s. dull mauve and blue (surch as T T **4**, narrow spacing) (R. 5/6)	£275	£300

For T T **3** the space between the bar obliterating "REVENUE" and the overprinted "TELEGRAPH" is 1.8 mm, for the narrow spacing varieties the space measures 1.2 mm. For the 1s. the word "SHILLING" is 9.3 mm long, but on Nos. T15b, T17b and T19b it measures 9.7 mm.

All values were surcharged in settings of 30 (6×5), eight of which made up the sheet of 240. For the 3d. the top row of the setting comprised T T **3**, the second and third row (1-4), T T **3** (narrow), the third row (5 and 6) and the fourth row, T T **4** and the fifth row T T **5**.

For the 1s. the top row was as T T **3**, the second, third and fourth rows as T T **3** (narrow) and the fifth row as T T **3** (large "SHILLING"), apart from R. 5/6, which was as T T **4**.

Natal became a province of the Union of South Africa on 31 May 1910. Stamps used during the Interprovincial Period (1 June 1910–31 August 1913) are listed under South Africa.

IV. NEW REPUBLIC

During the unrest following the death of Cetshwayo, the Zulu king, in 1884, a group of Boers from the Transvaal offered their support to his son, Dinizulu. The price for this support was the cession of a sizeable portion of Zulu territory to an independent Boer republic. The New Republic, centred on Vryheid, was proclaimed on 16 August 1884 with the remaining Zulu territory becoming a protectorate of the new administration. The first reference to an organised postal service occurs in December 1884.

Alarmed by these developments the British authorities annexed the southernmost part of the land grant, around St. Lucia Bay, to prevent access to the Indian Ocean. The remainder of the New Republic was, however, recognised as independent on 22 October 1886. Zululand was annexed by the British on 22 May 1887.

Difficulties beset the New Republic, however, and its Volksraad voted for union with the South African Republic (Transvaal). The two republics united on 21 July 1888. In 1903 the territory of the former New Republic was transferred to Natal.

Mail from Vryheid in 1884–85 was franked with issues of Transvaal (for dispatches made via Utrecht) or Natal (for those sent via Dundee from August 1885 onwards). Issues of the New Republic were never accepted as internationally valid by these administrations so that all external mail continued to show Transvaal or Natal stamps used in combination with those of the republic.

PRICES FOR STAMPS ON COVER	
No. 1	—
Nos. 2/5	*from* × 50
Nos. 6/25	
Nos. 26/9	*from* × 50
Nos. 30/47	
Nos. 48/50	*from* × 50
No. 51	—
Nos. 52/3	*from* × 50
Nos. 72/5	*from* × 50
Nos. 76/7b	
Nos. 78/80	*from* × 50
Nos. 81/95	—

1

Printed with a rubber handstamp on paper bought in Europe and sent out ready gummed and perforated.

1886 (7 Jan)–**87.** Various dates indicating date of printing. P 11½.

A. Without Arms

(i) Yellow paper

1	**1**	1d. black (9.1.86)	—	£3000
2		1d. violet (9.1.86)	20·00	22·00
		a. "1d." omitted (in pair with normal) (24.4.86)	£2500	
3		2d. violet (9.1.86)	22·00	26·00
		a. "d" omitted (13.10.86)	£4250	
		b. "2d." omitted (in pair with normal) (30.8.86)	£3000	
4		3d. violet (13.1.86)	48·00	60·00
		a. "d" omitted (13.10.86)	£4250	
		b. Tête-bêche (pair) (13.10.86)		
5		4d. violet (30.8.86)	85·00	
		a. "4" omitted (in pair with normal) (13.10.86)	£2500	
6		6d. violet (20.2.86)	65·00	70·00
		a. "6d." omitted (in pair with normal) (2.7.86)	£2500	
7		9d. violet (13.1.86)	£120	
8		1s. violet (30.8.86)	£120	
		a. "1s." omitted (in pair with normal) (6.9.86)	£2500	
9		1/s. violet (13.10.86)	£750	
10		1/6 violet (30.8.86)	£120	
11		1s.6d. violet (13.1.86)	£550	
		a. Tête-bêche (pair) (6.9.86)	£140	
		b. "d" omitted (13.10.86)		
12		2s. violet (30.8.86)	75·00	
		a. Tête-bêche (pair) (6.9.86)	£800	
13		2/6 violet (13.1.86)	£170	
14		2s.6d. violet (1.86)	£170	
15		4/s. violet (17.1.87)	£750	
15a		4/s. violet (17.1.87)		
16		5s. violet (1.86)	55·00	65·00
		a. "s" omitted (in pair with normal) (7.3.86)	£3250	

17		5/6 violet (20.2.86)	£275	
18		5s.6d. violet (13.1.86)	£500	
19		7/6 violet (13.1.86)	£225	
20		7s.6d. violet (24.5.86)	£160	
21		10s. violet (13.1.86)	£225	£275
22		10s.6d. violet (2.7.86)	£225	
		a. "d" omitted (1.86)	£200	
23		13s. violet (24.11.86)	£550	
24		£1 violet (13.1.86)	£140	
		a. Tête-bêche (pair) (13.10.86)	£600	
25		30s. violet (13.1.86)	£130	
		a. Tête-bêche (pair) (24.11.86)	£600	

(ii) Blue granite paper

26	**1**	1d. violet (20.1.86)	28·00	30·00
		a. "d" omitted (24.11.86)	£650	
		b. "1" omitted (in pair with normal) (24.11.86)		
27		2d. violet (24.11.86)	21·00	23·00
		a. "d" omitted (24.4.86)	£1200	
		b. "2d." omitted (in pair with normal) (24.4.86)		
28		3d. violet (30.8.86)	38·00	38·00
		a. "d" omitted (13.10.86)	£350	
29		4d. violet (24.5.86)	55·00	60·00
30		6d. violet (20.2.86)	90·00	90·00
		a. "6" omitted in pair with normal (24.5.86)	£2500	
31		9d. violet (6.9.86)	£150	
32		1s. violet (1.86)	42·00	48·00
		a. Tête-bêche (pair) (21.5.86)	£375	
		b. "1s." omitted (in pair with normal) (29.4.86)	£2500	
32c		1–s. violet (2.7.86) (f.c. £250)	†	—
33		1s.6d. violet (2.7.86)	£120	
		a. Tête-bêche (pair) (6.9.86)	£650	
		b. "d" omitted (13.10.86)		
34		1/6 violet (13.1.86)	£180	
35		2s. violet (21.5.86)	£150	
		a. "2s." omitted (in pair with normal) (24.5.86)	£3000	
36		2s.6d. violet (19.8.86)	£225	
37		2/6 violet (13.1.86)	£225	
38		4/s. violet (17.1.87)	£500	
39		5/6 violet (13.1.86)	£300	
		a. "/" omitted (13.1.87)		
		b. "6" omitted (13.1.86)	£4000	
40		5s.6d. violet (13.1.86)	£375	
41		7/6 violet (13.1.86)	£300	
41a		7s.6d. violet (13.1.86)	£400	
42		10s. violet (1.86)	£200	£200
		a. Tête-bêche (pair) (2.7.86)	£475	
		b. "s" omitted (13.1.86)		
43		10s.6d. violet (13.1.86)	£250	
		a. Tête-bêche (pair) (13.1.86)		
		b. "d" omitted (1.86)	£550	
44		12s. violet (13.1.86)	£400	
45		13s. violet (17.1.87)	£500	
46		£1 violet (13.1.86)	£350	
47		30s. violet (13.1.86)	£300	

B. With embossed Arms of New Republic

(i) Yellow paper

48	**1**	1d. violet (20.1.86)	22·00	24·00
		a. Arms inverted (20.1.86)	28·00	32·00
		b. Arms tête-bêche (pair) (14.4.86)	£100	£120
		c. Tête-bêche (pair) (3.11.86)	£800	
49		2d. violet (30.8.86)	26·00	28·00
		a. Arms inverted (24.11.86)	30·00	35·00
50		4d. violet (2.12.86)	80·00	80·00
		a. Arms inverted (12.86)	£110	85·00
		b. Arms tête-bêche (pair) (12.86)	£275	
51		6d. violet (2.12.86)	£350	

(ii) Blue granite paper

52	**1**	1d. violet (20.1.86)	28·00	28·00
		a. Arms inverted (10.2.86)	40·00	42·00
		b. Arms tête-bêche (pair) (3.11.86)	£500	
53		2d. violet (24.5.86)	29·00	29·00
		a. Arms inverted (30.8.86)	50·00	60·00
		b. Arms tête-bêche (pair) (2.12.86)	£500	£500
		c. Arms reversed (20.1.87)	£400	

Stamps as Type **1** were produced as and when stocks were required, each printing including in its design the date on which it was prepared. The dates quoted above for Nos. 1/53 are those on which the various stamps first appeared. Details of the various printing dates are given below. From these dates it can be seen that some values share common printing dates, and, it is believed, that the different values were produced *se-tenant* within the same sheet, at least in some instances. A reported proof sheet of Nos. 79/95 in the Pretoria Postal Museum, on yellow paper and embossed, contains four examples of the 6d. value and three each of the 3d., 4d., 9d., 1s., 1/6, 2/-, 2/6, 3s., 4s., 5s., 5/6, 7/6, 10s., 10/6, £1 and 30s.

The date on No. 1 measures 17 mm; on all others it is 15 mm.

The significance, if any, of the two coloured papers and the use of the embossing machine have never been satisfactorily explained. Both the different papers and the embossing machine were introduced in January 1886, and occur throughout the period that the stamps with dates were used.

PRINTINGS

Date	Paper	Face value	Cat No.	Unused	Used
Jan 86	Yellow	5s.	16	55·00	65·00
		10s.6d.	22	£250	
		10s.6	22a	£250	
	Blue	1s.	32		
		10s.	42	£200	£200
		10s.6d.	43		
		10s.6	43b	£600	
7 Jan 86	Yellow	10s.6d.	22	£250	
	Blue	10s.	42		
		10s.6d.	43	£475	
9 Jan 86	Yellow	1d. blk	1	—	£3000
		1d. vio	2	20·00	22·00
		2d.	3	45·00	55·00
13 Jan 86	Yellow	1d.	2	42·00	
		2d.	3	38·00	42·00
		3d.	4	85·00	
		9d	7	£200	
		1s.6d.	11	£600	
		2/6	13	£200	

Date	Paper	Face value	Cat No.	Unused	Used
		2s.6d.	14	£350	
		5s.6d.	18		
		7/6	19	£225	
		10s.	21		
		£1	24	£225	
		30s.	25	£225	
	Blue	5/6	39	£300	
		5s.6d.	40	£375	
		7/6	41	£300	
		7s.6d.	41a	£400	
		10s.	42	£400	
		10s.	42b		
		10s.6d.	43	£250	
		10s.6d.	43a		
		12s.	44	£400	
		£1	46	£350	
		30s.	47	£300	
20 Jan 86	Yellow	1d.	2		
	Blue	1d.	26	£275	
	Yellow, embossed	1d.	48	80·00	
		1d.	48a	£100	
	Blue, embossed	1d.	52	£140	
Jan 20 86	Blue	1d.	26	75·00	
	Yellow, embossed	1d.	48a	£275	
	Blue, embossed	1d.	52	£130	
24 Jan 86	Blue	1d.	26	38·00	
		2d.	27	60·00	
10 Feb 86	Yellow	1d.	2		
	Yellow, embossed	1d.	48	£100	
		1d.	48a	80·00	
	Blue, embossed	1d.	52	£130	
		1d.	52a	50·00	
20 Feb 86	Yellow	6d.	6		
		1s.6d.	11		
		2s.6d.	14	£200	
		5/6	17	£275	
		5s.6d.	18		
	Blue	6d.	30		
7 Mar 86	Yellow	1d.	2	£120	
		2/6	13		
		2s.6d.	14	£190	
		5s.	16	£225	£120
		5s.	16a	£3250	
		5/6	17	£300	
		5s.6d.	18	£500	
	Blue	2d.	27	£100	
		6d.	30		
		1s.	32		
17 Mar 86	Yellow	1d.	2	£110	
	Yellow, embossed	1d.	48	50·00	
	Blue, embossed	1d.	52	£150	
		1d.	52a	£130	
26 Mar 86	Blue, embossed	1d.	52a	£150	
14 Apr 86	Yellow	1d.	2		
		1d.	48	35·00	
		1d.	48a	60·00	
		1d.	48b	£100	£120
	Blue, embossed	1d.	52	55·00	
		1d.	52a		
24 Apr 86	Yellow	1d.	2	£110	
		1d.	2a	£2500	
		5s.	16		
	Blue	2d.	27	85·00	
		2d.	27a	£1200	
		2d.	27b		
29 Apr 86	Blue	1s.	32	£120	
		1s.	32b		
21 May 86	Yellow	6d.	6	£130	
	Blue	1d.	26	90·00	
		1s.	32	42·00	48·00
		1s.	32a	£375	
		1s.	32b	£2500	
		2s.	35	£300	
23 May 86	Blue, embossed	1d.	52a	£120	
24 May 86	Yellow	1d.	2	£130	£140
		2d.	3	£120	
		5s.	16	£225	
		7/6	19	£225	
		7s.6d.	20	£160	
	Blue	1d.	26	45·00	48·00
		2d.	27	£300	£300
		4d.	29	£120	
		6d.	30	£120	
		6d.	30a	£2500	
		1s.	32	£200	
		1s.	32b	£2500	
		2s.	35	£170	
		2s.	35a	£3000	
	Blue, embossed	2d.	53	£110	
26 May 86	Yellow	1d.	2		
	Blue	1d.	26	£120	
	Yellow, embossed	1d.	48	£250	
		1d.	48a	£100	
	Blue, embossed	1d.	52	£130	
		1d.	52a	50·00	55·00
28 May 86	Yellow, embossed	1d.	48	£200	
30 Jun 86	Blue	1d.	26	28·00	30·00
	Yellow, embossed	1d.	48	24·00	26·00
		1d.	48a	28·00	32·00
		1d.	48b	£200	£225
	Blue, embossed	1d.	52	48·00	42·00
2 July 86	Yellow	6d.	6	£200	
		6d.	6a		
		9d	7	£275	£275
		10s.	21		
		10s.	21a		
	Blue	1–s	32c (f.c. £250)		
		1s.6d.	33	£130	
		10s.	42	£200	
		10s.	42a	£475	
		10s.6d.	43		
		10s.6	43b	£550	
3 July 86	Blue	10s.	42		
7 July 86	Yellow	1d.	2		
	Blue	1d.	26		
	Yellow, embossed	1d.	48	90·00	
		1d.	48a	£110	£110
	Blue, embossed	1d.	52	30·00	32·00
		1d.	52a	60·00	45·00
4 Aug 86	Yellow	1d.	2		
	Yellow, embossed	1d.	48	65·00	

Date	Paper	Face value	Cat No.	Unused	Used
	Blue, embossed	1d.	52	75·00	
		1d.	52a		
19 Aug 86	Yellow	2/6	13		
		2s.6d.	14	£170	
	Blue	2s.6d.	36	£225	
		2/6	37	£225	
30 Aug 86	Yellow	1d.	2	20·00	22·00
		2d.	3	80·00	
		2d.	3b	£3000	
		3d.	4	90·00	
		4d.	5	85·00	
		6d.	6	£120	
		9d.	7	£120	
		1s.	8	£120	
		1/6	10	£120	
		2s.	12	£130	
		2/6	13	£190	
	Blue	2d.	27	22·00	23·00
		3d.	28		
	Yellow, embossed	2d.	49	£110	
	Blue, embossed	2d.	53	50·00	
		2d.	53a	£110	
6 Sept 86	Yellow	1d.	2	£100	
		2d.	3	38·00	42·00
		3d.	4	55·00	
		4d.	5	85·00	
		6d.	6	£100	
		9d.	7	£120	
		1s.	8	£130	
		1s.	8a		
		1/6	10	£200	
		1s.6d.	11	£550	
		1s.6d.	11a		
		2s.	12	£160	
		2s.	12a	£800	
		2/6	13	£170	
		2s.6d.	14	£200	
		5s.	16	£200	
		7s.6d.	20	£275	
		10s.	21	£225	
		£1	24	£180	
	Blue	6d.	30	90·00	90·00
		9d.	31	£150	
		1s.	32	85·00	
		1s.6d.	33	£120	
		1s.6d.	33a	£650	
		1/6	34		
		2s.6d.	36		
		2/6	37	£425	
		7s.6d.	41a	£400	
		10s.6d.	43 (f.c. £200)	†	—
13 Sept 86	Yellow	1d.	2		
	Yellow, embossed	1d.	48	85·00	
		1d.	48a	85·00	
	Blue, embossed	1d.	52	£110	
6 Oct 86	Yellow	1d.	2		
	Blue	1d.	26	£100	
	Yellow, embossed	1d.	48	85·00	70·00
		1d.	48a		
	Blue, embossed	1d.	52	48·00	28·00
		1d.	52a	90·00	
13 Oct 86	Yellow	1d.	2	30·00	30·00
		2d.	3	28·00	35·00
		2d.	3a	£4250	
		3d.	4	48·00	60·00
		3d.	4a	£4250	
		3d.	4b		
		4d.	5	90·00	
		4d.	5a	£2500	
		6d.	6	65·00	70·00
		9d.	7	£130	
		1s.	8	£250	
		1/s	9	£750	
		1/6	10	£170	
		1s6	11b	£140	
		2s.	12	75·00	
		2/6	13	£200	
		5s.	16	£100	£130
		10s.	21	£250	£275
		10s.6	22a	£200	
		£1	24	£140	
		£1	24a	£600	
	Blue	2d.	27	21·00	23·00
		3d.	28	38·00	38·00
		3d.	28a	£350	
		4d.	29	55·00	60·00
		1s.	32	60·00	
		1s6	33b		
		1/6	34	£180	
		2s.	35	£150	
3 Nov 86	Yellow	1d.	2	50·00	
	Blue	1d.	26		
	Yellow, embossed	1d.	48	22·00	24·00
		1d.	48a	28·00	32·00
		1d.	48b	£100	£120
		1d.	48c	£800	
	Blue, embossed	1d.	52	28·00	
		1d.	52a	40·00	42·00
		1d.	52b	£500	
13 Nov 86	Yellow	1d.	2	£180	
24 Nov 86	Yellow	1d.	2	£130	£140
		2d.	3	22·00	26·00
		3d.	4	60·00	65·00
		1/6	10	£200	
		10s.	21	£250	
		13s.	23	£550	
		30s.	25	£130	
		30s.	25a	£600	
	Blue	1d.	26	48·00	35·00
		1d.	26a	£650	
		1d.	26b		
		2d.	27	55·00	
		2d.	27a		
		4d.	29	55·00	60·00
		6d.	30	£110	£110
		9d.	31	£190	
		1s.	32	£120	£130
		1/6	34	£300	
		2s.	35	£180	
		2s.	35a	£3250	

Date	Paper	Face value	Cat No.	Unused	Used
	Yellow, embossed	2d.	49	£160	
		2d.	49a		
26 Nov 86	Yellow	1/6	10	£200	
2 Dec 86	Yellow	1d.	2		
		2d.	3		
	Blue	2d.	27		
	Yellow, embossed	2d.	48	32·00	35·00
		1d.	48a	£160	
		2d.	49	26·00	28·00
		2d.	49a	30·00	35·00
		4d.	50	£275	
		6d.	51	£400	
	Blue, embossed	1d.	52	40·00	
		1d.	52a	£160	
		2d.	53	29·00	29·00
		2d.	53a	50·00	60·00
		2d.	53b	£500	£500
3 Dec 86	Yellow, embossed	6d.	51		
Dec 86	Yellow	6d.	6		
	Blue	4d.	29		
	Yellow, embossed	4d.	50	80·00	80·00
		4d.	50a	£110	85·00
		4d.	50b	£275	
		6d.	51	£350	
4 Jan 87	Yellow	1d.	2	£110	
		2d.	3	45·00	
		13s.	23	£550	
	Blue	1d.	26	28·00	30·00
		2d.	27	28·00	28·00
	Blue, embossed	2d.	53	45·00	
13 Jan 87	Yellow	7/6	19		
	Blue	5/6	39	£450	
		5/6	39a		
		7/6	41	£500	
17 Jan 87	Yellow	1d.	2	75·00	
		2d.	3	80·00	
		3d.	4	85·00	
		4/s	15	£750	
		4s.	15a		
	Blue	1d.	26	85·00	
		4/s	38	£500	
		13s.	45	£500	
		30s.	47	£350	
20 Jan 87	Blue	2d.	27	40·00	
	Yellow, embossed	2d.	49	75·00	
		2d.	49a	£140	
	Blue, embossed	2d.	53	55·00	
		2d.	53a	£100	
		2d.	53c	£400	
20 Jan 87	Yellow, embossed	1d.	48a	£400	

1887 (Jan–Mar). As T **1**, but without date. With embossed Arms.

(a) Blue granite paper

			Unused	Used
72	1d. violet		32·00	18·00
	b. Stamps *tête-bêche* (pair)		£550	
	c. Arms *tête-bêche* (pair)			
	d. Arms inverted		27·00	25·00
	e. Arms omitted		£140	£140
	f. Arms sideways			
73	2d. violet		18·00	18·00
	a. Stamps *tête-bêche* (pair)		£375	
	b. Arms inverted		50·00	50·00
	c. Arms omitted		£120	£110
	d. Arms *tête-bêche* (pair)			
74	3d. violet		32·00	32·00
	a. Stamps *tête-bêche* (pair)		£400	
	b. Arms *tête-bêche* (pair)			
	c. Arms inverted		65·00	65·00
75	4d. violet		27·00	27·00
	a. Stamps *tête-bêche* (pair)		£350	
	b. Arms *tête-bêche* (pair)		£275	
	c. Arms inverted		£100	
76	6d. violet		35·00	35·00
	a. Arms inverted		95·00	
	ab. Arms inverted and reversed		£400	
77	1/6 violet		50·00	42·00
	a. Arms inverted		£150	
	b. Arms *tête-bêche* (pair)		£425	
77c	2/6 violet		†	£1000

(b) Yellow paper (March 1887)

			Unused	Used
78	2d. violet (arms omitted)		40·00	50·00
79	3d. violet		26·00	26·00
	b. Stamps *tête-bêche* (pair)		£350	£400
	c. Arms omitted		£200	
	d. Arms inverted		28·00	29·00
	e. Arms sideways		£350	
80	4d. violet		17·00	17·00
	a. Arms inverted		24·00	24·00
81	6d. violet		17·00	17·00
	a. Arms *tête-bêche* (pair)		£350	
	b. Arms inverted		45·00	45·00
	c. Arms omitted		90·00	
82	9d. violet		16·00	19·00
	a. Arms inverted		£225	
	b. Arms *tête-bêche* (pair)		£375	
83	1s. violet		20·00	20·00
	a. Arms inverted		70·00	
84	1/6 violet		55·00	45·00
85	2s. violet		40·00	42·00
	a. Arms inverted		60·00	55·00
	b. Arms omitted		£140	
86	2/6 violet		38·00	38·00
	a. Arms inverted		42·00	42·00
87	3s. violet		65·00	65·00
	a. Arms inverted		75·00	75·00
	b. Stamps *tête-bêche* (pair)		£550	
88	4s. violet		£650	
	a. Arms omitted			
88b	4/s violet		65·00	65·00
	ba. Arms inverted		£250	
89	5s. violet		60·00	60·00
	b. Arms inverted		—	£150
90	5/6 violet		28·00	32·00
91	7/6 violet		35·00	38·00
	a. Arms *tête-bêche* (pair)			
	b. Arms inverted		£110	
92	10s. violet		32·00	35·00
	b. Arms *tête-bêche* (pair)		£130	
	c. Arms inverted		40·00	
	d. Arms omitted		£120	80·00

93		10/6 violet	28·00	32·00
	b.	Arms inverted	55·00	
94		£1 violet	75·00	80·00
	a.	Stamps *tête-bêche* (pair)	£500	£600
	b.	Arms inverted	80·00	£100
95		30s. violet		£190

A £15 value as Nos. 78/95 exists, but is only known fiscally used (*Price* £9000).

Many values exist with double impressions of the handstamp.

New Republic united with the South African Republic (Transvaal) on 21 July 1888. In 1903 the territory of the former New Republic was transferred to Natal.

V. ORANGE FREE STATE

PRICES FOR STAMPS ON COVER	
Nos. 1/9	*from* × 20
Nos. 10/13	*from* × 30
Nos. 18/19	*from* × 20
No. 20	—
Nos. 21/42	*from* × 40
Nos. 48/51	*from* × 25
Nos. 52/138	*from* × 10
Nos. 139/51	*from* × 7
Nos. RO1/17	—
Nos. PF1/3	*from* × 20
No. M1	*from* × 25
Nos. F1/17	—

Supplies of Cape of Good Hope stamps were available at Bloemfontein and probably elsewhere in the Orange Free State, from mid-1856 onwards for use on mail to Cape Colony and beyond. Such arrangements continued after the introduction of Orange Free State stamps in 1868. It is not known if the dumb cancellations used on the few surviving covers were applied in the Free State or at Cape Town.

1

(Typo D.L.R.)

1868 (1 Jan)–**94**. P 14.

1	**1**	1d. pale brown	32·00	2·50
2		1d. red-brown	21·00	45
3		1d. deep brown	32·00	55
4		6d. pale rose (1868)	65·00	8·00
5		6d. rose (1871)	35·00	5·50
6		6d. rose-carmine (1891)	28·00	12·00
7		6d. bright carmine (1894)	17·00	2·00
8		1s. orange-buff	£100	7·00
9		1s. orange-yellow	60·00	1·50
	a.	Double print	—	£3000

4 **4** **4** **4**

(2) *(a)* *(b)* *(c)* *(d)*

1877. No. 5 surcharged T **2** *(a)* to *(d)*.

10	**1**	4d. on 6d. rose *(a)*	£400	65·00
	a.	Surch inverted	—	£550
	b.	Surch double *(a + c)*		
	c.	Surch double, one inverted *(a + c* inverted)	†	£3750
	d.	Surch double, one inverted *(a* inverted *+ c)*	†	£5000
11		4d. on 6d. rose *(b)*	£1300	£180
	a.	Surch inverted	—	£1100
	b.	Surch double *(b + d)*		
12		4d. on 6d. rose *(c)*	£200	40·00
	a.	Surch inverted	—	£350
	b.	Surch double		
13		4d. on 6d. rose *(d)*	£250	42·00
	a.	Surch inverted	£1200	£375
	b.	Surch double, one inverted *(d + c* inverted)	†	£3750

The setting of 60 comprised nine stamps as No. 10, four as No. 11, 27 as No. 12 and 20 as No. 13.

1878 (July). P 14.

18	**1**	4d. pale blue	25·00	5·00
19		4d. ultramarine	6·00	4·25
20		5s. green	13·00	21·00

1d. **1d.** **1d.** **1d.** **1d.** **1d.**

(3) *(a)* *(b)* *(c)* *(d)* *(e)* *(f)*

Type **3**: *(a)* Small "1" and "d." *(b)* Sloping serif. *(c)* Same size as *(b)*, but "1" with straighter horizontal serif. *(d)* Taller "1" with horizontal serif and antique "d". *(e)* Same size as *(d)* but with sloping serif and thin line at foot. *(f)* as *(d)* but with Roman "d".

1881 (19 May). No. 20 surch T **3** *(a)* to *(f)* with heavy black bar cancelling the old value.

21	**1**	1d. on 5s. green *(a)*	£110	30·00
22		1d. on 5s. green *(b)*	60·00	30·00
	a.	Surch inverted	—	£900
	b.	Surch double	—	£1200
23		1d. on 5s. green *(c)*	£275	85·00
	a.	Surch inverted	—	£1300
	b.	Surch double	—	£1500
24		1d. on 5s. green *(d)*	90·00	30·00
	a.	Surch inverted	£1800	£900
	b.	Surch double	—	£1200

25		1d. on 5s. green *(e)*	£550	£250
	a.	Surch inverted	†	£2250
	b.	Surch double	†	£2250
26		1d. on 5s. green *(f)*	85·00	30·00
	a.	Surch inverted	—	£800
	b.	Surch double	—	£800

No. 21 was the first printing in one type only. Nos. 22 to 25 constitute the second printing about a year later, and are all found on the same sheet; and No. 26 the third printing of which about half have the stop raised.

Owing to defective printing, examples of Nos. 22 and 24/5 may be found with the obliterating bar at the top of the stamps or, from the top row, without the bar.

½d

(4)

1882 (Aug). No. 20 surch with T **4** and with a thin black line cancelling old value.

36	**1**	½d. on 5s. green	24·00	6·50
	a.	Surch double	£475	£350
	b.	Surch inverted	£1300	£800

3d **3d** **3d** **3d** **3d**

(5) *(a)* *(b)* *(c)* *(d)* *(e)*

1882. No. 19 surch with T **5** *(a)* to *(e)* with thin black line cancelling value.

38	**1**	3d. on 4d. ultramarine *(a)*	90·00	35·00
	a.	Surch double	†	£1200
39		3d. on 4d. ultramarine *(b)*	90·00	18·00
	a.	Surch double	†	£1200
40		3d. on 4d. ultramarine *(c)*	50·00	24·00
	a.	Surch double	†	£1200
41		3d. on 4d. ultramarine *(d)*	90·00	23·00
	a.	Surch double	†	£1200
42		3d. on 4d. ultramarine *(e)*	£250	70·00
	a.	Surch double	†	£2750

Examples of Nos. 39 and 41/2 exist without the cancelling bar due to the misplacement of the surcharge.

1883–84. P 14.

48	**1**	½d. chestnut	8·00	50
49		2d. pale mauve	19·00	1·50
50		2d. bright mauve	22·00	30
51		3d. ultramarine	8·00	2·00

For 1d. purple, see No. 68.

2d **2d** **2d**

(6) *(a)* *(b)* *(c)*

1888 (Sept–Oct). No. 51 surch with T **6** *(a)*, *(b)* or *(c)*.

(a) Wide "2". (b) Narrow "2"

52	**1**	2d. on 3d. ultramarine *(a)* (9.88)	70·00	9·00
	a.	Surch inverted	—	£750
53		2d. on 3d. ultramarine *(b)*	55·00	2·00
	a.	Surch inverted	—	£300
	b.	"2" with curved foot *(c)*	£1300	£500

1d **1d** **Id**

(7) *(a)* *(b)* *(c)*

1890 (Dec)–**91**. Nos. 51 and 19 surch with T **7** *(a)* to *(c)*.

54	**1**	1d. on 3d. ultramarine *(a)*	8·50	1·00
	a.	Surch double	90·00	70·00
	c.	"1" and "d" wide apart	£150	£110
	d.	Dropped "d" (Right pane R. 5/6)	£160	£120
55		1d. on 3d. ultramarine *(b)*	24·00	2·75
	a.	Surch double	£300	£275
57		1d. on 4d. ultramarine *(a)*	45·00	14·00
	a.	Surch inverted	£150	£120
	b.	Surch double *(a + b)*	£400	
	c.	Surch triple	—	£2750
	d.	Raised "1" (Left pane R. 3/1)	£150	60·00
58		1d. on 4d. ultramarine *(b)*	85·00	55·00
	a.	Surch double	£425	£325
59		1d. on 4d. ultramarine *(c)*	£2000	£600

The settings of the 1d. on 3d. and on 4d. are not identical. The variety *(c)* does not exist on the 3d.

2½d. **2½d.**

(8)

Printer's quad after surcharge (Lower right pane No. 43)

1892 (Oct). No. 51 surch with T **8**.

67	**1**	2½d. on 3d. ultramarine	21·00	70
	a.	No stop after "d"	90·00	50·00
	b.	Printer's quad after surcharge	90·00	50·00

1894 (Sept). Colour changed. P 14.

68	**1**	1d. purple	5·00	30

½d **½d** **½d**
½d **½d** **½d** **½d**

(9) *(a)* *(b)* *(c)*
(d) *(e)* *(f)* *(g)*

Types *(a)* and *(e)* differ from types *(b)* and *(f)* respectively, in the serifs of the "**1**", but owing to faulty overprinting this distinction is not always clearly to be seen.

1896 (Sept). No. 51 surch with T **9** *(a)* to *(g)*.

69	**1**	½d. on 3d. ultramarine *(a)*	7·50	11·00
70		½d. on 3d. ultramarine *(b)*	14·00	14·00
71		½d. on 3d. ultramarine *(c)*	13·00	2·75
72		½d. on 3d. ultramarine *(d)*	13·00	2·25
73		½d. on 3d. ultramarine *(e)*	13·00	2·25
74		½d. on 3d. ultramarine *(f)*	14·00	15·00

75		½d. on 3d. ultramarine *(g)*	8·00	5·00
	a.	Surch double	13·00	10·00
	b.	Surch triple	70·00	70·00

The double and triple surcharges are often different types, but are always type *(g)*, or in combination with type *(g)*.

Double surcharges in the same type, but without the "d" and bar, also exist, probably from a trial sheet prepared by the printer. Both unused and used examples are known.

Halve Penny.

2½ **½**

(10) **(11)** **(12)**

1896. No. 51 surch with T **10**.

77	**1**	½d. on 3d. ultramarine	1·00	50
		(i) Errors in setting		
78	**1**	½d. on 3d. (no stop)	22·00	35·00
79		½d. on 3d. ("Peuny")	22·00	35·00
		(ii) Surch inverted		
81	**1**	½d. on 3d.	60·00	65·00
81a		½d. on 3d. (no stop)	£2000	
81b		½d. on 3d. ("Peuny")	£1500	
		(iii) Surch double, one inverted		
81c	**1**	½d. on 3d. (Nos. 77 and 81)	£180	£200
81d		½d. on 3d. (Nos. 77 and 81a)	£800	£800
81e		½d. on 3d. (Nos. 77 and 81b)	£900	£900
81f		½d. on 3d. (Nos. 81 and 78)	£1500	£900
82		½d. on 3d. (Nos. 81 and 79)	—	£900

Examples from the top horizontal row can be found without the bar due to the surcharge being misplaced.

Nos. 69 to 75 also exist surcharged as last but they are considered not to have been issued with authority (*Prices from* £30 *each, unused*).

1897 (1 Jan). No. 51 surch with T **11**. *(a)* or **12** *(b)* With Roman "1" and antique "2" in fraction.

83	**1**	2½d. on 3d. ultramarine *(a)*	10·00	1·25
83a		2½d. on 3d. ultramarine *(b)*	£170	90·00

1897. P 14.

84	**1**	½d. yellow (3.97)	2·75	35
85		½d. orange	2·75	50
87		1s. brown (8.97)	20·00	4·00

The 6d. blue was prepared for use in the Orange Free State, but had not been brought into use when the stamps were seized in Bloemfontein. A few have been seen without the "V.R.I." overprint but they were not authorized or available for postage (*Price* £65).

BRITISH OCCUPATION

V.R.I. **V.R.I.** **V.R.I.**

4d **½d** **½d**

31 (Level stops) **(32)** Thin "V" (Raised stops) **(33)** Thick "V"

V.R.I.

Inserted "R"

(Surch by Curling & Co, Bloemfontein)

1900. T **1** surch as T **31/33** (2½d. on 3d. optd "V.R.I." only).

(a) First printings surch as T **31** *with stops level (March)*

101		½d. on ½d. orange	4·75	7·00
	a.	No stop after "V" (R.10/3)	23·00	29·00
	b.	No stop after "I" (R.1/3)	£160	£160
	c.	"½" omitted (R.7/5)	£190	£190
	d.	"I" and stops after "I" and "R" omitted (R. 2/3)	£275	£250
	e.	"V.R.I." omitted	£180	
	f.	Value omitted	£120	
	g.	Small "½" (R. 1/1, 1/3 or R. 5/1, 8/1)	60·00	60·00
	h.	Surch double	£180	
102		1d. on 1d. purple	2·75	1·75
	a.	Surch on 1d. deep brown (No. 3)	£600	£400
	b.	No stop after "V" (R. 10/3)	19·00	18·00
	c.	No stop after "R"	£180	£190
	d.	No stop after "I"	£1000	
	e.	"1" omitted (R. 7/5)	£200	£200
	f.	"I" omitted (with stops present)	£350	£350
	g.	"I" and stop after "R" omitted (R. 2/3)	£275	£275
	ga.	"I" omitted, with raised stop after "R" (R. 2/3)	£250	£250
	h.	"V.R.I." omitted	£160	£180
	i.	"d" omitted	£400	£400
	j.	Value omitted	90·00	£100
	k.	Inverted stop after "R"	£250	£275
	l.	Wider space between "1" and "d"	£100	£100
	m.	"V" and "R" close	£160	£160
	n.	Pair, one without surch	£550	
	o.	"V" omitted	£850	
103		2d. on 2d. bright mauve	4·25	2·75
	a.	No stop after "V" (R. 10/3)	21·00	24·00
	b.	No stop after "R"	£325	£325
	c.	No stop after "I"	£325	£325
	d.	"V.R.I." omitted	£300	£300
	e.	Value omitted	£300	
104		2½d. on 3d. ultramarine *(a)*	22·00	22·00
	a.	No stop after "V" (R. 10/3)	95·00	95·00
105		2½d. on 3d. ultramarine *(b)*	£250	£250
106		3d. on 3d. ultramarine	3·25	4·75
	a.	No stop after "V" (R. 10/3)	25·00	30·00
	b.	Pair, one without surch	£650	
	c.	"V.R.I." omitted	£250	£250
	d.	Value omitted	£250	£250
107		4d. on 4d. ultramarine	11·00	17·00
	a.	No stop after "V" (R.10/3)	65·00	75·00
108		6d. on 6d. bright carmine	45·00	40·00
	a.	No stop after "V" (R. 10/3)	£250	£275
	b.	"6" omitted (R. 7/5)	£300	£300
109		6d. on 6d. blue	15·00	7·00
	a.	No stop after "V" (R. 10/3)	55·00	50·00

	b. "6" omitted (R. 7/5)	85·00	90·00
	c. "V.R.I." omitted	£500	£375
110	1s. on 1s. brown	7·00	2·75
	a. Surch on 1s. orange-yellow (No. 9)	£3500	£2500
	b. No stop after "V" (R. 10/3)	55·00	32·00
	c. "1" omitted (R. 4/6)	£150	£140
	ca. "1" inserted by hand	†	£1000
	d. "1" omitted and spaced stop after "s" (R. 4/6)	£160	£160
	e. "V.R.I." omitted	£200	£200
	f. Value omitted	£200	£200
	g. Raised stop after "s" (R. 1/5, 6/6, 7/2)	27·00	12·00
	h. Wider space between "1" and "s" (R. 4/6)	£150	£150
111	5s. on 5s. green	32·00	55·00
	a. No stop after "V" (R. 10/3)	£275	£325
	b. "5" omitted	£950	£1000
	c. Inverted stop after "R" (R. 2/2)	£800	£850
	d. Wider space between "5" and "s" (R. 3/6)	£130	£140
	e. "V.R.I." omitted	£425	£450

All values are found with a rectangular, instead of an oval, stop after "R". Misplaced surcharges (upwards or sideways) occur.

No. 110ca shows the missing "1" replaced by a handstamp in a different type face.

On No. 111c the stop is near the top of the "R". On 111d there is a 2mm space between "5" and "s"; lesser displacements exist on other positions.

(b) Subsequent printings
(i) Surch as T 32

112	½d. on ½d. orange	30	20
	a. Raised and level stops mixed	3·25	2·00
	b. Pair, one with level stops	15·00	19·00
	c. No stop after "V" (R. 6/1)	4·00	4·25
	d. No stop after "I" (R. 4/6)	42·00	42·00
	e. "V" omitted (R. 4/6)	£600	
	f. Small "½" (R. 7/3 or 10/6)	19·00	21·00
	g. As a, and small "½"		
	i. Space between "V" and "R"	75·00	80·00
	j. Value omitted	£120	£120
113	1d. on 1d. purple	30	20
	a. Raised and level stops mixed	2·50	3·00
	b. Pair, one with level stops	25·00	27·00
	c. No stop after "V" (R. 6/1)	4·25	8·50
	d. No stop after "R" (R. 1/2, 1/6, 5/5 or 7/6)	18·00	18·00
	e. No stop after "I" (R. 1/4, 1/5, 6/6, 7/6 or 9/1)	18·00	18·00
	f. No stops after "V" and "I" (R. 9/1)	£350	
	g. Surch inverted	£400	
	h. Surch double	£120	£110
	i. Pair, one without surch	£300	
	j. Short figure "1" (R. 1/5)	£110	£110
	k. Space between "V" and "R" (R. 7/5 or 7/6)	50·00	55·00
	l. Space between "R" and "I" (R. 7/6)	£120	£130
	m. Space between "1" and "d" (R. 10/5)	£190	£190
	n. Inserted "R"	£450	£450
	o. Inserted "V"	£750	
	p. Stamp doubly printed, one impression inverted	£2500	
114	2d. on 2d. bright mauve	3·50	30
	a. Raised and level stops mixed	8·50	5·00
	b. Pair, one with level stops	14·00	15·00
	c. Surch inverted	£350	£350
	d. "I" and stop raised	75·00	75·00
	e. Pair, one without surch	£300	£350
	f. No stop after "V" (R. 6/6)	£1000	
	g. No stop after "I"		
115	2½d. on 3d. ultramarine (a)	£225	£200
	a. Level stop after "V" (R.10/6)	£800	
116	2½d. on 3d. ultramarine (b)	£1200	
117	3d. on 3d. ultramarine	2·50	30
	a. Raised and level stops mixed	10·00	10·00
	b. Pair, one with level stops	24·00	25·00
	c. No stop after "V"	£140	£140
	d. No stop after "R"	£400	£475
	e. "I" and stop omitted (R. 6/6)	£425	£450
	ea. "I" and stop inserted		
	f. Surch double	£400	
	g. Surch double, one diagonal	£375	
	h. Ditto, diagonal surch with mixed stops	£6500	
	n. Inserted "R"		
	o. Space between "3" and "d"	£150	
118	4d. on 4d. ultramarine	3·00	4·75
	a. Raised and level stops mixed	10·00	15·00
	b. Pair, one with level stops	22·00	35·00
119	6d. on 6d. bright carmine	40·00	50·00
	a. Raised and level stops mixed	£140	£160
	b. Pair, one with level stops	£225	£300
120	6d. on 6d. blue	1·00	40
	a. Raised and level stops mixed	11·00	12·00
	b. Pair, one with level stops	25·00	29·00
	c. No stop after "V"	£550	£550
	d. No stop after "R"	£375	
	e. Value omitted	£450	
121	1s. on 1s. brown	11·00	45
	a. Surch on 1s. orange-yellow (No. 9)	£1300	£1300
	b. Raised and level stops mixed	27·00	23·00
	c. Pair, one with level stops	50·00	50·00
	f. "s" omitted	£250	
	g. "V.R.I." omitted	£400	
122	5s. on 5s. green	9·50	18·00
	a. Raised and level stops mixed	£350	£350
	b. Pair, one with level stops	£1000	
	c. Short top to "5" (R. 1/2)	60·00	70·00
	s. Handstamped "SPECIMEN"	55·00	

In the initial ("second") setting with raised stops (T **32**), there were still level stops at R. 7/4, and three positions showed raised and level stops mixed: R. 9/4 (level stops after "V" and "I"), R. 9/5 (level stops after "V") and R. 10/4 (level stop after "R" and "I"). No. 115a comes from a later setting, as do examples of a level stop after "V" at R. 1/6 and a level stop after "I" at R. 3/2, both on the 1d. value.

(ii) Surch as T 33

123	½d. on ½d. orange	8·50	5·00
124	1d. on 1d. purple	8·50	35
	a. Inverted "1" for "I" (R. 7/1)	27·00	27·00
	b. No stop after "R" and "I" (R. 10/4)	£160	£160
	c. No stop after "R" (R. 10/4)	65·00	70·00
	d. Surch double	£375	£375
	n. Inserted "R"	£400	£400

---

	p. Stamp doubly printed, one impression inverted	£6500	
125	2d. on 2d. bright mauve	20·00	18·00
	a. Inverted "1" for "I" (R. 7/1)	42·00	45·00
126	2½d. on 3d. ultramarine (a)	£750	£850
127	2½d. on 3d. ultramarine (b)	£3750	
128	3d. on 3d. ultramarine	10·00	18·00
	a. Inverted "1" for "I" (R. 7/1)	65·00	75·00
	b. Surch double	£550	
	ba. Surch double, one diagonal	£550	
129	6d. on 6d. bright carmine	£425	£450
130	6d. on 6d. blue	23·00	32·00
131	1s. on 1s. brown	40·00	13·00
132	5s. on 5s. green	65·00	55·00
	s. Handstamped "SPECIMEN"	£170	

Stamps with thick "V" occur in seven or later six positions in *later* settings of the type with stops above the line (T **32**). *Earlier* settings with stops above the line have all stamps with thin "V".

Some confusion has previously been caused by the listing of certain varieties as though they occurred on stamps with thick "V" in fact they occur on stamps showing the normal thin "V", included in the settings which also contained the thick "V".

For a short period small blocks of unsurcharged Free State stamps could be handed in for surcharging so that varieties occur which are not found in the complete settings. Nos. 102a, 110a and 121a also occur from such stocks.

The inserted "R" variety occurs on positions 6 (T **32**) and 12 (T **33**) of the forme. The "R" of the original surcharge failed to print and the "R", but not the full stop, was added by the use of a handstamp. Traces of the original letter are often visible. The broken "V" flaw, also shown in the illustration, does not appear on No. 124n.

ORANGE RIVER COLONY

CROWN COLONY

E. R. I.

ORANGE
RIVER   **4d**
COLONY.   **6d**
(34)   (35)   (36)

1900 (10 Aug)–02. Nos. 58, 59a and 63a of Cape of Good Hope (wmk Cabled Anchor. P 14) optd with T **34** by W. A. Richards and Sons, Cape Town.

133	½d. green (13.10.00)	65	10
	a. No stop	12·00	25·00
	b. Opt double	£650	£700
134	1d. carmine (5.1902)	2·00	10
	a. No stop	25·00	32·00
135	2½d. ultramarine	5·00	1·50
	a. No stop	75·00	75·00
133/5 Set of 3		7·00	1·50

In the ½d. and 2½d., the "no stop" after "COLONY" variety was the first stamp in the left lower pane. In the 1d. it is the twelfth stamp in the right lower pane on which the stop was present at the beginning of the printing but became damaged and soon failed to print.

1902 (14 Feb). Surch with T **35** by "Bloemfontein Express".

136	4d. on 6d. on 6d. blue (No. 120) (R.)	1·50	3·00
	a. No stop after "R" (R. 5/5)	38·00	55·00
	b. No stop after "I"	£1200	
	c. Surch on No. 130 (Thick "V")	2·50	9·50
	ca. Inverted "1" for "I" (R. 7/1)	6·50	24·00

1902 (Aug). Surch with T **36**.

137	**1** 6d. on 6d. blue	7·00	20·00
	a. Surch double, one inverted	£550	
	b. Wide space between "6" and "d" (R. 4/2)	60·00	£100

One Shilling
*
(37)

38 King Edward VII, Springbok and Gnu

1902 (Sept). Surch with T **37**.

138	**1** 1s. on 5s. green (O.)	10·00	25·00
	a. Thick "V"	17·00	50·00
	b. Short top to "5"	70·00	85·00
	c. Surch double	£1000	

(Typo D.L.R.)

1903 (3 Feb)–04. Wmk Crown CA. P 14.

139	**38** ½d. yellow-green (6.7.03)	9·00	2·25
	w. Wmk inverted	£250	£100
140	1d. scarlet	11·00	10
	w. Wmk inverted	£250	80·00
141	2d. brown (6.7.03)	9·50	1·50
142	2½d. bright blue (6.7.03)	7·50	2·00
143	3d. mauve (6.7.03)	9·50	1·25
144	4d. scarlet and sage-green (6.7.03)	38·00	7·00
	a. "IOSTAGE" for "POSTAGE"	£1200	£450
145	6d. scarlet and mauve (6.7.03)	8·50	1·75
146	1s. scarlet and bistre (6.7.03)	50·00	3·75
147	5s. blue and brown (31.10.04)	£160	30·00
139/47 Set of 9		£275	45·00
139s/47s Optd "SPECIMEN" Set of 9		£275	

No. 144a occurs on R. 10/2 of the upper left pane.

The 2d. exists from coils constructed from normal sheets for use in stamp machines introduced in 1911.

1905 (Nov)–09. Wmk Mult Crown CA. P 14.

148	**38** ½d. yellow-green (28.7.07)	18·00	1·25
149	1d. scarlet	10·00	30
150	4d. scarlet and sage-green (8.11.07)	4·50	6·50
	a. "IOSTAGE" for "POSTAGE"	£200	£250
151	1s. scarlet and bistre (2.09)	80·00	26·00
148/51 Set of 4		£100	30·00

POSTCARD STAMPS

From 1889 onwards the Orange Free State Post Office sold postcards franked with adhesives as Type **1**, some subsequently surcharged, over which the State Arms had been overprinted by Curling and Co., Bloemfontein. Examples are known of adhesives being affixed to cards upside-down, resulting in the overprint being inverted on loose stamps.

There are five known dies of the Arms overprint which can be identified as follows:

(a) Shield without flags. Single 15 mm diameter circle. Three cows (two lying down, one standing) at left. Point of shield complete.

(b) Shield with flags. Single 13 mm diameter circle. Four cows (two lying down, two standing) at left (*illustrated*).

(c) Shield with flags. Double 13 mm diameter circle. Three cows (one lying down, two standing) at left.

(d) Shield without flags. Single 14.5 mm diameter circle. Three cows (one lying down, two standing) at left.

(e) Shield without flags. Double 15 mm diameter circle. Three cows (two lying down, one standing) at left. Point of shield broken. There are also other differences between the dies.

PRICES. Those in the left-hand column are for unused examples on complete postcard; those on the right for used examples off card. Examples used on postcard are worth more.

1889 (Feb). No. 2 (placed sideways on card) optd Shield Type (a).

P1	**1** 1d. red-brown	£250	42·00
	a. Optd Shield Type (b)	40·00	8·00

1891 (Aug)–**94**. No. 48 optd Shield Type (b).

P2	**1** ½d. chestnut	7·00	2·00
	a. Optd Shield Type (c)	16·00	4·50
	b. Optd Shield Type (d)	7·50	2·50
	ba. Error. Optd with *Bloemfontein Express* die (1894)	£200	
	c. Optd Shield Type (e)	17·00	5·50

No. P2ba was caused when the trademark of the *Bloemfontein Express* newspaper was substituted for Type d in error.

1892 (June). No. 54 optd Shield Type (c).

P3	**1** 1d. on 3d. ultramarine	18·00	3·50

1½d.   **1½d.**   **1½d.**
(P 1)   (P 2)   (P 3)

1892 (Sept)–**95**. Nos. 50/1 optd Shield Type (b) or (d) (No. P6) and surch with Types P **1**/**3**.

P4	**1** 1½d. on 2d. bright mauve (Type P **1**) (11.92)	9·50	4·00
P5	1½d. on 2d. bright mauve (Type P **2**) (9.93)	7·50	2·00
	a. Surch inverted	£150	
P6	1½d. on 2d. bright mauve (Type P **3**) (R.) (6.95)	16·00	4·75
P7	1½d. on 3d. ultramarine (Type P **1**)	9·00	2·50

No. P5a shows the stamp affixed to the card upside down with the surcharge correctly positioned in relation to the card.

½d.
(P 4)

1895 (Aug). No. 48 optd Shield Type (e) and surch with Type P **4**.

P8	**1** ½d. on ½d. chestnut	16·00	3·00

1½d.   **1½d.**
(P 5)   (P 6)

1895 (Dec)–**97**. No. 50 optd Shield Type (e) and surch with Types P **5**/**6**.

P9	1½d. on 2d. bright mauve (Type P **5**)	8·00	3·00
P10	1½d. on 2d. bright mauve (Type P **6**) (12.97)	9·00	3·50
P11	1½d. on 2d. bright mauve (as Type P **6**, but without stop) (12.97)	9·00	3·50

1897 (Mar). No. 85 optd Shield Type (d).

P12	**1** ½d. orange	16·00	2·00
	a. Optd Shield Type (e)	17·00	3·00

V.R.I.
(P 7)

1900. Nos. P10/11 optd as T **31**/2 or with Type P **7**.

P13	**1** 1½d. on 2d. bright mauve (No. P10) (T **31**)	32·00	6·50
P14	1½d. on 2d. bright mauve (No. P11) (T **31**)	32·00	6·50
P15	1½d. on 2d. bright mauve (No. P10) (T **32**)	32·00	6·50
P16	1½d. on 2d. bright mauve (No. P11) (T **32**)	32·00	6·50
P17	1½d. on 2d. bright mauve (No. P10) (Type P **7**)	45·00	12·00
P18	1½d. on 2d. bright mauve (No. P11) (Type P **7**)	45·00	12·00

RAILWAY OFFICIAL STAMPS

The following stamps were provided for use on official correspondence of the Central Southern Africa Railways.

C.S.A.R.

(RO **1**)

1905 (Feb). Nos. 139/41 and 143/6 optd with T RO **1** at CSAR's Departmental Printing Office, Germiston.

RO1	½d. yellow-green	£100	25·00
RO2	1d. scarlet	£100	20·00
RO3	2d. brown	£200	75·00
RO4	3d. mauve	£375	£150
RO5	4d. scarlet and sage-green	£375	£150
RO6	6d. scarlet and mauve	£425	£200
RO7	1s. scarlet and bistre	£100	50·00

The overprint on Nos. RO1/7 was applied in a setting of 120 and was normally placed either at the top or bottom of the stamps, although central placings are known. The stamps were withdrawn on 13 October 1905, but examples of genuine late use have been recorded. Dangerous forgeries exist.

(RO **2**)

1907. Nos. 139/41 and 143/6 punctured with Type RO **2**.

RO8	½d. yellow-green	£100	50·00
RO9	1d. scarlet	£150	75·00
RO10	2d. brown	£200	£100
RO11	3d. mauve	—	£150
RO12	4d. scarlet and sage-green	£250	
RO13	6d. scarlet and mauve		
RO14	1s. scarlet and bistre		

1907. Nos. 148/50 punctured with Type RO **2**.

RO15	½d. yellow-green	£100	50·00
RO16	1d. scarlet	£100	50·00
RO17	4d. scarlet and sage-green	—	£200

Nos. RO8/17 were replaced by Transvaal stamps punctured "S/AR" and finally withdrawn on 1 April 1912, although later usages are known.

POLICE FRANK STAMPS

The following frank stamps were issued to members of the Orange Free State Mounted Police ("Rijdende Dienst Macht") for use on official correspondence.

PF **1** (eight ornaments at left and right)   PF **2**

1896. P 12.

PF1	PF **1**	(–) Black	£400	£500

No. PF1 was printed in horizontal strips of five surrounded by wide margins.

1898. As Type PF **1**, but with nine ornaments at left and right. P 12.

PF2		(–) Black	£250	£300
		a. No stop after "V"	£500	£600

No. PF2 was printed in blocks of four (2×2) surrounded by wide margins. No. PF2a occurs on R1/1 of the setting.

1899. P 12.

PF3	PF **2**	(–) Black/*yellow*	£225	£300
		a. No stop after "V"	£650	£850

No. PF3 was printed in sheets of 24 (6×4) with the edges of the sheet imperforate. It is believed that they were produced from a setting of eight (2×4) repeated three times. No. PF3a occurs on R. 1/2 of the setting.

Examples of No. PF3 are known postmarked as late as 28 April 1900. The O.F.S. Mounted Police were disbanded by the British authorities at the end of the following month.

MILITARY FRANK STAMP

M **1**

(Typeset Curling & Co, Bloemfontein)

1899 (15 Oct). P 12.

M1	M **1**	(–) Black/*bistre-yellow*	33·00	65·00

Supplies of No. M1 were issued to members of the Orange Free State army on active service during the Second Boer War. To pass free through the O.F.S. fieldpost system, letters had to be franked with No. M1 or initialled by the appropriate unit commander. The franks were in use between October 1899 and February 1900.

No. M1 was printed in sheets of 20 (5×4) using a setting of five different types in a horizontal row. The colour in the paper runs in water.

Typeset forgeries can be identified by the appearance of 17 pearls, instead of the 16 of the originals, in the top and bottom frames. Forgeries produced by lithography omit the stops after "BRIEF" and "FRANKO".

FISCAL STAMPS USED FOR POSTAGE

The following were issued in December 1877 (Nos. F1 and F3 in 1882) and were authorised for postal use between 1882 and 1886.

F **1**   F **2**

F **3**

(Typo D.L.R.)

1882–86. P 14.

F1	F **1**	6d. pearl-grey	20·00	22·00
F2		6d. purple-brown	90·00	45·00
F3	F **2**	1s. purple-brown	26·00	28·00
F4		1s. pearl-grey	£120	£120
F5		1s.6d. blue	45·00	35·00
F6		2s. magenta	40·00	32·00
F7		3s. chestnut	50·00	90·00
F8		4s. grey		
F9		5s. rose	45·00	40·00
F10		6s. green	—	£150
F11		7s. violet		
F12		10s. orange	£100	55·00
F13	F **3**	£1 purple	£130	55·00
		a. "VRY-STAAT" (R. 1/5)		
F14		£2 red-brown	£160	£130
		a. "VRY-STAAT" (R. 1/5)		
F14b		£4 carmine		
		ba. "VRY-STAAT" (R. 1/5)		
F15		£5 green	£250	85·00
		a. "VRY-STAAT" (R. 1/5)		

Die proofs of Type F **3** showed a hyphen in error between "VRY" and "STAAT". This was removed from each impression on the plate before printing, but was missed on R. 1/5.

A fiscally used example of No. F2 exists showing "ZES PENCE" double, one inverted.

The 8s. yellow was prepared but we have no evidence of its use postally without surcharge Type F **4** (*Price* £150, *unused*).

ZES PENCE.

(F **4**)

1886. Surch with Type F **4**.

F16	F **2**	6d. on 4s. grey	
F17		6d. on 8s. yellow	£600

TELEGRAPH STAMPS

TELE-GRAAF.

(T T **1**)

1885 (Sept). Postage stamps as T **1** handstamped as T T **1**.

T1	1d. red-brown (No. 2) (V.)	24·00	7·00
T2	3d. ultramarine (No. 51) (V.)	35·00	8·00
T3	3d. ultramarine (No. 51) (C.)	80·00	21·00
T4	6d. rose (No. 5) (V.)	35·00	9·00
T5	6d. rose (No. 5) (Blk.)	80·00	27·00
T6	1s. orange-yellow (No. 9) (V.)	£225	40·00

The handstamp is known reading vertically up or down or diagonally; double handstamps also exist. The 5s. (No. 20) has also been reported with T T **1** handstamp but it is believed not to have been issued.

1886 (Feb). Fiscal stamps as T F **2** handstamped as T T **1**.

T7	1s. purple-brown (No. F3) (V.)	55·00	14·00
T8	1s. purple-brown (No. F3) (Blk.)	70·00	22·00
T9	1s. pearl-grey (No. F4) (V.)	50·00	12·00

The handstamp is known reading horizontally, diagonally and inverted.

T F   **Een Shilling.**

(T **2**)   (T **3**)

1888 (Apr). Fiscal stamps as T F **2** optd and surch T T **2** and T T **3** by C. Borckenhagen, Bloemfontein.

T10	1s. on 7s. violet (No. F11)	75·00	14·00
T11	1s. on 8s. yellow (small "TF")	85·00	22·00
	a. Large "T" in "TF"	£170	40·00
T12	1s. on 8s. yellow (large "TF")	75·00	14·00
T13	1s. on 9s. olive-bistre (small "TF")	£120	35·00
	a. Large "T" in "TF"	£250	70·00
T14	1s. on 9s. olive-bistre (large "TF")	85·00	23·00

The "TF" overprint measures 8.2×2.9 mm on No. T10, 6.6×3.4 mm on Nos. T12 and T14 and 6.6×2.9 mm on T11 and T13.

No. T10 exists with an additional manuscript line through the original value, to correct misplacement of the T T **3** surcharge. The type used for T T **3** was in poor condition and numerous broken letter varieties exist, including "Ecn", "E-n" and damage to the first or second "I" or "n" of "Shilling".

T F   **T F**   **T F**   **T F**

(T **4**)   (T **5**)   (T **6**)   (T **7**)

1888 (May). Postage stamps as T **1** optd as T T **4** by C. Borckenhagen, Bloemfontein.

T15	1d. red-brown (No. 2)	35·00	11·00
T16	3d. ultramarine (No. 51)	6·00	2·00
T17	6d. rose (No. 5)	7·00	2·00
	a. Opt double	70·00	28·00
T18	1s. orange-yellow (No. 9)	8·00	2·00

Opt T T **4** measures 6.5×2.8 mm.

1890 (July). Postage stamps as T **1** optd as T T **5/6** by C. Borckenhagen, Bloemfontein.

T19	6d. rose (No. 5) (Optd T **5**)	£100	29·00
T20	1s. orange-yellow (No. 9) (Optd T **6**)	£130	40·00

In T19/20 the letters are smaller than other issues, the overprint measuring 5.5×2.1 mm on No. T19 and 6.0×2.25 mm on T20.

1891 (Jan). Postage stamps as T **1** optd as T T **7** by C. Borckenhagen, Bloemfontein.

T21	3d. ultramarine (No. 51)	7·00	2·00
	a. "FT" for "TF"	70·00	30·00
T22	6d. rose-carmine (No. 6)	7·00	2·00
	a. "FT" for "TF"	70·00	30·00
	b. Wide "TF"	29·00	8·50
	c. Opt double	£110	80·00
	d. Opt inverted		
T23	1s. orange-yellow (No. 9)	8·00	2·00
	a. "FT" for "TF"	80·00	35·00
	b. Wide "TF"	29·00	8·50

T T **7** is similar to T T **4** but the letters are thicker, the lower stroke of the "F" forms a triangle touching the upright, without the horizontal line found in T T **4**. In the "wide 'TF'" varieties there is a 4 mm space between the letters.

T F   **T F**   **T F.**

(T **8**)   (T **9**)   (T **10**)

1891 (Jan?). Postage stamps as T **1** optd as T T **8/9** by C. Borckenhagen, Bloemfontein.

T24	1d. red-brown (No. 2) (optd T T **8**)	7·50	1·50
	a. Opt inverted		
	b. Optd T T **9**	7·50	1·50
	ba. Ditto, opt inverted		
	c. Vert pair No. T24/b		
T25	6d. rose (No. 5) (optd T T **8**)	8·50	1·50
	a. Opt double		
	b. Optd T T **9**	8·50	1·50
	ba. Ditto, opt double		
	c. Vert pair Nos. T25/b		
T26	1s. orange-yellow (No. 9)	15·00	1·50
	a. Optd T T **9**	15·00	1·50
	c. Vert pair No. T26/a		

Opts T T **8** (9.3×3.9 *mm*) and T T **9** (8.5×3.3 *mm*) appeared in the same sheet, T T **8** in the upper part and T T **9** in the lower.

1892 (Oct). No. 6 optd T T **10** by C. Borckenhagen, Bloemfontein.

T27	6d. rose-carmine	32·00	11·00
	a. Stop omitted	65·00	22·00
	b. "TE." For "TF."	£100	40·00
	c. Inverted "L" for "T"		

T T **10** measures 5.4×2.5 mm, excluding the stop.

T.F.   **T F**

(T **11**)   (T **12**)

1892 (Nov). No 9 optd with T T **11** by C. Borckenhagen, Bloemfontein.

T28	1s. orange-yellow	26·00	5·00
	a. Stop omitted after "T"	55·00	14·00
	b. Stop omitted after "F"	55·00	14·00
	c. Stops omitted after "T" and "F"	65·00	17·00
	d. Comma for stop after "F"	55·00	14·00

1893. Postage stamps as T **1** opt with T T **12** by C. Borckenhagen, Bloemfontein.

T29	1d. red-brown (No. 2)	5·00	1·00
	a. Opt inverted	75·00	35·00
T30	3d. ultramarine (No. 51)	5·00	1·00
T31	6d. rose-carmine (No. 6)	6·00	1·25
T32	1s. orange-yellow (No. 9)	8·00	1·25

T T **12** measures 4.7×2.6 mm.

1898 (June)–**99**. As Nos. T29 and T31/2 but colours changed.

T33	1d. purple (No. 68) (5.99)	2·00	1·00
T34	6d. blue (8.98)	2·00	1·25
T35	6d. brown (No. 87)	2·00	1·25

The 6d. blue was not issued without the T T **12** opt.

British Occupation

The Army controlled the telegraph system from the start of the British occupation in 1900. Initially existing telegraph stamps were overprinted "V.R.I.," they were later supplemented by stamps overprinted "V.R.I./AT".

1900 (Apr). Nos. T30 and T33/5 optd "V.R.I." (as T **32**, thin "V", raised stops).

T36	1d. purple	3·00	2·00
	a. Raised and level stops mixed	12·00	8·50
	b. Horiz gutter pair, right stamp "V.R.I." omitted		£750
T37	3d. ultramarine	12·00	9·00
	a. Raised and level stops mixed	40·00	28·00
	b. "V.R.I." double	£325	£250
T38	6d. blue	24·00	12·00
	a. Raised and level stops mixed	70·00	35·00
T39	1s. brown	6·00	4·00
	a. Raised and level stops mixed	17·00	13·00

The "V.R.I." overprint is usually positioned at the top of the stamp but lower positions are not uncommon.

Mixed stop varieties occur as follows: level stop after "V" at R. 1/6, R. 5/6, R. 9/5 and R. 10/1, level stops after "V" at R. 9/4, level stops after "R" and "I" at R. 7/4 and R. 10/4, level stop after "R" at R. 8/4, level stop after "I" at R. 2/5 and R. 6/6.

V. R. I.   **V. R. I.**

T F   **A T**   **A T**

(T **13**)   (T **14**)   (T **15**)

T
Six Pence

(T **16**)

1900 (Apr). As No. T38 but optd as T T **13** and "V.R.I." (as T **32**).
T40		6d. mauve	55·00	30·00
	a.	Raised and level stops mixed	£150	85·00

T T **13** measures 7.1×3.0 mm.

1900 (Apr). No. T33 surcharged as T **32**.
T41	1d. on 1d. purple	

It is believed that No. T41 was the result of a sheet of telegraph stamps receiving the overprint due for the postage stamp in error. Forgeries exist.

1900 (Apr?). Postage stamps as T **1** and fiscal stamps as T F **2** optd with T T **14** (Nos. T42/5) or T T **15** (others).
T42		1d. purple	2·75	1·00
	a.	Thick "V" (as T **33**)	8·50	3·50
T43		3d. ultramarine	5·50	3·00
	a.	Thick "V" (as T **33**)	16·00	9·00
	b.	Opt inverted	£350	£300
T44		6d. mauve	6·50	4·00
	a.	Thick "V" (as T **33**)	19·00	12·00
T45		1s. brown	5·50	3·00
	a.	Thick "V" (as T **33**)	16·00	9·00
	b.	Opt double	£300	
T46		5s. mauve	19·00	10·00
	a.	Thick "V" (as T **33**)	55·00	28·00
	b.	No stop after "V" (R. 6/1)	£110	55·00
	c.	Low stop after "V" (R. 10/6)	£110	55·00
	d.	Broad short "A" in "AT" (R. 6/5)	£110	55·00
	e.	"V.R.I." omitted (lower stamp of vertical pair)		
T47		10s. orange	35·00	25·00
	a.	Thick "V" (as T **33**)	85·00	60·00
	b.	No stop after "V" (R. 6/1)	£200	£130
	c.	Low stop after "V" (R. 10/6)	£200	£130
	d.	Broad short "A" in "AT" (R. 6/5)	£200	£130
	e.	Opt inverted	£900	
T48		£1 purple	45·00	30·00
	a.	Thick "V" (as T **33**)	£110	75·00
	b.	No stop after "V" (R. 6/1)	£250	£150
	c.	Low stop after "V" (R. 10/6)	£250	£150
	d.	Broad short "A" in "AT" (R. 6/5)	£250	£150
	e.	"VRY-STAAT"	£300	
T49		£4 carmine	£110	80·00
	a.	Thick "V" (as T **33**)	£275	£180
	b.	No stop after "V" (R. 6/1)	£600	£400
	c.	Low stop after "V" (R. 10/6)	£600	£400
	d.	Broad short "A" in "AT" (R. 6/5)	£600	£400
	e.	"VRY-STAAT"	£700	

In T T **14** "AT" measures 6.5 mm, in T T **15** it measures 7.5 mm.
The thick "V" occurs at R. 1/5, R. 3/5, R. 4/5, R. 7/3, R. 8/3 and R. 8/6 in the case of Nos. T42a/5a and at R. 1/2, R. 3/2, R. 4/2, R. 7/4, R. 8/1 and R. 8/4 in the case of Nos. T46a/9a.

1903 (Mar). Postage stamps Nos. 114 and 117 additionally surch as T T **16**.
T50		6d. on 2d. on 2d. bright mauve	90·00	90·00
	a.	Thick "V" (as T **33**)	£180	£180
	ab.	Inverted "1" for "I" (R. 7/1)	£325	£325
T51		1s. on 3d. on 3d. ultramarine	75·00	75·00
	a.	Thick "V" (as T **33**)	£150	£150
	ab.	Inverted "1" for "I" (R. 7/1)	£300	£300

The "One Shilling" surcharge of No. T51 includes numerous wrong fount letters.

Orange Free State became a province of the Union of South Africa on 31 May 1910. Stamps used during the Interprovincial Period (1 June 1910–31 August 1913) are listed under South Africa.

VI. TRANSVAAL

(formerly South African Republic)

From 1852 mail from the Transvaal was forwarded to the Cape of Good Hope, via the Orange Free State, by a post office at Potchefstroom. In 1859 the Volksraad voted to set up a regular postal service and arrangements were made for letters sent to the Cape and for overseas to be franked with Cape of Good Hope stamps.

The Potchefstroom postmaster placed his first order for these on 23 August 1859 and examples of all four triangular values are known postmarked there. From 1868 mail via the Orange Free State required franking with their issues also.

A similar arrangement covering mail sent overseas via Natal was in operation from 9 July 1873 until the first British Occupation. Such letters carried combinations of Transvaal stamps, paying the rate to Natal, and Natal issues for the overseas postage. Such Natal stamps were sold, but not postmarked, by Transvaal post offices.

PRICES FOR STAMPS ON COVER	
Nos. 1/6 are rare used on cover.	
Nos. 7/80	from × 20
Nos. 86/155	from × 3
Nos. 156/62	from × 6
Nos. 163/9	from × 5
Nos. 170/225	from × 10
Nos. 226/34	from × 20
Nos. 235/7	—
Nos. 238/43	from × 12
Nos. 244/55	from × 4
Nos. 256/7	from × 6
Nos. 258/9	—
Nos. 260/76	from × 20
Nos. F1/5	from × 5
Nos. D1/7	from × 20
Nos. RO1/27	—

The issues for Pietersburg, Lydenburg, Rustenburg, Schweizer Renecke and Wolmaransstad are very rare when on cover.

1 (Eagle with   **2**   **3**
spread wings)

(Typo Adolph Otto, Gustrow, Mecklenburg-Schwerin)
1870 (1 May). Thin paper, clear and distinct impressions.

(a) Imperf
1	**1**	1d. brown-lake	£550	
	a.	Orange-red	£700	£700
2		6d. bright ultramarine	£300	£300
	a.	Pale ultramarine	£325	£325
3		1s. deep green	£850	£850
	a.	Tête-bêche (pair)		

(b) Fine roulette, 15½ to 16
4	**1**	1d. brown-lake	£200	
	a.	Brick-red	£180	
	b.	Orange-red	£180	
	c.	Vermilion	£180	
5		6d. bright ultramarine	£160	£160
	a.	Pale ultramarine	£170	£170
6		1s. deep green	£325	£350
	a.	Yellow-green	£275	£250
	b.	Emerald-green	£200	£200

Examples of Nos. 1/6 may have been sold to dealers at some stage between their arrival in Transvaal during August 1869 and the sale of stamps to the public for postal purposes on 1 May 1870.

PLATES. The German printings of the 1d., 6d. and 1s. in Type **1** were from two pairs of plates, each pair printing sheets of 80 in two panes of five horizontal rows of eight.

One pair of plates, used for Nos. 4a, 4c, 5a and 6/a, produced stamps spaced 1¼ to 1½ mm apart with the rouletting close to the design on all four sides. The 1d. from these "narrow" plates shows a gap in the outer frame line at the bottom right-hand corner. The second pair, used for Nos. 1/3, 4, 4b, 5/a and 6b, had 2½ to 3½ mm between the stamps. These "wide" plates were sent to the Transvaal in 1869 and were used there to produce either single or double pane printings until 1883.

The 6d. and 1s. "wide" plates each had an inverted *cliché*. When printed these occurred on right-hand pane R. 4/1 of the 6d. and right-hand pane R. 1/1 of the 1s. These were never corrected and resulted in tête-bêche pairs of these values as late as 1883.

REPRINTS AND IMITATIONS. A number of unauthorised printings were made of these stamps by the German printer. Many of these can be identified by differences in the central arms, unusual colours or, in the case of the 1d., by an extra frame around the numeral tablets at top.

Genuine stamps always show the "D" of "EENDRAGT" higher than the remainder of the word, have no break in the border above "DR" and depict the flagstaff at bottom right, behind "MAGT", stopping short of the central shield. They also show the eagle's eye as a clear white circle. On the forgeries the eye is often blurred.

The most difficult of the reprints to detect is the 1s. yellow-green which was once identified as genuine, but was subsequently identified, by J. N. Luff in *The Philatelic Record* 1911–12, as coming from an unauthorised plate of four. Stamps from this plate show either a white dot between "EEN" and "SHILLING" or a white flaw below the wagon pole.

(Typo M. J. Viljoen, Pretoria)
1870 (1 May–4 July).

I. Thin gummed paper from Germany. Impressions coarse and defective

(a) Imperf
8	**1**	1d. dull rose-red	£130	
	a.	Reddish pink	£120	
	b.	Carmine-red	£100	£120
9		6d. dull ultramarine	£425	£100
	a.	Tête-bêche (pair)		

(b) Fine roulette, 15½ to 16
10	**1**	1d. carmine-red	£850	£350
11		6d. dull ultramarine	£300	£130
	a.	Imperf between (vert pair)	£1300	

(c) Wide roulette, 6½
12	**1**	1d. carmine-red	—	£1100

II. Thick, hard paper with thin yellow smooth gum (No. 15) or yellow streaky gum (others)

(a) Imperf
13	**1**	1d. pale rose-red	£110	
	a.	Carmine-red	£110	£120
14		1s. yellow-green	£200	£170
	a.	Tête-bêche (pair)	£28000	
	b.	Bisected (6d.) (on cover)	†	£2750

(b) Fine roulette, 15½ to 16
15	**1**	1d. carmine-red (24.5)	£130	
16		6d. dull ultramarine (10.5)	£150	£130
	a.	Tête-bêche (pair)	£35000	£25000
17		1s. yellow-green	£850	£850

III. Medium paper, blotchy heavy printing and whitish gum.
Fine roulette 15½ to 16 (4 July)
18	**1**	1d. rose-red	£110	£130
	a.	Carmine-red	85·00	90·00
	b.	Crimson. From over-inked plate	£190	£160
19		6d. ultramarine	£140	95·00
	a.	Tête-bêche (pair)		
	b.	Deep ultramarine. From over-inked plate	£550	£200
20		1s. deep green	£250	£120
	a.	From over-inked plate	£650	£225

The rouletting machine producing the wide 6½ gauge was not introduced until 1875.

Nos. 18b, 19b and 20a were printed from badly over-inked plates giving heavy blobby impressions.

(Typo J. P. Borrius, Potchefstroom)
1870 (Sept)–**71**. Stout paper, but with colour often showing through, whitish gum.

(a) Imperf
21	**1**	1d. black	£190	£170

(b) Fine roulette, 15½ to 16
22	**1**	1d. black	30·00	40·00
	a.	Grey-black	30·00	40·00

23		6d. blackish blue (7.71)	£200	85·00
	a.	Dull blue	£140	£110

(Typo Adolph Otto, Gustrow, Mecklenburg-Schwerin)
1871 (July). Thin paper, clear and distinct impressions. Fine roulette, 15½ to 16.
24	**2**	3d. pale reddish lilac	90·00	£100
	a.	Deep lilac	£110	£120
	b.	Vert laid paper		

No. 24 and later printings in the Transvaal were produced from a pair of plates in the same format as the 1869 issue. All genuine stamps have a small dot on the left leg of the eagle.

Imperforate examples in the issued shade, without the dot on eagle's leg, had been previously supplied by the printer, probably as essays, but were not issued for postal purposes. (*Price* £550 *unused*.) They also exist tête-bêche (*Price for un pair* £3250).

Imperforate and rouletted stamps in other colours are reprints.

(Typo J. P. Borrius, Potchefstroom)
1872–74. Fine roulette, 15½ to 16.

(a) Thin transparent paper
25	**1**	1d. black	£300	£750
26		1d. bright carmine	£250	85·00
27		6d. ultramarine	£190	65·00
28		1s. green	£225	90·00

(b) Thinnish opaque paper, clear printing (Dec 1872)
29	**1**	1d. reddish pink	£100	60·00
	a.	Carmine-red	£100	60·00
30	**2**	3d. grey-lilac	£150	70·00
31	**1**	6d. ultramarine	£100	40·00
	a.	Pale ultramarine	£110	45·00
32		1s. yellow-green	£130	70·00
	a.	Green	£130	70·00
	aa.	Bisected (6d.) (on cover)	†	£2750

(c) Thickish wove paper (1873–74)
33	**1**	1d. dull rose	£500	£110
	a.	Brownish rose	£650	£150
	b.	Printed on both sides		
34		6d. milky blue	£225	70·00
	a.	Deep dull blue	£130	55·00
	aa.	Imperf (pair)	£900	
	ab.	Imperf between (horiz pair)	£950	
	ac.	Wide roulette 6½		

(d) Very thick dense paper (1873–74)
35	**1**	1d. dull rose	£800	£190
	a.	Brownish rose	£600	£170
36		6d. dull ultramarine	£275	85·00
	a.	Bright ultramarine	£300	85·00
37		1s. yellow-green	£1300	£850

(Typo P. Davis & Son, Pietermaritzburg)
1874 (Sept). P 12½.

(a) Thin transparent paper
38	**1**	1d. pale brick-red	£180	60·00
	a.	Brownish red	£180	60·00
39		6d. deep blue	£250	85·00

(b) Thicker opaque paper
40	**1**	1d. pale red	£225	95·00
41		6d. blue	£225	75·00
	a.	Imperf between (pair)		
	b.	Deep blue	£225	75·00

(Typo Adolph Otto, Gustrow, Mecklenburg-Schwerin)
1874 (Oct). Thin smooth paper, clearly printed. Fine roulette 15½ to 16.
42	**3**	6d. bright ultramarine	85·00	32·00
	a.	Bisected (3d.) (on cover)	†	£1800

Stamps in other shades of blue, brown or red, often on other types of paper, are reprints.

(Typo J. F. Celliers on behalf of Stamp Commission, Pretoria)
1875 (29 Apr)–**77**.

I. Very thin, soft opaque (semi-pelure) paper

(a) Imperf
43	**1**	1d. orange-red	£180	70·00
	a.	Pin-perf	£950	£450
44	**2**	3d. lilac	£130	70·00
45	**1**	6d. blue	£120	55·00
	a.	Milky blue	£180	60·00
	aa.	Tête-bêche (pair)	£21000	
	ab.	Pin-perf	—	£450

(b) Fine roulette 15½ to 16
46	**1**	1d. orange-red	£650	£180
47	**2**	3d. lilac	£700	£200
48	**1**	6d. blue	£650	£190

(c) Wide roulette, 6½
49	**1**	1d. orange-red	—	£300
50	**2**	3d. lilac	£850	£400
51	**1**	6d. blue	—	£200
	a.	Bright blue	—	£200
	b.	Milky blue	—	£200

II. Very thin, hard transparent (pelure) paper (1875–76)

(a) Imperf
52	**1**	1d. brownish red	80·00	42·00
	a.	Orange-red	70·00	35·00
	b.	Dull red	75·00	65·00
	ba.	Pin-perf	£750	£450
53	**2**	3d. lilac	80·00	55·00
	a.	Pin-perf	—	£475
	b.	Deep lilac	90·00	55·00
54	**1**	6d. pale blue	80·00	70·00
	a.	Blue	80·00	55·00
	ab.	Tête-bêche (pair)		
	ac.	Pin-perf	—	£425
	b.	Deep blue	85·00	60·00

(b) Fine roulette 15½ to 16
55	**1**	1d. orange-red	£450	£170
	a.	Brown-red	£450	£170
56	**2**	3d. lilac	£500	£180
57	**1**	6d. blue	£225	£130
	a.	Deep blue	£225	£150

(c) Wide roulette, 6½
58	**1**	1d. orange-red	£1200	£250
	a.	Bright red	—	£250
59	**2**	3d. lilac	£1100	£325
60	**1**	6d. deep blue	£1200	£140

III. Stout hard-surfaced paper with smooth, nearly white, gum (1876)

(a) Imperf

61	1	1d. bright red	38·00	29·00
62	2	3d. lilac	£475	£160
63	1	6d. bright blue	£140	32·00
		a. Tête-bêche (pair)		
		b. Pale blue	£140	32·00
		c. Deep blue (deep brown gum)	85·00	28·00
		ca. Tête-bêche (pair)	—	£22000

(b) Fine roulette, 15½ to 16

64	1	1d. bright red	£550	£200
65	2	3d. lilac	£500	
66	1	6d. bright blue	£900	£130
		a. Deep blue (deep brown gum)	£750	£350

(c) Wide roulette, 6½

67	1	1d. bright red	£750	£200
68		6d. pale blue	—	£300
		a. Deep blue (deep brown gum)	£800	£350

IV. Coarse, soft white paper (1876–77)

(a) Imperf

69	1	1d. brick-red	£250	75·00
70		6d. deep blue	£300	£650
		a. Milky blue	£450	£140
71		1s. yellow-green	£600	£180
		a. Bisected (6d.) (on cover)	†	£2250

(b) Fine roulette, 15½ to 16

72	1	1d. brick-red	—	£500
73		6d. deep blue	—	£250
74		1s. yellow-green	£1000	£450

(c) Wide roulette, 6½

75	1	1d. brick-red	—	£550
76		6d. deep blue	—	£1300
77		1s. yellow-green	—	£1400

(d) Fine × wide roulette

78	1	1d. brick-red	£850	£425

V. Hard, thick, coarse yellowish paper (1876–77)

79	1	1d. brick-red (imperf)	—	£450
80		1d. brick-red (wide roulette)	—	£600

The pin-perforated stamps have various gauges and were probably produced privately or by one or more post offices other than Pretoria.

On Nos. 63c/ca, 66a and 68a the brown gum used was so intense that it caused staining of the paper which is still visible on used examples.

See also Nos. 171/4.

FIRST BRITISH OCCUPATION

By 1876 conditions in the Transvaal had deteriorated and the country was faced by economic collapse, native wars and internal dissension. In early 1877 Sir Theophilus Shepstone, appointed Special Commissioner to the South African Republic by the British Government, arrived in Pretoria and on 12 April annexed the Transvaal with the acquiesence of at least part of the European population.

V. R.   **V. R.**

TRANSVAAL.   **TRANSVAAL.**
   (4)   (5)

T **4** is the normal overprint, but Setting I No. 11 (R. 2/3) has a wider-spaced overprint as T **5**.

1877 (Apr). Optd with T **4** in red.

(a) Imperf

86	2	3d. lilac (*semi-pelure*) (No. 44)	£1700	£400
		a. Opt Type 5		
87		3d. lilac (*pelure*) (No. 53)	£1700	£275
		a. Opt Type 5	£8500	£2750
		b. Opt on back	£4000	£3750
		c. Opt double, in red and in black	£7500	
88	1	6d. milky blue (No. 70)	£2250	£275
		a. Opt inverted	—	£5500
		b. Opt double	£5000	£1200
		c. Opt Type 5	£9000	£3250
		d. Deep blue	—	£350
89		1s. yellow-green (No. 71)	£850	£275
		a. Bisected (6d.) (on cover)	†	£2750
		b. Opt inverted	—	£4750
		c. Opt Type 5	£6000	£1700
		d. Tête-bêche (pair)		

(b) Fine roulette, 15½ to 16

90	2	3d. lilac (*pelure*) (No. 56)	—	£1700
91	1	6d. deep blue (No. 73)	—	£1800
92		1s. yellow-green (No. 74)	£19000	£850
		a. Opt Type 5		

(c) Wide roulette, 6½

93	2	3d. lilac (*pelure*) (No. 59)	—	£2500
		a. Opt Type 5		
94	1	6d. deep blue (No. 76)	—	£2500
		a. Opt Type 5		
95		1s. yellow-green (No. 77)	£4500	£2250
		a. Opt inverted	—	£6500

Nos. 88a, 89b and 95a occurred on the inverted *cliché* of the basic stamps.

1877 (June). Optd with T **4** in black.

I. Very thin, hard transparent (pelure) paper

96	1	1d. orange-red (imperf) (No. 52a)	£375	£180
97		1d. orange-red (fine roulette) (No. 55)	—	£1100

II. Stout hard-surfaced paper with smooth, nearly white, gum

98	1	1d. bright red (imperf) (No. 61)	40·00	30·00
		a. Opt inverted	£650	£600
		b. Opt Type 5	£850	£900
99		1d. bright red (fine roulette) (No. 64)	£250	70·00
		a. Opt inverted		
		b. Opt double	—	£1300
		c. Imperf between (horiz pair)	£1200	
		d. Imperf vert (horiz pair)	£1200	

100		1d. bright red (*wide roulette*) (No. 67)	£800	£250
100a		1d. bright red (*fine×wide roulette*) (No. 78)	—	£250

III. New ptgs on coarse, soft white paper

(a) Imperf

101	1	1d. brick-red (5.77)	40·00	32·00
		a. Opt double	—	£1400
		b. Opt Type 5	£900	
102	2	3d. lilac	£140	70·00
		a. Opt inverted		
		b. Deep lilac	£250	£120
103	1	6d. dull blue	£160	42·00
		a. Opt double	£3750	£2250
		b. Opt inverted	£1600	£200
		c. Opt Type 5	—	£1300
		da. Opt Type 5 inverted		
		e. Blue (bright to deep)	£250	42·00
		ea. Bright blue, opt inverted	—	£550
		f. Pin-perf	—	£700
104		1s. yellow-green	£200	80·00
		a. Opt inverted	£1500	£300
		b. Tête-bêche (pair)	£27000	£27000
		c. Opt Type 5	£5500	£1700
		d. Bisected (6d.) (on cover)	†	£2000

(b) Fine roulette, 15½ to 16

105	1	1d. brick-red	£120	£110
		a. Imperf horiz (vert strip of 3)		
		b. Imperf between (horiz pair)	†	£750
		c. Imperf vert (horiz pair)	£1500	
106	2	3d. lilac	£325	90·00
107	1	6d. dull blue	£375	80·00
		a. Opt inverted	—	£850
		b. Opt Type 5	£6000	
108		1s. yellow-green	£400	£130
		a. Opt inverted	£1600	£600
		b. Opt Type 5	—	£3000

(c) Wide roulette, 6½

109	1	1d. brick-red	£800	£180
		a. Opt Type 5	—	£1300
110	2	3d. lilac	—	£900
111	1	6d. dull blue	—	£1500
		a. Opt inverted	—	£4750
112		1s. yellow-green	£700	£180
		a. Opt inverted	£2250	£750

1877 (31 Aug). Optd with T **4** in black.

113	1	6d. blue/*rose* (imperf)	£140	65·00
		a. Bisected (3d.) (on cover)	†	—
		b. Opt inverted	£160	65·00
		c. Tête-bêche (pair)		
		d. Opt omitted	£3750	£2500
114		6d. blue/*rose* (fine roulette)	£400	85·00
		a. Opt inverted	£700	85·00
		b. Tête-bêche (pair)		
		c. Opt omitted		
		d. Bisected (3d.) (on cover)	†	—
115		6d. blue/*rose* (wide roulette)		
		a. Opt inverted	—	£800
		b. Opt omitted		

Nos. 113/15 were overprinted from a setting of 40 which was applied upright to one pane in each sheet and inverted on the other.

V. R.   **V. R.**

Transvaal   **Transvaal**
   (6)   (7)

1877 (28 Sept)–**79**. Optd with T **6** in black.

(a) Imperf

116	1	1d. red/*blue*	80·00	40·00
		a. "Transvral" (Right pane R. 2/3)	£5500	£2500
		b. Opt double	£4250	
		c. Opt inverted	£950	£475
		d. Opt omitted		
117		1d. red/*orange* (6.12.77)	38·00	28·00
		a. Pin-perf		
		b. Printed both sides		
		c. Opt double	£3750	
		d. Optd with Type 7 (15.4.78)	90·00	60·00
		e. Pair. Nos. 117 and 117d	£275	
118	2	3d. mauve/*buff* (24.10.77)	85·00	38·00
		a. Opt inverted	—	£850
		b. Pin-perf		
		c. Bisected (1½d) (on cover)	†	—
		d. Optd with Type 7 (15.4.78)	£100	48·00
		da. Pin-perf	£850	£850
		e. Pair. Nos. 118 and 118d	£400	
119		3d. mauve/*green* (18.4.79)	£275	55·00
		a. Pin-perf		
		b. Opt inverted	—	£2500
		c. Opt omitted		
		d. Printed both sides	†	—
		e. Optd with Type 7	£225	48·00
		ea. Opt inverted	—	£2500
		eb. Printed both sides	—	£1200
		f. Opt omitted	—	£4000
		g. Pair. Nos. 119 and 119e	£850	
120	1	6d. blue/*green* (27.11.77)	£150	48·00
		a. Deep blue/*green*	£160	50·00
		b. Small "v" in "Transvaal" (Left pane R. 5/2)	—	£850
		d. "V.R." (Right pane R. 3/4)	—	£850
		e. Tête-bêche (pair)	—	£22000
		f. Opt inverted	—	£1400
		g. Pin-perf		
		h. Bisected (3d.) (on cover)	†	—
121		6d. blue/*blue* (20.3.78)	£110	38·00
		a. Bisected (3d.) (on cover)		
		b. Opt inverted	—	£1400
		c. Opt omitted	—	£2500
		d. Opt double	—	£3750
		e. Pin-perf		
		f. Bisected (3d.) (on cover)	†	£1100
		g. Optd with Type 7	£225	40·00
		ga. Tête-bêche (pair)	£19000	
		gb. Opt inverted	—	£850
		gc. Bisected (3d.) (on cover)	†	—
		h. Pair. Nos. 121 and 121g	£650	

(b) Fine roulette, 15½ to 16

122	1	1d. red/*blue*	£150	48·00
		a. "Transvral" (Right pane R. 2/3)	—	£3000
123		1d. red/*orange* (6.12.77)	50·00	38·00
		a. Imperf between (pair)	£700	
		b. Optd with Type 7 (15.4.78)	£225	£160
		c. Pair. Nos. 123 and 123b	£600	
124	2	3d. mauve/*buff* (24.10.77)	£150	38·00
		a. Imperf between (pair)	£950	
		b. Opt inverted	—	£3500
		c. Optd with Type 7 (15.4.78)	£275	£150
		ca. Imperf between (pair)	£900	
		d. Pair. Nos. 124 and 124c		
125		3d. mauve/*green* (18.4.79)	£850	£225
		a. Optd with Type 7	£850	£225
		b. Pair. Nos. 125 and 125a		
126	1	6d. blue/*green* (27.11.77)	£130	38·00
		a. "V.R" (Right pane R. 3/4)	—	£1400
		b. Tête-bêche (pair)		
		c. Opt inverted	—	£800
		d. Opt omitted	—	£4250
		e. Bisected (3d.) (on cover)	†	£950
127		6d. blue/*blue* (20.3.78)	£375	75·00
		a. Opt inverted	—	£1100
		b. Opt omitted	—	£3750
		c. Imperf between (pair)		
		d. Bisected (3d.) (on cover)	†	£1000
		e. Optd with Type 7	£600	£150
		ea. Opt inverted	—	£1400

(c) Wide roulette, 6¼

128	1	1d. red/*orange* (15.4.78)	£350	£130
		a. Optd with Type 7	—	£375
129	2	3d. mauve/*buff* (24.10.77)	—	£130
		a. Optd with Type 7 (15.4.78)	—	£425
130		3d. mauve/*green* (18.4.79)	£850	£375
		a. Optd with Type 7	—	£400
131	1	6d. blue/*green* (27.11.77)	—	£1400
132		6d. blue/*blue* (20.3.78)	—	£375
		a. Opt inverted		
		b. Optd with Type 7	—	£425
		ba. Opt inverted		

(d) Fine×wide roulette

132c	1	1d. red/*orange*		£850

Nos. 116/32c were overprinted from various settings covering sheets of 80 or panes of 40 (8×5). Initially these settings contained Type 6 only, but from March 1878 settings also contained examples of Type 7. Details of these mixed settings are as follows:

1d. red/*orange* (sheets of 80): all Type 6 except for 16 Type 7.
3d. mauve/*buff* (panes of 40): 16 Type 7.
3d. mauve/*green* (panes of 40): uncertain, some panes at least contained 27 Type 7.
6d. blue/*blue* (sheets of 80): either 24 or 27 Type 7.

9

(Recess B.W.)

1878 (26 Aug)–**80**. P 14, 14½.

133	9	½d. vermilion (1.9.80)	30·00	95·00
134		1d. pale red-brown	22·00	7·50
		a. Brown-red	22·00	7·00
135		3d. dull rose (25.11.78)	35·00	10·00
		a. Claret	40·00	12·00
136		4d. sage-green	45·00	12·00
137		6d. olive-black (25.11.78)	20·00	10·00
		a. Black-brown	22·00	7·50
138		1s. green (25.11.78)	£180	55·00
139		2s. blue (25.11.78)	£325	£100
133/39		Set of 7	£600	£250

The ½d. is printed on paper bearing the sheet watermark 'R TURNER/CHAFFORD MILLS' in double-lined block capitals. Other values are generally on unwatermarked paper, but examples of the 1s. are known with the same watermark as the ½d.

The above prices are for examples perforated on all four sides. Stamps from margins of sheets, with perforations absent on one or two sides, can be supplied for about 30% less.

The used price quoted for No. 139 is for an example with telegraphic cancel, a 23.5 mm circular datestamp of Pretoria (or more rarely Heidelberg or Standerton). Postally used examples are worth much more.

1 Penny   **1 Penny**   **1 Penny**
  (10)   (11)   (12)

1 Penny   **1 Penny**
  (13)   (14)

1 PENNY   **1 Penny**
  (15)   (16)

1879 (22 Apr). No. 137a surch with T **10** to **16** in black.

140	10	1d. on 6d.	£110	48·00
		a. Surch in red	£350	£180
141	11	1d. on 6d.	£300	90·00
		a. Surch in red	£800	£400
142	12	1d. on 6d.	£300	90·00
		a. Surch in red	£800	£400
143	13	1d. on 6d.	£130	60·00
		a. Surch double	£400	£200
		b. Surch in red	£750	£180
144	14	1d. on 6d.	£750	£180
		a. Surch in red	£6500	£1700
145	15	1d. on 6d.	65·00	27·00
		a. Surch in red	£200	90·00
146	16	1d. on 6d.	£275	85·00
		a. Surch in red	£750	£375

Nos. 140/6 were surcharged from a setting of 60 containing 11 examples of Type **10**, four of Type **11**, four of Type **12**, nine of Type **13**, two of Type **14** (although there may have been only one in the first two ptgs), 25 of Type **15** and five of Type **16**.

The red surcharges may have been produced first.

V. R.　　　V. R.

Transvaal　**Transvaal**
(16a)

Small "T" (R. 2/8, 3/8, 4/8, 5/8 on right pane of 1d. and left pane of 3d.)

1879 (Aug–Sept). Optd with T **16a** in black.

		(a) Imperf		
147	**1**	1d. red/yellow	70·00	45·00
		a. Small "T"	£375	£250
		b. Red/orange	70·00	38·00
		ba. Small "T"	£350	£200
148	**2**	3d. mauve/green (9.79)	60·00	32·00
		a. Small "T"	£300	£130
149		3d. mauve/blue (9.79)	70·00	38·00
		a. Small "T"	£350	£130
		(b) Fine roulette 15½ to 16		
150	**1**	1d. red/yellow	£425	£275
		a. Small "T"	£1300	£800
		b. Red/orange	£950	£450
		ba. Small "T"	£2500	
151	**2**	3d. mauve/green	£900	£325
		a. Small "T"	—	£1000
152		3d. mauve/blue	—	£250
		a. Small "T"	—	£800
		(c) Wide roulette 6½		
153	**1**	1d. red/yellow	£850	£750
		a. Small "T"		
		b. Red/orange	£1800	£1400
154	**2**	3d. mauve/green	£1300	£750
		a. Small "T"		
155		3d. mauve/blue	—	£850
		(d) Pin-perf about 17		
156	**1**	1d. red/yellow	—	£850
157	**2**	3d. mauve/blue	—	£1400

SECOND REPUBLIC

Following the first Boer War the independence of the South African Republic was recognised by the Convention of Pretoria from 8 August 1881.

Nos. 133/9 remained valid and some values were available for postage until 1885.

Een Penny
(17)

1882 (11 Aug). No. 136 surch with T **17**.

170	**9**	1d. on 4d. sage-green	25·00	8·50
		a. Surch inverted	£350	£200

Used examples of a similar, but larger, surcharge (width 20 *mm*) are known. These were previously considered to be forgeries, but it is now believed that some, at least, may represent a trial printing of the "EEN PENNY" surcharge.

(Typo J. F. Celliers)

1883 (20 Feb–3 Aug). Re-issue of T **1** and **2**. P 12.

171	**1**	1d. grey (to black) (5.4)	9·00	3·50
		a. Imperf vert (horiz pair)	£350	
		b. Imperf horiz (vert pair)	£650	£475
172	**2**	3d. grey-black (to black)/rose	38·00	8·50
		a. Bisected (1d.) (on cover)	†	£800
173		3d. pale red (7.5)	18·00	3·75
		a. Bisected (1d.) (on cover)	†	£800
		b. Imperf horiz (vert pair)	†	£1200
		c. Chestnut	38·00	7·50
		ca. Imperf between (horiz pair)	†	—
		d. Vermilion	38·00	8·00
174		1s. green (to deep) (3.8)	90·00	8·50
		a. Bisected (6d.) (on cover)	†	£600
		b. Tête-bêche (pair)	£1300	£180

Reprints are known of Nos. 172, 173, 173b and 173c. The paper of the first is *bright rose* in place of *dull rose*, and the impression is brownish black in place of grey-black to deep black. The reprints on white paper have the paper thinner than the originals, and the gum yellowish instead of white. The colour is a dull deep orange-red.

The used price quoted for No. 174b is for an example with telegraphic cancel. Postally used examples are worth much more. (See note below No. 139).

18

PERFORATIONS. Stamps perforated 11½×12 come from the first vertical row of sheets of the initial printing otherwise perforated 12½×12.

REPRINTS. Reprints of the general issues 1885–93, 1894–95, 1895–96 and 1896–97 exist in large quantities produced using the original plates from 1911 onwards. They cannot readily be distinguished from genuine originals except by comparison with used stamps, but the following general characteristics may be noted. The reprints are all perf 12½, large holes; the paper is whiter and thinner than that usually employed for the originals and their colours lack the lustre of those of the genuine stamps.

Forged surcharges have been made on these reprints.

(Des J. Vurtheim. Typo Enschedé)

1885 (13 Mar)–**93**. P 12½.

175	**18**	½d. grey (30.3.85)	2·50	10
		a. Perf 13½	9·50	1·75
		b. Perf 12½×12	4·00	10
		ba. Perf 11½×12	35·00	9·00
176		1d. carmine	2·25	10
		a. Perf 12½×12	2·25	10
		aa. Perf 11½×12	22·00	3·75
		b. Rose	2·00	10
		ba. Perf 12½×12	2·00	10
177		2d. brown-purple (P 12½×12) (9.85)	3·50	4·75
178		2d. olive-bistre (14.4.87)	3·50	10
		a. Perf 12½×12	5·50	10
179		2½d. mauve (to bright) (8.93)	4·50	55
180		3d. mauve (to bright)	5·00	3·25
		a. Perf 12½×12	10·00	2·75
		aa. Perf 11½×12	40·00	20·00
181		4d. bronze-green	7·00	2·25
		a. Perf 13½	14·00	2·75
		b. Perf 12½×12	20·00	2·25
		ba. Perf 11½×12	£200	80·00
182		6d. pale dull blue	5·00	4·50
		a. Perf 13½	8·00	2·50
		b. Perf 12½×12	10·00	1·00
		ba. Perf 11½×12		
183		1s. yellow-green	4·75	2·50
		a. Perf 13½	40·00	7·50
		b. Perf 12½×12	16·00	1·50
184		2s.6d. orange-buff (to buff) (2.12.85)	17·00	4·25
		a. Perf 12½×12	27·00	10·00
185		5s. slate (2.12.85)	10·00	7·50
		a. Perf 12½×12	50·00	12·00
186		10s. dull chestnut (2.12.85)	45·00	17·00
		a. Yellow-brown (1891)		
187		£5 deep green (3.92)*	£3250	£190
		s. Optd "Monster"	£170	

Singles of the 6d. pale dull blue imperforate have been reported used in 1893.

*Most examples of No. 187 on the market are either forgeries or reprints.

HALVE PENNY
(19)

1885 (22 May–Aug). Surch with T **19**. Reading up or down.

188	**2**	½d. on 3d. (No. 173)	10·00	15·00
189	**1**	½d. on 1s. (No. 174) (8.85)	42·00	70·00
		a. Tête-bêche (pair)	£1000	£450

Nos. 188/9 were surcharged by a setting of 40. After the left pane had been surcharged reading down, the sheets were turned so that the right pane had the surcharges reading up.

HALVE PENNY / Z.A.R
(20)

TWEE PENCE / Z. A. R.
(21)

HALVE PENNY
(22)

1885 (1 Sept). No. 137a surch with T **20/1** in red.

190	**9**	½d. on 6d. black-brown	85·00	£120
191		2d. on 6d. black-brown	16·00	20·00

1885 (28 Sept). No. 180a surch with T **22**.

192	**18**	½d. on 3d. mauve	9·50	9·50
		a. "PRNNY" (R. 6/6)	65·00	85·00
		b. 2nd "N" inverted (R. 3/8)	£110	£130
		c. Perf 11½×12	20·00	20·00

2d　　**2d**
(23)　　(24)

1887 (15 Jan). No. 180a surch with T **23/4**.

193	**18**	2d. on 3d. mauve (Type **23**)	15·00	13·00
		a. Surch double	—	£400
		b. Perf 11½×12	38·00	28·00
194		2d. on 3d. mauve (Type **24**)	3·00	6·00
		a. Surch double	£225	£225
		b. Perf 11½×12	10·00	16·00

Nos. 193/4 were surcharged from the same setting of 60 (10×6) which showed Type **24** on the top five horizontal rows and Type **23** on the sixth horizontal row.

Halve Penny　**1 Penny**
(25)　　(26)

2½ Pence　　**2½ Pence**
(27)　　(28)

Two types of surcharge:
A. Vertical distance between bars 12½ mm.
B. Distance 13½ mm.

1893. T **18** surch. P 12½.

		(a) In red		
195	**25**	½d. on 2d. olive-bistre (A) (27.5)	1·50	3·50
		a. Surch inverted	3·25	4·00
		b. Surch Type B	2·25	4·25
		ba. Surch inverted	6·50	13·00
		(b) In black		
196	**25**	½d. on 2d. olive-bistre (A) (2.7)	1·75	3·50
		a. Surch inverted	5·00	6·00
		b. Extra surch on back inverted	£170	
		c. Surch Type B	2·50	4·50
		ca. Surch inverted	22·00	19·00
		cb. Extra surch on back inverted	£300	
197	**26**	1d. on 6d. blue (A) (26.1)	2·75	2·50
		a. Surch double	60·00	48·00
		b. Surch inverted	3·25	3·50
		c. Surch treble		
		d. Surch Type B	3·50	3·50
		da. Surch inverted	7·00	5·50
		db. Surch double	—	90·00
		e. Pair, one without surch	£300	
198	**27**	2½d. on 1s. green (A) (2.1)	3·25	8·00
		a. "2/½d" for "2½" (R. 1/10)	50·00	90·00
		b. Surch inverted	8·50	9·00
		ba. Surch inverted and "2/½d" for "2½"	£375	£325
		c. Extra surch on back inverted	£475	£475
		d. Surch double, one inverted	£750	
		e. Surch Type B	4·00	10·00
		ea. Surch inverted	11·00	20·00
199	**28**	2½d. on 1s. green (A) (24.6)	12·00	9·50
		a. Surch double	55·00	50·00
		b. Surch inverted	12·00	12·00
		c. Surch Type B	15·00	15·00
		ca. Surch double	90·00	£100
		cb. Surch inverted	24·00	24·00

Surcharge Types **25/8** all show a similar setting of the horizontal bars at top and bottom. On horizontal rows 1 to 4 and 6, the bars are 12½ mm apart and on row 5 the distance is 13½ mm.

29 (Wagon with shafts)　**30** (Wagon with pole)

1894 (July). P 12½.

200	**29**	½d. grey	2·50	1·50
201		1d. carmine	4·00	20
202		2d. olive-bistre	4·00	30
203		6d. pale dull blue	4·50	1·00
204		1s. yellow-green	23·00	30·00

For note *re* reprints, see below T **18**.

1895 (16 Mar)–**96**. P 12½.

205	**30**	½d. pearl-grey (1895)	2·25	10
		a. Lilac-grey	2·25	10
206		1d. rose-red	2·25	10
207		2d. olive-bistre (1895)	2·75	30
208		3d. mauve (1895)	3·75	1·25
209		4d. olive-black (1895)	4·00	1·00
210		6d. pale dull blue (1895)	4·00	1·00
211		1s. yellow-green (18.3.95)	5·00	1·50
212		5s. slate (1896)	23·00	42·00
212a		10s. pale chestnut (1896)	23·00	9·00
205s/8s, 211s Optd "Monster" *Set of 5*			£170	

For note *re* reprints, see below T **18**.

Halve Penny
(31)

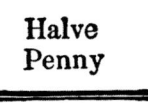

1d.　　**1d.**
(32—Round dot)　(32a—Square dot)

1895 (July–Aug). Nos. 211 and 179 surch with T **31/2**.

213	**30**	½d. on 1s. green (R.)	2·25	40
		a. Surch spaced	3·75	2·25
		b. "Pennij" for "Penny" (R. 6/6)	70·00	80·00
		c. Surch inverted	5·50	5·00
		d. Surch double	75·00	£100
214	**18**	1d. on 2½d. bright mauve (G.)	50	30
		a. Surch inverted	23·00	15·00
		b. Surch double	75·00	75·00
		c. Surch on back only	85·00	
		d. Surch Type **32a**	1·75	1·75
		da. Surch inverted	75·00	
		e. Surch treble	£600	

The normal space between "Penny" and the bars is 3 mm. On No. 213a, which comes from the fifth horizontal row of the setting, this is increased to 4 mm. Copies may be found in which one or both of the bars have failed to print.

Type **32a** with square stop occurred on R. 3/3-4, 3/6-8, 4/4-5, 4/7-8, 4/10, 6/3, 6/7-8 and 6/10 of the setting of 60.

33   **34**

1895 (July). Fiscal stamp optd "POSTZEGEL". P 11½.
215	**33**	6d. bright rose (G.)	3·25	3·00
		a. Imperf between (pair)		
		b. Opt inverted		

(Litho The Press Printing and Publishing Works, Pretoria)
1895 (6 Sept). Introduction of Penny Postage. P 11.
215c	**34**	1d. red (pale *to* deep)	2·75	3·25
		ca. Imperf between (pair)	£225	£250
		cb. Imperf vert (horiz pair)		
		cc. Imperf (pair)		

1896–97. P 12½.
216	**30**	½d. green (1896)	1·75	10
217		1d. rose-red and green (1896)	1·75	10
218		2d. brown and green (2.97)	2·00	20
219		2½d. dull blue and green (6.96)	3·00	30
220		3d. purple and green (3.97)	3·25	3·00
221		4d. sage-green and green (3.97)	3·25	4·00
222		6d. lilac and green (11.96)	3·00	2·75
223		1s. ochre and green (3.96)	2·50	1·50
224		2s.6d. dull violet and green (6.96)	3·75	4·50

For note *re* reprints, see below T **18**.

SECOND BRITISH OCCUPATION

The Second Boer War began on 11 October 1899 and was concluded by the Peace of Vereeniging on 31 May 1902. Pretoria was occupied by the British on 5 June 1900 and a civilian postal service began operating 13 days later.

FORGERIES. The forgeries of the "V.R.I." and "E.R.I." overprints most often met with can be recognised by the fact that the type used is perfect and the three stops are always in alignment with the bottom of the letters. In the genuine overprints, which were made from old type, it is impossible to find all three letters perfect and all three stops perfect and in exact alignment with the bottom of the letters.

E. R. I.

Half

V. R. I.   E. R. I.   Penny

(35)   (36)   (37)

1900 (18 June). Optd with T **35**.
226	**30**	½d. green	40	1·50
		a. No stop after "V"	14·00	17·00
		b. No stop after "R"	11·00	13·00
		c. No stop after "I"	9·50	12·00
		d. Opt inverted	13·00	18·00
		e. Opt double		
		f. "V.I.R." (R. 4/4)	£850	
227		1d. rose-red and green	75	1·50
		a. No stop after "V"	15·00	18·00
		b. No stop after "R"	12·00	14·00
		c. No stop after "I"	9·00	11·00
		d. Opt inverted	14·00	23·00
		e. Opt double	90·00	£120
		f. No stops after "R" and "I"	90·00	90·00
		g. Opt omitted (in pair with normal)	£325	
228		2d. brown and green	4·25	4·00
		a. No stop after "V"	40·00	45·00
		c. No stop after "I"	48·00	50·00
		d. Opt inverted	26·00	30·00
		e. Opt double		
		f. "V.I.R." (R. 4/4)	£900	£950
		g. Opt albino		
229		2½d. dull blue and green	1·25	3·50
		a. No stop after "V"	22·00	30·00
		b. No stop after "R"	50·00	70·00
		c. No stop after "I"	18·00	24·00
		d. Opt inverted	16·00	18·00
230		3d. purple and green	1·50	3·50
		a. No stop after "V"	27·00	38·00
		b. No stop after "R"	55·00	70·00
		c. No stop after "I"	38·00	50·00
		d. Opt inverted	90·00	£100
		f. "V.I.R." (R. 4/4)	£900	
231		4d. sage-green and green	3·75	4·25
		a. No stop after "V"	50·00	50·00
		b. No stop after "R"	70·00	70·00
		c. No stop after "I"	45·00	45·00
		d. Opt inverted	35·00	40·00
232		6d. lilac and green	4·00	3·00
		a. No stop after "V"	28·00	28·00
		b. No stop after "R"	38·00	38·00
		c. No stop after "I"	38·00	38·00
		d. Opt inverted	40·00	48·00
233		1s. ochre and green	4·00	5·00
		a. No stop after "V"	30·00	38·00
		b. No stop after "R"	30·00	38·00
		c. No stop after "I"	55·00	60·00
		d. Opt inverted	55·00	60·00
		e. Opt double	95·00	£100
234		2s.6d. dull violet and green	4·75	17·00
		a. No stop after "V"	60·00	
		b. No stop after "R"	£100	
		c. No stop after "I"	—	£500

235		5s. slate	10·00	25·00
		a. No stop after "V"	£170	
236		10s. pale chestnut	13·00	27·00
		a. No stop after "V"	£170	
		b. No stop after "R"	£170	
		c. No stop after "I"	£170	
237	**18**	£5 deep green*	£2000	£800
		a. No stop after "V"		
		234s/7s Handstamped "SPECIMEN" *Set of 4*	£225	

*Many examples of No. 237 on the market are forgeries and the stamps should only be purchased if accompanied by a recent expert committee certificate.

The error "V.I.R." occurred on R. 4/4 in the first batch of stamps to be overprinted—a few sheets of the ½d., 2d. and 4d. The error was then corrected and stamps showing it are very rare. The corrected overprint shows the "I" dropped by 0.75mm. This variety is known on all values apart from the £5, but was later corrected.

A number of different settings were used to apply the overprint on Nos. 226/37. The missing stop varieties listed above developed during overprinting and occur on different positions in the various settings.

1901 (Jan)–**02**. Optd with T **36**.
238	**30**	½d. green	50	2·75
		a. Opt double		
239		1d. rose-red and green (20.3.01)	50	10
		a. "E." of opt omitted	80·00	
240		3d. purple and green (6.02)	2·25	4·75
241		4d. sage-green and green (6.02)	2·75	11·00
242		2s.6d. dull violet and green (10.02)	15·00	40·00

1901 (July). Surch with T **37**.
243	**30**	½d. on 2d. brown and green	65	2·00
		a. No stop after "E" (R. 4/6)	50·00	65·00

38 (POSTAGE REVENUE)   **39** (POSTAGE POSTAGE)

(Typo D.L.R.)

1902 (1 Apr–17 Dec). Wmk Crown CA. P 14.
244	**38**	½d. black and bluish green	2·75	20
		w. Wmk inverted	£170	£100
245		1d. black and carmine	1·50	15
		w. Wmk inverted	£130	85·00
246		2d. black and purple	8·50	1·25
247		2½d. black and blue	16·00	2·25
		w. Wmk inverted	£100	60·00
248		3d. black and sage-green (17.12.02)	18·00	2·00
249		4d. black and brown (17.12.02)	18·00	3·25
250		6d. black and orange-brown	4·50	1·50
251		1s. black and sage-green	21·00	26·00
252		2s. black and brown	75·00	85·00
253	**39**	2s.6d. magenta and black	18·00	19·00
254		5s. black and purple/*yellow*	42·00	50·00
255		10s. black and purple/*red*	80·00	50·00
		244/55 *Set of 12*	£250	£200
		244s/55s (inc 247ws) Optd "SPECIMEN" *Set of 12*	£200	

The colour of the "black" centres varies from brownish grey or grey to black.

1903 (1 Feb). Wmk Crown CA. P 14.
256	**39**	1s. grey-black and red-brown	19·00	6·00
257		2s. grey-black and yellow	22·00	25·00
258		£1 green and violet	£375	£225
259		£5 orange-brown and violet	£2250	£950
		256s/9s Optd "SPECIMEN" *Set of 4*	£275	

1904–09. Ordinary paper. Wmk Mult Crown CA. P 14.
260	**38**	½d. black and bluish green	13·00	3·00
		w. Wmk inverted	£250	£110
		y. Wmk inverted and reversed	£190	80·00
261		1d. black and carmine	12·00	1·75
262		2d. black and purple (*chalk-surfaced paper*) (1906)	28·00	2·00
263		2½d. black and blue (1905)	32·00	14·00
		aw. Wmk inverted	£190	£130
		b. Chalk-surfaced paper	28·00	8·00
264		3d. black and sage-green (1906) (*chalk-surfaced paper*)	4·25	50
265		4d. black and brown (1906) (*chalk-surfaced paper*)	6·50	70
		w. Wmk inverted	£190	£110
266		6d. black and orange	19·00	2·00
		a. Chalk-surfaced paper. *Black and brown-orange* (1906)	6·00	50
		w. Wmk inverted	£225	£120
267	**39**	1s. black and red-brown (1905)	15·00	50
268		2s. black and yellow (1906)	35·00	16·00
269		2s.6d. magenta and black (1909)	60·00	12·00
270		5s. black and purple/*yellow*	35·00	1·75
271		10s. black and purple/*red* (1907)	90·00	4·75
272		£1 green and violet (1908)	£425	50·00
		a. Chalk-surfaced paper	£300	24·00
		260/72a *Set of 13*	£550	65·00

There is considerable variation in the "black" centres as in the previous issue.

1905–09. Wmk Mult Crown CA. P 14.
273	**38**	½d. yellow-green	4·00	10
		a. Deep green (1908)	4·00	20
		w. Wmk inverted	£250	£130
274		1d. scarlet	1·25	10
		aw. Wmk inverted	—	£325
		b. Error. Wmk Cabled Anchor, T **13** of Cape of Good Hope (3.3.06*)	—	£325
275		2d. purple (1909)	3·50	1·25
276		2½d. bright blue (1909)	28·00	14·00
		273/6 *Set of 4*	32·00	14·00
		273s/6s Optd "SPECIMEN" *Set of 4*	£110	

*Earliest known date of use.

The monocoloured ½d. and 1d. are printed from new combined plates. These show a slight alteration in that the frame does not touch the crown.

1909. Prepared for use but not issued. Wmk Mult Crown CA. P 14.
277s	**38**	2d. grey (optd "SPECIMEN")		£300

Although this stamp was distributed in " SPECIMEN" form by the UPU, the entire supply sent to Transvaal was destroyed.

The ½d., 1d. and 2d. exist from coils constructed from normal sheets for use in stamp machines introduced in 1911. These coils were originally joined horizontally but the 1d. was subsequently issued joined vertically.

STAMP BOOKLETS

1905 (July). Black on red cover showing arms. Stapled.
SB1	2s.7d. booklet containing 30×1d. (No. 261) in blocks of 6	£3250

1905. Black on red cover. Stapled.
SB2	2s.7d. booklet containing 30×1d. (No. 274) in blocks of 6	£3500

1909. Black on red cover. Stapled.
SB3	2s.6d. booklet containing 10×½d. (No. 273) in block of 6 and block of 4, and 24×1d. (No. 274) in blocks of 6	£4000

Stocks of No. SB3 were supplied containing twelve examples of the ½d., it being intended that the postal clerks would remove two stamps before the booklets were sold. In some instances this did not occur.

POSTAL FISCAL STAMPS

1900–02. Fiscal stamps as in T **33**, but optd with T **35**. P 11½.
F1		1d. pale blue	—	45·00
F2		6d. dull carmine	—	75·00
F3		1s. olive-bistre	—	90·00
F4		1s.6d. brown	—	£120
F5		2s.6d. dull purple	—	£150

Nos. F1/5, previously listed as Nos. 1/5 of Volksrust, are fiscal issues which are known postally used from various Transvaal post offices between June 1900 and June 1902.

Nos. F1/5, and higher values to £5, were also used on telegrams.

POSTAGE DUE STAMPS

D 1   Inverted "p" for "d" (Right pane R. 10/6)

(Typo D.L.R.)

1907. Wmk Mult Crown CA. P 14.
D1	D **1**	½d. black and blue-green	3·50	1·25
D2		1d. black and scarlet	4·00	85
D3		2d. brown-orange	7·50	1·25
D4		3d. black and blue	7·50	6·50
D5		5d. black and violet	4·00	12·00
		a. Inverted "p" for "d"	60·00	
D6		6d. black and red-brown	4·25	12·00
D7		1s. scarlet and black	18·00	12·00
		D1/7 *Set of 7*	42·00	42·00

RAILWAY OFFICIAL STAMPS

The following stamps were provided for use on official correspondence of the Central Southern Africa Railways.

RO 1

1904. Nos, 244/5 stencil-cut as T RO **1** at CSAR's Departmental Printing Office, Germiston.
RO1	½d. grey-black and bluish green	†	£750
RO2	1d. grey-black and carmine	†	£750

Contemporary reports exist of these stamps with "CSAR" stencil-cut in a single line, but no examples are known. The stencil-cut exists sideways on No. RO1 and inverted on No. RO2. They were probably trials, only used at CSAR's head office in Johannesburg.

1905 (Feb). Nos, 244/6, 228/50 and 256 optd with Type RO **1** of Orange River Colony at CSAR's Departmental Printing Office, Germiston.
RO3	½d. grey-black and bluish green	50·00	15·00
RO4	1d. grey-black and carmine	50·00	10·00
	a. Opt double	£150	—
RO5	2d. grey-black and purple	£100	50·00
RO6	3d. grey-black and sage-green	£150	75·00
RO7	4d. grey-black and brown	£150	75·00
RO8	6d. black and orange brown	£200	£100
RO9	1s. bluish grey and red-brown	£350	£250

1905. As Nos. RO3/4 but Wmk Multiple Crown CA.
RO10	½d. grey-black and bluish green	75·00	45·00
RO11	1d. grey-black and carmine	75·00	45·00

The overprint on Nos. RO3/11 was applied in a setting of 120 and was normally placed either at the top or the bottom of the stamp, although central placings are known. The stamps were withdrawn on 13 October 1905, but examples of genuine late usage have been recorded. Dangerous forgeries, including a 2½d. duty, exist.

1907. No. 246 punctured with Type RO **2** of Orange River Colony.
RO12	2d. black and purple	—	£100

1907. Nos, 262, 264/7, and 273/5 punctured with Type RO **2** of Orange River Colony.
RO13	2d. black and purple	—	50·00
RO14	3d. black and sage-green	—	£100
RO15	4d. black and brown	—	£120
RO16	6d. black and orange	—	£120
RO17	1s. black and red-brown		

1907. No. 273/5 punctured with Type RO **2** of Orange River Colony.

RO18	½d. yellow-green	—	20·00
RO19	1d. scarlet	—	15·00
RO20	2d. purple	—	75·00

RO **2**

1910 (Sept). Nos, 262, 264/7, and 273/5 punctured with Type RO **2**.

RO21	½d. yellow-green	—	25·00
RO22	1d. scarlet	—	25·00
RO23	2d. black and purple		
RO24	2d. purple		
RO25	3d. black and sage-green		
RO26	4d. black and brown		
RO27	6d. black and brown-orange		
RO28	1s. black and red-brown		

Nos. RO21/7 were produced by removing the "C" from the perforating heads used to prepare Nos. RO12/20.

Forgeries of the punctured initials stamps are known but the height of the "CS/AR" or "S/AR" is 17-17.5 mm, compared with 13.5 mm of genuine examples.

Nos. RO12/27 were withdrawn on 1 April 1912.

TELEGRAPH STAMPS

In the 1880s Queen's Head postage stamps (Type **9**) and fiscal stamps were used for the prepayment of telegraph communication. Once these were used up it would seem that just postage stamps were used until the British occupation in 1900. In the early period of the occupation, postage stamps overprinted "V.R.I." up to the value of 2s.6d. and high value fiscal stamps similarly overprinted were used for telegraph purposes (Cape of Good Hope "Hope standing" 6d. and 1s. fiscal stamps overprinted "TRANSVAAL" were also used). The following stamps were overprinted or surcharged specifically for telegraphic use.

Transvaal
Telegraphs

(T 1)

Transvaal
Telegraphs.

(T 1)

ONE
Shilling.

(T 2)

Transvaal
Telegraphs.

FIVE
Shillings.

(T 3)

Transvaal
Telegraphs

(T 4)

1901 (Sept–Oct). Nos. 217, 222 and 224 optd as T T **1** or optd and surch as T T **2**.

T1	1d. rose-red and green (10.01)	45·00	30·00
T2	6d. lilac and green (10.01)	70·00	40·00
T3	1s. on 2s.6d. dull violet and green	45·00	30·00
T4	2s.6d. dull violet and green (10.01)	70·00	40·00

Forgeries of T1-4 exist, used examples should have a clear "Army Telegraphs" cancellation.

1902. Fiscal stamp (as T **33**) optd T **35** and surch as T T **3**. Perf 11, 11×11½ or 11½.

T5	5s. on £2 red-brown (shades)	—	£275

1902 (June?). No 222 optd T **36** and handstamped as T T **4**.

T6	6d. lilac and green	£400	£250

1902 (June?). Nos. 217 and 222 handstamped as T T **4**.

T7	1d. rose-red and green	
T8	6d. lilac and green	

Only unused examples of Nos. T7/8 are known, and it is possible that they were not issued.

1902 (June). King Edward VII fiscal stamps handstamped as T T **4**.

T9	10s. grey-black and bright blue	£450	£225
T10	£1 grey-black and sage-green	£850	£375
T11	£5 grey-black and purple	£4000	

Forgeries of the T T **4** handstamp are known on cleaned fiscally used stamps.

There are two versions of the T T **4** handstamp, one as illustrated and the other with "T" of "Transvaal" above the "T" of "Telegraphs".

From 1903 postage stamps were once again used to pay telegraph charges.

Transvaal became a province of the Union of South Africa on 31 May 1910.

Stamps used during the Interprovincial Period (1 June 1910–31 August 1913) are listed under South Africa.

PIETERSBURG

After the fall of Pretoria to the British in June 1900 the Transvaal government withdrew to the north of the country. Those post offices in areas not occupied by the British continued to function. The following stamps were then authorised by the State Secretary. Pietersburg itself was taken by British forces on 9 April 1901.

PRICES. Genuinely used examples are very rare. Stamps cancelled by favour exist and are worth the same as the unused prices quoted.

The issued stamps were initialled by the Controller, J. T. de V. Smit. All values exist without his signature and these come from clandestine printings in excess of the official government print order. Unsigned stamps were not issued by the Post Office.

P 1   P 2

P 3

TYPES P 1/3. Each value was printed in sheets of 24 (6×4) of which the first two horizontal rows were as Type P **1** (Large "P" in "POSTZEGEL" and large date), the third row as Type P **2** (Large "P" in "POSTZEGEL" and small date) and the fourth as Type P **3** (Small "P" in "POSTZEGEL" and small date).

(Type-set *De Zoutpansberg Wachter* Press, Pietersburg)

1901 (20 Mar (1d.)–3 Apr (others)).

A. Imperf

(a) Controller's initials in black

1	P **1**	½d. black/green		15·00
		e. Controller's initials omitted		95·00
2	P **2**	½d. black/green		45·00
		d. Controller's initials omitted		95·00
3	P **3**	½d. black/green		45·00
		d. Controller's initials omitted		95·00
4	P **1**	1d. black/red		3·50
5	P **2**	1d. black/red		5·50
6	P **3**	1d. black/red		7·00
7	P **1**	2d. black/orange		6·00
8	P **2**	2d. black/orange		14·00
9	P **3**	2d. black/orange		22·00
10	P **1**	4d. black/blue		5·50
11	P **2**	4d. black/blue		9·50
12	P **3**	4d. black/blue		32·00
13	P **1**	6d. black/green		9·50
14	P **2**	6d. black/green		15·00
15	P **3**	6d. black/green		40·00
16	P **1**	1s. black/yellow		8·00
17	P **2**	1s. black/yellow		14·00
18	P **3**	1s. black/yellow		25·00

(b) Controller's initials in red

19	P **1**	½d. black/green		15·00
20	P **2**	½d. black/green		35·00
21	P **3**	½d. black/green		40·00

B. P 11½

(a) Controller's initials in red

22	P **1**	½d. black/green		5·50
		c. Imperf vert (horiz pair)		95·00
23	P **2**	½d. black/green		17·00
		f. Imperf vert (horiz pair)		£120
24	P **3**	½d. black/green		12·00
		b. Imperf vert (horiz pair)		£120

(b) Controller's initials in black

25	P **1**	1d. black/red		2·00
		m. Imperf vert (horiz pair)		55·00
		n. Imperf between (vert pair: No. 25+No. 26)		75·00
		o. Imperf horiz (vert pair)		55·00
26	P **2**	1d. black/red		2·75
		f. Imperf vert (horiz pair)		80·00
		g. Imperf horiz (vert pair: No. 26+No. 27)..		60·00
27	P **3**	1d. black/red		4·00
		f. Imperf vert (horiz pair)		80·00
28	P **1**	2d. black/orange		5·50
29	P **2**	2d. black/orange		8·00
30	P **3**	2d. black/orange		14·00

For the ½d. the First printing had initials in red, those of the Second printing had them in black or red, and all of the Third were in red.

CONSTANT VARIETIES

½d. value

First printing

R.3/5	Centre figures "½" level	Imperf	(No. 20a)	70·00
		Perf	(No. 23d)	40·00
R.3/6	No stop after right "AFR"	Imperf	(No. 20b)	70·00
		Perf	(No. 23e)	40·00
R.4/6	Hyphen between right "AFR" and "REP"	Imperf	(No. 21a)	70·00
		Perf	(No. 24a)	40·00

Second printing—Imperf

R.1/1 & 4	Top left "½" inverted, no stop after right "AFR"	(No. 19c)	70·00
R.1/2	Top right "½" inverted	(No. 19d)	90·00
R.1/3	"1/3" at lower right	(No. 19e)	90·00
R.1/5	"POSTZFGEL"	(No. 19f)	90·00
R.1/6	Left spray inverted, "AFB" at right	(No. 19g)	90·00
R.2/1	"REB" at left, left side of inner frame 3 mm too high	(No. 19h)	90·00
R.2/2	"BEP" at left	(No. 19i)	90·00
R.2/3	"POSTZEOEL"	(No. 19j)	90·00
R.2/4	"AER" at right, left side of inner frame 2 mm too high	(No. 19k)	90·00
R.2/5	No stop after date	(No. 19l)	90·00
R.2/6	No stop after "PENNY"	(No. 19m)	
R.3/1	"1/3" at top left, "PE" of "PENNY" spaced	(No. 20c)	90·00
R.3/2	Right spray inverted	(No. 20d)	90·00
R.3/3	Top left "½" inverted	(No. 20e)	90·00
R.3/4	No stop after "Z" at left	(No. 20f)	
R.3/5	Centre figures "½" level	(No. 20g)	

R.3/6	"POSTZEGFL", no stop after right "AFR"	(No. 20h)	
R.4/3	"1/3" at top right	(No. 21b)	90·00
R.4/4	Lower left "½" inverted	(No. 21c)	90·00
R.4/5	"¼" at top left	(No. 21d)	90·00
R.4/6	Left spray inverted, "901" for "1901"..	(No. 21e)	

Third printing

R.1/2	No stop after left "AFR"	Imperf	(No. 1a)	60·00
R.1/3	"1/3" at top left, no bar over lower right "½"	Imperf	(No. 1b)	60·00
R.1/6	No stop after date	Imperf	(No. 1c)	60·00
R.2/5	"BEP" at left, no stop after date	Imperf	(No. 1d)	60·00
R.3/3	"AFB" at left	Imperf	(No. 2a)	60·00
		Perf	(No. 23a)	
R.3/4	"POSTZEGEI"	Imperf	(No. 2b)	60·00
		Perf	(No. 23b)	
R.3/6	No bar over lower right "½"	Imperf	(No. 2c)	60·00
R.4/1	No stop after right "AFR"	Imperf	(No. 3a)	60·00
R.4/4	No stop after left "Z", no bar under top right "½"	Imperf	(No. 3b)	60·00
		Perf	(No. 23c)	
R.4/5	"POSTZECEL, AER" at left	Imperf	(No. 3c)	60·00

1d. value

First printing

R.1/2	First "1" in date dropped	Imperf	(No. 4l)	35·00
		Perf	(No. 25l)	22·00
R.3/6	No stop after right "AFR"	Imperf	(No. 5e)	35·00
		Perf	(No. 26e)	22·00
R.4/5	Dropped "P" in "PENNY"	Imperf	(No. 6e)	35·00
		Perf	(No. 27e)	22·00

Second printing

R.1/2	Inverted "1" at lower left, first "1" of date dropped	Imperf	(No. 4a)	35·00
		Perf	(No. 25a)	22·00
R.1/3	No bar under top left "1"	Imperf	(No. 4b)	35·00
		Perf	(No. 25b)	22·00
R.1/4	No bar over lower right "1"	Imperf	(No. 4c)	35·00
		Perf	(No. 25c)	22·00
R.1/5	"POSTZFGEL"	Imperf	(No. 4d)	35·00
		Perf	(No. 25d)	22·00
R.1/6	"AFB" at right	Imperf	(No. 4e)	35·00
		Perf	(No. 25e)	22·00
R.2/1	"REB" at left	Imperf	(No. 4f)	35·00
		Perf	(No. 25f)	22·00
R.2/2	"BEP" at left	Imperf	(No. 4g)	35·00
		Perf	(No. 25g)	22·00
R.2/3	"POSTZEOEL"	Imperf	(No. 4h)	35·00
		Perf	(No. 25h)	22·00
R.2/4	"AER" at right	Imperf	(No. 4i)	35·00
		Perf	(No. 25i)	22·00
R.2/5	No stop after date	Imperf	(No. 4j)	35·00
		Perf	(No. 25j)	22·00
R.2/6	No stop after "PENNY"	Imperf	(No. 4k)	35·00
		Perf	(No. 25k)	22·00
R.3/2	Right spray inverted	Imperf	(No. 5a)	35·00
		Perf	(No. 26a)	22·00
R.3/3	No bar over lower left "1"	Imperf	(No. 5b)	35·00
		Perf	(No. 26b)	22·00
R.3/4	No stop after left "Z"	Imperf	(No. 5c)	35·00
		Perf	(No. 26c)	22·00
R.3/6	"POSTZEGFL", no stop after right "AFR"	Imperf	(No. 5d)	35·00
		Perf	(No. 26d)	22·00
R.4/1	No stop after right "AFR"	Imperf	(No. 6a)	35·00
		Perf	(No. 27a)	22·00
R.4/2 & 6	Left spray inverted	Imperf	(No. 6b)	22·00
		Perf	(No. 27b)	13·00
R.4/3	"POSTZEGEI"	Imperf	(No. 6c)	35·00
		Perf	(No. 27c)	22·00
R.4/4	No bar under top right "1"	Imperf	(No. 6d)	35·00
		Perf	(No. 27d)	22·00

2d. value

First printing

R.1/2	First "1" in date dropped	Imperf	(No. 7m)	45·00
		Perf	(No. 28a)	30·00
R.2/1	No stop after left "REP"	Imperf	(No. 7n)	45·00
		Perf	(No. 28b)	30·00
R.3/6	No stop after right "AFR"	Imperf	(No. 8f)	45·00
		Perf	(No. 29a)	30·00
R.4/1	Centre 2 wider, no stop after right "AFR"	Imperf	(No. 9a)	38·00
		Perf	(No. 30a)	30·00
R.4/2	Centre "2" wider	Imperf	(No. 9g)	45·00
		Perf	(No. 30b)	30·00
R.4/5	"P" in "PENCE" dropped	Imperf	(No. 9h)	45·00
		Perf	(No. 30c)	30·00

The variety at R. 4/1 is also found in the second and third printings, while the varieties at R. 2/1 and R. 4/2 recur in the third printing.

Second printing—Imperf

R.1/1	"1" in lower right	(No. 7a)	45·00
R.1/3	"PENNY" for "PENCE"	(No. 7d)	45·00
R.1/5	"POSTZFGEL"	(No. 7e)	45·00
R.1/6	"AFB" at right	(No. 7f)	45·00
R.2/1	"REB" at left	(No. 7g)	45·00
R.2/2	"AFB" at left	(No. 7h)	45·00
R.2/3	"POSTZEOEL"	(No. 7i)	45·00
R.2/4	"AER" at right	(No. 7j)	45·00
R.2/5	No stop after date	(No. 7k)	45·00
R.2/6	No stop after date (part printing only) and vertical line after "POSTZEGEL"	(No. 7l)	45·00
R.3/2	Right spray inverted	(No. 8a)	45·00
R.3/3	No bar over lower left "2"	(No. 8b)	45·00
R.3/4	Centre "2" inverted, no stop after left "Z"	(No. 8c)	45·00
R.3/6	"POSTZEGFL", no stop after right "AFR"	(No. 8d)	45·00
R.4/2	Centre "2" wider, left spray inverted..	(No. 9b)	45·00
R.4/3	"POSTZEGEI"	(No. 9c)	45·00
R.4/4	No bar under top right "2"	(No. 9d)	45·00
R.4/5	"1" at lower left, "P" in "PENCE" dropped	(No. 9e)	45·00
R.4/6	Left spray inverted	(No. 9f)	45·00

The varieties at R. 2/5 and R. 4/4 recur in the third printing.

Third Printing — Imperf

R. 1/2	No stop after left "AFR"	(No. 7o)	60·00	
R. 1/3	No bar over lower right "2"	(No. 7p)	60·00	
R. 1/5	"POSTZEGEI"	(No. 7q)	60·00	
R. 3/4	No stop after left "Z"	(No. 8g)	60·00	
R. 3/5	"4" at lower right	(No. 8h)	60·00	
R. 4/5	"4" at upper left and "AER" at left	(No. 9i)	60·00	

4d. value

First printing

R.2/1	Left inner frame too high	(No. 10k)	45·00
R.4/1–2	Centre "4" wider	(No. 12g)	35·00
R.4/5	"P" in "PENCE" dropped	(No. 12h)	45·00

The variety at R. 4/1 recurs in the third printing.

Second printing

R.1/3	"PENNY" for "PENCE" (on small part of printing)	(No. 10c)	90·00
R.1/5	"POSTZFGEL"	(No. 10d)	45·00
R.1/6	"AFB" at right	(No. 10e)	45·00
R.2/1	"REB" at left	(No. 10f)	45·00
R.2/2	"AFB" at left	(No. 10g)	45·00
R.2/3	"POSTZEOEL"	(No. 10h)	45·00
R.2/4	"AER" at right	(No. 10i)	45·00
R.2/5	No stop after date	(No. 10j)	45·00
R.3/2	Right spray inverted	(No. 11a)	45·00
R.3/3	No bar over lower left "4" (on small part of printing)	(No. 11b)	90·00
R.3/4	No stop after left "Z"	(No. 11c)	45·00
R.3/6	"POSTZEGFL"	(No. 11d)	45·00
R.4/1	Centre "4" wider, no stop after right "AFR"	(No. 12a)	45·00
R.4/2	Centre "4" wider, left spray inverted	(No. 12b)	45·00
R.4/3	"POSTZEGEI"	(No. 12c)	45·00
R.4/4	No bar under top right "4"	(No. 12d)	45·00
R.4/5	"P" in "PENCE" dropped	(No. 12e)	45·00
R.4/6	Left spray inverted	(No. 12f)	45·00

Varieties at R. 1/5, R. 2/1, R. 2/2, R. 2/3, R. 2/4, R. 2/5, R. 3/2, R. 3/4, R. 3/6, R. 4/2, R. 4/4 and R. 4/6 also occur on the third printing.

Third printing

R. 1/2	No stop after left "AFR"	(No. 10l)	60·00
R. 1/3	No bar over lower right "4"	(No. 10m)	60·00
R. 3/5	"4" at lower right	(No. 11e)	60·00
R. 4/5	"AER" at left and "P" in "PENCE" dropped	(No. 12i)	60·00

6d. value

First printing

R.2/1	Left inner frame too high, no stop after left "REP"	(No. 13k)	55·00
R.4/1–2	Centre "6" wider	(No. 15g)	40·00
R.4/5	"P" in "PENCE" dropped	(No. 15h)	55·00

Second printing

R.1/3	"PENNY" for "PENCE" (on small part of printing)	(No. 13c)	£110
R.1/5	"POSTZFGEL"	(No. 13d)	55·00
R.1/6	"AFB" at right	(No. 13e)	55·00
R.2/1	"REB" at left	(No. 13f)	55·00
R.2/2	"AFB" at left	(No. 13g)	55·00
R.2/3	"POSTZEOEL"	(No. 13h)	55·00
R.2/4	"AER" at right	(No. 13i)	55·00
R.2/5	No stop after date	(No. 13j)	55·00
R.3/2	Right spray inverted	(No. 14a)	55·00
R.3/4	Centre "6" inverted, no stop after left "Z" (on small part of printing)	(No. 14b)	£150
R.3/4	No stop after left "Z"	(No. 14c)	55·00
R.3/6	"POSTZEGFL"	(No. 14d)	55·00
R.4/1	Centre "6" wider, no stop after right "AFR"	(No. 15a)	55·00
R.4/2	Centre "6" wider, left spray inverted	(No. 15b)	55·00
R.4/3	"POSTZEGEI"	(No. 15c)	55·00
R.4/4	No bar under top right "6"	(No. 15d)	55·00
R.4/5	"P" in "PENCE" dropped	(No. 15e)	55·00
R.4/6	Left spray inverted	(No. 15f)	55·00

Varieties at R. 1/5, R. 1/6, R. 2/1, R. 2/2, R. 2/3, R. 2/4, R. 2/5, R. 3/2, R. 3/4, R. 3/6, R. 4/1, R. 4/2, R. 4/3, R. 4/4 and R. 4/6 also occur on the third printing.

Third printing

R. 1/2	No stop after left "AFR"	(No. 13l)	75·00
R. 1/3	No bar over lower right "6"	(No. 13m)	75·00
R. 4/5	"AER" at left, "P" in "PENCE" dropped	(No. 15i)	75·00

1s. value

R.1/2	No stop after left "AFR"	(No. 16a)	40·00
R.1/3	No bar over lower right "1"	(No. 16b)	40·00
R.2/5	No stop after date	(No. 16c)	40·00
R.3/3	Centre "1" inverted (on small part of printing)	(No. 17a)	
R.3/4	"POSTZEGEI", no stop after left "Z"	(No. 17b)	40·00
R.4/1	No stop after right "AFR"	(No. 18a)	40·00
R.4/4	No bar under top right "1"	(No. 18b)	40·00
R.4/5	"AER" at left	(No. 18c)	40·00

LOCAL BRITISH OCCUPATION ISSUES DURING THE SOUTH AFRICAN WAR 1900–02

Stamps of the Transvaal Republic, unless otherwise stated, variously overprinted or surcharged.

LYDENBURG

Lydenburg was occupied by the British on 6 September 1900.

V.R.I.
3d.
(L 1)

1900 (Sept). Nos. 215c and 217 surch as Type L **1**, others optd "V.R.I" only.

1	**30**	½d. green	£190	£190
2		1d. rose-red and green	£180	£170
3	**30**	2d. brown and green	£1500	£1000
4		2½d. blue and green	£2500	£1100

5		3d. on 1d. rose-red and green	£160	£140
7		4d. sage-green and green	£3750	£1100
8		6d. lilac and green	£3750	£1000
9		1s. ochre and green	£5500	£3750

The above were cancelled by British Army postal service postmarks. These overprints with Transvaal cancellations are believed to be forgeries.

RUSTENBURG

British forces in Rustenburg, west of Pretoria, utilised Transvaal stamps, handstamped "V.R" on the command of Colonel Baden-Powell.

V.R.
(R 1)

1900 (22 June). Handstamped with Type R **1** in violet.

1	**30**	½d. green	£200	£150
2		1d. rose-red and green	£150	£110
3		2d. brown and green	£425	£180
4		2½d. purple and green	£275	£150
5		3d. purple and green	£350	£200
6		6d. lilac and green	£1500	£600
7		1s. ochre and green	£2250	£1400
8		2s.6d. dull violet and green	£9000	£4500
		a. Handstamp in black	†	£8000

Nos. 2 and 5 exist with the handstamp inverted.

SCHWEIZER RENECKE

BESIEGED
(SR 1)

1900 (Sept). Handstamped with Type SR **1** in black, reading vert up or down.

(a) On stamps of Transvaal

1	**30**	½d. green	†	£350
2		1d. rose-red and green	†	£350
3		2d. brown and green	†	£475
4		6d. lilac and green	†	£1300

(b) On stamps of Cape of Good Hope

5	**17**	½d. green	†	£600
6		1d. carmine	†	£600

Schweizer Renecke, near the Bechuanaland border, was occupied by a British garrison, besieged by a large Boer force, from July 1900 to 9 January 1901. The British commander authorised the above stamps shortly after 19 August. All stamps were cancelled with the dated circular town postmark ("Schweizer Renecke, Z.A.R."), usually after having been stuck on paper before use. Unused, without the postmark, do not exist.

No. 4 exists with double handstamp.

WOLMARANSSTAD

A British party occupied this town in the south-west of the Transvaal from 15 June to 27 July 1900. Transvaal stamps, to a face value of £5. 2s.6d., were found at the local firm of Thos. Leask and Co. and surcharged as below. The first mail left on 24 June and the last on 21 July.

Cancelled   Cancelled
V-R-I.   V-R-I.
(L 3)   (L 4)

1900 (24 June). Optd with Type L **3**.

1	**30**	½d. green (B.)	£375	£500
		a. Opt inverted	£1500	
		b. Opt in black		
1c		½d. on 1s. green (B.)	£5000	
2		1d. rose-red and green (B.)	£250	£400
		a. Opt in green	£2000	
		b. Opt in black	£3000	
3		2d. brown and green (B.)	£2250	£2250
		a. Opt in black	£3500	
4		2½d. blue and green (R.)	£2250	
		a. Opt in blue	£2750	£2750
		b. Opt in black	£3500	
5		3d. purple and green (B.)	£3500	£3500
6		4d. sage-green and green (B.)	£5000	£5000
7		6d. lilac and green (B.)	£6000	£6500
8		1s. ochre and green (B.)	—	£13000

The two lines of the overprint were handstamped separately. The ½d. exists with two impressions of the "Cancelled" handstamp, the 2½d. with two impressions of "V-R-I", one in red and one in blue and the 3d. with "Cancelled" in green and "V.R.I." in blue.

1900 (24 June). Optd with Type L **4**.

9	**34**	1d. red (B.)	£250	£450

The ½d., 1d. and 3d. in Type **30** are also known with this overprint.

VII. ZULULAND

Zululand remained an independent kingdom until annexed by Great Britain on 19 May 1887 when it was declared a Crown Colony.

The first European postal service was operated by a Natal postal agency at Eshowe opened in 1876 which cancelled Natal stamps with a "No. 56 P.O. Natal" postmark. The agency closed during the Zulu War of 1879 and did not re-open until 1885 when an Eshowe postmark was provided. "ZULULAND" was added to the cancellation in 1887 and stamps of Natal continued to be used until replaced by the overprinted series on 1 May 1888.

PRICES FOR STAMPS ON COVER	
Nos. 1/2	from × 100
Nos. 3/10	from × 20
No. 11	—
Nos. 12/16	from × 20
Nos. 20/3	from × 30
No. 24	from × 20
Nos. 25/6	from × 12
Nos. 27/9	—
No. F1	from × 100

ZULULAND   ZULULAND.
(1)   (2)

1888 (1 May)–93.

(a) Nos. 173, 180, 197, 200/2, 205a, 207a/8, 209 and 211 of Great Britain (Queen Victoria) optd with T **1** *by D.L.R.*

1		½d. vermilion (11.88)	8·50	3·00
2		1d. deep purple	28·00	6·50
3		2d. grey-green and carmine	29·00	50·00
4		2½d. purple/*blue* (9.91)	42·00	23·00
5		3d. purple/*yellow*	32·00	22·00
6		4d. green and deep brown	60·00	75·00
7		5d. dull purple and blue (3.93)	£100	£120
		w. Wmk inverted	†	£1800
8		6d. purple/*rose-red*	23·00	17·00
9		9d. dull purple and blue (4.92)	£120	£130
10		1s. dull green (4.92)	£150	£170
11		5s. rose (4.92)	£700	£800
1/11	Set of 11		£1100	£1300
1s/11s (ex 1d.) H/S "SPECIMEN" Set of 10			£650	

(b) No. 97a of Natal optd with T **2** *at Pietermaritzburg*

12		½d. dull green (with stop) (7.88)	55·00	95·00
		a. Opt double	£1100	£1200
		d. Opt omitted (vert pair with normal)	£7000	
13		½d. dull green (without stop)	29·00	50·00

The T **2** opt has been extensively forged. Examples of No. 12 with opt inverted and No. 13 with opt double are now considered to be forgeries.

1893 (29 Nov*). T **15** of Natal optd with T **1** by D.L.R. (Wmk Crown CA. P 14).

16		6d. dull purple	65·00	55·00

*Earliest known date of use. No. 16 was, apparently, originally supplied in 1889 for fiscal purposes.

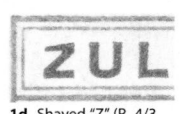

3   4

ZUL

1d. Shaved "Z" (R. 4/3 and R. 6/3)

(Typo D.L.R.)

1894 (18 Apr)–96. Wmk Crown CA. P 14.

20	**3**	½d. dull mauve and green	7·50	7·00
		w. Wmk inverted	£325	£400
21		1d. dull mauve and carmine	6·50	2·75
		a. Shaved "Z"	£120	70·00
22		2½d. dull mauve and ultramarine	14·00	11·00
23		3d. dull mauve and olive-brown	8·00	3·00
24	**4**	6d. dull mauve and black	20·00	16·00
25		1s. green	50·00	38·00
26		2s.6d. green and black (2.96)	90·00	£110
27		4s. green and carmine	£150	£225
28		£1 purple/*red*	£600	£650
29		£5 purple and black/*red*	£5500	£1600
		s. Optd "SPECIMEN"	£475	
20/8	Set of 9		£850	£950
20s/8s Optd "SPECIMEN" Set of 9			£500	

Dangerous forgeries exist of the £1 and £5.

FISCAL STAMP USED FOR POSTAGE

ZULULAND
F 1

1891 (5 May*). F **1**, Fiscal stamp of Natal optd with T **1**. Wmk Crown CA. P 14.

F1		1d. dull mauve	4·50	3·00
		a. Top left triangle detached	£250	£190
		s. Handstamped "SPECIMEN"	65·00	

*Earliest known date of use. A proclamation published in the *Natal Government Gazette* on 27 June 1891 authorised the use of this stamp for postal purposes, but it is clear from the wording that such use had already commenced.

For illustration of "top left triangle detached" variety see above No. 21 of Antigua.

Other values, 1s. to £20 as No. F1 exist apparently with postmarks, but, as these were never authorised for postal use, they are no longer listed.

Zululand was annexed to Natal on 31 December 1897 and its stamps were withdrawn from sale on 30 June 1898.

VIII. BRITISH ARMY FIELD OFFICES DURING SOUTH AFRICAN WAR, 1899–1902

Z **1**   Z **2**

Stamps of GREAT BRITAIN used by British Army Field Offices in South Africa cancelled as Types Z **1**, Z **2** or similar postmarks.

1881. Stamp of Queen Victoria.

Z1	1d. lilac (16 *dots*)	6·00

1883–84. Stamps of Queen Victoria.

Z1*a*	2s.6d lilac	£350
Z2	5s. rose	£475
Z2*a*	10s. ultramarine	£950

1887–92. Stamps of Queen Victoria.

Z3	½d. vermilion	7·00
Z4	1½d. dull purple and green	45·00
Z5	2d. grey-green and carmine	20·00
Z6	2½d. purple/*blue*	7·00
Z7	3d. purple/*yellow*	18·00
Z8	4d. green and brown	30·00
Z9	4½d. green and carmine	£120
Z10	5d. dull purple and blue (Die II)	20·00
Z11	6d. purple/*rose-red*	16·00
Z12	9d. dull purple and blue	£110
Z13	10d. dull purple and carmine	£100
Z14	1s. dull green	£160
Z15	£1 green	£1800

1900. Stamps of Queen Victoria.

Z16	½d. blue-green	7·00
Z17	1s. green and carmine	£225

1902. Stamps of King Edward VII.

Z18	½d. blue-green	16·00
Z19	1d. scarlet	11·00
Z20	1½d. purple and green	90·00
Z21	2d. yellowish green and carmine-red	65·00
Z22	2½d. ultramarine	25·00
Z23	3d. purple/*orange-yellow*	80·00
Z24	4d. green and grey-brown	90·00
Z25	5d. dull purple and ultramarine	90·00
Z26	6d. pale dull purple	40·00
Z27	9d. dull purple and ultramarine	£160
Z28	10d. dull purple and carmine	£170
Z29	1s. dull green and carmine	£110

ARMY OFFICIAL STAMPS

1896–1901. Stamps of Queen Victoria optd "ARMY OFFICIAL".

ZO1	½d. vermilion	£120
ZO2	½d. blue-green	£120
ZO3	1d. lilac (16 *dots*)	95·00
ZO4	6d. purple/*rose-red*	

ARMY TELEGRAPH STAMPS

Army Telegraph stamps were used between November 1899 and August 1900, during the second Anglo-Boer War in South Africa.

ARMY TELEGRAPHS
(T **1**)

ARMY TELEGRAPHS
(T **2**)

ARMY TELEGRAPHS
(T **3**)

(T **4**)

1899–1900. Nos. 197 and 213 of Great Britain opt with T **1** by D.L.R. or as T **2/4**.

AT1	T **1**	½d. vermilion	35·00	38·00
AT2		½d. blue-green (1900)	£140	
AT3	T **2**	1d. lilac and black	25·00	5·00
AT4		2d. lilac and blue	25·00	6·00
		a. Bisected (1d.) *on piece* (1900)	†	£425
AT5		3d. lilac and brown	55·00	10·00
AT6		6d. lilac and green	25·00	8·00
		a. Bisected (3d.) *on piece* (1900)	†	£275
AT7		8d. lilac and carmine	£140	£140
AT8	T **3**	1s. green and black	55·00	12·00
		a. Bisected (6d.) *on piece* (1900)	†	£475
AT9		2s.6d. green and brown	55·00	50·00
AT10		5s. green and mauve	80·00	25·00
AT11		10s. green and red	£120	25·00
AT12	T **4**	£1 lilac and black	£225	50·00
AT13		£5 lilac and green	£500	

Nos. AT3/4, AT6 and AT8/12 had originally been issued in 1895, and were used in small quantities during the Ashanti expedition. Nos. AT1, AT5 and AT7 followed in 1896, and were used with other values to 2s.6d. during Autumn manoeuvres in England, but the main usage of these stamps was in South Africa.

TWO
PENCE
(T **5**)

1900 (Feb). Nos. AT9 and AT10 surch as T **5**.

AT14		"TWO PENCE" on 2s.6d.green and brown (Verm.)	£3000	£120
		a. Bisected (1d.) *on piece*	†	£475
AT15		"ONE SHILLING" on 5s. green and mauve (B.)	£3000	£110
		a. Bisected (6d.) *on piece*	†	£600

Used stamps usually bear a metal "ARMY TELEGRAPHS" datestamp with code letters either side of the date.

As the Anglo-Boer War progressed the "Army Telegraphs" stamps were replaced by overprinted Telegraph stamps in the occupied Orange Free State and by Fiscal and postage stamps in the Transvaal.

IX. UNION OF SOUTH AFRICA

The Interprovincial Period (1 June 1910 – 31 August 1913)

With the establishment of the Union on 31 May 1910, the only definitive stamps available were those of the four provinces; Cape of Good Hope, Natal, Orange River Colony and Transvaal. These became available for use throughout the Union from 1 June, although the public was not officially informed of the fact until it was published in the *Government Gazette* on 19 August.

The collecting of 'Interprovincials' is best thought of as the study of the period from 1 June 1910 until the issue of the first Union definitives on 1 September 1913, although in the case of the postage dues of Transvaal, the period can be extended until the issue of the relevant Union values in 1914–15. The only provincial stamps reprinted and issued during this period were those of Transvaal. As collectors generally include the use of provincial stamps in their 'home' province during the period, these are included in the listings below.

Usage of provincial stamps continued after 1 September 1913, until demonetisation on 1 January 1938, although during this period usage became increasingly philatelic and included stocks of earlier stamps, such as the Orange Free State 'V.R.I.' overprints. Our listings comprise only those stamps which were generally available at the time of Union. The 2½d. values are relatively scarce used in the true Interprovincial period, but there were considerable stocks left in September 1913 and their use outside the period is more common.

Our prices are for fine used stamps clearly dated within the period and showing the place they were used. Stamps on piece or cover showing full cancellations, and stamps used in smaller offices are worth more. Collectors are warned against the Natal high values with faked interprovincial cancels.

Cape of Good Hope

(i) Used in Cape of Good Hope

Z1	½d. green (No. 70)	50
Z2	1d. carmine (No. 71)	50
Z3	2d. brown (No. 72)	1·50
Z4	2½d. ultramarine (No. 73)	15·00
Z5	3d. magenta (No. 74)	2·00
Z6	4d. olive-green (No. 75)	3·00
Z7	6d. bright mauve (No. 76)	3·00
Z8	1s. yellow-ochre (No. 77)	6·00
Z9	5s. brown-orange (No. 78)	40·00

(ii) Used in Natal

Z10	½d. green (No. 70)	2·00
Z11	1d. carmine (No. 71)	1·50
Z12	2d. brown (No. 72)	3·00
Z13	2½d. ultramarine (No. 73)	25·00
Z14	3d. magenta (No. 74)	4·00
Z15	4d. olive-green (No. 75)	6·00
Z16	6d. bright mauve (No. 76)	7·00
Z17	1s. yellow-ochre (No. 77)	12·00
Z18	5s. brown-orange (No. 78)	65·00

(iii) Used in Orange River Colony

Z19	½d. green (No. 70)	5·00
Z20	1d. carmine (No. 71)	3·00
Z21	2d. brown (No. 72)	4·00
Z22	2½d. ultramarine (No. 73)	30·00
Z23	3d. magenta (No. 74)	6·00
Z24	4d. olive-green (No. 75)	9·00
Z25	6d. bright mauve (No. 76)	10·00
Z26	1s. yellow-olive (No. 77)	20·00
Z27	5s. brown-orange (No. 78)	90·00

(iv) Used in Transvaal

Z28	½d. green (No. 70)	2·00
Z29	1d. carmine (No. 71)	1·50
Z30	2d. brown (No. 72)	2·50
Z31	2½d. ultramarine (No. 73)	22·00
Z32	3d. magenta (No. 74)	3·00
Z33	4d. olive-green (No. 75)	6·00
Z34	6d. bright mauve (No. 76)	6·00
Z35	1s. yellow-ochre (No. 77)	12·00
Z36	5s. brown-orange (No. 78)	60·00

Natal

(i) Used in Natal

Z37	½a. blue-green (No. 146)	50
Z38	1d. carmine (No. 147)	50
Z39	1d. deep carmine (No. 148)	1·00
Z40	1½d. green and black (No. 129)	12·00
Z41	2d. red and olive-green (No. 149)	4·00
Z42	2½d. bright blue (No. 131)	8·00
Z43	3d. purple and grey (No. 132)	3·50
Z44	4d. carmine and cinnamon (No. 152)	8·00
Z45	5d. black and orange (No. 153)	10·00
Z46	6d. dull and bright purple (No. 165)	5·00
Z47	1s. black/*green* (No. 166)	25·00
Z48	2s. purple and bright blue/*blue* (No. 167)	15·00
Z49	2s.6d. black and green/*blue* (No. 168)	15·00
Z50	5s. green and red/*yellow* (No. 169)	75·00
Z51	10s. green and red/*green* (No. 170)	£200
Z52	£1 purple and black/*red* (No. 171)	£500

(ii) Used in Cape of Good Hope

Z53	½d. blue-green (No. 146)	1·00
Z54	1d. carmine (No. 147)	1·00
Z55	1d. deep carmine (No. 148)	2·00
Z56	1½d. green and black (No. 129)	40·00
Z57	2d. red and olive-green (No. 149)	5·00
Z58	2½d. bright blue (No. 131)	12·00
Z59	3d. purple and grey (No. 132)	5·00
Z60	4d. carmine and cinnamon (No. 152)	12·00
Z61	5d. black and orange (No. 153)	20·00
Z62	6d. dull and bright purple (No. 165)	10·00
Z63	1s. black/*green* (No. 166)	£100
Z64	2s. purple and bright blue/*blue* (No. 167)	25·00
Z65	2s.6d. black and green/*blue* (No. 168)	25·00
Z66	5s. green and red/*yellow* (No. 169)	£150
Z67	10s. green and red/*green* (No. 170)	£350
Z68	£1 purple and black/*red* (No. 171)	£900

(iii) Used in Orange River Colony

Z69	½d. blue-green (No. 146)	5·00
Z70	1d. carmine (No. 147)	5·00
Z71	1d. deep carmine (No. 148)	8·00
Z72	1½d. green and black (No. 129)	80·00
Z73	2d. red and olive-green (No. 149)	12·00
Z74	2½d. bright blue (No. 131)	40·00
Z75	3d. purple and grey (No. 132)	18·00
Z76	4d. carmine and cinnamon (No. 152)	30·00
Z77	5d. black and orange (No. 153)	38·00

Z78	6d. dull and bright purple (No. 165)	28·00
Z79	1s. black/*green* (No. 166)	£350
Z80	2s. purple and bright blue/*blue* (No. 167)	£350
Z81	2s.6d. black and red/*blue* (No. 168)	£350
Z82	5s. green and red/*yellow* (No. 169)	£250
Z83	10s. green and red/*green* (No. 170)	£800
Z84	£1 purple and black/*red* (No. 171)	—

(iv) Used in Transvaal

Z85	½d. blue-green (No. 146)	1·00
Z86	1d. carmine (No. 147)	1·00
Z87	1d. bright carmine (No. 148)	2·00
Z88	1½d. green and black (No. 129)	45·00
Z89	2d. red and olive-green (No. 149)	5·00
Z90	2½d. bright blue (No. 131)	15·00
Z91	3d. purple and grey (No. 132)	5·00
Z92	4d. carmine and cinnamon (No. 152)	12·00
Z93	5d. black and orange (No. 153)	20·00
Z94	6d. dull and bright purple (No. 165)	12·00
Z95	1s. black/*green* (No. 166)	£100
Z96	2s. purple and bright blue/*blue* (No. 167)	30·00
Z97	2s.6d. black and red/*blue* (No. 168)	40·00
Z98	5s. green and red/*yellow* (No. 169)	80·00
Z99	10s. green and red/*green* (No. 170)	£350
Z100	£1 purple and black/*red* (No. 171)	£900

Orange River Colony

(i) Used in Orange River Colony

Z101	½d. yellow-green (No. 148)	2·00
Z102	1d. scarlet (No. 149)	1·00
Z103	2d. brown (No. 141)	2·50
Z104	2½d. bright blue (No. 142)	3·00
Z105	3d. mauve (No. 143)	3·00
Z106	4d. scarlet and sage-green (No. 150)	7·00
Z107	6d. scarlet and mauve (No. 145)	3·00
Z108	1s. scarlet and bistre (No. 146)	12·00
Z109	1s. scarlet and bistre (No. 151)	28·00
Z110	5s. blue and brown (No. 147)	40·00

(ii) Used in Cape of Good Hope

Z111	½d. yellow-green (No. 148)	3·00
Z112	1d. scarlet (No. 149)	1·50
Z113	2d. brown (No. 141)	3·50
Z114	2½d. bright blue (No. 142)	4·00
Z115	3d. mauve (No. 143)	4·00
Z116	4d. scarlet and sage-green (No. 150)	9·00
Z117	6d. scarlet and mauve (No. 145)	5·00
Z118	1s. scarlet and bistre (No. 146)	24·00
Z119	1s. scarlet and bistre (No. 151)	50·00
Z120	5s. blue and brown (No. 147)	50·00

(iii) Used in Natal

Z121	½d. yellow-green (No. 148)	4·00
Z122	1d. scarlet (No. 149)	2·00
Z123	2d. brown (No. 141)	4·50
Z124	2½d. bright blue (No. 142)	6·00
Z125	3d. mauve (No. 143)	5·00
Z126	4d. scarlet and sage-green (No. 150)	11·00
Z127	6d. scarlet and mauve (No. 145)	7·00
Z128	1s. scarlet and bistre (No. 146)	30·00
Z129	1s. scarlet and bistre (No. 151)	65·00
Z130	5s. scarlet blue and brown (No. 147)	70·00

(iv) Used in Transvaal

Z131	½d. yellow-green (No. 148)	3·00
Z132	1d. scarlet (No. 149)	1·50
Z133	2d. brown (No. 141)	3·50
Z134	2½d. bright blue (No. 142)	4·50
Z135	3d. mauve (No. 143)	4·50
Z136	4d. scarlet and sage-green (No. 150)	10·00
Z137	6d. scarlet and mauve (No. 145)	5·00
Z138	1s. scarlet and bistre (No. 146)	26·00
Z139	1s. scarlet and bistre (No. 151)	55·00
Z140	5s. blue and brown (No. 147)	60·00

Transvaal

(i) Used in Transvaal

Z141	½d. yellow-green (No. 273)	50
Z142	1d. scarlet (No. 274)	50
Z143	2d. purple (No. 275)	70
Z144	2½d. bright blue (No. 276)	15·00
Z145	3d. black and sage-green (No. 264)	1·00
Z146	4d. black and brown (No. 265)	1·50
Z147	6d. black and orange (No. 266a)	1·50
Z148	1s. black and red-brown (No. 267)	2·00
Z149	2s. black and yellow (No. 268)	16·00
Z150	2s.6d. magenta and black (No. 269)	14·00
Z151	5s. black and purple/*yellow* (No. 270)	4·00
Z152	10s. black and purple/*red* (No. 271)	6·00
Z153	£1 green and violet (No. 272a)	28·00

(ii) Used in Cape of Good Hope

Z154	½d. yellow-green (No. 273)	50
Z155	1d. scarlet (No. 274)	50
Z156	2d. purple (No. 275)	1·00
Z157	2½d. bright blue (No. 276)	15·00
Z158	3d. black and sage-green (No. 264)	2·00
Z159	4d. black and brown (No. 265)	2·50
Z160	6d. black and orange (No. 266a)	2·00
Z161	1s. black and red-brown (No. 267)	3·00
Z162	2s. black and yellow (No. 268)	20·00
Z163	2s.6d. magenta and black (No. 269)	16·00
Z164	5s. black and purple/*yellow* (No. 270)	6·00
Z165	10s. black and purple/*red* (No. 271)	8·00
Z166	£1 green and violet (No. 272a)	30·00

(iii) Used in Natal

Z167	½d. yellow-green (No. 273)	50
Z168	1d. scarlet (No. 274)	50
Z168	2d. brown (No. 275)	1·50
Z170	2½d. bright blue (No. 276)	18·00
Z171	3d. black and sage-green (No. 264)	3·00
Z172	4d. black and brown (No. 265)	3·00
Z173	6d. black and orange (No. 266a)	3·00
Z174	1s. black and red-brown (No. 267)	4·00
Z175	2s. black and yellow (No. 268)	22·00
Z176	2s.6d. magenta and black (No. 269)	20·00
Z177	5s. black and purple/*yellow* (No. 270)	7·00
Z178	10s. black and purple/*red* (No. 271)	10·00
Z179	£1 green and violet (No. 272a)	35·00

(iv) Used in Orange River Colony

Z180	½d. yellow-green (No. 273)	1·00
Z181	1d. scarlet (No. 274)	1·00

Z182	2d. brown (No. 275)			2·00
Z183	2½d. bright blue (No. 276)			20·00
Z184	3d. black and sage-green (No. 264)			4·00
Z185	4d. black and brown (No. 265)			4·00
Z186	6d. black and orange (No. 266a)			4·00
Z187	1s. black and red-brown (No. 267)			5·00
Z188	2s. black and yellow (No. 268)			28·00
Z189	2s.6d. magenta and black (No. 269)			24·00
Z190	5s. black and purple/*yellow* (No. 270)			10·00
Z191	10s. black and purple/*red* (No. 271)			12·00
Z192	£1 green and violet (No. 272a)			£130

PRICES FOR STAMPS ON COVER TO 1945

Nos. 1/15	from × 4
Nos. 16/17	—
Nos. 18/21	from × 6
Nos. 26/32	from × 2
No. 33	from × 4
Nos. 34/110	from × 1
Nos. D1/7	from × 4
Nos. D8/33	from × 6
Nos. O1/33	from × 4

1

(Des H. S. Wilkinson. Recess D.L.R.)

1910 (4 Nov). Opening of Union Parliament. Inscribed bilingually. Wmk Multiple Rosettes. P 14.

1	**1**	2½d. deep blue	3·75	1·75
		s. Handstamped "*Specimen*."	£550	
2		2½d. blue	2·75	1·00

The deep blue shade is generally accompanied by a blueing of the paper.

2	3	4 Springbok's Head

(Typo D.L.R.)

1913 (1 Sept)–**24**. Inscribed bilingually. W **4**.

(a) P 14

3	**2**	½d. green	1·75	30
		a. Stamp doubly printed	£10000	
		b. Blue-green	2·00	20
		c. Yellow-green	2·75	1·00
		d. Printed on the gummed side	£1500	
		w. Wmk inverted	2·00	1·00
4		1d. rose-red (*shades*)	1·75	10
		a. Carmine-red	2·25	10
		b. Scarlet (*shades*)	4·25	1·00
		w. Wmk inverted	2·50	1·00
5		1½d. chestnut (*shades*) (23.8.20)	80	10
		a. Tête-bêche (pair)	1·75	18·00
		c. Wmk sideways	†	£1800
		w. Wmk inverted	80	10
6	**3**	2d. dull purple	1·75	10
		a. Deep purple	2·50	10
		w. Wmk inverted	2·25	2·25
7		2½d. bright blue	4·50	1·00
		a. Deep blue	4·00	3·00
		w. Wmk inverted	£140	£170
8		3d. black and orange-red	13·00	30
		a. Black and dull orange-red	10·00	70
		w. Wmk inverted	25·00	9·50
9		3d. ultramarine (*shades*) (4.10.22)	4·75	1·00
		w. Wmk inverted	13·00	5·50
10		4d. orange-yellow and olive-green	10·00	75
		a. Orange-yellow and sage-green	6·50	55
		w. Wmk inverted	8·00	1·50
11		6d. black and violet	7·00	60
		a. Black and bright violet	10·00	1·50
		aw. Wmk inverted	18·00	10·00
12		1s. orange	10·00	60
		a. Orange-yellow	15·00	1·00
		w. Wmk inverted	24·00	2·25
13		1s.3d. violet (*shades*) (1.9.20)	11·00	6·00
		w. Wmk inverted	£160	£225
14		2s.6d. purple and green	55·00	1·50
15		5s. purple and blue	£120	9·50
		a. Reddish purple and light blue	£120	9·50
		w. Wmk inverted	£9000	£3500
16		10s. deep blue and olive-green	£180	7·50
		w. Wmk inverted	£6000	£2000
17		£1 green and red (7.16)	£650	£350
		a. Pale olive-green and red (1924)	£850	£1200
3/17 *Set of 15*			£950	£350

3s/8s, 10s/17s Optd or H/S (1½d. and 1s.3d. in violet,
£1 in green) "SPECIMEN" *Set of 14* £1600

(b) Coil stamps. P 14×imperf

18	**2**	½d. green	6·00	1·00
		w. Wmk inverted	—	£600
19		1d. rose-red (13.2.14)	23·00	3·00
		a. Scarlet	27·00	8·50
		w. Wmk inverted	£1000	£400
20		1½d. chestnut (15.11.20)	11·00	15·00
		w. Wmk inverted	†	£3500
21	**3**	2d. dull purple (7.10.21)	16·00	4·75
18/21 *Set of 4*			50·00	21·00

The 6d. exists with "Z" of "ZUID" wholly or partly missing at R. 8/3, lower right pane, due to wear of plate (*Price wholly missing, £95 un, £55 us*).

5 de Havilland
D.H.9 Biplane

(Eng A. J. Cooper. Litho *Cape Times* Ltd)

1925 (26 Feb). Air. Inscr bilingually. P 12.

26	**5**	1d. carmine	5·50	16·00
27		3d. ultramarine	8·00	12·00
28		6d. magenta	12·00	14·00
29		9d. green	25·00	75·00
26/9 *Set of 4*			45·00	£100

Beware of forgeries of all values perforated 11, 11½ or 13.

INSCRIPTIONS. From 1926 until 1951 most issues were inscribed in English and Afrikaans alternately throughout the sheets.

PRICES for Nos. 30/135 are for unused horizontal pairs, used horizontal pairs and used singles (either inscription), *unless otherwise indicated*. Vertical pairs are worth between 20% and 35% of the prices quoted for horizontal pairs.

6 Springbok	7 *Dromedaris* (Van Riebeeck's ship)

 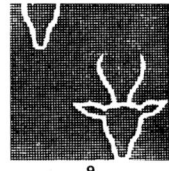

8 Orange Tree	9

(Typo Waterlow until 1927, thereafter Govt Printer, Pretoria)

1926 (2 Jan)–**27**. W **9**. P 14½×14.

			Un pair	Used pair	Used single
30	**6**	½d. black and green	2·75	3·25	10
		a. Missing "1" in "½"	£2750		
		b. Centre omitted (in pair with normal)	£3500		
		cw. Wmk inverted	5·00	8·00	20
		d. Frame printed double (horiz pair)	£22000		
		e. Perf 13½×14 (1927)	90·00	90·00	4·00
		ea. Tête-bêche (pair)	£1500		
		ew. Wmk inverted	90·00	90·00	4·00
		f. Wmk sideways**	—	£3250	
31	**7**	1d. black and carmine	1·50	50	10
		a. Imperf (vert pair)*	£1100		
		b. Imperf 3 sides (vert pair)*	£1100	£1200	
		c. Centre omitted (in pair with normal) (R. 20/9)	£5000		
		dw. Wmk inverted	6·00	2·75	20
		e. Perf 13½×14 (1927)	£120	85·00	4·00
		ea. Tête-bêche (pair)	£1500		
		ew. Wmk inverted	£120	85·00	4·00
		f. Wmk sideways**	£2750	£2500	
32	**8**	6d. green and orange (1.5.26)	42·00	48·00	1·50
		w. Wmk inverted	70·00	75·00	
30/2 *Set of 3*			42·00	48·00	1·50

No. 30a exists in Afrikaans only. Nos. 30e and 31e were only issued in booklets.

No. 30d occurred on the bottom left-hand corner of one sheet and included the bottom four stamps in the first vertical row and the bottom two in the second. As listed No. 30d shows the left-hand stamp with the frame completely double and the right-hand stamp with two-thirds of the frame double.

*Both Nos. 31a and 31b occur in blocks of four with the other vertical pair imperforate at left.

**Nos. 30f and 31f are known with the top of the Springbok's head to the left or to the right, *as seen from the back of the stamp*.

No 31c. developed from a plate crack during the second Pretoria printing, affecting R. 18/9, 19/9 and 20/9. On 20/9 the vignette failed to print altogether for a few sheets, but was soon repaired.

For ½d. with pale grey centre, see No. 126.
For rotogravure printing see Nos. 42, etc.

10 "Hope"

(Recess B.W.)

1926 (2 Jan). T **10**. Inscribed in English or Afrikaans. W **9** (upright or inverted in equal quantities).

			Single stamps	
33		4d. grey-blue (English inscr) (*shades*)	1·75	1·25
		a. Inscr in Afrikaans	1·75	1·25

In this value the English and Afrikaans inscriptions are on separate sheets.

This stamp is known with private perforations or roulettes.

---

11 Union Buildings, Pretoria	12 Groot Schuur

12a A Native Kraal	13 Black and Blue Wildebeest

14 Ox-wagon inspanned	15 Ox-wagon outspanned

16 Cape Town and Table Bay	2d. "Split 'd'" (Right pane, R. 8/2)

(Recess B.W.)

1927 (1 Mar)–**30**. "SUIDAFRIKA" in one word on Afrikaans stamps. W **9**. P 14.

			Un pair	Used pair	Used single
34	**11**	2d. grey and maroon	16·00	32·00	60
		aa. Split "d"	£300		
		aw. Wmk inverted	£900	£1000	60·00
		b. Perf 14×13½ (2.30)	50·00	55·00	1·00
		ba. Split "d"	£160		
35	**12**	3d. black and red	17·00	32·00	60
		a. Perf 14×13½ (1930)	80·00	80·00	1·25
35*b*	**12a**	4d. brown (23.3.28)	32·00	50·00	1·00
		c. Perf 14×13½ (1930)	60·00	70·00	1·25
		cw. Wmk inverted	£1000	£1000	55·00
36	**13**	1s. brown and deep blue	30·00	55·00	1·00
		a. Perf 14×13½ (1930)	75·00	90·00	2·00
37	**14**	2s.6d. green and brown	£150	£500	17·00
		a. Perf 14×13½ (1930)	£400	£700	24·00
38	**15**	5s. black and green	£300	£900	35·00
		a. Perf 14×13½ (1930)	£500	£1100	42·00
39	**16**	10s. bright blue and brown	£200	£160	10·00
		a. Centre inverted (*single stamp*)	£22000		
		b. Perf 14×13½ (1930)	£250	£200	12·00
34/9 *Set of 7*			£650	£1400	55·00

34s/9s H/S "SPECIMEN" *Set of 7* £1100

Two vertical pairs and a few single unused examples of No. 39a are known.

17 de Havilland
D.H.60 Cirrus Moth

(Typo Govt Ptg Wks, Pretoria)

1929 (16 Aug). Air. Inscribed bilingually. No wmk. P 14×13½.

			Un single	Us single
40	**17**	4d. green	6·00	1·75
41		1s. orange	10·00	14·00

PRINTER. All the following issues to 1961, *except where stated otherwise*, are printed by rotogravure (the design having either plain lines or a dotted screen) by the Government Printer, Pretoria.

I	II

I

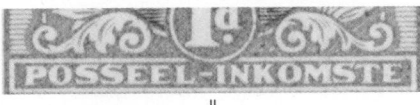

II

The two types of the 1d. differ in the spacing of the horizontal lines in the side panels:—Type I close; Type II wide. The Afrikaans had the spacing of the words POSSEEL-INKOMSTE close in Type I and more widely spaced in Type II.

½d. "Cobweb" variety (retouch between horns) (Cyl. 1 R. 9/5)

½d. "Dollar" variety (Cyl. 2 R. 10/9)

2d. Airship flaw (Cyl 34 R. 9/4)

3d. Window flaw (R. 20/4 on all ptgs before 1937)

4d. Spear flaw (R. 9/2)

4d. "Monkey" in tree (R. 2/2)

1s. Twisted horn (Cyl 7020 R. 1/5)

1s. Dart in Gnu's back (Cyl 6926 R. 20/1)

1930–44. T **6** to **8** and **11** to **14** redrawn, "SUIDAFRIKA" (in one word) on Afrikaans stamps. W **9**. P 15×14 (½d., 1d., and 6d.) or 14.

		Un pair	Used pair	Used single
42	½d. black and green (5.30)	6·50	3·50	10
	a. Two English or two Afrikaans stamps *se-tenant* (vert strip of 4)	40·00		
	b. *Tête-bêche*	£1400		
	c. "Cobweb" variety	50·00		
	d. "Dollar" variety	50·00		
	w. Wmk inverted	6·50	3·50	10
43	1d. black and carmine (I) (4.30)	7·00	3·00	10
	a. *Tête-bêche*	£1400		
	b. Frame omitted (*single stamp*)	£600		
	cw. Wmk inverted	7·00	3·00	10
	cwa. Vignette omitted	£1800		
43d	1d. black and carmine (II) (8.32)	60·00	4·00	10
	dw. Wmk inverted	50·00	4·00	10

44	2d. slate-grey and lilac (4.31)	28·00	26·00	40
	a. *Tête-bêche*	£8000		
	bw. Wmk inverted	22·00	12·00	20
	c. Frame omitted (*single stamp*)	£6000		
	cwa. Frame omitted (*single stamp*)	£6000	£6500	
	d. Airship flaw	£140	£150	
44e	2d. blue and violet (3.38)	£350	75·00	2·50
	ea. Airship flaw	£950	£350	
45	3d. black and red (11.31)	£130	£100	2·25
	aw. Wmk inverted	38·00	60·00	1·25
	b. Window flaw	£200		
	bw. Ditto. Wmk inverted	£150		
45c	3d. blue (10.33)	25·00	7·00	20
	cw. Wmk inverted	6·00	6·00	10
	d. Window flaw	£110		
	dw. Ditto. Wmk inverted	60·00		
	e. Centre omitted	£32000		
	f. Frame omitted (*single stamp*)	£16000		
46	4d. brown (19.11.32)	£325	£150	6·50
	aw. Wmk inverted	35·00	32·00	40
	b. Spear flaw	£400	£325	
	bw. Ditto. Wmk inverted	£170	£170	
46c	4d. brown (*shades*) (*again redrawn*) (1936)	3·75	2·75	10
	ca. "Monkey" in tree	50·00		
	cw. Wmk inverted	13·00	12·00	30
47	6d. green and orange (*wmk inverted*) (13.5.31)	13·00	5·50	10
	w. Wmk upright (8.32)	75·00	22·00	30
48	1s. brown and deep blue (14.9.32)	£120	60·00	55
	a. Dart in gnu's back	£375	£400	
	bw. Wmk inverted	35·00	26·00	35
	c. Twisted horn flaw	£350	£425	
	cw. Ditto. Wmk inverted	£225	£325	
49	2s.6d. green and brown (*shades*) (24.12.32)	£120	£120	3·25
	aw. Wmk inverted	£225	£250	3·25
49b	2s.6d. blue and brown (11.44)	26·00	15·00	20
42/9b	Set of 13	£500	£275	6·50

For similar designs with "SUID-AFRIKA" hyphenated, see Nos. 54 etc. and Nos. 114 etc.

Nos. 42/3, 43d/4 exist in coils.

The unused prices quoted for Nos. 44e and 49b are for unmounted examples.

No. 42a comes from the coil printing on the cylinder for which two horizontal rows were incorrectly etched so that two Afrikaans-inscribed stamps were followed by two English. This variety is normally without a coil join, although some examples do occur showing a repair join.

The 1d. (Type I) exists without watwermark from a trial printing (*Price* £30 *un*).

No. 44 exists in sepia and mauve with smaller vignettes. Believed to be an early or trial printing replaced due to the vignette being too narrow for the frames. (*Price* £900 *unused*, £700 *used*).

Although it appears to be printed in one colour No. 45c was produced from vignette and frame cylinders in the same way as the bicoloured version. The clouds in the background, which are present on No. 45e, were printed from the frame cylinder.

The Rotogravure printings may be distinguished from the preceding Typographed and Recess printed issues by the following tests:—

Typo   Roto

2d. Recess

2d. Recess   **2d.** Roto

3d. Recess   **3d.** Roto

4d. No. 35b Recess   **4d.** No. 46 Roto   **4d.** No. 46c Roto

1s. Recess   **1s.** Roto

2s.6d. Recess   **2s.6d.** Roto

5s. Recess

5s. Roto

ROTOGRAVURE:

½d. 1d. and 6d. Leg of "R" in "AFR" ends squarely on the bottom line.

2d. The newly built War Memorial appears to the left of the value.

3d. Two fine lines have been removed from the top part of the frame.

4d. No. 46. The scroll is in solid colour.
No. 46c. The scroll is white with a crooked line running through it. (No. 35b. The scroll is shaded by the diagonal lines.)

1s. The shading of the last "A" partly covers the flower beneath.

2s.6d. The top line of the centre frame is thick and leaves only one white line between it and the name.

5s. (Nos. 64/b). The leg of the "R" is straight.

Rotogravure impressions are generally coarser.

18 Church of the Vow   **19** *The Great Trek* (C. Michell)

20 A Voortrekker   **21** Voortrekker Woman

1d. Blurred "SOUTH AFRICA" and red "comet" flaw (Cyls 6917/6922 R. 2/7)

(Des J. Prentice (½d., 2d., 3d.))

1933 (3 May)–**36.** Voortrekker Memorial Fund. W **9** (sideways). P 14.

50	**18**	½d. +½d. black and green (16.1.36)	4·50	12·00	1·00
51	**19**	1d. +½d. grey-black and pink	3·25	2·25	25
		a. Blurred "SOUTH AFRICA" and red "comet" flaw	75·00	80·00	
		w. Wmk horns pointing to left	3·25	2·25	25
52	**20**	2d. +1d. grey-green and purple	4·50	4·25	55
53	**21**	3d. +1½d. grey-green and blue	7·00	5·00	70
50/3		Set of 4	17·00	21·00	2·25

The normal sideways watermark shows the horns of the springbok pointing to the right, *as seen from the back of the stamp.*

22 Gold Mine   **22a** Groot Schuur

Dies of 6d.

I   II   III

23 Groot Constantia

1½d. Broken chimney and fainter headgear (Cyl 62 R. 11/6)

1½d. Flag on chimney at right (Cyl 62 R. 20/2)

6d. "Falling ladder" flaw (R. 5/10)

6d. "Molehill" flaw (R. 20/11)

1933–48. "SUID-AFRIKA" (hyphenated) on Afrikaans stamps. W **9**. P 15×14 (½d., 1d. and 6d.) or 14 (others).

54	6	½d. grey and green (*wmk inverted*) (9.35)	7·50	3·00	10
		aw. Wmk upright (1936)	18·00	10·00	20
		b. Coil stamp. Perf 13½×14 (1935)	40·00	70·00	1·00
		bw. Wmk upright	40·00	70·00	1·00
		c. Booklet pane of 6 (with adverts on margins) (*wmk inverted*)	32·00		
56	7	1d. grey and carmine (*shades*) (19.4.34)	1·75	2·25	10
		a. Imperf (pair) (*wmk inverted*)	£180		
		b. Frame omitted (*single stamp*)	£350		
		cw. Wmk inverted	1·75	2·25	10
		d. Coil stamp. Perf 13½×14 (1935)	45·00	70·00	1·40
		dw. Wmk inverted	45·00	70·00	1·40
		e. Booklet pane of 6 (with adverts on margins) (wmk inverted) (1935)	38·00		
		f. Booklet pane of 6 (with blank margins) (1937)	38·00		
		h. Booklet pane of 6 (with postal slogans on margins) (1948)	4·00		
		i. *Grey and bright rose-carmine* (7.48)	70	2·75	10
57	22	1½d. green and bright gold (12.11.36)	7·00	3·75	10
		a. Shading omitted from mine dump (in pair with normal)	£275	£180	
		b. Broken chimney and faint headgear	28·00		

		c. Flag on chimney at right	28·00		
		dw. Wmk inverted	1·75	3·25	10
		dwa. Gold omitted	£25000		
		e. *Blue-green and dull gold* (8.40)	8·50	3·75	10
58	11	2d. blue and violet (11.38)	75·00	50·00	1·00
58a		2d. grey and dull purple (5.41)	65·00	£110	2·00
59	22a	3d. ultramarine (2.40)	15·00	4·00	10
61	8	6d. green and vermilion (I) (10.37)	70·00	50·00	1·00
		a. "Falling ladder" flaw	£300	£350	
		b. "Molehill" flaw	£250	£275	
61c		6d. green and vermilion (II) (6.38)	42·00	1·00	10
61d		6d. green and red-orange (III) (11.46)	20·00	75	10
62	13	1s. brown and chalky blue (2.39) (*shades*)	55·00	18·00	20
		a. Frame omitted (vert pair with normal)	£13000		
		b. Frame omitted (*single stamp*)	£9000		
64	15	5s. black and green (10.33)	60·00	75·00	1·75
		aw. Wmk inverted	£120	£150	3·00
		b. *Black and blue-green* (9.44)	42·00	21·00	35
64c	23	10s. blue and sepia (*shades*) (8.39)	65·00	10·00	70
		ca. *Blue and charcoal* (1944)	45·00	5·50	30
54/9, 61d/64ca Set of 10			£300	£190	3·25

The ½d. and 1d. coil stamps may be found in blocks emanating from the residue of the large rolls which were cut into sheets and distributed to Post Offices.

Nos. 54 and 56 also exist in coils.

1d. Is printed from Type II. Frames of different sizes exist due to reductions made from time to time for the purpose of providing more space for the perforations.

3d. In No. 59 the frame is unscreened and composed of solid lines. Centre is diagonally screened. Scrolls above "3d." are clear lined, light in the middle and dark at sides.

6d. Die I. Green background lines faint. "SUID-AFRIKA" 16¼ mm long.
Die II. Green background lines heavy. "SUID-AFRIKA" 17 mm long. "S" near end of tablet. Scroll open.
Die III. Scroll closed up and design smaller (18×22 mm).

Single specimens of the 1933–48 issue inscribed in English may be distinguished from those of 1930–45 as follows:—
½d. and 1d. Centres in grey instead of varying intensities of black.
2d. The letters of "SOUTH AFRICA" are narrower and thinner.
3d. The trees are taller and the sky is without lines.
6d. The frame is vermilion.
1s. The frame is chalky blue.

For similar designs, but printed in screened rotogravure, see Nos. 114 to 122a.

BOOKLET PANES. Booklets issued in 1935 contained ½d. and 1d. stamps in panes with advertisements in the top and bottom margins and no margin at right (Nos. 54c and 56e). These were replaced in 1937 by editions showing blank margins on all four sides (Nos. 56f and 75ca). Following a period when the booklet panes were without margins a further 3s. booklet was issued in 1948 which had four margins on the panes and postal slogans at top and bottom (Nos. 56h, 87c and 114a).

24

"Cleft skull" flaw (R. 14/2)

Spots above head and behind neck (R. 12/5)

JIPEX

1936

(24a)

(Des J. Booysen)

1935 (1 May). Silver Jubilee. Inscr bilingually. W **9**. P 15×14.

65	24	½d. black and blue-green	3·00	16·00	20
		a. "Cleft skull" flaw	8·50	32·00	
		b. Spots above head and behind neck	9·50	40·00	
66		1d. black and carmine	3·00	8·50	10
		a. "Cleft skull" flaw	8·50	21·00	
		b. Spots above head and behind neck	11·00	29·00	
67		3d. blue	15·00	60·00	2·25
		a. "Cleft skull" flaw	50·00	£130	
		b. Spots above head and behind neck	55·00	£140	
68		6d. green and orange	30·00	80·00	3·25
		a. "Cleft skull" flaw	80·00	£190	
		b. Spots above head and behind neck	85·00	£200	
65/8 Set of 4			45·00	£140	5·00

In stamps with English at top the ½d., 3d. and 6d. have "SILWER JUBILEUM" to left of portrait, and "POSTAGE REVENUE" or "POSTAGE" (3d. and 6d.) in left value tablet. In the 1d., "SILVER JUBILEE" is to the left of portrait. In alternate stamps the positions of English and Afrikaans inscriptions are reversed.

1936 (2 Nov). Johannesburg International Philatelic Exhibition. Optd with T **24a**. W **9** (inverted).

			Un sheet	Us sheet
MS69	6	½d. grey and green (No. 54)	4·75	13·00
MS70	7	1d. grey and carmine (No. 56)	3·50	8·50

Issued each in miniature sheet of six stamps with marginal advertisements. Ten different arrangements of advertisements exist on the ½d. sheets, 21 different on the 1d.

25 **1½d.** "Mouse" flaw (R. 4/1)

(Des J. Prentice)

1937 (12 May). Coronation. W **9** (sideways*). P 14.

			Un pair	Used pair	Used single
71	25	½d. grey-black and blue-green	1·00	1·25	10
		w. Wmk horns pointing to left	1·00	1·25	10
72		1d. grey-black and carmine	1·00	1·00	10
		w. Wmk horns pointing to left	1·00	1·00	10
73		1½d. orange and greenish blue	1·00	80	10
		a. "Mouse" flaw	12·00		
		w. Wmk horns pointing to left	1·00	80	10
74		3d. ultramarine	1·50	3·00	10
		w. Wmk horns pointing to left	1·50	3·00	10
75		1s. red-brown and turquoise-blue	3·25	5·00	15
		a. Hyphen on Afrikaans stamp omitted (R. 2/13)	80·00	90·00	
		bw. Wmk horns pointing to left	3·25	5·00	15
71/5 Set of 5			7·00	10·00	40

*The normal sideways watermark shows the horns of the springbok pointing to the right, *as seen from the back of the stamp*.

No. 75a shows the hyphen completely omitted and the top of the "K" damaged. A less distinct flaw, on which part of the hyphen is still visible and with no damage to the "K", occurs on R. 4/17.

25a **½d.** "Tick" flaw on ear and spot on nose (multipositive flaw (occurring in 1947) (R. 3/4 or 3/1 on some ptgs of No. 114))

1937–40. W **9**. P 15×14.

75c	25a	½d. grey and green	13·00	2·50	10
		ca. Booklet pane of 6 (with blank margins) (1937)	65·00		
		cd. *Grey and blue green* (1940)	10·00	1·25	10
		ce. "Tick" flaw and spot on nose	75·00		

The lines of shading in T **25a** are all horizontal and thicker than in T **6**. In Nos. 75c and 75cd the design is composed of solid lines. For stamps with designs composed of dotted lines, see No. 114. Later printings of No. 75cd have a smaller design.

26 Voortrekker Ploughing **27** Wagon crossing Drakensberg

28 Signing of Dingaan–Retief Treaty

29 Voortrekker Monument

(Des W. Coetzer and J. Prentice)

1938 (14 Dec). Voortrekker Centenary Memorial Fund. W **9**. P 14 (Nos. 76/7) or 15×14 (others).

76	**26**	½d. +½d. blue and green ..	18·00	8·00	50
77	**27**	1d. +1d. blue and carmine	22·00	5·50	40
78	**28**	1½d. +1½d. chocolate and blue-green	26·00	10·00	1·00
79	**29**	3d. +3d.bright blue	26·00	10·00	1·00
76/9 Set of 4			80·00	29·00	2·50

30 Wagon Wheel

31 Voortrekker Family

1d. Three bolts in wheel rim (R. 15/5)

(Des W. Coetzer and J. Prentice)

1938 (14 Dec). Voortrekker Commemoration. W **9**. P 15×14.

80	**30**	1d. blue and carmine	9·50	3·50	30
		a. Three bolts in wheel rim	65·00	40·00	
81	**31**	1½d. greenish blue and brown	12·00	3·50	30

32 Old Vicarage, Paarl, now a museum

33 Symbol of the Reformation

34 Huguenot Dwelling, Drakenstein Mountain Valley

(Des J. Prentice)

1939 (17 July). 250th Anniv of Huguenot Landing in South Africa and Huguenot Commemoration Fund. W **9**. P 14 (Nos. 82/3) or 15×14 (No. 84).

82	**32**	½d. +½d. brown and green.	9·00	8·00	40
83	**33**	1d. +1d. green and carmine	15·00	8·00	40
84	**34**	1½d. +1½d. blue-green and purple	32·00	22·00	1·25
82/4 Set of 3			50·00	35·00	1·90

34a Gold Mine

Large gold blob on headgear (Cyl 31, R. 3/4)

1941 (Aug)–**48**. W **9** (sideways). P 14×15.

87	**34a**	1½d. blue-green and yellow-buff (*shades*)	3·50	1·50	10
		a. Yellow-buff (centre) omitted	£5000	£2500	
		ab. Ditto (one stamp in pair)	£3000		
		b. Gold blob on headgear	42·00		
		c. Booklet pane of 6 (with postal slogans on margins) (1948)	9·00		

Due to changes in the frame-plate make-up, the "Gold blob on headgear" variety may be found on stamps with both Afrikaans and English inscriptions.

35 Infantry

36 Nurse and Ambulance

37 Airman

38 Sailor, Destroyer and Lifebelts

39 Women's Auxiliary Services

40 Artillery

41 Electric Welding

42 Tank Corps

42a Signaller

1d. "Stain" on uniform (R. 14/11)

3d. "Cigarette" flaw (R. 18/2)

1941–46. War Effort. W **9** (sideways on 2d., 4d., 6d.). P 14 (2d., 4d., 6d.) or 15×14 (others).

(a) Inscr alternately

88	**35**	½d. green (19.11.41)	1·50	4·00	15
		a. Blue-green (7.42)	3·75	5·50	15
89	**36**	1d. carmine (3.10.41)	2·00	4·00	15
		a. "Stain" on uniform flaw	38·00	55·00	
90	**37**	1½d. myrtle-green (12.1.42)	1·50	4·00	15
91	**39**	3d. blue (1.8.41)	23·00	50·00	80
		a. "Cigarette" flaw	£120	£225	
92	**40**	4d. orange-brown (20.8.41)	27·00	35·00	25
		a. Red-brown (6.42)	38·00	42·00	1·25
93	**41**	6d. red-orange (3.9.41)	12·00	19·00	20
94	**42a**	1s.3d. olive-brown (2.1.43)	20·00	16·00	30
		a. Blackish brown (5.46)	7·00	10·00	20

(b) Inscr bilingually

			Un single	Us single
95	**38**	2d. violet (15.9.41)	1·00	75
96	**42**	1s. brown (27.10.41)	3·75	1·00
88/96 Set of 7 pairs and 2 singles			70·00	£110

43 Infantry

44 Nurse

45 Airman

46 Sailor

47 Women's Auxiliary Services

48 Electric Welding

49 Heavy Gun in Concrete Turret

50 Tank Corps

Unit (*pair*)

Unit (*triplet*)

Ear Flap flaw (Cyl 43 R. 13/3)

Apostrophe flaw (Cyl 6931 R. 19/1) (later corrected)

Line on Cap (Cyl 39 R. 12/11)

1s. "Bursting Shell" (Cyl 46 R. 11/20)

1½d. Smoking "L" (Cyl 46 R. 8/2)

1942–44. War Effort. Reduced sizes. In pairs perf 14 (P) or strips of three, perf 15×14 (T), subdivided by roulette 6½. W **9** (sideways* on 3d., 4d. and 1s.).

(a) Inscr alternately

			Un unit	Us unit	Us single
97	**43**	½d. blue-green (T) (10.42)	2·00	1·50	10
		a. Green (3.43)	3·00	2·50	10
		b. Greenish blue (7.44)	2·00	2·25	10
		c. Roulette omitted	£1400	£1300	
98	**44**	1d. carmine-red (T) (5.1.43)	1·50	1·50	10
		a. Bright carmine (3.44)	1·00	1·25	10
		b. Both roulettes omitted	£1200	£1200	
		ba. Left-hand roulette omitted	£1500		
99	**45**	1½d. red-brown (P) (9.42)	65	2·25	10
		aa. Nos. 99 and 99a se-tenant (strip of 4)	15·00	22·00	
		a. Roulette 13 (8.42)	1·50	5·00	30
		b. Roulette omitted	£375	£400	
		c. Ear flap flaw	20·00		
100	**46**	2d. violet (P) (2.43)	1·00	2·00	10
		a. Reddish violet (6.43)	1·50	1·00	10
		b. Roulette omitted	£1300	£1300	
		c. Apostrophe flaw	75·00	80·00	
		d. Line on cap	75·00	80·00	
101	**47**	3d. blue (T) (10.42)	10·00	18·00	10
102	**48**	6d. red-orange (P) (10.42) ..	2·00	2·25	10

(b) Inscr bilingually

103	**49**	4d. slate-green (T) (10.42)	20·00	11·00	10
104	**50**	1s. brown (P) (11.42)	20·00	4·25	10
		a. "Bursting shell"	95·00	95·00	
		b. Smoking "L"	95·00	95·00	
97/104 Set of 8			50·00	38·00	65

*The sideways watermark shows springbok horns pointing to left on the 3d. and 1s., and to right on the 4d., *all as seen from the back of the stamp.*

52

53

1943. Coil stamps. Redrawn. In single colours with plain background. W **9**. P 15×14.

			Un pair	Used pair	Used single
105	**52**	½d. blue-green (6.8.43*)	3·75	7·50	25

| 106 | **53** | 1d. carmine (4.11.43*)........ | 4·50 | 6·50 | 15 |

Quoted prices are for *vertical pairs*.
* Earliest recorded dates.

54 Union Buildings, Pretoria

1945–47. Redrawn. W **9**. P 14.

107	**54**	2d. slate and deep reddish violet (3.45).....	24·00	2·50	10
		a. Slate and deep lilac (10.46).................	24·00	6·00	20
		b. Slate and bright violet (1947).................	4·50	10·00	20

In Nos. 107 to 107*b* the Union Buildings are shown at a different angle from Nos. 58 and 58*a*. Only the centre is screened i.e., composed of very small square dots of colour arranged in straight diagonal lines. For whole design screened and colours changed, see No. 116. No. 107*a/b* also show "2" of "2d." clear of white circle at top.

55 "Victory"

56 "Peace"

57 "Hope"

1d. "Barbed wire" (R. 9/6)

1945 (3 Dec). Victory. W **9**. P 14.

108	**55**	1d. brown and carmine.....	20	1·25	10
		a. barbed wire flaw........	15·00		
109	**56**	2d. slate-blue and violet ...	20	1·25	10
110	**57**	3d. deep blue and blue.....	20	1·50	10
108/10		*Set of 3*....................	55	3·50	25

58 King George VI

59 King George VI and Queen Elizabeth

60 Queen Elizabeth II as Princess, and Princess Margaret

"Bird" on "2" (Cyl 6912 R. 10/6)

3d. "Black-eyed Princess" (R. 19/2)

(Des J. Prentice)

1947 (17 Feb). Royal Visit. W **9**. P 15×14.

111	**58**	1d. black and carmine	10	35	10
112	**59**	2d. violet	15	60	10
		a. "Bird" on "2" flaw..............	6·00	9·00	
113	**60**	3d. blue	15	60	10
		a. "Black-eyed Princess".....	7·50	12·00	
111/13		*Set of 3*........................	35	1·40	20

3d. "Flying saucer" flaw (Cyl 17 R. 17/2)

II **5s.**

5s. "Rain" flaw (R. 20/6)

1947–54. "SUID-AFRIKA" hyphenated on Afrikaans stamps. Printed from new cylinders with design in screened rotogravure. W **9**. P 15×14 (½d., 1d. and 6d.) or 14 (others).

114	**25a**	½d. grey and green (frame only screened) (9.47)	3·00	7·00	10
		a. Booklet pane of 6 (with postal slogans on margins) (1948)	6·00		
		b. "Tick" flaw and spot on nose	45·00		
		c. Entire design screened (7.1.49)	2·75	7·00	10
		ca. Booklet pane of 6 (with margin at right) (1951).	6·00		
		cb. "Tick" flaw and spot on nose	45·00		
115	**7**	1d. grey and carmine (1.9.50).................	2·25	5·00	10
		a. Booklet pane of 6 (with margin at right) (1951).	6·00		
116	**54**	2d. slate-blue and purple (3.50)	5·50	24·00	1·00
117	**22a**	3d. dull blue (4.49)	3·75	8·00	10
117*a*		3d. blue (3.51)	4·50	7·00	10
		ab. "Flying saucer" flaw	90·00	£100	
118	**12a**	4d. brown (22.8.52).............	4·50	20·00	80
119	**8**	6d. green and red-orange (III) (1.50)...............	3·75	1·50	10
		a. Green and brown-orange (III) (1951)	3·75	1·25	10
120	**13**	1s. brown and chalky blue (1.50)................	11·00	14·00	10
		a. Blackish brown and ultramarine (4.52)	15·00	21·00	15
121	**14**	2s.6d. green and brown (8.49)	11·00	30·00	1·00
122	**15**	5s. black and pale blue-green (I) (9.49)............	45·00	80·00	2·00
		a. "Rain" flaw	70·00	£120	
122*b*		5s. black and deep yellow-green (II) (1.54)............	50·00	£100	4·25
114/22		*Set of 9*....................	80·00	£170	4·50

In screened rotogravure the design is composed of very small squares of colour arranged in straight diagonal lines.

½d. Size 17¾×21¾ mm. Early printings have only the frame screened.

Due to changes in the frame-plate make-up, the "Tick" flaw and spot on nose may be found on stamps with bold Afrikaans and English inscriptions.

For the final printing of 114c, issued December 1951, the "Tick" flaw was removed, leaving a white "tick", but the spot on nose remained on R. 2/4.

1d. Size 18×22 mm. For smaller, redrawn design, see No. 135.

2d. For earlier issue with centre only screened, and in different colours, see Nos. 107/*a*.

3d. No. 117. Whole stamp screened with irregular grain. Scrolls above "3d." solid and toneless. Printed from two cylinders.

No. 117*a*. Whole stamp diagonally screened. Printed from one cylinder. Clouds more pronounced. Late printings were often in deep shades.

4d. Two groups of white leaves below name tablet and a clear white line down left and right sides of stamp.

61 Gold Mine

62 King George VI and Queen Elizabeth

1948 (1 Apr). Unit of four, perf 14, sub-divided by roulette 6½. W **9** (sideways).

			Un unit of 4	Us unit	Used single
124	**61**	1½d. blue-green and yellow-buff..................	2·50	6·50	10

(Des J. Booysen and J. Prentice)

1948 (26 Apr). Silver Wedding. W **9**. P 14.

			Un pair	Used pair	Used single
125	**62**	3d. blue and silver..............	1·50	1·25	10

(Typo Government Printer, Pretoria)

1948 (July). W **9**. P 14½×14.

| 126 | **6** | ½d. pale grey and blue-green.................. | 2·25 | 13·00 | 1·40 |

This was an economy printing made from the old plates of the 1926 issue for the purpose of using up a stock of cut paper. For the original printing in black and green, see No. 30.

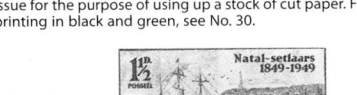

63 *Wanderer* (emigrant ship) entering Durban

Extended rigging on mainmast (R. 14/2)

"Pennant" flaw (R. 17/5)

(Des J. Prentice)

1949 (2 May). Centenary of Arrival of British Settlers in Natal. W **9**. P 15×14.

127	**63**	1½d. claret	80	80	10
		a. Extended rigging..........	16·00	18·00	
		b. "Pennant" flaw..............	16·00	18·00	

64 Hermes

3d. Serif on "C" (R. 1/1)

3d. "Lake" in East Africa (R. 2/19)

(Des J. Booysen and J. Prentice)

1949 (1 Oct). 75th Anniv of Universal Postal Union. As T **64** inscr "UNIVERSAL POSTAL UNION" and "WERELDPOSUNIE" alternately. W **9** (sideways). P 14×15.

128	**64**	½d. blue-green	50	1·00	10
129		1½d. brown-red	50	1·00	10
130		3d. bright blue	60	1·00	10
		a. Serif on "C"	55·00		
		b. "Lake" in East Africa..........	55·00		
128/30		*Set of 3*..........	1·40	2·75	25

65 Wagons approaching Bingham's Berg

67 Bible, candle and Voortrekkers

66 Voortrekker Monument, Pretoria

(Des W. Coetzer and J. Prentice)

1949 (1 Dec). Inauguration of Voortrekker Monument, Pretoria. T **65** and similar horiz designs. W **9**. P 15×14.

			Un single	Us single
131		1d. magenta................	10	10
132		1½d. blue-green	10	10
133		3d. blue	15	15
131/3		*Set of 3*....................	30	30

Designs:—1½d. Voortrekker Monument, Pretoria; 3d. Bible, candle and Voortrekkers.

68 Union Buildings, Pretoria

1950 (Apr)–**51**. W **9** (sideways). P 14×15.

			Un pair	Used pair	Used single
134	**68**	2d. blue and violet..............	1·00	1·00	10
		a. Booklet pane of 6 (with margin at right) (1951)................	4·00		

1951 (22 Feb). As No. 115, but redrawn with the horizon clearly defined. Size reduced to 17¼×21¼ mm.

| 135 | **7** | 1d. grey and carmine .... | 1·75 | 2·50 | 10 |

SOUTH AFRICA *Union of South Africa*

69 Seal and monogram

70 *Maria de la Quellerie* (D. Craey)

2d. "Full Moon" flaw under "R" of "AFRICA" (R. 6/3)

2d. Line through sails consists of a vertical line from near the top of the upper stamp, extending through the sails to the stamp below (pair comprising R. 11/2 and R. 12/12)

(Des Miss R. Reeves and J. Prentice (1d., 4½d.), Mrs. T. Campbell and J. Prentice (others))

1952 (14 Mar). Tercentenary of Landing of Van Riebeeck. T **69/70** and similar designs. W **9** (sideways on 1d. and 4½d.) P 14×15 (1d. and 4½d.) or 14×15 (others).

136	½d. brown-purple and olive-grey		10	10
137	1d. deep blue-green		10	10
138	2d. deep violet		50	10
	a. "Full Moon"		12·00	
	b. "Line through sails" (vert pair)		17·00	
139	4½d. blue		15	15
140	1s. brown		1·00	10
136/40 Set of 5			1·50	45

Designs: Horiz—2d. Arrival of Van Riebeeck's ships; 1s. *Landing at the Cape* (C. Davidson Bell). Vert—4½d. *Jan van Riebeeck* (D. Craey).

SATISE SADIPU
(74)　　　(75)

1952 (26 Mar). South African Tercentenary International Stamp Exhibition, Cape Town. No. 137 optd with T **74** and No. 138 with T **75**.

141	1d. deep blue-green		40	1·25
142	2d. deep violet		60	1·00
	a. "Full Moon"		14·00	
	b. "Line through sails" (vert pair)		19·00	

76 Queen Elizabeth II

Scar on neck (Cyls 66 and 98, R. 4/7)

(Des H. Kumst)

1953 (3 June). Coronation. W **9** (sideways). P 14×15.

143	76	2d. deep violet-blue	50	10
		a. *Ultramarine*	60	10
		b. Scar on neck	10·00	

77 1d. "Cape Triangular" Stamp

4d. Broken knee (lower pane, R. 10/4)

(Des H. Kumst)

1953 (1 Sept). Centenary of First Cape of Good Hope Stamp. T **77** and similar horiz design. W **9**. P 15×14.

144		1d. sepia and vermilion	10	10
145		4d. deep blue and light blue	50	20
		a. Broken knee	10·00	

Design:—4d. Four pence "Cape Triangular" stamp.

79 Merino Ram

80 Springbok

81 Aloes

(Des A. Hendriksz and J. Prentice (4½d.))

1953 (1 Oct). W **9**. P 14.

146	79	4½d. slate-purple and yellow	20	10
		a. Yellow omitted	†	£3000
147	80	1s.3d. chocolate	1·25	10
148	81	1s.6d. vermilion and deep blue-green	50	35
146/8 Set of 3			1·75	45

82 Arms of Orange Free State and Scroll

(Des H. Kumst)

1954 (23 Feb). Centenary of Orange Free State. W **9**. P 15×14.

149	82	2d. sepia and pale vermilion	10	10
150		4½d. purple and slate	20	50

83 Warthog

84 Black Wildebeest

85 Leopard

86 Mountain Zebra

87 White Rhinoceros

88 African Elephant

89 Hippopotamus

90 Lion

91 Greater Kudu

92 Springbok

93 Gemsbok

94 Nyala

95 Giraffe

96 Sable Antelope

(Des H. Kumst)

1954 (14 Oct). T **83/96** and similar designs. W **9** (sideways on large vert designs). P 15×14 (½d. to 2d.), 14 (others).

151	83	½d. deep blue-green	10	10
152	84	1d. brown-lake	10	10
153	85	1½d. sepia	10	10
154	86	2d. plum	10	10
155	87	3d. chocolate and turquoise-blue	1·00	10
156	88	4d. indigo and emerald	1·00	30
157	89	4½d. blue-black and grey-blue	60	1·00
158	90	6d. sepia and orange	50	10
159	91	1s. deep brown and pale chocolate	1·25	10
160	92	1s.3d. brown and bluish green	3·25	10
161	93	1s.6d. brown and rose	1·75	60
162	94	2s.6d. brown-black and apple-green	3·50	20
163	95	5s. black-brown and yellow-orange	12·00	1·60
164	96	10s. black and cobalt	12·00	3·50
151/64 Set of 14			32·00	6·50

No. 152 exists in coils.
See also Nos. 170/7 and 185/97.

97 President Kruger

98 President M. Pretorius

6d. "Scar" on chin (R. 1/7)

(Des H. Kumst)

1955 (21 Oct). Centenary of Pretoria. W **9** (sideways). P 14×15.

165	97	3d. slate-green	10	10
166	98	6d. maroon	10	30
		a. "Scar" on chin	8·00	

99 A. Pretorius, Church of the Vow and Flag

100 Settlers' Block-wagon and House

(Des H. Kumst)

1955 (1 Dec). Voortrekker Covenant Celebrations, Pietermaritzburg. W **9**. P 14.

			Un pair	Us pair	Us single
167	99	2d. blue and magenta	45	2·75	10

(Des H. Kumst)

1958 (1 July). Centenary of Arrival of German Settlers in South Africa. W **9**. P 14.

168	100	2d. chocolate and pale purple	10	10

101 Arms of the Academy

(Des H. Kumst)

1959 (1 May). 50th Anniv of the South African Academy of Science and Art, Pretoria. W **9**. P 15×14.

169	101	3d. deep blue and turquoise-blue	10	10
		a. Deep blue printing omitted	£6500	

102 Union Coat of Arms　　I　　II

584

1959–60. As Nos. 151/2, 155/6, 158/9 and 162/3, but W **102** (sideways on Nos. 172/3 and 175/7).

170	**83**	½d. deep greenish blue (12.60)	15	7·00
171	**84**	1d. brown-lake (I) (11.59)...................	10	10
		a. Redrawn. Type II (10.60).............	20	10
172	**87**	3d. chocolate and turquoise-blue (9.59)..	25	10
173	**88**	4d. indigo and emerald (1.60)	50	20
174	**90**	6d. sepia and orange (2.60)	70	2·75
175	**91**	1s. deep brown and pale chocolate (11.59).........................	7·00	1·75
176	**94**	2s.6d. brown-black and apple-green (12.59)......................................	2·75	4·00
177	**95**	5s. black-brown and yellow-orange (10.60)...........................	9·00	35·00
170/7 *Set of 8*...			18·00	45·00

Nos. 171/a. In Type II "1d. Posgeld Postage" is more to the left in relation to "South Africa", with "1" almost central over "S" instead of to right as in Type I.

No. 171 exists in coils.

103 Globe and Antarctic Scene

(Des H. Kumst)

1959 (16 Nov). South African National Antarctic Expedition. W **102**. P 14×15.

178	**103**	3d. blue-green and orange................	20	10

104 Union Flag   **105** Union Arms

106 "Wheel of Progress"

107 Union Festival emblem

(Des V. Ivanoff and H. Kumst (1s.), H. Kumst (others))

1960 (2 May). 50th Anniv of Union of South Africa. T **104/107**. W **102** (sideways on 4d. and 6d.). P 14×15 (4d., 6d.) or 15×14 (others).

179	**104**	4d. orange-red and blue....................	30	10
180	**105**	6d. red, brown and light green	30	10
181	**106**	1s. deep blue and light yellow	30	10
182	**107**	1s. 6d. black and light blue	70	1·00
179/82 *Set of 4*..			1·40	1·00

See also No. 190, 192/3.

108 Steam Locomotives *Natal* (1860) and Class 25 (1950s)

(Des V. Ivanoff)

1960 (2 May). Centenary of South African Railways. W **102**. P 15×14.

183	**108**	1s.3d. deep blue.............................	1·10	30

109 Prime Ministers Botha, Smuts, Hertzog, Malan, Strijdom and Verwoerd

1960 (31 May). Union Day. W **102**. P 15×14.

184	**109**	3d. brown and pale brown	15	10
		a. Pale brown omitted*..................	£9000	

*This is due to a rectangular piece of paper adhering to the background cylinder, resulting in R.2/1 missing the colour completely and six adjoining stamps having it partially omitted. The item in block of eight is probably unique.

(New Currency. 100 cents = 1 rand)

1961 (14 Feb). As previous issues but with values in cents and rand. W **102** (sideways on 3½c., 7½c., 20c., 50c., 1r.). P 15×14 (½c., to 2½c., 10c.), 14×15 (3½c., 7½c.) or 14 (others).

185	**83**	½c. deep bluish green (as 151)........	10	10
186	**84**	1c. brown-lake (as 152)..................	10	10
187	**85**	1½c. sepia (as 153)........................	10	10
188	**86**	2c. plum (as 154)...........................	10	1·00
189	**109**	2½c. brown (as 184).........................	20	10
190	**104**	3½c. orange-red and blue (as 179)....	20	2·50
191	**90**	5c. sepia and orange (as 158)..........	20	10
192	**105**	7½c. red, brown and light green (as 180)..	20	3·50
193	**106**	10c. deep blue and light yellow (as 181)...	40	60
194	**92**	12½c. brown and bluish green (as 160)..	1·00	1·25
195	**93**	20c. brown and rose (as 161)............	2·75	3·50
196	**95**	50c. black-brown and orange-yellow (as 163)..........................	4·75	11·00
197	**96**	1r. black and cobalt (as 164)	15·00	25·00
185/97 *Set of 13*..			22·00	42·00

X. REPUBLIC OF SOUTH AFRICA

OUTSIDE THE COMMONWEALTH

110 African Pygmy Kingfisher   **111** Kafferboom Flower   **112** Afrikander Bull

113 Pouring Gold   **114** Groot Constantia

115 Burchell's Gonolek   **116** Baobab Tree

117 Maize   **118** Cape Town Castle Entrance   **119** Protea

120 Secretary Bird   **121** Cape Town Harbour

122 Strelitzia

I

II

Two types of ½c.:

Type I from sheets. Reeds indistinct.
Type II from coils. Reeds strengthened.

Three types of 1c.:

I   II

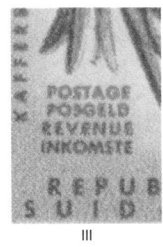

III

Type I. Lowest point of flower between "OS" of "POSTAGE". Right-hand petal over "E".
Type II. Flower has moved fractionally to the right so that lowest point is over "S" of "POSTAGE". Right-hand petal over "E .
Type III. Lowest point directly over "O". Right-hand petal over "G".

Two types of 2½c.

I

II

In Type I the lines of the building are quite faint.
In Type II all lines of the building have been strengthened by re-engraving.

(Des Mrs. T. Campbell (½c., 3c., 1r.); Miss N. Desmond (1c.); De La Rue (2½c., 5c., 12½c.); H. L. Prager (50c.); Govt. Ptg Dept artist (others))

1961 (31 May)–**63**. Unsurfaced paper. W **102** (sideways* on ½c., 1½c., 2½c., 5c. to 20c.). P 14×15 (½c., 1½c.), 15×14 (1c.) or 14 (others).

198	110	½c. bright blue, carmine and brown (I)	10	10
		a. Perf 14 (3.63)	10	15
		b. Type II (coils) (18.5.63)	1·25	3·00
199	111	1c. red and olive-grey (I)	10	10
		a. Type II (1.62)	10	10
		b. Type III (coils) (5.63)	2·00	3·75
200	112	1½c. brown-lake and light purple	10	10
201	113	2c. ultramarine and yellow	2·00	10
202	114	2½c. violet and green (I)	15	10
		aw. Wmk top of Arms to right	1·75	10
		b. Type II. *Deep violet and green* (9.61)	20	10
203	115	3c. red and deep blue	2·50	1·00
204	116	5c. yellow and greenish blue	30	10
205	117	7½c. yellow-brown and light green	60	10
206	118	10c. sepia and green	75	10
207	119	12½c. red, yellow and black-green	2·00	30
		a. Yellow omitted	£1600	
		b. Red omitted	£2750	
208	120	20c. turquoise-blue, carmine and brown-orange	3·00	30
209	121	50c. black and bright blue	14·00	2·00
210	122	1r. orange, olive-green and light blue	7·00	2·00
198/210		*Set of 13*	29·00	5·00

*The normal sideways watermark shows the top of the Arms to left, as seen from the back of the stamp.

1961–74 Definitives
Key to designs, perfs, watermarks, papers and phosphors

Value	Type	Perf	W 102 Ordinary	No wmk Ordinary	W 127 Chalky
½c.	110	(I)	14×15	198	
		(I)	14	198a	
		(II)	14×15	198b	
1c.	111	(I)	15×14	199	211
		(II)	14	199a	211a
		(II)			227
		(III)		199b	
1½c.	112		14×15	200	228
2c.	113		14	201	212	229
2½c.	114	(I)	14	202	
		(II)		202b	213/a	230/a
3c.	115		14	203	214	
5c.	116		14	204	215	231
7½c.	117		14	205	216	232
10c.	118		14	206	217/b	233/a
12½c.	119		14	207		
20c.	120		14	208	218	234/a
50c.	121		14	209	219	235
1r.	122		14	210		236

Redrawn Designs

Value	Type	Perf	W 127	W 127a plain or phos	W 127 Phos frame	W 127a Phos frame	No wmk. Phosphorised Glossy	Chalky
½c.	130a	14	A238	B238	—	—	—	—
		14×15	A238b	—				
		14	—	B238c/d	—	—		
1c.	131	15×14	A239	B239	—	—		
		13½×14	A239a	B239a	—			
1½c.	132	14×15	—	B240/b	284			
		14×13½	—	B240c	—			
2c.	133	14	A241	B241/b	—	285/a	315a	
		12½	—	—	—	315	315b	
2½c.	134	14	A242	B242a	286aa	286/a	—	
3c.	135	14	A243	B243/a	287			
		12½	—	—	—	316	316a	
4c.	134	14	—	B243b	288			
5c.	136	14	—	B244/a	289	318a		
		12½	—	—	—	318	318b	
6c.	137	14	—	—	290			
		12½	—	—	—	319		
7½c.	137	14	—	B245	291			

Value	Type	Perf	W 127	W 127a plain or phos	W 127 Phos frame	W 127a Phos frame	No wmk. Phosphorised Glossy	Chalky
9c.	139	14	—	B245a	—	292		
		12½	—	—	—	—	320/a	
10c.	138	14	—	B246/a	—	293	321/a	
		12½	—	—	—	—	321	321b
12½c.	139	14	A247/a	—	—	294		
15c.	140	14	A248	B248	—	295		
20c.	141	14	—	B249/a	—	296/a		
		12½	—	—	—	—	323	323a
50c.	142	14	—	B250	—	—		
		12½	—	—	—	—	324	324a
1r.	143	14	A251	B251	—	—		
		12½	—	—	—	—	325	

New Designs

Value	Type	Perf	W 127a Plain or phos	W 127a Phos frame	No wmk. Phosphorised Glossy	Chalky
½c.	168	14×13½	276	282	—	—
		14×14½	276a	—	313	—
		14×15	—	282a	—	—
1c.	169	13½×14	277	283	—	—
		14	—	—	314	—
4c.	182	14	310/a	—	—	—
		12½	—	—	317/b	317c
15c.	182a	14	311	—	—	322
		12½	—	—	—	—

Although several of the stamps included in this table were issued after 1970 and are therefore not listed in this catalogue, the table has been shown here in full for the convenience of collectors

1961 (1 Aug)–**63**. As Nos. 199, 201/6 and 208/9 but without wmk.

211	111	1c. red and olive-grey (I)	10	50
		a. Type II (9.62)	1·00	1·25
212	113	2c. ultramarine and yellow (8.63)	9·00	3·50
213	114	2½c. deep violet and green (II)	20	10
		a. *Violet and green (12.61)*	20	10
214	115	3c. red and deep blue (10.61)	45	10
		a. Deep blue (face value, etc) omitted	£3250	
215	116	5c. yellow and greenish blue (12.61)	35	10
216	117	7½c. yellow-brown and light green (3.62)	60	15
217	118	10c. sepia and green (11.61)	2·00	70
		a. Sepia and emerald (12.61)	50·00	18·00
		b. Sepia-brown and light green (7.63)	2·25	1·50
218	120	20c. turquoise-blue carmine and brown-orange (4.63)	8·00	2·75
219	121	50c. black and bright blue (8.62)	8·00	3·00
211/19		*Set of 9*	25·00	9·00

123 Blériot XI Monoplane and Boeing 707 Airliner over Table Mountain

124 Folk-dancers

1961 (1 Dec). 50th Anniv of First South African Aerial Post. W **102** (sideways). P 14×15.

220	123	3c. blue and red	50	10

(Des K. Esterhuysen)

1962 (1 Mar). 50th Anniv of Volkspele (folk-dancing) in South Africa. W **102** (sideways). P 14×15.

221	124	2½c. orange-red and brown	15	10

125 The Chapman (emigrant ship)

1962 (20 Aug). Unveiling of Precinct Stone, British Settlers Monument Grahamstown. W **102**. P 15×14.

222	125	2½c. turquoise-green and purple	50	10
223		12½c. blue and deep chocolate	1·75	1·00

126 Red Disa (orchid), Castle Rock and Gardens

(Des M. F. Stern)

1963 (14 Mar). 50th Anniv of Kirstenbosch Botanic Gardens, Cape Town. P 13½×14.

224	126	2½c. multicoloured	20	10
		a. Red (orchid, etc) omitted	£3750	£2250

127 RSA (upright)

127a RSA (*tête-bêche*)

128 Centenary Emblem and Nurse

129 Centenary Emblem and Globe

1963 (30 Aug). Centenary of Red Cross. Chalk-surfaced paper. Wmk **127** (sideways on 2½c.). P 14×13½ (2½c.) or 15×14 (12½c.).

225	128	2½c. red, black and reddish purple	20	10
		w. Wmk reversed	3·25	1·75
226	129	12½c. red and indigo	1·75	1·00
		a. Red cross omitted	£5000	£3000

1963–67. As 1961–63 but chalk-surfaced paper and W **127** (sideways on 1½c., 2½c., (Nos. 230, 230aw) and 5c.), (sideways inverted on 2½c. (No. 230a), 7½c., 10c. and 20c.). P 15×14 (1c.) 14×15 (1½c.), or 14 (others).

227	111	1c. red and olive-grey (II) (9.63)	10	10
		w. Wmk reversed	65	65
228	112	1½c. brown-lake and light purple (1.67)	1·75	3·00
229	113	2c. ultramarine and yellow (11.64)	15	20
230	114	2½c. violet and green (II) (10.63)	10	10
		a. *Bright reddish violet and emerald (II) (wmk sideways inverted) (3.66)*	20	20
		aw. Wmk sideways (top of triangle to right)	2·50	1·00
231	116	5c. yellow and greenish blue (9.66)	1·00	75
232	117	7½c. yellow-brown and bright green (23.2.66)	3·50	6·50
		w. Wmk sideways (top of triangle to right)	15·00	7·50
233	118	10c. sepia-brown and light emerald (9.64)	40	10
		a. Sepia-brown and green (1.67)	45	20
234	120	20c. turquoise-blue, carmine and brown orange (7.64)	1·00	2·25
		a. *Deep turquoise-blue, carmine and flesh (20.7.65)*	1·75	1·25
235	121	50c. black and ultramarine (4.66)	30·00	10·00
236	122	1r. orange, light green and pale blue (7.64)	48·00	48·00
227/36		*Set of 10*	80·00	60·00

In the 2½c. (No. 230a), 5c., 7½c., 10c. (Jan 1967 printing only) and 50c. the watermark is indistinct but they can easily be distinguished from the stamps without watermark by their shades and the chalk-surfaced paper which is appreciably thicker and whiter.

The normal sideways watermark shows the top of the triangle pointing left (*as seen from the back of the stamp*), i.e. sideways inverted. On Nos. 228, 230, 230aw, 231 and 232w the top of the triangle points to the right.

130 Assembly Building, Umtata

1963 (11 Dec). First Meeting of Transkei Legislative Assembly. Chalk-surfaced paper. W **127**. P 15×14.

237	130	2½c. sepia and light green	10	10
		a. Light green omitted	£3250	

130a African Pygmy Kingfisher

131 Kafferboom Flower

132 Afrikander Bull

133 Pouring Gold

134 Groot Constantia

135 Burchell's Gonolek

136 Baobab Tree

137 Maize

138 Cape Town Castle Entrance

139 Protea

140 Industry

141 Secretary Bird

142 Cape Town Harbour

143 Strelitzia

(15c. des C. E. F. Skotnes)

Redrawn types.

½c. "½C" larger and REPUBLIEK VAN REPUBLIC OF" smaller.
3c. and 12½c. Inscriptions and figures of value larger.
Others. "SOUTH AFRICA" and SUID-AFRIKA larger and bolder. The differences vary in each design but are easy to see by comparing the position of the letters of the country name with "REPUBLIC OF" and "REPUBLIEK VAN".

1964–72. As 1961–63 but redrawn and new values (4c, 9c and 15c). Chalk-surfaced paper.

(a) wmk **127** *(sideways on ½, 1½, 2½, 4, 5, 7½, 9, 10, 15, 20c.).*
P 14×15 (1½c.), 15×14 (1c.) or 14 (others)

A238	½c. bright blue, carmine and brown (21.5.64)	10	10
	a. Imperf (pair)	£375	
	b. Perf 14×15	20	20
A239	1c. red and olive-grey (9.3.67)	10	10
	a. Perf 13½×14 (7.68)	30	10
A241	2c. ultramarine and yellow (8.1.68)	20	10
	a. Yellow omitted	£1400	
A242	2½c. violet and green (19.4.67)	20	10
	w. Wmk top of RSA to left	£450	75.00
A243	3c. red and deep blue (11.64)	30	10
A247	12½c. red, yellow and black-green (3.64)	1.00	40
	a. Red, pale yellow and blue-green (2.2.66)	2.75	40
A248	15c. black, light olive-yellow and red-orange (1.3.67)	1.25	25
A251	1r. orange, light green and light blue (6.65)	2.00	1.00
	w. Wmk inverted		
A238/A251 Set of 8		4.50	2.00

(b) wmk **127a**. *P 14×15 (1½c.), 15×14 (1c.) or 14 (others)*

B238	½c. bright blue, carmine and yellow-brown (1.68)	10	10
	c. Perf 14. Bright blue, lake and yellow-brown (3.68)	60	70
	d. Perf 14. Bright blue, carmine-lake and yellow-brown (3.98)	30	10
B239	1c. red and olive-grey (7.67)	10	10
	a. Perf 13½×14 (9.68)	30	10
B240	1½c. dull red-brown and light purple (21.9.67)	15	10
	a. Purple-brown and light purple (1968)	15	10
	b. Bright red-brown and light purple (5.68)	15	10
	c. Perf 14×13½. Red-brown and light purple (14.8.69)	2.00	2.25
B241	2c. Ultramarine and yellow	1.50	20
	b. Blue and yellow	80	10
B242a	2½c. reddish violet and green (7.67)	30	10
B243	3c. red and deep blue (19.12.67)	30	10
	a. Brown-red and deep blue (3.72)	4.25	30
B243b	4c. violet and green (10.71)	1.00	30

B244	5c. orange-yellow and greenish blue (14.2.68)	40	10
	a. Lemon and deep greenish blue	8.50	1.00
B245	7½c. yellow-brown and bright green (26.7.67)	60	10
B245a	9c. red, yellow and slate-green (2.72)	7.50	7.50
B246	10c. sepia and green (10.6.68)	1.75	1.25
	a. Brown and pale green (7.68)	4.50	4.50
B248	15c. black, light olive-yellow and red-orange (4.3.69)	3.00	50
B249	20c. turquoise-blue, carmine and brown-orange (2.68)	6.50	15
	a. Turquoise-blue, carmine and orange-buff (12.71)	8.50	2.00
B250	50c. black and bright blue (17.6.68)	2.00	40
B251	1r. orange, light green and light blue (6.68)	2.00	1.00
B238/B251 Set of 14		30.00	10.00

The normal sideways watermark shows the top of RSA to right as seen from the back of the stamp.

WATERMARK. The first stamps on Type **127** showed a reasonably clear watermark, but a new paper introduced in late 1966 had a much fainter watermark. Type **127a** was introduced in mid-1967 and is invariably quite difficult to see, so care should be exercised in correctly identifying single stamps from this issue.

GUM. The 2, 3, 5, 20, 50c. and 1r. on W **127a** exist with PVA gum as well as gum arabic.

PHOSPHORISED PAPER. From October 1971 onwards phosphor bands (see Nos. 282/96) gave way to phosphorised paper which cannot be distinguished from non-phosphor stamps without the aid of a lamp. For this reason we do not distinguish these printings in the above issue, but some are slightly different shades and all have PVA gum. The 4c. and 9c. are on phosphorised paper only and differ from Nos. 288 and 292 by the lack of phosphor bands.

145 "Springbok" Badge of Rugby Board

147 Calvin

1964 (8 May). 75th Anniv of South African Rugby Board. Chalk-surfaced paper. T **145** and similar horiz design. W **127** (sideways on 2½c.). P 14×15 (2½c.) or 15×14 (12½c.).

252	2½c. yellow-brown and deep green	15	10
253	12½c. black and light yellow-green	1.50	1.50

Design:—12½c. Rugby footballer.

1964 (10 July). 400th Death Anniv of Calvin (Protestant reformer). Chalk-surfaced paper. W **127** (sideways). P 14×13½.

254	**147** 2½c. cerise, violet and brown	10	10

148 Nurse's Lamp

149 Nurse holding Lamp

I. Screened base to lamp

II. Clear base to lamp

1964 (12 Oct). 50th Anniv of South African Nursing Association. Chalk-surfaced paper. W **127** (sideways on 2½c.). P 14×15 (2½ c.) or 15×14 (12½c.)

255	**148** 2½c. ultramarine and dull gold (Type I)	10	10
256	2½c. bright blue and yellow-gold (Type II)	30	10
	a. *Ultramarine and dull gold*	15	10
257	**149** 12½c. bright blue and gold	1.75	1.25
	a. Gold omitted	£3750	
255/7 Set of 3		1.75	1.25

150 ITU Emblem and Satellites

1965 (17 May). ITU Centenary. T **150** and similar horiz design. Chalk-surfaced paper. W **127**. P 15×14.

258	2½c. orange and blue	25	10
259	12½c. brown-purple and green	1.25	1.00

Design:—12½ c. ITU emblem and symbols.

152 Pulpit in Groote Kerk, Cape Town

153 Church Emblem

1965 (21 Oct). Tercentenary of Nederduites Gereformeerde Kerk (Dutch Reformed Church) in South Africa. Chalk-surfaced paper. W **127** (sideways on 2½c., inverted on 12½c.). P 14×15 (2½c.) or 15×14 (12½c.).

260	**152** 2½c. brown and light yellow	15	10
261	**153** 12½c. black, light orange and blue	70	70

154 Diamond

155 Bird in flight

(Des C.E.F. Skotnes)

1966 (31 May). Fifth Anniv of Republic. T **154/5** and similar designs. Chalk-surfaced paper. W **127** (sideways on 1c., 3c.). P 14×13½ (1c.), 13½×14 (2½c.), 14×15 (3c.) or 15×14 (7½c.).

			Us	Us
		Un pair	pair	single
262	1c. black, bluish green and olive-yellow	45	60	10
263	2½c. blue, deep blue and yellow-green	50	1.00	10
264	3c. red, greenish yellow and red-brown	1.25	1.75	10
265	7½c. blue, ultramarine and yellow	1.25	1.75	10
262/5 Set of 4		3.00	4.50	35

Designs:—3c. Maize plants. Horiz—7½c. Mountain landscape. Nos. 262/5 exist on Swiss made paper with *tête bêche* watermark from a special printing made for use in presentation albums for delegates to the UPU Congress in Tokyo in 1969 as supplies of the original Harrison paper were by then exhausted (Set of 4 *pairs price* £140 *mint*).

158 Verwoerd and Union Buildings, Pretoria

(Des from portrait by Dr. Henkel)

1966 (6 Dec). Verwoerd Commemoration. T **158** and similar designs. Chalk-surfaced paper. W **127** (sideways on 3c.). P 14×15 (3c.) or 15×14 (others).

266	2½ c. blackish brown and turquoise	10	10
267	3c. blackish brown and yellow-green	10	10
	a. Blackish brown (portrait) omitted	£8000	
268	12½ c. blackish brown and greenish blue	60	60
266/8 Set of 3		70	60

Designs: Vert—3c. "Dr. H.F. Verwoerd" (I. Henkel). Horiz—12½c. Verwoerd and map of South Africa.

161 *Martin Luther* (Cranach the Elder)

162 Wittenberg Church Door

1967 (31 Oct). 450th Anniv of Reformation. W **127** ((sideways), on 2½c., W **127a** on 12½c.). P 14×15.

269	**161** 2½c. black and rose-red	10	10
270	**162** 12½c. black and yellow-orange	1.00	1.50

163 "Profile of Pres. Fouche" (I. Henkel)

164 Portrait of Pres. Fouche

1968 (10 Apr). Inauguration of President Fouche. W **127** (sideways). P 14×15.

271	**163** 2½c. chocolate and pale chocolate	10	10

272	164	12½c. deep blue and light blue	60	1·00
		a. Wmk **127a**	1·00	1·50

165 Hertzog in 1902

1968 (21 Sept). Inauguration of General Hertzog Monument, Bloemfontein. T **165** and similar designs. W **127**, (inverted on 3c., sideways on 12½c. or **127a** (2½c.)). P 14×13½ (12½c.) or 13½×14 (others).

273		2½c. black, brown and olive-yellow	10	10
274		3c. black, red-brown, red-orange and yellow	15	10
275		12½c. red and yellow-orange	1·00	1·00
273/5 *Set of 3*			1·00	1·00

Designs: Horiz—3c. Hertzog in 1924. Vert—12½c. Hertzog Monument.

168 African Pygmy Kingfisher **169** Kafferboom Flower

1969. W **127a** (sideways on ½c.). P 14×13½ (½c.) or 13½×14 (1c.)

276	168	½c. new blue, carmine-red and yellow-ochre (1.69)	10	60
		a. Coil. Perf 14×14½ (5.69)	1·75	4·25
277	169	1c. rose-red and olive-brown (1.69)	10	10

See also Nos. 282/3.

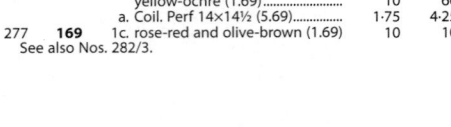

170 Springbok and Olympic Torch **171** Professor Barnard and Groote Schuur Hospital

1969 (15 Mar). South African Games, Bloemfontein. W **127a** (sideways). P 14×13½.

278	170	2½c. black, blue-black, red and sage-green	15	10
279		12½c. black, blue-black, red and cinnamon	70	1·00

1969 (7 July). World's First Heart Transplant and 47th South African Medical Association Congress. T **171** and similar horiz design. W **127a**. P 13½×14 (2½c.) or 15×14 (12½c.).

280		2½c. plum and rose-red	15	10
281		12½c. carmine-red and royal blue	1·25	1·40

Design:—12½c. Hands holding heart.

1969–72. As 1964–72 issue, Nos. 276/7, and new value (6c.), but with phosphor bands printed horizontally and vertically between the stamp designs, over the perforations, producing a frame effect. W **127a** (upright on 1, 2 and 3c., sideways on others). P 14×13½ (½, 1½c.), 13½×14 (1c.), or 14 (others).

282	168	½c. new blue, carmine-red and yellow-ochre (1.70)	15	70
		a. Coil. Perf 14×15 (2.71)	3·50	7·50
		w. Wmk reversed	65	2·50
283	169	1c. rose-red and olive-brown (12.69)	15	10
		w. Wmk reversed	60	1·00
284	132	1½c. red-brown and light purple (12.69)	20	1·00
285	133	2c. ultramarine and yellow (11.69)	1·00	10
		aa. Yellow omitted	£1500	
		a. *Deep ultramarine and yellow* (8.70)	1·00	1·00
286	134	2½c. violet and green (1.70)	15	10
		aa. Wmk **127**	1·00	1·00
		a. *Purple and green* (24.7.70)	1·75	10
		w. Wmk reversed	20·00	17·00
287	135	3c. red and deep blue (30.9.69)	1·00	1·50
288	134	4c. violet and green (1.3.71)	40	2·25
289	136	5c. yellow and greenish blue (17.11.69)	60	10
290	137	6c. yellow-brown and bright green (3.5.71)	70	2·00
291		7½c. yellow-brown and bright green (17.11.69)	2·00	30
292	139	9c. red, yellow and black-green (17.5.71)	3·50	2·50
293	138	10c. brown and pale green (1.70)	1·00	10
294	139	12½c. red, yellow and black-green (2.5.70)	4·00	7·00
295	140	15c. black, light olive-yellow and red-orange (1.70)	1·00	2·25

296	141	20c. turquoise-blue, carmine and brown-orange 18.2.70)	8·00	4·50
		a. Turquoise-blue, carmine and orange-buff (9.72)	11·00	4·50
282/96 *Set of 15*			21·00	22·00

The 1, 2, 2½, 3, 10, 15 and 20c. exist with PVA gum as well as gum arabic, but the 4, 6 and 9c. exist with PVA gum only. Stamps without watermark in these designs were issued between 1972 and 1974.

173 Mail Coach **174** Transvaal Stamp of 1869

1969 (6 Oct). Centenary of First Stamps of South African Republic (Transvaal). Phosphor bands on all four sides (2½c.). W **127a** (sideways on 12½c.). P 13½×14 (2½c.) or 14×13½ (12½c.)

297	173	2½c. yellow, indigo and yellow-brown	15	10
298	174	12½c. emerald, gold and yellow-brown	2·25	3·00

PHOSPHOR FRAME. Nos. 299/302 have phosphor applied on all four sides as a frame.

175 "Water 70" Emblem **177** "The Sower"

1970 (14 Feb). Water 70 Campaign. T **175** and similar design. W **127a** (sideways on 2½c.). P 14×13½ (2½c.) or 13½×14 (3c.)

299		2½c. green, bright blue and chocolate	30	10
300		3c. Prussian blue, royal blue and buff	30	20

Design: Horiz—3c. Symbolic waves.

1970 (24 Aug). 150th Anniv of Bible Society of South Africa. T **177** and similar horiz design (gold die-stamped on 12½c.). W **127a** (sideways on 2½c.). P 14×13½ (2½c.) or 13½×14 (12½c.)

301		2½c. multicoloured	15	10
302		12½c. gold, black and blue	1·00	1·40

Design:—12½c. "Biblia" and open book.

STAMP BOOKLETS

1913. Black on red cover. With "UNION OF SOUTH AFRICA" at top and "UNIE VAN ZUID AFRIKA" at foot. Stapled.

SB1	2s.6d. booklet containing 12×½d. and 24×1d. (Nos. 3/4) in blocks of 6	£10000	

B 1

1913–20. Black on red cover with "UNION OF SOUTH AFRICA" and "UNIE VAN ZUID AFRIKA" both at top. as Type B **1** Stapled.

SB2	2s.6d. booklet containing 12×½d. and 24×1d. (Nos. 3/4) in blocks of 6	£10000	
	a. Black on pink cover (1920)	£10000	

B **1a**

1921. Black on salmon-pink cover with "UNION OF SOUTH AFRICA" and "UNIE VAN ZUID AFRIKA" either side of Arms and telegraph rates beneath as Type B **1a**. Stapled.

SB3	3s. booklet containing 12×½d., 12×1d. and 12×1½d. (Nos. 3/5) in blocks of 6	£500	

1922. Black on salmon-pink cover as Type B **1a** surch. Stapled.

SB4	3s.6d. on 3s. booklet containing 12×½d., 12×1d. and 12×2d. (Nos. 3/4, 6) in blocks of 6	£1400	

1926. Black on salmon-pink cover as Type B **1a**. Stitched.

SB5	2s.6d. booklet containing 12×½d. and 24×1d. (Nos. 30/1)	£4000	

B **1b**

1927. Black on salmon-pink cover as No. SB3, but inscr "Union of South Africa" and "Unie van Suidafrika" as Type B **1b**. Stitched.

SB6	2s.6d. booklet containing 12×½d. and 24×1d. (Nos. 30e, 31e)	£8500	

B **1c**

1930. Black on pink cover as No. SB6, but with advertisement at foot instead of telegraph rates as Type B **1c**. Stitched.

SB7	2s.6d. booklet containing 12×½d. and 24×1d. (Nos. 42/3) in blocks of 6	£3500	

1931. Black on pink cover. As Type B **1c** but with smaller inscr and advertisement on front cover. Stitched.

SB8	3s. booklet containing 12×1d. (No. 43) in blocks of 6 and 12×2d. (No. 44) in blocks of 4	£3750	

B **1d**

1935. Black on lemon cover. Advertisement on front cover as Type B **1d**. Stitched.

SB9	2s.6d. booklet containing two panes of six ½d. (No. 54c) and four panes of six 1d. (No. 56e), all with adverts on margins	£350	

1937. Black on lemon cover. Advertisement on front cover as Type B **1d**. Stitched.

SB10	2s.6d. booklet containing two panes of six ½d. (No. 75ca) and four panes of six 1d. (No. 56f), all with blank margins	£750	

B **1e**

1937. Machine vended booklets. Red cover as Type B **1e**. Stitched.

SB11	6d. booklet containing 4×½d. and 4×1d. (Nos. 75c, 56) in pairs	7·00	

1938. Machine vended booklets. As Type B **1e** but blue cover. Stitched.

SB12	3d. booklet containing ½d. and 1d. (Nos. 75c, 56), each in pair	42·00	

B **1f**

1938. Black on buff cover. Union Arms at top left with advertisement at foot as Type B **1f**. Stitched.

SB13	2s.6d. booklet containing 12×½d. and 24×1d. (Nos. 75c, 56) in blocks of 6	£1200	

1939. Black on buff cover. As Type B **1f** but Union Arms centred at top with advertisement at foot. Stitched.

SB14	2s.6d. booklet containing 12×½d. and 24×1d. (Nos. 75c, 56) in blocks of 6	£1200	

B 1g

1939–40. Green on buff cover. Union Arms centred at top with large advertisement at bottom left as Type B **1g**. Stitched.

SB15 2s.6d. booklet containing 12×½d. and 24×1d.
(Nos. 75c, 56) in blocks of 6 .... £3500
      a. Blue on buff cover (1940) £180

1941. As Type B **1g** but blue on buff cover as No. SB15. Stitched.

SB17 2s.6d. booklet containing12×½d. and 12×1d.
(Nos. 75c, 56) in blocks of 6 and 12×1½d.
(No. 57) in blocks of 4 .... £180

B 1h

1948. Black on buff cover. With advertisement as Type B **1h**. Stitched.

SB18 3s. booklet containing two panes of six ½d., 1d. and 1½d. (Nos. 114a, 56h, 87c), all with postal slogans on margins, and pane of air mail labels .... 32·00

B 1i

1951. Black on buff cover as Type B **1i**. Stitched.

SB19 3s.6d. booklet containing two panes of six ½d., 1d. and 2d. (Nos. 114ca, 115a, 134a), each with margins at right .... 13·00

POSTAGE DUE STAMPS

The Interprovincial Period (1 June 1912–1914-15)

For postage due stamps the Interprovincial period is extended until the replacement of the relevant Transvaal stamps by the first Union issues on 12 December 1914 (2d.), 2 February 1915 (3d.) or 19 March 1915 (all other values).

Postage due stamps of Transvaal

(i) Used in Transvaal

ZD1	½d. black and green (No. D1)	2·00
ZD2	1d. black and scarlet (No. D2)	1·50
ZD3	2d. brown-orange (No. D3)	1·50
ZD4	3d. black and blue (No. D4)	7·50
ZD5	5d. black and violet (No. D5)	15·00
ZD6	6d. black and red-brown (No. D6)	18·00
ZD7	1s. scarlet and black (No. D7)	14·00

(ii) Used in Cape of Good Hope

ZD8	½d. black and green (No. D1)	3·00
ZD9	1d. black and scarlet (No. D2)	2·00
ZD10	2d. brown-orange (No. D3)	1·50
ZD11	3d. black and blue (No. D4)	8·00
ZD12	5d. black and violet (No. D5)	18·00
ZD13	6d. black and red-brown (No. D6)	18·00
ZD14	1s. scarlet and black (No. D7)	21·00

(iii) Used in Natal

ZD15	½d. black and green (No. D1)	4·00
ZD16	1d. black and scarlet (No. D2)	3·00
ZD17	2d. brown-orange (No. D3)	2·00
ZD18	3d. black and blue (No. D4)	9·50
ZD19	5d. black and violet (No. D5)	25·00
ZD20	6d. black and red brown (No. D6)	25·00
ZD21	1s. scarlet and black (No. D7)	27·00

(iv) Used in Orange River Colony

ZD22	½d. black and green (No. D1)	8·00
ZD23	1d. black and scarlet (No. D2)	5·00
ZD24	2d. brown-orange (No. D3)	5·00
ZD25	3d. black and blue (No. D4)	18·00
ZD26	5d. black and violet (No. D5)	£100
ZD27	6d. black and red-brown (No. D6)	45·00
ZD28	1s. scarlet and black (No. D7)	£100

D 1

    (A)   (B)

(Typo D.L.R.)

1914–22. Inscribed bilingually. Lettering as A. W **4**. P 14.

			Un	*Used*
			single	*single*
D1	D **1**	½d. black and green (19.3.15)	2·25	3·75
D2		1d. black and scarlet (19.3.15)	2·25	15
		a. Black ptd double	£3250	
		w. Wmk inverted	£150	£150
D3		2d. black and reddish violet (12.12.14)	6·50	50
		a. Black and bright violet (1922)	7·00	60
		w. Wmk inverted	£190	
D4		3d. black and bright blue (2.2.15)	2·25	60
		w. Wmk inverted	48·00	75·00
D5		5d. black and sepia (19.3.15)	4·00	38·00
D6		6d. black and slate (19.3.15)	7·00	42·00
D7		1s. red and black (19.3.15)	60·00	£170
D1/7	*Set of 7*	....	75·00	£225

There are interesting minor varieties in some of the above values, e.g. ½d. to 3d., thick downstroke to "d"; 1d., short serif to "1"; raised "d"; 2d., forward point of "2" blunted; 3d., raised "d"; very thick "d".

(Litho Govt Printer, Pretoria)

1922. Lettering as A. No wmk. Rouletted 7-8.

D8	D **1**	½d. black and bright green (6.6.22) ...	2·00	17·00
D9		1d. black and rose-red (3.10.22)	1·00	1·25
D10		1½d. black and yellow-brown (3.6.22).	1·25	1·75
D8/10	*Set of 3*	....	3·75	18·00

(Litho Govt Printer, Pretoria)

1922–26. Type D **1** redrawn. Lettering as B. P 14.

D11		½d. black and green (1.8.22)	80	1·25
D12		1d. black and rose (16.5.23)	90	15
D13		1½d. black and yellow-brown (12.1.24)......	1·00	1·25
D14		2d. black and pale violet (16.5.23)	1·00	70
		a. Imperf (pair)	£400	£500
		b. Black and deep violet	16·00	1·00
D15		3d. black and blue (3.7.26)	8·00	22·00
D16		6d. black and slate (9.23)	12·00	25·00
D11/16	*Set of 6*	....	21·00	25·00

The locally printed stamps, perf 14, differ both in border design and in figures of value from the rouletted stamps. All values except the 3d. and 6d. are known with closed "G" in "POSTAGE" usually referred to as the "POSTADE" variety. This was corrected in later printings.

  D 2   **D 3**   **D 4**

Blunt "2" (R. 3/6, 8/6)

(Typo Pretoria)

1927–28. Inscribed bilingually. No wmk. P 13½×14.

D17	D **2**	½d. black and green	1·00	2·25
		a. Blunt "2"	11·00	
D18		1d. black and carmine	1·25	30
D19		2d. black and mauve	1·25	30
		a. Black and purple	20·00	80
D20		3d. black and blue	8·50	24·00
D21		6d. black and slate	21·00	2·75
D17/21	*Set of 5*	....	30·00	27·00

On Nos. D20 and D21 there is no dot below "d".

1932–42. Type D **2** redrawn. W **9**. P 15×14.

(a) Frame roto, value typo

D22		½d. black and blue-green (1934)	2·75	1·25
		w. Wmk inverted	2·50	1·25
D23		2d. black and deep purple (10.4.33)	22·00	1·50
		w. Wmk inverted	22·00	1·50

(b) Whole stamp roto

D25		1d. black and carmine (wmk inverted) (3.34)	2·50	10
D26		2d. black and deep purple (10.39)	50·00	10
		a. Thick (double) "2d." (R. 5/6, R. 18/2)..	£500	50·00
		w. Wmk inverted	50·00	50
D27		3d. black and Prussian blue (3.8.32)	25·00	6·00
D28		3d. deep blue and blue (wmk inverted) (1935)	7·00	30
		a. Indigo and milky blue (wmk inverted) (1942)	75·00	3·25
		w. Wmk upright	50·00	3·00
D29		6d. green and brown-ochre (wmk inverted) (7.6.33)	25·00	2·25
		a. Green and bright orange (wmk inverted) (1938)	16·00	2·00
D22/9a	*Set of 7*	....	£110	10·00

In No. D26 the value is screened, whereas in No. D23 the black of the value is solid.

1943–44. Inscr bilingually. Roto. W **9**. In units of three, perf 15×14 subdivided by roulette 6½.

			Un unit	*Us unit*	*Us single*
D30	D **3**	½d. blue-green (1944)	17·00	65·00	60
D31		1d. carmine	10·00	5·50	10

D32		2d. dull violet	6·50	11·00	15
		a. Bright violet	16·00	50·00	65
D33		3d. indigo...........................	55·00	60·00	1·25
D30/3	*Set of 4*	....	80·00	£130	1·90

Split "D" (R. 7/5 on every fourth sheet)

1948–49. New figure of value and capital "D". Whole stamp roto. W **9**. P 15×14.

D34	D **4**	½d. black and blue-green	6·00	18·00
D35		1d. black and carmine	19·00	5·50
D36		2d. black and violet (1949)	23·00	11·00
		a. Thick (double) "2D." (R. 15/5-6, R. 16/5-6, ...	£100	50·00
D37		3d. deep blue and blue	15·00	17·00
		a. Split "D"	£450	£450
D38		6d. green and bright orange (1949)..	25·00	8·00
D34/8	*Set of 5*	....	80·00	55·00

3d. "Swallow in flight" (R. 16/8)

4d. Crude retouch to flaw on "4" (R. 1/1)

1950–58. As Type D **4**, but "SUID-AFRIKA" hyphenated. Whole stamp roto. W **9**. P 15×14.

D39		1d. black and carmine (5.50)	1·00	30
D40		2d. black and violet (4.51)	50	20
		a. Thick (double) "2D." (R. 15/5-6, R. 16/5-6)	8·00	11·00
		b. Black and reddish violet (12.52)......	1·00	1·00
		ba. Thick (double) "2D."	13·00	16·00
		bb. Black (value) omitted	£5500	
D41		3d. deep blue and blue (5.50)	4·50	2·50
		a. Split "D"	£140	90·00
		b. "Swallow" variety	90·00	75·00
D42		4d. deep myrtle-green and emerald (2.58)	12·00	15·00
		a. Retouch	70·00	70·00
D43		6d. green and bright orange (3.50)	7·00	9·00
D44		1s. black-brown and purple-brown (2.58)	12·00	15·00
D39/44	*Set of 6*	....	32·00	38·00

No. D40bb occurs in horizontal pair with a normal.

  D 5   **D 6** Afrikaans   **D 7** English
          at top   at top

1961 (14 Feb). Values in cents as Type D **5**. Whole stamp roto. W **102**. P 15×14.

D45		1c. black and carmine	20	3·75
D46		2c. black and violet	35	3·75
D47		4c. deep myrtle-green and emerald.......	80	8·50
D48		5c. deep blue and blue	1·75	8·50
D49		6c. green and orange-red	5·00	8·50
D50		10c. sepia and brown-lake	6·00	10·00
D45/50	*Set of 6*	....	13·00	38·00

1961 (31 May)**–69.** Roto. W **102**. P 15×14.

D51	D **6**	1c. black and carmine	40	60
D52	D **7**	1c. black and carmine (6.62)	40	3·75
D53		2c. black and deep reddish violet...	40	55
D54	D **6**	4c. deep myrtle-green and light emerald*	2·25	2·25
D54a	D **7**	4c. deep myrtle-green and light emerald (6.69)*	12·00	27·00
D55		5c. deep blue and grey-blue................	2·00	4·25
D56		5c. black and grey-blue (6.62)	1·25	4·00
D57	D **6**	6c. deep green and red-orange.............	8·00	4·75
D58		10c. sepia and purple-brown................	2·25	1·40
D51/8	*Set of 9*	....	26·00	45·00

1967 (1 Dec)**–71.** Roto. W **127** (Nos. D62b/c) or **127a** (others)*. P 15×14.

D59	D **6**	1c. black and carmine	20	55
D60	D **7**	1c. black and carmine	20	30
D61	D **6**	2c. black and deep reddish violet...	30	2·00

D62	D **7**	2c. black and deep reddish violet...		30	2·00
D62b		4c. deep myrtle-green and emerald (6.69)*		35·00	42·00
D62c	D **6**	4c. deep myrtle-green and emerald (6.69)*		£375	£375
D63		4c. dark green and pale green (4.71)		32·00	42·00
D64	D **7**	4c. dark green and pale green (4.71)		32·00	42·00
D65	D **6**	5c. black and deep blue		50	1·50
D66	D **7**	5c. black and deep blue		50	50
D67	D **7**	6c. green and orange-red (1968)		3·50	11·00
D68	D **7**	6c. green and orange-red (1968)		3·50	11·00
D69	D **6**	10c. black and purple-brown		1·00	4·50
		a. Black and brown-lake (12.69)		1·00	3·00
D70	D **7**	10c. black and purple-brown		1·00	4·50
		a. Black and brown-lake (12.69)		1·00	3·00
D59/70a *except* D62b/c *Set of 12*				70·00	£110

Nos. D59/70 were printed in two panes, one with inscriptions as Type D **6** and the other as Type D **7**.

*Nos. D54a, D62b/c and further supplies of D54 were part of a printing released in June 1969. Most sheets were printed on paper with the Arms watermark, but some were printed on RSA paper with the watermark upright and faint (W **127**). Of these many were spoilt, but a few sheets were issued in Types D **7** and D **6**, the latter being very scarce.

The 2c. (Types D **6** and D **7**) and 4c. (Type D **7** only) were reissued in 1971, perf 14.

OFFICIAL STAMPS

OFFICIAL.

OFFISIEEL.

OFFISIEEL

OFFICIAL

(O **1**)   (O **2**)

(Approximate measurements of the space between the two lines of overprint are quoted in millimetres, either in the set headings or after individual listings.)

1926 (1 Dec). Optd with Type O **1** (reading upwards with stops and 12½ mm between lines of opt).

(a) On 1913 issue (No. 6)

O1	**3**	2d. purple	25·00	1·75

(b) On 1926 issue (Nos. 30/2)

			Us pair	*Us single*
			Un pair	
O2	**6**	½d. black and green	9·00	26·00	2·00
O3	**7**	1d. black and carmine	4·00	8·00	50
O4	**8**	6d. green and orange	650·00	75·00	10·00
		w. Wmk inverted	£1700	£475	32·00

The overprint occurs on both the London and Pretoria printings of Nos. 30/2. For the lower two values the overprinted London printings are scarcer than the Pretoria, but for the 6d. the ratio is reversed.

1928–30. Nos. 32 and 34 optd as Type O **1** (reading upwards without stops).

O5	**11**	2d. grey and maroon (P 14) (17½ mm)		6·00	23·00	2·00
		a. Lines of opt 19 mm apart (1929)		7·00	32·00	2·25
		ab. Split "d"		£170		
		ac. On No. 34b (P 14×13½) (1930)		95·00	£100	6·50
		aca. Split "d"		£500		
O6	**8**	6d. green and orange (11½–12 mm)		24·00	55·00	3·00

1929–31. Optd with Type O **2**.

(a) On 1926 (Typo) issue (Nos. 30/2) (13½–15 mm between lines of opt)

O7	**6**	½d. black and green		2·75	4·50	35
		a. Stop after "OFFISIEEL" on English inscr stamp (1930)		50·00	55·00	3·25
		b. Ditto, but on Afrikaans inscr stamp (1930)		70·00	75·00	3·25
O8	**7**	1d. black and carmine		3·00	7·00	45
O9	**8**	6d. green and orange		7·00	42·00	3·25
		a. Stop after "OFFISIEEL" on English inscr stamp (1930)		95·00	£170	10·00
		b. Ditto, but on Afrikaans inscr stamp (1930)		£100	£180	12·00

(b) On 1927 (Recess) issue (Nos. 36a/7) (17½–19 mm between lines of opt)

O10	**13**	1s. brown and deep blue (1931)		45·00	£100	9·50
		a. Stop after "OFFICIAL" on Afrikaans inscr stamp (R. 10/1, 10/7)		£160	£300	
		b. Lines of opt 20½–21 mm apart		£1600		
		ba. Stop after "OFFICIAL" on Afrikaans inscr stamp		£4000		
O11	**14**	2s.6d. green and brown (1931)		70·00	£190	19·00
		a. Stop after "OFFICIAL" on Afrikaans inscr stamp (R. 10/1)		£375	£700	
O7/11 *Set of 5*				£110	£300	29·00

The "stop" varieties for the ½d., and 6d. occur on R. 5/3, 5/11, 8/12, 15/3, 15/11, 18/12 with English inscriptions and R. 9/10, 9/12, 19/10, 19/12 with Afrikaans on the 1930 overprinting only.

The 1932 printing of the 2s.6d. did not include No. O11a.

1930–47. Nos. 42/4 and 47/9 ("SUIDAFRIKA" in one word) optd with Type O **2**.

O12	**6**	½d. black and green (9½–12½ mm) (1931)		2·25	5·00	40
		a. Stop after "OFFISIEEL" on English inscr stamp		50·00	75·00	4·00
		b. Ditto, but on Afrikaans inscr stamp		28·00	60·00	3·50
		c. "Cobweb" variety		65·00		

---

		d. "Dollar" variety		65·00		
		e. Opt double		£500		
		f. Opt double, one inverted		£600		
		w. Wmk inverted (1934)		6·50	11·00	60
O13	**7**	1d. black and carmine (I) (12½–14 mm)		4·50	7·00	55
		a. Stop after "OFFISIEEL" on English inscr stamp		65·00	90·00	4·00
		b. Ditto, but on Afrikaans inscr stamp		40·00	65·00	3·50
		cw. Wmk inverted (1931)		4·50	7·00	55
		d. On Type II (No. 43d) (12½–13½ mm) (1933)		17·00	9·00	90
		da. Opt double		£300	£400	
O14	**11**	2d. slate-grey and lilac (20½–22½ mm) (1931)		6·50	11·00	1·50
		w. Wmk inverted (1934)		£120	£130	8·00
O15		2d. blue and violet (20½–22½ mm) (1938)		£160	£100	9·00
		a. Airship flaw		£1000		
O16	**8**	6d. green and orange (12½–13½ mm) (wmk inverted) (1931)		6·50	8·50	85
		a. Stop after "OFFISIEEL" on English inscr stamp		£130	£150	6·50
		b. Ditto, but on Afrikaans inscr stamp		£100	£120	5·50
		c. "OFFISIEEL" reading upwards (R. 17/12, 18/12, 19/12, 20/12) (1933)		£2000		
		w. Wmk upright (1935)		£110	£130	7·00
O17	**13**	1s. brown and deep blue (19 mm) (wmk inverted) (1932)		65·00	95·00	8·50
		a. Twisted horn flaw		£500		
		b. Lines of opt 21 mm apart (wmk inverted) (1933)		70·00	£110	7·50
		ba. Twisted horn flaw		£500		
		bw. Wmk inverted (1936)		£100	£180	10·00
O18	**14**	2s.6d. green and brown (17½–18½ mm) (1933)		85·00	£170	15·00
		a. Lines of opt 21 mm apart (1934)		60·00	75·00	8·50
		aw. Wmk inverted (1937)		£850	£900	
O19		2s.6d. blue and brown (19–20.5 mm) (1946)		55·00	£110	6·50
		a. Diaeresis over second "E" of "OFFISIEEL" on Afrikaans and English inscr stamps (1946)		£2750	£3000	
		b. Ditto, but on Afrikaans inscr stamp only		£1500	£1600	
		c. Ditto, but on English inscr stamp only		£1500	£1600	

The stop varieties for the ½d., 1d. and 6d. occur on R. 9/10, 9/12, 19/10, 19/12 with English inscriptions and R. 5/3, 5/11, 8/12, 15/3, 15/11, 18/12 with Afrikaans on the 1930 and 1931 overprintings only.

OFFICIAL

OFFISIEEL OFFISIEEL

OFFICIAL

(O **3**)   (O **4**)

1935–49. Nos. 54, 56/8, 61/2 and 64b/c ("SUID-AFRIKA" hyphenated) optd.

*(a) With Type O **2** (reading downwards with "OFFICIAL" at right)*

O20	**6**	½d. grey and green (12½ mm) (wmk inverted) (1936)		75·00	85·00	2·75
		w. Wmk upright (1937)		11·00	42·00	1·75
O21	**7**	1d. grey and carmine (11½–13 mm) (wmk inverted)		7·50	9·00	35
		aa. Pair, one stamp "OFFICIAL OFFICIAL"		†	£3500	—
		aw. Wmk upright (1937)		5·50	3·00	20
		b. Grey and bright rose-carmine (No. 56i) (1949)		4·00	6·50	40
O22	**22**	1½d. green and bright gold (20 mm) (wmk inverted) (1937)		50·00	35·00	1·75
		ab. Broken chimney and faint headgear		£160		
		ac. Flag on chimney at right		£160		
		aw. Wmk upright (1939)		32·00	24·00	1·00
		b. Blue-green and dull gold (No. 57e) (1941)		50·00	11·00	1·10
O23	**11**	2d. blue and violet (20 mm) (1939)		£150	50·00	2·25
O24	**8**	6d. green and vermilion (I) (11½–13 mm) (1937)		85·00	55·00	3·75
		a. "Falling ladder" flaw		£1400	£1100	
		b. "Molehill" flaw		£1200	£950	
		c. Die II (No. 61c) (1938)		14·00	10·00	1·25
		d. Die III Green and red-orange (No. 61d) (11.47)		4·00	8·50	90
O25		1s. brown and chalky blue (18.5–20 mm) (shades) (1939)		80·00	50·00	2·25
		a. Diaeresis over second "E" of "OFFISIEEL" on Afrikaans and English inscr stamps (1946)		£3750	£2750	
		b. Ditto, but on Afrikaans inscr stamp only		£2000	£1500	
		c. Ditto, but on English inscr stamp only		£2000	£1500	

O26	**15**	5s. black and blue-green (20 mm) (6.48)		65·00	£160	13·00
O27	**23**	10s. blue and blackish brown (No. 64c) (20 mm) (6.48)		£110	£275	23·00

*(b) With Type O **3** (reading downwards with "OFFICIAL" at left and 18–19 mm between lines of opt)*

O28	**15**	5s. black and blue-green (1940)		£120	£140	12·00
O29	**23**	10s. blue and sepia (1940)		£500	£500	38·00

*(c) With Type O **4** (reading upwards with "OFFICIAL" at right and 18½ mm between lines of opt)*

O30	**11**	2d. grey and dull purple (No. 58a) (1941)		11·00	38·00	2·25

Nos. O19a/c and O25a/c first appeared in a 1946 overprinting where the variety occurs on R. 1/5 (Afrikaans) and R. 1/6 (English). A setting of 60 (6×10) was applied to the top halves of the sheets only. The same setting was used for a printing of the 2d. value, applied twice to each sheet of 120, resulting in O36a. The diaeresis variety reappeared in the November 1947 printing of the 1s. and 2s.6d. values in position R. 6/2 on the Afrikaans stamp and R. 6/3 on the English stamp.

Horizontal rows of six of the 1s. exist with "OFFICIAL" twice on the first stamp and "OFFISIEEL" twice on the last stamp. Such rows are believed to come from two half sheets which were overprinted in 1947, but not placed into normal stock (*Price for row of 6, £4000, unused*).

OFFICIAL

OFFISIEEL

OFFICIAL

OFFISIEEL

(O **5**)   (O **6**)

1937–44. No. 75c (redrawn design) optd.

*(a) With Type O **2** (reading downwards with "OFFICIAL" at right and 11–12½ mm between lines of opt)*

O31	**25a**	½d. grey and green		35·00	35·00	1·50
		a. Grey and blue-green (No. 75cd) (1944)		4·00	11·00	60

*(b) With Type O **5** (reading up and down with "OFFICIAL" at left and diaeresis over the second "E" of "OFFISIEEL". 10 mm between lines of opt)*

O32	**25a**	½d. grey and blue-green (No. 75cd) (1944)		50·00	30·00	2·00

1944–50. Nos. 87 and 134 optd.

*(a) With Type O **2** (reading downwards with "OFFICIAL" at right)*

O33	**34a**	1½d. blue-green and yellow-buff (14½ mm)		2·50	10·00	80
		a. With diaeresis over second "E" of "OFFISIEEL"		£800	£475	30·00
		b. Gold blob on headgear		55·00		
		c. Lines of opt 16½ mm apart (6.48)		2·25	12·00	60

*(b) With Type O **6** (reading upwards with "OFFICIAL" at left and 16 mm between lines of opt)*

O34	**34a**	1½d. blue-green and yellow-buff (1949)		85·00	90·00	4·00
O35	**68**	2d. blue and violet (1950)		£4250	£4750	£275

Two different formes were used to overprint Type **34a** between 1944 and 1946. The first, applied to the left halves of sheets only, had a diaeresis over the second "E" of "OFFISIEEL" on all positions of the setting, except for R. 1/2, 2/2, 3/2 and 8/1. The second form, from which the majority of the stamps came, was applied twice to overprint complete sheets, had no diaeresis.

Examples of T **34a** overprinted with Type O **2** horizontally exist, but their status is unclear. (*Price £1000, unused pair*).

1947 (Nov)–**49**. No. 107a optd with Type O **2** (reading downwards with "OFFICIAL" at right and 20 mm between lines of opt).

O36	**54**	2d. slate and deep lilac		5·50	29·00	2·00
		a. With diaeresis over second "E" of "OFFISIEEL" (R. 1/5-6, 11/5-6)		£700	£1000	
		b. Slate and bright violet (No. 107b) (1949)		12·00	16·00	1·60

1949–50. Nos. 114 and 120 optd with Type O **2** (reading downwards with "OFFICIAL" at right).

O37	**25a**	½d. grey and green (11 mm)		5·00	17·00	1·25
		a. "Tick" flaw and spot on nose		75·00		
		b. Entire design screened (No. 114c)		5·50	13·00	1·00
		ba. "Tick" flaw and spot on nose		75·00		
O38	**13**	1s. brown and chalky blue (17½–18½ mm) (1950)		16·00	28·00	2·50

OFFISIEEL OFFICIAL

(O **7**)

1950 (June)–**54**. Optd as Type O **7** using stereo blocks measuring either 10 (½d., 1d., 6d.), 14½ (1½d., 2d.) or 19 mm (others) between the lines of opt.

O39	**25a**	½d. grey and green (No. 114c) (6.51)		70	1·50	15
O41	**7**	1d. grey and bright rose-carmine (No. 56i)		1·00	6·00	50
O42		1d. grey and carmine (No. 115) (3.51)		1·00	3·25	20
O43		1d. grey and carmine (No. 135) (6.52)		1·25	2·00	20

O44	34a	1½d. blue-green and yellow-buff (No. 87) (3.51)	4·25	4·50	30
O45	68	2d. blue and violet (No. 134)	1·00	2·00	20
		a. Opt inverted	£1100	†	
O46	8	6d. green and red-orange (No. 119)	2·75	4·00	35
		a. Green and brown-orange (No. 119a) (6.51)	1·75	3·50	35
O47	13	1s. brown and chalky blue (No. 120)	5·50	18·00	2·00
		a. Blackish brown and ultramarine (No. 120a) (2.53)	£170	£190	18·00
O48	14	2s.6d. green and brown (No. 121)	8·50	35·00	3·50
O49	15	5s. black and blue-green (No. 64b) (3.51)	£180	£140	9·00
O50		5s. black and pale blue-green (I) (No. 122) (2.53)	70·00	95·00	6·50
		aa. "Rain" flaw	£150	£200	
		a. Black and deep yellow-green (II) (No. 122b) (1.54)	75·00	£100	9·00
O51	23	10s. blue and charcoal (No. 64ca)	80·00	£250	22·00

The use of the official stamps ceased in January 1955.

South Arabian Federation

Comprising Aden and most of the territories of the former Western Aden Protectorate plus one from the Eastern Aden Protectorate.

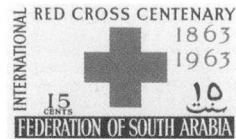

1 Red Cross Emblem

1963 (25 Nov). Red Cross Centenary. W w **12**. P 13½.

1	**1**	15c. red and black	30	30
2		1s.25 red and blue	70	1·25

(New Currency. 1000 fils = 1 dinar)

2 Federal Crest **3** Federal Flag

(Des V. Whiteley. Photo Harrison)

1965 (1 Apr). P 14½×14 (T **2**) or 14½ (T **3**).

3	**2**	5f. blue	20	10
4		10f. violet-blue	20	10
5		15f. turquoise-green	20	10
6		20f. green	20	10
7		25f. yellow-brown	20	10
8		30f. yellow-bistre	20	10
9		35f. chestnut	20	10
10		50f. red	20	10
11		65f. yellow-green	30	30
12		75f. crimson	30	10
13	**3**	100f. multicoloured	50	10
14		250f. multicoloured	5·00	1·50
15		500f. multicoloured	9·00	1·50
16		1d. multicoloured	16·00	19·00
3/16	*Set of 14*		29·00	21·00

4 ICY Emblem

(Des V. Whiteley. Litho Harrison)

1965 (24 Oct). International Co-operation Year. W w **12**. P 14½.

17	**4**	5f. reddish purple and turquoise-green	25	10
18		65f. deep bluish green and lavender	1·00	30

5 Sir Winston Churchill and St. Paul's Cathedral in Wartime

(Des Jennifer Toombs. Photo Harrison)

1966 (24 Jan). Churchill Commemoration. No wmk. P 14.

19	**5**	5f. black, cerise, gold and new blue	15	10
20		10f. black, cerise, gold and deep green	55	10
21		65f. black, cerise, gold and brown	1·25	20
22		125f. black, cerise, gold and bluish violet	1·75	1·75
19/22	*Set of 4*		3·25	1·90

6 Footballer's Legs, Ball and Jules Rimet Cup

(Des V. Whiteley. Litho Harrison)

1966 (1 July). World Cup Football Championship, England. No wmk. P 14.

23	**6**	10f. violet, yellow-green, lake and yellow brown	40	10
24		50f. chocolate, blue-green, lake and yellow-brown	1·00	30

7 WHO Building

(Des M. Goaman. Litho Harrison)

1966 (20 Sept). Inauguration of WHO Headquarters, Geneva. No wmk. P 14.

25	**7**	10f. black, yellow-green and light blue	50	10
26		75f. black, light purple and yellow-brown	1·25	55

8 "Education"

9 "Science"

10 "Culture"

(Des Jennifer Toombs. Litho Harrison)

1966 (15 Dec). 20th Anniv of UNESCO. No wmk. P 14.

27	**8**	10f. slate-violet, red, yellow and orange	30	20
28	**9**	65f. orange-yellow, violet and deep olive	1·25	1·40
29	**10**	125f. black, bright purple and orange	3·25	4·75
27/9	*Set of 3*		4·25	5·75

The South Arabian Federation became fully independent on 30 November 1967. Later issues for this area will be found listed in the Stanley Gibbons *Arabia catalogue* under Yemen People's Democratic Republic.

KATHIRI STATE OF SEIYUN

SOUTH ARABIA	SOUTH ARABIA	SOUTH ARABIA
5 FILS	500 FILS	50 FILS
19	**(20)**	**(21)**

1966 (1 Apr). New Currency. Nos. 29/41 of Aden-Kathiri State of Seiyun surch as T **19/21**.

42		5f. on 5c. (**19**)	30	20
		a. Surch quadruple, one inverted	75·00	
43		5f. on 10c. (**19**) (R.)	30	1·50
44		10f. on 15c. (**21**) (R.)	30	2·00
		a. Surch inverted	£140	
45		15f. on 25c. (**20**)	1·25	1·00
		w. Wmk inverted	65·00	
46		20f. on 35c. (**20**) (R.)	40	1·50
47		25f. on 50c. (**21**) (R.)	1·25	1·50
48		35f. on 70c. (**20**) (R.)	1·50	2·50
49		50f. on 1s. (**21**)	50	50
50		65f. on 1s.25 (**21**)	50	20
51		75f. on 1s.50 (**21**)	1·75	30
52		100f. on 2s. (**20**) (R.)	40·00	55·00
53		250f. on 5s. (**21**) (R.)	2·50	4·00
54		500f. on 10s. (**20**)	2·50	4·00
42/54	*Set of 13*		48·00	65·00

SOUTH ARABIA	SOUTH ARABIA	SOUTH ARABIA
5 FILS	50 FILS	15 FILS
(22)	**(23)**	**(24)**

1966 (13 Aug). Nos. 29/41 surch with T **22/4**.

55		5f. on 5c. (**22**) (B.)	1·75	40
		a. Surch inverted	85·00	
56		5f. on 10c. (**22**) (R.)	2·25	40
57		10f. on 15c. (**23**) (Y.)	2·25	1·75
		a. Surch inverted	65·00	
58		15f. on 25c. (**24**) (B.)	2·25	50
		a. Surch inverted	75·00	
59		20f. on 35c. (**23**) (Y.)	2·25	50
60		25f. on 50c. (**23**) (B.)	2·25	50

61	35f. on 70c. (24) (Br.)	2·50	75
62	50f. on 1s. (23) (G.)	2·75	1·75
	a. Stop after FILS" (R. 1/3)	32·00	
63	65f. on 1s.25 (23) (Y.)	4·00	1·50
64	75f. on 1s.50 (23) (G.)	5·00	2·75
	a. Surch inverted	75·00	
65	100f. on 2s. (23) (Y.)	6·00	2·50
	a. Surch inverted	75·00	
66	250f. on 5s. (23) (Y.)	5·50	4·00
	a. Surch inverted	60·00	
67	500f. on 10s. (24) (G.)	5·50	8·50
55/67	*Set of 13*	40·00	23·00

HELSINKI 1952

(25)   **(26)**

1966 (13 Aug). History of Olympic Games. Nos. 57, 59 and 61/7 optd T **25**/6 in red.

68	10f. on 15c. deep bluish green (25 ("LOS ANGELES 1932"))	35	70
	a. Optd as T **25** inverted		
69	20f. on 35c. deep blue (25 ("BERLIN 1936"))	45	75
70	35f. on 70c. black (26)	45	75
	a. Opt T **26** inverted	50·00	
71	50f. on 1s. brown-orange (25 ("LONDON 1948"))	50	1·00
	a. Stop after "FILS" (R. 1/3)	19·00	
72	65f. on 1s.25, blue-green (25)	50	1·00
73	75f. on 1s.50, deep reddish violet (25 ("MELBOURNE 1956"))	60	1·50
74	100f. on 2s. deep yellow-green (25 ("ROME 1960"))	70	1·75
75	250f. on 5s. deep blue and violet (25 ("TOKYO 1964"))	1·00	3·75
	a. Surch inverted	75·00	
76	500f. on 10s. yellow-brown and violet (25 ("MEXICO CITY 1968"))	1·25	4·50
68/76	*Set of 9*	5·25	14·00

CHAMPION: ENGLAND   **FOOTBALL 1966**

(27)   **(28)**

1966 (19 Sept). World Cup Football Championships. Nos. 57, 59, 61/2, 65/7 optd with T **27**/8.

77	10f. on 15c. deep bluish green (27)	70	1·00
78	20f. on 35c. deep blue (28)	90	1·00
79	35f. on 70c. black (28)	1·25	1·00
80	50f. on 1s. brown-orange (27)	1·40	1·00
	a. Stop after "FILS" (R. 1/3)	30·00	
81	100f. on 2s. deep yellow-green (28)	2·75	2·75
82	250f. on 5s. deep blue and violet (27)	6·00	9·50
83	500f. on 10s. yellow-brown and violet (28)	7·50	13·00
77/83	*Set of 7*	18·00	26·00

29 *Telstar*

(Photo State Ptg Wks, Vienna)

1966 (25 Oct). ITU Centenary (1965). T **29** and similar vert designs. P 13½.

84	5f. blackish green, black and reddish violet	2·50	15
85	10f. maroon, black and bright green	2·75	20
86	15f. Prussian blue, black and orange	3·25	20
87	25f. blackish green, black and orange-red	3·75	20
88	35f. maroon, black and deep olive-yellow	3·75	20
89	50f. Prussian blue, black and orange-brown	3·75	25
90	65f. blackish green, black and orange-yellow	4·00	30
84/90	*Set of 7*	21·00	1·25

Designs:—10, 35f. *Relay*; 15, 50f. *Ranger*; others, Type **29**.

32 Churchill at Easel

(Photo State Ptg Wks, Vienna)

1966 (1 Dec). Sir Winston Churchill's Paintings. T **32** and similar designs in black and gold (5f.) or multicoloured (others). P 13½.

91	5f. Type **32**	1·75	15
92	10f. *Antibes*	2·00	15
93	15f. *Flowers* (vert)	2·00	20
94	20f. *Tapestries*	2·00	35
95	25f. *Village, Lake Lugano*	2·00	35
96	35f. *Church, Lake Como* (vert)	2·00	40
97	50f. *Flowers at Chartwell* (vert)	2·25	65
98	65f. Type **32**	2·75	90
91/8	*Set of 8*	15·00	2·75

WORLD PEACE PANDIT NEHRU
(39)

40 *Master Crewe as Henry VIII*
(Sir Joshua Reynolds)

1967 (1 Jan). "World Peace". Nos. 57, 59 and 61/7 optd as T **39** in various sizes of type.

99	10f. on 15c. deep bluish green (Type **39**) (R.)	5·00	2·00
100	20f. on 35c. deep blue ("WINSTON CHURCHILL") (R.)	7·00	2·75
101	35f. on 70c. black ("DAG HAMMAR SKJOLD") (B.)	50	80
102	50f. on 1s. brown-orange ("JOHN F. KENNEDY") (R.)	60	90
	a. Stop after "FILS"	22·00	
103	65f. on 1s.25 blue-green ("LUDWIG ERHARD") (Pk.)	70	1·10
104	75f. on 1s.50 deep reddish violet ("LYNDON JOHNSON") (B.)	80	1·25
105	100f. on 2s. deep yellow-green ("ELEANOR ROOSEVELT") (B.)	1·00	2·25
106	250f. on 5s. deep blue and violet ("WINSTON CHURCHILL") (R.)	18·00	12·00
107	500f. on 10s. yellow-brown and violet ("JOHN F. KENNEDY") (R.)	5·00	13·00
99/107	*Set of 9*	35·00	32·00

(Photo State Ptg Wks, Vienna)

1967 (1 Feb). Paintings. T **40** and similar multicoloured designs. P 13½.

108	5f. Type **40**	40	25
109	10f. *The Dancer* (Degas)	45	30
110	15f. *The Filet* (Manet)	50	35
111	20f. *Stag at Sharkey's* (boxing match, G. Bellows)	55	40
112	25f. *Don Manuel Osorio* (Goya)	60	45
113	35f. *St. Martin distributing his Cloak* (A. van Dyck)	70	65
114	50f. *The Blue Boy* (Gainsborough)	80	75
115	65f. *The White Horse* (Gauguin)	90	1·00
116	75f. *Mona Lisa* (Da Vinci) (45×62 mm)	1·10	1·25
108/16	*Set of 9*	5·50	4·75

SCOTT CARPENTER
(49)

50 Churchill Crown

1967. American Astronauts. Nos. 57, 59, 61/2 and 65/6 optd as T **49** in various sizes of type, in red.

117	10f. on 15c. deep bluish green ("ALAN SHEPARD, JR.")	55	1·25
118	20f. on 35c. deep blue ("VIRGIL GRISSOM")	70	1·25
119	35f. on 70c. black ("JOHN GLENN, JR.")	95	1·50
120	50f. on 1s. brown-orange (Type **49**)	95	1·50
	a. Stop after "FILS"	26·00	
121	100f. on 2s. deep yellow-green ("WALTER SCHIRRA, JR.")	1·75	3·50
122	250f. on 5s. deep blue and violet ("GORDON COOPER, JR.")	2·50	8·00
	a. Opt (as T **49**) double	£120	
117/122	*Set of 6*	6·50	15·00

1967 (1 Mar). Churchill Commemoration Photo. P 13½.

123	**50** 75f. multicoloured	8·00	7·50

Appendix

The following stamps have either been issued in excess of postal needs, or have not been made available to the public in reasonable quantities at face value. Miniature sheets, imperforate stamps etc., are excluded from this section.

1967

Hunting. 20f.
Olympic Games, Grenoble. Postage 10, 25, 35, 50, 75f. Air 100, 200f.
Scout Jamboree, Idaho. Air 150f.
Paintings by Renoir. Postage 10, 35, 50, 65, 75f. Air 100, 200, 250f.
Paintings by Toulouse-Lautrec. Postage 10, 35, 50, 65, 75f. Air 100, 200, 250f.

The National Liberation Front is said to have taken control of Kathiri State of Seiyun on 1 October 1967.

QU'AITI STATE IN HADHRAMAUT

(New Currency. 1000 fils = 1 dinar)

1966 (1 Apr). New currency. Nos. 41/52 of Aden-Qu'aiti State in Hadhramaut surch as T **20**/21 of Kathiri State of Seiyun.

53	5f. on 5c. greenish blue (20) (R.)	10	1·25
54	5f. on 10c. grey-black (20) (R.)	1·50	1·75
55	10f. on 15c. bronze-green (20) (R.)	10	1·00
56	15f. on 25c. carmine-red (20)	10	2·00
57	20f. on 35c. blue (20) (R.)	10	3·00
58	25f. on 50c. red-orange (20)	10	2·25
59	35f. on 70c. deep brown (20) (R.)	10	1·75
60	50f. on 1s. black and deep lilac (21) (R.)	65	30
61	65f. on 1s.25 black and red-orange (21) (R.)	1·50	40
62	100f. on 2s. black and indigo-blue (21) (R.)	4·25	1·25
63	250f. on 5s. black and bluish green (21) (R.)	2·25	1·50
64	500f. on 10s. black and lake (21) (R.)	28·00	3·00
53/64	*Set of 12*	35·00	17·00

1874–1965   **1917–1963**
WINSTON CHURCHILL   **JOHN F. KENNEDY**
(23)   **(24)**

1966 (1 Apr). Churchill Commemoration. Nos. 54/6 optd with T **23**.

65	5f. on 10c. grey-black (R.)	9·00	17·00
66	10f. on 15c. bronze-green (R.)	10·00	18·00
	a. Opt T **23** inverted	90·00	
67	15f. on 25c. carmine-red (B.)	11·00	18·00
65/7	*Set of 3*	27·00	48·00

1966 (1 Apr). President Kennedy Commemoration. Nos. 57/9 optd with T **24**.

68	20f. on 35c. blue (R.)	1·25	6·00
69	25f. on 50c. red-orange (B.)	1·25	6·50
70	35f. on 70c. deep brown (B.)	1·25	7·50
68/70	*Set of 3*	3·25	18·00

25 World Cup Emblem

(Photo State Ptg Wks, Vienna)

1966 (11 Aug). World Cup Football Championship, England. T **25** and similar diamond-shaped designs. P 13½.

71	5f. maroon and yellow-orange	2·25	25
72	10f. slate-violet and light green	2·50	25
73	15f. maroon and yellow-orange	2·75	30
74	20f. slate-violet and light green	3·00	30
75	25f. blackish green and orange-red	3·25	30
76	35f. blue and yellow	3·75	35
77	50f. blackish green and orange-red	4·25	40
78	65f. blue and yellow	5·00	40
71/8	*Set of 8*	24·00	2·25
MS78a	110×110 mm. Nos. 77/8	55·00	7·50

Designs:—10, 35f. Wembley Stadium; 15, 50f. Footballers; 20f. Jules Rimet Cup and football; 25, 65f. Type **25**.

29 Mexican Hat and Blanket

(Photo State Ptg Wks, Vienna)

1966 (25 Oct). Pre-Olympic Games, Mexico (1968). P 13½.

79	**29** 75f. sepia and light yellow-green	1·75	75

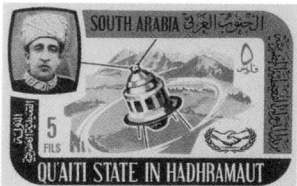

30 Telecommunications Satellite

(Photo State Ptg Wks, Vienna)

1966 (1 Dec). International Co-operation Year (1965). T **30** and similar horiz designs. P 13½.

80		5f. maroon, bright purple and emerald	2·75	30
81		10f. violet, orange, blue-green and new blue	3·00	30
82		15f. maroon, new blue and red	3·25	35
83		20f. Prussian blue, purple and red	3·50	40
84		25f. violet, olive-yellow, red and emerald	3·50	40
85		35f. maroon, rose-red and new blue	4·00	40
		a. New blue (face value) omitted	£450	
86		50f. maroon, green and red	4·75	45
87		65f. chocolate, bluish violet and red	5·50	45
80/87 *Set of 8*			27·00	2·75

Designs:—10f. Olympic runner (inscribed "ROME 1960"); 15f. Fish; 25f. Olympic runner (inscribed "TOKIO 1964"); 50f. Tobacco plant; others, Type **30**.

Appendix

The following stamps have either been issued in excess of postal needs, or have not been made available to the public in reasonable quantities at face value. Miniature sheets, imperforate stamps etc. are excluded from this section.

1967

Stampex Stamp Exhibition, London. Postage 5, 10, 15, 20, 25f. *Air* 50, 65f.
Amphilex International Stamp Exhibition, Amsterdam. Air 75f.
Olympic Games, Mexico (1968). 75f.
Paintings. Postage 5, 10, 15, 20, 25f. *Air* 50, 65f.
Scout Jamboree, Idaho. Air 35f.
Space Research. Postage 10, 25, 35, 50, 75f. *Air* 100, 250f.

The National Liberation Front is said to have taken control of Qu'aiti State in Hadhramaut on 17 September 1967.

MAHRA SULTANATE OF QISHN AND SOCOTRA

1 Mahra Flag

(Des and litho Harrison)

1967 (12 Mar). Flag in green, black and vermilion; inscriptions in black; background colours given. P 14×14½.

1	**1**	5f. mauve	4·75	55
2		10f. buff	4·75	55
3		15f. sage-green	4·75	55
4		20f. red-orange	4·75	55
5		25f. yellow-brown	4·75	55
6		35f. turquoise-green	4·75	55
7		50f. new blue	4·75	55
8		65f. blackish brown	5·50	55
9		100f. violet	5·50	55
10		250f. rose-red	5·50	55
11		500f. grey-black	5·50	55
1/11 *Set of 11*			50·00	5·50

Appendix

The following stamps have either been issued in excess of postal needs, or have not been made available to the public in reasonable quantities at face value. Miniature sheets, imperforate stamps etc., are excluded from this section.

1967

Scout Jamboree, Idaho. 15, 75, 100, 150f.
President Kennedy Commemoration. Postage 10, 15, 25, 50, 75, 100, 150f. *Air* 250, 500f.
Olympic Games, Mexico (1968). *Postage* 10, 25, 50f. *Air* 250, 500f.

The National Liberation Front is said to have taken control of Mahra Sultanate of Qishn and Socotra on 1 October 1967.

South Australia *see* Australia

Southern Cameroons *see* Cameroon

Southern Nigeria *see* Nigeria

Southern Rhodesia

PRICES FOR STAMPS ON COVER TO 1945
Nos. 1/61   *from* × 2

SELF-GOVERNMENT

The southern part of Rhodesia, previously administered by the British South Africa Company, was annexed by the British Government and granted the status of a self-governing colony from 1 October 1923.

The existing stamps of Rhodesia (the "Admiral" design first issued in 1913) remained in use until 31 March 1924 and continued to be valid for postal purposes until 30 April of that year.

1   **2** King George V   **3** Victoria Falls

(Recess Waterlow)

1924 (1 Apr)–**29**. P 14.

1	**1**	½d. blue-green	4·50	1·00
		a. Imperf between (horiz pair)	£1200	£1300
		b. Imperf between (vert pair)	£1200	£1300
		c. Imperf vert (horiz pair)	£1300	
2		1d. bright rose	4·00	10
		a. Imperf between (horiz pair)	£950	£1100
		b. Imperf between (vert pair)	£1700	
		c. Perf 12½ (coil) (1929)	4·25	80·00
3		1½d. bistre-brown	4·50	80
		a. Imperf between (horiz pair)	£15000	
		b. Imperf between (vert pair)	£8000	
		c. Printed double, one albino	£400	
4		2d. black and purple-grey	7·50	2·50
		a. Imperf between (horiz pair)	£17000	
5		3d. blue	6·50	6·50
6		4d. black and orange-red	6·50	2·75
7		6d. black and mauve	6·50	8·50
		a. Imperf between (horiz pair)	£45000	
8		8d. purple and pale green	16·00	50·00
		a. Frame double, one albino	£550	
9		10d. blue and rose	20·00	55·00
10		1s. black and light blue	9·00	13·00
11		1s.6d. black and yellow	23·00	42·00
12		2s. black and brown	17·00	20·00
13		2s.6d. blue and sepia	35·00	65·00
14		5s. blue and blue-green	90·00	£170
1/14 *Set of 14*			£225	£375

Prices for "imperf between" varieties are for adjacent stamps from the same pane and not for those separated by wide gutter margins between vertical or horizontal pairs, which come from the junction of two panes.

(T **2** recess by B.W.; T **3** typo by Waterlow)

1931 (1 Apr)–**37**. T **2** (line perf 12 unless otherwise stated) and **3** (comb perf 15×14). (The 11½ perf is comb.).

15	**2**	½d. green	3·25	1·00
		a. Perf 11½ (1933)	2·75	20
		b. Perf 14 (1935)	2·75	1·00
16		1d. scarlet	3·50	1·00
		a. Perf 11½ (1933)	4·00	20
		b. Perf 14 (1935)	1·25	20
16c		1½d. chocolate (3.3.33)	55·00	38·00
		d. Perf 11½ (1.4.32)	2·50	80
17	**3**	2d. black and sepia	12·00	1·40
18		3d. deep ultramarine	10·00	11·00
19	**2**	4d. black and vermilion	1·50	1·50
		a. Perf 11½ (1935)	19·00	6·50
		b. Perf 14 (10.37)	38·00	70·00
20		6d. black and magenta	2·25	3·00
		a. Perf 11½ (1933)	15·00	2·00
		b. Perf 14 (1936)	7·00	2·00
21		8d. violet and olive-green	1·75	4·25
		a. Perf 11½ (1934)	18·00	35·00
21b		9d. vermilion and olive-green (1.9.34)	11·00	14·00
22		10d. blue and scarlet	7·00	2·25
		a. Perf 11½ (1933)	6·00	13·00
23		1s. black and greenish blue	2·00	2·50
		a. Perf 11½ (1935)	£140	50·00
		b. Perf 14 (10.37)	£225	£160
24		1s.6d. black and orange-yellow	15·00	27·00
		a. Perf 11½ (1936)	75·00	£140
25		2s. black and brown	35·00	8·00
		a. Perf 11½ (1933)	35·00	32·00
26		2s.6d. blue and drab	50·00	35·00
		a. Perf 11½ (1933)	32·00	50·00
27		5s. blue and blue-green	50·00	50·00
		a. Printed on gummed side	£8500	
15/27 *Set of 15*			£160	£140

No. 16c was only issued in booklets.

PRINTERS. All stamps from Types **4** to **29** were recess-printed by Waterlow and Sons, Ltd, London, *except where otherwise stated.*

4

1932 (1 May). P 12½.

29	**4**	2d. green and chocolate	14·00	2·00
30		3d. deep ultramarine	14·00	3·00
		a. Imperf horiz (vert pair)	£17000	£18000
		b. Imperf between (vert pair)	£38000	

5 Victoria Falls

1935 (6 May). Silver Jubilee. P 11×12.

31	**5**	1d. olive and rose-carmine	5·00	3·25
32		2d. emerald and sepia	8·50	8·50
33		3d. violet and deep blue	6·50	11·00
34		6d. black and purple	11·00	24·00
31/4 *Set of 4*			28·00	42·00

1935–41. Inscr "POSTAGE AND REVENUE".

35	**4**	2d. green and chocolate (P 12½)	7·00	20·00
		a. Perf 14 (1941)	3·25	10
35b		3d. deep blue (P 14) (1938)	6·00	1·25

6 Victoria Falls and Railway Bridge   **7** King George VI

1937 (12 May). Coronation. P 12½.

36	**6**	1d. olive and rose-carmine	60	1·25
37		2d. emerald and sepia	60	1·75
38		3d. violet and blue	3·25	9·50
39		6d. black and purple	1·75	4·00
36/9 *Set of 4*			5·50	15·00

1937 (25 Nov). P 14.

40	**7**	½d. green	50	10
41		1d. scarlet	50	10
42		1½d. red-brown	1·00	30
43		4d. red-orange	2·00	10
44		6d. grey-black	1·50	50
45		8d. emerald-green	2·00	4·25
46		9d. pale blue	1·50	1·00
47		10d. purple	3·00	3·50
48		1s. black and blue-green	3·75	10
		a. Frame double, one albino	£3750	
49		1s.6d. black and orange-yellow	18·00	3·00
50		2s. black and brown	30·00	75
51		2s.6d. ultramarine and purple	17·00	8·50
52		5s. blue and blue-green	18·00	3·75
40/52 *Set of 13*			85·00	23·00

Nos. 40/1 exist in coils, constructed from normal sheets.
On No. 48a the frame appears blurred and over-inked.

8 British South Africa Co's Arms   **9** Fort Salisbury, 1890

10 Cecil John Rhodes (after S. P. Kendrick)   **11** Fort Victoria

12 Rhodes makes peace   **13** Victoria Falls Bridge

14 Statue of Sir Charles Coghlan   **15** Lobengula's Kraal and Govt House, Salisbury

Recut shirt collar (R. 6/1)

"Cave" flaw (R. 6/6)

(Des Mrs. L. E. Curtis (½d., 1d., 1½d., 3d.), Mrs I. Mount (others))

1940 (3 June). British South Africa Company's Golden Jubilee. P 14.

53	**8**	½d. slate-violet and green	10	65
54	**9**	1d. violet-blue and scarlet	80	10
55	**10**	1½d. black and red-brown	15	80
		a. Recut shirt collar	28·00	55·00
56	**11**	2d. green and bright violet..............	30	70
57	**12**	3d. black and blue........................	1·50	1·50
		a. Cave flaw	£110	£140
58	**13**	4d. green and brown.....................	2·50	3·75
59	**14**	6d. chocolate and green	2·50	4·50
60	**15**	1s. blue and green........................	3·75	4·50
53/60 Set of 8			10·00	15·00

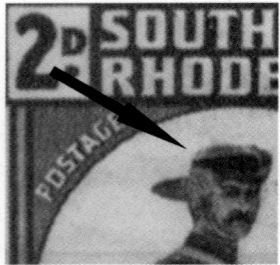

16 Mounted Pioneer

Hat brim retouch (Pl 1B R. 1/8)

Line under saddlebag (Pl 1A R. 6/10)

(Roto South African Govt Printer, Pretoria)

1943 (1 Nov). 50th Anniv of Occupation of Matabeleland. W **9** of South Africa (Mult Springbok) sideways. P 14.

61	**16**	2d. brown and green.......................	25	2·00
		a. Hat brim retouch.....................	27·00	45·00
		b. Line under saddlebag................	27·00	45·00

17 Queen Elizabeth II when Princess and Princess Margaret

18 King George VI and Queen Elizabeth

1947 (1 Apr). Royal Visit. T **17/18**. P 14.

62	**17**	½d. black and green.......................	30	60
63	**18**	1d. black and scarlet......................	30	60

19 Queen Elizabeth | **20** King George VI | **21** Queen Elizabeth II when Princess

22 Princess Margaret

Damage to right-hand frame (R. 1/10)

1947 (8 May). Victory. P 14.

64	**19**	1d. carmine	10	15
65	**20**	2d. slate	15	15
		a. Double print............................	£3500	
		b. Damaged frame........................	£375	
66	**21**	3d. blue.......................................	1·00	2·25
67	**22**	6d. orange	40	1·40
64/7 Set of 4			1·50	3·50

(Recess B.W.)

1949 (10 Oct). 75th Anniv of UPU As Nos. 115/16 of Antigua.

68		2d. slate-green............................	70	25
69		3d. blue......................................	80	4·50

23 Queen Victoria, Arms and King George VI

1950 (12 Sept). Diamond Jubilee of Southern Rhodesia. P 14.

70	**23**	2d. green and brown.....................	1·25	2·00

24 "Medical Services"

25 "Agriculture"

26 "Building"

27 "Water Supplies"

28 "Transport"

(Des A. R. Winter (2d.), Mrs. J. M. Enalim (others))

1953 (15 Apr). Birth Centenary of Cecil Rhodes. P 14.

71	**24**	½d. pale blue and sepia...................	15	2·50
72	**25**	1d. chestnut and blue-green	1·75	10
73	**26**	2d. grey-green and violet................	20	10
74	**27**	4½d. deep blue-green and deep ultramarine	80	3·50
75	**28**	1s. black and red-brown	3·00	2·25
71/5 Set of 5			5·50	7·50

No. 74 also commemorates the Diamond Jubilee of Matabeleland.

1953 (30 May). Rhodes Centenary Exhibition, Bulawayo. As No. 171 of Nyasaland, but without watermark.

76		6d. violet.....................................	1·00	1·00

30 Queen Elizabeth II

(Recess D.L.R.)

1953 (1 June). Coronation. P 12×12½.

77	**30**	2s.6d. carmine	7·00	7·00

31 Sable Antelope | **32** Tobacco planter

33 Rhodes's Grave | **34** Farm Worker

35 Flame Lily | **36** Victoria Falls

37 Baobab tree | **38** Lion

39 Zimbabwe Ruins | **40** Birchenough Bridge

41 Kariba Gorge | **42** Basket Maker

43 Balancing Rocks | **44** Coat of Arms

(Recess, centre typo (4d.), B.W.)

1953 (31 Aug). P 13½×14 (2d., 6d., 5s.), 14 (10s., £1) or 14×13½ (others).

78	**31**	½d. grey-green and claret.................	30	50
79	**32**	1d. green and brown......................	30	10
80	**33**	2d. deep chestnut and reddish violet.....................................	30	10
81	**34**	3d. chocolate and rose-red...............	55	2·75
82	**35**	4d. red, green and indigo................	3·50	40
83	**36**	4½d. black and deep bright blue.........	2·50	4·50
84	**37**	6d. brown-olive and deep turquoise-green.......................	4·50	1·75
85	**38**	9d. deep blue and reddish brown ..	4·50	4·75
86	**39**	1s. reddish violet and light blue	2·25	10
87	**40**	2s. purple and scarlet....................	16·00	9·50
88	**41**	2s.6d. yellow-olive and orange-brown...................................	8·50	9·50
89	**42**	5s. yellow-brown and deep green ..	12·00	12·00
90	**43**	10s. red-brown and olive................	22·00	38·00
91	**44**	£1 rose-red and black...................	25·00	45·00
78/91 Set of 14			90·00	£110

For issues from 1954 to 1963 see under RHODESIA AND NYASALAND.

45 Maize

46 African Buffalo

47 Tobacco

48 Greater Kudu

49 Citrus

50 Flame Lily

51 Ansellia Orchid

52 Emeralds

53 Aloe

54 Lake Kyle

55 Tigerfish

56 Cattle

57 Helmet Guineafowl

58 Coat of Arms

2s. Large white dot over "IA" of "RHODESIA" (R. 5/8)

10s. A large coloured flaw on the small guinea fowl gives the appearance of an extra feather (R. 2/2)

(Des V. Whiteley. Photo Harrison)

1964 (19 Feb). T **45/58**. P 14½ (½d. to 4d.), 13½×13 (6d. to 2s.6d.) or 14½×14 (others).

92	**45**	½d. yellow, yellow-green and light blue	20	2·75
93	**46**	1d. reddish violet and yellow-ochre	15	10
		a. Reddish violet omitted	£4000	
94	**47**	2d. yellow and deep violet	60	10
95	**48**	3d. chocolate and pale blue	20	10
96	**49**	4d. yellow-orange and deep green	30	10
97	**50**	6d. carmine-red, yellow and deep dull green	40	10
98	**51**	9d. red-brown, yellow and olive-green	2·75	1·50

99	**52**	1s. blue-green and ochre	3·75	30
		a. Blue-green (Queen and emeralds) omitted	£6000	
100	**53**	1s.3d. red, violet and yellow-green	3·00	10
101	**54**	2s. blue and ochre	2·50	3·50
		a. Dot over "IA"	22·00	
102	**55**	2s.6d. ultramarine and vermilion	4·00	1·00
		a. Vermilion omitted	£6000	
		b. Ultramarine omitted	£18000	
103	**56**	5s. light brown, bistre-yellow and light blue	3·50	2·75
104	**57**	10s. black, yellow-ochre, light blue and carmine-red	11·00	10·00
		a. Extra "feather"	26·00	45·00
105	**58**	£1 brown, yellow-green, buff and salmon-pink	9·00	23·00
92/105 *Set of 14*			38·00	40·00

Nos. 92 and 93 exist in coils constructed from normal sheets.

Nos. 102a and 102b occur on different sheets and involve one or two vertical rows of stamps in each instance. They were caused by the printing press being stopped and then restarted. Three such sheets showing No. 102a have been reported.

See also Nos. 359/72 of Rhodesia.

In October 1964 Southern Rhodesia was renamed Rhodesia.

STAMP BOOKLETS

1928 (1 Jan). Black on blue cover. Stitched.

SB1	2s.6d. booklet containing 12×½d. and 24×1d. (Nos. 1/2) in blocks of 6	£6500

1931. Black on blue cover. Stitched.

SB2	2s.6d. booklet containing 12×½d. and 24×1d. (Nos. 15/16) in blocks of 6	£7500

1933 (3 Mar). Black on red cover, size 69×53 mm. Stitched.

SB3	3s. booklet containing 12×½d., 12×1d. and 12×1½d. (Nos. 15, 16, 16c) in blocks of 6	£4500

The 1½d. postage rate was reduced to 1d. eight weeks after No. SB3 was issued. Postal officials were instructed to detach the 1½d. panes and use them for other purposes. The remaining stocks of the booklet were then sold for 1s.6d.

1938 (Oct)–45. Black on yellow cover. Stitched.

SB4	2s.6d. booklet containing 24×½d. and 18×1d. (Nos. 40/1) in blocks of 6 with postage rates on inside front cover	£325
	a. Label with new rates affixed to inside front cover (1945)	£375
	b. Inside front cover blank	£350

No. SB4b was issued sometime between 1945 and 1949.

1954 (Jan). Black on yellow cover, size 71×54 mm. Stitched.

SB5	2s.6d. booklet containing 12×½d. and 24×1d. (Nos. 78/9) in blocks of 6	75·00

1964 (19 Feb). Black on orange cover, size 57×45 mm. Stitched.

SB6	1s. booklet containing 3d. (No. 95) in block of 4.	3·25

POSTAGE DUE STAMPS

SOUTHERN

RHODESIA

(D **1**)

1951 (1 Oct). Postage Due stamps of Great Britain optd with Type D **1**.

D1	D **1**	½d. emerald (No. D27)	3·25	19·00
D2		1d. violet-blue (No. D36)	3·00	2·00
D3		2d. agate (No. D29)	2·50	1·75
D4		3d. violet (No. D30)	2·75	3·25
D5		4d. blue (No. D38)	1·75	4·00
D6		4d. dull grey-green (No. D31)	£300	£700
D7		1s. deep blue (No. D33)	2·50	6·50
D1/5, 7 *Set of 6*			14·00	32·00

No. D6 is reported to have been issued to Fort Victoria and Gwelo main post offices only.

South West Africa

Walvis (or Walfish) Bay, the major anchorage on the South West Africa coast, was claimed by Great Britain as early as 1796. In 1878 the 430 sq. mile area around the port, together with a number of offshore islands, was annexed to Cape Province, passing to the Union in 1910. Stamps of Cape of Good Hope and, later, South Africa, were used at Walvis Bay, often cancelled with the numeral obliterator "300", until the enclave was transferred to the South West African administration on 1 October 1922.

Germany declared a protectorate over the southern part of the territory, around Luderitzbucht, in 1884, extending its reach and establishing boundaries with surrounding administrations by 1890, establishing authority over the entire country, apart from the Walvis Bay enclave.

German post offices were opened from 1888, selling current German stamps which may be identified by their cancellations. In 1897 the German stamps overprinted "Deutsch-/Sudwest-Afrika" and, later, "Deutsch-/Sudwestafrica" were introduced, to be followed by the colonial "Yacht" series in 1901.

After a rebellion in South Africa, aided by arms supplied from German South West Africa, had been defeated in December 1914, South African troops invaded the protectorate, with the German forces finally capitulating on 9 July 1915.

As civil post offices were opened by the occupying forces, they sold South African stamps, generally postmarked by altered German colonial cancellers.

On 17 December 1920 the League of Nations conferred a mandate of administration of the territory on His Britannic Majesty, to be exercised by the government in South Africa. The Mandate came into force on 1 January 1923, on which date the first South African stamps overprinted for use in the territory were issued.

The following listing covers South African stamps used in South West Africa up to 31 January 1923 when they ceased to be valid. The cancellations during this period are of great interest with many provisional and altered German types; the prices given are for the more common markings.

Stamps of SOUTH AFRICA cancelled by South West Africa postmarks (various types).

1910 (Nos. 1/2).

Z1	2½d. blue		75·00

1913-24 (Nos. 3/17).

Z2	½d. green		1·00
Z3	1d. red		1·00
Z4	1½d. chesnut		1·50
Z5	2d. purple		1·50
Z6	2½d. blue		3·00
Z7	3d. black and orange-red		6·00
Z8	3d. ultramarine		£100
Z9	4d. orange-yellow and sage-green		4·00
Z10	6d. black and violet		8·00
Z11	1s. orange		12·00
Z12	1s. 3d. violet		£130
Z13	2s. 6d. purple and green		70·00
Z14	5s. purple and blue		80·00
Z15	10s. deep blue and olive-green		90·00
Z16	£1 green and red		£750

1913-21 Coil stamps (Nos. 18/21).

Z17	½d. green		35·00
Z18	1d. red		50·00
Z19	1½d. chesnut		£160
Z20	2d. purple		£250

Interprovincial stamps (see South Africa Nos. Z1/Z192) were also valid for use in South West Africa, but their use was almost entirely philatelic and they are not listed.

PRICES FOR STAMPS ON COVER TO 1945	
Nos. 1/40a	*from* × 6
Nos. 41/133	*from* × 2
Nos. D1/5	*from* × 10
Nos. D6/51	*from* × 20
Nos. O1/4	*from* × 3
Nos. O5/20	*from* × 15
No. O21	*from* × 2
No. O22	*from* × 15

INSCRIPTIONS. Most of the postage stamps up to No. 140 are inscribed alternately in English and Afrikaans throughout the sheets and the same applies to all the Official stamps and to Nos. D30/33.

PRICES for Nos. 1/140 are for unused horizontal pairs, used horizontal pairs or used singles (either inscr), *unless otherwise indicated*.

OVERPRINT SETTINGS. Between 1923 and 1928 the King George V definitives of South Africa, Types **2** and **3**, and the various postage due stamps were issued overprinted for use in South West Africa. A number of overprint settings were used:

Setting I – Overprint Types **1** and **2** ("Zuid-West Afrika"). 14 mm between lines of overprint. See Nos. 1/12 and D1/9.

Setting II – As Setting I, but 10 mm between lines of overprint. See Nos. 13/15 and D10/13.

Setting III – Overprint Types **3** ("Zuidwest Afrika") and **4.** "South West" 14 mm long. "Zuidwest" 11 mm long. 14 mm between lines of overprint. See Nos. 16/27 and D14/17

Setting IV – As Setting III, but "South West" 16 mm long, "Zuidwest" 12 mm long and 14 mm between lines of overprint. See Nos. 28 and D17a/20

Setting V – As Setting IV, but 12 mm between lines of overprint. See Nos. D21/4

Setting VI – As Setting V, but 9½ mm between lines of overprint. See Nos. 29/40 and D25/32.

South West   **Zuid-West**

Africa. (1)   **Afrika.** (2)

1923 (1 Jan–17 June). Nos. 3/4, 6 and 9/17 of South Africa optd alternately with T **1** and **2** by typography.

(a) Setting I (14 mm between lines of opt)

		Un pair	Us pair	Us single
1	½d. green	4·50	9·00	1·00
	a. "Wes" for "West" (R. 20/8)	£120	£160	
	b. "Afr ica" (R. 20/2)	£130		
	c. "Afrika" without stop			
	d. Litho opt in shiny ink (17 June)	12·00	65·00	5·00
2	1d. rose-red	8·00	9·50	1·00
	a. Opt inverted	£500		
	b. "Wes" for "West" (R. 12/2)	£190		
	c. "Af.rica" for "Africa" (R. 20/6)	£180	£300	
	d. Opt double	£1000		
	e. "Afr ica" (R. 20/2)	£130		
	f. "Afrika" without stop (R. 17/8)	£350		
3	2d. dull purple	10·00	16·00	1·50
	a. Opt inverted	£700	£800	
	b. "Wes" for "West" (R. 20/8)	£325		
	c. Litho opt in shiny ink (30 Mar)	75·00	£150	10·00
4	3d. ultramarine	12·00	19·00	2·75
5	4d. orange-yellow and sage-green	20·00	50·00	4·50
	a. Litho opt in shiny ink (19 Apr)	48·00	70·00	8·00
6	6d. black and violet	8·50	50·00	4·50
	a. Litho opt in shiny ink (19 Apr)	38·00	85·00	7·50
7	1s. orange-yellow	18·00	50·00	5·00
	a. Litho opt in shiny ink (19 Apr)	65·00	£130	11·00
	b. "Afrika" without stop (R. 17/8)	£6000		
8	1s.3d. pale violet	45·00	60·00	5·50
	a. Opt inverted	£400		
	b. Litho opt in shiny ink (19 Apr)	85·00	£160	14·00
9	2s.6d. purple and green	70·00	£140	18·00
	a. Litho opt in shiny ink (19 Apr)	£150	£300	35·00
10	5s. purple and blue	£225	£375	50·00
11	10s. blue and olive-green	£1400	£3250	£400
12	£1 green and red	£750	£1900	£250
1/12	Set of 12	£2250	£5250	£650
1s/12s	Optd "SPECIMEN" Set of 12 singles	£1700		

Nos. 1/12 were overprinted in complete sheets of 240 (4 panes 6×10).

No. 3b shows traces of a type spacer to the right of where the "t" should have been. This spacer is not visible on Nos. 1a and 2b.

Minor varieties, such as broken "t" in "West", were caused by worn type. Stamps showing one line of overprint only or with the lower line above the upper line due to overprint misplacement may also be found. All values exist showing a faint stop after "Afrika" on R. 17/8, but only examples of the 1d. and 1s. have been seen with it completely omitted.

(b) Setting II (10 mm between lines of opt) (31 Mar)

		Un pair	Us pair	Us single
13	5s. purple and green	£160	£275	45·00
	a. "Afrika" without stop (R. 6/1)	£1200	£1400	£225
14	10s. blue and olive-green	£500	£850	£140
	a. "Afrika" without stop (R. 6/1)	£2500	£3000	£550
15	£1 green and red	£1000	£1400	£200
	a. "Afrika" without stop (R. 6/1)	£4500	£5500	£1000
13/15	Set of 3	£1500	£2250	£350

Nos. 13/15 were overprinted in separate panes of 60 (6×10).

Examples of most values are known showing a forged Windhoek postmark dated "30 SEP 24".

Zuidwest   **South West**

Afrika. (3)   **Africa.** (4)

1923 (15 July)–26. Nos. 3/4, 6 and 9/17 of South Africa optd as T **3** ("Zuidwest" in one word, without hyphen) and **4** alternately.

(a) Setting III ("South West" 14 mm long, "Zuidwest" 11 mm long, 14 mm between lines of opt)

		Un pair	Us pair	Us single
16	½d. green (5.9.24)	12·00	40·00	4·25
	a. "outh" for "South" (R. 1/1)	£2250		
17	1d. rose-red (28.9.23)	6·00	9·00	1·40
	a. "outh" for "South" (R. 1/1)	£2000		
18	2d. dull purple (28.9.23)	11·00	16·00	1·50
	a. Opt double	£1000		
19	3d. ultramarine	5·00	14·00	1·40
20	4d. orange-yellow and sage-green	7·00	21·00	2·75
21	6d. black and violet (28.9.23)	12·00	45·00	5·00
22	1s. orange-yellow	12·00	45·00	5·00
23	1s.3d. pale violet	28·00	50·00	5·50
24	2s.6d. purple and green	50·00	90·00	10·00
25	5s. purple and blue	75·00	£140	18·00
26	10s. blue and olive-green	£170	£275	40·00
27	£1 green and red (28.9.23)	£325	£475	60·00
16/27	Set of 12	£650	£1100	£140

Nos. 16/27 were overprinted in complete sheets of 240 (4 panes 6×10).

Two sets may be made with this overprint, one with bold lettering, and the other from September 1924, with thinner lettering and smaller stops.

(b) Setting IV ("South West" 16 mm long, "Zuidwest" 12 mm long, 14 mm between lines of opt)

		Un pair	Us pair	Us single
28	2s.6d. purple and green (29.6.24)	90·00	£170	28·00

No. 28 was overprinted on two panes of 60 horizontally side by side.

(c) Setting VI ("South West" 16 mm long, "Zuidwest" 12 mm long, 9½ mm between lines of opt)

		Un pair	Us pair	Us single
29	½d. green (16.12.25)	7·00	48·00	5·50
30	1d. rose-red (9.12.24)	5·00	10·00	1·40
	a. Opt omitted (in pair with normal)	£2000		
31	2d. dull purple (9.12.24)	4·00	22·00	1·75
32	3d. ultramarine (31.1.26)	5·50	40·00	3·00
	a. Deep bright blue (20.4.26)	42·00	£100	12·00
33	4d. orange-yellow and sage-green (9.12.24)	6·50	48·00	4·00
34	6d. black and violet (9.12.24)	10·00	48·00	5·00
35	1s. orange-yellow (9.12.24)	8·50	48·00	5·00
36	1s.3d. pale violet (9.12.24)	11·00	48·00	5·00
37	2s.6d. purple and green (9.12.24)	45·00	75·00	10·00
38	5s. purple and blue (31.1.26)	60·00	£120	14·00
39	10s. blue and olive-green (9.12.24)	95·00	£180	20·00
40	£1 green and red (9.1.26)	£300	£450	55·00
	a. Pale olive-green and red (8.11.26)	£300	£475	65·00
	as. Ditto. H/S "SPECIMEN"	£250		
29/40	Set of 12	£500	£1000	£120
35s, 39s/40 H/S "SPECIMEN" Set of 3*		£500		

Nos. 29/40 were overprinted in complete sheets of 240 (4 panes of 6×10) with, initially, "South West Africa" 16½ mm long on the upper two panes and 16 mm long on the lower two. This order was subsequently reversed. For printings from 8 November 1926 all four panes showed the 16½ mm measurement. No. 40a only comes from this printing.

* The UPU distribution of Nos. 35s, 39s, 40s in 1928 included mixed stock of the £1 value (in both shades).

Examples of most values are known showing a forged Windhoek postmark dated "30 SEP 24".

Suidwes Afrika. (5)   **South West Africa.** (6)

1926 (1 Jan–1 May). Nos. 30/2 of South Africa (Waterlow printings) optd with T **5** (on stamps inscr in Afrikaans) and **6** (on stamps inscr in English) sideways, alternately in black.

		Un pair	Us pair	Us single
41	½d. black and green	4·75	13·00	1·50
42	1d. black and carmine	4·00	8·00	90
43	6d. green and orange (1.5)	27·00	55·00	7·00
41/3	Set of 3	32·00	70·00	8·50

SOUTH WEST AFRICA (7)   **SUIDWES-AFRIKA** (8)

1926. No. 33 of South Africa, imperf optd.

(a) With T 7 (English)

		Single Stamps	
44A	4d. grey-blue	75	3·00

(b) With T 8 (Afrikaans)

		Single Stamps	
44B	4d. grey-blue	75	3·00

1927. As Nos. 41/3, but Afrikaans opt on stamp inscr in English and vice versa.

		Un pair	Us pair	Us single
45	½d. black and green	2·00	13·00	1·50
	a. "Africa" without stop (R. 13/8)	£160		
46	1d. black and carmine	4·75	2·50	50
	a. "Africa" without stop (R. 13/8)	£300		
47	6d. green and orange	8·00	35·00	3·00
	a. "Africa" without stop (R. 13/8)	£180		
45/7	Set of 3	13·00	45·00	4·50

The overprints on Nos. 45/7 were applied to both the Waterlow and Pretoria printings of South Africa Nos. 30/2.

SOUTH WEST AFRICA (9)   **S.W.A.** (10)   **S.W.A.** (11)

1927. As No. 44A, but overprint T **9**.

		Single Stamps	
48	4d. grey-blue	8·00	19·00
	s. Handstamped "SPECIMEN"	70·00	

1927 (Apr). Nos. 34/9 of South Africa optd alternately as T **5** and **6**, in blue, but with lines of overprint spaced 16 mm.

		Un pair	Us pair	Us single
49	2d. grey and purple	6·50	16·00	1·75
50	3d. black and red	4·75	32·00	2·50
51	1s. brown and blue	16·00	32·00	4·00
52	2s.6d. green and brown	40·00	95·00	13·00
53	5s. black and green	75·00	£190	20·00
54	10s. blue and bistre-brown	65·00	£160	20·00
49/54	Set of 6	£180	£475	50·00
49s/51s, 54s H/S "SPECIMEN" Set of 4		£400		

A variety of Nos. 49, 50, 51 and 54 with spacing 16½ mm between lines of overprint, occurs in the third vertical row of each sheet.

1927. As No. 44, but perf 11½ by John Meinert Ltd, Windhoek.

(a) Optd with T 7 (English)

		Single Stamps	
55A	4d. grey-blue	1·25	6·00
	a. Imperf between (pair)	50·00	90·00
	s. Handstamped "SPECIMEN"	70·00	

(b) Optd with T 8 (Afrikaans)

		Single Stamps	
55B	4d. grey-blue	1·25	6·00
	a. Imperf between (pair)	50·00	90·00
	s. Handstamped "SPECIMEN"	70·00	

1927 (Aug)–30. Optd with T **10**.

(a) On Nos. 13 and 17a of South Africa

		Single Stamps	
56	1s.3d. pale violet	1·25	6·50
	a. Without stop after "A" (R. 3/4)	£100	
	s. Handstamped "SPECIMEN"	75·00	
57	£1 pale olive-green and red	95·00	£170
	a. Without stop after "A" (R. 3/4)	£1600	£2500

(b) On Nos. 30/2 and 34/9 of South Africa

		Un pair	Us pair	Us single
58	½d. black and green	2·50	8·50	80
	a. Without stop after "A"	42·00	75·00	
	b. "S.W.A." opt above value	2·75	16·00	2·25
	c. As b, in vert pair, top stamp without opt	£650		
59	1d. black and carmine	1·25	4·25	55
	a. Without stop after "A"	40·00	75·00	
	b. "S.W.A." opt at top (30.4.30)	1·75	14·00	1·60
	c. As b, in vert pair, top stamp without opt	£700		
60	2d. grey and maroon	9·00	42·00	2·50
	c. Perf 14×13½	29·00	55·00	
	ca. Without stop after "A"	85·00	£150	
	cb. Opt double, one inverted	£750	£1000	
	cc. Split "d"	£160		
61	3d. black and red	5·00	30·00	3·25
	a. Without stop after "A"	75·00	£130	
	b. Perf 14×13½	17·00	50·00	
	ba. Without stop after "A"	95·00	£170	
	bb. Without stop after "W"	£190		
62	4d. brown (4.28)	12·00	50·00	7·00
	a. Without stop after "A"	90·00	£140	
	b. Perf 14×13½	50·00	70·00	
63	6d. green and orange	6·00	30·00	2·75
	a. Without stop after "A"	£190		
64	1s. brown and deep blue	10·00	50·00	5·00
	b. Perf 14×13½	60·00	90·00	
	ba. Without stop after "A"	£1700	£1900	£350
65	2s.6d. green and brown	42·00	85·00	12·00
	a. Without stop after "A"	£160	£275	
	b. Perf 14×13½	80·00	£140	
	ba. Without stop after "A"	£225	£350	
66	5s. black and green	65·00	£120	18·00
	a. Without stop after "A"	£250	£375	
	b. Perf 14×13½	£110	£180	
	ba. Without stop after "A"	£300	£450	
67	10s. bright blue and brown	£110	£200	28·00
	a. Without stop after "A"	£375	£600	
58/67	Set of 10	£225	£550	70·00
58s/61s, 63s/7s H/S "SPECIMEN" Set of 9		£600		

On the ½d., 1d. and 6d. the missing stop variety occurs three times on each sheet, R. 1/7, 13/4 and one position not yet identified. For the other values it comes on R. 2/3 of the right pane and, for the 2s.6d., 5s. and 10s., on R. 8/1 of the left pane.

The missing stop after "W" on the 3d. occurs on R. 10/5 of the right pane.

The overprint is normally found at the base of the ½d., 1d., 6d., 1s.3d. and £1 values and at the top of the remainder.

Examples of all values are known showing a forged Windhoek postmark dated "20 MAR 31".

1930–31. Nos. 42 and 43 of South Africa (rotogravure printing) optd with T **10**.

		Un pair	Us pair	Us single
68	½d. black and green (1931)	24·00	50·00	5·00
69	1d. black and carmine	16·00	27·00	2·75

1930 (27 Nov–Dec). Air. Nos. 40/1 of South Africa optd.

(a) As T 10

		Un single	Us single
70	4d. green (first printing)	7·00	28·00
	a. No stop after "A" of "S.W.A."	70·00	£140
	b. Later printings	3·50	28·00
71	1s. orange (first printing)	70·00	£120
	a. No stop after "A" of "S.W.A."	£450	£650
	b. Later printings	5·00	55·00

First printing: Thick letters, blurred impression. Stops with rounded corners.

Later printings: Thinner letters, clear impression. Clean cut, square stops.

(b) As T 11 (12.30)

72	4d. green	1·25	6·00
	a. Opt double	£200	
	b. Opt inverted	£200	
73	1s. orange	2·50	15·00
	a. Opt double	£550	

12 Kori Bustard

13 Cape Cross

14 Bogenfels

15 Windhoek

16 Waterberg

17 Luderitz Bay

18 Bush Scene

19 Elands

20 Mountain Zebra and Blue Wildebeests

21 Herero Huts

22 Welwitschia Plant

23 Okuwahaken Falls

24 Monoplane over Windhoek

25 Biplane over Windhoek

(Recess B.W.)

1931 (5 Mar). T **12** to **25** (inscr alternately in English and Afrikaans). W **9** of South Africa. P 14×13½.

(a) Postage

74	½d. black and emerald	3·00	2·50	10
75	1d. indigo and scarlet	3·00	2·50	10
76	2d. blue and brown	2·25	9·50	20
	w. Wmk inverted	£900		
77	3d. grey-blue and blue	1·50	4·50	15
78	4d. green and purple	1·75	7·00	20
79	6d. blue and brown	1·50	11·00	20
80	1s. chocolate and blue	3·50	18·00	25
81	1s.3d. violet and yellow	6·00	11·00	50
82	2s.6d. carmine and grey	29·00	24·00	1·75
83	5s. sage-green and red-brown	16·00	35·00	2·75
84	10s. red-brown and emerald	50·00	50·00	6·00
85	20s. lake and blue-green	75·00	80·00	10·00

(b) Air

86	3d. brown and blue	29·00	35·00	2·50
87	10d. black and purple-brown	55·00	85·00	7·00
74/87 *Set of 14*		£225	£300	28·00

Examples of most values are known showing a forged Windhoek postmark dated "20 MAR 31".

26

(Recess B.W.)

1935 (1 May). Silver Jubilee. Inscr bilingually. W **9** of South Africa. P 14×13½.

			Un single	Us single
88	**26**	1d. black and scarlet	1·00	25
89		2d. black and sepia	1·50	25
90		3d. black and blue	7·50	25·00
91		6d. black and purple	3·00	15·00
88/91 *Set of 4*			11·50	35·00

1935–36. Voortrekker Memorial Fund. Nos. 50/3 of South Africa optd with T **10**.

92	½d. +½d. black and green	1·75	5·50	75
	a. Opt inverted	£275		
93	1d. +1½d. grey-black and pink	2·25	3·25	40
	a. Blurred "SOUTH AFRICA" and red "comet" flaw	80·00		
94	2d. +1d. grey-green and purple	7·00	6·00	80
	a. Without stop after "A"	£200	£225	
	b. Opt double	£250		
95	3d. +1½d. grey-green and blue	21·00	50·00	4·25
	a. Without stop after "A"	£275	£375	
92/5 *Set of 4*		29·00	60·00	5·50

27 Mail Train

28

Re-entry (R. 6/3)

(Recess B.W.)

1937 (1 Mar). W **9** of South Africa. P 14×13½.

96	**27**	1½d. purple-brown	29·00	4·50	35

(Recess B.W.)

1937 (12 May). Coronation. W **9** of South Africa (sideways). P 13½×14.

97	**28**	½d. black and emerald	40	15	10
98		1d. black and scarlet	40	15	10
99		1½d. black and orange	40	15	10
100		2d. black and brown	40	15	10
101		3d. black and blue	50	15	10
102		4d. black and purple	50	20	10
		a. Re-entry	22·00	20·00	
103		6d. black and yellow	50	3·25	20
104		1s. black and grey-black	55	3·50	25
97/104 *Set of 8*			3·25	7·00	65

On. No. 102a the frame and leaves at lower left are doubled. The stamp is inscribed in Afrikaans.

1938 (14 Dec). Voortrekker Centenary Memorial. Nos. 76/9 of South Africa optd as T **11**.

105	½d. +½d. blue and green	12·00	32·00	2·25
106	1d. +1d. blue and carmine	30·00	22·00	1·50
107	1½d. +1½d. chocolate and blue-green	32·00	38·00	3·25
108	3d. +3d. bright blue	55·00	95·00	8·50
105/8 *Set of 4*		£110	£160	14·00

1938 (14 Dec). Voortrekker Commemoration. Nos. 80/1 of South Africa optd as T **11**.

109	1d. blue and carmine	16·00	25·00	1·50
	a. Three bolts in wheel rim	85·00		
110	1½d. greenish blue and brown	22·00	30·00	2·00

1939 (17 July). 250th Anniv of Landing of Huguenots in South Africa and Huguenot Commemoration Fund. Nos. 82/4 of South Africa optd as T **11**.

111	½d. +½d. brown and green	14·00	18·00	1·40
112	1d. +1d. green and carmine	23·00	18·00	1·40
113	1½d. +1½d. blue-green and purple	38·00	17·00	1·25
111/13 *Set of 3*		65·00	48·00	3·50

SWA **SWA** **SWA** **S W A**
(29)   (30)   (31)   (32)

1941 (1 Oct)–43. War Effort. Nos. 88/96 of South Africa optd with T **29** or **30** (3d. and 1s.).

(a) Inscr alternately

114	½d. green (1.12.41)	1·50	6·00	40
	a. Blue-green (1942)	2·50	2·50	15
115	1d. carmine (1.11.41)	2·50	3·75	20
	a. "Stain" on uniform	27·00		
116	1½d. myrtle-green (21.1.42)	2·50	4·00	20
117	3d. blue	24·00	29·00	1·00
	a. Cigarette flaw	£130		
118	4d. orange-brown	10·00	21·00	1·00
	a. Red-brown	21·00	38·00	3·25
119	6d. red-orange	7·50	9·00	50
120	1s.3d. olive-brown (15.1.43)	13·00	23·00	1·25

(b) Inscr bilingually

			Un single	Us single
121	2d. violet		50	1·75
122	1s. brown (17.11.41)		1·60	2·00
114/22 *Set of 7 pairs and 2 singles*			50·00	85·00

1943–44. War Effort (reduced sizes). Nos. 97/104 of South Africa, optd with T **29** (1½d. and 1s., No. 130), or T **31** (others).

(a) Inscr alternately

			Un unit	Us unit	Us single
123	½d. blue-green (T)		50	9·50	55
	a. Green		7·00	13·00	70
	b. Greenish blue		4·25	10·00	55
124	1d. carmine-red (T)		4·50	8·50	30
	a. Bright carmine		3·50	8·50	30
125	1½d. red-brown (P)		50	1·75	15
	a. Ear flap flaw		16·00		
126	2d. violet (P)		8·50	5·50	20
	a. Reddish violet		14·00	8·50	30
	b. Apostrophe flaw		65·00		
127	3d. blue (T)		3·25	27·00	1·00
128	6d. red-orange (P)		5·00	3·00	30
	a. Opt inverted		£650		

(b) Inscr bilingually

129	4d. slate-green (T)		2·00	23·00	75
	a. Opt inverted		£900	£650	70·00
130	1s. brown (opt T **29**) (P)		19·00	40·00	2·00
	a. Opt inverted		£800	£450	
	b. Opt T **31** (1944)		4·00	6·00	30
	c. Opt T **31** inverted		£650	£425	48·00
	d. "Bursting shell"		50·00		
	e. Smoking "L"		50·00		
123/30b *Set of 8*			25·00	75·00	3·25

The "units" referred to above consist of pairs (P) or triplets (T). No. 128 exists with another type of opt as Type **31**, but with broader "s", narrower "w" and more space between the letters.

1945. Victory. Nos. 108/10 of South Africa optd with T **30**.

131	1d. brown and carmine	25	75	10
	a. Opt inverted	£400	£425	
	b. Barbed wire flaw	15·00		
132	2d. slate-blue and violet	30	75	10
133	3d. deep blue and blue	1·50	1·75	10
131/3 *Set of 3*		1·75	3·00	20

1947 (17 Feb). Royal Visit. Nos. 111/13 of South Africa optd as T **31**, but 8½×2 mm.

134	1d. black and carmine	10	10	10
135	2d. violet	10	60	10
	a. "Bird" on "2"	8·50		
136	3d. blue	15	40	10
	a. "Black-eyed Princess"	10·00		
134/6 *Set of 3*		30	1·00	15

1948 (26 Apr). Royal Silver Wedding. No. 125 of South Africa, optd as T **31**, but 4×2 mm.

137	3d. blue and silver	1·00	35	10

1949 (1 Oct). 75th Anniv of UPU. Nos. 128/30 of South Africa optd as T **30**, but 13×4 mm.

138	½d. blue-green	75	2·25	25
139	1½d. brown-red	75	1·75	15
140	3d. bright blue	1·25	1·00	25
	a. Serif on "C"	65·00		
	b. "Lake" in East Africa	65·00		
138/40 *Set of 3*		2·50	4·50	60

1949 (1 Dec). Inauguration of Voortrekker Monument, Pretoria. Nos. 131/3 of South Africa optd with T **32**.

			Un single	Us single
141	1d. magenta		10	10
142	1½d. blue-green		10	10
143	3d. blue		15	60
141/3 *Set of 3*			30	70

1952 (14 Mar). Tercentenary of Landing of Van Riebeeck. Nos. 136/40 of South Africa optd as T **30**, but 8×3½ mm (1d., 4½d.) or 11×4 mm (others).

144	½d. brown-purple and olive-grey	10	50	
145	1d. deep blue-green	10	10	
146	2d. deep violet	50	10	
	a. "Full Moon"	12·00		
	b. "Line through sails" (vert pair)	17·00		
147	4½d. blue	30	1·75	
148	1s. brown	75	20	
144/8 *Set of 5*		1·50	2·25	

33 Queen Elizabeth II and *Catophracies alexandrii*

1953 (2 June). Coronation. T **33** and similar horiz designs. W **9** of South Africa. P 14.

149	1d. bright carmine		40	10
150	2d. deep bluish green		40	10
151	4d. magenta		50	35
152	6d. dull ultramarine		50	85
153	1s. deep orange-brown		65	30
149/53 *Set of 5*			2·25	1·50

Designs:—2d. *Bauhinia macrantha*, 4d. *Caralluma nebrownii*, 6d. *Gloriosa virescens*, 1s. *Rhigozum trieholotum*.

34 "Two Bucks" (rock painting)

35 "White Lady" (rock painting)

36 "Rhinoceros Hunt" (rock painting)

37 "White Elephant and Giraffe" (rock painting)

38 Karakul Lamb

39 Ovambo Woman blowing Horn

40 Ovambo woman

41 Herero woman

42 Ovambo girl

43 Lioness

44 Gemsbok

45 African Elephant

(Des O. Schroeder (1d. to 4d.), M. Vandenschen (4½d. to 10s.))

1954 (15 Nov). T **34/45**. W **9** of South Africa (sideways* on vert designs). P 14.

154	**34**	1d. brown-red	30	10
		w. Wmk horns of springbok to right	18·00	13·00
155	**35**	2d. deep brown	35	10
156	**36**	3d. dull purple	1·25	10
157	**37**	4d. blackish olive	1·50	10
158	**38**	4½d. deep blue	70	40
159	**39**	6d. myrtle-green	70	70
		w. Wmk horns of springbok to right	80·00	40·00
160	**40**	1s. deep mauve	70	50
161	**41**	1s.3d. cerise	2·00	1·25
162	**42**	1s.6d. purple	2·00	50
163	**43**	2s.6d. bistre-brown	4·50	70
164	**44**	5s. deep bright blue	6·00	2·75
165	**45**	10s. deep myrtle-green	38·00	16·00
154/65 Set of 12			50·00	21·00

*The normal sideways watermark shows the horns of the springbok pointing left, *as seen from the back of the stamp.*

1960. As Nos. 154/7, 159, 162, but W **102** of South Africa (sideways on vert designs). P 14.

166	**34**	1d. brown-red	55	2·25
167	**35**	2d. deep brown	70	2·25
168	**36**	3d. dull purple	1·40	5·00
169	**37**	4d. blackish olive	2·75	4·25
169a	**39**	6d. myrtle-green	£1700	£550
170	**42**	1s.6d. purple	20·00	11·00
166/70 (ex 169a) Set of 5			23·00	22·00

(New Currency. 100 cents = 1 South African rand)

46 GPO Windhoek

47 Finger Rock

48 Mounted Soldier Monument

49 Quivertree

50 SWA House, Windhoek

50a Greater Flamingoes and Swakopmund Lighthouse

51 Fishing Industry

52 Greater Flamingo

53 German Lutheran Church, Windhoek

54 Diamond

55 Fort Namutoni

55a Hardap Dam

56 Topaz

57 Tourmaline

58 Heliodor

1961 (14 Feb)–**63**. Unsurfaced paper. W **102** of South Africa (sideways on vert designs). P 14.

171	**46**	½c. brown and pale blue	60	10
172	**47**	1c. sepia and reddish lilac	15	10
173	**48**	1½c. slate-violet and salmon	20	10
174	**49**	2c. deep green and yellow	75	1·40
175	**50**	2½c. red-brown and pale blue	35	10
176	**50a**	3c. ultramarine and rose-red (1.10.62)	6·00	40
177	**51**	3½c. indigo and blue-green	1·00	15
178	**52**	5c. scarlet and grey-blue	8·00	15
179	**53**	7½c. sepia and pale lemon	70	15
180	**54**	10c. blue and greenish yellow	1·75	60
181	**55**	12½c. indigo and lemon	60	40
182	**55a**	15c. chocolate and light blue (16.3.63)	18·00	3·25
183	**56**	20c. brown and red-orange	4·00	30
184	**57**	50c. deep bluish green and yellow-orange	4·50	1·50
185	**58**	1r. yellow, maroon and blue	7·50	12·00
171/185 Set of 15			48·00	18·00

See also Nos. 186/91, 202/16 and 224/6.

1962–66. As No. 171, etc., but without watermark.

186	**46**	½c. brown and pale blue (8.62)	50	1·50
187	**48**	1½c. slate-violet and salmon (9.62)	5·00	45
188	**49**	2c. deep green and yellow (5.62)	3·50	3·50
189	**50**	2½c. red-brown and light blue (1964)	13·00	6·50
190	**51**	3½c. indigo and blue-green (1966)	8·00	3·75
191	**52**	5c. scarlet and grey-blue (9.62)	7·00	15
186/91 Set of 6			32·00	15·00

59 "Agricultural Development"

60 Centenary Emblem and Map

61 Centenary Emblem and part of Globe

1963 (16 Mar). Opening of Hardap Dam. W **102** of South Africa (sideways). P 14.

192	**59**	3c. chocolate and light green	30	15

1963 (30 Aug). Centenary of Red Cross. P 14.

193	**60**	7½c. red, black and light blue	4·50	5·00
194	**61**	15c. red, black and orange-brown	6·50	8·00

62 Interior of Assembly Hall

63 Calvin

1964 (14 May). Opening of Legislative Assembly Hall, Windhoek. W **102** of South Africa. P 14.

195	**62**	3c. ultramarine and salmon	50	30

1964 (1 Oct). 400th Death Anniv of Calvin (Protestant reformer). P 14.

196	**63**	2½c. brown-purple and gold	50	15
197		15c. deep bluish green and gold	2·25	3·75

64 Mail Runner of 1890

65 Kurt von Francois (founder)

66 Dr. H. Vedder

(Des D. Aschenborn)

1965 (18 Oct). 75th Anniv of Windhoek. Chalk-surfaced paper. W **127** of South Africa (sideways). P 14.

198	**64**	3c. sepia and scarlet	50	15
199	**65**	15c. red-brown and blue-green	90	1·75

1966 (4 July). 90th Birth Anniv. of Dr. H. Vedder (philosopher and writer). Chalk-surfaced paper. W **127** of South Africa (sideways). P 14.

200	**66**	3c. blackish green and salmon	30	15
201		15c. deep sepia and light blue	70	40

No. 200 exists on Swiss-made paper with *tête-bêche* watermark from a special printing made for use in presentation albums for delegates to the UPU Congress in Tokyo in 1969, as supplies of the original Harrison paper were by then exhausted (*Price £30 mint*).

1966–72. As 1961–66 but W **127** or **127a** of South Africa and new values (4c., 6c., 9c.).

*(a) wmk **127** (sideways on vertical designs)*

A202	½c. brown and pale blue (1967)		10·00	2·50
A203	1c. sepia and light reddish lilac (1967)		1·50	10
	a. Wmk top of triangle to right		2·50	
A205	2c. deep green and yellow		5·50	10
A206	2½c. deep red-brown and light turquoise-blue		2·50	3·00
A208	3½c. indigo and blue-green (1967)		5·00	8·50
A212	7½c. sepia and pale lemon (1967)		3·50	30
	w. Wmk top of triangle to right		3·75	30
A202/212 Set of 6			25·00	13·00

*(b) wmk **127a***

B202	½c. brown and pale blue (1968)		1·25	10
B203a	1c. sepia and light reddish lilac (1972)		4·00	10
B204	1½c. slate-violet and salmon (1968)		7·50	50
B206a	2½c. deep red-brown and pale blue (1967)		70	10
B207	3c. ultramarine and rose-red (1970)		8·50	3·50
B209	4c. deep red-brown and light turquoise-blue (1.4.71)		1·50	2·50
B210	5c. scarlet and grey-blue (1968)		3·50	10
B211	6c. sepia and greenish yellow (31.8.71)		11·00	12·00
B213	9c. indigo and greenish yellow (1.7.71)		13·00	13·00
B214	10c. bright blue and greenish yellow (6.70)		18·00	3·00
	a. Whiter background (9.72)**		18·00	4·00
B215	15c. chocolate and light blue (1.72)		25·00	7·00
B216	20c. brown and red-orange (1968)		16·00	1·75
B202/216 Set of 12			£100	38·00

*The watermarks in this issue are indistinct but the stamps can be distinguished from each other and the stamps without watermark by their shades and the chalk-surfaced paper which is appreciably thicker and whiter.

†The normal sideways watermark shows top of triangle pointing to left, *as seen from the back of the stamp.*

**No. B214a, printed from sheets, has a much whiter background around the value and behind "SOUTH WEST AFRICA" compared with No. B214, which was issued in coils only.

See also Nos. 224/6.

67 Camelthorn Tree

(Des D. Aschenborn (2½c., 3c.), Govt Printer, Pretoria (15c.))

1967 (6 Jan). Verwoerd Commemoration. Chalk-surfaced paper. T **67** and similar designs. W **127** of South Africa (sideways on vert designs). P 14.

217		2½c. black and emerald-green	15	10
218		3c. brown and new blue	15	10
219		15c. blackish brown and reddish purple	55	45
217/19 Set of 3			75	60

Designs: *Vert.*—3c. Waves breaking against rock; 15c. Dr. H. F. Verwoerd.

70 President Swart

71 President and Mrs. Swart

1968 (2 Jan). Swart Commemoration. Chalk-surfaced paper. W **127** of South Africa (*tête-bêche*, sideways). P 14×15.

220	**70**	3c. orange-red, black and turquoise-blue		
		G. Inscribed in German	35	20
		A. Inscribed in Afrikaans	35	20
		E. Inscribed in English	35	20
221	**71**	15c. red, blackish olive and dull green		
		G. Inscribed in German	1·50	1·75
		A. Inscribed in Afrikaans	1·50	1·75
		E. Inscribed in English	1·50	1·75
		a. Red, brownish olive and bronze-green		
		G. Inscribed in German	3·00	3·25
		A. Inscribed in Afrikaans	3·00	3·25
		E. Inscribed in English	3·00	3·25
220/1 Set of 2 values in strips of three			5·00	5·50
Set of 6 singles			2·00	2·25

The three languages appear, *se-tenant*, both horizontally and vertically, throughout the sheet.

The 15c. also exists on Harrison paper, wmk w **102** of South Africa, from a special printing made for use in presentation albums for delegates to the UPU Congress in Tokyo in 1965. (*Price £30 mint*).

1970 (14 Feb). Water 70 Campaign. As Nos. 299/300 of South Africa, but with phosphor band and inscr "SWA".

222		2½c. green, bright blue and chocolate	50	30
223		3c. Prussian blue, royal blue and buff	50	30

72 GPO, Windhoek

1970–71. As Nos. 202 and 204/5 but "POSGELD INKOMSTE" omitted and larger figure of value as in T **72**. W **127a** of South Africa (sideways on 1½ and 2c.).

224	**72**	½c. brown and pale blue (6.70)	1·00	30
225	–	1½c. slate-violet and salmon (1.6.71)	17·00	22·00
226	–	2c. deep bluish green and lemon (11.70)	5·00	40
224/6 Set of 3			21·00	22·00

1970 (24 Aug). 150th Anniv of Bible Society of South Africa. As Nos. 301/2 of South Africa, but inscr "SWA".

228		2½c. multicoloured	75	10
229		12½c. gold, black and blue	3·50	4·50

No. 228 has a phosphor frame, probably added in error.

A mint example of No. 229 exists with a second, blind, impression of the die-stamped features.

POSTAGE DUE STAMPS

At the outset of the campaign in South West Africa, Transvaal postage due stamps were in general use in South Africa, before being replaced by South Africa Nos. D1/7.

Postage Due stamps of TRANSVAAL cancelled with South West Africa postmarks (various types).

1907 (Nos. D1/7).
ZD1	½d. black and blue green	22·00
ZD3	2d. brown orange	4·00
ZD5	5d. black and violet	40·00
ZD6	6d. black and red-brown	50·00
ZD7	1s. scarlet and black	70·00

Postage due stamps of SOUTH AFRICA cancelled with South West Africa postmarks (various types).

1914-22 (Nos. D1/7).
ZD8	½d. black and green	22·00
ZD9	1d. black and scarlet	4·00
ZD10	2d. black and violet	5·00
ZD11	3d. black and bright blue	28·00
ZD12	5d. black and sepia	£125
ZD14	1s. red and black	£400

PRICES for Nos. D1/39 are for unused horizontal pairs, used horizontal pairs and used singles.

1923 (1 Jan–July). Optd with T **1** and **2** alternately.

(a) Setting I (14 mm between lines of overprint)

(i) On Nos. D5/6 of Transvaal

			Un pair	Us pair	Us single
D1	5d. black and violet		4·00	55·00	11·00
	a. "Wes" for "West" (R. 8/6, 10/2 left pane)		£200		
	b. "Afrika" without stop (R. 6/1)		£140		
D2	6d. black and red-brown		17·00	50·00	11·00
	a. "Wes" for "West" (R. 10/2)		£500		
	b. "Afrika" without stop (R. 6/1, 7/2)		£275		
	c. 12 mm between lines of opt (R. 1/1)		£325		

(ii) On Nos. D3/4 and D6 of South Africa (De La Rue printing)
D3	2d. black and violet		50·00	55·00	10·00
	a. "Wes" for "West" (R. 10/2)		£350	£450	
	b. "Afrika" without stop (R. 6/1, 7/2)		£300		
D4	3d. black and blue		21·00	55·00	10·00
	a. "Wes" for "West" (R. 8/6, 10/2)		£200		
	b. "Afrika" without stop (R. 9/1)		£350		
D5	6d. black and slate (20.4)		50·00	70·00	13·00
	a. "Wes" for "West" (R. 8/6)		£350		

(iii) On Nos. D9/10, D11 and D14 of South Africa (Pretoria printings)
D6	½d. black and green (P 14)		6·00	32·00	6·00
	a. Opt inverted		£600		
	b. Opt double		£1500	£1700	
	c. "Wes" for "West" (R. 10/2)		£160		
	d. "Afrika" without stop (R. 6/1, 7/2)		£130		
D7	1d. black and rose (roul)		7·00	32·00	6·00
	a. "Wes" for "West" (R. 10/2)		£150	£350	
	b. "Afrika" without stop (R. 6/1)		£150		
	c. Imperf between (horiz pair)		£1800		
D8	1½d. black and yellow-brown (roul)		1·25	14·00	2·75
	a. "Wes" for "West" (R. 8/6, 10/2)		£130		
	b. "Afrika" without stop (R. 6/1)		£110		
D9	2d. black and violet (P 14) (21.6)		4·75	28·00	5·00
	a. "Wes" for "West" (R. 8/6)		£150		
	b. "Afrika" without stop (R. 6/1)		£180		

Nos. D1/9 were initially overprinted as separate panes of 60, but some values were later done as double panes of 120.

A variety of Nos. D1, D4/5 and D9 with 15 mm between the lines of overprint occurs on four positions in each pane from some printings.

(b) Setting II (10 mm between lines of overprint)

(i) On No. D5 of Transvaal
D10	5d. black and violet (20.4)		55·00	£200

(ii) On Nos. D3/4 of South Africa (De La Rue printing)
D11	2d. black and violet (20.4)		19·00	55·00	9·50
	a. "Afrika" without stop (R. 6/1)		£300		
D12	3d. black and blue (20.4)		7·50	29·00	5·50
	a. "Afrika" without stop (R. 6/1)		£130		

(iii) On No. D9 of South Africa (Pretoria printing). Roul.
D13	1d. black and rose (7.23)	£22000	—	£1800

1923 (30 July)–**26**. Optd as T **3** ("Zuidwest" in one word without hyphen) and **4**.

(a) Setting III ("South West" 14 mm long, "Zuidwest" 11 mm long and 14 mm between lines of overprint)

(i) On No. D6 of Transvaal
D14	6d. black and red-brown		21·00	90·00	20·00

(ii) On Nos. D9 and D11/12 of South Africa (Pretoria printing).
D15	½d. black and green (P 14)		20·00	45·00	6·50
D16	1d. black and rose (roul)		13·00	45·00	6·50
D17	1d. black and rose (P 14) (2.8.23)		42·00	45·00	6·50

(b) Setting IV ("South West" 16 mm long, "Zuidwest" 12 mm long and 14 mm between lines of overprint)

(i) On No. D5 of Transvaal
D17a	5d. black and violet (1.7.24)		£950	£1500

(ii) On Nos. D11/12 and D16 of South Africa (Pretoria printing). P 14
D18	½d. black and green (1.7.24)		7·50	38·00	5·50
D19	1d. black and rose (1.7.24)		10·00	30·00	5·50
D20	6d. black and slate (1.7.24)		2·25	42·00	9·00
	a. "Africa" without stop (R. 9/5)		£130	£325	

(c) Setting V (12 mm. between lines of overprint)

(i) On No. D5 of Transvaal
D21	5d. black and violet (6.8.24)		11·00	70·00	10·00

(ii) On No. D4 of South Africa (De La Rue printing)
D22	3d. black and blue (6.8.24)		16·00	55·00	11·00

(iii) On Nos. D11 and D13 of South Africa (Pretoria printing). P 14
D23	½d. black and green (6.8.24)		3·00	30·00	6·50
D24	1½d. black and yellow-brown (6.8.24)		6·00	50·00	8·00

(d) Setting VI (9½ mm between lines of overprint)

(i) On No. D5 of Transvaal
D25	5d. black and violet (7.9.24)		2·75	22·00	3·50
	a. "Africa" without stop (R. 9/5)		85·00		

(ii) On No. D4 of South Africa (De La Rue printing)
D26	3d. black and blue (3.2.26)		12·00	65·00	11·00

(iii) On Nos. D11/16 of South Africa (Pretoria printing). P 14
D27	½d. black and green (1.3.26)		15·00	35·00	7·50
D28	1d. black and rose (16.3.25)		2·00	12·00	1·60
	a. "Africa" without stop (R. 9/5 right pane)		85·00		
D29	1½d. black and yellow-brown (1.10.26)		4·50	40·00	8·00
	a. "Africa" without stop (R. 9/5 right pane)		95·00		
D30	2d. black and violet (7.9.24)		2·50	18·00	3·50
	a. "Africa" without stop (R. 9/5) right pane)		80·00		
D31	3d. black and blue (6.5.26)		4·50	19·00	3·75
	a. "Africa" without stop (R. 9/5) right pane)		90·00		
D32	6d. black and slate (1.10.26)		17·00	55·00	14·00
	a. "Africa" without stop (R. 9/5) right pane)		£180		
D27/32 *Set of 6*			40·00	£160	35·00

For Setting VI the overprint was applied to sheets of 120 (2 panes of 60) of the 1d., 3d. and 6d., and to individual panes of 60 for the other values. The two measurements of "South West", as detailed under No. 40, also occur on the postage dues. Nos. D25 and D31/2 show 16 mm long, No. 27 16½ mm and the other stamps can be found with either measurement. In addition to the complete panes the 16½ mm long "South West" also occurs on R. 2/4 in the 16 mm left pane for Nos. D28 and D30/2.

Suidwes	**South West**
Afrika.	**Africa.**
(D **1**)	(D **2**)

1927 (14 May–27 Sept). Optd as Types D **1** and D **2**, alternately, 12 mm between lines of overprint.

(a) On No. D5 of Transvaal
D33	5d. black and violet (27.9)		24·00	£100	23·00

(b) On Nos. D13/16 of South Africa (Pretoria printing). P 14
D34	1½d. black and yellow-brown		1·00	21·00	3·50
D35	2d. black and pale violet (27.9)		4·75	18·00	3·25
	a. Black and deep violet		9·00	18·00	3·50
D37	3d. black and blue (27.9)		16·00	50·00	11·00
D38	6d. black and slate (27.9)		14·00	40·00	8·50

(c) On No. D18 of South Africa (Pretoria printing). P 14
D39	1d. black and carmine		1·00	12·00	2·25
D33/9 *Set of 6*			55·00	£225	45·00

No. D33 was overprinted in panes of 60 and the remainder as complete sheets of 120.

Examples of all values can be found with very small or very faint stops from various positions in the sheet.

1928–29. Optd with T **10**.

(a) On Nos. D15/16 of South Africa
			Un single	Us single
D40	3d. black and blue		1·50	18·00
	a. Without stop after "A" (R. 3/6)		45·00	
D41	6d. black and slate		6·00	35·00
	a. Without stop after "A" (R. 3/6)		£150	

(b) On Nos. D17/21 of South Africa
D42	½d. black and green		50	10·00
D43	1d. black and carmine		50	3·25
	a. Without stop after "A" (R. 3/6)		40·00	
D44	2d. black and mauve		50	4·50
	a. Without stop after "A" (R. 3/6)		55·00	
D45	3d. black and blue		2·25	26·00
D46	6d. black and slate		1·50	26·00
	a. Without stop after "A" (R. 3/6)		60·00	£225
D42/6 *Set of 5*			4·75	60·00

D **3**	D **4**

(Litho B.W.)

1931 (23 Feb). Inscribed bilingually. W **9** of South Africa. P 12.
D47	D **3**	½d. black and green		1·00	7·50
D48		1d. black and scarlet		1·00	1·25
D49		2d. black and violet		1·00	2·75
D50		3d. black and blue		4·25	13·00
D51		6d. black and slate		13·00	25·00
D47/51 *Set of 5*				18·00	45·00

PRINTER. The following issues have been printed by the South African Government Printer, Pretoria.

1959 (18 May). Centre typo; frame roto. W **9** of South Africa. P 15×14.
D52	D **4**	1d. black and scarlet		1·50	15·00
D53		2d. black and reddish violet		1·50	15·00
D54		3d. black and blue		1·50	15·00
D52/4 *Set of 3*				4·00	40·00

1960 (1 Dec). As Nos. D52 and D54 but W **102** of South Africa.
D55	1d. black and scarlet		1·50	2·50
D56	3d. black and blue		1·50	3·00

1961 (14 Feb). As Nos. D52 etc, but whole stamp roto, and value in cents. W **102** of South Africa.
D57	1c. black and blue-green		70	3·25
D58	2c. black and scarlet		70	3·25
D59	4c. black and reddish violet		70	4·50
D60	5c. black and light blue		80	3·25
D61	6c. black and green		1·00	5·00
D62	10c. black and yellow		3·00	6·50
D57/62 *Set of 6*			6·00	23·00

OFFICIAL STAMPS

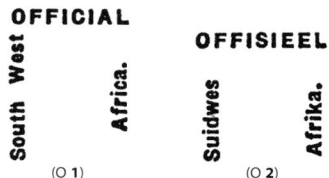

(O **1**)	(O **2**)

1927 (16 Mar). Nos. 30, 31, 6 and 32 of South Africa optd with Type O **1** on English stamp and O **2** on Afrikaans stamp alternately.

			Un pair	Us pair	Us single
O1	½d. black and green		£100	£225	30·00
O2	1d. black and carmine		£110	£225	30·00
O3	2d. dull purple		£275	£400	45·00
O4	6d. green and orange		£140	£250	30·00
O1/4 *Set of 4*			£550	£1000	£120

Overprints O1 and O2 were applied to the London printing of the ½d. and the Pretoria printings of the 1d. and 6d.

OFFICIAL	**OFFISIEEL**
S.W.A.	**S.W.A.**
(O **3**)	(O **4**)

1929 (May). Nos. 30, 31, 32 and 34 of South Africa optd with Type O **3** on English stamp and O **4** on Afrikaans stamp.
O5	½d. black and green		1·00	17·00	2·75
O6	1d. black and carmine		1·00	17·00	2·75
	w. Wmk inverted		£500		
O7	2d. grey and purple		1·50	24·00	3·50
	a. Pair, one stamp without stop after "OFFICIAL"		9·00	60·00	
	b. Pair, one stamp without stop after "OFFISIEEL"		9·00	60·00	
	c. Pair, comprising a and b		15·00	90·00	
	d. Split "d"		65·00		
O8	6d. green and orange		2·00	20·00	3·75
O5/8 *Set of 4*			5·00	70·00	11·50

Types O **3** and O **4** are normally spaced 17 mm between lines on all except the 2d. value, which is spaced 13 mm.

Except on No. O7, the words "OFFICIAL" or "OFFISIEEL" normally have no stops after them.

The setting of 60 (5×10) used for No. O11 (and subsequently, after re-arrangement, for No. O11) showed no stop after "OFFICIAL" at R. 1/1, 2/6, 6/6, 7/5, 8/6 and 9/5, and no stop after "OFFISIEEL" at R. 5/6, 7/6, 8/5, 9/6 and 10/5. No. O7c therefore occurs only at R. 7/5-6, 8/5-6 and 9/5-6.

(O **5**)	(O **6**)
OFFICIAL. **S.W.A.**	**OFFISIEEL.** **S.W.A.**
(O **7**)	(O **8**)

1929 (Aug). Nos. 30, 31 and 32 of South Africa optd with Types O **5** and O **6**, and No. 34 with Types O **7** and O **8**, languages to correspond.
O9	½d. black and green		75	16·00	2·75
O10	1d. black and carmine		1·00	17·00	2·75
O11	2d. grey and purple		1·00	18·00	3·25
	a. Pair, one stamp without stop after "OFFICIAL"		6·00	50·00	
	b. Pair, one stamp without stop after "OFFISIEEL"		6·00	50·00	
	c. Pair, comprising a and b		10·00	85·00	
	d. Split "d"		65·00		
O12	6d. green and orange		2·50	27·00	6·50
O9/12 *Set of 4*			4·75	70·00	13·50

Examples of Nos. O1/12 are known showing forged Windhoek postmarks dated "30 SEP 24" or "20 MAR 31".

OFFICIAL	**OFFISIEEL**
(O **9**)	(O **10**)

1931. English stamp optd with Type O **9** and Afrikaans stamp with Type O **10** in red.
O13	**12**	½d. black and emerald		10·00	24·00	3·75
O14	**13**	1d. indigo and scarlet		1·00	19·00	3·50
O15	**14**	2d. blue and brown		2·25	10·00	2·25
O16	**17**	6d. blue and brown		4·00	14·00	3·25
O13/16 *Set of 4*				15·00	60·00	11·50

OFFICIAL   OFFISIEEL
(O **11**)   (O **12**)

1938 (1 July). English stamp optd with Type O **11** and Afrikaans with Type O **12** in red.

O17	**27**	1½d. purple-brown	32·00	50·00	6·00
		a. "OFFICIAI" for			
		"OFFICIAL" (R. 10/2)	£250		

OFFICIAL   OFFISIEEL
(O **13**)   (O **14**)

1945–50. English stamp optd with Type O **13**, and Afrikaans stamp with Type O **14** in red.

O18	**12**	½d. black and emerald	13·00	38·00	5·00
O19	**13**	1d. indigo and scarlet			
		(1950)	17·00	22·00	3·25
		a. Opt double	£700		
O20	**27**	1½d. purple-brown	35·00	55·00	7·00
O21	**14**	2d. blue and brown			
		(1947?)	£700	£850	£100
O22	**17**	6d. blue and brown	25·00	70·00	8·00
O18/20, O22 Set of 4			80·00	£170	21·00

OFFICIAL   OFFISIEEL
(O **15**)   (O **16**)

1951 (16 Nov)–**52.** English stamp optd with Type O **15** and Afrikaans stamp with Type O **16**, in red.

O23	**12**	½d. black and emerald			
		(1952)	18·00	24·00	4·50
O24	**13**	1d. indigo and scarlet	5·00	26·00	3·00
		a. Opts transposed	£100	£250	
O25	**27**	1½d. purple-brown	30·00	32·00	5·00
		a. Opts transposed	75·00	95·00	
O26	**14**	2d. blue and brown	4·75	32·00	4·00
		a. Opts transposed	75·00	£250	
O27	**17**	6d. blue and brown	2·75	55·00	7·50
		a. Opts transposed	29·00	£170	
O23/7 Set of 5			55·00	£150	21·00

The above errors refer to stamps with the English overprint on Afrikaans stamp and *vice versa.*

The transposed overprint varieties occur on the lower five rows of the right pane from the first printing of Nos. O24/27 and on alternate horizontal rows of both panes from the second printing (Nos. O25 and O27 only).

The use of official stamps ceased in January 1955.

Sudan

ANGLO-EGYPTIAN CONDOMINIUM

An Egyptian post office was opened at Suakin in 1867 and the stamps of Egypt, including postage dues and the official (No. O64). were used in the Sudan until replaced by the overprinted "SOUDAN" issue of 1897. Cancellations have been identified from eleven post offices, using the following postmark types:

A   B

C   D

E   F

G   H

I   J

K

L

BERBER (spelt BARBAR). *Open 1 October 1873 to 20 May 1884. Postmark type G.*

DABROUSSA. *Open 1891 onwards. Postmark as type J but with 11 bars in arcs.*

DONGOLA. *Open 1 October 1873 to 13 June 1885 and 1896 onwards. Postmark types F, G, K, L.*

GEDAREF. *Open August 1878 to April 1884. Postmark type H.*

KASSALA. *Open 15 May 1875 to 30 July 1885. Postmark type G.*

KHARTOUM. *Open 1 October 1873 to 14 December 1885. Postmark types E (spelt KARTUM), G (spelt HARTUM), I (with or without line of Arabic above date).*

KORTI. *Open January to March 1885 and 1897. Postmark type K.*

SUAKIN. *Open November 1867 onwards. Postmark types A, B, C (spelt SUAKIM), D (spelt SUAKIM and also with year replaced by concentric arcs), I (spelt SOUAKIN), J (spelt SAWAKIN, number of bars differs).*

TANI. *Open 1885. Postmark type K.*

TOKAR. *Open 1891 onwards. Postmark type J (7 bars in arcs).*

WADI HALFA. *Open 1 October 1873 onwards. Postmark types F (spelt WADI HALFE), G (spelt WADI HALFE), I, J (number of bars differs).*

WADI HALFA CAMP. *Open 1896 onwards. Postmark type I.*

Official records also list post offices at the following locations, but no genuine postal markings from them have yet been reported: Chaka, Dara, Debeira, El Abiad, El Fasher, El Kalabat, Faras, Fashoda, Fazogl, Ishkeit, Kalkal, Karkok, Mesellemia, Sara, Sennar and Taoufikia (not to be confused with the town of the same name in Egypt).

M

The post office at Kassala was operated by Italy from 1894 until 1896, using stamps of Eritrea cancelled with postmark type M.

From the last years of the 19th-century that part of Sudan lying south of the 5 degree North latitude line was administered by Uganda (the area to the east of the Nile) (until 1912) or by Belgium (the area to the west of the Nile, known as the Lado Enclave) (until 1910).

Stamps of Uganda or East Africa and Uganda were used at Gondokoro and Nimuli between 1901 and 1911, usually cancelled with circular date stamps or, probably in transit at Khartoum, by a lozenge-shaped grid of 18×17 dots.

Stamps of Belgian Congo were used from the Lado Enclave between 1897 and 1910, as were those of Uganda (1901–10) and Sudan (1902–10), although no local postmarks were supplied, examples being initially cancelled in manuscript.

Stamps of Sudan were used at Gambeila (Ethiopia) between 1910 and 10 June 1940 and from 22 March 1941 until 15 October 1956. Sudan stamps were also used at Sabderat (Eritrea) between March 1910 and 1940.

PRICES FOR STAMPS ON COVER TO 1945	
Nos. 1/9	*from* × 20
Nos. 10/17	*from* × 6
Nos. 18/29	*from* × 5
Nos. 30/95	*from* × 2
Nos. D1/11	*from* × 30
Nos. O1/3	*from* × 10
No. O4	*from* × 15
Nos. O5/10	*from* × 50
No. O11	*from* × 10
Nos. O12/31	*from* × 15
Nos. O32/42	*from* × 10
No. A1	*from* × 20
Nos. A2/5	—
Nos. A6/10	*from* × 50
Nos. A11	*from* × 15
Nos. A12/13	—
Nos. A14	*from* × 15
Nos. A15/16	—
Nos. A17/22	*from* × 20
Nos. A23/6	—
Nos. A27/8	*from* × 10

السودان
SOUDAN
(1)

1897 (1 Mar). Nos. 54*b*, 55, 56*a*, 58/*a*, 59*a*, 61*a*, 63 and 64 of Egypt optd as T **1** by Govt Ptg Wks, Bûlaq, Cairo.

1	1m. pale brown	4·50	2·00
	a. Opt inverted	£225	
	b. Opt omitted (in vert pair with normal)	£1500	
	c. Deep brown	4·25	2·50
	w. Wmk inverted		
3	2m. green	1·25	1·75
4	3m. orange-yellow	1·40	1·50
5	5m. rose-carmine	2·00	70
	a. Opt inverted	£250	£300
	b. Opt omitted (in vert pair with normal)	£1600	
6	1p. ultramarine	7·00	2·00
7	2p. orange-brown	80·00	16·00
8	5p. slate	80·00	24·00
	a. Opt double	£6000	
	b. Opt omitted (in vert pair with normal)	£6000	
9	10p. mauve	50·00	60·00
1/9 Set of 8		£200	£100

Numerous forgeries exist including some which show the characteristics of the varieties mentioned below.

There are six varieties of the overprint on each value. Vertical strips of six showing them are worth a premium.

Four settings of the overprint were previously recognised by specialists, but one of these is now regarded as an unauthorised reprint from the original type. Here reprints can only be detected when in multiples. The 2pi. with inverted watermark only exists with this unauthorised overprint so it is not listed.

In some printings the large dot is omitted from the left-hand Arabic character on one stamp in the pane of 60.

Only two examples, one unused and the other used (in the Royal Collection), are known of No. 8a. In both instances one impression is partially albino.

PRINTERS. All stamps of Sudan were printed by De La Rue & Co, Ltd, London, *except where otherwise stated.*

(Currency. 10 milliemes = 1 piastre. 100 piastres = £1 Sudanese)

2 Arab Postman

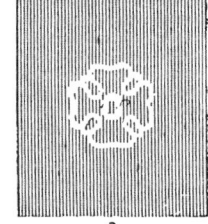

3

(Des E. A. Stanton. Typo)

1898 (1 Mar). W **3**. P 14.

10	**2**	1m. brown and pink	1·00	3·00
11		2m. green and brown	2·25	2·75
12		3m. mauve and green	2·25	2·25
13		5m. carmine and black	2·00	1·50
14		1p. blue and brown	21·00	2·75
15		2p. black and blue	50·00	3·50
16		5p. brown and green	50·00	17·00
17		10p. black and mauve	42·00	2·25
10/17 *Set of 8*			£150	32·00

4

5 Milliemes

(5)

Damaged stereos (R. 2/5 and 2/6)

1902–21. Ordinary paper. W **4**. P 14.

18	**2**	1m. brown and carmine (5.05)	1·25	65
19		2m. green and brown (11.02)	1·75	10
20		3m. mauve and green (3.03)	2·25	25
21		4m. blue and bistre (20.1.07)	1·50	2·50
22		4m. vermilion and brown (10.07)	1·50	75
23		5m. scarlet and black (12.03)	2·00	10
		w. Wmk inverted	—	£200
24		1p. blue and brown (12.03)	2·50	30
25		2p. black and blue (2.08)	50·00	1·25
26		2p. purple and orange-yellow (chalk-surfaced paper) (22.12.21)	13·00	14·00
27		5p. brown and green (2.08)	35·00	30
		a. Chalk-surfaced paper	50·00	4·00
28		10p. black and mauve (2.11)	29·00	4·25
		a. Chalk-surfaced paper	50·00	15·00
18/28 *Set of 11*			£120	22·00

1903 (Sept). No. 16 surch at Khartoum with T **5**, in blocks of 30.

29	**2**	5m. on 5 pi. brown and green	6·50	9·50
		a. Surch inverted	£325	£275
		b. Damaged stereos horiz (pair)	£180	

The stereos on R. 2/5 and 2/6 were damaged towards the end of production of No. 29. They were replaced by new stereos showing a gap between the "m" and second "e" of "Milliemes" (R. 2/5) and a narrower than usual gap between "5" and "M" (R. 2/6).

6

7

1921–23. Chalk-surfaced paper. Typo. W **4**. P 14.

30	**6**	1m. black and orange (4.2.22)	80	5·50
31		2m. yellow-orange and chocolate (1922)	9·00	11·00
		a. Yellow and chocolate (1923)	12·00	16·00
32		3m. mauve and green (25.1.22)	2·50	13·00
33		4m. green and chocolate (21.3.22)	10·00	15·00
34		5m. olive-brown and black (4.2.22)	2·25	10
35		10m. carmine and black (1922)	8·50	10
36		15m. bright blue and chestnut (14.12.21)	5·50	1·00
30/36 *Set of 7*			35·00	40·00

1927–41. Chalk-surfaced paper. W **7**. P 14.

37	**6**	1m. black and orange	70	40
38		a. Ordinary paper (1941)	70	1·75
38		2m. orange and chocolate	75	10
		aw. Wmk inverted	†	£300
		b. Ordinary paper (1941)	1·50	10
39		3m. mauve and green	70	10
		a. Ordinary paper (1941)	2·75	30
40		4m. green and chocolate	60	10
		a. Ordinary paper (1941)	4·00	1·00
		aw. Wmk inverted	80·00	90·00
41		5m. olive-brown and black	60	10
		a. Ordinary paper (1941)	4·00	10
42		10m. carmine and black	1·50	10
		a. Ordinary paper (1941)	9·00	10
43		15m. bright blue and chestnut	4·00	10
		aw. Wmk inverted	†	£300
		b. Ordinary paper (1941)	6·00	10
44	**2**	2p. purple and orange-yellow	4·50	10
		a. Ordinary paper (1941)	12·00	10
44b		3p. red-brown and blue (1.1.40)	11·00	10
		ba. Ordinary paper (1941)	21·00	10
44c		4p. ultramarine and black (2.11.36)	4·25	10
45		5p. chestnut and green	1·25	10
		a. Ordinary paper (1941)	16·00	3·75
45b		6p. greenish blue and black (2.11.36)	19·00	3·00
		ba. Ordinary paper (1941)	65·00	6·50
45c		8p. emerald and black (2.11.36)	19·00	7·50
		ca. Ordinary paper (1941)	75·00	11·00
46		10p. black and reddish purple	9·50	50
		a. Ordinary paper. Black and bright mauve (1941)	18·00	70
46b		20p. pale blue and blue (17.10.35)	15·00	60
		ba. Ordinary paper (1941)	15·00	20
37/46b *Set of 15*			80·00	10·50

The ordinary paper of this issue is thick, smooth and opaque and was a wartime substitute for chalk-surfaced paper.

For similar stamps, but with different Arabic inscriptions, see Nos. 96/111.

AIR MAIL (8) **AIR MAIL** (9) **AIR** Extended foot to "R" (R. 5/12)

1931 (15 Feb–Mar). Air. Nos. 41/2 and 44 optd with T **8** or **9** (2p.).

47	**6**	5m. olive-brown and black (3.31)	35	70
48		10m. carmine and black	1·00	17·00
49	**2**	2p. purple and orange-yellow	85	7·50
		a. Extended foot to "R"	30·00	
47/9 *Set of 3*			2·00	23·00

2½ **2⅛**

AIR MAIL

10 Statue of Gen. Gordon (11)

1931 (1 Sept)–**37**. Air. Recess. W **7** (sideways*). P 14.

49b	**10**	3m. green and sepia (1.1.33)	3·50	6·50
50		5m. black and orange	1·00	10
51		10m. black and carmine	1·00	20
52		15m. red-brown and sepia	40	10
		aw. Wmk sideways inverted (top of G to right)	£275	£250
		b. Perf 11½×12½ (1937)	4·50	10
		bx. Wmk reversed	†	£375
		by. Wmk sideways inverted (top of G to right) and reversed	£425	
53		2p. black and orange	50	10
		ab. Frame printed double, one albino	£850	
		ax. Wmk reversed	£300	
		ay. Wmk sideways inverted (top of G to right) and reversed	£300	
		b. Perf 11½×12½ (1937)	4·50	23·00
53c		2½p. magenta and blue (1.1.33)	4·75	10
		cw. Wmk sideways inverted (top of G to right)	—	£375
		cy. Wmk sideways inverted (top of G to right) and reversed	£375	
		d. Perf 11½×12½ (1936)	5·00	10
		da. Aniline magenta and blue	13·00	3·50
		dx. Wmk reversed	£250	
		dy. Wmk sideways inverted (top of G to right) and reversed	£300	£325
54		3p. black and grey	60	15
		a. Perf 11½×12½ (1937)	1·00	35
55		3½p. black and violet	1·50	80
		a. Perf 11½×12½ (1937)	2·50	21·00
		ay. Wmk sideways inverted (top of G to right) and reversed	£325	£350
56		4½p. red-brown and grey	13·00	15·00
57		5p. black and ultramarine	1·00	30
		a. Perf 11½×12½ (1937)	3·75	35
57b		7½p. green and emerald (17.10.35)	9·50	7·50
		bx. Wmk reversed	£275	
		by. Wmk sideways inverted (top of G to right) and reversed	£275	£275
		c. Perf 11½×12½ (1937)	4·00	11·00
57d		10p. brown and greenish blue (10.35)	10·00	1·75
		e. Perf 11½×12½ (1937)	8·00	28·00
		ey. Wmk sideways inverted (top of G to right) and reversed	£325	
49b/57d *Set of 12* (P 14)			40·00	29·00
52b/7e *Set of 8* (P 11½×12½)			30·00	75·00

*The normal sideways watermark shows the top of the G pointing left *as seen from the back of the stamp.*

1932 (18 July). Air. No. 44 surch with T **11**.

58	**2**	2½p. on 2p. purple and orange-yellow	1·40	4·50

12 Gen. Gordon (after C. Ouless)

13 Gordon Memorial College, Khartoum

14 Gordon Memorial Service, Khartoum (after R. C. Woodville)

1935 (1 Jan). 50th Death Anniv of General Gordon, Recess. W **7**. P 14.

59	**12**	5m. green	35	10
60		10m. yellow-brown	85	25
61		13m. ultramarine	85	14·00
62		15m. scarlet	1·75	25
63	**13**	2p. blue	2·50	20
64		5p. orange-vermilion	2·50	1·25
65		10p. purple	9·50	9·50
66	**14**	20p. black	32·00	65·00
67		50p. red-brown	£100	£150
59/67 *Set of 9*			£130	£200

7½ PIASTRES ٧ ١/٢ قروش (15)

5 MILLIEMES ٥ مليمت (16)

1935. Air. Nos. 49b/51 and 56 surch as T **15** at Khartoum.

68	**10**	15m. on 10m. black and carmine (4.35)	40	10
		a. Surch double	£1000	£1400
69		2½p. on 3m. green and sepia (4.35)	85	3·25
		a. Second arabic letter from left missing	50·00	£110
		b. Small "½"	2·25	21·00
70		2½p. on 5m. black and green (4.35)	50	1·00
		a. Second Arabic letter from left missing	25·00	60·00
		b. Small "½"	1·25	2·50
		c. Surch inverted	£1000	£1400
		d. Ditto with variety a.	£30000	
		e. Ditto with variety b.	£4500	£6000
71		3p. on 4½p. red-brown and grey (4.35)	1·75	22·00
72		7½p. on 4½p. red-brown and grey (3.35)	6·50	55·00
73		10p. on 4½p. red-brown and grey (3.35)	6·50	55·00
68/73 *Set of 6*			15·00	£120

Nos. 69a and 70a occur on R. 10/4 of the sheet of 50; the small "½" variety occurs on R. 4/2, R. 6/2, R. 7/2, R. 8/1, R. 9/1, R. 9/2 and R. 10/1.

The 15m. on 10m. surcharged in red (*Price*, £375) and the 2½p. on 3m. and 2½p. on 5m. in green are from proof sheets; the latter two items being known cancelled (*Price*, £225 each, unused).

There were four proof sheets of the 7½p. on 4½p., two in red and two in black. The setting on these proof sheets showed three errors subsequently corrected before No. 72 was surcharged. 12 positions showed an Arabic "⅓" instead of "½", one an English "¼" for "½" and another one of the Arabic letters inverted. (*Price for red surcharge*, £375).

1938 (1 July). Air. Nos. 53d, 55, 57b and 57d surch as T **16** by De La Rue.

74	**10**	5m. on 2½p. magenta and blue (P 11½×12½)	3·50	10
		w. Wmk sideways inverted (top of G to right)	£250	£225
		x. Wmk reversed		
75		3p. on 3½p. black and violet (P 14)	48·00	60·00
		a. Perf 11½×12½	£750	£850
76		3p. on 7½p. green and emerald (P 14)	6·00	6·50
		ax. Wmk reversed		
		ay. Wmk sideways inverted (top of G to right) and reversed	£120	£140
		b. Perf 11½×12½	£750	£850
77		5p. on 10p. brown and greenish blue (P 14)	1·75	4·75
		ax. Wmk reversed	£225	
		b. Perf 11½×12½	£750	£850
74/7 *Set of 4*			55·00	65·00

A 5p. on 2½p., perf 11½×12½ exists either mint or cancelled from a trial printing (*Price £400 unused*).

5 Mills. ٥ مليم (17) Normal ("Malime")

"Malmime" (Left-hand pane R. 5/1) Short "mim" (Right-hand pane R. 3/1) Broken "lam" (Right-hand pane R. 6/2)

5 M

Inserted "5" (Bottom
right-hand pane R. 4/5)

1940 (25 Feb). No. 42 surch with T **17** by McCorquodale (Sudan) Ltd, Khartoum.

78	**6**	5m. on 10m. carmine and black........	2·00	2·00
		a. "Malmime".................................	65·00	85·00
		b. Two dots omitted (Right-hand pane R. 8/6)........	65·00	85·00
		c. Short "mim"..............................	65·00	85·00
		d. Broken "lam".............................	65·00	85·00
		e. Inserted "5"...............................	£190	

4½ Piastres

(18)

(19)

1940–41. Nos. 41 and 45c surch as T **18** or **19** at Khartoum.

79	**6**	4½p. on 5m. olive-brown and black (9.2.41)........	48·00	15·00
80	**2**	4½p. on 8p. emerald and black (12.12.40)........	42·00	9·00

20 Tuti Island, R. Nile, near Khartoum

21 Tuti Island, R. Nile near Khartoum

(Des Miss H. M. Hebbert. Litho Security Printing Press, Nasik, India)

1941 (25 Mar–10 Aug). P 14×13½ (T **20**) or P 13½×14 (T **21**).

81	**20**	1m. slate and orange (10.8)........	5·00	4·00
82		2m. orange and chocolate (10.8)........	5·00	6·50
83		3m. mauve and green (10.8)........	5·50	20
84		4m. green and chocolate (10.8)........	1·00	1·75
85		5m. olive-brown and black (10.8)........	50	10
86		10m. carmine and black (10.8)........	30·00	7·00
87		15m. bright blue and chestnut........	1·50	10
88	**21**	2p. purple and orange-yellow (10.8)........	7·50	60
89		3p. red-brown and blue........	1·25	10
90		4p. ultramarine and black........	6·50	10
91		5p. chestnut and green (10.8)........	11·00	16·00
92		6p. greenish blue and black (10.8)........	27·00	2·25
93		8p. emerald and black (10.8)........	30·00	2·25
94		10p. slate and purple (10.8)........	£120	2·00
95		20p. pale blue and blue (10.8)........	£100	50·00
81/95		Set of 15........	£325	80·00

22 | **23**

 (arrow)

1m.–15m. "nun" flaw (R. 2/3)

1948 (1 Jan–June). Arabic inscriptions below camel altered. Typo. Ordinary paper (8, 10, 20p.) or chalk-surfaced paper (others). W **7**. P 14.

96	**22**	1m. black and orange........	35	7·00
		a. "nun" flaw........	9·00	
97		2m. orange and chocolate........	80	6·00
		a. "nun" flaw........	17·00	
98		3m. mauve and green........	30	9·50
		a. "nun" flaw........	9·00	35·00
99		4m. deep green and chocolate........	50	4·00
		a. "nun" flaw........	22·00	
100		5m. olive-brown and black........	12·00	3·00
		a. "nun" flaw........	30·00	15·00
		w. Wmk inverted........	80·00	
101		10m. rose-red and black........	5·50	10
		a. Centre inverted........	† £40000	
		b. "nun" flaw........	21·00	5·50
102		15m. ultramarine and chestnut........	5·00	20
		a. "nun" flaw........	21·00	6·50
103	**23**	2p. purple and orange-yellow........	12·00	5·00
104		3p. red-brown and deep blue........	7·50	30
105		4p. ultramarine and black........	4·00	1·75
106		5p. brown-orange and deep green........	4·00	7·00
107		6p. greenish blue and black........	4·50	3·50
108		8p. bluish green and black........	4·50	6·00
109		10p. black and mauve........	16·00	10·00
		a. Chalk-surfaced paper (6.48)........	55·00	6·00
110		20p. pale blue and deep blue........	4·50	50
		a. Perf 13. Chalk-surfaced paper (6.48)........	40·00	£250
111		50p. carmine and ultramarine........	8·00	3·00
96/111		Set of 16........	75·00	55·00

A single used example is known of No. 101a.
The 2m. and 4m. are known without the "nun" flaw on R. 2/3.
For similar stamps, but with different Arabic inscriptions, see Nos. 37/46b.

24 | **25**

1948 (1 Oct). Golden Jubilee of "Camel Postman" design. Chalk-surfaced paper. Typo. W **7**. P 13.

112	**24**	2p. black and light blue........	50	10

1948 (23 Dec). Opening of Legislative Assembly, Chalk-surfaced paper. Typo. W **7**. P 13.

113	**25**	10m. rose-red and black........	1·25	10
114		5p. brown-orange and deep green........	1·75	3·00

26 Blue Nile Bridge, Khartoum

27 Kassala Jebel

28 Sagia (water wheel)

29 Port Sudan

30 Gordon Memorial College

31 Gordon Pasha (Nile mail boat)

32 Suakin

33 GPO, Khartoum

(Des Col. W. L. Atkinson (2½p., 6p.), G. R. Wilson (3p.), others from photographs. Recess)

1950 (1 July). Air. T **26/33**. W **7**. P 12.

115	**26**	2p. black and blue-green........	6·50	1·50
116	**27**	2½p. light blue and red-orange........	1·25	2·00
117	**28**	3p. reddish purple and blue........	4·50	1·25
118	**29**	3½p. purple-brown and yellow-brown........	6·50	6·50
119	**30**	4p. brown and light blue........	1·75	3·50
120	**31**	4½p. blue and ultramarine........	3·50	7·00
		a. Black and steel-blue........	23·00	11·00
121	**32**	6p. black and carmine........	4·75	4·00
122	**33**	20p. black and purple........	3·00	8·00
115/122		Set of 8........	28·00	30·00

34 Ibex

35 Whale-headed stork

36 Giraffe

37 Baggara girl

38 Shilluk warrior

39 Hadendowa

40 Policeman

41 Cotton Picking

42 Ambatch reed canoe

43 Nuba wrestlers

44 Weaving | **45** Saluka farming

46 Gum tapping | **47** Darfur chief

48 Stack Laboratory | **49** Nile Lechwe

50 Camel postman

(Des Col. W. L. Atkinson (1m., 2m., 4m., 5m., 10m., 3p., 3½p., 20p.), Col. E. A. Stanton (50p.) others from photographs. Typo)

1951 (1 Sept)–**61**. Designs as T **34/50**. Chalk-surfaced paper. W **7**. P 14 (millieme values) or 13 (piastre values).

123	**34**	1m. black and orange........	4·00	1·50
124	**35**	2m. black and bright blue........	4·00	1·50
125	**36**	3m. black and green........	13·00	7·50
126	**37**	4m. black and yellow-green........	3·50	7·50
127	**38**	5m. black and purple........	2·25	10
		a. Black and reddish purple (8.6.59)........	7·00	70
128	**39**	10m. black and pale blue........	30	10
129	**40**	15m. black and chestnut........	11·00	10
		a. Black and brown-orange (1961*)........	7·00	10
130	**41**	2p. deep blue and pale blue........	30	10
		a. Deep blue and very pale blue (9.58*)........	7·00	1·25
131	**42**	3p. brown and dull ultramarine........	25·00	10
		a. Brown and deep blue (11.58*)........	14·00	2·75
132	**43**	3½p. bright green and red-brown (11.61*)........	3·00	10
		a. Light emerald and red-brown (11.61*)........	6·00	10
133	**44**	4p. ultramarine and black........	7·50	25
		a. Deep blue and black (7.59*)........	8·50	10
134	**45**	5p. orange-brown and yellow-green........	3·75	10
135	**46**	6p. blue and black........	9·00	3·50
		a. Deep blue and black (8.61*)........	16·00	7·00
136	**47**	8p. blue and brown........	14·00	5·00
		a. Deep blue and brown (5.60*)........	17·00	9·50
137	**48**	10p. black and green........	1·50	1·50
138	**49**	20p. blue-green and black........	12·00	3·75
139	**50**	50p. carmine and black........	20·00	5·50
123/39		Set of 17........	£100	35·00

*Earliest known postmark date.

SELF-GOVERNMENT

51 Camel Postman

1954 (9 Jan). Self-Government. Chalk-surfaced paper. Typo. W **7**. P 13.

140	**51**	15m. orange-brown and bright green........	50	1·25
141		3p. blue and indigo........	75	5·00
142		5p. black and reddish purple........	50	2·50
140/2		Set of 3........	1·60	8·00

Stamps as Type **51**, but dated "1953" were released in error at the Sudan Agency in London. They had no postal validity (Price per set £18 un).

Sudan became an independent republic on 1 January 1956. Later issues will be found in the Stanley Gibbons *North East Africa catalogue*.

STAMP BOOKLETS

Nos. SB1/3 have one cover inscribed in English and one in Arabic. Listings are provided for booklets believed to have been issued, with prices quoted for those known to still exist.

1912 (Dec). Black on pink cover, size 74×29 mm. Stapled.
SB1   100m. booklet containing 20×5m. (No. 23) in pairs.   £900

1924. Black on pink cover, size 45×50 mm. Stapled.
SB2   105m. booklet containing 20×5m. (No. 34) in blocks of 4........

1930. Black on pink cover, size 45×50 mm. Stapled.
SB3   100m. booklet containing 20×5m. (No. 41) in
     blocks of 4 .... £1800
Some supplies of No. SB3 included a page of air mail labels.

POSTAGE DUE STAMPS

1897 (1 Mar). Type D **24** of Egypt, optd with T **1** at Būlaq.
D1	2m. green	1·75	5·00
	a. Opt omitted (in horiz pair with normal)	£3250	
D2	4m. maroon	1·75	5·00
D3	1p. ultramarine	10·00	3·50
	a. Bisected (2m.) (on cover)	†	—
D4	2p. orange	10·00	7·00
	a. Bisected (1p.) (on cover)	†	£1400
D1/4 Set of 4		21·00	18·00

In some printings the large dot is omitted from the left-hand Arabic character on one stamp in the pane.
No. D1 has been recorded used as a bisect.

D **1** Gunboat *Zafir*   D **2**

1901 (1 Jan)–**26.** Typo. Ordinary paper. W **4** (sideways). P 14.
D5	D **1**	2m. black and brown	55	60
		a. Wmk upright (1912)	£225	75·00
		b. Chalk-surfaced paper (6.24*)	3·00	15·00
D6		4m. brown and green	2·00	90
		a. Chalk-surfaced paper (9.26*)	12·00	15·00
D7		10m. green and mauve	9·00	4·00
		a. Wmk upright (1912)	£130	60·00
		b. Chalk-surfaced paper (6.24*)	18·00	17·00
D8		20m. ultramarine and carmine	3·25	3·50
D5/8 Set of 4			13·50	8·00

*Dates quoted for the chalk-surfaced paper printings are those of the earliest recorded postal use. These printings were despatched to the Sudan in March 1922 (10m.) or September 1922 (others).
The 4m. is known bisected at Khartoum or Omdurman in November/December 1901 and the 20m. at El Obeid in 1904–05.

1927–30. Chalk-surfaced paper. W **7.** P 14.
D9	D **1**	2m. black and green (1930)	2·50	2·50
D10		4m. brown and green	1·00	80
D11		10m. green and mauve	1·75	1·25
		a. Ordinary paper	22·00	8·00
D9/11 Set of 3			4·75	4·00

1948 (1 Jan). Arabic inscriptions altered. Chalk-surfaced paper. Typo. W **7.** P 14.
D12	D **2**	2m. black and brown-orange	4·75	50·00
D13		4m. brown and green	11·00	55·00
D14		10m. green and mauve	20·00	21·00
D15		20m. ultramarine and carmine	20·00	40·00
D12/15 Set of 4			50·00	£150

The 10 and 20m. were reissued in 1979 on Sudan Arms watermarked paper.

OFFICIAL STAMPS

(O **1**)

1900 (8 Feb). 5 mils of 1897 punctured as Type O **1** by hand.
O1	5m. rose-carmine	60·00	16·00

1901 (Jan). 1m. wmk Quatrefoil, punctured as Type O **1.**
O2	1m. brown and pink	55·00	30·00

Due to the method of production, Nos. O1/2 are found with the punctured "SG" upright, inverted, reversed or inverted and reversed.

O.S.G.S, (O **1a**) ("On Sudan Government Service")
O.S.G.S. (O **2**) ("On Sudan Government Service")

O.S.G.S.
Malformed "O" (lower pane, R. 1/7)

O.S.G.S.
Accent over "G" (upper pane, R. 4/12)

1902. No. 10 optd at Khartoum as Type O **1a** in blocks of 30 stamps.
O3	**2**	1m. brown and pink	3·50	15·00
		a. Oval "O" (No. 19)	40·00	£110
		b. Round stops. (Nos. 25 to 30)	7·50	45·00
		c. Opt inverted	£350	£475
		d. Ditto and oval "O"	£4250	£5000
		e. Ditto and round stops	£900	£1200
		f. Opt double	£500	
		g. Ditto and round stops	£1500	
		h. Ditto and oval "O"	£5000	

1903–12. T **2** optd as Type O **2,** by D.L.R. in sheets of 120 stamps.
*(i) W **3** (Quatrefoil)*
O4		10p. black and mauve (3.06)	23·00	26·00
		a. Malformed "O"	£150	

*(ii) W **4** (Mult Star and Crescent)*
O5		1m. brown and carmine (9.04)	50	10
		a. Opt double		
		b. Malformed "O"	20·00	10·00
O6		3m. mauve and green (2.04)	2·50	15
		a. Opt double	£850	£850
		b. Malformed "O"	45·00	12·00

O7		5m. scarlet and black (1.1.03)	2·50	10
		a. Malformed "O"	45·00	10·00
		b. Accent over "G"		
O8		1p. blue and brown (1.1.03)	13·00	10
		a. Malformed "O"	£100	10·00
		b. Accent over "G"		
O9		2p. black and blue (1.1.03)	45·00	20
		a. Malformed "O"	£250	14·00
		b. Accent over "G"		
O10		5p. brown and green (1.1.03)	3·00	30
		a. Malformed "O"	60·00	15·00
		b. Accent over "G"		
O11		10p. black and mauve (9.12)	4·00	70·00
		a. Malformed "O"	70·00	
O4/11 Set of 8			85·00	85·00

(O **2a**)   (O **2b**)

1913 (1 Jan)–**22.** Nos. 18/20 and 23/8 punctured as Type O **2a** by machine.
O12	**2**	1m. brown and carmine	21·00	25
O13		2m. green and brown (1915)	18·00	7·50
O14		3m. mauve and green	30·00	70
O15		5m. scarlet and black	12·00	15
O16		1p. blue and brown	17·00	35
O17		2p. black and blue	42·00	65
O18		2p. purple and orange-yellow (chalk-surfaced paper) (1922)	15·00	14·00
O19		5p. brown and green	60·00	3·25
		a. Chalk-surfaced paper	70·00	9·00
O20		10p. black and mauve (1914)	80·00	50·00
		a. Chalk-surfaced paper	90·00	50·00
O12/20 Set of 9			£250	65·00

1922. Nos. 32/5 punctured as Type O **2b** by machine.
O21	**6**	3m. mauve and green	25·00	14·00
O22		4m. green and chocolate	40·00	9·00
O23		5m. olive-brown and black	10·00	3·00
O24		10m. carmine and black	12·00	3·00
O21/4 Set of 4			80·00	26·00

1927–30. Nos. 39/42 punctured as Type O **2b** and Nos. 44, 45 and 46 as Type O **2a.**
O25	**6**	3m. mauve and green (1928)	32·00	5·50
O26		4m. green and chocolate (1930)	90·00	50·00
O27		5m. olive-brown and black	13·00	10
O28		10m. carmine and black	35·00	35
O29	**2**	2p. purple and orange-yellow	42·00	1·00
O30		5p. chestnut and green	32·00	3·50
O31		10p. black and reddish purple	65·00	10·00
O25/31 Set of 7			£275	60·00

The use of Nos. O25/31 on internal official mail ceased in 1932, but they continued to be required for official mail to foreign destinations until replaced by Nos. O32/46 in 1936.

S.G. (O **3**)   **S.G.** (O **4**)   **S.G.** (O **4a**)

1936 (19 Sept)–**46.** Nos. 37a, 38b, 39/43 optd with Type O **3,** and 44, 44ba, 44c, 45, 45ba, 45ca, 46 and 46ba with Type O **4.** W **7.** P 14.
O32	**6**	1m. black and orange (22.11.46)	2·50	17·00
		a. Opt double	†	£225
O33		2m. orange and chocolate (ordinary paper) (4.45)	6·00	9·00
		a. Chalk-surfaced paper	£120	70·00
O34		3m. mauve and green (chalk-surfaced paper) (1.37)	5·50	10
O35		4m. green and chocolate (chalk-surfaced paper)	11·00	5·00
		a. Ordinary paper		
O36		5m. olive-brown and black (chalk-surfaced paper) (3.40)	8·00	10
		a. Ordinary paper	32·00	40
O37		10m. carmine and black (chalk-surfaced paper) (6.46)	1·75	10
O38		15m. bright blue and chestnut (chalk-surfaced paper) (21.6.37)	16·00	30
		a. Ordinary paper	85·00	4·50
O39	**2**	2p. purple and orange-yellow (chalk-surfaced paper) (4.37)	20·00	10
		a. Ordinary paper	50·00	10
O39b		3p. red-brown and blue (4.46)	7·50	2·75
O39c		4p. ultramarine and black (chalk-surfaced paper) (4.46)	55·00	9·00
		ca. Ordinary paper	85·00	4·50
O40		5p. chestnut and green (chalk-surfaced paper)	17·00	10
		a. Ordinary paper	£100	6·50
O40b		6p. greenish blue and black (4.46)	15·00	13·00
O40c		8p. emerald and black (4.46)	7·00	45·00
O41		10p. black and reddish purple (chalk-surfaced paper) (10.37)	65·00	24·00
		a. Ordinary paper. Black and bright mauve (1941)	65·00	10·00
O42		20p. pale blue and blue (6.46)	38·00	35·00
O32/42 Set of 15			£250	£130

1948 (1 Jan). Nos. 96/102 optd with Type O **3,** and 103/111 with Type O **4.**
O43	**22**	1m. black and orange	30	7·00
		a. "nun" flaw	9·00	
O44		2m. orange and chocolate	2·50	1·75
		a. "nun" flaw	20·00	
O45		3m. mauve and green	5·00	13·00
		a. "nun" flaw	25·00	
O46		4m. deep green and chocolate	4·25	8·00
		a. "nun" flaw	50·00	
O47		5m. olive-brown and black	4·00	10
		a. "nun" flaw	22·00	
O48		10m. rose-red and black	4·25	3·00
		a. "nun" flaw	22·00	
O49		15m. ultramarine and chestnut	4·50	10
		a. "nun" flaw	22·00	
O50	**23**	2p. purple and orange-yellow	4·50	10
O51		3p. red-brown and deep blue	4·50	10

O52		4p. ultramarine and black	5·00	40
		a. Perf 13 (optd Type O **4a**)	13·00	24·00
O53		5p. brown-orange and deep green	6·50	10
O54		6p. greenish blue and black	3·50	10
O55		8p. bluish green and black	3·50	9·00
O56		10p. black and mauve	8·00	30
O57		20p. pale blue and deep blue	6·50	1·75
O58		50p. carmine and ultramarine	70·00	60·00
O43/58 Set of 16			£120	90·00

1950 (1 July). Air. Nos. 115/22 optd with Type O **4a.**
O59	**26**	2p. blue and blue-green (R.)	16·00	4·50
O60	**27**	2½p. light blue and red-orange	1·50	1·75
O61	**28**	3p. reddish purple and blue	1·00	1·00
O62	**29**	3½p. purple-brown and yellow-brown	1·25	13·00
O63	**30**	4p. brown and light blue	1·00	11·00
O64	**31**	4½p. black and ultramarine (R.)	4·75	24·00
		a. Black and steel-blue	21·00	29·00
O65	**32**	6p. black and carmine (R.)	1·00	6·00
O66	**33**	20p. black and purple (R.)	4·50	12·00
O59/66 Set of 8			28·00	65·00

1951 (1 Sept)–**62?.** Nos. 123/9 optd with Type O **3,** and 130/9 with Type O **4a.**
O67	**34**	1m. black and orange (R.)	50	7·00
O68	**35**	2m. black and bright blue (R.)	50	3·50
O69	**36**	3m. black and green (R.)	14·00	23·00
O70	**37**	4m. black and yellow-green (R.)	10	5·50
O71	**38**	5m. black and purple (R.)	10	10
		a. Black and reddish purple		
O72	**39**	10m. black and pale blue (R.)	10	10
O73	**40**	15m. black and chestnut (R.)	1·00	10
		a. Black and brown-orange		
O74	**41**	2p. deep blue and pale blue	10	10
		a. Opt inverted	£1200	
		b. Deep blue and very pale blue (9.61*)	2·25	10
O75	**42**	3p. brown and dull ultramarine	35·00	10
		a. Brown and deep blue (8.60*)	35·00	3·25
O76	**43**	3½p. bright green and red-brown	30	10
		a. Light emerald and red-brown (1962?)	9·00	6·00
O77	**44**	4p. ultramarine and black	8·00	10
		a. Deep blue and black (1961)	8·50	10
O78	**45**	5p. orange-brown and yellow-green	40	10
		a. Deep blue and black (1962?)	16·00	11·00
O79	**46**	6p. blue and black	70	4·50
O80	**47**	8p. blue and brown	1·00	30
		a. Deep blue and brown (1962?)	12·00	6·00
O81	**48**	10p. black and green (R.)	70	10
O81a		10p. black and green (Blk.) (1958)	22·00	4·00
O82	**49**	20p. blue-green and black	1·50	30
		a. Opt inverted	†	£4500
O83	**50**	50p. carmine and black	6·00	1·50
O67/83 Set of 18			75·00	45·00

The 5, 10 and 15m. values were reissued between 1957 and 1960 with a thinner overprint with smaller stops.
*Earliest known postmark date.

ARMY SERVICE STAMPS

ARMY (A **1**)   **OFFICIAL ARMY** (A **2**)   **OFFICIAL Army Service** (A **3**)

1905 (1 Jan). T **2** optd at Khartoum as Types A **1** or A **2.** W **4** (Mult Star and Crescent).
(i) "ARMY" reading up
A1	1m. brown and carmine (A **1**)	11·00	4·00
	a. "I" for "1"	85·00	50·00
	b. Opt Type A **2**	65·00	32·00
	c. Pair. Types A **1** and A **2** se-tenant	£130	£180

(ii) Overprint horizontal
A2	1m. brown and carmine (A **1**)	£600	†
	a. "I" for "1"	£6500	†
	b. Opt Type A **2**	£4250	†

The horizontal overprint exists with either "ARMY" or "OFFICIAL" reading the right way up. It did not fit the stamps, resulting in misplacements where more than one whole overprint appears, or when the two words are transposed.

(iii) "ARMY" reading down
A3	1m. brown and carmine (A **1**)	£200	£100
	a. "I" for "1"	£1500	£1500
	b. Opt Type A **2**	£1300	£800

1905 (Nov). As No. A1, W **3** (Quatrefoil).
A4	1m. brown and pink (A **1**)	£225	£250
	a. "I" for "1"	£6000	£4000
	b. Opt Type A **2**	£3500	£3500
	c. Pair. Types A **1** and A **2** se-tenant	£5000	

The setting used for overprinting Nos. A1/4 was 30 (6×5). The "!" for first "I" variety occurs on R. 5/4 and overprint Type A **2** on R. 1/6 and 2/6 of the setting.

Two varieties of the 1 millieme.
A. 1st Ptg. 14 mm between lines of opt.
B. Later Ptgs. 12 mm between lines.

All other values are Type B.

1906 (Jan)–**11.** T **2** optd as Type A **3.**
*(i) W **4** (Mult Star and Crescent)*
A5	1m. brown and carmine (Type A)	£700	£450
	a. Opt double, one albino	£800	
A6	1m. brown and carmine (Type B)	4·25	20
	a. Opt double, one diagonal	†	£1600
	b. Opt inverted	£800	£800
	c. Pair, one without opt	†	£7500
	d. "Service" omitted	†	£4750
A7	2m. green and brown	29·00	1·00
	a. Pair, one without opt	£5000	
	b. "Army" omitted	£4500	£4500

A8		3m. mauve and green	25·00	40
	a.	Opt inverted	£2000	
A9		5m. scarlet and black	5·00	10
	a.	Opt. double	£400	£250
	ab.	Opt double, one diagonal	£350	
	b.	Opt inverted	†	£450
	c.	"Amry"	†	£2750
	e.	Opt double, one inverted	£1800	£700
	f.	"Armv" for "Army" (R. 4/9)		
A10		1p. blue and brown	30·00	15
	a.	"Army" omitted	—	£3500
	b.	Opt double	†	£3000
A11		2p. black and blue (1.09)	£100	13·00
	a.	Opt double	—	£3000
A12		5p. brown and green (5.08)	£190	70·00
A13		10p. black and mauve (5.11)	£600	£750
A6s/10s Optd "SPECIMEN" Set of 5			£130	

There were a number of printings of these Army Service stamps; the earlier are as Type A **3**; the 1908 printing has a narrower "A" in "Army" and the 1910–11 printings have the tail of the "y" in "Army" much shorter.

The two overprints on No. A11a are almost coincident. The error comes from the 'short "y"' printing.

A variety with no cross-bar to "A" of "Army" is known on some values, but does not appear to be constant.

No. A13 has been extensively forged, and should only be purchased with a reliable guarantee.

(ii) W **3** (Quatrefoil)

A14	2p. black and blue		95·00	10·00
A15	5p. brown and green		£130	£275
A16	10p. black and mauve		£160	£425
A14/16 Set of 3			£350	£650
A14s/16s Optd "SPECIMEN" Set of 3			£120	

(A **4**)

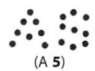
(A **5**)

1913 (1 Jan)–**22**. Nos. 18/20 and 23/8 punctured as Type A **4**.

A17	**2**	1m. brown and carmine	60·00	7·00
A18		2m. green and brown	16·00	70
A19		3m. mauve and green	75·00	6·00
A20		5m. scarlet and black	22·00	50
	a.	On No. 13		
A21		1p. blue and brown	50·00	1·50
A22		2p. black and blue	90·00	8·00
A23		2p. purple and orange-yellow (chalk-surfaced paper) (1922)	£130	60·00
A24		5p. brown and green	£110	50·00
	a.	Chalk-surfaced paper	£140	50·00
A25		10p. black and mauve (1914)	£500	£275
A17/25 Set of 9			£950	£375

1922–24. Nos. 31a and 34/5 punctured as Type A **5**.

A26	**6**	2m. yellow and chocolate (1924)	£110	55·00
A27		5m. olive-brown and black (4.2.22)	27·00	8·00
A28		10m. carmine and black	38·00	12·00
A26/8 Set of 3			£160	65·00

The use of Nos. A17/28 on internal Army mail ceased when the Egyptian units were withdrawn at the end of 1924, but existing stocks continued to be used on Army mail to foreign destinations until supplies were exhausted.

MILITARY TELEGRAPH STAMPS

From March to May 1885 the Military Telegraph stamps of Great Britain (Bechuanaland Nos. MT1/8) were in use in Sudan. Identifying postmark codes are "SK" (Suakin), "QI" (Quarantine Island), "HQ" (Headquarters), "WR" (Western Redoubt) and "ZA" (No.1 Post and, later, 2nd Brigade HQ).

1885. Nos. MT1/8 of Bechuanaland.

(a) Wmk Orb. P 14

MT1	1d. lilac and black	£200
MT2	3d. lilac and brown	£200
MT3	6d. lilac and green	£200

(b) Wmk script "VR" (sideways). P 13½

MT4	1s. green and black	£300
MT5	2s. green and blue	£500
MT6	5s. green and mauve	£600
MT7	10s. green and red	£7500

(c) Wmk Two Orbs (sideways). P 14×13½

MT8	£1 lilac and black	

Used prices for Nos. MT1/8 are for stamps with identifiable Sudan cancellations. For mint prices see Bechuanaland Nos. T1/8.

Telegraph stamps were reintroduced during the Sudan campaign of 1896–8.

(T **1**)

T **2**

1897 (July?). Nos. 5/9 handstamped as Type T **1**.

T1	5m. rose-carmine	7·00	2·00
	a. Opt in blue	21·00	6·00
T2	1p. ultramarine	14·00	4·00
	a. Opt in blue	22·00	10·00
T3	2p. orange-brown	25·00	5·00
T4	5p. slate	30·00	8·00
	a. Opt in blue	50·00	20·00
T5	10p. mauve	25·00	10·00
	a. Opt in blue	80·00	40·00

Handstamp T T **1** is known sideways, diagonal and inverted.

Nos. 1, 3 and 4 are also known handstamped T T **1**, but their authenticity is in doubt.

(Typo D.L.R.)

1898 (1 March). W **3**. P 14.

			Un whole stamp	Used whole stamp	Used half
T6	T **2**	5m. brown-purple and violet	5·00	6·00	75
T7		1p. black and bright carmine	5·00	6·00	75
T8		2p. green and lilac-brown	5·00	6·00	75
T9		5p. violet and black	5·00	6·00	75

PRICES for Nos. T6/17 are for unused whole stamps, used whole stamps or used half stamps. Each stamp has an extra central vertical line of perforations to allow "bisection" in use.

1898 (June). W **8a** of Egypt (sideways). P 14.

T10	T **2**	10p. bright rose and bluish green	75·00	95·00	21·00

1898–99. W **4**. P 14.

T11	T **2**	5m. brown-purple and violet	1·50	3·00	50
T12		5m. brown and blue (1899)	3·00	5·00	75
T13		1p. black and bright carmine	1·50	3·00	50
T14		2p. green and lilac-brown (1899)	15·00	20·00	2·00
T15		5p. violet and black (1899)	2·00	3·00	50
T16		10p. bright rose and bluish green	2·50	3·50	50
T17		25p. blue and brown (1899)	3·00	5·00	75

The use of telegraph stamps was discontinued in 1902. Postage stamps which had been used for telegraph purposes in parallel with telegraph stamps throughout, were exclusively used thereafter.

Swaziland

TRIPARTITE GOVERNMENT

Following internal unrest and problems caused by the multitude of commercial concessions granted by the Swazi king the British and Transvaal governments intervened during 1889 to establish a tripartite administration under which the country was controlled by their representatives, acting with the agent of the Swazi king.

The Pretoria government had previously purchased the concession to run the postal service and, on the establishment of the tripartite administration, provided overprinted Transvaal stamps for use from a post office at Embekelweni and later at Bremersdorp and Darkton.

Swazieland
(1)

1889 (18 Oct)–**90**. Stamps of Transvaal (South African Republic) optd with T **1**, in black.

(a) P 12½×12

1	**18**	1d. carmine	25·00	25·00
		a. Opt inverted	£700	£650
2		2d. olive-bistre	85·00	38·00
		a. Opt inverted	—	£1700
		b. "Swazielan"	£1100	£650
		c. "Swazielan" inverted		
3		1s. green	20·00	13·00
		a. Opt inverted	£800	£475

(b) P 12½

4	**18**	½d. grey	9·00	26·00
		a. Opt inverted	£1200	£850
		b. "Swazielan"	£2000	£1100
		c. "Swazielan" inverted	—	£8000
5		2d. olive-bistre	32·00	18·00
		a. Opt inverted	£950	£450
		b. "Swazielan"	£475	£400
		c. "Swazielan" inverted	£7500	£5000
6		6d. blue	45·00	60·00
7		2s.6d. buff (20.10.90)	£325	£475
8		5s. slate-blue (20.10.90)	£170	£325
		a. Opt inverted	£1900	£3000
		b. "Swazielan"	£4500	
9		10s. dull chestnut (20.10.90)	£7000	£4750

The "Swazielan" variety occurs on R. 6/1 in each sheet of certain printings.

A printing of the ½d., 1d., 2d. and 10s. yellow-brown with stop after "Swazieland" was made in July 1894, but such stamps were not issued.

It is possible that the dates quoted above were those on which the overprinting took place in Pretoria and that the stamps were issued slightly later in Swaziland itself.

1892 (Aug). Optd in carmine. P 12½.

10	**18**	½d. grey	7·50	16·00
		a. Opt inverted	£500	
		b. Opt double	£500	£500
		c. Pair, one without opt	†	£2000

No. 10 was overprinted in Pretoria during August 1892 when Swaziland was under quarantine due to smallpox. It is unlikely that it saw much postal use before all the overprints were withdrawn, although cancelled-to-order examples are plentiful.

It appears likely that no further supplies of stamps overprinted "Swaziland" were provided by Pretoria after December 1892, although stocks held at post offices were used up. The overprinted stamps were declared to be invalid from 7 November 1894. They were replaced by unoverprinted issues of the Transvaal (South African Republic).

Stamps of TRANSVAAL (SOUTH AFRICAN REPUBLIC) used in Swaziland between December 1892 and January 1900.

1885–93. (Nos. 175/87).

Z1	½d. grey	45·00
Z2	1d. carmine	45·00
Z3	2d. olive-bistre	25·00
Z4	2½d. mauve	65·00
Z5	3d. mauve	65·00
Z6	4d. bronze-green	60·00
Z9	2s.6d. orange-buff	

1893. (Nos. 195/9).

Z10	½d. on 2d. olive-bistre (Type A surch in red)	70·00
	a. Surch Type B	
Z11	½d. on 2d. olive-bistre (Type A surch in black)	
Z12	1d. on 6d. blue (Type A surch)	60·00
	a. Surch Type B	70·00
Z13	2½d. on 1s. green ("2½ Pence" in one line) (Type A surch)	60·00
	a. Surch Type B	70·00

1894. (Nos. 200/4).

Z16	1d. carmine	45·00
Z17	2d. olive-bistre	45·00

1895–96. (Nos. 205/12a).

Z20	½d. pearl-grey	45·00
Z21	1d. rose-red	25·00
Z22	2d. olive-bistre	25·00
Z24	4d. olive-black	55·00
Z25	6d. pale dull blue	50·00

1895. (Nos. 213/14).

Z27	½d. on 1s. green	

1895. Introduction of Penny Postage (No. 215b).

Z29	1d. red	90·00

1896–97. (Nos. 216/24).

Z30	½d. green	45·00
Z31	1d. rose-red and green	25·00
Z32	2d. brown and green	55·00
Z33	2½d. dull blue and green	50·00
Z34	3d. purple and green	55·00
Z35	4d. sage-green and green	45·00
Z36	6d. lilac and green	45·00
Z37	1s. ochre and green	90·00
Z38	2s.6d. dull violet and green	£160

Prices are for clear and fairly complete postmarks. Examples dated in 1892 and 1893 are worth a premium. For list of post offices open during this period see boxed note below. Most known examples are from Bremersdorp (squared circle inscr "SWAZIEL" later replaced by "Z.A.R." or c.d.s.) or Darkton (c.d.s.).

Shortly after the outbreak of the Boer War in 1899 the Transvaal administration withdrew from Swaziland, although the post office at Darkton, which was on the border, was still operating in early 1900. There was, however, no further organised postal service in Swaziland until the country became a British Protectorate in March 1902.

BRITISH PROTECTORATE

Stamps of Transvaal used in Swaziland from 1902.

1900. (Nos. 226/36).

Z41	1d. rose-red and green	£100
Z44	3d. purple and green	£150
Z45	4d. sage-green and green	£150

1902. (Nos. 244/55).

Z51	½d. black and bluish green	12·00
Z52	1d. black and carmine	10·00
Z54	2½d. black and violet	27·00
Z57	6d. black and orange-brown	30·00
Z60	2s.6d. magenta and black	50·00

1903. (Nos. 256/8).

Z63	1s. grey-black and red-brown	38·00
Z64	2s. grey-black and yellow	70·00

1904–09. (Nos. 260/72).

Z67	1d. black and carmine	10·00
Z68	2d. black and purple	16·00
Z70	3d. black and sage-green	20·00
Z71	4d. black and brown	16·00
Z72	6d. black and orange	16·00
Z73	1s. black and red-brown	20·00
Z74	2s. black and yellow	55·00
Z75	2s.6d. magenta and black	55·00
Z76	5s. black and purple/*yellow*	55·00
Z77	10s. black and purple/*red*	55·00
Z78	£1 green and violet	£190

1905–09. (Nos. 273/6).

Z79	½d. yellow-green	12·00
Z80	1d. scarlet	10·00
Z81	2d. purple	16·00
Z82	2½d. bright blue	38·00

The stamps of South Africa replaced those of Transvaal from 1913. Stamps of the other provinces were also valid for postal use.

2 King George V   **3** King George VI

(Des Rev. C. C. Tugman. Recess D.L.R.)

1933 (3 Jan). Wmk Mult Script CA. P 14.

11	**2**	½d. green	30	30
12		1d. carmine	30	20
13		2d. brown	30	45
14		3d. blue	45	40
15		4d. orange	3·50	4·00
16		6d. bright purple	1·25	1·75
17		1s. olive	1·50	3·25
18		2s.6d. bright violet	15·00	22·00
19		5s. bright violet	38·00	55·00
20		10s. sepia	£140	£180
		11/20 *Set of 10*	£180	£225
		11s/20s Perf "SPECIMEN" *Set of 10*	£325	

The ½d., 1d., 2d. and 6d. values exist overprinted "OFFICIAL", but authority for their use was withdrawn before any were actually used. However, some stamps had already been issued to the Secretariat staff before instructions were received to invalidate their use (*Price £50000 per set un*).

1935 (4 May). Silver Jubilee. As Nos. 91/4 of Antigua, but ptd by B.W. P 11×12.

21		1d. deep blue and scarlet	50	1·50
		a. Extra flagstaff	£300	£400
		b. Short extra flagstaff	£550	
		c. Lightning conductor	£550	
		d. Flagstaff on right-hand turret	£130	£250
		e. Double flagstaff	£130	£250
22		2d. ultramarine and grey-black	2·75	4·75
		a. Extra flagstaff	£140	£250
		b. Short extra flagstaff	£170	£275
		c. Lightning conductor	£150	£250
23		3d. brown and deep blue	1·25	8·50
		a. Extra flagstaff	£110	£300
		b. Short extra flagstaff	£150	£325
		c. Lightning conductor	£130	£325
24		6d. slate and purple	4·50	7·00
		a. Extra flagstaff	£140	£250
		b. Short extra flagstaff	£170	£300
		c. Lightning conductor	£170	£300
		21/4 *Set of 4*	8·00	20·00
		21s/4s Perf "SPECIMEN" *Set of 4*	£140	

For illustrations of plate varieties see Omnibus section following Zanzibar.

1937 (12 May). Coronation. As Nos. 95/7 of Antigua. P 11×11½.

25		1d. carmine	50	2·50
26		2d. yellow-brown	50	50
27		3d. blue	50	1·25
		25/7 *Set of 3*	1·40	3·75
		25s/7s Perf "SPECIMEN" *Set of 3*	£120	

(Recess D.L.R.)

1938 (1 Apr)–**54**. Wmk Mult Script CA. P 13½×13.

28	**3**	½d. green	2·50	1·25
		a. Perf 13½×14 (1.43)	30	2·75
		b. Perf 13½×14. *Bronze-green* (2.50)	3·25	12·00
29		1d. rose-red	2·75	1·25
		a. Perf 13½×14 (1.43)	1·00	1·75
30		1½d. light blue	6·50	75
		a. Perf 14 (1941)	2·75	1·00
		b. Perf 13½×14 (1.43)	40	1·00
		ba. Printed on the gummed side	£6000	
31		2d. yellow-brown	2·50	1·25
		a. Perf 13½×14 (1.43)	40	50
32		3d. ultramarine	11·00	1·75
		a. *Deep blue* (10.38)	17·00	1·75
		b. Perf 13½×14. *Ultramarine* (1.43)	9·50	10·00
		c. Perf 13½×14. *Light ultramarine* (10.46)	26·00	30·00
		d. Perf 13½×14. *Deep blue* (10.47)	20·00	12·00
33		4d. orange	14·00	3·50
		a. Perf 13½×14 (1.43)	1·25	1·40
34		6d. deep magenta	26·00	2·75
		a. Perf 13½×14. *Reddish purple (shades)* (7.44)	4·50	1·50
		c. Perf 13½×14. *Claret* (13.10.54)	10·00	8·50
35		1s. brown-olive	28·00	2·00
		a. Perf 13½×14 (1.43)	1·25	65
36		2s.6d. bright violet	35·00	6·00
		a. Perf 13½×14. *Violet* (1.43)	32·00	7·00
		b. Perf 13½×14. *Reddish violet* (10.47)	27·00	18·00
37		5s. grey	70·00	20·00
		a. Perf 13½×14. *Slate* (1.43)	60·00	55·00
		b. Perf 13½×14. *Grey* (5.44)	50·00	20·00
38		10s. sepia	75·00	9·00
		a. Perf 13½×14 (1.43)	10·00	7·00
		28/38a *Set of 11*	95·00	35·00
		28s/38s Perf "SPECIMEN" *Set of 11*	£325	

The above perforations vary slightly from stamp to stamp, but the average measurements are respectively: 13.3×13.2 comb (13½×13), 14.2 line (14) and 13.3×13.8 comb (13½×14).

Swaziland
(4)

1945 (3 Dec). Victory. Nos. 108/10 of South Africa optd with T **4**.

			Us	Us
			Un pair	pair	single
39		1d. brown and carmine	65	80	10
		a. Barbed wire flaw	15·00		
40		2d. slate-blue and violet	65	80	10
41		3d. deep blue and blue	65	2·50	20
		39/41 *Set of 3*	1·75	3·75	35

1947 (17 Feb). Royal Visit. As Nos. 32/5 of Basutoland.

			Un	Us
42		1d. scarlet	10	10
43		2d. green	10	10
44		3d. ultramarine	10	10
45		1s. mauve	10	10
		42/5 *Set of 4*	35	35
		42s/5s Perf "SPECIMEN" *Set of 4*	£150	

1948 (1 Dec). Royal Silver Wedding. As Nos. 112/13 of Antigua.

46		1½d. ultramarine	50	1·00
47		10s. purple-brown	40·00	45·00

1949 (10 Oct). 75th Anniv of UPU. As Nos. 114/17 of Antigua.

48		1½d. blue	15	30
		a. "A" of "CA" missing from wmk	£750	
49		3d. deep blue	2·00	4·50
50		6d. magenta	30	1·00
51		1s. olive	30	4·75
		a. "A" of "CA" missing from wmk	£1000	
		48/51 *Set of 4*	2·25	9·50

1953 (3 June). Coronation. As No. 120 of Antigua.

52		2d. black and yellow-brown	45	20

5 Havelock Asbestos Mine   **6** A Highveld view

7 Swazi Married Woman

8 Swazi courting couple

9 Swazi warrior in ceremonial dress

10 Greater Kudu

(Recess B.W.)

1956 (2 July). T **5/10**. Wmk Mult Script CA. P 13×13½ (horiz) or 13½×13 (vert).

53	**5**	½d. black and orange	50	10
54	**6**	1d. black and emerald	30	10
55	**7**	2d. black and brown	50	10
56	**8**	3d. black and rose-red	30	10
57	**9**	4½d. black and deep bright blue	1·25	1·00
58	**10**	6d. black and magenta	3·00	10
59	**5**	1s. black and deep olive	1·25	10
60	**8**	1s.3d. black and sepia	6·50	7·50
61	**6**	2s.6d. emerald and carmine-red	4·50	4·25
62	**9**	5s. deep lilac and slate-black	15·00	9·50
63	**7**	10s. black and deep lilac	26·00	22·00
64	**10**	£1 black and turquoise-blue	60·00	48·00
53/64 *Set of 12*			£100	80·00

(New Currency. 100 cents = 1 rand)

½c (11) 1c (12) 2c (13) 3½c (14)

2½c (I) 2½c (II) 4c (I) 4c (II)

5c (I) 5c (II) 25c (I) 25c (II)

50c (I) 50c (II) 50c (III)

R1 (I) R1 (II) R1 (III) R2 (I) R2 (II)

1961 (14 Feb–May). Nos. 53/64 surch as T **11** to **14**.

65	½c. on ½d.	4·50	8·50
	a. Surch inverted	£1900	
66	1c. on 1d.	10	2·25
	a. Surch double*	£2250	
67	2c. on 2d.	10	3·00
68	2½c. on 2d.	10	1·25
69	2½c. on 3d. (Type I)	10	50
	a. Type II	10	2·00
70	3½c. on 2d. (5.61)	10	1·25
71	4c. on 4½d. (Type I)	10	30
	a. Type II	60	1·75
72	5c. on 6d. (Type I)	50	10
	a. Type II	20	1·75
73	10c. on 1s.	42·00	10·00
	a. Surch double*	£2500	
74	25c. on 2s.6d. (Type I)	40	1·50
	a. Type II (central)	2·00	2·25
	ab. Surch double, one albino	£850	
	b. Type II (bottom left)	£700	£850
75	50c. on 5s. (Type I)	50	2·00
	a. Type II	15·00	4·25
	b. Type III	£900	£1100
76	1r. on 10s. (Type I)	1·50	1·75
	a. Type II	5·50	10·00
	b. Type III	£120	£160
77	2r. on £1 (Type I)	26·00	22·00
	a. Type II (middle left)	16·00	25·00
	b. Type II (bottom)	£150	£275
65/77a *Set of 13*		55·00	48·00

*On both Nos. 66a and 73a the second surcharge falls across the horizontal perforations.

No. 74b has the thin Type II surcharge at bottom left, in similar position to the thicker Type I, No. 74, with which it should not be confused.

No. 77b has the surcharge centrally placed at bottom. No. 77a has it at middle left, above "KUDU".

No. 66 with surcharge central (instead of bottom left) and No. 75a bottom left (instead of middle left) are believed to be from trial sheets released with the normal stocks. They do not represent separate printings. (No. 66 *price* £120 *un*, No. 75a *price* £325 *un*.)

(Recess B.W.)

1961. As 1956 issue, but with values in cents and rands. Wmk Mult Script CA. P 13×13½ (horiz) or 13½×13 (vert).

78	½c. black and orange (as ½d.) (14.2)	10	1·25
79	1c. black and emerald (as 1d.) (14.2)	10	10
80	2c. black and brown (as 2d.) (10.9)	10	2·50
81	2½c. black and rose-red (as 3d.) (14.2)	15	10

82	4c. black and deep bright blue (as 4½d.) (10.9)	20	1·50
83	5c. black and magenta (as 6d.) (10.9)	1·25	15
84	10c. black and deep olive (as 1s.) (14.2)	20	10
85	12½c. black and sepia (as 1s 3d.) (14.2)	1·25	70
86	25c. emerald and carmine-red (as 2s 6d.) (1.8)	4·50	8·00
87	50c. deep lilac and slate-black (as 5s.) (10.9)	6·00	3·50
88	1r. black and deep lilac (as 10s.) (10.9)	14·00	17·00
89	2r. black and turquoise-blue (as £1) (1.8)	22·00	14·00
78/89 *Set of 12*		45·00	42·00

15 Swazi Shields

16 Battle Axe

(Des Mrs. C. Hughes. Photo Enschedé)

1962 (24 Apr)–**66**. Various designs as T **15/16**. W w **12**. P 14×13 (horiz) or 13×14 (vert).

90	½c. black, brown and yellow-brown	10	10
	w. Wmk inverted	45·00	23·00
91	1c. yellow-orange and black	10	10
	w. Wmk inverted	1·75	2·25
92	2c. deep bluish green, black and yellow-olive	10	1·75
	w. Wmk inverted	50·00	42·00
93	2½c. black and vermilion	10	10
	a. Black and dull red (5.66)	3·00	80
	w. Wmk inverted	2·50	2·00
94	3½c. yellow-green and deep grey	10	40
	w. Wmk inverted	10·00	7·50
95	4c. black and turquoise-green	10	50
	a. Black and deep turquoise-green (5.66)	3·00	1·00
	w. Wmk inverted	11·00	8·00
96	5c. black, red and orange-red	1·50	10
	w. Wmk inverted	13·00	8·00
97	7½c. deep brown and buff	2·00	1·50
	a. Blackish brown and yellowish buff (5.66)	9·00	5·50
	w. Wmk inverted	13·00	12·00
98	10c. black and light blue	5·00	35
	w. Wmk inverted	80·00	40·00
99	12½c. carmine and grey-olive	2·50	3·50
	w. Wmk inverted	80·00	
100	15c. black and bright purple	1·50	1·75
101	20c. black and green	40	1·00
	w. Wmk inverted	—	£225
102	25c. black and bright blue	50	1·00
	w. Wmk inverted	55·00	40·00
103	50c. black and rose-red	20·00	7·00
	w. Wmk inverted	—	£200
104	1r. emerald and ochre	3·00	2·50
105	2r. carmine-red and ultramarine	24·00	15·00
90/105 *Set of 16*		50·00	30·00

Designs: Vert—2c. Forestry; 2½c. Ceremonial headdress; 3½c. Musical instrument; 4c. Irrigation; 5c. Long-tailed Whydah; 7½c. Rock paintings; 10c. Secretary Bird; 12½c. Pink Arum; 15c. Swazi married woman; 20c. Malaria control; 25c. Swazi warrior; 1r. Aloes. Horiz—50c. Southern Ground Hornbill; 2r. Msinsi in flower.

1963 (4 June). Freedom from Hunger. As No. 146 of Antigua.

106	15c. reddish violet	50	15

1963 (2 Sept). Red Cross Centenary. As Nos. 147/8 of Antigua.

107	2½c. red and black	30	10
108	15c. red and blue	70	90

31 Goods Train and Map of Swaziland Railway

(Des R. A. H. Street. Recess B.W.)

1964 (5 Nov). Opening of Swaziland Railway. W w **12**. P 11½.

109	**31**	2½c. emerald-green and purple	65	10
110		3½c. turquoise-blue and deep yellow-olive	65	1·00
111		15c. red-orange and deep chocolate	1·00	70
112		25c. olive-yellow and deep ultramarine	1·10	80
109/12 *Set of 4*			3·00	2·25

1965 (17 May). ITU Centenary. As Nos. 166/7 of Antigua.

113	2½c. light blue and bistre	15	10
114	15c. bright purple and rose	35	20

1965 (25 Oct). International Co-operation Year. As Nos. 168/9 of Antigua.

115	½c. reddish purple and turquoise-green	10	30
116	15c. deep bluish green and lavender	40	20

1966 (24 Jan). Churchill Commemoration. As Nos. 170/3 of Antigua.

117	½c. new blue	10	3·00
118	2½c. deep green	35	10
119	15c. brown	75	25
	w. Wmk inverted	75·00	55·00
120	25c. bluish violet	80	1·10
117/20 *Set of 4*		1·75	4·00

1966 (1 Dec). 20th Anniv of UNESCO. As Nos. 196/8 of Antigua.

121		2½c. slate-violet, red, yellow and orange	30	10
122		7½c. orange-yellow, violet and deep olive	85	85
123		15c. black, bright purple and orange	1·40	1·60
121/3 *Set of 3*			2·25	2·25

PROTECTED STATE

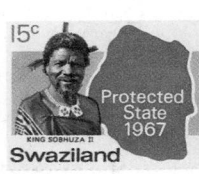

32 King Sobhuza II and Map

33 King Sobhuza II

(Des and photo Harrison)

1967 (25 Apr). Protected State. W w **12** (sideways on horiz designs). P 14½.

124	**32**	2½c. multicoloured	10	10
125	**33**	7½c. multicoloured	15	20
126	**32**	15c. multicoloured	20	30
127	**33**	25c. multicoloured	25	55
124/7 *Set of 4*			65	1·00

34 Students and University

(Des V. Whiteley. Photo Harrison)

1967 (7 Sept). First Conferment of University Degrees. P 14×14½.

128	**34**	2½c. sepia, ultramarine and light yellow-orange	10	10
129		7½c. sepia, ultramarine and light greenish blue	15	15
130		15c. sepia, ultramarine and rose	25	30
131		25c. sepia, ultramarine and light violet	30	35
128/31 *Set of 4*			65	75

35 Incwala Ceremony

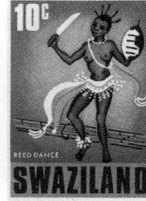

36 Reed Dance

(Des Mrs. G. Ellison. Photo Harrison)

1968 (5 Jan). Traditional Customs. P 14.

132	**35**	3c. silver, vermilion and black	10	10
133	**36**	10c. silver, light brown, orange and black	10	10
134	**35**	15c. gold, vermilion and black	15	20
135	**36**	25c. gold, light brown, orange and black	15	20
132/5 *Set of 4*			40	50

(37) **38** Cattle Ploughing

1968 (1 May). No. 96 surch with T **37**.

136	3c. on 5c. black, red and orange-red	1·50	10
	w. Wmk inverted	8·00	2·00

INDEPENDENT

(Des Mrs. G. Ellison. Photo Enschedé)

1968 (6 Sept). Independence. T **38** and similar horiz designs. W w **12** (sideways). P 14×12½.

137	3c. multicoloured	10	10
	a. Imperf (pair)	£250	
138	4½c. multicoloured	10	45
	a. Imperf (pair)	£250	
139	17½c. yellow, green, black and gold	15	70
140	25c. slate, black and gold	45	90
137/40 *Set of 4*		65	1·75
MS141	180×162 mm. Nos. 137/40 each×5	14·00	23·00
	a. Error Imperf	£2250	

Designs: —4½c. Overhead cable carrying asbestos; 17½c. Cutting sugar cane; 25c. Iron ore mining and railway map.

Nos. 137/40 were printed in sheets of 50, but also in miniature sheets of 20 (4×5) containing *se-tenant* strips of each value.

INDEPENDENCE
1968
(42)   **43** Cape Porcupine

1968 (6 Sept). Nos. 90/105 optd as T **42**, and No. 93 additionally surch 3c., by Enschedé.

(a) Wmk upright

142	½c. black, brown and yellow-brown........	10	10
	a. Brown omitted...............................	£425	
	b. Albino opt......................................	50·00	
143	1c. yellow-orange and black..................	10	10
	w. Wmk inverted...............................	50·00	40·00
144	2c. deep bluish green, black and yellow-olive	10	10
	w. Wmk inverted...............................	—	40·00
145	2½c. black and vermilion........................	1·25	1·40
	a. Black and dull red...........................	3·75	10
	w. Wmk inverted...............................	42·00	32·00
146	3c. on 2½c. black and vermilion...........	10	10
	a. Black and dull red...........................	10	10
	w. Wmk inverted...............................	40·00	32·00
147	3½c. yellow-green and deep grey............	15	10
	w. Wmk inverted...............................	50·00	40·00
148	4c. black and turquoise-green..............	10	10
	a. Black and deep turquoise-green........	25	15
	b. Black and pale turquoise-green........	20	1·50
149	5c. black, red and orange-red..............	4·25	10
	w. Wmk inverted...............................	65·00	40·00
150	7½c. deep brown and buff......................	60	10
151	10c. black and light blue......................	4·50	10
152	12½c. carmine and grey-olive..................	25	1·00
	w. Wmk inverted...............................	2·00	3·00
153	15c. black and bright purple................	25	1·25
154	20c. black and green..........................	75	2·00
155	25c. black and bright blue..................	35	1·25
156	50c. black and rose-red......................	6·00	4·00
157	1r. emerald and ochre........................	2·00	4·50
158	2r. carmine-red and ultramarine........	4·00	9·00

(b) Wmk sideways

159	50c. black and rose-red......................	3·50	12·00
160	2r. carmine-red and ultramarine........	8·50	5·50
142/60 *Set of 19*		32·00	35·00

The 2½c., 3½c., 5c., 12½c., 50c. (No. 156) and 2r. (No. 158) exist with gum arabic only, the 1c., 2c., 3c., 4c., and 15c. with both gum arabic and PVA gum and the remainder with PVA gum only.

(Des and litho D.L.R.)

1969 (1 Aug)–**75**. T **43** and similar designs showing animals. Multicoloured. W w **12** (sideways on 3c., 3½c., 1r., 2r.). P 13×13½ (3, 3½c.), 12½×13 (1, 2r.) or 13×12½ (others).

161		½c. Caracal................................	10	10
162		1c. Type **43**.............................	10	10
163		2c. Crocodile.............................	20	10
		aw. Wmk inverted........................	4·25	
		b. Perf 12½×12 (29.9.75)...........	3·25	5·50
164		3c. Lion......................................	1·00	10
165		3½c. African Elephant..................	1·00	10
166		5c. Bush Pig...............................	30	10
167		7½c. Impala..................................	35	10
168		10c. Charmer Baboon..................	45	10
169		12½c. Ratel....................................	70	4·00
170		15c. Leopard...............................	1·25	70
171		20c. Blue Wildebeest...................	1·00	60
172		25c. White Rhinoceros.................	1·75	1·75
		aw. Wmk inverted........................	3·75	
173		50c. Common Zebra.....................	1·50	3·25
174		1r. Waterbuck (*vert*).................	3·00	6·50
175		2r. Giraffe (*vert*)......................	11·00	11·00
161/75 *Set of 15*			21·00	25·00

Nos. 161/73 are horizontal as Type **43** but the 3c. and 3½c. are larger, 35×24½ mm.
No. 163b was printed by the D.L.R. works in Bogota, Colombia.
Nos. 174 and 175 were reissued in new currency and No. 164 with Ww **12** upright in 1975.

   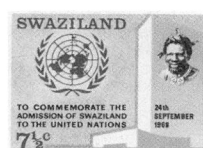

44 King Sobhuza II and Flags   **45** King Sobhuza II, UN Building and Emblem

(Des D.L.R. Litho P.B.)

1969 (24 Sept). Admission of Swaziland to the United Nations. W w **12** (sideways). P 13½.

176	**44**	3c. multicoloured...........................	10	10
177	**45**	7½c. multicoloured...........................	15	10
178	**44**	12½c. multicoloured...........................	25	10
179	**45**	25c. multicoloured...........................	40	40
176/9 *Set of 4*			75	55

46 Athlete, Shield and Spears

(Des L. Curtis. Litho Format)

1970 (16 July). Ninth Commonwealth Games, Edinburgh. T **46** and similar vert designs. Multicoloured. W w **12**. P 14.

180	3c. Type **46**............................	10	10
181	7½c. Runner..............................	20	10
182	12½c. Hurdler.............................	25	10
183	25c. Procession of Swaziland competitors	35	40
180/3 *Set of 4*		75	55

POSTAGE DUE STAMPS

Postage Due stamps of Transvaal used in Swaziland.

1907. (Nos. D1/7).

ZD1	½d. black and blue-green..............	28·00
ZD2	1d. black and scarlet.....................	23·00
ZD3	2d. brown-orange.........................	21·00
ZD4	3d. black and blue........................	35·00
ZD5	5d. black and violet......................	35·00
ZD6	6d. black and red-brown...............	60·00

These stamps were replaced by those of South Africa from 1914.

   Postage Due 2d

D **1**   (D **2**)   D **3**

(Typo D.L.R.)

1933 (23 Jan)–**57**. Wmk Mult Script CA. P 14.

D1	D **1**	1d. carmine...............................	2·25	18·00
		a. Chalk-surfaced paper. Deep carmine (24.10.51)..................	1·25	22·00
		ac. Error. St Edward's Crown, W **9b**	£425	
D2		2d. pale violet............................	5·00	38·00
		a. Chalk-surfaced paper (22.2.57)...	6·50	55·00
		ab. Large "d"................................	55·00	
D1s/2s Perf "SPECIMEN" *Set of 2*			75·00	

For illustration of No. D2ab see above No. D1 of Basutoland.

1961 (8 Feb). No. 55 surch with Type D **2**.

D3	**7**	2d. on 2d..................................	1·25	2·75

Another 2d. on 2d. Postage Due, with small surcharge as Type D **5**, was produced *after the currency change*, to meet the philatelic demand (*Price* 30p *unused*, £1·00 *used*).

1961 (14 Feb). Chalk-surfaced paper. Wmk Mult Script CA. P 14.

D4	D **3**	1c. carmine...............................	15	1·10
D5		2c. violet...................................	15	1·10
D6		5c. green...................................	20	1·10
D4/6 *Set of 3*			45	3·00

Postage Due 1c (D **4**)   **Postage Due 1c** (D **5**)   **2c** Narrow '2' (R. 8/4)

1961. No. 55 surcharged.

a. As Type D 4. (14 Feb)

D7	**7**	1c. on 2d..................................	1·25	2·50
D8		2c. on 2d..................................	1·25	2·50
		a. Narrow "2"..............................	25·00	
D9		5c. on 2d..................................	2·25	2·50
D7/9 *Set of 3*			4·25	6·75

b. As Type D 5. (Date?)

D10	**7**	1c. on 2d..................................	70	4·25
D11		2c. on 2d..................................	50	2·75
D12		5c. on 2d..................................	90	2·25
D10/12 *Set of 3*			1·90	8·25

Tanganyika

The stamps of GERMANY were used in the colony between October 1890 and July 1893 when issues for GERMAN EAST AFRICA were provided.

PRICES FOR STAMPS ON COVER TO 1945
The Mafia Island provisionals (Nos. M1/52) are very rare used on cover.

Nos. N1/5	*from* × 8
Nos. 45/59	*from* × 6
Nos. 60/2	—
Nos. 63/73	*from* × 6
Nos. 74/86	*from* × 8
Nos. 87/8	—
Nos. 89/92	*from* × 6
Nos. 93/106	*from* × 3
No. 107	—

MAFIA ISLAND

BRITISH OCCUPATION

Mafia Island was captured by the British from the Germans in January 1915. Letters were first sent out unstamped, then with stamps handstamped with Type M **1**. Later the military were supplied with handstamps by the post office in Zanzibar. These were used to produce Nos. M11/52.

There is continuing debate about the status of the Mafia provisional issues, but we are satisfied that they were produced with proper authorisation, under wartime conditions.

(Currency. 100 heller = 1 rupee)

G.B. MAFIA (M **1**)   (M **3**)

1915 (Jan). German East Africa Yacht types, handstamped with Type M **1**. Wmk Lozenges, or no wmk (1r., 2r.). A. In black (2½h. in blackish lilac). B. In deep purple. C. In reddish violet.

		A	B	C
M1	2½h. brown.............................	£1100	†	£225
	a. Pair, one without handstamp		†	£4000
M2	4h. green................................	£1000	£1100	£325
	a. Pair, one without handstamp		†	£4000
M3	7½h. carmine............................	£650	£700	£100
	a. Pair, one without handstamp	£8500	†	£2750
M4	15h. ultramarine......................	£650	£900	£170
	a. Pair, one without handstamp		†	£3500
M5	20h. black and red/yellow..........	£950	£950	£350
	a. Pair, one without handstamp		†	£4000
M6	30h. black and carmine.............	£1100	£1300	£425
	a. Pair, one without handstamp	£9000	†	£3750
M7	45h. black and mauve...............	£1100	£1300	£500
	a. Pair, one without handstamp	£9000	†	£4750
M8	1r. carmine.............................	£14000	†	£8500
M9	2r. green.................................	£15000	†	£9500
M10	3r. blue-black and red..............	£16000	†	£11000

Prices are for unused examples.
A few contemporary Zanzibar stamps (1, 3, 6 and 15c.) and India – I.E.F. ½a and 1a are known with the above handstamp.

(Currency. 100 cents = 1 rupee)

1915 (May). German East Africa Yacht types with handstamped four-line surcharge "G.R.—POST—6 CENTS—MAFIA" in black, green or violet. Wmk Lozenges or no wmk (1r., 2r.).

M11	6c. on 2½h. brown...................	£2500	£2500
	a. Pair, one without handstamp...........	†	£7500
M12	6c. on 4h. green.......................	£2750	£2750
	a. Pair, one without handstamp...........	£8000	
M13	6c. on 7½h. carmine.................	£2500	£2500
	a. Pair, one without handstamp...........	£8000	
M14	6c. on 15h. ultramarine............	£2250	£2500
M15	6c. on 20h. black and red/yellow	£3500	£3500
M16	6c. on 30h. black and carmine...	£4000	£4250
M17	6c. on 45h. black and mauve.....	£4000	£4000
	a. Pair, one without handstamp...........	£9000	
M18	6c. on 1r. carmine...................	£40000	
M19	6c. on 2r. green.......................	£45000	
M20	6c. on 3r. blue-black and red.....	£50000	

The 5, 20 and 40 pesa values of the 1901 Yacht issue are also known with the above surcharge as are the contemporary 1c. and 6c. Zanzibar stamps.

1915 (Sept).

(a) German East African fiscal stamps. "Statistik des Waaren-Verkehrs" (*Trade Statistical Charge*) handstamped in bluish green or violet, "O.H.B.M.S. Mafia" in a circle, as Type M **3**

M21	24 pesa, vermilion/buff...............	£900	£1400
M22	12½ heller, drab.........................	£1100	£1500
	a. Pair, one without handstamp..........	£12000	
M23	25 heller, dull green....................	£1100	£1500
M24	50 heller, slate...........................	£1100	£1500
	a. Pair, one without handstamp..........	£12000	
M25	1 rupee, lilac..............................	£1100	£1500

(b) German East African "Übersetzungs- Gebühren" (*Fee*) stamp, overprinted as before

M26	25 heller, grey...........................	£1100	£1500

G. R. POST MAFIA
(M **4**)

G. R. Post MAFIA.
(M **5**)

(c) Stamps as above, but with further opt as Type M 4, in bluish green or violet

M27	24 pesa, vermilion/*buff*	£1400
M28	12½ heller, drab	£1500
M29	25 heller, dull green	£1500
M30	50 heller, slate	£1500
M31	1 rupee, lilac	£1500
M32	25 heller, grey (No. M26)	£1500
	a. Pair, one without handstamp	
	Type M 4	£8000

Type M **3** is also known handstamped on the 7½h., 20h. and 30h. values of German East Africa 1905 Yacht issue and also on contemporary 1, 3, 6 and 25c. Zanzibar stamps.

(Currency. 12 pies = 1 anna. 16 annas = 1 rupee)

1915 (Nov)–**16**. Nos. E1/2, E4/9, E11 and E13 of Indian Expeditionary Forces (India King George V optd "I.E.F.") with a further opt Type M **4** handstruck in green, greenish black or dull blue.

M33	3p. grey	42·00	£110
	a. Pair, one stamp without handstamp	—	£1900
M34	½a. light green	65·00	£110
	a. Pair, one stamp without handstamp	£2500	£1900
M35	1a. aniline carmine	65·00	90·00
M36	2a. purple	£110	£190
M37	2½a. ultramarine	£120	£200
M38	3a. orange	£130	£200
	a. Pair, one stamp without handstamp	†	£3500
M39	4a. olive-green	£200	£300
M40	8a. deep magenta	£375	£475
	a. Pair, one stamp without handstamp	†	£3750
M41	12a. carmine-lake	£475	£650
M42	1r. red-brown and deep blue-green	£500	£750
	a. "I.E.F." opt double, one albino	£1000	
M33/42 *Set of 10*		£1900	£2750

All values exist with the overprint inverted, and several are known with overprint double or sideways.

Type M **4** (a handstamp made up from metal type) was originally applied as a combined overprint and postmark, between November 1915 and July 1916, and can be found tying the 3p., ½a. and 1a. values to *piece* or *cover*. A "MAFIA" circular datestamp was supplied from Zanzibar in early July 1916, and from July to September 1916 type M **4** was used as an overprint only, mainly for philatelic purposes.

Until early April 1917 India "I.E.F." stamps were in use on Mafia without additional overprint, but the new overprint Type M **5** (a rubber handstamp) was then introduced, producing Nos. M43/52.

1917 (Apr). Nos. E1/2, E4/9, E11 and E13 of Indian Expeditionary Forces (India King George V optd "I.E.F.") with further opt Type M **5** handstruck in green, greenish black, dull blue or violet.

M43	3p. grey	£150	£160
M44	½a. light green	£160	£160
	a. Pair, one without handstamp	†	£3750
M45	1a. aniline carmine	£120	£130
M46	2a. purple	£190	£190
M47	2½a. ultramarine	£200	£200
M48	3a. orange	£225	£225
M49	4a. olive-green	£300	£300
M50	8a. deep magenta	£475	£475
M51	12a. carmine-lake	£475	£600
M52	1r. red-brown and deep blue-green	£650	£750
M43/52 *Set of 10*		£2500	£2750

Stamps with handstamp inverted are known.

Used examples of Nos. M43/52 with black double-ring backdated postmarks of "JA 23 1915" and other dates prior to April 1917 are worth about 50% of the prices quoted.

Nos. M43/52 were in use until August 1918, when they were replaced by the Tanganyika "G.E.A." issue (Nos. 45/61). India "I.E.F." stamps without additional overprint also remained in use during the period.

NYASALAND-RHODESIAN FORCE

This issue was sanctioned for use by the Nyasaland-Rhodesian Force during operations in German East Africa, Mozambique and Nyasaland. Unoverprinted Nyasaland stamps were used by the Force prior to the introduction of Nos. N1/5 and, again, in 1918.

N. F.
(N **1**)

1916 (7 Aug–18 Sept*). Nos. 83, 86, 90/1 and 93 of Nyasaland optd with Type N **1** by Govt Printer, Zomba.

N1	½d. green	1·50	8·00
N2	1d. scarlet	1·50	3·25
N3	3d. purple/*yellow* (15.9*)	27·00	17·00
	a. Opt double	†	£22000
N4	4d. black and red/*yellow* (13.9*)	50·00	40·00
N5	1s. black/*green* (18.9*)	70·00	70·00
N1/5 *Set of 5*		£130	£120
N1s/5s Optd "SPECIMEN" *Set of 5*		£250	

*Earliest known dates of use.

Of No. N3a only six examples were printed, these being the bottom row on one pane issued at M'bamba Bay FPO, German East Africa in March 1918.

This overprint was applied in a setting of 60 (10 rows of 6) and the following minor varieties occur on all values: small stop after "N" (R. 1/1); broken "F" (R. 4/3); very small stop after "F" (R. 6/5); no serifs at top left and bottom of "N" (R. 10/1).

TANGANYIKA

BRITISH OCCUPATION OF GERMAN EAST AFRICA

Following the invasion of German East Africa by Allied forces civilian mail was accepted by the Indian Army postal service, using Indian stamps overprinted "I.E.F.". Some offices reverted to civilian control on 1 June 1917 and these used stamps of East Africa and Uganda until the "G.E.A." overprints were ready. The last field post offices, in the southern part of the country, did not come under civilian control until 15 March 1919.

(Currency. 100 cents = 1 rupee)

G.E.A.
(1)

G.E.A.
(2)

G.E.A.
(3)

1917 (Oct)–**21**. Nos. 44/5, 46a/51, 52b, 53/9 and 61 of Kenya and Uganda optd with T **1** and **2** by De La Rue. Ordinary paper (1c. to 15c.) or chalk-surfaced paper (others). Wmk Mult Crown CA.

45	1c. black (R.)	15	80
	aw. Wmk inverted	£350	
	ay. Wmk inverted and reversed	£200	
	b. Vermilion opt	20·00	16·00
47	3c. green	20	15
48	6c. scarlet	20	10
	a. Wmk sideways	£2250	£2500
	w. Wmk inverted	£375	£250
49	10c. yellow-orange	50	60
	y. Wmk inverted and reversed	£275	
50	12c. slate-grey	75	3·75
	y. Wmk inverted and reversed	£275	
51	15c. bright blue	2·00	6·00
	w. Wmk inverted	£350	
	y. Wmk inverted and reversed	£350	
52	25c. black and red/*yellow*	80	7·00
	a. On pale yellow (1921)	2·00	18·00
	as. Optd "SPECIMEN"	40·00	
53	50c. black and lilac	2·50	6·00
54	75c. black/*blue-green, olive back* (R.)	1·00	4·75
	a. On emerald back (1921)	3·50	50·00
	as. Optd "SPECIMEN"	50·00	
55	1r. black/*green* (R.)	6·50	7·50
	a. On emerald back (1919)	14·00	65·00
56	2r. red and black/*blue*	14·00	60·00
	x. Wmk reversed	£650	£650
57	3r. violet and green	17·00	80·00
58	4r. red and green/*yellow*	26·00	£120
59	5r. blue and dull purple	50·00	£140
60	10r. red and green/*green*	£150	£450
	a. On emerald back	£200	£700
61	20r. black and purple/*red*	£325	£700
62	50r. carmine and green	£750	£1200
	s. Optd "SPECIMEN"	£300	
45/61 *Set of 16*		£550	£1400
45s/61s Optd "SPECIMEN" *Set of 16*		£600	

Early printings of the rupee values exist with very large stop after the "E" in "G.E.A." (R. 5/3). There are round stops after "E" varieties, which in one position of later printings became a small stop.

Examples of Nos. 45/55 can also be found handstamped with Type M **5**, but these were not issued.

1921. Nos. 69/74 of Kenya and Uganda optd with T **1** or **2** by De La Rue. Chalk-surfaced paper (50c. to 5r.). Wmk Mult Script CA.

63	12c. slate-grey	11·00	£130
	a. Raised stop after "A"	£100	
64	15c. bright blue	9·00	18·00
	a. Raised stop after "A"	£100	
65	50c. black and dull purple	17·00	£120
	a. Raised stop after "A"	£150	
66	2r. red and black/*blue*	55·00	£160
67	3r. violet and green	£130	£400
68	5r. blue and dull purple	£170	£500
63/8 *Set of 6*		£350	£1200
63s/8s Optd "SPECIMEN" *Set of 6*		£300	

The raised stop after "A" occurs on R. 1/6, right pane.

1922. Nos. 65 and 68 of Kenya and Uganda optd by the Government Printer at Dar-es-Salaam with T **3**. Wmk Mult Script CA.

72	1c. black (R.)	2·00	24·00
73	10c. orange	4·25	14·00
	y. Wmk inverted and reversed	£250	

No. 73 is known with the overprint inverted, but this is of clandestine origin.

BRITISH MANDATED TERRITORY
(New Currency. 100 cents = 1 shilling)

4 Giraffe

5 Giraffe

(Recess B.W.)

1922–24. Head in black.

(a) Wmk Mult Script CA. P 15×14

74	**4**	5c. slate-purple	3·00	20
75		10c. green	4·25	85
76		15c. carmine-red	4·50	10
77		20c. orange	6·50	10
78		25c. black	9·50	6·50
79		30c. blue	6·50	5·00
80		40c. yellow-brown	7·00	4·50
81		50c. slate-grey	8·00	1·50
82		75c. yellow-bistre	7·00	25·00

(b) Wmk Mult Script CA (sideways). P 14

83	**5**	1s. carmine-red	14·00	32·00
		a. Wmk upright (1923)	8·50	12·00
84		2s. purple	12·00	32·00
		a. Wmk upright (1924)	9·00	50·00
85		3s. black	60·00	60·00
86		5s. scarlet	90·00	£140
		a. Wmk upright (1923)	45·00	£110
87		10s. deep blue	£275	£475
		a. Wmk upright (1923)	£130	£225
88		£1 yellow-orange	£475	£750
		a. Wmk upright (1923)	£425	£700
74/88a *Set of 15*			£650	£1100
74s/88s Optd "SPECIMEN" (Nos. 74/82) or "SPECIMEN." *Set of 15*			£850	

On the £1 stamp the words of value are on a curved scroll running across the stamp above the words "POSTAGE AND REVENUE".

Nos. 83/8 are known showing a forged Dodoma postmark, dated "16 JA 22". This issue was extensively used for fiscal purposes, and collectors are warned against examples which have been cleaned and regummed, or provided with forged postmarks.

1925. As 1922. Frame colours changed.

89	**4**	5c. green	14·00	1·50
90		10c. orange-yellow	14·00	1·50
91		25c. blue	4·75	18·00
92		30c. purple	9·50	32·00
89/92 *Set of 4*			38·00	48·00
89s/92s Optd "SPECIMEN." *Set of 4*			£150	

6

7

(Typo D.L.R.)

1927–31. Head in black. Chalk-surfaced paper (5s., 10s., £1). Wmk Mult Script CA. P 14.

93	**6**	5c. green	1·75	10
94		10c. yellow	2·00	10
95		15c. carmine-red	1·75	10
96		20c. orange-buff	2·75	10
97		25c. bright blue	3·75	2·00
98		30c. dull purple	2·75	3·50
98a		30c. bright blue (1931)	26·00	30
99		40c. yellow-brown	2·00	9·50
100		50c. grey	2·50	1·00
101		75c. olive-green	2·00	26·00
102	**7**	1s. green	4·25	2·75
103		2s. deep purple	30·00	9·00
104		3s. black	50·00	£110
105		5s. carmine-red	45·00	29·00
		a. Ordinary paper		
106		10s. deep blue	£100	£160
		a. Ordinary paper. *Deep dark blue*		
107		£1 brown-orange	£275	£425
93/107 *Set of 16*			£500	£700
93s/107s Optd or Perf (No. 98as) "SPECIMEN" *Set of 16*			£375	

Examples of Nos. 104/7 are known showing a forged Dar-es-Salaam postmark dated "20 NO 1928".

Tanganyika became part of the joint East African postal administration on 1 January 1933 and subsequently used the stamps of KENYA, UGANDA AND TANGANYIKA.

INDEPENDENT REPUBLIC

8 Teacher and Pupils

9 District Nurse and Child

14 "Maternity"

15 Freedom Torch over Mt Kilimanjaro

30c. "UHURU 196" (Pl. 1C R. 10/10, later corrected)

20s. Mountain flaw (R. 8/8)

(Des V. Whiteley. Photo Harrison)

1961 (9 Dec)–**64**. Independence. T **8/9**, **14/15** and similar designs. P 14×15 (5c., 30c.), 15×14 (10c.,15c., 20c., 50c.) or 14½ (others).

108	5c. sepia and light apple-green..............	10	10
109	10c. deep bluish green........................	10	10
110	15c. sepia and blue.............................	10	10
	a. Blue omitted...........................	£1700	
111	20c. orange-brown...............................	10	10
112	30c. black, emerald and yellow.............	10	10
	a. Inscr "UHURU 196"................	£950	£425
	b. "1" inserted after "196"........	30·00	
113	50c. black and yellow...........................	10	10
114	1s. brown, blue and olive-yellow...........	15	10
115	1s.30 red, yellow, black, brown and blue ..	4·50	10
	a. Red, yellow, black, brown and deep blue (10.3.64)................	9·50	1·00
116	2s. blue, yellow, green and brown	1·00	10
117	5s. deep bluish green and orange-red..	1·00	50
118	10s. black, reddish purple and light blue...	15·00	4·75
	a. Reddish purple (diamond) omitted................................	£275	£190
119	20s. red, yellow, black, brown and green	4·00	9·00
	a. Mountain flaw	45·00	
108/19 *Set of 12*		23·00	13·50

Designs: Vert (as T **9**)—15c. Coffee-picking; 20c. Harvesting maize; 50c. Serengeti lions. Horiz (as T **8**)—30c. Tanganyikan flag. (As T **14**)—2s. Dar-es-Salaam waterfront; 5s. Land tillage; 10s. Diamond and mine. Vert—20s. Type **15**.

On the corrected version of No. 112a the number "1" is very slightly shorter and the figure is more solid than normal.

19 Pres. Nyerere inaugurating Self-help Project

20 Hoisting Flag on Mt Kilimanjaro

(Photo Harrison)

1962 (9 Dec). Inauguration of Republic. Vert designs as T **19/20**. P 14½.

120	30c. emerald......................................	10	10
121	50c. yellow, black, green, red and blue....	10	10
122	1s.30 multicoloured............................	10	10
123	2s.50 black, red and blue.....................	30	50
120/3 *Set of 4*		55	70

Designs:—1s.30, Presidential emblem; 2s.50, Independence Monument.

23 Map of Republic

24 Torch and Spear Emblem

(Des M. Goaman. Photo Harrison)

1964 (7 July). United Republic of Tanganyika and Zanzibar Commemoration. P 14×14½.

124	**23**	20c. yellow-green and light blue.......	30	10
125	**24**	30c. blue and sepia........................	10	10
126		1s.30 orange-brown and ultramarine.......................	10	10
127	**23**	2s.50 purple and ultramarine.............	2·00	1·75
124/7 *Set of 4*			2·25	1·75

Despite the inscription on the stamps the above issue was only on sale in Tanganyika and had no validity in Zanzibar.

STAMP BOOKLETS

1922–25. Black on red cover.

SB1	3s. booklet containing 5c., 10c., 15c. and 20c. (Nos. 74/7), each in block of 6............................	£3500
	a. As No. SB1, but contents changed (Nos. 89/90, 76/7) (1925)	

1922–26. Black on red cover. Stapled.

SB2	3s. booklet containing 6×10c., and 12×5c. and 12×15c. (Nos. 74/6) in blocks of 6......................	
	a. As No. SB2, but contents changed (Nos. 74, 90, 76) (1925)	
	b. As No. SB2, but contents changed (Nos. 89/90, 76) (1926)	£3000

1927. Black on red covers. Stapled.

SB3	3s. booklet containing 6×10c., and 12×5c. and 12×15c. (Nos. 93/5) in blocks of 6........................	£1500
SB4	3s. booklet containing 5c., 10c. and 15c. (Nos. 93/5), each in block of 10	£1900

1961 (9 Dec). Black on blue-green cover, size 48×46 mm. Stitched.

SB5	5s. booklet containing 10c., 15c., 20c. 30c. and 50c. (Nos. 109/13), each in block of 4.................	5·00

OFFICIAL STAMPS

OFFICIAL OFFICIAL
(O **1**) (O **2**) (3½ *mm* tall)

1961 (9 Dec). Nos. 108/14 and 117 optd with Type O **1** (10, 15, 20, 50c. or larger (17 *mm*) 5, 30c.) or with Type O **2** (1s. or larger (22 *mm*) 5s.).

O1	5c. sepia and light apple-green..............	10	10
O2	10c. deep bluish green........................	10	10
O3	15c. sepia and blue.............................	10	10
O4	20c. orange-brown...............................	10	10
O5	30c. black, emerald and yellow.............	10	10
O6	50c. black and yellow...........................	10	10
O7	1s. brown, blue and olive-yellow...........	10	10
O8	5s. deep bluish green and orange-red..	75	85
O1/8 *Set of 8*		1·00	1·00

Tanzania

The United Republic of Tanganyika and Zanzibar, formed 26 April 1964, was renamed the United Republic of Tanzania on 29 October 1964.

Issues to No. 176, except Nos. Z142/5, were also valid in Kenya and Uganda.

(Currency. 100 cents = 1 shilling)

25 Hale Hydro Electric Scheme

26 Tanzanian Flag

27 National Servicemen

33 Dar-es-Salaam Harbour

38 Arms of Tanzania

(Des V. Whiteley. Photo Harrison)

1965 (9 Dec). T **25/7**, **33**, **38** and similar designs. P 14×14½ (5c., 10c., 20c., 50c., 65c.), 14½×14 (15c., 30c., 40c.), or 14 (others).

128	5c. ultramarine and yellow-orange........	10	10
129	10c. black, greenish yellow, green and blue..	10	10
130	15c. multicoloured..............................	10	10
131	20c. sepia, grey-green and greenish blue..	10	10
132	30c. black and red-brown.....................	10	10
133	40c. multicoloured..............................	1·00	20
134	50c. multicoloured..............................	1·00	10
135	65c. green, red-brown and blue.............	2·75	2·50
136	1s. multicoloured...............................	1·50	10
137	1s.30 multicoloured............................	6·50	1·50
138	2s.50 blue and orange-brown...............	6·50	1·25
139	5s. lake-brown, yellow-green and blue..	80	20
140	10s. olive-yellow, olive-green and blue...	1·00	4·00
141	20s. multicoloured..............................	7·00	19·00
128/41 *Set of 14*		25·00	26·00

Designs: Horiz (as T **25**)—20c. Road-building; 50c. Common Zebras, Manyara National Park; 65c. Mt Kilimanjaro. Vert (as T **27**)—30c. Drum, spear, shield and stool; 40c. Giraffes, Mikumi National Park. Horiz (As T **33**)—1s.30, Skull of *Zinjanthropus* and excavations, Olduvai Gorge, 2s.50, Fishing; 5s. Sisal industry; 10s. State House, Dar-es-Salaam.

Z **39** Pres. Nyerere and First Vice-Pres. Karume within Bowl of Flame

Z **40** Hands supporting Bowl of Flame

(Des J. Ahmed (Type Z **39**), G. Vasarhelyi (Type Z **40**). Photo Enschedé)

1966 (26 Apr). Second Anniv of United Republic. P 14×13.

Z142	Z **39**	30c. multicoloured..............................	20	45
Z143	Z **40**	50c. multicoloured..............................	20	45
Z144		1s.30, multicoloured...........................	30	45
Z145	Z **39**	2s.50, multicoloured...........................	40	1·25
Z142/5 *Set of 4*			1·00	2·40

Nos. Z142/5 were on sale in Zanzibar only.

39 Black-footed Cardinalfish

40 Sobrinus Mudskipper

41 Lionfish

(Des Rena Fennesy. Photo Harrison)

1967 (9 Dec)–**73**. Designs as T **39/41**. Chalk-surfaced paper. P 14×15 (5c. to 70c.) or 14½ (others).

142	5c. magenta, yellow-olive and black.......	10	2·75
	a. Glazed, ordinary paper (22.1.71)........	30	3·75

143	10c. brown and bistre	10	10
	a. Glazed, ordinary paper (27.9.72)	50	2·25
144	15c. grey, turquoise-blue and black	10	2·00
	a. Glazed, ordinary paper (22.1.71)	45	6·50
145	20c. brown and turquoise-green	10	10
	a. Glazed, ordinary paper (16.7.73)	50	9·50
146	30c. sage-green and black	20	10
	a. Glazed, ordinary paper (3.5.71)	17·00	4·75
147	40c. yellow, chocolate and bright green	1·00	10
	a. Glazed, ordinary paper (10.2.71)	1·00	60
148	50c. multicoloured	20	10
	a. Glazed, ordinary paper (10.2.71)	50	3·00
149	65c. orange-yellow, bronze-green and black	1·25	4·50
150	70c. multicoloured (15.9.69)	1·00	3·50
	a. Glazed, ordinary paper (22.1.71)	4·25	12·00
151	1s. orange-brown, slate-blue and maroon	30	10
	a. Glazed ordinary paper (3.2.71)	1·00	10
152	1s.30 multicoloured	3·00	10
153	1s.50 multicoloured (15.9.69)	2·00	50
	a. Glazed, ordinary paper (27.9.72)	2·25	10
154	2s.50 multicoloured	2·25	3·25
	a. Glazed, ordinary paper (27.9.72)	17·00	10
155	5s. greenish yellow, black and turquoise-green	4·00	2·75
	a. Glazed, ordinary paper (12.12.70*)	3·25	10
156	10s. multicoloured	1·00	3·75
	a. Glazed, ordinary paper (dull blue-green background) (12.12.70*)	1·00	10
	ab. Deep dull green background (12.9.73)	1·75	50
157	20s. multicoloured	1·25	7·00
	a. Glazed, ordinary paper (12.12.70*)	5·50	15
142/57 Set of 16		15·00	27·00
142a/57a Set of 14		48·00	38·00

*Earliest known postmark date.

Designs: Horiz as T **39/40**—15c. White-spotted Puffer; 20c. Thorny Seahorse; 30c. Dusky Batfish; 40c. Black-spotted Sweetlips 50c. Blue Birdwrasse; 65c. Bennett's Butterflyfish; 70c. Black-tipped Grouper. Horiz as T **41**:—1s.30, Powder-blue Surgeonfish; 1s.50, Yellow-finned Fusilier; 2s.50, Emperor Snapper; 5s. Moorish Idol; 10s. Painted Triggerfish; 20s. Horned Squirrelfish.

On chalk-surfaced paper all values except the 30c. exist with PVA gum as well as gum arabic, but the 70c. and 1s.50 exist with PVA gum only. Stamps on glazed, ordinary paper come only with PVA gum.

STAMP BOOKLETS

1965 (9 Dec). Black on blue (No. SB6) or buff (No. SB7) covers, size 48×46 mm. Stitched.

SB6	3s. booklet containing 4×15c. and 8×30c. (Nos. 130, 132) in blocks of 4	5·50
SB7	5s. booklet containing 4×15c. and 4×50c. and 8×30c. (Nos. 130, 132, 134) in blocks of 4	6·00

1967 (9 Dec). Black on blue (No. SB8) or buff (No. SB9) covers, size 48×45 mm. Stitched.

SB8	3s. booklet containing 4×15c. and 8×30c. (Nos. 144, 146) in blocks of 4	3·00
SB9	5s. booklet containing 10c., 15c., 20c., 30c. and 50c. and 8×30c. (Nos. 143/6, 148), each in blocks of 4	3·50

OFFICIAL STAMPS

(Opt photo Harrison)

1965 (9 Dec). Nos. 128/32, 134, 136, 139 optd as Types O **1** (15c., 30c. or larger (17 *mm*) 5c., 10c., 20c., 50c.), or with O **2** of Tanganyika (1s., 5s.).

O9	5c. ultramarine and yellow-orange	10	2·50
O10	10c. black, greenish yellow, green and blue	10	1·50
O11	15c. multicoloured	10	1·50
O12	20c. sepia, grey-green and greenish blue	10	2·75
O13	30c. black and red-brown	10	1·75
O14	50c. multicoloured	15	1·50
O15	1s. multicoloured	30	1·50
O16	5s. lake-brown, yellow-green and blue	1·75	10·00
O9/16 Set of 8		2·25	21·00

OFFICIAL

(O **3**)

(Opt litho Govt Printer, Dar-es-Salaam)

1967 (10–18 Nov). Nos. 134, 136 and 139 optd as No. O14 (50c.) or with Type O **3** (others).

O17	50c. multicoloured (18.11)	—	17·00
O18	1s. multicoloured (18.11)	22·00	9·50
O19	5s. lake-brown, yellow-green and blue	10·00	17·00

The issue dates given are for the earliest known postmarked examples.

Nos. O9/16 were overprinted by Harrison in photogravure and Nos. O17/19 have litho overprints by the Government Printer, Dar-es-Salaam. On No. O17 the overprint is the same size (17 *mm* long) as on No. O14.

1967 (9 Dec)–**71**. Nos. 142/6, 148, 151 and 155 optd as Type O **1**, but larger (measuring 17 *mm*) (5c. to 50c.) or as Type O **2** of Tanganyika (1s. and 5s.). Chalk-surfaced paper.

O20	5c. magenta, yellow-olive and black	10	5·00
	a. Glazed, ordinary paper (22.1.71)	3·50	4·75
O21	10c. brown and bistre	10	1·00
	a. Glazed, ordinary paper (1971)	15·00	4·25
O22	15c. grey turquoise-blue and black	10	7·00
	a. Glazed, ordinary paper (22.1.71)	3·50	5·50
O23	20c. brown and turquoise-green	10	1·00
O24	30c. sage-green and black	10	30
O25	50c. multicoloured	15	1·60
	a. Glazed, ordinary paper (22.1.71)	3·50	5·50
O26	1s. orange-brown, slate-blue and maroon	30	3·00
	a. Glazed, ordinary paper (3.2.71)	17·00	5·50
O27	5s. greenish yellow, black and turquoise-green	2·50	17·00
	a. Glazed, ordinary paper (3.2.71)	20·00	22·00
O20/7 Set of 8		3·00	32·00
O20a/7a Set of 6		55·00	42·00

The chalk-surfaced paper exists with both PVA gum and gum arabic, but the glazed, ordinary paper exists PVA gum only.

OFFICIAL

(O **4**)

1970 (10 Dec)–**73**. Nos. 142/8, 151 and 155 optd locally by letterpress as Type O **4** (5 to 50c.) or as Type O **2** of Tanganyika, but measuring 28 mm (1s. and 5s.).

(a) Chalk-surfaced paper

O28	5c. magenta, yellow-olive and black	75	11·00
	a. "OFFCIAL" (R.7/6)	—	£150
O29	10c. brown and bistre	1·25	4·00
	a. "OFFICIAL" (R.7/6)		
O30	20c. brown and turquoise-green	1·60	4·50
O31	30c. sage-green and black	1·90	4·50
O28/31 Set of 4		5·00	22·00

(b) Glazed, ordinary paper (1973)

O32	5c. magenta, yellow-olive and black	20·00	7·50
	a. "OFFCIAL" (R.7/6)	£500	90·00
	b. "OFFICIA" (R.10/9)	—	£110
O33	10c. brown and bistre	85·00	7·50
	a. "OFFICIAL" (R.7/6)	—	£120
O34	15c. grey, turquoise-blue and black	85·00	7·50
	a. "OFFICIAL" (R.7/6)	—	£110
O35	20c. brown and turquoise-green	—	5·00
O36	40c. yellow, chocolate and bright green	45·00	4·25
	a. Opt double	—	£200
	b. "OFFICIA" (R.10/9)	£500	£110
O37	50c. multicoloured	—	4·25
	a. "OFFICIAL" (R.7/6)	—	£100
O38	1s. orange-brown, slate-blue and maroon	65·00	13·00
	a. Opt double	—	£400
O39	5s. greenish yellow, black and turquoise green	75·00	65·00

The letterpress overprint can be distinguished from the photogravure by its absence of screening dots and the overprint showing through to the reverse, apart from the difference in length.

The "OFFICIA" error (Nos. O32b, O36b) occurred initially only on R10/9 of the setting of 100. Subsequently the "L" of "OFFICIAL" deteriorated on R10/10 also, and examples of the 40c. value have been seen with complete omission from this second position.

No. O36a comes from a sheet used at Kasulu in 1973-74. A second overprint was deliberately applied to part of the sheet to correct a weak first impression.

No. O38a comes from a sheet used at Masasi in 1973.

POSTAGE DUE STAMPS

Postage Due stamps of Kenya and Uganda wre issued for provisional use as such in Tanganyika on 1 July 1933. The postmark is the only means of identification.

The Postage Due stamps of Kenya, Uganda and Tanganyika were used in Tanganyika/Tanzania until 2 January 1967.

D 1

(Litho D.L.R.)

1967 (3 Jan). P 14×13½.

D1	D **1**	5c. scarlet	35	10·00
D2		10c. green	45	10·00
D3		20c. deep blue	50	13·00
D4		30c. red-brown	50	15·00
D5		40c. bright purple	50	18·00
D6		1s. orange	80	12·00
D1/6 Set of 6			2·75	70·00

1969 (12 Dec)–**71**. Chalk-surfaced paper. P 14×15.

D7	D **1**	5c. scarlet	30	14·00
		a. Glazed, ordinary paper (13.7.71)	4·00	8·00
D8		10c. green	65	6·00
		a. Glazed, ordinary paper (13.7.71)	75	5·50
D9		20c. deep blue	70	13·00
		a. Glazed, ordinary paper (13.7.71)	2·50	9·00
D10		30c. red-brown	65	23·00
		a. Glazed, ordinary paper (13.7.71)	85	6·50
D11		40c. bright purple	2·00	23·00
		a. Glazed, ordinary paper (13.7.71)	6·50	48·00
D12		1s. orange (glazed, ordinary paper) (13.7.71)	4·75	38·00
D7/11 Set of 5			3·75	70·00
D7a/12 Set of 6			17·00	£100

The stamps on chalk-surfaced paper exist only with gum arabic, but the stamps on glazed paper exist only with PVA gum.

Tasmania *see* **Australia**

Tobago *see* **Trinidad and Tobago**

Togo

The stamps of GERMANY were used in the colony from March 1888 until June 1897 when issues for TOGO were provided.

PRICES FOR STAMPS ON COVER	
Nos. H1/7	from × 6
No. H8	—
No. H9	from × 6
No. H10	from × 2
No. H11	—
Nos. H12/13	from × 6
Nos. H14/16	—
Nos. H17/19	from × 12
Nos. H20/6	—
Nos. H27/8	from × 20
No. H29	—
Nos. H30/1	from × 6
Nos. H32/3	—
Nos. H34/58	from × 5

ANGLO-FRENCH OCCUPATION

French forces invaded southern Togo on 8 August 1914 and the British had entered Lomé by the same date, examples of Gold Coast stamps being known cancelled there on the 8th. The German administration surrendered on 26 August 1914.

The territory was jointly administered under martial law, but was formally divided between Great Britain and France, effective 1 October 1920. League of Nations mandates were issued for both areas from 20 July 1922.

(Currency. 100 pfennig = 1 mark)

Stamps of German Colonial issue Yacht Types 1900 and 1909–14 (5pf. and 10pf.)

TOGO	
Anglo-French	
Occupation	**Half penny**
(1)	(2)

SETTINGS. Nos. H1/33 were all overprinted or surcharged by the Catholic Mission, Lomé.

The initial setting for the 3pf. to 80pf. was of 50 (10×5), repeated twice on each sheet of 100. Overprints from this setting, used for Nos. H1/9, had the lines of type 3 mm apart.

Nos. H1/2 were subsequently surcharged, also from a setting of 50, to form Nos. H12/13. The surcharge setting showed a thin dropped "y" with small serifs on R. 1/1–2, 2/1, 3/1, 4/1 and 5/1–2.

The type from the overprint and surcharge was then amalgamated in a new setting of 50 on which the lines of the overprint were only 2 mm apart. On this amalgamated setting, used for Nos. H27/8, the thin "y" varieties were still present and R. 4/7 showed the second "O" of "TOGO" omitted.

The surcharge was subsequently removed from this "2 mm" setting which was then used to produce Nos. H17/19. The missing "O" was spotted and corrected before any of the 30pf. stamps were overprinted.

The remaining low values of the second issue, Nos. H14/16 and H20/2, were overprinted from settings of 25 (5×5), either taken from the last setting of 50 or from an amended version on which there was no space either side of the hyphen. This slightly narrower overprint was subsequently used for Nos. H29/33. It shows the top of the second "O" broken so that it resembles a "U" on R. 1/5.

The mark values were overprinted from settings of 20 (5×4), showing the same differences in the spacing of the lines as on the low values.

It is believed that odd examples of some German colonial values were overprinted from individual settings in either spacing.

1914 (17 Sept*). Optd with T **1** by Catholic Mission, Lomé. Wide setting. Lines 3 mm apart.

H1	3pf. brown	£130	£100
H2	5pf. green	£130	£100
H3	10pf. carmine (Wmk Lozenges)	£130	£100
	a. Opt inverted	£10000	£3000
	b. Opt tête-bêche in vert pair	†	£8500
	c. No wmk	†	£5500
H4	20pf. ultramarine	42·00	50·00
H5	25pf. black and red/yellow	40·00	50·00
H6	30pf. black and orange/buff	50·00	60·00
H7	40pf. black and carmine	£225	£250
H8	50pf. black and purple/buff	£13000	£11000
H9	80pf. black and carmine/rose	£275	£275
H10	1m. carmine	£5000	£2750
H11	2m. blue	£13000	£15000
	a. "Occupation" double	£24000	£16000
	b. Opt inverted	£16000	

*The post office at Lomé was open for four hours on 17 September, before closing again on instructions from Accra. It finally reopened on 24 September.

The *tête-bêche* overprint on the 10pf. is due to the sheet being turned round after the upper 50 stamps had been overprinted so that vertical pairs from the two middle rows have the overprint *tête-bêche*.

1914 (1 Oct). Nos. H1 and H2 surch as T **2**.

H12	½d. on 3pf. brown	£160	£140
	a. Thin "y" in "penny"	£400	£350
H13	1d. on 5pf. green	£160	£140
	a. Thin "y" in "penny"	£400	£350

TOGO	**TOGO**
Anglo-French	**Anglo-French**
Occupation	**Occupation**
	Half penny
(3)	(4)

1914 (Oct).

(a) Optd with T 3. Narrow Setting. Lines 2 mm apart. "Anglo-French" measures 16 mm

H14	3pf. brown	£6500	£1100
H15	5pf. green	£1500	750
H16	10pf. carmine	†	£3000
	a. No wmk	†	£7000
H17	20pf. ultramarine	32·00	12·00
	a. "TOG"	£3500	£2500
	b. Nos. H4 and H17 se-tenant (vert pair)		£9000
H18	25pf. black and red/*yellow*	42·00	35·00
	a. "TOG"		£12000
H19	30pf. black and orange/*buff*	20·00	29·00
H20	40pf. black and carmine	£6000	£1600
H21	50pf. black and purple/*buff*	†	£9000
H22	80pf. black and carmine/*rose*	£3250	£2250
H23	1m. carmine	£8000	£4250
H24	2m. blue	†	£100000
H25	3m. violet-black	†	£100000
H26	5m. lake and black	†	£100000

(b) Narrow setting, but including value, as T 4

H27	½d. on 3pf. brown	48·00	26·00
	a. "TOG"	£425	£300
	b. Thin y" in "penny"	75·00	60·00
H28	1d. on 5pf. green	7·00	4·25
	a. "TOG"	£130	£110
	b. Thin "y" in "penny"	12·00	15·00

In the 20pf. one half of a sheet was overprinted with the wide setting (3 mm), and the other half with the narrow setting (2 *mm*), so that vertical pairs from the middle of the sheet show the two varieties of the overprint.

TOGO
Anglo-French
Occupation
(6)

1915 (7 Jan). Optd as T **6**. The words "Anglo-French" measure 15 mm instead of 16 mm as in T **3**.

H29	3pf. brown	£9000	£2500
H30	5pf. green	£225	£130
	a. "Occupation" omitted	£12000	
H31	10pf. carmine	£200	£130
	a. No wmk	†	£7000
H32	20pf. ultramarine	£1400	£400
H32a	40pf. black and carmine	†	£9000
H33	50pf. black and purple/*buff*	£16000	£11000

This printing was made on another batch of German Togo stamps, found at Sansane-Mangu.

TOGO
ANGLO-FRENCH
OCCUPATION

OCCU OCCU

(7)	Accra opt	London opt

Stamps of Gold Coast overprinted

1915 (May). Nos. 70/81, 82b and 83/4 of Gold Coast (King George V) optd at Govt Press, Accra, with T **7** ("OCCUPATION" 14½ mm long).

H34	½d. green (*shades*)	75	4·75
	a. Small "F" in "FRENCH"	2·25	12·00
	b. Thin "G" in "TOGO"	4·50	22·00
	c. No hyphen after "ANGLO"	4·50	22·00
	e. "CUPATION" for "OCCUPATION"	£140	
	f. "CCUPATION" for "OCCUPATION"	80·00	
	g. Opt double		
H35	1d. red	1·25	75
	a. Small "F" in "FRENCH"	2·75	3·75
	b. Thin "G" in "TOGO"	9·00	15·00
	c. No hyphen after "ANGLO"	9·00	15·00
	f. "CCUPATION" for "OCCUPATION"	£200	
	g. Opt double	£350	£475
	h. Opt inverted	£250	
	ha. Ditto. "TOGO" omitted	£8000	
H36	2d. grey	1·25	2·25
	a. Small "F" in "FRENCH"	5·00	8·00
	b. Thin "G" in "TOGO"	6·50	19·00
	c. No hyphen after "ANGLO"	£250	
	d. Two hyphens after "ANGLO"	55·00	
	f. "CCUPATION" for "OCCUPATION"	£250	
H37	2½d. bright blue	4·75	8·50
	a. Small "F" in "FRENCH"	9·00	15·00
	b. Thin "G" in "TOGO"	17·00	38·00
	c. No hyphen after "ANGLO"	£170	
	d. Two hyphens after "ANGLO"	60·00	
	f. "CCUPATION" for "OCCUPATION"	£170	
H38	3d. purple/*yellow*	4·25	7·50
	a. Small "F" in "FRENCH"	8·00	15·00
	b. Thin "G" in "TOGO"	22·00	40·00
	c. No hyphen after "ANGLO"	55·00	
	f. "CCUPATION" for "OCCUPATION"	£225	
	g. White back	4·75	27·00
	ga. Small "F" in "FRENCH"	27·00	80·00
	gb. Thin "G" in "TOGO"	65·00	£160
H40	6d. dull and bright purple	3·50	3·25
	a. Small "F" in "FRENCH"	9·00	15·00
	b. Thin "G" in "TOGO"	22·00	32·00
	f. "CCUPATION" for "OCCUPATION"	£300	
H41	1s. black/*green*	3·00	14·00
	a. Small F" in "FRENCH"	4·75	25·00
	b. Thin "G" in "TOGO"	21·00	65·00
	f. "CCUPATION" for "OCCUPATION"	£170	
	g. Opt double	£1500	
H42	2s. purple and blue/*blue*	18·00	26·00
	a. Small "F" in "FRENCH"	50·00	80·00
	b. Thin "G" in "TOGO"	£100	£160
	c. No hyphen after "ANGLO"	£275	
	f. "CCUPATION" for "OCCUPATION"	£450	
H43	2s.6d. black and red/*blue*	5·50	32·00
	a. Small "F" in "FRENCH"	23·00	£100
	b. Thin "G" in "TOGO"	55·00	£200
	c. No hyphen after "ANGLO"	£275	
	f. "CCUPATION" for "OCCUPATION"	£600	

H44	5s. green and red/*yellow* (*white back*)	12·00	15·00
	a. Small "F" in "FRENCH"	65·00	£100
	b. Thin "G" in "TOGO"	90·00	£200
	c. No hyphen after "ANGLO"	£325	
	f. "CCUPATION" for "OCCUPATION"	£550	
H45	10s. green and red/*green*	50·00	60·00
	a. Small "F" in "FRENCH"	£120	
	b. Thin "G" in "TOGO"	£225	
	f. "CCUPATION" for "OCCUPATION"	£650	
H46	20s. purple and black/*red*	£150	£160
	a. Small "F" in "FRENCH"	£350	
	b. Thin "G" in "TOGO"	£650	
	f. "CCUPATION" for "OCCUPATION"	£850	
H34/46 Set of 12		£200	£275

Nos. H34/46 were overprinted in panes of 60 (6×10), using a setting of movable type. There were three printings:
1st printing (all values, 3d. No. H38 only).
2nd printing (all values, 3d. No. H38g only).
3rd printing (recorded on 1d., 3d. (H38), 2s., 2s.6d., 5s. only.)

Varieties occur as follows (Nos. indicate position in setting)
a. Small "F" in "FRENCH" (25, 58, 59). Present in all three printings on pos. 25, and on pos. 58 and 59 in first and second printings.
b. Thin "G" in "TOGO" (24) Constant in all three printings. The letter is from a slightly smaller fount.
c. No hyphen after "ANGLO" (5, 28). Occurs on pos. 5 during the first printing (½d., 1d., 2d., 2½d., 3d. (No. H38), rare on the 2d. and 2½d.), and again on the third printing (½d., 1d., 3d., (No. H38), 2s., 2s.6d., 5s.). It is also found on pos. 28 in the first printing (½d. and 1d. only).
d. Two hyphens after "ANGLO" (5). Occurs on pos. 5 during the first printing (2d., 2½d. only). The two hyphens vary in character. The same two values are also found with misplaced hyphen from this position.
e. "CUPATION" for "OCCUPATION" (33) ½d. value only, first printing.
f. "CCUPATION" for "OCCUPATION" (57). All values, first printing.

CHARACTERISTICS OF THE ACCRA OVERPRINT

Being set up from movable type, no two positions are exactly the same and there are many minor varieties of broken type. The two "C"s in "OCCUPATION" often differ slightly in shape and one or both usually have closed jaws. The word "OCCUPATION" is generally fractionally shorter (at 14½ to 14¾ mm) than in the subsequent London overprint, where the length is consistently 15 mm. The impression is variable, but usually appears weaker than the London overprint, which is normally bold and well-inked.

The position of the overprint on the stamp varies greatly, with the word "TOGO" often encroaching on the crown above the King's head (high position) or the word "OCCUPATION" encroaching on the value tablet (low position). The subsequent London overprint is invariably well-centred, leaving both crown and value tablet clear.

Note that the 3d. (No. H38g) and 5s. (No. H44) with white back do not occur with the London overprint.

The 1d. opt inverted (No. H35h) exists with small "F" (Price £1700 *unused*), thin "G" (Price £4500 *unused*) and "No hyphen" (Price £4500 *unused*).

Examples of all values, and especially the varieties, are known showing a forged Lomé postmark dated "22 1 15".

TOGO
ANGLO-FRENCH
OCCUPATION
8

1916 (Apr)–**20**. Nos. 70/84 of Gold Coast (King George V) optd in London with T **8** ("OCCUPATION" 15 *mm* long). Heavy type and thicker letters showing through on back.

H47	½d. green	30	2·75
H48	1d. red	30	85
H49	2d. grey	1·00	3·75
H50	2½d. bright blue	1·25	1·50
H51	3d. purple/*yellow*	7·50	1·25
	a. On buff-yellow (1919)	10·00	3·00
H52	6d. dull and bright purple	2·75	2·25
	w. Wmk inverted	£160	£275
H53	1s. black/*green*	10·00	16·00
	a. On blue-green (olive back) (1918)	15·00	18·00
	b. On emerald-green (olive back) (1920)	£1100	
	c. On emerald-green (emerald-green back) (1920)	£425	£900
H54	2s. purple and blue/*blue*	6·00	8·50
	a. Wmk sideways	£3250	£3250
H55	2s.6d. black and red/*blue*	4·50	7·00
H56	5s. green and red/*yellow*	42·00	27·00
	a. On buff-yellow (1919)	38·00	50·00
H57	10s. green and red/*green*	28·00	65·00
	a. On blue-green (olive back) (1920)	22·00	75·00
H58	20s. purple and black/*red*	£160	£190
H47/58 Set of 12		£200	£275
H47s/58s Optd "SPECIMEN" Set of 12		£350	

Nos. H47/58 were overprinted by De La Rue using a stereotyped plate, probably of 120 (two panes, each 6×10). The overprint is much more consistent than the Accra printings and is usually bold and well-inked, with letters that appear thicker, particularly in the word "TOGO". "OCCUPATION" measures 15 mm in length. The two "C"s in "OCCUPATION" are identical in size and style, with open jaws.

The overprint is invariably well-centred, with the top of the word "TOGO" placed just below the top of the King's head on the 1d. and just below the base of the crown on the other values, leaving the value tablet completely clear.

Nos. H51a, 53a/c, 56/a and 57a are all shades which were overprinted only in London and do not exist with the Accra overprint. Nos. H51a and 56a, described as on "buff-yellow" paper, include second printings made in 1920, which are not easy to distinguish. Viewed from the back, the paper appears rather pale and dull, in comparison with the bright (almost lemon) yellow of Nos. H51 and 56.

Nos. H47/58 were withdrawn in October 1920 when Gold Coast stamps were introduced.

The mandates were transferred to the United Nations in January 1946. The inhabitants of the British mandate voted to join Ghana in 1957.

■ **Tokelau** *see after* **New Zealand**

Tonga

The Tongan Post Office was established in 1885 and FIJI 2d. and 6d. stamps are recorded in use until the arrival of Nos. 1/4.

PRICES FOR STAMPS ON COVER TO 1945	
Nos. 1/4	from × 60
Nos. 5/9	from × 20
Nos. 10/28	from × 8
Nos. 29/31	from × 7
Nos. 32/7	from × 6
Nos. 38/54	from × 5
Nos. 55/63	from × 6
Nos. 64/70	from × 3
Nos. 71/87	from × 2
Nos. O1/10	from × 25

PROTECTORATE KINGDOM
King George I, 1845–93

1 King George I	2

(Eng Bock and Cousins. Plates made and typo Govt Ptg Office, Wellington)

1886–88. W **2**. P 12½ (line) or 12×11½ (comb)*.

1	**1**	1d. carmine (P 12½) (27.8.86)	£450	6·00
		a. Perf 12½×10		
		b. Perf 12×11½ (15.7.87)	10·00	3·25
		ba. Pale carmine (P 12×11½)	16·00	9·00
2		2d. pale violet (P 12½) (27.8.86)	50·00	10·00
		a. Bright violet	70·00	3·50
		b. Perf 12×11½ (15.7.87)	45·00	2·75
		ba. Bright violet (P 12×11½)	55·00	3·00
3		6d. blue (P 12½) (9.10.86)	60·00	2·25
		a. Perf 12×11½ (15.10.88)	50·00	2·25
		ab. Dull blue (P 12×11½)	35·00	2·25
4		1s. pale green (P 12½) (9.10.86)	95·00	4·50
		a. Deep green (P 12½)	£100	2·25
		b. Perf 12×11½ (15.10.88)	55·00	6·00
		ba. Deep green (P 12×11½)	55·00	3·25

*See note after New Zealand, No. 186.

FOUR PENCE.

EIGHT PENCE.

(3)	(4)

(Surch Messrs Wilson & Horton, Auckland, N.Z.)

1891 (10 Nov). Nos. 1b and 2b surch.

5	**3**	4d. on 1d. carmine	3·00	14·00
		a. No stop after "PENCE"	50·00	£130
6	**4**	8d. on 2d. violet	45·00	£110
		a. Short "T" in "EIGHT"	£170	£325

No. 5a occurred on R. 6/8 and 9, R. 10/11, all from the right-hand pane.

1891 (23 Nov). Optd with stars in upper right and lower left corners by lithography. P 12½.

7	**1**	1d. carmine	50·00	70·00
		a. Three stars	£400	
		b. Four stars	£550	
		c. Five stars	£800	
		d. Perf 12×11½	£300	
		da. Three stars	£550	
		db. Four stars	£700	
		dc. Five stars	£950	
8		2d. violet	80·00	38·00
		a. Perf 12×11½	£400	

Stamps with forged stars are known, but the stars are invariably applied by typography (letterpress) and indent the paper.

The varieties with three, four or five stars emanate from sheets which received a double overprint, one impression being sideways.

1892 (15 Aug). W **2**. P 12×11½.

9	**1**	6d. yellow-orange	16·00	38·00

5 Arms of Tonga	6 King George I

Damaged "O" in "TONGA" (R. 1/1, later corrected)

(Dies eng A. E. Cousins. Typo at Govt Printing Office, Wellington, N.Z.)

1892 (10 Nov). W **2**. P 12×11½.

10	**5**	1d. pale rose	23·00	35·00
		a. Bright rose	18·00	35·00

	b. Bisected diag (½d.) (1893) *(on cover)*		†	£850
	c. Damaged "O"		£110	£160
11	6	2d. olive	40·00	16·00
12	5	4d. chestnut	50·00	75·00
13	6	8d. bright mauve	70·00	£180
14		1s. brown	85·00	£140
10/14	*Set of 5*		£225	£400

No. 10b was used from 31 May 1893 to provide a 2½d. rate before the arrival of No. 15, and on subsequent occasions up to 1895.

(7) (8) (9) (10)

1893. Printed in new colours and surch with T **7/10** by Govt Printing Office, Wellington.

(a) In carmine. P 12½ (21 Aug)

15	5	½d. on 1d. bright ultramarine	23·00	27·00
		a. Surch omitted		
16	6	2½d. on 8d. carmine	26·00	12·00
17		5d. on 4d. orange	4·50	8·00
18	6	7½d. on 8d. carmine	32·00	80·00

(b) In black. P 12×11½ (Nov)

19	5	½d. on 1d. dull blue	42·00	50·00
20	6	2½d. on 2d. green	17·00	17·00
		a. Surch double	£2000	£2000
		b. Fraction bar completely omitted (R. 3/3)		

King George II, 1893–1918

(11) (12) Small "F" in "HALF"

(Surch at the *Star* Office, Auckland, N.Z.)

1894 (June–Nov). Surch with T **11** or **12**.

21	5	½d. on 4d. chestnut (B.) (11.94)	2·00	7·00
		a. "SURCHARCE"	9·00	22·00
		b. Small "F"	9·00	22·00
22	6	½d. on 1s. brown	2·50	11·00
		a. "SURCHARCE"	11·00	42·00
		b. Small "F"	11·00	42·00
		c. Surch double	£275	
		d. Surch double with "SURCHARCE"	£900	
		e. Surch double with small "F"	£750	
23		2½d. on 8d. mauve	13·00	8·00
		a. No stop after "SURCHARGE"	48·00	55·00
		b. Mixed perfs 12×11½ and 12½		
24	1	2½d. on 1s. deep green (No. 4a) (11.94)	65·00	28·00
		a. No stop after "SURCHARGE"	£200	
		b. Perf 12×11½	15·00	48·00
		ba. No stop after "SURCHARGE"	55·00	

Nos. 21/4 were surcharged in panes of 60 (6×10) with No. 21a occurring on R. 2/6, 4/6, 5/6, 8/6 and 10/6, No. 21b on R. 1/4, 3/4, 6/4, 7/4 and 9/4, No. 22a on R. 1/6, 3/6, 5/6, 8/6 and 10/6, No. 22b on R. 2/4, 4/4, 6/4, 7/4 and 9/4 (both after the setting had been rearranged), No. 23a on R. 3/1–3 and Nos. 24a and 24ba on R. 6/3 and R. 7/3 or R. 7/1–2.

Sheets used for these provisionals were surcharged with the remains of the tissue interleaving still in place. This sometimes subsequently fell away taking parts of the surcharge with it.

Deformed "E" in "PENI" (R. 2/2)

(Design resembling No. 11 litho and surch at *Star* Office Auckland, N.Z.)

1895 (22 May*). As T **6** surch as T **11** and **12**. No wmk. P 12.

25	11	1d. on 2d. pale blue (C.)	50·00	40·00
		a. Deformed "E"	£130	£100
26	12	1½d. on 2d. pale blue (C.)	65·00	50·00
		a. Deformed "E"	£170	£120
		b. Perf 12×11	50·00	50·00
		ba. Deformed "E"	£130	£120
27		2½d. on 2d. pale blue (C.)†	40·00	50·00
		a. No stop after "SURCHARGE"	£225	£225
		b. Deformed "E"	£110	£130
28		7½d. on 2d. pale blue (C.)	£500	
		a. Deformed "E"		
		b. Perf 12×11	65·00	50·00
		ba. Deformed "E"	£170	£140

*Earliest known date of use.

†The 2½d. on 2d. is the only value which normally has a stop after the word "SURCHARGE".

No. 27a occurs on R. 1/3 of the right-hand pane.

12a King George II

13 King George II

(14)

"BU" joined (R. 1/1)   Missing eyebrow (R. 2/4)

"7" for "1" in "½d." (R. 2/1)

1895 (20 June*). Unissued stamp surch as in T **12a**. No wmk. P 12.

29	11	½d. on 2½d. vermilion	50·00	32·00
		a. "BU" joined	£100	75·00
		b. "SURCHARCE"	90·00	70·00
		c. Missing eyebrow	£100	75·00
		d. Stop after "POSTAGE" (R. 2/5)	£100	75·00
		e. "7" for "1" in "½d."	£100	75·00
30		1d. on 2½d. vermilion	£100	50·00
		a. "BU" joined	£170	£110
		c. Missing eyebrow	£170	£110
		d. Stop after "POSTAGE" (R. 2/5)	£170	£110
		e. "7" for "1" in "½d."	£170	£110
31	12	7½d. on 2½d. vermilion	60·00	75·00
		a. "BU" joined	£110	£120
		c. Missing eyebrow	£110	£120
		d. Stop after "POSTAGE" (R. 2/5)	£110	£120
		e. "7" for "1" in "½d."	£110	£120

*Earliest known date of use.

No. 29b occurs on R. 1/6 and 3/6 of both the right and the left pane. In the ½d. surcharge there is a stop after "SURCHARGE" and not after "PENNY". In the 1d. and 7½d. the stop is after the value only.

"Black Eye" flaw (Rt pane R. 2/4)

(Litho *Star* Office, Auckland, N.Z.)

1895 (9 July–Sept). No wmk. P 12.

32	13	1d. olive-green	32·00	30·00
		a. Bisected diagonally (½d.) *(on cover)* (9.95)	†	£750
		b. Imperf between (horiz pair)	—	£7500
33		2½d. rose	30·00	9·00
		a. Stop (flaw) after "POSTAGE" (R. 4/5)	85·00	50·00
34		5d. blue	42·00	70·00
		a. "Black eye" flaw	£110	
		b. Perf 12×11	23·00	65·00
		ba. "Black eye" flaw	70·00	
		c. Perf 11	£400	
		ca. "Black eye" flaw		
35		7½d. orange-yellow	45·00	55·00
		a. Yellow	45·00	55·00

1896 (May). Nos. 26b and 28b with typewritten surcharge "Half-Penny-", in violet, and Tongan surcharge, in black, as T **14**.

a. Tongan surch reading downwards (right panes)

36A	6	½d. on 1½d. on 2d.		£450
		a. Perf 12	£425	£425
		e. "Halef"	£7000	
		f. "H" over "G"		
		g. "Pen?y"	£6000	
37A		½d. on 7½d. on 2d.	85·00	£120
		a. "Hafl" for "Half"	£2250	£2500
		b. "Hafl" ("Penny" omitted)	£5500	
		c. "PPenny"	£750	
		d. Stops instead of hyphens	£1100	
		e. "Halyf"		
		f. "Half-Penny-" inverted	£3250	
		g. No hyphen after "Penny"		
		i. No hyphen after "Half"	£1000	
		l. Capital "P" over small "p"		
		m. Hyphen after "Penny" over capital "Y"	£2250	
		p. Perf 12	£800	
		pa. No hyphen after "Half"		

---

		b. Tongan surch reading upwards (left panes)		
36B	6	½d. on 1½d. on 2d.	£450	£450
		a. Perf 12	£475	£475
		ab. "Haalf"	£3500	
		c. "H" double		
		e. "Penny"	£3500	
37B		½d. on 7½d. on 2d.	85·00	£120
		c. "PPenny"	£950	
		d. Stops instead of hyphens	£1100	
		f. "Half-Penny-" inverted	£4500	
		g. Comma instead of hyphen after "Penny"	£750	
		h. "Hwlf"		
		i. No hyphen after "Half"	£1500	
		j. "Penny" double		
		k. "Penny" twice, with "Half" on top of upper "Penny"	£4750	
		m. "Half H"	£1000	
		n. Tongan surch double	£1600	
		o. Two hyphens between "Half" and "Penny"		
		p. Perf 12	£800	

Nos. 26b and 28b were in sheets of 48 (2 panes 6×4). The panes were separated before the surcharges were applied.

There are variations in the relative positions of the words "Half" and "Penny", both vertically and horizontally.

Dangerous forgeries of the above issue are known to exist, particularly of the ½d. on 1½d. on 2d. (Nos. 36A/B), and no rarity should be acquired without a reliable guarantee. But note that whereas the violet typewritten part of the surcharge has been cleverly imitated, using a machine of the same model as was used for the original issue, such fakes also have a forged version of the black typeset Tongan surcharge.

Genuine typewritten surcharges show the letters "Hal" or "Half" spaced as in T **14**, with the "a" much closer to the "H". Examples with "Hal" evenly spaced are forged.

15 Arms

16 Ovava Tree, Kana-Kubolu

17 King George II

18 Prehistoric Trilith at Haamonga

19 Bread Fruit

20 Coral

21 View of Haapai

22 Red Shining Parrot

23 View of Vavau Harbour

24 Tortoises (*upright*)

Types of Type **17**:

Type I. Top of hilt showing   Type II. No sword hilt

1d. Normal

1d. Lopped branch (R. 8/5)
(ptgs from 1934 onwards)

Normal

Smaller "2" (R. 1/2, 1/4–5,
2/8, 4/4, 5/4 and 6/1)

10d. Normal

10d. Both "O"s small in "HOGOFULU"
(R. 1/7)

10d. Small second "O" in "HOGOFULU"
(R. 2/7)

WATERMARKS. Stamps with W **24** upright show all the tortoise heads pointing upwards, or downwards if inverted. On stamps with sideways watermark the heads point upwards or downwards alternately. Stamps with inverted or sideways inverted watermarks are not separately listed and should be assumed to have the same value as the upright (or sideways) versions.

(Recess D.L.R.)

1897 (1 June). W **24**. P. 14.

38	**15**	½d. indigo.................................	7·50	3·50
		a. Wmk sideways.....................	70	3·00
39	**16**	1d. black and scarlet................	80	80
		a. Wmk sideways.....................	10·00	3·50
		b. Lopped branch.....................	£150	
40	**17**	2d. sepia and bistre (I).............	32·00	9·00
		a. Wmk sideways.....................	20·00	3·50
		b. Smaller "2".........................	60·00	15·00
41		2d. sepia and bistre (II)............	50·00	10·00
		a. Wmk sideways.....................	45·00	10·00
		b. Smaller "2".........................	85·00	27·00
42		2d. grey and bistre (II)..............	50·00	3·25
		a. Wmk sideways.....................	30·00	3·50
		b. Smaller "2".........................	70·00	10·00
43		2½d. black and blue...................	12·00	1·40
		a. No fraction bar in "½" (R. 2/10).....................	£130	60·00
		b. Wmk sideways.....................	12·00	1·60
		ba. No fraction bar in "½" (R. 2/10).....................	£120	60·00
44	**18**	3d. black and yellow-green........	3·50	17·00
		a. Wmk sideways.....................	2·50	6·50
45	**19**	4d. green and purple.................	5·00	4·00
		a. Wmk sideways.....................	4·00	4·50
46	**17**	5d. black and orange (II)..........	32·00	12·00
		a. Wmk sideways.....................		
47	**20**	6d. red.....................................	13·00	8·00
		a. Wmk sideways.....................	8·50	14·00
48	**17**	7½d. black and green (II)...........	20·00	21·00
		a. Centre inverted....................	£9000	
49		10d. black and lake (II).............	48·00	45·00
		a. Wmk sideways.....................		
		b. Both "O"s small...................	£225	£225
		c. Small second "O".................	£225	£225
50		1s. black and red-brown (II).....	14·00	11·00
		a. No hyphen before "TAHA" (R. 3/5)	£160	£140
		b. Wmk sideways.....................		
51	**21**	2s. black and ultramarine.........	£130	£140
		a. Wmk sideways.....................	32·00	32·00
52	**22**	2s.6d. deep purple....................	50·00	30·00
		a. Wmk sideways.....................	65·00	50·00
53	**23**	5s. black and brown-red...........	48·00	50·00
		a. Wmk sideways.....................	26·00	32·00
38a/53a		Set of 14.................................	£225	£180

The 1d., 3d. and 4d. are known bisected and used for half their value.

T – L

(25)

Ⅰ June, 1899.

26 Queen Salote

1899 (1 June). Royal Wedding. No. 39a optd with T **25** at *Star Office*, Auckland, N.Z.

54	**16**	1d. black and scarlet (hyphen 2 *mm* long)........................	42·00	70·00
		a. "1889" for "1899" (R. 8/1, 8/4)......	£250	£400
		b. Hyphen 3 mm long.............	60·00	85·00
		c. Wmk upright.......................	65·00	95·00

	ca. "1889" for "1899" (R. 8/1, 8/4)......	£450	£700
	cb. Hyphen 3 mm long.............	90·00	£150

The letters "T L" stand for Taufa'ahau, the King's family name, and Lavinia, the bride.
No. 54 was overprinted from a setting of 30 (3×10) applied twice to the sheets of 60. The setting contains twenty-one examples of the 2 mm hyphen and nine of the 3 mm.

Queen Salote, 1918–65

Dies of the 2d.:

Die I (As used for 1897 issue)

Die II

Normal

"2½" recut (note lines on "2" and different "½") (R. 1/1)

Retouched (small) hyphen (R. 3/5)

(Recess D.L.R.)

1920 (Apr)–**35**. W **24** (sideways). P. 14.

55	**15**	½d. yellow-green (1934)..........	1·00	1·25
		a. Wmk upright.......................	55·00	75·00
56	**26**	1½d. grey-black (1935).............	50	2·50
57		2d. agate and aniline violet (Die I)..	17·00	13·00
		a. Wmk sideways.....................	45·00	50·00
		b. Smaller "2".........................	65·00	85·00
		c. *Black and slate-violet* (1924)	21·00	2·25
		ca. Wmk upright.......................		
		cb. Smaller "2".........................	70·00	20·00
		d. *Black and deep purple* (1925)......	20·00	3·00
		db. Smaller "2".........................	70·00	25·00
57e		2d. black and blackish lilac (Die II) (1932)...........................	10·00	10·00
58		2½d. black and blue (3.21)........	9·00	48·00
59		2½d. bright ultramarine (1934)...	10·00	1·00
		a. Recut "2½"...........................	50·00	9·50
60		5d. black and orange-vermilion (1921)...............................	3·25	8·00
61		7½d. black and yellow-green (1921) .	1·75	1·75
62		10d. black and lake (1921).........	2·50	4·75
		a. Both "O"s small...................	28·00	45·00
		b. Small second "O".................	28·00	45·00
		c. *Black and aniline carmine* (9.25)	7·00	20·00
		ca. Both "O"s small...................	75·00	£140
		cb. Small second "O".................	75·00	£140
63		1s. black and red-brown (1921)..	1·25	2·50
		a. Retouched (small) hyphen	16·00	26·00
		b. Wmk upright.......................	55·00	55·00
		ba. Retouched (small) hyphen	£200	£200
55/63		Set of 10.................................	50·00	75·00
55s/63s		Optd or Perf (Nos. 55s/6s and 59s) "SPECIMEN" Set of 9		£275

In Die II the ball of the "2" is larger and the word "PENI-E-UA" is re-engraved and slightly shorter; the "U" has a spur on the left side.
For illustrations of Nos. 62a/b see above No. 38.

TWO PENCE

TWO PENCE

PENI-E-UA   **PENI-E-UA**
(27)   (28)

1923 (20 Oct)–**24**. Nos. 46, 48/9, 50, 51/2 and 53a surch as T **27** (vert stamps) or **28** (horiz stamps).

64	**17**	2d. on 5d. black and orange (II) (B.)	1·00	85
		a. Wmk sideways.....................	30·00	20·00
65		2d. on 7½d. black and green (II) (B.)	35·00	45·00
		a. Wmk sideways.....................	£140	£150
66		2d. on 10d. black and lake (II) (B.)	24·00	70·00
		a. Wmk sideways.....................	£100	£130
		b. Both "O"s small...................	£120	
		c. Small second "O".................	£120	
67		2d. on 1s. black and red-brown (II) (B.)	75·00	22·00
		a. No hyphen before "TAHA" (R. 3/5)............................	£375	£200
		b. Wmk sideways.....................	£150	£120
68	**21**	2d. on 2s. black and ultramarine (R)	45·00	
		a. Wmk sideways.....................	12·00	13·00
69	**22**	2d. on 2s.6d. deep purple (R.)..	32·00	6·50
		a. Wmk sideways.....................	£170	90·00
70	**23**	2d. on 5s. black and brown-red (R.)	40·00	40·00
		a. Wmk sideways.....................	3·25	2·50
64/70a		Set of 7...................................	£160	£140

29 Queen Salote

(Recess D.L.R.)

1938 (12 Oct). 20th Anniv of Queen Salote's Accession. Tablet at foot dated "1918–1938". W **24** (sideways). P. 13½.

71	**29**	1d. black and scarlet................	1·25	9·00
72		2d. black and purple................	16·00	9·00
73		2½d. black and ultramarine.......	16·00	11·00
71/3		Set of 3...................................	30·00	26·00
71s/3s		Perf "SPECIMEN" Set of 3........		£100

For Silver Jubilee issue in a similar design, see Nos. 83/7.

Further die of 2d.:

Die III

(Recess D.L.R.)

1942–49. Wmk Mult Script CA (sideways on 5s.). P. 14.

74	**15**	½d. yellow-green.....................	30	3·50
		a. "A" of "CA" missing from wmk....	£650	
75	**16**	1d. black and scarlet................	2·50	3·00
		a. Lopped branch.....................	£140	£160
76	**26**	2d. black and purple (Die II).....	7·00	2·75
		a. Die III (4.49).......................	13·00	15·00
77		2½d. bright ultramarine.............	1·75	2·75
		a. Recut "2½"..........................	35·00	
78	**18**	3d. black and yellow-green........	65	6·00
79	**20**	6d. red.....................................	3·50	2·50
80	**26**	1s. black and red-brown............	5·00	3·50
		a. Retouched (small) hyphen.....	55·00	40·00
81	**22**	2s.6d. deep purple (1943).........	38·00	40·00
82	**23**	5s. black and brown-red (1943)..	16·00	60·00
74/82		Set of 9...................................	65·00	£110
74s/82s		Perf "SPECIMEN" Set of 9........		£250

In Die III the foot of the "2" is longer than in Die II and extends towards the right beyond the curve of the loop; the letters of "PENI-E-UA are taller and differently shaped.
Damage to the "2" on R. 4/9 of No. 77 was frequently corrected by hand-painting.
For illustration of No. 75a see above No. 38 and of No. 77a see above No. 55.
The ½d. 1d., 3d. and 1s. exist perforated from either line or comb machines. The other values only come line perforated.

30

(Recess D.L.R.)

1944 (25 Jan). Silver Jubilee of Queen Salote's Accession. As T **29**, but inscr "1918–1943" at foot, as T **30**. Wmk Mult Script CA. P. 14.

83		1d. black and carmine..............	15	1·25
84		2d. black and purple................	15	1·25
85		3d. black and green.................	15	1·25
86		6d. black and orange...............	1·00	2·00
87		1s. black and brown................	75	2·00
83/7		Set of 5...................................	2·00	7·00
83s/7s		Perf "SPECIMEN" Set of 5........		£140

1949 (10 Oct). 75th Anniv of UPU. As Nos. 114/17 of Antigua.

88		2½d. ultramarine......................	20	1·00
89		3d. olive.................................	2·00	4·50
90		6d. carmine-red.......................	20	1·00
91		1s. red-brown.........................	25	1·00
88/91		Set of 4...................................	2·40	6·75

31 Queen Salote

33 Queen Salote

32 Queen Salote

(Photo Waterlow)

1950 (1 Nov). Queen Salote's 50th Birthday. Wmk Mult Script CA. P. 12½.

92	**31**	1d. carmine.............................	1·40	5·00
93	**32**	5d. green.................................	1·40	4·25
94	**33**	1s. violet.................................	1·40	4·25
92/4		Set of 3...................................	3·75	12·00

34 Map

35 Palace, Nuku'alofa

36 Beach scene

37 HMNZS *Bellona*

38 Flag

39 Arms of Tonga and Great Britain

(Recess Waterlow)

1951 (2 July). 50th Anniv of Treaty of Friendship between Great Britain and Tonga. T **34/9**. Wmk Mult Script CA. P 12½ (3d.), 13×13½ (½d.), 13½×13 (others).

95	**34**	½d. green	30	4·25
96	**35**	1d. black and carmine	30	5·00
97	**36**	2½d. green and brown	30	4·25
98	**37**	3d. yellow and bright blue..............	2·75	3·00
99	**38**	5d. carmine and green	5·50	2·00
100	**39**	1s. yellow-orange and violet	4·50	2·00
95/100 *Set of 6*			12·00	18·00

40 Royal Palace, Nuku'alofa

41 Shore fishing with throw-net

42 *Hifofua* and *Aoniu* (ketches)

43 Swallows' Cave, Vava'u

44 Map of Tongatapu

45 Vava'u harbour

46 Post Office, Nuku'alofa

47 Aerodrome, Fua'amotu

48 *Matua* (inter-island freighter)

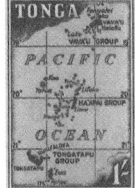

49 Map of Tonga Islands

50 Lifuka, Ha'apai

51 Mutiny on the *Bounty*

52 Queen Salote

53 Arms of Tonga

(Des J. Berry. Centre litho, frame recess (£1), recess (others) B.W.)

1953 (1 July). T **40/53**. W **24** (sideways). P 11×11½ (vert) or 11½×11 (horiz).

101	**40**	1d. black and red-brown	10	10
102	**41**	1½d. blue and emerald........................	20	10
103	**42**	2d. deep turquoise-green and black...........................	1·25	20
104	**43**	3d. blue and deep bluish green......	2·50	20
105	**44**	3½d. yellow and carmine-red..............	1·75	70
106	**45**	4d. yellow and deep rose-carmine	2·50	10
107	**46**	5d. blue and red-brown..............	1·00	10
108	**47**	6d. black and deep blue	1·50	30
109	**48**	8d. emerald and deep reddish violet	1·50	2·25
110	**49**	1s. blue and black.......................	2·00	10
111	**50**	2s. sage-green and brown	10·00	1·25
112	**51**	5s. orange-yellow and slate-lilac ..	25·00	9·50
113	**52**	10s. yellow and black....................	14·00	9·50
114	**53**	£1 yellow, scarlet, ultramarine and deep bright blue	14·00	6·50
101/14 *Set of 14*			70·00	26·00

54 Stamp of 1886

55 Whaling Ship and Whaleboat

(Des D. Bakeley. Photo Harrison)

1961 (1 Dec). 75th Anniv of Tongan Postal Service. T **54/5** and similar horiz designs. W **24** (sideways). P 14½×13½.

115		1d. carmine and brown-orange...............	10	10
116		2d. ultramarine	1·25	45
117		4d. blue-green	20	45
118		5d. violet	1·25	45
119		1s. red-brown	1·25	45
115/19 *Set of 5*			3·50	1·60

Designs:—4d. Queen Salote and Post Office, Nuku'alofa; 5d. *Aoniu II* (inter-island freighter); 1s. Douglas DC-4 mailplane over Tongatapu.

1862 TAU'ATĀINA EMANCIPATION 1962 (**59**)

60 "Protein Foods"

1962 (7 Feb). Centenary of Emancipation. Nos. 101, 104, 107/10, 112, 117 optd with T **59** (No. 126 surch also), in red, by R. S. Wallbank Govt Printer.

120		1d. black and red-brown	10	2·25
121		4d. blue-green	10	90
122		5d. blue and red-brown	15	90
123		6d. black and deep blue	20	1·25
124		8d. emerald and deep reddish violet	40	3·25
125		1s. blue and black..........................	20	1·00
		a. Opt inverted..........................	£600	£200
126		2s. on 3d. blue and deep bluish green...	40	8·00
		a. Missing fraction-bar in surch....	12·00	50·00
127		5s. orange-yellow and slate-lilac ...	6·50	8·00
		a. Opt inverted...........................	£225	£300
120/127 *Set of 8*			7·00	23·00

Nos. 120/4 and 127 were overprinted in sheets of 60 (5×12), using a 5×6 setting which was applied first to the lower half sheets, then to the upper. One full sheet of the 5s. (No. 127) received inverted opts on both halves.

Nos. 125/6 were overprinted or surcharged in half-sheets of 30 (6×5), using adjusted settings. The missing fraction bar variety (No. 126a) occurred at R. 3/1 on both upper and lower half sheets. One upper half sheet of the 1s (No. 125) inadvertently received an inverted opt (intended for a lower half sheet), from which only two unused examples survived, with the remainder used on first day covers at Vava'u.

(Des M. Goaman. Photo Harrison)

1963 (4 June). Freedom from Hunger. W **24**. P 14×14½.

128	**60**	11d. ultramarine..	50	40

61 Coat of Arms

62 Queen Salote

63 Queen Salote

(Des Ida West. Die-cut Walsall)

1963 (17 June). First Polynesian Gold Coinage Commemoration. Circular designs. Embossed on gold foil backed with paper, inscr overall "TONGA THE FRIENDLY ISLANDS". Imperf.

(a) Postage. ¼ koula coin. Diameter 1⅝in

129	**61**	1d. carmine	10	10
130	**62**	2d. deep blue	10	10
131	**61**	6d. blue-green	20	15
132	**62**	9d. bright purple.......................	20	15
133	**61**	1s.6d. violet..............................	30	30
134	**62**	2s. light emerald	40	40

(b) Air. (i) ½ koula coin. Diam 2⅛in

135	**63**	10d. carmine	20	20
136	**61**	11d. blue-green	30	30
137	**63**	1s.1d. deep blue	30	30

(ii) 1 koula coin. Diam 3⅛in

138	**63**	2s.1d. bright purple	45	50
139	**61**	2s.4d. light emerald	50	60
140	**63**	2s.9d. violet	50	60
129/140 *and* O17 *Set of 13*			14·00	15·00

Examples of a 9d. Postage value in the design of the 1s.6d. exists, but these have been identified as proofs.

64 Red Cross Emblem

(Des V. Whiteley. Litho B.W.)

1963 (7 Oct). Red Cross Centenary. W **24** (sideways). P 13½.

141	**64**	2d. red and black.................................	30	10
142		11d. red and blue.................................	1·00	1·50

65 Queen Salote

66 Map of Tongatapu

(Des M. Meers. Die-cut Walsall)

1964 (19 Oct). Pan-Pacific South-East Asia Women's Association Meeting, Nuku'alofa. Embossed on gold foil, backed with paper inscr overall "TONGA THE FRIENDLY ISLANDS". Imperf.

(a) Postage

143	**65**	3d. pink......................................	25	40
144		9d. light blue	35	40
145		2s. yellow-green	55	65
146		5s. lilac	90	1·50

		(b) Air			
147	66	10d. blue-green		35	30
148		1s.2d. black		45	45
149		3s.6d. cerise		75	1·50
150		6s.6d. violet		1·10	2·75
143/150		*Set of 8*		4·25	7·00

(67)

1965 (18 Mar). "Gold Coin" stamps of 1963 surch as T **67** by Walsall Lithographic Co. New figures of value in gold; obliterating colours shown in brackets.

(a) Postage

151	61	1s.3d. on 1s.6d. violet (R.)	25	25
152	62	1s.9d. on 9d. bright purple (W.)	25	25
153	61	2s.6d. on 6d. blue-green (R.)	30	55
154		5s. on 1d. carmine	17·00	27·00
155	62	5s. on 2d. deep blue	2·75	4·00
156		5s. on 2s. light emerald	70	1·25

(b) Air

157	63	2s.3d. on 10d. carmine	25	40
158	61	2s.9d. on 11d. blue-green (W.)	30	55
159	63	4s.6d. on 11d. bright purple (R.)	13·00	17·00
		a. Opt double	13·00	17·00
160	61	4s.6d. on 2s.4d. light emerald (R.)	13·00	17·00
161	63	4s.6d. on 2s.9d. violet (R.)	7·50	16·00
151/161 and O18		*Set of 12*	50·00	75·00

Examples of No. 160 are known with a larger surcharge panel. These may have come from a trial printing which was subsequently released to the stamp trade.

King Taufa'ahau IV, 16 December 1965

1866-1966
TUPOU COLLEGE
& SECONDARY
EDUCATION
(68)

AIRMAIL
1866 CENTENARY 1966
TUPOU COLLEGE
&
SECONDARY EDUCATION
10d
(69)

OU COLLE
&
ARY EDUC
Misplaced "&"
(R. 5/5)

1966 (18 June). Centenary of Tupou College and Secondary Education. Nos. 115/16 and 118/19 optd or surch.

(a) Postage. As T 68

162		1d. carmine and brown-orange (P.)	10	10
163		3d. on 1d. carmine and brown-orange (P.)	10	10
		a. Misplaced "3d" (R. 2/5)	2·75	
		b. Surch inverted	†	£900
164		6d. on 2d ultramarine (R.)	15	10
165		1s.2d. on 2d. ultramarine (R.)	25	10
166		2s. on 2d ultramarine (R.)	30	10
167		3s. on 2d. ultramarine (R.)	30	15

(b) Air. As T 69

168		5d. violet	15	10
		b. Misplaced "&"	2·75	
169		10d. on 1d. carmine and brown-orange	15	10
		b. Misplaced "&"	2·75	
170		1s. red-brown	30	10
		b. Misplaced "&"	2·75	
171		2s.9d. on 2d ultramarine	35	15
		a. Sideways second "X" (R. 3/4)	9·00	
		b. Misplaced "&"	8·00	
172		3s.6d. on 5d. violet	35	15
		a. Sideways second "X" (R. 3/4)	9·00	
		b. Misplaced "&"	8·00	
173		4s.6d. on 1s. red-brown	45	15
		a. Sideways second "X" (R. 3/4)	9·00	
		b. Misplaced "&"	8·00	
162/173 and O19/20		*Set of 14*	3·75	1·75

On No. 163a the "d" is 20 mm from the "X" instead of the normal 22 mm.

(70)

(71)

1966 (16 Dec). Queen Salote Commemoration. Nos. 143/4 and 147/8 optd as T **70/1**, or surch also, by Walsall Lithographic Co. Inscriptions and new figures of value in first colour and obliterating shapes in second colour given.

(a) Postage. Optd as T 70

174	65	3d. (silver and ultramarine)	35	20
175		5d. on 9d. (silver and black)	40	20
176		9d. (silver and black)	40	20

177		1s.7d. on 3d. (silver and ultramarine)	1·40	1·00
178		3s.6d. on 9d. (silver and black)	2·00	1·25
179		6s.6d. on 3d. (silver and ultramarine)	2·50	3·50

(b) Air. Optd as T 71

180	66	10d. (silver and black)	70	20
181		1s.2d. (black and gold)	80	35
182		4s. on 10d. (silver and black)	2·25	1·25
183		5s.6d. on 1s.2d. (black and gold)	2·50	2·50
184		10s.6d. on 1s.2d. (gold and black)	3·00	4·00
174/184		*Set of 11*	14·50	13·00

(New Currency. 100 seniti = 1 pa'anga)

10
Seniti

1 SENITI 1
(72)

10
(73)

1967 (25 Mar). Decimal currency. Various stamps surch as T **72/3**.

185		1s. on 1d. (No. 101)	10	20
186		2s. on 4d. (No. 106)	20	20
187		3s. on 5d. (No. 107)	10	20
188		4s. on 5d. (No. 107)	30	50
189		5s. on 3½d. (No. 105)	10	20
190		6s. on 8d. (No. 109)	30	20
191		7s. on 1½d. (No. 102)	10	20
192		8s. on 2d. (No. 108)	30	20
193		9s. on 3d. (No. 104)	15	20
194		10s. on 1s. (No. 110)	25	20
195		11s. on 3d. on 1d. (No. 163)	30	30
		a. Misplaced "3d" (R. 2/5)	14·00	
196		21s. on 3s. on 2d. (No. 167)	25	35
197		23s. on 1d. (No. 101)	25	35
198		30s. on 2s. (No. 111)* (R.)	2·75	4·25
199		30s. on 2s. (No. 111)* (R.)	2·75	4·25
200		50s. on 6d. (No. 108) (R.)	1·25	2·25
201		60s. on 3d. (No. 103) (R.)	1·50	2·50
185/201 and O21		*Set of 18*	17·00	18·00

The above surcharges come in a variety of types and sizes.
*No. 198 has the surcharged value expressed horizontally; No. 199 has the figures "30" above and below "SENITI".

74 Coat of Arms (reverse)

75 King Taufa'ahau IV (obverse)

(Die-cut Walsall)

1967 (4 July). Coronation of King Taufa'ahau IV. Circular designs. Embossed on palladium foil, backed with paper inscr overall "The Friendly Islands Tonga", etc. Imperf.

Sizes

(a) Diameter 1½ in.	(d) Diameter 2³/₁₀ in.	
(b) Diameter 1⁷/₁₀in.	(e) Diameter 2⁷/₁₀ in.	
(c) Diameter 2 in.	(f) Diameter 2⁹/₁₀ in.	

(a) Postage

202	74	1s. orange and greenish blue (b)	10	30
203	75	2s. greenish blue and deep magenta (d)	10	30
204	74	4s. emerald and bright purple (d)	15	25
205	75	15s. turquoise and violet (e)	55	25
206	74	28s. black and bright purple (a)	1·25	60
207	75	50s. carmine-red and ultramarine (c)	2·00	2·00
208	74	1p. blue and carmine (f)	2·75	3·25

(b) Air

209	75	7s. carmine-red and black (b)	25	10
210	74	9s. brown-purple and emerald (c)	35	10
211	75	11s. greenish blue and orange (d)	40	15
212	74	21s. black and emerald (e)	75	30
213	75	23s. bright purple and light emerald (a)	85	45
214	75	29s. ultramarine and emerald (c)	1·10	45
215	75	2p. bright purple and orange (f)	3·75	4·50
202/15		*Set of 14*	13·00	11·50

The commemorative coins depicted in reverse (Type **74**) are inscribed in various denominations as follows: 1s.—"20 SENITI"; 4s.—"PA'ANGA"; 9s.—"50 SENITI"; 21s.—"TWO PA'ANGA"; 28s.—"QUARTER HAU"; 29s.—"HALF HAU"; 1p. "HAU".

The
Friendly Islands
welcome the
United States
Peace Corps
(76)

S

1967 (15 Dec). Arrival of US Peace Corps in Tonga. As Nos. 101/14, but imperf in different colours and surch as T **76**.

(a) Postage

216		1s. on 1d. black and orange-yellow	10	20
217		2s. on 2d. ultramarine and carmine-red	10	20
218		3s. on 3d. chestnut and yellow	10	20
219		4s. on 4d. reddish violet and yellow	10	20
220		5s. on 5d. green and yellow	10	10
221		10s. on 1s. carmine-red and yellow	10	10
222		20s. on 2s. claret and new blue	30	15
223		50s. on 5s. sepia and orange-yellow	2·75	1·75
224		1p. on 10s. orange-yellow	70	2·00

(b) Air

225		11s. on 3½d. ultramarine (R.)	15	20
226		21s. on 1½d. emerald	30	20
227		23s. on 3½d. ultramarine	30	20
216/27 and O26/8		*Set of 15*	6·00	9·00

On Nos. 219 and 224 the opt is smaller, and in four lines instead of five. On Nos. 216/20 the surcharge takes the form of an alteration to the currency name as in T **76**.

10
SENITI

2 SENITI 2
(77)

10
(78)

1968 (6 Apr). Various stamps surch as T **77/8**.

(a) Postage

228		1s. on 1d. (No. 101) (R.)	10	10
229		2s. on 4d. (No. 106) (R.)	10	20
230		3s. on 3d. (No. 104) (B.)	10	20
231		4s. on 5d. (No. 107) (R.)	10	20
232		5s. on 3d. (No. 103) (R.)	10	20
233		6s. on 6d. (No. 108) (R.)	10	20
234		7s. on 1½d.(No. 102) (R.)	10	15
235		8s. on 8d. (No. 109) (R.)	10	25
236		9s. on 3½d. (No. 105) (R.)	20	30
237		10s. on 1s. (No. 110) (R.)	20	20
238		20s. on 5s. (No. 112) (R.)	1·75	70
239		2p. on 10s. (No. 111) (R.)	1·50	2·75

(b) Air. Surch as T 78 with "AIRMAIL" added

240		11s. on 10s. (No. 113) (R.)	25	30
241		21s. on 10s. (No. 113) (R.)	40	50
242		23s. on 10s. (No. 113) (R.)	40	50
228/42 and O22/5		*Set of 19*	8·75	12·50

Friendly Islands
Field & Track Trials
South Pacific Games
Port Moresby
1969

H.M'S BIRTHDAY
4 JULY 1968
(79)
(80)

S

1968 (4 July). 50th Birthday of King Taufa'ahau IV. Nos. 202/15 optd as T **79**.

(a) Postage

243	74	1s. orange and greenish blue (b) (R.)	10	60
244	75	2s. greenish blue and deep magenta (b) (B.)	20	60
245	74	4s. emerald and bright purple (d) (R.)	40	60
246	75	15s. turquoise and violet (e) (R.)	1·75	35
247	74	28s. black and bright purple (a) (R.)	2·50	45
248	75	50s. carmine-red and ultramarine (c) (B.)	3·25	2·25
249	74	1p. blue and carmine (f) (R.)	6·50	8·00

(b) Air

250	75	7s. carmine-red and black (b) (B.)	80	20
251	74	9s. brown-purple and emerald (c) (R.)	85	20
252	75	11s. greenish blue and orange (d) (B.)	1·00	25
253	74	21s. black and emerald (e) (R.)	2·25	30
		a. Opt (gold only) double	£275	
254	75	23s. bright purple and light emerald (a) (B.)	2·25	30
255	74	29s. ultramarine and emerald (c) (R.)	2·50	40
256	75	2p. bright purple and orange (f) (B.)	10·00	14·00
243/56 and O29/32		*Set of 18*	50·00	42·00

The overprints vary in size, but are all crescent-shaped as Type **79** and inscribed "H.M'S BIRTHDAY 4 JULY 1968" (Type **79**) or "HIS MAJESTY'S 50th BIRTHDAY" (others).

1968 (19 Dec). South Pacific Games Field and Track Trials, Port Moresby, Papua New Guinea. Nos. 101/13, but imperf, in different colours and surch as T **80**.

(a) Postage

257		5s. on 5d green and yellow (R.)	10	15
258		10s. on 1s. carmine-red and yellow	20	15
259		15s. on 2s. claret and new blue	30	20
260		25s. on 2d. ultramarine and carmine-red	30	25
261		50s. on 1d. black and orange-yellow	35	65
262		75s. on 10s. orange-yellow (G.)	60	1·50

		(b) Air		
263		6s. on 6d. black and yellow*......................	10	15
264		7s. on 4d. reddish violet and yellow.......	10	15
265		8s. on 8d. black and greenish yellow......	25	15
		a. Surch 11½ mm as on 6d...................	£140	£100
266		9s. on 1½d. emerald	10	15
267		11s. on 3d. chestnut and yellow.............	15	15
268		21s. on 3½d. ultramarine	20	20
269		38s. on 5s. sepia and orange-yellow.......	3·00	1·25
270		1p. on 10s. orange-yellow........................	70	2·00
257/70 *and* O33/4 *Set of 16*.............................			6·25	8·25

*On No. 263 the surcharge is smaller (11½ mm wide).

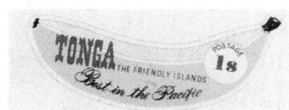

(81) (82)

1969. Emergency Provisionals. Various stamps (Nos. 273/6 are imperf and in different colours) surch as T **81** or **82**.

		(a) Postage		
271		1s. on 1s.2d. on 2d. ultramarine (No. 165)	2·75	5·00
272		1s. on 2s. on 2d. ultramarine (No. 166)..	2·75	5·00
273		1s. on 6d. black and yellow (as No. 108)	70	2·00
274		2s. on 3½d. ultramarine (as No. 105)......	75	2·00
275		3s. on 1½d. emerald (as No. 102)...........	75	2·00
276		4s. on 8d. black and greenish yellow (as No. 109)	1·00	2·00
		(b) Air. Nos. 171/3 surch with T **82**		
277		1s. on 2s.9d. on 2d. ultramarine.............	3·00	5·00
		a. Sideways second "X" (R. 3/4)	42·00	
		b. Misplaced "&"	40·00	
278		1s. on 3s.6d. on 5d. violet.......................	3·00	5·00
		a. Sideways second "X" (R. 3/4)	42·00	
		b. Misplaced "&"	40·00	
279		1s. on 4s.6d. on 1s. red-brown................	3·00	5·00
		a. Sideways second "X" (R. 3/4)	42·00	
		b. Misplaced "&"	40·00	
271/9 *Set of 9*..			16·00	30·00

SELF-ADHESIVE ISSUES. From No. 280 until No. 344 all stamps were manufactured by Walsall Security Printers Ltd and are self-adhesive. This also applies to the Official stamps.

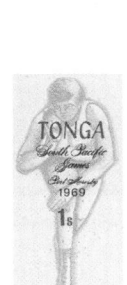

83 Banana

1969 (21 Apr). Coil stamps.

280	**83**	1s. scarlet, black and greenish yellow	1·40	2·50
281		2s. bright green, black and greenish yellow	1·50	2·50
282		3s. violet, black and greenish yellow	1·60	2·50
283		4s. ultramarine, black and greenish yellow	1·75	2·50
284		5s. bronze-green, black and greenish yellow	1·90	2·50
280/4 *Set of 5*..			7·25	11·00

Nos. 280/4 were produced in rolls of 200, each even stamp having a number applied to the front of the backing paper, with the usual inscription on the reverse.

See also Nos. 325/9.

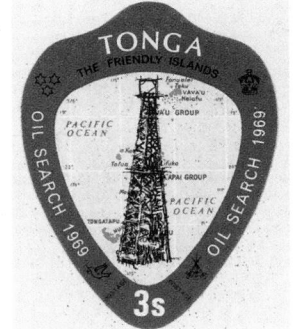

84 Putting the Shot	**86** Oil Derrick and Map

1969 (13 Aug). Third South Pacific Games, Port Moresby. T **84** and similar design.

		(a) Postage		
285	**84**	1s. black, red and buff..............	10	15
286		3s. bright green, red and buff..........	10	15
287		6s. blue, red and buff	10	15
288		10s. bluish violet, red and buff	15	15
289		30s. blue, red and buff	30	30
		(b) Air		
290	–	9s. black, violet and orange......	15	15
291	–	11s. black, ultramarine and orange..	15	15
292	–	20s. black, bright green and orange	25	15
293	–	60s. black, cerise and orange......	75	1·25
294	–	1p. black, blue-green and orange...	1·10	2·00
285/94 *and* O35/6 *Set of 12*......................			4·25	7·00
Design:—9, 11, 20, 60s., 1p. Boxing.				

1969 (23 Dec). First Oil Search in Tonga. T **86** and similar vert design.

		(a) Postage		
295	**86**	3s. multicoloured	65	25
296		7s. multicoloured	85	25
297		20s. multicoloured	1·50	50
298		25s. multicoloured	1·50	50
299		35s. multicoloured	1·75	80
		(b) Air		
300	–	9s. multicoloured	85	25
301	–	10s. multicoloured	85	25
302	–	24s. multicoloured	1·50	50
303	–	29s. multicoloured	1·75	70
304	–	38s. multicoloured	2·00	80
295/304 *and* O37/8 *Set of 12*..................			19·00	15·00
Design:—Nos. 300/4, Oil derrick and island of Tongatapu.				

87 Members of the British and Tongan Royal Families

1970 (7 Mar). Royal Visit. T **87** and similar design. Multicoloured.

		(a) Postage		
305	**87**	3s. multicoloured	60	30
306		5s. multicoloured	70	30
307		10s. multicoloured	1·00	40
308		25s. multicoloured	2·50	75
309		50s. multicoloured	4·25	4·00
		(b) Air		
310	–	7s. multicoloured	90	25
311	–	9s. multicoloured	1·00	30
312	–	24s. multicoloured	2·50	75
313	–	29s. multicoloured	2·75	80
314	–	38s. multicoloured	3·75	1·50
305/14 *and* O39/41 *Set of 13*..................			45·00	29·00

Design:—Nos. 310/14, Queen Elizabeth II and King Taufaʻahau Tupou IV.

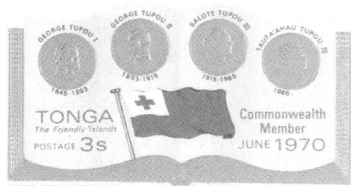

89 Book, Tongan Rulers and Flag

1970 (4 June). Entry into British Commonwealth. T **89** and similar design.

		(a) Postage		
315	**89**	3s. multicoloured	65	25
316		7s. multicoloured	90	30
317		15s. multicoloured	1·40	40
318		25s. multicoloured	1·75	90
319		50s. multicoloured	2·75	2·50
		(b) Air		
320	–	9s. turquoise-blue, gold and scarlet	20	20
321	–	10s. bright purple, gold and greenish blue	20	20
322	–	24s. olive-yellow, gold and green	50	30
323	–	29s. new blue, gold and orange-red..	55	30
324	–	38s. deep orange-yellow, gold and bright emerald	70	55
315/24 *and* O42/4 *Set of 13*....................			35·00	19·00

Design: "*Star*" shaped (44×51 *mm*)—Nos. 320/4, King Taufaʻahau Tupou IV.

90 Coconut

1970 (9 June). Coil stamps.

		(a) As T **83** *but colours changed*		
325	**83**	1s. greenish yellow, bright purple and black	1·00	1·50
326		2s. greenish yellow, ultramarine and black	1·00	1·50
327		3s. greenish yellow, chocolate and black	1·00	1·50
328		4s. greenish yellow, emerald and black	1·00	1·50
329		5s. greenish yellow, orange-red and blue..	1·00	1·50

		(b) T **90**. *Multicoloured; colour of face value given*		
330	**90**	6s. rose-carmine.................................	1·00	1·50
331		7s. bright purple...............................	1·10	1·50
332		8s. bluish violet.................................	1·25	1·50
333		9s. turquoise....................................	1·40	1·50
334		10s. pale orange................................	1·40	1·50
325/34 *Set of 10*..			10·00	13·50

Nos. 325/34 and O45/54 were produced in rolls of 200, each even stamp having a number applied to the front of the backing paper, with the usual inscription on the reverse.

91 "Red Cross"

(Litho (postage) or litho and die-stamped (air))

1970 (17 Oct). Centenary of British Red Cross. T **91** and similar "cross" shaped design.

		(a) Postage		
335	**91**	3s. vermilion, black and light green	40	30
336		7s. vermilion, black and ultramarine	55	20
337		15s. vermilion and bright purple	1·25	60
338		25s. vermilion, black and turquoise-blue	1·60	90
339		75s. vermilion and deep red-brown ...	7·50	9·50
		(b) Air		
340	–	9s. vermilion and silver.................	60	20
341	–	10s. vermilion and bright purple	60	20
342	–	18s. vermilion and green.................	1·25	60
343	–	38s. vermilion and ultramarine	3·25	2·25
344	–	1p. vermilion and turquoise-blue ...	8·50	13·00
335/44 *and* O55/7 *Set of 13*......................			48·00	42·00

Design: As T **91**—Nos. 340/4 as Nos. 335/9 but with inscription rearranged and Coat of Arms omitted.

On Nos. 335/6 and 338 the black colour is produced as a composite of the other two colours used.

OFFICIAL STAMPS

G.F.B. (O **1**)   (O **2**)

(G.F.B. = Gaue Faka Buleaga = On Government Service)

1893 (13 Feb). Optd with Type O **1** by Govt Printing Office, Wellington, N.Z. W **2**. P 12×11½.

O1	**5**	1d. ultramarine (C.)	24·00	50·00
		a. Bisected diagonally (½d.) (on cover)............................	†	—
O2	**6**	2d. ultramarine (C.)	40·00	55·00
O3	**5**	4d. ultramarine (C.)	50·00	£100
O4	**6**	8d. ultramarine (C.)	95·00	£180
O5	**5**	1s. ultramarine (C.)	£110	£200
O1/5 *Set of 5*...			£275	£500

Above prices are for stamps in good condition and colour. Faded and stained stamps from the remainders are worth much less.

1893 (Dec). Nos. O1 to O5 variously surch with new value, sideways as Type O **2**.

O6	**5**	½d. on 1d. ultramarine	26·00	50·00
O7	**6**	2½d. on 2d. ultramarine	32·00	50·00
O8	**5**	5d. on 4d. ultramarine	32·00	50·00
O9	**6**	7½d. on 8d. ultramarine	32·00	80·00
		a. "D" of "7½D." omitted	£1300	
		b. Surch double..........................	£2250	
O10		10d. on 1s. ultramarine	40·00	85·00
O6/10 *Set of 5*...			£150	£275

The surcharges on Nos. O6/10 were applied by two-unit handstamps to each vertical pair. The two types of each value show slight differences.

OFFICIAL AIRMAIL

OFFICIAL	AIR MAIL	
1862		**40**
TAUʻATAINA		
EMANCIPATION		SENITI
1962		
(O **3**)		(O **4**)

1962 (7 Feb). Air. Centenary of Emancipation. Nos. 112/14, 116 and 118/19 optd with Type O **3** in red by R. S. Wallbank, Govt Printer.

O11	–	2d. ultramarine	23·00	7·50
		a. "OFFICIAI"	65·00	25·00
		b. "MAII"	90·00	40·00
O12	–	5d. violet....................................	23·00	7·50
		a. "OFFICIAI"	65·00	25·00
		b. "MAII"	90·00	40·00
O13	–	1s. red-brown	20·00	4·50
		a. "OFFICIAI"	65·00	15·00
		b. "MAII"	90·00	25·00
		c. Opt double..............................	£350	
		ca. "OFFICIAI"	£900	
		cb. "MAII"	£900	
O14	–	5s. orange-yellow and slate-lilac	£150	80·00
		a. "MAII"	£425	150
		b. "OFFICIAI"	£150	150

O15	52	10s. yellow and black		60·00	30·00
		a. "MAII"		£200	
O16	53	£1 yellow, scarlet, ultramarine and deep bright blue		85·00	50·00
		a. "MAII"		£300	
		b. "OFFICIAI"			
O11/16		Set of 6		£325	£160

Nos. O11/14 were overprinted in sheets of 60 (5×12), using a 5×6 setting which was applied first to the lower half sheets, then to the upper. The variety "OFFICIAI" occurred at R. 4/2 on both the upper and lower halves, whereas "MAII" occurred at R. 2/5 on the upper halves only. One sheet of the 1s. value (No. O13) received a double overprint on the upper half only, making Nos. O13ca and O13cb both unique.

Nos O15/16 were overprinted in sheets of 60 (6×10), using adjusted 5×6 settings, with a smaller space between "OFFICIAL" and "AIR MAIL" at top. The variety "MAII" occurred at R. 2/5, probably on both halves of each sheet, but the position of No. O16b has not been established.

The listed "I" for "L" must show no trace of horizontal bar. Varieties with a short horizontal bar occur on other positions in the settings, but are worth much less.

SET PRICES. Official stamps from here onwards are included in the complete commemorative set prices given for any corresponding Postage issues.

1963 (15 July). Air. First Polynesian Gold Coinage Commemoration. As T **63** but inscr "OFFICIAL AIRMAIL". 1 koula coin (diam 3¹/₈in.). Imperf.

O17	63	15s. black	12·00	13·00

1965 (18 Mar). No. O17 surch as T **67**.

O18	63	30s. on 15s. black	3·75	5·00

1966 (18 June). Air. Centenary of Tupou College and Secondary Education. No. 117 surch with "OFFICIAL AIRMAIL" and new value, with commemorative inscription as in T **69** but in italic capital letters.

O19		10s. on 4d. blue-green	50	35
		a. Surch inverted	£275	£120
O20		30s. on 4d. blue-green	70	50

1967 (25 Mar). Air. Decimal currency. No. 112 surch "OFFICIAL AIRMAIL ONE PA' ANGA" in three lines, in red.

O21		1p. on 5s. yellow and lilac	8·00	3·50
		a. "AIRMAIL" above "OFFICIAL"	£180	

No. O21a occurred at R.8/3 in a number of sheets until it was corrected.

1967 (4 July). Air. No. 114 surch in various denominations as Type O **4**.

O22	53	40s. on £1 yellow, red and blue	60	75
O23		60s. on £1 yellow, red and blue	80	1·25
O24		1p. on £1 yellow, red and blue	1·10	2·00
O25		2p. on £1 yellow, red and blue	1·75	3·00

Nos. O22/5 were first used on 4 July 1967, but supplies of unused stamps were not made available until April 1968.

(O 5)   (O 6)

1967 (15 Dec). Air. Arrival of US Peace Corps in Tonga. As No. 114, but imperf, and background colour changed, and surch as Type O **5**.

O26	53	30s. on £1 yellow, scarlet, ultramarine and emerald-green	50	30
O27		70s. on £1 yellow, scarlet, ultramarine and emerald-green	70	1·50
O28		1p.50 on £1 yellow, scarlet, ultramarine and emerald-green	1·00	2·75

1968 (4 July). Air. 50th Birthday of King Taufa'ahua IV. No. 207 surch "HIS MAJESTY'S 50th BIRTHDAY" (as T **79**), "OFFICIAL AIRMAIL" and new value.

O29	75	40s. on 50s. (Turq.)	3·25	80
O30		60s. on 50s. (G.)	3·75	2·00
O31		1p. on 50s. (V.)	5·00	5·00
O32		2p. on 50s. (P.)	9·00	12·00

1968 (19 Dec). Air. South Pacific Games Field and Track Trials, Port Moresby, New Guinea. As No. 114, but imperf, background colour changed and surch as Type O **6**.

O33	53	20s. on £1 yellow, scarlet, ultramarine and emerald-green	20	30
O34		1p. on £1 yellow, scarlet, ultramarine and emerald-green	70	1·75

1969 (13 Aug). Air. Third South Pacific Games, Port Moresby. Design as Nos. 290/4.

O35		70s. carmine-red, bright green and turquoise	75	1·60
O36		80s. carmine-red, orange and turquoise	85	1·60

OFFICIAL AIRMAIL

(O 7)   (O 8)

1969 (23 Dec). Air. First Oil Search in Tonga. As No. 114 but imperf, background colour changed to emerald-green, and surch as Type O **7**.

O37	53	90s. on £1 multicoloured	4·25	6·00
		a. "1966" for "1969" (R. 3/5)	£160	

O38		1p.10 on £1 multicoloured (R.)	4·25	6·00
		a. "1966" for "1969" (R. 3/5)	£160	

The "1966" error was later corrected.
No. O38 is surch as Type O **7**, but without "OFFICIAL AIRMAIL".

1970 (7 Mar). Royal Visit. As No. 110 but imperf colours changed, and surch as Type O **8**.

O39		75s. on 1s. carmine-red and yellow	9·50	6·50
O40		1p. on 1s. carmine-red and yellow (B.)	10·00	7·50
O41		1p.25 on 1s. carmine-red and yellow (G.)	11·00	9·00

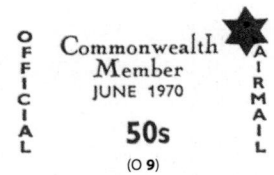

(O 9)

1970 (4 June). Air. Entry into British Commonwealth. As No. 112 but imperf, background colour changed, and surch as Type O **9**.

O42		50s. on 5s. orange-yellow and sepia	9·00	2·25
O43		90s. on 5s. orange-yellow and sepia (R.)	10·00	4·25
O44		1p.50 on 5s. orange-yellow and sepia (G.)	12·00	9·50

1970 (4 June). As Nos. 325/34, but inscr "OFFICIAL POST". Colour of "TONGA" given for 6 to 10s.

O45	83	1s. greenish yellow, bright purple and black	90	1·60
O46		2s. greenish yellow, ultramarine and black	1·00	1·60
O47		3s. greenish yellow, chocolate and black	1·00	1·60
O48		4s. greenish yellow, emerald and black	1·00	1·60
O49		5s. greenish yellow, orange-red and black	1·00	1·60
O50	90	6s. ultramarine	1·10	1·60
O51		7s. deep mauve	1·25	1·60
O52		8s. gold	1·25	1·60
O53		9s. bright carmine	1·40	1·60
O54		10s. silver	1·40	1·60
O45/54		Set of 10	10·00	14·50

The note after No. 334 also applies here.

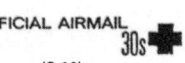

(O 10)

1970 (17 Oct). Centenary of British Red Cross. As Nos. 102 and 112 but imperf, colours changed and surch as Type O **10**.

O55		30s. on 1½d. emerald (Blk. and R.)	2·00	2·25
O56		80s. on 5s. orange-yellow and sepia (B. & R.)	13·00	8·50
O57		90s. on 5s. orange-yellow and sepia (B. & R.)	13·00	8·50

Transjordan

PRICES FOR STAMPS ON COVER

Nos. 1/88a	from × 10
Nos. 89/142	from × 5
Nos. 143/243	from × 3
Nos. D112/24	from × 6
Nos. D159/248	from × 4
No. O117	—

Transjordan was part of the Turkish Empire from 1516 to 1918.

Turkish post offices are known to have existed at Ajlun ("Adjiloun"), Amman ("Omman"), Amman Station, Kerak ("Kerek"), Ma'an ("Mohan" or "Maan"), Qatrana, Salt and Tafila ("Tafile"). Stamps cancelled "Ibin" may have been used at Ibbin.

The area was overrun by British and Arab forces, organised by Colonel T. E. Lawrence, in September 1918, and as Occupied Enemy Territory (East), became part of the Syrian state under the Emir Faisal, who was king of Syria from 11 March to 24 July 1920. During 1920 the stamps of the Arab Kingdom of Syria were in use. On 25 April 1920 the Supreme Council of the Allies assigned to the United Kingdom a mandate to administer both Palestine and Transjordan, as the area to the east of the Jordan was called. The mandate came into operation on 29 September 1923.

E.E.F. post offices, using the stamps of Palestine, operated in the area from September 1918.

FORGERIES. Collectors are warned that the early provisional overprints and surcharges on T **3** or Palestine have been extensively forged. This particularly concerns Nos. 1/8, 20/88a and 98A/109. Nos. 9/19 and 106A/B and 107A/B must, however, always be genuine, as the underlying stamps of Palestine T **3** were never issued perf 14 without opt.

BRITISH MANDATED TERRITORY
(Currency. 1000 milliemes = 100 piastres = £1 Egyptian)

"EAST". Where the word "East" appears in Arabic overprints it is not used in its widest sense but as implying the land or government "East of Jordan".

شرقي الاردن   شرقي الاردن

(1) ("East of Jordan")   (1a)

(Optd at Greek Orthodox Convent, Jerusalem)

1920 (Nov). T **3** of Palestine optd with T **1**.

(a) P 15×14

1	**1**	1m. sepia	3·75	6·00
		a. Opt inverted	£140	£275
2		2m. blue-green	23·00	26·00
		a. Silver opt		
3		3m. yellow-brown	4·00	4·75
		a. Opt Type 1a	£1100	
4		4m. scarlet	4·25	4·50
		a. Arabic "40"	75·00	
5		5m. yellow-orange	11·00	3·75
5a		1p. deep indigo (Silver)	£2000	
6		2p. olive	15·00	17·00
		a. Opt Type 1a	£850	
7		5p. deep purple	50·00	80·00
		a. Opt Type 1a	£1400	
8		9p. ochre	£850	£1400
1/7 (ex 5a)		Set of 7	95·00	£120

(b) P 14

9	**1**	1m. sepia	1·40	6·00
		a. Opt inverted	£170	
10		2m. blue-green	3·50	5·50
		a. Silver opt	£550	£600
11		3m. yellow-brown	23·00	32·00
12		4m. scarlet	17·00	48·00
		a. Arabic "40"	£150	
13		5m. orange	2·75	3·75
14		1p. deep indigo (Silver)	3·75	4·75
15		2p. deep olive	15·00	15·00
16		5p. purple	7·50	17·00
17		9p. ochre	7·50	55·00
18		10p. ultramarine	18·00	55·00
19		20p. pale grey	20·00	90·00
9/19		Set of 11	£100	£300

Nos. 1/19 were surcharged from five different settings of 120 (12×10) which produced eight sub-types of Type 1. Type 1a occurred on R. 8/12 from one setting. The 9p. also exists with this overprint, but no example appears to have survived without further overprint or surcharge.

Nos. 9/19 (P 14) were never issued without opt, and the Type 1 opt on this perforation must always be genuine.

The Type **1** opt ("Sharqi Al-urdun") comprises seven Arabic characters, reading (from right to left) Sh-R-Qi-Al-R-D-N. The key features of the rare Type **1a** are a) the absence of the dots above "Qi" and b) the short left stroke of the "Al". Other variants exist with the missing dots, but only Type **1a** also has the short left stroke. Type **1a** is often misidentified, and forgeries exist.

1b Moab District Seal *(full size)*

1920 (Nov). Issued at Kerak. Handstamped. Manuscript initials "AK" in violet. Imperf.

19a **1b** (1p.) pale blue... £3500 £4000

No. 19a was issued in November 1920 by the political officer for Moab District, Captain (later Sir) Alex Kirkbride, and was used until supplies of Nos. 1/19 reached the area in March 1921. The local Turkish canceller was used as a postmark.

Emir Abdullah, 1 April 1921–22 May 1946

Abdullah, a son of the King of the Hejaz, was made Emir of Transjordan in 1921. On 26 May 1923 Transjordan was recognised as an autonomous state and on 20 February 1928 it was accorded a degree of independence.

(2) ("Tenth of a piastre") (3) ("Piastre") (4) ("Arab Government of the East, April 1921")

1922 (Nov). Nos. 1/19 additionally handstamped with steel dies at Amman as T **2** or **3**.

(a) P 15×14

20	**2**	¹/₁₀p. on 1m. sepia	29·00	50·00
		a. Red surch	70·00	70·00
		b. Violet surch	70·00	70·00
21		²/₁₀p. on 2m. blue-green	35·00	35·00
		a. Error. Surch "³/₁₀" for "²/₁₀"	£120	£110
		b. Red surch	80·00	80·00
		c. Violet surch	£100	£100
		ca. Error. Surch "³/₁₀" for "²/₁₀"		
22		³/₁₀p. on 3m. yellow-brown	15·00	15·00
		a. Pair, one without surch	£800	
		b. Opt Type **1a**	£1200	£1200
		c. Error. "²/₁₀" for "³/₁₀"		
		d. Violet surch	£150	£150
		da. Opt Type **1a**	£2750	
23		⁴/₁₀p. on 4m. scarlet	60·00	65·00
		a. Violet surch		
24		⁵/₁₀p. on 5m. yellow-orange	£180	£100
		a. Pair, one without surch		
		b. Violet surch	£250	£225
25	**3**	2p. on 2p. olive	£250	75·00
		a. Opt Type **1a**	£1300	
		b. Red surch	£325	80·00
		ba. Opt Type **1a**		
		c. Violet surch	£300	90·00
26		5p. on 5p. deep purple	65·00	80·00
		a. Opt Type **1a**	£1600	
		b. Violet surch		
27		9p. on 9p. ochre	£300	£350
		a. Red surch	£130	£140
		b. Violet surch		

(b) P 14

28	**2**	¹/₁₀p. on 1m. sepia	25·00	30·00
		a. Pair, one without surch	£1500	
		b. Red surch	60·00	60·00
		c. Violet surch	£250	£300
29		²/₁₀p. on 2m. blue-green	29·00	29·00
		a. Pair, one without surch	£1500	
		b. Error. Surch "³/₁₀" for "²/₁₀"	£110	£110
		c. Red surch	80·00	80·00
		ca. Error. Surch "³/₁₀" for "²/₁₀"		
		d. Violet surch	80·00	80·00
30		⁵/₁₀p. on 5m. orange	£225	£100
		a. Pair, one without surch	†	£2000
		b. Violet surch	£275	
31	**3**	1p. on 1p. deep indigo (R.)	£200	60·00
		a. Pair, one without surch	£1800	
		b. Violet surch	£400	
32		9p. on 9p. ochre (R.)	£550	£550
33		10p. on 10p. ultramarine	£850	£1000
		a. Violet surch inverted		
34		20p. on 20p. pale grey	£650	£850
		a. Violet surch	£900	£950

*T **3** of Palestine (perf 15×14) similarly surch*

35	**3**	10p. on 10p. ultramarine	£1800	£2500
36		20p. on 20p. pale grey	£2500	£3000
		a. Violet surch		

T **2** reads "tenths of a piastre" and T **3** "the piastre", both with Arabic figures below. These surcharges were applied in order to translate the Egyptian face values of the stamps into the currency of the Arab Kingdom of Syria, but the actual face value of the stamps remained unchanged.

Being handstamped the surcharge may be found either at the top or bottom of the stamp, and exists double on most stamps.

The Types **2/3** handstamped surcharges have been extensively forged. Forged examples of Nos. 20/7 also often have a forged Type **1** opt.

1922 (Dec). Stamps of 1920 handstamped with a steel die as T **4** in red-purple, violet or black*.

(a) P 15×14

37	**4**	1m. sepia (R.P.)	29·00	30·00
		a. Violet opt	30·00	35·00
		b. Black opt	26·00	26·00
38		2m. blue-green (R.P.)	27·00	27·00
		a. Violet opt	24·00	24·00
		b. Black opt	23·00	23·00
39		3m. yellow-brown (R.P.)	48·00	48·00
		a. Violet opt	£1600	
		b. Black opt	9·00	9·00
		ba. Pair, one without opt	£1300	
		bb. Opt Type **1a**	£1500	£2000
		c. Black surch	10·00	10·00
		ca. Opt Type **1a**		

40		4m. scarlet (R.P.)	60·00	65·00
		b. Violet opt	60·00	65·00
		c. Black opt	60·00	65·00
41		5m. yellow-orange (R.P.)	45·00	12·00
		a. Violet opt	19·00	12·00
42		2p. olive (R.P.)	60·00	45·00
		a. Opt Type **1a**	£1500	
		b. Violet opt	26·00	18·00
		ba. Opt Type **1a**	£1500	£1300
		c. Black opt	17·00	12·00
43		5p. deep purple (R.P.)	£100	£120
		a. Pair, one without opt	£1600	
		b. Violet opt	65·00	85·00
		c. Black opt		
44		9p. ochre (R.P.)	£400	£450
		a. Violet opt	£200	£250
		ab. Opt Type **1a**	£2250	
		b. Black opt	70·00	85·00

(b) P 14

45	**4**	1m. sepia (R.P.)	16·00	20·00
		a. Pair, one without opt	£1300	
		b. Violet opt	27·00	24·00
		c. Black opt	23·00	23·00
46		2m. blue-green (R.P.)	32·00	32·00
		a. Violet opt	10·00	10·00
		b. Black opt	15·00	15·00
46c		3m. yellow-brown (V.)	£800	£350
47		5m. orange (R.P.)	£300	75·00
		a. Violet opt	32·00	22·00
48		1p. deep indigo (R.P.)	38·00	17·00
		a. Violet opt	22·00	11·00
49		2p. deep olive (V.)	80·00	85·00
50		5p. purple (R.P.)	£100	£110
		a. Violet opt	£110	£120
		b. Black opt		
51		9p. ochre (V.)	£900	£1000
52		10p. ultramarine (R.P.)	£1800	£1900
		a. Violet opt	£1100	£1600
		b. Black opt		
53		20p. pale grey (R.P.)	£1600	£2000
		a. Violet opt	£1100	£1800
		b. Black opt		

*The ink of the "black" overprint is not a true black, but is caused by a mixture of inks from different ink-pads. The colour is, however, very distinct from either of the others.

Most values are known with inverted and/or double overprints.

The Type **4** handstamp has been extensively forged, often in conjunction with a forged Type **1** opt on stamps perf 15×14.

(5) ("Arab Government of the East, April 1921")

1923 (1 Mar). Stamps of 1920, with typographed overprint, T **5** applied by Govt Printing Press, Amman.

(a) P 15×14

54	**5**	1m. sepia (Gold)	£1500	£1800
55		2m. blue-green (Gold)	24·00	26·00
56		3m. yellow-brown (Gold)	18·00	19·00
		a. Opt double	£500	
		b. Opt inverted	£550	
		c. Black opt	75·00	85·00
57		4m. scarlet	20·00	19·00
58		5m. yellow-orange	60·00	50·00
		a. Opt Type **1** albino	£1200	£1400
59		2p. olive (Gold)	23·00	21·00
		a. Opt Type **1a**	£1200	£1000
		b. Black opt	£250	£250
		ba. Opt Type **1a**		
60		5p. deep purple (Gold)	75·00	£100
		a. Opt inverted	£225	
		b. Opt Type **1a**	£2000	
		ba. Opt inverted	£2500	
		c. Black opt inverted	£1500	

(b) P 14

62	**5**	1m. sepia (Gold)	19·00	32·00
		a. Opt inverted	£750	
63		2m. blue-green (Gold)	18·00	21·00
		a. Opt inverted	£350	£350
		b. Opt double	£300	
		c. Black opt	£300	
		ca. Opt double	£1500	
64		5m. orange	14·00	14·00
65		1p. deep indigo (Gold)	14·00	18·00
		a. Opt double	£500	£550
		b. Black opt	£800	£850
66		9p. ochre	90·00	£130
		a. Gold opt	£3000	
67		10p. ultramarine (Gold)	85·00	£130
		a. Black opt		
68		20p. pale grey (Gold)	85·00	£130
		a. Opt inverted	£375	
		b. Opt double	£450	
		c. Opt double, one inverted	£450	
		e. Opt double, one gold, one black, latter inverted	£750	
		f. Opt treble, one inverted	£1100	
		g. Black opt	£850	
		ga. Opt double	£1100	
		gb. Opt double, one inverted	£1300	

The gold overprints were created by sprinkling gold dust on wet black ink.

There are numerous constant minor varieties in this overprint in all values.

The 9p. perforated 15×14 was also prepared with this overprint, but the entire stock was used for No. 85.

The 20p. exists with top line of overprint only or with the lines transposed, both due to misplacement.

(6) (7) (8) (9)

1923 (Apr–Oct). Stamps of the preceding issues further surch by means of handstamps.

(a) Issue of Nov 1920

70	–	2½ /10ths p. on 5m. (13) (B.–Blk.)	£170	£170
		a. Black surch	£170	£170
		b. Violet surch	£170	£170
70c	**6**	⁵/₁₀p. on 3m. (3)	†	£5000
70d		⁵/₁₀p. on 5m. (13)	£2500	
70e	**9**	2p. on 20p. (19)		

(b) Stamp of Palestine

71	**6**	⁵/₁₀p. on 3m. (P 15×14)	£3000	

(c) Issue of Nov 1922

72	**6**	⁵/₁₀p. on 3m. (22)	£7000	
		a. Pair, one without surch	£7500	
73		⁵/₁₀p. on 5p. (26) (V.)	75·00	85·00
		a. Black surch		
		ab. Opt Type **3** omitted	£1200	
73b		⁵/₁₀p. on 9p. (27a)	£1300	
74	**7**	½p. on 5p. (26)	75·00	85·00
		a. Pair, one without surch	£750	
75		½p. on 9p. (27)	£3500	
		a. On No. 27a	£350	£400
		ab. Opt Type **1a**	£3500	
76		½p. on 9p. (32)	—	£8000
77	**8**	1p. on 5p. (26)	85·00	£110

(d) Issue of Dec 1922

78	**6**	⁵/₁₀p. on 3m. (39) (V.)	85·00	£100
		a. Black surch	£750	
		ab. Opt Type **1a**		
		b. On No. 39b	50·00	60·00
		ba. Pair, one without surch	£1400	
		bb. Without numeral of value		
		bc. Black surch	£750	
79		⁵/₁₀p. on 5p. (43b) (Blk.)	10·00	19·00
		a. Opt Type **1a**	£2000	
		b. Pair, one without surch	£500	
		c. Violet surch		
79d		⁵/₁₀p. on 9p. (44b)	—	£1200
		da. On No. 44a. Violet surch	—	£1300
80	**7**	½p. on 2p. (42)	£100	£120
		a. Opt Type **1a**	£2000	
		b. On No. 42b	80·00	£110
		c. On No. 42c	60·00	£110
		ca. Pair, one without surch	£1000	
		w. Wmk inverted		
81		½p. on 5p. (43)	£3000	
		a. On No. 43b	£1000	
82		½p. on 5p. (50)	£2000	
		a. On No. 50a	£2500	
83	**8**	1p. on 5p. (43)	£3750	
		b. On No. 43b	£2000	£2250
83c		1p. on 5p. (50)	£2500	

(e) Issue of 1 March 1923

84	**6**	⁵/₁₀p. on 3m. (56)	29·00	45·00
		a. On No. 56c	£750	
85	**7**	½p. on 9p. (P 15×14)	95·00	£160
		a. Pair, one without surch	£5000	
86		½p. on 9p. (66)	£170	
87	**9**	1p. on 5p. (67)	£2250	£2500
		a. Violet surch	£2750	
88		2p. on 20p. (68)	65·00	85·00
88a		2p. on 20p. (68g)	£2000	

The handstamp on Nos. 70c, 88 and 88a has an Arabic "2" in place of the "1" shown in the illustration of Type **9**.

Being handstamped any of the above exist inverted or double.

The Types **6/9** provisional surcharges have been extensively forged and should only be acquired from reliable sources.

Types of Saudi Arabia overprinted

11 20

21 22

(10) ("Arab Government of the East, 9 Sha'ban 1341")

(11) ("Arab Government of the East. Commemoration of Independence, 25 May 1923")

It should be noted that as Arabic is read from right to left, the overprint described as reading downwards appears to the English reader as though reading upwards. Our illustration of Type **11** shows the overprint reading downwards.

1923 (Apr). Stamps of Saudi Arabia. T **11**, with typographed opt, T **10**.

89	**10**	⅛p. chestnut	5·50	4·25
		a. Opt double	£200	
		b. Opt inverted	£110	
90		½p. scarlet	5·50	4·25
		a. Opt inverted	£120	
91		1p. blue	4·25	1·25
		a. Opt inverted	£120	140
92		1½p. lilac	4·50	2·50
		a. Opt double	£150	
		b. Top line omitted	—	£250
		c. Pair, one without opt	£250	
		d. Imperf between (horiz pair)	£170	
93		2p. orange	5·50	8·00
94		3p. brown	14·00	20·00
		a. Opt inverted	£225	
		b. Opt double	£225	£250
		c. Pair, one without opt	£375	
95		5p. olive	32·00	45·00
89/95 *Set of 7*			65·00	75·00

On same stamps, surcharged with new values (Saudi Arabia, Nos. 47 and 49)

96	**10**	¼p. on ⅛p. chestnut	16·00	8·00
		a. Opt and surch inverted	£150	
		b. Ditto but 2nd and 3rd lines of opt omitted	£200	
		c. Opt double	†	£200
97		10p. on 5p. olive	35·00	40·00
		a. Top line omitted	£350	

In this setting the third line of the overprint measures 19–21 mm. On 35 stamps out of the setting of 36 the Arabic "9" (right-hand character in bottom line) is widely spaced from the rest of the inscription. Minor varieties of this setting exist on all values.

For later setting, varying from the above, see Nos. 121/4.

Normal. "923"   Error. "933"

An error reading "933" instead of "923" occurs as No. 3 in the setting of 24 on all values. Only 24 stamps are believed to have been overprinted for each of Nos. 103A, 108A, 105B and 107B so that for these stamps only one example of the error can exist. No example has yet been confirmed for Nos. 103A or 105B.

1923 (25 May). T **3** of Palestine optd with T **11**, reading up or down, in black or gold by Govt Press, Amman, in a setting of 24 (12×2). P 14 (9p., 10p.) or 15×14 (other values).

A. Reading downwards

98A	1m. (Blk.)	23·00	23·00
	a. Opt double, one inverted (Blk.)	£650	£650
	b. Arabic "933"	£100	
	c. Gold opt	£150	£160
	ca. Opt double, one inverted (Gold)	£900	
	cb. Opt double (Blk.+Gold)	£900	£900
	cc. Arabic "933"	£550	
99A	2m. (Blk.)	42·00	50·00
	a. Arabic "933"	£180	
100A	3m. (Blk.)	14·00	18·00
	a. Arabic "933"	80·00	
101A	4m. (Blk.)	15·00	18·00
	a. Arabic "933"	85·00	
102A	5m. (Blk.)	70·00	80·00
	a. Arabic "933"	£375	
103A	1p. (Blk.)	£750	£850
	a. Opt double	£800	£900
104A	2p. (Blk.)	70·00	90·00
	a. Arabic "933"	£375	
105A	5p. (Gold)	80·00	90·00
	a. Opt double (Gold)	£650	
	b. Arabic "933"	£400	
	c. Opt double (Blk.)	£1500	
106A	9p. (Blk.)	90·00	£130
	a. Arabic "933"	£425	
107A	10p. (Blk.)	80·00	£100
	a. Arabic "933"	£400	
108A	20p. (Blk.)	£800	£800
	a. Arabic "933"	£3000	

B. Reading upwards

98B	1m. (Blk.)	95·00	£120
	b. Arabic "933"	£400	
	c. Gold opt	£150	£160
	cc. Arabic "933"	£550	
99B	2m. (Blk.)	60·00	70·00
	a. Arabic "933"	£300	
100B	3m. (Blk.)	£100	£130
	a. Arabic "933"	£400	
101B	4m. (Blk.)	32·00	45·00
	a. Arabic "933"	£150	
103B	1p. (Gold)	70·00	85·00
	a. Opt double	£600	
	b. Black opt		
	c. Arabic "933"	£375	

105B	5p. (Gold)		£800	£650
	a. Opt double			
106B	9p. (Blk.)		70·00	85·00
	a. Arabic "933"		£375	
107B	10p. (Blk.)		£700	
	a. Arabic "933"		£3000	
108B	20p. (Blk.)		85·00	£110
	a. Arabic "933"		£425	

The Type **11** opt has been extensively forged for all values, but note that the 9p. and 10p. (Nos. 106A/B and 107A/B) will always be genuine, if correctly perf 14. The genuine Type **11** opt shows numerous breaks in the Arabic lettering, which tend to be absent from the more heavily printed forged opts.

No. 107A surch with T **9**.

109	1p. on 10p. ultramarine	£6000	

(12)

1923 (Sept). No. 92 surch with T **12**.

(a) Handstamped

110	**12**	½p. on 1½p. lilac	12·00	14·00
		a. Surch and opt inverted	55·00	
		b. Opt inverted	75·00	
		c. Opt double, one inverted	90·00	£100
		d. Pair, one without opt	£150	

This handstamp is known inverted, double and double, one inverted.

(b) Typographed

111	**12**	½p. on 1½p. lilac	55·00	55·00
		a. Surch inverted	£150	
		b. Surch double	£180	
		c. Pair, one without surch	£500	

(13a)   **(13b)**

("Arab Government of the East, 9 Sha'ban, 1341")

These two types differ in the spacing of the characters and in the position of the bottom line which is to the left of the middle line in T **13a** and centrally placed in T **13b**.

1923 (Oct). T **11** of Saudi Arabia handstamped as T **13a** or **13b**.

112	**13a**	½p. scarlet	15·00	16·00
113	**13b**	½p. scarlet	15·00	16·00

No. 112 exists with handstamp inverted.

د.ق.ج

15 ("Arab Government of the East")

16 ("Commemorating the coming of His Majesty the King of the Arabs" and date)

1924 (Jan). T **11** of Saudi Arabia with typographed opt T **15**.

114	**15**	½p. scarlet	22·00	16·00
		a. Opt inverted	£180	
115		1p. blue	£300	£200
116		1½p. lilac	£350	
		a. Pair, one without opt	£1500	

The ½p. exists with thick, brown gum, which tints the paper, and with white gum and paper.

The 2p. in the same design was also overprinted, but was not issued without the subsequent Type **16** overprint.

1924 (18 Jan). Visit of King Hussein of Hejaz. Nos. 114/16 and unissued 2p. with further typographed opt T **16** in black.

117	**16**	½p. scarlet	3·25	3·25
		a. Type **15** omitted	£150	
		b. Type **16** inverted	£150	
		c. Imperf between (pair)	£110	
		d. Type **16** in gold	3·25	3·25
		dc. Imperf between (pair)	£250	
118		1p. blue	4·00	3·50
		a. Type **15** omitted	£150	
		b. Both opts inverted	£200	
		c. Imperf between (pair)		
		d. Type **16** in gold	4·00	3·50
		db. Both opts inverted	£300	
		dc. Imperf between (pair)	£225	
119		1½p. lilac	4·25	4·50
		a. Type **15** omitted		
		b. Type **16** inverted	£130	
		d. Type **16** in gold	4·25	4·50
		da. Type **15** inverted	£150	
120		2p. orange	13·00	5·00
		d. Type **16** in gold	12·00	12·00

The spacing of the lines of the overprint varies considerably, and a variety dated "432" for "342" occurs on the twelfth stamp in each sheet (*Price* £75 un).

(16a)

"Shaban" (normal)   "Shabal" (R. 4/6)   "Shabn" (R. 5/3)

1924 (Mar–May). T **11** of Saudi Arabia optd with T **16a** (new setting of Type **10**).

121	⅛p. chestnut		45·00	22·00
	a. Opt inverted		£100	
122	½p. scarlet		14·00	4·50
	a. "Shabal"		55·00	
	b. "Shabn"		55·00	
	c. Opt inverted		£120	
123	1p. blue		24·00	2·25
	a. "Shabal"		80·00	
	b. "Shabn"		80·00	
	c. Opt double		£120	
	d. Imperf between (horiz pair) with opt double		£500	
124	1½p. lilac		28·00	28·00
	a. "Shabal"		95·00	
	b. "Shabn"		95·00	

This setting is from fresh type with the third line measuring 18¼ mm.

On all stamps in this setting (except Nos. 1, 9, 32 and 33) the Arabic "9" is close to the rest of the inscription.

The dots on the character "Y" (the second character from the left in the second line) are on many stamps vertical (:) instead of horizontal (..).

On some sheets of the ⅛p. and ½p. the right-hand character, "H", in the first line, was omitted from the second stamp in the first row of the sheet.

(17) ("Government of the Arab East, 1342")

(18) ("Government of the Arab East, 1343")

"Hukumat" (normal)   "Jakramat" (R. 2/1)

"1342" (normal)   "1343" (R. 4/2)   "1242" (R. 6/1)

1924 (Sept–Nov). T **11** of Saudi Arabia with type-set opt as T **17** by Govt Press, Amman.

125	**17**	⅛p. chestnut	1·50	1·25
		a. Opt inverted	£130	
		b. "Jakramat"	30·00	
		c. "1242"	30·00	
126		¼p. green	1·50	70
		a. Tête-bêche (pair, both opts normal)	9·00	12·00
		b. Opt inverted	85·00	
		c. Tête-bêche (pair, one with opt inverted)	£300	
		d. "Jakramat"	30·00	
		e. "1242"	30·00	
127		½p. bright scarlet	1·50	70
		a. Deep rose-red		
		b. "1343"	30·00	
129		1p. blue	10·00	1·50
		a. Imperf between (horiz pair)	£130	
		b. Opt inverted		
		c. "Jakramat"	50·00	
		d. "1242"	50·00	
130		1½p. lilac	6·50	6·50
		a. "1343"	55·00	
131		2p. orange	4·75	3·50
		a. Opt double		
		b. "1343"	55·00	
132		3p. brown-red	4·75	4·75
		a. Opt inverted	£100	
		b. Opt double	£100	
		c. "1343"	75·00	
133		5p. olive	6·50	6·50
		a. "Jakramat"	60·00	
		b. "1242"	60·00	
134		10p. brown-purple and mauve (R.)	15·00	16·00
		a. Centre inverted	£2500	
		b. Black opt	£250	
		c. "Jakramat"	£100	
		d. "1242"	£100	
125/34 *Set of 9*			45·00	38·00

Type **11** of Saudi Arabia was printed in sheets of 36 (6×6). The ¼p. value had the bottom three rows inverted, giving six vertical *tête-bêche* pairs. A few sheets were overprinted with the normal setting of Type **17**, with the result that the overprints on the bottom rows were inverted in relation to the stamps, including on one of the stamps in the *tête-bêche* pair (No. 126c). A corrected setting with the overprint inverted on the lower rows was used for the majority of the printing giving *tête-bêche* pairs with the overprints both normal in relation to the stamps (No. 126a).

1925 (2 Aug). T **20/2** of Saudi Arabia with lithographed opt T **18** applied in Cairo.

135	**18**	½p. chocolate	1·00	1·50
		a. Imperf vert (horiz pair)	£130	£150
		b. Opt inverted	70·00	
136		¼p. ultramarine	2·00	3·00
		a. Opt inverted	70·00	
137		½p. carmine	1·50	60
		a. Opt inverted	70·00	
138		1p. green	1·50	1·50
139		1½p. orange	3·50	4·00
		a. Opt inverted	70·00	
140		2p. blue	4·50	6·00
		a. Opt treble	£160	£225
141		3p. sage-green (R.)	5·00	8·00
		a. Imperf vert (horiz pair)	£130	£170
		b. Opt inverted	90·00	
		c. Black opt	£130	£160
142		5p. chestnut	7·50	15·00
		a. Opt inverted	85·00	
135/42 Set of 8			24·00	35·00

All values exist imperforate.
No. 141 imperforate with gold overprint comes from a presentation sheet for the Emir.

(19) ("East of the Jordan") | **22** Emir Abdullah | **23** Emir Abdullah

(Opt typo by Waterlow)

1925 (1 Nov)–**26**. Stamps of Palestine, 1922 (without the three-line Palestine opt), optd with T **19**. Wmk Mult Script CA. P 14.

143	**19**	1m. deep brown	55	3·50
144		2m. yellow	1·00	75
145		3m. greenish blue	2·75	1·75
146		4m. carmine-pink	2·75	4·00
147		5m. orange	3·25	50
		a. Yellow-orange	42·00	22·00
148		6m. blue-green	2·75	2·50
149		7m. yellow-brown	2·75	2·50
150		8m. scarlet	2·75	1·25
151		1p. grey	2·75	70
152		13m. ultramarine	3·25	3·00
153		2p. olive	4·25	4·75
		a. Olive-green	£120	35·00
154		5p. deep purple	9·50	10·00
155		9p. ochre	14·00	27·00
		a. Perf 15×14 (1926)	£900	£1400
156		10p. light blue	29·00	40·00
		a. Error. "E.F.F." in bottom panel (R.10/3)	£800	£1000
		b. Perf 15×14 (1926)	80·00	£100
157		20p. light violet	48·00	85·00
		a. Perf 15×14 (1926)	£850	£1000
143/57 Set of 15			£110	£160
143s/57s Optd "SPECIMEN" Set of 15			£350	

(New Currency. 1000 milliemes = £1 Palestinian)

(Recess Perkins Bacon & Co)

1927 (1 Nov)–**29**. New Currency. Wmk Mult Script CA. P 14.

159	**22**	2m. greenish blue	3·50	1·75
160		3m. carmine-pink	4·75	4·00
161		4m. green	6·50	8·00
162		5m. orange	3·25	30
163		10m. scarlet	5·50	8·00
164		15m. ultramarine	4·50	65
165		20m. olive-green	4·50	4·75
166	**23**	50m. purple	4·50	14·00
167		90m. bistre	7·50	35·00
168		100m. blue	8·50	25·00
169		200m. violet	17·00	50·00
170		500m. brown (5.29)	60·00	85·00
171		1000m. slate-grey (5.29)	£100	£150
159/71 Set of 13			£200	£350
159s/71s Optd or Perf (500, 1000m.) "SPECIMEN" Set of 13			£375	

(24) ("Constitution") | **(27)**

1928 (1 Sept). New Constitution of 20 February 1928. Optd with T **24** by lithography by Atwood, Morris & Co., Cairo.

172	**22**	2m. greenish blue	7·00	7·00
173		3m. carmine-pink	8·00	12·00
174		4m. green	8·00	15·00
175		5m. orange	8·00	4·25
176		10m. scarlet	8·00	16·00
177		15m. ultramarine	8·00	4·75
178		20m. olive-green	16·00	26·00
179	**23**	50m. purple	21·00	29·00
180		90m. bistre	25·00	£100
181		100m. blue	25·00	£100
182		200m. violet	90·00	£180
172/82 Set of 11			£200	£450

1930 (1 Apr). Locust Campaign. Optd as T **27** by lithography by Whitehead, Morris & Co, Alexandria.

183	**22**	2m. greenish blue	3·25	7·50
		a. Opt inverted	£300	£600
184		3m. carmine-pink	2·50	6·50
185		4m. green	3·75	19·00
186		5m. orange	23·00	14·00
		a. Opt double	£425	£700
		b. Vert pair, top stamp opt double. Lower stamp without bottom line of opt	£1800	
187		10m. scarlet	2·25	4·25

188		15m. ultramarine	2·25	4·00
		a. Opt inverted	£225	£450
189		20m. olive-green	4·00	4·00
190	**23**	50m. purple	5·00	11·00
191		90m. bistre	10·00	48·00
192		100m. blue	12·00	50·00
193		200m. violet	32·00	85·00
194		500m. brown	75·00	£200
		a. "C" of "LOCUST" omitted (R. 5/3)	£800	£1200
183/94 Set of 12			£150	£400

No. 186a was sold at Kerak.

28 | **29**

(Re-engraved with figures of value at left only. Recess Perkins, Bacon)

1930 (1 June)–**39**. Wmk Mult Script CA. P 14.

194b	**28**	1m. red-brown (6.2.34)	9·00	1·00
		c. Perf 13½×13 (1939)	18·00	7·00
195		2m. greenish blue	2·00	50
		a. Perf 13½×13. Bluish green (1939)	24·00	4·50
196		3m. carmine-pink	5·50	70
196a		3m. green (6.2.34)	10·00	85
		b. Perf 13½×13 (1939)	35·00	8·00
197		4m. green	5·50	8·00
197a		4m. carmine-pink (6.2.34)	10·00	1·00
		b. Perf 13½×13 (1939)	£140	45·00
198		5m. orange	3·50	40
		a. Coil stamp. Perf 13½×14 (29.2.36)	32·00	23·00
		b. Perf 13½×13 (1939)	70·00	3·00
199		10m. scarlet	4·50	15
		a. Perf 13½×13 (1939)	£190	4·25
200		15m. ultramarine	4·50	20
		a. Coil stamp. Perf 13½×14 (29.2.36)	29·00	22·00
		b. Perf 13½×13 (1939)	42·00	5·50
201		20m. olive-green	4·75	35
		a. Perf 13½×13 (1939)	65·00	12·00
202	**29**	50m. purple	6·00	1·25
203		90m. bistre	3·50	4·25
204		100m. blue	4·50	4·25
205		200m. violet	22·00	14·00
206		500m. brown	32·00	55·00
207		£P1 slate-grey	70·00	£110
194b/207 Set of 16			£170	£180
194bs/207s Perf "SPECIMEN" Set of 16			£375	

For stamps perf 12 see Nos. 230/43, and for T **28** lithographed, perf 13½, see Nos. 222/9.

30 Mushetta | **30a** Nymphaeum, Jerash

30b Kasr Kharana | **30c** Kerak Castles

30d Temple of Artemis, Jerash | **31** Ajlun Castle

31a The Khazneh at Petra | **31b** Allenby Bridge over the Jordan

31c Threshing scene | **31d** Kasr Kharana

32 Temple of Artemis, Jerash | **32a** Ajlun Castle

32b The Khazneh at Petra | **33** Emir Abdullah

(Vignettes from photographs; frames des Yacoub Sukker. Recess Bradbury, Wilkinson)

1933 (1 Feb). As T **30/3**. Wmk Mult Script CA. P 12.

208	**30**	1m. black and maroon	1·75	1·60
209	**30a**	2m. black and claret	6·00	1·40
210	**30b**	3m. blue-green	6·00	1·75
211	**30c**	4m. black and brown	12·00	7·00
212	**30d**	5m. black and orange	7·00	1·40
213	**31**	10m. carmine	15·00	4·75
214	**31a**	15m. blue	8·50	1·40
215	**31b**	20m. black and sage-green	8·50	5·50
216	**31c**	50m. black and purple	35·00	21·00
217	**31d**	90m. black and yellow	35·00	60·00
218	**32**	100m. black and blue	35·00	60·00
219	**32a**	200m. black and violet	65·00	£150
220	**32b**	500m. scarlet and red-brown	£250	£500
221	**33**	£P1 black and yellow-green	£550	£1300
208/21 Set of 14			£900	£1900
208s/21s Perf "SPECIMEN" Set of 14			£900	

34

(Litho Survey Dept, Cairo)

1942 (18 May). T **28**, but with Arabic characters above portrait and in top left circle modified as in T **34**. No wmk. P 13½.

222	**34**	1m. red-brown	1·25	8·50
223		2m. green	3·50	3·25
224		3m. yellow-green	4·00	7·50
225		4m. carmine-pink	4·00	7·50
226		5m. yellow-orange	7·50	1·75
227		10m. scarlet	14·00	3·75
228		15m. blue	27·00	8·50
229		20m. olive-green	48·00	50·00
222/9 Set of 8			95·00	80·00

Forgeries of the above exist on whiter paper with rough perforations.

(Recess Bradbury Wilkinson)

1943 (1 Jan)–**46**. Wmk Mult Script CA. P 12.

230	**28**	1m. red-brown	30	75
231		2m. bluish green	4·25	2·75
232		3m. green	2·00	3·50
233		4m. carmine-pink	1·75	3·50
234		5m. orange	1·75	20
235		10m. red	3·00	1·25
236		15m. blue	3·00	2·75
237		20m. olive-green (26.8.46)	3·00	1·00
238	**29**	50m. purple (26.8.46)	3·00	1·00
239		90m. bistre (26.8.46)	5·50	9·00
240		100m. blue (26.8.46)	5·50	1·75
241		200m. violet (26.8.46)	12·00	16·00
242		500m. brown (26.8.46)	14·00	12·00
243		£P1 slate-grey (26.8.46)	26·00	22·00
230/43 Set of 14			75·00	70·00

Nos. 237/43 were released in London by the Crown Agents in May 1944, but were not put on sale in Transjordan until 26 August 1946. Printings of the 3, 4, 10, 15 and 20m. in changed colours, together with a new 12m. value, were released on 12 May 1947.

POSTAGE DUE STAMPS

حكومة
مستحق
الشرق العربية
٩ شعبان ١٣٤١   مستحق

(D 12 "Due") | **(D 13)**

1923 (Sept). Issue of April 1923, with opt T **10** with further typographed opt Type D **12** (the 3p. with handstamped surch as T **12** at top).

D112		½p. on 3p. brown	40·00	42·00
		a. "Due" inverted	50·00	55·00
		b. "Due" double	50·00	60·00
		ba. "Due" double, one inverted	£150	
		c. Arabic "t" & "h" transposed (R. 1/2)	£110	
		ca. As c, inverted	£350	
		d. Surch at foot of stamp	48·00	
		da. Ditto, but with var. c	£130	
		e. Surch omitted	£200	
D113		1p. brown	24·00	26·00
		a. Type **10** inverted	80·00	
		b. "Due" inverted	48·00	42·00
		c. "Due" double	50·00	
		d. "Due" double, one inverted	£150	
		e. Arabic "t" & "h" transposed (R. 1/2)	75·00	
		f. "Due" omitted (in vertical pair with normal)	£200	
D114		1½p. lilac	35·00	38·00
		a. "Due" inverted	48·00	48·00
		b. "Due" double	50·00	
		ba. "Due" double, one diagonal	75·00	

	c. Arabic "t" & "h" transposed (R. 1/2) ...	75·00	
	ca. As c, inverted	£275	
	d. "Due" omitted (in pair with normal)	£200	
D115	2p. orange	38·00	40·00
	a. "Due" inverted	60·00	60·00
	b. "Due" double	65·00	
	ba. "Due" double, one diagonal.............	£100	
	c. "Due" treble	£150	
	d. Arabic "t" & "h" transposed (R. 1/2) ...	80·00	
	e. Arabic "h" omitted	£100	

The variety, Arabic "t" and "h" transposed, occurred on R. 1/2 of all values in the first batch of sheets printed. The variety, Arabic "h" omitted, occurred on every stamp in the first three rows of at least three sheets of the 2p.

Genuine examples of Nos. D113/15 are known with additional forged Type D **12** opts, in imitation of the "double" and "double, one inverted" errors. Most such forged opts show the left-hand Arabic character dropped out of alignment with the other characters.

Handstamped in four lines as Type D **13** and surch as on No. D112

D116	½p. on 3p. brown..............	55·00	60·00
	a. Opt and surch inverted..........	£200	
	b. Opt double	£200	
	c. Surch omitted	£225	
	d. Opt inverted. Surch normal, but at foot of stamp	£150	
	e. Opt omitted and opt inverted (pair)	£300	
	f. "Due" double, one inverted........	£160	
	h. Surch double....................	£250	

(D **14**)

(D **20**) ("Due. East of the Jordan")

1923 (Oct). T **11** of Saudi Arabia handstamped with Type D **14**.

D117	½p. scarlet	4·25	9·00
D118	1p. blue	8·50	8·50
	a. Pair, one without handstamp.............	£180	
D119	1½p. lilac	6·00	9·50
D120	2p. orange	8·50	10·00
D121	3p. brown	20·00	26·00
	a. Pair, one without handstamp.............	£600	
D122	5p. olive	22·00	42·00
D117/22 Set of 6		60·00	95·00

There are three types of this handstamp, differing in some of the Arabic characters. They occur inverted, double etc.

1923 (Nov). T **11** of Saudi Arabia with opt similar to Type D **14** but first three lines typo and fourth handstruck.

D123	1p. blue	80·00	
D124	5p. olive	28·00	
	a. Imperf between (vert pair)	£750	

(Opt typo by Waterlow)

1925 (Nov). Stamps of Palestine 1922 (without the three-line Palestine opt), optd with Type D **20**. P 14.

D159	1m. deep brown................	2·50	15·00
D160	2m. yellow	4·75	9·50
D161	4m. carmine-pink...............	4·75	22·00
D162	8m. scarlet	7·00	23·00
D163	13m. ultramarine	11·00	24·00
D164	5p. deep purple	13·00	40·00
	a. Perf 15×14....................	65·00	£100
D159/64 Set of 6		38·00	£120
D159s/64s Optd "SPECIMEN" Set of 6			£140

Stamps as No. D164, but with a different top line to overprint Type D **20**, were for revenue purposes.

(Surch typo at Jerusalem)

(D **21**) (1m.) (2m.) (4m.)

(8m.) (13m.) (5p.)

1926 (Feb–May). Postage stamps of 1 November 1925, surch "Due" and new value as Type D **21** by Greek Orthodox Printing Press, Jerusalem. Bottom line of surcharge differs for each value as illustrated.

D165	1m. on 1m. deep brown..............	14·00	38·00
	a. Red opt........................	£160	
D166	2m. on 1m. deep brown..............	13·00	38·00
D167	4m. on 3m. greenish blue.............	14·00	40·00
D168	8m. on 3m. greenish blue.............	14·00	40·00
D169	13m. on 13m. ultramarine............	19·00	45·00
D170	5p. on 13m. ultramarine.............	23·00	65·00
D165/70 Set of 6		85·00	£225

(D **25** "Due")

Extra Arabic character in opt (R. 4/10)

1929 (1 Jan). Nos. 159 etc. optd only or surch in addition as Type D **25** by lithography by Whitehead, Morris & Co, Alexandria.

D183	**22**	1m. on 3m. carmine-pink	1·75	8·00
		a. Extra Arabic character	40·00	
D184		2m. greenish blue	4·00	7·50
		a. Pair, one without opt	£475	
D185		4m. on 15m. ultramarine	4·75	18·00
		a. Surch inverted	£190	£325
D186		10m. scarlet	9·00	9·50
D187	**23**	20m. on 100m. blue	7·50	29·00
		a. Horiz pair, one without surch...	£800	
D188		50m. purple	6·00	27·00
		a. Horiz pair, one without opt......	£800	
D183/8 Set of 6			30·00	90·00

D **26**   D **35**

(Recess Perkins, Bacon)

1929 (1 Apr)–**39**. Wmk Mult Script CA. P 14.

D189	D **26**	1m. red-brown	2·50	15·00
		a. Perf 13½×13 (1939)................	£160	£130
D190		2m. orange-yellow	5·00	8·00
D191		4m. green	6·50	18·00
D192		10m. scarlet	12·00	14·00
D193		16m. olive-green................	16·00	27·00
D194		50m. blue	20·00	35·00
D189/94 Set of 6			55·00	£100
D189s/94s Perf "SPECIMEN" Set of 6				£150

(Litho Survey Dept, Cairo)

1942 (22 Dec). Redrawn. Top line of Arabic in taller lettering. No wmk. P 13½.

D230	D **35**	1m. red-brown	4·50	25·00
D231		2m. orange-yellow	12·00	13·00
D232		10m. scarlet	19·00	7·00
D230/2 Set of 3			32·00	40·00

Forgeries of the above exist on whiter paper with rough perforations.

(Recess Bradbury Wilkinson)

1944–49. Wmk Mult Script CA. P 12.

D244	D **26**	1m. red-brown	1·50	8·50
D245		2m. orange-yellow	2·50	8·50
D246		4m. green	2·50	13·00
D247		10m. carmine	7·50	16·00
D248		20m. olive-green (1949)	80·00	£100
D244/8 Set of 5			85·00	£130

OFFICIAL STAMP

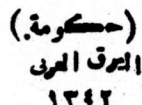

(O **16**) ("Arab Government of the East, 1342" = 1924)

1924. T **11** of Saudi Arabia with typographed opt, Type O **16**.

O117	½p. scarlet	32·00	£110
	a. Arabic "1242" (R. 2/2, 3/6, 4/5, 4/6)....	£160	
	b. Imperf between (vert pair)		

By treaty of 22 March 1946 with the United Kingdom, Transjordan was proclaimed an independent kingdom on 25 May 1946.

Later issues are listed under JORDAN in the Stanley Gibbons *Middle East catalogue.*

Transvaal *see* **South Africa**

Trinidad and Tobago

TRINIDAD

CROWN COLONY

The first post office was established at Port of Spain in 1800 to deal with overseas mail. Before 1851 there was no post office inland service, although a privately-operated one along the coast did exist, for which rates were officially fixed (see No. 1). During 1851 the colonial authorities established an inland postal system which commenced operation on 14 August. Responsibility for the overseas mails passed to the local post authorities in 1858.

No. CC1 is recorded in the G.P.O. Record Book on 21 March 1852, but no examples have been recorded used on cover before February 1858. The prepayment of postage on mail to Great Britain was made compulsory from 9 October 1858. From March 1859 it was used with the early Britannia 1d. stamps to indicate prepayment of the additional overseas rate in cash or, later, to show that letters were fully franked with adhesive stamps. This is the normal usage of the handstamp and commands little, if any premium over the cover price quoted below for the stamps involved. The use of the handstamp without an adhesive is rare.

PORT OF SPAIN

CROWNED-CIRCLE HANDSTAMPS

CC 1

CC1	CC **1** TRINIDAD (R.) (*without additional adhesive stamp*) (21.3.52)......................*Price on cover*	£3000

PRICES FOR STAMPS ON COVER		
No. 1	*from × 2*	
Nos. 2/12	*from × 10*	
Nos. 13/20	*from × 4*	
Nos. 25/9	*from × 10*	
No. 30	—	
Nos. 31/44	*from × 4*	
No. 45	—	
Nos. 46/59	*from × 4*	
Nos. 60/3	*from × 5*	
Nos. 64/8	*from × 4*	
Nos. 69/74	*from × 20*	
Nos. 75/8	*from × 50*	
No. 79	—	
No. 87	*from × 20*	
Nos. 98/102	*from × 6*	
No. 103	—	
Nos. 104/5	*from × 20*	
Nos. 106/12	*from × 12*	
No. 113	—	
Nos. 114/21	*from × 4*	
Nos. 122/4	—	
No. 125	*from × 10*	
Nos. 126/30	*from × 5*	
No. 131	—	
Nos. 132/43	*from × 3*	
Nos. 144/5	—	
Nos. 146/8	*from × 3*	
Nos. D1/17	*from × 15*	

1   2 Britannia

1847 (16 Apr). Litho. Imperf.

1	**1**	(5c.) blue..............................	£30000	£10000

The "LADY McLEOD" stamps were issued in April 1847, by David Bryce, owner of the SS *Lady McLeod*, and sold at five cents each for the prepayment of the carriage of letters by his vessel between Port of Spain and San Fernando.

The price quoted for used examples of No. 1 is for pen-cancelled. Stamps cancelled by having a corner skimmed-off are worth less.

(Recess P.B.)

1851 (14 Aug)–**55**. No value expressed. Imperf. Blued paper.

2	**2**	(1d.) purple-brown (1851)................	21·00	80·00
3		(1d.) blue to deep blue (12.51)........	23·00	65·00
4		(1d.) deep blue (1852)*...............	£150	85·00
5		(1d.) grey (12.51)...................	80·00	70·00
6		(1d.) brownish grey (2.53)...........	55·00	80·00
7		(1d.) brownish red (1853)...........	£300	70·00
8		(1d.) brick-red (8.55)...............	£180	75·00

No. 2 is known on paper bearing the sheet watermark "STACEY WISE/RUSH MILLS".

*No. 4 shows the paper deeply and evenly blued, especially on the back. It has more the appearance of having been printed on blue paper rather than on white paper that has become blued.

1854 (Aug)–**57**. Imperf. White paper.

9	**2**	(1d.) deep purple....................	32·00	95·00
10		(1d.) dark grey	55·00	90·00
12		(1d.) rose-red (1857)	£2500	70·00

PRICES. Prices quoted for the unused of most of the above issues and Nos. 25 and 29 are for "remainders" with original gum, found in London. Old colours that have been out to Trinidad are of much greater value.

3 Britannia   **4** Britannia

The following provisional issues were lithographed in the Colony (from die engraved by Charles Petit), and brought into use to meet shortages of the Perkins Bacon stamps during the following periods: (1) Sept 1852–May 1853; (2) March 1855–June 1855; (3) Dec 1856–Jan 1857; (4) Oct 1858–Jan 1859; (5) March 1860–June 1860.

1852–60. No value expressed. Imperf.

A. First Issue (September 1852). Fine impression; lines of background clear and distinct

(i) Yellowish paper

13	**3**	(1d.) blue	£9000	£1700

(ii) Bluish cartridge paper (February 1853)

14	**3**	(1d.) blue	—	£1900

B. Second issue (March 1855). Thinner paper. Impression less distinct than before.

15	**3**	(1d.) pale blue to greenish blue	—	£1000

C. Third issue (August 1856). Background often of solid colour, but with clear lines in places

16	**3**	(1d.) bright blue to deep blue	£4500	£1000

D. Fourth issue (October 1858). Impression less distinct, and rarely showing more than traces of background lines

17	**3**	(1d.) very deep greenish blue	—	£750
18		(1d.) slate-blue	£4000	£650

E. Fifth issue (March 1860). Impression shows no (or hardly any) background lines

19	**3**	(1d.) grey to bluish grey	£4000	£400
20		(1d.) red (*shades*)	16·00	£600

In the worn impression of the fourth and fifth issues, the impression varies according to the position on the stone. Generally speaking, stamps of the fifth issue have a flatter appearance and cancellations are often less well defined. The paper of both these issues is thin or very thin. In all issues except 1853 (Feb) the gum tends to give the paper a toned appearance.

Stamps in the slate-blue shade (No. 18) also occur in the fifth issue, but are not readily distinguishable.

PERKINS BACON "CANCELLED". For notes on these handstamps, showing "CANCELLED" between horizontal bars forming an oval, see Catalogue Introduction.

(Recess P.B.)

1859 (9 May). Imperf.

25	**4**	4d. grey-lilac (H/S "CANCELLED" in oval £9000)	£120	£325
28		6d. deep green (H/S "CANCELLED" in oval £9000)	£12000	£425
29		1s. indigo	£100	£350
30		1s. purple-slate	£7000	

"CANCELLED" examples of No. 25 are in lilac rather than grey-lilac. No. 30 may be of unissued status.

1859 (Sept). Pin-perf with a spiked wheel.

(a) Pin-perf 12½

31	**2**	(1d.) rose-red	£1600	55·00
32		(1d.) carmine-lake	£1800	50·00
33	**4**	4d. dull lilac	—	£900
34		4d. dull purple	£6500	£900
35		6d. yellow-green	£2750	£200
36		6d. deep green	£2750	£200
37		1s. purple-slate	£7000	£1300

(b) Pin-perf 13½–14

38	**2**	(1d.) rose-red	£250	40·00
39		(1d.) carmine-lake	£325	38·00
40	**4**	4d. dull lilac	£1200	80·00
40*a*		4d. brownish purple	£225	£110
41		4d. dull purple	£500	£110
42		6d. yellow-green	£600	80·00
43		6d. deep green	£600	75·00
43*a*		6d. bright yellow-green	£160	£110
		b. Imperf between (vert pair)	£7500	
44		1s. purple-slate	£7500	£800

(c) Compound pin-perf 13½–14×12½

45	**2**	(1d.) carmine-lake	†	£3750
45*a*	**4**	4d. dull purple	†	—

PRICES. The Pin-perf stamps are very scarce with perforations on all sides and the prices quoted above are for good average specimens.

The note after No. 12 also applies to Nos. 38, 40*a*, 43*a*, 46, 47 and 50.

1860 (Aug). Clean-cut perf 14–16½.

46	**2**	(1d.) rose-red	£190	55·00
		a. Imperf vert (horiz pair)	£1100	
47	**4**	4d. brownish lilac	£200	80·00
48		4d. lilac	—	£350
49		6d. bright yellow-green	£550	£110
50		6d. deep green	£275	£160

1861 (June). Rough perf 14–16½.

52	**2**	(1d.) rose-red (H/S "CANCELLED" in oval £9000)	£170	40·00
53		(1d.) rose	£180	35·00
54	**4**	4d. brownish lilac	£275	70·00
55		4d. lilac	£600	95·00
		a. Imperf		
56		6d. yellow-green	£325	80·00
57		6d. deep green	£400	70·00
58		1s. indigo	£850	£275
59		1s. deep bluish purple (H/S "CANCELLED" in oval £9000)	£1500	£425

(Recess D.L.R.)

1862–63. Thick paper.

(a) P 11½, 12

60	**2**	(1d.) crimson-lake	£150	27·00

61	**4**	4d. deep purple	£225	60·00
62		6d. deep green	£1300	85·00
63		1s. bluish slate	£2250	£110

(b) P 11½, 12, compound with 11

63*a*	**2**	(1d.) crimson-lake	£1600	£500
63*b*	**4**	6d. deep green	†	£6500

(c) P 13 (1863)

64	**2**	(1d.) lake	50·00	27·00
65	**4**	6d. emerald-green	£500	60·00
67		1s. bright mauve	£4500	£300

(d) P 12½ (1863)

68	**2**	(1d.) lake	60·00	27·00

1863–80.

(a) Wmk Crown CC. P 12½

69	**2**	(1d.) lake	65·00	8·00
		a. Wmk sideways	£120	21·00
		b. Rose	65·00	3·00
		ba. Imperf (pair)		
		c. Scarlet	70·00	3·50
		d. Carmine	70·00	3·75
		w. Wmk inverted	†	65·00
		x. Wmk reversed	70·00	4·00
		y. Wmk inverted and reversed	—	75·00
70	**4**	4d. bright violet	£130	20·00
		a. Pale mauve	£200	23·00
		b. Dull lilac	£160	23·00
		w. Wmk inverted	£275	75·00
		x. Wmk reversed	£140	21·00
71		4d. grey (1872)	£130	8·00
		a. Bluish grey	£120	8·50
		ax. Wmk reversed	£120	10·00
		w. Wmk inverted	—	75·00
72		6d. emerald-green	£120	18·00
		a. Deep green	£400	9·50
		b. Yellow-green	£110	6·00
		c. Apple-green	£110	7·50
		d. Blue-green	£180	9·00
		w. Wmk inverted	—	75·00
		x. Wmk reversed	£130	7·50
73		1s. bright deep mauve	£190	11·00
		a. Lilac-rose	£160	11·00
		b. Mauve (aniline)	£140	7·00
		bw. Wmk inverted		
		bx. Wmk reversed	—	8·50
74		1s. chrome-yellow (1872)	£170	2·25
		w. Wmk inverted	—	85·00
		x. Wmk reversed	£200	7·50

(b) P 14 (1876)

75	**2**	(1d.) lake	50·00	2·75
		a. Bisected (½d.) (*on cover*)	†	£600
		b. Rose-carmine	50·00	2·75
		c. Scarlet	60·00	2·75
		w. Wmk inverted	—	60·00
		x. Wmk reversed	55·00	2·75
76	**4**	4d. bluish grey	£130	2·00
		w. Wmk inverted	†	90·00
		y. Wmk inverted and reversed	†	90·00
77		6d. bright yellow-green	£120	3·00
		a. Deep yellow-green	£150	3·00
		w. Wmk inverted	†	80·00
		x. Wmk reversed	£130	4·00
78		1s. chrome-yellow	£160	4·50
		w. Wmk inverted		
		x. Wmk reversed		

(c) P 14×12½ (1880)

79	**4**	6d. yellow-green	†	£6500

The 1s. perforated 12½ in purple-slate is a colour changeling.

5

(Typo D.L.R.)

1869. Wmk Crown CC. P 12½.

87	**5**	5s. rose-lake	£170	75·00

HALFPENNY   **ONE PENNY**

(**6**)   (**7**)

1879–82. Surch with T **6** or **7**. P 14.

(a) Wmk Crown CC (June 1879)

98	**2**	½d. lilac	20·00	13·00
		w. Wmk inverted	£110	38·00
		x. Wmk reversed	20·00	13·00
99		½d. mauve	20·00	13·00
		a. Wmk sideways	50·00	50·00
		w. Wmk inverted	†	£300

(b) Wmk Crown CA (1882)

100	**2**	½d. lilac (wmk reversed)	£180	75·00
101		1d. rosy carmine	75·00	2·50
		a. Bisected (½d.) (*on cover*)	†	£550
		x. Wmk reversed	75·00	2·75

1882. Wmk Crown CA. P 14.

102	**4**	4d. bluish grey	£200	16·00
		x. Wmk reversed		

1d   1d   1d

(**8**) Various styles

1882 (9 May). Surch by hand in various styles as T **8** in red or black ink and the original value obliterated by a thick or thin bar or bars, of the same colour.

103		1d. on 6d. (No. 77) (Bk.)	—	£1600
104		1d. on 6d. (No. 77) (R.)	15·00	9·00
		x. Wmk reversed	20·00	14·00
105		1d. on 6d. (No. 77*a*) (R.)	15·00	9·00
		a. Bisected (½d.) (*on cover*)	†	£300

10   **11** Britannia   **12** Britannia

(Typo D.L.R.)

1883–94. P 14.

(a) Wmk Crown CA

106	**10**	½d. dull green	11·00	1·25
107		1d. carmine	24·00	50
		a. Bisected (½d.) (*on cover*)	†	£950
		w. Wmk inverted	†	£200
108		2½d. bright blue	27·00	60
110		4d. grey	5·00	60
		w. Wmk inverted	†	£250
111		6d. olive-black (1884)	8·00	6·50
112		1s. orange-brown (1884)	15·00	6·50

(b) Wmk Crown CC

113	**5**	5s. maroon (1894)	55·00	£110
106/13 *Set of 7*			£130	£110
106s/13 Optd "SPECIMEN" *Set of 6*			£750	

Two types of 1d. value:

ONE PENNY   **ONE PENNY**
(I) (round "o")   (II) (oval "o")

(Typo D.L.R.)

1896 (17 Aug)–**1906.** P 14.

(a) Wmk Crown CA

114	**11**	½d. dull purple and green	3·25	30
115		1d. dull purple and rose (I)	3·50	10
		w. Wmk inverted		
116		1d. dull purple and rose (II) (1900)	£325	4·00
117		2½d. dull purple and blue	6·00	20
118		4d. dull purple and orange	9·00	26·00
119		5d. dull purple and mauve	11·00	15·00
120		6d. dull purple and black	7·50	5·50
121		1s. green and brown	7·50	6·50

(b) Wmk CA over Crown. Ordinary paper

122	**12**	5s. green and brown	60·00	£100
123		10s. green and ultramarine	£325	£550
124		£1 green and carmine	£200	£325
		a. Chalk-surfaced paper (1906)	£350	
114/24 *Set of 10*			£550	£950
114s/24s Optd "SPECIMEN" *Set of 10*			£200	

Collectors are warned against apparently postally used examples of this issue which bear "REGISTRAR-GENERAL" obliterations and are of very little value.

13 Landing of Columbus

(Recess D.L.R.)

1898 (31 July). 400th Anniv of Discovery of Trinidad. Wmk Crown CC. P 14.

125	**13**	2d. brown and dull violet	3·25	1·25
		s. Optd "SPECIMEN"	65·00	

3ᵈ.

(**13a**)

1899 (Oct). No. 119 surch T **13a** by D.L.R. Prepared for use but not issued.

126	**11**	3d. on 5d. dull purple and mauve	£3250	
		s. Optd "SPECIMEN"	£1400	

1901–06. Colours changed. Ordinary paper. Wmk Crown CA or CA over Crown (5s.). P 14.

127	**11**	½d. grey-green (1902)	1·00	2·00
128		1d. black/*red* (II)	5·00	10
		a. Value omitted	£32000	
		w. Wmk inverted	†	£200
129		2½d. purple and blue/*blue* (1902)	26·00	30
130		4d. green and blue/*buff* (1902)	4·00	22·00
		a. Chalk-surfaced paper	3·50	14·00
131		1s. black and blue/*yellow* (1903)	19·00	5·50
132	**12**	5s. lilac and mauve	75·00	90·00
		a. Chalk-surfaced paper. *Deep purple and mauve* (1906)	85·00	£100
127/32 *Set of 6*			£110	£100
127s/32s Optd "SPECIMEN" *Set of 6*			£150	

A pane of 60 of No. 128a was found at the San Fernando post office of which 51 were subsequently returned to London and destroyed. Only three unused examples, one of which is in the Royal Collection, are now thought to survive; all show traces of the value still present.

1904–09. Ordinary paper (½d., 1d., 2½d. (No. 137)) or chalk-surfaced paper (others). Wmk Mult Crown CA. P 14.

133	11	½d. grey-green	9·50	1·00
		a. Chalk-surfaced paper	12·00	2·25
		b. blue-green (1906)	15·00	3·00
134		1d. black/red (II)	14·00	10
		a. Chalk-surfaced paper	14·00	10
135		1d. rose-red (1906)	3·25	10
		w. Wmk inverted	†	£225
136		2½d. purple and blue/blue	26·00	90
137		2½d. purple and blue/blue	11·00	15
138		4d. grey and red/yellow (1909)	7·00	16·00
		a. Black and red/yellow	13·00	25·00
139		6d. dull purple and black (1905)	23·00	16·00
140		6d. dull and bright purple (1909)	11·00	16·00
141		1s. black and blue/yellow	25·00	11·00
142		1s. purple and blue/golden yellow (1906)	17·00	28·00
143		1s. black/green (1909)	3·00	1·25
144	12	5s. deep purple and mauve (1907)	80·00	£110
145		£1 green and carmine (1907)	£300	£375
133/45 Set of 13			£475	£500

135s/43s (*ex Nos.* 136, 139, 141) Optd "SPECIMEN"
Set of 6 .... £150

No. 135 is from a new die, the letters of "ONE PENNY" being short and thick, while the point of Britannia's spear breaks the uppermost horizontal line of shading in the background.

14	14	16

(Typo D.L.R.)

1909 (Dec). Wmk Mult Crown CA. P 14.

146	14	½d. green	10·00	10
		y. Wmk inverted and reversed	—	£200
147	15	1d. rose-red	13·00	10
148	16	2½d. blue	27·00	4·50
146/8 Set of 3			45·00	4·50
146s/8s Optd "SPECIMEN" Set of 3			85·00	

TOBAGO

Although a Colonial Postmaster was appointed in January 1765 it was not until 1841 that the British GPO established a branch office at Scarborough, the island capital, to handle the overseas mail.

The stamps of Great Britain were in use from May 1858 to the end of April 1860 when the control of the postal service passed to the local authorities.

From April 1860 Nos. CC1/2 were again used on overseas mail, pending the introduction of Tobago stamps in 1879.

SCARBOROUGH

CROWNED-CIRCLE HANDSTAMPS

CC 1	CC 2

CC1	CC 1 TOBAGO (R.) (31.10.1851)	*Price on cover*	£1300
CC2	CC 2 TOBAGO (R.) (1875)	*Price on cover*	£5000

Stamps of GREAT BRITAIN cancelled "A 14" as Type Z 1 of Jamaica.

1858–60.

Z1	1d. rose-red (1857), perf 14	£900
Z2	4d. rose (1857)	£425
Z3	6d. lilac (1856)	£275
Z4	1s. green (1856)	£2250

PRICES FOR STAMPS ON COVER	
Nos. 1/2	—
Nos. 3/4	from × 30
Nos. 5/7	—
Nos. 8/12	from × 10
Nos. 13/19	from × 6
Nos. 20/4	from × 40
Nos. 26/33	from × 25

CANCELLATIONS. Beware of early stamps of Tobago with fiscal endorsements removed and forged wide "A 14" postmarks added.

2½ PENCE

1	2	(3)

(T **1** and **2** Typo D.L.R.)

1879 (1 Aug). Fiscal stamps issued provisionally pending the arrival of stamps inscr "POSTAGE". Wmk Crown CC. P 14.

1	1	1d. rose	£140	£100
2		3d. blue	£140	85·00
3		6d. orange	65·00	80·00
		w. Wmk inverted	£140	£180
4		1s. green	£400	80·00
		a. Bisected (6d.) (on cover)	†	—
5		5s. slate	£900	£800
6		£1 mauve	£4250	

The stamps were introduced for fiscal purposes on 1 July 1879. Stamps of T **1**, watermark Crown CA, are fiscals which were never admitted to postal use.

1880 (Nov). No. 3 bisected vertically and surch with pen and ink.

7	1	1d. on half of 6d. orange	£6000	£850
		w. Wmk inverted	£7000	£1200

1880 (20 Dec). Wmk Crown CC. P 14.

8	2	½d. purple-brown	75·00	£110
9		1d. Venetian red	£140	70·00
		a. Bisected (½d.) (on cover)	†	£2000
10		4d. yellow-green	£300	38·00
		a. Bisected (2d.) (on cover)	†	£2000
		b. Malformed "CE" in "PENCE"	£1900	£400
		w. Wmk inverted	—	£250
11		6d. stone	£400	£120
12		1s. yellow-ochre	£110	£140
		w. Wmk inverted	—	£325

For illustration of Nos. 10b, 18a, 22b, 30b, 31a and 33b see above No. 4 of Dominica.

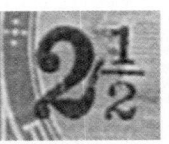

Large "2" with long tail
(R. 2/6, 4/6, 6/6, 8/6 and 10/6)

1883 (Apr). No. 11 surch with T **3** by the Government Printing Office, Scarborough.

13	2	2½d. on 6d. stone	£100	£100
		a. Surch double	£4000	£2250
		b. Large "2" with long tail	£190	£200

"SLASH" FLAW. Stamps as Type **2** were produced from Key and Duty plates. On the Key plate used for consignments between 2 October 1892 and 16 December 1896, damage in the form of a large cut or "slash" shows after the "E" of "POSTAGE" on R. 1/4.

After 1896 an attempt was made to repair the "slash". This resulted in its disappearance, but left an incomplete edge to the circular frame at right.

1882–84. Wmk Crown CA. P 14.

14	2	½d. purple-brown (1882)	3·25	20·00
15		1d. Venetian red (1882)	14·00	3·50
		a. Bisected diag. (½d.) (on cover)		
16		2½d. dull blue (1883)	65·00	3·50
		a. Bright blue	16·00	1·50
		b. Ultramarine	17·00	1·50
		c. "Slash" flaw	£140	60·00
		ca. "Slash" flaw repaired	£225	
18		4d. yellow-green (1882)	£225	95·00
		a. Malformed "CE" in "PENCE"	£1400	£500
19		6d. stone (1884)	£550	£500

1885–96. Colours changed and new value. Wmk Crown CA. P 14.

20	2	½d. dull green (1886)	5·50	2·25
		a. "Slash" flaw	80·00	70·00
		ab. "Slash" flaw repaired	£140	
		w. Wmk inverted		
21		1d. carmine (1889)	9·00	1·75
		a. "Slash" flaw	£110	60·00
		ab. "Slash" flaw repaired	£170	
22		4d. grey (1885)	9·00	4·00
		a. Imperf (pair)	£2000	
		b. Malformed "CE" in "PENCE"	90·00	£100
		c. "Slash" flaw	£190	£200
		ca. "Slash" flaw repaired	£250	
23		6d. orange-brown (1886)	2·50	9·00
		a. "Slash" flaw	£190	£275
		ab. "Slash" flaw repaired	£275	
24		1s. olive-yellow (1894)	4·75	30·00
		a. Pale olive-yellow	7·00	
		b. "Slash" flaw	£250	£550
		ba. "Slash" flaw repaired	£375	
24c		1s. orange-brown (1896)	28·00	£140
		c. "Slash" flaw	£425	
20s/3s (ex 4d.) Optd "SPECIMEN" Set of 3			£170	

No. 24c was printed in the colour of the 6d. by mistake.

½ PENNY 2½ PENCE POSTAGE

(4)	(5)	(6)

1886–89. Nos. 16, 19 and 23 surch as T **4** by the Government Printing Office, Scarborough.

26		½d. on 2½d. dull blue (4.86)	11·00	27·00
		a. Figure further from word	40·00	80·00
		b. Surch double	£2750	£2500
		c. Surch omitted. Vert pair with No. 26	£15000	
		d. Ditto with No. 26a	£25000	
27		½d. on 6d. stone (1.86)	4·00	27·00
		a. Figure further from word	26·00	£110
		b. Surch inverted	£3250	
		c. Surch double	£3750	
28		½d. on 6d. orange-brown (8.87)	£150	£200

		a. Figure further from word	£375	£450
		b. Surch double	—	£2750
29		1d. on 2½d. dull blue (7.89)	£110	24·00
		a. Figure further from word	£300	90·00

The surcharge is in a setting of 12 (two rows of six), repeated five times in a pane.

The measurements given below (and below Nos. 31 and 33) are to the nearest ¼ mm and are for the space between the upright of "1" of "½" or "1" and the upright of the "P".

On Nos. 26/9 the normal spacing is 3¼ mm, but there are slightly narrower spacings on stamps 1 (3 mm) and 7 (2¾ mm) of most settings. The listed wider spacing (4¼ mm) occurs on stamp 10 of Nos. 26, 28, one of the four settings of No. 27 and one of the two settings of No. 29. It occurs on stamps 3 and 10 of a second setting of No. 29 and on stamp 7 in a second setting of No. 29. The "P" may be found raised in various positions in some settings.

1891–92. No. 22 surch with T **4** or **5** by the Government Printing Office, Scarborough.

30		½d. on 4d. grey (3.92)	30·00	85·00
		a. Figure further from word	75·00	
		b. Malformed "CE" in "PENCE"	£325	£750
		c. Surch double	£3500	
31		2½d. on 4d. grey (8.91)	24·00	10·00
		a. Malformed "CE" in "PENCE"	£200	£200
		b. Surch double	£3500	

On Nos. 30/1 the normal spacing is 2¾ mm, but there is a slightly wider space (3 mm) on stamps 3 and 7 of No. 30 and stamp 12 of No. 31. There is a slightly narrower space (2½ mm) on stamp 9 of No. 30. A new setting of No. 30 gave rise to the listed wider space (3¼ mm) on stamp 7.

1896. Fiscal stamp (T **1**, value in second colour, wmk Crown CA, P 14), surch with T **6** by the Government Printing Office, Scarborough.

33		½d. on 4d. lilac and carmine	£100	55·00
		a. Space between "½" and "d"	£140	80·00
		b. Malformed "CE" in "PENCE"	£1300	£800
		c. Surch double	£3500	

On No. 33 there are two settings, a scarcer one with a normal space of 3½ mm between the "1" of "½" and the upright of the "d" and a more common one with wide spacings on stamp 5 (5 mm), stamps 6 and 8 (4½ mm) and stamps 9 and 11 (4¼ mm).

Tobago became a ward of Trinidad on 1 January 1899. Stamps of Trinidad were used until issues inscribed "TRINIDAD AND TOBAGO" appeared in 1913.

TRINIDAD AND TOBAGO

PRICES FOR STAMPS ON COVER	
Nos. 149/55	from × 3
Nos. 156/7	—
Nos. 174/89	from × 10
Nos. 206/56	from × 2
Nos. D18/25	from × 12

17	18

(Typo D.L.R.)

1913–23. Ordinary paper (½d. to 2½d.) or chalk-surfaced paper (others). Wmk Mult Crown CA. P 14.

149	17	½d. green	3·00	10
		a. Yellow-green (1915)	6·00	20
		b. Blue-green (thick paper) (1917)	7·00	1·00
		ba. Wmk sideways	†	£2000
		c. Blue-green/bluish (3.18)	15·00	12·00
		w. Wmk inverted		
150		1d. bright red	1·50	10
		a. Red (thick paper) (1916)	3·25	30
		b. Pink (1918)	50·00	4·50
		c. Carmine-red (5.18)	2·50	10
		w. Wmk inverted		
151		2½d. ultramarine	13·00	50
		a. Bright blue (thick paper) (1916)	6·50	50
		b. Bright blue (thin paper) (1918)	8·00	50
152		4d. black and red/yellow	70	6·00
		a. Ordinary paper.		
		b. White back (12.13)	1·75	11·00
		bs. Optd "SPECIMEN"	25·00	
		c. On lemon (1917)	10·00	
		d. On pale yellow (1923)	6·50	12·00
		ds. Optd "SPECIMEN"	40·00	
153		6d. dull and reddish purple	10·00	11·00
		a. Dull and deep purple (1918)	20·00	13·00
		b. Dull purple and mauve (2.18)	10·00	8·00
154		1s. black/green	1·75	4·50
		a. White back	1·50	16·00
		as. Optd "SPECIMEN"	25·00	
		b. On blue-green, olive back	17·00	9·00
		c. On emerald back	1·50	3·00
		cs. Optd "SPECIMEN"	40·00	
155	18	5s. dull purple and mauve (1914)	75·00	£110
		a. Deep purple and mauve (1918)	80·00	£110
		b. Lilac and violet	£120	£170
		c. Dull purple and violet	£130	£180
		d. Brown-purple and violet	£110	£140
156		£1 grey-green and carmine (1914)	£250	£325
		a. Deep yellow-green and carmine (1918)	£250	£300
149/56 Set of 8			£325	£400
149s/56s Optd "SPECIMEN" Set of 8			£275	

No. 156a is from a plate showing background lines very worn.

18a

1914 (18 Sept). Red Cross Label authorised for use as ½d. stamp. Typo. P 11–12.
157   **18a**   (½d.) red .... 28·00   £225

The above was authorised for internal postal use on one day only, to frank circular letters appealing for funds for the Red Cross. It had gone on sale the previous day (advertised price 24c. per 100) but has long been accepted as a ½d. value as this was the rate it covered during its one day of postal validity. The used price is for stamp on cover cancelled on 18 Sept 1914. Labels affixed to earlier or later items of mail had no postal validity.

19. 10. 16.

 21. 10. 15.
    (19)   **(19a)**

1915 (21 Oct). Optd with T **19**. Cross in red with outline and date in black.
174   **17**   1d. red .... 3·25   5·50
      a. Cross 2 mm to right .... 38·00   70·00
      b. "1" of "15" forked foot .... 18·00   35·00
      c. Broken "0" in "10" .... 18·00   35·00

The varieties occur in the following positions on the pane of 60: a. No. 11. b. No. 42. c. No. 45. Variety a. is only found on the right-hand pane.

1916 (19 Oct). Optd with T **19a**. Cross in red with outline and date in black.
175   **17**   1d. scarlet 50   2·00
      a. No stop after "16" .... 20·00   60·00
      b. "19.10.16" omitted ....
      c. Red shading on cross omitted ...

No. 175a appears on stamp No. 36 on the right-hand pane only.

PRINTING METHOD. The "War Tax" overprints, types **19a** to **26a**, were lithographed locally by the Govt Printer, using settings of 120.

FORGERIES. Beware of forgeries of the "War Tax" errors listed below. There are also other unlisted errors which are purely fakes.

WAR TAX   **WAR TAX**   **WAR TAX**   **WAR TAX**
 (19b)   **(20)**   **(21)**   **(22)**

1917 (29 Mar). Optd with T **19b**.
176   **17**   1d. red .... 4·50   3·25
      a. Opt inverted £225   £300
      b. Scarlet .... 4·50   3·25
      w. Wmk inverted ....

1917 (May). Optd with T **20**.
177   **17**   ½d. green (10.5.17) .... 1·50   40
      a. Pair, one without opt £900   £1400
178   1d. red (7.5.17) .... 4·75   2·25
      a. Pair, one without opt £900   £1400
      b. Scarlet .... 6·00   1·00
      ba. Opt double £160

The varieties without overprint were caused by the overprint being shifted over towards the left so that some stamps in the right-hand column of each pane escaped.

1917 (June). Optd with T **21**.
179   **17**   ½d. yellow-green (21.6.17) ... 7·00   27·00
      a. Pale green .... 1·00   17·00
      b. Deep green .... 4·00   17·00
180   1d. red (25.6.17) 15   75
      a. Pair, one without opt ....

No. 180a was caused by a shifting of the overprint to the left-hand side, but only a few stamps on the right-hand vertical row escaped the overprint and such pairs are very rare.

1917 (21 July–Sept). Optd with T **22**.
181   **17**   ½d. yellow-green .... 7·00   14·00
      a. Deep green 10   5·00
      aw. Wmk inverted £150
182   1d. red (6.9.17) .... 7·50   1·00

WAR TAX   **WAR TAX**   **WAR TAX**
 (23)   **(24)**   **(25)**

1917 (1 Sept). Optd with T **23** (closer spacing between lines of opt).
183   **17**   ½d. deep green 10   2·75
      a. Pale yellow-green ....
184   1d. red .... 70·00   60·00

1917 (31 Oct). Optd with T **24**.
185   **17**   1d. scarlet 60   1·00
      a. Opt inverted £170

1918 (7 Jan). Optd with T **25**.
186   **17**   1d. scarlet .... 2·25   15
      a. Opt double £225   £225
      b. Opt inverted £150   £160

War Tax   **War Tax**
 (26)   **(26a)**   **27**

1918 (13 Feb–Dec). Optd with T **26**.
187   **17**   ½d. bluish green 10   3·50
      a. Pair, one without opt £1500
      y. Wmk inverted and reversed ... £150
188   1d. scarlet .... 2·25   1·25
      a. Opt double £160
      b. Rose-red (12.18) 10   60

Both values exist with "Tax" omitted, the ½d. due to a paper fold and the 1d. due to misplacement.

1918 (14 Sept). New printing as T **26**, but 19 stamps on each sheet have the letters of the word "Tax" wider spaced, the "x" being to the right of "r" of "War" as T **26a**. Thick bluish paper.
189   **17**   1d. scarlet ("Tax" spaced) ... 7·00   24·00
      a. Opt double £300
      b. Opt inverted £1600
      c. Opt inverted on back £1600

The sheet positions of No. 189 are as follows: Left pane; R. 3/2, 3/4, 5/2, 5/6, 6/3, 7/6, 8/1, 8/5 and 10/3. Right pane; R. 1/3, 2/2, 5/3, 5/5, 6/6, 7/3, 8/6, 9/3 and 9/4.

The varieties 189b and 189c are caused by a paper fold.

1921–22. Chalk-surfaced paper (6d. to £1). Wmk Mult Script CA. P 14.
206   **17**   ½d. green .... 3·50   2·25
207   1d. scarlet 60   30
208   1d. brown (17.2.22) 60   1·50
209   2d. grey (17.2.22) .... 1·00   1·25
210   2½d. bright blue 80   24·00
211   3d. bright blue (17.2.22) .... 8·50   3·00
212   6d. dull and bright purple .... 5·00   16·00
213   **18**   5s. dull purple and purple (1921) ... 75·00   £170
      a. deep purple and purple (1922) ... £100   £180
215   £1 green and carmine £180   £375
206/15 Set of 9 .... £225   £550
206s/15s Optd "SPECIMEN" Set of 9 .... £300

(Typo D.L.R.)
1922–28. Chalk-surfaced paper (4d. to £1). P 14.
(a) Wmk Mult Crown CA
216   **27**   4d. black and red/pale yellow ... 4·75   20·00
217   1s. black/emerald .... 6·00   9·50
(b) Wmk Mult Script CA
218   **27**   ½d. green 50   10
219   1d. brown 50   10
      w. Wmk inverted .... 35·00   38·00
220   1½d. bright rose .... 3·75   60
      aw. Wmk inverted .... 70·00   70·00
      b. Scarlet .... 2·25   30
      bw. Wmk inverted ....
222   2d. grey 50   1·25
      w. Wmk inverted .... —   £170
223   3d. blue 50   1·25
224   4d. black and red/pale yellow (1928) ... 3·25   3·25
      w. Wmk inverted .... —   £325
225   6d. dull purple and bright magenta ... 2·25   27·00
226   6d. green and red/emerald (1924) ... 1·25   60
227   1s. black/emerald .... 5·50   1·75
228   5s. dull purple and mauve .... 30·00   38·00
229   £1 green and bright rose £150   £275
216/29 Set of 13 .... £180   £325
216s/29s Optd "SPECIMEN" Set of 13 .... £400

(New Currency. 100 cents = 1 West Indian dollar)

28 First Boca

29 Imperial College of Tropical Agriculture

30 Mt. Irvine Bay, Tobago

31 Discovery of Lake Asphalt

32 Queen's Park, Savannah

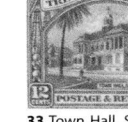
33 Town Hall, San Fernando

34 Government House

35 Memorial Park

36 Blue Basin

(Recess B.W.)
1935 (1 Feb)–**37**. T **28/36**. Wmk Mult Script CA (sideways). P 12.
230   **28**   1c. blue and green 40   85
      a. Perf 12½ (1936) 30   10
231   **29**   2c. ultramarine and yellow-brown ... 2·75   1·00
      a. Perf 12½ (1936) .... 3·00   10
232   **30**   3c. black and scarlet .... 2·00   30
      a. Perf 12½ (1936) .... 3·25   30
233   **31**   6c. sepia and blue .... 4·25   2·50
      a. Perf 12½ (1937) .... 18·00   11·00
234   **32**   8c. sage-green and vermilion ... 3·75   3·50
235   **33**   12c. black and violet .... 4·50   1·75
      a. Perf 12½ (1937) .... 19·00   13·00
236   **34**   24c. black and olive-green .... 10·00   2·75
      a. Perf 12½ (1937) .... 28·00   22·00
237   **35**   48c. deep green .... 10·00   15·00
238   **36**   72c. myrtle-green and carmine ... 42·00   30·00
230/8 Set of 9 .... 70·00   50·00
230s/8s Perf "SPECIMEN" Set of 9 .... £180

The original printings of Nos. 230/8 were P 12 (line). Later printings (Nos. 230a/6a) were comb perforated (exact gauge P 12·7 × 12·6).

1935 (6 May). Silver Jubilee. As Nos. 91/4 of Antigua, but ptd by B.W. P 11×12.
239   2c. ultramarine and grey-black ... 30   75
      a. Extra flagstaff .... 35·00   55·00
      b. Short extra flagstaff .... 95·00
      c. Lightning conductor .... 50·00
      d. Flagstaff on right-hand turret ... £130
      e. Double flagstaff £140
240   3c. deep blue and scarlet 30   2·50
      a. Extra flagstaff .... 60·00   £120
      c. Lightning conductor .... 80·00
241   6c. brown and deep blue .... 3·00   2·50
      a. Extra flagstaff .... 90·00   £150
      b. Short extra flagstaff £200
      c. Lightning conductor £120   £180
242   24c. slate and purple .... 14·00   27·00
      a. Extra flagstaff £180   £325
      c. Lightning conductor £200
      d. Flagstaff on right-hand turret ... £325
      e. Double flagstaff £350
239/42 Set of 4 .... 16·00   29·00
239s/42s Perf "SPECIMEN" Set of 4 .... £110

For illustrations of plate varieties see Omnibus section following Zanzibar.

1937 (12 May). Coronation. As Nos. 95/7 of Antigua, but ptd by D.L.R. P 14.
243   1c. carmine 15   60
244   2c. yellow-brown 40   15
245   8c. orange .... 1·10   2·25
243/5 Set of 3 .... 1·50   2·75
243s/5s Perf "SPECIMEN" Set of 3 .... 95·00

37 First Boca

38 Imperial College of Tropical Agriculture

39 Mt. Irvine Bay, Tobago

40 Memorial Park

41 GPO and Treasury

42 Discovery of Lake Asphalt

43 Queen's Park, Savannah

44 Town Hall, San Fernando

45 Government House

46 Blue Basin

47 King George VI

(Recess B.W.)

1938 (2 May)–**44**. T **37/47**. Wmk Mult Script CA (sideways on 1c. to 60c.).

(a) P 11½×11

246	37	1c. blue and green	1·00	30
247	38	2c. blue and yellow-brown	1·25	20
248	39	3c. black and scarlet	11·00	1·00
248a		3c. green and purple-brown (1941)	30	20
		ab. "A" of "CA" missing from wmk		
249	40	4c. chocolate	30·00	3·00
249a		4c. scarlet (1941)	50	1·00
249b	41	5c. magenta (1.5.41)	50	15
250	42	6c. sepia and blue	2·75	80
251	43	8c. sage-green and vermilion	2·75	1·00
		a. "A" of "CA" missing from wmk	£950	
252	44	12c. black and purple	35·00	2·50
		a. *Black and slate-purple* (1944)	5·50	50
253	45	24c. black and olive-green	8·50	50
254	46	60c. myrtle-green and carmine	16·00	1·50

(b) T 47. P 12

255	47	$1.20 blue-green (1.40)	13·00	1·75
256		$4.80 rose-carmine (1.40)	40·00	55·00
246/56 *Set of 14*			£110	60·00
246s/56s (*ex 5c.*) Perf "SPECIMEN" *Set of 13*			£400	

1946 (1 Oct). Victory. As Nos. 110/11 of Antigua.

257		3c. chocolate	10	10
258		6c. blue	55	1·50
257s/8s Perf "SPECIMEN" *Set of 2*			85·00	

1948 (22 Nov). Royal Silver Wedding. As Nos. 112/13 of Antigua, but $4.80 in recess.

259		3c. red-brown	10	10
260		$4.80 carmine	30·00	48·00

1949 (10 Oct). 75th Anniv of UPU. As Nos. 114/17 of Antigua.

261		5c. bright reddish purple	35	1·00
262		6c. deep blue	2·00	2·50
263		12c. violet	55	1·75
264		24c. olive	55	1·25
261/4 *Set of 4*			3·00	6·00

1951 (16 Feb). Inauguration of BWI University College. As Nos. 118/19 of Antigua.

265		3c. green and red-brown	20	1·25
266		12c. black and reddish violet	30	1·25

Nos. 265/6 are inscribed "TRINIDAD".

48 First Boca

49 Mt. Irvine Bay, Tobago

(Recess B.W.)

1953 (20 Apr)–**59**. Designs previously used for King George VI issue, but with portrait of Queen Elizabeth II as is T **48** (1c., 2c., 12c.) or **49** (other values). Wmk Mult Script CA. P 12 (dollar values) or 11½×11 (others).

267	48	1c. blue and green	20	40
		a. *Blue and bluish green* (10.6.59)	6·00	7·00
268	38	2c. indigo and orange-brown	20	40
269	49	3c. deep emerald and purple-brown	20	10
270	40	4c. scarlet	30	40
271	41	5c. magenta	40	30
272	42	6c. brown and greenish blue	60	30
273	43	8c. deep yellow-green and orange-red	2·50	30
274	44	12c. black and purple	40	10
275	45	24c. black and yellow-olive	2·75	30
		a. *Black and olive* (16.11.55)	6·50	1·50
		b. *Black and greenish olive* (12.12.56)	11·00	1·25
276	46	60c. blackish green and carmine	27·00	1·75
277	47	$1.20 bluish green	1·00	2·00
		a. Perf 11½ (19.1.55)	2·00	30
278		$4.80 cerise	8·50	27·00
		a. Perf 11½ (16.12.55)	12·00	20·00
267/78a *Set of 12*			40·00	22·00

1953 (3 June). Coronation. As No. 120 of Antigua.

279		3c. black and green	30	10

ONE CENT
(50)

1956 (20 Dec). No. 268 surch with T **50**.

280		1c. on 2c. indigo and orange-brown	1·25	2·25

1958 (22 Apr). Inauguration of British Caribbean Federation. As Nos. 135/7 of Antigua.

281		5c. deep green	50	10
282		6c. blue	55	1·50
283		12c. scarlet	60	10
281/3 *Set of 3*			1·50	1·50

PRINTERS. Nos. 284 to 354 were printed in photogravure by Harrison & Sons, unless otherwise stated.

51 Cipriani Memorial

52 Queen's Hall

53 Whitehall

54 Treasury Building

55 Governor General's House

56 General Hospital, San Fernando

57 Oil refinery

58 Crest

58a Coat of Arms

59 Scarlet Ibis

60 Pitch Lake

61 Mohammed Jinnah Mosque

62 Anthurium Lilies

63 Copper-rumped Hummingbird

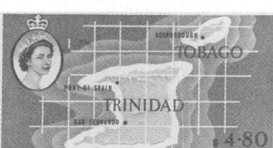

64 Map of Trinidad and Tobago

(Des V. Whiteley (1, 2, 12, 35, 60c., $4.80), J. Matthews (5c.), H. Baxter (6, 8, 10, 15c.), M. Goaman (25c., 50c., $1.20))

1960 (24 Sept)–**67**. Designs as T **51/64**. W w **12** (upright). P 13½×14½ (1c., 60c., $1.20, $4.80) or 14½×13½ (others).

284	51	1c. stone and black	1·25	20
285	52	2c. bright blue	45	20
		a. *Blue* (23.6.64)	5·50	1·00
		b. *New blue* (18.4.67)	5·50	1·00
		w. Wmk inverted	7·00	
286	53	5c. chalky blue	10	10
		w. Wmk inverted	9·50	2·25
287	54	6c. red-brown	50	1·00
		a. *Pale chestnut* (13.4.67)	8·50	3·25
		w. Wmk inverted	70·00	
288	55	8c. yellow-green	10	1·50
289	56	10c. deep lilac	10	10
290	57	12c. vermilion	10	1·25
291	58	15c. orange	3·50	10
291a	58a	15c. orange (15.9.64)	14·00	10
292	59	25c. rose-carmine and deep blue	80	10
		w. Wmk inverted	3·50	1·75
293	60	35c. emerald and black	3·75	10
		w. Wmk inverted	—	£225
294	61	50c. yellow, grey and blue	35	1·50
295	62	60c. vermilion, yellow-green and indigo	55	30
		a. Perf 14½ (17.7.65*)	£140	50·00
296	63	$1.20 multicoloured	15·00	4·00
297	64	$4.80 apple-green and pale blue	22·00	21·00
284/97 *Set of 15*			50·00	29·00

*This is the earliest date reported to us. It comes from an unannounced printing which was despatched to Trinidad on 3 December 1964.

The 2, 5, 6, 12 and 25c. exist with PVA gum as well as gum arabic. See also No. 317.

65 Scouts and Gold Wolf Badge

1961 (4 Apr). Second Caribbean. Scout Jamboree. Design multicoloured; background colours below. W w **12**. P 13½×14½.

298	65	8c. light green	15	10
299		25c. light blue	15	10
		w. Wmk inverted	£170	85·00

INDEPENDENT

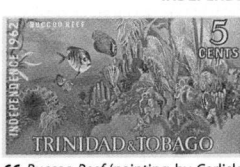

66 *Buccoo Reef* (painting by Carlisle Chang)

71 "Protein Foods"

1962 (31 Aug). Independence. T **66** and similar horiz designs. W w **12**. P 14½.

300		5c. bluish green	10	10
301		8c. grey	40	1·00
302		25c. reddish violet	15	10
303		35c. brown, yellow, green and black	2·25	10
304		60c. red, black and blue	2·75	3·75
300/4 *Set of 5*			5·00	4·50

Designs:—8c. Piarco Air Terminal; 25c. Hilton Hotel, Port-of-Spain; 35c. Greater Bird of Paradise and map; 60c. Scarlet Ibis and map.

(Des M. Goaman)

1963 (4 June). Freedom from Hunger. W w **12**. P 14×13½.

305	71	5c. brown-red	35	10
306		8c. yellow-bistre	50	85
307		25c. violet-blue	80	20
305/7 *Set of 3*			1·50	1·00

72 Jubilee Emblem

1964 (15 Sept). Golden Jubilee of Trinidad and Tobago Girl Guides' Association. W w **12**. P 14½×14.

308	72	6c. yellow, ultramarine and rose-red	10	70
309		25c. yellow, ultramarine and bright blue	15	20
310		35c. yellow, ultramarine and emerald-green	20	20
308/10 *Set of 3*			40	1·00

73 ICY Emblem

(Litho State Ptg Wks, Vienna)

1965 (15 Nov). International Co-operation Year. P 12.

311	73	35c. red-brown, deep green and ochre-yellow	65	20

74 Eleanor Roosevelt, Flag and UN Emblem

1965 (10 Dec). Eleanor Roosevelt Memorial Foundation. W w **12**. P 13½×14½.

312	74	25c. black, red and ultramarine	15	10

75 Parliament Building

FIFTH YEAR OF INDEPENDENCE 31st AUGUST 1967
(79)

1966 (8 Feb). Royal Visit. T **75** and similar horiz designs. Multicoloured. W w **12** (sideways). P 13½×14½.

313		5c. Type 75	1·10	10
314		8c. Map, Royal Yacht *Britannia* and Arms	1·90	1·00
315		25c. Map and flag	1·90	55
316		35c. Flag and panorama	1·90	70
313/16 *Set of 4*			6·00	2·00

1966 (15 Nov). As No. 284 but W w **12** (sideways*).
317	1c. stone and black	10	70
	w. Wmk Crown to right of CA		

*The normal sideways watermark shows Crown to left of CA, *as seen from the back of the stamp*.
No. 317 exists with PVA gum as well as gum arabic.

1967 (31 Aug). Fifth Year of Independence. Nos. 288/9, 291a and 295 optd as T **79**.
318	8c. yellow-green	10	10
319	10c. deep lilac	10	10
320	15c. orange	10	10
321	60c. vermilion, yellow-green and indigo.	25	15
318/21	Set of 4	30	30

On No. 321 the overprint is in five lines.

80 Musical Instruments

81 Calypso King

1968 (17 Feb). Trinidad Carnival. Horiz designs as T **80** (15 and 25c.), or vert designs as T **81** (35 and 60c.). Multicoloured. P 12.
322	5c. Type **80**	10	10
323	10c. Type **81**	10	10
324	15c. Steel band	15	10
325	25c. Carnival procession	20	10
326	35c. Carnival King	20	10
327	60c. Carnival Queen	40	1·00
322/7	Set of 6	1·00	1·10

86 Doctor giving Eye-Test

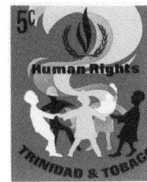
87 Peoples of the World and Emblem

1968 (7 May). 20th Anniv of World Health Organization. W w **12** (sideways). P 14.
328	**86**	5c. red, blackish brown and gold ...	15	10
329		25c. orange, blackish brown and gold	35	15
330		35c. bright blue, black and gold	40	25
328/30		Set of 3	80	45

1968 (5 Aug). Human Rights Year. W w **12** (sideways). P 13½×14.
331	**87**	5c. cerise, black and greenish yellow	10	10
332		10c. new blue, black and greenish yellow	15	10
333		25c. apple-green, black and greenish yellow	30	15
331/3		Set of 3	45	30

88 Cycling

(Des G. Vasarhelyi. Islands additionally die-stamped in gold (5c. to 35c.))

1968 (14 Oct). Olympic Games, Mexico. T **88** and similar horiz designs. Multicoloured. W w **12**. P 14.
334	5c. Type **88**	80	10
	w. Wmk inverted	†	£200
335	15c. Weightlifting	20	10
	w. Wmk inverted	9·00	
336	25c. Relay-racing	20	10
337	35c. Sprinting	20	10
338	$1.20 Maps of Mexico and Trinidad	1·60	1·10
334/8	Set of 5	2·75	1·25

93 Cocoa Beans

94 Green Hermit

(Des G. Vasarhelyi. Queen's profile die-stamped in gold (G.) or silver (S.), also the Islands on 20, 25c.)
1969 (1 Apr)–72. Designs as T **93/4**. W w **12** (sideways* on 1 to 8c., 40c., 50c.). Chalk-surfaced paper. P 14×14½ ($2.50, $5) or 14 (others).
339	1c. multicoloured (S.)	20	1·25
	a. Queen's head omitted	£170	

	bw. Wmk Crown to right of CA		
	c. Glazed, ordinary paper (24.3.72)	10	45
	cw. Wmk Crown to right of CA		
340	3c. multicoloured (G.)	10	10
	aw. Wmk Crown to right of CA		
	b. Glazed, ordinary paper (24.3.72)	10	10
	bw. Wmk Crown to right of CA		
341	5c. multicoloured (G.)	3·50	10
	a. Glazed, ordinary paper (24.3.72)	2·00	10
	ab. Queen's head omitted	£250	
	ac. Imperf (pair)	£275	
	ad. Ditto and Queen's head omitted	£400	
	aw. Wmk Crown to right of CA	7·50	
342	6c. multicoloured (G.)	10	10
	a. Queen's head omitted	£300	
	b. Imperf (pair)	£350	
	c. Glazed, ordinary paper (24.3.72)	2·75	10·00
	cw. Wmk Crown to right of CA	4·75	
343	8c. multicoloured (S.)	5·00	3·25
344	10c. multicoloured (G.)	4·50	20
	a. Glazed, ordinary paper (24.3.72)	2·00	20
	aw. Wmk inverted	11·00	
345	12c. multicoloured (blue-green leaves) (S.)	15	3·75
	a. Myrtle-green leaves	4·75	8·50
	b. Glazed, ordinary paper (24.3.72)	50	6·50
346	15c. multicoloured (S.)	10	10
	a. Queen's head omitted	£475	
	b. Glazed, ordinary paper (24.3.72)	20	10
347	20c. scarlet, black and grey (G.)	30	10
	a. Glazed, ordinary paper (24.3.72)	50	3·75
348	25c. scarlet, black and new blue (S.)	30	1·00
	a. Glazed, ordinary paper (24.3.72)	4·75	4·00
	ab. Silver (Queen's head and island) omitted	£325	
349	30c. multicoloured (S.)	30	10
	a. Glazed, ordinary paper (24.3.72)	50	2·25
	aw. Wmk inverted	18·00	
350	40c. multicoloured (G.)	5·50	10
	a. Glazed, ordinary paper (24.3.72)	6·50	60
351	50c. multicoloured (S.)	30	4·25
	a. Glazed, ordinary paper (24.3.72)	1·50	8·50
	aw. Wmk Crown to right of CA	7·00	
352	$1 multicoloured (G.)	60	15
	a. Gold (Queen's head) omitted	£275	
	b. Glazed, ordinary paper (24.3.72)	1·50	7·00
	ba. Gold (Queen's head) omitted		
353	$2.50 multicoloured (G.)	1·00	5·50
	a. Perf 14 (1972)	5·00	12·00
	aw. Wmk inverted	40·00	
354	$5 multicoloured (G.)	1·00	5·50
	a. Gold (Queen's head) omitted	£450	
	b. Perf 14 (1972)	6·00	25·00
	bw. Wmk inverted	38·00	50·00
339/54	Set of 16	20·00	22·00
339c/352b	Set of 13	21·00	38·00

Designs: Horiz as T **93**—3c. Sugar refinery; 5c. Rufous vented Chachalaca; 6c. Oil refinery; 8c. Fertilizer plant 40c. Scarlet Ibis; 50c. Maracas Bay; $2.50, Fishing; $5 Red House. Vert as T **94**—12c. Citrus fruit; 15c. Arms of Trinidad and Tobago; 20c, 25c. Flag and outline of Trinidad and Tobago; 30c. Chaconia plant; $1, Poui tree.
*The normal sideways watermark shows the Crown to the left of CA, *as seen from the back of the stamp*.
The date quoted for the glazed, ordinary paper printings is that of receipt at the GPO; the dates of issue are not known.

The listed missing die-stamped heads have the heads completely omitted and, except for No. 352a which results from a shift, show a blind impression of the die. They should not be confused with stamps from sheets containing a row of partially missing heads progressing down to mere specks of foil. The 20c. value also exists with the gold omitted from the map only. We have also seen stamps with an additional "blind" profile cutting into the rear of the head but without a second die-stamped impression. Varieties of this nature are outside the scope of this catalogue.
Nos. 340/2 were later reissued with W w **12** upright and No. 344a with W w **14**.

108 Captain A. A. Cipriani (labour leader) and Entrance to Woodford Square

(Photo State Ptg Works, Vienna)
1969 (1 May). 50th Anniv of International Labour Organization. T **108** and similar horiz design. P 12.
355	6c. black, gold and carmine-red	15	25
356	15c. black, gold and new blue	15	25

Design:—15c. Arms of Industrial Court and entrance to Woodford Square.

110 Cornucopia and Fruit

111 "CARIFTA" Countries

(Des and photo State Ptg Works, Vienna)
1969 (1 Aug). First Anniv of CARIFTA (Caribbean Free Trade Area). T **110/11** and similar multicoloured designs. P 13½.
357	6c. Type **110**	10	10
358	10c. British and member nations' flags (horiz)	10	10
359	30c. Type **111**	20	20
360	40c. Boeing 727-100 "Sunjet" in flight (horiz)	40	90
357/60	Set of 4	65	1·10

114 Space Module landing on Moon

(Des G. Vasarhelyi. Litho D.L.R.)
1969 (2 Sept). First Man on the Moon. T **114** and similar multicoloured designs. P 14.
361	6c. Type **114**	20	10
362	40c. Space module and astronauts on Moon (vert)	30	10
363	$1 Astronauts seen from inside space module	60	35
361/3	Set of 3	1·00	50

The above were released by the Philatelic Agency in the USA on 1 September, but not sold locally until 2 September.

117 Parliamentary Chamber, Flags and Emblems

(Photo Harrison)
1969 (23 Oct*). 15th Commonwealth Parliamentary Association Conference, Port-of-Spain. T **117** and similar horiz designs. Multicoloured. W w **12**. P 14½×13½.
364	10c. Type **117**	10	10
365	15c. J.F. Kennedy College	10	10
366	30c. Parliamentary maces	25	50
367	40c. Cannon and emblem	25	50
364/7	Set of 4	60	1·00

*This was the local release date; the Philatelic Agency in New York released the stamps ten days earlier.

121 Congress Emblem

122 Emblem and Islands at Daybreak

(Photo Rosenbaum Bros, Vienna)
1969 (3 Nov). International Congress of the Junior Chamber of Commerce. T **121/2** and similar vert design. P 13½.
368	6c. black, red and gold	10	10
369	30c. gold, lake and light blue	25	40
370	40c. black, gold and ultramarine	25	40
368/70	Set of 3	50	75

Design:—40c. Emblem palm-trees and ruin.
The above were released by the Philatelic Agency in the USA on 2 November, but not sold locally until 3 November.

124 "Man in the Moon"

129 Statue of Gandhi

(Des V. Whiteley. Litho Questa)
1970 (6 Feb). Carnival Winners. T **124** and similar multicoloured designs. W w **12** (sideways on 40c.). P 14.
371	5c. Type **124**	10	10
372	6c. "City beneath the Sea"	10	10
373	15c. "Antelope" God Bamibara	15	10
	w. Wmk inverted	—	16·00
374	30c. "Chanticleer" Pheasant Queen of Malaya	25	10
375	40c. Steel Band of the Year (horiz)	25	30
371/5	Set of 5	70	50

The above were released by the Philatelic Agency in the USA on 2 February, but not sold locally until 6 February.

(Photo State Printing Works, Vienna)
1970 (2 Mar). Gandhi Centenary Year (1969). T **129** and similar multicoloured design. P 12.
376	10c. Type **129**	40	10
377	30c. Head of Gandhi and Indian flag (horiz)	85	20

131 Symbols of Culture, Science, Arts and Technology

132 New UPU HQ Building

(Des G. Lee. Photo State Printing Works, Vienna)

1970 (26 June). 25th Anniv of United Nations. T **131**/2 and similar designs. Multicoloured. P 12 (30c.) 13½×14 (10c.) or 13½ (others).

378		5c. Type **131**	10	10
379		10c. Children of different races, map and flag (34×25 *mm*)	20	10
380		20c. Noah's Ark, rainbow and dove (35×24 *mm*)	20	45
381		30c. Type **132**	25	30
378/81		*Set of 4*	65	75

(133) **134** *East Indian Immigrants* (J. Cazabon)

1970 (1 July). Inauguration of National Commercial Bank. No. 341 optd with T **133**.

382		5c. multicoloured	30	10

(Des from paintings by Cazabon. Litho Questa)

1970 (1 Oct). 125th Anniv of San Fernando. T **134** and similar designs. W w **12** (sideways on 5c. and 40c.). P 13½.

383		3c. multicoloured	10	90
		w. Wmk inverted	—	40·00
384		5c. black, blue and yellow-ochre	10	10
385		40c. black, blue and yellow-ochre	95	20
383/5		*Set of 3*	1·00	1·10

Designs: Horiz—5c. *San Fernando Town Hall*; 40c. *San Fernando Harbour, 1860*

135 *The Adoration of the Shepherds* (detail, School of Seville)

(Des G. Drummond. Litho Format)

1970 (8 Dec). Christmas. Paintings. T **135** and similar vert designs. Multicoloured. P 13½.

386		3c. Type **135**	10	10
387		5c. *Madonna and Child with Saints* (detail, Titian)	10	10
388		30c. *The Adoration of the Shepherds* (detail, Le Nain)	15	20
389		40c. *The Virgin and Child, St. John and an Angel* (Morando)	15	10
390		$1 *The Adoration of the Kings* (detail, Veronese)	35	2·50
386/90		*Set of 5*	75	2·75
MS391		114×153 mm. Nos. 386/9	1·00	1·25

STAMP BOOKLETS

1925.
SB1	2s. booklet containing 8×½d., 8×1d. and 8×1½d. (Nos. 218/20) in blocks of 4		

1931–32. Black on pink covers.
SB2	1s.8d. booklet containing 8×½d. and 16×1d. (Nos. 218/19) in blocks of 8		
SB3	2s. booklet containing 8×½d., 8×1d. and 8×1½d. (Nos. 218/20) in blocks of 8 (1932)		

1936.
SB4	48c. booklet containing 8×1, 8×2 and 8×3c. (Nos. 230a/2a) in blocks of 4		

1970 (8 Dec). Christmas. Olive-green printed cover inscr "CHRISTMAS GREETINGS".
SB5	$1.78 booklet containing 6×3c., 4×5c. and 2×30c. and 2×40c. (Nos. 386/9) in pairs	4·50	

POSTAGE DUE STAMPS

D 1 **D 2**

1/- **1/-**

Column 4 Column 5

The degree of inclination of the stroke on the 1s. value varies for each vertical column of the sheet: Columns 1, 2 and 6 104°, Column 3 108°, Column 4 107° and Column 5 (Nos. D9a, D17a, D25a) 100°.

(Typo D.L.R.)

1885 (1 Jan). Wmk Crown CA. P 14.

D1	D **1**	½d. slate-black	19·00	50·00
D2		1d. slate-black	16·00	20
D3		2d. slate-black	50·00	20
		w. Wmk inverted	†	£450
D4		3d. slate-black	60·00	40
D5		4d. slate-black	50·00	7·00
D6		5d. slate-black	24·00	60
D7		6d. slate-black	50·00	15·00
D8		8d. slate-black	60·00	5·50
D9		1s. slate-black	80·00	5·00
		a. Upright stroke	£150	15·00
D1/9		*Set of 9*	£350	70·00

1905–06. Wmk Mult Crown CA. P 14.

D10	D **1**	1d. slate-black	9·00	20
D11		2d. slate-black	40·00	20
		w. Wmk inverted	†	£350
D12		3d. slate-black	14·00	3·75
		w. Wmk inverted	—	£180
D13		4d. slate-black	14·00	22·00
		w. Wmk inverted		
D14		5d. slate-black	21·00	23·00
D15		6d. slate-black	6·50	17·00
D16		8d. slate-black	21·00	23·00
D17		1s. slate-black	29·00	45·00
		a. Upright stroke	45·00	75·00
D10/17		*Set of 8*	£140	£120

1923–45. Wmk Mult Script CA. P 14.

D18	D **1**	1d. black	4·00	4·00
D19		2d. black	8·50	1·50
D20		3d. black (1925)	12·00	6·50
D21		4d. black (1929)	8·50	30·00
D22		5d. black (1944)	40·00	£140
D23		6d. black (1945)	75·00	55·00
D24		8d. black (1945)	45·00	£200
D25		1s. black (1945)	85·00	£160
		a. Upright stroke	£140	£275
D18/25		*Set of 8*	£250	£550
D18s/25s		Optd or Perf (5d. to 1s.) "SPECIMEN" *Set of 8*	£200	

1947 (1 Sept)–**61**. Values in cents. Ordinary paper. Wmk Mult Script CA. P 14.

D26	D **1**	2c. black	5·50	9·50
		a. Chalk-surfaced paper (20.1.53)	20	6·00
		ab. Error. Crown missing. W **9a**	£150	
		ac. Error. St. Edward's Crown. W **9b**	38·00	
D27		4c. black	2·75	3·00
		a. Chalk-surfaced paper (10.8.55)	10·00	4·50
D28		6c. black	5·00	7·00
		a. Chalk-surfaced paper (20.1.53)	30	7·50
		ab. Error. Crown missing. W **9a**	£450	
		ac. Error. St. Edward's Crown. W **9b**	95·00	
D29		8c. black	1·25	42·00
		a. Chalk-surfaced paper (10.9.58)	35	32·00
D30		10c. black	3·25	9·50
		a. Chalk-surfaced paper (10.8.55)	9·50	23·00
D31		12c. black	4·25	29·00
		a. Chalk-surfaced paper (20.1.53)	40	25·00
		ab. Error. Crown missing. W **9a**	£650	
		ac. Error. St. Edward's Crown. W **9b**	£170	
D32		16c. black	2·00	55·00
		a. Chalk-surfaced paper (22.8.61)	16·00	70·00
D33		24c. black	13·00	15·00
		a. Chalk-surfaced paper (10.8.55)	14·00	55·00
D26/33		*Set of 8*	32·00	£150
D26a/33a		*Set of 8*	45·00	£200
D26s/33s		Perf "SPECIMEN" *Set of 8*	£140	

(Litho B.W.)

1969 (25 Nov)–**70**. Size 19×24 mm. P 14×13½.

D34	D **2**	2c. pale blue-green	15	2·50
D35		4c. magenta (1970)	25	8·50
D36		6c. brown (1970)	50	4·50
D37		8c. slate-lilac (1970)	65	4·50
D38		10c. dull red (1970)	1·00	8·50
D39		12c. pale orange (1970)	80	6·50
D40		16c. bright apple-green (1970)	1·00	6·50
D41		24c. grey (1970)	1·00	11·00
D42		50c. grey-blue (1970)	1·00	4·50
D43		60c. sage-green (1970)	1·00	4·00
D34/43		*Set of 10*	6·50	55·00

Postage due stamps as T D **2** but smaller (17×21 *mm*) were issued in 1976 and 1977.

"TOO LATE" STAMPS

A handstamp with the words "TOO LATE" was used upon letters on which a too-late fee had been paid, and was sometimes used for cancelling the stamps on such letters.

OFFICIAL STAMPS

O S **OFFICIAL** **OFFICIAL**
(O **1**) (O **2**) (O **3**)

1894. Optd with Type O **1**.

(a) On Nos. 106/12. Wmk Crown CA. P 14

O1	**10**	½d. dull green	48·00	65·00
O2		1d. carmine	50·00	70·00
O3		2½d. bright blue	55·00	£100
O4		4d. grey	60·00	£130
O5		6d. olive-black	60·00	£140
O6		1s. orange-brown	80·00	£190

(b) On No. 87. Wmk Crown CC. P 12½

O7	**5**	5s. rose-lake	£180	£900

1909. Nos. 133 and 135 optd with Type O **2**. Wmk Mult Crown CA. P 14.

O8	**11**	½d. blue-green	3·75	11·00
O9		1d. rose-red	3·50	12·00
		a. Opt double	—	£325
		b. Opt vertical	£130	£150
		c. Opt inverted	£750	£225

1910. No. 146 optd with Type O **2**. Wmk Mult Crown CA. P 14.

O10	**14**	½d. green	12·00	16·00
		w. Wmk inverted	£170	

1913. No. 149 optd with Type O **3** by lithography.

O11	**17**	½d. green	2·75	17·00
		a. Opt vertical		

OFFICIAL **OFFICIAL** **OFFICIAL**
(O **4**) (O **5**) (O **6**)

1914. No. 149 optd with Type O **4**.

O12	**17**	½d. green	4·25	24·00

1914–17. No. 149 optd with Type O **5** (without stop).

O13	**17**	½d. green	6·50	27·00
		a. Blue-green (*thick paper*) (1917)	65	10·00

1916. No. 149a optd with Type O **5** (with stop).

O14	**17**	½d. yellow-green	5·50	9·50
		a. Opt double	55·00	

1917 (22 Aug). No. 149 optd with Type O **6**.

O15	**17**	½d. green	6·50	30·00
		a. Yellow-green	6·50	32·00
		b. Blue-green (*thick paper*)	3·25	30·00

Tristan da Cunha

Although first settled in 1817 no surviving mail is known from Tristan da Cunha until two whaler's letters written in 1836 and 1843, these being carried home in other whaling ships. Then there is a long gap until the late 1800's when other letters are known—surprisingly only some seven in number, up to 1908 when the first of the island cachet handstamps came into use.

The collecting of postal history material from 1908 to 1952, when Tristan's first stamps were issued, revolves around the numerous cachets of origin which were struck on mail from the island during these 44 years. The handstamps producing these cachets were supplied over the years by various people particularly interested in the island and the islanders, and were mostly used by the clergymen who volunteered to go and serve as the community's ministers.

The postal cachets are illustrated below. The use of the different cachets on mail frequently overlapped, at one period in 1930 there were five different types of handstamp in use. As there was no official source for providing them they appeared on the island from various donors; then disappeared without trace once they became worn out. Only one of these early rubber handstamps has apparently survived, Cachet Va.

Covers bearing the cachets are recognised collector's items, but are difficult to value in general terms. As elsewhere the value is discounted by poor condition of the cover, and may be increased by use on a scarce date or with additional postal markings. Some cachets are known in more than one colour, but we do not list these variations.

Cachet Types V and VII on cover are the commonest, Type Va, used only for three months, and Type IVa are the scarcest, equalling the scarcest use of Type I examples. All cacheted covers, particularly if non-philatelic, are desirable forerunner items. Even a philatelic cover of Type V is, at present, worth in the region of £35.

Dates given are of the first recorded use.

Cachet I   Cachet II

Cat. No.				Value on cover
C1	**1908** (May). Cachet I		*from*	£4000
C2	**1919** (31 July). Cachet II		*from*	£425

Cachet III

C3	**1921** (8 Feb). Cachet III	*from*	£300

Cachet IVa

C4	**1927** (1 Oct). Cachet IV (*as IVa, but without centre label*)	*from*	£850
C5	**1928** (28 Oct). Cachet IVa	*from*	£5500

Cachet V   Cachet VI

C6	**1929** (24 Feb). Cachet V	*from*	35·00
C7	**1929** (15 May). Cachet Va (*as V, but without break in inner ring. Shows "T" "C" and "N" damaged*)	*from*	£6500
C8	**1936** (Aug). Cachet VI	*from*	60·00

Cachet VII

C9	**1936** (1 Feb). Cachet VII	*from*	22·00

During World War II there was little mail from the island as its function as a meteorological station was cloaked by security. Such covers as are known are generally struck with the "tombstone" naval censor mark and postmarked "maritime mail" or have South African postal markings. A few philatelic items from early in the war bearing cachets exist, but this usage was soon stopped by the military commander and the handstamps were put away until peace returned. Covers from the period would be worth from £75 to at least £350.

Cachet VIII

C10	**1946** (8 May). Cachet VIII	*from*	90·00

Cachet IX

C11	**1948** (29 Feb). Cachet IX	*from*	55·00

Cachet X

C12	**1948** (2 Feb). Cachet X	*from*	45·00

This cachet with "A.B.C." below the date was in private use between 1942 and 1946.

Although an earlier example of Cachet X is now known, we have retained the traditional sequence insofar as Cachets IX and X are concerned, for the convenience of collectors.

Cachet XI

Cachet XII

RESETTLEMENT SURVEY – 1962

Cachet XIII

Cachets XI to XIII from the 1961/63 "volcano eruption" and "return to the island" period vary in value from £30 to £120, due to philatelic usage on the one hand and scarce mailings from the small survey parties on shore during this period on the other.

TRISTAN DA CUNHA
(1)

1952 (1 Jan). Nos. 131, 135a/40 and 149/51 of St. Helena optd with T **1**.

1	½d. violet	15	3·50
2	1d. black and green	1·00	1·50
3	1½d. black and carmine	1·00	1·50
4	2d. black and scarlet	1·00	1·50
5	3d. grey	1·00	1·50
6	4d. ultramarine	7·00	2·50
7	6d. light blue	7·00	2·50
8	8d. olive-green	7·00	8·50
9	1s. sepia	5·50	2·00
10	2s.6d. maroon	24·00	19·00
11	5s. chocolate	38·00	25·00
12	10s. purple	60·00	42·00
1/12	*Set of 12*	£140	£100

1953 (2 June). Coronation. As No. 120 of Antigua.

13	3d. black and grey-green	1·25	2·00

2 Tristan Crawfish   **3** Carting Flax for Thatching

4 Rockhopper Penguin   **5** Big Beach factory

6 Yellow-nosed Albatross   **7** Island longboat

8 Tristan from the south-west   **9** Girls on donkeys

10 Inaccessible Island from Tristan   **11** Nightingale Island

 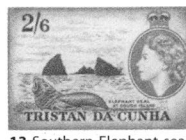

12 St. Mary's Church   **13** Southern Elephant seal at Gough Island

14 Inaccessible Island Rail   **15** Island spinning wheel

(Des D.L.R. (5d. and 10s.), H. Elliott (others). Recess D.L.R.)

1954 (2 Jan). T **2/15**. Wmk Mult Script CA. P 12½×13 (horiz) or 13×12½ (vert).

14	**2**	½d. red and deep brown..................	10	10
15	**3**	1d. sepia and bluish green..............	10	50
16	**4**	1½d. black and reddish purple...........	1·75	1·75
17	**5**	2d. grey-violet and brown-orange...	30	20
18	**6**	2½d. black and carmine-red..............	1·75	60
19	**7**	3d. ultramarine and olive-green.......	2·50	1·75
20	**8**	4d. turquoise-blue and deep blue..	60	70
21	**9**	5d. emerald and black.....................	60	70
22	**10**	6d. deep green and violet................	60	75
23	**11**	9d. reddish violet and Venetian red	60	45
24	**12**	deep yellow-green and sepia..........	60	45
25	**13**	2s.6d. deep brown and light blue........	17·00	11·00
26	**14**	5s. black and red-orange................	50·00	15·00
27	**15**	10s. brown-orange and purple	24·00	14·00
14/27 Set of 14...			90·00	42·00

16 Starfish   **17** Concha Wrasse

18 Two-spined Thornfish   **19** Atlantic Saury

20 Bristle Snipefish   **21** Tristan Crawfish

22 False Jacopever   **23** Five-fingered Morwong

24 Long-finned Scad   **25** Christophersen's Medusafish

26 Blue Medusafish   **27** Snoek

28 Blue Shark   **29** Black Right Whale

(Des Mr. and Mrs. G. F. Harris. Recess Waterlow)

1960 (1 Feb). Marine Life. T **16/29**. W w **12**. P 13.

28	**16**	½d. black and orange	15	40

29	**17**	1d. black and bright purple..............	15	20
30	**18**	1½d. black and light turquoise-blue .	20	1·00
31	**19**	2d. black and bluish green..............	30	1·25
32	**20**	2½d. black and sepia.......................	55	60
33	**21**	3d. black and brown-red.................	1·25	2·00
34	**22**	4d. black and yellow-olive..............	1·25	1·25
35	**23**	6d. black and orange-yellow..........	1·50	1·00
36	**24**	6d. black and blue.........................	1·75	1·00
37	**25**	9d. black and rose-carmine............	1·75	1·50
38	**26**	1s. black and light brown...............	3·50	1·00
39	**27**	2s.6d. black and ultramarine..............	11·00	11·00
40	**28**	5s. black and light emerald............	12·00	12·00
41	**29**	10s. black and violet.......................	48·00	32·00
28/41 Set of 14...			75·00	60·00

1961 (15 Apr). As Nos. 28/30 and 32/41 but values in South African decimal currency.

42	½c. black and orange (as ½d.)........	20	1·25
43	1c. black and bright purple (as 1d.)........	20	1·25
44	1½c. black and light turquoise-blue (as 1½d.)	35	1·25
45	2c. black and sepia (as 2½d.)........	65	1·25
46	2½c. black and brown-red (as 3d.)....	1·00	1·25
47	3c. black and yellow-olive (as 4d.)..	1·00	1·25
48	4c. black and orange-yellow (as 5d.)..	1·25	1·25
49	5c. black and blue (as 6d.).............	1·25	1·25
50	7½c. black and rose-carmine (as 9d.)..	1·25	1·25
51	10c. black and light brown (as 1s.)....	2·00	1·25
52	25c. black and ultramarine (as 2s. 6d.)..	7·00	7·50
53	50c. black and light emerald (as 5s.)..	24·00	18·00
54	1r. black and violet (as 10s.).........	50·00	35·00
42/54 Set of 13...		80·00	65·00

Following a volcanic eruption the island was evacuated on 10 October 1961, but resettled in 1963.

TRISTAN DA CUNHA RESETTLEMENT 1963
(30)

1963 (12 Apr). Tristan Resettlement. As Nos. 176/88 of St. Helena, but Wmk Mult Script CA (sideways on 1d., 2d., 7d., 10d., 2s. 6d., 10s), optd with T **30**.

55		1d. bright blue, dull violet, yellow and carmine	15	1·00
56		1½d. yellow, green, black and light drab..	2·00	70
57		2d. scarlet and grey	25	1·00
58		3d. light blue, black, pink and deep blue......................	30	1·00
		a. Black printed double*	£300	
		w. Wmk inverted.........................	£750	£850
59		4½d. yellow-green, green, brown and grey......................	50	60
60		6d. red, sepia and light yellow-olive	3·00	30
61		7d. red-brown, black and violet.......	50	30
62		10d. brown-purple and light blue.......	50	30
63		1s. greenish yellow, bluish green and brown	50	30
64		1s.6d. grey, black and slate-blue........	6·50	1·00
65		2s.6d. red, pale yellow and turquoise	1·00	45
66		5s. yellow, brown and green	5·00	1·00
		w. Wmk inverted.........................	90·00	80·00
67		10s. orange-red, black and blue...............	6·00	1·00
55/67 Set of 13...			23·00	8·00

*No. 58a shows the outline round the Queen's head printed double.

1963 (2 Oct). Freedom from Hunger. As No. 146 of Antigua.

68	1s.6d. carmine	50	30

1964 (1 Feb). Red Cross Centenary. As Nos. 147/8 of Antigua.

69	3d. red and black..........................	20	15
70	1s.6d. red and blue..........................	30	20

31 South Atlantic Map   **32** Flagship of Tristao da Cunha, 1506

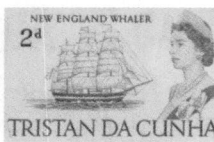

33 *Heemstede* (Dutch East Indiaman), 1643   **34** *Edward* (American Whaling ship), 1864

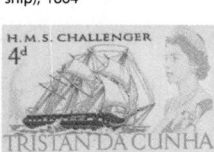

35 *Shenandoah* (Confederate warship), 1873   **35a** HMS *Challenger* (survey ship), 1873

36 HMS *Galatea* (screw frigate), 1867   **37** HMS *Cilicia* (transport), 1942

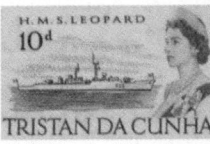

38 Royal Yacht *Britannia*   **39** HMS *Leopard* (frigate)

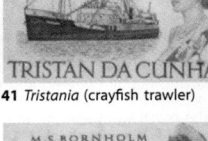

40 *Tjisadane* (liner)   **41** *Tristania* (crayfish trawler)

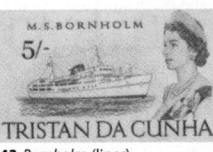

42 *Boissevain* (cargo liner)   **43** *Bornholm* (liner)

44 Queen Elizabeth II   **44a** *RSA* (research vessel)

(Queen's portrait by Anthony Buckley. Des, eng and recess B.W.)

1965 (17 Feb)–**67**. Designs as T **31/44a**. W w **12** (sideways on £1). P 11½×11 (vert) or 11×11½ (horiz).

71	**31**	½d. black and ultramarine	15	30
72	**32**	1d. black and emerald-green.........	1·00	15
73	**33**	1½d. black and blue.........................	1·00	15
74	**34**	2d. black and purple.....................	1·00	15
75	**35**	3d. black and turquoise-blue..........	1·00	15
75a	**35a**	4d. black and orange (1.9.67).........	3·00	4·00
76	**36**	4½d. black and brown......................	1·00	15
77	**37**	6d. black and green......................	1·25	15
78	**38**	7d. black and rose-red..................	2·25	30
79	**39**	10d. black and chocolate.................	1·25	55
80	**40**	1s. black and slate-blue...............	1·25	30
81	**41**	1s.6d. black and yellow-olive............	7·50	2·50
82	**42**	2s.6d. black and orange-brown........	3·50	4·00
83	**43**	5s. black and violet.....................	9·50	3·50
84	**44**	10s. deep blue and carmine..............	1·75	1·25
84a	**44a**	10s. black and deep turquoise-blue (1.9.67)..............	14·00	11·00
84b		£1 deep blue and orange-brown (1.9.67)..............	8·00	11·00
71/84b Set of 17...			50·00	35·00

1965 (11 May*). ITU Centenary. As Nos. 166/7 of Antigua.

85	3d. orange-red and grey................	20	15
86	6d. reddish violet and yellow-orange.....	30	15

*This is the local date of issue; the stamps were not released in London until 17 May.

1965 (25 Oct). International Co-operation Year. As Nos. 168/9 of Antigua.

87	1d. reddish purple and turquoise-green........	20	15
88	6d. deep bluish green and lavender.......	50	25

1966 (24 Jan). Churchill Commemoration. As Nos. 170/3 of Antigua.

89	1d. new blue..............................	35	40
	a. Value omitted.........................	£1400	
90	3d. deep green............................	1·00	50
91	6d. brown.................................	1·25	65
92	1s.6d. bluish violet.........................	1·40	70
89/92 Set of 4...		3·50	2·00

No. 89a was caused by misplacement of the gold and also shows the country inscription moved to the right.

45 HMS *Falmouth* (frigate) at Tristan and Soldier of 1816

(Des V. Whiteley. Litho Harrison)

1966 (15 Aug). 150th Anniv of Tristan Garrison. W w **12** (sideways*). P 14½.

93	**45**	3d. multicoloured..........................	15	10
		w. Wmk Crown to right of CA.........	7·00	
94		6d. multicoloured..........................	15	15
95		1s.6d. multicoloured..........................	20	25
96		2s.6d. multicoloured..........................	25	25
93/6 Set of 4...			65	65

*The normal sideways watermark shows Crown to left of CA, *as seen from the back of the stamp.*

1966 (1 Oct*). World Cup Football Championship. As Nos. 176/7 of Antigua.

97		3d. violet, yellow-grn, lake and yellow-brown	20	10
98		2s.6d. chocolate, blue-green, lake and yellow-brown	50	20

*Released in St. Helena on 1 July in error.

1966 (1 Oct). Inauguration of W... Headquarters, Geneva. As Nos. 178/9 of Antigua.

99		6d. black, yellow-green and light blue	65	30
100		5s. black, light purple and yellow-brown	1·10	70

1966 (1 Dec). 20th Anniv of UNESCO. As Nos. 196/8 of Antigua.

101		10d. slate-violet, red, yellow and orange	25	15
		w. Wmk Crown to right of CA	45·00	
102		1s.6d. orange-yellow, violet and deep olive	40	20
103		2s.6d. black, bright purple and orange	45	25
101/3	Set of 3		1·00	55

*The normal sideways watermark shows Crown to left of CA, as seen from the back of the stamp.

46 Calshot Harbour

(Des V. Whiteley. Litho D.L.R.)

1967 (2 Jan). Opening of Calshot Harbour. P 14×14½.

104	**46**	6d. multicoloured	10	10
105		10d. multicoloured	10	10
106		1s.6d. multicoloured	10	15
107		2s.6d. multicoloured	15	20
104/7	Set of 4		30	45

(47)

48 Prince Alfred, First Duke of Edinburgh

1967 (10 May). No. 76 surch with T **47**.

108	4d. on 4½d. black and brown	10	10

(Des M. Goaman. Litho Harrison)

1967 (10 July). Centenary of First Duke of Edinburgh's Visit to Tristan. W w **12**. P 14½.

109	**48**	3d. multicoloured	10	10
110		6d. multicoloured	10	10
111		1s.6d. multicoloured	10	10
112		2s.6d. multicoloured	15	15
109/12	Set of 4		30	30

49 Wandering Albatross

(Des V. Whiteley. Photo Harrison)

1968 (15 May). Birds. T **49** and similar horiz designs. Multicoloured. W w **12**. P 14×14½.

113		4d. Type **49**	30	30
114		1s. Wilkins's Finch	35	30
115		1s.6d. Tristan Thrush	40	55
116		2s.6d. Greater Shearwater	60	65
113/16	Set of 4		1·50	1·60

53 Union Jack and Dependency Flag

(Des Jennifer Toombs. Litho D.L.R.)

1968 (1 Nov). 30th Anniv of Tristan da Cunha as a Dependency of St. Helena. T **53** and similar horiz design. W w **12** (sideways). P 14.

117	**53**	6d. multicoloured	20	30
118	–	9d. sepia, blue and turquoise-blue	20	35
119	**53**	1s.6d. multicoloured	30	40
120	–	2s.6d. carmine, blue and turquoise-blue	40	40
117/20	Set of 4		1·00	1·25

Design:—9d., 2s.6d. St. Helena and Tristan on chart.

55 Frigate

(Des and recess B.W.)

1969 (1 June). Clipper Ships. T **55** and similar horiz designs. W w **12**. P 11×11½.

121		4d. new blue	60	50
122		1s. carmine (full-rigged ship)	60	60
123		1s.6d. blue-green (barque)	65	95
124		2s.6d. chocolate (full-rigged clipper)	70	1·10
121/4	Set of 4		2·25	2·75

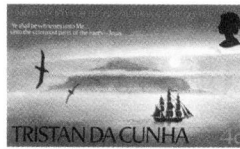

59 Sailing Ship off Tristan da Cunha

(Des Jennifer Toombs. Litho Format)

1969 (1 Nov). United Society for the Propagation of the Gospel. T **59** and similar horiz designs. Multicoloured. W w **12** (sideways). P 14½×14.

125		4d. Type **59**	60	30
126		9d. Islanders going to first Gospel service	15	30
127		1s.6d. Landing of the first minister	15	40
128		2s.6d. Procession outside St. Mary's Church	20	40
125/8	Set of 4		1·00	1·25

63 Globe and Red Cross Emblem

(Des and litho B.W.)

1970 (1 June). Centenary of British Red Cross. T **63** and similar designs. W w **12** (sideways on vert designs). P 13.

129	**63**	4d. light emerald, scarlet and deep bluish green	10	25
130		9d. bistre, scarlet and deep bluish green	15	30
131	–	1s.9d. light drab, scarlet and ultramarine	40	45
132	–	2s.6d. reddish purple, scarlet and ultramarine	45	55
129/32	Set of 4		1·00	1·40

Design: Vert—1s.9d., 2s.6d., Union Jack and Red Cross Flag.

64 Crawfish and Longboat

(Des Harrison. Litho Enschedé)

1970 (1 Nov). Crawfish Industry. T **64** and similar horiz design. Multicoloured. W w **12**. P 12½×13.

133		4d. Type **64**	30	30
134		10d. Packing and storing Crawfish	35	35
135		1s.6d. Type **64**	45	60
136		2s.6d. As 10d.	45	70
133/6	Set of 4		1·40	1·75

STAMP BOOKLETS

1957 (30 May)–**58**. Black on blue cover. Postmarked "MY 30 57" on back cover. Stapled.

SB1	3s.6d. booklet containing 8×½d. and 4×1d., 4×1½d., 4×3d. and 4×4d. (Nos. 14/16, 19/20) in blocks of 4	£350	
	a. Postmarked "JA 24 58" on back cover (24.1.58)	£300	
	b. Without postmark	£325	

1958 (Jan). Black on red cover. Without postmark. Stapled.

SB2	3s.6d. Contents as No. SB1	55·00	

1960 (Feb). Black on green cover. Stitched.

SB3	3s.6d. booklet containing 8×½d. and 4×1d., 4×1½d., 4×3d. and 4×4d. (Nos. 28/30, 33/4) in blocks of 4	30·00	

1965 (17 Feb). Black on green cover. Stapled.

SB4	4s.2d. booklet containing 8×½d. and 4×1d., 4×1½d., 4×3d. and 4×6d. (Nos. 71/3, 75, 77) in blocks of 4	6·00	

The booklet covers were reprinted with amended postage rates and released by the Crown Agents on 21 September 1970.

POSTAGE DUE STAMPS

D **1**

Normal	Lower serif at left of "3" missing (R. 9/1)	4d. Ball of "d" broken and serif at top damaged (R. 9/5). Other stamps in the fifth vertical row show slight breaks to the ball of the "d".

(Typo D.L.R.)

1957 (1 Feb). Chalk-surfaced paper. Wmk Mult Script CA. P 14.

D1	D **1**	1d. scarlet	1·75	16·00
D2		2d. orange-yellow	2·50	4·75
		a. Large "d"	30·00	
D3		3d. green	2·50	5·50
		a. Missing serif	50·00	
D4		4d. ultramarine	4·50	7·00
		a. Broken "d"	60·00	
D5		5d. lake	2·50	27·00
D1/5	Set of 5		12·00	55·00

For illustration of No. D2a see above No. D1 of Basutoland.

POSTAL FISCAL STAMPS

NATIONAL SAVINGS

(F **1**)

1970 (15 May). No. 77 optd with Type F **1** in red.

F1	6d. black and green	20	30

No. F1 was originally intended as a National Savings Stamp, but also retained postal validity.

Trucial States

The Trucial States consisted of Abu Dhabi, Ajman (with Manama), Dubai, Fujeira, Ras al Khaima. Sharjah and Umm al Qiwain. However the following issue of stamps was only put into use in Dubai, despite the inscription "TRUCIAL STATES".

The first organised postal service in Dubai commenced on 19 August 1909 when an Indian Branch Office, administered from Karachi, was opened, using the unoverprinted stamps of India, principally the ½a. and 1a. values.

The initial cancellation was a single-ring type inscribed "DUBAI B.O. PERSIAN GULF", which remained in use until 1933.

1909 Cancellation

Its replacement was of the Indian double-circle type showing a similar inscription.

Dubai was upgraded to Sub-Post Office status on 1 April 1942 and this change was reflected in a new double-ring mark inscribed "DUBAI" only. At the same time the office was provided with a single-ring handstamp which also incorporated a cancelling device of seven wavy lines.

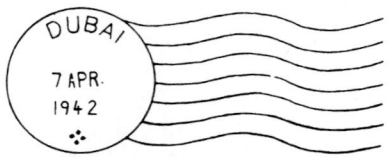

1942 Handstamp (*illustration reduced: actual size 65×27 mm*)

A further version of the double-ring type appeared in 1946, showing the "PERSIAN GULF" inscription restored to the lower segment of the postmark.

In October 1947 control of the Dubai Post Office passed to Pakistan whose stamps were used there until the end of March 1948.

On 1 April 1948 the post office was transferred, yet again, to British control and Great Britain stamps surcharged for use in the British Postal Agencies in Eastern Arabia were then sold in Dubai until 6 January 1961, being cancelled with British style single and double-ring postmarks.

Stamps of the British Postal Agencies in Eastern Arabia (Nos. 81, 83 and 85/6) overprinted "AJMAN", "FUJAIRAH" or "UMM AL QAIWAIN" are bogus.

(Currency. 100 naye paise = 1 rupee)

1 Palms   **2** Dhow

(Des M. Goaman. Photo Harrison (T **1**). Des M. Farrar-Bell. Recess D.L.R. (T **2**))

1961 (7 Jan). P 15×14 (T **1**) or 13×12½ (T **2**).

1	1	5n.p. green	1·75	1·75
2		15n.p. red-brown	60	1·50
3		20n.p. bright blue	1·75	2·00
4		30n.p. orange-red	60	50
5		40n.p. reddish violet	60	50
6		50n.p. bistre	60	75
7		75n.p. grey	60	1·50
8	2	1r. green	9·50	4·50
9		2r. black	8·50	22·00
10		5r. carmine-red	12·00	28·00
11		10r. deep ultramarine	15·00	30·00
1/11		*Set of 11*	45·00	80·00

The Dubai Post Department took over the postal services on 14 June 1963. Later issues for Dubai will be found in the Stanley Gibbons *Arabia catalogue*.

Turks and Caicos Islands

TURKS ISLANDS

DEPENDENCY OF JAMAICA

A branch of the British Post Office opened at Grand Turk on 11 December 1854 replacing an earlier arrangement under which mail for the islands was sorted by local R.M.S.P. agents.

No. CC 1 is known used between 22 October 1857 and 20 April 1862.

GRAND TURK

CROWNED-CIRCLE HANDSTAMPS

CC 1

CC1	CC **1** TURKS-ISLANDS (Oct 1857)	*Price on cover*	£5500

PRICES FOR STAMPS ON COVER TO 1945	
Nos. 1/5	*from* × 30
No. 6	—
Nos. 7/20	*from* × 50
Nos. 20a/48	—
Nos. 49/52	*from* × 12
Nos. 53/7	*from* × 10
Nos. 58/65	*from* × 20
Nos. 66/9	*from* × 5
Nos. 70/2	*from* × 10
Nos. 101/9	*from* × 8
Nos. 110/26	*from* × 6
Nos. 129/39	*from* × 4
Nos. 140/53	*from* × 12
Nos. 154/90	*from* × 3
Nos. 191/3	*from* × 10
Nos. 194/205	*from* × 2

1

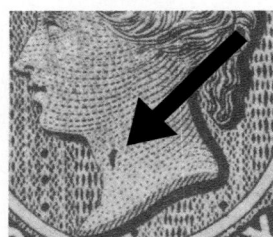

Throat flaw (R. 3/4)

(Recess P.B.)

1867 (4 Apr). No wmk. P 11–12½.

1	**1**	1d. dull rose	65·00	60·00
		a. Throat flaw	£250	£250
2		6d. black	£120	£140
3		1s. dull blue	£100	60·00

1873–79. Wmk Small Star. W w 2 (sideways on Nos. 5 and 6). P 11–12½×14½–15½.

4	**1**	1d. dull rose-lake (7.73)	55·00	50·00
		a. Throat flaw	£225	£225
		b. Wmk sideways	90·00	90·00
		ba. Throat flaw	£325	£350
5		1d. dull red (1.79)	60·00	60·00
		a. Imperf between (horiz pair)	£30000	
		b. Throat flaw	£250	£250
		c. Wmk upright		
6		1s. lilac (1.79)	£5000	£2000

1881 (1 Jan). Stamps of the preceding issues surcharged locally, in black. Sheets of 30 (10×3).
There are 12 different settings of the ½d., nine settings of the 2½d., and six settings of the 4d.

Setting 1. T **2**. Long fraction bar. Two varieties in a horizontal pair repeated fifteen times in the sheet.

7	½ on 6d black	£100	£170

Setting 2. T **3**. Short fraction bar. Three varieties in a vertical strip repeated ten times in sheet.

Setting 3. Similar to setting 2, but the middle stamp of the three varieties has a longer bar.

8	½ on 6d. black (*setting 2 only*)	£100	£150
9	½ on 1s. dull blue	£140	£200
	a. Surch double	£8000	

Three varieties in a vertical strip repeated ten times in sheet.

Setting 4. Types **4**, **5**, **6**.
Setting 5. Types **4** (without bar), **5**, **6**.
Setting 6. Types **4**, **5**, **6** (without bar).
Setting 7. Types **4** (shorter thick bar), **6**, **6**.

10	½ on 1d. dull red (*setting 7 only*) (T **6**).		
	a. Type **4** (shorter thick bar)	£16000	
11	½ on 1s. dull blue (*setting 6 and 7*) (T **4**)	£2000	
	a. Type **4** (shorter thick bar)	£3000	
	b. Type **5**	£1500	
	c. Type **6**	£1200	
	d. Type **6** (without bar)	£2500	
	e. Surch double (T **4**)	£14000	
	f. Surch double (T **5**)	£14000	
	g. Surch double (T **6** without bar)	£14000	
12	½ on 1s. lilac (T **4**)	£275	£425
	a. Without bar	£600	
	b. With short thick bar	£550	£750
	c. Surch double	£4000	
	cb. Surch double and short thick bar	£14000	
13	½ on 1s. lilac (T **5**)	£160	£300
	a. Surch double	£3750	
14	½ on 1s. lilac (T **6**)	£150	£275
	a. Without bar	£700	
	b. Surch double	£8000	
	ba. Surch double and without bar	£14000	

Care should be taken in the identification of Types **6** and **7** which are very similar. For the 1s. value some varieties of No. 9 are often confused with Nos. 11b/c.

Setting 8. T **7**. Three varieties in a vertical strip. All have a very short bar.

15	½. on 1d dull red	85·00	£160
	a. Throat flaw	£350	
	b. Surch double	£7500	

Setting 9. T **8**. Single unit surcharge. Bar long and thick and "1" leaning a little to left.

16	½ on 1d. dull red	£200	£350
	a. Surch double	£6000	
	b. Throat flaw	£700	

Setting 10. T **9** and **10**. 15 varieties repeated twice in a sheet. Ten are of T **9** (Rows 1 and 2), five of T **10** (Row 3).

17	½ on 1d. dull red (T **9**)	60·00	£150
	a. Surch double	£6500	
18	½ on 1d. dull red (T **10**)	95·00	£200
	a. Surch double	£11000	
	b. Throat flaw	£350	
19	½ on 1s. lilac (T **9**)	£100	£225
20	½ on 1s. lilac (T **10**)	£180	£400
20a	½. on 1s dull blue (T **9**)	£12000	
20b	½ on 1s dull blue (T **10**)	£22000	

Types **9** and **11**. The difference is in the position of the "2" in relation to the "1". In setting 10 the "2" is to the left of the "1" except on No. 10 (where it is directly below the "1") and in setting 11 it is to the right except on No. 2 (where it is to the left, as in setting 10).

Setting 11. T **9** and **11** to **14**. 15 varieties repeated twice in a sheet. Nine of T **11**, three of T **12**, and one each of T **9**, **13** and **14**.

Setting 12. Similar to last, but T **13** replaced by another T **12**.

21	½ on 1d. dull red (T **11**)	£120	£225
22	½ on 1d. dull red (T **12**)	£325	
	a. Throat flaw	£1300	
23	½ on 1d. dull red (T **13**)	£1100	
	a. Throat flaw	£1100	
24	½ on 1d. dull red (T **14**)	£700	
24a	½. on 1d dull blue (T **11**)	£22000	

Type **9** from these settings, where it occurs on position 2, can only be distinguished from similar stamps from setting 10 when se-tenant with Type **11**.

In setting 11 Type **13** occupied R. 3/4 in the setting (5×3), corresponding to the position of the "Throat flaw" on the left half of each sheet of 30 (10×3). Nos. 23 and 23a therefore exist in equal quantities.

Setting 1. T **15**. Single unit surcharge. Fraction in very small type.

25	2½ on 6d. black	£16000	

Setting 2. T **16**. Two varieties repeated 15 times in a sheet. Large "2" on level with top of the "1", long thin bar.
26		2½ on 6d. black	£400	£600
	a. Imperf between (horiz pair)		£42000	
	b. Surch double		£18000	

$2\frac{1}{2}$ (17) $2\frac{1}{2}$ (18) $2\frac{1}{2}$ (19)

Setting 3. T **17**. Single unit surcharge. As T **16**, but large "2" not so high up.
27   2½ on 1s. lilac..................... £4000

Setting 4. T **18**. Three varieties in a vertical strip repeated ten times in sheet. Large "2" placed lower and small bar.
28   2½ on 6d. black £250   £450
     a. Surch double £17000

Setting 5. T **19**. Three varieties in a vertical strip repeated ten times in sheet. "2" further from "½", small fraction bar.
29   2½ on 1s. lilac..................... £550   £1000

$2\frac{1}{2}$ (20) $2\frac{1}{2}$ (21)

Setting 6. T **20** and **21**. Fifteen varieties. Ten of T **20** and five of T **21**, repeated twice in a sheet.
30   2½ on 1s. lilac (T **20**)..................... £14000
31   2½ on 1s. lilac (T **21**)..................... £25000

$2\frac{1}{2}$ (22) $2\frac{1}{2}$ (23) $2\frac{1}{2}$ (24)

Setting 7. T **22**. Three varieties in a vertical strip, repeated ten times in a sheet.
32   2½ on 6d. black £9500
33   2½ on 1s. dull blue..................... £28000

Setting 8. T **23** and **24**. 15 varieties. Ten of T **23** and five of T **24** repeated twice in a sheet.
34   2½ on 1d. dull red (T **23**)..................... £800
35   2½ on 1d. dull red (T **24**)..................... £1600
     a. Throat flaw £4750
36   2½ on 1s. lilac (T **23**)..................... £600   £900
     a. Surch "½" double £4750
37   2½ on 1s. lilac (T **24**)..................... £1200
     a. Surch "½" double £9000

$2\frac{1}{2}$ (25) $2\frac{1}{2}$ (26) $2\frac{1}{2}$ (27)

Setting 9. T **25**, **26**, and **27**. 15 varieties. Ten of T **25**, three of T **26**, one of T **26** without bar, and one of T **27**, repeated twice in a sheet.
38   2½ on 1s. dull blue (T **25**)..................... £1100
39   2½ on 1s. dull blue (T **26**)..................... £3750
40   2½ on 1s. dull blue (T **26**) (without bar).... £15000
41   2½ on 1s. dull blue (T **27**)..................... £15000

4 (28)   **4** (29)   **4** (30)

Setting 1. T **28**. "4" 8 mm high, pointed top.
42   4 on 6d. black..................... £750   £350

Settings 2-6. T **29** and **30**.
43   4 on 6d. black (T **29**)..................... £110   £160
44   4 on 6d. black (T **30**)..................... £400   £550
45   4 on 1s. lilac (T **29**)..................... £475   £750
     a. Surch double.....................
46   4 on 1s. lilac (T **30**)..................... £2500
     a. Surch double.....................
47   4 on 1d. dull red (T **29**)..................... £750   £475
48   4 on 1d. dull red (T **28**)..................... £850   £550
     The components of these settings can only be distinguished when in blocks. Details are given in the handbook by John J. Challis.

31 | **One Penny** (32)

(Typo (No. 50) or recess D.L.R.)
1881. Wmk Crown CC (sideways* on T **1**). P 14.
49   1   1d. brown-red (10.81)..................... 85·00   £100
     a. Throat flaw £300   £375
50   31   4d. ultramarine (Die I) (8.81)..................... £170   60·00
     w. Wmk inverted..................... —   £400
51   1   6d. olive-black (10.81)..................... £160   £200
52   1   1s. slate-green (10.81)..................... £200   £150

*The normal sideways watermark shows Crown to right of CC, *as seen from the back of the stamp*.
Nos. 49 and 51/2 also exist showing Crown to left of CC, but due to the position of the watermark such varieties are difficult to detect on single stamps. Reversed watermarks are also known.

1882–85. Wmk Crown CA (reversed on 1d.). P 14.
53   31   ½d. blue-green (Die I) (2.82)..................... 25·00   30·00
     a. Pale green (12.85) .... 7·00   6·50
     b. Top left triangle detached £400
     w. Wmk inverted..................... £250
55   1   1d. orange-brown (10.83)..................... £100   38·00
     a. Bisected (½d.) (on cover)..................... †   £5000
     b. Throat flaw £375   £150
     x. Wmk normal (not reversed) £190   £110
56   31   2½d. red-brown (2.82)..................... 45·00   17·00
57   4d. grey (Die I) (10.84)..................... 40·00   4·25
     a. Bisected (2d.) (on cover)..................... †   £5000
For illustration of "top left triangle detached" variety see above No. 21 of Antigua.

1887 (July)**–89**. Wmk Crown CA.

(a) P 12
58   1   1d. crimson-lake..................... 38·00   9·00
     a. Imperf between (horiz pair)..... £28000
     b. Throat flaw .... 90·00   23·00
     x. Wmk reversed..................... 23·00   6·00

(b) P 14
59   1   6d. yellow-brown (2.89)..................... 5·00   6·50
     s. Optd "SPECIMEN"..................... 50·00
60   1s. sepia..................... 7·00   5·00

> During a shortage of 1d. stamps a supply of JAMAICA No. 27 was sent to the Turks and Caicos Islands in April 1889 and used until replaced by No. 61. *Price from £250 used.*

1889 (May). Surch at Grand Turk with T **32**.
61   31   1d. on 2½d. red-brown..................... 24·00   20·00
     a. "One" omitted..................... £1600
     b. Bisected (½d.) (on cover)..................... †   £5000
No. 61a was caused by misplacement of the surcharge. Stamps from the same sheet can be found with the surcharge reading "Penny One".

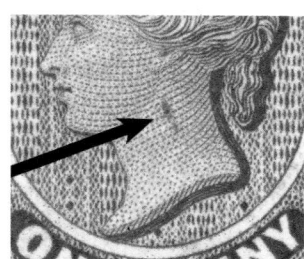

Neck flaw (R. 3/2)

1889–93. Wmk Crown CA. P 14.
62   1   1d. crimson-lake (7.89) .... 8·50   6·50
     a. Bisected (½d.) (on cover)..................... †   £4750
     b. Throat flaw .... 28·00   28·00
     c. Neck flaw .... 48·00   48·00
     x. Wmk reversed..................... 75·00
63   1d. lake..................... 7·00   4·50
     a. Bisected (½d.) (on cover)..................... †   £4750
     b. Throat flaw .... 22·00   22·00
     c. Neck flaw .... 40·00   40·00
64   1d. pale rosy lake..................... 7·00   8·50
     b. Throat flaw .... 22·00   35·00
     c. Neck flaw .... 40·00   50·00
65   31   2½d. ultramarine (Die II) (4.93)..................... 7·00   4·75
     s. Optd "SPECIMEN"..................... 50·00

(33)   **34**

1893 (10 June). No. 57 surch at Grand Turk with T **33**.
Setting 1. Bars between "1d." and "2" separate, instead of continuous across the rows of stamps.
66   ½d. on 4d. grey..................... £3500   £1500

Setting 2. Continuous bars. Thin and thick bar 10¾ mm apart. "2" under the "1".
67   ½d. on 4d. grey..................... £200   £140

Setting 3. As last, but bars 11¾ mm apart.
68   ½d. on 4d. grey..................... £180   £190

Setting 4. Bars 11 mm apart. Five out of the six varieties in the strip have the "2" below the space between the "1" and "d".
69   ½d. on 4d. grey..................... £225   £180
There is a fifth setting, but the variation is slight.

(Typo D.L.R.)
1893–95. Wmk Crown CA. P 14.
70   31   ½d. dull green (Die II) (12.93)..................... 7·00   4·25
71   4d. dull purple and ultramarine (5.95)..................... 25·00   27·00
72   34   5d. olive-green and carmine (6.94)..................... 12·00   27·00
     a. Bisected (2½d.) (on cover)..................... †   £4750
70/2 *Set of 3*..................... 40·00   50·00
71s/2s Optd "SPECIMEN" *Set of 2*..................... £100

TURKS AND CAICOS ISLANDS

35 Badge of the Islands   **36** Badge of the Islands

The dates on the stamps have reference to the political separation from Bahamas.

(Recess D.L.R.)
1900 (10 Nov)**–04**. Wmk Crown CA (½d. to 1s.) or Wmk Crown CC (2s., 3s.). P 14.
101   35   ½d. green..................... 2·75   4·00
     x. Wmk reversed..................... £170
     xs. Ditto. Optd "SPECIMEN"..................... £190
102   1d. red..................... 3·50   75
     w. Wmk inverted..................... £110
     x. Wmk reversed..................... £170
103   2d. sepia..................... 1·00   1·25
     w. Wmk inverted..................... £130
     x. Wmk reversed..................... £130
104   2½d. blue..................... 11·00   16·00
     a. Greyish blue (1904)..................... 1·75   1·00
     aw. Wmk inverted..................... £110
     ay. Wmk inverted and reversed.... —   £200
105   4d. orange..................... 3·75   7·00
106   6d. dull mauve..................... 2·50   6·50
107   1s. purple-brown..................... 3·25   23·00
108   36   2s. purple..................... 50·00   80·00
109   3s. lake..................... 80·00   £110
101/9 *Set of 9*..................... £130   £200
101s/9s Optd "SPECIMEN" *Set of 9*..................... £250
Nos. 101/7 exist without watermark or with double-lined lettering from the marginal watermark due to the way in which full sheets were cut for printing.

1905–08. Wmk Mult Crown CA. P 14.
110   35   ½d. green..................... 6·50   15
     x. Wmk reversed..................... —   £200
111   1d. red..................... 20·00   50
     w. Wmk inverted..................... £200
     x. Wmk reversed..................... £200
112   3d. purple/*yellow* (1908)..................... 2·25   6·00
     s. Optd "SPECIMEN"..................... 50·00
     w. Wmk inverted.....................
110/12 *Set of 3*..................... 26·00   6·00

37 Turk's-head Cactus   **38**

(Recess D.L.R.)
1909 (2 Sept)**–11**. Wmk Mult Crown CA. P 14.
115   37   ¼d. rosy mauve (1910)..................... 1·75   1·00
     w. Wmk inverted..................... £200
116   ¼d. red (1911)..................... 60   40
     w. Wmk inverted.....................
117   38   ½d. yellow-green..................... 75   40
     x. Wmk reversed..................... 65·00
     y. Wmk inverted and reversed.... £170
118   1d. red..................... 1·25   40
119   2d. greyish slate..................... 6·00   1·40
120   2½d. blue..................... 8·50   2·25
     w. Wmk inverted.....................
     x. Wmk reversed..................... 80·00   90·00
     xs. Ditto opt "SPECIMEN"..................... £110
121   3d. purple/*yellow*..................... 2·50   2·00
122   4d. red/*yellow*..................... 3·25   5·00
123   6d. purple..................... 7·00   3·00
124   1s. black/*green*..................... 7·50   4·50
     w. Wmk inverted..................... £275
125   2s. red/*green*..................... 45·00   75·00
126   3s. black/*red*..................... 48·00   40·00
115/26 *Set of 12*..................... £110   £120
115s/26s Optd "SPECIMEN" *Set of 12*..................... £275
See also Nos. 154 and 162.

39   # WAR TAX (40)

1913 (1 Apr)**–21**. Wmk Mult Crown CA. P 14.
129   39   ½d. green..................... 50   1·75
     w. Wmk inverted.....................
130   1d. red..................... 1·00   2·25
     a. Bright rose-scarlet..................... 1·10   2·00
     ax. Wmk reversed..................... 85·00
     b. Rose-carmine (1918)..................... 3·75   7·00
131   2d. greyish slate..................... 2·25   3·50
132   2½d. ultramarine..................... 2·25   3·00
     aw. Wmk inverted.....................
     b. Bright blue (1918)..................... 4·25   3·00
133   3d. purple/*yellow*..................... 2·25   11·00
     a. On lemon..................... 16·00
     b. On yellow-buff..................... 4·00   12·00
     c. On orange-buff..................... 1·75
     cx. Wmk reversed..................... £110
     d. On pale yellow..................... 2·75   12·00

134		4d. red/yellow	1·00	9·50
	a.	On orange-buff	1·75	7·50
	ab.	"A" of "CA" missing from wmk		
	as.	Optd "SPECIMEN"	48·00	
	b.	Carmine on pale yellow	7·50	16·00
135		5d. pale olive-green (18.5.16)	6·50	22·00
136		6d. dull purple	2·50	3·50
	w.	Wmk inverted		
	x.	Wmk reversed		
137		1s. brown-orange	1·50	5·00
	w.	Wmk inverted		
138		2s. blue-green	27·00	60·00
	a.	On greenish white (1919)	30·00	70·00
	b.	On emerald (3.21)	48·00	75·00
	bs.	Optd "SPECIMEN"	55·00	
	bx.	Wmk reversed	£275	
139		3s. black/red	15·00	26·00
129/39 Set of 11			55·00	£120
129s/39s Optd "SPECIMEN" Set of 11			£200	

1917 (3 Jan). Optd locally with T **40** at bottom of stamp.

140	**39**	1d. red	10	1·75
	a.	Opt double	£180	£250
	ab.	Opt double (in horiz pair with normal)	£400	
	b.	"TAX" omitted	£700	
	c.	"WAR TAX" omitted in vert pair with normal	£700	
	d.	Opt inverted at top	65·00	85·00
	e.	Opt double, one inverted	£110	
	f.	Opt inverted only, in pair with No. 140e	£600	
141		3d. purple/yellow-buff	1·25	9·50
	a.	Opt double	£100	
	b.	On lemon	4·25	15·00
	ba.	Opt double	£100	£130
	bb.	Opt double, one inverted	£325	

The overprint was in a setting of 60, using a plate supplied by De La Rue, applied twice to the sheets of 120. One sheet of the 1d. exists with the right-hand impression of the setting misplaced one row to the left so that stamps in vertical row 6 show a double overprint (No. 140ab). It appears that the right-hand vertical row on this sheet had the overprint applied at a third operation.

In Nos. 140e/f the inverted overprint is at foot and reads "TAX WAR" owing to displacement. No. 140e also exists with "WAR" omitted from the inverted overprint.

In both values of the first printings the stamp in the bottom left-hand corner of the sheet has a long "T" in "TAX", and on the first stamp of the sixth row the "X" is damaged and looks like a reversed "K". The long "T" was subsequently converted.

1917 (Oct). Second printing with overprint at top or in middle of stamp.

143	**39**	1d. red	10	1·25
	a.	Inverted opt at bottom or centre	50·00	
	c.	Opt omitted (in pair with normal)	£650	
	d.	Opt double, one at top, one at bottom	65·00	
	e.	As d., but additional opt in top margin	£120	
	f.	Pair, one as d., the other normal	£325	
	g.	Pair, one opt inverted, one normal	£650	
	h.	Double opt at top (in pair with normal)	£275	
	i.	Opt double	48·00	60·00
144		3d. purple/yellow	60	2·50
	a.	Opt double	50·00	
	b.	Opt double, one inverted	£350	
	c.	On lemon	4·50	

1918 (18 Dec). Overprinted with T **40**.

145	**39**	3d. purple/yellow (R.)	22·00	60·00
	a.	Opt double	£325	

W A R

WAR

WAR	W A R		TAX
TAX	**T A X**		**(43)**
(41)	**(42)**		

1918 (26 June). Optd with T **41** in London by D.L.R.

146	**39**	1d. rose-carmine	20	2·75
	a.	Bright rose-scarlet	15	2·25
	aw.	Wmk inverted	75·00	
147		3d. purple/yellow	6·50	8·00
146s/7s Optd "SPECIMEN" Set of 2			85·00	

1919 (14 Apr). Optd with T **41** in London by D.L.R.

148	**39**	3d. purple/orange-buff (R.)	20	6·00
	s.	Optd "SPECIMEN"	45·00	

1919 (17 Apr). Local overprint. T **40**, in violet.

149	**39**	1d. bright rose-scarlet	1·75	7·00
	a.	"WAR" omitted (in pair with normal)	£200	
	b.	Opt double	21·00	
	c.	Opt double in pair with normal	£120	
	d.	Opt double, one inverted		
	e.	Opt triple		
	f.	Rose-carmine	9·00	19·00
	fa.	Opt double		
	w.	Wmk inverted	32·00	

1919 (20 Aug). Optd locally with T **42**.

150	**39**	1d. scarlet	10	2·25
	a.	Opt double	£150	£180
151		3d. purple/orange-buff	45	2·75
	w.	Wmk inverted	40·00	
	x.	Wmk reversed	40·00	

1919 (17 Dec). Optd locally with T **43**.

152	**39**	1d. scarlet	20	4·00
	a.	Opt inverted		
153		3d. purple/orange-buff	1·75	4·00
	w.	Wmk inverted	40·00	

---

	x.	Wmk reversed	25·00	
	y.	Wmk inverted and reversed	12·00	35·00

The two bottom rows of this setting have the words "WAR" and "TAX" about 1 mm further apart.

1921 (23 Apr). Wmk Mult Script CA. P 14.

154	**37**	¼d. rose-red	4·75	26·00
155	**39**	½d. green	3·50	7·00
156		1d. carmine-red	1·00	5·50
157		2d. slate-grey	1·00	20·00
	y.	Wmk inverted and reversed	95·00	
158		2½d. bright blue	1·75	7·50
	x.	Wmk reversed	£130	
159		5d. sage-green	12·00	70·00
160		6d. purple	6·50	70·00
	w.	Wmk inverted	£100	
	x.	Wmk reversed	£100	
161		1s. brown-orange	13·00	48·00
154/61 Set of 8			38·00	£225
154s/61s Optd "SPECIMEN" Set of 8			£150	

44	**45**

(Recess D.L.R.)

1922 (20 Nov)–**26**. P 14.

(a) Wmk Mult Script CA

162	**37**	¼d. black (11.10.26)	1·25	1·00
163	**44**	½d. yellow-green	5·50	4·75
	a.	Bright green	5·50	4·75
	b.	Apple-green	8·00	12·00
164		1d. brown	50	3·25
165		1½d. scarlet (24.11.25)	9·00	17·00
166		2d. slate	50	5·00
167		2½d. purple/pale yellow	50	1·75
168		3d. bright blue	50	5·00
169		4d. red/pale yellow	1·25	19·00
	ax.	Wmk reversed	£100	
	b.	Carmine/pale yellow	4·50	17·00
170		5d. sage-green	85	22·00
	y.	Wmk inverted and reversed	£110	
171		6d. purple	70	13·00
	x.	Wmk reversed	£120	
172		1s. brown-orange	80	23·00
173		2s. red/emerald (24.11.25)	2·00	12·00

(b) Wmk Mult Crown CA

174	**44**	2s. red/emerald	25·00	£110
175		3s. black/red	5·00	40·00
162/75 Set of 14			45·00	£250
162s/75s Optd "SPECIMEN" Set of 14			£250	

1928 (1 Mar). Inscr "POSTAGE & REVENUE". Wmk Mult Script CA. P 14.

176	**45**	½d. green	75	50
177		1d. brown	75	70
178		1½d. scarlet	75	4·50
179		2d. grey	75	50
180		2½d. purple/yellow	75	5·00
181		3d. bright blue	75	11·00
182		6d. purple	75	7·50
183		1s. brown-orange	3·75	7·50
184		2s. red/emerald	7·50	38·00
185		5s. green/yellow	13·00	35·00
186		10s. purple/blue	60·00	£120
176/86 Set of 11			80·00	£200
176s/86s Optd "SPECIMEN" Set of 11			£190	

1935 (6 May). Silver Jubilee. As Nos. 91/4 of Antigua, but ptd by Waterlow. P 11×12.

187		½d. black and green	30	1·00
	k.	Kite and vertical log	45·00	70·00
	l.	Kite and horizontal log	50·00	70·00
188		3d. brown and deep blue	5·50	4·00
	k.	Kite and vertical log	£120	£150
189		6d. light blue and olive-green	1·75	5·50
	k.	Kite and vertical log	£100	£160
190		1s. slate and purple	1·75	4·00
	k.	Kite and vertical log	£100	£150
187/90 Set of 4			8·50	14·00
187s/90s Perf "SPECIMEN" Set of 4			£100	

For illustrations of plate varieties see Omnibus section following Zanzibar.

1937 (12 May). Coronation. As Nos. 95/7 of Antigua, but ptd by D.L.R. P 14.

191		½d. myrtle-green	10	10
	a.	Deep green	40·00	40·00
192		2d. grey-black	80	65
193		3d. bright blue	80	65
191/3 Set of 3			1·50	1·25
191s/3s Perf "SPECIMEN" Set of 3			90·00	

46 Raking Salt	**47** Salt Industry

(Recess Waterlow)

1938 (18 June)–**45**. Wmk Mult Script CA. P 12½.

194	**46**	¼d. black	20	10
195		½d. yellowish green	8·50	15
	a.	Deep green (6.11.44)	2·75	70
196		1d. red-brown	75	10
197		1½d. scarlet	75	15
198		2d. grey	1·00	30
199		2½d. yellow-orange	12·00	15·00
	a.	Orange (6.11.44)	6·00	3·50

200		3d. bright blue	70	30
201		6d. mauve	22·00	3·50
201a		6d. sepia (9.2.45)	50	20
202		1s. yellow-bistre	5·00	14·00
202a		1s. grey-olive (9.2.45)	50	20
203	**47**	2s. deep rose-carmine	48·00	19·00
	a.	Bright rose-carmine (6.11.44)	22·00	22·00
204		5s. yellowish green	60·00	27·00
	a.	Deep green (6.11.44)	55·00	30·00
205		10s. bright violet	32·00	7·50
194/205 Set of 14			£130	60·00
194s/205s Perf "SPECIMEN" Set of 14			£375	

1946 (4 Nov). Victory. As Nos. 110/11 of Antigua.

206		2d. black	10	15
207		3d. blue	15	20
206s/7s Perf "SPECIMEN" Set of 2			80·00	

1948 (13 Sept). Royal Silver Wedding. As Nos. 112/13 of Antigua.

208		1d. red-brown	15	10
209		10s. mauve	14·00	20·00

50 Badge of the Islands	**51** Flag of Turks and Caicos Islands

52 Map of islands	**53** Queen Victoria and King George VI

(Recess Waterlow)

1948 (14 Dec). Centenary of Separation from Bahamas. T **50/53**. Wmk Mult Script CA. P 12½.

210	**50**	½d. blue-green	2·00	15
211		2d. carmine	2·00	15
212	**51**	3d. blue	1·75	15
213	**52**	6d. violet	1·75	30
214	**53**	2s. black and bright blue	1·25	2·25
215		5s. black and green	1·50	7·50
216		10s. black and brown	4·25	7·50
210/16 Set of 7			13·00	16·00

1949 (10 Oct). 75th Anniv of UPU. As Nos. 114/17 of Antigua.

217		2½d. red-orange	20	2·50
218		3d. deep blue	2·25	1·75
219		6d. brown	30	2·75
220		1s. olive	20	50
217/20 Set of 4			2·75	6·75

54 Bulk Salt Loading	**55** Salt Cay

56 Caicos mail	**57** Grand Turk

58 Sponge diving	**59** South Creek

60 Map	**61** Grand Turk Light

62 Government House	**63** Cockburn Harbour

64 Government offices	**65** Loading salt

66 Dependency's Badge

(Recess Waterlow)

1950 (1 Aug). T **54/66**. Wmk Mult Script CA. P 12½.

221	54	½d. green	85	40
222	55	1d. red-brown	1·25	75
223	56	1½d. deep carmine	1·25	55
224	57	2d. red-orange	1·25	40
225	58	2½d. grey-olive	1·25	50
226	59	3d. bright blue	1·00	40
227	60	4d. black and rose	4·00	70
228	61	6d. black and blue	3·50	50
229	62	1s. black and blue-green	3·00	40
230	63	1s.6d. black and scarlet	16·00	3·25
231	64	2s. emerald and ultramarine	7·00	4·50
232	65	5s. blue and black	27·00	8·50
233	66	10s. black and violet	28·00	28·00
221/33 *Set of 13*			85·00	42·00

1953 (2 June). Coronation. As No. 120 of Antigua, but ptd by B.W. & Co.

234		2d. black and orange-red	60	1·25

67 MV *Kirksons*   **68** Greater Flamingoes in flight

(Recess Waterlow)

1955 (1 Feb). T **67/8**. Wmk Mult Script CA. P 12½.

235		5d. black and bright green	1·75	1·00
236		8d. black and brown	3·00	70

69 Queen Elizabeth II (after Annigoni)   **70** Bonefish

71 Red Grouper   **72** Spiny Lobster

73 Albacore   **74** Mutton Snapper

 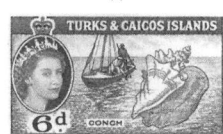

75 Permit   **76** Queen or Pink Conch

 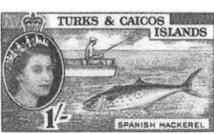

77 Greater Flamingoes   **78** Spanish Mackerel

 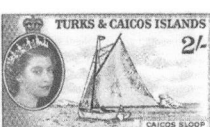

79 Salt Cay   **80** *Uakon* (Caicos sloop)

81 Cable Office   **82** Dependency's Badge

(Recess B.W.)

1957 (25 Nov). T **69/82**. W w **12**. P 13½×14 (1d.), 14 (10s.) or 13½ (others).

237	69	1d. deep blue and carmine	60	20
238	70	1½d. grey-green and orange	30	30
239	71	2d. red-brown and olive	30	15
240	72	2½d. carmine and green	30	15
241	73	3d. turquoise-blue and purple	30	15
242	74	4d. lake and black	1·25	15
243	75	5d. slate-green and brown	1·25	40
244	76	6d. carmine-rose and blue	2·00	55
245	77	8d. vermilion and black	3·25	20
246	78	1s. deep blue and black	1·25	10
247	79	1s.6d. sepia and deep ultramarine	20·00	2·25
248	80	2s. deep ultramarine and brown	16·00	3·00
249	81	5s. black and carmine	10·00	2·50
250	82	10s. black and purple	26·00	8·00
237/250 *and* 253 *Set of 15*			£120	30·00

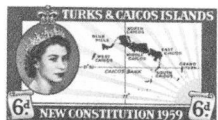

83 Map of the Turks and Caicos Islands

(Photo D.L.R.)

1959 (4 July). New Constitution. Wmk Mult Script CA. P 13½×14.

251	83	6d. deep olive and light orange	80	70
252		8d. violet and light orange	80	40

84 Brown Pelican

(Des Mrs. S. Hurd. Photo Harrison)

1960 (1 Nov). W w **12**. P 14×14½.

253	84	£1 sepia and deep red	48·00	16·00

CROWN COLONY

1963 (4 June). Freedom from Hunger. As No. 146 of Antigua.

254		8d. carmine	30	15

1963 (2 Sept). Red Cross Centenary. As Nos. 147/8 of Antigua.

255		2d. red and black	15	50
256		8d. red and blue	30	50

1964 (23 Apr). 400th Birth Anniv of William Shakespeare. As No. 164 of Antigua.

257		8d. green	30	10

1965 (17 May). ITU Centenary. As Nos. 166/7 of Antigua.

258		1d. vermilion and brown	10	10
259		2s. light emerald and turquoise-blue	20	20

1965 (25 Oct). International Co-operation Year. As Nos. 168/9 of Antigua.

260		1d. reddish purple and turquoise-green	10	15
261		8d. deep bluish green and lavender	20	15

1966 (24 Jan). Churchill Commemoration. As Nos. 170/3 of Antigua.

262		1d. new blue	10	10
263		2d. deep green	20	10
264		8d. brown	35	10
		a. Gold ptg double	£160	
265		1s.6d. bluish violet	50	1·10
262/5 *Set of 4*			1·00	1·25

The price quoted for No. 264a is for examples with the two impressions clearly separated. Examples with the two impressions nearly co-incident are worth considerably less.

1966 (4 Feb). Royal Visit. As Nos. 271/2 of Bahamas.

266		8d. black and ultramarine	40	10
267		1s. 6d. black and magenta	60	20

85 Andrew Symmer going ashore

(Des V. Whiteley. Photo D.L.R.)

1966 (1 Oct). Bicentenary of "Ties with Britain" T **85** and similar horiz designs. P 13½.

268		1d. deep blue and orange	10	10
269		8d. red, blue and orange-yellow	20	15
270		1s.6d. multicoloured	25	20
268/70 *Set of 3*			50	40

Designs:—8d. Andrew Symmer and Royal Warrant; 1s.6d. Arms and Royal Cypher.

1966 (1 Dec). 20th Anniv of UNESCO. As Nos. 196/8 of Antigua.

271		1d. slate-violet, red, yellow and orange	10	10
272		8d. orange-yellow, violet and deep olive	40	10
273		1s.6d. black, bright purple and orange	65	40
271/3 *Set of 3*			1·00	50

88 Turk's-head Cactus   **89** Boat-building

90 Arms of Turks and Caicos Islands   **91** Queen Elizabeth II

(Des V. Whiteley. Photo Harrison)

1967 (1 Feb). Designs as T **88/91**. W w **12**. P 14½×14 (vert) or 14×14½ (horiz).

274		1d. olive-yellow, vermilion and bright bluish violet	10	10
275		1½d. brown and orange-yellow	1·50	10
276		2d. deep slate and deep orange-yellow	20	10
277		3d. agate and dull green	20	10
278		4d. bright mauve, black and turquoise	2·75	10
279		6d. sepia and new blue	2·25	10
280		8d. yellow, turquoise-blue and deep blue	55	10
281		1s. maroon and turquoise	20	10
282		1s.6d. orange-yellow, lake-brown and deep turquoise-blue	50	20
283		2s. multicoloured	1·25	2·00
284		3s. maroon and turquoise-blue	3·00	40
285		5s. ochre, blue and new blue	2·00	2·75
286		10s. multicoloured	4·75	3·00
287		£1 Prussian blue, silver and crimson	4·75	12·00
274/287 *Set of 14*			21·00	18·00

Designs: Vert as T **88**—2d. Donkey; 3d. Sisal industry 6d. Salt industry; 8d. Skin-diving; 1s.6d. Water-skiing. Horiz as T **89**—4d. Conch industry; 1s. Fishing; 2s. Crawfish industry; 3s. Maps of Turks and Caicos Islands and West Indies; 5s. Fishing industry.

102 Turks Islands 1d. Stamp of 1867

(Des R. Granger Barrett. Photo Harrison)

1967 (1 May). Stamp Centenary. T **102** and similar horiz designs. W w **12**. P 14½.

288		1d. black and light magenta	15	10
		w. Wmk inverted	50·00	
289		6d. black and bluish grey	25	15
290		1s. black and turquoise-blue	25	15
288/90 *Set of 3*			60	30

Designs:—6d. Queen Elizabeth "stamp" and Turks Islands 6d. stamp of 1867; 1s. Turks Islands 1s. stamp of 1867.

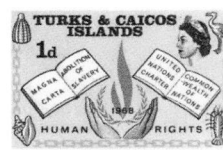

104 Human Rights Emblem and Charter

(Des R. Granger Barrett. Photo Harrison)

1968 (1 Apr). Human Rights Year. W w **12**. P 14×14½.

291	104	1d. multicoloured	10	10
292		8d. multicoloured	15	15
293		1s.6d. multicoloured	15	15
291/3 *Set of 3*			30	30

105 Dr Martin Luther King and "Freedom March"

(Des V. Whiteley. Photo Harrison)

1968 (1 Oct). Martin Luther King Commemoration. W w **12**. P 14×14½.

294	105	2d. yellow-brown, blackish brown and deep blue	10	10
295		8d. yellow-brown, blackish brown and lake	15	15
296		1s.6d. yellow-brown, blackish brown and violet	15	15
294/6 *Set of 3*			30	30

(106)

107 The Nativity with John the Baptist

1c

1969 (8 Sept)–71. Decimal currency. Nos. 274/87 surch as T **106** by Harrison & Sons, and new value (¼c.) as T **90**.

297	¼c.	pale greenish grey and multicoloured	10	10
	a.	Bronze-green and multicoloured (2.2.71)	1·75	30
298	1c.	on 1d.olive-yellow, vermilion and bright bluish violet	10	10
	a.	Wmk sideways	10	10
299	2c.	on 2d. deep slate and deep orange-yellow	10	10
	a.	Wmk sideways	10	10
300	3c.	on 3d. agate and dull green	10	10
	a.	Wmk sideways	10	10
301	4c.	on 4d. bright mauve, black and turquoise	3·00	10
302	5c.	on 6d. sepia and new blue	10	10
	a.	Wmk sideways	10	60
303	7c.	on 8d. yellow, turquoise-blue and deep blue	10	10
	a.	Wmk sideways	10	40
304	8c.	on 1½d. brown and orange-yellow	10	10
	w.	Wmk inverted	35·00	
305	10c.	on 1s. maroon and turquoise	20	10
306	15c.	on 1s.6d. orange-yellow, lake-brown and deep turquoise-blue	25	10
	a.	Wmk sideways	20	25
307	20c.	on 2s. multicoloured	30	25
308	30c.	on 3s. maroon and turquoise-blue	55	35
309	50c.	on 5s. ochre, blue and new blue	1·25	45
310	$1	on 10s. multicoloured	2·50	2·75
311	$2	on £1 Prussian blue, silver and crimson	2·75	15·00
	a.	Wmk sideways	2·75	7·00
297/311	Set of 15		10·00	17·00
298a/311a	Set of 7		3·00	7·50

The 4, 8, 10, 20, 30, 50c., and $1 exist with PVA gum as well as gum arabic.

No. 311 was only on sale through the Crown Agents.

(Des adapted by V. Whiteley. Litho D.L.R.)

1969 (20 Oct). Christmas. Scenes from 16th-cent Book of Hours. T **107** and similar vert design. Multicoloured. W w **12**. P 13×12½.

312	1c.	Type **107**	10	10
313	3c.	The Flight into Egypt	10	10
314	15c.	Type **107**	15	10
315	30c.	As 3c.	25	20
312/15	Set of 4		40	40

109 Coat of Arms

110 Christ bearing the Cross

(Des L. Curtis. Litho B.W.)

1970 (2 Feb). New Constitution. Multicoloured; background colours given. W w **12** (sideways). P 13×12½.

316	**109**	7c. brown	20	25
317		35c. deep violet-blue	35	25

(Des, recess and litho Enschedé)

1970 (17 Mar). Easter. Details from the Small Engraved Passion by Dürer. T **110** and similar vert designs. W w **12** (sideways). P 13×13½.

318	5c.	olive-grey and blue	10	10
319	7c.	olive-grey and vermilion	10	10
320	50c.	olive-grey and red-brown	60	1·00
318/20	Set of 3		70	1·10

Designs:—7c. Christ on the Cross; 50c. The Lamentation of Christ

113 Dickens and Scene from Oliver Twist

(Des Sylvia Goaman. Recess and litho D.L.R.)

1970 (17 June). Death Centenary of Charles Dickens. T **113** and similar horiz designs. W w **12** (sideways). P 13.

321	1c.	black and yellow-brown/yellow	10	50

322	3c.	black and Prussian blue/flesh	20	40
323	15c.	black and grey blue/flesh	60	20
324	30c.	black and drab/blue	80	40
321/4	Set of 4		1·50	1·40

Designs (each incorporating portrait of Dickens as in T **113**, and a scene from one of his novels):—3c. A Christmas Carol; 15c. Pickwick Papers; 30c. The Old Curiosity Shop.

114 Ambulance—1870

(Des Harrison. Litho B.W.)

1970 (4 Aug). Centenary of British Red Cross. T **114** and similar horiz design. Multicoloured. W w **12**. P 13½×14.

325	1c.	Type **114**	10	20
326	5c.	Ambulance—1970	20	10
	a.	Wmk sideways	30	10
	ab.	Grey omitted	£350	
327	15c.	Type **114**	40	15
	a.	Wmk sideways	50	10
328	30c.	As 5c.	50	20
	a.	Wmk sideways	60	40
325/8	Set of 4		1·00	55

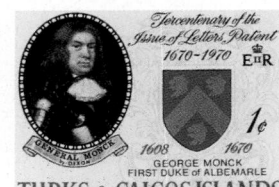

115 Duke of Albemarle and Coat of Arms

(Des V. Whiteley. Litho Enschedé)

1970 (1 Dec). Tercentenary of Issue of Letters Patent. T **115** and similar horiz design. Multicoloured. W w **12**. P 12½×13½.

329	1c.	Type **115**	10	30
330	8c.	Arms of Charles II and Elizabeth II	25	40
331	10c.	Type **115**	25	15
332	35c.	As 8c.	55	75
329/32	Set of 4		1·00	1·40

Uganda

PROTECTORATE

Following a period of conflict between Islamic, Protestant and Roman Catholic factions, Uganda was declared to be in the British sphere of influence by the Anglo-German Agreement of July 1890. The British East Africa Company exercised a variable degree of control until 27 August 1894 when the country was declared a British Protectorate.

Before the introduction of Nos. 84/91 the stamps of Uganda were only valid for internal postage. Letters for overseas were franked with British East Africa issues on arrival at Mombasa.

(Currency. 200 cowries = 1 rupee)

```
 ┌ ─ ─ ┐        ┌ ─ ─ ┐
 'U    G'       'U    G'
 '     '        '     '
 '  50 '        '  20 '
 '     '        '     '
 '     '        '     '
 └ ─ ─ ┘        └ ─ ─ ┘
    1              2
```

TYPE-WRITTEN STAMPS. Nos. 1/53 were type-written by the Revd. E. Millar at Mengo for the Uganda administration. For all "printings" a thin laid paper was used, and all issues were imperforate and ungummed. The laid lines are invariably horizontal, with the exception of Nos. 19a, 20a and 38b.

The original typewriter used had wide letters, but in late April, 1895 Millar obtained a new machine on which the type face was in a narrower fount.

Each sheet was made up of whatever values were required at the time, so that different values can be found se-tenant or tête-bêche. These last were caused by the paper being inverted in the machine so that space at the foot could be utilised.

For the first issue the sheets were of 117 (9×13), but with the introduction of the narrower width (Nos. 17 onwards) a larger number of stamps per sheet, 143 (11×13), was adopted.

PRICES. The prices of Nos. 1/53 vary greatly according to condition. The thin paper used is subject to creasing, staining and thinning. Catalogue quality is for fine examples, with borders visible on at least three sides. Used stamps are usually found with manuscript crosses in pencil, crayon or ink; examples with initials, dates or place names may command a premium, but note that stamps cancelled to order with circular datestamps (usually at Kampala in 1898) tend to be worth less.

1895 (20 Mar). Wide letters. Wide stamps, 20 to 26 mm wide.

1	**1**	10 (c.) black	£4250	£2250
2		20 (c.) black	£7500	£1800
		a. "U A" for "U G"	†	£6500
3		30 (c.) black	£2000	£1600
4		40 (c.) black	£6000	£2250
5		50 (c.) black	£1400	£1100
		a. "U A" for "U G"	†	£8500
6		60 (c.) black	£2500	£2250

It is now believed that the 5, 15 and 25 cowries values in this width, formerly listed, do not exist.

1895 (May). Wide stamps with pen-written surcharges, in black.

8	**1**	5 on 10 (c.) black	†	£70000
9		10 on 30 (c.) black	†	£70000
10		10 on 50 (c.) black	†	£70000
11		15 on 10 (c.) black	†	£50000
12		15 on 20 (c.) black	†	£70000
13		15 on 40 (c.) black	†	£60000
14		15 on 50 (c.) black	†	£70000
15		25 on 50 (c.) black	†	£70000
16		50 on 60 (c.) black	†	£70000

The manuscript provisionals, Nos. 9/16 come from the Mission at Ngogwe, most of the manuscript surcharges including the initials of the Revd. G. R. Blackledge stationed there. But No. 8, known only in se-tenant form with an unsurcharged pair of No. 1 on cover, was initialled "E.M." by Revd. E. Millar, presumably at Mengo.

1895 (Apr). Wide letters. Narrow stamps, 16 to 18 mm wide.

17	**1**	5 (c.) black	£3250	£1300
18		10 (c.) black	£3250	£1600
19		15 (c.) black	£2000	£1500
		a. Vertically laid paper	†	£5000
20		20 (c.) black	£3250	£1500
		a. Vertically laid paper	†	£6500
21		25 (c.) black	£1800	£1600
22		30 (c.) black	£8500	£8500
23		40 (c.) black	£8000	£8000
24		50 (c.) black	£3750	£4250
25		60 (c.) black	£8000	£8500

A used pair of No. 19a and two used examples of No. 20a have been seen. With the exception of No. 38b, Nos. 1/53 otherwise show the laid lines horizontal.

To qualify as Nos. 22/5, which are very rare stamps, examples must show borders on both vertical sides and not exceed 18 mm in width. Examples not fulfilling both criteria can only be classified as belonging to the "Wide stamps" group, Nos. 3/6.

1895 (May). Narrow letters. Narrow stamps 16 to 18 mm wide.

26	**2**	5 (c.) black		£1700
27		10 (c.) black		£1800

28		15 (c.) black	£1800	
29		20 (c.) black	£1500	
30		25 (c.) black	£1700	
31		30 (c.) black	£2000	
32		40 (c.) black	£1700	
33		50 (c.) black	£1800	
34		60 (c.) black	£2500	

1895 (Nov). Narrow letters. Narrow stamps, 16–18 mm wide. Change of colour.

35	**2**	5 (c.) violet	£700	£650
36		10 (c.) violet	£650	£650
37		15 (c.) violet	£1100	£600
38		20 (c.) violet	£475	£300
		a. "G U" for "U G"	£3000	
		b. Vertically laid paper	£3000	
39		25 (c.) violet	£1800	£1600
40		30 (c.) violet	£2250	£1100
41		40 (c.) violet	£2250	£1500
42		50 (c.) violet	£2000	£1500
43		100 (c.) violet	£2500	£3000

Stamps of 35 (c.) and 45 (c.) have been recorded in violet, on vertically laid paper. They were never prepared for postal use, and did not represent a postal rate, but were type-written to oblige a local official. (*Price* £2750 *each, unused*)

3

1896 (June).

44	**3**	5 (c.) violet	£750	£1000
45		10 (c.) violet	£850	£650
46		15 (c.) violet	£750	£750
47		20 (c.) violet	£400	£225
48		25 (c.) violet	£700	£900
49		30 (c.) violet	£800	£850
50		40 (c.) violet	£900	£900
51		50 (c.) violet	£750	£800
52		60 (c.) violet	£1600	£2000
53		100 (c.) violet	£1500	£2000

(New Currency. 16 annas = 1 rupee)

4 (Thin "1")   **5** (Thick "1")

6   **7**

In the 2a. and 3a. the dagger points upwards; the stars in the 2a. are level with the top of "VR". The 8a. is as T **6** but with left star at top and right star at foot. The 1r. has three stars at foot. The 5r. has central star raised and the others at foot.

(Type-set by the Revd. F. Rowling at Lubwa's, in Usoga)

1896 (7 Nov). Thick white wove paper (Nos. 54/8) or thin yellowish paper ruled with vertical lines 9 mm apart (Nos. 59/61).

(a) Types 4/6

54	**4**	1a. black	£110	£100
		a. Small "o" in "POSTAGE"	£600	£600
55	**5**	1a. black	23·00	26·00
		a. Small "o" in "POSTAGE"	85·00	£100
56	**6**	2a. black	29·00	35·00
		a. Small "o" in "POSTAGE"	£100	£120
57		3a. black	29·00	45·00
		a. Small "o" in "POSTAGE"	£120	£180
58		4a. black	32·00	38·00
		a. Small "o" in "POSTAGE"	£120	£130
59		8a. black	40·00	48·00
		a. Small "o" in "POSTAGE"	£140	£180
60		1r. black	85·00	£100
		a. Small "o" in "POSTAGE"	£350	£425
61		5r. black	£275	£350
		a. Small "o" in "POSTAGE"	£900	£1100

(b) Optd "L", in black as in T 7 for local use, by a postal official, R. R. Racey, at Kampala

70	**4**	1a. black	£190	£170
		a. Small "o" in "POSTAGE"	£1400	£1200
71	**6**	2a. black	£120	£120
		a. Small "o" in "POSTAGE"	£550	£600
72		3a. black	£275	£325
		a. Small "o" in "POSTAGE"	£1700	£2000
73		4a. black	£120	£160
		a. Small "o" in "POSTAGE"	£550	
74		8a. black	£200	£300
		a. Small "o" in "POSTAGE"	£1500	£1900
75		1r. black	£375	£450
		a. Small "o" in "POSTAGE"	£2000	
76		5r. black	£22000	£22000

Tête-bêche pairs of all values may be found owing to the settings of 16 (4×4) being printed side by side or above one another. They are worth a premium. The variety with small "O" occurs on R. 3/1.

---

8   **9**   **(10)**

(Recess D.L.R.)

1898 (Nov)–**1902**. P 14.

(a) Wmk Crown CA

84	**8**	1a. scarlet	6·50	4·50
		a. Carmine-rose (1902)	2·25	1·75
86		2a. red-brown	10·00	11·00
87		3a. pale grey	21·00	45·00
		a. Bluish grey	21·00	20·00
		x. Wmk reversed	£325	
88		4a. deep green	16·00	10·00
89		8a. pale olive	15·00	30·00
		a. Grey-green	38·00	50·00

(b) Wmk Crown CC

90	**9**	1r. dull blue	55·00	60·00
		a. Bright blue	65·00	75·00
91		5r. brown	£100	£120
84/91 *Set of 7*			£190	£225
84s/91s Optd "SPECIMEN" *Set of 7*			£190	

Examples of No. 86 are known bisected to pay the 1 anna rate during a shortage of 1a. stamps at the post office in Masindi in late 1899 and early 1900.

Nos. 84/9 exist without watermark or with double-lined lettering from the marginal watermark due to the way in which sheets were cut for printing.

On 1 April 1901 the postal administrations of British East Africa and Uganda were merged. Subsequent issues to 1962 are listed under KENYA, UGANDA and TANGANYIKA.

1902 (Feb). T **11** of British East Africa (Kenya, Uganda, and Tanganyika) optd with T **10**.

92		½a. yellow-green	3·00	2·00
		a. Opt omitted (in pair with normal)	£5500	
		b. Opt inverted (at foot)	£2250	
		c. Opt double	£2750	
		w. Wmk inverted	£375	
		x. Wmk reversed	—	£300
93		2½a. deep blue (R.)	5·00	3·00
		a. Opt double	£600	
		b. Inverted "S" (R. 1/1)	£120	£100
		x. Wmk reversed	£350	
		y. Wmk inverted and reversed	£350	

The Eastern Province of Uganda was transferred to British East Africa on 1 April 1902.

SELF-GOVERNMENT

(New Currency. 100 cents = 1 East African, later Uganda shilling)

11 Ripon Falls and Speke Memorial

1962 (28 July). Centenary of Speke's Discovery of Source of the Nile. W w **12**. P 14.

95	**11**	30c. black and red	20	25
96		50c. black and slate-violet	20	10
97		1s.30 black and green	1·00	25
98		2s.50 black and blue	2·25	2·25
95/8 *Set of 4*			3·25	2·50

INDEPENDENT

12 Murchison Falls   **13** Tobacco-growing

14 Mulago Hospital

1s.30 Dome flaw - a large white flaw to left of dome of Namirembe Cathedral (Pl. 1A-1A, R. 9/10)

(Des V. Whiteley. Photo Harrison)

1962 (9 Oct)–**64**. Independence. Various designs as T **12/14**. P 15×14 (5c. to 50c.) or 14½ (others).

99		5c. deep bluish green	10	10
100		10c. reddish brown	10	10
		a. Brown (coil)	10	75
		b. Deep yellow-brown (17.10.64)	10	10
101		15c. black, red and green	10	10
102		20c. plum and buff	10	10
103		30c. blue	10	10
104		50c. black and turquoise-green	10	10
105		1s. sepia, red and green	1·25	20
106		1s.30 yellow-orange and violet	25	10
		a. Dome flaw	32·00	
107		2s. black, carmine and light blue	50	70
108		5s. vermilion and deep green	8·00	2·00
109		10s. slate and chestnut	4·25	4·50
110		20s. brown and blue	4·50	21·00
99/110 *Set of 12*			17·00	26·00

Designs: As T **12/13**—10c. Tobacco growing, 15c. Coffee growing; 20c. Ankole cattle; 30c. Cotton; 50c. Mountains of the Moon. As T **14**—1s.30, Cathedrals and Mosque; 2s. Makerere College; 5s. Copper mining; 10s. Cement industry; 20s. Parliament Buildings.

15 South African Crowned Crane

(Photo Harrison)

1965 (20 Feb). International Trade Fair, Kampala. P 14½×14.

111	**15**	30c. multicoloured	15	10
112		1s.30 multicoloured	25	10

16 Black Bee-eater   **17** African Jacana

18 Ruwenzori Turaco

(Des Mrs. R. Fennessy. Photo Harrison)

1965 (9 Oct). Birds. Various designs as T **16/18**. P 15×14 (5c., 15c., 20c., 40c., 50c.), 14×15 (10c., 30c., 65c.) or 14½ (others).

113		5c. multicoloured	10	10
114		10c. chestnut, black and light blue	10	10
115		15c. yellow and sepia	20	10
116		20c. multicoloured	20	10
117		30c. black and brown-red	1·50	10
118		40c. multicoloured	1·00	1·75
119		50c. grey-blue and reddish violet	25	10
		a. White bird (grey-blue omitted)	£1700	
120		65c. orange-red, black and light grey	2·00	2·75
121		1s. multicoloured	50	10
122		1s.30 chestnut, black and yellow	4·50	30
123		2s.50 multicoloured	3·50	65
124		5s. multicoloured	6·00	4·00
125		10s. multicoloured	9·00	11·00
126		20s. multicoloured	20·00	38·00
113/26 *Set of 14*			42·00	48·00

Designs: Vert as T **16**—15c. Orange Weaver; 20c. Narina Trogon; 40c. Blue-breasted Kingfisher; 50c. Whale-headed Stork. Horiz as T **17**—30c. Red-crowned Bishop. As T **18**. Vert—1s.30, African Fish Eagle; 5s. Lilac-breasted Roller. Horiz—2s.50, Great Blue Turaco; 10s. Black-collared Lovebird; 20s. South African Crowned Crane. The 15c., 40c., 65c., and 1s. exist with PVA gum as well as gum arabic.

19 Carved Screen

(Des Mrs. R. Fennessy. Photo Harrison)

1967 (26 Oct). 13th Commonwealth Parliamentary Association Conference. T **19** and similar horiz designs. Multicoloured. P 14.

127		30c. Type **19**	10	10
128		50c. Arms of Uganda	10	10
129		1s.30 Parliamentary Building	10	10
130		2s.50 Conference Chamber	15	1·75
127/30 *Set of 4*			30	1·75

20 *Cordia* **21** *Acacia*
abyssinica *drepanolobium*

(Des Mrs. R. Fennessy. Photo Harrison)

1969 (9 Oct)–**74**. Flowers. Various designs as T **20**/1. Chalk-surfaced paper. P 14½×14 (5c. to 70c.) or 14 (others).

131	5c. brown, green and light olive-yellow	10	1·00
	a. Glazed, ordinary paper (11.4.73)	40	10
132	10c. multicoloured	10	10
	a. Glazed, ordinary paper (27.9.72)	40	10
133	15c. multicoloured	40	10
134	20c. bluish violet, yellow-olive and pale sage-green	15	10
	a. Glazed, ordinary paper (27.9.72)	40	10
135	30c. multicoloured	20	10
136	40c. reddish violet, yellow-green and pale olive-grey	20	10
137	50c. multicoloured	20	10
138	60c. multicoloured	45	2·75
	a. Glazed, ordinary paper (9.5.73)	17·00	40
139	70c. multicoloured	25	30
	a. Glazed, ordinary paper (27.9.72)	1·00	45
140	1s. multicoloured	20	10
	a. Glazed, ordinary paper (22.1.71)	1·00	10
141	1s.50 multicoloured (cobalt background)	25	10
	a. Glazed, ordinary paper (3.2.71)	50	10
	b. Azure background (chalk-surfaced paper) (21.1.74)	55	30
142	2s.50 multicoloured	30	1·25
	a. Glazed, ordinary paper (3.2.71)	1·25	10
143	5s. multicoloured	40	1·60
	a. Glazed, ordinary paper (3.2.71)	1·75	10
144	10s. multicoloured	50	4·50
	a. Glazed, ordinary paper (3.2.71)	3·75	10
145	20s. multicoloured	1·00	6·00
	a. Glazed, ordinary paper (22.1.71)	12·00	15
131/45 *Set of 15*		3·50	15·00
131a/45a *Set of 11*		35·00	1·40

Designs: As T **20**—10c. *Grewia similis*; 15c. *Cassia. didymobotrya*; 20c. *Coleus barbatus*; 30c. *Ockna ovata*; 40c. *Ipomoea spathulata*; 50c. *Spathodea nilotica*; 60c. *Oncoba spinosa*; 70c. *Carissa edulis*. As T **21**—1s.50, *Clerodendrum myricoides*; 2s.50, *Acanthus arboreus*; 5s. *Kigelia aethiopium*; 10s. *Erythrina abyssinica*; 20s. *Monodora myristica*.

Some of the glazed ordinary paper printings were available in Uganda some time before the London release dates which are quoted in the listings.

STAMP BOOKLETS

1962 (9 Oct). Black on buff cover. Stitched.
SB1	5s. booklet containing 10c., 15c., 20c., 30c. and 50c. (Nos. 100/4), each in block of 4		6·50

1965. Black on blue (No. SB2) or buff (No. SB3) covers. Stitched.
SB2	3s. booklet containing 4×15c. and 8×30c. (Nos. 115, 117) in blocks of 4		10·00
SB3	5s. booklet containing 4×15c. and 4×50c., and 8×30c. Nos. 115, 117, 119) in blocks of 4		11·00

1970. Black on blue (No. SB4) or buff (No. SB5) covers. Stitched.
SB4	3s. booklet containing four 5c. and 10c., and eight 30c. (Nos. 131/2, 135) in blocks of 4		15·00
SB5	5s. booklet containing 4×5c., 4×10c. and 4×50c., and 8×30c. (Nos. 131/2, 135, 137) in blocks of 4		15·00

POSTAGE DUE STAMPS

The Postage Due stamps of Kenya, Uganda and Tanganyika were used in Uganda until 2 January 1967.

D 1

(Litho D.L.R.)

1967 (3 Jan). Chalk-surfaced paper. P 14×13½.
D1	D **1**	5c. scarlet	20	4·50
D2		10c. green	20	5·00
D3		20c. deep blue	35	5·00
D4		30c. red-brown	40	6·50
D5		40c. bright purple	60	15·00
D6		1s. orange	1·50	13·00
D1/6 *Set of 6*			3·00	45·00

1970 (31 Mar). As Nos. D1/6, but on glazed ordinary paper. P 14×15.
D7	D **1**	5c. scarlet	15	3·25
D8		10c. green	15	2·50
D9		20c. deep blue	25	3·00
D10		30c. red-brown	35	4·25
D11		40c. bright purple	55	5·50
D7/11 *Set of 5*			1·25	17·00

TELEGRAPH STAMPS

T **1** T **2**

1902 (1 June). Black on coloured paper. Pin perf 12.
T1	T **1**	2a. on blue-green	£110	70·00
		a. Seriffed "G" in lower "TELEGRAPHS"	£180	£110
T2		4a. on yellow	£120	85·00
		a. Seriffed "G" in lower "TELEGRAPHS"	£190	£130
T3		6a. on magenta	£130	95·00
		a. "SIK" for "SIX" in upper half	£225	
		b. Seriffed "G" in lower "TELEGRAPHS"	£225	£140
T4		8a. on rose	£160	£110
		a. Seriffed "G" in lower "TELEGRAPHS"	£250	£170
T5		12a. on green	£225	£170
		a. On greyish blue	£275	£225
		b. Seriffed "G" in lower "TELEGRAPHS"	£350	£250
T6	T **2**	1r. on white laid paper	£300	95·00
		a. Stop for comma after lower "TELEGRAPHS"	£325	£110
		b. No stop after lower "RUPEE"	£325	£110
T7		2r. on yellow	£300	£120
		a. Stop for comma after lower "TELEGRAPHS"	£325	£130
T8		3r. on blue-green	£475	£275
		a. Stop for comma after lower "TELEGRAPHS"	£550	£300
T9		4r. on magenta	£650	£325
		a. Stop for comma after lower "TELEGRAPHS"	£750	£350
		b. No stop after lower "RUPEES"	£750	£350
T10		5r. on rose	£750	£350
		a. Stop for comma after lower "TELEGRAPHS"	£850	£375
T11		10r. on greyish blue	£1200	£600
		a. Stop for comma after lower "TELEGRAPHS"	£1400	£650
T12		20r. on white laid paper	£1900	£950
		a. Stop for comma after lower "TELEGRAPHS"	£2250	£1000
		b. No stop after lower "RUPEES"	£2250	£1000

Nos. T1/5 were printed in sheets of 56 (14×4), from stereotyped plates formed from an original typeset row of seven. Nos. T6/12 were in sheets of 48 (12×4), similarly formed from an original typeset row of six.

No. T3a occurs on the seventh and 14th stamp of each row.

The variety with seriffed "G" occurs on the first and eighth stamp of each row.

Nos. T7/9 are known with the "S" of "RUPEES" omitted but these are of proof status.

Unused prices are for whole stamps. Used prices are for lower halves. Upper halves are worth more.

Victoria *see* **Australia**

Virgin Islands *see* **British Virgin Islands**

Western Australia *see* **Australia**

Western Samoa *see* **Samoa**

Zambia

INDEPENDENT

11 Pres. Kaunda **12** College of Further
and Victoria Falls Education, Lusaka

(Des M. Goaman (3d., 6d.), Gabriel Ellison (1s.3d.). Photo Harrison)

1964 (24 Oct). Independence. T **11**/12 and similar vert design. P 13½×11½ (6d.) or 14½×13½ (others).
91	3d. sepia, yellow-green and blue	10	10
92	6d. deep violet and yellow	15	20
93	1s.3d. red, black, sepia and orange	20	25
91/3 *Set of 3*		40	50

Design:—1s.3d. Barotse dancer.

14 Maize-Farmer **15** Health—
and Silo Radiographer

21 Fishing at Mpulungu **22** Tobacco Worker

(Des Gabriel Ellison. Photo Harrison)

1964 (24 Oct). T **14**/15, **21**/2 and similar designs. P 14½ (½d. to 4d.), 14½×13½ (1s.3d., 2s. and £1) or 13½×14½ (others).
94	½d. red, black and yellow-green	10	1·50
95	1d. brown, black and bright blue	10	10
96	2d. red, deep brown and orange	10	10
97	3d. black and red	10	10
98	4d. black, brown and orange	15	10
99	6d. orange, deep brown and deep bluish green	30	10
100	9d. carmine, black and bright blue	15	10
101	1s. black, yellow-bistre and blue	15	10
102	1s.3d. light red, yellow, black and blue	20	10
103	2s. bright blue, black, deep brown and orange	25	30
	a. Black (detail of heads) omitted	£300	
104	2s.6d. black and orange-yellow	1·00	35
105	5s. black, yellow and green	1·00	1·00
106	10s. black and orange	4·50	4·75
107	£1 black, brown, yellow and red	2·00	7·50
94/107 *Set of 14*		9·00	14·00

Designs: Vert (as T **15**)—2d. Chinyau dancer; 3d. Cotton-picking. (As T **22**)—2s. Tonga basket-making; £1 Makishi dancer. Horiz (as T **14**)—4d. Angoni bull. (As T **21**)—6d. Communications, old and new; 9d. Zambezi sawmills and Redwood flower; 2s.6d. Luangwa Game Reserve; 5s. Education—student; 10s. Copper mining.

Nos. 94/5 and 97 exist in coils, constructed from normal sheets.

28 ITU Emblem and **29** ICY Emblem
Symbols

(Photo Harrison)

1965 (26 July). ITU Centenary. P 14×14½.
108	**28**	6d. light reddish violet and gold	15	10
109		2s.6d. brownish grey and gold	85	1·50

(Photo Harrison)

1965 (26 July). International Co-operation Year. P 14½.
110	**29**	3d. turquoise and gold	15	10
111		1s.3d. ultramarine and gold	45	45

30 State House, Lusaka **34** WHO Building and UN Flag

(Des Gabriel Ellison. Photo Harrison)

1965 (18 Oct). First Anniv of Independence. T **30** and similar multicoloured designs. No wmk. P 13½×14½ (3d.), 14×13½ (6d.) or 13½×14 (others).

112		3d. Type **30**	10	10
113		6d. Fireworks, Independence Stadium...	10	10
		a. Bright purple (fireworks) omitted......	£160	
114		1s.3d. *Clematopsis* (*vert*)	15	10
115		2s.6d. *Tithonia diversifolia* (*vert*)	30	1·25
112/15		*Set of 4*	50	1·25

(Des M. Goaman. Photo Harrison)

1966 (18 May). Inauguration of WHO Headquarters, Geneva. P 14½.

116	**34**	3d. lake-brown, gold and new blue .	40	10
		a. Gold omitted	£120	
117		1s.3d. gold, new blue and deep bluish violet	1·40	95

35 Proposed University Building   **36** National Assembly Building

(Des Gabriel Ellison. Photo Harrison)

1966 (12 July). Opening of Zambia University. P 14½.

118	**35**	3d. blue-green and copper-bronze	10	10
119		1s.3d. reddish violet and copper-bronze	20	10

The building shown on Type **35** was never built.

(Des Gabriel Ellison. Photo Harrison)

1967 (2 May). Inauguration of National Assembly Building. P 14½.

120	**36**	3d. black and copper-bronze	10	10
121		6d. olive-green and copper-bronze	10	10

37 Airport Scene

(Des Gabriel Ellison. Photo Harrison)

1967 (2 Oct). Opening of Lusaka International Airport. P 13½×14½.

122	**37**	6d. violet-blue and copper-bronze.	15	10
123		2s.6d. brown and copper-bronze	60	1·00

38 Youth Service Badge   **39** "Co-operative Farming"

(Des Gabriel Ellison. Photo Harrison)

1967 (23 Oct). National Development. T **38/9** and similar designs. P 13½×14½ (6d., 1s.6d.) or 14½×13½ (others).

124		4d. black, red and gold	10	10
125		6d. black, gold and violet-blue	10	10
126		9d. black, grey-blue and silver	15	50
127		1s. multicoloured	50	10
128		1s.6d. multicoloured	70	2·25
124/8		*Set of 5*	1·40	2·75

Designs: Vert—9d. "Communications"; 1s. Coalfields. Horiz—1s.6d. Road link with Tanzania.

(New Currency. 100 ngwee = 1 kwacha)

43 Lusaka Cathedral   **44** Baobab Tree

52 Chokwe Dancer   **53** Kafue Railway Bridge

(Des Gabriel Ellison. Photo Harrison)

1968 (16 Jan). Decimal Currency. T **43/4**, **52/3** and similar designs. P 13½×14½ (1, 3, 15, 50n.) or 14½×13½ (others).

129		1n. multicoloured	˙10	10

	a. Copper-bronze (including value) omitted		£180
	b. Ultramarine (windows) omitted		£225
130	2n. multicoloured	10	10
131	3n. multicoloured	10	10
132	5n. bistre-brown and copper-bronze	10	10
	a. Coil stamp. P 14½	1·00	1·50
133	8n. multicoloured	15	10
	a. Copper-bronze (background) omitted		£160
	b. Blue (of costumes) omitted		£160
134	10n. multicoloured	35	10
135	15n. multicoloured	2·75	10
136	20n. multicoloured	4·75	10
137	25n. multicoloured	25	10
138	50n. chocolate, red-orange and copper-bronze	30	15
139	1k. royal blue and copper-bronze	7·50	20
140	2k. black and copper-bronze	1·25	1·25
129/40	*Set of 12*	15·00	1·75

Designs: Horiz (as T **43**)—3n. Zambia Airways Vickers VC-10 jetliner. (As T **53**)—15n. *Imbrasia zambesina* (moth); 2k. Eland. Vert (as T **44**)—5n. National Museum, Livingstone; 8n. Vimbuza dancer; 10n. Tobacco picking. (As T **52**)—20n. South African Crowned Cranes; 25n. Angoni warrior.

All values exist with PVA gum as well as gum arabic.

Nos. 129/30 and 132 exist in coils, constructed from normal sheets it is believed that the 5n. perf 14½ came from a late release.

55 Ndola on Outline of Zambia   **56** Human Rights Emblem and Heads

(Des Gabriel Ellison. Photo Harrison)

1968 (29 June). Trade Fair, Ndola. P 14.

141	**55**	15n. green and gold	10	10

(Des Gabriel Ellison. Photo and die-stamped (gold emblem) Harrison)

1968 (23 Oct). Human Rights Year. P 14.

142	**56**	3n. deep blue, pale violet and gold	10	10

57 WHO Emblem   **58** Group of Children

(Des Gabriel Ellison. Photo and die-stamped (gold staff and "20") Harrison)

1968 (23 Oct). 20th Anniv of World Health Organization. P 14.

143	**57**	10n. gold and bluish violet	10	10

(Des Gabriel Ellison. Photo and die-stamped (gold children) Harrison)

1968 (23 Oct). 22nd Anniv of UNICEF. P 14.

144	**58**	25n. black, gold and ultramarine	15	70

59 Copper Miner   **61** Zambia outlined on Map of Africa

(Des Gabriel Ellison. Photo Harrison)

1969 (18 June). 50th Anniv of International Labour Organization. T **59** and similar design. P 14½×13½ (3n.) or 13½×14½ (25n.).

145		3n. copper-bronze and deep violet	25	10
146		25n. pale yellow copper-bronze and blackish brown	1·00	1·00

Design: Horiz—25n. Poling a furnace.

A used example of No. 145 exists with the copper-bronze omitted.

(Des Gabriel Ellison. Photo Harrison)

1969 (23 Oct). International African Tourist Year. T **61** and similar multicoloured designs. P 14×14½ (5n., 25n.) or 14½×14 (others).

147		5n. Type **61**	10	10
148		10n. Waterbuck (*horiz*)	15	10
149		15n. Kasaba Bay Golden Perch (*horiz*)	35	40
150		25n. Carmine Bee-eater	1·00	1·75
147/50		*Set of 4*	1·40	2·00

PREVENTIVE MEDICINE

65 Satellite *Nimbus 3* orbiting the Earth   **66** Woman collecting Water from Well

(Des Gabriel Ellison. Litho Enschedé)

1970 (23 Mar). World Meteorological Day. P 13×10½.

151	**65**	15n. multicoloured	20	50

(Des V. Whiteley (from local designs). Litho B.W.)

1970 (4 July). Preventive Medicine. T **66** and similar vert designs. P 13½×12.

152		3n. multicoloured	15	10
153		15n. multicoloured	30	30
154		25n. greenish blue, rosine and sepia	65	70
152/4		*Set of 3*	1·00	1·00

Designs:—15n. Child on scales; 25n. Child being immunized.

67 *Masks* (mural by Gabriel Ellison)   **68** Ceremonial Axe

(Des Gabriel Ellison. Litho Harrison)

1970 (8 Sept). Conference of Non-Aligned Nations. P 14×14½.

155	**67**	15n. multicoloured	30	30

(Des Gabriel Ellison. Litho D.L.R.)

1970 (30 Nov). Traditional Crafts. T **68** and similar multicoloured designs. P 13½ (15n.), 12½ (25n.) or 14 (others).

156		3n. Type **68**	10	10
157		5n. Clay Smoking-Pipe Bowl	10	10
158		15n. Makishi Mask (30×47 *mm*)	35	30
159		25n. Kuomboka Ceremony (72×19 *mm*)	55	1·00
156/9		*Set of 4*	1·00	1·40
MS160		133×83 mm. Nos. 156/9. Imperf	5·00	13·00

STAMP BOOKLETS

Republic of Zambia
POSTAGE STAMPS
8 at 1n
4 at 3n
20n

B **2**

1968. Black on buff covers as Type B **2** (No. SB2), or size 82×58 mm (No. SB3). Stitched.

SB2	20n. booklet containing 8×1n. and 4×3n. (Nos. 129, 131) in blocks of 4.	4·25
SB3	30n. booklet containing 12×1n. and 6×3n. (Nos. 129, 131) in blocks of 6.	4·25

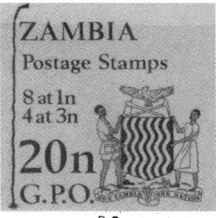

ZAMBIA
Postage Stamps
8 at 1n
4 at 3n
20n
G.P.O.

B **3**

1970 (26 Aug). Black on green cover as Type B **3** (No. SB4) or black on rose cover, size 82×58 mm (No. SB5). Stitched.

SB4	20n. booklet containing 8×1n. and 4×3n. (Nos. 129, 131) in blocks of 4.	6·50
SB5	30n. booklet containing 12×1n. and 6×3n. (Nos. 129, 131) in blocks of 6.	6·50

POSTAGE DUE STAMPS

POSTAGE DUE
ONE PENNY
1D
ZAMBIA

D **3**

(Des D. Smith. Litho Govt Printer, Lusaka)

1964 (24 Oct). P 12½.

D11	D **3**	1d. orange	35	2·50
D12		2d. deep blue	35	2·50
D13		3d. lake	45	1·75
D14		4d. ultramarine	45	2·25
D15		6d. purple	45	2·25
D16		1s. light emerald	55	4·25
D11/16		*Set of 6*	2·25	14·00

In all values the left-hand vertical row of the sheet is imperf at left and the bottom horizontal row is imperf at foot. The above were crudely perforated, resulting in variations in the sizes of the stamps.

The above were withdrawn on 15 January 1968 and thereafter decimal currency postage stamps were used for postage due purposes with appropriate cancellations.

Zanzibar

An Indian post office opened in Zanzibar in November 1868, but was closed for political reasons on 1 April of the following year. Little has survived from this period. Subsequently mail was forwarded via Seychelles or, later, Aden.

Stamps of INDIA were used in Zanzibar from 1 October 1875 until 10 November 1895, when the administration of the postal service was transferred from India to British East Africa. Separate cancellations for Zanzibar are known from 1 June 1878.

Z 1   Z 1a

Stamps of INDIA cancelled with Type Z **1** (1878–79)

1865. (Nos. 54/65).
Z1	1a. deep brown	£650
Z2	2a. orange	£650

1866–78. (Nos. 69/72).
Z2a	4a. green (Die I)	£650
Z3	4a. blue-green (Die II)	£650

1865. (Nos. 54/65).
Z4	½a. blue (Die II)	£600

Surviving covers show that Type Z **1** was normally used as a datestamp, struck clear of the stamps which were obliterated by a rhomboid of bars, but examples of the c.d.s. used as a cancel are known.

Stamps of INDIA cancelled with Type Z **1a**.

1865. (Nos. 54/65).
Z7	2a. orange	£750

In Type Z **1a** the word "ZANZIBAR" is shorter than in Types Z **1** and Z **3**. It was generally used as an arrival mark but cancellations on adhesives are known.

Z 2

Stamps of INDIA cancelled with Type Z **2** (1879–82).

1865. (Nos. 54/65).
Z10	8p. mauve	£500
Z11	1a. deep brown	19·00
Z12	2a. orange	32·00
	a. Brown-orange	18·00

1866–78. (Nos. 69/72).
Z13	4a. green (Die I)	£120
Z14	4a. blue-green (Die II)	30·00

1868. (Nos. 73/4).
Z15	8a. rose (Die II)	£120

1873. (Nos. 75/6).
Z16	½a. blue (Die II)	19·00

1874. (Nos. 77/9).
Z17	1r. slate	£400

1876. (Nos. 80/2).
Z18	6a. pale brown	£150
Z19	12a. Venetian red	£325

1882. (No. 90).
Z19a	1a.6p. sepia	£275

OFFICIAL STAMPS

1874–82. (Nos. O31/7).
Z19b	1a. brown	£425
Z20	2a. orange	£375
Z21	4a. green (Die I)	£475
Z22	8a. rose (Die II)	£650

Z 3

Stamps of INDIA cancelled with Type Z **3** (1882–84)

1865. (Nos. 54/65).
Z25	1a. deep brown	75·00
Z26	2a. brown-orange	45·00
	aa. Orange	75·00

1866–78. (Nos. 69/72).
Z26a	4a. green (Die I)	£110
Z27	4a. blue-green (Die II)	50·00

1868. (Nos. 73/4).
Z28	8a. rose (Die II)	90·00

1873. (Nos. 75/6).
Z29	½a. blue (Die II)	40·00

1874. (Nos. 77/9).
Z29a	1r. slate	£300

1876. (Nos. 80/2).
Z30	6a. pale brown	85·00
Z31	12a. Venetian red	£300

1882–83. (Nos. 84/101).
Z32	1a. brown-purple	55·00
Z33	1a.6p. sepia	60·00
Z34	3a. orange	55·00

OFFICIAL STAMPS

1867–73. (Nos. O20/30a).
Z35	2a. orange	£425
Z36	8a. rose	£550

Z 4   Z 5

Stamps of INDIA cancelled with Type Z **4** (June 1884–May 1887) (between January and September 1885 the postmark was used without year numerals).

1865. (Nos. 54/65).
Z38	8p. purple	£550
Z39	1a. deep brown	£225
Z40	2a. brown-orange	40·00

1866–78. (Nos. 69/72).
Z41	4a. green (Die I)	£250
Z41a	4a. blue-green (Die II)	38·00

1868. (Nos. 73/4).
Z42	8a. rose (Die II)	48·00

1873. (Nos. 75/6).
Z43	½a. blue (Die II)	30·00

1874. (Nos. 77/9).
Z44	1r. slate	£350

1876. (Nos. 80/2).
Z45	6a. pale brown	£100
Z45a	12a. Venetian red	£275

1882–86. (Nos. 84/101).
Z46	½a. blue-green	25·00
Z47	1a. brown-purple	27·00
Z48	1a.6p. sepia	21·00
Z49	2a. blue	60·00
Z50	3a. orange	15·00
Z51	4a. olive-green	45·00
Z52	4a.6p. yellow-green	24·00
Z53	8a. dull mauve	60·00
Z54	1r. slate	48·00

OFFICIAL STAMPS

1867–73. (Nos. O20/30a).
Z55	2a. orange	£375

1874–82. (Nos. O31/7).
Z55a	½a. blue	£140
Z56	1a. brown	£140
Z56a	2a. orange	£350

1883–95. (Nos. O37a/48).
Z57	1a. brown-purple	£250

Stamps of INDIA cancelled with Type Z **5** (1887–94).

1865. (Nos. 54/65).
Z58	8p. purple	£475
Z59	2a. brown-orange	£225

1868. (Nos. 73/4).
Z59a	8a. rose (Die II)	£350

1873. (Nos. 75/6).
Z59b	½a. blue (Die II)	£170

1876. (Nos. 80/2).
Z60	6a. pale brown	24·00
Z61	12a. Venetian red	£100

1882–90. (Nos. 84/101).
Z62	½a. blue-green	8·00
Z63	9p. aniline carmine	85·00
Z64	1a. brown-purple	6·00
Z65	1a.6p. sepia	10·00
Z66	2a. blue	8·00
Z67	3a. orange	10·00
Z68	3a. brown-orange	7·50
Z69	4a. olive-green	40·00
Z70	4a.6p. yellow-green	12·00
Z71	8a. dull mauve	24·00
Z72	12a. purple/red	85·00
Z73	1r. slate	18·00

1891. (No. 102).
Z74	2½a. on 4a.6p. yellow-green	9·00

1892–95. (Nos. 103/6).
Z75	2a.6p. yellow-green	6·00

OFFICIAL STAMPS

1867–73. (Nos. O20/30a).
Z75a	4a. green	£550

1874–82. (Nos. O31/71).
Z76	½a. blue	£100
Z77	1a. brown	£160
Z78	2a. yellow	£350

Z 6   Z 7

Stamps of INDIA cancelled with Type Z **6**, inscribed "REG" (registration) or "PAR" (parcel) (1888–95).

1876. (Nos. 80/2).
Z80	6a. pale brown	30·00
Z80a	12a. Venetian red	£250

1882–90. (Nos. 84/101).
Z81	½a. blue-green	45·00
Z82	9p. aniline carmine	£100
Z83	1a. brown-purple	10·00
Z84	1a.6p. sepia	15·00
Z85	2a. blue	16·00
Z86	3a. orange	30·00
Z87	3a. brown-orange	25·00
Z88	4a. olive-green	17·00
Z89	4a.6p. yellow-green	32·00
Z90	8a. dull mauve	28·00
Z91	12a. purple/red	95·00
Z92	1r. slate	24·00

1891. (No. 102).
Z93	2½a. on 4a.6p. yellow-green	38·00

1892–95. (Nos. 103/6).
Z94	2a.6p. yellow-green	20·00

Stamps of INDIA cancelled with Type Z **7** (1894–95).

1876. (Nos. 80/2).
Z95	6a. pale brown	£120

1882–90. (Nos. 84/101).
Z100	½a. blue-green	32·00
Z101	9p. aniline carmine	£140
Z102	1a. brown-purple	40·00
Z103	1a.6p. sepia	95·00
Z104	2a. blue	32·00
Z105	3a. brown-orange	95·00
Z106	4a. olive-green	95·00
Z107	8a. dull mauve	£110
Z108	12a. purple/red	£140
Z109	1r. slate	£130

1892–95. (Nos. 103/6).
Z110	2a.6p. yellow-green	19·00

1895. (Nos. 107/9).
Z111	2r. carmine and yellow-brown	£800

A French post office was opened on the island on 1 February 1889 and this service used the stamps of FRANCE until 1894 when specific stamps for this office were provided. The French postal service on the island closed on 31 July 1904 and it is known that French stamps were again utilised during the final month.

A German postal agency operated in Zanzibar between 27 August 1890 and 31 July 1891, using stamps of GERMANY.

PRICES FOR STAMPS ON COVER TO 1945
Nos. 1/2	—
Nos. 3/16	from × 30
No. 17	from × 8
No. 18	from × 25
Nos. 19/21	—
No. 22	from × 40
Nos. 23/5	from × 25
No. 26	from × 40
Nos. 27/40	—
Nos. 41/6	from × 25
Nos. 156/68	from × 15
Nos. 169/77	
Nos. 178/87	from × 20
Nos. 188/204	from × 15
Nos. 205/9	from × 20
Nos. 210/38	from × 15
Nos. 239/45	—
Nos. 246/59	from × 8
Nos. 260/f	
Nos. 261/330	from × 4
Nos. D1/3	from × 8
No. D4	from × 1
No. D5	from × 15
No. D6	—
No. D7	from × 1
Nos. D8/12	from × 15
No. D13	from × 1
No. D14	—
Nos. D15/16	from × 6
No. D17	from × 4
Nos. D18/24	from × 15
Nos. D25/30	from × 30

PROTECTORATE
(Currency. 12 pies = 1 anna. 16 annas = 1 rupee)

Zanzibar
(1)

1895 (14 Nov)–**96**. Nos. 81, 85, 90/6, 98/101, 103 and 106/9 of India (Queen Victoria) optd with T **1** by *Zanzibar Gazette*.

(a) In blue

1		½a. blue-green	£25000	£5500
2		1a. plum	£3000	£500
		j. "Zanzidar" (R. 4/6, 8/5)	†	£25000

(b) In black

3		½a. blue-green	4·50	5·00
		j. "Zanzidar" (R. 4/6, 8/5)	£1300	£700
		k. "Zanibar" (R. 7/2)	£1300	£1700
		l. Diaeresis over last "a" (R. 10/5)	£2000	£2000
		m. Opt double, one albino	£225	
4		1a. plum	4·75	3·75
		j. "Zanzidar" (R. 4/6, 8/5)	—	£3500
		k. "Zanibar" (R. 7/2)	£1700	£2000
		l. Diaeresis over last "a" (R. 10/5)	£4750	
5		1a.6p. sepia	5·00	4·75
		j. "Zanzidar" (R. 4/6, 8/5)	£4000	£1200
		k. "Zanibar" (R. 7/2)	£1600	£1700
		l. "Zanzibar" (R. 1/9)		
		m. Diaeresis over last "a" (R. 10/5)	£1600	
6		2a. pale blue	9·50	8·50
7		2a. blue	10·00	9·00
		j. "Zanzidar" (R. 4/6, 8/5)	£7500	£3000
		k. "Zanibar" (R. 7/2)	£6000	£2750
		l. Diaeresis over last "a"	£3000	
		m. Opt double	£275	
		n. Opt double, one albino	£275	
8		2½a. yellow-green	9·00	5·00
		j. "Zanzidar" (R. 4/6, 8/5)	£7500	£1800
		k. "Zanibar" (R. 7/2)	£700	£1400
		l. "Zapzibar"		
		n. Diaeresis over last "a" (R.10/5)	£2500	£1900
		o. Second "z" italic (R. 10/1)	£450	£650
		p. Opt double, one albino	£275	
10		3a. brown-orange	12·00	17·00
		j. "Zanzidar" (R. 4/6, 8/5)	£1000	£1900
		k. "Zanzibar" (R. 1/9)	£6500	£7000
11		4a. olive-green	20·00	18·00
		j. "Zanzidar" (R. 4/6, 8/5)	£10000	£4250
12		4a. slate-green	21·00	24·00
		l. Diaeresis over last "a" (R. 10/5)	£5000	
		m. Opt double, one albino		
13		6a. pale brown	20·00	11·00
		j. "Zanzidar" (R. 4/6, 8/5)	£10000	£4250
		k. "Zanibar" (R. 7/2)	£800	£1400
		l. "Zanzibarr"	£6500	£5000
		m. Opt double		
		n. Opt double, one albino	£170	
		o. Opt triple, two albino	£225	
14		8a. dull mauve	48·00	28·00
		j. "Zanzidar" (R. 4/6, 8/5)	£10000	£8000
15		8a. magenta (6.96)	25·00	30·00
		l. Diaeresis over last "a" (R. 10/5)	£8000	
16		12a. purple/*red*	18·00	11·00
		j. "Zanzidar" (R.4/6, 8/5)	£10000	£4500
17		1r. slate	£130	90·00
		j. "Zanzidar" (R 4/6, 8/5)	£9500	£6000
18		1r. green and aniline carmine (7.96)	21·00	40·00
		j. Opt vert downwards	£425	
19		2r. carmine and yellow-brown	£110	£120
		j. "r" omitted	£28000	
		k. "r" inverted	£4000	£5000
20		3r. brown and green	95·00	£100
		j. "r" omitted	£28000	
		k. "r" inverted	£6000	£6000
		l. Opt double, one albino	£1600	
21		5r. ultramarine and violet	£100	£130
		j. "r" omitted	£28000	
		k. "r" inverted	£4750	£7500
		l. Opt double, one inverted	£850	
		m. Opt double, one albino	£1600	
3/21 *Set of 15*			£500	£500

Forged examples of the blue overprints, Nos. 1/2, can be found on piece with genuine cancellations as type Z **7**, dated "13 FE 97".

There were a number of different settings for this overprint. Values to 1r. were initially overprinted from settings of 120 (12×10) including one which showed "Zanzidar" on R. 4/6 and R. 8/5 (soon corrected) and "Zanzibar" on R. 1/9 (also soon corrected). Later supplies of these values were overprinted from settings of 80 (8×10) for the 6a. only or 60 (6×10) for the others. One of these settings included "Zanibar" on R. 7/2. Another late setting, size unknown, showed a diaeresis over last "a" on R. 10/5.

Many forgeries of this overprint exist and also bogus errors.

MINOR VARIETIES. The following minor varieties of type exist on Nos. 1/21:

A. First "Z" antique (sloping serifs) (all values)
B. Broken "p" for "n" (all values to 1r.)
C. Tall second "z" (all values)
D. Small second "z" (all values)
E. Small second "z" and inverted "q" for "b" (all values)
F. Second "z" Gothic (lower limb bent upwards) (½a. to 12a. and 1r.) (No. 18) (black opts only)
G. No dot over "i" (all values to 1r.)
H. Inverted "q" for "b" (all values to 1r.)
I. Arabic "2" for "r" (all values to 1r.) (black opts only)

Varieties D and E are worth the same as normal examples, A (2, 3, 5r.) and C normal plus 50%, G and I from 3 times normal, A (values to 1r.), F and H from 4 times normal and B from 5 times normal.

2½ **(2)**	2½ **(3)**	2½ **(4)**	2½ **(5)**	

1895–98. Provisionals.

I. Stamps used for postal purposes
(a) No. 5 surch in red (30.11.95)

22	**2**	2½ on 1½a. sepia	75·00	55·00
		j. "Zanzibar"	£1600	£1300
		k. "Zanzibar"	£4750	£1900
		l. Inverted "1" in "½"	£1100	£900

(b) No. 4 surch in black (11.5.96)

23	**3**	2½ on 1a. plum	£180	£100
24	**4**	2½ on 1a. plum	£475	£275
		j. Inverted "1" in "½"	£2750	
25	**5**	2½ on 1a. plum	£200	£110

2½ **(6)**	2½ **(7)**	2½ **(8)**

(c) No. 6 surch in red (15.8.96)

26	**6**	2½ on 2a. pale blue	70·00	42·00
		j. Inverted "1" in "½"	£450	£275
		k. Roman "I" in "½"	£250	£160
		l. "Zanzibar" double, one albino	£160	
		m. "Zanzibar" triple, two albino	£300	
27	**7**	2½ on 2a. pale blue	£190	£110
		j. "2" of "½" omitted	£16000	
		k. "2" for "2½"	£24000	
		l. "1" of "½" omitted	£16000	£6500
		m. Inverted "1" in "½"	£3500	£1700
		n. "Zanzibar" double, one albino	£500	
28	**8**	2½ on 2a. pale blue	£500	£2500

No. 28 only exists with small "z" and occurs on R. 2/2 in the setting of 60.

(d) No. 5 surch in red (15.11.96)

29	**6**	2½ on 1½a. sepia	£180	£180
		j. Inverted "1 in "½"	£1500	£1200
		k. Roman "I" in "½"	£900	£900
		l. Surch double, one albino	£350	
30	**7**	2½ on 1½a. sepia	£425	£400
		j. Surch double, one albino	£800	
31	**8**	2½ on 1½a. sepia	£24000	£17000

No. 31 only exists with small "z" and occurs on R. 2/2 in the setting of 60.

II. Stamps prepared for official purposes. Nos. 4, 5 and 7 surch as before in red (1.98).

32	**3**	2½ on 1a. plum	£250	£700
33	**4**	2½ on 1a. plum	£450	£1000
34	**5**	2½ on 1a. plum	£275	£700
35	**3**	2½ on 1½a. sepia	90·00	£250
		j. Diaeresis over last "a"	£8000	
36	**4**	2½ on 1½a. sepia	£225	£600
37	**5**	2½ on 1½a. sepia	£130	£350
		j. "b" and "r" of "Zanzibar" inserted by hand	£2250	
38	**3**	2½ on 2a. dull blue	£140	£350
39	**4**	2½ on 2a. dull blue	£325	£650
40	**5**	2½ on 2a. dull blue	£160	£425

It is doubtful whether Nos. 32/40 were issued to the public.

1896. Nos. 65/6, 68 and 71/3 of British East Africa (Queen Victoria), optd with T **1**.

41		½a. yellow-green (23.5)	42·00	24·00
42		1a. carmine-rose (1.6)	45·00	17·00
		j. Opt double	£750	£900
		k. Opt double, one albino	£325	
43		2½a. deep blue (R.) (24.5)	90·00	48·00
		j. Inverted "S" in "ANNAS" (R. 1/1)	£1200	£750
44		4½a. orange-yellow (12.8)	50·00	60·00
45		5a. yellow-bistre (12.8)	65·00	40·00
		j. "r" omitted	—	£4000
46		7½a. mauve (12 Aug)	55·00	65·00
41/6 *Set of 6*			£300	£225

MINOR VARIETIES. The various minor varieties of type detailed in the note below No. 21 also occur on Nos. 22 to 46 as indicated below:

A. Nos. 23, 25, 27, 30, 35, 38, 41/6
B. Nos. 22/3, 26, 29/30, 32/3, 36, 39, 44/6
C. Nos. 22, 25/6, 32, 36, 38, 40/6
D. Nos. 22/46
E. Nos. 22/46
F. Nos. 22, 25/6, 29, 41/6
G. Nos. 25/6, 29, 35, 37/8, 40/6
H. Nos. 22, 41/6 (on the British East Africa stamps this variety occurs in the same position as variety C)
I. Nos. 26, 29, 35, 38, 41/6

The scarcity of these varieties on the surcharges (Nos. 22/40) is similar to those on the basic stamps, but examples on the British East Africa values (Nos. 41/6) are more common.

PRINTERS. All Zanzibar stamps up to Type **37** were printed by De La Rue & Co.

12

13

14 Sultan Seyyid Hamad-bin-Thwain

No right serif to left-hand "4" (R. 1/1)

No fraction bar at right (R. 2/1)

1896 (Dec). Recess. Flags in red on all values. W **12**. P 14.

156	**13**	½a. yellow-green	4·00	2·50
157		1a. indigo	4·00	1·75
158		1a. violet-blue	7·00	4·50
159		2a. red-brown	4·50	75
160		2½a. bright blue	16·00	1·50
161		2½a. pale blue	18·00	1·50
162		3a. grey	19·00	10·00
163		3a. bluish grey	22·00	12·00
164		4a. myrtle-green	13·00	6·00
165		4½a. orange	8·00	8·00
		a. No right serif to left-hand "4"	£275	£275
		b. No fraction bar at right (R. 2/1)	£275	£275
166		5a. bistre	9·00	5·50
		a. Bisected (2½a.) (on cover)	†	£4500
167		7½a. mauve	8·00	8·00
168		8a. grey-olive	11·00	8·50
169	**14**	1r. blue	25·00	9·00
170		1r. deep blue	38·00	14·00
171		2r. green	30·00	9·50
172		3r. dull purple	32·00	9·50
173		4r. lake	25·00	13·00
174		5r. sepia	32·00	13·00
156/74 *Set of 15*			£200	95·00
156s/74s *Optd "SPECIMEN" Set of 15*			£275	

The ½, 1, 2, 2½, 3 and 8a. are known without wmk, these being from edges of the sheets.

1897 (5 Jan). No. 164 surch as before, in red by the *Zanzibar Gazette*.

175	**3**	2½ on 4a. myrtle-green	90·00	55·00
176	**4**	2½ on 4a. myrtle-green	£300	£275
177	**5**	2½ on 4a. myrtle-green	£110	80·00
175/7 *Set of 3*			£450	£375

There are two settings of the surcharge, the first comprised 26 of Type **3**, 10 of Type **4** and 24 of Type **5**. The composition of the second setting is unknown.

18

1898 (Apr). Recess. W **18**. P 14.

178	**13**	½a. yellow-green	1·50	35
179		1a. indigo	5·50	1·25
		a. Greenish black	7·00	1·50
180		2a. red-brown	10·00	2·00
		a. Deep brown	12·00	2·00
181		2½a. bright blue	5·00	30
182		3a. grey	9·00	1·00
183		4a. myrtle-green	3·75	1·75
184		4½a. orange	16·00	1·25
		a. No right serif to left-hand "4"	£375	£100
		b. No fraction bar at right (R. 2/1)	£375	£100
185		5a. bistre	21·00	2·25
		a. Pale bistre	23·00	2·75
186		7½a. mauve	20·00	2·75
187		8a. grey-olive	22·00	3·00
178/87 *Set of 10*			£100	14·00

19

20 Sultan Seyyid Hamoud-bin-Mohammed bin Said

1899 (June)–**1901**. Recess. Flags in red. W **18** (Nos. 188/99) or W **12** (others). P 14.

188	**19**	½a. yellow-green	2·75	60
		a. Wmk sideways	25·00	8·50
189		1a. indigo	4·50	20
		a. Wmk sideways	50·00	2·25
190		1a. carmine (1901)	4·50	20
191		2a. red-brown	5·50	1·50
192		2½a. bright blue	5·50	1·00
193		3a. grey	7·50	3·00
194		4a. myrtle-green	7·50	3·75
195		4½a. orange	18·00	10·00
196		4½a. blue-black (1901)	21·00	15·00
197		5a. bistre	8·00	3·25
198		7½a. mauve	8·00	9·00
199		8a. grey-olive	8·00	7·00
200	**20**	1r. blue	25·00	15·00
201		2r. green	28·00	24·00
202		3r. dull purple	50·00	50·00
203		4r. lake	60·00	75·00
204		5r. sepia	80·00	£100
188/204 *Set of 17*			£300	£275
188s/204s *Optd "SPECIMEN" Set of 17*			£325	

Two & One **(21)**	Two & Half **(22)**	Two & Half **(22a)** Thin open "w" (R. 2/2, 3/4)	Two & Half **(22b)** Serif to foot of "f" (R. 3/1)

1904 (June). Nos. 194/6 and 198/9 surch as T **21** and **22**, in black or lake (L.) by *Zanzibar Gazette* in setting of 30 (6×5).

205	**19**	1 on 4½a. orange	4·00	6·50
206		1 on 4½a. blue-black (L.)	6·50	18·00
207		2 on 4a. myrtle-green (L.)	14·00	18·00

208		2½ on 7½a. mauve	17·00	24·00
	a.	Opt Type **22a**	90·00	£110
	b.	Opt Type **22b**	£150	£190
	c.	"Hlaf" for "Half"	£16000	
209		2½ on 8a. grey-olive	30·00	40·00
	a.	Opt Type **22a**	£150	£180
	b.	Opt Type **22b**	£250	£300
	c.	"Hlaf" for "Half"	£15000	£10000
205/9 *Set of 5*			65·00	95·00

23 **24**

Monogram of Sultan Seyyid Ali bin Hamoud bin Naherud

1904 (8 June). Typo. Background of centre in second colour. W **18**. P 14.

210	**23**	½a. green	2·75	50
211		1a. rose-red	2·75	10
212		2a. brown	5·00	45
213		2½a. blue	4·75	35
214		3a. grey	6·00	2·25
215		4a. deep green	4·50	1·60
216		4½a. black	5·50	2·50
217		5a. yellow-brown	7·00	3·00
218		7½a. purple	8·50	8·00
219		8a. olive-green	6·50	6·50
220	**24**	1r. blue and red	38·00	28·00
	a.	Wmk sideways	£100	35·00
221		2r. green and red	45·00	50·00
	a.	Wmk sideways	£275	£375
222		3r. violet and red	65·00	95·00
223		4r. claret and red	70·00	£110
224		5r. olive-brown and red	70·00	£110
210/24 *Set of 15*			£300	£375
210s/24s Optd "SPECIMEN" *Set of 15*			£200	

25 **26**

27 Sultan Ali bin Hamoud **28** View of Port

1908 (May)–**09**. Recess. W **18** (sideways on 10r. to 30r.). P 14.

225	**25**	1c. pearl-grey (10.09)	2·25	30
226		3c. yellow-green	16·00	10
	a.	Wmk sideways	9·00	1·25
227		6c. rose-carmine	11·00	10
	a.	Wmk sideways	13·00	3·00
228		10c. brown (10.09)	7·00	2·75
229		12c. violet	19·00	3·75
	a.	Wmk sideways	16·00	1·25
230	**26**	15c. ultramarine	21·00	40
	a.	Wmk sideways	20·00	6·50
231		25c. sepia	8·50	1·00
232		50c. blue-green	12·00	8·50
233		75c. grey-black (10.09)	16·00	19·00
234	**27**	1r. yellow-green	50·00	12·00
	a.	Wmk sideways	£120	15·00
235		2r. violet	24·00	20·00
	a.	Wmk sideways	£300	80·00
236		3r. orange-bistre	42·00	60·00
237		4r. vermilion	70·00	£110
238		5r. steel-blue	75·00	75·00
239	**28**	10r. blue-green and brown	£225	£375
	s.	Optd "SPECIMEN"	70·00	
240		20r. black and yellow-green	£650	£850
	s.	Optd "SPECIMEN"	£100	
241		30r. black and sepia	£750	£1100
	a.	Wmk upright		
	s.	Optd "SPECIMEN"	£120	
242		40r. black and orange-brown	£950	
	s.	Optd "SPECIMEN"	£150	
243		50r. black and mauve	£850	
	s.	Optd "SPECIMEN"	£150	
244		100r. black and steel-blue	£1300	
	s.	Optd "SPECIMEN"	£200	
245		200r. brown and greenish black	£1800	
	s.	Optd "SPECIMEN"	£275	
225/38 *Set of 14*			£325	£275
225s/38s Optd "SPECIMEN" *Set of 14*			£325	

The 3, 6, 12, 15c. "SPECIMEN" always show wmk sideways.

29 Sultan Khalifa bin Harub **30** Sailing Canoe

---

31 Dhow

1913. Recess. W **18** (sideways on 75c. and 10r. to 200r.). P 14.

246	**29**	1c. grey	40	75
247		3c. yellow-green	1·50	75
248		6c. rose-carmine	1·75	20
249		10c. brown	1·25	3·75
250		12c. violet	1·50	75
251		15c. blue	4·00	1·00
252		25c. sepia	1·50	3·00
253		50c. blue-green	4·75	8·00
254		75c. grey-black	3·00	7·00
	a.	Wmk upright	£150	
	as.	Optd "SPECIMEN"	95·00	
255	**30**	1r. yellow-green	28·00	20·00
256		2r. violet	22·00	40·00
257		3r. orange-bistre	27·00	65·00
258		4r. scarlet	42·00	90·00
259		5r. steel-blue	55·00	55·00
260	**31**	10r. green and brown	£225	£425
260b		20r. black and brown	£375	£700
	bs.	Optd "SPECIMEN"	90·00	
260c		30r. black and brown	£400	£850
	cs.	Optd "SPECIMEN"	90·00	
260d		40r. black and vermilion	£700	£1100
	ds.	Optd "SPECIMEN"	£160	
260e		50r. black and purple	£700	£1200
	es.	Optd "SPECIMEN"	£150	
260f		100r. black and blue	£950	
	fs.	Optd "SPECIMEN"	£180	
260g		200r. brown and black	£1400	
	gs.	Optd "SPECIMEN"	£225	
246/60 *Set of 15*			£350	£650
246s/60as Optd "SPECIMEN" *Set of 15*			£375	

1914–22. Wmk Mult Crown CA (sideways on 10r.). P 14.

261	**29**	1c. grey	80	25
		w. Wmk inverted	†	£450
262		3c. yellow-green	1·25	10
		a. Dull green	9·50	20
		w. Wmk inverted	†	£300
263		6c. deep carmine	1·25	20
		a. Bright rose-carmine	1·00	10
		aw. Wmk inverted	†	£300
		ay. Wmk inverted and reversed	†	£350
264		8c. purple/*pale yellow* (1922)	1·50	7·50
265		10c. myrtle/*pale yellow* (1922)	85	30
266		15c. deep ultramarine	1·75	8·50
268		50c. blue-green	5·00	8·00
269		75c. grey-black	3·00	38·00
270	**30**	1r. yellow-green	5·50	3·75
271		2r. violet	19·00	20·00
272		3r. orange-bistre	27·00	50·00
273		4r. scarlet	32·00	85·00
		y. Wmk inverted and reversed	£275	
274		5r. steel-blue	17·00	65·00
		w. Wmk inverted	£275	
275	**31**	10r. green and brown	£225	£750
261/75 *Set of 14*			£300	£950
261s/75s Optd "SPECIMEN" *Set of 14*			£375	

1921–29. Wmk Mult Script CA (sideways on 10r. to 30r.). P 14.

276	**29**	1c. slate-grey	30	12·00
		x. Wmk reversed	£300	
277		3c. yellow-green	4·25	7·50
278		3c. orange-yellow (1922)	40	10
		w. Wmk inverted		
279		4c. green (1922)	60	3·00
280		6c. carmine-red	40	50
		w. Wmk inverted	£325	
		x. Wmk reversed	†	£425
281		6c. purple/*blue* (1922)	45	10
		w. Wmk inverted	†	£425
282		10c. brown	80	16·00
283		12c. violet	50	30
		w. Wmk inverted		
284		12c. carmine-red (1922)	50	40
285		15c. blue	65	15·00
286		20c. indigo (1922)	1·00	30
287		25c. sepia	1·00	32·00
288		50c. myrtle-green	4·00	8·50
		y. Wmk inverted and reversed	£200	£300
289		75c. slate	2·50	65·00
290	**30**	1r. yellow-green	7·00	3·50
291		2r. deep violet	3·50	17·00
292		3r. orange-bistre	6·50	7·50
293		4r. scarlet	12·00	48·00
294		5r. Prussian blue	26·00	75·00
		w. Wmk inverted	£350	
295	**31**	10r. green and brown	£225	£500
296		20r. black and green	£425	£800
		s. Optd "SPECIMEN"	£150	
297		30r. black and brown (1929)	£350	£750
		s. Perf "SPECIMEN"	£150	
276/95 *Set of 20*			£275	£750
276s/95s Optd "SPECIMEN" *Set of 20*			£425	

32 Sultan Khalifa bin Harub **33**

1926–27. T **32** ("CENTS" in serifed capitals). Recess. Wmk Mult Script CA. P 14.

299	**32**	1c. brown	1·00	10
300		3c. yellow-orange	30	15
301		4c. deep dull green	30	1·00

302		6c. violet	30	10
303		8c. slate	1·00	4·50
304		10c. olive-green	1·00	40
305		12c. carmine-red	3·00	10
306		20c. bright blue	60	30
307		25c. purple/*yellow* (1927)	16·00	2·50
308		50c. claret	4·75	35
309		75c. sepia (1927)	38·00	42·00
299/309 *Set of 11*			60·00	45·00
299s/309s Optd "SPECIMEN" *Set of 11*			£200	

(New Currency. 100 cents = 1 shilling)

1936 (1 Jan). T **33** ("CENTS" in sans-serif capitals), and T **30/1**, but values in shillings. Recess. Wmk Mult Script CA. P 14×13½–14.

310	**33**	5c. green	10	10
311		10c. black	15	10
312		15c. carmine-red	20	1·25
313		20c. orange	20	10
314		25c. purple/*yellow*	20	10
315		30c. ultramarine	20	10
316		40c. sepia	20	20
317		50c. claret	30	10
318	**30**	1s. yellow-green	75	10
319		2s. slate-violet	4·00	1·75
320		5s. scarlet	26·00	6·50
321		7s.50 light blue	45·00	42·00
322	**31**	10s. green and brown	45·00	32·00
310/22 *Set of 13*			£110	75·00
310s/22s Perf "SPECIMEN" *Set of 13*			£250	

Nos. 310/22 remained current until 1952 and the unused prices are therefore for unmounted examples.

36 Sultan Khalifa bin Harub

1936 (9 Dec). Silver Jubilee of Sultan. Recess. Wmk Mult Script CA. P 14.

323	**36**	10c. black and olive-green	3·25	30
324		20c. black and bright purple	4·50	2·75
325		30c. black and deep ultramarine	15·00	1·00
326		50c. black and orange-vermilion	15·00	7·00
323/6 *Set of 4*			35·00	10·00
323s/6s Perf "SPECIMEN" *Set of 4*			£120	

37 Sham Alam (Sultan's dhow) **(38)**

1944 (20 Nov). Bicentenary of Al Busaid Dynasty. Recess. Wmk Mult Script CA. P 14.

327	**37**	10c. ultramarine	1·00	5·50
	a.	"C" of "CA" missing from wmk	£800	
328		20c. red	1·50	3·75
	a.	"C" of "CA" missing from wmk	£800	
329		50c. blue-green	1·50	30
	a.	"A" of "CA" missing from wmk	—	£850
330		1s. dull purple	1·50	1·50
	a.	"A" of "CA" missing from wmk	£950	
327/30 *Set of 4*			5·00	10·00
327s/30s Perf "SPECIMEN" *Set of 4*			£120	

1946 (11 Nov). Victory. Nos. 311 and 315 optd with T **38**.

331	**33**	10c. black (R.)	20	50
332		30c. ultramarine (R.)	30	50
331s/2s Perf "SPECIMEN" *Set of 2*			90·00	

1949 (10 Jan). Royal Silver Wedding. As Nos. 112/13 of Antigua.

333		20c. orange	30	1·50
334		10s. brown	25·00	40·00

1949 (10–13 Oct). 75th Anniv of UPU. As Nos. 114/17 of Antigua.

335		20c. red-orange (13.10)	30	4·00
336		30c. deep blue	1·75	2·50
	a.	"C" of "CA" missing from wmk	£900	
337		50c. magenta	1·00	3·25
	a.	"A" of "CA" missing from wmk	£900	
338		1s. blue-green (13.10)	1·00	4·50
335/8 *Set of 4*			3·50	13·00

39 Sultan Khalifa bin Harub **40** Seyyid Khalifa Schools, Beit-el-Ras

1952 (26 Aug)–**55**. Wmk Mult Script CA. P 12½ (cent values) or 13 (shilling values).

339	**39**	5c. black	10	10
340		10c. red-orange	10	10
341		15c. green	2·75	3·75
		a. Yellow-green (12.11.53)	6·00	3·75

342		20c. carmine-red	75	70
343		25c. reddish purple	1·00	10
344		30c. deep bluish green	1·25	10
	a.	Deep green (29.3.55)	16·00	4·75
345		35c. bright blue	1·25	4·00
346		40c. deep brown	1·25	1·25
	a.	Sepia (12.11.53)	6·00	2·00
347		50c. violet	3·50	10
	a.	Deep violet (29.3.55)	8·00	1·00
348	40	1s. deep green and deep brown	60	10
349		2s. bright blue and deep purple	3·00	2·50
350		5s. black and carmine-red	3·50	9·00
351		7s.50 grey-black and emerald	28·00	26·00
352		10s. carmine-red and black	10·00	18·00
339/52	Set of 14		50·00	60·00

41 Sultan Khalifa bin Harub

(Photo Harrison)

1954 (26 Aug). Sultan's 75th Birthday. Wmk Mult Script CA. Chalk-surfaced paper. P 13×12.

353	41	15c. deep green	15	10
354		20c. rose-red	15	10
355		30c. bright blue	20	10
356		50c. purple	30	10
357		1s.25 orange-red	30	75
353/7	Set of 5		1·00	1·00

42 Cloves

43 Urnmoja Wema (dhow)

44 Sultan's Barge

45 Map of East African Coast

46 Minaret Mosque

47 Dimbani Mosque

48 Kibweni Palace

(Des W. J. Jennings (T 42), A. Farhan (T 43), Mrs. M. Broadbent (T 44, 46), R. A. Sweet (T 45), A. S. B. New (T 47), B. J. Woolley (T 48). Recess B.W.)

1957 (26 Aug). W w **12**. P 11½ (5c., 10c.), 11×11½ (15c., 30c., 1s.25), 14×13½ (20c., 25c., 35c., 50c.,), 13½×14 (40c., 1s., 2s.) or 13×13½ (5s., 7s.50, 10s.).

358	42	5c. orange and deep green	10	40
359		10c. emerald and carmine-red	10	10
360	43	15c. green and sepia	30	2·75
361	44	20c. ultramarine	15	10
362	45	25c. orange-brown and black	45	1·25
363	43	30c. carmine-red and black	20	1·25
364	45	35c. slate and emerald	45	20
365	46	40c. brown and black	15	10
366	45	50c. blue and grey-green	60	30
367	47	1s. carmine and black	20	30
368	43	1s.25 slate and carmine	3·50	20
369	47	2s. orange and deep green	4·00	2·25
370	48	5s. deep bright blue	5·00	2·00
371		7s.50 green	17·00	4·00
372		10s. carmine	17·00	6·50
358/72	Set of 15		45·00	19·00

The 10c. exists from coils made up from normal sheets.

49 Sultan Seyyid Sir Abdullah bin Khalifa

50 "Protein Foods"

(Recess B.W.)

1961 (17 Oct). As T 42/8, but with portrait of Sultan Sir Abdullah as in T 49. W w **12**. P 13×13½ (20s.), others as before.

373	49	5c. orange and deep green	50	1·25
374	43	10c. emerald and carmine-red	40	1·75
375	43	15c. green and sepia	75	3·75
376	44	20c. ultramarine	40	30
377	45	25c. orange-brown and black	2·50	1·75
378	43	30c. carmine-red and black	3·00	3·25

379	45	35c. slate and emerald	3·75	5·50
380	46	40c. brown and black	40	20
381	45	50c. blue and grey-green	4·00	2·00
382	47	1s. carmine and black	50	1·50
383	43	1s.25 slate and carmine	4·00	8·00
384	47	2s. orange and deep green	1·00	4·50
385	48	5s. deep bright blue	3·50	13·00
386		7s.50 green	3·50	22·00
387		10s. carmine	4·50	13·00
388		20s. sepia	17·00	28·00
373/88	Set of 16		42·00	95·00

The 10c. exists from coils made up from normal sheets.

(Des M. Goaman. Photo Harrison)

1963 (4 June). Freedom from Hunger. W w **12**. P 14×14½.

389	50	1s.30 sepia	1·25	75

INDEPENDENT

51 Zanzibar Clove

53 "Religious Tolerance" (mosques and churches)

(Photo Harrison)

1963 (10 Dec). Independence. Portrait of Sultan Seyyid Jamshid bin Abdullah. T **51**, **53** and similar vert designs. P 12½.

390		30c. multicoloured	25	1·25
391		50c. multicoloured	25	1·00
392		1s.30, multicoloured	25	4·00
393		2s.50, multicoloured	35	4·75
	a.	Green omitted	†	£700
390/3	Set of 4		1·00	10·00

Designs:—50c. "To Prosperity" (Zanzibar doorway); 2s.50, "Towards the Light" (Mangapwani Cave).

REPUBLIC

When the Post Office opened on 14 January 1964, after the revolution deposing the Sultan, the stamps on sale had the portrait cancelled by a manuscript cross. Stamps thus cancelled *on cover* or *piece* used between January 14 and 17 are therefore of interest.

JAMHURI 1964

(55= "Republic")

1964 (17 Jan). Locally handstamped as T **55** in black.

(i) Nos. 373/88

394	49	5c. orange and deep green	1·25	65
395		10c. emerald and carmine-red	1·25	10
396	43	15c. green and sepia	2·50	2·75
397	44	20c. ultramarine	1·75	1·25
398	45	25c. orange-brown and black	2·75	20
399	43	30c. carmine-red and black	1·50	60
400	45	35c. slate and emerald	2·75	1·50
401	46	40c. brown and black	1·75	1·50
402	45	50c. blue and grey-green	2·75	10
403	47	1s. carmine and black	1·50	1·00
404	43	1s.25 slate and carmine	1·25	2·50
405	47	2s. orange and deep green	2·00	2·00
406	48	5s. deep bright blue	1·75	1·75
407		7s.50 green	2·00	1·75
408		10s. carmine	2·00	1·75
409		20s. sepia	2·50	7·00

(ii) Nos. 390/3 (Independence)

410		30c. multicoloured	1·00	3·00
411		50c. multicoloured	60	1·50
412		1s.30 multicoloured	1·25	2·00
413		2s.50 multicoloured	1·40	4·00
	a.	Green omitted	£425	
394/413	Set of 20		32·00	32·00

T **55** occurs in various positions—diagonally, horizontally or vertically.

NOTE. Nos. 394 to 413 are the only stamps officially authorised to receive the handstamp but it has also been seen on Nos. 353/7, 389 and the D25/30 Postage Dues. There are numerous errors such as inverted and double opts, and pairs, one without handstamp, but it is impossible to distinguish between cases of genuine oversight and those made deliberately at the request of purchasers.

JAMHURI

JAMHURI 1964
(56)

JAMHURI 1964
(57)

1964 (28 Feb). Optd by Bradbury Wilkinson.

(i) As T 56 on Nos. 373/88

414	49	5c. orange and deep green	10	10
415		10c. emerald and carmine-red	10	10
416	43	15c. green and sepia	20	10
417	44	20c. ultramarine	10	10
418	45	25c. orange-brown and black	30	10
419	43	30c. carmine-red and black	20	10
420	45	35c. slate and emerald	30	10
421	46	40c. brown and black	10	10
422	45	50c. blue and grey-green	30	10
423	47	1s. carmine and black	10	10
424	43	1s.25 slate and carmine	2·00	3·00
425	47	2s. orange and deep green	50	40
426	48	5s. deep bright blue	50	35
427		7s.50 green	65	7·00
428		10s. carmine	1·25	8·00
429		20s. sepia	2·25	8·00

The opt T **56** is set in two lines on Types **46/8**.
The 10c. exists from coils made up from normal sheets.

(ii) As T 57 on Nos. 390/3 (Independence)

430		30c. multicoloured	10	10
431		50c. multicoloured	10	10
432		1s.30, multicoloured	10	10
433		2s.50, multicoloured	15	65
	a.	Green omitted	£160	
414/33	Set of 20		8·00	25·00

The opt T **57** is set in one line on No. 432.
For the set inscribed "UNITED REPUBLIC OF TANGANYIKA AND ZANZIBAR" see Nos. 124/7 of Tanganyika.

58 Axe, Spear and Dagger

59 Zanzibari with Rifle

(Litho German Bank Note Ptg Co, Leipzig)

1964 (21 June). T **58/9** and similar designs inscr. "JAMHURI ZANZIBAR 1964". Multicoloured. P 13×13½ (vert) or 13½×13 (horiz).

434		5c. Type 58	20	10
435		10c. Bow and arrow breaking chains	30	10
436		15c. Type 58	30	10
437		20c. As 10c	50	10
438		25c. Type 59	50	10
439		30c. Zanzibari breaking manacles	30	10
440		40c. Type 59	50	10
441		50c. As 30c	30	10
442		1s. Zanzibari, flag and Sun	30	10
443		1s.30 Hands breaking chains (horiz)	30	1·75
444		2s. Hand waving flag (horiz)	30	30
445		5s. Map of Zanzibar and Pemba on flag (horiz)	1·00	5·50
446		10s. Flag on Map	4·75	7·50
447		20s. National Flag (horiz)	4·50	26·00
434/47	Set of 14		12·50	38·00

68 Soldier and Maps

69 Building Construction

(Litho German Bank Note Ptg Co, Leipzig)

1965 (12 Jan). First Anniv of Revolution. P 13×13½ (vert) or 13½×13 (horiz).

448	68	20c. apple-green and deep green	10	10
449	69	30c. chocolate and yellow-orange	10	10
450	68	1s.30 light blue and ultramarine	15	15
451	69	2s.50 reddish violet and rose	20	75
448/51	Set of 4		50	1·00

Type 68 is inscribed "PEMPA" in error for "PEMBA".

70 Planting Rice

(Litho German Bank Note Ptg Co, Leipzig)

1965 (17 Oct). Agricultural Development. T **70** and similar horiz design. P 13×12½.

452	70	20c. sepia and blue	10	1·00
453	–	30c. sepia and magenta	10	1·00
454	–	1s.30 sepia and yellow-orange	25	2·00
455	70	2s.50 sepia and emerald	35	7·00
452/5	Set of 4		70	10·00

Design:—30c., 1s.30, Hands holding rice.

72 Freighter, Tractor, Factory, and Open Book and Torch

73 Soldier

(Litho German Bank Note Ptg Co, Leipzig)

1966 (12 Jan). Second Anniv of Revolution. P 12½×13.

456	72	20c. multicoloured	25	20
457	73	50c. multicoloured	25	50
458	72	1s.30 multicoloured	30	30
459	73	2s.50 multicoloured	30	2·25
456/9	Set of 4		1·00	3·00

For stamps with similar inscription or inscribed "TANZANIA" only, and with commemorative date 26th April 1966, see Nos. Z142/5 of TANZANIA.

74 Tree-felling   **75** Zanzibar Street

(Litho German Bank Note Ptg Co, Leipzig)

1966 (5 June). Horiz designs as T **74**, and T **75**. P 12½×13 (50c., 10s.) or 13×12½ (others).

460	5c. maroon and yellow-olive	70	80
461	10c. brown-purple and bright emerald	70	80
462	15c. brown-purple and light blue	70	80
463	20c. ultramarine and light orange	40	20
464	25c. maroon and orange-yellow	40	30
465	30c. maroon and ochre-yellow	70	20
466	40c. purple-brown and rose-pink	80	20
467	50c. green and pale greenish yellow	80	20
468	1s. maroon and bright blue	80	20
469	1s. 30 maroon and turquoise	80	3·00
470	2s. brown-purple and light blue-green	80	40
471	5s. rose-red and pale blue	1·25	6·50
472	10s. crimson and pale yellow	2·25	18·00
473	20s. deep purple-brown and magenta	6·50	42·00
460/473	Set of 14	16·00	65·00

Designs:—5c., 20s. Type **74**; 10c., 1s. Clove cultivation; 15, 40c. Chair-making; 20c., 5s. Lumumba College; 25c., 4s. 30, Agriculture; 30c., 2s. Agricultural workers; 50c.,10s. Type **75**.

81 "Education"

(Litho D.L.R.)

1966 (25 Sept). Introduction of Free Education. P 13½×13.

474	**81**	50c. black, light blue and orange	10	1·00
475		1s.30 black, light blue and yellow-green	25	1·75
476		2s.50 black, light blue and pink	80	4·50
474/6		Set of 3	1·00	6·50

82 ASP Flag

(Litho D.L.R.)

1967 (5 Feb). Tenth Anniv of Afro-Shirazi Party (ASP). T **82** and similar multicoloured design. P 14.

477		30c. Type **82**	35	1·75
478		50c. Vice-President M. A. Karume of Tanzania, flag and crowd (vert)	20	1·00
479		1s.30 As 50c	35	2·25
480		2s.50 Type **82**	50	3·75
477/80		Set of 4	1·25	8·00

84 Voluntary Workers

(Photo Delrieu)

1967 (20 Aug). Voluntary Workers Brigade. P 12½×12.

481	**84**	1s.30 multicoloured	25	2·25
482		2s.50 multicoloured	75	5·50

POSTAGE DUE STAMPS

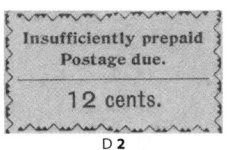

D **1**   D **2**

(Types D **1** and D **2** typo by the Government Printing Office)

1926–30. Rouletted 10, with imperf sheet edges. No gum.

D1	D **1**	1c. black/orange (1930)	11·00	£160
D2		2c. black/orange (1930)	4·50	85·00
D3		3c. black/orange (1929)	5·00	70·00
	a.	"cent.s" for "cents."	£160	£550
D4		6c. black/orange	—	£7000
	a.	"cent.s" for "cents."	†	£24000
D5		9c. black/orange (1929)	2·75	45·00
	a.	"cent.s" for "cents."	27·00	£200

D6		12c. black/orange (1929)	£15000	£12000
	a.	"cent.s" for "cents"	†	£21000
	b.	"I" of "Insufficiently" omitted (R. 3/2)	†	£21000
D7		12c. black/green	£1500	£600
	a.	"cent.s" for "cents."	£4000	£1700
D8		15c. black/orange (1929)	2·75	45·00
	a.	"cent.s" for "cents."	27·00	£200
D9		18c. black/salmon	5·50	60·00
	a.	"cent.s" for "cents."	55·00	£300
D10		18c. black/orange (1929)	29·00	90·00
	a.	"cent.s" for "cents."	85·00	£400
D11		20c. black/orange (1929)	4·50	80·00
	a.	"cent.s" for "cents."	55·00	£375
D12		21c. black/orange (1929)	3·50	55·00
	a.	"cent.s" for "cents."	48·00	£275
D13		25c. black/magenta	£2750	£1300
	a.	"cent.s" for "cents."	£7000	£4000
D14		25c. black/orange (1929)	£20000	£18000
D15		31c. black/orange (1929)	9·50	£130
	a.	"cent.s" for "cents."	70·00	£1200
D16		50c. black/orange (1929)	21·00	£275
	a.	"cent.s" for "cents."	£130	£1700
D17		75c. black/orange (1929)	80·00	£750
	a.	"cent.s" for "cents."	£300	

Initial printings, except the 1c. and 2c., contained the error "cent.s" for "cents" on R. 4/1 in the sheets of ten (2×5). The error was corrected on subsequent supplies of the 3c., 9c. and 15c.

It is known that examples of these stamps used before early 1929 were left uncancelled on the covers. Uncancelled examples of Nos. D4, D6/7 and D13/14 which are not in very fine condition, must be assumed to have been used.

1930–33. Rouletted 5. No gum.

D18	D **2**	2c. black/salmon (1932)	28·00	42·00
	a.	Wide space between "2" and "cents" (R. 1/2)	—	£325
D19		3c. black/rose (1933)	3·50	70·00
D21		6c. black/yellow	3·25	45·00
D22		12c. black/blue (1931)	4·50	32·00
D23		25c. black/rose	10·00	£150
D24		25c. black/lilac (1933)	30·00	90·00
D18/24		Set of 6	70·00	£375

The wide space variety No. D18a occurred only on one of the four printings of the 2c. value.

D **3**

(Typo D.L.R.)

1936 (1 Jan)–62. Wmk Mult Script CA. P 14.

D25	D **3**	5c. violet	8·50	14·00
	a.	Chalk-surfaced paper (18.7.56)	35	20·00
D26		10c. scarlet	7·50	2·75
	a.	Chalk-surfaced paper (6.3.62)	35	13·00
D27		20c. green	2·50	7·00
	a.	Chalk-surfaced paper (6.3.62)	35	30·00
D28		30c. brown	19·00	24·00
	a.	Chalk-surfaced paper (18.7.56)	35	14·00
D29		40c. ultramarine	10·00	29·00
	a.	Chalk-surfaced paper (18.7.56)	75	50·00
D30		1s. grey	16·00	38·00
	a.	Chalk-surfaced paper (18.7.56)	1·00	25·00
D25/30		Set of 6	55·00	£100
D25a/30a		Set of 6	2·75	£140
D25s/30s Perf "SPECIMEN" Set of 6			£140	

For postage due stamps handstamped "JAMHURI 1964", see note below No. 413.

All Zanzibar issues were withdrawn on 1 January 1968 and replaced by Tanzania issues. Zanzibar stamps remained valid for postage in Zanzibar for a limited period.

Zululand *see* **South Africa**

Set Prices for British Empire Omnibus Issues

The composition of these sets is in accordance with the tables on the following pages. Only such items considered basic stamps are included; varieties such as shades, perforation changes and watermark changes are excluded.

Stamps issued in connection with any of the events by countries which are no longer in the British Commonwealth and which are not listed in the Part 1 Catalogue are omitted.

1935 SILVER JUBILEE

		PRICE	
		Un	Used
1935. Silver Jubilee.			
Complete set of 250 stamps		£1500	£2000

Country	Catalogue Nos.	Stamps
Great Britain	453/6	4
Antigua	91/4	4
Ascension	31/4	4
Australia	156/8	3
Nauru	40/3	4
New Guinea	206/7	2
Papua	150/3	4
Bahamas	141/4	4
Barbados	241/4	4
Basutoland	11/14	4
Bechuanaland	111/14	4
Bermuda	94/7	4
British Guiana	301/4	4
British Honduras	143/6	4
British Solomon Islands	53/6	4
Canada	335/40	6
Newfoundland	250/3	4
Cayman Islands	108/11	4
Ceylon	379/82	4
Cyprus	144/7	4
Dominica	92/5	4
Egypt-British Forces	A10	1
Falkland Islands	139/42	4
Fiji	242/5	4
Gambia	143/6	4
Gibraltar	114/17	4
Gilbert and Ellice Islands	36/9	4
Gold Coast	113/16	4
Grenada	145/8	4
Hong Kong	133/6	4
India	240/6	7
Jamaica	114/17	4
Kenya, Uganda and Tanganyika	124/7	4
Leeward Islands	88/91	4
Malaya-Straits Settlements	256/9	4
Malta	210/13	4
Mauritius	245/8	4
Montserrat	94/7	4
Morocco Agencies		
British Currency	62/5	4
Spanish Currency	149/52	4
French Currency	212/15	4
Tangier	238/40	3
New Zealand	573/5	3
Cook Islands	113/15	3
Niue	69/71	3
Western Samoa	177/9	3
Nigeria	30/3	4
Northern Rhodesia	18/21	4
Nyasaland	123/6	4
St. Helena	124/7	4
St. Kitts-Nevis	61/4	4
St. Lucia	109/12	4
St. Vincent	142/5	4
Seychelles	128/31	4
Sierra Leone	181/4	4
Somaliland Protectorate	86/9	4
South Africa	65/8	4×2
Southern Rhodesia	31/4	4
South West Africa	88/91	4
Swaziland	21/4	4
Trinidad and Tobago	239/42	4
Turks and Caicos Islands	187/9	4
Virgin Islands	103/6	4
Total		**250**

The concept initiated by the 1935 Silver Jubilee omnibus issue has provided a pattern for a series of Royal commemoratives over the past 50 years which have introduced countless collectors to the hobby.

The Crown Colony Windsor Castle design by Hugo Fleury is, surely, one of the most impressive produced to the 20th-century and its reproduction in the recess process by three of the leading stamp-printing firms of the era has provided a subject for philatelic research which has yet to be exhausted.

Each of the three, Bradbury, Wilkinson & Co. and Waterlow and Sons, who both produced fifteen issues, together with De La Rue & Co. who printed fourteen, used a series of vignette (centre) plates coupled with individual frame plates for each value. All were taken from dies made by Waterlow. Several worthwhile varieties exist on the frame plates but most interest has been concentrated on the centre plates, each of which was used to print a considerable number of different stamps.

Sheets printed by Bradbury, Wilkinson were without printed plate numbers, but research has now identified twelve centre plates which were probably used in permanent pairings. Stamps from some of these centre plates have revealed a number of prominent plate flaws, the most famous of which, the extra flagstaff, has been eagerly sought by collectors for many years.

Extra flagstaff (Plate "1" R. 9/1)

Short extra flagstaff (Plate "2" R. 2/1)

Lightning conductor (Plate "3" R. 2/5)

Flagstaff on right-hand turret (Plate "5" R. 7/1)

Double flagstaff (Plate "6" R. 5/2)

De La Rue sheets were initially printed with plate numbers, but in many instances these were subsequently trimmed off. Surviving examples do, however, enable a positive identification of six centre plates, 2A, 2B, (2A), (2B), 4 and 4/ to be made. The evidence of sheet markings and plate flaws clearly demonstrates that there were two different pairs of plates numbered 2A 2B. The second pair is designated (2A) (2B) by specialist collectors to avoid further confusion. The number of major plate flaws is not so great as on the Bradbury, Wilkinson sheets, but four examples are included in the catalogue.

Diagonal line by turret (Plate 2A R. 10/1 and 10/2)

Dot to left of chapel (Plate 2B R. 8/3)

Dot by flagstaff (Plate 4 R. 8/4)

Dash by turret (Plate 4/ R. 3/6)

Much less is known concerning the Waterlow centre plate system as the sheets did not show plate numbers. Ten individual plates have, so far, been identified and it is believed that these were used in pairs. The two versions of the kite and log flaw from plate "2" show that this plate exists in two states.

Damaged turret (Plate "1" R. 5/6)

Kite and vertical log (Plate "2A" R. 10/6)

Kite and horizontal log (Plate "2B" R. 10/6)

Bird by turret (Plate "7" R. 1/5)

1937 CORONATION

		PRICE	
1937. Coronation.			
Complete set of 202 stamps		£200	£260

Country	Catalogue Nos	Stamps
Great Britain	461	1
Aden	13/15	3
Antigua	95/7	3
Ascension	35/7	3
Australia	44/7	4
Nauru	208/11	4
New Guinea	154/7	4
Papua		
Bahamas	146/8	3
Barbados	245/7	3
Basutoland	15/17	3
Bechuanaland	115/17	3
Bermuda	107/9	3
British Guiana	305/7	3
British Honduras	147/9	3
British Solomon Islands	57/9	3
Canada	356	1
Newfoundland	254/6, 257/67	14
Cayman Islands	112/14	3
Ceylon	383/5	3
Cyprus	148/50	3
Dominica	96/8	3
Falkland Islands	143/5	3
Fiji	246/8	3
Gambia	147/9	3
Gibraltar	118/20	3
Gilbert and Ellice Islands	40/2	3
Gold Coast	117/19	3
Grenada	149/51	3
Hong Kong	137/9	3
Jamaica	118/20	3
Kenya, Uganda and Tanganyika	128/30	3
Leeward Islands	92/4	3
Malaya-Straits Settlements	275/7	3
Malta	214/16	3
Mauritius	249/51	3
Montserrat	98/100	3
Morocco Agencies		
Spanish Currency	164	1
French Currency	229	1
Tangier	244	1
New Zealand	599/601	3
Cook Islands	124/6	3
Niue	72/4	3
Nigeria	46/8	3
Northern Rhodesia	22/4	3
Nyasaland	127/9	3
St. Helena	128/30	3
St. Kitts-Nevis	65/7	3
St. Lucia	125/7	3
St. Vincent	146/8	3
Seychelles	132/4	3
Sierra Leone	185/7	3
Somaliland Protectorate	911/2	3
South Africa	71/5	5×2
Southern Rhodesia	36/9	4
South West Africa	97/104	8×2
Swaziland	25/7	3
Trinidad and Tobago	243/5	3
Turks and Caicos Islands	191/3	3
Virgin Islands	107/9	3
Total		**202**

1945–46 VICTORY

1945–46. Victory.
Complete set of 164 stamps.. 60·00   90·00

Country	Catalogue Nos.	Stamps
Great Britain	491/2	2
Aden	28/9	2
Seiyun	12/13	2
Shihr and Mukalla	12/13	2
Antigua	110/11	2
Ascension	48/9	2
Australia	213/15	3
Bahamas	176/7	2
Barbados	262/3	2
Basutoland	29/31	3×2
Bechuanaland	129/31	3×2
Bermuda	123/4	2
British Guiana	320/1	2
British Honduras	162/3	2
British Solomon Islands	73/4	2
Burma	64/7	4
Cayman Islands	127/8	2
Ceylon	400/1	2
Cyprus	164/5	2
Dominica	110/11	2
Falkland Islands	164/5	2
Falkland Islands Dependencies	G17/18	2
Fiji	268/9	2
Gambia	162/3	2
Gibraltar	132/3	2
Gilbert and Ellice Islands	55/6	2
Gold Coast	133/4	2
Grenada	164/5	2
Hong Kong	169/70	2
India	278/81	4
Hyderabad	53	1
Jamaica	141/2	2
Kenya, Uganda and Tanganyika	155/6	2
Leeward Islands	115/16	2
Malta	232/3	2
Mauritius	264/5	2
Montserrat	113/14	2
Morocco Agencies		
Tangier	253/4	2
New Zealand	667/77	11
Cook Islands	146/9	4
Niue	98/101	4
Western Samoa	215/18	4
Nigeria	60/1	2
Northern Rhodesia	46/7	2
Nyasaland	158/9	2
Pakistan		
Bahawalpur	O19	1
Pitcairn Islands	9/10	2
St. Helena	141/2	2
St. Kitts-Nevis	78/9	2
St. Lucia	142/3	2
St. Vincent	160/1	2
Seychelles	150/1	2
Sierra Leone	201/2	2
Somaliland Protectorate	117/18	2
South Africa	108/10	3×2
Southern Rhodesia	64/7	4
South West Africa	131/3	3×2
Swaziland	39/41	3×2
Trinidad and Tobago	257/8	2
Turks and Caicos Islands	206/7	2
Virgin Islands	122/3	2
Zanzibar	331/2	2
Total		164

1948 ROYAL SILVER WEDDING

1948–49. Royal Silver Wedding.
Complete set of 138 stamps.. £2250   £2500

Country	Catalogue Nos.	Stamps
Great Britain	493/4	2
Aden	30/1	2
Seiyun	14/15	2
Shihr and Mukalla	14/15	2
Antigua	112/13	2
Ascension	50/1	2
Bahamas	194/5	2
Bahrain	61/2	2
Barbados	265/62	2
Basutoland	36/7	2
Bechuanaland	136/7	2
Bermuda	125/6	2
British Guiana	322/3	2
British Honduras	164/5	2

Country	Catalogue Nos.	Stamps
British Postal Agencies in Eastern Arabia	25/6	2
British Solomon Islands	75/6	2
Cayman Islands	129/30	2
Cyprus	166/7	2
Dominica	112/13	2
Falkland Islands	166/7	2
Falkland Islands Dependencies	G19/20	2
Fiji	270/1	2
Gambia	164/5	2
Gibraltar	134/5	2
Gilbert and Ellice Islands	57/8	2
Gold Coast	147/8	2
Grenada	166/7	2
Hong Kong	171/2	2
Jamaica	143/4	2
Kenya, Uganda and Tanganyika	157/8	2
Kuwait	74/5	2
Leeward Islands	117/18	2
Malaya		
Johore	131/2	2
Kedah	70/1	2
Kelantan	55/6	2
Malacca	1/2	2
Negri Sembilan	40/1	2
Pahang	47/8	2
Penang	1/2	2
Perak	122/3	2
Perlis	1/2	2
Selangor	88/9	2
Trengganu	61/2	2
Malta	249/50	2
Mauritius	270/1	2
Montserrat	115/16	2
Morocco Agencies		
Spanish Currency	176/7	2
Tangier	255/6	2
Nigeria	62/3	2
North Borneo	350/1	2
Northern Rhodesia	48/9	2
Nyasaland	161/2	2
Pitcairn Islands	11/12	2
St. Helena	143/4	2
St. Kitts-Nevis	80/1	2
St. Lucia	144/5	2
St. Vincent	162/3	2
Sarawak	165/6	2
Seychelles	152/3	2
Sierra Leone	203/4	2
Singapore	31/2	2
Somaliland Protectorate	119/20	2
South Africa	125	1×2
South West Africa	137	1×2
Swaziland	46/7	2
Trinidad and Tobago	259/60	2
Turks and Caicos Islands	208/9	2
Virgin Islands	124/5	2
Zanzibar	333/4	2
Total		138

1949 75th ANNIVERSARY OF U.P.U.

1949. U.P.U. 75th Anniversary.
Complete set of 310 stamps.. £325   £675

Country	Catalogue Nos.	Stamps
Great Britain	449/502	4
Aden	32/5	4
Seiyun	16/19	4
Shihr and Mukalla	16/19	4
Antigua	114/17	4
Ascension	52/5	4
Australia	232	1
Bahamas	196/9	4
Bahrain	67/70	4
Barbados	267/70	4
Basutoland	38/41	4
Bechuanaland	138/41	4
Bermuda	130/3	4
British Guiana	324/7	4
British Honduras	172/5	4
British Postal Agencies in Eastern Arabia	31/4	4
British Solomon Islands	77/80	4
Brunei	96/9	4
Cayman Islands	131/4	4
Ceylon	410/12	3
Cyprus	168/71	4
Dominica	114/17	4
Falkland Islands	168/71	4
Falkland Islands Dependencies	G31/4	4
Fiji	272/5	4
Gambia	166/9	4
Gibraltar	136/9	4

Country	Catalogue Nos.	Stamps
Gilbert and Ellice Islands	59/62	4
Gold Coast	149/52	4
Grenada	168/71	4
Hong Kong	173/6	4
India	325/8	4
Jamaica	145/8	4
Kenya, Uganda and Tanganyika	159/62	4
Kuwait	80/3	4
Leeward Islands	119/22	4
Malaya		
Johore	148/51	4
Kedah	72/5	4
Kelantan	57/60	4
Malacca	18/21	4
Negri Sembilan	63/6	4
Pahang	49/52	4
Penang	23/6	4
Perak	124/7	4
Perlis	3/6	4
Selangor	111/14	4
Trengganu	63/6	4
Malta	251/4	4
Mauritius	272/5	4
Montserrat	117/20	4
Morocco Agencies		
Tangier	276/9	4
New Hebrides	64/7, F77/80	4+4
Nigeria	64/7	4
North Borneo	352/5	4
Northern Rhodesia	50/3	4
Nyasaland	163/6	4
Pakistan		
Bahawalpur	43/6, O28/31	4+4
Pitcairn Islands	13/16	4
St. Helena	145/8	4
St. Kitts-Nevis	82/5	4
St. Lucia	160/3	4
St. Vincent	178/81	4
Sarawak	167/70	4
Seychelles	154/7	4
Sierra Leone	205/8	4
Singapore	33/6	4
Somaliland Protectorate	121/4	4
South Africa	128/30	3×2
Southern Rhodesia	68/9	2
South West Africa	138/40	3×2
Swaziland	48/51	4
Tonga	88/91	4
Trinidad and Tobago	261/4	4
Turks and Caicos Islands	217/20	4
Virgin Islands	126/9	4
Zanzibar	335/8	4
Total		310

1951 INAUGURATION OF B.W.I. UNIVERSITY COLLEGE

1951. B.W.I. University College.
Complete set of 28 stamps .... 12·00   30·00

Country	Catalogue Nos.	Stamps
Antigua	118/19	2
Barbados	283/4	2
British Guiana	328/9	2
British Honduras	176/7	2
Dominica	118/19	2
Grenada	185/6	2
Jamaica	149/50	2
Leeward Islands	123/4	2
Montserrat	121/2	2
St. Kitts-Nevis	92/3	2
St. Lucia	164/5	2
St. Vincent	182/3	2
Trinidad and Tobago	265/6	2
Virgin Islands	130/1	2
Total		28

1953 CORONATION

1953. Coronation.
Complete set of 106 stamps.. £140   £150

1953–54 ROYAL VISIT

1953–54. Royal Visit.
Complete set of 13 stamps .... 7·50   4·50

1958 CARIBBEAN FEDERATION

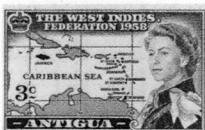

1958. Caribbean Federation.
Complete set of 30 stamps .... 26·00   21·00

1963 FREEDOM FROM HUNGER

1963. Freedom from Hunger.
Complete set of 77 stamps £160   £110

1963 RED CROSS

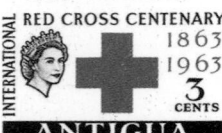

1963. Red Cross Centenary.
Complete set of 108 stamps and 2 miniature sheets. £190   £225

1964 SHAKESPEARE

1964. Shakespeare. 400th Birth Anniversary.
Complete set of 25 stamps .... 22·00   20·00

1965 I.T.U. CENTENARY

1965. I.T.U. Centenary.
Complete set of 112 stamps and 1 miniature sheet... £150   £120

1965 I.C.Y.

1965. I.C.Y.
Complete set of 107 stamps and 2 miniature sheets. £110   90·00

1965–67 CHURCHILL

1965–67. Churchill.
Complete set of 182 stamps £260   £225

1966 ROYAL VISIT

1966. Royal Visit to the Caribbean.
Complete set of 34 stamps .... 35·00   18·00

1966 FOOTBALL WORLD CUP

1966. World Cup Football Championship.
Complete set of 68 stamps and 2 miniature sheets... £140   90·00

1966 W.H.O. HEADQUARTERS

1966. W.H.O. New Headquarters.
Complete set of 58 stamps and 1 miniature sheet... 90·00   75·00

1966-67 U.N.E.S.C.O. ANNIVERSARY

1966–67. U.N.E.S.C.O. 20th Anniversary.
Complete set of 110 stamps and 1 miniature sheet... £180   £170

1935 SILVER JUBILEE TO 1966 U.N.E.S.C.O.

Issuing countries	1935 Silver Jubilee	1937 Coronation	1945–47 Victory	1948 Silver Wedding	1949 U.P.U.	1951 B.W.I. Univ	1953 Coronation	1953–54 Royal Visit	1958 Caribbean Federation	1963 F.F.H.	1963 Red Cross	1964 Shakespeare	1965 I.T.U.	1965–66 I.C.Y.	1965–66 Churchill	1966 Royal Visit	1966 Football Cup	1966 W.H.O.	1966 U.N.E.S.C.O.
Great Britain	4	1	2	2	4	—	4	—	—	2+2	3+3	5+4	2+2	2+2	2+2	—	3+3	—	—
Aden / South Arabian Federation	—	3	2	2	4	—	1	1	—	1	2	—	2+2	2	4	—	2	2	3
Seiyun	—	—	2	2	4	—	1	—	—	—	—	—	7	—	1	—	7	—	—
Shihr and Mukalla	—	—	2	2	4	—	1	—	—	—	—	—	—	8	3	—	8+MS	—	—
Antigua	4	3	2	2	4	2	1	—	3	1	2	1	2	2	4	2	2	2	3
Ascension	4	3	2	2	4	—	1	—	—	1	2	—	2	2	4	—	2	2	3
Australia	3	—	3	—	1	—	3	3	—	—	1	—	1	1	1	—	—	—	—
Bahamas	4	3	2	2	4	—	1	—	—	1	2	1	2	2	4	2	2	2	3
Bahrain	—	—	—	2	4	—	4	—	—	—	—	—	—	—	—	—	—	—	—
Barbados	4	3	2	2	4	2	1	—	3	—	—	—	2	—	4	2	—	—	3
Basutoland / Lesotho	4	3	3×2	2	4	—	1	—	—	—	2	—	2	2	4	—	—	—	4
Bechuanaland / Botswana	4	3	3×2	2	4	—	1	—	—	1	2	1	2	2	4	—	—	—	—
Bermuda	4	3	2	2	4	—	1	1	—	1	2	—	2	2	4	—	2	—	3
British Antarctic Territory	—	—	—	—	—	—	—	—	—	—	—	—	—	—	4	—	—	—	—
British Guiana / Guyana	4	3	2	2	4	2	1	—	—	1	2	—	2	2	4	2	—	—	—
British Honduras	4	3	2	2	4	—	1	—	—	1	2	—	2	2	4	—	—	—	—
British P.A's in Eastern Arabia	—	—	—	2	4	—	4	—	—	—	—	—	—	—	—	—	—	—	—
British Solomon Islands	4	3	2	2	4	—	1	—	—	1	2	—	2	2	4	—	2	2	3
British Virgin Islands	4	3	2	2	4	2	1	—	—	1	2	1	2	2	4	2	—	—	3
Brunei	—	—	—	—	4	—	—	—	—	1	—	—	2	2	4	—	2	2	3
Burma	—	—	4	—	—	—	—	—	—	—	—	—	—	—	—	—	—	—	—
Canada	6	1	—	—	—	—	1	—	—	—	—	—	—	1	1	—	—	—	—
Newfoundland	4	14	—	—	—	—	—	—	—	—	—	—	—	—	—	—	—	—	—
Cayman Islands	4	3	2	2	4	—	1	—	—	1	2	1	2	2	4	2	2	2	3
Ceylon	4	3	2	—	3	—	1	1	—	2	—	—	2	2	—	—	—	2	2
Cook Islands	3	3	4	—	—	—	2	—	—	—	—	—	—	—	6	—	—	—	—
Cyprus	4	3	2	2	4	—	1	—	—	2	2	4	3	2	—	—	—	—	1
Dominica	4	3	2	2	4	2	1	—	3	1	2	1	2	2	4	2	2	2	3
Egypt/ British Forces in Egypt	1	—	—	—	—	—	—	—	—	—	—	—	—	—	—	—	—	—	—
Falkland Islands	4	3	2	2	4	—	1	—	—	1	2	1	2	2	4	—	—	—	—
Falkland Island Dependencies	—	—	2	2	4	—	1	—	—	—	—	—	—	—	—	—	—	—	—
Fiji	4	3	2	2	4	—	1	1	—	1	2	—	2	2	4	—	2	2	—
Gambia	4	3	2	2	4	—	1	—	—	1	2	1	2	—	3	—	—	—	—
Gibraltar	4	3	2	2	4	—	1	1	—	1	2	1	2	2	4	—	2	2	3
Gilbert and Ellice Islands	4	3	2	2	4	—	1	—	—	1	2	—	2	2	4	—	2	2	3
Gold Coast / Ghana	4	3	2	2	4	—	1	—	—	3	4+MS	—	4+MS	4+MS	—	—	5+MS	4+MS	5+MS
Grenada	4	3	2	2	4	2	1	—	3	1	2	—	2	2	4	2	2	2	3
Hong Kong	4	3	2	2	4	—	1	—	—	1	2	—	2	2	4	—	—	2	3
India	7	—	4	—	4	—	1	—	—	1	1	—	1	1	—	—	—	—	—
Hyderabad	—	—	1	—	—	—	—	—	—	—	—	—	—	—	—	—	—	—	—
Ireland	—	—	—	—	—	—	—	—	—	2	2	—	2	2	—	—	—	—	—
Jamaica	4	3	2	2	4	2	1	1	3	2	2	—	1	—	2	4	—	—	—
K.U.T. / East Africa	4	3	2	2	4	—	1	—	—	4	2	—	4	4	—	—	—	—	4
Kuwait	—	—	—	2	4	—	4												
Leeward Islands	4	3	2	—	4	2	1												
Malayan States, etc.	4	3	—	22	44	—	11	—	—	3	—	—	3	—	—	—	—	—	—
North Borneo	—	—	—	2	4	—	1	—	—	1	—	—	—	—	—	—	—	—	—
Sarawak	—	—	—	2	4	—	1	—	—	1	—	—	—	—	—	—	—	—	—
Maldive Islands	—	—	—	—	—	—	1	—	—	7	5	—	—	5+MS	6	—	—	—	6
Malta	4	3	2	2	4	—	1	1	—	1	2	—	2	—	4	—	—	—	—
Mauritius	4	3	2	2	4	—	1	—	—	1	2	—	2	2	4	—	—	—	3
Montserrat	4	3	2	2	4	2	1	—	3	1	2	1	2	2	4	2	—	2	3
Morocco Agencies / Tangier	15	3	2	4	4	—	4												
Nauru	4	4																	
New Hebrides / Vanuatu (English and French inscr)	—	—	—	—	4+4	—	1	—	—	1+1	2+2	—	2+2	2+2	4+4	—	2+2	2+2	3+3
New Zealand	3	3	11	—	—	—	5	2	—	—	—	—	1	1	1	—	—	—	—
Tokelau Islands	—	—	—	—	—	—	1												
Nigeria	4	3	2	2	4	—	1	—	—	2	3+MS	—	3	3	—	—	—	—	3
Niue	3	3	4	—	—	—	2												
Northern Rhodesia / Zambia	4	3	2	2	4	—	1	—	—	—	—	—	2	2	—	—	—	2	—
Nyasaland / Malawi	4	3	2	2	4	—	1												
Pakistan	—	—	—	—	—	—	—	—	—	2	1	—	1	2	—	—	—	—	1
Bahawalpur	—	—	1	—	4+4														
Papua New Guinea / Papua	4	4	—	—	—	—	—	—	—	—	1								
New Guinea	2	4																	
Pitcairn Islands	—	—	2	2	4	—	1	—	—	1	2	—	2	2	4	—	2	2	3
Rhodesia and Nyasaland	—	—	—	—	—	—	—	—	—	—	1								
St. Helena	4	3	2	2	4	—	1	—	—	1	2	—	2	2	4	—	2	2	3
St. Kitts-Nevis	4	3	2	2	4	2	1	—	3	—	2	—	2	2	4	2	2	2	3
St. Lucia	4	3	2	2	4	2	1	—	3	1	2	1	2	2	4	2	2	2	3
St. Vincent	4	3	2	2	4	2	1	—	3	1	2	—	2	—	4	2	—	2	3
Samoa	3	—	4	—	2	—	2	—	—	—	—	—	—	—	—	—	—	4	—
Seychelles	4	3	2	2	4	—	1	—	—	1	2	—	2	2	4	—	2	—	3
Sierra Leone	4	3	2	2	4	—	1	—	—	2	3	—	—	—	11				
Singapore	—	—	—	2	4	—	1												
Somaliland Protectorate	4	3	2	2	4	—	1												
South Africa	4×2	5×2	3×2	1×2	3×2	—	1	—	—	—	2	—	2						
Southern Rhodesia	4	4	4	—	2	—	1	—	—	—	—	—	3	—	1				
South West Africa	4	8×2	3×2	1×2	3×2	—	5												
Swaziland	4	3	3×2	2	4	—	1	—	—	1	2	—	2	2	4	—	—	—	3
Tonga	—	—	—	—	4	—	—	—	—	1	2								
Trinidad and Tobago	4	3	2	2	4	2	1	—	3	3	2	—	—	1	—	4	—	—	—
Tristan da Cunha	—	—	—	—	—	—	1	—	—	1	2	—	2	2	4	—	2	2	3
Turks and Caicos islands	4	3	2	2	4	—	1	—	—	1	2	1	2	2	4	2	—	—	3
Zanzibar	—	—	2	2	4														
Total number of stamps	250	202	164	138	310	28	106	13	30	77	108 +2MS	25	112 +MS	107 +2MS	182	34	68 +2MS	58 +MS	110 +MS

Index

Are You THINKING of SELLING?

This is

HOW THE STAMP TRADE WORKS

Philatelic Expert Lets You into his *Selling Secrets* so you can benefit from a *totally different* (and New) Selling Experience

by Andrew McGavin

1 **If You want to learn** how the stamp trade works, please read on… When I was 15, I did. I wondered if there was some secret source of supply? So, I bought my 1st stamp mixture, (wholesale I thought), broke it into 50 smaller units, advertised it in Stamp Magazine 'Classifieds', and waited for the orders to roll in… I'm still waiting, 48 years later !…

Wrong Offer ✗ *Wrong Price* ✗ *Wrong Place* ✗
(naïve seller ✔ *=* 😞 *me but I was only 15 at the time!)*

2 **Three years later,** attending my first public stamp auctions I wondered how some bidders seemed to buy everything, paying the highest price? It didn't occur to me that they were probably Auction Bidding Agents, paid by absent (dealer) bidders to represent them. I wondered why two collectors sitting side by side muttered to each other **"he's a dealer"** as if that justified him paying the highest price…

> **About The Author** ➺ Andrew found his Father's stamps at the age of 10. A year later at Senior School he immediately joined the School Stamp Club. He 'specialised'(!) in British, but soon was interested in Queen Victoria which he could not afford. The 2nd to last boy wearing short trousers in his school year, he religiously bought Post Office New Issues on Tuesdays with his pocket money. He soon found that he enjoyed swapping / trading stamps as much as collecting them. Aged 19, eschewing University he quickly found a philatelic career in London, leading to creating his own companies in stamps. Andrew has authored many internationally published Stamp 'Tips' articles, appearing on Local Radio and National TV promoting Philately with Alan Titchmarsh. Andrew's area of expertise is unusual – in so far as his grounding in collecting and wide philatelic knowledge has given him a deep understanding of Philately. He has studied Philately for the past 45 years, in combination with Commerce and Marketing Expertise, enabling him to create synergies in 'lifetime' interlinked Stamp Selling Systems, selling unit-priced stamps through to handling collections & Rarities up to £700,000 each. Today Andrew is fortunate to be co-owner with his Wife, of Universal Philatelic Auctions (aka UPA) – the Largest No Buyer's Premium Reducing-Estimate System Stamp Auction in the World, creating records selling stamps to 2,261 different bidders from 54 different countries in his latest auction. Andrew stopped collecting stamps aged 18 reasoning that his enjoyment of stamps would be in handling them and selling them…

…but did it really? What was the real reason? How could a Dealer pay a higher price than a Collector? It doesn't make sense, does it? Collectors are customers. Customers usually pay the highest price, unless… for a Collector, this was…

Wrong Presentation ✗ *Wrong Place* ✗
therefore Wrong Price ✗

3 **Fast-forward 48 years later** to a British Empire collection, lot #1 in an International Stamp Auction – Estimated at £3,000, but we were the highest bidder at £21,000 – **YES** – some 7×higher. Including Buyer's Premium in the extraordinary sum of £4,788 we actually paid GBP£25,788= upon a £3,000 estimate… **however,** we broke it down into sets, singles, mini-collections etc. We made a profit. Some might say it found its price. Others may say:

Wrong Estimate ✗ *Wrong Presentation* ✗
Wrong Structure ✗ *Wrong Protection of Price* ✗

– *Lucky for the seller that 2 well-healed bidders saw the potential value that day* or it could have been given away… the seller could easily have lost out couldn't he? or she?

So, by un-peeling the layers of obfuscation, hopefully we can all agree:

The Secret is Simple –

> it's ALL About: TIMING,

Plus the 3 Philatelic 'P's –

Presentation ✔ **Place** ✔ and **Price** ✔

4 **Understanding the problem…** I always remember the car trade had their own little 'bible' – Glass's Guide. I've no idea, I've not even looked - in this internet-dominated world, it may even have disappeared. Well, there's an insider Stamp Trade publication for Stamp Dealers called "The Philatelic Exporter". There's nothing that special about it – and you won't learn much or find massively reduced prices by subscribing – **BUT** – it is a forum, a paper focal point, a last 'bastion' in this on-line transparent world that we inhabit… whereby dealers (and auctioneers) can try and communicate with each other. I publish my own articles there…

Recently I discussed the outcome of my 10 years' simple research, asking dealers and auctioneers **'what is your biggest problem?'**

To a man, (why are we almost all men), they replied – **"my biggest problem is stock, if I can get more of the right stock I can sell it easily"**

Strange that, nobody ever asked me the same question back – because my answer would have been entirely different (and I don't treat it as a problem) – **I seek to satisfy collectors**

This is the reason why my company has such massive advertising. This is the reason why we spend up to 8% of turnover – up to £200,000 per annum in marketing costs. (Most dealers don't even sell £200K per annum).

5 **Why is that?** Because, as the world revolved **the Stamp Market, imperceptibly *Changed*, and incrementally – Massively**

So, although few will tell you this, it's clearly evident that the problem for most Sellers of Stamps today is no longer absent stock – but **absent collectors in the place they choose to sell their stamps in.** Simply put, other Dealers, Auctions, Stamp Fairs have not invested in marketing to have a strong Customer-core. To be fair, this is not true of all – but it is true of most – so that our nearest competitor 'Apex' had 800 bidders in a recent auction. In my most recent 20,000+ lot UPA 65th Auction we had 2,261 different bidders from 54 different countries, 95% of whom were Collectors. Some other well-advertised auctions only have 200 bidders (a high percentage of whom are dealers – so that, essentially they are Dealer-dominated auctions) – so that when you sell through them – you're paying up to 18% (including VAT) seller's commission and the buyer is paying up to 25% **and** more in Buyer's Premium, credit card fees, on-line bidding fee, delivery and insurance etc… **AND all of that so that your stamps may be sold, wait for it – TO DEALERS (and some collectors),** but Dealers, that naturally must make a profit to survive…

6 **Now, let's examine the cost implications – Example:** Your stamp collection sells in public auction for £800. Upon a 25% buyer's premium, the dealer pays £1,000 and it could be more. He breaks it into £2,000+ selling price (much lower and he'll go out of business). The auction charges you a seller's commission of up to 18% (VAT included) upon the £800 sale price. This is GBP£144. Therefore you receive approaching £656 – which is approximately 33% of the dealer's £2,000+/- retail selling price - **BUT… now that we have identified the problem…**

> *Isn't the Solution Staring us Right in The Face ?*

7 **Why Pay an Auction to Sell to Dealers:** Sell to Collectors instead ? In our example with buyer's premium, sellers commission, lotting fees, extra credit card charges, VAT and even insurance - you're already being charged in different ways up to 40% of the selling price to sell, possibly or probably, **to the wrong person**.

Why not direct that 40% cost you're paying to sell to Collectors instead? Sounds good, so why hasn't this been done before ?

8 **Truth is, it *Has* been done before…** Sometimes the 'old' ways are the best ways aren't they? But in today's enthusiasm to obscure the obvious so that money may be taken, almost surreptitiously, in numerous different ways, (without us apparently noticing until we see the cheque in our pocket) – the transparent 'seller pays' has been deliberately 'obscured' – so much so that, **amazingly,** the latest 2017 European Auction Selling Legislation just introduced – now requires auctions

ANDREW PROMOTING PHILATELY ON THE ALAN TITCHMARSH SHOW ITV

Universal Philatelic Auctions present

TIPS OF THE TRADE
Your Expert Guide to Stamp Collecting
Volume 1
➤ How to buy: How to sell
➤ Catalogue value: common misconceptions
➤ How to insure reasonably
➤ Which Accessories do you really need?
➤ and Much More ...

£55 OFF
The UPA STAMP AUCTIONS PURCHASES

£55 OFF: Do You Qualify? INSIDE: see pages 15/16 ➔

REQUEST MY 'TIPS OF THE TRADE' FREE BOOKLET

that charge 'buyer's premiums' **to warn the buyer in advance.** Just imagine going into the petrol station, and being warned that the price you're paying to put fuel in you tank is not the real price, you have to pay a premium! Obviously, there would be an uproar…

9 How can you cut out the middleman and sell to Collectors instead?
Well, I can think of two ways. 1). **DIY** - Do It Yourself selling on eBay. That may be fine for lower grade material – but, would you risk auctioning relatively unprotected rare material on eBay ? We don't and we're professionals, so we should know what we're doing. Or 2). Cut out the extra middle-man. **Use my company UPA, which reaches collectors instead.** Here's how it works: Continuing from our previous **Example**:

The auction sold your stamps to a dealer for £1,000 – but You received circa £656

UPA sells them to collectors for you for up to £2,000 – even after 40% commission you receive up to £1,200. Up to £544 more. Now that's amazing, isn't it? 🏆

10 Sounds Good Andrew, but Can You 'Deliver'?
Obviously, nothing is as simple as that, and as we auction stamps to collectors some collections may 'break' to the example £2,000+/- but the stamps may be sold for more or less – especially as we reserve all lots at 20% below, (Estimate £2,000 = £1,600 reserve) and not everything sells first or even 2nd time so prices may come down… Naturally, it's not that straightforward for a dealer either – he may sell at a discount to 'move' stock **OR**, like many dealers he may be sitting on the same unsold stamps, that you see time and time again, in dealer's stocks years later and still at the same unattractive prices… So, I think it is more reasonable for you to expect up to 36% to 50% more, indirectly or directly via my **Collector's Secret Weapon:** Universal Philatelic Auctions, which moves material more quickly, by incrementally reducing estimate (and reserve) price in a structured selling system…

11 Q.) What is the Collector's 'Secret Weapon'?

A.) It's called the Unique UPA Reducing Estimate System… ⭐⭐
This is a rather long explanation, I don't want to bore you, but 17 years ago, when my wife and I set up Universal Philatelic Auctions I detected that the stamp trade's biggest problem then was not what sold – **but what didn't sell…** So, because I didn't want to try to keep on offering the same either unsaleable or overpriced stock I created the unique UPA Reducing Estimate (and reserve) Selling System. Simply put, if a lot doesn't sell in the 1st auction we reduce the estimate (and reserve) by 11% and unlike other dealers and auctions **WE TELL YOU – 'US'** = once unsold. If unsold after the following auction we **reduce by a further 12%** and **WE TELL YOU 'US2',** if unsold after a 3rd U̅P̅A̅ auction we reduce by a further 13% and **WE TELL YOU 'US3'** and so on till the lot finds its price, is sold or virtually given away… ✔

12 Any Scientist will tell you
that combinations of ingredients can produce powerful results. So we created the unique combination of my UPA Reducing Estimate System, married (in stone), with UPA's fair 'NO BUYER'S Premium' policy, PLUS each lot carries my total 'no quibble' guarantee – this formula is the reason why within the span of 4 auctions (one year)… 90%-95% of lots broken from a collection have sold. This Unique Philatelic Selling System **Formula** is the reason why we are the largest stamp auction in the UK today with 2,261 different bidders in my recent auction. 🌐

SCOTTISH & NORTH CONTACT

COTSWOLDS MIDLANDS & SOUTH CONTACT

Contact UPA: 01451 861 111

In Hindsight Dealers warned me 17 years ago that my idea wouldn't work. 17 years later I think I've proven that it does. (Reader: Please Request a complimentary UPA catalogue – using the contact details further below)

13 OK, Cut to the Chase Andrew, what's the offer?
All of my Selling Systems are based upon **selling to Collectors Globally,** so that 95% of stamps sold by UPA are sold directly to Collectors. If you wish to benefit by up to 50% or more, depending upon your circumstance and type of material, by cutting out the middleman – then this offer may be for you. Generally 'time' is the enemy in our lives, and for most dealers not being able to sell stock. Now is the time to let 'time' do the 'heavy-lifting' and consider making 'time' work for you, so that at UPA you can make time your friend. 👍

14 AND the SMALL PRINT?
Some lots are too small in value for us to offer this system. Other lots may not be suited to selling in this manner (e.g. surplus mint British decimal stamps best used for postage) – especially if the market is heavily compromised by stock overhang in specific areas. Some Collectors will not wish to use time and systems to leverage price, others will

want to agree a specific price and know that they are paid precisely this amount. No client is treated like a number and no client is forced like a square peg into a round hole. ☀

15 OK, What Do I Do Next?
a). You contact UPA to discuss with Andrew or a highly-qualified Auction Valuer/ Describer what you have to dispose of and your options bearing in mind your specific interests / requirements

b). If you wish, get a 2nd opinion, but investigate what type of auction / dealer you are dealing with. Is it a Dealer's auction with relatively few collectors? Can you see where / how the Dealer sells? If you can't easily see any pricelists or high quality selling catalogues – that Dealer may sell your stamps to other dealers…

c). Finally you ask U P A to collect your stamps, insure in transit for an estimated replacement retail value…☎ 🖥 🚚

16 What Happens then?
A member of my Team telephones/e-mails you to confirm safe receipt. 'Overnight' valuations, unless simple, are rare. Valuing stamp collections that have taken tens of years to create takes time. Depending upon your priorities / timescale I, or an experienced member of my Team will contact you to discuss your requirements and the options available to you for the sale of your collection. Provided only that you feel well-informed and comfortable do we agree strategy 🧮 🤝

17 How Strong is the Stamp and Cover Market?
Everybody knows that the strongest areas are GB and British Empire. Post-Independence / QEII material sells but if hinged at considerable discount. Mint hinged material pre 1952 is regarded as the industry 'norm' and therefore desirable – but genuine never-hinged commands a premium. Europe sells but at reduced levels, Americas is good, as generally is Asia but the 'heat' has come off China which is still good – and Russia which can still be good. East Europe is weaker. Overall, Rarities throughout can command their own price levels and real Postal History has good demand.

18 What Should I Do Next?
Discuss your collection with U P A. Contact Andrew or an experienced member of his Team now… 🖥 ☎

19 Guarantee: I want You to be absolutely Sure
So If You're not sure we'll transport and return your stamps for FREE up to £200 in actual shipping cost at our expense. It sounds generous (and it is), but it's far less than the cost of driving 100+ miles each way and 3 to 6 hours in your home valuing your stamps 😊

20 My Double Cast Iron Guarantee:
We can do a better job valuing your stamps in our office than in your home. If you don't agree I'll pay you an extra £50 for you to pay somebody trusted to open the boxes and put your albums back, in the same place, on the shelf they came from. 😊 😊

21 Act NOW: Contact Andrew
or an experienced member of his Team using the on-line selling form at our website, by fax, telephone or by mail. We'll work harder for you not to regret the decision to sell all or part of your collection…☎ 🖥

Andrew

Andrew McGavin, Philatelic Expert, Author, Managing Director
Universal Philatelic Auctions UPA

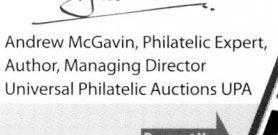

Request Your Next FREE Catalogue NOW

Don't think we can pay you up to 36% more?

COLLECTORS ARE RIGHT TO BE WARY OF LOFTY CLAIMS BUT THERE MAY BE GOOD REASONS WHY YOU MAY FIND SOME OF THEM TO BE TRUE

The stamp market constantly fluctuates so that at any given moment **if there is too much of what you wish to sell on the market,** despite what anybody claims, no dealer can offer you **massively** more.

However, there may be good reasons why some stamp organisations can offer you significantly more and pay you immediately rather than waiting months for the unknown of what you may or may not sell at auction – and you will be waiting even longer for payment.

It all depends upon that stamp dealer's/auction's business model. UPA buys and sells globally but if for example the nearest stamp dealer you approach only sells British stamps to a small market place then there is a strong possibility that he/she may be fully stocked already – so that if a price is proffered to you there is an increased likelihood of your receiving a lower offer as your collection, or part of your collection may be 'traded on' to a larger dealer. Worse still, other unrelated areas of your collection may be neglected or not valued in any offer you receive.

If you consign your collection to auction and it is unsuitable or too time-consuming for that auction to 'break' it into smaller lots – then there is a very strong probability that you will be paying an auction to sell your stamps to a stamp dealer WHO could afford to pay you up to 36% more than you will receive. Don't forget most auctions charge the buyer of your collection up to twice the commission, or more, that they charge you.

It doesn't make sense for you to pay an auction to sell your stamps to a stamp dealer, when – if you handle the transaction wisely – you can receive the up to 36% more for yourself.

What happens when you ask UPA to make you an offer?

First we ask you to tell us about your collection and we listen. Then we ask you how much you know about the market for your type of collection? At this stage we add to your knowledge, informing you of current conditions you may be unaware of. Then we discuss whether we may be well placed to assist you and how that may be achieved.

Providing your collection has sufficient potential we may offer to visit without charge or obligation, or we will offer to uplift your collection from your home at our expense, insured in transit (and whilst in our care) free of charge. If you are situated in mainland UK and your collection is too bulky for you to pack, provided your collection is valuable enough, we may even provide a free packing service in addition to shipping to our office.

Now we assess your collection and offer you the choice of agreeing a price that will be paid immediately – or of our bidding against other dealers so that you know you are achieving the best possible price.

Guarantee: We guarantee that you will never be under pressure at any stage of the process; you will always be in control. E-mail or Contact UPA now: 01451 861 111

Why can UPA often pay considerably more?

We often buy at auction. That auction takes the "**up to 36% more**" that we pay that YOU DO NOT RECEIVE.

However – there is another equally important

SCOTTISH & NORTH OFFICE – BUYER

COTSWOLD, MIDLANDS & SOUTH – BUYER

National number please contact: Andrew McGavin or John Cowell on 01451 861 111 number please contact: Andrew McGavin or John Cowell on 01451 861 111

reason …. namely **The UPA Business Model.** Unlike most dealers we believe that if an item is not selling, then it must be too expensive. This is the reason why when you receive our quarterly catalogues of up to 20,671 different lots (you can request a sample one free) … you will find that if an item has been previously unsold **we actually tell you.** Furthermore each time an item is unsold we reduce the price and **we keep on reducing the price – until finally the lot sells** or it is given away. In practice good material sells quickly whilst other material finally finds its own price and sells. This is the reason why there are always 1,000's of new offers at UPA …. and part of the reason why

we are usually in a position to pay you more and pay you immediately.

Furthermore, unlike some, UPA has not one but **4 different selling systems** selling 95% of stamps to collectors, so that when a collection is purchased the most valuable/interesting stamps go into our Universal Philatelic Auctions (a UK record 1,750 different bidders in the last auction). Intermediate/lower-priced sets/singles enter our Omniphil and Avon Approvals systems (established 56 years and over 1,200 regular collector clients), inexpensive stamps enter the Avon Mixtures system and eBay (universalphilatelic) for surplus material. All of which is why UPA can purchase and pay for almost literally anything…..

WHAT DOES UPA BUY?

UPA literally purchases almost any country collection worth £200 upwards from sets and singles to classics and entire British, British Empire, Europe and World collections. At the moment UPA has **exceptional demand for original collections of Great Britain and British Empire** in particular.

What do I do next?

You contact UPA and talk to one of our friendly Team who will help to inform you so that you can decide how to progress matters … there is no charge and no obligation … **please CONTACT UPA NOW.**

Remember, if you are selling a collection … collectors buy the stamps they are missing; this is why dealers exist. Most intact collections offered at auction sell to dealers. **Save commissions and uncertainty by contacting UPA today.** We guarantee that you will never be under pressure at any stage of the process, you will always be in control.

CONTACT our friendly UPA Team NOW: 01451 861 111

To read the rest of this series 'SELLING YOUR STAMPS?' see the relevant pages listed below:
Summary Tip 18 – page 42 (Australia)
Summary Tip 19 – page 98 (Bechuanaland)
Summary Tip 20 – page 210 (Egypt)
Summary Tip 21 – page 272 (India)
To read the final instalment, Summary Tip 22 – 'Selling via Online Auction' simply e-mail and request to: *info@upastampauctions.co.uk*

If you'd like to discuss the sale of your collection please contact Elaine or Andrew on 01451 861111

ANDREW PROMOTING PHILATELY ON THE ALAN TITCHMARSH SHOW ITV

Visit www.upastampauctions.co.uk **when you want to buy or sell stamps.**

UNIVERSAL PHILATELIC AUCTIONS (PART1)

4 The Old Coalyard, West End Northleach, Glos. GL54 3HE UK
Tel: 01451 861111 • Fax: 01451 861297

www.upastampauctions.co.uk • info@upastampauctions.co.uk

Universal Philatelic Auctions present

TIPS OF THE TRADE
Your Expert Guide to Stamp Collecting
Volume 1

£55 OFF

REQUEST MY 'TIPS OF THE TRADE' FREE BOOKLET